Graduate Medical Education Directory

Including programs accredited by the
Accreditation Council for Graduate Medical Education

M000087763

AMA
AMERICAN
MEDICAL
ASSOCIATION

ACGME

2009–2010

American Medical Association

Executive Vice President, Chief Executive Officer: Michael D Maves, MD, MBA
Chief Operating Officer: Bernard L Hengesbaugh
Senior Vice President, Publishing and Business Services: Robert A Musacchio, PhD
Vice President and General Manager, Publishing: Frank J. Krause
Vice President, Business Operations: Vanessa Hayden
Senior Acquisitions Editor: Suzanne Fraker
Director, Production and Manufacturing: Jean Roberts
Director, Business Marketing and Communication: Pam Palmersheim
Director, Sales and Strategic Partnerships: J D Kinney
Developmental Editor: Elizabeth Kennedy
Production Manager: Rosalyn Carlton
Senior Print Production Specialist: Ronnie Summers
Marketing Manager: Cara Zimmerman
Senior Production Specialist: Boon Ai Tan
Manager, Developmental Editing: Nancy Baker
Director, Fulfillment Operations: Allen Novak
Customer Service Coordinator: Paula Coyne
Catalog and Direct Marketing Manager: Lori Hollacher
Manager, TeleSales: Mark Daniels

Copyright 2009 by the American Medical Association
All Rights Reserved
Printed in the United States of America
Internet address: www.ama-assn.org

No part of this publication may be reproduced, stored in a retrieval system, or transmitted in any form or by any means, electronic, mechanical, photocopying, recording, or otherwise, without the prior written permission of the publisher.

The American Medical Association and its authors and editors have checked with sources believed to be reliable to confirm that the information presented herein is accurate and complete and in accordance with current accepted practices. However, the AMA does not warrant that the information is in every respect accurate and complete, and is not responsible for any errors or omissions or for any consequences from application of the information in this book. This book is intended for information purposes only. It is not intended to constitute legal advice. If legal advice is desired or needed, a licensed attorney should be consulted.

Order Information
To order additional copies of the *Graduate Medical Education Directory*,
call the American Medical Association toll free at 800 621-8335
Or access the secure AMA Web site at www.amabookstore.com.
Mention product number OP416709.

For other correspondence address inquiries to:
Fred Donini-Lenhoff
Medical Education Products
American Medical Association
515 N State St
Chicago, IL 60654
312 464-5333
312 464-5830 Fax
E-mail: fred.lenhoff@ama-assn.org
www.ama-assn.org/go/meded

ISBN: 978-1-60359-101-0
BP17:09-P-014:04/09

Table of Contents

1 Section I—Graduate Medical Education Information

1   A. Residency Application and Career Planning Resources Match Timeline
2   Fellowship and Residency Electronic Interactive Database Access (FREIDA) Online®
3   GME Library on CD-ROM
4   Careers in Medicine
4   Choosing a Medical Specialty
4   ERAS®
5   Succeeding from Medical School to Practice
5   Transitioning to Residency: What Medical Students Need to Know
5   The Residency Interview: A Guide for Medical Students
6   Find a Residency or Fellowship
6   AMA Alliance Resident Physician Spouses and Medical Student Spouses (RPS-MSS)

7   B. Information on Matching Programs
7   National Resident Matching Program
8   San Francisco Matching Program
8   Urology Match
9   Canadian Resident Matching Service
9   Military Matches
9   Couple's Matching
10   Match Outcomes

10   C. GME Information for IMGs
10   Educational Commission for Foreign Medical Graduates (ECFMG®) Certification
11   Entry of Foreign-Born Medical Graduates to the United States
15   AMA International Medical Graduates Section

16   D. AMA Medical Education Products, Services, and Activities
16   AMA Council on Medical Education
16   AMA Section on Medical Schools
17   AMA Medical Education Group
17   National GME Census
17   Medical Education Issue of *JAMA*
17   Medical Education Data Service, Mailing Labels
17   Electronic State-level GME Data
18   GME e-Letter
18   GME Articles from *American Medical News*
18   Medical Education Bulletin
18   Guidebook for GME Directors and Coordinators
18   AMA Introduction to the Practice of Medicine Educational Series
19   AMA Continuing Medical Education
20   Gifts to Physicians from Industry
20   Virtual Mentor

21   E. GME-related Organizations
21   Accreditation Council for Graduate Medical Education (ACGME)
25   Association of American Medical Colleges (AAMC)
27   Association for Hospital Medical Education (AHME)
28   Organization of Program Directors Associations (OPDA)
29   Training Administrators of Graduate Medical Education (TAGME)

31 Section II—Specialty/Subspecialty Information and Data

37   Allergy and Immunology   → 2 + IM (3)
39   Anesthesiology
40   Adult Cardiothoracic Anesthesiology
41   Critical Care Medicine
42   Pediatric Anesthesiology
44   Colon and Rectal Surgery   1 + GS (5)
46   Dermatology
47   Clinical and Laboratory Dermatological Immunology
48   Dermatopathology
48   Pediatric Dermatology
48   Procedural Dermatology
49   Emergency Medicine
50   Medical Toxicology
50   Pediatric Emergency Medicine
51   Sports Medicine
52   Undersea and Hyperbaric Medicine
53   Family Medicine   (3)
55   Adolescent Medicine
55   Geriatric Medicine (1)
56   Sports Medicine (1)
57   Hospice and Palliative Medicine
58   Internal Medicine   (3)
60   Adolescent Medicine
60   Cardiovascular Disease
61   Clinical Cardiac Electrophysiology
62   Critical Care Medicine
63   Endocrinology, Diabetes, and Metabolism
64   Gastroenterology (3)
65   Geriatric Medicine (1)
67   Hematology
68   Hematology and Oncology
69   Infectious Disease (2)
70   Interventional Cardiology
71   Nephrology (2)
72   Oncology
73   Pulmonary Disease
74   Pulmonary Disease and Critical Care Medicine
75   Rheumatology (2)
76   Sports Medicine
76   Transplant Hepatology
77   Internal Medicine/Pediatrics
78   Medical Genetics
80   Clinical Biochemical Genetics
80   Clinical Cytogenetics
80   Clinical Genetics (MD)
81   Clinical Molecular Genetics
81   Medical Biochemical Genetics
81   Molecular Genetic Pathology
82   Neurological Surgery
83   Endovascular Surgical Neuroradiology
84   Neurology
85   Child Neurology
86   Clinical Neurophysiology
87   Neurodevelopmental Disabilities
87   Neuromuscular Medicine
88   Vascular Neurology
88   Nuclear Medicine

90 Obstetrics and Gynecology
91   Critical Care Medicine
92   Gynecologic Oncology
92   Maternal-Fetal Medicine
92   Reproductive Endocrinology/Infertility
93 Ophthalmology
94 Orthopaedic Surgery (5)
96   Adult Reconstructive Orthopaedics
96   Foot and Ankle Orthopaedics
96   Hand Surgery
97   Musculoskeletal Oncology
97   Orthopaedic Sports Medicine (1)
99   Orthopaedic Surgery of the Spine (1)
100   Orthopaedic Trauma (1)
100   Pediatric Orthopaedics
100 Otolaryngology
102   Neurotology
102   Pediatric Otolaryngology
103   Plastic Surgery within the Head and Neck
104 Pain Medicine
105 Pathology
107   Blood Banking/ Transfusion Medicine
108   Chemical Pathology
108   Cytopathology
109   Dermatopathology
109   Forensic Pathology
109   Hematology
110   Medical Microbiology
111   Molecular Genetic Pathology
112   Neuropathology
113   Pediatric Pathology
113   Selective Pathology
114 Pediatrics
116   Adolescent Medicine
116   Developmental-Behavioral Pediatrics
116   Medical Toxicology
116   Neonatal-Perinatal Medicine
118   Neurodevelopmental Disabilities
118   Pediatric Cardiology
119   Pediatric Critical Care Medicine
120   Pediatric Emergency Medicine
121   Pediatric Endocrinology
122   Pediatric Gastroenterology
123   Pediatric Hematology/Oncology
124   Pediatric Infectious Diseases
125   Pediatric Nephrology
126   Pediatric Pulmonology
127   Pediatric Rheumatology
127   Pediatric Sports Medicine
128   Pediatric Transplant Hepatology
128 Physical Medicine and Rehabilitation
130   Neuromuscular Medicine
130   Pediatric Rehabilitation Medicine
130   Spinal Cord Injury Medicine
131   Sports Medicine
132 Plastic Surgery
133   Craniofacial Surgery (Plastic Surgery within the Head and Neck)
134   Hand Surgery
135 Preventive Medicine
137   Aerospace Medicine
137   Occupational Medicine
137   Public Health and General Preventive Medicine
138   Medical Toxicology

138   Undersea and Hyperbaric Medicine
138 Psychiatry
140   Addiction Psychiatry
141   Child and Adolescent Psychiatry
142   Forensic Psychiatry
143   Geriatric Psychiatry
144   Psychosomatic Medicine
145 Radiation Oncology
146 Radiology–Diagnostic (4)
148   Abdominal Radiology
149   Cardiothoracic Radiology
149   Endovascular Surgical Neuroradiology
150   Musculoskeletal Radiology
151   Neuroradiology
152   Nuclear Radiology
153   Pediatric Radiology
154   Vascular and Interventional Radiology (1)
155 Sleep Medicine
156 Surgery-General (5)
158   Hand Surgery
158   Pediatric Surgery
159   Surgical Critical Care
160   Vascular Surgery (5+2, 5)
162 Thoracic Surgery
164   Congenital Cardiac Surgery
164 Transitional Year
166 Urology (GS × 1y + 3 or 4)
167   Pediatric Urology
168 Salary Information Supplement from *Modern Healthcare*

(handwritten annotations:) discontinued June 30, 2010 → ; integrated ↙

175 Section III—Accredited Graduate Medical Education Programs

177 Specialties/Subspecialties with ACGME-accredited Programs
178 Abdominal Radiology (Radiology–Diagnostic)
179 Addiction Psychiatry (Psychiatry)
182 Adolescent Medicine (Pediatrics)
184 Adult Cardiothoracic Anesthesiology
187 Adult Reconstructive Orthopaedics (Orthopaedic Surgery)
189 Allergy and Immunology
194 Anesthesiology
203 Blood Banking/Transfusion Medicine (Pathology)
206 Cardiothoracic Radiology (Radiology–Diagnostic)
206 Cardiovascular Disease (Internal Medicine)
218 Chemical Pathology (Pathology)
218 Child and Adolescent Psychiatry (Psychiatry)
227 Child Neurology (Neurology)
232 Clinical Cardiac Electrophysiology (Internal Medicine)
238 Clinical Neurophysiology (Neurology)
244 Colon and Rectal Surgery
248 Congenital Cardiac Surgery (Thoracic Surgery)
249 Craniofacial Surgery (Plastic Surgery)
249 Critical Care Medicine (Anesthesiology)
253 Critical Care Medicine (Internal Medicine)
255 Cytopathology (Pathology)
261 Dermatology
269 Dermatopathology (Dermatology)
273 Developmental-Behavioral Pediatrics (Pediatrics)
275 Emergency Medicine
285 Endocrinology, Diabetes, and Metabolism (Internal Medicine)

294 Endovascular Surgical Neuroradiology (Neurological Surgery)
294 Endovascular Surgical Neuroradiology (Neurology)
294 Endovascular Surgical Neuroradiology (Radiology)
295 Family Medicine
323 Foot and Ankle Orthopaedics (Orthopaedic Surgery)
323 Forensic Pathology (Pathology)
326 Forensic Psychiatry (Psychiatry)
329 Gastroenterology (Internal Medicine)
340 Geriatric Medicine (Family Medicine)
343 Geriatric Medicine (Internal Medicine)
350 Geriatric Psychiatry (Psychiatry)
354 Hand Surgery (General Surgery)
355 Hand Surgery (Orthopaedic Surgery)
359 Hand Surgery (Plastic Surgery)
360 Hematology (Internal Medicine)
361 Hematology (Pathology)
366 Hematology and Oncology (Internal Medicine)
375 Hospice and Palliative Medicine
378 Infectious Disease (Internal Medicine)
388 Internal Medicine
411 Internal Medicine/Pediatrics
417 Interventional Cardiology (Internal Medicine)
426 Medical Biochemical Genetics (Medical Genetics)
426 Medical Genetics
430 Medical Microbiology (Pathology)
431 Medical Toxicology (Emergency Medicine)
433 Medical Toxicology (Preventive Medicine)
433 Molecular Genetic Pathology (Medical Genetics and Pathology)
435 Musculoskeletal Oncology (Orthopaedic Surgery)
436 Musculoskeletal Radiology (Radiology–Diagnostic)
437 Neonatal-Perinatal Medicine (Pediatrics)
444 Nephrology (Internal Medicine)
453 Neurodevelopmental Disabilities (Neurology)
454 Neurological Surgery
461 Neurology
470 Neuromuscular Medicine (Neurology)
472 Neuropathology (Pathology)
475 Neuroradiology (Radiology–Diagnostic)
481 Neurotology (Otolaryngology)
482 Nuclear Medicine
486 Nuclear Radiology (Radiology–Diagnostic)
488 Obstetrics and Gynecology
504 Oncology (Internal Medicine)
505 Ophthalmology
513 Orthopaedic Sports Medicine (Orthopaedic Surgery)
519 Orthopaedic Surgery
530 Orthopaedic Surgery of the Spine (Orthopaedic Surgery)
531 Orthopaedic Trauma (Orthopaedic Surgery)
532 Otolaryngology
539 Pain Medicine
546 Pathology-Anatomic and Clinical
556 Pediatric Anesthesiology (Anesthesiology)
559 Pediatric Cardiology (Pediatrics)
562 Pediatric Critical Care Medicine (Pediatrics)
567 Pediatric Emergency Medicine (Emergency Medicine)
568 Pediatric Emergency Medicine (Pediatrics)
572 Pediatric Endocrinology (Pediatrics)
576 Pediatric Gastroenterology (Pediatrics)
580 Pediatric Hematology/Oncology (Pediatrics)
585 Pediatric Infectious Diseases (Pediatrics)
589 Pediatric Nephrology (Pediatrics)
592 Pediatric Orthopaedics (Orthopaedic Surgery)

594 Pediatric Otolaryngology (Otolaryngology)
594 Pediatric Pathology (Pathology)
596 Pediatric Pulmonology (Pediatrics)
600 Pediatric Radiology (Radiology–Diagnostic)
603 Pediatric Rehabilitation Medicine (Physical Medicine and Rehabilitation)
604 Pediatric Rheumatology (Pediatrics)
606 Pediatric Sports Medicine (Pediatrics)
607 Pediatric Surgery (General Surgery)
610 Pediatric Transplant Hepatology (Pediatrics)
610 Pediatric Urology (Urology)
612 Pediatrics
625 Physical Medicine and Rehabilitation
631 Plastic Surgery
636 Plastic Surgery–Integrated
639 Preventive Medicine: Aerospace Medicine
639 Preventive Medicine: General Preventive Medicine
641 Preventive Medicine: Occupational Medicine
644 Preventive Medicine: Public Health and General Preventive Medicine
645 Procedural Dermatology (Dermatology)
647 Psychiatry
660 Psychosomatic Medicine (Psychiatry)
663 Pulmonary Disease (Internal Medicine)
664 Pulmonary Disease and Critical Care Medicine (Internal Medicine)
673 Radiation Oncology
679 Radiology–Diagnostic
691 Rheumatology (Internal Medicine)
699 Selective Pathology (Pathology)
702 Sleep Medicine
707 Spinal Cord Injury Medicine (Physical Medicine and Rehabilitation)
709 Sports Medicine (Emergency Medicine)
710 Sports Medicine (Family Medicine)
717 Surgery-General
733 Surgical Critical Care (General Surgery)
739 Thoracic Surgery
745 Thoracic Surgery–Integrated
745 Transitional Year
753 Transplant Hepatology (Internal Medicine)
755 Undersea and Hyperbaric Medicine (Emergency Medicine)
756 Undersea and Hyperbaric Medicine (Preventive Medicine)
756 Urology
765 Vascular and Interventional Radiology (Radiology–Diagnostic)
772 Vascular Neurology (Neurology)
776 Vascular Surgery (General Surgery)
783 Vascular Surgery-Integrated (General Surgery)

785 Section IV—New and Withdrawn Programs

785 New Programs
793 Withdrawn Programs

797 Section V—Graduate Medical Education Teaching Institutions

877 Appendix A—Combined Specialty Programs

877 Note on Combined Internal Medicine/Pediatrics Programs
877 Diagnostic Radiology/Nuclear Medicine/Nuclear Radiology
878 Emergency Medicine/Family Medicine
878 Internal Medicine/Dermatology
879 Internal Medicine/Emergency Medicine
880 Internal Medicine/Emergency Medicine/Critical Care Medicine
880 Internal Medicine/Family Medicine
881 Internal Medicine/Medical Genetics
881 Internal Medicine/Neurology
882 Internal Medicine/Nuclear Medicine
882 Internal Medicine/Physical Medicine and Rehabilitation
882 Internal Medicine/Preventive Medicine
883 Internal Medicine/Psychiatry
884 Neurology/Diagnostic Radiology/Neuroradiology
884 Pediatrics/Dermatology
884 Pediatrics/Emergency Medicine
885 Pediatrics/Medical Genetics
885 Pediatrics/Physical Medicine and Rehabilitation
885 Pediatrics/Psychiatry/Child and Adolescent Psychiatry
886 Psychiatry/Family Medicine
887 Psychiatry/Neurology

903 Appendix B—Medical Specialty Board Certification Requirements

904 Member Boards of the American Board of Medical Specialties
905 The American Board of Medical Specialties (ABMS) and Board Certification
American Board of:
927 Allergy and Immunology
927 Anesthesiology
928 Colon and Rectal Surgery
929 Dermatology
929 Emergency Medicine
930 Family Medicine
930 Internal Medicine
931 Medical Genetics
932 Neurological Surgery
932 Nuclear Medicine
933 Obstetrics and Gynecology
934 Ophthalmology
935 Orthopaedic Surgery
935 Otolaryngology
936 Pathology
937 Pediatrics
938 Physical Medicine and Rehabilitation
939 Plastic Surgery
940 Preventive Medicine
941 Psychiatry and Neurology
942 Radiology
942 Surgery
943 Thoracic Surgery
943 Urology

945 Appendix C—Medical Schools in the United States

949 Appendix D—Graduate Medical Education Glossary

953 Appendix E—Listings of Subspecialty and Fellowship Programs

953 Introduction
953 Abdominal Transplant Surgery Fellowships
953 Aesthetic Plastic Surgery Fellowships
954 Breast Fellowships
954 Dermatology Fellowships
954 Electrodiagnostic Medicine Fellowships
954 Endocrine Surgery Fellowships
955 General Internal Medicine Fellowships
955 Advanced Gynecologic Endoscopy Fellowships
955 Hospitalist and Hospital Medicine Programs
956 Minimally Invasive and GI Surgery Fellowships
956 Neurology Fellowship Programs
957 Obstetrics-Gynecology Subspecialty Programs
957 Ophthalmology Fellowship Programs
957 Palliative Medicine Fellowship Programs
958 Pathology Fellowship Programs
958 Spine Programs
958 Surgical Oncology Fellowships
959 Trauma Fellowships

961 Appendix F—Medical Licensure Information

961 Obtaining a Medical License: The Basics
963 State Medical Licensure Requirements and Statistics: Contents
965 Table 1: Administration of the US Medical Licensing Examination Step 3: Graduate Medical Education Requirements
967 Table 2: Administration of the US Medical Licensing Examination Step 3: Time Limits for Completion
970 Table 3: Initial Licensure of US Medical/Osteopathic School Graduates
973 Table 4: Initial Licensure of Canadian Citizens Who Are Graduates of Accredited Canadian Medical Schools
977 Table 5: Initial Licensure of International Medical Graduates
980 Table 6: Medical Student Clerkship Regulations
983 Table 7: Additional Policies Concerning IMGs and DOs
986 Table 8: Accredited Subspecialties and Nonaccredited Fellowships That Satisfy GME Requirements for Licensure
989 Table 9: Licensure Requirement Exemptions for Eminent Physicians and Medical School Faculty
992 Table 10: Teaching (Visiting Professor) Licenses
996 Table 11: Resident/Fellow Physician Licenses
999 Contact Information for State Medical/Osteopathic Boards

Preface

The *Graduate Medical Education Directory* (94th edition), published by the American Medical Association (AMA), lists programs accredited by the Accreditation Council for Graduate Medical Education (ACGME).

The *Directory* provides medical students with a list of accredited graduate medical education (GME) programs in the United States, which aids them in making important professional decisions. State licensing boards, specialty societies, and hospitals refer to the *Directory* to verify the authenticity of programs presented by physicians who wish to qualify for licensure, certification, or hospital privileges. The *Directory* provides a unique historical record of accredited GME programs and background information about the ACGME accreditation process.

Contents of the Directory

- Section I—Graduate Medical Education Information—provides descriptions of various organizations involved in GME, including the ACGME, National Resident Matching Program (NRMP), Electronic Residency Application Service (ERAS), and Educational Commission for Foreign Medical Graduates (ECFMG), as well as information on AMA products, projects, and initiatives relevant to medical students, residents/fellows, program directors, and academic physicians.
- Section II—Specialty/Subspecialty Information and Data—provides descriptions of and data for all specialties/subspecialties with ACGME-accredited residency/fellowship programs and/or ACGME Program Requirements in effect. Also included are subspecialties for which a member board of the American Board of Medical Specialties (ABMS) offers certification.
- Section III—Accredited Graduate Medical Education Programs—as the official list of ACGME-accredited programs, generally reflects accreditation actions completed by December of the previous year. The data published in this edition were transferred from the ACGME to the AMA on January 15, 2009. *Programs with withdrawal dates after this date are included in Section III.* Section III provides program name, sponsoring institution, major participating institution(s), program director name, address, and phone/fax numbers, e-mail address, accredited program length, ACGME approved/offered positions, and program ID number. Specialties and subspecialties are listed in alphabetical order. Programs within each specialty or subspecialty are listed in alphabetical order by state and city. A list of accredited transitional year programs offered by hospitals or groups of hospitals is also included. Newly appointed program directors since the publication of last year's *Directory* are noted with an asterisk. (*Note:* The *Directory* may include programs on probation. To check a program's current accreditation status, go to the ACGME Web site, www.acgme.org, click on "public," then click on "Search Through Accredited Programs and Sponsors" to look up information about programs and sponsors, including current accreditation status.)
- Section IV—New and Withdrawn Programs—lists GME programs newly accredited since the publication of the 2008-2009 edition of the *Directory* and programs that are no longer accredited to offer GME as of December 31, 2008, or earlier.
- Section V—Graduate Medical Education Teaching Institutions—lists institutions and organizations that sponsor or participate in GME programs. Teaching institution listings include type of affiliation (sponsor and/or participant) and are listed alphabetically by state and city. Institution listings include the name and address of the institution, medical school affiliations (as verified biennially by the deans of accredited US medical schools), a list of the specialties and subspecialties in which the institution provides training, and the institution identification number.
- Appendix A—Combined Specialty Programs—provides information on programs that offer combined specialty training. Combined training consists of a coherent educational experience in two or more closely related specialty or subspecialty programs. The educational plan for combined training is approved by the specialty board of each of the specialties to assure that resident physicians completing combined training are eligible for board certification in each of the component specialties. Each specialty or subspecialty program is separately accredited by the ACGME through its respective specialty review committee. The duration of combined training is longer than any one of its component specialty programs standing alone, and shorter than all of its component specialty programs together.
- Appendix B—Medical Specialty Board Certification Requirements—contains information about the American Board of Medical Specialties (ABMS) and the certification requirements for each of the 24 member boards of the ABMS. Certification is the process by which a medical specialty board grants recognition to a physician who has met certain predetermined qualifications, as specified by the board. Certification requirements are also published by and available from each medical specialty board. Questions concerning certification requirements should be directed to the particular specialty board office listed in Appendix B.
- Appendix C—Medical Schools in the United States—contains a list of US medical schools accredited by the Liaison Committee on Medical Education (LCME), including the identification number, name, and location of each LCME-accredited medical school.
- Appendix D—Graduate Medical Education Glossary—defines various terms commonly used in GME.
- Appendix E—Listings of Subspecialty and Fellowship Programs—provides information on subspecialty and fellowship programs outside the purview of the ACGME accreditation process.
- Appendix F—Medical Licensure Information—contains an article on the basics of medical licensure, in addition to information on GME-related licensure policies of state medical boards, as published in 2009 edition of the AMA's *State Medical Licensure Requirements and Statistics.*

Production of the Directory

The work of the ACGME's review committees, which review and evaluate programs and sponsoring institutions, provide the basis for program and institutional information included in Sections III through V of the *Directory.* The ACGME shares its data on accreditation actions and program changes with the AMA quarterly for the exclusive purpose of maintaining an accurate database to benefit programs, residents, applicants, and the public. The AMA, in turn, shares with the ACGME information collected through its annual survey of GME programs, but program directors are reminded that most review committees require prompt notification in writing of changes in the program's leadership. Providing information on program director changes through the National GME Census does not meet this requirement. In addition, most review committees require a current copy of the curriculum vitae for new program directors.

The *Directory,* as the official list of ACGME-accredited programs, generally reflects accreditation actions completed by December of the previous year. The data published in this edition were transferred from the ACGME to the AMA in January 2008. Readers are reminded that accreditation actions and related changes can alter the ACGME program population on a daily basis, and that the *Directory* serves only as a "snapshot" of this population at a given moment. For the most current information on ACGME-accredited programs, consult the ACGME Web site: www.acgme.org.

The data for combined programs listed in Appendix A were obtained via the National GME Census (see Section I for more information).

Disclaimer

It is the AMA's understanding that all institutions listed in the *Graduate Medical Education Directory* are required by law to include the phrase "EEO, M/F/D/V" (Equal Employment Opportunity, Minority/Female/Disabled/Veteran) on any information distributed for public view.

Back Issues of the Directory

Copies of previous editions of the *Directory* are available for purchase at $25 per copy. For more information or to order, please call 312 464-5333. In addition, the CD-ROM version of the *Directory* contains Adobe Acrobat files of editions from 1996-1997 to the present.

Special Acknowledgment to the ACGME

The AMA gratefully acknowledges the cooperation of the Accreditation Council for Graduate Medical Education (ACGME) in supplying the list of programs accredited by the ACGME and sponsoring/participating institutions and relevant information about the ACGME and its accreditation process. The AMA thanks all RRC executive directors and accreditation administrators as well as ACGME staff Jeanne Heard, MD, PhD, Ingrid Philibert, John Nylen, MBA, Rebecca Miller, MS, and Julie Jacob for their many ongoing contributions to the *Directory*.

Acknowledgments

Many people contributed to the publication of this edition of the *Graduate Medical Education Directory*. In addition to collaborative efforts with the ACGME (see "Special Acknowledgment," above), the ABMS and staff of the member boards of the ABMS provided requirements for certification in each of the medical specialties and subspecialties.

Special acknowledgment is also given to the following groups and individuals:

- **AMA Department of Data Collection**, for data collection and information resources management: Chris Mathews, Lydia Cruz, John Wilson, and Tammy Stockton.
- **Association of American Medical Colleges**, for its collaboration with the AMA in collecting data on combined programs (see Appendix A) via the National GME Census: Jennifer Faerberg and Fesum Kebede.
- **AMA Book Group** (listed on p. ii).
- **AMA Medical Education Group**, for data cleaning, QA, and editorial advising and assistance: Sarah Brotherton, PhD, Sylvia Etzel, Jacqueline Drake, Barbara Barzansky, PhD, Jeanette Harmon, Dorothy Grant-Bryant, Enza Perrone, and Arecia Washington.

In addition, we would like to acknowledge the many contributions of the following individuals/organizations for assistance with the indicated sections/appendices of this book:

Section I
- Careers in Medicine—George V Richard, PhD
- Choosing a Medical Specialty—Rebecca Gierhahn, AMA Medical Student Section
- Succeeding from Medical School to Practice— Jon Fanning, Anu Gupta, AMA Resident and Fellow Section
- Transitioning to Residency: What Medical Students Need to Know—Phyllis Kopriva, AMA Minority Affairs Consortium

- The Residency Interview: A Guide for Medical Students—Phyllis Kopriva, AMA Women Physicians Congress
- Electronic Residency Application Service—Renee Overton, Moira Edwards
- Find a Residency or Fellowship—Jon Fanning, Anu Gupta, AMA Resident and Fellow Section
- National Resident Matching Program—Mona Signer
- Information on Matching Programs—Henry Sondheimer, MD, Association of American Medical Colleges; Dennis S Thomatos, San Francisco Matching Program, American Academy of Ophthalmology; Susan Banner, Canadian Resident Matching Service; Hope Thompkins, American Urological Association Residency Matching Program
- Entry of Foreign-born Medical Graduates to the United States—Tracy A Cuddy, Eleanor M Fitzpatrick, Elizabeth M Ingraham, Tracy Wallowicz, Educational Commission for Foreign Medical Graduates; Ann H Lance, Bruce R Larson, Esq, Mayo Clinic
- AMA International Medical Graduates Section—J Mori Johnson
- Virtual Mentor—Faith Lagay, PhD
- Association of American Medical Colleges—Sunny Yoder
- Organization of Program Directors Associations—Sandi Trusky
- Training Administrators of Graduate Medical Education— Linda Gacioch and Ruth Nawotniak

Section II
- American Board of Medical Specialties—Lori Boukas, Sylvia McGreal
- *Modern Healthcare*—Dave Burda, Rebecca Mielcarski

We would also like to recognize the many contributions of Rod Hill of North Coast Associates, the typesetter of this publication.

Fred Donini-Lenhoff, MA, Editor
Paul H Rockey, MD, MPH, Director, Division of Undergraduate and Graduate Medical Education

Section I

Graduate Medical Education Information

A. Residency Application and Career Planning Resources

Match Timeline

Class Year	Period	Suggested Activities and Tasks
Year 3	October - March	• Begin working on your curriculum vitae (CV). Crafting a high quality CV can take 8-10 hours. Information for the CV can be used in the ERAS application and provided to those writing your letters of recommendation • Review the AAMC/NRMP *Charting Outcomes in the Match* report to assess qualifications and competitiveness for different specialties
	February - June	• Review residency programs and physician workforce data through the AAMC Careers in Medicine Specialty Pages and FREIDA Online • Depending on your school's schedule, make an appointment with your Associate Dean to discuss the Medical School Performance Evaluation (MSPE) process (at some schools this may occur later in the year) • Write your personal statement
	Summer	• Obtain your ERAS token (a special code) from your advisor or the Student Affairs dean's office • Register with the National Resident Matching Program (NRMP) for the Main Residency Match • Register for early Match, if applicable
Year 4	July - September	• Complete the ERAS application using the MyERAS site (www.aamc.org/students/eras/start.htm), including the designation of programs where your application is to be transmitted • Identify additional faculty for writing letters of recommendation
	September - October	• Begin preparing for residency interviews • If you haven't taken the USMLE Step 2, consider using this time to prepare
	October - January	• MSPE released November 1 • Residency interviews • Early Match deadlines usually occur in early or mid-January
	January - February	• Begin entering your Rank Order List for the NRMP match
	March	• Match Day—typically the third Thursday in March; results are formally announced at 12:00pm EST
	April - June	• Sign the contract with your residency program • Graduate and prepare to begin residency – Congratulations! • Begin preparations for moving
	June - July	• Residency begins

Reprinted with permission from the Association of American Medical Colleges, 2450 N St, NW, Washington, DC 20037-1126 USA. Copyright © 2008. All rights reserved.

Fellowship and Residency Electronic Interactive Database Access (FREIDA) Online®

FREIDA Online is a free Internet database of approximately 8,500 graduate medical education programs accredited by the Accreditation Council for Graduate Medical Education (ACGME) or approved by member boards of the American Board of Medical Specialties.

Users of FREIDA Online can search the database by specialty/subspecialty or state/region, among other criteria. The SearchPlus feature also allows users to compare programs by features of importance, such as number of first year positions, salary, and program setting. In addition, FREIDA Online also displays aggregate statistics for each specialty and subspecialty, providing averages and percents, for example, on the average number of faculty per program in the specialty, or the average number of hours on-duty.

AMA student and resident members can save their favorite programs in an electronic folder and can print their own mailing labels to contact programs.

GME programs update data for FREIDA Online via the National GME Census, an annual survey conducted by the AMA and Association of American Medical Colleges. The survey instrument, GME Track, is available online at www.aamc.org/gmetrack.

Programs: Modifying Your FREIDA Online Listing

In addition to providing data via the National GME Census, as explained above, program directors and staff can also modify the basic information that appears on FREIDA Online throughout the year by accessing www.ama-assn.org/go/freida.

For example, if there is a new program director or a new contact person, you can make these changes on FREIDA Online directly. Changes are reviewed by FREIDA staff before the data are updated; changes take approximately 2 weeks to process.

FREIDA Online Listings: Basic and Expanded

All programs listed in FREIDA include the following *Basic Listing*:
- Program name
- Program identifier (eg, 120-36-21-000)
- Specialty/subspecialty (eg, family medicine)
- Program director (name, mailing address, phone, fax, e-mail, Web address)
- Person to contact for more information about the program (name, mailing address, phone, fax, e-mail)
- Accredited length; required length
- Accepting applications
- Program start date
- Participates in ERAS
- Affiliated with US government
- Institution list (sponsor and participant[s])

In addition, programs that select the *Expanded Detailed Listing* option (as the majority of programs do) provide the following information to students and residents:

General information
- Comments (used to highlight special qualities about the program, such as special features or description of surrounding hospital setting)
- Total program size (by year)
- Primary teaching site (eg, City University Hospital)
- Primary teaching site uses electronic medical records
- Program best described as (eg, community-based hospital)
- Previous GME required
- Preliminary positions offered
- Information on USMLE Step 2-CS

- Participation in National Resident Matching Program (NRMP); code(s)
- Participation in San Francisco match
- Participation in another matching program
- Number of interviews conducted last year for first year positions
- Required letters of recommendation
- Earliest date for applications; latest date for applications; interview period

Program faculty
- Number of faculty (physician and nonphysician)
- Full-time and part-time physicians and nonphysicians
- Percentage of full-time paid female physician faculty
- Ratio of full-time equivalent paid faculty to positions

Work schedule
- Average hours/week on duty during first year (excluding beeper call)
- Maximum consecutive hours on duty during first year (excluding beeper call)
- Average number of 24-hour off duty periods per week during first year
- Moonlighting allowed within institution
- Night float system (residents do/do not participate during first year)
- Call schedule (by year)
- Most taxing schedule and frequency per year
- Beeper or home call (weeks/year)

Educational environment
Educational setting
- Average hours/week of regularly scheduled lectures/conferences
- Percent training at hospital outpatient clinics
- Percent training in ambulatory non-hospital community-based settings, eg, physician offices, community clinics

Educational benefits
- Curriculum on management of tobacco dependence
- Program to assess/enhance medical professionalism
- Debt management/financial counseling
- Formal program to develop teaching skills
- Formal program to foster interdisciplinary teamwork
- Formal mentoring program
- Continuous quality improvement training
- International experience
- Resident/fellow retreats
- Off-campus electives
- Hospice/home care experience
- Cultural competence awareness
- Instruction in medical Spanish or other non-English language
- Alternative/complementary medicine curriculum
- Training in identifying and reporting of domestic violence/abuse
- MPH/MBA or PhD training
- Research rotation

Educational features
- Offers additional training or educational experience beyond accredited length
- Residents supervise medical students
- Offers a primary care track, rural track, women's health track, hospitalist track, research track/nonaccredited fellowship, and/or another special track

Resident Evaluation
- Yearly specialty in-service examination required
- Patient surveys
- Portfolio system
- 360-degree evaluations
- Objective structured clinical examinations (OSCE)

Program evaluation
- Program graduation rates
- Board certification rates
- In-training examination scores
- Performance-based assessment scores (eg, OSCE)

Employment policies and benefits
- Part-time/shared positions
- On-site child care; subsidized child care
- Allowance/stipend for professional expenses
- Leave for educational meetings/conferences
- Moving allowance
- Housing stipend
- On-call meal allowance
- Parking
- PDAs available
- Job placement assistance
- Cross coverage in case of illness/disability

Compensation and leave (by year)
- Salary compensation
- Vacation weeks
- Sick days

Leave availability
- Maximum number of paid and unpaid days for family/medical leave

Major medical benefits
- Major medical insurance for residents and dependents
- Outpatient/inpatient mental health insurance
- Group life insurance
- Dental insurance
- Disability insurance
- Disability insurance for occupationally acquired HIV
- When medical insurance coverage begins

Pricing for Expanded Detailed Listing in FREIDA
- $90 Subspecialty program
- $160 Specialty program

Note: As an added bonus for those programs that choose an expanded listing in FREIDA Online, the *GME Library on CD-ROM* (see below) includes a direct link to those programs' FREIDA Online listings, under "Other information."

Information

www.ama-assn.org/go/freida
800 266-3966
312 464-5830 Fax
E-mail: freida@ama-assn.org
To view a sample FREIDA Online listing, visit
www.ama-assn.org/go/freidasample

GME Library on CD-ROM

The *Graduate Medical Education Library on CD-ROM* combines all information from the text version of the *Directory* with advanced search functions to help users find the program or institution they're seeking. Its Web browser interface—no installation required—allows for quick, easy access to all program and institution data and many clickable links, including hyperlinks to program Web sites.

The CD-ROM also includes archive copies of each year's *Directory* since 1996-1997. The CD's XML capabilities allow for quick data sorts and program comparison by a large number of data variables, including the majority of those listed below. These data are derived from the National GME Census, as are the data for FREIDA Online.

Note: As an added bonus for those programs that choose an expanded listing in FREIDA Online, the CD-ROM includes a link to those programs' FREIDA Online listing, under "Other Information."

Program Information
- Program name
- Program setting
- Accredited length (years)
- Years required
- Program size
- Graduate Year 1 (GY1) positions
- Requires prior GME (years)

Work Schedule
- Average hours/week duty
- Maximum hours consecutive duty
- Most taxing call schedule
- Duration
- Moonlighting allowed
- Employment policies/benefits
- Salary, program year one
- On-site child care
- Part-time/shared positions
- Multiple start dates

Educational Curriculum
- Continuous quality improvement
- International experience
- Resident/fellow retreats
- Off-campus electives
- Hospice/home care experience
- Cultural competence awareness
- Non-English language instruction
- Alternative/complementary medicine
- Research rotation/duration

Additional Training
- MPH/MBA training or PhD training
- Offers additional training
- Requires additional training
- Additional training length

Other Information
- FREIDA listing
- Plastic surgery integrated model
- Preventive medicine specialty area
- Military
- Subspecialty code(s)
- Sponsoring specialty

Contact Information
- Sponsoring institution
- Major participating institution(s)
- Program director and program codirector
- Address
- Phone/fax/e-mail

Information

The CD-ROM is $115 list price or $85 for AMA members, plus shipping/handling and state tax, if applicable. To order, contact:
AMA Order Department
PO Box 930876
Atlanta, GA 31193-0876
800 621-8335
312 464-5600 Fax
www.amabookstore.com

Careers in Medicine

Careers in Medicine is a comprehensive, four-phase career planning and development program sponsored by the Association of American Medical Colleges (AAMC). Designed to equip medical students with the skills and information needed to make informed career decisions, it focuses on helping students understand their medical career options, select their specialty, and apply to a residency program that fits their career goals. The program is offered in conjunction with medical school staff, and can also be accessed via the Internet at www.aamc.org/careersinmedicine.

As students work through the program they engage in a process of self-understanding, career exploration, decision-making, and career planning. They can assess their career interests, values, personality, and skills online and view results at any time through their private Personal Profile. Of special interest to students exploring specialty options are the Careers in Medicine Specialty Pages, which provide comprehensive information for 122 specialty and subspecialty areas, including nature of the work, personal characteristics, residency/ fellowship training requirements, Match results, workforce statistics, physician compensation, and links to over 1,000 specialty associations, journals, and newsletters.

Careers in Medicine offers guidance and interactive decision-making tools for making these important career decisions. Students can cycle through the program several times during medical school as they develop increasingly more refined views of their preferred career paths. The program is currently available to all AAMC-member US and Canadian medical schools. It is also available to medical students in osteopathic medical schools that have completed licensing agreements with the AAMC. Staffs in medical schools offer workshops using the Careers in Medicine model throughout all 4 years of medical school.

To obtain information about the program and to find out more about accessing the password-protected Web site, students should contact their Careers in Medicine Liaison, or the student affairs dean, in their medical school. Residents should contact the Careers in Medicine Office at careersinmedicine@aamc.org.

Choosing a Medical Specialty

Since 1994, the AMA Medical Student Section has maintained *Choosing a Medical Specialty*, a bibliography of current sources for information on the medical and surgical specialties for students preparing to enter into the residency selection process. This online publication directs students to numerous resources available to help them make informed career choices.

Information

www.ama-assn.org/go/choosingyourspecialty
AMA Medical Student Section
800 621-8335 x4746
E-mail: mss@ama-assn.org

ERAS

ERAS®—the Electronic Residency Application Service, provided by the AAMC—has been working together with applicants, medical schools, and training programs to streamline the application process for 14 years. Using the ERAS service, applicants to residency and fellowship programs transmit applications and supporting documents to training programs over the Internet. Each year, the ERAS system transmits more than 25 million documents, bypassing the laborious paper process and the US Postal Service.

Specialties using ERAS 2010 (residency positions begin July 2010) include:

- Anesthesiology (most positions begin July 2011)
- Dermatology (most positions begin July 2011)
- Diagnostic Radiology (positions begin July 2011)
- Emergency Medicine
- Family Medicine
- Family Medicine/Physical Medicine and Rehabilitation combined programs
- Internal Medicine (preliminary and categorical)
- Internal Medicine/Dermatology combined programs
- Internal Medicine/Emergency Medicine combined programs
- Internal Medicine/Family Medicine combined programs
- Internal Medicine/Pediatrics combined programs
- Internal Medicine/Physical Medicine and Rehabilitation combined programs
- Internal Medicine/Psychiatry combined programs
- Neurological Surgery
- Neurology
- Nuclear Medicine
- Obstetrics/Gynecology
- Orthopaedic Surgery
- Otolaryngology
- Pathology
- Pediatrics
- Pediatrics/Emergency Medicine combined programs
- Pediatrics/Physical Medicine and Rehabilitation combined programs
- Pediatrics/Psychiatry/Child Psychiatry Triple Board programs
- Physical Medicine and Rehabilitation (most positions begin July 2011)
- Plastic Surgery Integrated Programs offering PGY1 positions
- Preventive Medicine*
- Psychiatry
- Psychiatry/Neurology
- Radiation Oncology
- Surgery (General)
- Thoracic Surgery - Integrated
- Transitional Year
- Urology
- Vascular Surgery - Integrated
- All US Army/Navy programs offering PGY1 positions
  * Specialties debuting in ERAS 2010

Having successfully implemented ERAS in residency specialties, the service focused its attention on offering fellowship applicants and programs the same benefits available to residency participants. ERAS Fellowships, introduced in 2003, offers two cycles for fellowship applications. The July application cycle has fellowship programs receiving applications in July for positions that commence 12 months later. The December application cycle has programs receiving applications in December for positions that begin 18 months later. Fellowship specialties using ERAS 2010 include:

July Application Cycle Specialties

(Apply July 2009; Positions begin July 2010)

- Colon and Rectal Surgery
- Geriatric Medicine (Family Practice and Internal Medicine)
- Pediatric Critical Care*
- Pediatric Rheumatology
- Pediatric Emergency Medicine (Emergency Medicine and Pediatrics)

December Application Cycle Specialties

(Apply December 2009; Positions begin July 2011)

- Asthma, Allergy and Immunology
- Cardiovascular Disease
- Endocrinology, Diabetes and Metabolism
- Female Pelvic Medicine and Reconstructive Surgery*
- Gastroenterology
- Gynecologic Oncology
- Hematology and Oncology
- Infectious Diseases
- Interventional Cardiology
- Maternal-Fetal Medicine
- Neonatal-Perinatal Medicine
- Nephrology
- Pediatric Endocrinology*
- Pediatric Gastroenterology
- Pediatric Hematology-Oncology
- Pediatric Infectious Diseases*
- Pediatric Nephrology
- Pediatric Surgery
- Pulmonary Disease and Critical Care Medicine
- Rheumatology
- Thoracic Surgery
- Vascular Surgery
  * Specialties debuting in ERAS 2010

Residency students and graduates of US medical schools should contact the student affairs office at their medical schools of graduation for information about ERAS. Students and graduates of foreign medical schools should contact the Educational Commission for Foreign Medical Graduates (ECFMG). All fellowship applicants, including US and international graduates, should contact the ERAS Fellowships Document Office (EFDO). General information about ERAS, including EFDO contact information and participating programs, is available at www.aamc.org/eras.

Succeeding from Medical School to Practice

Succeeding from Medical School to Practice (www.ama-assn.org/go/succeeding) is a comprehensive resource that helps medical students, residents, fellows, and young physicians prepare for a successful career in medicine and confront the many nonclinical demands of training and the practice environment. Developed by your physician colleagues, this easy-to-navigate resource features tips, links, and streaming video organized into three sections.

Medical school and residency

- How to prepare for the match
- What are the duty hour standards and how to deal with violations
- What are the requirements for board certification
- How is medical education funded
- How to take advantage of foreign residency rotations

- How to budget and manage personal finances

Preparing for practice

- How to get credentialed and obtain hospital privileges
- Weighing your options—medical practice start-up, purchase or buy-in
- What to look for in medical liability and disability insurance policies
- What does physician profiling mean to you
- What to consider in selecting a practice setting and geographical location

Joining, purchasing, or starting a practice

- How to negotiate an employment contract
- How to value a medical practice for purchase or buy-in
- How to write a business plan, estimate costs and set up a practice
- How to build a practice through marketing
- How to deal with the challenges of managed care and claims management

www.ama-assn.org/go/succeeding
AMA Resident and Fellow Section
312 464-4748
E-mail: rfs@ama-assn.org

Transitioning to Residency: What Medical Students Need to Know

The AMA's Minority Affairs Consortium (MAC) has developed this online resource for medical students transitioning into residency training programs. The information is meant to provide an overview of the planning, application, and selection process from the personal viewpoints of MAC members who have successfully gone through the process themselves.

Sections include the following:
- Getting Ready: Medical School Years 1-3
- The Residency Application: Information & Procedures
- The Application Process: A Timetable for Success
- Writing Your Personal Statement
- Selecting Your Residency Programs
- The Residency Interview: Making the Most of It
- Not Matched? The Decision to Reapply
- Making the Most of Your Residency
- Residency Programs: An Inside Look
- General Residency Questions

Visit the MAC Web Site: www.ama-assn.org/go/mac
AMA Minority Affairs Consortium
312 464-5622
E-mail: mps@ama-assn.org

The Residency Interview: A Guide for Medical Students

This online resource guide, available to AMA members, is published by the AMA Women Physicians Congress (AMA WPC), a special interest group comprised of physicians and medical students who are advocates for women's health issues and women in medicine professional and life balancing issues.

This resource addresses the following topics:
- Handling gender-based questions
- Couples match

- Shared and part-time residencies
- Preparing for your interview
- Interview questions to ask
- Common and uncommon questions that will be asked of you
- What to bring with you

Both men and women medical students report anxiety and confusion when faced with interviews for residency placement. Women medical students reported that they had difficulty with their residency training interviews when asked questions dealing with gender. Some women reported that they were never asked gender-based questions, but others reported being asked questions about their marriages and plans for childbearing. Men and women respondents alike said they were often asked questions which they found to be vague or provocative.

The interview process is stressful for all medical students, and medical schools seldom coach their students in how to approach residency placement. In publishing this guide, the AMA Women Physician Congress (WPC) Governing Council felt that it would meet the needs of all medical students and would include a special section for women on gender- based questions.

This guide is not intended to help students pick a specialty or how to interview specifically in the different specialties, nor does it suggest how to plan electives. Rather, it is an overview of the interviewing process, intended as a guide to start students' thinking about what they will encounter.

Information

Visit the WPC web site: www.ama-assn.org/go/wpc
AMA Women Physicians Congress
312 464-5622
312 464-5845 Fax
E-mail: wpc@ama-assn.org

Find a Residency or Fellowship

In response to many requests from medical school graduates seeking unfilled positions in residency programs, the AMA Resident and Fellow Section (AMA-RFS) offers a Web-based list of open residency and fellowship positions.

Postings on the "Find a Residency or Fellowship" Web site include a short description of the position and the program, as provided by program officials, as well as contact information. The site also provides links to specialty societies that offer information on residency vacancies.

www.ama-assn.org/go/rfs

Programs that wish to list a vacant position can enter the required data at www.ama-assn.org/go/rfs.

For information on positions in a given specialty, applicants for positions may also wish to contact the appropriate specialty society, as shown in Section II.

AMA Alliance Resident Physician Spouses and Medical Student Spouses (RPS-MSS) Groups

The American Medical Association Alliance (Alliance), a nationwide grass roots network of more than 25,000 physician spouses and physicians, is the largest volunteer arm of the AMA. The Alliance offers support and advocacy for the family of medicine, a convenient portal for help when you need it, and the opportunity to make a difference in your community while advancing personal development and leadership skills.

Resident physicians and their spouses (RPS) and medical students and their spouses (MSS) are encouraged to join this resource for "surviving the training years." Annual membership is only $10.

Special features include scholarship resources, Physicians in Training Host Program for medical students traveling to interview for residency, access to a nationwide network of physician families that help introduce new physicians' families to their new community, and opportunities to have a voice in legislative issues that affect physicians and health care. Children's activity books and resources on the medical marriage are also available.

Information

American Medical Association Alliance
515 N State St
Chicago, IL 60654
312 464-4470
312 464-5020 Fax
www.amaalliance.org
E-mail: amaa@ama-assn.org

B. Information on Matching Programs

Most US medical students and other applicants to US GME programs secure positions through a "matching program." The National Resident Matching Program (NRMP) is the largest matching program; other residency matching programs include the San Francisco Matching Program and the matching programs sponsored by the American Urology Association (AUA) and the American Osteopathic Association (AOA). In addition, the various US Armed Services select applicants participating in military programs at US medical schools for Armed Forces-sponsored GME programs. Finally, the Canadian Resident Matching Service (CaRMS) sponsors a two-phased match for Canadian medical school students and other applicants.

National Resident Matching Program

The National Resident Matching Program (NRMP) has been matching the preferences of applicants and programs for residency positions since 1952. The program was created to provide both applicants and residency program directors a fair opportunity to consider their options for appointment, to make reasoned decisions, and to have their decisions announced at a specified time. Participants in the NRMP agree to honor the commitment to offer or to accept an appointment if a match results.

In 2008, in addition to 15,696 US medical students, another 20,564 "independent" applicants competed for 22,240 graduate year one (GY1) positions and 2,826 graduate year two positions offered in the NRMP. Independent applicants include prior graduates of US allopathic medical schools and eligible students/graduates of osteopathic, Canadian, and international medical schools, and Fifth Pathway programs. The numbers of US medical students, independent applicants, and programs participating in the 2007 match increased slightly from the previous year.

Since July 2001, all NRMP services have been Web-based. Participants register for the Match, pay their registration fees, submit rank order lists, and receive match results via the NRMP Web site at www.nrmp.org.

The NRMP is not a centralized application service. Applicants apply through ERAS or directly to residency programs, and the programs administer their own selection process, including requests for interviews. Programs that participate in the NRMP require applicants to register with the NRMP. In January and February, after interviewing has been completed, applicants and programs submit to the NRMP via the Web rank order lists indicating their choices in order of preference. The system is in real time with up-to-the-minute information on applicants and programs participating in the match.

Both applicants and programs must agree that neither will ask the other to make a commitment before Match Day, although a high level of interest may be expressed. Verbal or written contracts prior to Match Day should not be made and are violations of the NRMP Match Participation Agreement signed by all participants. The final preferences of program directors and applicants as reflected on the submitted rank order lists will determine the offering of positions and the placement of applicants.

Through the NRMP process, each applicant and program submits a list of preferences in rank order. The matching algorithm places an applicant into a program he or she prefers that 1) has ranked the applicant and 2) has not been filled with other applicants who also prefer the program and are ranked higher on the program's list. Match results are announced in mid-March and are available on the NRMP Web site to participants. Applicants who fail to obtain a position and programs that do not fill all their offered positions are informed 2 days before the general announcement so that they may contact one another to secure appointments. The majority of appointments to residency programs begin on or about July 1.

Positions Offered Through the NRMP

The positions offered by programs participating in the NRMP are typically those sought by US medical school seniors; that is, positions that provide the first year of graduate medical education. In addition, specialties that start their training at graduate year two offer positions in the NRMP so that applicants may link their first and second years of training on their rank order lists.

- Categorical positions are offered by programs that expect applicants who enter in graduate year one to continue until completion of training required for specialty certification, provided their performance is satisfactory (normally 3 to 4 years).
- Preliminary positions provide 1 or 2 years of prerequisite training for entry into advanced programs that require 1 or more years of clinical training. Internal medicine, surgery, and transitional year programs commonly offer preliminary positions.
- Advanced positions at graduate year two, which do not commence until a year after the Match, are in specialty programs that require completion of 1 or more years of preliminary training. Applicants without prior graduate medical education may apply for these positions while also applying for preliminary positions that are compatible with their plans.
- Resident positions at graduate year two that begin in July of the year of the match are reserved for physicians who have had prior graduate medical education. These positions are not available to senior US medical students.

Couples and Shared Residency Positions

Applicants who are members of a couple may link their program choices together. In creating pairs of program choices, couples can mix specialties, program types, and geographic locations.

Some programs offer shared residency positions. In a shared residency, two residents share one position, usually alternating months on clinical rotations with time off to devote to family, research, or other interests. Obtaining a shared residency position through the NRMP requires that two applicants who have enrolled separately in the NRMP become partners to be matched together in a single position.

Specialties Matching Service

In addition to conducting the match for graduate year one and graduate year two residency positions, the NRMP conducts matches for advanced residency or fellowship positions through the Specialties Matching Service. These specialty matches occur throughout the year, and each requires its own registration with the NRMP.

Specialty matches currently include the following:

- Combined Musculoskeletal Matching Program (participating subspecialties of orthopaedic surgery)
- Abdominal transplant surgery
- Allergy and immunology
- Child and adolescent psychiatry
- Colon and rectal surgery
- Medical Specialties Matching Program (participating subspecialties of internal medicine)
- Neonatal-perinatal medicine
- Obstetrics-Gynecology Fellowship Match (participating subspecialties of obstetrics and gynecology)
- Ophthalmic plastic and reconstructive surgery
- Pediatric cardiology
- Pediatric critical care medicine

- Pediatric emergency medicine
- Pediatric gastroenterology
- Pediatric hematology/oncology
- Pediatric nephrology
- Pediatric pulmonology
- Pediatric rheumatology
- Pediatric surgery
- Primary care sports medicine
- Radiology (participating subspecialties in radiology)
- Surgical critical care
- Thoracic surgery
- Vascular surgery

Important Dates

August 15   The NRMP Main Residency Match Web site opens for applicant registration. US seniors and independent applicants begin registering for the following year's Match.

September 1   Registration opens for institutions and programs participating in the Main Match.

November 30   Deadline for applicant registration. Registration after November 30 requires an additional $50 late registration fee.

January 15   The submission of rank order lists begins on the Web at www.nrmp.org.

February   The ranking process culminates with the closing of rank order lists in the third week of February.

March   Applicants and institutions receive the Match results the third week of March. Unmatched applicants are notified at noon on Monday, and unfilled specialty positions are posted to the Web that Tuesday at noon Eastern Standard Time.

July 1   Most appointments to residency programs begin.

Information and Inquiries

The National Resident Matching Program is sponsored by the Council of Medical Specialty Societies, American Board of Medical Specialties, American Hospital Association, American Medical Association, and Association of American Medical Colleges. The NRMP is managed and operated by the Association of American Medical Colleges.

Inquiries regarding the NRMP should be directed to:
National Resident Matching Program
2450 N St, NW
Washington, DC 20037-1127
202 828-0566
E-mail: nrmp@aamc.org
www.nrmp.org

San Francisco Matching Program

For 2008, the San Francisco Matching Program offered residency positions in specialties that do not participate in the National Resident Matching Program (NRMP), including child neurology, ophthalmology, orthopedic trauma, and plastic surgery. It also offered fellowship positions in several subspecialties, including Mohs micrographic surgery, ophthalmology fellowships, rhinology, pediatric otolaryngology, facial plastic surgery, and craniofacial surgery. Applicants are advised to review carefully the information provided on the San Francisco Match Web site at www.sfmatch.org.

Because the San Francisco Match does not offer GY1 positions, applicants must obtain their preliminary positions outside of the San Francisco Match. Some programs have designated preliminary positions in the same institution for applicants who match through

the San Francisco Match; therefore, these applicants do not have to go through a matching program to obtain a GY1 position. The programs are not required to be ACGME-accredited to participate in the matching program.

To participate in the San Francisco Match, applicants complete the online registration form, print it, and mail or fax it along with the required payment to the San Francisco Matching Program. Applicants are then e-mailed a registration number, as well as additional information on matching procedures. Most, but not all, of the programs participating in the San Francisco Match use the Central Application Service (CAS); programs in those specialties not using the CAS must be contacted directly for their individual applications. The Central Application can be downloaded and saved to one's personal computer for completion and electronic submission.

The ranking function for the San Francisco Match is completed online for applicants and on paper for programs. Applicants complete the rank form that is posted on the San Francisco Match Web site and submit online. Receipt is confirmed by e-mail. The San Francisco Match uses an "applicant-proposing algorithm," and all matches are tentative until the matching process has been completed, with the outcome determined by the rank order lists submitted by programs and applicants. All matches are binding commitments.

Registration for the San Francisco Match begins in May for ophthalmology and throughout the year for other specialties. The period for submitting rank order lists varies according to specialty. Unfilled positions are posted on the San Francisco Match Web site throughout the year, and all programs participating have access to statistical data not provided to the general public.

Information and Inquiries

San Francisco Matching Program
655 Beach Street
San Francisco, CA 94109
415 447-0350, ext 0
415 561-8535 Fax
E-mail: help@sfmatch.org
www.sfmatch.org

[*Note:* The following information is reprinted from the Association of American Medical Colleges, *Roadmap to Residency: From Application to the Match and Beyond*, 2007. www.aamc.org/publications © 2006-2007 Association of American Medical Colleges. All rights reserved. Reproduced with permission of the Association of American Medical Colleges.]

Urology Match

The American Urological Association (AUA) monitors a match for residency positions in urology only. Each year, about 350 applicants compete for approximately 235 positions, virtually all of which are filled through the AUA Match. AUA Match statistics, as well as general information about the AUA matching process, can be found on the AUA Residency Match Web site at www.auanet.org/content/residency/residency-match.cfm. Applicants are advised to review this Web site information carefully.

The prerequisite training for a prospective urology resident is 1 or 2 years, preferably in a general surgery program. Because the Urology Match does not offer GY1 positions, applicants obtain their preliminary positions outside of the AUA Match. Some programs have designated preliminary positions in the same institution for applicants who match through the Urology Match; therefore, those applicants do not have to go through a matching program to obtain a GY1 position. Other programs require applicants to participate in the NRMP Main Residency Match to obtain a position for preliminary training. Preliminary positions for US allopathic medical school seniors must be offered through the NRMP Main Residency Match.

The registration form and fee for the AUA Match are submitted using an online form that can be accessed on the AUA Web site. The Web site also lists participating programs and indicates whether each uses ERAS or another method for receipt of applications. It is important to note that registration for the AUA Match does not register an applicant with ERAS, or vice versa.

The AUA Match ranking function is Web-based. Preference lists must be submitted to the AUA Match by the first week in January, and they cannot be changed after the deadline date. As with the NRMP, the AUA Match uses an "applicant-proposing algorithm," and the AUA Match outcome is determined by applicants' and programs' preference lists. All matches are binding commitments.

Applicants can register for the AUA Match as early as the spring of the year prior to the AUA Match; the final registration deadline is the third week of December. The period for submitting rank order lists is December through the first week of January, and Match Day is in the third week in January. Vacancies available after the AUA Match may be listed on the AUA Web site. Unmatched applicants may make individual arrangements with programs that have vacant positions.

Information and Inquiries

AUA Residency Matching Program
1000 Corporate Boulevard
Linthicum, MD 21090
866 746-4282, ext 3913
410 689-3939 Fax
E-mail: resmatch@auanet.org
www.auanet.org/content/residency/residency-match.cfm

Canadian Resident Matching Service

The Canadian Resident Matching Service (CaRMS) is a two-phased match. The First Iteration Match is open to Canadian medical school seniors and international medical graduates who are Canadian citizens or permanent residents. They compete for approximately 2,600 positions. The Second Iteration Match is open to unmatched First Iteration applicants and applicants with prior North American GME experience.

CaRMS receives directly from the Canadian medical schools a list of current year graduates and automatically sends them a token to access the Applicant Webstation. All other applicants are considered independent applicants and, as such, must complete the online request for registration. Once eligibility has been confirmed by CaRMS, an access token is sent by e-mail. Registration for the First Iteration match opens in August, and the application process continues through the fall. The Applicant Webstation opens for First Iteration Match participants in September, and for those in the Second Iteration Match in January. For the First Iteration Match, the ranking function opens in the beginning of February and closes on February 25, and Match Day is March 8. For the Second Iteration Match, the ranking function opens in late March, and Match Day is in mid-April.

CaRMS also allows couples to link their rank order lists so they will match to programs suited to their needs. The partners enroll individually in the CaRMS Match and indicate in the system that they want to participate as a couple. Both partners of a couple must submit the same number of ranks on their rank order lists. The couple matches to the most preferred pair of programs on the rank order lists where each partner has been offered a position.

Information and Inquiries

Canadian Resident Matching Service
171 Nepean Street, Suite 300
Ottawa, ON K2P 0B4
613 237-0075
613 563-2860 Fax
E-mail: help@carms.ca
www.carms.ca

Military Matches

Positions in US military residency training programs are open only to applicants who are graduates of the Uniformed Services University of the Health Sciences (USUHS), medical students with an individual military commitment through the Health Professions Scholarship Programs (HPSP), and participants in the Reserve Officers Training Corps (ROTC). Although applicants and programs submit rank order lists, and applicants to Army and Navy programs apply through the Electronic Residency Application Service (ERAS) as their civilian counterparts do, only the Army uses a computerized matching process similar to the NRMP matching process to select residents. The Navy and the Air Force employ a scoring board, using applicant and program rank order lists to make their selections. Decisions are made in early December, and results are sent to the NRMP so that applicants who registered for the NRMP Main Residency Match, but who obtained a military residency training position, can be withdrawn from the NRMP. Applicants who have been notified by the military in early December that they are authorized to seek civilian deferred residency training can participate in the NRMP or another appropriate civilian matching program.

Couple's Matching

Some matching programs, including the NRMP and CaRMS, offer the opportunity for two partners to link their rank order lists so that both residency applicants can match to programs suited to their needs. The partners enroll individually in the match and indicate that they want to be in the match as a couple. They form pairs of choices on their rank order lists, which are then considered in rank order in the match. The couple matches to the most preferred pair of programs on the rank order lists for which each partner has been offered a position.

No matching program has access to information from another matching program. Applicants, therefore, should not accept advice to try to find out about another match under the guise of creating a "couple's match," since that attempt would represent a match violation. More specifically, a matching program may advise an applicant that it offers a couple's match when a couple's match is not possible. When two partners participate in different matching programs, they cannot link rank order lists between matches. If one matching program requests that an applicant's partner contact a residency program that participates in another match in order to inquire about the likelihood of matching, the partner is being asked to violate the terms of that match. Almost every match contract prohibits applicants and programs from inquiring about how one plans to rank the other. Consequently, when partners participate in different matches, the only way to ensure that both partners will match to programs in the same geographic region is for the partner participating in the later match to rank only programs in the same geographic area in which the partner in the earlier match obtained a position.

Match Outcomes

1. A Binding Commitment

It is the policy of every matching program that a match between an applicant and a program is a binding commitment. Failure to honor that commitment is a violation of the contract signed during the registration process. Penalties for violations vary among the matches. Some matches permit applicants to seek a waiver of their match commitment, either by mutual agreement of the applicant and program or by contacting the match office directly. The applicable rules are available on each match program's Web site.

2. The "Early Matches"

Applicants participating in some early matches—the San Francisco Match and the AUA Urology Match—receive their match results in January or early February. In some cases, a preliminary position will be "held" by the same institution to which the applicant matched. In other cases, applicants who obtained positions through the early matches will be required to register for the NRMP Main Residency Match to secure a position for their preliminary training. (In all cases, US allopathic medical school seniors must participate in the NRMP for their preliminary positions.)

3. Unmatched "Early Match" Applicants

Applicants who do not match in one of the early matches may seek positions after the match concludes, using the list of available positions that is typically posted on the relevant matching program's Web site.

The San Francisco Matching Program uses a Vacancy Information System that lists vacant post-Match positions, as well as positions that become available throughout the year. Applicants must complete the "Applying to Post Match Vacancies" form that is posted on the San Francisco Match Web site (www.sfmatch.org).

The AUA Urology Match posts vacancies in urology on its Web site (www.auanet.org/residents/resmatch.cfm) after the AUA Match concludes and throughout the year. Applicants must contact programs directly.

The NRMP begins to release the results of the Main Residency Match on Monday of Match Week, when applicants are told whether, but not to which programs, they have been matched. At Noon EST on Tuesday of Match Week, when the NRMP releases the list of unfilled programs, "the Scramble" begins. Information about vacant positions is posted to the NRMP R3 System (www.nrmp.org) in a "dynamic" format so that programs can delete positions from the list as they are filled. The list indicates how the program will receive applications: through ERAS or by e-mail or fax. The List of Unfilled Programs remains on the NRMP Web site until May 1.

After May 1, services such as FindAResident (www.aamc.org/findaresident) provide a continuously updated list of residency vacancies.

C. GME Information for IMGs

Educational Commission for Foreign Medical Graduates (ECFMG®) Certification

[*Note:* The following information is provided by the Educational Commission for Foreign Medical Graduates.]

The Educational Commission for Foreign Medical Graduates (ECFMG), through its program of certification, assesses the readiness of international medical graduates (IMGs) to enter US residency or fellowship programs that are accredited by the Accreditation Council for Graduate Medical Education (ACGME).

ECFMG and its organizational members define an IMG as a physician who received his/her basic medical degree or qualification from a medical school located outside the United States and Canada. For IMGs seeking ECFMG Certification, the physician's medical school and graduation year must be listed in the *International Medical Education Directory* (*IMED*) of the Foundation for Advancement of International Medical Education and Research (FAIMER®). US citizens who have completed their medical education in schools outside the United States and Canada are considered IMGs; non-US citizens who have graduated from medical schools in the United States and Canada are not considered IMGs. ECFMG Certification provides assurance to the directors of ACGME-accredited residency and fellowship programs, and to the people of the United States, that IMGs have met minimum standards of eligibility required to enter such programs. ECFMG Certification is one of the eligibility requirements to take Step 3 of the United States Medical Licensing Examination (USMLE), and is required to obtain an unrestricted license to practice medicine in the United States.

To be eligible for certification by ECFMG, applicants must meet medical education credential requirements and examination requirements.

Medical Education Credential Requirements

1. Applicants must have had at least 4 credit years (academic years for which credit has been given toward completion of the medical curriculum) in attendance at a medical school that is listed in the FAIMER *IMED*. There are restrictions on credits transferred to the medical school that awards an applicant's medical degree that can be used to meet this requirement. The physician's graduation year must be included in the medical school's *IMED* listing. (The FAIMER *IMED* contains information supplied by countries about their medical schools. FAIMER is not an accrediting agency.)

2. Applicants must document the completion of all requirements for, and receipt of, the final medical diploma. ECFMG verifies every applicant's medical diploma with the appropriate officials of the medical school that issued the diploma. When ECFMG sends an applicant's medical diploma to the medical school for verification, ECFMG requests that the medical school include the applicant's final medical school transcript when the school returns the verification of the medical diploma to ECFMG. Verification by ECFMG with the issuing school may also be required for transcripts that are submitted by applicants to document transferred credits. ECFMG medical education credential requirements are not fulfilled until ECFMG receives and accepts verification of the final medical diploma, final medical school

transcript, and, if required, transfer credit transcript(s) directly from the issuing school(s).

For more information on the medical education credential requirements for ECFMG Certification, refer to the ECFMG *Information Booklet*, available on the ECFMG Web site at www.ecfmg.org.

Examination Requirements

The current examination requirements for ECFMG Certification include passing Step 1 and Step 2 of the USMLE. The Step 2 exam has two separately administered components, the Clinical Knowledge (CK) component and the Clinical Skills (CS) component. Step 1, Step 2 CK, and Step 2 CS are the same exams taken by graduates of US and Canadian medical schools. Detailed information on the USMLE is available on the USMLE Web site at www.usmle.org.

To meet the examination requirements for ECFMG Certification, applicants must:

1. **Satisfy the medical science examination requirement**. Step 1 and Step 2 CK of the USMLE are the exams currently administered that satisfy this requirement. ECFMG also accepts a passing performance on certain former medical science examinations to satisfy this requirement. Some of these former examinations have been recognized by the US Secretary of Health and Human Services as meeting the medical science examination requirement to obtain a visa to enter the United States, while others have not. For more information, refer to the ECFMG *Information Booklet*, available on the ECFMG Web site.

2. **Satisfy the clinical skills requirement**. Step 2 CS of the USMLE is the exam currently administered that satisfies the clinical skills requirement for ECFMG Certification. Applicants who have both passed the former ECFMG Clinical Skills Assessment (CSA®) and achieved a score acceptable to ECFMG on an English language proficiency test (such as the Test of English as a Foreign Language [TOEFL] exam or the former ECFMG English Test) can use these passing performances to satisfy the clinical skills requirement.

There are specific time requirements for completing the exams for ECFMG Certification. These requirements are described in the ECFMG *Information Booklet*, available on the ECFMG Web site.

Standard ECFMG Certificate

The Standard ECFMG Certificate is issued to applicants who fulfill the medical education credential requirements, meet the examination requirements, and clear their financial accounts with the ECFMG. The Standard ECFMG Certificate may be used for entry into accredited GME programs in the United States.

For further information on ECFMG Certification, including exam eligibility, fees, applying for examination, scheduling, test centers, preparation, orientation and practice materials, and the validity of certain exams for entry to GME, refer to the ECFMG *Information Booklet* or contact:

ECFMG
3624 Market St
Philadelphia, PA 19104-2685
215 386-5900
215 386-9196 Fax
E-mail: info@ecfmg.org
www.ecfmg.org

Entry of Foreign-Born Medical Graduates to the United States

[*Note:* The following information is provided by the Educational Commission for Foreign Medical Graduates and the International Personnel Office, Mayo Clinic.]

International medical graduates (IMGs), regardless of country of citizenship, must be ECFMG-certified in order to train or practice medicine in the United States. All foreign national physicians, both IMGs and graduates of Canadian or US medical schools, must obtain an appropriate visa to participate in US programs of graduate medical education (GME).

The typical pathway for foreign national physicians to enter US programs of GME involves the following steps:

- Completion of all ECFMG Certification requirements, *IMGs only*
- Application to US residency program, which may involve travel to the United States for personal interviews at teaching hospitals
- Securing a contract for a residency training position
- Satisfying state medical licensure requirements
- Securing an appropriate immigration status that will permit US GME training

Understanding and complying with immigration guidelines is critical for teaching hospitals and foreign national physicians who pursue US residency training positions. The following sections outline the immigration guidelines and visa options available to foreign national physicians for US training.

Immigration and GME

US immigration law is governed by specific federal regulations and defined in the US Immigration and Nationality Act (INA), as amended. Various agencies of the US Department of Homeland Security (DHS) and the Department of State (DOS) are responsible for overseeing particular aspects of the US visa and immigration process, as shown in Table 1.

Table 1:
Roles of Department of Homeland Security (DHS) and Department of State (DOS) in Visa Oversight

Agencies within DHS Responsible for Immigration Policies, Procedures, and Enforcement	Agencies within DOS Responsible for Management of Visa Processes
US Customs and Border Protection (CBP): entry of foreign nationals at US ports-of-entry	Bureau of Educational and Cultural Affairs: oversight of all J-1 Exchange Visitor Programs
US Immigration and Customs Enforcement (ICE): investigations, detention, removal, intelligence, SEVIS	Bureau of Consular Affairs: US consulates abroad determine visa eligibility for all classifications
US Citizenship and Immigration Services (USCIS): adjudications of immigration benefits	

In reviewing the immigration process as it relates to foreign national physicians, it is important to be familiar with the following basic terms:

"Visa"—A "nonimmigrant" (temporary) visa is a document issued at a US embassy or consulate and stamped or affixed into the visa applicant's passport. The visa constitutes a permit for the individual to seek entry into the United States for specific temporary purposes allowed under that particular visa category (such as B-1/B-2 visitor, J-1 exchange visitor, H-1B temporary worker, etc.). The individual may seek entry only during the validity period shown on the visa. Note that the visa is only an entry permit and does *not* control how long the person may stay in the United States.

"**Visa Status**"—This term refers to the specific visa classification in which the foreign national is formally admitted into the United States. It also confirms the duration of approved stay. Visa status is conferred by Customs and Border Protection (CBP) at the port-of-entry for initial admission to the country, or through a US Citizenship and Immigration Services (USCIS) Regional Service Center for individuals who seek a change of status while in the United States. All foreign nationals must abide by the terms and dates of the visa status as noted on the I-94 card, Arrival/Departure Record or Notice of Action.

Visa Options for US GME

A foreign national physician who secures a contract for a US GME position must obtain an appropriate visa prior to beginning the training program. There are various temporary, nonimmigrant visa options available for GME training. The most common include the J-1 "Exchange Visitor" and the H-1B "Temporary Worker in a Specialty Occupation" visas. Foreign national physicians may also qualify to train as medical residents/fellows with valid employment authorization documents (EADs). USCIS grants work authorization in conjunction with a variety of immigrant and nonimmigrant petitions, (ie, "F-1 Student" on Optional Practical Training [OPT], J-2 dependent of a J-1 principal, family of a US citizen or legal permanent resident, refugee or asylee status, etc). In exceptional cases, foreign national physicians may also qualify for O-1 visas that are reserved for "Individuals of Extraordinary Ability." The O-1 visa requires superior credentials and documented international renown and, therefore, is rarely used for residency training purposes.

Teaching hospitals, like all US employers, are responsible for complying with federal rules governing the hiring of non-US citizens. Immigration and employment laws mandate that teaching hospitals pay certain filing fees and assume administrative oversight of foreign national physicians participating in their residency programs. It is not uncommon for hospitals to limit the types of visas they will accept for trainees enrolling in their programs. Foreign national physicians are advised to inquire about the immigration options offered by the programs they are considering prior to making application. It is important to understand clearly the specific regulatory requirements, restrictions, costs, timelines, and institutional policies that apply to the various visa/immigration options.

Below is an overview of the visa options for residency training.

J-1 Sponsorship for Residency Training

Historically, the J-1 has been the most common visa classification used for foreign national physicians in residency training. The J-1 is a nonimmigrant visa reserved for participants in the Exchange Visitor Program. As a public diplomacy initiative of DOS, the Exchange Visitor Program was established to enhance international exchange and mutual understanding between the people of the United States and other nations. In keeping with the J-1 program's goals of educational exchange, J-1 physicians are encouraged to maintain strong ties to the home country and to return home upon completion of training.

DOS designated ECFMG as the sole visa sponsor for all J-1 physicians who participate in clinical training programs in the mid-1970s. ECFMG administers its sponsorship program in accordance with the provisions set forth in a Memorandum of Understanding between ECFMG and the DOS and the federal regulations established to implement the Mutual Educational and Cultural Exchange Act of 1961. ECFMG is responsible for ensuring that J-1 physicians and teaching institutions meet the federal requirements for participation. ECFMG does not sponsor physicians for other US visa types.

Foreign national physicians who seek J-1 sponsorship to enroll in GME programs must fulfill a number of general requirements as detailed in the application materials published by ECFMG. At a minimum, J-1 physician applicants must have:

• Adequate prior education/training and English competency
• Statement of Need from the home country's Ministry of Health
• Contract for a residency position

J-1 physicians must demonstrate "adequate prior education and training to participate satisfactorily in the program for which they are coming to the United States" [22 CFR §62.27(b)(1)] and have "competency in oral and written English" [22 CFR §62.27(b)(4)]. Possession of a valid Standard ECFMG Certificate ensures that these educational prerequisites have been met. For information on the requirements for ECFMG Certification, refer to "Educational Commission for Foreign Medical Graduates (ECFMG®) Certification," above.

J-1 physician applicants must provide ECFMG with a Statement of Need from the central office of the Ministry of Health of the country of most recent legal permanent residence [22 CFR §62.27(6); 64 Fed.Reg. 34982-83 (June 30, 1999)]. The Statement of Need, which follows specific regulatory language, documents the home government's support for the specific training that the J-1 physician will pursue and confirms the physician's intent to return home to practice medicine upon completion of training in the United States. The Statement of Need is consistent with the compulsory obligation of the INA 212(e) two-year home residency requirement for all J-1 physicians and their J-2 dependents. As stipulated in the regulations, the home residency requirement mandates that J-1 physicians and accompanying J-2 dependents reside in the home country for an aggregate of at least 2 years before being eligible for certain changes in visa status in the United States [INA §212(e)(iii); 22 CFR §62.27(g)(2)]. Various legal options have evolved to allow J-1 physicians to waive the return home obligation following training, including employment in a US Medically Underserved Area (MUA) or Health Professional Shortage Area (HPSA).

J-1 sponsorship for residency training is dependent on a contract or official letter of offer for a GME position [22 CFR §62.27(7)]. The J-1 physician applicant must secure the training contract prior to applying to ECFMG for visa sponsorship. ECFMG is authorized to sponsor physicians for training in base residencies and subspecialty fellowships that are ACGME-accredited as well as for advanced, "non-standard" fellowships for which accreditation is not available. J-1 sponsorship is generally issued in increments of 1 year corresponding with the GME academic year of July 1 through June 30. Specific instructions and materials for each application type can be found on the ECFMG Web site at www.ecfmg.org/evsp.

Once a physician has been approved for J-1 sponsorship, ECFMG creates an electronic record for the physician in the Student and Exchange Visitor Information System (SEVIS) and issues Form DS-2019, "Certificate of Eligibility for Exchange Visitor (J-1) Status." Through an interagency partnership between DOS and DHS, SEVIS tracks and monitors the activities of all J, F, and M visa holders [22 CFR §62.70(a)(6)]. The foreign national physician with an active SEVIS record and an original Form DS-2019 may apply for J-1 visa and/or visa status from agencies of the U.S. government. ECFMG validates the arrival of J-1 physicians in SEVIS upon notification from the teaching hospital and confirms ongoing program participation through direct communication with designated hospital representatives.

J-1 physicians may request ECFMG sponsorship for dependent spouse and children. The J-2 spouse may seek employment authorization through USCIS to work in any position for which he/she is qualified, including residency training. The duration of stay for the J-2 is limited to the approved timeline for the J-1 principal and cannot be extended independently of the primary visa holder.

Federal regulations define the scope, pathway, and duration of J-1 program participation. J-1 physicians must predefine their educational objectives and may be eligible to pursue progressive training beginning at the base residency level through advanced subspecialty fellowships. ECFMG's sponsorship approval is based on a specific training contract, which reflects the current program location, specialty, level, salary, and contract dates. J-1 physicians are permitted to change specialty once within the first 2 years of sponsorship. A request to change medical specialty requires reestablishing eligibility for sponsorship, including confirmation that the proposed training can be completed within the maximum duration of participation. J-1 physicians are eligible for a maximum of 7 years of training, provided that they are advancing through an approved GME track. The duration of sponsorship is linked directly to the standard board certification requirements as established by the member boards of the American Board of Medical Specialties (ABMS) and/or the ACGME-accredited length of the program. In select cases, a request for an exceptional extension beyond 7 years for training can be requested from the DOS through ECFMG. J-1 sponsorship can also be briefly extended to allow a J-1 physician to sit for an ABMS member board certification exam. For a comprehensive outline of pertinent regulations related to the J-1 sponsorship of foreign national physicians, refer to the *Exchange Visitor Sponsorship Program Reference Guide*, available on the ECFMG Web site at www.ecfmg.org/evsp.

To ensure strict regulatory compliance, the J-1 visa sponsorship process requires close coordination between the teaching institution, the physician applicant, and ECFMG. Each academic institution designates a Training Program Liaison (TPL) to serve as the official representative to communicate with ECFMG regarding all J-1 matters. Physicians must establish contact with the TPL at each program in which they enroll and maintain contact throughout the duration of their J-1 sponsorship.

H-1B Visa for Residency Training

The H-1B visa is reserved for temporary workers in professional or "specialty" occupations. Today, the option of H-1B visa sponsorship is offered by many institutions for residency training. In addition to a medical degree and a valid Standard ECFMG Certificate, foreign national physicians who are interested in obtaining an H-1B visa must pass USMLE Step 3 and qualify for the appropriate medical license in the state where the training will take place. (Most states offer some form of "resident permit," a provisional/temporary medical license for physicians practicing under supervision in a GME

program.) Competency in English is also required for the H-1B. Passing USMLE Step 2 CS satisfies the language requirement as this exam includes an assessment of spoken English.

H-1B status is employer-specific and requires visa sponsorship directly through the teaching hospital. To sponsor a qualified foreign national physician for a residency position on an H-1B visa, the teaching hospital must file a preliminary "labor condition application" with the US Department of Labor (DOL) and an H-1B petition with USCIS. These filings require detailed information regarding the position being offered, including program dates, location and wage rate, and evidence of the physician's credentials. Additionally, the hospital must confirm that the foreign national physician will be paid the appropriate salary for the position. An appropriate salary is defined as the higher of either the "actual wage" as paid by the hospital to a US citizen holding the same position, or the "prevailing wage," which is the average wage paid for the same position by all employers in the geographic area. As the prospective employer, the teaching hospital must pay applicable government fees associated with filing all H-1B petitions and must agree to cover the return home transportation costs in the event it should dismiss the physician from the training program before its full completion.

H-1B petitions are approved based on the length of the training program, not to exceed 3 years at one time. An approved H-1B petition is valid only for work with the specific sponsoring institution, program, and position. The H-1B physician may seek to change positions or transfer to a different hospital/employer, but only if the new institution itself first files an H-1B petition for the physician. An individual pursuing continuous stay in H-1B status is subject to the maximum duration of 6 years.

The H-1B physician's dependent spouse and children may accompany the principal H-1B to the United States in H-4 status. Unlike J-2 dependents, H-4s are not eligible to obtain independent work authorization. However, they may participate in educational studies.

In contrast to the J-1, the H-1B visa does not impose a mandatory home residency requirement upon completion of training. Therefore, foreign national physicians who train on H-1B visas may be eligible, in some cases, to pursue direct steps toward permanent resident status after training.

GME Following a J-1 Program of Nonclinical Observation, Consultation, Teaching, and Research

Foreign national physicians frequently enter the United States as J-1 research scholars or professors for nonclinical activities involving observation, consultation, teaching, or research. Many physicians choose to pursue GME as an extension of their original J-1 program. The federal regulations stipulate, however, that an individual in J-1 status may not, as a matter of course, change from one J-1 category to another. Physicians seeking to change from J-1 re-

Table 2: Summary and Comparison of J-1 and H-1B Visas for Residency

	J-1	H-1B
Regulatory Oversight	Department of State, Department of Homeland Security, ECFMG	Department of Labor, Department of Homeland Security
Exams	USMLE Steps 1, 2 CK, 2 CS	USMLE Steps 1, 2 CK, 2 CS, 3
Time Limit	7 years maximum	6 years maximum
Funding	Multiple sources acceptable	US employer salary only
214(b) & 212(e) of INA	Strong ties to home country **Two-year** home residency requirement	Not Applicable
Employment for Spouse?	Yes, J-2 can apply for work authorization	No, H-4 ineligible to work

search to J-1 clinical to enter a GME program must obtain pre-approval from DOS through ECFMG. For information on the requirements for a change of J-1 category, please contact ECFMG.

J-1 research scholars or professors may qualify for an H-1B for GME, provided they meet the meet the credential requirements and are not subject to the home residency requirement [INA 212(e)].

Other Possible Immigration Options for GME Trainees

F-1 Student - Optional Practical Training

Individuals in F-1 status who are graduating from a US medical school may be eligible to extend their student status for up to 12 months of optional practical training (OPT). OPT requires an Employment Authorization Document (EAD) issued by USCIS and can be used for the first year of residency training. F-1 students are advised to contact the designated school official at their US medical school to determine their eligibility for OPT. If the GME program requires more than 12 months of training, the physician will need to acquire a different visa status, such as J-1 or H-1B, before the OPT expires.

Employment Authorization Document (EAD) for J-2 Dependents and Applicants for Permanent Immigrant Status

Physicians in J-2 status (dependents of J-1 principals) are eligible to apply for work authorization for general employment including residency training. The J-2 dependent must obtain an EAD through USCIS. The EAD is generally limited to the approved J-1 sponsorship dates as indicated on Form DS-2019.

Individuals applying for adjustment to permanent immigrant (green card) status are also eligible to apply for EAD to participate in GME.

Lawful Permanent Resident (LPR, Immigrant, or "Green Card") Status

Persons who hold lawful permanent resident status are permitted to remain in the United States permanently and to accept employment in the same way as a US citizen. Physicians in LPR status who are IMGs or Canadian medical graduates are required to meet certain credential and state licensure requirements in order to train or practice medicine in this country.

Initial Visa Application Process

Generally, all nonimmigrant visa applicants seeking a visa for initial entry to the United States must appear for a personal interview at a US embassy or consulate, usually in the home country. Scheduling the visa interview and then waiting for the security clearance can take several months. Therefore, advance preparation and planning are essential. Foreign national physicians should contact the appropriate US consulate to determine scheduling times and specific application requirements (including Form DS-156 "Nonimmigrant Visa Application," Form DS-157 "Supplemental Nonimmigrant Visa Application," biometric finger printing, fees, name check, and security clearance procedures, etc). Web sites for US embassies and consulates can be accessed through the DOS Web site at www.usembassy.gov. Timelines for visa appointments and general processing information can be found at http://travel.state.gov/visa/temp/wait/tempvisitors_wait.php

Maintaining Visa Status

In addition to meeting the academic standards required to progress through residency, foreign national physicians must maintain valid visa status in order to continue to train at a US teaching hospital. Maintaining status requires, but is not limited to, the following:

- Active participation in approved training program: specific site, salary, dates, etc.
  - J-1 physicians must maintain full-time status in the program
  - *Unauthorized employment is considered a violation of status*
- Possession of required documents/records confirming visa status
  - For J-1: DS-2019; for H-1B: I-797 with valid dates
  - I-94 record with "Duration of Status" (D/S) or future end date
  - Valid passport
- Compliance with all reporting requirements
  - Reporting US residential address to US government (Form AR-11) within 10 days of any move
  - Notification to appropriate offices (ie, ECFMG, TPL, program director, GME office, or US government) of proposed changes in location or course of training, leaves of absence, terminations, extensions, etc
  - Complying with any special registration requirement as instructed by US government official at port-of-entry, etc

Table 3: Documentation Typically Required When Applying for a J-1 or H-1B Visa

J-1	H-1B
Form DS-2019, "Certificate of Eligibility for Exchange Visitor (J-1) Status," signed in blue ink by the Regional Advisor at ECFMG, with a future expiration/end date	Original Form I-797, "Notice of Action," issued by USCIS showing approval of an H-1B petition, with a future expiration/end date
Form DS-158, "Contact Information and Work History for Nonimmigrant Visa Applicant"	Copy of H-1B petition filed by employer on physician's behalf (in some cases a copy of the Form I-129 petition and Labor Condition Application may be sufficient; check with consulate)
Form DS-156, "Nonimmigrant Visa Application," with photos	Form DS-156, "Nonimmigrant Visa Application," with photos
Form DS-157, "Supplemental Nonimmigrant Visa Application" (generally required of all male applicants between the ages of 16 and 45)	Form DS-157, "Supplemental Nonimmigrant Visa Application" (generally required of all male applicants between the ages of 16 and 45)
Valid passport	Valid passport
Application and Reciprocity fees (check with the consulate for the current fee amounts and how they must be paid)	Application and Reciprocity fees (check with the consulate for the current fee amounts and how they must be paid)
SEVIS fee, if applying for a J-1 visa to begin a new program	
Documents that demonstrate nonimmigrant intent (ie, proof of intent to return home)	

- Strict adherence to all applicable US laws and regulations

International Travel and Visas

Foreign national physicians who travel outside the United States during the course of residency training can experience problems and delays. Most critically, individuals must posses a currently valid visa in order to reenter the United States.

As a general rule, it is not advisable for foreign national physicians with expired visas and/or those who changed visa status within the United States to travel internationally during the training year. Such individuals will need to apply for a new visa for reentry, and the current US visa application process can involve long waits for consular appointments and security clearances. At present, there is no expedited processing available for background checks for anyone; therefore, it is impossible to guarantee timely return to the training program.

Foreign national physicians who must travel outside the United States are advised to review the dates and purpose of their travel with the residency program director(s) and administrative staff prior to finalizing their plans. A discussion about potential delays and contract provisions to make up lost time should take place before departure. Physicians should also contact the specific US embassy or consulate where they intend to apply for the visa to inquire about application procedures, documentation, requirements, and timeframes. It is critical for the foreign national physician (and dependents) to be aware of the documents that will be required for reentry to the United States.

Additional information on travel is available on the ECFMG Web site at www.ecfmg.org/evsp.

The Implications of Personal and Professional Difficulties During Residency

In general, foreign national physicians enrolled in residency training face similar personal and professional challenges as their US citizen counterparts. Health, family, or academic issues can result in an interruption or change in a resident's contract. Foreign national physicians whose visa status is based on enrollment in medical residencies must understand clearly the immigration implications of diverting from the preapproved activities and timelines. US immigration regulations and labor laws are complex, and teaching hospitals and foreign national physicians must be careful to maintain continuous training and immigration records.

Requests for program transfers, leaves of absence, change to parttime status, resignations from training, etc, must be preapproved by the visa sponsor (ECFMG for J-1s, teaching hospitals for H-1Bs, etc). No change should be made without first verifying permissibility of altering the approved educational plan and then clarifying the necessary steps to return to training or depart the United States. Teaching hospitals and physicians should contact the visa sponsor or an immigration attorney to consult on specific questions and regulations.

Conclusions

Foreign national physicians and US teaching hospitals are encouraged to thoroughly research the visa options available for GME. Policies, procedures, budgets, and deadlines vary widely among teaching hospitals and even among programs within the same institution. Ultimately, foreign national physicians and teaching hospitals must understand and comply fully with all US immigration laws and regulatory guidelines.

Resource List

ECFMG Exchange Visitor Sponsorship Program
Visit ECFMG's Web site at www.ecfmg.org/evsp for access to:
- *J-1 Visa Sponsorship Fact Sheet*

- *Exchange Visitor Sponsorship Program Reference Guide*
- Application materials
- Important updates

ECFMG Certification
Visit ECFMG's Web site at www.ecfmg.org for access to:
- *ECFMG® Certification Fact Sheet*
- *ECFMG® Information Booklet*

US Department of State Exchange Visitor Program (DOS-EVP)
http://exchanges.state.gov/jexchanges

US Citizenship and Immigration Services
www.uscis.gov

US Department of Homeland Security
www.dhs.gov

US Embassies and Consulates
www.usembassy.gov

American Board of Medical Specialties (ABMS)
www.abms.org

Accreditation Council for Graduate Medical Education (ACGME)
www.acgme.org

[*Note*: Portions of this section were previously published in *The International Medical Graduate's Guide to US Medicine & Residency Training*, Chapter 4, Transitioning to the United States, pages 57-66, copyright 2008, American College of Physicians, Philadelphia.]

AMA International Medical Graduates Section

The International Medical Graduates Section (IMG) of the AMA advocates for IMG physicians by enhancing their participation in organized medicine, increasing AMA communication and interchange among IMGs, and studying issues of concern to IMGs such as the impact of IMGs on the physician workforce. An IMG member of the AMA is automatically a member of the IMG Section and can participate in the Section's annual elections and Caucus activities. The IMG Section is dedicated to improving opportunities for IMGs in the areas of licensure, training, and practicing medicine in the US.

The IMG Section Web site contains information of interest to IMGs, including:
- ECFMG certification
- Immigration
- Residency program requirements, including application tips and interview hints
- State licensure board requirements for IMGs
- IMG Governing Council and leadership opportunities
- AMA policies related to IMGs and IMG issues
- Significant dates in US immigration policy affecting IMGs
- IMG physician demographics
- History and development of the AMA IMG Section

Information
International Medical Graduates Section
312 464-5678
www.ama-assn.org/go/imgs

D. AMA Medical Education Products, Services, and Activities

Note: For a Reference List of AMA Contacts and Web Sites, see the QuickConsult insert included with this publication.

AMA Council on Medical Education

Recognizing the relationship between quality medical education and quality health care, the AMA established the Council on Medical Education in 1904 to formulate and implement policy. After studying and evaluating medical education across the continuum, the current Council recommends educational policies and standards to the AMA House of Delegates (HOD) and to the medical education community. The council also prepares numerous reports responding to AMA HOD actions and initiates relevant studies in areas of high concern to the educational community. For example, recent initiatives have focused on:

- The need for workforce policy that supports an adequate continuing supply of well-qualified physicians to meet the medical needs of the public
- Medical student debt and its possible influence on the decision to apply to medical school and on the career choices of graduates
- Resident working conditions, duty hours and the impact of sleep deprivation and fatigue on medical student and resident education and patient safety

The council also reviews and recommends nominees to the AMA Board of Trustees for appointment or nomination to accrediting bodies, specialty-certifying boards and other national organizations.

Key Dates in the History of the Council on Medical Education and GME

1847 American Medical Association organized; Committee on Medical Education appointed

1901 First publication of the Annual Medical Education issue of the *Journal of the American Medical Association*

1904 Formation of the Council on Medical Education

1910 Publication of "Flexner Report" evaluating medical schools

1912 First survey of hospitals for the training of interns

1914 First publication of what was to become the *GME Directory*, as the *Provisional List of Hospitals Furnishing Acceptable Internships for Medical Graduates* (15 cents per copy)

1919 Establishment of the Essentials for Approved Internships

1927 Beginning of approval of residency programs in hospitals; publication of *Hospitals Approved for Residencies in Specialties*, with 270 hospitals in 14 different specialties

1928 Establishment of Essentials for registered hospitals and for approved residencies and fellowships

1934 Approval of examining boards for the certification of specialists; establishment of standards for the formation of American boards in the specialties

1948 Establishment of the Liaison Committee for Specialty Boards between the AMA Council on Medical Education and Advisory Board for Medical Specialties

1949 Conference Committee on Internal Medicine, established in 1939, reactivated

1950 Conference Committee on Graduate Training in Surgery established

1951 First operation of the National Intern Matching Program

1956 Educational Commission for Foreign Medical Graduates established

1958 Two-year integrated training program for family practice approved by the AMA House of Delegates

1966 Report of the Citizens Commission on Graduate Medical Education (Millis Report) published

1966 Council Report on Education for Family Practice (Willard Report) published

1970 Advisory Board for Medical Specialties reorganized as American Board of Medical Specialties

1972 Liaison Committee on Graduate Medical Education (LCGME) established

1975 LCGME formally began to accredit programs

1981 Accreditation Council for Graduate Medical Education replaces LCGME

1982 CME Report B, Recommendations for "Future Directions for Medical Education," adopted by AMA House of Delegates

1987 CME Report C, "Resident Physician Working Hours and Supervision," adopted by AMA House of Delegates

1991 AMA Fellowship and Residency Electronic Interactive Data Access (FREIDA) System established

1992 ACGME declares 1-year moratorium on considering accreditation requirements for new subspecialties

1996 AMA FREIDA becomes FREIDA Online

1996 First CD-ROM version of the *GME Directory* published

2000 ACGME becomes incorporated

2000 In collaboration with the Association of American Medical Colleges (AAMC), AMA develops online survey, the National GME Census

2002 CME Report 9, "Resident Physician Working Conditions," adopted by AMA House of Delegates

2004 Council celebrates its 100th anniversary

2005 Council begins its Initiative to Transform Medical Education (ITME)

2005 AMA and AAMC sign Statement of Cooperation

Information

312 464-4627
E-mail: daniel.winship@ama-assn.org
www.ama-assn.org/go/councilmeded

AMA Section on Medical Schools

The AMA Section on Medical Schools (AMA-SMS) provides all LCME- and AOA-accredited medical schools and their faculty an opportunity both to express their opinions through debate and to participate in the formulation of policy through a vote in the AMA House of Delegates. During each Annual and Interim meeting, the AMA-SMS provides informative educational programs on current issues of relevance to the medical education community. Uniquely positioned to address key education and practice issues affecting physicians and their patients, the AMA-SMS plays an important role in helping the AMA develop policy in areas such as medical education reform, clinical research, workforce planning, patient care, and the financing of medical education.

Information

312 464-4655
E-mail: section@ama-assn.org
www.ama-assn.org/go/sms

AMA Medical Education Group

The AMA Medical Education Group, under the guidance of the Council on Medical Education and the Section on Medical Schools, supports the development, promulgation, and implementation of policies that fulfill the profession's responsibility to ensure the competence of its members.

The group facilitates the development of national medical education policy, collects survey data, and widely disseminates information on undergraduate, graduate, and continuing medical education as well as educational programs in 77 health-related professions. The group serves as a valuable resource for physicians, educators, policymakers, researchers, and the public.

Information

Jacqueline Drake
312 464-4389
E-mail: jacqueline.drake@ama-assn.org
www.ama-assn.org/go/meded

National GME Census

The National GME Census is a joint effort of the AMA and the Association of American Medical Colleges (AAMC) and replaces the AMA Annual Survey of GME Programs. Every summer, all programs accredited by the ACGME and combined specialty programs approved by their respective boards are asked to complete this online census, available at www.aamc.org/gmetrack.

The census collects data on program characteristics, such as program size, work hours, program evaluation, educational characteristics, and health benefits. GME program directors also confirm or edit information about individual residents and provide information on new residents, if necessary. These data are stored in the AMA Physician Masterfile and are used to verify the education and training credentials of physicians. Program data are used to update listings in FREIDA Online and Appendix A of the *Graduate Medical Education Directory*.

During the 2008 survey cycle, 90% of programs completed the census as of January 31, 2009, either online via the AAMC Web site or by completing a paper survey.

Information

www.aamc.org/gmetrack
800 866-6793
E-mail: gmetrack@aamc.org

Medical Education Issue of *JAMA*

Every September, the *Journal of the American Medical Association (JAMA)* publishes a special issue on medical education.

The GME tables in the appendix are based on data collected through the National GME Census. Program directors, specialty societies, and health workforce researchers and planners at national and state levels all rely on the data published in this issue of *JAMA*. The contributions of program directors to the Census are very important to the provision of accurate and timely data to the GME community. Program directors' early and complete participation in the Census is thus strongly encouraged and appreciated; without the information they provide, such reporting on GME data would be difficult, if not impossible.

The September 10, 2008 issue included:

- Student Body Racial and Ethnic Composition and Diversity-Related Outcomes in US Medical Schools
- Association of Workload of On-Call Medical Interns With On-Call Sleep Duration, Shift Duration, and Participation in Educational Activities
- Factors Associated With Medical Students' Career Choices Regarding Internal Medicine
- Characteristics and Career Intentions of the Emerging MD/PhD Workforce
- US Residency Training Before and After the 1997 Balanced Budget Act
- Internet-Based Learning in the Health Professions: A Meta-analysis
- Building Physician Work Hour Regulations From First Principles and Best Evidence
- Emotional Intelligence and Graduate Medical Education
- Diversifying the Medical Classroom: Is More Evidence Needed?
- Improving Accountability for the Public Investment in Health Profession Education: It's Time to Try Health Workforce Planning
- MD/PhD Programs—A Call for an Accounting
- Future Salary and US Residency Fill Rate Revisited
- Participation in and Perceptions of Unprofessional Behaviors Among Incoming Internal Medicine Interns

Information

www.jama.com

Medical Education Data Service, Mailing Labels

The AMA Medical Education Data Service provides published information, existing tables, custom tables, electronic data and mailing labels to students, educational institutions, professional associations, government agencies, foundations and others interested in collecting, analyzing and disseminating medical education data. Written requests for data are screened for merit and must include the purpose of the project, specific data service requested, expected due date for data, and name, address, phone and fax number of the project contact. When requests require staff contribution or organizational overhead, a fee is assessed; program directors requesting data receive a substantial discount.

Information

Sarah Brotherton, PhD, Director
AMA Data Acquisition Services
312 464-4487
E-mail: sarah.brotherton@ama-assn.org

Electronic State-level GME Data

The AMA offers aggregate statistics for each state on all resident physicians, in Adobe Acrobat format. There are six different tables for each state, including Puerto Rico and the District of Columbia, as well as a set of six tables for the United States:
- Total Number of Resident Physicians and Program Year 1 Resident Physicians in GME Programs
- Resident Physicians by Type of Medical School Attended
- Resident Physicians by Gender and Race/Ethnicity
- Resident Physicians Without Prior US GME in GY1 Positions by Type of Medical School Attended
- Resident Physicians Who Completed a Graduate Medical Education Program or Completed a Preliminary Year

- Plans of Resident Physicians Completing a Program

Information

For more information on these tables, or for inquiries about other GME data, contact

AMA Data Acquisition Services
312 464-4487

Price for state-level GME data is $20 to $50 (based on number of states ordered). To order, contact:
Jackie Edwards
312 464-4659
E-mail: jacqueline.edwards@ama-assn.org
www.ama-assn.org/go/mededproducts

GME e-Letter

The *GME e-Letter*, a free monthly e-mail newsletter from the AMA, is a popular source of news and information for the GME community. Comments from subscribers include:
- "Clear, concise, and relevant!"
- "Very useful since it is focused, brief and contains information of importance to program directors."
- "Loved the e-letter. Thought it was well-written, informative and appropriately succinct."
- "A great resource and the best way to share cutting-edge news re: GME."

Since its debut in May 2001, the *GME e-Letter* has grown to encompass more than 13,000 subscribers, including:
- Program directors and staff of residency and fellowship programs
- Hospital administrators
- Professional associations
- Certifying/licensing boards
- Physician recruiters
- Governmental and regulatory organizations

The *e-Letter* covers a wide range of issues affecting GME—everything from resident work hours and pharmaceutical industry access to residency programs to updates on accreditation activities and development of new subspecialties. The publication also references peer-reviewed studies and articles in the medical literature that are related to GME.

Information

Current issue of the *e-Letter*
www.ama-assn.org/go/gmenews

Subscriptions

www.ama-assn.org/go/enews

GME Articles from *American Medical News*

American Medical News (AMNews) is a weekly newspaper for physicians, published by the AMA, that covers professional, educational, social, economic, and policy issues in medicine. *AMNews* frequently covers key issues in medical education; recent articles, for example, include:
- Teaching hospitals, residencies win reprieve on Medicaid cuts
- AMA meeting: Resident work hours stir passionate debate
- AMA meeting: Delegates respond to rising student debt
- IMGs, other visa holders in Michigan free to drive again

- Medical schools on target to reach enrollment goals
- New rule excludes medical graduates from federal loan deferment plan
- Gearing up for a graying generation: Training more doctors in geriatrics skills
- Shortage of general surgeons is straining some facilities

Links to these and other articles of specific interest to academic physicians, program directors, medical students, and physicians in training are available free of charge at www.ama-assn.org/ama/pub/category/8731.html.

Information

American Medical News (AMNews)
312 464-4429
312 464-4445 fax
www.amednews.com

Medical Education Bulletin

The *Medical Education Bulletin* is a newsletter published twice a year by the AMA Medical Education Group. It covers issues of interest to the undergraduate and graduate medical education community, including updates on AMA actions related to medical education at the annual and interim meetings of the AMA House of Delegates.

Recent issues have included such articles as:
- AMA House of Delegates Actions, 2008 Annual Meeting
- New toolkit from AMA Ethical Force Program
- New health literacy report available
- After 40 years, AMA PRA is still the gold standard

The *Bulletin* is mailed to GME program directors, medical education directors at teaching hospitals, members of the Section on Medical Schools, medical school deans, and the AMA appointees to the Residency Review Committees.

Information

Sylvia I. Etzel, Editor
312 464-4693
312 464-5830 Fax
E-mail: sylvia.etzel@ama-assn.org

Guidebook for GME Directors and Coordinators

Published by the AMA Division of Graduate Medical Education, this 87-page guidebook provides residency/fellowship program directors, program coordinators, institution officials, and others information about AMA services, products, and activities related to GME. Also included are descriptions of and contact information for a number of organizations involved in GME, including American Board of Medical Specialties (ABMS) certification boards and medical licensing boards.

The book is available as an Adobe Acrobat .pdf file at www.ama-assn.org/go/gmeguidebook.

AMA Introduction to the Practice of Medicine Educational Series

The AMA is offering the Introduction to the Practice of Medicine (IPM) program, a Web-based educational series developed through collaboration with the Ohio State Medical Association and The Ohio

State University Medical Center. The series is designed to help meet the dual challenges of educating residents in ACGME general competency requirements and supplementing their education in a variety of nontraditional curricular topics. IPM features include:

- 24/7 accessibility, so residents can complete the modules and post-assessments at their own convenience.
- Easy navigation, with quick and easy access to learning modules, asessments, reports and a host of other features.
- Comprehensive library of more than 20 learning modules, assembled by experts from across the country, covering such topics as Health Care Quality, Physician Employment Contracts, and Sleep Deprivation, with more modules under construction. Each module includes a formal lecture, post-assessment, evaluation, and course certificate of completion.
- Extensive reporting features, making it simple to track and document progress. The IPM features easy-to-use tools for GME departments to seamlessly track how their institution—and residents—are using the program. Reports can be produced to show which residents have completed each module and how they scored on each post-assessment. Administrators can view aggregate evaluation scores to measure performance at the resident, program, and institution level. These documentation capabilities can present a real-time picture of an institution's overall progress toward fulfilling competency requirements.

Information

Marie Cruz
312 464-4698
E-mail: ipm@ama-assn.org

AMA Continuing Medical Education

Advances in biomedical science and changes in the other facets of the US health care delivery environment engage physicians in a continuous process of professional development. To ensure that they provide patients with the most current and appropriate treatment, services, and information, physicians keep learning through participation in a wide array of conferences and other educational experiences, as well as through independent study of published materials. The AMA supports these physician efforts by:

- Administering the only nonspecialty-specific credit system that recognizes physician completion of continuing medical education (CME) activities
- Offering CME publications and programs (both conferences and enduring materials, such as online and print activities)
- Establishing new learning modalities (performance improvement and Internet point of care) appropriate for physician professional development and investigating international opportunities for reciprocal CME relationships

The AMA Physician's Recognition Award

In 1968, the AMA House of Delegates established the AMA Physician's Recognition Award (PRA) to both encourage physicians to participate in CME and acknowledge when individual physicians complete CME activities. Activities that meet education standards established by the AMA can be designated *AMA PRA Category 1 Credit*[TM] by educational institutions accredited by the Accreditation Council for Continuing Medical Education (ACCME) or a recognized state medical society to provide CME to physicians. These typically include state medical societies, medical specialty societies, medical schools, and hospitals. Other activities, usually independent or physician directed learning, may be reported for *AMA PRA Category 2 Credit*[TM]. AMA PRA certificates are awarded in lengths of 1, 2, or 3 years.

The AMA also offers the AMA PRA with Commendation, awarded to physicians who exceed the credit required to earn the standard PRA. For more information, visit www.ama-assn.org/go/pra.

Through partnership arrangements, the AMA will also award the AMA PRA certificate if the CME requirements of other organizations are met. In addition, 38 states accept the AMA PRA certificate or the AMA-approved AMA PRA application as evidence that physicians have met the CME requirements for license reregistration.

The AMA sends information about applying for the AMA PRA to physicians who have had a valid AMA PRA certificate within the past 3 years and physicians whose current certificate is expiring within 3 months.

Information

The AMA PRA application form and the *Physician's Recognition Award and Credit System Information Booklet (2006 revision)* are available via:
Department of AMA PRA Standards and Policy
Continuing Physician Professional Development
312 464-4941
312 464-4567 fax
E-mail: pra@ama-assn.org
www.ama-assn.org/go/prabooklet and
www.ama-assn.org/go/applypra

For bulk orders of the booklet, contact the AMA at 800 621-8335.

AMA PRA Rules for Performance Improvement and Internet Point of Care (PoC) CME

In 2004, the AMA Council on Medical Education approved new rules governing how Performance Improvement (PI) activities could be conducted for *AMA PRA Category 1 Credit*. Performance improvement activities describe structured, long-term processes by which a physician or group of physicians can learn about specific performance measures, retrospectively assess their practice, apply these measures prospectively over a useful interval, and reevaluate their performance. The AMA helped the ACCME develop guidance for providers on how to implement the requirements for this format to develop effective PI activities.

Similarly, in 2005, the Council approved new rules governing how Internet PoC activities could be conducted for *AMA PRA Category 1 Credit*. Internet PoC CME describes a process developed by accredited CME providers that provides structured, self-directed, online learning by physicians on topics relevant to their clinical practice. Learning for this activity is driven by a reflective process in which physicians must document their clinical question, the sources consulted, and the application to practice for the accredited CME provider. The AMA also assisted the ACCME in developing guidance for providers on how to implement the requirements for this format.

For more information on either of these two new formats, visit www.ama-assn.org/go/prabooklet.

AMA CME Program

As an ACCME-accredited provider, the AMA offers CME activities in a variety of formats for physicians' professional development. All activities must be congruent with the mission of the AMA and are planned and implemented to meet AMA's rigorous CME standards.

Enduring CME activities

The AMA offers a number of enduring CME activities that provide physician self-assessment. Available in print, CD-ROM, and Internet formats, these enduring CME activities are intended to provide physicians with clinical and nonclinical information that will meet their professional development needs.

A list of activities is available at www.ama-assn.org/go/cme, or e-mail cme@ama-assn.org for more information.

Journal CME

The AMA offers online journal CME activities in the *Journal of the American Medical Association* and the six AMA Archives journals. Physicians can earn *AMA PRA Category 1 Credit* by reading the designated articles online and completing a post-test.

AMA-sponsored conferences and live events

The AMA sponsors multiple conferences and live events designated for *AMA PRA Category 1 Credit*. Physicians receive education on topics of interest to all disciplines and specialties. Recently, AMA-sponsored conferences and live events have included Basic and Advanced Disaster Life Support programs, the AMA Medical Communications Conference, and the Federation of State Physician Health Programs.

International CME

The International Conference Recognition Program began in 1990 by an act of the AMA House of Delegates. The AMA recognized that international congresses present opportunities for physicians to participate in quality educational programs and provide opportunities for US physicians to collaborate with colleagues overseas. The AMA recognizes a small number of events each year and provides American physicians with an opportunity to earn *AMA PRA Category 1 Credit* at these approved events. For more information, visit www.ama-assn.org/go/internationalcme.

Information

For more information on AMA CME programs and activities, visit www.ama-assn.org/go/cme or contact:

AMA CME credits/courses	312 464-4941
Physician's Recognition Award	312 464-4664
International CME	312 464-5196

For general information, contact:
AMA Continuing Physician Professional Development
312 464-4671
312 464-5830 Fax
E-mail: cppd@ama-assn.org

Gifts to Physicians from Industry

Starting in 2001, the AMA led this initiative to create awareness among physicians and physicians-in-training about the ethical implications of receiving gifts from industry.

The initiative consists of a series of four free online educational modules available at www.ama-assn.org/go/ethicalgifts. Each module presents important general concepts, then uses gifts as the context to illustrate the idea. Every module is rich with case examples. The educational modules will also help satisfy the requirements from the Accreditation Council for Graduate Medical Education (ACGME) for education on professionalism as one of the six competencies expected of residents in training.

The four educational modules cover these topics:
- An overview of ethical, professional, and legal issues for physicians' relationships with industry
- Physicians' expectations from industry and sales personnel
- Professionalism, including the issues of gifts to physicians from industry
- The AMA guidelines on gifts to physicians from industry

Using the Internet, each module is available in two formats at no cost and with 24-hour access:
- Downloadable resource materials for instructors, at any level of medical education, to use to build 1-hour learning experiences. Materials include a presenter's guide, PowerPoint slides, and a participant's handout. CME providers can adapt these resources for use in their local sites.
- Online self-study modules designed for individual learners, designated for *AMA PRA Category 1 Credit*.

The material in the educational modules is based on the 1990 AMA Council on Ethical and Judicial Affairs (CEJA) Opinion 8.061, "Gifts to Physicians from Industry," which is part of the AMA Code of Medical Ethics. There are no new policies or guidelines in the modules.

The modules also refer to the Pharmaceutical Research and Manufacturers of America (PhRMA) guidelines, as well as those developed by other medical, industry, and government groups, as appropriate, to give a broad-based understanding of the issues involved in the ethics of gift giving. The PhRMA code and others are very similar in spirit and substance to the AMA Ethical Opinion. The recent guidance to pharmaceutical and device companies by the Office of the Inspector General is provided as a reference.

Related Resources

Resident Physician and Medical Industry Interactions: Guiding Principles

Association of American Medical Colleges
Organization of Resident Representatives
www.aamc.org/members/orr/interactionguidelines.pdf

Principles to Guide the Relationship Between Graduate Medical Education and Industry

Accreditation Council for Graduate Medical Education
www.acgme.org/acWebsite/positionPapers/pp_GMEGuide.pdf

Information

E-mail: cppd@ama-assn.org
www.ama-assn.org/go/ethicalgifts

Virtual Mentor

Virtual Mentor is the AMA's online ethics journal. Published since 1999, *Virtual Mentor* (*VM*) explores the ethical issues and challenges that students, residents, and other physicians are likely to confront in their training and daily practice. For this reason, the journal is a valuable teaching resource for medical educators at all levels as well as for doctors and doctors-to-be. Each monthly issue of *VM* contains original articles and commentary on a given theme—eg, access to care, quality of life considerations in clinical decisionmaking, public roles of physicians, ethical issues in endocrinology, conflict of values in the clinic.

Virtual Mentor is student- and resident-driven. Theme issue editors are selected each year through a competitive process from among medical students and residents who seek to broaden and deepen their education by taking the time to examine medicine's ever-increasing ethical challenges. The issue editors meet annually with *VM* editorial staff, based in Chicago, where we discuss potential topics for the upcoming year. Each editor identifies a theme and month of publication for his or her issue and then solicits articles and case commentary from experienced physicians and other experts in the field who can help *VM* readers think productively about the topic under discussion. The application process for theme issue editors is announced in *VM* each September. In 2008, VM was accepted by the National Library of Medicine for indexing in MEDLINE. MEDLINE indexing will make *VM*'s articles readily accessible to anyone who searches PubMed online.

Virtual Mentor is also home to the John Conley Ethics Essay Contest, publishing the winning student essay in an appropriately

GME Information

themed issue of *VM*. Announcement of the annual Conley Contest topic and instructions for entering appear in the February *VM*.

Themes for upcoming issues of *VM* are listed at the bottom of each month's home page. If you have expertise in a field or topic that will be a *VM* focus in the future and you would like to contribute to the journal, contact *VM* at virtualmentor@ama-assn.org.

Information

www.virtualmentor.org
312 464-5438
E-mail: virtualmentor@ama-assn.org

E. GME-related Organizations

Accreditation Council for Graduate Medical Education (ACGME)

The Accreditation Council for Graduate Medical Education (ACGME) is a separately incorporated organization, responsible for the accreditation of more than 8,500 allopathic graduate medical education programs. It has five member organizations:

- American Board of Medical Specialties
- American Hospital Association
- American Medical Association
- Association of American Medical Colleges
- Council of Medical Specialty Societies

Each member organization nominates four individuals to the ACGME's Board of Directors. In addition, the Board of Directors includes three public representatives, two resident representatives, and the chair of the Council of Review Committee Chairs. A representative for the federal government also serves on the Board in a non-voting capacity.

The mission of the ACGME is to improve health care by assessing and advancing the quality of resident physicians' education through accreditation. The ACGME's vision is exemplary accreditation and its values are:

- Accountability through processes and results that are open and transparent; responsive to the educational community and the health care community; and reliable, valid, and consistent.
- Excellence through accreditation that is efficient and effective, outcomes-based, improvement-oriented, and innovative.
- Professionalism through actions that are respectful and collaborative, responsive, ethical, and fair.

Under the aegis of the ACGME, the accreditation of graduate medical education programs and the institutions that sponsor them is carried out by 27 residency review committees and an institutional review committee. These committees have been delegated accreditation authority by the ACGME. A Residency Review Committee (RRC) consists of representatives appointed by the American Medical Association, the appropriate specialty board, and, in some cases, a national specialty organization (see table on p. 22).

The Transitional Year Review Committee is composed of ten members who are appointed by the chair of the ACGME in conjunction with the Executive Committee. The term "review committee" is used to denote a Residency Review Committee, the Transitional Year Review Committee, and the Institutional Review Committee. The Institutional Review Committee (IRC) is composed of ten members appointed by the Chair of the ACGME in conjunction with the Executive Committee. The Institutional Review Committee assumes the responsibility for accrediting institutions which sponsor multiple programs. It evaluates institutions for substantial compliance with the Institutional Requirements.

GME programs are accredited when they are judged to be in substantial compliance with the institutional, common, and specialty program requirements. The requirements are developed and periodically revised by a review committee for its area(s) of competence, and are approved by the ACGME. The activities of the ACGME extend to programs and institutions within the jurisdiction of the United States of America.

ACGME institutional and program requirements are posted on the ACGME Web site: www.acgme.org. The institutional and program requirements describe curricular content for GME programs and may also address program resources and personnel, program length and other issues. Accredited programs and institutions are

Residency Review Committee Appointing Organizations

Residency Review Committees	Sponsoring Organizations	Residency Review Committees	Sponsoring Organizations
Allergy and Immunology	American Board of Allergy and Immunology (A Conjoint Board of the American Board of Internal Medicine and the American Board of Pediatrics) AMA Council on Medical Education	Ophthalmology	American Academy of Ophthalmology American Board of Ophthalmology AMA Council on Medical Education
Anesthesiology	American Board of Anesthesiology American Society of Anesthesiologists AMA Council on Medical Education	Orthopaedic Surgery	American Academy of Orthopaedic Surgeons American Board of Orthopaedic Surgery AMA Council on Medical Education
Colon and Rectal Surgery	American Board of Colon and Rectal Surgery American College of Surgeons AMA Council on Medical Education	Otolaryngology	American Board of Otolaryngology American College of Surgeons AMA Council on Medical Education
Dermatology	American Board of Dermatology AMA Council on Medical Education	Pathology	American Board of Pathology AMA Council on Medical Education
Diagnostic Radiology	American Board of Radiology American College of Radiology AMA Council on Medical Education	Pediatrics	American Academy of Pediatrics American Board of Pediatrics AMA Council on Medical Education
Emergency Medicine	American Board of Emergency Medicine American College of Emergency Physicians AMA Council on Medical Education	Physical Medicine and Rehabilitation	American Academy of Physical Medicine and Rehabilitation American Board of Physical Medicine and Rehabilitation AMA Council on Medical Education
Family Practice	American Academy of Family Physicians American Board of Family Practice AMA Council on Medical Education	Plastic Surgery	American Board of Plastic Surgery American College of Surgeons AMA Council on Medical Education
Internal Medicine	American Board of Internal Medicine American College of Physicians AMA Council on Medical Education	Preventive Medicine	American Board of Preventive Medicine AMA Council on Medical Education
Medical Genetics	American Board of Medical Genetics American College of Medical Genetics AMA Council on Medical Education	Psychiatry	American Board of Psychiatry and Neurology American Psychiatric Association AMA Council on Medical Education
Neurological Surgery	American Board of Neurological Surgery American College of Surgeons AMA Council on Medical Education	Radiation Oncology	American Board of Radiology American College of Radiology AMA Council on Medical Education
Neurology	American Academy of Neurology American Board of Psychiatry and Neurology AMA Council on Medical Education	Surgery	American Board of Surgery American College of Surgeons AMA Council on Medical Education
Nuclear Medicine	American Board of Nuclear Medicine Society of Nuclear Medicine AMA Council on Medical Education	Thoracic Surgery	American Board of Thoracic Surgery American College of Surgeons AMA Council on Medical Education
Obstetrics-Gynecology	American Board of Obstetrics and Gynecology American College of Obstetricians and Gynecologists AMA Council on Medical Education	Urology	American Board of Urology American College of Surgeons AMA Council on Medical Education

judged to be in substantial compliance with ACGME institutional, common, and specialty-specific program requirements.

Also available on the ACGME Web site are the ACGME *Policies and Procedures*, *Bylaws*, and *Glossary*. The *Policies and Procedures* provides information on the review process, definitions of accreditation statuses, and other useful information.

A list of programs accredited by the ACGME, including detailed information about each program, is published by the AMA annually in the *Directory* (see Section III) using information provided by the ACGME. The ACGME lists accredited programs and institutions on its Web site: www.acgme.org. Click on "Search Programs/Institutions" in the left-hand navigation bar to look up the accreditation status of a program or institution. In addition, the Web site contains comprehensive information about accreditation of graduate medical education programs and sponsoring institutions.

ACGME Program Requirements Additions/Updates in 2008

The ACGME Board of Directors meets three times a year, in February, June, and September. One of its functions is to approve revisions to existing ACGME program requirements or the development of program requirements for new specialties/subspecialties.

At its February 2008 meeting, the ACGME recognized pediatric transplant hepatology (pediatrics) as a new subspecialty and approved program requirements in the field; it also approved new program requirements for hospice and palliative medicine. In addition, minor revisions were approved for the following:

- Neuromuscular Medicine
- Sports Medicine
- Vascular Surgery
- Sleep Medicine
- Psychiatry

At its June 2008 meeting, the ACGME approved major revisions to the following program requirements, effective July 1, 2009:
- Neurological Surgery
- Plastic Surgery
- Radiation Oncology
- Six subspecialties of pediatrics (Pediatric Endocrinology, Pediatric Nephrology, Pediatric Pulmonology, Pediatric Gastroenterology, Pediatric Infectious Diseases, Developmental-Behavioral Pediatrics)

In addition, minor revisions, effective August 10, 2008, were approved in:
- Surgery
- Pediatric Surgery

Finally, it was announced that accreditation of cardiothoracic radiology programs would be discontinued in June 2010; at the time, two programs were accredited.

At its September 2008 meeting, the ACGME approved major revisions to the program requirements in the following specialties, effective July 1, 2009:
- Internal Medicine
- Urology
- Pediatric Urology

In addition, the ACGME approved addition of 1-year fellowship common requirements for the following subspecialties, effective September 16, 2008 (unless noted):
- Surgical Critical Care (Surgery)
- Spinal Cord Injury Medicine (Physical Medicine and Rehabilitation)
- Pediatric Rehabilitation Medicine (Physical Medicine and Rehabilitation)
- Pediatric Transplant Hepatology (Pediatrics) (effective November 16, 2008)

Parker J. Palmer Courage to Teach Award

In February 2001, the ACGME established the Parker J. Palmer Courage to Teach Award to recognize outstanding GME program directors. Criteria for selection include a demonstrated commitment to education with evidence of successful mentoring, program development, and improvement. The ACGME recognizes ten outstanding program directors each year with the award. The winners of the Parker J. Palmer award from 2002 to 2009 are listed below:

2002
- Robert W. Block, MD, University of Oklahoma, Tulsa (Pediatrics)
- Virginia U. Collier, MD, Christiana Care Health Services (Internal Medicine)
- George C. Curry, MD, University of Texas Southwestern Medical Center (Diagnostic Radiology)
- Alfred D. Fleming, MD, Creighton University (Obstetrics-Gynecology/Maternal Fetal Medicine)
- William H. Hester, MD, McLeod Family Medicine Center (Family Medicine)
- Earl D. Kemp, MD, Sioux Falls Family Medicine Residency (Family Medicine)
- Gail A. McGuinness, MD, University of Iowa (Pediatrics)
- Claude H. Organ, Jr, MD, University of California-San Francisco-East Bay (General Surgery)
- Keith D. Wrenn, MD, Vanderbilt University Medical Center (Emergency Medicine)
- Nikitas J. Zervanos, MD, Lancaster General Hospital (Family Medicine)

2003
- C. Bruce Alexander, MD, University of Alabama, Birmingham (Pathology)

- Keith B. Armitage, MD, University Hospitals of Cleveland (Internal Medicine)
- Eugene V. Beresin, MD, Massachusetts General Hospital (Child-Adolescent Psychiatry)
- Frank J. Eismont, MD, Jackson Memorial Hospital/Jackson Health System (Orthopaedic Surgery)
- Steven K. Feske, MD, Brigham and Women's Hospital (Neurology)
- Joseph T. Gilhooly, MD, Oregon Health & Sciences University (Pediatrics)
- Harold L. Johnston, MD, Alaska Family Medicine/Providence Hospital (Family Medicine)
- Henry J. Schultz, MD, Mayo Clinic (Retired, Internal Medicine)
- John L. Tarpley, MD, Vanderbilt University (General Surgery)
- Bennett S. Vogelman, MD, University of Wisconsin-Madison (Internal Medicine)
- Kathleen V. Watson, MD, University of Minnesota (Internal Medicine)

2004
- William L. Bockenek, MD, Charlotte Institute of Rehabilitation (Physical Medicine & Rehabilitation)
- Carol Carraccio, MD, University of Maryland Medical System (Pediatrics)
- Carlyle H. Chan, MD, Medical College of Wisconsin (Psychiatry)
- Paul H. Gerst, MD, Bronx-Lebanon Hospital Center, (General Surgery)
- DuPont Guerry, IV, MD, University of Pennsylvania (Hematology-Oncology)
- J. Peter Harris, MD, Golisano Children's Hospital at Strong University of Rochester (Pediatrics)
- John B. Jeffers, MD, Wills Eye Hospital (Ophthalmology)
- Catherine K. Lineberger, MD, Duke University Medical Center (Anesthesiology)
- Gordon E. Schutze, MD, University of Arkansas for Medical Sciences/Arkansas Children's Hospital (Pediatrics)
- Eric Walsh, MD, Oregon Health & Science University (Family Medicine)

2005
- Patricia L. Blanchette, MD, University of Hawaii (Geriatric Medicine)
- Francis L. Counselman, MD, Eastern Virginia Medical School (Emergency Medicine)
- Daniel Dedrick, MD, Brigham and Women's Hospital (Anesthesiology)
- Richard W. Dow, MD, Dartmouth-Hitchcock Medical Center (General Surgery)
- David L. George, MD, Reading Hospital and Medical Center (Transitional Year)
- Mark S. Juzych, MD, Kresge Eye Institute (Ophthalmology)
- Teresa L. Massagli, MD, University of Washington (Physical Medicine & Rehabilitation)
- Anthony A. Meyer, MD, PhD, University of North Carolina, Chapel Hill (General Surgery)
- Glenn C. Newell, MD, UMDNJ-Robert Wood Johnson (Internal Medicine)
- Eric Scher, MD, Henry Ford Hospital (Internal Medicine)

2006
- Steven R. Cohen, MD, MPH, Mount Sinai School of Medicine (Dermatology)
- Deborah S. Cowley, MD, University of Washington School of Medicine (Psychiatry)
- Karen E. Deveney, MD, Oregon Health and Sciences University (General Surgery)

- Jehan El-Bayoumi, MD, George Washington University (Internal Medicine)
- Ralph S. Greco, MD, Stanford University School of Medicine (General Surgery)
- Kirk A. Keegan, Jr, MD, University of California, Orange (Obstetrics-Gynecology)
- Dorothy S. Lane, MD, Stony Brook University (Preventive Medicine)
- Shahla Masood, MD, University of Florida, Jacksonville (Pathology)
- Kemuel L. Philbrick, MD, Mayo Clinic (Psychiatry)
- Volkner K. H. Sonntag, MD, Barrow Institute for Neurological Institute (Neurosurgery)

2007

- David Allen, MD, University of Wisconsin Children's Hospital, Madison (Pediatrics)
- Hasan Bazari, MD, Massachusetts General Hospital, Boston (Internal Medicine)
- Carey Chisholm, MD, Indiana University School of Medicine, Indianapolis (Emergency Medicine)
- Gary Clark, MD, MetroHealth Rehabilitation Institute, Cleveland (Physical Medicine and Rehabilitation)
- Javier Alfonso Gonzalez del Rey, MD, Cincinnati Children's Hospital, Ohio (Pediatric Emergency Medicine)
- Robert Heros, MD, University of Miami (Neurological Surgery)
- Neil Mitnick, DO, Albany Medical College, New York (Family Medicine)
- Humberto Quintana, MD, Louisiana State University Health Sciences Center, New Orleans (Child and Adolescent Psychiatry)
- Allen Silbergleit, MD, St. Joseph Mercy Oakland, Pontiac, Michigan (General Surgery)
- Jeffrey Wiese, MD, Tulane University School of Medicine, New Orleans (Internal Medicine)

2008

- Robert Brown, MD, Beth Israel Deaconess Medical Center, Boston (Nephrology)
- Steve Galetta, MD, University of Pennsylvania, Philadelphia (Neurology)
- Kalpalatha Guntupalli, MD, Baylor College of Medicine, Houston (Pulmonary/Critical Care)
- Karen Horvath, MD, University of Washington, Seattle (General Surgery)
- Richard Lackman, MD, University of Pennsylvania, Philadelphia (Orthopaedic Surgery)
- John Jane, MD, University of Virginia, Charlottesville (Neurosurgery)
- Mukta Panda, MD, University of Tennessee, Knoxville (Internal Medicine)
- Susan Promes, MD, Duke University, Durham (Emergency Medicine)
- Richard Shugarman, MD, University of Washington (Pediatrics)
- William Sonis, MD, Drexel University College of Medicine, Friends Hospital, Philadelphia (Child and Adolescent Psychiatry)

2009

- Michael S. Beeson, MD, Summa Health System, Akron, Ohio (Emergency Medicine)
- James Burks, MD, Texas Tech University, Lubbock (Internal Medicine)
- Peter Carek, MD, Medical University of South Carolina, Charleston (Family Medicine)
- Edmund Cibas, MD, Brigham and Women's Hospital, Boston, Massachusetts (Cytopathology)

- Nancy Gaba, MD, George Washington University, Washington, DC (Obstetrics and Gynecology)
- Sheela Kapre, MD, San Joaquin General Hospital, French Camp, California (Internal Medicine)
- Gail Manos, MD, Naval Medical Center, Portsmouth, Virginia (Psychiatry)
- D. Karl Montague, MD, Cleveland Clinic, Ohio (Urology)
- Lori Schuh, MD, Henry Ford Hospital, Detroit, Michigan (Neurology)
- James Valentine, MD, University of Texas Southwestern Medical School, Dallas (Surgery)
- James Welling, MD, Good Samaritan Hospital, Cincinnati, Ohio (Surgery)

Parker J. Palmer, educator and author of *The Courage to Teach*, promotes the concept of "living divided no more," which has proven relevant to teaching in academic health centers.

ACGME Staff

The following list is updated as of January 2009.
Main Office: 312 755-5000

Office of the Executive Director

Thomas J. Nasca, MD, MACP, executive director
312 755-7492   tnasca@acgme.org
Marsha A. Miller, associate vice president, Office of Resident Services
312 755-5041   mmiller@acgme.org
Rose Cross, executive secretary
312 755-5008   rmc@acgme.org

Department of Accreditation Committees

Jeanne K. Heard, MD, PhD, senior vice president
312 755-5040   jkh@acgme.org
Mary Cleveland, executive assistant
312 755-5010   mcleveland@acgme.org
Caroline Fischer, MBA, executive director, Accreditation Standards
312 755-5044   cfischer@acgme.org

Residency Review Committees (RRCs) for

Allergy and Immunology
Patricia Levenberg, PhD, executive director
312 755-5048   plevenberg@acgme.org
Eileen Anthony, MJ, associate executive director
312 755-5047   eanthony@acgme.org

Anesthesiology
Missy Fleming, MEd, PhD, executive director
312 755-5043   mfleming@acgme.org
Linda Thorsen, MA, associate executive director
312 755-5029   lmt@acgme.org

Colon and Rectal Surgery
Louise King, executive director
312 755-5498   lking@acgme.org

Dermatology
Georgia Andrianopoulos, PhD, executive director
312 755-5031   gpa@acgme.org

Emergency Medicine
Lynne Meyer, PhD, MPH, executive director
312 755-5006   lmeyer@acgme.org
Susan Mansker, associate executive director
312 755-5028   smansker@acgme.org

Family Medicine
Jerry Vasilias, PhD, executive director
312 755-7477   jvasilias@acgme.org

Internal Medicine
William E. Rodak, PhD, executive director
312 755-5497   wer@acgme.org

Karen L. Lambert, associate executive director
312 755-5785   kll@acgme.org
Debra L. Dooley, associate executive director
312 755-5496   dld@acgme.org

Medical Genetics
Georgia Andrianopoulos, PhD, executive director
312 755-5031   gpa@acgme.org

Neurological Surgery
Larry D. Sulton, PhD, executive director
312 755-5027   lds@acgme.org
Susan Mansker, associate executive director
312 755-5028   smansker@acgme.org

Neurology
Lynne Meyer, PhD, MPH, executive director
312 755-5006   lmeyer@acgme.org
Susan Mansker, associate executive director
312 755-5028   smansker@acgme.org

Nuclear Medicine
Missy Fleming, MEd, PhD, executive director
312 755-5043   mfleming@acgme.org

Obstetrics and Gynecology
Patricia M. Surdyk, PhD, executive director
312 755-5005   psurdyk@acgme.org

Ophthalmology
Patricia Levenberg, PhD, executive director
312 755-5048   plevenberg@acgme.org
Eileen Anthony, MJ, associate executive director
312 755-5047   eanthony@acgme.org

Orthopaedic Surgery
Steven P. Nestler, PhD, executive director
312 755-5025   spn@acgme.org

Otolaryngology
Patricia Levenberg, PhD, executive director
312 755-5048   plevenberg@acgme.org
Eileen Anthony, MJ, associate executive director
312 755-5047   eanthony@acgme.org

Pathology
Georgia Andrianopoulos, PhD, executive director
312 755-5031   gpa@acgme.org

Pediatrics
Jerry Vasilias, PhD, executive director
312 755-7477   jvasilias@acgme.org
Caroline Fischer, associate executive director
312 755-5044   cfischer@acgme.org

Physical Medicine and Rehabilitation
Steven P. Nestler, PhD, executive director
312 755-5025   spn@acgme.org

Plastic Surgery
Peggy Simpson , EdD, executive director
312 755-5499   psimpson@acgme.org

Preventive Medicine
Patricia Levenberg, PhD, executive director
312 755-5048   plevenberg@acgme.org
Eileen Anthony, MJ, associate executive director
312 755-5047   eanthony@acgme.org

Psychiatry
Lynne Meyer, PhD, MPH, executive director
312 755-5006   lmeyer@acgme.org
Susan Mansker, associate executive director
312 755-5028   smansker@acgme.org

Radiation Oncology
Linda Thorsen, MA, executive director
312 755-5029   lmt@acgme.org

Radiology—Diagnostic
Missy Fleming, MEd, PhD, executive director
312 755-5043   mfleming@acgme.org

Linda Thorsen, MA, associate executive director
312 755-5029   lmt@acgme.org

Surgery
Peggy Simpson , EdD, executive director
312 755-5499   psimpson@acgme.org

Thoracic Surgery
Peggy Simpson , EdD, executive director
312 755-5499   psimpson@acgme.org

Urology
Louise King, executive director
312 755-5498   lking@acgme.org

Transitional Year Review Committee
Linda Thorsen, MA, executive director
312 755-5029   lmt@acgme.org

Institutional Review Committee
Patricia M. Surdyk, PhD, executive director
312 755-5005   psurdyk@acgme.org

Department of Field Activities
Ingrid Philibert, PhD, senior vice president
312 755-5003   iphilibert@acgme.org
Other ACGME personnel
Cynthia Taradejna, associate director, Strategic Planning
312 755-5004   cat@acgme.org
Susan R. Swing, PhD, vice president, Outcome Assessment
312 755-7447   srs@acgme.org
John H. Nylen, chief operations officer
Office of Operations
312 755-7121   jhn@acgme.org
Rebecca Miller, vice president
Department of Operations and Data Analysis
312 755-7119   rmiller@acgme.org
Timothy P. Brigham, MDiv, PhD, senior vice president, Department of Education
312 755-5050   tbrigham@acgme.org
Richard Murphy, director
Human Resources
312 755-7122   rmurphy@acgme.org
Julie Jacob, manager
Corporate Communications
312 755-7133   juliej@acgme.org
Linda Gordon, manager
Department of Meeting Services
312 755-7142   lgordon@acgme.org

Association of American Medical Colleges (AAMC)

The Association of American Medical Colleges is a not-for-profit association representing all 130 accredited US and 17 accredited Canadian medical schools; nearly 400 major teaching hospitals and health systems, including 68 Department of Veterans Affairs medical centers; and nearly 90 academic and scientific societies.
Through these institutions and organizations, the AAMC represents 125,000 faculty members, 70,000 medical students, and 104,000 resident physicians. The AAMC seeks to improve the nation's health by enhancing the effectiveness of academic medicine. The AAMC assists academic medicine's institutions, organizations, and individuals in the three main mission areas of medical education, medical research, and patient care.

In GME, the AAMC represents and supports members in improving educational quality, strengthening institutional GME leadership and institutional accountability for GME, developing faculty, and setting a national agenda for the support of GME. It carries out this work through a variety of activities.

Compact Between Resident Physicians and Their Teachers

www.aamc.org/meded/residentcompact
Contact: Nicole Buckley
E-mail: nbuckley@aamc.org

The Compact is a declaration of the fundamental principles of GME and the major commitments of both residents and faculty to the educational process, to each other, and to the patients they serve. The Compact's purpose is to provide institutional GME sponsors, program directors, and residents with a model statement that will foster more open communication, clarify expectations, and re-energize the commitment to the primary educational mission of training tomorrow's doctors.

Medical Education Initiatives

www.aamc.org/meded/iime
Contact: Carol A. Aschenbrener, MD
E-mail: caschenbrener@aamc.org

The AAMC has a number of programs and initiatives aimed at improving the health of Americans by fostering innovations in medical education to better align the knowledge, skills, and professionalism of medical students, residents, and practicing physicians with the needs and expectations of the public. Employing expert panels, convening special topic colloquia, and collaborating with external funding partners to administer school-based curriculum improvement grants, the AAMC strives to highlight creative and dynamic approaches employed by medical educators to develop enriching learning experiences and teaching models.

MedEdPORTAL^{SM}

www.aamc.org/mededportal
Contact: Robby Reynolds
E-mail: mededportal@aamc.org

This free online resource enables faculty to publish, share, and discover peer-reviewed educational materials. It is designed to promote collaboration and educational scholarship by facilitating the exchange of peer-reviewed teaching resources such as animations, tutorials, lab manuals, assessment instruments, faculty development materials, and computer-based resources, including an inventory of virtual patients. The AAMC and the McGill University Faculty of Medicine have also announced a new collaboration between MedEdPORTAL and the McGill Molson Medical Informatics (MMMI) project. Through this collaboration, MedEdPORTAL will serve as the primary outlet for more than 8,000 MMMI multimedia teaching materials, helping significantly expand the existing collection of free, high-quality MedEdPORTAL publications currently available online. Recently, MedEdPORTAL has added user comment functionality to promote interactivity and has launched free online training workshops that have reached participants across the globe. In Spring 2008, MedEdPORTAL launched a new Web site, including an online repository, to host online its entire collection of peer-reviewed, high-quality published resources online covering the continuum of medical education.

Project Medical Education (PME)

www.aamc.org/members/pme
Contact: Chris Tucker
E-mail: ctucker@aamc.org

Project Medical Education (PME) helps educate policymakers and others about the missions of medical schools and teaching hospitals. During visits to medical schools and teaching hospitals, policymakers assume the roles of medical students, resident physicians, and faculty physicians in a 1- to 2-day program that shows them first-hand how medical education benefits all Americans.

More than 600 legislators and staff members have participated in at least one PME program held in conjunction with over 60 AAMC member institutions in 24 states since the program's inception in 1999.

Organization of Resident Representatives (ORR)

www.aamc.org/members/orr
Contact: Alexis L. Ruffin
E-mail: alruffin@aamc.org

The mission of the AAMC's Organization of Resident Representatives (ORR) is to improve resident physician education and training, and the quality of health care, by providing a venue for resident voices and offering leadership development to resident physicians pursuing careers in academic medicine. ORR members are appointed through the AAMC Council of Academic Societies, representing program directors or department chairs.

Group on Education Affairs (GEA)

www.aamc.org/members/gea
Contact: M. Brownell (Brownie) Anderson
E-mail: mbanderson@aamc.org

The group's purpose is to promote excellence in the education of physicians throughout their professional lives and, thereby, to contribute to improving the health of the public. Reflecting the continuum of medical education, the GEA is organized by four sections, including the Graduate Medical Education Section, which focuses on supporting the development and continued improvement of GME programs. The Research in Medical Education (RIME) Conference, held in conjunction with the AAMC Annual Meeting, includes research papers, symposia, and abstract sessions. The Innovations in Medical Education Exhibits (IME) also are held during the Annual Meeting.

Group on Resident Affairs (GRA)

www.aamc.org/members/gra
Contact: Sunny Yoder
E-mail: syoder@aamc.org

This group's purpose is to develop leaders who are responsible for GME oversight, administration, organization, financing, and quality in their respective medical schools and teaching hospitals. The Group offers a GME Leadership Development Course—a "school for DIOs"—that explores the DIO's responsibility, from leading a sponsoring institution successfully through an accreditation review to improving the GME enterprise and developing advanced leadership skills. The foundation of the course is the GRA document, "Core Competencies of Institutional GME Leaders/DIOs," available on the GRA Web site at www.aamc.org/members/gra/corecompetencies08.pdf.

Other AAMC Activities

The AAMC also helps students make career decisions and enter residency programs. It assists residents in managing their medical education loans. In collaboration with the AMA, it tracks residents from entry to residency through completion and beyond. The AAMC also offers GME-related online publications.

Careers in Medicine^{SM}

www.aamc.org/students/careersinmedicine
Contact: George V. Richard, PhD
E-mail: grichard@aamc.org

This program helps students choose a medical specialty and select and apply to residency programs (see listing under "Residency Application and Career Planning Resources" for more information).

Visiting Student Application Service (VSAS®)

www.aamc.org/vsas
Contact: Melissa Donner
E-mail: mdonner@aamc.org

The Visiting Student Application Service (VSAS) is a new centralized application service for senior clinical electives piloting in 2008-09. The goal is to streamline what is currently a time-consuming and cumbersome process of locating and applying to away electives. Ten schools will pilot VSAS starting in March 2008 and the service is expected to be open to all schools in spring 2009.

Electronic Resident Application Service (ERAS®)

www.aamc.org/audienceeras.htm
Contact: B. Renée Overton, MBA
E-mail: broverton@aamc.org

ERAS®—the Electronic Resident Application Service—works with applicants, designated dean's offices, and training programs to streamline the residency and fellowship application process for all involved. ERAS users transmit application materials and supporting credentials to training programs using the Internet. ERAS serves almost 48,000 residency and fellowship applicants, 163 medical schools and designated dean's offices, and almost 6,000 training programs annually (see listing under "Residency Application and Career Planning Resources" for more information).

FindAResident®

www.aamc.org/audiencefindaresident.htm
Contact: B. Renée Overton, MBA
E-mail: broverton@aamc.org

FindAResident is a Web-based service designed to provide a direct and efficient way for program administrators to connect with residency and fellowship candidates. Residency and fellowship programs can share information about their programs as well as open positions with applicants; applicants post their resume and contact information for programs to review. FindAResident is a supplement to ERAS®— the Electronic Residency Application Service, providing services not fulfilled by ERAS.

FIRST

www.aamc.org/programs/first
Contact: Nancy-Pat Weaver
E-mail: nweaver@aamc.org

FIRST for Medical Education is designed to help members of the academic medicine community navigate the complexities of student debt. FIRST offers a full range of resources to help medical school borrowers expand their financial literacy, make smart decisions about student loans, and manage their student debt wisely.

GME Track

www.aamc.org/programs/gmetrack/start.htm
Contact: Gwen Garrison
E-mail: ggarrison@aamc.org

GME Track is a Web-based application designed to assist with the collection and management of GME data. GME Track contains the National GME Census, jointly conducted by the AAMC and AMA, which collects detailed information on residents/fellows and training programs. Data collected in the National GME Census are used for national GME statistics and workforce studies as well updating FREIDA Online. Programs, institutions, and medical schools have the ability to download their data and create customized data files on current or previous residents/graduates.

Center for Workforce Studies

www.aamc.org/workforce/
Contact: Edward Salsberg
E-mail: esalsberg@aamc.org

In light of the need to increase medical school and GME capacity to meet the needs of the nation in 2015 and beyond, the Center for Workforce Studies works to:
- Develop the capacity to effectively document and study physician workforce issues related to physician supply, demand, utilization, and distribution across specialty and geographic region
- Support informed decision-making by the medical education community (medical schools, teaching hospitals, faculty, medical students and residents) and policy makers
- Support AAMC policy goals that related to physician workforce, such as increasing underrepresented minorities in medicine

AAMC Publications

The following publications are available via the AAMC Web site at www.aamc.org/publications:
- After the Boston Medical Center Case: The Nuts and Bolts of Resident Unions
- Terrorism Education for Medical Students: Knowledge of Public Health System Key to Preparing Future Physicians
- GME Core Curriculum
- Institutional Accountability for Graduate Medical Education (Report of a Working Group)
- Integrating Education and Patient Care: Observations from the GME Task Force
- Managed Care and Medical Education: The Impact on Physician Education and Teaching Institutions
- Medicaid Direct and Indirect Graduate Medical Education Payments: A 50-State Survey
- Medical School Tuition and Young Physician Indebtedness
- Medicare Payments for Graduate Medical Education: What Every Medical Student, Resident, and Advisor Needs to Know
- Medicare Resident Limits Laws and Regulations: A Reference Guide for the Academic Medical Community
- Patient Safety and Graduate Medical Education
- Resident Physician Duty Hours CD-ROM
- The Handbook of Academic Medicine: How Medical Schools and Teaching Hospitals Work
- Washington Highlights (Periodical)
- Charting Outcomes in the Match: Characteristics of Applicants Who Matched to Their Preferred Specialty in the 2005 NRMP Main Residency Match
- Medical Educational Costs and Student Debt
- Roadmap to Residency: From Application to the Match and Beyond

Information

Association of American Medical Colleges
2450 N Street, NW
Washington, DC 20037-1126
202 828-0400
202 828-1125 Fax
www.aamc.org

Association for Hospital Medical Education (AHME)

The Association for Hospital Medical Education (AHME), founded in 1956, is a national, nonprofit professional organization involved in the continuum of hospital-based medical education—undergraduate, graduate, and continuing medical education. AHME's more than 600 members represent hundreds of teaching hospitals, academic medical centers, and consortia nationwide.

The mission of AHME is to:

- Promote improvement in medical education to meet health care needs
- Serve as a forum and resource for medical education information
- Develop professionals in the field of medical education
- Advocate the value of medical education in health care

AHME offers training and current information for medical education professionals; mentoring and training from national experts on GME institutional administration; and collaboration with accreditation, regulatory, governmental, and other professional organizations in medical education.

AHME celebrated its 50th anniversary in Chicago, Illinois, in May 2006. To commemorate this occasion, AHME published the "50th Anniversary Celebration: 1956-2006" book to describe AHME's history of service and honor AHME's leaders, friends, and supporters.

Publications

AHME News
www.ahme.org/publications/news.html

AHME News, published as a paper copy once per year, with quarterly "electronic" versions, offers news about the Association's divisions, committees, and councils in addition to updates on governmental and accreditation issues affecting medical education.

Guide to Medical Education in the Teaching Hospital
www.ahme.org/publications/guide.html

A practical guide to help navigate the constantly changing landscape of GME. Originally published in 1994, the third edition is now available online in a special section of the AHME Web site, with new chapters added periodically and existing chapters updated as they are completed.

Information

Association for Hospital Medical Education
109 Brush Creek Road
Irwin, PA 15642
724 864-7321
724 864-6153 Fax
E-mail: info@ahme.org
www.ahme.org

Organization of Program Directors Associations (OPDA)

The Organization of Program Directors Associations (OPDA), a component group of the Council of Medical Specialty Societies (CMSS), works to promote the role of the residency director and residency program director societies in achieving excellence in GME.

Created in 2000, OPDA is a leadership consortium of residency program director (or chair) societies in each of the 27 medical and surgical specialties that correspond to 27 ACGME Residency Review Committees. Consisting of one liaison representative from each program director society, OPDA meets regularly to provide peer interaction, information sharing, and collaborative problem solving. In addition, OPDA sponsors periodic symposia and meetings on timely GME issues, provides a forum for communication with leaders in GME, and monitors and promotes GME excellence in the activities of the AAMC, ACGME, NRMP, NBME, ECFMG, and other organizations that regulate and impact GME.

Recently, OPDA was invited to appoint representatives to two key organizations in medical education (ie, the NRMP and the ACGME) to represent OPDA and program director interests in matters of relevance to GME.

The following societies of program directors (or chairs) are currently represented on OPDA:

Allergy and immunology
Allergy/Immunology Training Program Directors (A/ITPD)
www.acaai.org/Member/Committees/allergy_training_program_directors_advisory.htm
Anesthesiology
Association of Anesthesiology Program Directors (AAPD)
www.aapd-saac.org
Society of Academic Anesthesiology Chairs (SAAC)
Colon and rectal surgery
Association of Program Directors for Colon and Rectal Surgery (APDCRS)
www.abcrs.org/pda/
Dermatology
Association of Professors of Dermatology (APD)
www.dermatologyprofessors.org
Emergency medicine
Council of Emergency Medicine Residency Directors (CORD)
www.cordem.org
Family medicine
Association of Family Medicine Residency Directors (AFMRD)
www.afmrd.org/cms
Internal medicine
Association of Program Directors in Internal Medicine (APDIM)
www.im.org/APDIM
Medical genetics
Association of Professors of Human and Medical Genetics (APHMG)
http://genetics.faseb.org/genetics/aphmg/aphmg1.htm
Neurological surgery
Society of Neurological Surgeons (SNS)
www.societyns.org
Neurology
Consortium of Neurology Program Directors of the American Academy of Neurology (AAN-CNPD)
www.aan.com/go/education/directors/consortium
Nuclear medicine
Society of Nuclear Medicine (SNM)
www.snm.org
Obstetrics and gynecology
Council on Residency Education in Obstetrics and Gynecology (CREOG)
www.acog.org/departments/dept_web.cfm?recno=1
Ophthalmology
Association of University Professors of Ophthalmology (AUPO)
www.aupo.org
Orthopedic Surgery
American Orthopedic Association
www.aoassn.org
Otolaryngology
Association of Academic Departments of Otolaryngology (AADO)
www.suo-aado.org
Pathology
Pathology Residency Directors Society (PRODS), Association of Pathology Chairs (APC)
www.apcprods.org
Pediatrics
Association of Pediatrics Program Directors (APPD)
www.appd.org
Council of Pediatric Subspecialties (CoPS)
www.pedsubs.org

Physical medicine and rehabilitation
Association of Academic Physiatrists/Resident Program Directors
Council (AAP/AAPMR)
www.physiatry.org

Plastic surgery
Association of Academic Chairs of Plastic Surgery (AACPS)
www.aacplasticsurgery.org

Preventive and occupational medicine
American College of Occupational and Environmental Medicine's
Section for Residency Program Directors (ACOEM-SRPD)
Joint Council of Preventive Medicine Residency Programs
(JCPMRP)

Psychiatry
American Association of Directors of Psychiatric Residency Training (AADPRT)
www.aadprt.org

Radiation oncology
Association for Directors of Radiation Oncology Programs
www.adrop.org

Radiology
Association of Program Directors of Radiology (APDR)
www.apdr.org

Surgery
Association of Program Directors in Surgery (APDS)
www.apds.org

Thoracic surgery
Thoracic Surgery Directors Association (TSDA)
www.tsda.org

Urology
Society of University Urologists (SUU)
www.suunet.org
Society for Urologists, Chairs and Program Directors (SUCPD)
www.sucpd.org

Transitional year
Council of Transitional Year Program Directors (CTYPD)

Council of Medical Specialty Societies

As noted above, OPDA is a component group of the Council of Medical Specialty Societies (CMSS), founded in 1965 to provide an independent forum for the discussion by medical specialists of issues of
national interest and mutual concern. CMSS serves to represent the
views of specialist physicians in influencing policy, medical education, and accreditation from a broad, cross-specialty perspective.

Information

Organization of Program Directors Associations
c/o Council of Medical Specialty Societies
51 Sherwood Terrace, Suite M
Lake Bluff, IL 60044-2232
847 295-3456
847 295-3759 Fax
E-mail: mailbox@cmss.org

Training Administrators of Graduate Medical Education (TAGME)

The National Board for Certification of Training Administrators
of Graduate Medical Education (TAGME) programs was created in
2003 to establish standards for the profession, acknowledge the expertise needed to successfully manage GME programs, and recognize those training program administrators who have achieved
competence in all fields related to their profession.

Criteria for Certification

- Years of on-the-job experience: at least 3 continuous years in the
  same clinical specialty
- National meeting attendance: at least one GME-related meeting
  within the past 3 years
- Site visit/internal review: participation in at least one site visit or
  internal review within the past 3 years
- Personal professional development within the past 3 years:
  – Oral/poster presentations
  – Abstracts and/or publications
  – Participation and/or leadership in national organizations
    within the profession
  – Participation and/or leadership in sponsoring institutional/
    GME committees
  – Departmental presentations, such as orientation or in-service
    training sessions on program procedures for attendings and/or
    residents
- Successful completion of the Assessment Tools

Criteria for Recertification

- Five years between certification periods
- National meeting attendance: at least two GME-related meetings
  within the 5-year period
- Institution/Department Committee participation: at least one
  committee per year
- Personal professional development activities (3 activities within
  the 5-year period)
- Oral or poster presentations
- GME-related workshop attendance
- Abstracts and/or publications
- Committee leadership
- Participation on a national or regional level committee
- Continued education coursework to enhance professional devel-
  opment (eg, online professional education modules, such as
  SoftSkills or institutional-based learning courses)
- Higher education coursework
- Successful completion of the Maintenance of Certification Tool

Information

National Board for Certification of Training Administrators of
   Graduate Medical Education
E-mail: resicoordinator@tagme.biz
www.tagme.org

Section II

Specialty/ Subspecialty Information and Data

Included in this section are descriptions of the specialties/ subspecialties with residency/fellowship programs accredited by the Accreditation Council for Graduate Medical Education (ACGME) and/or ACGME Program Requirements in effect. Also included are subspecialties for which a member board of the American Board of Medical Specialties (ABMS) offers certification. Subspecialties are listed alphabetically under each specialty. [*Note*: Links to national medical specialty society Web sites are available via the AMA Web site at www.ama-assn.org/ama/pub/category/7634.html.]

Sources for the information and data in this section include:

* *Guide to Physician Specialties*, ABMS. [*Note*: Unless otherwise indicated, all text in the "Professional Description" section of each specialty/subspecialty is taken from this document.]
* ACGME, Number and Percent of New Program Directors, July 1, 2007-June 30, 2008 academic year, www.acgme.org/adspublic/ (*Note*: Overall program director turnover rate was 1,061 out of 8,491ACGME-accredited programs, or 12.5%)
* National Resident Matching Program (NRMP) 2008 Match Data, Association of American Medical Colleges (AAMC), www.nrmp.org/data/resultsanddata2007.pdf
* "Hot Commodity," *Modern Healthcare*, July 14, 2008
[*Note*: Generally, data are shown for specialties/subspecialties in which at least one third of programs in that specialty/subspecialty selected an expanded listing in FREIDA Online®.]

History of ABMS certification and ACGME accreditation of medical specialties/subspecialties
(inactive specialties/subspecialties shown in italics)

Name	AMA/ ACGME Code	Approved by ABMS	Certificates First Issued	ACGME Essentials Approved	ACGME Programs Accredited	Notes
Allergy and immunology	020	1971	1972	1975	1946	
Clinical and laboratory immunology[1]	025	1986	1986	1990	1991	ACGME programs discontinued 2005
Anesthesiology	040	1941	1938	-	1924	
Adult cardiothoracic anesthesiology	041	-	-	2006	2006	
Critical care medicine	045	1985	1986	1988	1989	
Pain medicine[2]	048	1991	1993	1992	1992	Became multidisciplinary ACGME subspecialty (code 530), 2007
Pediatric anesthesiology	042	-	-	1997	1998	
Colon and rectal surgery	060	1949	1940	1962	1962	Anorectal surgery, 1949-1954; proctology 1940-1956
Dermatology	080	1933	1932	-	1924	
Clinical and laboratory dermatological immunology[3]		1983	1985	-	-	ABMS certificate 1985-1991
Dermatopathology	100	1973	1974	1977	1977	Subspecialty of dermatology and pathology
Pediatric dermatology		2000	2004	-	-	
Procedural dermatology	081	-	-	2003	2004	
Emergency medicine	110	1979	1980	1982	1982	
Medical toxicology	118	1992	1995	1998	2000	
Pediatric emergency medicine	114	1991	1993	1998	1999	
Sports medicine	116	1991	1993	1994	1998	
Undersea and hyperbaric medicine	119	2000	2000	2002	2004	
Family medicine	120	1969	1970	1970	1970	Family practice, 1970-2004
Adolescent medicine		2000	2001	-	-	
Geriatric medicine	125	1985	1988	1988	1988	

Name	AMA/ ACGME Code	Approved by ABMS	Certificates First Issued	ACGME Essentials Approved	ACGME Programs Accredited	Notes
Sports medicine	127	1989	1993	1994	1996	
Medical genetics	130	1991	1982	1994	1995	
Clinical biochemical genetics	-		1982	-	-	
Clinical biochemical/molecular genetics		1990		-	-	ABMS certificate 1990-1993
Clinical cytogenetics	-		1982	-	-	
Clinical genetics—MD	-		1982	-	-	
Clinical molecular genetics	-		1993	-	-	
PhD medical genetics	-		1982	-	-	
Medical biochemical genetics	131	2007	2009	2007	2008	
Molecular genetic pathology	190	1999	2001	2001	2002	Subspecialty of medical genetics and pathology
Internal medicine	140	1936	1937	-	1924	
Allergy and immunology		1936	1936	-	-	ABMS certificate 1936-1971
Adolescent medicine		1992	1994	-	-	
Cardiovascular disease	141	*	1937	1981	1987	
Clinical and laboratory immunology		1986	1986			Diagnostic laboratory immunology, 1986-1990; clinical and laboratory immunology, 1990-2003
Clinical cardiac electrophysiology	154	1989	1992	1994	1995	Cardiac electrophysiology, 1989-1991
Critical care medicine	142	1985	1987	1988	1989	
Endocrinology, diabetes, and metabolism	143	1971	1972	1981	1987	Endocrinology and metabolism, 1972-1992
Gastroenterology	144	*	1936	1981	1987	
Geriatric medicine	151	1985	1988	1988	1988	
Hematology	145	1971	1972	1981	1987	
Hematology and oncology	155	-	-	1994	1994	
Infectious disease	146	1971	1972	1981	1987	
Interventional cardiology	152	1996	1999	1998	1999	
Nephrology	148	1971	1972	1981	1987	
Oncology	147	1972	1973	1981	1987	
Pulmonary disease	149	*	1937	1981	1987	
Pulmonary disease and critical care medicine	156	-	-	1994	1994	
Rheumatology	150	1971	1972	1981	1987	
Sports medicine	157	1992	1993	1994	1996	ACGME programs discontinued 6/2006; 1 existing program moved into sports medicine/family medicine
Transplant Hepatology	158	2003	2006	2006	2007	
Neurological surgery	160	1940	1940	-	1932	
Critical care medicine			1985			ABMS certificate discontinued 1994
Endovascular surgical neuroradiology	163	-	-	2000	2008	
Neurology	180	1935	1935	-	1933	
Child neurology	185		1968	1988	1988	
Clinical neurophysiology	187	1990	1992	1994	1996	
Neurodevelopmental disabilities	186	1999	2001	2002	2002	
Neuromuscular medicine	183	2005	2008	2005	2005	
Pain medicine[2]	181	1998	2000	2000	2003	Became multidisciplinary ACGME subspecialty (code 530), 2007

Name	AMA/ ACGME Code	Approved by ABMS	Certificates First Issued	ACGME Essentials Approved	ACGME Programs Accredited	Notes
Vascular neurology	188	2003	2005	2002	2002	
Nuclear medicine	200	1971	1972	1974	1974	
Obstetrics and gynecology	220	1933	1930	-	1924	
Critical care medicine		1985	1991	-	-	Programs approved by the American Board of Obstetrics and Gynecology
Gynecologic oncology		1972	1974	-	-	
Maternal and fetal medicine		1973	1974	-	-	
Reproductive endocrinology/infertility[4]		1973	1974	-	-	
Ophthalmology	240	1933	1916	-	1924	
Orthopaedic surgery	260	1935	1935	-	1924	
Adult reconstructive orthopaedics	261	-	-	1990	1990	
Foot and ankle orthopaedics	262	-	-	1994	1995	
Hand surgery	263	1986	1989	1986	1988	
Musculoskeletal oncology	270	-	-	1987	1989	
Orthopaedic sports medicine	268	2003	2007	1987	1988	
Orthopaedic surgery of the spine	267	-	-	1991	1991	
Orthopaedic trauma	269	-	-	1990	1990	
Pediatric orthopaedics	265	-	-	1986	1988	
Otolaryngology	280	1933	1925	-	1924	
Neurotology	286	1992	2004	1995	1997	Otology/neurotology, 1992-2002
Pediatric otolaryngology	288	1992	Not issued	1995	1998	
Plastic surgery within the head and neck		2000	-	-	-	
Pathology-anatomic and clinical	300	1936	1936	-	1924	
Selective pathology	301	-	-	-	1996	
Blood banking/transfusion medicine	305	1972	1973	1993	1993	Blood banking, 1983-1988
Chemical pathology	306	*	1951	1983	1986	
Cytopathology	307	1988	1989	1991	1991	
Forensic pathology	310	*	1959	1976	1960	
Hematology	311	*	1955	1983	1986	
Immunopathology	313	1983	1983	1988	1988	ABMS certificate discontinued 1999; ACGME programs discontinued 2001
Medical microbiology	314	*	1950	1983	1986	
Neuropathology	315	*	1948	1978	1978	
Pediatric pathology	316	1989	1990	1994	1995	
Radioisotopic pathology		1974	1974			ABMS certificate discontinued 1983
Pediatrics	320	1935	1934	-	1924	
Allergy and immunology		1936	1944	-	-	ABMS certificate discontinued 1971
Adolescent medicine	321	1991	1994	1997	1998	
Child abuse pediatrics		2006	2009			
Clinical and laboratory immunology		1986	1986			ABMS certificate (diagnostic laboratory immunology) discontinued 1990
Developmental-behavioral pediatrics	336	1999	2002	2002	2003	
Medical toxicology		1992	1994	-	-	
Neonatal-perinatal medicine	329	1974	1975	1983	1984	
Neurodevelopmental disabilities		1999	2001	-	-	
Pediatric cardiology	325	*	1961	1965	1962	
Pediatric critical care medicine	323	1985	1987	1989	1990	

Specialty Data

Name	AMA/ ACGME Code	Approved by ABMS	Certificates First Issued	ACGME Essentials Approved	ACGME Programs Accredited	Notes
Pediatric emergency medicine	324	1991	1992	1998	1999	
Pediatric endocrinology	326	1976	1978	1983	1985	
Pediatric gastroenterology	332	1988	1990	1993	1994	
Pediatric hematology/oncology	327	1973	1974	1983	1985	
Pediatric infectious diseases	335	1991	1994	1996	1998	
Pediatric nephrology	328	1973	1974	1983	1985	
Pediatric pulmonology	330	1984	1986	1989	1990	
Pediatric rheumatology	331	1990	1992	1995	1997	
Pediatric sports medicine	333	1990	1993	1994	1999	
Pediatric transplant hepatology	338	2004	2006	2008	2008	
Physical medicine and rehabilitation	340	1947	1947	-	1936	
Neuromuscular Medicine	343	2005	2006	2008	-	
Pain medicine[2]	341	1998	2000	2000	2001	Became multidisciplinary ACGME subspecialty (code 530), 2007
Pediatric rehabilitation medicine	346	1999	2004	2002	2004	
Spinal cord injury medicine	345	1995	1998	1996	1997	
Sports Medicine	342	2006	2007	2008	-	
Plastic surgery	360	1941	1939	-	1935	
Plastic Surgery-Integrated	362	2008	-	2008	2008	
Craniofacial surgery	361	-	-	1997	2000	
Hand surgery	363	1986	1989	1986	1990	
Plastic surgery of the head and neck		2000	-			Joint certificate of the ABPS and the ABOto
Preventive medicine	380	1949	1953	-	1924	Includes general preventive medicine, occupational medicine, aerospace medicine, & public health/general preventive medicine
Medical toxicology	399	1992	1995	1998	2000	
Undersea and hyperbaric medicine	398	1989	1993	2002	2003	Undersea medicine, 1989-1993
Psychiatry	400	1935	1935	-	1932	
Addiction psychiatry	401	1991	1993	1994	1995	
Child and adolescent psychiatry	405	*	1959	1960	1959	Child psychiatry, 1959-1987
Forensic psychiatry	406	1992	1994	1996	1997	
Geriatric psychiatry	407	1989	1991	1993	1995	
Pain medicine[2]	402	1998	2000	2000	2004	Became multidisciplinary ACGME subspecialty (code 530), 2007
Psychosomatic medicine	409	2003	2005	2003	2004	
Radiology-diagnostic	420	1935	1965	1970	1970	
Abdominal radiology	421	-	-	1998	2000	
Cardiothoracic radiology	429	-	-	2002	2003	ACGME accreditation ends 6/30/2010
Diagnostic and Medical Nuclear Physics			1976			ABMS certificate discontinued 1998
Diagnostic radiological physics		-	1974	-	-	
Diagnostic Roentgenology			1934			ABMS certificate discontinued 1968
Endovascular surgical neuroradiology	422	-	-	2000	2002	
Medical nuclear physics		-	1949	-	-	
Musculoskeletal radiology	426	-	-	1996	1997	
Neuroradiology	423	1994	1995	1990	1991	
Nuclear Medicine			1957			ABMS certificate discontinued 1966

Name	AMA/ ACGME Code	Approved by ABMS	Certificates First Issued	ACGME Essentials Approved	ACGME Programs Accredited	Notes
Nuclear radiology	425	1972	1974	1983	1983	
Pediatric radiology	424	1993	1994	1990	1991	
Radiologic physics		-	1947	-	-	
Radiological Physics			1947			ABMS certificate discontinued 1998
Radiology			1934			ABMS certificate discontinued 1996
Radium Therapy			1939			ABMS certificate discontinued 1960
Roentgen Ray and Gamma Ray Physics			1961			ABMS certificate discontinued 1975
Roentgenology			1934			ABMS certificate discontinued 1964
Therapeutic and Diagnostic Radiological Physics			1973			ABMS certificate discontinued 1998
Therapeutic and Medical Nuclear Physics			1976			ABMS certificate discontinued 1998
Therapeutic radiological physics		-	1973	-	-	
Therapeutic Roentgenology			1935			ABMS certificate discontinued 1953
Vascular and interventional radiology	427	1994	1994	1991	1991	
X-Ray and Radium Physics			1947			ABMS certificate discontinued 1966
Radiation oncology	430	-	1987			Therapeutic radiology, 1934-1986
Surgery-general	440	1937	1937	-	1924	
Hand surgery	443	1986	1989	1986	1991	
Pediatric surgery	445	1973	1974	1975	1978	
Surgical critical care	442	1985	1986	1988	1989	
Vascular surgery	450	-	1982	1983	1984	
Vascular surgery-integrated	451	-	-	2007	2007	
Thoracic surgery	460	1971	1948	-	1934	
Thoracic surgery-integrated	461	-	-	2008	2008	
Congenital cardiac surgery	466	2007	2009	2006	2006	
Urology	480	1935	1935	-	1924	
Pediatric urology	485	2006	2008	1990	1991	
Sleep medicine	520	2005	2007	2004	2005	Subspecialty of family medicine, internal medicine, pediatrics, psychiatry, neurology, otolaryngology
Pain medicine (Multidisciplinary)	530	1991	1993	2007	2007	Subspecialty of anesthesiology, physical medicine and rehabilitation, psychiatry, and neurology
Hospice and palliative medicine	540	2006	2008	2008	2008	Subspecialty of anesthesiology, emergency medicine, family medicine, internal medicine, obstetrics-gynecology, pediatrics, physical medicine and rehabilitation, preventive medicine, neurology, psychiatry, radiology – diagnostic, and general surgery
Internal medicine/pediatrics	700	-	-	2006	2007	Programs board-approved prior to 2007
Transitional year	999	-	-	1982	1985	

Notes:

* Certificate issued prior to 1972, when ABMS recognition procedures were established.

1. ABMS certificate in Diagnostic Laboratory Immunology (1986-1990). Clinical Laboratory Immunology certificates issued from 1994-2003.

2. "Pain Management" until 2002.

3. ABMS certificate in Dermatological Immunology/Diagnostic and Laboratory Immunology (1985-1991).

4. ABMS certificate in Reproductive Endocrinology, 1973-2004.

Specialty Data

Data

Following are 2008 data, showing totals or averages for all ACGME-accredited and ABMS board-approved programs in Section III and in Appendix A.

Number of accredited programs	8,570
Number of programs providing data	4,698
Average number of interviews for program year 1 positions	16.2
Percent new program directors, 2006-2007 academic year (source: ACGME)	13.3%

Residents/Fellows

Total number of active residents/fellows	105,699
Average number of residents/fellows per program	8.1
Average percent female	40.1%
Average percent international medical graduate (IMG)	28.9%

Program Faculty

Average number of full-time physician faculty	21.5
Average number of part-time physician faculty	4.9
Average percent female full-time physician faculty	24.9%
Average ratio of full-time physician faculty to resident/fellow	3.3

Work Schedule (Program Year 1)

Average hours on duty per week	48.3
Average maximum consecutive hours on duty	17.5
Average days off duty per week	1.6
Moonlighting allowed within institution	52.3%
Night float system	30.2%
Offers awareness and management of fatigue in residents/fellows	87.4%

Educational Setting (Program Year 1)

Average hours/week of regularly scheduled lectures/conferences	5.4
Average percent of training in hospital outpatient clinics	28%
Average percent of training in nonhospital ambulatory care community settings	6.4%

Educational Benefits

Curriculum on management of tobacco dependence	13.0%
Program to assess/enhance medical professionalism	73.9%
Debt management/financial counseling	54.0%
Formal program to develop teaching skills	80.4%
Formal mentoring program	64.1%
Formal program to foster interdisciplinary teamwork	23.8%
Continuous quality improvement training	86.3%
International experience	27.2%
Resident/fellow retreats	48.5%
Off-campus electives	67.2%
Hospice/home care experience	30.1%
Cultural competence awareness	74.8%
Instruction in medical Spanish or other non-English language	22.1%
Alternative/complementary medicine curriculum	28.7%
Training in identifying and reporting of domestic violence/abuse	52.4%
MPH/MBA or PhD training	23.3%
Research rotation	41.4%

Educational Features

Offers additional training or educational experience beyond accredited length	25.2%
Offers a primary care track	12.1%
Offers a rural track	3.4%
Offers a women's health track	5.0%
Offers a hospitalist track	2.8%
Offers a research track/nonaccredited fellowship	18.0%
Offers an other track	11.0%

Resident Evaluation

Yearly specialty in-service examination required	74.7%
Patient surveys	41.9%
Portfolio system	45.0%
360 degree evaluations	76.6%
Objective structured clinical examinations (OSCE)	18.5%

Program Evaluation

Program graduation rates	82.9%
Board certification rates	94.1%
In-training examinations	74.7%
Performance-based assessments	47.1%

Employment Policies and Benefits

Part-time/shared positions	7.7%
On-site child care	39.2%
Subsidized child care	6.8%
Allowance/stipend for professional expenses	92.2%
Leave for educational meetings/conferences	73.0%
Moving allowance	12.9%
Housing stipend	6.0%
On-call meal allowance	74.1%
Free parking	63.6%
PDAs	29.1%
Placement assistance upon completion of program	30.8%
Cross coverage in case of illness/disability	83.3%

Compensation and Leave (Graduate Year 1)

Average resident/fellow compensation	$49,171
Average number weeks of vacation	5.3
Sick days (paid)	24.7
Maximum number of paid days for family/medical leave	34
Maximum number of unpaid days for family/medical leave	47

Major Medical Benefits

Major medical insurance for residents	99.0%
Major medical insurance for dependents	94.5%
Outpatient mental health insurance	91.8%
Inpatient mental health insurance	91.4%
Group life insurance	90.2%
Dental insurance	88.0%
Disability insurance	89.3%
Disability insurance for occupationally acquired HIV	71.5%
Medical insurance coverage begins when starting program	85.2%

Allergy and Immunology

Professional Description

An allergist-immunologist is trained in evaluation, physical and laboratory diagnosis, and management of disorders involving the immune system. Selected examples of such conditions include asthma, anaphylaxis, rhinitis, eczema, and adverse reactions to drugs, foods, and insect stings as well as immune deficiency diseases (both acquired and congenital), defects in host defense, and problems related to autoimmune disease, organ transplantation or malignancies of the immune system. As our understanding of the immune system develops, the scope of this specialty is widening.

Training programs are available at some medical centers to provide individuals with expertise in both allergy/immunology and adult rheumatology, or in both allergy/immunology and pediatric pulmonology. Such individuals are candidates for dual certification.

Source: American Board of Medical Specialties, *Guide to Physician Specialties*

A certified specialist in allergy and immunology is a physician who previously has passed the certification examination of the American Board of Internal Medicine (ABIM) and/or the American Board of Pediatrics (ABP) with additional certification by the American Board of Allergy and Immunology (ABAI), a Conjoint Board of the ABIM and the ABP. Diplomates of the ABAI have detailed knowledge of the underlying pathophysiology and the diagnosis, treatment, and prevention of allergic diseases such as allergic rhinitis, allergic asthma, urticaria, anaphylaxis, hypersensitivity pneumonitis, atopic and contact dermatitis, and allergic gastrointestinal disorders, as well as comparable clinical problems without an apparent allergic etiology or component such as vasomotor rhinitis, nonallergic asthma, and idiopathic and/or hereditary forms of urticaria and/or angioedema. Diplomates also have expertise in the management of pulmonary complications of certain of these diseases.

Diplomates of the ABAI also possess advanced understanding of the biology of inflammation, immunochemistry, immunobiology, and pharmacology and experience in the application of this knowledge to the diagnosis, management, and therapy of immunologic diseases. This includes inborn or acquired defects of host resistance, autoimmune diseases, bone marrow and solid organ transplantation, gene replacement therapy, adverse drug reactions, and related conditions. Diplomates have demonstrated to the satisfaction of their peers that they possess the general qualifications specified and are ethical and humanistic practitioners of medicine.

Source: American Board of Allergy and Immunology

Prerequisites; Length of Training

Prior completion of internal medicine or pediatrics program; length of accredited programs is 2 years.

Subspecialties

No subspecialty programs accredited by the Accreditation Council for Graduate Medical Education; no subspecialty certificates offered by the ABAI. The ABAI, however, does offer formal special pathways for physicians seeking dual certification in allergy/immunology and pediatric pulmonology; allergy/immunology and pediatric rheumatology; and allergy/immunology and adult rheumatology. Additional information regarding special pathways is available upon request to the ABAI.

Data

Unless otherwise noted, all data are for 2008.

Table 1. Allergy and Immunology Programs

Number of accredited programs	73

Program Data

length of accredited training	2
Minimum number of prior years of GME required	3
Offers graduate year 1 positions, available immediately upon medical school completion	No
Average number of interviews for program year 1 positions	12.0
Percent new program directors, 2007-2008 academic year (source: ACGME)	18.3%

Residents/Fellows

Total number of active residents/fellows	276
Average number of residents/fellows per program	3.8
Average percent female	55.1%
Average percent international medical graduate (IMG)	14.5%

Program Faculty

Average number of full-time physician faculty	7.8
Average number of part-time physician faculty	2.1
Average percent female full-time physician faculty	25.0%
Average ratio of full-time physician faculty to resident/fellow	1.2

Table 2. Data for Allergy and Immunology Programs Listed in FREIDA

Number of programs providing data	23

Work Schedule (Program Year 1)

Average hours on duty per week	44.3
Average maximum consecutive hours on duty	14.4
Average days off duty per week	1.6
Moonlighting allowed within institution	56.5%
Night float system	8.7%
Offers awareness and management of fatigue in residents/fellows	91.3%

Educational Setting (Program Year 1)

Average hours/week of regularly scheduled lectures/conferences	5.1
Average percent of training in hospital outpatient clinics	49.5%
Average percent of training in nonhospital ambulatory care community settings	16.1%

Educational Benefits

Curriculum on management of tobacco dependence	21.7%
Program to assess/enhance medical professionalism	87.0%
Debt management/financial counseling	43.5%
Formal program to develop teaching skills	73.9%
Formal mentoring program	73.9%
Formal program to foster interdisciplinary teamwork	26.1%
Continuous quality improvement training	82.6%
International experience	13.0%
Resident/fellow retreats	39.1%
Off-campus electives	69.6%
Hospice/home care experience	0.0%
Cultural competence awareness	73.9%
Instruction in medical Spanish or other non-English language	8.7%
Alternative/complementary medicine curriculum	13.0%
Training in identifying and reporting of domestic violence/abuse	43.5%
MPH/MBA or PhD training	39.1%
Research rotation	95.7%

Educational Features

Offers additional training or educational experience beyond accredited length	63.2%
Offers a primary care track	0.0%
Offers a rural track	0.0%
Offers a women's health track	0.0%
Offers a hospitalist track	0.0%

Specialty Data

Offers a research track/nonaccredited fellowship	17.4%
Offers an other track	8.7%
Resident Evaluation	
Yearly specialty in-service examination required	95.6%
Patient surveys	73.9%
Portfolio system	78.3%
360 degree evaluations	91.3%
Objective structured clinical examinations (OSCE)	8.7%
Program Evaluation	
Program graduation rates	65.2%
Board certification rates	100.0%
In-training examinations	95.7%
Performance-based assessments	34.8%
Employment Policies and Benefits	
Part-time/shared positions	4.3%
On-site child care	43.5%
Subsidized child care	4.3%
Allowance/stipend for professional expenses	73.9%
Leave for educational meetings/conferences	78.1%
Moving allowance	4.3%
Housing stipend	0.0%
On-call meal allowance	30.4%
Free parking	43.5%
PDAs	17.4%
Placement assistance upon completion of program	26.1%
Cross coverage in case of illness/disability	69.6%
Compensation and Leave (Graduate Year 1)	
Average resident/fellow compensation	$50,990
Average number weeks of vacation	8.0
Sick days (paid)	21.6
Maximum number of paid days for family/medical leave	36
Maximum number of unpaid days for family/medical leave	55
Major Medical Benefits	
Major medical insurance for residents	100.0%
Major medical insurance for dependents	87.0%
Outpatient mental health insurance	87.0%
Inpatient mental health insurance	82.6%
Group life insurance	82.6%
Dental insurance	82.6%
Disability insurance	73.9%
Disability insurance for occupationally acquired HIV	60.9%
Medical insurance coverage begins when starting program	82.6%

For more information

Professional Association(s)

American Academy of Allergy Asthma & Immunology
555 East Wells Street, Suite 1100
Milwaukee, WI 53202-3823
414 272-6071
E-mail: info@aaaai.org
www.aaaai.org

American College of Allergy, Asthma and Immunology
85 West Algonquin Road, Suite 550
Arlington Heights, IL 60005
847 427-1200
847 427-1294 Fax
E-mail: mail@acaai.org
www.acaai.org

Certification

American Board of Allergy and Immunology
111 South Independence Mall East, Suite 701
Philadelphia, PA 19106-3699
215 592-9466
215 592-9411 Fax
E-mail: abai@abai.org
www.abai.org

Program Accreditation

Accreditation Council for Graduate Medical Education
Residency Review Committee for Allergy and Immunology
Patricia Levenberg, PhD, RN, Executive Director
515 North State Street
Chicago, IL 60654
312 755-5048
E-mail: plevenberg@acgme.org
www.acgme.org

Anesthesiology

Professional Description

An anesthesiologist is trained to provide pain relief and maintenance, or restoration, of a stable condition during and immediately following an operation or an obstetric or diagnostic procedure. The anesthesiologist assesses the risk of the patient undergoing surgery and optimizes the patient's condition prior to, during, and after surgery. In addition to these management responsibilities, the anesthesiologist provides medical management and consultation in pain management and critical care medicine. Anesthesiologists

- Diagnose and treat acute, long-standing and cancer pain problems
- Diagnose and treat patients with critical illnesses or severe injuries
- Direct resuscitation in the care of patients with cardiac or respiratory emergencies, including the need for artificial ventilation
- Supervise post-anesthesia recovery

Prerequisites; Length of Training

length of accredited programs is 3 years or 4 years (the latter includes the clinical base year).

Subspecialties

Subspecialty programs accredited by the ACGME

- Adult cardiothoracic anesthesiology
- Critical care medicine
- Pain medicine*
- Pediatric anesthesiology
  * In 2007, ACGME-accredited pain medicine programs under anesthesiology, neurology, physical medicine and rehabilitation, and psychiatry were combined into a multidisciplinary pain medicine subspecialty.

Subspecialty certificates offered by the American Board of Anesthesiology

- Critical care medicine
- Hospice and palliative medicine
- Pain medicine

Data

Unless otherwise noted, all data are for 2008.

Table 1. Anesthesiology Programs

Number of accredited programs	131
Program Data	
length of accredited training	3/4
Minimum number of prior years of GME required	1/0
Offers graduate year 1 positions, available immediately upon medical school completion	Some
Average number of interviews for program year 1 positions	100.6
Percent new program directors, 2007-2008 academic year (source: ACGME)	16.8%
Residents/Fellows	
Total number of active residents/fellows	4,829
Average number of residents/fellows per program	36.9
Average percent female	36.5%
Average percent international medical graduate (IMG)	13.8%
Program Faculty	
Average number of full-time physician faculty	44.6
Average number of part-time physician faculty	3.7
Average percent female full-time physician faculty	26.6%
Average ratio of full-time physician faculty to resident/fellow	0.9

Table 2. Data for Anesthesiology Programs Listed in FREIDA

Number of programs providing data	92
Work Schedule (Program Year 1)	
Average hours on duty per week	61.4
Average maximum consecutive hours on duty	24.9
Average days off duty per week	1.6
Moonlighting allowed within institution	58.7%
Night float system	31.5%
Offers awareness and management of fatigue in residents/fellows	95.7%
Educational Setting (Program Year 1)	
Average hours/week of regularly scheduled lectures/conferences	4.3
Average percent of training in hospital outpatient clinics	11.8%
Average percent of training in nonhospital ambulatory care community settings	5.8%
Educational Benefits	
Curriculum on management of tobacco dependence	10.9%
Program to assess/enhance medical professionalism	83.7%
Debt management/financial counseling	78.3%
Formal program to develop teaching skills	77.2%
Formal mentoring program	90.2%
Formal program to foster interdisciplinary teamwork	34.8%
Continuous quality improvement training	100.0%
International experience	42.4%
Resident/fellow retreats	41.3%
Off-campus electives	75.0%
Hospice/home care experience	6.5%
Cultural competence awareness	67.4%
Instruction in medical Spanish or other non-English language	18.5%
Alternative/complementary medicine curriculum	30.4%
Training in identifying and reporting of domestic violence/abuse	33.7%
MPH/MBA or PhD training	17.4%
Research rotation	6.5%
Educational Features	
Offers additional training or educational experience beyond accredited length	34.1%
Offers a primary care track	1.1%
Offers a rural track	0.0%
Offers a women's health track	0.0%
Offers a hospitalist track	0.0%
Offers a research track/nonaccredited fellowship	52.2%
Offers an other track	12.0%
Resident Evaluation	
Yearly specialty in-service examination required	96.8%
Patient surveys	47.8%
Portfolio system	68.5%
360 degree evaluations	85.9%
Objective structured clinical examinations (OSCE)	20.7%
Program Evaluation	
Program graduation rates	89.1%
Board certification rates	100.0%
In-training examinations	100.0%
Performance-based assessments	70.7%
Employment Policies and Benefits	
Part-time/shared positions	4.3%
On-site child care	42.4%
Subsidized child care	5.4%
Allowance/stipend for professional expenses	98.9%
Leave for educational meetings/conferences	83.8%
Moving allowance	8.7%
Housing stipend	7.6%
On-call meal allowance	96.7%
Free parking	52.2%

PDAs	32.6%
Placement assistance upon completion of program	48.9%
Cross coverage in case of illness/disability	82.6%
Compensation and Leave (Graduate Year 1)	
Average resident/fellow compensation	$46,151
Average number weeks of vacation	3.5
Sick days (paid)	17.7
Maximum number of paid days for family/medical leave	36
Maximum number of unpaid days for family/medical leave	65
Major Medical Benefits	
Major medical insurance for residents	98.9%
Major medical insurance for dependents	94.6%
Outpatient mental health insurance	93.5%
Inpatient mental health insurance	94.6%
Group life insurance	95.7%
Dental insurance	87.0%
Disability insurance	91.3%
Disability insurance for occupationally acquired HIV	78.3%
Medical insurance coverage begins when starting program	81.5%

Table 3. Anesthesiology Match Data

GY1	2008
Number of positions offered	666
Number filled by US seniors	524
Percent filled by US seniors	78.7
Total positions filled	649
Percent total positions filled	97.4
GY2	
Number of positions offered	698
Number filled by US seniors	546
Percent filled by US seniors	78.2
Total positions filled	679
Percent total positions filled	97.3
All	
Total Positions*	1,361
Preferred by US Seniors*	1,138
Preferred Positions per US Senior	1.2
Preferred by Independent Applicants†	509
Preferred Positions per IA	2.7

Source: National Resident Matching Program 2008 Match Data
* Includes all positions offered in a specialty, except preliminary positions.
† Preferred means the number of applicants for whom the specialty was the only or first choice.

For more information

Professional Association(s)

American Society of Anesthesiologists
520 N Northwest Highway
Park Ridge, IL 60068-2573
847 825-5586
847 825-1692 Fax
E-mail: mail@asahq.org
www.asahq.org

Certification

American Board of Anesthesiology
4101 Lake Boone Trail, Suite 510
Raleigh, NC 27607-7506
919 881-2570
919 881-2575 Fax
www.theABA.org

Program Accreditation

Accreditation Council for Graduate Medical Education
Residency Review Committee for Anesthesiology
Missy Fleming, MEd, PhD, Executive Director
515 North State Street
Chicago, IL 60654
312 755-5043
E-mail: mfleming@acgme.org
www.acgme.org

Adult Cardiothoracic Anesthesiology

Professional Description

Adult cardiothoracic anesthesiology is "devoted to the preoperative, intraoperative, and postoperative care of adult patients undergoing cardiothoracic surgery and related invasive procedures."

Fellows "should be proficient in providing anesthesia care for patients undergoing cardiac surgery with and without extracorporeal circulation, and thoracic surgery including operations on the lung, esophagus, and thoracic aorta. The curriculum should also include experience with patients undergoing nonoperative diagnostic and interventional cardiac, thoracic, and electrophysiological procedures. In addition, the cardiothoracic anesthesiology fellow should develop skills in the conduct of preoperative patient evaluation and interpretation of cardiovascular and pulmonary diagnostic test data, hemodynamic and respiratory monitoring, advanced- level perioperative transesophageal echocardiography (TEE), management of cardiopulmonary bypass (CPB), pharmacological and mechanical hemodynamic support, perioperative critical care, including ventilatory support and perioperative pain management."

Source: Adult Cardiothoracic Anesthesiology Program Requirements, ACGME
www.acgme.org/acWebsite/downloads/RRC_progReq/041pr206.pdf

Prerequisites; Length of Training

Completion of an anesthesiology residency is required; length of accredited programs is 1 year.

Data

Unless otherwise noted, all data are for 2008.

Table 1. Adult Cardiothoracic Anesthesiology Programs

Number of accredited programs	44
Program Data	
Length of accredited training	1
Minimum number of prior years of GME required	4
Offers graduate year 1 positions, available immediately upon medical school completion	No
Average number of interviews for program year 1 positions	6.2
Percent new program directors, 2007-2008 academic year (source: ACGME)	6.1%
Residents/Fellows	
Total number of active residents/fellows	84
Average number of residents/fellows per program	1.9

Average percent female	25.0%
Average percent international medical graduate (IMG)	21.4%
Program Faculty	
Average number of full-time physician faculty	8.5
Average number of part-time physician faculty	0.2
Average percent female full-time physician faculty	16.8%
Average ratio of full-time physician faculty to resident/fellow	1.8

Table 2. Data for Adult Cardiothoracic Anesthesiology Programs Listed in FREIDA

Number of programs providing data	14
Work Schedule (Program Year 1)	
Average hours on duty per week	34.3
Average maximum consecutive hours on duty	15.4
Average days off duty per week	1.7
Moonlighting allowed within institution	57.1%
Night float system	7.1%
Offers awareness and management of fatigue in residents/fellows	85.7%
Educational Setting (Program Year 1)	
Average hours/week of regularly scheduled lectures/conferences	2.9
Average percent of training in hospital outpatient clinics	30.0%
Educational Benefits	
Curriculum on management of tobacco dependence	42.9%
Program to assess/enhance medical professionalism	71.4%
Debt management/financial counseling	42.9%
Formal program to develop teaching skills	50.0%
Formal mentoring program	64.3%
Formal program to foster interdisciplinary teamwork	35.7%
Continuous quality improvement training	85.7%
International experience	7.1%
Resident/fellow retreats	14.3%
Off-campus electives	35.7%
Hospice/home care experience	7.1%
Cultural competence awareness	42.9%
Instruction in medical Spanish or other non-English language	0.0%
Alternative/complementary medicine curriculum	14.3%
Training in identifying and reporting of domestic violence/abuse	35.7%
MPH/MBA or PhD training	7.1%
Research rotation	7.1%
Educational Features	
Offers additional training or educational experience beyond accredited length	9.5%
Offers a primary care track	0.0%
Offers a rural track	0.0%
Offers a women's health track	0.0%
Offers a hospitalist track	0.0%
Offers a research track/nonaccredited fellowship	14.3%
Offers an other track	0.0%
Resident Evaluation	
Yearly specialty in-service examination required	10.7%
Patient surveys	42.9%
Portfolio system	35.7%
360 degree evaluations	78.6%
Objective structured clinical examinations (OSCE)	0.0%
Program Evaluation	
Program graduation rates	71.4%
Board certification rates	92.9%
In-training examinations	35.7%
Performance-based assessments	28.6%
Employment Policies and Benefits	
Part-time/shared positions	0.0%
On-site child care	35.7%

Subsidized child care	7.1%
Allowance/stipend for professional expenses	85.7%
Leave for educational meetings/conferences	59.1%
Moving allowance	7.1%
Housing stipend	7.1%
On-call meal allowance	85.7%
Free parking	35.7%
PDAs	14.3%
Placement assistance upon completion of program	35.7%
Cross coverage in case of illness/disability	57.1%
Compensation and Leave (Graduate Year 1)	
Average resident/fellow compensation	$55,348
Average number weeks of vacation	3.5
Sick days (paid)	31.5
Maximum number of paid days for family/medical leave	16
Maximum number of unpaid days for family/medical leave	12
Major Medical Benefits	
Major medical insurance for residents	100.0%
Major medical insurance for dependents	100.0%
Outpatient mental health insurance	92.9%
Inpatient mental health insurance	92.9%
Group life insurance	92.9%
Dental insurance	100.0%
Disability insurance	92.9%
Disability insurance for occupationally acquired HIV	78.6%
Medical insurance coverage begins when starting program	100.0%

For more information

American Society of Anesthesiologists
520 N Northwest Highway
Park Ridge, IL 60068-2573
847 825-5586
847 825-1692 Fax
E-mail: mail@asahq.org
www.asahq.org

Critical Care Medicine

Professional Description

An anesthesiologist who specializes in critical care medicine diagnoses, treats and supports patients with multiple organ dysfunction. This specialist may have administrative responsibilities for intensive care units and may also facilitate and coordinate patient care among the primary physician, the critical care staff, and other specialists.

Prerequisites; Length of Training

Completion of an anesthesiology residency is required; length of accredited programs is 1 year.

Data

Unless otherwise noted, all data are for 2008.

Table 1. Critical Care Medicine Programs

Number of accredited programs	45
Program Data	
Length of accredited training	1
Minimum number of prior years of GME required	4
Offers graduate year 1 positions, available immediately upon medical school completion	No
Average number of interviews for program year 1 positions	3.9

Specialty Data

Percent new program directors, 2007-2008 academic year (source: ACGME)	10.0%

Residents/Fellows

Total number of active residents/fellows	81
Average number of residents/fellows per program	1.8
Average percent female	25.9%
Average percent international medical graduate (IMG)	27.2%

Program Faculty

Average number of full-time physician faculty	12.4
Average number of part-time physician faculty	0.4
Average percent female full-time physician faculty	17.0%
Average ratio of full-time physician faculty to resident/fellow	3.2

Table 2. Data for Critical Care Medicine Programs Listed in FREIDA

Number of programs providing data	25

Work Schedule (Program Year 1)

Average hours on duty per week	58.8
Average maximum consecutive hours on duty	23.8
Average days off duty per week	1.4
Moonlighting allowed within institution	68.0%
Night float system	20.0%
Offers awareness and management of fatigue in residents/fellows	96.0%

Educational Setting (Program Year 1)

Average hours/week of regularly scheduled lectures/conferences	5.4
Average percent of training in hospital outpatient clinics	10.0%
Average percent of training in nonhospital ambulatory care community settings	10.0%

Educational Benefits

Curriculum on management of tobacco dependence	12.0%
Program to assess/enhance medical professionalism	68.0%
Debt management/financial counseling	44.0%
Formal program to develop teaching skills	84.0%
Formal mentoring program	48.0%
Formal program to foster interdisciplinary teamwork	36.0%
Continuous quality improvement training	92.0%
International experience	8.0%
Resident/fellow retreats	28.0%
Off-campus electives	64.0%
Hospice/home care experience	16.0%
Cultural competence awareness	60.0%
Instruction in medical Spanish or other non-English language	12.0%
Alternative/complementary medicine curriculum	20.0%
Training in identifying and reporting of domestic violence/abuse	24.0%
MPH/MBA or PhD training	12.0%
Research rotation	24.0%

Educational Features

Offers additional training or educational experience beyond accredited length	13.8%
Offers a primary care track	0.0%
Offers a rural track	0.0%
Offers a women's health track	0.0%
Offers a hospitalist track	0.0%
Offers a research track/nonaccredited fellowship	8.0%
Offers an other track	12.0%

Resident Evaluation

Yearly specialty in-service examination required	71.0%
Patient surveys	16.0%
Portfolio system	32.0%
360 degree evaluations	80.0%
Objective structured clinical examinations (OSCE)	4.0%

Program Evaluation

Program graduation rates	84.0%
Board certification rates	96.0%

In-training examinations	68.0%
Performance-based assessments	32.0%

Employment Policies and Benefits

Part-time/shared positions	8.0%
On-site child care	48.0%
Subsidized child care	8.0%
Allowance/stipend for professional expenses	100.0%
Leave for educational meetings/conferences	85.7%
Moving allowance	4.0%
Housing stipend	0.0%
On-call meal allowance	84.0%
Free parking	36.0%
PDAs	20.0%
Placement assistance upon completion of program	44.0%
Cross coverage in case of illness/disability	76.0%

Compensation and Leave (Graduate Year 1)

Average resident/fellow compensation	$53,601
Average number weeks of vacation	3.4
Sick days (paid)	25.8
Maximum number of paid days for family/medical leave	31
Maximum number of unpaid days for family/medical leave	63

Major Medical Benefits

Major medical insurance for residents	100.0%
Major medical insurance for dependents	96.0%
Outpatient mental health insurance	88.0%
Inpatient mental health insurance	88.0%
Group life insurance	88.0%
Dental insurance	88.0%
Disability insurance	96.0%
Disability insurance for occupationally acquired HIV	76.0%
Medical insurance coverage begins when starting program	92.0%

For more information

Society of Critical Care Medicine
500 Midway Drive
Mount Prospect, IL 60056
847 827-6869
847 827-6886 Fax
E-mail: info@sccm.org
www.sccm.org

Hospice and Palliative Medicine

See page 57.

Pain Medicine

See page 104.

Pediatric Anesthesiology

Professional Description

A pediatric anesthesiologist is a fully trained anesthesiologist who has completed at least 1 year of specialized training in anesthesia care of infants and children. Most pediatric surgeons deliver care to children in the operating room along with a pediatric anesthesiologist. Many children who need surgery have very complex medical problems that affect many parts of the body. The pediatric anesthesiologist is best qualified to evaluate these complex problems and plan a safe anesthetic for each child.

Pediatric anesthesiologists treat children from the newborn period through the teenage years. They choose to make pediatric care the core of their medical practice, and the unique nature of medical and surgical care of children is learned from advanced training and experience in practice.

Pediatric anesthesiologists are responsible for the general anesthesia, sedation, and pain management needs of infants and children. Pediatric anesthesiologists generally provide the following services:

- Evaluation of complex medical problems in infants and children when surgery is needed
- Planning and care for before and after surgery
- A nonthreatening environment for children in the operating room
- Pain control, if needed after surgery, either with intravenous (IV) medications or other anesthetic techniques
- Anesthesia and sedation for many procedures out of the operating room such as MRI, CT scan, and radiation therapy

Source: American Academy of Pediatrics, *What is a Pediatric Anesthesiologist?*
www.aap.org/sections/sap/he3003.pdf

Prerequisites; Length of Training

Completion of an anesthesiology residency is required; length of accredited programs is 1 year.

Data

Unless otherwise noted, all data are for 2008.

Table 1. Pediatric Anesthesiology Programs

Number of accredited programs	45

Program Data

length of accredited training	1
Minimum number of prior years of GME required	4
Offers graduate year 1 positions, available immediately upon medical school completion	No
Average number of interviews for program year 1 positions	8.6
Percent new program directors, 2007-2008 academic year (source: ACGME)	17.8%

Residents/Fellows

Total number of active residents/fellows	123
Average number of residents/fellows per program	2.7
Average percent female	47.2%
Average percent international medical graduate (IMG)	13.8%

Program Faculty

Average number of full-time physician faculty	20.6
Average number of part-time physician faculty	2.8
Average percent female full-time physician faculty	34.2%
Average ratio of full-time physician faculty to resident/fellow	3.0

Table 2. Data for Pediatric Anesthesiology Programs Listed in FREIDA

Number of programs providing data	23

Work Schedule (Program Year 1)

Average hours on duty per week	46.0
Average maximum consecutive hours on duty	21.7
Average days off duty per week	1.8
Moonlighting allowed within institution	56.5%
Night float system	8.7%
Offers awareness and management of fatigue in residents/fellows	78.3%

Educational Setting (Program Year 1)

Average hours/week of regularly scheduled lectures/conferences	3.5
Average percent of training in hospital outpatient clinics	20.8%

Average percent of training in nonhospital ambulatory care community settings	5.0%

Educational Benefits

Curriculum on management of tobacco dependence	8.7%
Program to assess/enhance medical professionalism	56.5%
Debt management/financial counseling	34.8%
Formal program to develop teaching skills	82.6%
Formal mentoring program	78.3%
Formal program to foster interdisciplinary teamwork	21.7%
Continuous quality improvement training	87.0%
International experience	34.8%
Resident/fellow retreats	21.7%
Off-campus electives	43.5%
Hospice/home care experience	4.3%
Cultural competence awareness	60.9%
Instruction in medical Spanish or other non-English language	17.4%
Alternative/complementary medicine curriculum	13.0%
Training in identifying and reporting of domestic violence/abuse	17.4%
MPH/MBA or PhD training	17.4%
Research rotation	17.4%

Educational Features

Offers additional training or educational experience beyond accredited length	22.0%
Offers a primary care track	8.7%
Offers a rural track	0.0%
Offers a women's health track	0.0%
Offers a hospitalist track	8.7%
Offers a research track/nonaccredited fellowship	21.7%
Offers an other track	4.3%

Resident Evaluation

Yearly specialty in-service examination required	10.4%
Patient surveys	17.4%
Portfolio system	52.2%
360 degree evaluations	78.3%
Objective structured clinical examinations (OSCE)	13.0%

Program Evaluation

Program graduation rates	87.0%
Board certification rates	65.2%
In-training examinations	17.4%
Performance-based assessments	56.5%

Employment Policies and Benefits

Part-time/shared positions	13.0%
On-site child care	30.4%
Subsidized child care	4.3%
Allowance/stipend for professional expenses	100.0%
Leave for educational meetings/conferences	86.5%
Moving allowance	21.7%
Housing stipend	0.0%
On-call meal allowance	82.6%
Free parking	47.8%
PDAs	0.0%
Placement assistance upon completion of program	21.7%
Cross coverage in case of illness/disability	82.6%

Compensation and Leave (Graduate Year 1)

Average resident/fellow compensation	$54,346
Average number weeks of vacation	7.5
Sick days (paid)	14.9
Maximum number of paid days for family/medical leave	25
Maximum number of unpaid days for family/medical leave	55

Major Medical Benefits

Major medical insurance for residents	95.7%
Major medical insurance for dependents	95.7%

Specialty Data

Outpatient mental health insurance	95.7%
Inpatient mental health insurance	95.7%
Group life insurance	91.3%
Dental insurance	78.3%
Disability insurance	91.3%
Disability insurance for occupationally acquired HIV	73.9%
Medical insurance coverage begins when starting program	100.0%

For more information

Society for Pediatric Anesthesia
2209 Dickens Road
Richmond, VA 23230-2005
804 282-9780
804 282-0090 Fax
E-mail: spa@societyhq.com
www.pedsanesthesia.org

Colon and Rectal Surgery

Professional Description

A colon and rectal surgeon is trained to diagnose and treat various diseases of the intestinal tract, colon, rectum, anal canal, and perianal area by medical and surgical means. This specialist also deals with other organs and tissues (such as the liver, urinary, and female reproductive system) involved with primary intestinal disease.

Colon and rectal surgeons have the expertise to diagnose and often manage anorectal conditions such as hemorrhoids, fissures (painful tears in the anal lining), abscesses, and fistulae (infections located around the anus and rectum) in the office setting. They also treat problems of the intestine and colon and perform endoscopic procedures to evaluate and treat problems such as cancer, polyps (precancerous growths), and inflammatory conditions.

Prerequisites; Length of Training

Prior completion a minimum of 5 years of a general surgery program; length of accredited programs is 1 year.

Subspecialties

No subspecialty programs accredited by the Accreditation Council for Graduate Medical Education; no subspecialty certificates offered by the American Board of Colon and Rectal Surgery.

Data

Unless otherwise noted, all data are for 2008.

Table 1. Colon and Rectal Surgery Programs	
Number of accredited programs	47
Program Data	
length of accredited training	1
Minimum number of prior years of GME required	5
Offers graduate year 1 positions, available immediately upon medical school completion	No
Average number of interviews for program year 1 positions	20.6
Percent new program directors, 2007-2008 academic year (source: ACGME)	17.8%
Residents/Fellows	
Total number of active residents/fellows	69
Average number of residents/fellows per program	1.5
Average percent female	31.9%
Average percent international medical graduate (IMG)	18.8%
Program Faculty	
Average number of full-time physician faculty	5.1
Average number of part-time physician faculty	0.8
Average percent female full-time physician faculty	16.4%
Average ratio of full-time physician faculty to resident/fellow	1.5

Table 2. Data for Colon and Rectal Surgery Programs Listed in FREIDA	
Number of programs providing data	26
Work Schedule (Program Year 1)	
Average hours on duty per week	51.2
Average maximum consecutive hours on duty	15.9
Average days off duty per week	1.4
Moonlighting allowed within institution	19.2%
Night float system	11.5%
Offers awareness and management of fatigue in residents/fellows	84.6%
Educational Setting (Program Year 1)	
Average hours/week of regularly scheduled lectures/conferences	3.8
Average percent of training in hospital outpatient clinics	28.4%

Average percent of training in nonhospital ambulatory care community settings	25.4%

Educational Benefits

Curriculum on management of tobacco dependence	15.4%
Program to assess/enhance medical professionalism	61.5%
Debt management/financial counseling	30.8%
Formal program to develop teaching skills	73.1%
Formal mentoring program	50.0%
Formal program to foster interdisciplinary teamwork	30.8%
Continuous quality improvement training	96.2%
International experience	3.8%
Resident/fellow retreats	23.1%
Off-campus electives	34.6%
Hospice/home care experience	7.7%
Cultural competence awareness	69.2%
Instruction in medical Spanish or other non-English language	11.5%
Alternative/complementary medicine curriculum	11.5%
Training in identifying and reporting of domestic violence/abuse	30.8%
MPH/MBA or PhD training	11.5%
Research rotation	11.5%

Educational Features

Offers additional training or educational experience beyond accredited length	18.4%
Offers a primary care track	7.7%
Offers a rural track	0.0%
Offers a women's health track	0.0%
Offers a hospitalist track	0.0%
Offers a research track/nonaccredited fellowship	19.2%
Offers an other track	3.8%

Resident Evaluation

Yearly specialty in-service examination required	42.6%
Patient surveys	46.2%
Portfolio system	15.4%
360 degree evaluations	69.2%
Objective structured clinical examinations (OSCE)	3.8%

Program Evaluation

Program graduation rates	69.2%
Board certification rates	100.0%
In-training examinations	30.8%
Performance-based assessments	30.8%

Employment Policies and Benefits

Part-time/shared positions	3.8%
On-site child care	30.8%
Subsidized child care	3.8%
Allowance/stipend for professional expenses	92.3%
Leave for educational meetings/conferences	80.8%
Moving allowance	3.8%
Housing stipend	0.0%
On-call meal allowance	69.2%
Free parking	84.6%
PDAs	7.7%
Placement assistance upon completion of program	26.9%
Cross coverage in case of illness/disability	65.4%

Compensation and Leave (Graduate Year 1)

Average resident/fellow compensation	$55,454
Average number weeks of vacation	3.2
Sick days (paid)	19.1
Maximum number of paid days for family/medical leave	29
Maximum number of unpaid days for family/medical leave	28

Major Medical Benefits

Major medical insurance for residents	100.0%
Major medical insurance for dependents	84.6%

Outpatient mental health insurance	88.5%
Inpatient mental health insurance	84.6%
Group life insurance	80.8%
Dental insurance	92.3%
Disability insurance	76.9%
Disability insurance for occupationally acquired HIV	65.4%
Medical insurance coverage begins when starting program	88.5%

For more information

Professional Association

American Society of Colon and Rectal Surgeons
85 West Algonquin Road, Suite 550
Arlington Heights, IL 60005
847 290-9184
847 290-9203 Fax
E-mail: ascrs@fascrs.org
www.fascrs.org

Certification

American Board of Colon and Rectal Surgery
20600 Eureka Road, Suite 600
Taylor, MI 48180
734 282-9400
734 282-9402 Fax
E-mail: admin@abcrs.org
www.abcrs.org

Program Accreditation

Accreditation Council for Graduate Medical Education
Residency Review Committee for Colon and Rectal Surgery
Louise King, MS, Executive Director
515 North State Street
Chicago, IL 60654
312 755-5498
E-mail: lking@acgme.org
www.acgme.org

Specialty Data

Dermatology

Professional Description

A dermatologist is trained to diagnose and treat pediatric and adult patients with benign and malignant disorders of the skin, mouth, external genitalia, hair, and nails, and those with a number of sexually transmitted diseases. The dermatologist has had additional training and experience in the diagnosis and treatment of skin cancers, melanomas, moles, and other tumors of the skin, the management of contact dermatitis, and other allergic and nonallergic skin disorders, and in the recognition of the skin manifestations of systemic (including internal malignancy) and infectious diseases. Dermatologists have special training in dermatopathology and in the surgical techniques used in dermatology. They also have expertise in the management of cosmetic disorders of the skin, such as hair loss and scars, and the skin changes associated with aging.

Source: American Board of Medical Specialties, *Guide to Physician Specialties*

Dermatologists perform many specialized diagnostic procedures including microscopic examination of skin biopsy specimens, cytological smears, patch tests, photo tests, potassium hydroxide (KOH) preparations, fungus cultures, and other microbiologic examination of skin scrapings and secretions. Treatment methods used by dermatologists include externally applied, injected, and internal medications, selected x-ray and ultraviolet light therapy, and a range of dermatologic surgical procedures. The training and experience of dermatologists in dermatologic surgery include electrosurgery, cryosurgery with the use of freezing surgical units, laser surgery, nail surgery, biopsy techniques and excisional surgery with appropriate closures, including flaps and grafts. Among some of the techniques used by dermatologists for the correction of cosmetic defects are dermabrasion, chemical face peels, hair transplants, injections of materials into the skin for scar revision, sclerosis of veins, and laser surgery of vascular lesions of the skin, including certain birth marks. Patients seeking a dermatologist may come directly or may be referred by another physician. A certified specialist in dermatology may subspecialize and become certified for Special Qualification.
Source: American Academy of Dermatology

Prerequisites; Length of Training

No prerequisites required when entering programs with an accredited length of 4 years. A broad-based clinical year of training in an ACGME-accredited program is required when entering a 3-year program.

Subspecialties

Subspecialty programs accredited by the ACGME

- Dermatopathology
- Procedural dermatology

American Board of Dermatology subspecialty certificates:

- Clinical and laboratory dermatological immunology
- Dermatopathology
- Pediatric dermatology

Data

Unless otherwise noted, all data are for 2008.

Table 1. Dermatology Programs

Number of accredited programs	111

Program Data

length of accredited training	3/4

Minimum number of prior years of GME required	1/0
Offers graduate year 1 positions, available immediately upon medical school completion	Some
Average number of interviews for program year 1 positions	29.7
Percent new program directors, 2007-2008 academic year (source: ACGME)	10.9%

Residents/Fellows

Total number of active residents/fellows	1,044
Average number of residents/fellows per program	9.4
Average percent female	63.0%
Average percent international medical graduate (IMG)	4.2%

Program Faculty

Average number of full-time physician faculty	8.8
Average number of part-time physician faculty	3.4
Average percent female full-time physician faculty	41.2%
Average ratio of full-time physician faculty to resident/fellow	0.7

Table 2. Data for Dermatology Programs Listed in FREIDA

Number of programs providing data	47

Work Schedule (Program Year 1)

Average hours on duty per week	44.3
Average maximum consecutive hours on duty	12.4
Average days off duty per week	1.9
Moonlighting allowed within institution	53.2%
Night float system	2.1%
Offers awareness and management of fatigue in residents/fellows	74.5%

Educational Setting (Program Year 1)

Average hours/week of regularly scheduled lectures/conferences	8.1
Average percent of training in hospital outpatient clinics	78.3%
Average percent of training in nonhospital ambulatory care community settings	15.2%

Educational Benefits

Curriculum on management of tobacco dependence	10.6%
Program to assess/enhance medical professionalism	74.5%
Debt management/financial counseling	38.3%
Formal program to develop teaching skills	61.7%
Formal mentoring program	42.6%
Formal program to foster interdisciplinary teamwork	19.1%
Continuous quality improvement training	70.2%
International experience	21.3%
Resident/fellow retreats	40.4%
Off-campus electives	78.7%
Hospice/home care experience	2.1%
Cultural competence awareness	59.6%
Instruction in medical Spanish or other non-English language	17.0%
Alternative/complementary medicine curriculum	14.9%
Training in identifying and reporting of domestic violence/abuse	46.8%
MPH/MBA or PhD training	14.9%
Research rotation	6.4%

Educational Features

Offers additional training or educational experience beyond accredited length	19.0%
Offers a primary care track	2.1%
Offers a rural track	0.0%
Offers a women's health track	0.0%
Offers a hospitalist track	2.1%
Offers a research track/nonaccredited fellowship	21.3%
Offers an other track	8.5%

Resident Evaluation

Yearly specialty in-service examination required	100.0%
Patient surveys	61.7%
Portfolio system	46.8%
360 degree evaluations	80.9%

Specialty Data

Objective structured clinical examinations (OSCE)	12.8%
Program Evaluation	
Program graduation rates	78.7%
Board certification rates	97.9%
In-training examinations	100.0%
Performance-based assessments	40.4%
Employment Policies and Benefits	
Part-time/shared positions	0.0%
On-site child care	40.4%
Subsidized child care	4.3%
Allowance/stipend for professional expenses	89.4%
Leave for educational meetings/conferences	87.2%
Moving allowance	6.4%
Housing stipend	0.0%
On-call meal allowance	48.9%
Free parking	55.3%
PDAs	17.0%
Placement assistance upon completion of program	8.5%
Cross coverage in case of illness/disability	87.2%
Compensation and Leave (Graduate Year 1)	
Average resident/fellow compensation	$47,157
Average number weeks of vacation	3.4
Sick days (paid)	22.6
Maximum number of paid days for family/medical leave	39
Maximum number of unpaid days for family/medical leave	50
Major Medical Benefits	
Major medical insurance for residents	100.0%
Major medical insurance for dependents	93.6%
Outpatient mental health insurance	85.1%
Inpatient mental health insurance	83.0%
Group life insurance	89.4%
Dental insurance	83.0%
Disability insurance	93.6%
Disability insurance for occupationally acquired HIV	74.5%
Medical insurance coverage begins when starting program	91.5%

Table 3. Dermatology Match Data

GY1	2008
Number of positions offered	30
Number filled by US seniors	26
Percent filled by US seniors	86.7
Total positions filled	30
Percent total positions filled	100
GY2	
Number of positions offered	297
Number filled by US seniors	230
Percent filled by US seniors	77.4
Total positions filled	297
Percent total positions filled	100
All	
Total Positions*	327
Preferred by US Seniors*	359
Preferred Positions per US Senior	0.9
Preferred by Independent Applicants†	177
Preferred Positions per IA	1.8

Source: National Resident Matching Program 2008 Match Data
* Includes all positions offered in a specialty, except preliminary positions.
† Preferred means the number of applicants for whom the specialty was the only or first choice.

For more information

Professional Associations

American Academy of Dermatology
PO Box 4014
Schaumburg, IL 60168-4014
847 240-1280
847 240-1859 Fax
E-mail: mrc@aad.org
www.aad.org

American Society for Dermatologic Surgery
5550 Meadowbrook Drive, Suite 120
Rolling Meadows, IL 60008
847 956-0900
847 956-0999 Fax
E-mail: info@asds.net
www.asds.net

Society for Investigative Dermatology
526 Superior East, Suite 540
Cleveland, OH 44114-1900
216 579-9300
216 579-9333 Fax
E-mail: sid@sidnet.org
www.sidnet.org

Certification

American Board of Dermatology
Henry Ford Health System
One Ford Place
Detroit, MI 48202-3450
313 874-1088
313 872-3221 Fax
E-mail: abderm@hfhs.org
www.abderm.org

Program Accreditation

Accreditation Council for Graduate Medical Education
Residency Review Committee for Dermatology
Georgia Andrianopoulos, PhD, Executive Director
515 North State Street
Chicago, IL 60654
312 755-5031
E-mail: gda@acgme.org
www.acgme.org

Clinical and Laboratory Dermatological Immunology

Professional Description

A dermatologist who utilizes various specialized laboratory procedures to diagnose disorders characterized by defective responses of the body's immune system. Immunodermatologists also may provide consultation in the management of these disorders and administer specialized forms of therapy for these diseases.

Prerequisites; Length of Training

Completion of an dermatology residency is required; length of accredited programs is 1 year.

For more information

American Academy of Dermatology
PO Box 4014
Schaumburg, IL 60168-4014
847 240-1280
847 240-1859 Fax
E-mail: mrc@aad.org
www.aad.org

Dermatopathology

Professional Description

A dermatopathologist has the expertise to diagnose and monitor diseases of the skin including infectious, immunologic, degenerative, and neoplastic diseases. This entails the examination and interpretation of specially prepared tissue sections, cellular scrapings, and smears of skin lesions by means of routine and special (electron and fluorescent) microscopes.

Prerequisites; Length of Training

Completion of an dermatology or pathology residency is required; length of accredited programs is 1 year.

For more information

American Society of Dermatopathology
111 Deer Lake Road, Suite 100
Deerfield, IL 60015
847 400-5820
847 480-9282 Fax
E-mail: info@asdp.org
www.asdp.org

Pediatric Dermatology

Professional Description

A pediatric dermatologist has, through additional special training, developed expertise in the treatment of specific skin disease categories with emphasis on those diseases which predominate in infants, children, and adolescents.

Prerequisites; Length of Training

Completion of an dermatology residency is required; length of accredited programs is 1 or 2 years.

For more information

Society for Pediatric Dermatology
8365 Keystone Crossing, Suite 107
Indianapolis, IN 46240
317 202-0224
317 202-9481 Fax
E-mail: spd@hp-assoc.com
www.pedsderm.net

Procedural Dermatology

Professional Description

A pediatric dermatologist has, through additional special training, developed expertise in the treatment of specific skin disease

categories with emphasis on those diseases which predominate in infants, children, and adolescents.

Source: American Board of Medical Specialties, *Guide to Physician Specialties*

Prerequisites; Length of Training

Completion of an dermatology residency is required; length of accredited programs is 1 year.

For more information

American Society for Dermatologic Surgery
5550 Meadowbrook Drive, Suite 120
Rolling Meadows, IL 60008
847 956-0900
847 956-0999 Fax
E-mail: info@asds.net
www.asds.net

Emergency Medicine

Professional Description

An emergency physician focuses on the immediate decision making and action necessary to prevent death or any further disability both in the pre-hospital setting by directing emergency medical technicians and in the emergency department. The emergency physician provides immediate recognition, evaluation, care, stabilization, and disposition of a generally diversified population of adult and pediatric patients in response to acute illness and injury.

Prerequisites; Length of Training

No prerequisites required when entering programs with an accredited length of 4 years. A broad-based clinical year of training in an ACGME-accredited program is required when entering a 3-year program.

Subspecialties

Subspecialty programs accredited by the ACGME

- Hospice and palliative medicine
- Medical toxicology
- Pediatric emergency medicine
- Sports medicine
- Undersea and hyperbaric medicine

American Board of Emergency Medicine subspecialty certificates

- Hospice and palliative medicine
- Medical toxicology
- Pediatric emergency medicine
- Sports medicine
- Undersea and hyperbaric medicine

Data

Unless otherwise noted, all data are for 2008.

Table 1. Emergency Medicine Programs

Number of accredited programs	148

Program Data	
length of accredited training	3/4
Minimum number of prior years of GME required	1/0
Offers graduate year 1 positions, available immediately upon medical school completion	Some
Average number of interviews for program year 1 positions	107.5
Percent new program directors, 2007-2008 academic year (source: ACGME)	13.8%

Residents/Fellows	
Total number of active residents/fellows	4,608
Average number of residents/fellows per program	31.1
Average percent female	39.5%
Average percent international medical graduate (IMG)	6.0%

Program Faculty	
Average number of full-time physician faculty	26.1
Average number of part-time physician faculty	5.4
Average percent female full-time physician faculty	27.2%
Average ratio of full-time physician faculty to resident/fellow	0.6

Table 2. Data for Emergency Medicine Programs Listed in FREIDA

Number of programs providing data	105

Work Schedule (Program Year 1)	
Average hours on duty per week	55.5
Average maximum consecutive hours on duty	20.5
Average days off duty per week	1.6

Moonlighting allowed within institution	59.0%
Night float system	20.0%
Offers awareness and management of fatigue in residents/fellows	100.0%

Educational Setting (Program Year 1)	
Average hours/week of regularly scheduled lectures/conferences	5.1
Average percent of training in hospital outpatient clinics	10.9%
Average percent of training in nonhospital ambulatory care community settings	6.0%

Educational Benefits	
Curriculum on management of tobacco dependence	9.5%
Program to assess/enhance medical professionalism	86.7%
Debt management/financial counseling	82.9%
Formal program to develop teaching skills	92.4%
Formal mentoring program	85.7%
Formal program to foster interdisciplinary teamwork	33.3%
Continuous quality improvement training	99.0%
International experience	69.5%
Resident/fellow retreats	83.8%
Off-campus electives	90.5%
Hospice/home care experience	5.7%
Cultural competence awareness	88.6%
Instruction in medical Spanish or other non-English language	26.7%
Alternative/complementary medicine curriculum	26.7%
Training in identifying and reporting of domestic violence/abuse	98.1%
MPH/MBA or PhD training	16.2%
Research rotation	44.8%

Educational Features	
Offers additional training or educational experience beyond accredited length	8.1%
Offers a primary care track	5.7%
Offers a rural track	4.8%
Offers a women's health track	1.0%
Offers a hospitalist track	1.9%
Offers a research track/nonaccredited fellowship	18.1%
Offers an other track	13.3%

Resident Evaluation	
Yearly specialty in-service examination required	99.3%
Patient surveys	44.8%
Portfolio system	67.6%
360 degree evaluations	77.1%
Objective structured clinical examinations (OSCE)	40.0%

Program Evaluation	
Program graduation rates	84.8%
Board certification rates	97.1%
In-training examinations	99.0%
Performance-based assessments	82.9%

Employment Policies and Benefits	
Part-time/shared positions	1.0%
On-site child care	34.3%
Subsidized child care	6.7%
Allowance/stipend for professional expenses	98.1%
Leave for educational meetings/conferences	85.6%
Moving allowance	15.2%
Housing stipend	9.5%
On-call meal allowance	91.4%
Free parking	64.8%
PDAs	43.8%
Placement assistance upon completion of program	43.8%
Cross coverage in case of illness/disability	93.3%

Compensation and Leave (Graduate Year 1)	
Average resident/fellow compensation	$45,950

Specialty Data

Average number weeks of vacation	3.4
Sick days (paid)	17.2
Maximum number of paid days for family/medical leave	42
Maximum number of unpaid days for family/medical leave	67
Major Medical Benefits	
Major medical insurance for residents	99.0%
Major medical insurance for dependents	96.2%
Outpatient mental health insurance	90.5%
Inpatient mental health insurance	90.5%
Group life insurance	92.4%
Dental insurance	90.5%
Disability insurance	93.3%
Disability insurance for occupationally acquired HIV	76.2%
Medical insurance coverage begins when starting program	82.9%

Table 3. Emergency Medicine Match Data

GY1	2008
Number of positions offered	1,399
Number filled by US seniors	1,083
Percent filled by US seniors	77.4
Total positions filled	1,370
Percent total positions filled	97.9
GY2	
Number of positions offered	76
Number filled by US seniors	45
Percent filled by US seniors	59.2
Total positions filled	75
Percent total positions filled	98.7
All	
Total Positions*	1471
Preferred by US Seniors*	1,166
Preferred Positions per US Senior	1.3
Preferred by Independent Applicants†	524
Preferred Positions per IA	2.8

Source: National Resident Matching Program 2008 Match Data
* Includes all positions offered in a specialty, except preliminary positions.
† Preferred means the number of applicants for whom the specialty was the only or first choice.

For more information

Professional Association(s)

American College of Emergency Physicians
1125 Executive Circle
Irving, TX 75038-2522
800 798-1822
972 580-2816 Fax
E-mail: membership@acep.org
www.acep.org

Certification

American Board of Emergency Medicine
3000 Coolidge Road
East Lansing, MI 48823-6319
517 332-4800
517 332-2234 Fax
www.abem.org

Program Accreditation

Accreditation Council for Graduate Medical Education
Residency Review Committee for Emergency Medicine
Lynne Meyer, PhD, MPH, Executive Director
515 North State Street
Chicago, IL 60654
312 755-5006
E-mail: lmeyer@acgme.org
www.acgme.org

Hospice and Palliative Medicine

See page 57.

Medical Toxicology

Professional Description

An emergency physician who has special knowledge about the evaluation and management of patients with accidental or purposeful poisoning through exposure to prescription and nonprescription medications, drugs of abuse, household or industrial toxins, and environmental toxins.

Areas of medical toxicology include acute pediatric and adult drug ingestion; drug abuse, addiction, and withdrawal; chemical poisoning exposure and toxicity; hazardous materials exposure and toxicity; and occupational toxicology.

Prerequisites; Length of Training

Completion of an ACGME-accredited residency is required; length of accredited programs is 2 years.

For more information

American College of Medical Toxicology
10645 N Tatum Blvd, Suite 200-111
Phoenix, AZ 85028
623 533-6340
E-mail: info@acmt.net
www.acmt.net

Pediatric Emergency Medicine

Professional Description

An emergency physician who has special qualifications to manage emergencies in infants and children.

Prerequisites; Length of Training

Completion of an ACGME-accredited emergency medicine residency is required; length of accredited programs is 2 years (3 years for those planning to seek certification from the American Board of Pediatrics).

Data

Unless otherwise noted, all data are for 2008.

Table 1. Pediatric Emergency Medicine Programs	
Number of accredited programs	19
Program Data	
length of accredited training	2
Minimum number of prior years of GME required	4

Offers graduate year 1 positions, available immediately upon medical school completion	No
Average number of interviews for program year 1 positions	12.9
Percent new program directors, 2007-2008 academic year (source: ACGME)	23.5%
Residents/Fellows	
Total number of active residents/fellows	46
Average number of residents/fellows per program	2.4
Average percent female	69.6%
Average percent international medical graduate (IMG)	23.9%
Program Faculty	
Average number of full-time physician faculty	13.2
Average number of part-time physician faculty	2.7
Average percent female full-time physician faculty	37.4%
Average ratio of full-time physician faculty to resident/fellow	3.0

Table 2. Data for Pediatric Emergency Medicine Programs Listed in FREIDA

Number of programs providing data	8
Work Schedule (Program Year 1)	
Average hours on duty per week	34.6
Average maximum consecutive hours on duty	12.1
Average days off duty per week	1.8
Moonlighting allowed within institution	75.0%
Night float system	0.0%
Offers awareness and management of fatigue in residents/fellows	87.5%
Educational Setting (Program Year 1)	
Average hours/week of regularly scheduled lectures/conferences	4.4
Average percent of training in hospital outpatient clinics	8.2%
Average percent of training in nonhospital ambulatory care community settings	7.0%
Educational Benefits	
Curriculum on management of tobacco dependence	25.0%
Program to assess/enhance medical professionalism	87.5%
Debt management/financial counseling	37.5%
Formal program to develop teaching skills	75.0%
Formal mentoring program	75.0%
Formal program to foster interdisciplinary teamwork	50.0%
Continuous quality improvement training	100.0%
International experience	75.0%
Resident/fellow retreats	100.0%
Off-campus electives	87.5%
Hospice/home care experience	12.5%
Cultural competence awareness	62.5%
Instruction in medical Spanish or other non-English language	37.5%
Alternative/complementary medicine curriculum	37.5%
Training in identifying and reporting of domestic violence/abuse	75.0%
MPH/MBA or PhD training	50.0%
Research rotation	75.0%
Educational Features	
Offers additional training or educational experience beyond accredited length	58.8%
Offers a primary care track	0.0%
Offers a rural track	0.0%
Offers a women's health track	0.0%
Offers a hospitalist track	0.0%
Offers a research track/nonaccredited fellowship	0.0%
Offers an other track	25.0%
Resident Evaluation	
Yearly specialty in-service examination required	100.0%
Patient surveys	37.5%
Portfolio system	50.0%
360 degree evaluations	100.0%

Objective structured clinical examinations (OSCE)	25.0%
Program Evaluation	
Program graduation rates	87.5%
Board certification rates	100.0%
In-training examinations	100.0%
Performance-based assessments	37.5%
Employment Policies and Benefits	
Part-time/shared positions	0.0%
On-site child care	50.0%
Subsidized child care	0.0%
Allowance/stipend for professional expenses	100.0%
Leave for educational meetings/conferences	70.0%
Moving allowance	12.5%
Housing stipend	0.0%
On-call meal allowance	87.5%
Free parking	87.5%
PDAs	25.0%
Placement assistance upon completion of program	25.0%
Cross coverage in case of illness/disability	25.0%
Compensation and Leave (Graduate Year 1)	
Average resident/fellow compensation	$50,567
Average number weeks of vacation	3.8
Sick days (paid)	10.9
Maximum number of paid days for family/medical leave	31
Maximum number of unpaid days for family/medical leave	15
Major Medical Benefits	
Major medical insurance for residents	100.0%
Major medical insurance for dependents	87.5%
Outpatient mental health insurance	62.5%
Inpatient mental health insurance	62.5%
Group life insurance	100.0%
Dental insurance	87.5%
Disability insurance	87.5%
Disability insurance for occupationally acquired HIV	62.5%
Medical insurance coverage begins when starting program	100.0%

For more information

American College of Emergency Physicians
1125 Executive Circle
Irving, TX 75038-2522
800 798-1822
972 580-2816 Fax
E-mail: membership@acep.org
www.acep.org

Sports Medicine

Professional Description

An emergency physician with special knowledge in sports medicine is responsible for continuous care in the field of sports medicine, not only for the enhancement of health and fitness, but also for the prevention and management of injury and illness. A sports medicine physician has knowledge and experience in the promotion of wellness and the role of exercise in promoting a healthy lifestyle. Knowledge of exercise physiology, biomechanics, nutrition, psychology, physical rehabilitation, and epidemiology is essential to the practice of sports medicine.

Prerequisites; Length of Training

Completion of an ACGME-accredited residency is required; length of accredited programs is 1 year.

Specialty Data

Data

Unless otherwise noted, all data are for 2008.

Table 1. Sports Medicine Programs

Number of accredited programs	5

Program Data

length of accredited training	1
Minimum number of prior years of GME required	4
Offers graduate year 1 positions, available immediately upon medical school completion	No
Average number of interviews for program year 1 positions	7.0
Percent new program directors, 2007-2008 academic year (source: ACGME)	0.0%

Residents/Fellows

Total number of active residents/fellows	5
Average number of residents/fellows per program	1.0
Average percent female	20.0%
Average percent international medical graduate (IMG)	20.0%

Program Faculty

Average number of full-time physician faculty	11.8
Average number of part-time physician faculty	2.3
Average percent female full-time physician faculty	23.4%
Average ratio of full-time physician faculty to resident/fellow	5.2

Table 2. Data for Sports Medicine Programs Listed in FREIDA

Number of programs providing data	3

Work Schedule (Program Year 1)

Average hours on duty per week	41.2
Average maximum consecutive hours on duty	8.7
Average days off duty per week	1.5
Moonlighting allowed within institution	66.7%
Night float system	0.0%
Offers awareness and management of fatigue in residents/fellows	66.7%

Educational Setting (Program Year 1)

Average hours/week of regularly scheduled lectures/conferences	4.0
Average percent of training in hospital outpatient clinics	65.0%
Average percent of training in nonhospital ambulatory care community settings	26.7%

Educational Benefits

Curriculum on management of tobacco dependence	0.0%
Program to assess/enhance medical professionalism	100.0%
Debt management/financial counseling	33.3%
Formal program to develop teaching skills	66.7%
Formal mentoring program	100.0%
Formal program to foster interdisciplinary teamwork	33.3%
Continuous quality improvement training	66.7%
International experience	33.3%
Resident/fellow retreats	66.7%
Off-campus electives	100.0%
Hospice/home care experience	0.0%
Cultural competence awareness	33.3%
Instruction in medical Spanish or other non-English language	33.3%
Alternative/complementary medicine curriculum	66.7%
Training in identifying and reporting of domestic violence/abuse	33.3%
MPH/MBA or PhD training	33.3%
Research rotation	33.3%

Educational Features

Offers additional training or educational experience beyond accredited length	0.0%
Offers a primary care track	66.7%
Offers a rural track	0.0%
Offers a women's health track	0.0%
Offers a hospitalist track	0.0%
Offers a research track/nonaccredited fellowship	0.0%
Offers an other track	33.3%

Resident Evaluation

Yearly specialty in-service examination required	40.0%
Patient surveys	66.7%
Portfolio system	66.7%
360 degree evaluations	66.7%
Objective structured clinical examinations (OSCE)	66.7%

Program Evaluation

Program graduation rates	100.0%
Board certification rates	100.0%
In-training examinations	66.7%
Performance-based assessments	66.7%

Employment Policies and Benefits

Part-time/shared positions	0.0%
On-site child care	66.7%
Subsidized child care	0.0%
Allowance/stipend for professional expenses	100.0%
Leave for educational meetings/conferences	83.3%
Moving allowance	0.0%
Housing stipend	0.0%
On-call meal allowance	66.7%
Free parking	100.0%
PDAs	0.0%
Placement assistance upon completion of program	33.3%
Cross coverage in case of illness/disability	66.7%

Compensation and Leave (Graduate Year 1)

Average resident/fellow compensation	$51,185
Average number weeks of vacation	3.3
Sick days (paid)	90.0
Maximum number of paid days for family/medical leave	5
Maximum number of unpaid days for family/medical leave	0

Major Medical Benefits

Major medical insurance for residents	100.0%
Major medical insurance for dependents	100.0%
Outpatient mental health insurance	100.0%
Inpatient mental health insurance	100.0%
Group life insurance	100.0%
Dental insurance	100.0%
Disability insurance	66.7%
Disability insurance for occupationally acquired HIV	66.7%
Medical insurance coverage begins when starting program	66.7%

For more information

American College of Sports Medicine
401 West Michigan Street
Indianapolis, IN 46202-3233
317 637-9200
317 634-7817 Fax
www.acsm.org

Undersea and Hyperbaric Medicine

Professional Description

An emergency medicine physician who, with additional and specialized training, has expertise in the treatment of decompression illness and diving accident cases and uses hyperbaric oxygen therapy treatment for conditions such as carbon monoxide poisoning, gas gangrene, non-healing wounds, tissue damage from radiation and burns, and bone infections. This specialist also serves as consultant to other physicians in all aspects of hyperbaric chamber operations, and assesses risks and applies appropriate standards to prevent disease and disability in divers and other persons working in altered atmospheric conditions.

Prerequisites; Length of Training

Completion of an ACGME-accredited residency is required; length of accredited programs is 1 year.

For more information

Undersea & Hyperbaric Medicine Society
21 West Colony Place
Durham, NC 27705
919 490-5140
919 490-5149 Fax
uhms@uhms.org
www.uhms.org

Family Medicine

Professional Description

A family physician is concerned with the total health care of the individual and the family, and is trained to diagnose and treat a wide variety of ailments in patients of all ages. The family physician receives a broad range of training that includes internal medicine, pediatrics, obstetrics and gynecology, psychiatry, and geriatrics. Special emphasis is placed on prevention and the primary care of entire families, utilizing consultations and community resources when appropriate.

Source: American Board of Medical Specialties, *Guide to Physician Specialties*

Family medicine is the medical specialty which is concerned with the total health care of the individual and the family. It is the specialty in breadth which integrates the biological, clinical, and behavioral sciences. The scope of family medicine is not limited by age, sex, organ system, or disease entity.

Source: American Board of Family Medicine

Prerequisites; Length of Training

No prerequisites required; ACGME-accredited programs are 3 years.

Subspecialties

Subspecialty programs accredited by the ACGME

- Geriatric medicine
- Hospice and palliative medicine
- Sleep medicine
- Sports medicine

American Board of Family Medicine subspecialty certificates

- Adolescent medicine
- Geriatric medicine
- Hospice and palliative medicine
- Sleep medicine
- Sports medicine

Data

Unless otherwise noted, all data are for 2008.

Table 1. Family Medicine Programs

Number of accredited programs	453
Program Data	
length of accredited training	3
Minimum number of prior years of GME required	0
Offers graduate year 1 positions, available immediately upon medical school completion	Yes
Average number of interviews for program year 1 positions	53.5
Percent new program directors, 2007-2008 academic year (source: ACGME)	15.2%
Residents/Fellows	
Total number of active residents/fellows	8,991
Average number of residents/fellows per program	19.8
Average percent female	54.0%
Average percent international medical graduate (IMG)	40.5%
Program Faculty	
Average number of full-time physician faculty	10.7
Average number of part-time physician faculty	6.1
Average percent female full-time physician faculty	33.1%
Average ratio of full-time physician faculty to resident/fellow	0.4

Table 2. Data for Family Medicine Programs Listed in FREIDA

Number of programs providing data	380

Specialty Data

Work Schedule (Program Year 1)

Average hours on duty per week	63.1
Average maximum consecutive hours on duty	28.5
Average days off duty per week	1.3
Moonlighting allowed within institution	66.6%
Night float system	53.7%
Offers awareness and management of fatigue in residents/fellows	97.1%

Educational Setting (Program Year 1)

Average hours/week of regularly scheduled lectures/conferences	5.3
Average percent of training in hospital outpatient clinics	20.2%
Average percent of training in nonhospital ambulatory care community settings	16.5%

Educational Benefits

Curriculum on management of tobacco dependence	45.0%
Program to assess/enhance medical professionalism	85.5%
Debt management/financial counseling	82.1%
Formal program to develop teaching skills	83.7%
Formal mentoring program	74.2%
Formal program to foster interdisciplinary teamwork	43.2%
Continuous quality improvement training	96.3%
International experience	71.3%
Resident/fellow retreats	89.2%
Off-campus electives	97.9%
Hospice/home care experience	98.9%
Cultural competence awareness	96.1%
Instruction in medical Spanish or other non-English language	33.9%
Alternative/complementary medicine curriculum	61.6%
Training in identifying and reporting of domestic violence/abuse	94.2%
MPH/MBA or PhD training	17.6%
Research rotation	21.3%

Educational Features

Offers additional training or educational experience beyond accredited length	18.1%
Offers a primary care track	43.9%
Offers a rural track	20.5%
Offers a women's health track	20.0%
Offers a hospitalist track	9.2%
Offers a research track/nonaccredited fellowship	9.2%
Offers an other track	28.2%

Resident Evaluation

Yearly specialty in-service examination required	98.5%
Patient surveys	80.8%
Portfolio system	58.4%
360 degree evaluations	85.0%
Objective structured clinical examinations (OSCE)	37.1%

Program Evaluation

Program graduation rates	88.7%
Board certification rates	99.5%
In-training examinations	98.9%
Performance-based assessments	55.8%

Employment Policies and Benefits

Part-time/shared positions	8.7%
On-site child care	30.8%
Subsidized child care	8.2%
Allowance/stipend for professional expenses	98.4%
Leave for educational meetings/conferences	90.3%
Moving allowance	50.3%
Housing stipend	10.0%
On-call meal allowance	97.9%
Free parking	92.4%
PDAs	72.9%
Placement assistance upon completion of program	45.0%

Cross coverage in case of illness/disability	95.3%

Compensation and Leave (Graduate Year 1)

Average resident/fellow compensation	$45,145
Average number weeks of vacation	3.5
Sick days (paid)	11.6
Maximum number of paid days for family/medical leave	31
Maximum number of unpaid days for family/medical leave	69

Major Medical Benefits

Major medical insurance for residents	100.0%
Major medical insurance for dependents	95.3%
Outpatient mental health insurance	94.7%
Inpatient mental health insurance	93.4%
Group life insurance	96.6%
Dental insurance	89.7%
Disability insurance	91.8%
Disability insurance for occupationally acquired HIV	74.2%
Medical insurance coverage begins when starting program	88.4%

Table 3. Family Medicine Match Data

GY1	2008
Number of positions offered	2,636
Number filled by US seniors	1,156
Percent filled by US seniors	43.9
Total positions filled	2,387
Percent total positions filled	90.6
All	
Total Positions*	2,636
Preferred by US Seniors*	1,144
Preferred Positions per US Senior	2.3
Preferred by Independent Applicants†	2,109
Preferred Positions per IA	1.2

Source: National Resident Matching Program 2008 Match Data
* Includes all positions offered in a specialty, except preliminary positions.
† Preferred means the number of applicants for whom the specialty was the only or first choice.

For more information

Professional Association

American Academy of Family Physicians
PO Box 11210
Shawnee Mission, KS 66207-1210
800 274-2237
913 906-6075 Fax
E-mail: fp@aafp.org
www.aafp.org

Certification

American Board of Family Medicine
2228 Young Dr
Lexington, KY 40505-4294
859 269-5626
859 335-7501 Fax
E-mail: helpl@theabfm.org
www.theabfm.org

Program Accreditation

Accreditation Council for Graduate Medical Education
Residency Review Committee for Family Medicine
Jerry Vasilias, PhD, Executive Director
515 North State Street
Chicago, IL 60654
312 755-7477
E-mail: jvasilias@acgme.org
www.acgme.org

Adolescent Medicine

Professional Description

A family physician with multidisciplinary training in the unique physical, psychological, and social characteristics of adolescents, their health care problems and needs.

Prerequisites; Length of Training

Completion of an ACGME-accredited residency is required; programs are 2 years.

For more information

Society for Adolescent Medicine
1916 Copper Oaks Circle
Blue Springs, MO 64015
816 224-8010
816 224-8009 Fax
E-mail: sam@adolescenthealth.org
www.adolescenthealth.org

Geriatric Medicine

Professional Description

A family physician with special knowledge of the aging process and special skills in the diagnostic, therapeutic, preventive, and rehabilitative aspects of illness in the elderly. This specialist cares for geriatric patients in the patient's home, the office, long-term care settings such as nursing homes, and the hospital.

Prerequisites; Length of Training

Completion of an ACGME-accredited residency is required; ACGME-accredited programs are 1 year.

Data

Unless otherwise noted, all data are for 2008.

Table 1. Geriatric Medicine Programs

Number of accredited programs	40
Program Data	
length of accredited training	1
Minimum number of prior years of GME required	3
Offers graduate year 1 positions, available immediately upon medical school completion	No
Average number of interviews for program year 1 positions	5.0
Percent new program directors, 2007-2008 academic year (source: ACGME)	7.7%
Residents/Fellows	
Total number of active residents/fellows	62
Average number of residents/fellows per program	1.6
Average percent female	45.2%
Average percent international medical graduate (IMG)	61.3%
Program Faculty	
Average number of full-time physician faculty	5.9
Average number of part-time physician faculty	2.0
Average percent female full-time physician faculty	31.7%
Average ratio of full-time physician faculty to resident/fellow	1.6

Table 2. Data for Geriatric Medicine Programs Listed in FREIDA

Number of programs providing data	21
Work Schedule (Program Year 1)	
Average hours on duty per week	38.7
Average maximum consecutive hours on duty	14.1
Average days off duty per week	1.8
Moonlighting allowed within institution	76.2%
Night float system	4.8%
Offers awareness and management of fatigue in residents/fellows	61.9%
Educational Setting (Program Year 1)	
Average hours/week of regularly scheduled lectures/conferences	4.6
Average percent of training in hospital outpatient clinics	32.3%
Average percent of training in nonhospital ambulatory care community settings	24.3%
Educational Benefits	
Curriculum on management of tobacco dependence	4.8%
Program to assess/enhance medical professionalism	76.2%
Debt management/financial counseling	33.3%
Formal program to develop teaching skills	90.5%
Formal mentoring program	66.7%
Formal program to foster interdisciplinary teamwork	61.9%
Continuous quality improvement training	81.0%
International experience	4.8%
Resident/fellow retreats	57.1%
Off-campus electives	85.7%
Hospice/home care experience	100.0%
Cultural competence awareness	90.5%
Instruction in medical Spanish or other non-English language	14.3%
Alternative/complementary medicine curriculum	33.3%
Training in identifying and reporting of domestic violence/abuse	76.2%
MPH/MBA or PhD training	19.0%
Research rotation	57.1%
Educational Features	
Offers additional training or educational experience beyond accredited length	17.8%
Offers a primary care track	42.9%
Offers a rural track	9.5%
Offers a women's health track	0.0%
Offers a hospitalist track	0.0%
Offers a research track/nonaccredited fellowship	14.3%
Offers an other track	19.0%
Resident Evaluation	
Yearly specialty in-service examination required	22.7%
Patient surveys	52.4%
Portfolio system	38.1%
360 degree evaluations	90.5%
Objective structured clinical examinations (OSCE)	4.8%
Program Evaluation	
Program graduation rates	95.2%
Board certification rates	100.0%
In-training examinations	23.8%
Performance-based assessments	42.9%
Employment Policies and Benefits	
Part-time/shared positions	14.3%
On-site child care	42.9%
Subsidized child care	14.3%
Allowance/stipend for professional expenses	100.0%
Leave for educational meetings/conferences	84.0%
Moving allowance	47.6%
Housing stipend	4.8%
On-call meal allowance	52.4%
Free parking	81.0%
PDAs	47.6%
Placement assistance upon completion of program	42.9%
Cross coverage in case of illness/disability	76.2%

Specialty Data

Compensation and Leave (Graduate Year 1)

Average resident/fellow compensation	$50,767
Average number weeks of vacation	3.5
Sick days (paid)	13.9
Maximum number of paid days for family/medical leave	32
Maximum number of unpaid days for family/medical leave	44

Major Medical Benefits

Major medical insurance for residents	95.2%
Major medical insurance for dependents	90.5%
Outpatient mental health insurance	95.2%
Inpatient mental health insurance	95.2%
Group life insurance	85.7%
Dental insurance	81.0%
Disability insurance	76.2%
Disability insurance for occupationally acquired HIV	66.7%
Medical insurance coverage begins when starting program	85.7%

For more information

American Geriatrics Society
Empire State Building
350 Fifth Avenue, Suite 801
New York, NY 10118
212 308-1414
212 832-8646 Fax
E-mail: info@americangeriatrics.org
www.americangeriatrics.org

Hospice and Palliative Medicine

See page 57.

Sleep Medicine

See page 155.

Sports Medicine

Professional Description

A family physician who is trained to be responsible for continuous care in the field of sports medicine, not only for the enhancement of health and fitness, but also for the prevention of injury and illness. A sports medicine physician must have knowledge and experience in the promotion of wellness and the prevention of injury. Knowledge about special areas of medicine such as exercise physiology, biomechanics, nutrition, psychology, physical rehabilitation, epidemiology, physical evaluation, injuries (treatment and prevention and referral practice), and the role of exercise in promoting a healthy lifestyle are essential to the practice of sports medicine. The sports medicine physician requires special education to provide the knowledge to improve the health care of the individual engaged in physical exercise (sports) whether as an individual or in team participation.

Prerequisites; Length of Training

Completion of an ACGME-accredited residency is required; ACGME-accredited programs are 1 year.

Data

Unless otherwise noted, all data are for 2008.

Table 1. Sports Medicine Programs

Number of accredited programs	101

Program Data

length of accredited training	1
Minimum number of prior years of GME required	3
Offers graduate year 1 positions, available immediately upon medical school completion	No
Average number of interviews for program year 1 positions	8.5
Percent new program directors, 2007-2008 academic year (source: ACGME)	10.3%

Residents/Fellows

Total number of active residents/fellows	126
Average number of residents/fellows per program	1.2
Average percent female	29.4%
Average percent international medical graduate (IMG)	20.6%

Program Faculty

Average number of full-time physician faculty	4.5
Average number of part-time physician faculty	1.7
Average percent female full-time physician faculty	17.4%
Average ratio of full-time physician faculty to resident/fellow	1.5

Table 2. Data for Sports Medicine Programs Listed in FREIDA

Number of programs providing data	42

Work Schedule (Program Year 1)

Average hours on duty per week	42.4
Average maximum consecutive hours on duty	13.6
Average days off duty per week	1.3
Moonlighting allowed within institution	69.0%
Night float system	0.0%
Offers awareness and management of fatigue in residents/fellows	85.7%

Educational Setting (Program Year 1)

Average hours/week of regularly scheduled lectures/conferences	3.5
Average percent of training in hospital outpatient clinics	43.2%
Average percent of training in nonhospital ambulatory care community settings	55.5%

Educational Benefits

Curriculum on management of tobacco dependence	9.5%
Program to assess/enhance medical professionalism	69.0%
Debt management/financial counseling	40.5%
Formal program to develop teaching skills	81.0%
Formal mentoring program	47.6%
Formal program to foster interdisciplinary teamwork	26.2%
Continuous quality improvement training	76.2%
International experience	9.5%
Resident/fellow retreats	52.4%
Off-campus electives	76.2%
Hospice/home care experience	19.0%
Cultural competence awareness	73.8%
Instruction in medical Spanish or other non-English language	7.1%
Alternative/complementary medicine curriculum	40.5%
Training in identifying and reporting of domestic violence/abuse	45.2%
MPH/MBA or PhD training	7.1%
Research rotation	52.4%

Educational Features

Offers additional training or educational experience beyond accredited length	7.5%
Offers a primary care track	33.3%
Offers a rural track	2.4%
Offers a women's health track	0.0%
Offers a hospitalist track	0.0%

Offers a research track/nonaccredited fellowship	9.5%
Offers an other track	16.7%
Resident Evaluation	
Yearly specialty in-service examination required	51.0%
Patient surveys	33.3%
Portfolio system	38.1%
360 degree evaluations	66.7%
Objective structured clinical examinations (OSCE)	7.1%
Program Evaluation	
Program graduation rates	81.0%
Board certification rates	95.2%
In-training examinations	42.9%
Performance-based assessments	35.7%
Employment Policies and Benefits	
Part-time/shared positions	0.0%
On-site child care	45.2%
Subsidized child care	4.8%
Allowance/stipend for professional expenses	97.6%
Leave for educational meetings/conferences	79.5%
Moving allowance	33.3%
Housing stipend	0.0%
On-call meal allowance	50.0%
Free parking	88.1%
PDAs	35.7%
Placement assistance upon completion of program	19.0%
Cross coverage in case of illness/disability	73.8%
Compensation and Leave (Graduate Year 1)	
Average resident/fellow compensation	$50,308
Average number weeks of vacation	4.4
Sick days (paid)	18.3
Maximum number of paid days for family/medical leave	17
Maximum number of unpaid days for family/medical leave	25
Major Medical Benefits	
Major medical insurance for residents	100.0%
Major medical insurance for dependents	95.2%
Outpatient mental health insurance	92.9%
Inpatient mental health insurance	92.9%
Group life insurance	95.2%
Dental insurance	90.5%
Disability insurance	92.9%
Disability insurance for occupationally acquired HIV	66.7%
Medical insurance coverage begins when starting program	92.9%

For more information

American College of Sports Medicine
401 West Michigan Street
Indianapolis, IN 46202-3233
317 637-9200
317 634-7817 Fax
www.acsm.org

Hospice and Palliative Medicine

Professional Description

The subspecialty of hospice and palliative medicine represents the medical component of the broad therapeutic model known as palliative care. Subspecialists in this field reduce the burden of life-threatening conditions by supporting the best quality of life throughout the course of an illness and by managing factors that contribute to the suffering of the patient and the patient's family.
1. Palliative care addresses physical, psychological, social, and spiritual needs of patients and their families, and provides assistance with medical decision-making.
2. The major clinical skills central to the subspecialty are the prevention (when possible), assessment, and management of physical, psychological, and spiritual suffering faced by patients with life-limiting conditions and their families.
3. Hospice and palliative medicine is distinguished from other disciplines by:

- A high level of expertise in addressing the multidimensional needs of patients with life-threatening illnesses, including a practical skill set in symptom control interventions
- A high level of expertise in both clinical and nonclinical issues related to advanced illness, the dying process, and bereavement
- A commitment to an interdisciplinary team approach
- A strong focus on the patient and family as the unit of care

Source: Hospice and palliative medicine program requirements, ACGME
www.acgme.org/acWebsite/downloads/RRC_progReq/540_hospice_and_palliative_medicine_02122008.pdf

Prerequisites; Length of Training

Completion is required of an ACGME-accredited program in anesthesiology, emergency medicine, family medicine, internal medicine, neurology, obstetrics and gynecology, pediatrics, physical medicine and rehabilitation, psychiatry, radiation oncology, or surgery; length of accredited programs is 1 year.
Note: The RRC for Family Medicine reviews and accredits all hospice and palliative medicine programs regardless of the sponsoring specialty of the individual program.

For more information

Professional Association

American Academy of Hospice and Palliative Medicine
4700 West Lake Avenue
Glenview, IL 60025
847 375-4712
847 375-6475 Fax
E-mail: info@aahpm.org
www.aahpm.org

Certification

Certification is through the following ABMS boards:
- Anesthesiology
- Emergency Medicine
- Family Medicine
- Internal Medicine
- Neurology
- Obstetrics and Gynecology
- Pediatrics

Specialty Data

- Physical Medicine and Rehabilitation
- Psychiatry
- Radiology
- Surgery

Program Accreditation

Accreditation Council for Graduate Medical Education
Residency Review Committee for Family Medicine
Jerry Vasilias, PhD, Executive Director
515 North State Street
Chicago, IL 60654
312 755-7477
E-mail: jvasilias@acgme.org
www.acgme.org

Internal Medicine

Professional Description

Internal medicine is the largest primary care specialty in the United States and is an ever-changing and rapidly advancing discipline. Doctors of internal medicine are known as "internists" or "general internists," and should not be confused with "interns" who are doctors in their first year of training after medical school. Internists are not the same as "general practitioners" (GPs) or "family physicians" (FPs) whose practices may include surgery, obstetrics, and pediatrics and whose training is not solely concentrated on adults.

Because internal medicine is expansive, internists must continually update their knowledge in many areas including allergy, arthritis, blood diseases, cancer, diabetes, digestive diseases, illness in the elderly, diseases of the heart and blood vessels, hormonal disorders, infections, intensive care, kidney diseases, and respiratory disorders.

The practice of internal medicine also incorporates an understanding of wellness (disease prevention and health promotion), women's health, substance abuse, mental health, and medical ethics, as well as effective treatment of common problems of the eyes, ears, skin, nervous system, and reproductive organs.
Source: American Board of Internal Medicine, www.abim.org/resources/publications/whats_so_special.shtm

Prerequisites; Length of Training

No prerequisites; length of accredited programs is 3 years.

Subspecialties

Subspecialty programs accredited by the ACGME

- Cardiovascular disease
- Clinical cardiac electrophysiology
- Critical care medicine
- Endocrinology, diabetes, and metabolism
- Gastroenterology
- Geriatric medicine
- Hematology
- Hematology and oncology
- Hospice and palliative medicine
- Infectious disease
- Interventional cardiology
- Nephrology
- Oncology
- Pulmonary disease
- Pulmonary disease and critical care medicine
- Rheumatology
- Sleep medicine
- Transplant hepatology

American Board of Internal Medicine subspecialty certificates

- Adolescent medicine
- Cardiovascular disease
- Clinical cardiac electrophysiology
- Critical care medicine
- Endocrinology, diabetes, and metabolism
- Gastroenterology
- Geriatric medicine
- Hematology
- Hospice and palliative medicine
- Infectious disease
- Interventional cardiology
- Medical oncology
- Nephrology

- Pulmonary disease
- Rheumatology
- Sleep medicine
- Sports medicine
- Transplant hepatology

Data

Unless otherwise noted, all data are for 2008.

Table 1. Internal Medicine Programs

Number of accredited programs	382

Program Data

length of accredited training	3
Minimum number of prior years of GME required	0
Offers graduate year 1 positions, available immediately upon medical school completion	Yes
Average number of interviews for program year 1 positions	199.2
Percent new program directors, 2007-2008 academic year (source: ACGME)	13.0%

Residents/Fellows

Total number of active residents/fellows	20,705
Average number of residents/fellows per program	54.2
Average percent female	43.0%
Average percent international medical graduate (IMG)	44.5%

Program Faculty

Average number of full-time physician faculty	78.9
Average number of part-time physician faculty	18.8
Average percent female full-time physician faculty	26.9%
Average ratio of full-time physician faculty to resident/fellow	1.0

Table 2. Data for Internal Medicine Programs Listed in FREIDA

Number of programs providing data	303

Work Schedule (Program Year 1)

Average hours on duty per week	64.7
Average maximum consecutive hours on duty	27.6
Average days off duty per week	1.2
Moonlighting allowed within institution	66.7%
Night float system	84.5%
Offers awareness and management of fatigue in residents/fellows	97.7%

Educational Setting (Program Year 1)

Average hours/week of regularly scheduled lectures/conferences	8.4
Average percent of training in hospital outpatient clinics	23.2%
Average percent of training in nonhospital ambulatory care community settings	10.9%

Educational Benefits

Curriculum on management of tobacco dependence	48.2%
Program to assess/enhance medical professionalism	92.1%
Debt management/financial counseling	74.9%
Formal program to develop teaching skills	91.4%
Formal mentoring program	83.8%
Formal program to foster interdisciplinary teamwork	48.8%
Continuous quality improvement training	97.7%
International experience	47.9%
Resident/fellow retreats	71.3%
Off-campus electives	91.7%
Hospice/home care experience	89.8%
Cultural competence awareness	92.1%
Instruction in medical Spanish or other non-English language	29.0%
Alternative/complementary medicine curriculum	55.8%
Training in identifying and reporting of domestic violence/abuse	92.1%
MPH/MBA or PhD training	18.8%
Research rotation	16.8%

Educational Features

Offers additional training or educational experience beyond accredited length	12.7%
Offers a primary care track	29.4%
Offers a rural track	2.3%
Offers a women's health track	7.3%
Offers a hospitalist track	12.9%
Offers a research track/nonaccredited fellowship	13.5%
Offers an other track	16.2%

Resident Evaluation

Yearly specialty in-service examination required	98.8%
Patient surveys	68.6%
Portfolio system	66.7%
360 degree evaluations	91.4%
Objective structured clinical examinations (OSCE)	44.6%

Program Evaluation

Program graduation rates	91.4%
Board certification rates	99.7%
In-training examinations	98.0%
Performance-based assessments	73.9%

Employment Policies and Benefits

Part-time/shared positions	10.6%
On-site child care	41.6%
Subsidized child care	7.9%
Allowance/stipend for professional expenses	94.7%
Leave for educational meetings/conferences	73.2%
Moving allowance	17.8%
Housing stipend	9.6%
On-call meal allowance	95.4%
Free parking	76.6%
PDAs	39.3%
Placement assistance upon completion of program	53.8%
Cross coverage in case of illness/disability	99.3%

Compensation and Leave (Graduate Year 1)

Average resident/fellow compensation	$45,763
Average number weeks of vacation	3.5
Sick days (paid)	17.7
Maximum number of paid days for family/medical leave	34
Maximum number of unpaid days for family/medical leave	71

Major Medical Benefits

Major medical insurance for residents	100.0%
Major medical insurance for dependents	98.0%
Outpatient mental health insurance	96.4%
Inpatient mental health insurance	96.7%
Group life insurance	93.7%
Dental insurance	90.8%
Disability insurance	94.1%
Disability insurance for occupationally acquired HIV	77.6%
Medical insurance coverage begins when starting program	93.1%

Table 3. Internal Medicine Match Data

GY1	2008
Number of positions offered	4,858
Number filled by US seniors	2,660
Percent filled by US seniors	54.8
Total positions filled	4,751
Percent total positions filled	97.8

All	
Total Positions*	5,554
Preferred by US Seniors*	3,150
Preferred Positions per US Senior	1.8
Preferred by Independent Applicants†	4,788

Specialty Data

Preferred Positions per IA	1.2

Source: National Resident Matching Program 2008 Match Data
* Includes all positions offered in a specialty, except preliminary positions.
† Preferred means the number of applicants for whom the specialty was the only or first choice.

For more information

Professional Association

American College of Physicians
190 N Independence Mall West
Philadelphia, PA 19106-1572
800 523-1546, x2600
215 351-2400
www.acponline.org

Certification

American Board of Internal Medicine
510 Walnut Street, Suite 1700
Philadelphia, PA 19106
800 441-2246
215 446-3590 Fax
E-mail: request@abim.org
www.abim.org

Program Accreditation

Accreditation Council for Graduate Medical Education
Residency Review Committee for Internal Medicine
William Rodak, PhD, Executive Director
515 North State Street
Chicago, IL 60654
312 755-5497
E-mail: wer@acgme.org
www.acgme.org

Adolescent Medicine

Professional Description

An internist who specializes in adolescent medicine is a multi-disciplinary health care specialist trained in the unique physical, psychological, and social characteristics of adolescents and their health care problems and needs.

Prerequisites; Length of Training

Completion of an ACGME-accredited residency is required; programs are 2 years.

For more information

Society for Adolescent Medicine
1916 Copper Oaks Circle
Blue Springs, MO 64015
816 224-8010
816 224-8009 Fax
E-mail: sam@adolescenthealth.org
www.adolescenthealth.org

Cardiovascular Disease

Professional Description

An internist who specializes in diseases of the heart and blood vessels and manages complex cardiac conditions such as heart attacks and life-threatening, abnormal heart rhythms.

Prerequisites; Length of Training

Completion of a 3-year ACGME-accredited residency program in internal medicine is required; ACGME-accredited programs in cardiovascular disease are 3 years.

Data

Unless otherwise noted, all data are for 2008.

Table 1. Cardiovascular Disease Programs	
Number of accredited programs	178
Program Data	
length of accredited training	3
Minimum number of prior years of GME required	3
Offers graduate year 1 positions, available immediately upon medical school completion	No
Average number of interviews for program year 1 positions	42.0
Percent new program directors, 2007-2008 academic year (source: ACGME)	10.2%
Residents/Fellows	
Total number of active residents/fellows	2,308
Average number of residents/fellows per program	13.0
Average percent female	20.2%
Average percent international medical graduate (IMG)	33.2%
Program Faculty	
Average number of full-time physician faculty	22.1
Average number of part-time physician faculty	2.5
Average percent female full-time physician faculty	14.6%
Average ratio of full-time physician faculty to resident/fellow	1.2

Table 2. Data for Cardiovascular Disease Programs Listed in FREIDA	
Number of programs providing data	100
Work Schedule (Program Year 1)	
Average hours on duty per week	54.1
Average maximum consecutive hours on duty	21.3
Average days off duty per week	1.5
Moonlighting allowed within institution	78.0%
Night float system	12.0%
Offers awareness and management of fatigue in residents/fellows	93.0%
Educational Setting (Program Year 1)	
Average hours/week of regularly scheduled lectures/conferences	6.2
Average percent of training in hospital outpatient clinics	14.8%
Average percent of training in nonhospital ambulatory care community settings	12.8%
Educational Benefits	
Curriculum on management of tobacco dependence	21.0%
Program to assess/enhance medical professionalism	71.0%
Debt management/financial counseling	48.0%
Formal program to develop teaching skills	80.0%
Formal mentoring program	71.0%
Formal program to foster interdisciplinary teamwork	16.0%
Continuous quality improvement training	85.0%
International experience	11.0%
Resident/fellow retreats	30.0%
Off-campus electives	65.0%
Hospice/home care experience	8.0%
Cultural competence awareness	79.0%
Instruction in medical Spanish or other non-English language	22.0%
Alternative/complementary medicine curriculum	19.0%
Training in identifying and reporting of domestic violence/abuse	34.0%
MPH/MBA or PhD training	37.0%
Research rotation	86.0%

Educational Features

Offers additional training or educational experience beyond accredited length	37.6%
Offers a primary care track	3.0%
Offers a rural track	1.0%
Offers a women's health track	2.0%
Offers a hospitalist track	0.0%
Offers a research track/nonaccredited fellowship	29.0%
Offers an other track	12.0%

Resident Evaluation

Yearly specialty in-service examination required	33.3%
Patient surveys	43.0%
Portfolio system	38.0%
360 degree evaluations	89.0%
Objective structured clinical examinations (OSCE)	15.0%

Program Evaluation

Program graduation rates	77.0%
Board certification rates	100.0%
In-training examinations	32.0%
Performance-based assessments	31.0%

Employment Policies and Benefits

Part-time/shared positions	5.0%
On-site child care	41.0%
Subsidized child care	2.0%
Allowance/stipend for professional expenses	92.0%
Leave for educational meetings/conferences	83.4%
Moving allowance	2.0%
Housing stipend	5.0%
On-call meal allowance	70.0%
Free parking	62.0%
PDAs	18.0%
Placement assistance upon completion of program	26.0%
Cross coverage in case of illness/disability	92.0%

Compensation and Leave (Graduate Year 1)

Average resident/fellow compensation	$51,298
Average number weeks of vacation	3.6
Sick days (paid)	20.4
Maximum number of paid days for family/medical leave	46
Maximum number of unpaid days for family/medical leave	60

Major Medical Benefits

Major medical insurance for residents	100.0%
Major medical insurance for dependents	97.0%
Outpatient mental health insurance	95.0%
Inpatient mental health insurance	93.0%
Group life insurance	88.0%
Dental insurance	89.0%
Disability insurance	94.0%
Disability insurance for occupationally acquired HIV	80.0%
Medical insurance coverage begins when starting program	90.0%

For more information

American College of Cardiology
Heart House
2400 N Street, NW
Washington, DC 20037
202 375-6000
202 375-7000 Fax
E-mail: resource@acc.org
www.acc.org

Clinical Cardiac Electrophysiology

Professional Description

A field of special interest within the subspecialty of cardiovascular disease that involves intricate technical procedures to evaluate heart rhythms and determine appropriate treatment for them.

Prerequisites; Length of Training

Completion of a 3-year ACGME-accredited residency program in cardiovascular disease is required; ACGME-accredited programs in clinical cardiac electrophysiology are 1 year.

Data

Unless otherwise noted, all data are for 2008.

Table 1. Clinical Cardiac Electrophysiology Programs

Number of accredited programs	96
Program Data	
length of accredited training	1
Minimum number of prior years of GME required	5
Offers graduate year 1 positions, available immediately upon medical school completion	No
Average number of interviews for program year 1 positions	5.3
Percent new program directors, 2007-2008 academic year (source: ACGME)	10.5%
Residents/Fellows	
Total number of active residents/fellows	151
Average number of residents/fellows per program	1.6
Average percent female	7.3%
Average percent international medical graduate (IMG)	29.8%
Program Faculty	
Average number of full-time physician faculty	5.5
Average number of part-time physician faculty	0.4
Average percent female full-time physician faculty	12.4%
Average ratio of full-time physician faculty to resident/fellow	1.6

Table 2. Data for Clinical Cardiac Electrophysiology Programs Listed in FREIDA

Number of programs providing data	40
Work Schedule (Program Year 1)	
Average hours on duty per week	51.5
Average maximum consecutive hours on duty	17.1
Average days off duty per week	1.6
Moonlighting allowed within institution	77.5%
Night float system	2.5%
Offers awareness and management of fatigue in residents/fellows	90.0%
Educational Setting (Program Year 1)	
Average hours/week of regularly scheduled lectures/conferences	4.4
Average percent of training in hospital outpatient clinics	17.5%
Average percent of training in nonhospital ambulatory care community settings	10.0%
Educational Benefits	
Curriculum on management of tobacco dependence	22.5%
Program to assess/enhance medical professionalism	67.5%
Debt management/financial counseling	55.0%
Formal program to develop teaching skills	75.0%
Formal mentoring program	45.0%
Formal program to foster interdisciplinary teamwork	15.0%
Continuous quality improvement training	82.5%
International experience	7.5%
Resident/fellow retreats	35.0%
Off-campus electives	20.0%
Hospice/home care experience	7.5%

Cultural competence awareness	62.5%
Instruction in medical Spanish or other non-English language	15.0%
Alternative/complementary medicine curriculum	22.5%
Training in identifying and reporting of domestic violence/abuse	42.5%
MPH/MBA or PhD training	15.0%
Research rotation	52.5%
Educational Features	
Offers additional training or educational experience beyond accredited length	43.0%
Offers a primary care track	5.0%
Offers a rural track	0.0%
Offers a women's health track	2.5%
Offers a hospitalist track	2.5%
Offers a research track/nonaccredited fellowship	17.5%
Offers an other track	2.5%
Resident Evaluation	
Yearly specialty in-service examination required	25.5%
Patient surveys	32.5%
Portfolio system	37.5%
360 degree evaluations	87.5%
Objective structured clinical examinations (OSCE)	7.5%
Program Evaluation	
Program graduation rates	87.5%
Board certification rates	100.0%
In-training examinations	27.5%
Performance-based assessments	25.0%
Employment Policies and Benefits	
Part-time/shared positions	0.0%
On-site child care	37.5%
Subsidized child care	7.5%
Allowance/stipend for professional expenses	92.5%
Leave for educational meetings/conferences	86.1%
Moving allowance	2.5%
Housing stipend	2.5%
On-call meal allowance	47.5%
Free parking	50.0%
PDAs	12.5%
Placement assistance upon completion of program	12.5%
Cross coverage in case of illness/disability	77.5%
Compensation and Leave (Graduate Year 1)	
Average resident/fellow compensation	$56,680
Average number weeks of vacation	3.4
Sick days (paid)	25.2
Maximum number of paid days for family/medical leave	51
Maximum number of unpaid days for family/medical leave	47
Major Medical Benefits	
Major medical insurance for residents	97.5%
Major medical insurance for dependents	97.5%
Outpatient mental health insurance	95.0%
Inpatient mental health insurance	95.0%
Group life insurance	92.5%
Dental insurance	87.5%
Disability insurance	95.0%
Disability insurance for occupationally acquired HIV	80.0%
Medical insurance coverage begins when starting program	90.0%

For more information

American College of Cardiology
Heart House
2400 N Street, NW
Washington, DC 20037
202 375-6000
202 375-7000 Fax
E-mail: resource@acc.org
www.acc.org

Critical Care Medicine

Professional Description

An internist who diagnoses, treats, and supports patients with multiple organ dysfunction. This specialist may have administrative responsibilities for intensive care units and may also facilitate and coordinate patient care among the primary physician, the critical care staff, and other specialists.

Prerequisites; Length of Training

Completion of a 3-year ACGME-accredited residency program in internal medicine is required; ACGME-accredited programs in critical care medicine are 2 years.

Data

Unless otherwise noted, all data are for 2008.

Table 1. Critical Care Medicine Programs

Number of accredited programs	32
Program Data	
length of accredited training	1/2
Minimum number of prior years of GME required	3
Offers graduate year 1 positions, available immediately upon medical school completion	No
Average number of interviews for program year 1 positions	14.7
Percent new program directors, 2007-2008 academic year (source: ACGME)	13.3%
Residents/Fellows	
Total number of active residents/fellows	133
Average number of residents/fellows per program	4.2
Average percent female	19.5%
Average percent international medical graduate (IMG)	63.2%
Program Faculty	
Average number of full-time physician faculty	15.5
Average number of part-time physician faculty	2.4
Average percent female full-time physician faculty	18.6%
Average ratio of full-time physician faculty to resident/fellow	1.7

Table 2. Data for Critical Care Medicine Programs Listed in FREIDA

Number of programs providing data	17
Work Schedule (Program Year 1)	
Average hours on duty per week	55.4
Average maximum consecutive hours on duty	21.3
Average days off duty per week	1.5
Moonlighting allowed within institution	64.7%
Night float system	23.5%
Offers awareness and management of fatigue in residents/fellows	88.2%
Educational Setting (Program Year 1)	
Average hours/week of regularly scheduled lectures/conferences	5.6
Average percent of training in hospital outpatient clinics	10.0%
Average percent of training in nonhospital ambulatory care community settings	

Educational Benefits

Curriculum on management of tobacco dependence	17.6%
Program to assess/enhance medical professionalism	76.5%
Debt management/financial counseling	41.2%
Formal program to develop teaching skills	94.1%
Formal mentoring program	41.2%
Formal program to foster interdisciplinary teamwork	29.4%
Continuous quality improvement training	82.4%
International experience	23.5%
Resident/fellow retreats	29.4%
Off-campus electives	100.0%
Hospice/home care experience	29.4%
Cultural competence awareness	70.6%
Instruction in medical Spanish or other non-English language	17.6%
Alternative/complementary medicine curriculum	23.5%
Training in identifying and reporting of domestic violence/abuse	23.5%
MPH/MBA or PhD training	41.2%
Research rotation	70.6%

Educational Features

Offers additional training or educational experience beyond accredited length	10.8%
Offers a primary care track	0.0%
Offers a rural track	0.0%
Offers a women's health track	0.0%
Offers a hospitalist track	0.0%
Offers a research track/nonaccredited fellowship	11.8%
Offers an other track	11.8%

Resident Evaluation

Yearly specialty in-service examination required	43.3%
Patient surveys	5.9%
Portfolio system	52.9%
360 degree evaluations	82.4%
Objective structured clinical examinations (OSCE)	11.8%

Program Evaluation

Program graduation rates	88.2%
Board certification rates	100.0%
In-training examinations	76.5%
Performance-based assessments	41.2%

Employment Policies and Benefits

Part-time/shared positions	5.9%
On-site child care	70.6%
Subsidized child care	11.8%
Allowance/stipend for professional expenses	94.1%
Leave for educational meetings/conferences	54.3%
Moving allowance	17.6%
Housing stipend	0.0%
On-call meal allowance	82.4%
Free parking	52.9%
PDAs	17.6%
Placement assistance upon completion of program	11.8%
Cross coverage in case of illness/disability	100.0%

Compensation and Leave (Graduate Year 1)

Average resident/fellow compensation	$52,246
Average number weeks of vacation	3.4
Sick days (paid)	31.1
Maximum number of paid days for family/medical leave	39
Maximum number of unpaid days for family/medical leave	65

Major Medical Benefits

Major medical insurance for residents	100.0%
Major medical insurance for dependents	100.0%
Outpatient mental health insurance	94.1%
Inpatient mental health insurance	94.1%
Group life insurance	100.0%
Dental insurance	100.0%
Disability insurance	82.4%
Disability insurance for occupationally acquired HIV	64.7%
Medical insurance coverage begins when starting program	88.2%

For more information

Society of Critical Care Medicine
500 Midway Drive
Mount Prospect, IL 60056
847 827-6869
847 827-6886 Fax
E-mail: info@sccm.org
www.sccm.org

Endocrinology, Diabetes, and Metabolism

Professional Description

An internist who concentrates on disorders of the internal (endocrine) glands, such as the thyroid and adrenal glands. This specialist also deals with disorders such as diabetes, metabolic and nutritional disorders, obesity, pituitary diseases, and menstrual and sexual problems.

Prerequisites; Length of Training

Completion of a 3-year ACGME-accredited residency program in internal medicine is required; ACGME-accredited programs in endocrinology, diabetes, and metabolism are 2 years.

Data

Unless otherwise noted, all data are for 2008.

Table 1. Endocrinology, Diabetes, and Metabolism Programs

Number of accredited programs	125

Program Data

length of accredited training	2
Minimum number of prior years of GME required	3
Offers graduate year 1 positions, available immediately upon medical school completion	No
Average number of interviews for program year 1 positions	11.0
Percent new program directors, 2007-2008 academic year (source: ACGME)	6.6%

Residents/Fellows

Total number of active residents/fellows	546
Average number of residents/fellows per program	4.4
Average percent female	65.0%
Average percent international medical graduate (IMG)	37.7%

Program Faculty

Average number of full-time physician faculty	11.2
Average number of part-time physician faculty	1.4
Average percent female full-time physician faculty	31.3%
Average ratio of full-time physician faculty to resident/fellow	1.7

Table 2. Data for Endocrinology, Diabetes, and Metabolism Programs Listed in FREIDA

Number of programs providing data	52

Work Schedule (Program Year 1)

Average hours on duty per week	45.6
Average maximum consecutive hours on duty	14.6
Average days off duty per week	1.5
Moonlighting allowed within institution	75.0%

Night float system	1.9%
Offers awareness and management of fatigue in residents/fellows	88.5%

Educational Setting (Program Year 1)

Average hours/week of regularly scheduled lectures/conferences	4.6
Average percent of training in hospital outpatient clinics	48.5%
Average percent of training in nonhospital ambulatory care community settings	17.3%

Educational Benefits

Curriculum on management of tobacco dependence	13.5%
Program to assess/enhance medical professionalism	80.8%
Debt management/financial counseling	51.9%
Formal program to develop teaching skills	88.5%
Formal mentoring program	71.2%
Formal program to foster interdisciplinary teamwork	28.8%
Continuous quality improvement training	88.5%
International experience	5.8%
Resident/fellow retreats	38.5%
Off-campus electives	57.7%
Hospice/home care experience	9.6%
Cultural competence awareness	71.2%
Instruction in medical Spanish or other non-English language	28.8%
Alternative/complementary medicine curriculum	26.9%
Training in identifying and reporting of domestic violence/abuse	40.4%
MPH/MBA or PhD training	40.4%
Research rotation	96.2%

Educational Features

Offers additional training or educational experience beyond accredited length	46.0%
Offers a primary care track	3.8%
Offers a rural track	0.0%
Offers a women's health track	5.8%
Offers a hospitalist track	0.0%
Offers a research track/nonaccredited fellowship	32.7%
Offers an other track	11.5%

Resident Evaluation

Yearly specialty in-service examination required	37.4%
Patient surveys	51.9%
Portfolio system	69.2%
360 degree evaluations	88.5%
Objective structured clinical examinations (OSCE)	9.6%

Program Evaluation

Program graduation rates	86.5%
Board certification rates	98.1%
In-training examinations	38.5%
Performance-based assessments	28.8%

Employment Policies and Benefits

Part-time/shared positions	5.8%
On-site child care	48.1%
Subsidized child care	5.8%
Allowance/stipend for professional expenses	88.5%
Leave for educational meetings/conferences	79.5%
Moving allowance	1.9%
Housing stipend	3.8%
On-call meal allowance	38.5%
Free parking	59.6%
PDAs	11.5%
Placement assistance upon completion of program	38.5%
Cross coverage in case of illness/disability	84.6%

Compensation and Leave (Graduate Year 1)

Average resident/fellow compensation	$50,992
Average number weeks of vacation	3.5
Sick days (paid)	23.5

Maximum number of paid days for family/medical leave	37
Maximum number of unpaid days for family/medical leave	54

Major Medical Benefits

Major medical insurance for residents	98.1%
Major medical insurance for dependents	94.2%
Outpatient mental health insurance	88.5%
Inpatient mental health insurance	86.5%
Group life insurance	82.7%
Dental insurance	80.8%
Disability insurance	82.7%
Disability insurance for occupationally acquired HIV	69.2%
Medical insurance coverage begins when starting program	80.8%

For more information

American Association of Clinical Endocrinologists
245 Riverside Avenue, Suite 200
Jacksonville, FL 32202
904 353-7878
904 353-8185 Fax
E-mail: info@aace.org
www.aace.com

The Endocrine Society
8401 Connecticut Avenue, Suite 900
Chevy Chase, MD 20815
301 941-0200
301 941-0259 Fax
www.endo-society.org

Gastroenterology

Professional Description

An internist who specializes in diagnosis and treatment of diseases of the digestive organs, including the stomach, bowels, liver, and gallbladder. This specialist treats conditions such as abdominal pain, ulcers, diarrhea, cancer, and jaundice, and performs complex diagnostic and therapeutic procedures using endoscopes to visualize internal organs.

Prerequisites; Length of Training

Completion of a 3-year ACGME-accredited residency program in internal medicine is required; ACGME-accredited programs in gastroenterology are 3 years.

Data

Unless otherwise noted, all data are for 2008.

Table 1. Gastroenterology Programs

Number of accredited programs	154
Program Data	
length of accredited training	3
Minimum number of prior years of GME required	3
Offers graduate year 1 positions, available immediately upon medical school completion	No
Average number of interviews for program year 1 positions	20.7
Percent new program directors, 2007-2008 academic year (source: ACGME)	18.7%
Residents/Fellows	
Total number of active residents/fellows	1,231
Average number of residents/fellows per program	8.0
Average percent female	30.8%
Average percent international medical graduate (IMG)	27.9%

Program Faculty

Average number of full-time physician faculty	12.5
Average number of part-time physician faculty	1.5
Average percent female full-time physician faculty	16.5%
Average ratio of full-time physician faculty to resident/fellow	1.1

Table 2. Data for Gastroenterology Programs Listed in FREIDA

Number of programs providing data	69

Work Schedule (Program Year 1)

Average hours on duty per week	51.0
Average maximum consecutive hours on duty	15.1
Average days off duty per week	1.6
Moonlighting allowed within institution	66.7%
Night float system	1.4%
Offers awareness and management of fatigue in residents/fellows	94.2%

Educational Setting (Program Year 1)

Average hours/week of regularly scheduled lectures/conferences	5.2
Average percent of training in hospital outpatient clinics	23.8%
Average percent of training in nonhospital ambulatory care community settings	17.4%

Educational Benefits

Curriculum on management of tobacco dependence	10.1%
Program to assess/enhance medical professionalism	75.4%
Debt management/financial counseling	49.3%
Formal program to develop teaching skills	91.3%
Formal mentoring program	66.7%
Formal program to foster interdisciplinary teamwork	26.1%
Continuous quality improvement training	88.4%
International experience	7.2%
Resident/fellow retreats	37.7%
Off-campus electives	60.9%
Hospice/home care experience	8.7%
Cultural competence awareness	68.1%
Instruction in medical Spanish or other non-English language	18.8%
Alternative/complementary medicine curriculum	29.0%
Training in identifying and reporting of domestic violence/abuse	31.9%
MPH/MBA or PhD training	43.5%
Research rotation	95.7%

Educational Features

Offers additional training or educational experience beyond accredited length	23.0%
Offers a primary care track	8.7%
Offers a rural track	2.9%
Offers a women's health track	1.4%
Offers a hospitalist track	0.0%
Offers a research track/nonaccredited fellowship	17.4%
Offers an other track	8.7%

Resident Evaluation

Yearly specialty in-service examination required	71.1%
Patient surveys	49.3%
Portfolio system	42.0%
360 degree evaluations	88.4%
Objective structured clinical examinations (OSCE)	14.5%

Program Evaluation

Program graduation rates	85.5%
Board certification rates	95.7%
In-training examinations	85.5%
Performance-based assessments	42.0%

Employment Policies and Benefits

Part-time/shared positions	0.0%
On-site child care	40.6%
Subsidized child care	8.7%
Allowance/stipend for professional expenses	92.8%

Leave for educational meetings/conferences	87.7%
Moving allowance	0.0%
Housing stipend	7.2%
On-call meal allowance	56.5%
Free parking	65.2%
PDAs	10.1%
Placement assistance upon completion of program	15.9%
Cross coverage in case of illness/disability	85.5%

Compensation and Leave (Graduate Year 1)

Average resident/fellow compensation	$51,052
Average number weeks of vacation	5.3
Sick days (paid)	24.9
Maximum number of paid days for family/medical leave	38
Maximum number of unpaid days for family/medical leave	58

Major Medical Benefits

Major medical insurance for residents	100.0%
Major medical insurance for dependents	95.7%
Outpatient mental health insurance	97.1%
Inpatient mental health insurance	97.1%
Group life insurance	88.4%
Dental insurance	91.3%
Disability insurance	91.3%
Disability insurance for occupationally acquired HIV	76.8%
Medical insurance coverage begins when starting program	95.7%

Specialty Data

For more information

American College of Gastroenterology
PO Box 342260
Bethesda, MD 20827-2260
301 263-9000
www.acg.gi.org

American Gastroenterological Association
4930 Del Ray Avenue
Bethesda, MD 20814
301 654-2055
301 654-5920 Fax
www.gastro.org

American Society for Gastrointestinal Endoscopy
1520 Kensington Road, Suite 202
Oak Brook, IL 60523
630 573-0600
630 573-0691 Fax
www.asge.org

Society of American Gastrointestinal Endoscopic Surgeons
11300 West Olympic Boulevard, Suite 600
Los Angeles, CA 90064
310 437-0544
301 437-0585 Fax
E-mail: sagesweb@sages.org
www.sages.org

Geriatric Medicine

Professional Description

An internist who has special knowledge of the aging process and special skills in the diagnostic, therapeutic, preventive, and rehabilitative aspects of illness in the elderly. This specialist cares for geriatric patients in the patient's home, the office, long-term care settings such as nursing homes, and the hospital.

Prerequisites; Length of Training

Completion of a 3-year ACGME-accredited residency program in internal medicine is required; ACGME-accredited programs in geriatric medicine are 1 year.

Data

Unless otherwise noted, all data are for 2008.

Table 1. Geriatric Medicine Programs

Number of accredited programs	105

Program Data

length of accredited training	1
Minimum number of prior years of GME required	3
Offers graduate year 1 positions, available immediately upon medical school completion	No
Average number of interviews for program year 1 positions	11.4
Percent new program directors, 2007-2008 academic year (source: ACGME)	8.8%

Residents/Fellows

Total number of active residents/fellows	244
Average number of residents/fellows per program	2.3
Average percent female	56.6%
Average percent international medical graduate (IMG)	67.2%

Program Faculty

Average number of full-time physician faculty	10.5
Average number of part-time physician faculty	4.2
Average percent female full-time physician faculty	44.6%
Average ratio of full-time physician faculty to resident/fellow	2.0

Table 2. Data for Geriatric Medicine Programs Listed in FREIDA

Number of programs providing data	62

Work Schedule (Program Year 1)

Average hours on duty per week	44.1
Average maximum consecutive hours on duty	13.3
Average days off duty per week	1.8
Moonlighting allowed within institution	77.4%
Night float system	6.5%
Offers awareness and management of fatigue in residents/fellows	90.3%

Educational Setting (Program Year 1)

Average hours/week of regularly scheduled lectures/conferences	4.1
Average percent of training in hospital outpatient clinics	37.2%
Average percent of training in nonhospital ambulatory care community settings	18.3%

Educational Benefits

Curriculum on management of tobacco dependence	22.6%
Program to assess/enhance medical professionalism	79.0%
Debt management/financial counseling	40.3%
Formal program to develop teaching skills	91.9%
Formal mentoring program	71.0%
Formal program to foster interdisciplinary teamwork	69.4%
Continuous quality improvement training	90.3%
International experience	8.1%
Resident/fellow retreats	32.3%
Off-campus electives	66.1%
Hospice/home care experience	98.4%
Cultural competence awareness	83.9%
Instruction in medical Spanish or other non-English language	17.7%
Alternative/complementary medicine curriculum	25.8%
Training in identifying and reporting of domestic violence/abuse	69.4%
MPH/MBA or PhD training	46.8%
Research rotation	27.4%

Educational Features

Offers additional training or educational experience beyond accredited length	55.0%
Offers a primary care track	32.3%
Offers a rural track	1.6%
Offers a women's health track	4.8%
Offers a hospitalist track	4.8%
Offers a research track/nonaccredited fellowship	45.2%
Offers an other track	24.2%

Resident Evaluation

Yearly specialty in-service examination required	25.4%
Patient surveys	59.7%
Portfolio system	56.5%
360 degree evaluations	88.7%
Objective structured clinical examinations (OSCE)	30.6%

Program Evaluation

Program graduation rates	88.7%
Board certification rates	98.4%
In-training examinations	30.6%
Performance-based assessments	46.8%

Employment Policies and Benefits

Part-time/shared positions	4.8%
On-site child care	41.9%
Subsidized child care	4.8%
Allowance/stipend for professional expenses	87.1%
Leave for educational meetings/conferences	87.6%
Moving allowance	4.8%
Housing stipend	8.1%
On-call meal allowance	35.5%
Free parking	61.3%
PDAs	11.3%
Placement assistance upon completion of program	32.3%
Cross coverage in case of illness/disability	87.1%

Compensation and Leave (Graduate Year 1)

Average resident/fellow compensation	$51,889
Average number weeks of vacation	3.4
Sick days (paid)	19.6
Maximum number of paid days for family/medical leave	38
Maximum number of unpaid days for family/medical leave	61

Major Medical Benefits

Major medical insurance for residents	98.4%
Major medical insurance for dependents	95.2%
Outpatient mental health insurance	91.9%
Inpatient mental health insurance	91.9%
Group life insurance	88.7%
Dental insurance	80.6%
Disability insurance	93.5%
Disability insurance for occupationally acquired HIV	75.8%
Medical insurance coverage begins when starting program	82.3%

For more information

American Geriatrics Society
Empire State Building
350 Fifth Avenue, Suite 801
New York, NY 10118
212 308-1414
212 832-8646 Fax
E-mail: info@americangeriatrics.org
www.americangeriatrics.org

Hematology

Professional Description

An internist with additional training who specializes in blood diseases. This specialist treats diseases such as anemia, hemophilia, and sickle cell disease as well as cancers such as leukemia, lymphoma, and multiple myeloma.

Source: American Society of Hematology

Prerequisites; Length of Training

Completion of a 3-year ACGME-accredited residency program in internal medicine is required; ACGME-accredited programs in hematology are 2 years.

Data

Unless otherwise noted, all data are for 2008.

Table 1. Hematology Programs

Number of accredited programs	8

Program Data

length of accredited training	2
Minimum number of prior years of GME required	3
Offers graduate year 1 positions, available immediately upon medical school completion	No
Average number of interviews for program year 1 positions	11.2
Percent new program directors, 2007-2008 academic year (source: ACGME)	11.1%

Residents/Fellows

Total number of active residents/fellows	42
Average number of residents/fellows per program	5.3
Average percent female	35.7%
Average percent international medical graduate (IMG)	38.1%

Program Faculty

Average number of full-time physician faculty	10.0
Average number of part-time physician faculty	1.0
Average percent female full-time physician faculty	31.1%
Average ratio of full-time physician faculty to resident/fellow	1.1

Table 2. Data for Hematology Programs Listed in FREIDA

Number of programs providing data	3

Work Schedule (Program Year 1)

Average hours on duty per week	51.2
Average maximum consecutive hours on duty	16.0
Average days off duty per week	1.3
Moonlighting allowed within institution	100.0%
Night float system	0.0%
Offers awareness and management of fatigue in residents/fellows	66.7%

Educational Setting (Program Year 1)

Average hours/week of regularly scheduled lectures/conferences	4.7
Average percent of training in hospital outpatient clinics	20.0%
Average percent of training in nonhospital ambulatory care community settings	

Educational Benefits

Curriculum on management of tobacco dependence	0.0%
Program to assess/enhance medical professionalism	33.3%
Debt management/financial counseling	33.3%
Formal program to develop teaching skills	33.3%
Formal mentoring program	33.3%
Formal program to foster interdisciplinary teamwork	0.0%
Continuous quality improvement training	33.3%
International experience	0.0%
Resident/fellow retreats	0.0%
Off-campus electives	0.0%

Hospice/home care experience	0.0%
Cultural competence awareness	33.3%
Instruction in medical Spanish or other non-English language	0.0%
Alternative/complementary medicine curriculum	0.0%
Training in identifying and reporting of domestic violence/abuse	0.0%
MPH/MBA or PhD training	33.3%
Research rotation	66.7%

Educational Features

Offers additional training or educational experience beyond accredited length	76.2%
Offers a primary care track	0.0%
Offers a rural track	0.0%
Offers a women's health track	0.0%
Offers a hospitalist track	0.0%
Offers a research track/nonaccredited fellowship	100.0%
Offers an other track	0.0%

Resident Evaluation

Yearly specialty in-service examination required	21.7%
Patient surveys	33.3%
Portfolio system	33.3%
360 degree evaluations	33.3%
Objective structured clinical examinations (OSCE)	33.3%

Program Evaluation

Program graduation rates	66.7%
Board certification rates	100.0%
In-training examinations	0.0%
Performance-based assessments	33.3%

Employment Policies and Benefits

Part-time/shared positions	0.0%
On-site child care	66.7%
Subsidized child care	0.0%
Allowance/stipend for professional expenses	66.7%
Leave for educational meetings/conferences	53.2%
Moving allowance	0.0%
Housing stipend	0.0%
On-call meal allowance	66.7%
Free parking	33.3%
PDAs	0.0%
Placement assistance upon completion of program	0.0%
Cross coverage in case of illness/disability	66.7%

Compensation and Leave (Graduate Year 1)

Average resident/fellow compensation	$48,237
Average number weeks of vacation	3.7
Sick days (paid)	15.0
Maximum number of paid days for family/medical leave	36
Maximum number of unpaid days for family/medical leave	66

Major Medical Benefits

Major medical insurance for residents	100.0%
Major medical insurance for dependents	100.0%
Outpatient mental health insurance	100.0%
Inpatient mental health insurance	100.0%
Group life insurance	33.3%
Dental insurance	66.7%
Disability insurance	100.0%
Disability insurance for occupationally acquired HIV	100.0%
Medical insurance coverage begins when starting program	100.0%

Specialty Data

For more information

American Society of Hematology
1900 M Street NW, Suite 200
Washington, DC 20036
202 776-0544
202 776-0545 Fax
www.hematology.org

Hematology and Oncology

Professional Description

See descriptions of each component subspecialty elsewhere in this section.

Prerequisites; Length of Training

Completion of a 3-year ACGME-accredited residency program in internal medicine is required; ACGME-accredited programs in hematology and oncology are 2 years.

Data

Unless otherwise noted, all data are for 2008.

Table 1. Hematology and Oncology Programs

Number of accredited programs	128
Program Data	
length of accredited training	3
Minimum number of prior years of GME required	3
Offers graduate year 1 positions, available immediately upon medical school completion	No
Average number of interviews for program year 1 positions	26.8
Percent new program directors, 2007-2008 academic year (source: ACGME)	5.5%
Residents/Fellows	
Total number of active residents/fellows	1,366
Average number of residents/fellows per program	10.7
Average percent female	43.0%
Average percent international medical graduate (IMG)	38.9%
Program Faculty	
Average number of full-time physician faculty	23.0
Average number of part-time physician faculty	1.4
Average percent female full-time physician faculty	26.3%
Average ratio of full-time physician faculty to resident/fellow	1.6

Table 2. Data for Hematology and Oncology Programs Listed in FREIDA

Number of programs providing data	69
Work Schedule (Program Year 1)	
Average hours on duty per week	51.4
Average maximum consecutive hours on duty	15.9
Average days off duty per week	1.5
Moonlighting allowed within institution	79.7%
Night float system	10.1%
Offers awareness and management of fatigue in residents/fellows	87.0%
Educational Setting (Program Year 1)	
Average hours/week of regularly scheduled lectures/conferences	5.5
Average percent of training in hospital outpatient clinics	33.4%
Average percent of training in nonhospital ambulatory care community settings	21.9%
Educational Benefits	
Curriculum on management of tobacco dependence	10.1%
Program to assess/enhance medical professionalism	82.6%
Debt management/financial counseling	42.0%
Formal program to develop teaching skills	81.2%

Formal mentoring program	75.4%
Formal program to foster interdisciplinary teamwork	39.1%
Continuous quality improvement training	89.9%
International experience	15.9%
Resident/fellow retreats	47.8%
Off-campus electives	79.7%
Hospice/home care experience	75.4%
Cultural competence awareness	76.8%
Instruction in medical Spanish or other non-English language	21.7%
Alternative/complementary medicine curriculum	31.9%
Training in identifying and reporting of domestic violence/abuse	30.4%
MPH/MBA or PhD training	42.0%
Research rotation	92.8%
Educational Features	
Offers additional training or educational experience beyond accredited length	26.9%
Offers a primary care track	5.8%
Offers a rural track	0.0%
Offers a women's health track	1.4%
Offers a hospitalist track	0.0%
Offers a research track/nonaccredited fellowship	24.6%
Offers an other track	13.0%
Resident Evaluation	
Yearly specialty in-service examination required	63.4%
Patient surveys	55.1%
Portfolio system	47.8%
360 degree evaluations	89.9%
Objective structured clinical examinations (OSCE)	10.1%
Program Evaluation	
Program graduation rates	85.5%
Board certification rates	97.1%
In-training examinations	75.4%
Performance-based assessments	34.8%
Employment Policies and Benefits	
Part-time/shared positions	2.9%
On-site child care	47.8%
Subsidized child care	13.0%
Allowance/stipend for professional expenses	91.3%
Leave for educational meetings/conferences	90.3%
Moving allowance	0.0%
Housing stipend	4.3%
On-call meal allowance	55.1%
Free parking	55.1%
PDAs	27.5%
Placement assistance upon completion of program	30.4%
Cross coverage in case of illness/disability	82.6%
Compensation and Leave (Graduate Year 1)	
Average resident/fellow compensation	$52,198
Average number weeks of vacation	4.9
Sick days (paid)	24.9
Maximum number of paid days for family/medical leave	38
Maximum number of unpaid days for family/medical leave	51
Major Medical Benefits	
Major medical insurance for residents	98.6%
Major medical insurance for dependents	89.9%
Outpatient mental health insurance	92.8%
Inpatient mental health insurance	89.9%
Group life insurance	84.1%
Dental insurance	84.1%
Disability insurance	82.6%
Disability insurance for occupationally acquired HIV	60.9%
Medical insurance coverage begins when starting program	88.4%

For more information

American Society of Hematology
1900 M Street NW, Suite 200
Washington, DC 20036
202 776-0544
202 776-0545 Fax
www.hematology.org

American Society of Clinical Oncology
2318 Mill Road, Suite 800
Alexandria, VA 22314
571 483-1300
571 366-9530 Fax
E-mail: asco@asco.org
www.asco.org

Hospice and Palliative Medicine

See page 57.

Infectious Disease

Professional Description

An internist who deals with infectious diseases of all types and in all organ systems. Conditions requiring selective use of antibiotics call for this special skill. This physician often diagnoses and treats AIDS patients and patients who have fevers that have not been explained. Infectious disease specialists may also have expertise in preventive medicine and travel medicine.

Prerequisites; Length of Training

Completion of a 3-year ACGME-accredited residency program in internal medicine is required; ACGME-accredited programs in infectious disease are 2 years.

Data

Unless otherwise noted, all data are for 2008.

Table 1. Infectious Disease Programs

Number of accredited programs	143

Program Data

length of accredited training	2
Minimum number of prior years of GME required	3
Offers graduate year 1 positions, available immediately upon medical school completion	No
Average number of interviews for program year 1 positions	15.7
Percent new program directors, 2007-2008 academic year (source: ACGME)	6.3%

Residents/Fellows

Total number of active residents/fellows	714
Average number of residents/fellows per program	5.0
Average percent female	49.0%
Average percent international medical graduate (IMG)	42.9%

Program Faculty

Average number of full-time physician faculty	13.0
Average number of part-time physician faculty	1.4
Average percent female full-time physician faculty	33.2%
Average ratio of full-time physician faculty to resident/fellow	1.7

Table 2. Data for Infectious Disease Programs Listed in FREIDA

Number of programs providing data	82

Work Schedule (Program Year 1)

Average hours on duty per week	51.6
Average maximum consecutive hours on duty	14.4
Average days off duty per week	1.4
Moonlighting allowed within institution	81.7%
Night float system	2.4%
Offers awareness and management of fatigue in residents/fellows	87.8%

Educational Setting (Program Year 1)

Average hours/week of regularly scheduled lectures/conferences	4.3
Average percent of training in hospital outpatient clinics	16.3%
Average percent of training in nonhospital ambulatory care community settings	7.4%

Educational Benefits

Curriculum on management of tobacco dependence	13.4%
Program to assess/enhance medical professionalism	87.8%
Debt management/financial counseling	45.1%
Formal program to develop teaching skills	80.5%
Formal mentoring program	74.4%
Formal program to foster interdisciplinary teamwork	28.0%
Continuous quality improvement training	92.7%
International experience	54.9%
Resident/fellow retreats	29.3%
Off-campus electives	78.0%
Hospice/home care experience	28.0%
Cultural competence awareness	76.8%
Instruction in medical Spanish or other non-English language	19.5%
Alternative/complementary medicine curriculum	14.6%
Training in identifying and reporting of domestic violence/abuse	36.6%
MPH/MBA or PhD training	50.0%
Research rotation	96.3%

Educational Features

Offers additional training or educational experience beyond accredited length	53.1%
Offers a primary care track	4.9%
Offers a rural track	3.7%
Offers a women's health track	2.4%
Offers a hospitalist track	1.2%
Offers a research track/nonaccredited fellowship	35.4%
Offers an other track	18.3%

Resident Evaluation

Yearly specialty in-service examination required	72.4%
Patient surveys	46.3%
Portfolio system	41.5%
360 degree evaluations	91.5%
Objective structured clinical examinations (OSCE)	14.6%

Program Evaluation

Program graduation rates	82.9%
Board certification rates	98.8%
In-training examinations	74.4%
Performance-based assessments	26.8%

Employment Policies and Benefits

Part-time/shared positions	9.8%
On-site child care	41.5%
Subsidized child care	4.9%
Allowance/stipend for professional expenses	92.7%
Leave for educational meetings/conferences	88.8%
Moving allowance	1.2%
Housing stipend	2.4%
On-call meal allowance	42.7%
Free parking	59.8%
PDAs	11.0%
Placement assistance upon completion of program	28.0%

Specialty Data

Cross coverage in case of illness/disability	87.8%

Compensation and Leave (Graduate Year 1)

Average resident/fellow compensation	$51,281
Average number weeks of vacation	3.5
Sick days (paid)	21.0
Maximum number of paid days for family/medical leave	41
Maximum number of unpaid days for family/medical leave	70

Major Medical Benefits

Major medical insurance for residents	100.0%
Major medical insurance for dependents	92.7%
Outpatient mental health insurance	89.0%
Inpatient mental health insurance	89.0%
Group life insurance	87.8%
Dental insurance	87.8%
Disability insurance	80.5%
Disability insurance for occupationally acquired HIV	69.5%
Medical insurance coverage begins when starting program	87.8%

For more information

Infectious Diseases Society of America
1300 Wilson Blvd, Suite 300
Alexandria, VA 22209
703 299-0200
703 299-0204 Fax
E-mail: info@idsociety.org
www.idsociety.org

Interventional Cardiology

Professional Description

An area of medicine within the subspecialty of cardiology that uses specialized imaging and other diagnostic techniques to evaluate blood flow and pressure in the coronary arteries and chambers of the heart and uses technical procedures and medications to treat abnormalities that impair the function of the cardiovascular system.

Prerequisites; Length of Training

Completion of a 3-year ACGME-accredited residency program in cardiovascular disease is required; ACGME-accredited programs in interventional cardiology are 1 year.

Data

Unless otherwise noted, all data are for 2008.

Table 1. Interventional Cardiology Programs

Number of accredited programs	132

Program Data

length of accredited training	1
Minimum number of prior years of GME required	6
Offers graduate year 1 positions, available immediately upon medical school completion	No
Average number of interviews for program year 1 positions	8.7
Percent new program directors, 2007-2008 academic year (source: ACGME)	12.3%

Residents/Fellows

Total number of active residents/fellows	235
Average number of residents/fellows per program	1.8
Average percent female	6.4%
Average percent international medical graduate (IMG)	43.4%

Program Faculty

Average number of full-time physician faculty	6.3
Average number of part-time physician faculty	0.5
Average percent female full-time physician faculty	5.8%
Average ratio of full-time physician faculty to resident/fellow	1.6

Table 2. Data for Interventional Cardiology Programs Listed in FREIDA

Number of programs providing data	55

Work Schedule (Program Year 1)

Average hours on duty per week	49.2
Average maximum consecutive hours on duty	16.6
Average days off duty per week	1.6
Moonlighting allowed within institution	65.5%
Night float system	1.8%
Offers awareness and management of fatigue in residents/fellows	85.5%

Educational Setting (Program Year 1)

Average hours/week of regularly scheduled lectures/conferences	4.6
Average percent of training in hospital outpatient clinics	16.4%
Average percent of training in nonhospital ambulatory care community settings	13.1%

Educational Benefits

Curriculum on management of tobacco dependence	14.5%
Program to assess/enhance medical professionalism	80.0%
Debt management/financial counseling	43.6%
Formal program to develop teaching skills	72.7%
Formal mentoring program	61.8%
Formal program to foster interdisciplinary teamwork	18.2%
Continuous quality improvement training	81.8%
International experience	3.6%
Resident/fellow retreats	21.8%
Off-campus electives	29.1%
Hospice/home care experience	3.6%
Cultural competence awareness	67.3%
Instruction in medical Spanish or other non-English language	9.1%
Alternative/complementary medicine curriculum	12.7%
Training in identifying and reporting of domestic violence/abuse	32.7%
MPH/MBA or PhD training	12.7%
Research rotation	32.7%

Educational Features

Offers additional training or educational experience beyond accredited length	21.6%
Offers a primary care track	5.5%
Offers a rural track	0.0%
Offers a women's health track	0.0%
Offers a hospitalist track	0.0%
Offers a research track/nonaccredited fellowship	16.4%
Offers an other track	1.8%

Resident Evaluation

Yearly specialty in-service examination required	19.1%
Patient surveys	38.2%
Portfolio system	27.3%
360 degree evaluations	90.9%
Objective structured clinical examinations (OSCE)	1.8%

Program Evaluation

Program graduation rates	72.7%
Board certification rates	100.0%
In-training examinations	16.4%
Performance-based assessments	30.9%

Employment Policies and Benefits

Part-time/shared positions	0.0%
On-site child care	40.0%
Subsidized child care	5.5%
Allowance/stipend for professional expenses	92.7%

Leave for educational meetings/conferences	88.9%
Moving allowance	1.8%
Housing stipend	3.6%
On-call meal allowance	58.2%
Free parking	61.8%
PDAs	10.9%
Placement assistance upon completion of program	18.2%
Cross coverage in case of illness/disability	87.3%

Compensation and Leave (Graduate Year 1)

Average resident/fellow compensation	$57,064
Average number weeks of vacation	3.5
Sick days (paid)	21.5
Maximum number of paid days for family/medical leave	40
Maximum number of unpaid days for family/medical leave	49

Major Medical Benefits

Major medical insurance for residents	100.0%
Major medical insurance for dependents	96.4%
Outpatient mental health insurance	92.7%
Inpatient mental health insurance	94.5%
Group life insurance	92.7%
Dental insurance	92.7%
Disability insurance	96.4%
Disability insurance for occupationally acquired HIV	78.2%
Medical insurance coverage begins when starting program	90.9%

For more information

American College of Cardiology
Heart House
2400 N Street, NW
Washington, DC 20037
202 375-6000
202 375-7000 Fax
E-mail: resource@acc.org
www.acc.org

Nephrology

Professional Description

An internist who treats disorders of the kidney, high blood pressure, fluid and mineral balance, and dialysis of body wastes when the kidneys do not function. This specialist consults with surgeons about kidney transplantation.

Prerequisites; Length of Training

Completion of a 3-year ACGME-accredited residency program in internal medicine is required; ACGME-accredited programs in nephrology are 2 years.

Data

Unless otherwise noted, all data are for 2008.

Table 1. Nephrology Programs

Number of accredited programs	141

Program Data

length of accredited training	2
Minimum number of prior years of GME required	3
Offers graduate year 1 positions, available immediately upon medical school completion	No
Average number of interviews for program year 1 positions	16.6
Percent new program directors, 2007-2008 academic year (source: ACGME)	11.5%

Residents/Fellows

Total number of active residents/fellows	784
Average number of residents/fellows per program	5.6
Average percent female	34.7%
Average percent international medical graduate (IMG)	52.8%

Program Faculty

Average number of full-time physician faculty	11.0
Average number of part-time physician faculty	1.1
Average percent female full-time physician faculty	22.6%
Average ratio of full-time physician faculty to resident/fellow	1.2

Table 2. Data for Nephrology Programs Listed in FREIDA

Number of programs providing data	69

Work Schedule (Program Year 1)

Average hours on duty per week	53.4
Average maximum consecutive hours on duty	17.2
Average days off duty per week	1.5
Moonlighting allowed within institution	75.4%
Night float system	1.4%
Offers awareness and management of fatigue in residents/fellows	91.3%

Educational Setting (Program Year 1)

Average hours/week of regularly scheduled lectures/conferences	4.5
Average percent of training in hospital outpatient clinics	22.6%
Average percent of training in nonhospital ambulatory care community settings	13.6%

Educational Benefits

Curriculum on management of tobacco dependence	14.5%
Program to assess/enhance medical professionalism	75.4%
Debt management/financial counseling	43.5%
Formal program to develop teaching skills	78.3%
Formal mentoring program	63.8%
Formal program to foster interdisciplinary teamwork	37.7%
Continuous quality improvement training	92.8%
International experience	8.7%
Resident/fellow retreats	30.4%
Off-campus electives	49.3%
Hospice/home care experience	17.4%
Cultural competence awareness	76.8%
Instruction in medical Spanish or other non-English language	21.7%
Alternative/complementary medicine curriculum	20.3%
Training in identifying and reporting of domestic violence/abuse	44.9%
MPH/MBA or PhD training	30.4%
Research rotation	88.4%

Educational Features

Offers additional training or educational experience beyond accredited length	54.6%
Offers a primary care track	1.4%
Offers a rural track	0.0%
Offers a women's health track	1.4%
Offers a hospitalist track	0.0%
Offers a research track/nonaccredited fellowship	36.2%
Offers an other track	15.9%

Resident Evaluation

Yearly specialty in-service examination required	41.6%
Patient surveys	49.3%
Portfolio system	59.4%
360 degree evaluations	91.3%
Objective structured clinical examinations (OSCE)	14.5%

Program Evaluation

Program graduation rates	82.6%
Board certification rates	100.0%
In-training examinations	46.4%
Performance-based assessments	23.2%

Employment Policies and Benefits

Part-time/shared positions	1.4%
On-site child care	40.6%
Subsidized child care	4.3%
Allowance/stipend for professional expenses	92.8%
Leave for educational meetings/conferences	86.4%
Moving allowance	0.0%
Housing stipend	5.8%
On-call meal allowance	50.7%
Free parking	58.0%
PDAs	14.5%
Placement assistance upon completion of program	37.7%
Cross coverage in case of illness/disability	84.1%

Compensation and Leave (Graduate Year 1)

Average resident/fellow compensation	$51,315
Average number weeks of vacation	4.3
Sick days (paid)	22.3
Maximum number of paid days for family/medical leave	39
Maximum number of unpaid days for family/medical leave	54

Major Medical Benefits

Major medical insurance for residents	100.0%
Major medical insurance for dependents	92.8%
Outpatient mental health insurance	88.4%
Inpatient mental health insurance	88.4%
Group life insurance	84.1%
Dental insurance	82.6%
Disability insurance	88.4%
Disability insurance for occupationally acquired HIV	66.7%
Medical insurance coverage begins when starting program	85.5%

For more information

American Society of Nephrology
1725 I Street, NW, Suite 510
Washington, DC 20006
202 659-0599
202 659-0709 Fax
E-mail: email@asn-online.org
www.asn-online.org

Oncology

Professional Description

An internist who specializes in the diagnosis and treatment of all types of cancer and other benign and malignant tumors. This specialist decides on and administers therapy for these malignancies as well as consults with surgeons and radiotherapists on other treatments for cancer.

Prerequisites; Length of Training

Completion of a 3-year ACGME-accredited residency program in internal medicine is required; ACGME-accredited programs in oncology are 2 years.

Data

Unless otherwise noted, all data are for 2008.

Table 1. Oncology Programs

Number of accredited programs	17

Program Data

length of accredited training	2
Minimum number of prior years of GME required	3

Offers graduate year 1 positions, available immediately upon medical school completion	No
Average number of interviews for program year 1 positions	16.3
Percent new program directors, 2007-2008 academic year (source: ACGME)	11.8%

Residents/Fellows

Total number of active residents/fellows	115
Average number of residents/fellows per program	6.8
Average percent female	36.5%
Average percent international medical graduate (IMG)	53.9%

Program Faculty

Average number of full-time physician faculty	16.8
Average number of part-time physician faculty	2.0
Average percent female full-time physician faculty	23.4%
Average ratio of full-time physician faculty to resident/fellow	1.4

Table 2. Data for Oncology Programs Listed in FREIDA

Number of programs providing data	6

Work Schedule (Program Year 1)

Average hours on duty per week	50.7
Average maximum consecutive hours on duty	16.5
Average days off duty per week	1.5
Moonlighting allowed within institution	83.3%
Night float system	0.0%
Offers awareness and management of fatigue in residents/fellows	100.0%

Educational Setting (Program Year 1)

Average hours/week of regularly scheduled lectures/conferences	5.5
Average percent of training in hospital outpatient clinics	45.0%
Average percent of training in nonhospital ambulatory care community settings	23.3%

Educational Benefits

Curriculum on management of tobacco dependence	0.0%
Program to assess/enhance medical professionalism	50.0%
Debt management/financial counseling	50.0%
Formal program to develop teaching skills	83.3%
Formal mentoring program	50.0%
Formal program to foster interdisciplinary teamwork	16.7%
Continuous quality improvement training	50.0%
International experience	0.0%
Resident/fellow retreats	0.0%
Off-campus electives	83.3%
Hospice/home care experience	33.3%
Cultural competence awareness	50.0%
Instruction in medical Spanish or other non-English language	16.7%
Alternative/complementary medicine curriculum	16.7%
Training in identifying and reporting of domestic violence/abuse	16.7%
MPH/MBA or PhD training	16.7%
Research rotation	66.7%

Educational Features

Offers additional training or educational experience beyond accredited length	46.4%
Offers a primary care track	0.0%
Offers a rural track	0.0%
Offers a women's health track	0.0%
Offers a hospitalist track	0.0%
Offers a research track/nonaccredited fellowship	16.7%
Offers an other track	0.0%

Resident Evaluation

Yearly specialty in-service examination required	25.4%
Patient surveys	50.0%
Portfolio system	50.0%
360 degree evaluations	100.0%

Objective structured clinical examinations (OSCE)	16.7%
Program Evaluation	
Program graduation rates	83.3%
Board certification rates	100.0%
In-training examinations	66.7%
Performance-based assessments	50.0%
Employment Policies and Benefits	
Part-time/shared positions	0.0%
On-site child care	33.3%
Subsidized child care	0.0%
Allowance/stipend for professional expenses	100.0%
Leave for educational meetings/conferences	51.4%
Moving allowance	0.0%
Housing stipend	0.0%
On-call meal allowance	66.7%
Free parking	50.0%
PDAs	16.7%
Placement assistance upon completion of program	16.7%
Cross coverage in case of illness/disability	100.0%
Compensation and Leave (Graduate Year 1)	
Average resident/fellow compensation	$48,319
Average number weeks of vacation	3.3
Sick days (paid)	11.4
Maximum number of paid days for family/medical leave	55
Maximum number of unpaid days for family/medical leave	57
Major Medical Benefits	
Major medical insurance for residents	100.0%
Major medical insurance for dependents	100.0%
Outpatient mental health insurance	83.3%
Inpatient mental health insurance	83.3%
Group life insurance	83.3%
Dental insurance	83.3%
Disability insurance	100.0%
Disability insurance for occupationally acquired HIV	83.3%
Medical insurance coverage begins when starting program	83.3%

For more information

American Society of Clinical Oncology
2318 Mill Road, Suite 800
Alexandria, VA 22314
571 483-1300
571 366-9530 Fax
E-mail: asco@asco.org
www.asco.org

Pulmonary Disease

Professional Description

An internist who treats diseases of the lungs and airways. The pulmonologist diagnoses and treats cancer, pneumonia, pleurisy, asthma, occupational and environmental diseases, bronchitis, sleep disorders, emphysema, and other complex disorders of the lungs.

Prerequisites; Length of Training

Completion of a 3-year ACGME-accredited residency program in internal medicine is required; ACGME-accredited programs in pulmonary disease are 2 years.

Data

Unless otherwise noted, all data are for 2008.

Table 1. Pulmonary Disease Programs

Number of accredited programs	22
Program Data	
length of accredited training	2
Minimum number of prior years of GME required	3
Offers graduate year 1 positions, available immediately upon medical school completion	No
Average number of interviews for program year 1 positions	12.5
Percent new program directors, 2007-2008 academic year (source: ACGME)	12.0%
Residents/Fellows	
Total number of active residents/fellows	72
Average number of residents/fellows per program	3.3
Average percent female	26.4%
Average percent international medical graduate (IMG)	83.3%
Program Faculty	
Average number of full-time physician faculty	5.4
Average number of part-time physician faculty	1.0
Average percent female full-time physician faculty	12.1%
Average ratio of full-time physician faculty to resident/fellow	1.2

Table 2. Data for Pulmonary Disease Programs Listed in FREIDA

Number of programs providing data	8
Work Schedule (Program Year 1)	
Average hours on duty per week	48.5
Average maximum consecutive hours on duty	19.7
Average days off duty per week	1.4
Moonlighting allowed within institution	37.5%
Night float system	0.0%
Offers awareness and management of fatigue in residents/fellows	75.0%
Educational Setting (Program Year 1)	
Average hours/week of regularly scheduled lectures/conferences	5.6
Average percent of training in hospital outpatient clinics	20.0%
Average percent of training in nonhospital ambulatory care community settings	9.5%
Educational Benefits	
Curriculum on management of tobacco dependence	37.5%
Program to assess/enhance medical professionalism	100.0%
Debt management/financial counseling	25.0%
Formal program to develop teaching skills	100.0%
Formal mentoring program	75.0%
Formal program to foster interdisciplinary teamwork	37.5%
Continuous quality improvement training	87.5%
International experience	25.0%
Resident/fellow retreats	25.0%
Off-campus electives	62.5%
Hospice/home care experience	12.5%
Cultural competence awareness	75.0%
Instruction in medical Spanish or other non-English language	25.0%
Alternative/complementary medicine curriculum	37.5%
Training in identifying and reporting of domestic violence/abuse	37.5%
MPH/MBA or PhD training	12.5%
Research rotation	100.0%
Educational Features	
Offers additional training or educational experience beyond accredited length	17.9%
Offers a primary care track	0.0%
Offers a rural track	12.5%
Offers a women's health track	0.0%
Offers a hospitalist track	0.0%

Specialty Data

Offers a research track/nonaccredited fellowship	0.0%
Offers an other track	0.0%
Resident Evaluation	
Yearly specialty in-service examination required	28.4%
Patient surveys	75.0%
Portfolio system	62.5%
360 degree evaluations	100.0%
Objective structured clinical examinations (OSCE)	37.5%
Program Evaluation	
Program graduation rates	100.0%
Board certification rates	100.0%
In-training examinations	75.0%
Performance-based assessments	50.0%
Employment Policies and Benefits	
Part-time/shared positions	0.0%
On-site child care	37.5%
Subsidized child care	12.5%
Allowance/stipend for professional expenses	87.5%
Leave for educational meetings/conferences	56.8%
Moving allowance	0.0%
Housing stipend	12.5%
On-call meal allowance	87.5%
Free parking	62.5%
PDAs	12.5%
Placement assistance upon completion of program	12.5%
Cross coverage in case of illness/disability	100.0%
Compensation and Leave (Graduate Year 1)	
Average resident/fellow compensation	$51,028
Average number weeks of vacation	3.6
Sick days (paid)	27.4
Maximum number of paid days for family/medical leave	35
Maximum number of unpaid days for family/medical leave	90
Major Medical Benefits	
Major medical insurance for residents	100.0%
Major medical insurance for dependents	100.0%
Outpatient mental health insurance	100.0%
Inpatient mental health insurance	100.0%
Group life insurance	100.0%
Dental insurance	87.5%
Disability insurance	100.0%
Disability insurance for occupationally acquired HIV	75.0%
Medical insurance coverage begins when starting program	87.5%

For more information

American College of Chest Physicians
3300 Dundee Road
Northbrook, IL 60062-2348
847 498-1400
www.chestnet.org

Pulmonary Disease and Critical Care Medicine

Professional Description

See descriptions of each component subspecialty elsewhere in this section.

Prerequisites; Length of Training

Completion of a 3-year ACGME-accredited residency program in internal medicine is required; ACGME-accredited programs in pulmonary disease and critical care medicine are 3 years.

Data

Unless otherwise noted, all data are for 2008.

Table 1. Pulmonary Disease and Critical Care Medicine Programs

Number of accredited programs	133
Program Data	
length of accredited training	3
Minimum number of prior years of GME required	3
Offers graduate year 1 positions, available immediately upon medical school completion	No
Average number of interviews for program year 1 positions	25.2
Percent new program directors, 2007-2008 academic year (source: ACGME)	15.4%
Residents/Fellows	
Total number of active residents/fellows	1,185
Average number of residents/fellows per program	8.9
Average percent female	29.2%
Average percent international medical graduate (IMG)	42.7%
Program Faculty	
Average number of full-time physician faculty	16.7
Average number of part-time physician faculty	1.2
Average percent female full-time physician faculty	21.1%
Average ratio of full-time physician faculty to resident/fellow	1.3

Table 2. Data for Pulmonary Disease and Critical Care Medicine Programs Listed in FREIDA

Number of programs providing data	73
Work Schedule (Program Year 1)	
Average hours on duty per week	53.7
Average maximum consecutive hours on duty	20.7
Average days off duty per week	1.5
Moonlighting allowed within institution	82.2%
Night float system	15.1%
Offers awareness and management of fatigue in residents/fellows	97.3%
Educational Setting (Program Year 1)	
Average hours/week of regularly scheduled lectures/conferences	4.7
Average percent of training in hospital outpatient clinics	16.5%
Average percent of training in nonhospital ambulatory care community settings	6.7%
Educational Benefits	
Curriculum on management of tobacco dependence	38.4%
Program to assess/enhance medical professionalism	83.6%
Debt management/financial counseling	38.4%
Formal program to develop teaching skills	86.3%
Formal mentoring program	75.3%
Formal program to foster interdisciplinary teamwork	34.2%
Continuous quality improvement training	94.5%
International experience	16.4%
Resident/fellow retreats	30.1%
Off-campus electives	80.8%
Hospice/home care experience	30.1%
Cultural competence awareness	83.6%
Instruction in medical Spanish or other non-English language	23.3%
Alternative/complementary medicine curriculum	26.0%
Training in identifying and reporting of domestic violence/abuse	34.2%
MPH/MBA or PhD training	46.6%
Research rotation	94.5%

Educational Features

Offers additional training or educational experience beyond accredited length	45.5%
Offers a primary care track	1.4%
Offers a rural track	0.0%
Offers a women's health track	1.4%
Offers a hospitalist track	0.0%
Offers a research track/nonaccredited fellowship	28.8%
Offers an other track	30.1%

Resident Evaluation

Yearly specialty in-service examination required	77.8%
Patient surveys	58.9%
Portfolio system	60.3%
360 degree evaluations	93.2%
Objective structured clinical examinations (OSCE)	12.3%

Program Evaluation

Program graduation rates	89.0%
Board certification rates	98.6%
In-training examinations	82.2%
Performance-based assessments	41.1%

Employment Policies and Benefits

Part-time/shared positions	8.2%
On-site child care	39.7%
Subsidized child care	9.6%
Allowance/stipend for professional expenses	94.5%
Leave for educational meetings/conferences	88.3%
Moving allowance	1.4%
Housing stipend	4.1%
On-call meal allowance	69.9%
Free parking	56.2%
PDAs	16.4%
Placement assistance upon completion of program	27.4%
Cross coverage in case of illness/disability	90.4%

Compensation and Leave (Graduate Year 1)

Average resident/fellow compensation	$51,269
Average number weeks of vacation	3.5
Sick days (paid)	20.8
Maximum number of paid days for family/medical leave	44
Maximum number of unpaid days for family/medical leave	57

Major Medical Benefits

Major medical insurance for residents	97.3%
Major medical insurance for dependents	94.5%
Outpatient mental health insurance	89.0%
Inpatient mental health insurance	89.0%
Group life insurance	90.4%
Dental insurance	82.2%
Disability insurance	90.4%
Disability insurance for occupationally acquired HIV	79.5%
Medical insurance coverage begins when starting program	91.8%

For more information

American College of Chest Physicians
3300 Dundee Road
Northbrook, IL 60062-2348
847 498-1400
www.chestnet.org

Society of Critical Care Medicine
500 Midway Drive
Mount Prospect, IL 60056
847 827-6869
847 827-6886 Fax
E-mail: info@sccm.org
www.sccm.org

Rheumatology

Professional Description

An internist who treats diseases of joints, muscle, bones, and tendons. This specialist diagnoses and treats arthritis, back pain, muscle strains, common athletic injuries, and "collagen" diseases.

Prerequisites; Length of Training

Completion of a 3-year ACGME-accredited residency program in internal medicine is required; ACGME-accredited programs in rheumatology are 2 years.

Data

Unless otherwise noted, all data are for 2008.

Table 1. Rheumatology Programs

Number of accredited programs	109

Program Data

length of accredited training	2
Minimum number of prior years of GME required	3
Offers graduate year 1 positions, available immediately upon medical school completion	No
Average number of interviews for program year 1 positions	10.9
Percent new program directors, 2007-2008 academic year (source: ACGME)	11.0%

Residents/Fellows

Total number of active residents/fellows	405
Average number of residents/fellows per program	3.7
Average percent female	59.8%
Average percent international medical graduate (IMG)	36.0%

Program Faculty

Average number of full-time physician faculty	7.9
Average number of part-time physician faculty	1.4
Average percent female full-time physician faculty	33.7%
Average ratio of full-time physician faculty to resident/fellow	1.4

Table 2. Data for Rheumatology Programs Listed in FREIDA

Number of programs providing data	54

Work Schedule (Program Year 1)

Average hours on duty per week	45.8
Average maximum consecutive hours on duty	13.6
Average days off duty per week	1.4
Moonlighting allowed within institution	74.1%
Night float system	0.0%
Offers awareness and management of fatigue in residents/fellows	94.4%

Educational Setting (Program Year 1)

Average hours/week of regularly scheduled lectures/conferences	4.5
Average percent of training in hospital outpatient clinics	52.3%
Average percent of training in nonhospital ambulatory care community settings	14.4%

Educational Benefits

Curriculum on management of tobacco dependence	5.6%
Program to assess/enhance medical professionalism	77.8%
Debt management/financial counseling	40.7%

Formal program to develop teaching skills	85.2%
Formal mentoring program	61.1%
Formal program to foster interdisciplinary teamwork	22.2%
Continuous quality improvement training	87.0%
International experience	9.3%
Resident/fellow retreats	27.8%
Off-campus electives	66.7%
Hospice/home care experience	3.7%
Cultural competence awareness	75.9%
Instruction in medical Spanish or other non-English language	20.4%
Alternative/complementary medicine curriculum	29.6%
Training in identifying and reporting of domestic violence/abuse	25.9%
MPH/MBA or PhD training	50.0%
Research rotation	87.0%

Educational Features

Offers additional training or educational experience beyond accredited length	50.9%
Offers a primary care track	0.0%
Offers a rural track	1.9%
Offers a women's health track	0.0%
Offers a hospitalist track	0.0%
Offers a research track/nonaccredited fellowship	29.6%
Offers an other track	14.8%

Resident Evaluation

Yearly specialty in-service examination required	89.8%
Patient surveys	68.5%
Portfolio system	68.5%
360 degree evaluations	90.7%
Objective structured clinical examinations (OSCE)	29.6%

Program Evaluation

Program graduation rates	87.0%
Board certification rates	100.0%
In-training examinations	87.0%
Performance-based assessments	38.9%

Employment Policies and Benefits

Part-time/shared positions	5.6%
On-site child care	38.9%
Subsidized child care	7.4%
Allowance/stipend for professional expenses	96.3%
Leave for educational meetings/conferences	85.2%
Moving allowance	1.9%
Housing stipend	11.1%
On-call meal allowance	37.0%
Free parking	51.9%
PDAs	9.3%
Placement assistance upon completion of program	29.6%
Cross coverage in case of illness/disability	83.3%

Compensation and Leave (Graduate Year 1)

Average resident/fellow compensation	$50,696
Average number weeks of vacation	5.3
Sick days (paid)	21.8
Maximum number of paid days for family/medical leave	34
Maximum number of unpaid days for family/medical leave	70

Major Medical Benefits

Major medical insurance for residents	100.0%
Major medical insurance for dependents	94.4%
Outpatient mental health insurance	96.3%
Inpatient mental health insurance	94.4%
Group life insurance	85.2%
Dental insurance	92.6%
Disability insurance	96.3%
Disability insurance for occupationally acquired HIV	74.1%

Medical insurance coverage begins when starting program	87.0%

For more information

American College of Rheumatology
1800 Century Place, Suite 250
Atlanta, GA 30345-4300
404 633-3777
404 633-1870 Fax
www.rheumatology.org

Sleep Medicine

See page 155.

Sports Medicine

Professional Description

An internist trained to be responsible for continuous care in the field of sports medicine, not only for the enhancement of health and fitness, but also for the prevention of injury and illness. A sports medicine physician must have knowledge and experience in the promotion of wellness and the prevention of injury. Knowledge about special areas of medicine such as exercise physiology, biomechanics, nutrition, psychology, physical rehabilitation, epidemiology, physical evaluation, injuries (treatment and prevention and referral practice), and the role of exercise in promoting a healthy lifestyle are essential to the practice of sports medicine. The sports medicine physician requires special education to provide the knowledge to improve the health care of the individual engaged in physical exercise (sports) whether as an individual or in team participation.

Prerequisites; Length of Training

As of June 2006, programs in sports medicine as a subspecialty of internal medicine were no longer accredited by the ACGME.

For more information

American College of Sports Medicine
401 West Michigan Street
Indianapolis, IN 46202-3233
317 637-9200
317 634-7817 Fax
www.acsm.org

Transplant Hepatology

Professional Description

An internist with special knowledge and the skill required of a gastroenterologist to care for patients prior to and following hepatic transplantation that spans all phases of liver transplantation. Selection of appropriate recipients requires assessment by a team having experience in evaluating the severity and prognosis of patients with liver disease.

Prerequisites; Length of Training

Completion of a 3-year ACGME-accredited gastroenterology program is required; programs are 1 year.

For more information

American College of Gastroenterology
PO Box 342260
Bethesda, MD 20827-2260
301 263-9000
www.acg.gi.org

American Gastroenterological Association
4930 Del Ray Avenue
Bethesda, MD 20814
301 654-2055
301 654-5920 Fax
www.gastro.org

Internal Medicine/Pediatrics

Description

Internal medicine/pediatrics is a combined specialty program that allows physicians to meet eligibility requirements for dual certification by the American Board of Internal Medicine and American Board of Pediatrics. Internal medicine/pediatrics programs were formerly jointly approved (not accredited) by the two boards, but are now fully accredited through the ACGME (Program Requirements effective June 26, 2006).

Prerequisites; Length of Training

No prerequisites; length of accredited programs is 4 years.

Data

Unless otherwise noted, all data are for 2008.

Table 1. Internal Medicine/Pediatrics Programs

Number of accredited programs	80
Program Data	
length of accredited training	4
Minimum number of prior years of GME required	0
Offers graduate year 1 positions, available immediately upon medical school completion	Yes
Average number of interviews for program year 1 positions	35.5
Percent new program directors, 2007-2008 academic year (source: ACGME)	14.8%
Residents/Fellows	
Total number of active residents/fellows	1,370
Average number of residents/fellows per program	17.1
Average percent female	55.0%
Average percent international medical graduate (IMG)	13.5%
Program Faculty	
Average number of full-time physician faculty	161.9
Average number of part-time physician faculty	23.8
Average percent female full-time physician faculty	29.0%
Average ratio of full-time physician faculty to resident/fellow	8.3

Table 2. Data for Internal Medicine/Pediatrics Programs Listed in FREIDA

Number of programs providing data	66
Work Schedule (Program Year 1)	
Average hours on duty per week	66.5
Average maximum consecutive hours on duty	29.0
Average days off duty per week	1.2
Moonlighting allowed within institution	80.3%
Night float system	90.9%
Offers awareness and management of fatigue in residents/fellows	97.0%
Educational Setting (Program Year 1)	
Average hours/week of regularly scheduled lectures/conferences	7.7
Average percent of training in hospital outpatient clinics	28.2%
Average percent of training in nonhospital ambulatory care community settings	12.6%
Educational Benefits	
Curriculum on management of tobacco dependence	45.5%
Program to assess/enhance medical professionalism	93.9%
Debt management/financial counseling	92.4%
Formal program to develop teaching skills	100.0%
Formal mentoring program	89.4%
Formal program to foster interdisciplinary teamwork	33.3%
Continuous quality improvement training	100.0%
International experience	75.8%
Resident/fellow retreats	95.5%

Specialty Data

Off-campus electives	92.4%
Hospice/home care experience	86.4%
Cultural competence awareness	98.5%
Instruction in medical Spanish or other non-English language	42.4%
Alternative/complementary medicine curriculum	65.2%
Training in identifying and reporting of domestic violence/abuse	92.4%
MPH/MBA or PhD training	31.8%
Research rotation	13.6%

Educational Features

Offers additional training or educational experience beyond accredited length	3.6%
Offers a primary care track	21.2%
Offers a rural track	0.0%
Offers a women's health track	4.5%
Offers a hospitalist track	4.5%
Offers a research track/nonaccredited fellowship	1.5%
Offers an other track	9.1%

Resident Evaluation

Yearly specialty in-service examination required	98.3%
Patient surveys	69.7%
Portfolio system	65.2%
360 degree evaluations	87.9%
Objective structured clinical examinations (OSCE)	51.5%

Program Evaluation

Program graduation rates	95.5%
Board certification rates	100.0%
In-training examinations	98.5%
Performance-based assessments	68.2%

Employment Policies and Benefits

Part-time/shared positions	16.7%
On-site child care	45.5%
Subsidized child care	7.6%
Allowance/stipend for professional expenses	95.5%
Leave for educational meetings/conferences	59.9%
Moving allowance	19.7%
Housing stipend	1.5%
On-call meal allowance	97.0%
Free parking	74.2%
PDAs	43.9%
Placement assistance upon completion of program	40.9%
Cross coverage in case of illness/disability	98.5%

Compensation and Leave (Graduate Year 1)

Average resident/fellow compensation	$45,472
Average number weeks of vacation	3.5
Sick days (paid)	14.9
Maximum number of paid days for family/medical leave	49
Maximum number of unpaid days for family/medical leave	73

Major Medical Benefits

Major medical insurance for residents	100.0%
Major medical insurance for dependents	97.0%
Outpatient mental health insurance	97.0%
Inpatient mental health insurance	97.0%
Group life insurance	97.0%
Dental insurance	84.8%
Disability insurance	95.5%
Disability insurance for occupationally acquired HIV	81.8%
Medical insurance coverage begins when starting program	86.4%

Medical Genetics

Professional Description

A specialist trained in diagnostic and therapeutic procedures for patients with genetically linked diseases. This specialist uses modern cytogenetic, radiologic, and biochemical testing to assist in specialized genetic counseling, implements needed therapeutic interventions, and provides prevention through prenatal diagnosis.

A medical geneticist plans and coordinates large-scale screening programs for inborn errors of metabolism, hemoglobinopathies, chromosome abnormalities, and neural tube defects.

Prerequisites; Length of Training

No prerequisites are required when entering a 4-year program; 2 years of ACGME-accredited GME are required when entering a 2-year program. length of accredited programs is 2 years or 4 years.

Subspecialties

Subspecialty programs accredited by the ACGME

- Molecular genetic pathology
- Medical biochemical genetics

Note: Molecular genetic pathology programs are jointly accredited by the Residency Review Committees for Medical Genetics and Pathology.

American Board of Medical Genetics specialty certificates

- Clinical biochemical genetics
- Clinical cytogenetics
- Clinical genetics
- Clinical molecular genetics
- Molecular genetic pathology (subspecialty)

Note: Molecular genetic pathology certification is jointly offered by the American Board of Medical Genetics and American Board of Pathology.

Data

Unless otherwise noted, all data are for 2008.

Table 1. Medical Genetics Programs

Number of accredited programs	49
Program Data	
length of accredited training	2/4
Minimum number of prior years of GME required	2/0
Offers graduate year 1 positions, available immediately upon medical school completion	Some
Average number of interviews for program year 1 positions	3.3
Percent new program directors, 2007-2008 academic year (source: ACGME)	8.3%
Residents/Fellows	
Total number of active residents/fellows	71
Average number of residents/fellows per program	1.4
Average percent female	52.1%
Average percent international medical graduate (IMG)	46.5%
Program Faculty	
Average number of full-time physician faculty	11.1
Average number of part-time physician faculty	1.4
Average percent female full-time physician faculty	36.0%
Average ratio of full-time physician faculty to resident/fellow	3.6

Table 2. Data for Medical Genetics Programs Listed in FREIDA

Number of programs providing data	20
Work Schedule (Program Year 1)	
Average hours on duty per week	43.1

Average maximum consecutive hours on duty	13.5
Average days off duty per week	1.7
Moonlighting allowed within institution	45.0%
Night float system	0.0%
Offers awareness and management of fatigue in residents/fellows	70.0%

Educational Setting (Program Year 1)

Average hours/week of regularly scheduled lectures/conferences	5.6
Average percent of training in hospital outpatient clinics	65.1%
Average percent of training in nonhospital ambulatory care community settings	15.0%

Educational Benefits

Curriculum on management of tobacco dependence	0.0%
Program to assess/enhance medical professionalism	75.0%
Debt management/financial counseling	35.0%
Formal program to develop teaching skills	75.0%
Formal mentoring program	50.0%
Formal program to foster interdisciplinary teamwork	20.0%
Continuous quality improvement training	50.0%
International experience	10.0%
Resident/fellow retreats	60.0%
Off-campus electives	80.0%
Hospice/home care experience	5.0%
Cultural competence awareness	70.0%
Instruction in medical Spanish or other non-English language	30.0%
Alternative/complementary medicine curriculum	15.0%
Training in identifying and reporting of domestic violence/abuse	35.0%
MPH/MBA or PhD training	35.0%
Research rotation	80.0%

Educational Features

Offers additional training or educational experience beyond accredited length	64.0%
Offers a primary care track	10.0%
Offers a rural track	0.0%
Offers a women's health track	0.0%
Offers a hospitalist track	0.0%
Offers a research track/nonaccredited fellowship	25.0%
Offers an other track	20.0%

Resident Evaluation

Yearly specialty in-service examination required	41.5%
Patient surveys	30.0%
Portfolio system	40.0%
360 degree evaluations	90.0%
Objective structured clinical examinations (OSCE)	25.0%

Program Evaluation

Program graduation rates	80.0%
Board certification rates	100.0%
In-training examinations	65.0%
Performance-based assessments	45.0%

Employment Policies and Benefits

Part-time/shared positions	15.0%
On-site child care	50.0%
Subsidized child care	10.0%
Allowance/stipend for professional expenses	90.0%
Leave for educational meetings/conferences	82.8%
Moving allowance	25.0%
Housing stipend	0.0%
On-call meal allowance	45.0%
Free parking	60.0%
PDAs	15.0%
Placement assistance upon completion of program	25.0%
Cross coverage in case of illness/disability	80.0%

Compensation and Leave (Graduate Year 1)

Average resident/fellow compensation	$47,936
Average number weeks of vacation	8.3
Sick days (paid)	34.1
Maximum number of paid days for family/medical leave	29
Maximum number of unpaid days for family/medical leave	62

Major Medical Benefits

Major medical insurance for residents	100.0%
Major medical insurance for dependents	90.0%
Outpatient mental health insurance	85.0%
Inpatient mental health insurance	85.0%
Group life insurance	85.0%
Dental insurance	85.0%
Disability insurance	90.0%
Disability insurance for occupationally acquired HIV	80.0%
Medical insurance coverage begins when starting program	95.0%

Table 3. Medical Genetics Match Data

GY1	2008
Number of positions offered	4
Number filled by US seniors	1
Percent filled by US seniors	25
Total positions filled	1
Percent total positions filled	25
All	
Total Positions*	4
Preferred by US Seniors*	1
Preferred Positions per US Senior	4
Preferred by Independent Applicants†	0
Preferred Positions per IA	0

Source: National Resident Matching Program 2008 Match Data
* Includes all positions offered in a specialty, except preliminary positions.
† Preferred means the number of applicants for whom the specialty was the only or first choice.

For more information

Professional Association

American College of Medical Genetics
9650 Rockville Pike
Bethesda, MD 20814-3998
301 634-7127
301 634-7275
E-mail: acmg@acmg.net
www.acmg.net

Certification

American Board of Medical Genetics
9650 Rockville Pike
Bethesda, MD 20814-3998
301 634-7315
301 634-7320 Fax
E-mail: abmg@abmg.org
www.abmg.org

Program Accreditation

Accreditation Council for Graduate Medical Education
Residency Review Committee for Medical Genetics
Georgia Andrianopoulos, PhD, Executive Director
515 North State Street
Chicago, IL 60654
312 755-5031
E-mail: gda@acgme.org
www.acgme.org

Specialty Data

Clinical Biochemical Genetics

Professional Description

A clinical biochemical geneticist is an individual with a US- or Canadian-earned, or the equivalent of an earned, doctoral degree (MD, DO, PhD) who can correctly perform and interpret biochemical analyses relevant to the diagnosis and management of human genetic diseases and who acts as a consultant regarding laboratory diagnosis of a broad range of biochemical genetic disorders.

These requirements imply that the individual possesses:

- The ability to supervise and direct the operations of a clinical biochemical genetics diagnostic laboratory, including technical expertise and knowledge in quality control and quality assessment procedures
- Broad knowledge of (1) basic biochemistry and genetics, (2) the application of biochemical techniques to the diagnosis and management of genetic diseases, and (3) the etiology, pathogenesis, clinical manifestations, and management of human inherited biochemical disorders
- An understanding of the heterogeneity, variability, and natural history of biochemical genetic disorders
- Diagnostic and interpretive skills in a wide range of biochemical genetic problems
- The ability to communicate biochemical laboratory results in the capacity of consultant to medical genetics professionals and other clinicians and directly to patients in concert with other professional staff

Source: American Board of Medical Genetics

Prerequisites; Length of Training

A US-earned doctoral degree (MD, DO, PhD, or the equivalent) is required. Length of ABMG-accredited programs is 2 years.

For more information

American College of Medical Genetics
9650 Rockville Pike
Bethesda, MD 20814-3998
301 634-7127
301 634-7275 Fax
E-mail: acmg@acmg.net
www.acmg.net

Clinical Cytogenetics

Professional Description

A clinical cytogeneticist is an individual with a US- or Canadian-earned, or the equivalent of an earned, doctoral degree (MD, DO, PhD) who can correctly perform and interpret cytogenetic analyses relevant to the diagnosis and management of human genetic diseases and who acts as a consultant regarding laboratory diagnosis for a broad range of cytogenetic disorders, including inherited and acquired conditions.

These requirements imply that the individual possesses:

- The ability to supervise and direct the operations of a clinical cytogenetic diagnostic laboratory, including technical expertise and knowledge in quality control and quality assessment procedures
- Broad knowledge in human cytogenetics, including prenatal and postnatal cytogenetic diagnosis, infertility and pregnancy loss, cancer, and leukemia
- An understanding of the heterogeneity, variability, and natural history of cytogenetic disorders

- Diagnostic and interpretive skills in a wide range of cytogenetic problems
- The ability to communicate cytogenetic laboratory results in the capacity of consultant to medical genetics professionals and other clinicians and directly to patients in concert with other professional staff

Source: American Board of Medical Genetics

Prerequisites; Length of Training

A US earned doctoral degree (MD, DO, PhD, or the equivalent) is required. Length of ABMG-accredited programs is 2 years.

For more information

American College of Medical Genetics
9650 Rockville Pike
Bethesda, MD 20814-3998
301 634-7127
301 634-7275 Fax
E-mail: acmg@acmg.net
www.acmg.net

Clinical Genetics (MD)

Professional Description

A clinical geneticist is an individual who holds a US- or Canadian-earned, or the equivalent of an earned, MD or DO degree, has had 2 years in an ACGME-accredited clinical residency program in another medical specialty, 2 years in an ACGME-accredited residency in clinical genetics (or 4 years in an accredited clinical genetics residency program), a valid medical license, and demonstrates competence to provide comprehensive genetic diagnostic, management, therapeutic, and counseling services.

These requirements imply that the individual possesses

- Broad knowledge in human and medical genetics, including an understanding of heterogeneity, variability, and natural history of genetic disorders
- Diagnostic and therapeutic skills in a wide range of genetic disorders
- The ability to elicit and interpret individual and family histories
- The ability to integrate clinical and genetic information and understand the uses, limitations, interpretation, and significance of specialized laboratory and clinical procedures
- Expertise in genetic and mathematical principles to perform risk assessment
- Skills in interviewing and counseling techniques required to (1) elicit from the patient or family the information necessary to reach an appropriate conclusion; (2) anticipate areas of difficulty and conflict; (3) help families and individuals recognize and cope with their emotional and psychological needs; (4) recognize situations requiring psychiatric referral; and (5) transmit pertinent information in a way that is comprehensible to the individual or family
- knowledge of available health care resources (community, regional, and national) required for appropriate referral or support

Source: American Board of Medical Genetics

Prerequisites; Length of Training

No prerequisites are required when entering a 4-year program; 2 years of ACGME-accredited GME are required when entering a 2-year program. length of accredited programs is 2 years or 4 years.

For more information

American College of Medical Genetics
9650 Rockville Pike
Bethesda, MD 20814-3998
301 634-7127
301 634-7275 Fax
E-mail: acmg@acmg.net
www.acmg.net

Clinical Molecular Genetics

Professional Description

A clinical molecular geneticist is an individual with a US- or Canadian-earned, or the equivalent of an earned, doctoral degree (MD, DO, PhD) who can correctly perform and interpret molecular analyses relevant to the diagnosis and management of human genetic diseases and who can act as a consultant regarding laboratory diagnosis of a broad range of molecular genetic disorders.

These requirements imply that the individual possesses:

- The ability to supervise and direct the operations of a clinical molecular genetics diagnostic laboratory, including technical experience and knowledge in quality control and quality assessment procedures
- The ability to perform a variety of molecular diagnostic assays
- An understanding of the heterogeneity, variability, and natural history of molecular genetic disorders
- A broad knowledge of (1) basic molecular biology and genetics; (2) the application of recombinant DNA techniques and linkage analysis to the diagnosis of genetic diseases; and (3) the etiology, pathogenesis, clinical manifestations, and management of human genetic disorders
- Diagnostic and interpretive skills in a wide range of clinical molecular genetics problems
- The ability to communicate molecular diagnostic laboratory results in the capacity of a consultant to medical genetics professionals and other clinicians and directly to patients in concert with other professional staff

Source: American Board of Medical Genetics

Prerequisites; Length of Training

A US-earned doctoral degree (MD, DO, PhD, or the equivalent) is required. Length of ABMG-accredited programs is 2 years.

For more information

American College of Medical Genetics
9650 Rockville Pike
Bethesda, MD 20814-3998
301 634-7127
301 634-7275 Fax
E-mail: acmg@acmg.net
www.acmg.net

Medical Biochemical Genetics

Professional Description

Medical biochemical geneticists provide comprehensive diagnostic, management, and genetic counseling services for patients with inborn errors of metabolism. They focus on the treatment of genetic disorders of intermediary metabolism, lysosomal storage diseases, disorders of energy metabolism, and related disorders.

Source: Medical biochemical genetics' program requirements, ACGME
http://www.acgme.org/acWebsite/downloads/RRC_progReq/131medicalbiochemicalgenetics02132007.pdf

Prerequisites; Length of Training

Completion of a medical genetics residency program is required. Length of ACGME-accredited programs is 1 year.

For more information

American College of Medical Genetics
9650 Rockville Pike
Bethesda, MD 20814-3998
301 634-7127
301 634-7275 Fax
E-mail: acmg@acmg.net
www.acmg.net

Molecular Genetic Pathology

Professional Description

A molecular genetic pathologist is expert in the principles, theory, and technologies of molecular biology and molecular genetics. This expertise is used to make or confirm diagnoses of Mendelian genetic disorders, of human development, infectious diseases and malignancies, and to assess the natural history of those disorders. A molecular genetic pathologist provides information about gene structure, function, and alteration and applies laboratory techniques for diagnosis, treatment, and prognosis for individuals with related disorders.

Source: American Board of Medical Genetics

Prerequisites; Length of Training

Completion of a 4-year ACGME-accredited program in pathology or medical genetics is required. Length of ACGME-accredited molecular genetic pathology programs is 1 year.

For more information

American College of Medical Genetics
9650 Rockville Pike
Bethesda, MD 20814-3998
301 634-7127
301 634-7275 Fax
E-mail: acmg@acmg.net
www.acmg.net

Neurological Surgery

Professional Description

Neurological surgery is a discipline of medicine and the specialty of surgery that provides the operative and nonoperative management (ie, prevention, diagnosis, evaluation, treatment, critical care, and rehabilitation) of disorders of the central, peripheral, and autonomic nervous systems, including their supporting structures and vascular supply; the evaluation and treatment of pathological processes that modify the function or activity of the nervous system, including the hypophysis; and the operative and nonoperative management of pain. As such, neurological surgery encompasses the surgical, nonsurgical, and stereotactic radiosurgical treatment of adult and pediatric patients with disorders of the nervous system: disorders of the brain, meninges, skull, and skull base, and their blood supply, including the surgical and endovascular treatment of disorders of the intracranial and extracranial vasculature supplying the brain and spinal cord; disorders of the pituitary gland; disorders of the spinal cord, meninges, and vertebral column, including those that may require treatment by fusion, instrumentation, or endovascular techniques; and disorders of the cranial, peripheral, and spinal nerves throughout their distribution.

Source: American Board of Neurological Surgery

Prerequisites; Length of Training

length of accredited programs is 6 years (effective July 1, 2009).

Subspecialties

Subspecialty programs accredited by the ACGME

- Endovascular surgical neuroradiology

American Board of Neurological Surgery subspecialty certificates

None

Data

Unless otherwise noted, all data are for 2008.

Table 1. Neurological Surgery Programs

Number of accredited programs	99

Program Data

length of accredited training	6
Minimum number of prior years of GME required	0
Offers graduate year 1 positions, available immediately upon medical school completion	Yes
Average number of interviews for program year 1 positions	30.1
Percent new program directors, 2007-2008 academic year (source: ACGME)	11.3%

Residents/Fellows

Total number of active residents/fellows	936
Average number of residents/fellows per program	9.5
Average percent female	11.8%
Average percent international medical graduate (IMG)	10.7%

Program Faculty

Average number of full-time physician faculty	10.7
Average number of part-time physician faculty	0.9
Average percent female full-time physician faculty	7.5%
Average ratio of full-time physician faculty to resident/fellow	0.9

Table 2. Data for Neurological Surgery Programs Listed in FREIDA

Number of programs providing data	53

Work Schedule (Program Year 1)

Average hours on duty per week	76.3
Average maximum consecutive hours on duty	26.7
Average days off duty per week	1.3
Moonlighting allowed within institution	7.5%
Night float system	22.6%
Offers awareness and management of fatigue in residents/fellows	94.3%

Educational Setting (Program Year 1)

Average hours/week of regularly scheduled lectures/conferences	5.4
Average percent of training in hospital outpatient clinics	16.7%
Average percent of training in nonhospital ambulatory care community settings	13.7%

Educational Benefits

Curriculum on management of tobacco dependence	18.9%
Program to assess/enhance medical professionalism	75.5%
Debt management/financial counseling	56.6%
Formal program to develop teaching skills	75.5%
Formal mentoring program	71.7%
Formal program to foster interdisciplinary teamwork	28.3%
Continuous quality improvement training	96.2%
International experience	24.5%
Resident/fellow retreats	39.6%
Off-campus electives	60.4%
Hospice/home care experience	11.3%
Cultural competence awareness	66.0%
Instruction in medical Spanish or other non-English language	15.1%
Alternative/complementary medicine curriculum	9.4%
Training in identifying and reporting of domestic violence/abuse	45.3%
MPH/MBA or PhD training	32.1%
Research rotation	94.3%

Educational Features

Offers additional training or educational experience beyond accredited length	80.8%
Offers a primary care track	0.0%
Offers a rural track	0.0%
Offers a women's health track	0.0%
Offers a hospitalist track	3.8%
Offers a research track/nonaccredited fellowship	37.7%
Offers an other track	3.8%

Resident Evaluation

Yearly specialty in-service examination required	85.6%
Patient surveys	43.4%
Portfolio system	39.6%
360 degree evaluations	88.7%
Objective structured clinical examinations (OSCE)	15.1%

Program Evaluation

Program graduation rates	88.7%
Board certification rates	96.2%
In-training examinations	86.8%
Performance-based assessments	34.0%

Employment Policies and Benefits

Part-time/shared positions	0.0%
On-site child care	43.4%
Subsidized child care	0.0%
Allowance/stipend for professional expenses	96.2%
Leave for educational meetings/conferences	90.7%
Moving allowance	3.8%
Housing stipend	5.7%
On-call meal allowance	90.6%
Free parking	47.2%
PDAs	24.5%
Placement assistance upon completion of program	35.8%
Cross coverage in case of illness/disability	71.7%

Compensation and Leave (Graduate Year 1)

Average resident/fellow compensation	$45,206
Average number weeks of vacation	3.3
Sick days (paid)	24.7
Maximum number of paid days for family/medical leave	44
Maximum number of unpaid days for family/medical leave	67

Major Medical Benefits

Major medical insurance for residents	100.0%
Major medical insurance for dependents	96.2%
Outpatient mental health insurance	94.3%
Inpatient mental health insurance	94.3%
Group life insurance	94.3%
Dental insurance	83.0%
Disability insurance	94.3%
Disability insurance for occupationally acquired HIV	73.6%
Medical insurance coverage begins when starting program	94.3%

Table 3. Neurological Surgery Match Data

GY1	2008
Number of positions offered	19
Number filled by US seniors	14
Percent filled by US seniors	73.7
Total positions filled	16
Percent total positions filled	84.2
All	
Total Positions*	12
Preferred by US Seniors*	9
Preferred Positions per US Senior	1.3
Preferred by Independent Applicants†	3
Preferred Positions per IA	4

Source: National Resident Matching Program 2008 Match Data
* Includes all positions offered in a specialty, except preliminary positions.
† Preferred means the number of applicants for whom the specialty was the only or first choice.

For more information

American Association of Neurological Surgeons
5550 Meadowbrook Drive
Rolling Meadows, IL 60008
847 378-0500
847 378-0600 Fax
E-mail: info@aans.org
www.aans.org

Congress of Neurological Surgeons
10 North Martingale Road, Suite 190
Schaumburg, IL 60173
847 240-2500
847 240-0804 Fax
E-mail: info@1CNS.org
www.neurosurgeon.org

Certification

American Board of Neurological Surgery
6550 Fannin Street, Suite 2139
Houston, TX 77030-2701
713 441-6015
713 794-0207 Fax
E-mail: abns@tmhs.edu
www.abns.org

Program Accreditation

Accreditation Council for Graduate Medical Education
Residency Review Committee for Neurological Surgery
Larry D Sulton, PhD, Executive Director
515 North State Street
Chicago, IL 60654
312 755-5027
E-mail: lds@acgme.org
www.acgme.org

Endovascular Surgical Neuroradiology

Professional Description

Endovascular surgical neuroradiology is a subspecialty that uses catheter technology, radiologic imaging, and clinical expertise to diagnose and treat diseases of the central nervous system. Practitioners have training and experience in:

- Signs and symptoms of disorders amenable to diagnosis and treatment by endovascular surgical neuroradiology techniques
- Neurological examinations to evaluate patients with neurological disorders
- Pathophysiology and natural history of these disorders
- Indications and contraindications to endovascular surgical neuroradiology procedures
- Clinical and technical aspects of endovascular surgical neuroradiology procedures
- Medical and surgical alternatives
- Preoperative and postoperative management of endovascular patients
- Neurointensive care management
- Fundamentals of imaging physics and radiation biology
- Interpretation of radiographic studies pertinent to the practice

Source: Endovascular Surgical Neuroradiology Program Requirements, ACGME
www.acgme.org/acWebsite/downloads/RRC_progReq/422pr403.pdf

Prerequisites; Length of Training

A minimum of 4 years of prior GME is required. Length of ACGME-accredited programs is 1 year.

For more information

Professional Association

American Society of Neuroradiology
2210 Midwest Road, Suite 207
Oak Brook, IL 60523
630 574-0220
630 574-0661 Fax
www.asnr.org

Specialty Data

Neurology

Professional Description

A neurologist specializes in the diagnosis and treatment of all types of disease or impaired function of the brain, spinal cord, peripheral nerves, muscles, and autonomic nervous system, as well as the blood vessels that relate to these structures. A child neurologist has special skills in the diagnosis and management of neurologic disorders of the neonatal period, infancy, early childhood, and adolescence.

Prerequisites; Length of Training

Programs are either 3 years or 4 years. Residents entering a 3-year program must have completed 1 year in an accredited program in the US or Canada.

Subspecialties

Subspecialty programs accredited by the ACGME

- Child neurology
- Clinical neurophysiology
- Endovascular surgical neuroradiology
- Hospice and palliative medicine
- Neurodevelopmental disabilities
- Neuromuscular medicine
- Pain medicine*
- Sleep medicine
- Vascular neurology
  * In 2007, ACGME-accredited pain medicine programs under anesthesiology, neurology, physical medicine and rehabilitation, and psychiatry were combined into a multidisciplinary pain medicine subspecialty.

American Board of Psychiatry and Neurology subspecialty certificates

- Child neurology (special certification)
- Clinical neurophysiology
- Hospice and palliative medicine
- Neurodevelopmental disabilities
- Pain medicine
- Sleep medicine
- Vascular neurology

Data

Unless otherwise noted, all data are for 2008.

Table 1. Neurology Programs

Number of accredited programs	126
Program Data	
length of accredited training	3/4
Minimum number of prior years of GME required	1/0
Offers graduate year 1 positions, available immediately upon medical school completion	Some
Average number of interviews for program year 1 positions	43.0
Percent new program directors, 2007-2008 academic year (source: ACGME)	13.1%
Residents/Fellows	
Total number of active residents/fellows	1,614
Average number of residents/fellows per program	12.8
Average percent female	45.0%
Average percent international medical graduate (IMG)	36.8%
Program Faculty	
Average number of full-time physician faculty	28.0
Average number of part-time physician faculty	2.7
Average percent female full-time physician faculty	22.5%
Average ratio of full-time physician faculty to resident/fellow	1.5

Table 2. Data for Neurology Programs Listed in FREIDA

Number of programs providing data	74
Work Schedule (Program Year 1)	
Average hours on duty per week	62.8
Average maximum consecutive hours on duty	26.2
Average days off duty per week	1.2
Moonlighting allowed within institution	50.0%
Night float system	33.8%
Offers awareness and management of fatigue in residents/fellows	91.9%
Educational Setting (Program Year 1)	
Average hours/week of regularly scheduled lectures/conferences	7.1
Average percent of training in hospital outpatient clinics	25.1%
Average percent of training in nonhospital ambulatory care community settings	13.3%
Educational Benefits	
Curriculum on management of tobacco dependence	6.8%
Program to assess/enhance medical professionalism	78.4%
Debt management/financial counseling	56.8%
Formal program to develop teaching skills	83.8%
Formal mentoring program	79.7%
Formal program to foster interdisciplinary teamwork	24.3%
Continuous quality improvement training	85.1%
International experience	13.5%
Resident/fellow retreats	31.1%
Off-campus electives	75.7%
Hospice/home care experience	16.2%
Cultural competence awareness	70.3%
Instruction in medical Spanish or other non-English language	24.3%
Alternative/complementary medicine curriculum	21.6%
Training in identifying and reporting of domestic violence/abuse	60.8%
MPH/MBA or PhD training	25.7%
Research rotation	21.6%
Educational Features	
Offers additional training or educational experience beyond accredited length	26.8%
Offers a primary care track	9.5%
Offers a rural track	0.0%
Offers a women's health track	1.4%
Offers a hospitalist track	6.8%
Offers a research track/nonaccredited fellowship	21.6%
Offers an other track	6.8%
Resident Evaluation	
Yearly specialty in-service examination required	99.3%
Patient surveys	59.5%
Portfolio system	51.4%
360 degree evaluations	86.5%
Objective structured clinical examinations (OSCE)	50.0%
Program Evaluation	
Program graduation rates	87.8%
Board certification rates	95.9%
In-training examinations	98.6%
Performance-based assessments	77.0%
Employment Policies and Benefits	
Part-time/shared positions	1.4%
On-site child care	39.2%
Subsidized child care	9.5%
Allowance/stipend for professional expenses	97.3%
Leave for educational meetings/conferences	82.3%
Moving allowance	4.1%
Housing stipend	5.4%

On-call meal allowance	91.9%
Free parking	58.1%
PDAs	32.4%
Placement assistance upon completion of program	20.3%
Cross coverage in case of illness/disability	94.6%
Compensation and Leave (Graduate Year 1)	
Average resident/fellow compensation	$46,733
Average number weeks of vacation	3.4
Sick days (paid)	21.9
Maximum number of paid days for family/medical leave	53
Maximum number of unpaid days for family/medical leave	64
Major Medical Benefits	
Major medical insurance for residents	100.0%
Major medical insurance for dependents	91.9%
Outpatient mental health insurance	89.2%
Inpatient mental health insurance	89.2%
Group life insurance	93.2%
Dental insurance	89.2%
Disability insurance	94.6%
Disability insurance for occupationally acquired HIV	73.0%
Medical insurance coverage begins when starting program	81.1%

Table 3. Neurology Match Data

GY1	2008
Number of positions offered	177
Number filled by US seniors	105
Percent filled by US seniors	59.3
Total positions filled	165
Percent total positions filled	93.2
GY2	
Number of positions offered	398
Number filled by US seniors	226
Percent filled by US seniors	56.8
Total positions filled	371
Percent total positions filled	93.2
All	
Total Positions*	574
Preferred by US Seniors*	336
Preferred Positions per US Senior	1.7
Preferred by Independent Applicants†	360
Preferred Positions per IA	1.6

Source: National Resident Matching Program 2008 Match Data
* Includes all positions offered in a specialty, except preliminary positions.
† Preferred means the number of applicants for whom the specialty was the only or first choice.

For more information

Professional Association

American Academy of Neurology
1080 Montreal Avenue
Saint Paul, MN 55116
800 879-1960
651 695-2791 Fax
E-mail: memberservices@aan.com
www.aan.com

Certification

American Board of Psychiatry and Neurology
2150 East Lake Cook Road, Suite 900
Buffalo Grove, IL 60089
847 229-6500
847 229-6600 Fax
www.abpn.com

Program Accreditation

Accreditation Council for Graduate Medical Education
Residency Review Committee for Neurology
Lynne Meyer, PhD, MPH, Executive Director
515 North State Street
Chicago, IL 60654
312 755-5006
E-mail: lmeyer@acgme.org
www.acgme.org

Child Neurology

Professional Description

A child neurologist has special skills in the diagnosis and management of neurologic disorders of the neonatal period, infancy, early childhood, and adolescence.

Prerequisites; Length of Training

The three options for prerequisite training are 2 years of pediatrics training in the US or Canada; 1 year of internal medicine and 1 year of pediatrics; or 1 year of pediatrics and 1 year of basic neuroscience training. Length of ACGME-accredited programs is 3 years.

Data

Unless otherwise noted, all data are for 2008.

Table 1. Child Neurology Programs

Number of accredited programs	69
Program Data	
length of accredited training	3
Minimum number of prior years of GME required	2
Offers graduate year 1 positions, available immediately upon medical school completion	No
Average number of interviews for program year 1 positions	8.8
Percent new program directors, 2007-2008 academic year (source: ACGME)	10.5%
Residents/Fellows	
Total number of active residents/fellows	252
Average number of residents/fellows per program	3.7
Average percent female	62.3%
Average percent international medical graduate (IMG)	31.3%
Program Faculty	
Average number of full-time physician faculty	21.5
Average number of part-time physician faculty	1.8
Average percent female full-time physician faculty	29.4%
Average ratio of full-time physician faculty to resident/fellow	3.7

Table 2. Data for Child Neurology Programs Listed in FREIDA

Number of programs providing data	29
Work Schedule (Program Year 1)	
Average hours on duty per week	56.1
Average maximum consecutive hours on duty	23.8
Average days off duty per week	1.3
Moonlighting allowed within institution	48.3%
Night float system	27.6%
Offers awareness and management of fatigue in residents/fellows	89.7%
Educational Setting (Program Year 1)	
Average hours/week of regularly scheduled lectures/conferences	6.7
Average percent of training in hospital outpatient clinics	30.2%
Average percent of training in nonhospital ambulatory care community settings	10.0%

Specialty Data

Educational Benefits

Curriculum on management of tobacco dependence	6.9%
Program to assess/enhance medical professionalism	72.4%
Debt management/financial counseling	41.4%
Formal program to develop teaching skills	86.2%
Formal mentoring program	75.9%
Formal program to foster interdisciplinary teamwork	24.1%
Continuous quality improvement training	93.1%
International experience	24.1%
Resident/fellow retreats	51.7%
Off-campus electives	75.9%
Hospice/home care experience	13.8%
Cultural competence awareness	75.9%
Instruction in medical Spanish or other non-English language	27.6%
Alternative/complementary medicine curriculum	17.2%
Training in identifying and reporting of domestic violence/abuse	51.7%
MPH/MBA or PhD training	24.1%
Research rotation	27.6%

Educational Features

Offers additional training or educational experience beyond accredited length	25.3%
Offers a primary care track	13.8%
Offers a rural track	0.0%
Offers a women's health track	0.0%
Offers a hospitalist track	0.0%
Offers a research track/nonaccredited fellowship	20.7%
Offers an other track	13.8%

Resident Evaluation

Yearly specialty in-service examination required	94.0%
Patient surveys	44.8%
Portfolio system	58.6%
360 degree evaluations	75.9%
Objective structured clinical examinations (OSCE)	69.0%

Program Evaluation

Program graduation rates	93.1%
Board certification rates	100.0%
In-training examinations	96.6%
Performance-based assessments	72.4%

Employment Policies and Benefits

Part-time/shared positions	17.2%
On-site child care	55.2%
Subsidized child care	10.3%
Allowance/stipend for professional expenses	96.6%
Leave for educational meetings/conferences	77.2%
Moving allowance	13.8%
Housing stipend	6.9%
On-call meal allowance	89.7%
Free parking	55.2%
PDAs	31.0%
Placement assistance upon completion of program	37.9%
Cross coverage in case of illness/disability	69.0%

Compensation and Leave (Graduate Year 1)

Average resident/fellow compensation	$49,468
Average number weeks of vacation	3.4
Sick days (paid)	17.8
Maximum number of paid days for family/medical leave	50
Maximum number of unpaid days for family/medical leave	57

Major Medical Benefits

Major medical insurance for residents	100.0%
Major medical insurance for dependents	93.1%
Outpatient mental health insurance	100.0%
Inpatient mental health insurance	100.0%
Group life insurance	93.1%
Dental insurance	100.0%
Disability insurance	93.1%
Disability insurance for occupationally acquired HIV	72.4%
Medical insurance coverage begins when starting program	89.7%

For more information

American Academy of Neurology
1080 Montreal Avenue
Saint Paul, MN 55116
800 879-1960
651 695-2791 Fax
E-mail: memberservices@aan.com
www.aan.com

Clinical Neurophysiology

Professional Description

A neurologist who specializes in the diagnosis and management of central, peripheral, and autonomic nervous system disorders using a combination of clinical evaluation and electrophysiologic testing, such as electroencephalography (EEG), electromyography (EMG), and nerve conduction studies (NCS), among others.

Prerequisites; Length of Training

Completion of an accredited neurology, child neurology, or psychiatry program in the US or Canada is required. Length of ACGME-accredited programs is 1 year.

Data

Unless otherwise noted, all data are for 2008.

Table 1. Clinical Neurophysiology Programs

Number of accredited programs	89
Program Data	
length of accredited training	1
Minimum number of prior years of GME required	4
Offers graduate year 1 positions, available immediately upon medical school completion	No
Average number of interviews for program year 1 positions	8.2
Percent new program directors, 2007-2008 academic year (source: ACGME)	10.1%
Residents/Fellows	
Total number of active residents/fellows	140
Average number of residents/fellows per program	1.6
Average percent female	43.6%
Average percent international medical graduate (IMG)	37.9%
Program Faculty	
Average number of full-time physician faculty	12.5
Average number of part-time physician faculty	1.0
Average percent female full-time physician faculty	24.8%
Average ratio of full-time physician faculty to resident/fellow	2.9

Table 2. Data for Clinical Neurophysiology Programs Listed in FREIDA

Number of programs providing data	37
Work Schedule (Program Year 1)	
Average hours on duty per week	42.5
Average maximum consecutive hours on duty	14.0
Average days off duty per week	1.7
Moonlighting allowed within institution	48.6%
Night float system	2.7%
Offers awareness and management of fatigue in residents/fellows	81.1%

Educational Setting (Program Year 1)

Average hours/week of regularly scheduled lectures/conferences	4.8
Average percent of training in hospital outpatient clinics	34.6%
Average percent of training in nonhospital ambulatory care community settings	17.5%

Educational Benefits

Curriculum on management of tobacco dependence	2.7%
Program to assess/enhance medical professionalism	56.8%
Debt management/financial counseling	51.4%
Formal program to develop teaching skills	62.2%
Formal mentoring program	56.8%
Formal program to foster interdisciplinary teamwork	18.9%
Continuous quality improvement training	62.2%
International experience	10.8%
Resident/fellow retreats	48.6%
Off-campus electives	24.3%
Hospice/home care experience	8.1%
Cultural competence awareness	43.2%
Instruction in medical Spanish or other non-English language	2.7%
Alternative/complementary medicine curriculum	10.8%
Training in identifying and reporting of domestic violence/abuse	45.9%
MPH/MBA or PhD training	13.5%
Research rotation	32.4%

Educational Features

Offers additional training or educational experience beyond accredited length	28.6%
Offers a primary care track	0.0%
Offers a rural track	0.0%
Offers a women's health track	0.0%
Offers a hospitalist track	0.0%
Offers a research track/nonaccredited fellowship	16.2%
Offers an other track	16.2%

Resident Evaluation

Yearly specialty in-service examination required	82.6%
Patient surveys	32.4%
Portfolio system	35.1%
360 degree evaluations	73.0%
Objective structured clinical examinations (OSCE)	8.1%

Program Evaluation

Program graduation rates	78.4%
Board certification rates	91.9%
In-training examinations	91.9%
Performance-based assessments	32.4%

Employment Policies and Benefits

Part-time/shared positions	0.0%
On-site child care	40.5%
Subsidized child care	13.5%
Allowance/stipend for professional expenses	91.9%
Leave for educational meetings/conferences	74.7%
Moving allowance	2.7%
Housing stipend	0.0%
On-call meal allowance	48.6%
Free parking	48.6%
PDAs	10.8%
Placement assistance upon completion of program	13.5%
Cross coverage in case of illness/disability	75.7%

Compensation and Leave (Graduate Year 1)

Average resident/fellow compensation	$51,781
Average number weeks of vacation	3.3
Sick days (paid)	32.9
Maximum number of paid days for family/medical leave	40
Maximum number of unpaid days for family/medical leave	38

Major Medical Benefits

Major medical insurance for residents	100.0%
Major medical insurance for dependents	97.3%
Outpatient mental health insurance	91.9%
Inpatient mental health insurance	94.6%
Group life insurance	94.6%
Dental insurance	91.9%
Disability insurance	94.6%
Disability insurance for occupationally acquired HIV	78.4%
Medical insurance coverage begins when starting program	86.5%

For more information

American Academy of Neurology
1080 Montreal Avenue
Saint Paul, MN 55116
800 879-1960
651 695-2791 Fax
E-mail: memberservices@aan.com
www.aan.com

Endovascular Surgical Neuroradiology

See description under Neurological Surgery.

Hospice and Palliative Medicine

See page 57.

Neurodevelopmental Disabilities

Professional Description

A pediatrician or neurologist who specializes in the diagnosis and management of chronic conditions that affect the developing and mature nervous system, such as cerebral palsy, mental retardation, and chronic behavioral syndromes or neurologic conditions.

Prerequisites; Length of Training

Completion of 2 years of an accredited pediatrics program in the US or Canada is required. Length of ACGME-accredited programs is 4 years.

For more information

American Academy of Neurology
1080 Montreal Avenue
Saint Paul, MN 55116
800 879-1960
651 695-2791 Fax
E-mail: memberservices@aan.com
www.aan.com

Neuromuscular Medicine

Professional Description

A neurologist or child neurologist specializing in the diagnosis and management of disorders of nerve, muscle, or neuromuscular junction, including amyotrophic lateral sclerosis, peripheral neuropathies (eg, diabetic and immune mediated neuropathies), various muscular dystrophies, congenital and acquired myopathies,

Specialty Data

inflammatory myopathies (eg, polymyositis, inclusion body myositis), and neuromuscular transmission disorders (eg, myasthenia gravis, Lambert-Eaton myasthenic syndrome).

Source: American Board of Psychiatry and Neurology

Prerequisites; Length of Training

Successfully completion of an ACGME- or RCPSC-accredited residency program in either adult or pediatric neurology or physical medicine and rehabilitation is required. Length of ACGME-accredited programs is 1 year.

For more information

American Academy of Pain Medicine
4700 West Lake
Glenview, IL 60025
847 375-4731
847 375-6429 Fax
E-mail: info@painmed.org
www.painmed.org

Pain Medicine

See page 104.

Sleep Medicine

See page 155.

Vascular Neurology

Professional Description

A neurologist or child neurologist who specializes in the evaluation, prevention, treatment, and recovery from vascular diseases of the nervous system. This subspecialty includes the diagnosis and treatment of vascular events of arterial or venous origin from a large number of causes that affect the brain or spinal cord; such as ischemic stroke, intracranial hemorrhage, spinal cord ischemia, and spinal cord hemorrhage.

Source: American Board of Psychiatry and Neurology

Prerequisites; Length of Training

Completion of an accredited neurology program is required. Length of ACGME-accredited programs is 1 year.

For more information

American Academy of Pain Medicine
4700 West Lake
Glenview, IL 60025
847 375-4731
847 375-6429 Fax
E-mail: info@painmed.org
www.painmed.org

Nuclear Medicine

Professional Description

A nuclear medicine specialist employs the properties of radioactive atoms and molecules in the diagnosis and treatment of disease and in research. Radiation detection and imaging instrument systems are used to detect disease as it changes the function and metabolism of normal cells, tissues, and organs. A wide variety of diseases can be found in this way, usually before the structure of the organ involved by the disease can be seen to be abnormal by any other techniques. Early detection of coronary artery disease (including acute heart attack); early cancer detection and evaluation of the effect of tumor treatment; diagnosis of infection and inflammation anywhere in the body; and early detection of blood clot in the lungs are all possible with these techniques. Unique forms of radioactive molecules can attack and kill cancer cells (eg, lymphoma, thyroid cancer) or can relieve the severe pain of cancer that has spread to bone.

The nuclear medicine specialist has special knowledge in the biologic effects of radiation exposure, the fundamentals of the physical sciences, and the principles and operation of radiation detection and imaging instrumentation systems.

Prerequisites; Length of Training

Prior to entering a nuclear medicine program, residents must have completed 1 year of broad clinical education in an accredited program in the US or Canada. Nuclear medicine programs are 3 years (as of July 1, 2007).

Subspecialties

No subspecialty programs accredited by the Accreditation Council for Graduate Medical Education; no subspecialty certificates offered by the American Board of Nuclear Medicine.

Data

Unless otherwise noted, all data are for 2008.

Table 1. Nuclear Medicine Programs	
Number of accredited programs	55
Program Data	
length of accredited training	3
Minimum number of prior years of GME required	1
Offers graduate year 1 positions, available immediately upon medical school completion	No
Average number of interviews for program year 1 positions	6.7
Percent new program directors, 2007-2008 academic year (source: ACGME)	10.5%
Residents/Fellows	
Total number of active residents/fellows	128
Average number of residents/fellows per program	2.3
Average percent female	35.2%
Average percent international medical graduate (IMG)	63.3%
Program Faculty	
Average number of full-time physician faculty	5.3
Average number of part-time physician faculty	1.0
Average percent female full-time physician faculty	18.3%
Average ratio of full-time physician faculty to resident/fellow	1.2

Table 2. Data for Nuclear Medicine Programs Listed in FREIDA	
Number of programs providing data	20
Work Schedule (Program Year 1)	
Average hours on duty per week	46.7
Average maximum consecutive hours on duty	13.8

Average days off duty per week	1.8
Moonlighting allowed within institution	45.0%
Night float system	5.0%
Offers awareness and management of fatigue in residents/fellows	60.0%

Educational Setting (Program Year 1)

Average hours/week of regularly scheduled lectures/conferences	7.3
Average percent of training in hospital outpatient clinics	51.1%

Educational Benefits

Curriculum on management of tobacco dependence	0.0%
Program to assess/enhance medical professionalism	65.0%
Debt management/financial counseling	35.0%
Formal program to develop teaching skills	65.0%
Formal mentoring program	25.0%
Formal program to foster interdisciplinary teamwork	5.0%
Continuous quality improvement training	75.0%
International experience	5.0%
Resident/fellow retreats	15.0%
Off-campus electives	40.0%
Hospice/home care experience	0.0%
Cultural competence awareness	55.0%
Instruction in medical Spanish or other non-English language	10.0%
Alternative/complementary medicine curriculum	10.0%
Training in identifying and reporting of domestic violence/abuse	15.0%
MPH/MBA or PhD training	20.0%
Research rotation	35.0%

Educational Features

Offers additional training or educational experience beyond accredited length	26.2%
Offers a primary care track	5.0%
Offers a rural track	0.0%
Offers a women's health track	0.0%
Offers a hospitalist track	0.0%
Offers a research track/nonaccredited fellowship	35.0%
Offers an other track	10.0%

Resident Evaluation

Yearly specialty in-service examination required	88.9%
Patient surveys	50.0%
Portfolio system	55.0%
360 degree evaluations	75.0%
Objective structured clinical examinations (OSCE)	20.0%

Program Evaluation

Program graduation rates	85.0%
Board certification rates	95.0%
In-training examinations	90.0%
Performance-based assessments	30.0%

Employment Policies and Benefits

Part-time/shared positions	0.0%
On-site child care	25.0%
Subsidized child care	0.0%
Allowance/stipend for professional expenses	90.0%
Leave for educational meetings/conferences	75.0%
Moving allowance	0.0%
Housing stipend	15.0%
On-call meal allowance	55.0%
Free parking	40.0%
PDAs	5.0%
Placement assistance upon completion of program	20.0%
Cross coverage in case of illness/disability	75.0%

Compensation and Leave (Graduate Year 1)

Average resident/fellow compensation	$46,993
Average number weeks of vacation	8.5
Sick days (paid)	13.0

Maximum number of paid days for family/medical leave	34
Maximum number of unpaid days for family/medical leave	74

Major Medical Benefits

Major medical insurance for residents	100.0%
Major medical insurance for dependents	90.0%
Outpatient mental health insurance	90.0%
Inpatient mental health insurance	85.0%
Group life insurance	85.0%
Dental insurance	90.0%
Disability insurance	80.0%
Disability insurance for occupationally acquired HIV	65.0%
Medical insurance coverage begins when starting program	95.0%

Table 3. Nuclear Medicine Match Data

GY1	2008
Number of positions offered	0
Number filled by US seniors	0
Percent filled by US seniors	0
Total positions filled	0
Percent total positions filled	0
GY2	
Number of positions offered	4
Number filled by US seniors	0
Percent filled by US seniors	0
Total positions filled	4
Percent total positions filled	100
All	
Total Positions*	4
Preferred by US Seniors*	0
Preferred Positions per US Senior	0
Preferred by Independent Applicants†	4
Preferred Positions per IA	1

Source: National Resident Matching Program 2008 Match Data
* Includes all positions offered in a specialty, except preliminary positions.
† Preferred means the number of applicants for whom the specialty was the only or first choice.

For more information

Professional Association

American College of Nuclear Medicine
101 West Broad Street, Suite 614
Hazelton, PA 18201
570 501-9661
570 450-0863 Fax
E-mail: rpowell@ptd.net
www.acnucmed.com

American College of Nuclear Physicians
1850 Samuel Morse Drive
Reston, VA 20190-5316
703 326-1190
703 708-9015 Fax
www.acnponline.org

Society of Nuclear Medicine
1850 Samuel Morse Drive
Reston, VA 20190-5316
703 708-9000
703 708-9015
www.snm.org

Certification

American Board of Nuclear Medicine
4555 Forest Park Boulevard, Suite 119
St. Louis, MO 63108
314 367-2225
E-mail: abnm@abnm.org
www.abnm.org

Program Accreditation

Accreditation Council for Graduate Medical Education
Residency Review Committee for Nuclear Medicine
Missy Fleming, MEd, PhD, Executive Director
515 North State Street
Chicago, IL 60654
312 755-5043
E-mail: mfleming@acgme.org
www.acgme.org

Obstetrics and Gynecology

Professional Description

An obstetrician-gynecologist possesses special knowledge, skills, and professional capability in the medical and surgical care of the female reproductive system and associated disorders. This physician serves as a consultant to other physicians, and as a primary physician for women.

Prerequisites; Length of Training

No prerequisites required; length of ACGME-accredited programs is 4 years.

Subspecialties

Subspecialty programs accredited by the ACGME

- Hospice and palliative medicine

Subspecialty programs accredited by the American Board of Obstetrics and Gynecology

- Female pelvic medicine and reconstructive surgery
- Gynecologic oncology
- Maternal-fetal medicine
- Reproductive endocrinology/infertility

American Board of Obstetrics and Gynecology subspecialty certificates

- Critical care medicine
- Gynecologic oncology
- Hospice and palliative medicine
- Maternal-fetal medicine
- Reproductive endocrinology/infertility

Data

Unless otherwise noted, all data are for 2008.

Table 1. Obstetrics and Gynecology Programs	
Number of accredited programs	248
Program Data	
length of accredited training	4
Minimum number of prior years of GME required	0
Offers graduate year 1 positions, available immediately upon medical school completion	Yes
Average number of interviews for program year 1 positions	60.4
Percent new program directors, 2007-2008 academic year (source: ACGME)	17.6%
Residents/Fellows	
Total number of active residents/fellows	4,612
Average number of residents/fellows per program	18.6
Average percent female	77.7%
Average percent international medical graduate (IMG)	20.1%
Program Faculty	
Average number of full-time physician faculty	20.0
Average number of part-time physician faculty	6.5
Average percent female full-time physician faculty	45.0%
Average ratio of full-time physician faculty to resident/fellow	0.8

Table 2. Data for Obstetrics and Gynecology Programs Listed in FREIDA	
Number of programs providing data	204
Work Schedule (Program Year 1)	
Average hours on duty per week	72.3
Average maximum consecutive hours on duty	26.4
Average days off duty per week	1.3
Moonlighting allowed within institution	21.6%

Night float system	86.8%
Offers awareness and management of fatigue in residents/fellows	97.1%

Educational Setting (Program Year 1)

Average hours/week of regularly scheduled lectures/conferences	6.0
Average percent of training in hospital outpatient clinics	27.8%
Average percent of training in nonhospital ambulatory care community settings	12.7%

Educational Benefits

Curriculum on management of tobacco dependence	28.4%
Program to assess/enhance medical professionalism	84.8%
Debt management/financial counseling	73.0%
Formal program to develop teaching skills	86.3%
Formal mentoring program	83.3%
Formal program to foster interdisciplinary teamwork	37.7%
Continuous quality improvement training	94.1%
International experience	31.9%
Resident/fellow retreats	69.6%
Off-campus electives	76.5%
Hospice/home care experience	21.6%
Cultural competence awareness	88.7%
Instruction in medical Spanish or other non-English language	31.9%
Alternative/complementary medicine curriculum	38.7%
Training in identifying and reporting of domestic violence/abuse	91.7%
MPH/MBA or PhD training	12.7%
Research rotation	39.2%

Educational Features

Offers additional training or educational experience beyond accredited length	1.5%
Offers a primary care track	27.5%
Offers a rural track	2.0%
Offers a women's health track	39.2%
Offers a hospitalist track	2.9%
Offers a research track/nonaccredited fellowship	6.9%
Offers an other track	3.4%

Resident Evaluation

Yearly specialty in-service examination required	100.0%
Patient surveys	83.8%
Portfolio system	77.0%
360 degree evaluations	98.0%
Objective structured clinical examinations (OSCE)	33.3%

Program Evaluation

Program graduation rates	82.4%
Board certification rates	100.0%
In-training examinations	98.0%
Performance-based assessments	57.4%

Employment Policies and Benefits

Part-time/shared positions	0.5%
On-site child care	40.2%
Subsidized child care	6.9%
Allowance/stipend for professional expenses	97.1%
Leave for educational meetings/conferences	89.7%
Moving allowance	15.7%
Housing stipend	8.8%
On-call meal allowance	96.1%
Free parking	69.6%
PDAs	39.2%
Placement assistance upon completion of program	39.2%
Cross coverage in case of illness/disability	89.2%

Compensation and Leave (Graduate Year 1)

Average resident/fellow compensation	$45,465
Average number weeks of vacation	3.3
Sick days (paid)	16.0

Maximum number of paid days for family/medical leave	43
Maximum number of unpaid days for family/medical leave	63

Major Medical Benefits

Major medical insurance for residents	100.0%
Major medical insurance for dependents	97.1%
Outpatient mental health insurance	96.1%
Inpatient mental health insurance	95.6%
Group life insurance	94.1%
Dental insurance	89.7%
Disability insurance	93.1%
Disability insurance for occupationally acquired HIV	71.1%
Medical insurance coverage begins when starting program	89.2%

For more information

Professional Associations

American Association of Gynecologic Laparoscopists
6757 Katella Avenue
Cypress, CA 90630-5105
800 554-2245
714 503-6201 Fax
E-mail: generalmail@aagl.org
www.aagl.com

American College of Obstetricians and Gynecologists
409 12th Street, SW
PO Box 96920
Washington, DC 20090-6920
202 638-5577
www.acog.org

Certification

American Board of Obstetrics and Gynecology
2915 Vine Street, Suite 300
Dallas, TX 75204
214 871-1619
214 871-1943 Fax
E-mail: info@abog.org
www.abog.org

Program Accreditation

Accreditation Council for Graduate Medical Education
Residency Review Committee for Obstetrics and Gynecology
Patricia M Surdyk, PhD, Executive Director
515 North State Street
Chicago, IL 60654
312 755-5005
E-mail: psurdyk@acgme.org
www.acgme.org

Critical Care Medicine

Professional Description

An obstetrician-gynecologist who specializes in critical care medicine diagnoses, treats, and supports female patients with multiple organ dysfunction. This specialist may have administrative responsibilities for intensive care units and may also facilitate and coordinate patient care among the primary physician, the critical care staff, and other specialists.

Prerequisites; Length of Training

To earn the certificate in Obstetrics and Gynecology with Added Qualification in Critical Care from the ABOG, the applicant must have completed a program of no less than 1 year in length that fulfills the requirements of the American Board of Surgery for Surgical Critical Care or the American Board of Anesthesiology for Critical Care Medicine.

For more information

Society of Critical Care Medicine
500 Midway Drive
Mount Prospect, IL 60056
847 827-6869
847 827-6886 Fax
E-mail: info@sccm.org
www.sccm.org

American College of Obstetricians and Gynecologists
409 12th Street, SW
PO Box 96920
Washington, DC 20090-6920
202 638-5577
www.acog.org

Gynecologic Oncology

Professional Description

An obstetrician-gynecologist who provides consultation and comprehensive management of patients with gynecologic cancer, including those diagnostic and therapeutic procedures necessary for the total care of the patient with gynecologic cancer and resulting complications.

Prerequisites; Length of Training

Completion of an ACGME-accredited obstetrics-gynecology program is required. Length of ABOG-accredited gynecologic oncology programs is 3 years.

For more information

Professional Association

American College of Obstetricians and Gynecologists
409 12th Street, SW
PO Box 96920
Washington, DC 20090-6920
202 638-5577
www.acog.org

Hospice and Palliative Medicine

See page 57.

Maternal-Fetal Medicine

Professional Description

An obstetrician-gynecologist who cares for, or provides consultation on, patients with complications of pregnancy. This specialist has advanced knowledge of the obstetrical, medical, and surgical complications of pregnancy and their effect on both the mother and the fetus. He/she also possesses expertise in the most current diagnostic and treatment modalities used in the care of patients with complicated pregnancies.

Prerequisites; Length of Training

Completion of an ACGME-accredited obstetrics-gynecology program is required. Length of ABOG-accredited maternal-fetal medicine programs is 3 years.

For more information

American College of Obstetricians and Gynecologists
409 12th Street, SW
PO Box 96920
Washington, DC 20090-6920
202 638-5577
www.acog.org

Reproductive Endocrinology/Infertility

Professional Description

An obstetrician-gynecologist who is capable of managing complex problems relating to reproductive endocrinology and infertility.

Prerequisites; Length of Training

Completion of an ACGME-accredited obstetrics-gynecology program is required. Length of ABOG-accredited reproductive endocrinology/infertility programs is 3 years.

For more information

American College of Obstetricians and Gynecologists
409 12th Street, SW
PO Box 96920
Washington, DC 20090-6920
202 638-5577
www.acog.org

Ophthalmology

Professional Description

An ophthalmologist has the knowledge and professional skills needed to provide comprehensive eye and vision care. Ophthalmologists are medically trained to diagnose, monitor, and medically or surgically treat all ocular and visual disorders. This includes problems affecting the eye and its component structures, the eyelids, the orbit, and the visual pathways. In so doing, an ophthalmologist prescribes vision services, including glasses and contact lenses.

Prerequisites; Length of Training

One year of education in an accredited program is required prior to entry. Ophthalmology programs are 3 years.

Subspecialties

No subspecialty programs accredited by the Accreditation Council for Graduate Medical Education; no subspecialty certificates offered by the American Board of Ophthalmology.

Data

Unless otherwise noted, all data are for 2008.

Table 1. Ophthalmology Programs

Number of accredited programs	119

Program Data

length of accredited training	3/4
Minimum number of prior years of GME required	1
Offers graduate year 1 positions, available immediately upon medical school completion	No
Average number of interviews for program year 1 positions	44.4
Percent new program directors, 2007-2008 academic year (source: ACGME)	17.0%

Residents/Fellows

Total number of active residents/fellows	1,155
Average number of residents/fellows per program	9.7
Average percent female	42.5%
Average percent international medical graduate (IMG)	7.0%

Program Faculty

Average number of full-time physician faculty	16.0
Average number of part-time physician faculty	9.3
Average percent female full-time physician faculty	23.6%
Average ratio of full-time physician faculty to resident/fellow	1.1

Table 2. Data for Ophthalmology Programs Listed in FREIDA

Number of programs providing data	44

Work Schedule (Program Year 1)

Average hours on duty per week	50.8
Average maximum consecutive hours on duty	19.1
Average days off duty per week	1.7
Moonlighting allowed within institution	25.0%
Night float system	6.8%
Offers awareness and management of fatigue in residents/fellows	88.6%

Educational Setting (Program Year 1)

Average hours/week of regularly scheduled lectures/conferences	6.7
Average percent of training in hospital outpatient clinics	87.1%
Average percent of training in nonhospital ambulatory care community settings	14.6%

Educational Benefits

Curriculum on management of tobacco dependence	9.1%
Program to assess/enhance medical professionalism	77.3%
Debt management/financial counseling	56.8%
Formal program to develop teaching skills	68.2%

Formal mentoring program	47.7%
Formal program to foster interdisciplinary teamwork	13.6%
Continuous quality improvement training	95.5%
International experience	29.5%
Resident/fellow retreats	18.2%
Off-campus electives	36.4%
Hospice/home care experience	2.3%
Cultural competence awareness	56.8%
Instruction in medical Spanish or other non-English language	13.6%
Alternative/complementary medicine curriculum	15.9%
Training in identifying and reporting of domestic violence/abuse	38.6%
MPH/MBA or PhD training	6.8%
Research rotation	22.7%

Educational Features

Offers additional training or educational experience beyond accredited length	8.1%
Offers a primary care track	9.1%
Offers a rural track	0.0%
Offers a women's health track	0.0%
Offers a hospitalist track	0.0%
Offers a research track/nonaccredited fellowship	20.5%
Offers an other track	4.5%

Resident Evaluation

Yearly specialty in-service examination required	96.3%
Patient surveys	63.6%
Portfolio system	61.4%
360 degree evaluations	90.9%
Objective structured clinical examinations (OSCE)	36.4%

Program Evaluation

Program graduation rates	88.6%
Board certification rates	95.5%
In-training examinations	93.2%
Performance-based assessments	56.8%

Employment Policies and Benefits

Part-time/shared positions	2.3%
On-site child care	40.9%
Subsidized child care	6.8%
Allowance/stipend for professional expenses	90.9%
Leave for educational meetings/conferences	85.3%
Moving allowance	4.5%
Housing stipend	9.1%
On-call meal allowance	65.9%
Free parking	59.1%
PDAs	18.2%
Placement assistance upon completion of program	15.9%
Cross coverage in case of illness/disability	88.6%

Compensation and Leave (Graduate Year 1)

Average resident/fellow compensation	$46,642
Average number weeks of vacation	3.5
Sick days (paid)	20.8
Maximum number of paid days for family/medical leave	43
Maximum number of unpaid days for family/medical leave	47

Major Medical Benefits

Major medical insurance for residents	100.0%
Major medical insurance for dependents	100.0%
Outpatient mental health insurance	88.6%
Inpatient mental health insurance	88.6%
Group life insurance	97.7%
Dental insurance	84.1%
Disability insurance	90.9%
Disability insurance for occupationally acquired HIV	65.9%
Medical insurance coverage begins when starting program	86.4%

Specialty Data

Table 3. Ophthalmology Match Data

GY1	2008
Number of positions offered	3
Number filled by US seniors	1
Percent filled by US seniors	33.3
Total positions filled	1
Percent total positions filled	33.3

For more information

Professional Associations

American Academy of Ophthalmology
PO Box 7424
San Francisco, CA 94120-7424
415 561-8500
415 561-8533 Fax
www.aao.org

American Society of Cataract and Refractive Surgery
4000 Legato Road, Suite 700
Fairfax, VA 22033
703 591-2220
703 591-0614
www.ascrs.org

Contact Lens Association of Ophthalmologists
2025 Woodlane Drive
Saint Paul, MN 55125
877 501-3937
651 731-0410 Fax
E-mail: eyes@clao.org
www.clao.org

American Society of Retina Specialties
PMB #A
2485 Notre Dame Boulevard, Suite 370
Chico, CA 95928
530 566-9181
530 566-9192 Fax
E-mail: cordie@asrs.org
www.asrs.org

Certification

American Board of Ophthalmology
111 Presidential Boulevard, Suite 241
Bala Cynwyd, PA 19004-1075
610 664-1175
610 664-6503 Fax
E-mail: info@abop.org
www.abop.org

Program Accreditation

Accreditation Council for Graduate Medical Education
Residency Review Committee for Ophthalmology
Patricia Levenberg, PhD, RN, Executive Director
515 North State Street
Chicago, IL 60654
312 755-5048
E-mail: plevenberg@acgme.org
www.acgme.org

Orthopaedic Surgery

Professional Description

An orthopaedic surgeon is trained in preserving, investigating, and restoring the form and function of the extremities, spine, and associated structures by medical, surgical, and physical means.

An orthopaedic surgeon is involved with the care of patients whose musculoskeletal problems include congenital deformities, trauma, infections, tumors, metabolic disturbances of the musculoskeletal system, deformities, injuries, and degenerative diseases of the spine, hands, feet, knee, hip, shoulder, and elbow in children and adults. An orthopaedic surgeon is also concerned with primary and secondary muscular problems and the effects of central or peripheral nervous system lesions of the musculoskeletal system.

Prerequisites; Length of Training

No previous GME is required; length of accredited programs is 5 years.

Subspecialties

Subspecialty programs accredited by the ACGME

- Adult reconstructive orthopaedics
- Foot and ankle orthopaedics
- Hand surgery
- Musculoskeletal oncology
- Orthopaedic sports medicine
- Orthopaedic surgery of the spine
- Orthopaedic trauma
- Pediatric orthopaedics

American Board of Orthopaedic Surgery subspecialty certificates

- Orthopaedic sports medicine
- Surgery of the hand

Data

Unless otherwise noted, all data are for 2008.

Table 1. Orthopaedic Surgery Programs

Number of accredited programs	153
Program Data	
length of accredited training	5
Minimum number of prior years of GME required	1/0
Offers graduate year 1 positions, available immediately upon medical school completion	Some
Average number of interviews for program year 1 positions	53.0
Percent new program directors, 2007-2008 academic year (source: ACGME)	18.3%
Residents/Fellows	
Total number of active residents/fellows	3,098
Average number of residents/fellows per program	20.2
Average percent female	13.0%
Average percent international medical graduate (IMG)	2.5%
Program Faculty	
Average number of full-time physician faculty	16.4
Average number of part-time physician faculty	3.1
Average percent female full-time physician faculty	7.7%
Average ratio of full-time physician faculty to resident/fellow	0.6

Table 2. Data for Orthopaedic Surgery Programs Listed in FREIDA

Number of programs providing data	97
Work Schedule (Program Year 1)	
Average hours on duty per week	70.7

Average maximum consecutive hours on duty	26.4
Average days off duty per week	1.2
Moonlighting allowed within institution	25.8%
Night float system	33.0%
Offers awareness and management of fatigue in residents/fellows	91.8%

Educational Setting (Program Year 1)

Average hours/week of regularly scheduled lectures/conferences	5.9
Average percent of training in hospital outpatient clinics	30.7%
Average percent of training in nonhospital ambulatory care community settings	13.3%

Educational Benefits

Curriculum on management of tobacco dependence	7.2%
Program to assess/enhance medical professionalism	75.3%
Debt management/financial counseling	58.8%
Formal program to develop teaching skills	80.4%
Formal mentoring program	54.6%
Formal program to foster interdisciplinary teamwork	16.5%
Continuous quality improvement training	82.5%
International experience	19.6%
Resident/fellow retreats	30.9%
Off-campus electives	41.2%
Hospice/home care experience	4.1%
Cultural competence awareness	79.4%
Instruction in medical Spanish or other non-English language	14.4%
Alternative/complementary medicine curriculum	16.5%
Training in identifying and reporting of domestic violence/abuse	47.4%
MPH/MBA or PhD training	13.4%
Research rotation	63.9%

Educational Features

Offers additional training or educational experience beyond accredited length	25.3%
Offers a primary care track	5.2%
Offers a rural track	3.1%
Offers a women's health track	2.1%
Offers a hospitalist track	1.0%
Offers a research track/nonaccredited fellowship	16.5%
Offers an other track	6.2%

Resident Evaluation

Yearly specialty in-service examination required	99.4%
Patient surveys	35.1%
Portfolio system	33.0%
360 degree evaluations	82.5%
Objective structured clinical examinations (OSCE)	10.3%

Program Evaluation

Program graduation rates	84.5%
Board certification rates	97.9%
In-training examinations	99.0%
Performance-based assessments	38.1%

Employment Policies and Benefits

Part-time/shared positions	0.0%
On-site child care	36.1%
Subsidized child care	6.2%
Allowance/stipend for professional expenses	95.9%
Leave for educational meetings/conferences	91.5%
Moving allowance	11.3%
Housing stipend	4.1%
On-call meal allowance	96.9%
Free parking	61.9%
PDAs	27.8%
Placement assistance upon completion of program	18.6%
Cross coverage in case of illness/disability	74.2%

Compensation and Leave (Graduate Year 1)

Average resident/fellow compensation	$45,058
Average number weeks of vacation	3.3
Sick days (paid)	18.3
Maximum number of paid days for family/medical leave	41
Maximum number of unpaid days for family/medical leave	72

Major Medical Benefits

Major medical insurance for residents	100.0%
Major medical insurance for dependents	95.9%
Outpatient mental health insurance	89.7%
Inpatient mental health insurance	87.6%
Group life insurance	91.8%
Dental insurance	86.6%
Disability insurance	89.7%
Disability insurance for occupationally acquired HIV	75.3%
Medical insurance coverage begins when starting program	86.6%

Table 3. Orthopaedic Surgery Match Data

GY1	2008
Number of positions offered	636
Number filled by US seniors	592
Percent filled by US seniors	93.1
Total positions filled	635
Percent total positions filled	99.8
GY2	
Number of positions offered	0
Number filled by US seniors	0
Percent filled by US seniors	0
Total positions filled	0
Percent total positions filled	0
All	
Total Positions*	636
Preferred by US Seniors*	731
Preferred Positions per US Senior	0.9
Preferred by Independent Applicants†	173
Preferred Positions per IA	3.7

Source: National Resident Matching Program 2008 Match Data
* Includes all positions offered in a specialty, except preliminary positions.
† Preferred means the number of applicants for whom the specialty was the only or first choice.

For more information

Professional Associations

American Academy of Orthopaedic Surgeons
6300 North River Road
Rosemont, IL 60018-4262
847 823-7186
847 823-8125 Fax
www.aaos.org

American Association of Hip and Knee Surgeons
6300 North River Road, Suite 615
Rosemont, IL 60018-4237
847 698-1200
847 698-0704 Fax
www.aahks.org

American Orthopaedic Association
6300 North River Road, Suite 505
Rosemont, IL 60018
847 318-7330
847 318-7339
E-mail: info@aoassn.org
www.aoassn.org

Specialty Data

American Orthopaedic Foot and Ankle Society
6300 North River Road, Suite 510
Rosemont, IL 60018
847 698-4654
847 692-3315
E-mail: aofasinfo@aofas.org
www.aofas.org

Certification

American Board of Orthopaedic Surgery
400 Silver Cedar Court
Chapel Hill, NC 27514
919 929-7103
919 942-8988 Fax
www.abos.org

Program Accreditation

Accreditation Council for Graduate Medical Education
Residency Review Committee for Orthopaedic Surgery
Steven P Nestler, PhD, Executive Director
515 North State Street
Chicago, IL 60654
312 755-5025
E-mail: spn@acgme.org
www.acgme.org

Adult Reconstructive Orthopaedics

Professional Description

Adult reconstructive orthopaedics includes the in-depth study, prevention, and reconstructive treatment of musculoskeletal diseases, disorders, and sequelae of injuries by medical, physical, and surgical methods in patients 17 years and older. An educational program in adult reconstructive orthopaedics may include the care of arthritis and related disorders in many anatomic regions or be limited to areas such as the hip, knee, shoulder, elbow, or ankle and foot.

Source: Adult Reconstructive Orthopaedics Program Requirements, ACGME, www.acgme.org/acWebsite/downloads/RRC_progReq/09-2007PRs/261_Adult_Recon_Ortho_Surg_07012008.pdf

Prerequisites; Length of Training

Completion of an accredited residency is required. Length of ACGME-accredited programs is 1 year.

For more information

American Academy of Orthopaedic Surgeons
6300 North River Road
Rosemont, IL 60018-4262
847 823-7186
847 823-8125 Fax
www.aaos.org

Foot and Ankle Orthopaedics

Professional Description

Foot and ankle orthopaedics is a subspecialty of orthopaedic surgery which includes the in-depth study, prevention, and treatment of musculoskeletal diseases, disorders, and sequelae of injuries in this anatomic region by medical, physical, and surgical methods.

Source: Foot and Ankle Orthopaedics Program Requirements, ACGME, www.acgme.org/acWebsite/downloads/RRC_progReq/09-2007PRs/262_Foot_and_Ankle_Ortho_Surg_07012008.pdf

Prerequisites; Length of Training

Completion of an accredited residency is required. Length of ACGME-accredited programs is 1 year.

For more information

American Orthopaedic Foot and Ankle Society
6300 North River Road, Suite 510
Rosemont, IL 60018
847 698-4654
847 692-3315
E-mail: aofasinfo@aofas.org
www.aofas.org

Hand Surgery

Professional Description

A specialist trained in the investigation, preservation, and restoration by medical, surgical, and rehabilitative means of all structures of the upper extremity directly affecting the form and function of the hand and wrist.

Prerequisites; Length of Training

Completion of an accredited general surgery, orthopaedic surgery, or plastic surgery residency in the US or Canada is required. Length of ACGME-accredited programs is 1 year.

Data

Unless otherwise noted, all data are for 2008.

Table 1. Hand Surgery Programs	
Number of accredited programs	56
Program Data	
length of accredited training	1
Minimum number of prior years of GME required	5
Offers graduate year 1 positions, available immediately upon medical school completion	No
Average number of interviews for program year 1 positions	18.3
Percent new program directors, 2007-2008 academic year (source: ACGME)	7.1%
Residents/Fellows	
Total number of active residents/fellows	99
Average number of residents/fellows per program	1.8
Average percent female	19.2%
Average percent international medical graduate (IMG)	9.1%
Program Faculty	
Average number of full-time physician faculty	6.0
Average number of part-time physician faculty	0.5
Average percent female full-time physician faculty	10.5%
Average ratio of full-time physician faculty to resident/fellow	1.3

Table 2. Data for Hand Surgery Programs Listed in FREIDA	
Number of programs providing data	28
Work Schedule (Program Year 1)	
Average hours on duty per week	53.9
Average maximum consecutive hours on duty	20.3
Average days off duty per week	1.6
Moonlighting allowed within institution	25.0%
Night float system	0.0%
Offers awareness and management of fatigue in residents/fellows	78.6%
Educational Setting (Program Year 1)	
Average hours/week of regularly scheduled lectures/conferences	4.5
Average percent of training in hospital outpatient clinics	27.6%

Average percent of training in nonhospital ambulatory care community settings	31.3%

Educational Benefits

Curriculum on management of tobacco dependence	7.1%
Program to assess/enhance medical professionalism	53.6%
Debt management/financial counseling	35.7%
Formal program to develop teaching skills	67.9%
Formal mentoring program	39.3%
Formal program to foster interdisciplinary teamwork	10.7%
Continuous quality improvement training	42.9%
International experience	17.9%
Resident/fellow retreats	14.3%
Off-campus electives	39.3%
Hospice/home care experience	0.0%
Cultural competence awareness	46.4%
Instruction in medical Spanish or other non-English language	17.9%
Alternative/complementary medicine curriculum	3.6%
Training in identifying and reporting of domestic violence/abuse	25.0%
MPH/MBA or PhD training	3.6%
Research rotation	46.4%

Educational Features

Offers additional training or educational experience beyond accredited length	3.4%
Offers a primary care track	3.6%
Offers a rural track	0.0%
Offers a women's health track	3.6%
Offers a hospitalist track	0.0%
Offers a research track/nonaccredited fellowship	3.6%
Offers an other track	7.1%

Resident Evaluation

Yearly specialty in-service examination required	31.7%
Patient surveys	14.3%
Portfolio system	10.7%
360 degree evaluations	60.7%
Objective structured clinical examinations (OSCE)	3.6%

Program Evaluation

Program graduation rates	71.4%
Board certification rates	78.6%
In-training examinations	21.4%
Performance-based assessments	28.6%

Employment Policies and Benefits

Part-time/shared positions	3.6%
On-site child care	32.1%
Subsidized child care	10.7%
Allowance/stipend for professional expenses	85.7%
Leave for educational meetings/conferences	84.6%
Moving allowance	3.6%
Housing stipend	0.0%
On-call meal allowance	32.1%
Free parking	39.3%
PDAs	14.3%
Placement assistance upon completion of program	21.4%
Cross coverage in case of illness/disability	67.9%

Compensation and Leave (Graduate Year 1)

Average resident/fellow compensation	$55,152
Average number weeks of vacation	3.0
Sick days (paid)	23.0
Maximum number of paid days for family/medical leave	41
Maximum number of unpaid days for family/medical leave	38

Major Medical Benefits

Major medical insurance for residents	100.0%
Major medical insurance for dependents	96.4%

Outpatient mental health insurance	89.3%
Inpatient mental health insurance	89.3%
Group life insurance	89.3%
Dental insurance	92.9%
Disability insurance	82.1%
Disability insurance for occupationally acquired HIV	60.7%
Medical insurance coverage begins when starting program	85.7%

For more information

Professional Association

American Academy of Orthopaedic Surgeons
6300 North River Road
Rosemont, IL 60018-4262
847 823-7186
847 823-8125 Fax
www.aaos.org

Musculoskeletal Oncology

Professional Description

Musculoskeletal oncology is the component of orthopaedic surgery that is focused on the diagnosis and treatment of children and adults with benign and malignant tumors of bone and connective soft tissues. The field also includes the diagnosis, treatment, and palliative care of patients with metastatic carcinoma to the skeleton. Musculoskeletal oncologists work in concert with experts from musculoskeletal radiology, pathology, medical and pediatric oncology, radiotherapy, and surgery to care for patients with sarcomas of bone and soft tissue.

Source: Musculoskeletal Oncology Program Requirements, ACGME, www.acgme.org/acWebsite/downloads/RRC_progReq/09-2007PRs/270_Musculoskeletal_Oncology_07012008.pdf

Prerequisites; Length of Training

Completion of an accredited residency is required. Length of ACGME-accredited programs is 1 year.

For more information

American Academy of Orthopaedic Surgeons
6300 North River Road
Rosemont, IL 60018-4262
847 823-7186
847 823-8125 Fax
www.aaos.org

Orthopaedic Sports Medicine

Professional Description

An orthopaedic surgeon trained in sports medicine provides appropriate care for all structures of the musculoskeletal system directly affected by participation in sporting activity.

A sports medicine surgeon is proficient in areas including conditioning, training, and fitness; athletic performance and the impact of dietary supplements, pharmaceuticals, and nutrition on performance and health; coordination of care within the team setting and utilizing other health care professionals; field evaluation and management; and soft tissue biomechanics injury, healing and repair. The specialist understands treatment options, both surgical and nonsurgical, as they relate to sports specific injuries and competition. Knowledge in understanding the principles and techniques of rehabilitation, athletic equipment, and orthoptic devices enables the specialist to prevent and manage athletic injuries.

Prerequisites; Length of Training

Completion of an accredited residency is required. Length of ACGME-accredited programs is 1 year.

Data

Unless otherwise noted, all data are for 2008.

Table 1. Orthopaedic Sports Medicine Programs

Number of accredited programs	84

Program Data

length of accredited training	1
Minimum number of prior years of GME required	5
Offers graduate year 1 positions, available immediately upon medical school completion	No
Average number of interviews for program year 1 positions	13.6
Percent new program directors, 2007-2008 academic year (source: ACGME)	1.3%

Residents/Fellows

Total number of active residents/fellows	139
Average number of residents/fellows per program	1.7
Average percent female	3.6%
Average percent international medical graduate (IMG)	2.9%

Program Faculty

Average number of full-time physician faculty	5.8
Average number of part-time physician faculty	0.6
Average percent female full-time physician faculty	4.5%
Average ratio of full-time physician faculty to resident/fellow	1.4

Table 2. Data for Orthopaedic Sports Medicine Programs Listed in FREIDA

Number of programs providing data	33

Work Schedule (Program Year 1)

Average hours on duty per week	42.8
Average maximum consecutive hours on duty	13.5
Average days off duty per week	1.8
Moonlighting allowed within institution	30.3%
Night float system	3.0%
Offers awareness and management of fatigue in residents/fellows	60.6%

Educational Setting (Program Year 1)

Average hours/week of regularly scheduled lectures/conferences	3.6
Average percent of training in hospital outpatient clinics	41.9%
Average percent of training in nonhospital ambulatory care community settings	36.2%

Educational Benefits

Curriculum on management of tobacco dependence	6.1%
Program to assess/enhance medical professionalism	39.4%
Debt management/financial counseling	27.3%
Formal program to develop teaching skills	72.7%
Formal mentoring program	33.3%
Formal program to foster interdisciplinary teamwork	21.2%
Continuous quality improvement training	57.6%
International experience	6.1%
Resident/fellow retreats	18.2%
Off-campus electives	18.2%
Hospice/home care experience	0.0%
Cultural competence awareness	39.4%
Instruction in medical Spanish or other non-English language	18.2%
Alternative/complementary medicine curriculum	15.2%
Training in identifying and reporting of domestic violence/abuse	12.1%
MPH/MBA or PhD training	0.0%
Research rotation	63.6%

Educational Features

Offers additional training or educational experience beyond accredited length	3.3%
Offers a primary care track	6.1%
Offers a rural track	0.0%
Offers a women's health track	6.1%
Offers a hospitalist track	3.0%
Offers a research track/nonaccredited fellowship	0.0%
Offers an other track	9.1%

Resident Evaluation

Yearly specialty in-service examination required	74.2%
Patient surveys	12.1%
Portfolio system	9.1%
360 degree evaluations	45.5%
Objective structured clinical examinations (OSCE)	3.0%

Program Evaluation

Program graduation rates	54.5%
Board certification rates	48.5%
In-training examinations	54.5%
Performance-based assessments	30.3%

Employment Policies and Benefits

Part-time/shared positions	3.0%
On-site child care	18.2%
Subsidized child care	3.0%
Allowance/stipend for professional expenses	97.0%
Leave for educational meetings/conferences	70.6%
Moving allowance	3.0%
Housing stipend	3.0%
On-call meal allowance	30.3%
Free parking	60.6%
PDAs	9.1%
Placement assistance upon completion of program	15.2%
Cross coverage in case of illness/disability	66.7%

Compensation and Leave (Graduate Year 1)

Average resident/fellow compensation	$52,263
Average number weeks of vacation	10.1
Sick days (paid)	17.6
Maximum number of paid days for family/medical leave	18
Maximum number of unpaid days for family/medical leave	17

Major Medical Benefits

Major medical insurance for residents	97.0%
Major medical insurance for dependents	84.8%
Outpatient mental health insurance	87.9%
Inpatient mental health insurance	87.9%
Group life insurance	81.8%
Dental insurance	84.8%
Disability insurance	81.8%
Disability insurance for occupationally acquired HIV	60.6%
Medical insurance coverage begins when starting program	81.8%

For more information

American Academy of Orthopaedic Surgeons
6300 North River Road
Rosemont, IL 60018-4262
847 823-7186
847 823-8125 Fax
www.aaos.org

Orthopaedic Surgery of the Spine

Professional Description

Orthopaedic surgery of the spine is the component of orthopaedic surgery that is focused on the study and prevention of spinal column diseases, disorders, and injuries and their treatment by medical, physical, and surgical methods.

Source: Orthopaedic Surgery of the Spine Program Requirements, ACGME, www.acgme.org/acWebsite/downloads/RRC_progReq/09-2007PRs/267_Ortho_Surgery_of_the_Spine_07012008.pdf

Prerequisites; Length of Training

Completion of an accredited residency is required. Length of ACGME-accredited programs is 1 year.

Data

Unless otherwise noted, all data are for 2008.

Table 1. Orthopaedic Surgery of the Spine Programs

Number of accredited programs	13
Program Data	
length of accredited training	1
Minimum number of prior years of GME required	5
Offers graduate year 1 positions, available immediately upon medical school completion	No
Average number of interviews for program year 1 positions	9.0
Percent new program directors, 2007-2008 academic year (source: ACGME)	14.3%
Residents/Fellows	
Total number of active residents/fellows	24
Average number of residents/fellows per program	1.8
Average percent female	8.3%
Average percent international medical graduate (IMG)	20.8%
Program Faculty	
Average number of full-time physician faculty	6.2
Average number of part-time physician faculty	0.6
Average percent female full-time physician faculty	0.0%
Average ratio of full-time physician faculty to resident/fellow	1.6

Table 2. Data for Orthopaedic Surgery of the Spine Programs Listed in FREIDA

Number of programs providing data	5
Work Schedule (Program Year 1)	
Average hours on duty per week	51.9
Average maximum consecutive hours on duty	20.0
Average days off duty per week	2.0
Moonlighting allowed within institution	0.0%
Night float system	20.0%
Offers awareness and management of fatigue in residents/fellows	80.0%
Educational Setting (Program Year 1)	
Average hours/week of regularly scheduled lectures/conferences	2.8
Average percent of training in hospital outpatient clinics	20.3%
Average percent of training in nonhospital ambulatory care community settings	6.7%
Educational Benefits	
Curriculum on management of tobacco dependence	0.0%
Program to assess/enhance medical professionalism	80.0%
Debt management/financial counseling	40.0%
Formal program to develop teaching skills	100.0%
Formal mentoring program	60.0%
Formal program to foster interdisciplinary teamwork	40.0%
Continuous quality improvement training	60.0%

International experience	40.0%
Resident/fellow retreats	20.0%
Off-campus electives	0.0%
Hospice/home care experience	0.0%
Cultural competence awareness	80.0%
Instruction in medical Spanish or other non-English language	0.0%
Alternative/complementary medicine curriculum	20.0%
Training in identifying and reporting of domestic violence/abuse	60.0%
MPH/MBA or PhD training	0.0%
Research rotation	60.0%
Educational Features	
Offers additional training or educational experience beyond accredited length	12.5%
Offers a primary care track	40.0%
Offers a rural track	0.0%
Offers a women's health track	0.0%
Offers a hospitalist track	0.0%
Offers a research track/nonaccredited fellowship	0.0%
Offers an other track	0.0%
Resident Evaluation	
Yearly specialty in-service examination required	0.0%
Patient surveys	0.0%
Portfolio system	0.0%
360 degree evaluations	60.0%
Objective structured clinical examinations (OSCE)	0.0%
Program Evaluation	
Program graduation rates	60.0%
Board certification rates	40.0%
In-training examinations	20.0%
Performance-based assessments	20.0%
Employment Policies and Benefits	
Part-time/shared positions	0.0%
On-site child care	40.0%
Subsidized child care	0.0%
Allowance/stipend for professional expenses	100.0%
Leave for educational meetings/conferences	65.2%
Moving allowance	0.0%
Housing stipend	0.0%
On-call meal allowance	40.0%
Free parking	60.0%
PDAs	0.0%
Placement assistance upon completion of program	0.0%
Cross coverage in case of illness/disability	80.0%
Compensation and Leave (Graduate Year 1)	
Average resident/fellow compensation	$56,985
Average number weeks of vacation	3.2
Sick days (paid)	39.7
Maximum number of paid days for family/medical leave	83
Maximum number of unpaid days for family/medical leave	20
Major Medical Benefits	
Major medical insurance for residents	100.0%
Major medical insurance for dependents	80.0%
Outpatient mental health insurance	80.0%
Inpatient mental health insurance	80.0%
Group life insurance	80.0%
Dental insurance	80.0%
Disability insurance	80.0%
Disability insurance for occupationally acquired HIV	80.0%
Medical insurance coverage begins when starting program	80.0%

For more information

American Academy of Orthopaedic Surgeons
6300 North River Road
Rosemont, IL 60018-4262
847 823-7186
847 823-8125 Fax
www.aaos.org

Orthopaedic Trauma

Professional Description

Orthopaedic trauma is a subspecialty of orthopaedic surgery that includes the in-depth study and treatment of injuries to the locomotor system and their sequelae.

Source: ACGME Program Requirements for Graduate Medical Education in Orthopaedic Trauma,
www.acgme.org/acWebsite/downloads/RRC_progReq/09-2007PRs/269_Orthopaedic_Trauma_07012008.pdf

Prerequisites; Length of Training

Completion of an accredited residency is required. Length of ACGME-accredited programs is 1 year.

For more information

American Academy of Orthopaedic Surgeons
6300 North River Road
Rosemont, IL 60018-4262
847 823-7186
847 823-8125 Fax
www.aaos.org

Pediatric Orthopaedics

Professional Description

Pediatric orthopaedics is the medical specialty that includes the study and prevention of musculoskeletal diseases, disorders, and injuries and their treatment by medical, surgical, and physical methods in patients aged 16 years and younger.

Source: Pediatric Orthopaedics Program Requirements, ACGME,
www.acgme.org/acWebsite/downloads/RRC_progReq/09-2007PRs/265_Pediatric_Ortho_Surg_07012008.pdf

Prerequisites; Length of Training

Completion of an accredited residency is required. Length of ACGME-accredited programs is 1 year.

For more information

American Academy of Orthopaedic Surgeons
6300 North River Road
Rosemont, IL 60018-4262
847 823-7186
847 823-8125 Fax
www.aaos.org

Otolaryngology

Professional Description

An otolaryngologist-head and neck surgeon provides comprehensive medical and surgical care for patients with diseases and disorders that affect the ears, nose, throat, respiratory and upper alimentary systems, and related structures of the head and neck.

An otolaryngologist diagnoses and provides medical and/or surgical therapy or prevention of diseases, allergies, neoplasms, deformities, disorders, and/or injuries of the ears, nose, sinuses, throat, respiratory and upper alimentary systems, face, jaws, and the other head and neck systems. Head and neck oncology, facial plastic and reconstructive surgery, and the treatment of disorders of hearing and voice are fundamental areas of expertise.

Prerequisites; Length of Training

No previous GME is required; length of accredited programs is 5 years.

Subspecialties

Subspecialty programs accredited by the ACGME

- Neurotology
- Pediatric otolaryngology
- Sleep medicine

American Board of Otolaryngology subspecialty certificates

- Neurotology
- Pediatric otolaryngology
- Plastic surgery within the head and neck
- Sleep medicine

Data

Unless otherwise noted, all data are for 2008.

Table 1. Otolaryngology Programs	
Number of accredited programs	103
Program Data	
length of accredited training	5
Minimum number of prior years of GME required	0
Offers graduate year 1 positions, available immediately upon medical school completion	Yes
Average number of interviews for program year 1 positions	34.7
Percent new program directors, 2007-2008 academic year (source: ACGME)	16.5%
Residents/Fellows	
Total number of active residents/fellows	1,217
Average number of residents/fellows per program	11.8
Average percent female	29.7%
Average percent international medical graduate (IMG)	3.5%
Program Faculty	
Average number of full-time physician faculty	13.3
Average number of part-time physician faculty	2.1
Average percent female full-time physician faculty	15.3%
Average ratio of full-time physician faculty to resident/fellow	0.8

Table 2. Data for Otolaryngology Programs Listed in FREIDA	
Number of programs providing data	52
Work Schedule (Program Year 1)	
Average hours on duty per week	67.4
Average maximum consecutive hours on duty	26.2
Average days off duty per week	1.3
Moonlighting allowed within institution	23.1%
Night float system	17.3%

Offers awareness and management of fatigue in residents/fellows	90.4%

Educational Setting (Program Year 1)

Average hours/week of regularly scheduled lectures/conferences	5.3
Average percent of training in hospital outpatient clinics	36.2%
Average percent of training in nonhospital ambulatory care community settings	10.6%

Educational Benefits

Curriculum on management of tobacco dependence	23.1%
Program to assess/enhance medical professionalism	80.8%
Debt management/financial counseling	59.6%
Formal program to develop teaching skills	84.6%
Formal mentoring program	63.5%
Formal program to foster interdisciplinary teamwork	28.8%
Continuous quality improvement training	96.2%
International experience	21.2%
Resident/fellow retreats	46.2%
Off-campus electives	40.4%
Hospice/home care experience	9.6%
Cultural competence awareness	69.2%
Instruction in medical Spanish or other non-English language	21.2%
Alternative/complementary medicine curriculum	25.0%
Training in identifying and reporting of domestic violence/abuse	38.5%
MPH/MBA or PhD training	15.4%
Research rotation	96.2%

Educational Features

Offers additional training or educational experience beyond accredited length	16.0%
Offers a primary care track	7.7%
Offers a rural track	1.9%
Offers a women's health track	1.9%
Offers a hospitalist track	1.9%
Offers a research track/nonaccredited fellowship	19.2%
Offers an other track	3.8%

Resident Evaluation

Yearly specialty in-service examination required	100.0%
Patient surveys	53.8%
Portfolio system	65.4%
360 degree evaluations	96.2%
Objective structured clinical examinations (OSCE)	15.4%

Program Evaluation

Program graduation rates	84.6%
Board certification rates	100.0%
In-training examinations	100.0%
Performance-based assessments	44.2%

Employment Policies and Benefits

Part-time/shared positions	0.0%
On-site child care	36.5%
Subsidized child care	5.8%
Allowance/stipend for professional expenses	96.2%
Leave for educational meetings/conferences	95.6%
Moving allowance	5.8%
Housing stipend	11.5%
On-call meal allowance	84.6%
Free parking	57.7%
PDAs	17.3%
Placement assistance upon completion of program	17.3%
Cross coverage in case of illness/disability	88.5%

Compensation and Leave (Graduate Year 1)

Average resident/fellow compensation	$45,465
Average number weeks of vacation	3.2
Sick days (paid)	25.1
Maximum number of paid days for family/medical leave	37

Maximum number of unpaid days for family/medical leave	65

Major Medical Benefits

Major medical insurance for residents	98.1%
Major medical insurance for dependents	92.3%
Outpatient mental health insurance	92.3%
Inpatient mental health insurance	92.3%
Group life insurance	94.2%
Dental insurance	82.7%
Disability insurance	90.4%
Disability insurance for occupationally acquired HIV	82.7%
Medical insurance coverage begins when starting program	92.3%

Table 3. Otolaryngology Match Data

GY1	2008
Number of positions offered	273
Number filled by US seniors	253
Percent filled by US seniors	92.7
Total positions filled	269
Percent total positions filled	98.5
All	
Total Positions*	273
Preferred by US Seniors*	307
Preferred Positions per US Senior	0.9
Preferred by Independent Applicants†	48
Preferred Positions per IA	5.7

Source: National Resident Matching Program 2008 Match Data
* Includes all positions offered in a specialty, except preliminary positions.
† Preferred means the number of applicants for whom the specialty was the only or first choice.

For more information

Professional Associations

American Academy of Otolaryngic Allergy
1990 M Street, NW, Suite 680
Washington, DC 20036
202 955-5010
202 955-5016
E-mail: info@aaoaf.org
www.aaoaf.org

American Academy of Otolaryngology-Head and Neck Surgery
1650 Diagonal Road
Alexandria, VA 22314-2857
703 836-4444
www.entnet.org

Triological Society, The
555 North 30th Street
Omaha, NE 68131
402 346-5500
402 346-5300 Fax
E-mail: info@triological.org
www.triological.com

Certification

American Board of Otolaryngology
5615 Kirby Drive, Suite 600
Houston, TX 77005
713 850-0399
713 850-1104 Fax
www.aboto.org

Program Accreditation

Accreditation Council for Graduate Medical Education
Residency Review Committee for Otolaryngology
Patricia Levenberg, PhD, RN, Executive Director
515 North State Street
Chicago, IL 60654
312 755-5048
E-mail: plevenberg@acgme.org
www.acgme.org

Neurotology

Professional Description

An otolaryngologist who treats diseases of the ear and temporal
bone, including disorders of hearing and balance. The additional
training in otology and neurotology emphasizes the study of embry-
ology, anatomy, physiology, epidemiology, pathophysiology, pathology, genetics, immunology, microbiology, and the etiology of
diseases of the ear and temporal bone.

The neurotologist should have command of the core knowledge
and understanding of:

- The basic medical sciences relevant to the temporal bone, lateral
  skull base, and related structures; the communication sciences,
  including knowledge of audiology, endocrinology, and neurology
  as they relate to the temporal bone, lateral skull base, and
  related structures
- Advanced diagnostic expertise and advanced medical and surgical management skills for the care of diseases and disorders of
  the petrous apex, infratemporal fossa, internal auditory canals,
  cranial nerves, and lateral skull base (including the occipital
  bone, sphenoid bone, temporal bone, mesial aspect of the dura
  and intradural management), in conjunction with neurological
  surgery

A neurotologist has acquired expertise in the medical and surgical
management of diseases and disorders of the temporal bone, lateral
skull base, and related structures beyond that inherent to the practice of otolaryngology-head and neck surgery.
Source: American Board of Otolaryngology

Prerequisites; Length of Training

Completion of an accredited otolaryngology residency is required.
Length of ACGME-accredited programs is 2 years.

For more information

American Neurotology Society
www.otology-neurotology.org/ANS/ans-main.html

Pediatric Otolaryngology

Professional Description

A pediatric otolaryngologist has special expertise in the management of infants and children with disorders that include congenital
and acquired conditions involving the aerodigestive tract, nose and
paranasal sinuses, the ear, and other areas of the head and neck.
The pediatric otolaryngologist has special skills in diagnosing, treating, and managing childhood disorders of voice, speech, language,
and hearing.

Prerequisites; Length of Training

Completion of an accredited otolaryngology residency is required.
Length of ACGME-accredited programs is 1 year (as of July 1,
2006).

Data

Unless otherwise noted, all data are for 2008.

Table 1. Pediatric Otolaryngology Programs

Number of accredited programs	7
Program Data	
length of accredited training	2
Minimum number of prior years of GME required	5
Offers graduate year 1 positions, available immediately upon medical school completion	No
Average number of interviews for program year 1 positions	7.4
Percent new program directors, 2007-2008 academic year (source: ACGME)	0.0%
Residents/Fellows	
Total number of active residents/fellows	11
Average number of residents/fellows per program	1.6
Average percent female	27.3%
Average percent international medical graduate (IMG)	9.1%
Program Faculty	
Average number of full-time physician faculty	6.6
Average number of part-time physician faculty	0.2
Average percent female full-time physician faculty	27.3%
Average ratio of full-time physician faculty to resident/fellow	1.7

Table 2. Data for Pediatric Otolaryngology Programs Listed in FREIDA

Number of programs providing data	2
Work Schedule (Program Year 1)	
Average hours on duty per week	35.0
Average maximum consecutive hours on duty	8.9
Average days off duty per week	1.8
Moonlighting allowed within institution	50.0%
Night float system	0.0%
Offers awareness and management of fatigue in residents/fellows	100.0%
Educational Setting (Program Year 1)	
Average hours/week of regularly scheduled lectures/conferences	5.0
Average percent of training in hospital outpatient clinics	25.0%
Average percent of training in nonhospital ambulatory care community settings	10.0%
Educational Benefits	
Curriculum on management of tobacco dependence	0.0%
Program to assess/enhance medical professionalism	100.0%
Debt management/financial counseling	0.0%
Formal program to develop teaching skills	100.0%
Formal mentoring program	100.0%
Formal program to foster interdisciplinary teamwork	50.0%
Continuous quality improvement training	100.0%
International experience	50.0%
Resident/fellow retreats	50.0%
Off-campus electives	50.0%
Hospice/home care experience	0.0%
Cultural competence awareness	100.0%
Instruction in medical Spanish or other non-English language	0.0%
Alternative/complementary medicine curriculum	0.0%
Training in identifying and reporting of domestic violence/abuse	0.0%
MPH/MBA or PhD training	50.0%
Research rotation	50.0%

Educational Features

Offers additional training or educational experience beyond accredited length	66.7%
Offers a primary care track	0.0%
Offers a rural track	0.0%
Offers a women's health track	0.0%
Offers a hospitalist track	0.0%
Offers a research track/nonaccredited fellowship	50.0%
Offers an other track	50.0%

Resident Evaluation

Yearly specialty in-service examination required	0.0%
Patient surveys	0.0%
Portfolio system	50.0%
360 degree evaluations	100.0%
Objective structured clinical examinations (OSCE)	0.0%

Program Evaluation

Program graduation rates	50.0%
Board certification rates	0.0%
In-training examinations	0.0%
Performance-based assessments	100.0%

Employment Policies and Benefits

Part-time/shared positions	0.0%
On-site child care	50.0%
Subsidized child care	0.0%
Allowance/stipend for professional expenses	100.0%
Leave for educational meetings/conferences	57.1%
Moving allowance	50.0%
Housing stipend	0.0%
On-call meal allowance	0.0%
Free parking	50.0%
PDAs	0.0%
Placement assistance upon completion of program	50.0%
Cross coverage in case of illness/disability	100.0%

Compensation and Leave (Graduate Year 1)

Average resident/fellow compensation	$54,210
Average number weeks of vacation	3.0
Maximum number of paid days for family/medical leave	13
Maximum number of unpaid days for family/medical leave	68

Major Medical Benefits

Major medical insurance for residents	100.0%
Major medical insurance for dependents	100.0%
Outpatient mental health insurance	100.0%
Inpatient mental health insurance	100.0%
Group life insurance	100.0%
Dental insurance	100.0%
Disability insurance	100.0%
Disability insurance for occupationally acquired HIV	100.0%
Medical insurance coverage begins when starting program	100.0%

For more information

American Academy of Otolaryngology-Head and Neck Surgery
1650 Diagonal Road
Alexandria, VA 22314-2857
703 836-4444
www.entnet.org

Plastic Surgery within the Head and Neck

Professional Description

An otolaryngologist with additional training in plastic and reconstructive procedures within the head, face, neck, and associated structures, including cutaneous head and neck oncology and reconstruction, management of maxillofacial trauma, soft tissue repair, and neural surgery.

The field is diverse and involves a wide age range of patients, from the newborn to the aged. While both cosmetic and reconstructive surgery are practiced, there are many additional procedures which interface with them.

For more information

American Academy of Otolaryngology-Head and Neck Surgery
1650 Diagonal Road
Alexandria, VA 22314-2857
703 836-4444
www.entnet.org

Sleep Medicine

See page 155.

Pain Medicine

Note: In 2007, ACGME-accredited pain medicine programs under anesthesiology, neurology, physical medicine and rehabilitation, and psychiatry were combined into a multidisciplinary pain medicine subspecialty.

Professional Description

A psychiatrist who provides a high level of care, either as a primary physician or consultant, for patients experiencing problems with acute, chronic, or cancer pain in both hospital and ambulatory settings. Patient care needs may also be coordinated with other specialists.

Prerequisites; Length of Training

A minimum of 4 years of prior GME is required. Length of ACGME-accredited programs is 1 year.

Data

Unless otherwise noted, all data are for 2008.

Table 1. Pain Medicine Programs

Number of accredited programs	92

Program Data

length of accredited training	1
Minimum number of prior years of GME required	3/4
Offers graduate year 1 positions, available immediately upon medical school completion	No
Average number of interviews for program year 1 positions	15.3
Percent new program directors, 2006-2007 academic year (source: ACGME)	15.2%

Residents/Fellows

Total number of active residents/fellows	214
Average number of residents/fellows per program	2.3
Average percent female	27.1%
Average percent international medical graduate (IMG)	20.1%

Program Faculty

Average number of full-time physician faculty	6.7
Average number of part-time physician faculty	1.0
Average percent female full-time physician faculty	22.2%
Average ratio of full-time physician faculty to resident/fellow	1.2

Table 2. Data for Pain Medicine Programs Listed in FREIDA

Number of programs providing data	39

Work Schedule (Program Year 1)

Average hours on duty per week	45.1
Average maximum consecutive hours on duty	16.0
Average days off duty per week	1.8
Moonlighting allowed within institution	56.4%
Night float system	2.6%
Offers awareness and management of fatigue in residents/fellows	76.9%

Educational Setting (Program Year 1)

Average hours/week of regularly scheduled lectures/conferences	3.4
Average percent of training in hospital outpatient clinics	78.3%
Average percent of training in nonhospital ambulatory care community settings	16.8%

Educational Benefits

Curriculum on management of tobacco dependence	23.1%
Program to assess/enhance medical professionalism	82.1%
Debt management/financial counseling	53.8%
Formal program to develop teaching skills	64.1%
Formal mentoring program	61.5%
Formal program to foster interdisciplinary teamwork	35.9%

Continuous quality improvement training	89.7%
International experience	17.9%
Resident/fellow retreats	33.3%
Off-campus electives	43.6%
Hospice/home care experience	41.0%
Cultural competence awareness	64.1%
Instruction in medical Spanish or other non-English language	17.9%
Alternative/complementary medicine curriculum	71.8%
Training in identifying and reporting of domestic violence/abuse	33.3%
MPH/MBA or PhD training	7.7%
Research rotation	5.1%

Educational Features

Offers additional training or educational experience beyond accredited length	8.6%
Offers a primary care track	0.0%
Offers a rural track	0.0%
Offers a women's health track	0.0%
Offers a hospitalist track	5.1%
Offers a research track/nonaccredited fellowship	2.6%
Offers an other track	2.6%

Resident Evaluation

Yearly specialty in-service examination required	29.5%
Patient surveys	43.6%
Portfolio system	38.5%
360 degree evaluations	76.9%
Objective structured clinical examinations (OSCE)	10.3%

Program Evaluation

Program graduation rates	84.6%
Board certification rates	89.7%
In-training examinations	23.1%
Performance-based assessments	38.5%

Employment Policies and Benefits

Part-time/shared positions	0.0%
On-site child care	35.9%
Subsidized child care	5.1%
Allowance/stipend for professional expenses	92.3%
Leave for educational meetings/conferences	89.4%
Moving allowance	2.6%
Housing stipend	0.0%
On-call meal allowance	59.0%
Free parking	61.5%
PDAs	7.7%
Placement assistance upon completion of program	25.6%
Cross coverage in case of illness/disability	74.4%

Compensation and Leave (Graduate Year 1)

Average resident/fellow compensation	$52,496
Average number weeks of vacation	3.5
Sick days (paid)	30.7
Maximum number of paid days for family/medical leave	39
Maximum number of unpaid days for family/medical leave	48

Major Medical Benefits

Major medical insurance for residents	100.0%
Major medical insurance for dependents	100.0%
Outpatient mental health insurance	92.3%
Inpatient mental health insurance	92.3%
Group life insurance	97.4%
Dental insurance	92.3%
Disability insurance	87.2%
Disability insurance for occupationally acquired HIV	74.4%
Medical insurance coverage begins when starting program	84.6%

For more information

American Academy of Pain Medicine
4700 West Lake
Glenview, IL 60025
847 375-4731
847 375-6429 Fax
E-mail: info@painmed.org
www.painmed.org

Pathology

Professional Description

A pathologist deals with the causes and nature of disease and contributes to diagnosis, prognosis, and treatment through knowledge gained by the laboratory application of the biologic, chemical, and physical sciences.

A pathologist uses information gathered from the microscopic examination of tissue specimens, cells, and body fluids, and from clinical laboratory tests on body fluids and secretions, for the diagnosis, exclusion, and monitoring of disease.

Prerequisites; Length of Training

No previous GME is required; length of accredited programs is either 3 years or 4 years.

Subspecialties

Subspecialty programs accredited by the ACGME

- Selective pathology
- Blood banking/transfusion medicine
- Chemical pathology
- Cytopathology
- Dermatopathology
- Forensic pathology
- Hematology
- Medical microbiology
- Molecular genetic pathology
- Neuropathology
- Pediatric pathology

American Board of Pathology subspecialty certificates

- Blood banking/transfusion medicine
- Chemical pathology
- Cytopathology
- Dermatopathology
- Forensic pathology
- Hematology
- Medical microbiology
- Molecular genetic pathology
- Neuropathology
- Pediatric pathology

Data

Unless otherwise noted, all data are for 2008.

Table 1. Pathology-Anatomic and Clinical Programs

Number of accredited programs	149
Program Data	
length of accredited training	4
Minimum number of prior years of GME required	0
Offers graduate year 1 positions, available immediately upon medical school completion	Yes
Average number of interviews for program year 1 positions	34.0
Percent new program directors, 2007-2008 academic year (source: ACGME)	11.3%
Residents/Fellows	
Total number of active residents/fellows	2,237
Average number of residents/fellows per program	15.0
Average percent female	52.1%
Average percent international medical graduate (IMG)	30.8%
Program Faculty	
Average number of full-time physician faculty	26.2
Average number of part-time physician faculty	2.7

Specialty Data

Average percent female full-time physician faculty	33.5%
Average ratio of full-time physician faculty to resident/fellow	1.3

Table 2. Data for Pathology-Anatomic and Clinical Programs Listed in FREIDA

Number of programs providing data	100
Work Schedule (Program Year 1)	
Average hours on duty per week	49.3
Average maximum consecutive hours on duty	14.5
Average days off duty per week	1.7
Moonlighting allowed within institution	45.0%
Night float system	2.0%
Offers awareness and management of fatigue in residents/fellows	94.0%
Educational Setting (Program Year 1)	
Average hours/week of regularly scheduled lectures/conferences	6.9
Average percent of training in hospital outpatient clinics	9.8%
Average percent of training in nonhospital ambulatory care community settings	6.5%
Educational Benefits	
Curriculum on management of tobacco dependence	8.0%
Program to assess/enhance medical professionalism	68.0%
Debt management/financial counseling	52.0%
Formal program to develop teaching skills	76.0%
Formal mentoring program	42.0%
Formal program to foster interdisciplinary teamwork	14.0%
Continuous quality improvement training	90.0%
International experience	11.0%
Resident/fellow retreats	31.0%
Off-campus electives	85.0%
Hospice/home care experience	1.0%
Cultural competence awareness	57.0%
Instruction in medical Spanish or other non-English language	14.0%
Alternative/complementary medicine curriculum	6.0%
Training in identifying and reporting of domestic violence/abuse	25.0%
MPH/MBA or PhD training	22.0%
Research rotation	15.0%
Educational Features	
Offers additional training or educational experience beyond accredited length	35.7%
Offers a primary care track	1.0%
Offers a rural track	2.0%
Offers a women's health track	2.0%
Offers a hospitalist track	0.0%
Offers a research track/nonaccredited fellowship	25.0%
Offers an other track	5.0%
Resident Evaluation	
Yearly specialty in-service examination required	95.6%
Patient surveys	6.0%
Portfolio system	56.0%
360 degree evaluations	79.0%
Objective structured clinical examinations (OSCE)	12.0%
Program Evaluation	
Program graduation rates	82.0%
Board certification rates	100.0%
In-training examinations	98.0%
Performance-based assessments	45.0%
Employment Policies and Benefits	
Part-time/shared positions	2.0%
On-site child care	44.0%
Subsidized child care	8.0%
Allowance/stipend for professional expenses	100.0%
Leave for educational meetings/conferences	81.7%
Moving allowance	11.0%

Housing stipend	8.0%
On-call meal allowance	68.0%
Free parking	61.0%
PDAs	14.0%
Placement assistance upon completion of program	28.0%
Cross coverage in case of illness/disability	80.0%
Compensation and Leave (Graduate Year 1)	
Average resident/fellow compensation	$45,476
Average number weeks of vacation	4.3
Sick days (paid)	18.4
Maximum number of paid days for family/medical leave	46
Maximum number of unpaid days for family/medical leave	61
Major Medical Benefits	
Major medical insurance for residents	99.0%
Major medical insurance for dependents	95.0%
Outpatient mental health insurance	91.0%
Inpatient mental health insurance	91.0%
Group life insurance	92.0%
Dental insurance	88.0%
Disability insurance	92.0%
Disability insurance for occupationally acquired HIV	76.0%
Medical insurance coverage begins when starting program	88.0%

For more information

Professional Associations

American Society for Clinical Pathology
33 West Monroe, Suite 1600
Chicago, IL 60603
312 541-4999
312 541-4998 Fax
E-mail: info@ascp.org
www.ascp.org

American Society of Cytopathology
400 West 9th Street, Suite 201
Wilmington, DE 19801
302 429-8802
302 429-8807 Fax
www.cytopathology.org

College of American Pathologists
325 Waukegan Road
Northfield, IL 60093-2750
847 832-7000
847 832-8000 Fax
www.cap.org

US and Canadian Academy of Pathology
3643 Walton Way Extension
Augusta, GA 30909
706 733-7550
706 733-8033 Fax
E-mail: iap@uscap.org
www.uscap.org

Certification

American Board of Pathology
PO Box 25915
Tampa, FL 33622-5915
813 286-2444
813 289-5279 Fax
www.abpath.org

Program Accreditation

Accreditation Council for Graduate Medical Education
Residency Review Committee for Pathology
Georgia Andrianopoulos, PhD, Executive Director
515 North State Street
Chicago, IL 60654
312 755-5031
E-mail: gda@acgme.org
www.acgme.org

Blood Banking/ Transfusion Medicine

Professional Description

A physician who specializes in blood banking/transfusion medicine is responsible for the maintenance of an adequate blood supply, blood donor and patient-recipient safety, and appropriate blood utilization. Pretransfusion compatibility testing and antibody testing assure that blood transfusions, when indicated, are as safe as possible. This physician directs the preparation and safe use of specially prepared blood components, including red blood cells, white blood cells, platelets, plasma constituents, and marrow or stem cells for transplantation.

Prerequisites; Length of Training

A minimum of 3 years of prior GME is required. Length of ACGME-accredited programs is 1 year.

Data

Unless otherwise noted, all data are for 2008.

Table 1. Blood Banking/Transfusion Medicine Programs

Number of accredited programs	47
Program Data	
length of accredited training	1
Minimum number of prior years of GME required	3
Offers graduate year 1 positions, available immediately upon medical school completion	No
Average number of interviews for program year 1 positions	1.9
Percent new program directors, 2007-2008 academic year (source: ACGME)	6.5%
Residents/Fellows	
Total number of active residents/fellows	34
Average number of residents/fellows per program	0.7
Average percent female	41.2%
Average percent international medical graduate (IMG)	23.5%
Program Faculty	
Average number of full-time physician faculty	6.0
Average number of part-time physician faculty	1.0
Average percent female full-time physician faculty	35.3%
Average ratio of full-time physician faculty to resident/fellow	3.3

Table 2. Data for Blood Banking/Transfusion Medicine Programs Listed in FREIDA

Number of programs providing data	20
Work Schedule (Program Year 1)	
Average hours on duty per week	42.7
Average maximum consecutive hours on duty	13.5
Average days off duty per week	1.7
Moonlighting allowed within institution	40.0%
Night float system	5.0%
Offers awareness and management of fatigue in residents/fellows	70.0%
Educational Setting (Program Year 1)	
Average hours/week of regularly scheduled lectures/conferences	5.8

Average percent of training in hospital outpatient clinics	18.8%
Average percent of training in nonhospital ambulatory care community settings	29.6%
Educational Benefits	
Curriculum on management of tobacco dependence	15.0%
Program to assess/enhance medical professionalism	70.0%
Debt management/financial counseling	40.0%
Formal program to develop teaching skills	60.0%
Formal mentoring program	45.0%
Formal program to foster interdisciplinary teamwork	15.0%
Continuous quality improvement training	90.0%
International experience	10.0%
Resident/fellow retreats	25.0%
Off-campus electives	65.0%
Hospice/home care experience	10.0%
Cultural competence awareness	50.0%
Instruction in medical Spanish or other non-English language	10.0%
Alternative/complementary medicine curriculum	10.0%
Training in identifying and reporting of domestic violence/abuse	20.0%
MPH/MBA or PhD training	15.0%
Research rotation	40.0%
Educational Features	
Offers additional training or educational experience beyond accredited length	32.7%
Offers a primary care track	0.0%
Offers a rural track	0.0%
Offers a women's health track	0.0%
Offers a hospitalist track	0.0%
Offers a research track/nonaccredited fellowship	30.0%
Offers an other track	15.0%
Resident Evaluation	
Yearly specialty in-service examination required	30.0%
Patient surveys	10.0%
Portfolio system	25.0%
360 degree evaluations	70.0%
Objective structured clinical examinations (OSCE)	0.0%
Program Evaluation	
Program graduation rates	75.0%
Board certification rates	95.0%
In-training examinations	30.0%
Performance-based assessments	20.0%
Employment Policies and Benefits	
Part-time/shared positions	5.0%
On-site child care	40.0%
Subsidized child care	10.0%
Allowance/stipend for professional expenses	85.0%
Leave for educational meetings/conferences	79.0%
Moving allowance	10.0%
Housing stipend	5.0%
On-call meal allowance	20.0%
Free parking	70.0%
PDAs	15.0%
Placement assistance upon completion of program	10.0%
Cross coverage in case of illness/disability	65.0%
Compensation and Leave (Graduate Year 1)	
Average resident/fellow compensation	$52,103
Average number weeks of vacation	3.8
Sick days (paid)	24.6
Maximum number of paid days for family/medical leave	36
Maximum number of unpaid days for family/medical leave	48
Major Medical Benefits	
Major medical insurance for residents	100.0%

Major medical insurance for dependents	85.0%
Outpatient mental health insurance	80.0%
Inpatient mental health insurance	80.0%
Group life insurance	85.0%
Dental insurance	90.0%
Disability insurance	90.0%
Disability insurance for occupationally acquired HIV	75.0%
Medical insurance coverage begins when starting program	90.0%

For more information

American Society for Clinical Pathology
33 West Monroe, Suite 1600
Chicago, IL 60603
312 541-4999
312 541-4998 Fax
E-mail: info@ascp.org
www.ascp.org

Chemical Pathology

Professional Description

A chemical pathologist has expertise in the biochemistry of the human body as it applies to the understanding of the cause and progress of disease. This physician functions as a clinical consultant in the diagnosis and treatment of human disease. Chemical pathology entails the application of biochemical data to the detection, confirmation, or monitoring of disease.

Prerequisites; Length of Training

Completion of an ACGME-accredited residency in anatomic pathology and clinical pathology, anatomic pathology, or clinical pathology is required. Length of ACGME-accredited programs is 1 year.

For more information

American Society for Clinical Pathology
33 West Monroe, Suite 1600
Chicago, IL 60603
312 541-4999   312 541-4998 Fax
E-mail: info@ascp.org
www.ascp.org

Cytopathology

Professional Description

A cytopathologist is an anatomic pathologist trained in the diagnosis of human disease by means of the study of cells obtained from body secretions and fluids, by scraping, washing, or sponging the surface of a lesion, or by the aspiration of a tumor mass or body organ with a fine needle. A major aspect of a cytopathologist's practice is the interpretation of Papanicolaou-stained smears of cells from the female reproductive systems, the "Pap" test. However, the cytopathologist's expertise is applied to the diagnosis of cells from all systems and areas of the body. He/she is a consultant to all medical specialists.

Prerequisites; Length of Training

A minimum of 3 years of prior GME is required. Length of ACGME-accredited programs is 1 year.

Data

Unless otherwise noted, all data are for 2008.

Table 1. Cytopathology Programs

Number of accredited programs	86

Program Data

length of accredited training	1
Minimum number of prior years of GME required	3
Offers graduate year 1 positions, available immediately upon medical school completion	No
Average number of interviews for program year 1 positions	5.1
Percent new program directors, 2007-2008 academic year (source: ACGME)	17.4%

Residents/Fellows

Total number of active residents/fellows	104
Average number of residents/fellows per program	1.2
Average percent female	55.8%
Average percent international medical graduate (IMG)	47.1%

Program Faculty

Average number of full-time physician faculty	7.1
Average number of part-time physician faculty	0.6
Average percent female full-time physician faculty	41.8%
Average ratio of full-time physician faculty to resident/fellow	2.5

Table 2. Data for Cytopathology Programs Listed in FREIDA

Number of programs providing data	39

Work Schedule (Program Year 1)

Average hours on duty per week	43.7
Average maximum consecutive hours on duty	10.6
Average days off duty per week	1.9
Moonlighting allowed within institution	38.5%
Night float system	0.0%
Offers awareness and management of fatigue in residents/fellows	82.1%

Educational Setting (Program Year 1)

Average hours/week of regularly scheduled lectures/conferences	4.7
Average percent of training in hospital outpatient clinics	21.6%
Average percent of training in nonhospital ambulatory care community settings	20.0%

Educational Benefits

Curriculum on management of tobacco dependence	10.3%
Program to assess/enhance medical professionalism	51.3%
Debt management/financial counseling	38.5%
Formal program to develop teaching skills	69.2%
Formal mentoring program	46.2%
Formal program to foster interdisciplinary teamwork	15.4%
Continuous quality improvement training	82.1%
International experience	5.1%
Resident/fellow retreats	28.2%
Off-campus electives	35.9%
Hospice/home care experience	2.6%
Cultural competence awareness	46.2%
Instruction in medical Spanish or other non-English language	15.4%
Alternative/complementary medicine curriculum	7.7%
Training in identifying and reporting of domestic violence/abuse	23.1%
MPH/MBA or PhD training	10.3%
Research rotation	30.8%

Educational Features

Offers additional training or educational experience beyond accredited length	4.4%
Offers a primary care track	5.1%
Offers a rural track	0.0%
Offers a women's health track	12.8%
Offers a hospitalist track	2.6%

Offers a research track/nonaccredited fellowship	10.3%
Offers an other track	7.7%
Resident Evaluation	
Yearly specialty in-service examination required	46.8%
Patient surveys	2.6%
Portfolio system	30.8%
360 degree evaluations	69.2%
Objective structured clinical examinations (OSCE)	10.3%
Program Evaluation	
Program graduation rates	79.5%
Board certification rates	97.4%
In-training examinations	48.7%
Performance-based assessments	48.7%
Employment Policies and Benefits	
Part-time/shared positions	5.1%
On-site child care	35.9%
Subsidized child care	5.1%
Allowance/stipend for professional expenses	94.9%
Leave for educational meetings/conferences	82.8%
Moving allowance	2.6%
Housing stipend	0.0%
On-call meal allowance	33.3%
Free parking	46.2%
PDAs	7.7%
Placement assistance upon completion of program	23.1%
Cross coverage in case of illness/disability	74.4%
Compensation and Leave (Graduate Year 1)	
Average resident/fellow compensation	$51,612
Average number weeks of vacation	8.8
Sick days (paid)	23.5
Maximum number of paid days for family/medical leave	44
Maximum number of unpaid days for family/medical leave	34
Major Medical Benefits	
Major medical insurance for residents	100.0%
Major medical insurance for dependents	97.4%
Outpatient mental health insurance	94.9%
Inpatient mental health insurance	94.9%
Group life insurance	94.9%
Dental insurance	89.7%
Disability insurance	87.2%
Disability insurance for occupationally acquired HIV	76.9%
Medical insurance coverage begins when starting program	82.1%

For more information

American Society of Cytopathology
400 West 9th Street, Suite 201
Wilmington, DE 19801
302 429-8802
302 429-8807 Fax
www.cytopathology.org

Dermatopathology

Professional Description

A dermatopathologist is expert in diagnosing and monitoring diseases of the skin, including infectious, immunologic, degenerative, and neoplastic diseases. This entails the examination and interpretation of specially prepared tissue sections, cellular scrapings, and smears of skin lesions by means of light microscopy, electron microscopy, and fluorescence microscopy.

Prerequisites; Length of Training

Completion of an dermatology or pathology residency is required; length of accredited programs is 1 year.

For more information

American Society of Dermatopathology
111 Deer Lake Road, Suite 100
Deerfield, IL 60015
847 400-5820
847 480-9282 Fax
E-mail: info@asdp.org
www.asdp.org

Forensic Pathology

Professional Description

A forensic pathologist is expert in investigating and evaluating cases of sudden, unexpected, suspicious, and violent death as well as other specific classes of death defined by law. The forensic pathologist serves the public as coroner or medical examiner, or by performing medicolegal autopsies for such officials.

Prerequisites; Length of Training

A minimum of 3 years of prior GME is required. Length of ACGME-accredited programs is 1 year.

For more information

National Association of Medical Examiners
430 Pryor Street, SW
Atlanta, GA 30312
404 730-4781
404 730-4420 Fax
E-mail: name@thename.org
www.thename.org

Hematology

Professional Description

A physician who is expert in blood diseases and disorders, with the knowledge and technical skills essential for the laboratory diagnosis of diseases such as anemias, bleeding disorders, blood clotting disorders, leukemias, and lymphomas.
   Source: American Society of Hematology

Prerequisites; Length of Training

A minimum of 3 years of prior GME is required. Length of ACGME-accredited programs is 1 year.

Data

Unless otherwise noted, all data are for 2008.

Table 1. Hematology Programs	
Number of accredited programs	79
Program Data	
length of accredited training	1
Minimum number of prior years of GME required	3
Offers graduate year 1 positions, available immediately upon medical school completion	No
Average number of interviews for program year 1 positions	4.6
Percent new program directors, 2007-2008 academic year (source: ACGME)	9.0%

Specialty Data

Residents/Fellows

Total number of active residents/fellows	83
Average number of residents/fellows per program	1.1
Average percent female	50.6%
Average percent international medical graduate (IMG)	30.1%

Program Faculty

Average number of full-time physician faculty	7.2
Average number of part-time physician faculty	0.7
Average percent female full-time physician faculty	35.8%
Average ratio of full-time physician faculty to resident/fellow	2.8

Table 2. Data for Hematology Programs Listed in FREIDA

Number of programs providing data	27

Work Schedule (Program Year 1)

Average hours on duty per week	45.3
Average maximum consecutive hours on duty	12.0
Average days off duty per week	1.8
Moonlighting allowed within institution	33.3%
Night float system	0.0%
Offers awareness and management of fatigue in residents/fellows	81.5%

Educational Setting (Program Year 1)

Average hours/week of regularly scheduled lectures/conferences	5.2
Average percent of training in hospital outpatient clinics	5.6%
Average percent of training in nonhospital ambulatory care community settings	5.0%

Educational Benefits

Curriculum on management of tobacco dependence	3.7%
Program to assess/enhance medical professionalism	59.3%
Debt management/financial counseling	37.0%
Formal program to develop teaching skills	59.3%
Formal mentoring program	33.3%
Formal program to foster interdisciplinary teamwork	7.4%
Continuous quality improvement training	81.5%
International experience	3.7%
Resident/fellow retreats	18.5%
Off-campus electives	44.4%
Hospice/home care experience	0.0%
Cultural competence awareness	40.7%
Instruction in medical Spanish or other non-English language	11.1%
Alternative/complementary medicine curriculum	0.0%
Training in identifying and reporting of domestic violence/abuse	22.2%
MPH/MBA or PhD training	11.1%
Research rotation	29.6%

Educational Features

Offers additional training or educational experience beyond accredited length	31.3%
Offers a primary care track	0.0%
Offers a rural track	0.0%
Offers a women's health track	0.0%
Offers a hospitalist track	0.0%
Offers a research track/nonaccredited fellowship	22.2%
Offers an other track	3.7%

Resident Evaluation

Yearly specialty in-service examination required	61.2%
Patient surveys	0.0%
Portfolio system	33.3%
360 degree evaluations	77.8%
Objective structured clinical examinations (OSCE)	7.4%

Program Evaluation

Program graduation rates	81.5%
Board certification rates	96.3%
In-training examinations	70.4%
Performance-based assessments	29.6%

Employment Policies and Benefits

Part-time/shared positions	3.7%
On-site child care	44.4%
Subsidized child care	11.1%
Allowance/stipend for professional expenses	96.3%
Leave for educational meetings/conferences	81.1%
Moving allowance	0.0%
Housing stipend	3.7%
On-call meal allowance	48.1%
Free parking	59.3%
PDAs	11.1%
Placement assistance upon completion of program	22.2%
Cross coverage in case of illness/disability	66.7%

Compensation and Leave (Graduate Year 1)

Average resident/fellow compensation	$51,569
Average number weeks of vacation	3.8
Sick days (paid)	25.9
Maximum number of paid days for family/medical leave	36
Maximum number of unpaid days for family/medical leave	41

Major Medical Benefits

Major medical insurance for residents	100.0%
Major medical insurance for dependents	96.3%
Outpatient mental health insurance	96.3%
Inpatient mental health insurance	96.3%
Group life insurance	96.3%
Dental insurance	92.6%
Disability insurance	92.6%
Disability insurance for occupationally acquired HIV	77.8%
Medical insurance coverage begins when starting program	85.2%

For more information

American Society of Hematology
1900 M Street, NW, Suite 200
Washington, DC 20036
202 776-0544
202 776-0545 Fax
E-mail: ash@hematology.org
www.hematology.org

Medical Microbiology

Professional Description

A medical microbiologist is expert in the isolation and identification of microbial agents that cause infectious disease. Viruses, bacteria, and fungi, as well as parasites, are identified and, where possible, tested for susceptibility to appropriate antimicrobial agents.

Prerequisites; Length of Training

Required prerequisites are completion of an ACGME-accredited residency in anatomic pathology and clinical pathology, anatomic pathology, or clinical pathology, or completion of an ACGME-accredited residency in another primary medical specialty and completion of an ACGME-accredited fellowship in infectious disease. Length of ACGME-accredited programs is 1 year.

Data

Unless otherwise noted, all data are for 2008.

Table 1. Medical Microbiology Programs

Number of accredited programs	13

Program Data

length of accredited training	1
Minimum number of prior years of GME required	3
Offers graduate year 1 positions, available immediately upon medical school completion	No
Average number of interviews for program year 1 positions	2.3
Percent new program directors, 2007-2008 academic year (source: ACGME)	15.4%

Residents/Fellows

Total number of active residents/fellows	7
Average number of residents/fellows per program	0.5
Average percent female	71.4%
Average percent international medical graduate (IMG)	28.6%

Program Faculty

Average number of full-time physician faculty	4.1
Average number of part-time physician faculty	1.5
Average percent female full-time physician faculty	39.4%
Average ratio of full-time physician faculty to resident/fellow	3.0

Table 2. Data for Medical Microbiology Programs Listed in FREIDA

Number of programs providing data	7

Work Schedule (Program Year 1)

Average hours on duty per week	36.5
Average maximum consecutive hours on duty	9.4
Average days off duty per week	2.0
Moonlighting allowed within institution	28.6%
Night float system	0.0%
Offers awareness and management of fatigue in residents/fellows	85.7%

Educational Setting (Program Year 1)

Average hours/week of regularly scheduled lectures/conferences	5.0
Average percent of training in nonhospital ambulatory care community settings	12.0%

Educational Benefits

Curriculum on management of tobacco dependence	28.6%
Program to assess/enhance medical professionalism	71.4%
Debt management/financial counseling	42.9%
Formal program to develop teaching skills	85.7%
Formal mentoring program	57.1%
Formal program to foster interdisciplinary teamwork	28.6%
Continuous quality improvement training	71.4%
International experience	14.3%
Resident/fellow retreats	28.6%
Off-campus electives	42.9%
Hospice/home care experience	14.3%
Cultural competence awareness	85.7%
Instruction in medical Spanish or other non-English language	14.3%
Alternative/complementary medicine curriculum	14.3%
Training in identifying and reporting of domestic violence/abuse	28.6%
MPH/MBA or PhD training	42.9%
Research rotation	100.0%

Educational Features

Offers additional training or educational experience beyond accredited length	37.5%
Offers a primary care track	0.0%
Offers a rural track	0.0%
Offers a women's health track	0.0%
Offers a hospitalist track	0.0%
Offers a research track/nonaccredited fellowship	42.9%

Offers an other track	0.0%

Resident Evaluation

Yearly specialty in-service examination required	28.6%
Patient surveys	0.0%
Portfolio system	57.1%
360 degree evaluations	71.4%
Objective structured clinical examinations (OSCE)	0.0%

Program Evaluation

Program graduation rates	57.1%
Board certification rates	85.7%
In-training examinations	57.1%
Performance-based assessments	71.4%

Employment Policies and Benefits

Part-time/shared positions	0.0%
On-site child care	85.7%
Subsidized child care	14.3%
Allowance/stipend for professional expenses	100.0%
Leave for educational meetings/conferences	70.6%
Moving allowance	0.0%
Housing stipend	0.0%
On-call meal allowance	28.6%
Free parking	42.9%
PDAs	0.0%
Placement assistance upon completion of program	14.3%
Cross coverage in case of illness/disability	57.1%

Compensation and Leave (Graduate Year 1)

Average resident/fellow compensation	$51,256
Average number weeks of vacation	3.3
Sick days (paid)	48.0
Maximum number of paid days for family/medical leave	35
Maximum number of unpaid days for family/medical leave	28

Major Medical Benefits

Major medical insurance for residents	100.0%
Major medical insurance for dependents	100.0%
Outpatient mental health insurance	100.0%
Inpatient mental health insurance	100.0%
Group life insurance	100.0%
Dental insurance	85.7%
Disability insurance	100.0%
Disability insurance for occupationally acquired HIV	100.0%
Medical insurance coverage begins when starting program	85.7%

For more information

American Society for Clinical Pathology
33 West Monroe, Suite 1600
Chicago, IL 60603
312 541-4999
312 541-4998 Fax
E-mail: info@ascp.org
www.ascp.org

Molecular Genetic Pathology

Professional Description

A molecular genetic pathologist is expert in the principles, theory, and technologies of molecular biology and molecular genetics. This expertise is used to make or confirm diagnoses of Mendelian genetic disorders, disorders of human development, and infectious diseases and malignancies, and to assess the natural history of those disorders. A molecular genetic pathologist provides information about gene structure, function, and alteration and applies

Specialty Data

laboratory techniques for diagnosis, treatment, and prognosis for individuals with related disorders.

Prerequisites; Length of Training

Completion of a 4-year ACGME-accredited program in pathology or medical genetics is required. Length of ACGME-accredited molecular genetic pathology programs is 1 year.

For more information

American Society for Clinical Pathology
33 West Monroe, Suite 1600
Chicago, IL 60603
312 541-4999
312 541-4998 Fax
E-mail: info@ascp.org
www.ascp.org

Neuropathology

Professional Description

A neuropathologist is expert in the diagnosis of diseases of the nervous system and skeletal muscles and functions as a consultant primarily to neurologists and neurosurgeons. The neuropathologist is knowledgeable in the infirmities of humans as they affect the nervous and neuromuscular systems, be they degenerative, infectious, metabolic, immunologic, neoplastic, vascular, or physical in nature.

Prerequisites; Length of Training

A minimum of 3 years of prior GME is required. Length of ACGME-accredited programs is 2 years.

Data

Unless otherwise noted, all data are for 2008.

Table 1. Neuropathology Programs

Number of accredited programs	35
Program Data	
length of accredited training	2
Minimum number of prior years of GME required	3
Offers graduate year 1 positions, available immediately upon medical school completion	No
Average number of interviews for program year 1 positions	1.7
Percent new program directors, 2007-2008 academic year (source: ACGME)	5.7%
Residents/Fellows	
Total number of active residents/fellows	40
Average number of residents/fellows per program	1.1
Average percent female	35.0%
Average percent international medical graduate (IMG)	45.0%
Program Faculty	
Average number of full-time physician faculty	4.3
Average number of part-time physician faculty	0.8
Average percent female full-time physician faculty	26.4%
Average ratio of full-time physician faculty to resident/fellow	1.9

Table 2. Data for Neuropathology Programs Listed in FREIDA

Number of programs providing data	20
Work Schedule (Program Year 1)	
Average hours on duty per week	45.2
Average maximum consecutive hours on duty	13.6
Average days off duty per week	1.8
Moonlighting allowed within institution	30.0%

Night float system	0.0%
Offers awareness and management of fatigue in residents/fellows	75.0%
Educational Setting (Program Year 1)	
Average hours/week of regularly scheduled lectures/conferences	8.7
Average percent of training in hospital outpatient clinics	
Educational Benefits	
Curriculum on management of tobacco dependence	0.0%
Program to assess/enhance medical professionalism	65.0%
Debt management/financial counseling	40.0%
Formal program to develop teaching skills	50.0%
Formal mentoring program	55.0%
Formal program to foster interdisciplinary teamwork	5.0%
Continuous quality improvement training	80.0%
International experience	10.0%
Resident/fellow retreats	40.0%
Off-campus electives	70.0%
Hospice/home care experience	0.0%
Cultural competence awareness	60.0%
Instruction in medical Spanish or other non-English language	20.0%
Alternative/complementary medicine curriculum	0.0%
Training in identifying and reporting of domestic violence/abuse	20.0%
MPH/MBA or PhD training	25.0%
Research rotation	50.0%
Educational Features	
Offers additional training or educational experience beyond accredited length	21.4%
Offers a primary care track	0.0%
Offers a rural track	0.0%
Offers a women's health track	0.0%
Offers a hospitalist track	0.0%
Offers a research track/nonaccredited fellowship	25.0%
Offers an other track	0.0%
Resident Evaluation	
Yearly specialty in-service examination required	37.3%
Patient surveys	0.0%
Portfolio system	20.0%
360 degree evaluations	75.0%
Objective structured clinical examinations (OSCE)	0.0%
Program Evaluation	
Program graduation rates	80.0%
Board certification rates	85.0%
In-training examinations	50.0%
Performance-based assessments	45.0%
Employment Policies and Benefits	
Part-time/shared positions	15.0%
On-site child care	55.0%
Subsidized child care	15.0%
Allowance/stipend for professional expenses	95.0%
Leave for educational meetings/conferences	67.3%
Moving allowance	5.0%
Housing stipend	0.0%
On-call meal allowance	45.0%
Free parking	40.0%
PDAs	5.0%
Placement assistance upon completion of program	30.0%
Cross coverage in case of illness/disability	70.0%
Compensation and Leave (Graduate Year 1)	
Average resident/fellow compensation	$49,842
Average number weeks of vacation	4.2
Sick days (paid)	24.9
Maximum number of paid days for family/medical leave	34
Maximum number of unpaid days for family/medical leave	51

Major Medical Benefits

Major medical insurance for residents	100.0%
Major medical insurance for dependents	100.0%
Outpatient mental health insurance	95.0%
Inpatient mental health insurance	95.0%
Group life insurance	100.0%
Dental insurance	95.0%
Disability insurance	85.0%
Disability insurance for occupationally acquired HIV	70.0%
Medical insurance coverage begins when starting program	90.0%

For more information

American Association of Neuropathologists
George Perry, PhD, Secretary-Treasurer, AANP
University of Texas at San Antonio College of Sciences
6900 North Loop 1604 West
San Antonio, TX 78249-0661
216 368-3671
216 368-8964 Fax
E-mail: aanp@case.edu
www.aanp-jnen.com

Pediatric Pathology

Professional Description

A pediatric pathologist is expert in the laboratory diagnosis of diseases that occur during fetal growth, infancy, and child development. The practice requires a strong foundation in general pathology and substantial understanding of normal growth and development, along with extensive knowledge of pediatric medicine.

Prerequisites; Length of Training

A minimum of 3 years of prior GME is required. Length of ACGME-accredited programs is 2 years.

For more information

American Society for Clinical Pathology
33 West Monroe, Suite 1600
Chicago, IL 60603
312 541-4999
312 541-4998 Fax
E-mail: info@ascp.org
www.ascp.org

Selective Pathology

Professional Description

Selective pathology programs are typically sponsored by institutions that provide unique educational resources in a specialized area of pathology.

Length of Training

Length of ACGME-accredited programs is 1 year.

Data

Unless otherwise noted, all data are for 2008.

Table 1. Selective Pathology Programs

Number of accredited programs	58

Program Data

length of accredited training	1
Minimum number of prior years of GME required	3
Offers graduate year 1 positions, available immediately upon medical school completion	No
Average number of interviews for program year 1 positions	5.9
Percent new program directors, 2007-2008 academic year (source: ACGME)	8.8%

Residents/Fellows

Total number of active residents/fellows	67
Average number of residents/fellows per program	1.2
Average percent female	52.2%
Average percent international medical graduate (IMG)	43.3%

Program Faculty

Average number of full-time physician faculty	11.3
Average number of part-time physician faculty	1.0
Average percent female full-time physician faculty	38.0%
Average ratio of full-time physician faculty to resident/fellow	2.7

Table 2. Data for Selective Pathology Programs Listed in FREIDA

Number of programs providing data	22

Work Schedule (Program Year 1)

Average hours on duty per week	34.5
Average maximum consecutive hours on duty	8.9
Average days off duty per week	1.9
Moonlighting allowed within institution	18.2%
Night float system	0.0%
Offers awareness and management of fatigue in residents/fellows	90.9%

Educational Setting (Program Year 1)

Average hours/week of regularly scheduled lectures/conferences	5.3
Average percent of training in hospital outpatient clinics	1.0%

Educational Benefits

Curriculum on management of tobacco dependence	18.2%
Program to assess/enhance medical professionalism	72.7%
Debt management/financial counseling	50.0%
Formal program to develop teaching skills	72.7%
Formal mentoring program	59.1%
Formal program to foster interdisciplinary teamwork	18.2%
Continuous quality improvement training	90.9%
International experience	22.7%
Resident/fellow retreats	31.8%
Off-campus electives	59.1%
Hospice/home care experience	0.0%
Cultural competence awareness	68.2%
Instruction in medical Spanish or other non-English language	4.5%
Alternative/complementary medicine curriculum	18.2%
Training in identifying and reporting of domestic violence/abuse	22.7%
MPH/MBA or PhD training	13.6%
Research rotation	18.2%

Educational Features

Offers additional training or educational experience beyond accredited length	22.0%
Offers a primary care track	0.0%
Offers a rural track	0.0%
Offers a women's health track	4.5%
Offers a hospitalist track	0.0%
Offers a research track/nonaccredited fellowship	22.7%
Offers an other track	13.6%

Resident Evaluation

Yearly specialty in-service examination required	22.2%
Patient surveys	0.0%
Portfolio system	31.8%
360 degree evaluations	50.0%

Specialty Data

Objective structured clinical examinations (OSCE)	9.1%
Program Evaluation	
Program graduation rates	77.3%
Board certification rates	45.5%
In-training examinations	54.5%
Performance-based assessments	50.0%
Employment Policies and Benefits	
Part-time/shared positions	13.6%
On-site child care	50.0%
Subsidized child care	31.8%
Allowance/stipend for professional expenses	95.5%
Leave for educational meetings/conferences	60.0%
Moving allowance	0.0%
Housing stipend	0.0%
On-call meal allowance	68.2%
Free parking	59.1%
PDAs	13.6%
Placement assistance upon completion of program	50.0%
Cross coverage in case of illness/disability	68.2%
Compensation and Leave (Graduate Year 1)	
Average resident/fellow compensation	$51,938
Average number weeks of vacation	4.4
Sick days (paid)	30.7
Maximum number of paid days for family/medical leave	30
Maximum number of unpaid days for family/medical leave	17
Major Medical Benefits	
Major medical insurance for residents	100.0%
Major medical insurance for dependents	100.0%
Outpatient mental health insurance	100.0%
Inpatient mental health insurance	100.0%
Group life insurance	100.0%
Dental insurance	100.0%
Disability insurance	77.3%
Disability insurance for occupationally acquired HIV	68.2%
Medical insurance coverage begins when starting program	95.5%

Pediatrics

Professional Description

Pediatrics is the specialty of medical science concerned with the physical, emotional, and social health of children from birth to young adulthood. Pediatric care encompasses a broad spectrum of health services ranging from preventive health care to the diagnosis and treatment of acute and chronic diseases.

Pediatrics is a discipline that deals with biological, social, and environmental influences on the developing child and with the impact of disease and dysfunction on development. Children differ from adults anatomically, physiologically, immunologically, psychologically, developmentally, and metabolically.

The pediatrician understands this constantly changing functional status of his or her patients incident to growth and development and the consequent changing standards of "normal" for age. A pediatrician is a medical specialist who is primarily concerned with the health, welfare, and development of children and is uniquely qualified for these endeavors by virtue of interest and initial training. Maintenance of these competencies is achieved by experience, training, continuous education, self-assessment, and practice improvement.

A pediatrician is able to define accurately the child's health status as well as to serve as a consultant and to make use of other specialists as consultants. Because the child's welfare is heavily dependent on the home and family, the pediatrician supports efforts to create a nurturing environment. Such support includes education about healthful living and anticipatory guidance for both patients and parents.

A pediatrician participates at the community level in preventing or solving problems in child health care and publicly advocates the causes of children.

Source: American Board of Pediatrics, American Academy of Pediatrics

Prerequisites; Length of Training

No previous GME is required; length of accredited programs is 3 years.

Subspecialties

Subspecialty programs accredited by the ACGME

- Adolescent medicine
- Developmental-behavioral pediatrics
- Hospice and palliative medicine
- Neonatal-perinatal medicine
- Pediatric cardiology
- Pediatric critical care medicine
- Pediatric emergency medicine
- Pediatric endocrinology
- Pediatric gastroenterology
- Pediatric hematology/oncology
- Pediatric infectious diseases
- Pediatric nephrology
- Pediatric pulmonology
- Pediatric rheumatology
- Pediatric sports medicine
- Pediatric transplant hepatology
- Sleep medicine

American Board of Pediatrics subspecialty certificates/certificates of added qualifications

- Adolescent medicine
- Developmental-behavioral pediatrics
- Hospice and palliative medicine

- Medical toxicology
- Neonatal-perinatal medicine
- Neurodevelopmental disabilities
- Pediatric cardiology
- Pediatric critical care medicine
- Pediatric emergency medicine
- Pediatric endocrinology
- Pediatric gastroenterology
- Pediatric hematology/oncology
- Pediatric infectious diseases
- Pediatric nephrology
- Pediatric pulmonology
- Pediatric rheumatology
- Pediatric sports medicine
- Pediatric transplant hepatology
- Sleep medicine

Data

Unless otherwise noted, all data are for 2008.

Table 1. Pediatrics Programs

Number of accredited programs	194

Program Data

length of accredited training	3
Minimum number of prior years of GME required	0
Offers graduate year 1 positions, available immediately upon medical school completion	Yes
Average number of interviews for program year 1 positions	134.7
Percent new program directors, 2007-2008 academic year (source: ACGME)	14.7%

Residents/Fellows

Total number of active residents/fellows	7,755
Average number of residents/fellows per program	40.0
Average percent female	71.7%
Average percent international medical graduate (IMG)	23.8%

Program Faculty

Average number of full-time physician faculty	83.8
Average number of part-time physician faculty	18.4
Average percent female full-time physician faculty	40.2%
Average ratio of full-time physician faculty to resident/fellow	1.5

Table 2. Data for Pediatrics Programs Listed in FREIDA

Number of programs providing data	161

Work Schedule (Program Year 1)

Average hours on duty per week	67.2
Average maximum consecutive hours on duty	28.8
Average days off duty per week	1.3
Moonlighting allowed within institution	69.6%
Night float system	75.2%
Offers awareness and management of fatigue in residents/fellows	98.8%

Educational Setting (Program Year 1)

Average hours/week of regularly scheduled lectures/conferences	7.4
Average percent of training in hospital outpatient clinics	34.1%
Average percent of training in nonhospital ambulatory care community settings	12.0%

Educational Benefits

Curriculum on management of tobacco dependence	16.8%
Program to assess/enhance medical professionalism	90.7%
Debt management/financial counseling	76.4%
Formal program to develop teaching skills	98.1%
Formal mentoring program	96.9%
Formal program to foster interdisciplinary teamwork	36.0%
Continuous quality improvement training	96.3%
International experience	72.7%

Resident/fellow retreats	92.5%
Off-campus electives	95.7%
Hospice/home care experience	58.4%
Cultural competence awareness	96.3%
Instruction in medical Spanish or other non-English language	47.8%
Alternative/complementary medicine curriculum	35.4%
Training in identifying and reporting of domestic violence/abuse	93.2%
MPH/MBA or PhD training	23.6%
Research rotation	9.9%

Educational Features

Offers additional training or educational experience beyond accredited length	15.9%
Offers a primary care track	28.0%
Offers a rural track	3.7%
Offers a women's health track	0.6%
Offers a hospitalist track	3.7%
Offers a research track/nonaccredited fellowship	10.6%
Offers an other track	17.4%

Resident Evaluation

Yearly specialty in-service examination required	98.6%
Patient surveys	80.1%
Portfolio system	77.0%
360 degree evaluations	93.2%
Objective structured clinical examinations (OSCE)	38.5%

Program Evaluation

Program graduation rates	91.9%
Board certification rates	100.0%
In-training examinations	98.8%
Performance-based assessments	64.6%

Employment Policies and Benefits

Part-time/shared positions	16.8%
On-site child care	44.1%
Subsidized child care	6.2%
Allowance/stipend for professional expenses	95.7%
Leave for educational meetings/conferences	68.1%
Moving allowance	21.1%
Housing stipend	8.1%
On-call meal allowance	97.5%
Free parking	72.0%
PDAs	35.4%
Placement assistance upon completion of program	55.3%
Cross coverage in case of illness/disability	96.9%

Compensation and Leave (Graduate Year 1)

Average resident/fellow compensation	$45,740
Average number weeks of vacation	3.5
Sick days (paid)	16.5
Maximum number of paid days for family/medical leave	43
Maximum number of unpaid days for family/medical leave	69

Major Medical Benefits

Major medical insurance for residents	99.4%
Major medical insurance for dependents	95.7%
Outpatient mental health insurance	94.4%
Inpatient mental health insurance	93.2%
Group life insurance	93.2%
Dental insurance	88.2%
Disability insurance	95.0%
Disability insurance for occupationally acquired HIV	77.6%
Medical insurance coverage begins when starting program	87.6%

Table 3. Pediatrics Match Data

GY1	2008
Number of positions offered	2,382

Number filled by US seniors	1,610
Percent filled by US seniors	67.6
Total positions filled	2,295
Percent total positions filled	96.3
All	
Total Positions*	2,453
Preferred by US Seniors*	1,698
Preferred Positions per US Senior	1.4
Preferred by Independent Applicants†	1,177
Preferred Positions per IA	2.1

Source: National Resident Matching Program 2008 Match Data
* Includes all positions offered in a specialty, except preliminary positions.
† Preferred means the number of applicants for whom the specialty was the only or first choice.

For more information

Professional Association

American Academy of Pediatrics
141 Northwest Point Boulevard
Elk Grove Village, IL 60007
847 434-4000
847 434-8000 Fax
www.aap.org

Certification

American Board of Pediatrics
111 Silver Cedar Court
Chapel Hill, NC 27514-1513
919 929-0461
919 929-9255 Fax
E-mail: abpeds@abpeds.org
www.abp.org

Program Accreditation

Accreditation Council for Graduate Medical Education
Residency Review Committee for Pediatrics
Jerry Vasilias, PhD, Executive Director
515 North State Street
Chicago, IL 60654
312 755-7477
E-mail: jvasilias@acgme.org
www.acgme.org

Adolescent Medicine

Professional Description

A pediatrician who specializes in adolescent medicine is a multi-disciplinary health care specialist trained in the unique physical, psychological, and social characteristics of adolescents and their health care problems and needs.

Prerequisites; Length of Training

A minimum of 3 years of prior GME is required. Length of ACGME-accredited programs is 3 years.

For more information

Society for Adolescent Medicine
1916 Copper Oaks Circle
Blue Springs, MO 64015
816 224-8010
816 224-8009 Fax
E-mail: sam@adolescenthealth.org
www.adolescenthealth.org

Developmental-Behavioral Pediatrics

Professional Description

A developmental-behavioral specialist is a pediatrician with special training and experience who aims to foster understanding and promotion of optimal development of children and families through research, education, clinical care, and advocacy efforts. This physician assists in the prevention, diagnosis, and management of developmental difficulties and problematic behaviors in children, and in the family dysfunctions that compromise children's development.

Prerequisites; Length of Training

A minimum of 3 years of prior GME is required. Length of ACGME-accredited programs is 3 years.

For more information

Society for Developmental and Behavioral Pediatrics
6728 Old McLean Village Drive
McLean, VA 22101
703 556-9222
703 556-8729 Fax
E-mail: info@sdbp.org
www.sdbp.org

Hospice and Palliative Medicine

See page 57.

Medical Toxicology

Professional Description

A pediatrician who focuses on the evaluation and management of patients with accidental or intentional poisoning through exposure to prescription and non-prescription medications, drugs of abuse, household or industrial toxins, and environmental toxins.

Important areas of medical toxicology include acute pediatric and adult drug ingestion; drug abuse, addiction, and withdrawal; chemical poisoning exposure and toxicity; hazardous materials exposure and toxicity; and occupational toxicology.

Prerequisites; Length of Training

A minimum of 3 years of prior GME is required. Length of ACGME-accredited medical toxicology programs is 2 years.

For more information

American College of Medical Toxicology
10645 N Tatum Boulevard, Suite 200-111
Phoenix, AZ 85028
623 533-6340
623 633-6340 Fax
E-mail: info@acmt.org
www.acmt.net

Neonatal-Perinatal Medicine

Professional Description

A pediatrician who is the principal care provider for sick newborn infants. Clinical expertise is used for direct patient care and for consulting with obstetrical colleagues to plan for the care of mothers who have high-risk pregnancies.

Prerequisites; Length of Training

A minimum of 3 years of prior GME is required. Length of ACGME-accredited programs is 3 years.

Data

Unless otherwise noted, all data are for 2008.

Table 1. Neonatal-Perinatal Medicine Programs

Number of accredited programs	98
Program Data	
length of accredited training	3
Minimum number of prior years of GME required	3
Offers graduate year 1 positions, available immediately upon medical school completion	No
Average number of interviews for program year 1 positions	9.1
Percent new program directors, 2007-2008 academic year (source: ACGME)	16.5%
Residents/Fellows	
Total number of active residents/fellows	573
Average number of residents/fellows per program	5.8
Average percent female	60.4%
Average percent international medical graduate (IMG)	40.3%
Program Faculty	
Average number of full-time physician faculty	12.3
Average number of part-time physician faculty	1.0
Average percent female full-time physician faculty	42.6%
Average ratio of full-time physician faculty to resident/fellow	1.4

Table 2. Data for Neonatal-Perinatal Medicine Programs Listed in FREIDA

Number of programs providing data	61
Work Schedule (Program Year 1)	
Average hours on duty per week	56.5
Average maximum consecutive hours on duty	26.9
Average days off duty per week	1.5
Moonlighting allowed within institution	85.2%
Night float system	9.8%
Offers awareness and management of fatigue in residents/fellows	88.5%
Educational Setting (Program Year 1)	
Average hours/week of regularly scheduled lectures/conferences	4.8
Average percent of training in hospital outpatient clinics	7.4%
Average percent of training in nonhospital ambulatory care community settings	7.0%
Educational Benefits	
Curriculum on management of tobacco dependence	8.2%
Program to assess/enhance medical professionalism	77.0%
Debt management/financial counseling	34.4%
Formal program to develop teaching skills	96.7%
Formal mentoring program	91.8%
Formal program to foster interdisciplinary teamwork	41.0%
Continuous quality improvement training	86.9%
International experience	23.0%
Resident/fellow retreats	47.5%
Off-campus electives	45.9%
Hospice/home care experience	16.4%
Cultural competence awareness	72.1%
Instruction in medical Spanish or other non-English language	21.3%
Alternative/complementary medicine curriculum	21.3%
Training in identifying and reporting of domestic violence/abuse	26.2%
MPH/MBA or PhD training	57.4%
Research rotation	96.7%

Educational Features

Offers additional training or educational experience beyond accredited length	31.4%
Offers a primary care track	8.2%
Offers a rural track	0.0%
Offers a women's health track	0.0%
Offers a hospitalist track	3.3%
Offers a research track/nonaccredited fellowship	21.3%
Offers an other track	13.1%
Resident Evaluation	
Yearly specialty in-service examination required	88.8%
Patient surveys	54.1%
Portfolio system	60.7%
360 degree evaluations	91.8%
Objective structured clinical examinations (OSCE)	6.6%
Program Evaluation	
Program graduation rates	88.5%
Board certification rates	98.4%
In-training examinations	93.4%
Performance-based assessments	29.5%
Employment Policies and Benefits	
Part-time/shared positions	18.0%
On-site child care	49.2%
Subsidized child care	8.2%
Allowance/stipend for professional expenses	98.4%
Leave for educational meetings/conferences	90.8%
Moving allowance	4.9%
Housing stipend	1.6%
On-call meal allowance	82.0%
Free parking	54.1%
PDAs	26.2%
Placement assistance upon completion of program	44.3%
Cross coverage in case of illness/disability	75.4%
Compensation and Leave (Graduate Year 1)	
Average resident/fellow compensation	$51,285
Average number weeks of vacation	5.1
Sick days (paid)	22.2
Maximum number of paid days for family/medical leave	43
Maximum number of unpaid days for family/medical leave	80
Major Medical Benefits	
Major medical insurance for residents	100.0%
Major medical insurance for dependents	95.1%
Outpatient mental health insurance	86.9%
Inpatient mental health insurance	86.9%
Group life insurance	88.5%
Dental insurance	90.2%
Disability insurance	91.8%
Disability insurance for occupationally acquired HIV	57.4%
Medical insurance coverage begins when starting program	90.2%

For more information

American Academy of Pediatrics
141 Northwest Point Boulevard
Elk Grove Village, IL 60007
847 434-4000
847 434-8000 Fax
www.aap.org

Specialty Data

Neurodevelopmental Disabilities

Professional Description

A pediatrician who treats children having developmental delays, or learning disorders, including those associated with visual and hearing impairment, mental retardation, cerebral palsy, spina bifida, autism, and other chronic neurologic conditions. This specialist provides medical consultation and education and assumes leadership in the interdisciplinary management of children with neurodevelopmental disorders. They may also focus on the early identification and diagnosis of neurodevelopmental disabilities in infants and young children as well as on changes that occur as the child with developmental disabilities grows.

Prerequisites; Length of Training

Completion of 2 years of an accredited pediatrics program in the US or Canada is required. Length of ACGME-accredited programs is 4 years.

For more information

American Academy of Neurology
1080 Montreal Avenue
Saint Paul, MN 55116
800 879-1960
651 695-2791 Fax
E-mail: memberservices@aan.com
www.aan.com

Pediatric Cardiology

Professional Description

A pediatric cardiologist provides comprehensive care to patients with cardiovascular problems. This specialist is skilled in selecting, performing, and evaluating the structural and functional assessment of the heart and blood vessels and in the clinical evaluation of cardiovascular disease.

Prerequisites; Length of Training

A minimum of 3 years of prior GME is required. Length of ACGME-accredited programs is 3 years.

Data

Unless otherwise noted, all data are for 2008.

Table 1. Pediatric Cardiology Programs

Number of accredited programs	49
Program Data	
length of accredited training	3
Minimum number of prior years of GME required	3
Offers graduate year 1 positions, available immediately upon medical school completion	No
Average number of interviews for program year 1 positions	17.1
Percent new program directors, 2007-2008 academic year (source: ACGME)	18.4%
Residents/Fellows	
Total number of active residents/fellows	309
Average number of residents/fellows per program	6.3
Average percent female	38.2%
Average percent international medical graduate (IMG)	21.0%
Program Faculty	
Average number of full-time physician faculty	13.4
Average number of part-time physician faculty	2.4
Average percent female full-time physician faculty	29.5%
Average ratio of full-time physician faculty to resident/fellow	1.4

Table 2. Data for Pediatric Cardiology Programs Listed in FREIDA

Number of programs providing data	18
Work Schedule (Program Year 1)	
Average hours on duty per week	56.8
Average maximum consecutive hours on duty	23.4
Average days off duty per week	1.5
Moonlighting allowed within institution	77.8%
Night float system	11.1%
Offers awareness and management of fatigue in residents/fellows	88.9%
Educational Setting (Program Year 1)	
Average hours/week of regularly scheduled lectures/conferences	7.1
Average percent of training in hospital outpatient clinics	15.4%
Average percent of training in nonhospital ambulatory care community settings	10.8%
Educational Benefits	
Curriculum on management of tobacco dependence	5.6%
Program to assess/enhance medical professionalism	88.9%
Debt management/financial counseling	27.8%
Formal program to develop teaching skills	88.9%
Formal mentoring program	94.4%
Formal program to foster interdisciplinary teamwork	27.8%
Continuous quality improvement training	61.1%
International experience	22.2%
Resident/fellow retreats	33.3%
Off-campus electives	61.1%
Hospice/home care experience	11.1%
Cultural competence awareness	77.8%
Instruction in medical Spanish or other non-English language	11.1%
Alternative/complementary medicine curriculum	22.2%
Training in identifying and reporting of domestic violence/abuse	27.8%
MPH/MBA or PhD training	72.2%
Research rotation	100.0%
Educational Features	
Offers additional training or educational experience beyond accredited length	65.4%
Offers a primary care track	5.6%
Offers a rural track	0.0%
Offers a women's health track	0.0%
Offers a hospitalist track	0.0%
Offers a research track/nonaccredited fellowship	16.7%
Offers an other track	11.1%
Resident Evaluation	
Yearly specialty in-service examination required	98.1%
Patient surveys	55.6%
Portfolio system	50.0%
360 degree evaluations	83.3%
Objective structured clinical examinations (OSCE)	5.6%
Program Evaluation	
Program graduation rates	100.0%
Board certification rates	100.0%
In-training examinations	100.0%
Performance-based assessments	27.8%
Employment Policies and Benefits	
Part-time/shared positions	5.6%
On-site child care	38.9%
Subsidized child care	5.6%
Allowance/stipend for professional expenses	94.4%
Leave for educational meetings/conferences	87.9%
Moving allowance	5.6%

Housing stipend	0.0%
On-call meal allowance	77.8%
Free parking	50.0%
PDAs	16.7%
Placement assistance upon completion of program	44.4%
Cross coverage in case of illness/disability	83.3%
Compensation and Leave (Graduate Year 1)	
Average resident/fellow compensation	$50,518
Average number weeks of vacation	3.5
Sick days (paid)	31.5
Maximum number of paid days for family/medical leave	37
Maximum number of unpaid days for family/medical leave	47
Major Medical Benefits	
Major medical insurance for residents	100.0%
Major medical insurance for dependents	100.0%
Outpatient mental health insurance	88.9%
Inpatient mental health insurance	88.9%
Group life insurance	88.9%
Dental insurance	88.9%
Disability insurance	94.4%
Disability insurance for occupationally acquired HIV	88.9%
Medical insurance coverage begins when starting program	94.4%

For more information

American Academy of Pediatrics
141 Northwest Point Boulevard
Elk Grove Village, IL 60007
847 434-4000
847 434-8000 Fax
www.aap.org

Pediatric Critical Care Medicine

Professional Description

A pediatrician expert in advanced life support for children from the term or near-term neonate to the adolescent. This competence extends to the critical care management of life-threatening organ system failure from any cause in both medical and surgical patients and to the support of vital physiological functions.

This specialist may have administrative responsibilities for intensive care units and also facilitate patient care among other specialists.

Prerequisites; Length of Training

A minimum of 3 years of prior GME is required. Length of ACGME-accredited programs is 3 years.

Data

Unless otherwise noted, all data are for 2008.

Table 1. Pediatric Critical Care Medicine Programs

Number of accredited programs	62
Program Data	
length of accredited training	3
Minimum number of prior years of GME required	3
Offers graduate year 1 positions, available immediately upon medical school completion	No
Average number of interviews for program year 1 positions	9.8
Percent new program directors, 2007-2008 academic year (source: ACGME)	16.1%
Residents/Fellows	
Total number of active residents/fellows	349

Average number of residents/fellows per program	5.6
Average percent female	45.6%
Average percent international medical graduate (IMG)	23.5%
Program Faculty	
Average number of full-time physician faculty	12.0
Average number of part-time physician faculty	1.1
Average percent female full-time physician faculty	38.0%
Average ratio of full-time physician faculty to resident/fellow	1.5

Table 2. Data for Pediatric Critical Care Medicine Programs Listed in FREIDA

Number of programs providing data	35
Work Schedule (Program Year 1)	
Average hours on duty per week	62.7
Average maximum consecutive hours on duty	26.9
Average days off duty per week	1.5
Moonlighting allowed within institution	74.3%
Night float system	11.4%
Offers awareness and management of fatigue in residents/fellows	91.4%
Educational Setting (Program Year 1)	
Average hours/week of regularly scheduled lectures/conferences	4.4
Average percent of training in hospital outpatient clinics	5.0%
Educational Benefits	
Curriculum on management of tobacco dependence	11.4%
Program to assess/enhance medical professionalism	85.7%
Debt management/financial counseling	42.9%
Formal program to develop teaching skills	97.1%
Formal mentoring program	94.3%
Formal program to foster interdisciplinary teamwork	40.0%
Continuous quality improvement training	88.6%
International experience	28.6%
Resident/fellow retreats	57.1%
Off-campus electives	65.7%
Hospice/home care experience	31.4%
Cultural competence awareness	82.9%
Instruction in medical Spanish or other non-English language	31.4%
Alternative/complementary medicine curriculum	8.6%
Training in identifying and reporting of domestic violence/abuse	48.6%
MPH/MBA or PhD training	65.7%
Research rotation	100.0%
Educational Features	
Offers additional training or educational experience beyond accredited length	46.2%
Offers a primary care track	5.7%
Offers a rural track	0.0%
Offers a women's health track	0.0%
Offers a hospitalist track	2.9%
Offers a research track/nonaccredited fellowship	20.0%
Offers an other track	20.0%
Resident Evaluation	
Yearly specialty in-service examination required	97.1%
Patient surveys	42.9%
Portfolio system	34.3%
360 degree evaluations	88.6%
Objective structured clinical examinations (OSCE)	8.6%
Program Evaluation	
Program graduation rates	82.9%
Board certification rates	97.1%
In-training examinations	97.1%
Performance-based assessments	25.7%
Employment Policies and Benefits	
Part-time/shared positions	22.9%

Specialty Data

On-site child care	37.1%
Subsidized child care	8.6%
Allowance/stipend for professional expenses	91.4%
Leave for educational meetings/conferences	81.3%
Moving allowance	5.7%
Housing stipend	2.9%
On-call meal allowance	82.9%
Free parking	51.4%
PDAs	17.1%
Placement assistance upon completion of program	37.1%
Cross coverage in case of illness/disability	82.9%

Compensation and Leave (Graduate Year 1)

Average resident/fellow compensation	$50,504
Average number weeks of vacation	3.4
Sick days (paid)	17.8
Maximum number of paid days for family/medical leave	47
Maximum number of unpaid days for family/medical leave	71

Major Medical Benefits

Major medical insurance for residents	100.0%
Major medical insurance for dependents	97.1%
Outpatient mental health insurance	91.4%
Inpatient mental health insurance	91.4%
Group life insurance	94.3%
Dental insurance	91.4%
Disability insurance	100.0%
Disability insurance for occupationally acquired HIV	71.4%
Medical insurance coverage begins when starting program	94.3%

For more information

American Academy of Pediatrics
141 Northwest Point Boulevard
Elk Grove Village, IL 60007
847 434-4000
847 434-8000 Fax
www.aap.org

Society of Critical Care Medicine
500 Midway Drive
Mount Prospect, IL 60056
847 827-6869
847 827-6886 Fax
info@sccm.org
www.sccm.org

Pediatric Emergency Medicine

Professional Description

A pediatrician who has special qualifications to manage emergencies in infants and children.

Prerequisites; Length of Training

A minimum of 3 years of prior GME is required. Length of ACGME-accredited programs is 3 years.

Data

Unless otherwise noted, all data are for 2008.

Table 1. Pediatric Emergency Medicine Programs

Number of accredited programs	46

Program Data

length of accredited training	3
Minimum number of prior years of GME required	3

Offers graduate year 1 positions, available immediately upon medical school completion	No
Average number of interviews for program year 1 positions	18.5
Percent new program directors, 2007-2008 academic year (source: ACGME)	15.2%

Residents/Fellows

Total number of active residents/fellows	245
Average number of residents/fellows per program	5.3
Average percent female	62.9%
Average percent international medical graduate (IMG)	13.9%

Program Faculty

Average number of full-time physician faculty	14.1
Average number of part-time physician faculty	3.0
Average percent female full-time physician faculty	48.7%
Average ratio of full-time physician faculty to resident/fellow	1.8

Table 2. Data for Pediatric Emergency Medicine Programs Listed in FREIDA

Number of programs providing data	21

Work Schedule (Program Year 1)

Average hours on duty per week	41.6
Average maximum consecutive hours on duty	17.5
Average days off duty per week	2.1
Moonlighting allowed within institution	76.2%
Night float system	0.0%
Offers awareness and management of fatigue in residents/fellows	95.2%

Educational Setting (Program Year 1)

Average hours/week of regularly scheduled lectures/conferences	4.4
Average percent of training in hospital outpatient clinics	40.5%
Average percent of training in nonhospital ambulatory care community settings	7.2%

Educational Benefits

Curriculum on management of tobacco dependence	9.5%
Program to assess/enhance medical professionalism	85.7%
Debt management/financial counseling	33.3%
Formal program to develop teaching skills	95.2%
Formal mentoring program	90.5%
Formal program to foster interdisciplinary teamwork	33.3%
Continuous quality improvement training	100.0%
International experience	57.1%
Resident/fellow retreats	71.4%
Off-campus electives	95.2%
Hospice/home care experience	4.8%
Cultural competence awareness	100.0%
Instruction in medical Spanish or other non-English language	52.4%
Alternative/complementary medicine curriculum	14.3%
Training in identifying and reporting of domestic violence/abuse	85.7%
MPH/MBA or PhD training	38.1%
Research rotation	95.2%

Educational Features

Offers additional training or educational experience beyond accredited length	13.0%
Offers a primary care track	4.8%
Offers a rural track	0.0%
Offers a women's health track	0.0%
Offers a hospitalist track	0.0%
Offers a research track/nonaccredited fellowship	9.5%
Offers an other track	28.6%

Resident Evaluation

Yearly specialty in-service examination required	100.0%
Patient surveys	66.7%
Portfolio system	66.7%
360 degree evaluations	90.5%

Objective structured clinical examinations (OSCE)	14.3%

Program Evaluation

Program graduation rates	95.2%
Board certification rates	95.2%
In-training examinations	90.5%
Performance-based assessments	47.6%

Employment Policies and Benefits

Part-time/shared positions	9.5%
On-site child care	33.3%
Subsidized child care	4.8%
Allowance/stipend for professional expenses	95.2%
Leave for educational meetings/conferences	95.7%
Moving allowance	9.5%
Housing stipend	0.0%
On-call meal allowance	33.3%
Free parking	61.9%
PDAs	28.6%
Placement assistance upon completion of program	33.3%
Cross coverage in case of illness/disability	76.2%

Compensation and Leave (Graduate Year 1)

Average resident/fellow compensation	$51,489
Average number weeks of vacation	8.2
Sick days (paid)	27.9
Maximum number of paid days for family/medical leave	46
Maximum number of unpaid days for family/medical leave	73

Major Medical Benefits

Major medical insurance for residents	95.2%
Major medical insurance for dependents	90.5%
Outpatient mental health insurance	95.2%
Inpatient mental health insurance	95.2%
Group life insurance	100.0%
Dental insurance	85.7%
Disability insurance	90.5%
Disability insurance for occupationally acquired HIV	71.4%
Medical insurance coverage begins when starting program	90.5%

For more information

American Academy of Pediatrics
141 Northwest Point Boulevard
Elk Grove Village, IL 60007-1098
847 434-4000
847 434-8000 Fax
www.aap.org

Pediatric Endocrinology

Professional Description

A pediatrician who provides expert care to infants, children and adolescents who have diseases that result from an abnormality in the endocrine glands (glands that secrete hormones). These diseases include diabetes mellitus, growth failure, unusual size for age, early or late pubertal development, birth defects, the genital region, and disorders of the thyroid, adrenal, and pituitary glands.

Prerequisites; Length of Training

A minimum of 3 years of prior GME is required. Length of ACGME-accredited programs is 3 years.

Data

Unless otherwise noted, all data are for 2008.

Table 1. Pediatric Endocrinology Programs

Number of accredited programs	67

Program Data

length of accredited training	3
Minimum number of prior years of GME required	3
Offers graduate year 1 positions, available immediately upon medical school completion	No
Average number of interviews for program year 1 positions	4.9
Percent new program directors, 2007-2008 academic year (source: ACGME)	7.4%

Residents/Fellows

Total number of active residents/fellows	212
Average number of residents/fellows per program	3.2
Average percent female	78.3%
Average percent international medical graduate (IMG)	35.4%

Program Faculty

Average number of full-time physician faculty	5.8
Average number of part-time physician faculty	1.4
Average percent female full-time physician faculty	49.6%
Average ratio of full-time physician faculty to resident/fellow	1.2

Table 2. Data for Pediatric Endocrinology Programs Listed in FREIDA

Number of programs providing data	31

Work Schedule (Program Year 1)

Average hours on duty per week	43.0
Average maximum consecutive hours on duty	13.4
Average days off duty per week	1.5
Moonlighting allowed within institution	48.4%
Night float system	3.2%
Offers awareness and management of fatigue in residents/fellows	74.2%

Educational Setting (Program Year 1)

Average hours/week of regularly scheduled lectures/conferences	4.3
Average percent of training in hospital outpatient clinics	53.0%
Average percent of training in nonhospital ambulatory care community settings	21.6%

Educational Benefits

Curriculum on management of tobacco dependence	6.5%
Program to assess/enhance medical professionalism	87.1%
Debt management/financial counseling	32.3%
Formal program to develop teaching skills	90.3%
Formal mentoring program	83.9%
Formal program to foster interdisciplinary teamwork	32.3%
Continuous quality improvement training	74.2%
International experience	6.5%
Resident/fellow retreats	41.9%
Off-campus electives	45.2%
Hospice/home care experience	3.2%
Cultural competence awareness	67.7%
Instruction in medical Spanish or other non-English language	32.3%
Alternative/complementary medicine curriculum	22.6%
Training in identifying and reporting of domestic violence/abuse	32.3%
MPH/MBA or PhD training	41.9%
Research rotation	93.5%

Educational Features

Offers additional training or educational experience beyond accredited length	28.2%
Offers a primary care track	0.0%
Offers a rural track	0.0%
Offers a women's health track	0.0%
Offers a hospitalist track	0.0%

Offers a research track/nonaccredited fellowship	19.4%
Offers an other track	12.9%
Resident Evaluation	
Yearly specialty in-service examination required	74.7%
Patient surveys	58.1%
Portfolio system	38.7%
360 degree evaluations	71.0%
Objective structured clinical examinations (OSCE)	6.5%
Program Evaluation	
Program graduation rates	67.7%
Board certification rates	83.9%
In-training examinations	83.9%
Performance-based assessments	16.1%
Employment Policies and Benefits	
Part-time/shared positions	9.7%
On-site child care	51.6%
Subsidized child care	6.5%
Allowance/stipend for professional expenses	74.2%
Leave for educational meetings/conferences	80.7%
Moving allowance	6.5%
Housing stipend	6.5%
On-call meal allowance	29.0%
Free parking	51.6%
PDAs	16.1%
Placement assistance upon completion of program	35.5%
Cross coverage in case of illness/disability	71.0%
Compensation and Leave (Graduate Year 1)	
Average resident/fellow compensation	$50,995
Average number weeks of vacation	7.1
Sick days (paid)	26.3
Maximum number of paid days for family/medical leave	40
Maximum number of unpaid days for family/medical leave	69
Major Medical Benefits	
Major medical insurance for residents	96.8%
Major medical insurance for dependents	93.5%
Outpatient mental health insurance	83.9%
Inpatient mental health insurance	83.9%
Group life insurance	67.7%
Dental insurance	77.4%
Disability insurance	74.2%
Disability insurance for occupationally acquired HIV	54.8%
Medical insurance coverage begins when starting program	83.9%

For more information

American Academy of Pediatrics
141 Northwest Point Boulevard
Elk Grove Village, IL 60007
847 434-4000
847 434-8000 Fax
www.aap.org

Pediatric Gastroenterology

Professional Description

A pediatrician who specializes in the diagnosis and treatment of diseases of the digestive systems of infants, children, and adolescents. This specialist treats conditions such as abdominal pain, ulcers, diarrhea, cancer, and jaundice and performs complex diagnostic and therapeutic procedures using lighted scopes to see internal organs.

Prerequisites; Length of Training

A minimum of 3 years of prior GME is required. Length of ACGME-accredited programs is 3 years.

Data

Unless otherwise noted, all data are for 2008.

Table 1. Pediatric Gastroenterology Programs

Number of accredited programs	54
Program Data	
length of accredited training	3
Minimum number of prior years of GME required	3
Offers graduate year 1 positions, available immediately upon medical school completion	No
Average number of interviews for program year 1 positions	7.6
Percent new program directors, 2007-2008 academic year (source: ACGME)	13.7%
Residents/Fellows	
Total number of active residents/fellows	184
Average number of residents/fellows per program	3.4
Average percent female	51.1%
Average percent international medical graduate (IMG)	30.4%
Program Faculty	
Average number of full-time physician faculty	7.4
Average number of part-time physician faculty	0.4
Average percent female full-time physician faculty	35.1%
Average ratio of full-time physician faculty to resident/fellow	1.3

Table 2. Data for Pediatric Gastroenterology Programs Listed in FREIDA

Number of programs providing data	19
Work Schedule (Program Year 1)	
Average hours on duty per week	47.3
Average maximum consecutive hours on duty	14.5
Average days off duty per week	1.5
Moonlighting allowed within institution	84.2%
Night float system	0.0%
Offers awareness and management of fatigue in residents/fellows	100.0%
Educational Setting (Program Year 1)	
Average hours/week of regularly scheduled lectures/conferences	4.5
Average percent of training in hospital outpatient clinics	32.6%
Average percent of training in nonhospital ambulatory care community settings	5.7%
Educational Benefits	
Curriculum on management of tobacco dependence	21.1%
Program to assess/enhance medical professionalism	100.0%
Debt management/financial counseling	47.4%
Formal program to develop teaching skills	100.0%
Formal mentoring program	94.7%
Formal program to foster interdisciplinary teamwork	36.8%
Continuous quality improvement training	78.9%
International experience	26.3%
Resident/fellow retreats	73.7%
Off-campus electives	57.9%
Hospice/home care experience	10.5%
Cultural competence awareness	89.5%
Instruction in medical Spanish or other non-English language	26.3%
Alternative/complementary medicine curriculum	10.5%
Training in identifying and reporting of domestic violence/abuse	26.3%
MPH/MBA or PhD training	68.4%
Research rotation	94.7%

Educational Features

Offers additional training or educational experience beyond accredited length	24.6%
Offers a primary care track	5.3%
Offers a rural track	0.0%
Offers a women's health track	0.0%
Offers a hospitalist track	0.0%
Offers a research track/nonaccredited fellowship	21.1%
Offers an other track	10.5%

Resident Evaluation

Yearly specialty in-service examination required	75.0%
Patient surveys	47.4%
Portfolio system	42.1%
360 degree evaluations	78.9%
Objective structured clinical examinations (OSCE)	0.0%

Program Evaluation

Program graduation rates	78.9%
Board certification rates	100.0%
In-training examinations	94.7%
Performance-based assessments	36.8%

Employment Policies and Benefits

Part-time/shared positions	0.0%
On-site child care	57.9%
Subsidized child care	5.3%
Allowance/stipend for professional expenses	94.7%
Leave for educational meetings/conferences	76.1%
Moving allowance	0.0%
Housing stipend	5.3%
On-call meal allowance	36.8%
Free parking	36.8%
PDAs	21.1%
Placement assistance upon completion of program	15.8%
Cross coverage in case of illness/disability	78.9%

Compensation and Leave (Graduate Year 1)

Average resident/fellow compensation	$50,384
Average number weeks of vacation	3.5
Sick days (paid)	25.5
Maximum number of paid days for family/medical leave	37
Maximum number of unpaid days for family/medical leave	47

Major Medical Benefits

Major medical insurance for residents	100.0%
Major medical insurance for dependents	89.5%
Outpatient mental health insurance	78.9%
Inpatient mental health insurance	78.9%
Group life insurance	84.2%
Dental insurance	94.7%
Disability insurance	89.5%
Disability insurance for occupationally acquired HIV	57.9%
Medical insurance coverage begins when starting program	100.0%

For more information

American Academy of Pediatrics
141 Northwest Point Boulevard
Elk Grove Village, IL 60007
847 434-4000
847 434-8000 Fax
www.aap.org

North American Society for Pediatric Gastroenterology, Hepatology, and Nutrition
PO Box 6
Flourtown, PA 19031
215 233-0808
215 233-3918 Fax
E-mail: naspghan@naspghan.org
www.naspghan.org

Pediatric Hematology/Oncology

Professional Description

A pediatrician trained in pediatrics, hematology, and oncology who can diagnose and treat blood diseases such as leukemia and sickle cell disease.

Source: American Society of Hematology

Prerequisites; Length of Training

A minimum of 3 years of prior GME is required. Length of ACGME-accredited programs is 3 years.

Data

Unless otherwise noted, all data are for 2008.

Table 1. Pediatric Hematology/Oncology Programs

Number of accredited programs	66
Program Data	
length of accredited training	3
Minimum number of prior years of GME required	3
Offers graduate year 1 positions, available immediately upon medical school completion	No
Average number of interviews for program year 1 positions	13.3
Percent new program directors, 2007-2008 academic year (source: ACGME)	14.1%
Residents/Fellows	
Total number of active residents/fellows	381
Average number of residents/fellows per program	5.8
Average percent female	58.5%
Average percent international medical graduate (IMG)	27.0%
Program Faculty	
Average number of full-time physician faculty	14.1
Average number of part-time physician faculty	1.2
Average percent female full-time physician faculty	41.1%
Average ratio of full-time physician faculty to resident/fellow	1.7

Table 2. Data for Pediatric Hematology/Oncology Programs Listed in FREIDA

Number of programs providing data	40
Work Schedule (Program Year 1)	
Average hours on duty per week	53.4
Average maximum consecutive hours on duty	19.2
Average days off duty per week	1.6
Moonlighting allowed within institution	72.5%
Night float system	0.0%
Offers awareness and management of fatigue in residents/fellows	87.5%
Educational Setting (Program Year 1)	
Average hours/week of regularly scheduled lectures/conferences	5.2
Average percent of training in hospital outpatient clinics	30.1%
Average percent of training in nonhospital ambulatory care community settings	2.3%
Educational Benefits	
Curriculum on management of tobacco dependence	10.0%

Specialty Data

Program to assess/enhance medical professionalism	82.5%
Debt management/financial counseling	32.5%
Formal program to develop teaching skills	90.0%
Formal mentoring program	97.5%
Formal program to foster interdisciplinary teamwork	40.0%
Continuous quality improvement training	77.5%
International experience	17.5%
Resident/fellow retreats	55.0%
Off-campus electives	52.5%
Hospice/home care experience	67.5%
Cultural competence awareness	82.5%
Instruction in medical Spanish or other non-English language	20.0%
Alternative/complementary medicine curriculum	27.5%
Training in identifying and reporting of domestic violence/abuse	25.0%
MPH/MBA or PhD training	57.5%
Research rotation	100.0%

Educational Features

Offers additional training or educational experience beyond accredited length	51.4%
Offers a primary care track	5.0%
Offers a rural track	0.0%
Offers a women's health track	0.0%
Offers a hospitalist track	0.0%
Offers a research track/nonaccredited fellowship	12.5%
Offers an other track	5.0%

Resident Evaluation

Yearly specialty in-service examination required	75.6%
Patient surveys	70.0%
Portfolio system	42.5%
360 degree evaluations	92.5%
Objective structured clinical examinations (OSCE)	2.5%

Program Evaluation

Program graduation rates	87.5%
Board certification rates	100.0%
In-training examinations	85.0%
Performance-based assessments	20.0%

Employment Policies and Benefits

Part-time/shared positions	15.0%
On-site child care	47.5%
Subsidized child care	7.5%
Allowance/stipend for professional expenses	95.0%
Leave for educational meetings/conferences	79.3%
Moving allowance	7.5%
Housing stipend	2.5%
On-call meal allowance	27.5%
Free parking	52.5%
PDAs	12.5%
Placement assistance upon completion of program	32.5%
Cross coverage in case of illness/disability	65.0%

Compensation and Leave (Graduate Year 1)

Average resident/fellow compensation	$50,729
Average number weeks of vacation	3.5
Sick days (paid)	25.4
Maximum number of paid days for family/medical leave	44
Maximum number of unpaid days for family/medical leave	68

Major Medical Benefits

Major medical insurance for residents	100.0%
Major medical insurance for dependents	97.5%
Outpatient mental health insurance	87.5%
Inpatient mental health insurance	87.5%
Group life insurance	87.5%
Dental insurance	92.5%

Disability insurance	90.0%
Disability insurance for occupationally acquired HIV	60.0%
Medical insurance coverage begins when starting program	85.0%

For more information

American Society of Pediatric Hematology/Oncology
4700 West Lake
Glenview, IL 60025-1485
847 375-4716
847 375-6483 Fax
E-mail: info@aspho.org
www.aspho.org

Pediatric Infectious Diseases

Professional Description

A pediatrician trained to care for children in the diagnosis, treatment and prevention of infectious diseases. This specialist can apply specific knowledge to affect a better outcome for pediatric infections with complicated courses, underlying diseases that predispose to unusual or severe infections, unclear diagnoses, uncommon diseases, and complex or investigational treatments.

Prerequisites; Length of Training

A minimum of 3 years of prior GME is required. Length of ACGME-accredited programs is 3 years.

Data

Unless otherwise noted, all data are for 2008.

Table 1. Pediatric Infectious Diseases Programs

Number of accredited programs	61

Program Data

length of accredited training	3
Minimum number of prior years of GME required	3
Offers graduate year 1 positions, available immediately upon medical school completion	No
Average number of interviews for program year 1 positions	4.7
Percent new program directors, 2007-2008 academic year (source: ACGME)	14.8%

Residents/Fellows

Total number of active residents/fellows	149
Average number of residents/fellows per program	2.4
Average percent female	65.1%
Average percent international medical graduate (IMG)	34.9%

Program Faculty

Average number of full-time physician faculty	7.3
Average number of part-time physician faculty	0.5
Average percent female full-time physician faculty	39.7%
Average ratio of full-time physician faculty to resident/fellow	1.9

Table 2. Data for Pediatric Infectious Diseases Programs Listed in FREIDA

Number of programs providing data	23

Work Schedule (Program Year 1)

Average hours on duty per week	47.5
Average maximum consecutive hours on duty	14.2
Average days off duty per week	1.4
Moonlighting allowed within institution	73.9%
Night float system	0.0%
Offers awareness and management of fatigue in residents/fellows	91.3%

Educational Setting (Program Year 1)

Average hours/week of regularly scheduled lectures/conferences	4.9
Average percent of training in hospital outpatient clinics	17.3%
Average percent of training in nonhospital ambulatory care community settings	10.0%

Educational Benefits

Curriculum on management of tobacco dependence	13.0%
Program to assess/enhance medical professionalism	82.6%
Debt management/financial counseling	34.8%
Formal program to develop teaching skills	91.3%
Formal mentoring program	91.3%
Formal program to foster interdisciplinary teamwork	13.0%
Continuous quality improvement training	73.9%
International experience	60.9%
Resident/fellow retreats	52.2%
Off-campus electives	60.9%
Hospice/home care experience	13.0%
Cultural competence awareness	65.2%
Instruction in medical Spanish or other non-English language	34.8%
Alternative/complementary medicine curriculum	17.4%
Training in identifying and reporting of domestic violence/abuse	17.4%
MPH/MBA or PhD training	69.6%
Research rotation	100.0%

Educational Features

Offers additional training or educational experience beyond accredited length	38.1%
Offers a primary care track	0.0%
Offers a rural track	0.0%
Offers a women's health track	0.0%
Offers a hospitalist track	0.0%
Offers a research track/nonaccredited fellowship	21.7%
Offers an other track	8.7%

Resident Evaluation

Yearly specialty in-service examination required	75.0%
Patient surveys	26.1%
Portfolio system	30.4%
360 degree evaluations	73.9%
Objective structured clinical examinations (OSCE)	0.0%

Program Evaluation

Program graduation rates	91.3%
Board certification rates	100.0%
In-training examinations	87.0%
Performance-based assessments	13.0%

Employment Policies and Benefits

Part-time/shared positions	8.7%
On-site child care	47.8%
Subsidized child care	17.4%
Allowance/stipend for professional expenses	82.6%
Leave for educational meetings/conferences	89.2%
Moving allowance	13.0%
Housing stipend	4.3%
On-call meal allowance	30.4%
Free parking	39.1%
PDAs	13.0%
Placement assistance upon completion of program	30.4%
Cross coverage in case of illness/disability	56.5%

Compensation and Leave (Graduate Year 1)

Average resident/fellow compensation	$51,858
Average number weeks of vacation	3.3
Sick days (paid)	24.6
Maximum number of paid days for family/medical leave	57
Maximum number of unpaid days for family/medical leave	88

Major Medical Benefits

Major medical insurance for residents	100.0%
Major medical insurance for dependents	100.0%
Outpatient mental health insurance	87.0%
Inpatient mental health insurance	87.0%
Group life insurance	91.3%
Dental insurance	87.0%
Disability insurance	87.0%
Disability insurance for occupationally acquired HIV	73.9%
Medical insurance coverage begins when starting program	91.3%

For more information

Pediatric Infectious Diseases Society
1300 Wilson Blvd, Suite 300
Arlington, VA 22309
703 299-6764
703 299-0473 Fax
E-mail: pids@idsociety.org
www.pids.org

Pediatric Nephrology

Professional Description

A pediatrician who deals with the normal and abnormal development and maturation of the kidney and urinary tract, the mechanisms by which the kidney can be damaged, the evaluation and treatment of renal diseases, fluid and electrolyte abnormalities, hypertension, and renal replacement therapy.

Prerequisites; Length of Training

A minimum of 3 years of prior GME is required. Length of ACGME-accredited programs is 3 years.

Data

Unless otherwise noted, all data are for 2008.

Table 1. Pediatric Nephrology Programs

Number of accredited programs	37
Program Data	
length of accredited training	3
Minimum number of prior years of GME required	3
Offers graduate year 1 positions, available immediately upon medical school completion	No
Average number of interviews for program year 1 positions	2.8
Percent new program directors, 2007-2008 academic year (source: ACGME)	11.1%
Residents/Fellows	
Total number of active residents/fellows	94
Average number of residents/fellows per program	2.5
Average percent female	61.7%
Average percent international medical graduate (IMG)	42.6%
Program Faculty	
Average number of full-time physician faculty	5.2
Average number of part-time physician faculty	0.8
Average percent female full-time physician faculty	39.1%
Average ratio of full-time physician faculty to resident/fellow	1.2

Table 2. Data for Pediatric Nephrology Programs Listed in FREIDA

Number of programs providing data	15
Work Schedule (Program Year 1)	
Average hours on duty per week	44.8
Average maximum consecutive hours on duty	18.5

Average days off duty per week	1.5
Moonlighting allowed within institution	80.0%
Night float system	0.0%
Offers awareness and management of fatigue in residents/fellows	80.0%

Educational Setting (Program Year 1)

Average hours/week of regularly scheduled lectures/conferences	5.1
Average percent of training in hospital outpatient clinics	31.7%
Average percent of training in nonhospital ambulatory care community settings	10.0%

Educational Benefits

Curriculum on management of tobacco dependence	6.7%
Program to assess/enhance medical professionalism	80.0%
Debt management/financial counseling	40.0%
Formal program to develop teaching skills	100.0%
Formal mentoring program	93.3%
Formal program to foster interdisciplinary teamwork	20.0%
Continuous quality improvement training	80.0%
International experience	13.3%
Resident/fellow retreats	33.3%
Off-campus electives	53.3%
Hospice/home care experience	6.7%
Cultural competence awareness	80.0%
Instruction in medical Spanish or other non-English language	33.3%
Alternative/complementary medicine curriculum	26.7%
Training in identifying and reporting of domestic violence/abuse	26.7%
MPH/MBA or PhD training	73.3%
Research rotation	100.0%

Educational Features

Offers additional training or educational experience beyond accredited length	37.8%
Offers a primary care track	6.7%
Offers a rural track	0.0%
Offers a women's health track	0.0%
Offers a hospitalist track	0.0%
Offers a research track/nonaccredited fellowship	33.3%
Offers an other track	6.7%

Resident Evaluation

Yearly specialty in-service examination required	67.9%
Patient surveys	60.0%
Portfolio system	33.3%
360 degree evaluations	80.0%
Objective structured clinical examinations (OSCE)	6.7%

Program Evaluation

Program graduation rates	100.0%
Board certification rates	100.0%
In-training examinations	80.0%
Performance-based assessments	13.3%

Employment Policies and Benefits

Part-time/shared positions	20.0%
On-site child care	33.3%
Subsidized child care	6.7%
Allowance/stipend for professional expenses	86.7%
Leave for educational meetings/conferences	74.1%
Moving allowance	13.3%
Housing stipend	6.7%
On-call meal allowance	53.3%
Free parking	46.7%
PDAs	26.7%
Placement assistance upon completion of program	13.3%
Cross coverage in case of illness/disability	60.0%

Compensation and Leave (Graduate Year 1)

Average resident/fellow compensation	$50,558

Average number weeks of vacation	11.3
Sick days (paid)	14.1
Maximum number of paid days for family/medical leave	28
Maximum number of unpaid days for family/medical leave	85

Major Medical Benefits

Major medical insurance for residents	100.0%
Major medical insurance for dependents	86.7%
Outpatient mental health insurance	80.0%
Inpatient mental health insurance	80.0%
Group life insurance	80.0%
Dental insurance	73.3%
Disability insurance	86.7%
Disability insurance for occupationally acquired HIV	60.0%
Medical insurance coverage begins when starting program	80.0%

For more information

American Society of Pediatric Nephrology
3400 Research Forest Drive, Suite B7
The Woodlands, TX 77381
281 419-0052
281 419-0082 Fax
E-mail: info@aspneph.com
www.aspneph.com

Pediatric Pulmonology

Professional Description

A pediatrician dedicated to the prevention and treatment of all respiratory diseases affecting infants, children, and young adults. This specialist is knowledgeable about the growth and development of the lung, assessment of respiratory function in infants and children, and experienced in a variety of invasive and noninvasive diagnostic techniques.

Prerequisites; Length of Training

A minimum of 3 years of prior GME is required. Length of ACGME-accredited programs is 3 years.

Data

Unless otherwise noted, all data are for 2008.

Table 1. Pediatric Pulmonology Programs

Number of accredited programs	47

Program Data

length of accredited training	3
Minimum number of prior years of GME required	3
Offers graduate year 1 positions, available immediately upon medical school completion	No
Average number of interviews for program year 1 positions	3.6
Percent new program directors, 2007-2008 academic year (source: ACGME)	12.8%

Residents/Fellows

Total number of active residents/fellows	121
Average number of residents/fellows per program	2.6
Average percent female	47.1%
Average percent international medical graduate (IMG)	38.8%

Program Faculty

Average number of full-time physician faculty	6.9
Average number of part-time physician faculty	0.9
Average percent female full-time physician faculty	37.8%
Average ratio of full-time physician faculty to resident/fellow	1.7

Table 2. Data for Pediatric Pulmonology Programs Listed in FREIDA

Number of programs providing data	22

Work Schedule (Program Year 1)

Average hours on duty per week	47.2
Average maximum consecutive hours on duty	19.1
Average days off duty per week	1.5
Moonlighting allowed within institution	81.8%
Night float system	9.1%
Offers awareness and management of fatigue in residents/fellows	86.4%

Educational Setting (Program Year 1)

Average hours/week of regularly scheduled lectures/conferences	4.2
Average percent of training in hospital outpatient clinics	23.9%
Average percent of training in nonhospital ambulatory care community settings	3.2%

Educational Benefits

Curriculum on management of tobacco dependence	13.6%
Program to assess/enhance medical professionalism	77.3%
Debt management/financial counseling	31.8%
Formal program to develop teaching skills	81.8%
Formal mentoring program	77.3%
Formal program to foster interdisciplinary teamwork	40.9%
Continuous quality improvement training	81.8%
International experience	18.2%
Resident/fellow retreats	45.5%
Off-campus electives	59.1%
Hospice/home care experience	40.9%
Cultural competence awareness	63.6%
Instruction in medical Spanish or other non-English language	36.4%
Alternative/complementary medicine curriculum	13.6%
Training in identifying and reporting of domestic violence/abuse	27.3%
MPH/MBA or PhD training	68.2%
Research rotation	90.9%

Educational Features

Offers additional training or educational experience beyond accredited length	47.1%
Offers a primary care track	4.5%
Offers a rural track	0.0%
Offers a women's health track	4.5%
Offers a hospitalist track	0.0%
Offers a research track/nonaccredited fellowship	27.3%
Offers an other track	4.5%

Resident Evaluation

Yearly specialty in-service examination required	77.8%
Patient surveys	45.5%
Portfolio system	50.0%
360 degree evaluations	81.8%
Objective structured clinical examinations (OSCE)	4.5%

Program Evaluation

Program graduation rates	63.6%
Board certification rates	90.9%
In-training examinations	81.8%
Performance-based assessments	22.7%

Employment Policies and Benefits

Part-time/shared positions	9.1%
On-site child care	45.5%
Subsidized child care	4.5%
Allowance/stipend for professional expenses	81.8%
Leave for educational meetings/conferences	77.6%
Moving allowance	4.5%
Housing stipend	13.6%
On-call meal allowance	45.5%
Free parking	31.8%

PDAs	22.7%
Placement assistance upon completion of program	18.2%
Cross coverage in case of illness/disability	68.2%

Compensation and Leave (Graduate Year 1)

Average resident/fellow compensation	$50,578
Average number weeks of vacation	3.4
Sick days (paid)	13.4
Maximum number of paid days for family/medical leave	21
Maximum number of unpaid days for family/medical leave	56

Major Medical Benefits

Major medical insurance for residents	100.0%
Major medical insurance for dependents	95.5%
Outpatient mental health insurance	81.8%
Inpatient mental health insurance	81.8%
Group life insurance	81.8%
Dental insurance	95.5%
Disability insurance	90.9%
Disability insurance for occupationally acquired HIV	50.0%
Medical insurance coverage begins when starting program	95.5%

For more information

American Academy of Pediatrics
141 Northwest Point Boulevard
Elk Grove Village, IL 60007
847 434-4000
847 434-8000 Fax
www.aap.org

Pediatric Rheumatology

Professional Description

A pediatrician who treats diseases of joints, muscle, bones, and tendons. A pediatric rheumatologist diagnoses and treats arthritis, back pain, muscle strains, common athletic injuries, and "collagen" diseases.

Prerequisites; Length of Training

A minimum of 3 years of prior GME is required. Length of ACGME-accredited programs is 3 years.

For more information

American College of Rheumatology
1800 Century Place, Suite 250
Atlanta, GA 30345-4300
404 633-3777
404 633-1870 Fax
www.rheumatology.org

American Academy of Pediatrics
141 Northwest Point Boulevard
Elk Grove Village, IL 60007
847 434-4000
847 434-8000 Fax
www.aap.org

Pediatric Sports Medicine

Professional Description

A pediatrician responsible for continuous care in the field of sports medicine, not only for the enhancement of health and fitness, but

Specialty Data

also for the prevention of injury and illness. A sports medicine physician must have knowledge and experience in the promotion of wellness and the prevention of injury. Knowledge about special areas of medicine such as exercise physiology, biomechanics, nutrition, psychology, physical rehabilitation, epidemiology, physical evaluation, injuries (treatment and prevention and referral practice), and the role of exercise in promoting a healthy lifestyle are essential to the practice of sports medicine. The sports medicine physician requires special education to provide the knowledge to improve the health care of the individual engaged in physical exercise (sports) whether as an individual or as part of a team.

Prerequisites; Length of Training

A minimum of 3 years of prior GME is required. Length of ACGME-accredited programs is 1 year.

For more information

American College of Sports Medicine
401 West Michigan Street
Indianapolis, IN 46202-3233
317 637-9200
317 634-7817 Fax
www.acsm.org

American Academy of Pediatrics
141 Northwest Point Boulevard
Elk Grove Village, IL 60007
847 434-4000
847 434-8000 Fax
www.aap.org

Pediatric Transplant Hepatology

Professional Description

A pediatrician with expertise in transplant hepatology encompasses the special knowledge and skill required of pediatric gastroenterologists to care for patients prior to and following hepatic transplantation; it spans all phases of liver transplantation.

Prerequisites; Length of Training

A minimum of 3 years of prior GME is required. Length of ACGME-accredited programs is 3 years.

For more information

North American Society for Pediatric Gastroenterology, Hepatology, and Nutrition
PO Box 6
Flourtown, PA 19031
215 233-0808
215 233-3918 Fax
E-mail: naspghan@naspghan.org
www.naspghan.org

Sleep Medicine

See page 155.

Physical Medicine and Rehabilitation

Professional Description

A physician certified in physical medicine and rehabilitation is often called a physiatrist. The primary goal of the physiatrist is to achieve maximal restoration of physical, psychological, social, and vocational function through comprehensive rehabilitation. Pain management is often an important part of the role of the physiatrist. For diagnosis and evaluation, a physiatrist may include the techniques of electromyography to supplement the standard history, physical, X-ray, and laboratory examinations. The physiatrist has expertise in the appropriate use of therapeutic exercise, prosthetics (artificial limbs), orthotics, and mechanical and electrical devices.

Prerequisites; Length of Training

No previous GME is required when entering an accredited 4-year program that includes 12 months of fundamental clinical skills in areas other than physical medicine and rehabilitation; 1 year of previous GME (eg, Transitional Year) is required when entering a 3-year program.

Subspecialties

Subspecialty programs accredited by the ACGME

- Hospice and palliative medicine
- Neuromuscular medicine
- Pain medicine*
- Pediatric rehabilitation medicine
- Spinal cord injury medicine
- Sports medicine

* In 2007, ACGME-accredited pain medicine programs under anesthesiology, neurology, physical medicine and rehabilitation, and psychiatry were combined into a multidisciplinary pain medicine subspecialty.

American Board of Physical Medicine and Rehabilitation subspecialty certificates

- Hospice and palliative medicine
- Neuromuscular medicine
- Pain medicine
- Pediatric rehabilitation medicine
- Spinal cord injury medicine
- Sports medicine

Data

Unless otherwise noted, all data are for 2008.

Table 1. Physical Medicine and Rehabilitation Programs	
Number of accredited programs	79
Program Data	
length of accredited training	3/4
Minimum number of prior years of GME required	1/0
Offers graduate year 1 positions, available immediately upon medical school completion	Some
Average number of interviews for program year 1 positions	49.2
Percent new program directors, 2007-2008 academic year (source: ACGME)	10.1%
Residents/Fellows	
Total number of active residents/fellows	1,155
Average number of residents/fellows per program	14.6
Average percent female	40.2%

Average percent international medical graduate (IMG)	18.5%

Program Faculty

Average number of full-time physician faculty	14.8
Average number of part-time physician faculty	2.9
Average percent female full-time physician faculty	34.0%
Average ratio of full-time physician faculty to resident/fellow	0.7

Table 2. Data for Physical Medicine and Rehabilitation Programs Listed in FREIDA

Number of programs providing data	56

Work Schedule (Program Year 1)

Average hours on duty per week	53.1
Average maximum consecutive hours on duty	22.1
Average days off duty per week	1.6
Moonlighting allowed within institution	57.1%
Night float system	7.1%
Offers awareness and management of fatigue in residents/fellows	100.0%

Educational Setting (Program Year 1)

Average hours/week of regularly scheduled lectures/conferences	5.8
Average percent of training in hospital outpatient clinics	26.9%
Average percent of training in nonhospital ambulatory care community settings	12.1%

Educational Benefits

Curriculum on management of tobacco dependence	5.4%
Program to assess/enhance medical professionalism	75.0%
Debt management/financial counseling	64.3%
Formal program to develop teaching skills	73.2%
Formal mentoring program	64.3%
Formal program to foster interdisciplinary teamwork	39.3%
Continuous quality improvement training	91.1%
International experience	10.7%
Resident/fellow retreats	55.4%
Off-campus electives	85.7%
Hospice/home care experience	35.7%
Cultural competence awareness	78.6%
Instruction in medical Spanish or other non-English language	23.2%
Alternative/complementary medicine curriculum	64.3%
Training in identifying and reporting of domestic violence/abuse	32.1%
MPH/MBA or PhD training	14.3%
Research rotation	28.6%

Educational Features

Offers additional training or educational experience beyond accredited length	4.9%
Offers a primary care track	1.8%
Offers a rural track	0.0%
Offers a women's health track	3.6%
Offers a hospitalist track	1.8%
Offers a research track/nonaccredited fellowship	16.1%
Offers an other track	5.4%

Resident Evaluation

Yearly specialty in-service examination required	97.6%
Patient surveys	53.6%
Portfolio system	62.5%
360 degree evaluations	96.4%
Objective structured clinical examinations (OSCE)	30.4%

Program Evaluation

Program graduation rates	83.9%
Board certification rates	98.2%
In-training examinations	98.2%
Performance-based assessments	50.0%

Employment Policies and Benefits

Part-time/shared positions	1.8%
On-site child care	44.6%
Subsidized child care	10.7%
Allowance/stipend for professional expenses	98.2%
Leave for educational meetings/conferences	95.3%
Moving allowance	5.4%
Housing stipend	5.4%
On-call meal allowance	69.6%
Free parking	60.7%
PDAs	26.8%
Placement assistance upon completion of program	35.7%
Cross coverage in case of illness/disability	80.4%

Compensation and Leave (Graduate Year 1)

Average resident/fellow compensation	$46,789
Average number weeks of vacation	3.7
Sick days (paid)	20.1
Maximum number of paid days for family/medical leave	40
Maximum number of unpaid days for family/medical leave	62

Major Medical Benefits

Major medical insurance for residents	100.0%
Major medical insurance for dependents	96.4%
Outpatient mental health insurance	94.6%
Inpatient mental health insurance	92.9%
Group life insurance	85.7%
Dental insurance	92.9%
Disability insurance	83.9%
Disability insurance for occupationally acquired HIV	69.6%
Medical insurance coverage begins when starting program	87.5%

For more information

Professional Association

American Academy of Physical Medicine & Rehabilitation
330 North Wabash, Suite 2500
Chicago, IL 60611-7617
312 464-9700
312 464-0227 Fax
E-mail: info@aapmr.org
www.aapmr.org

Certification

American Board of Physical Medicine & Rehabilitation
3015 Allegro Park Lane SW
Rochester, MN 55902-4139
507 282-1776
507 282-9242 Fax
E-mail: info@abpmr.org
www.abpmr.org

Program Accreditation

Accreditation Council for Graduate Medical Education
Residency Review Committee for Physical Medicine & Rehabilitation
Steven P Nestler, PhD, Executive Director
515 North State Street
Chicago, IL 60654
312 755-5025
E-mail: spn@acgme.org
www.acgme.org

Hospice and Palliative Medicine

See page 57.

Specialty Data

Neuromuscular Medicine

Professional Description

A physiatrist who specializes in neuromuscular medicine possess specialized knowledge in the science, clinical evaluation, and management of these disorders. This encompasses the knowledge of the pathology, diagnosis, and treatment of these disorders at a level that is significantly beyond the training and knowledge expected of a general physiatrist.

Neuromuscular medicine includes the evaluation and treatment of a wide range of diseases, including motor neuron disease, myopathy/neuromuscular transmission disorders, peripheral neuropathy, cranial/spinal single and multiple mononeuropathies, polyneuropathy (infectious/inflammatory), inherited neuropathy, polyneuropathy (ischemia/physical agents/toxins), and polyneuropathy/systemic disease.

Prerequisites; Length of Training

Required for entry is successful completion of an ACGME-accredited program in either adult or pediatric neurology or physical medicine and rehabilitation; programs accredited by the Royal College of Physicians and Surgeons (Canada) are also accepted. Length of ACGME- accredited programs is 1 year.

For more information

American Association of Neuromuscular & Electrodiagnostic
  Medicine
2621 Superior Drive, NW
Rochester, MN 55901
507 288-0100
507 288-1225 Fax
E-mail: aanem@aanem.org
www.aanem.org

Pain Medicine

See description on p. 99.

Pediatric Rehabilitation Medicine

Professional Description

A physiatrist who utilizes an interdisciplinary approach and addresses the prevention, diagnosis, treatment, and management of congenital and childhood onset physical impairments including related or secondary medical, physical, functional, psychosocial, and vocational limitations or conditions, with an understanding of the life course of disability.

This physician is trained in the identification of functional capabilities and selection of the best of rehabilitation intervention strategies, with an understanding of the continuum of care.

Prerequisites; Length of Training

A minimum of 4 years of prior GME is required. Length of ACGME-accredited programs is 2 years (or 1 year for trainees who have completed ACGME-approved combined or consecutive programs in both physical medicine and rehabilitation and pediatrics).

For more information

American Academy of Physical Medicine & Rehabilitation
330 North Wabash, Suite 2500
Chicago, IL 60611-7617
312 464-9700
312 464-0227 Fax
E-mail: info@aapmr.org
www.aapmr.org

Spinal Cord Injury Medicine

Professional Description

A physician who addresses the prevention, diagnosis, treatment, and management of traumatic spinal cord injury and nontraumatic etiologies of spinal cord dysfunction by working in an interdisciplinary manner. Care is provided to patients of all ages on a lifelong basis and covers related medical, physical, psychological, and vocational disabilities and complications.

Prerequisites; Length of Training

A minimum of 3 years of prior GME is required in a specialty relevant to spinal cord injury medicine, such as anesthesiology, emergency medicine, family medicine, internal medicine, neurological surgery, neurology, orthopaedic surgery, pediatrics, physical medicine and rehabilitation, plastic surgery, surgery, or urology. Length of ACGME-accredited programs is 1 year.

Data

Unless otherwise noted, all data are for 2008.

Table 1. Spinal Cord Injury Medicine Programs	
Number of accredited programs	19
Program Data	
length of accredited training	1
Minimum number of prior years of GME required	4
Offers graduate year 1 positions, available immediately upon medical school completion	No
Average number of interviews for program year 1 positions	3.0
Percent new program directors, 2007-2008 academic year (source: ACGME)	15.0%
Residents/Fellows	
Total number of active residents/fellows	11
Average number of residents/fellows per program	0.6
Average percent female	63.6%
Average percent international medical graduate (IMG)	18.2%
Program Faculty	
Average number of full-time physician faculty	8.3
Average number of part-time physician faculty	0.6
Average percent female full-time physician faculty	30.2%
Average ratio of full-time physician faculty to resident/fellow	4.8

Table 2. Data for Spinal Cord Injury Medicine Programs Listed in FREIDA	
Number of programs providing data	12
Work Schedule (Program Year 1)	
Average hours on duty per week	44.6
Average maximum consecutive hours on duty	12.4
Average days off duty per week	2.0
Moonlighting allowed within institution	50.0%
Night float system	0.0%
Offers awareness and management of fatigue in residents/fellows	83.3%
Educational Setting (Program Year 1)	
Average hours/week of regularly scheduled lectures/conferences	4.0

Average percent of training in hospital outpatient clinics	39.2%
Average percent of training in nonhospital ambulatory care community settings	5.0%

Educational Benefits

Curriculum on management of tobacco dependence	8.3%
Program to assess/enhance medical professionalism	66.7%
Debt management/financial counseling	50.0%
Formal program to develop teaching skills	66.7%
Formal mentoring program	75.0%
Formal program to foster interdisciplinary teamwork	8.3%
Continuous quality improvement training	100.0%
International experience	0.0%
Resident/fellow retreats	41.7%
Off-campus electives	50.0%
Hospice/home care experience	50.0%
Cultural competence awareness	91.7%
Instruction in medical Spanish or other non-English language	16.7%
Alternative/complementary medicine curriculum	25.0%
Training in identifying and reporting of domestic violence/abuse	33.3%
MPH/MBA or PhD training	0.0%
Research rotation	41.7%

Educational Features

Offers additional training or educational experience beyond accredited length	27.3%
Offers a primary care track	8.3%
Offers a rural track	0.0%
Offers a women's health track	8.3%
Offers a hospitalist track	0.0%
Offers a research track/nonaccredited fellowship	16.7%
Offers an other track	8.3%

Resident Evaluation

Yearly specialty in-service examination required	13.0%
Patient surveys	41.7%
Portfolio system	50.0%
360 degree evaluations	83.3%
Objective structured clinical examinations (OSCE)	25.0%

Program Evaluation

Program graduation rates	75.0%
Board certification rates	91.7%
In-training examinations	16.7%
Performance-based assessments	33.3%

Employment Policies and Benefits

Part-time/shared positions	0.0%
On-site child care	25.0%
Subsidized child care	0.0%
Allowance/stipend for professional expenses	100.0%
Leave for educational meetings/conferences	83.3%
Moving allowance	0.0%
Housing stipend	8.3%
On-call meal allowance	25.0%
Free parking	58.3%
PDAs	8.3%
Placement assistance upon completion of program	50.0%
Cross coverage in case of illness/disability	58.3%

Compensation and Leave (Graduate Year 1)

Average resident/fellow compensation	$52,815
Average number weeks of vacation	3.3
Sick days (paid)	12.5
Maximum number of paid days for family/medical leave	22
Maximum number of unpaid days for family/medical leave	53

Major Medical Benefits

Major medical insurance for residents	100.0%
Major medical insurance for dependents	91.7%
Outpatient mental health insurance	83.3%
Inpatient mental health insurance	83.3%
Group life insurance	100.0%
Dental insurance	83.3%
Disability insurance	83.3%
Disability insurance for occupationally acquired HIV	50.0%
Medical insurance coverage begins when starting program	91.7%

For more information

American Academy of Physical Medicine & Rehabilitation
330 North Wabash, Suite 2500
Chicago, IL 60611-7617
312 464-9700
312 464-0227 Fax
E-mail: info@aapmr.org
www.aapmr.org

Sports Medicine

Professional Description

A physiatrist with special knowledge in sports medicine is responsible for continuous care in the field of sports medicine, not only for the enhancement of health and fitness, but also for the prevention and management of injury and illness. A sports medicine physician has knowledge and experience in the promotion of wellness and the role of exercise in promoting a healthy lifestyle. Knowledge of exercise physiology, biomechanics, nutrition, psychology, physical rehabilitation, and epidemiology is essential to the practice of sports medicine.

Prerequisites; Length of Training

Completion of an ACGME-accredited residency is required; length of accredited programs is 1 year.

Data

Unless otherwise noted, all data are for 2008.

For more information

American College of Sports Medicine
401 West Michigan Street
Indianapolis, IN 46202-3233
317 637-9200
317 634-7817 Fax
www.acsm.org

Specialty Data

Plastic Surgery

Professional Description

Plastic surgery deals with the repair, reconstruction, or replacement of physical defects of form or function involving the skin, musculoskeletal system, craniomaxillofacial structures, hand, extremities, breast and trunk, external genitalia or cosmetic enhancement of these areas of the body. Cosmetic surgery is an essential component of plastic surgery. The plastic surgeon uses cosmetic surgical principles both to improve overall appearance and to optimize the outcome of reconstructive procedures.

Special knowledge and skill in the design and surgery of grafts, flaps, free tissue transfer and replantation is necessary. Competence in the management of complex wounds, the use of implantable materials, and in tumor surgery is required. Plastic surgeons have been prominent in the development of innovative techniques such as microvascular and craniomaxillofacial surgery, liposuction, and tissue transfer. Anatomy, physiology, pathology, and other basic sciences are fundamental to the specialty.

Competency in plastic surgery implies an amalgam of basic medical and surgical knowledge, operative judgment, technical expertise, ethical behavior, and interpersonal skills to achieve problem resolution and patient satisfaction.

Source: American Board of Plastic Surgery

Prerequisites; Length of Training

Accredited plastic surgery programs are either *independent* (3 years length) or *integrated* (6 years). Prerequisites for the independent programs are 1) a minimum of 3 years clinical education with progressive responsibility in a general surgery program; 2) completion of a neurological surgery, orthopaedic surgery, otolaryngology, or urology residency; or 3) completion of an educational program in oral and maxillofacial surgery approved by the American Dental Association (for individuals holding the DMD/MD or DDS/MD degree).

Subspecialties

Subspecialty programs accredited by the ACGME

- Craniofacial surgery
- Hand surgery

American Board of Plastic Surgery subspecialty certificates

- Plastic surgery within the head and neck
- Surgery of the hand

Data

Unless otherwise noted, all data are for 2008.

Table 1. Plastic Surgery Programs

Number of accredited programs	89
Program Data	
length of accredited training	3/6
Minimum number of prior years of GME required	3/0
Offers graduate year 1 positions, available immediately upon medical school completion	Some
Average number of interviews for program year 1 positions	28.2
Percent new program directors, 2007-2008 academic year (source: ACGME)	8.0%
Residents/Fellows	
Total number of active residents/fellows	640
Average number of residents/fellows per program	7.2
Average percent female	24.1%
Average percent international medical graduate (IMG)	6.4%

Program Faculty

Average number of full-time physician faculty	8.1
Average number of part-time physician faculty	1.5
Average percent female full-time physician faculty	11.2%
Average ratio of full-time physician faculty to resident/fellow	0.7

Table 2. Data for Plastic Surgery Programs Listed in FREIDA

Number of programs providing data	47
Work Schedule (Program Year 1)	
Average hours on duty per week	64.6
Average maximum consecutive hours on duty	23.7
Average days off duty per week	1.2
Moonlighting allowed within institution	12.8%
Night float system	23.4%
Offers awareness and management of fatigue in residents/fellows	85.1%
Educational Setting (Program Year 1)	
Average hours/week of regularly scheduled lectures/conferences	4.4
Average percent of training in hospital outpatient clinics	18.1%
Average percent of training in nonhospital ambulatory care community settings	11.0%
Educational Benefits	
Curriculum on management of tobacco dependence	6.4%
Program to assess/enhance medical professionalism	70.2%
Debt management/financial counseling	53.2%
Formal program to develop teaching skills	80.9%
Formal mentoring program	48.9%
Formal program to foster interdisciplinary teamwork	10.6%
Continuous quality improvement training	83.0%
International experience	36.2%
Resident/fellow retreats	31.9%
Off-campus electives	42.6%
Hospice/home care experience	2.1%
Cultural competence awareness	57.4%
Instruction in medical Spanish or other non-English language	12.8%
Alternative/complementary medicine curriculum	4.3%
Training in identifying and reporting of domestic violence/abuse	31.9%
MPH/MBA or PhD training	10.6%
Research rotation	40.4%
Educational Features	
Offers additional training or educational experience beyond accredited length	13.7%
Offers a primary care track	6.4%
Offers a rural track	0.0%
Offers a women's health track	4.3%
Offers a hospitalist track	0.0%
Offers a research track/nonaccredited fellowship	8.5%
Offers an other track	4.3%
Resident Evaluation	
Yearly specialty in-service examination required	98.1%
Patient surveys	31.9%
Portfolio system	38.3%
360 degree evaluations	87.2%
Objective structured clinical examinations (OSCE)	10.6%
Program Evaluation	
Program graduation rates	85.1%
Board certification rates	97.9%
In-training examinations	100.0%
Performance-based assessments	55.3%
Employment Policies and Benefits	
Part-time/shared positions	0.0%
On-site child care	40.4%
Subsidized child care	8.5%
Allowance/stipend for professional expenses	93.6%

Leave for educational meetings/conferences	83.8%
Moving allowance	8.5%
Housing stipend	6.4%
On-call meal allowance	85.1%
Free parking	46.8%
PDAs	25.5%
Placement assistance upon completion of program	17.0%
Cross coverage in case of illness/disability	83.0%
Compensation and Leave (Graduate Year 1)	
Average resident/fellow compensation	$50,172
Average number weeks of vacation	5.2
Sick days (paid)	23.4
Maximum number of paid days for family/medical leave	36
Maximum number of unpaid days for family/medical leave	70
Major Medical Benefits	
Major medical insurance for residents	100.0%
Major medical insurance for dependents	95.7%
Outpatient mental health insurance	95.7%
Inpatient mental health insurance	93.6%
Group life insurance	95.7%
Dental insurance	87.2%
Disability insurance	85.1%
Disability insurance for occupationally acquired HIV	63.8%
Medical insurance coverage begins when starting program	89.4%

Table 3. Plastic Surgery Match Data

GY1	2008
Number of positions offered	92
Number filled by US seniors	86
Percent filled by US seniors	93.5
Total positions filled	92
Percent total positions filled	100
GY2	
Number of positions offered	0
Number filled by US seniors	0
Percent filled by US seniors	0
Total positions filled	0
Percent total positions filled	0
All	
Total Positions*	91
Preferred by US Seniors*	147
Preferred Positions per US Senior	0.6
Preferred by Independent Applicants†	23
Preferred Positions per IA	4

For more information

Professional Associations

American Academy of Facial Plastic and Reconstructive Surgery
310 South Henry Street
Alexandria, VA 22314
703 299-9291
703 299-8898 Fax
E-mail: info@aafprs.com
www.aafprs.org

American Association of Plastic Surgeons
900 Cummings Center, Suite 221-U
Beverly, MA 01915
978 927-8330
978 524-8890 Fax
www.aaps1921.org

American Society for Aesthetic Plastic Surgery
11081 Winners Circle
Los Alamitos, CA 90720-2813
888 272-7711
E-mail: findasurgeon@surgery.org
www.surgery.org

American Society of Ophthalmic Plastic and Reconstructive Surgery
5841 Cedar Lake Road, Suite 204
Minneapolis, MN 55416
952 646-2038
952 545-6073 Fax
E-mail: info@asoprs.org
www.asoprs.org

American Society of Plastic Surgeons
444 East Algonquin Road
Arlington Heights, IL 60005
847 228-9900
www.plasticsurgery.org

Certification

American Board of Plastic Surgery
Seven Penn Center, Suite 400
1635 Market Street
Philadelphia, PA 19103-2204
215 587-9322
215 587-9622 Fax
E-mail: info@abplsurg.org
www.abplsurg.org

Program Accreditation

Accreditation Council for Graduate Medical Education
Residency Review Committee for Plastic Surgery
Peggy Simpson, EdD, Executive Director
515 North State Street
Chicago, IL 60654
312 755-5499
E-mail: psimpson@acgme.org
www.acgme.org

Craniofacial Surgery (Plastic Surgery within the Head and Neck)

Professional Description

A plastic surgeon with additional training in plastic and reconstructive procedures within the head, face, neck, and associated structures, including cutaneous head and neck oncology and reconstruction, management of maxillofacial trauma, soft tissue repair, and neural surgery.

The field is diverse and involves a wide age range of patients, from the newborn to the aged. While both cosmetic and reconstructive surgery are practiced, there are many additional procedures that interface with them. Cosmetic procedures include otoplasty; surgery of the aging face (brow lift, blepharoplasty, face lift); rhinoplasty; facial implants (cheek, nasal, and chin); facial resurfacing; and liposuction/lipoplasty. Reconstructive procedures performed include maxillofacial trauma; skin grafts and flaps; repair of congenital facial defects (hemangiomata, cleft lip and palate, nasal abnormalities); reconstruction of the jaws and other facial bones; reanimation/rehabilitation of the paralyzed face; nerve repair; periorbital surgery; and biomedical implant insertion. Areas of research in this field include materials biocompatibility; wound healing adjuncts; skin repair/regeneration; and bone reconstruction.

Prerequisites; Length of Training

Completion of a 6-year plastic surgery program or other appropriate surgery training is required. Length of ACGME-accredited programs is 1 year.

For more information

Professional Association

American Academy of Facial Plastic and Reconstructive Surgery
310 South Henry Street
Alexandria, VA 22314
703 299-9291
E-mail: info@aafprs.com
www.aafprs.org

Hand Surgery

Professional Description

A plastic surgeon with additional training in the investigation, preservation, and restoration—by medical, surgical, and rehabilitative means—of all structures of the upper extremity directly affecting the form and function of the hand and wrist.

Prerequisites; Length of Training

Completion of an ACGME-accredited general surgery, orthopaedic surgery, or plastic surgery program is required. Length of ACGME-accredited programs is 1 year.

Data

Unless otherwise noted, all data are for 2008.

Table 1. Hand Surgery Programs

Number of accredited programs	14

Program Data	
length of accredited training	1
Minimum number of prior years of GME required	5
Offers graduate year 1 positions, available immediately upon medical school completion	No
Average number of interviews for program year 1 positions	8.3
Percent new program directors, 2007-2008 academic year (source: ACGME)	7.7%

Residents/Fellows	
Total number of active residents/fellows	17
Average number of residents/fellows per program	1.2
Average percent female	11.8%
Average percent international medical graduate (IMG)	17.6%

Program Faculty	
Average number of full-time physician faculty	6.5
Average number of part-time physician faculty	0.7
Average percent female full-time physician faculty	11.9%
Average ratio of full-time physician faculty to resident/fellow	2.5

Table 2. Data for Hand Surgery Programs Listed in FREIDA

Number of programs providing data	8

Work Schedule (Program Year 1)

Average hours on duty per week	53.9
Average maximum consecutive hours on duty	23.0
Average days off duty per week	1.3
Moonlighting allowed within institution	12.5%
Night float system	0.0%
Offers awareness and management of fatigue in residents/fellows	100.0%

Educational Setting (Program Year 1)

Average hours/week of regularly scheduled lectures/conferences	4.0
Average percent of training in hospital outpatient clinics	18.8%
Average percent of training in nonhospital ambulatory care community settings	20.0%

Educational Benefits	
Curriculum on management of tobacco dependence	0.0%
Program to assess/enhance medical professionalism	37.5%
Debt management/financial counseling	25.0%
Formal program to develop teaching skills	87.5%
Formal mentoring program	37.5%
Formal program to foster interdisciplinary teamwork	0.0%
Continuous quality improvement training	87.5%
International experience	25.0%
Resident/fellow retreats	37.5%
Off-campus electives	37.5%
Hospice/home care experience	0.0%
Cultural competence awareness	75.0%
Instruction in medical Spanish or other non-English language	25.0%
Alternative/complementary medicine curriculum	0.0%
Training in identifying and reporting of domestic violence/abuse	37.5%
MPH/MBA or PhD training	0.0%
Research rotation	12.5%

Educational Features	
Offers additional training or educational experience beyond accredited length	7.1%
Offers a primary care track	12.5%
Offers a rural track	0.0%
Offers a women's health track	0.0%
Offers a hospitalist track	0.0%
Offers a research track/nonaccredited fellowship	12.5%
Offers an other track	0.0%

Resident Evaluation	
Yearly specialty in-service examination required	50.0%
Patient surveys	37.5%
Portfolio system	37.5%
360 degree evaluations	87.5%
Objective structured clinical examinations (OSCE)	0.0%

Program Evaluation	
Program graduation rates	87.5%
Board certification rates	87.5%
In-training examinations	50.0%
Performance-based assessments	25.0%

Employment Policies and Benefits	
Part-time/shared positions	0.0%
On-site child care	25.0%
Subsidized child care	0.0%
Allowance/stipend for professional expenses	100.0%
Leave for educational meetings/conferences	65.2%
Moving allowance	0.0%
Housing stipend	0.0%
On-call meal allowance	50.0%
Free parking	12.5%
PDAs	0.0%

Placement assistance upon completion of program	0.0%
Cross coverage in case of illness/disability	87.5%
Compensation and Leave (Graduate Year 1)	
Average resident/fellow compensation	$57,466
Average number weeks of vacation	15.1
Sick days (paid)	37.7
Maximum number of paid days for family/medical leave	18
Maximum number of unpaid days for family/medical leave	53
Major Medical Benefits	
Major medical insurance for residents	100.0%
Major medical insurance for dependents	87.5%
Outpatient mental health insurance	100.0%
Inpatient mental health insurance	100.0%
Group life insurance	100.0%
Dental insurance	87.5%
Disability insurance	75.0%
Disability insurance for occupationally acquired HIV	37.5%
Medical insurance coverage begins when starting program	100.0%

For more information

Professional Association

American Society for Surgery of the Hand
6300 North River Road, Suite 600
Rosemont, IL 60018
847 384-8300
847 384-1435 Fax
E-mail: info@assh.org
www.assh.org

Preventive Medicine

Professional Description

A preventive medicine specialist focuses on the health of individuals and defined populations to protect, promote, and maintain health and well-being and to prevent disease, disability, and premature death. The distinctive components of preventive medicine include:

- Biostatistics and the application of biostatistical principles and methodology
- Epidemiology and its application to population-based medicine and research
- Health services management and administration, including developing, assessing, and assuring health policies; planning, implementing, directing, budgeting, and evaluating population health and disease management programs; and utilizing legislative and regulatory processes to enhance health
- Control of environmental factors that may adversely affect health
- Control and prevention of occupational factors that may adversely affect health safety
- Clinical preventive medicine activities, including measures to promote health and prevent the occurrence, progression, and disabling effects of disease and injury
- Assessment of social, cultural, and behavioral influences on health

A preventive medicine physician may be a specialist in general preventive medicine, public health, occupational medicine, or aerospace medicine. This specialist works with large population groups as well as with individual patients to promote health and understand the risks of disease, injury, disability, and death, seeking to modify and eliminate these risks.

Prerequisites; Length of Training

Accredited programs are either 1, 2, or 3 years in length.

Specialty Areas

Programs in specialty areas accredited by the ACGME

- Aerospace medicine
- Occupational medicine
- Public health and general preventive medicine

American Board of Preventive Medicine specialty area certificates

- Aerospace medicine
- Occupational medicine
- Public health and general preventive medicine

Subspecialties

Subspecialty programs accredited by the ACGME

- Medical toxicology
- Undersea and hyperbaric medicine

American Board of Preventive Medicine subspecialty certificates

- Medical toxicology
- Undersea and hyperbaric medicine

Specialty Data

Data

Unless otherwise noted, all data are for 2008.

Table 1. Preventive Medicine Programs

Number of accredited programs	69

Program Data

length of accredited training	1/2/3
Minimum number of prior years of GME required	1/0
Offers graduate year 1 positions, available immediately upon medical school completion	Some
Average number of interviews for program year 1 positions	6.6
Percent new program directors, 2007-2008 academic year (source: ACGME)	8.2%

Residents/Fellows

Total number of active residents/fellows	238
Average number of residents/fellows per program	3.4
Average percent female	44.5%
Average percent international medical graduate (IMG)	20.6%

Program Faculty

Average number of full-time physician faculty	9.5
Average number of part-time physician faculty	3.6
Average percent female full-time physician faculty	33.2%
Average ratio of full-time physician faculty to resident/fellow	1.3

Table 2. Data for Preventive Medicine Programs Listed in FREIDA

Number of programs providing data	22

Work Schedule (Program Year 1)

Average hours on duty per week	42.6
Average maximum consecutive hours on duty	12.2
Average days off duty per week	2.0
Moonlighting allowed within institution	68.2%
Night float system	4.5%
Offers awareness and management of fatigue in residents/fellows	81.8%

Educational Setting (Program Year 1)

Average hours/week of regularly scheduled lectures/conferences	8.4
Average percent of training in hospital outpatient clinics	17.4%
Average percent of training in nonhospital ambulatory care community settings	25.1%

Educational Benefits

Curriculum on management of tobacco dependence	36.4%
Program to assess/enhance medical professionalism	90.9%
Debt management/financial counseling	40.9%
Formal program to develop teaching skills	50.0%
Formal mentoring program	50.0%
Formal program to foster interdisciplinary teamwork	31.8%
Continuous quality improvement training	81.8%
International experience	31.8%
Resident/fellow retreats	31.8%
Off-campus electives	100.0%
Hospice/home care experience	4.5%
Cultural competence awareness	81.8%
Instruction in medical Spanish or other non-English language	13.6%
Alternative/complementary medicine curriculum	31.8%
Training in identifying and reporting of domestic violence/abuse	27.3%
MPH/MBA or PhD training	100.0%
Research rotation	63.6%

Educational Features

Offers additional training or educational experience beyond accredited length	17.1%
Offers a primary care track	13.6%
Offers a rural track	22.7%
Offers a women's health track	9.1%
Offers a hospitalist track	0.0%
Offers a research track/nonaccredited fellowship	13.6%
Offers an other track	63.6%

Resident Evaluation

Yearly specialty in-service examination required	80.6%
Patient surveys	22.7%
Portfolio system	54.5%
360 degree evaluations	63.6%
Objective structured clinical examinations (OSCE)	27.3%

Program Evaluation

Program graduation rates	95.5%
Board certification rates	100.0%
In-training examinations	100.0%
Performance-based assessments	40.9%

Employment Policies and Benefits

Part-time/shared positions	27.3%
On-site child care	27.3%
Subsidized child care	4.5%
Allowance/stipend for professional expenses	100.0%
Leave for educational meetings/conferences	81.0%
Moving allowance	0.0%
Housing stipend	13.6%
On-call meal allowance	18.2%
Free parking	59.1%
PDAs	18.2%
Placement assistance upon completion of program	40.9%
Cross coverage in case of illness/disability	45.5%

Compensation and Leave (Graduate Year 1)

Average resident/fellow compensation	$47,452
Average number weeks of vacation	3.1
Sick days (paid)	23.1
Maximum number of paid days for family/medical leave	37
Maximum number of unpaid days for family/medical leave	59

Major Medical Benefits

Major medical insurance for residents	95.5%
Major medical insurance for dependents	77.3%
Outpatient mental health insurance	81.8%
Inpatient mental health insurance	72.7%
Group life insurance	72.7%
Dental insurance	90.9%
Disability insurance	86.4%
Disability insurance for occupationally acquired HIV	50.0%
Medical insurance coverage begins when starting program	81.8%

For more information

Professional Association

American College of Preventive Medicine
1307 New York Avenue, NW, Suite 200
Washington, DC 20005
202 466-2044
202 466-2662 Fax
E-mail: info@acpm.org
www.acpm.org

Certification

American Board of Preventive Medicine
111 West Jackson Boulevard, Suite 1110
Chicago, IL 60604
312 939-2276
312 939-2218 Fax
E-mail: abpm@theabpm.org
www.abprevmed.org

Program Accreditation

Accreditation Council for Graduate Medical Education
Residency Review Committee for Preventive Medicine
Patricia Levenberg, PhD, Executive Director
515 North State Street
Chicago, IL 60654
312 755-5048
E-mail: plevenberg@acgme.org
www.acgme.org

Aerospace Medicine

Professional Description

Aerospace medicine concerns the determination and maintenance of the health, safety, and performance of persons involved in air and space travel. Aerospace medicine, as a broad field of endeavor, offers dynamic challenges and opportunities for physicians, nurses, physiologists, bioenvironmental engineers, industrial hygienists, environmental health practitioners, human factors specialists, psychologists, and other professionals. Those in the field are dedicated to enhancing health, promoting safety, and improving performance of individuals who work or travel in unusual environments. The environments of space and aviation provide significant challenges, such as microgravity, radiation exposure, G-forces, emergency ejection injuries, and hypoxic conditions, for those embarking in their exploration. Areas of interest range from space and atmospheric flight to undersea activities, and the environments that are studied cover a wide spectrum, extending from the "microenvironments" of space or diving suits to those of "Spaceship Earth."

Source: Aerospace Medical Association

For more information

Aerospace Medical Association
320 South Henry Street
Alexandria, VA 22314 -3579
703 739-2240
703 739-9652 Fax
E-mail: info@asma.org
www.asma.org

Occupational Medicine

Professional Description

Occupational and environmental medicine is perhaps the most wide ranging of all medical specialties. It is the medical specialty devoted to prevention and management of occupational and environmental injury, illness and disability, and promotion of health and productivity of workers, their families, and communities.

Occupational medicine was previously identified as "industrial medicine." This term was used when heavy industry (eg, lumbering, automobile manufacturing, mining, railroads, steel manufacturers, etc) employed physicians to provide acute medical and surgical care for employees. By 1945, medical programs had spread to business organizations with a predominance of clerical and service employees. Large banks, insurance companies, mercantile establishments, etc., could not be described as industrial; therefore, the broader designation of "occupational medicine" came into common use.

Today, the complexity and pervasiveness of modern industrial processes afford occupational and environmental medicine physicians the opportunity to address work site and environmental concerns and such community health and policy issues as atmospheric pollution, product safety, health promotion, and benefits value management. The term "environmental medicine" has also recently been used to describe this growing, challenging, modern medical specialty. Environmental medicine has been defined as the branch of medical science that addresses the impact of chemical and physical stressors on individuals and groups. Both occupational and environmental medicine use similar skills and focus on the recognition and prevention of hazardous exposures.

Source: American College of Occupational and Environmental Medicine

For more information

American College of Occupational and Environmental Medicine
25 Northwest Point Boulevard, Suite 700
Elk Grove Village, IL 60007-1030
847 818-1800
847 818-9266 Fax
www.acoem.org

Public Health and General Preventive Medicine

Professional Description

A public health physician helps guide a community, agency, health organization, medical office, or program in pursuit of group or community health goals. This includes physicians who plan, provide, and administer public health and preventive medicine services in public, private, or voluntary settings.

The public health practitioner:

- Performs epidemiological investigations of acute and chronic diseases and injuries
- Uses appropriate statistical techniques in the design of studies and interpretation of findings relative to disease interventions performed on individuals and in monitoring and experimental protocols
- Plans, administers, and evaluates programs to promote health and prevent disease in medical practice settings and in public health agencies
- Designs, performs, and evaluates clinical trials
- Applies clinical interventions in the general population
- Assesses health risk factors in individual persons and groups and prescribes appropriate interventions
- Assesses and ameliorates the impact of environmental and occupational risk factors on individual persons and on groups
- Assesses the clinical and public health program needs of populations, eg, workers, communities, and military groups

Source: American Association of Public Health Physicians

For more information

American Association of Public Health Physicians
3433 Kirchoff Road
Rolling Meadows, IL 60008
847 371-1502
847 255-0559 Fax
E-mail: aaphp@reachone.com
www.aaphp.org

Specialty Data

Medical Toxicology

Professional Description

A specialist who is expert in evaluating and managing patients with accidental or intentional poisoning through exposure to prescription and nonprescription medications, drugs of abuse, household or industrial toxins, and environmental toxins.

Important areas of medical toxicology include acute pediatric and adult drug ingestion; drug abuse, addiction, and withdrawal; chemical poisoning exposure and toxicity; hazardous materials exposure and toxicity; and occupational toxicology.

Prerequisites; Length of Training

Completion of an ACGME-accredited residency is required; length of accredited programs is 2 years.

For more information

American College of Medical Toxicology
10645 N Tatum Boulevard, Suite 200-111
Phoenix, AZ 85028
623 533-6340
623 533-6340 Fax
E-mail: info@acmt.net
www.acmt.net

Undersea and Hyperbaric Medicine

Professional Description

A specialist who treats decompression illness and diving accident cases and uses hyperbaric oxygen therapy to treat such conditions as carbon monoxide poisoning, gas gangrene, nonhealing wounds, tissue damage from radiation and burns, and bone infections. This specialist also serves as consultant to other physicians in all aspects of hyperbaric chamber operations, and assesses risks and applies appropriate standards to prevent disease and disability in divers and other persons working in altered atmospheric conditions.

Prerequisites; Length of Training

Completion of an ACGME-accredited residency is required; length of accredited programs is 1 year.

For more information

Undersea & Hyperbaric Medicine Society
21 West Colony Place, Suite 280
Durham, NC 27705
919 490-5140
919 490-5149 Fax
Email: uhms@uhms.org
www.uhms.org

Psychiatry

Professional Description

A psychiatrist specializes in the prevention, diagnosis, and treatment of mental, addictive, and emotional disorders such as schizophrenia and other psychotic disorders, mood disorders, anxiety disorders, substance-related disorders, sexual and gender identity disorders, and adjustment disorders. The psychiatrist is able to understand the biologic, psychologic, and social components of illness, and therefore is uniquely prepared to treat the whole person. A psychiatrist is qualified to order diagnostic laboratory tests and to prescribe medications, evaluate and treat psychologic and interpersonal problems, and intervene with families who are coping with stress, crises, and other problems in living.

Prerequisites; Length of Training

No previous GME is required. ACGME-accredited programs are 4 years.

Physicians may also enter programs at the GY2 level only after successfully completing one of the following:

- One clinical year of training in an ACGME-accredited internal medicine, family medicine, or pediatrics program
- An ACGME-accredited transitional year program
- One year of an ACGME-accredited residency in a clinical specialty requiring comprehensive and continuous patient care

For physicians entering at the GY2 level, the GY1 year may be credited toward the 48-month requirement.

Subspecialties

Subspecialty programs accredited by the ACGME

- Addiction psychiatry
- Child and adolescent psychiatry
- Forensic psychiatry
- Geriatric psychiatry
- Hospice and palliative medicine
- Pain medicine
- Psychosomatic medicine
- Sleep medicine

American Board of Psychiatry and Neurology subspecialty certificates

- Addiction psychiatry
- Child and adolescent psychiatry
- Forensic psychiatry
- Geriatric psychiatry
- Hospice and palliative medicine
- Pain medicine
- Psychosomatic medicine
- Sleep medicine

Data

Table 1. Psychiatry Programs	
Number of accredited programs	182
Program Data	
length of accredited training	4
Minimum number of prior years of GME required	0
Offers graduate year 1 positions, available immediately upon medical school completion	Yes
Average number of interviews for program year 1 positions	58.3
Percent new program directors, 2007-2008 academic year (source: ACGME)	18.8%

Residents/Fellows

Total number of active residents/fellows	4,610
Average number of residents/fellows per program	25.3
Average percent female	54.1%
Average percent international medical graduate (IMG)	33.1%

Program Faculty

Average number of full-time physician faculty	37.3
Average number of part-time physician faculty	16.8
Average percent female full-time physician faculty	33.0%
Average ratio of full-time physician faculty to resident/fellow	1.1

Table 2. Data for Psychiatry Programs Listed in FREIDA

Number of programs providing data	138

Work Schedule (Program Year 1)

Average hours on duty per week	55.0
Average maximum consecutive hours on duty	26.3
Average days off duty per week	1.5
Moonlighting allowed within institution	63.0%
Night float system	39.1%
Offers awareness and management of fatigue in residents/fellows	93.5%

Educational Setting (Program Year 1)

Average hours/week of regularly scheduled lectures/conferences	6.1
Average percent of training in hospital outpatient clinics	16.5%
Average percent of training in nonhospital ambulatory care community settings	9.1%

Educational Benefits

Curriculum on management of tobacco dependence	36.2%
Program to assess/enhance medical professionalism	81.2%
Debt management/financial counseling	45.7%
Formal program to develop teaching skills	94.9%
Formal mentoring program	71.0%
Formal program to foster interdisciplinary teamwork	38.4%
Continuous quality improvement training	89.9%
International experience	21.0%
Resident/fellow retreats	84.8%
Off-campus electives	91.3%
Hospice/home care experience	34.8%
Cultural competence awareness	99.3%
Instruction in medical Spanish or other non-English language	20.3%
Alternative/complementary medicine curriculum	40.6%
Training in identifying and reporting of domestic violence/abuse	83.3%
MPH/MBA or PhD training	26.8%
Research rotation	23.2%

Educational Features

Offers additional training or educational experience beyond accredited length	23.1%
Offers a primary care track	7.2%
Offers a rural track	8.0%
Offers a women's health track	7.2%
Offers a hospitalist track	2.9%
Offers a research track/nonaccredited fellowship	42.8%
Offers an other track	19.6%

Resident Evaluation

Yearly specialty in-service examination required	98.5%
Patient surveys	54.3%
Portfolio system	54.3%
360 degree evaluations	88.4%
Objective structured clinical examinations (OSCE)	35.5%

Program Evaluation

Program graduation rates	80.4%
Board certification rates	98.6%
In-training examinations	97.1%
Performance-based assessments	64.5%

Employment Policies and Benefits

Part-time/shared positions	25.4%
On-site child care	37.0%
Subsidized child care	5.8%
Allowance/stipend for professional expenses	85.5%
Leave for educational meetings/conferences	82.6%
Moving allowance	8.7%
Housing stipend	4.3%
On-call meal allowance	92.0%
Free parking	61.6%
PDAs	21.7%
Placement assistance upon completion of program	25.4%
Cross coverage in case of illness/disability	92.8%

Compensation and Leave (Graduate Year 1)

Average resident/fellow compensation	$46,374
Average number weeks of vacation	3.5
Sick days (paid)	17.4
Maximum number of paid days for family/medical leave	40
Maximum number of unpaid days for family/medical leave	64

Major Medical Benefits

Major medical insurance for residents	99.3%
Major medical insurance for dependents	95.7%
Outpatient mental health insurance	97.8%
Inpatient mental health insurance	98.6%
Group life insurance	91.3%
Dental insurance	85.5%
Disability insurance	85.5%
Disability insurance for occupationally acquired HIV	71.0%
Medical insurance coverage begins when starting program	84.8%

Table 3. Psychiatry Match Data

GY1	2008
Number of positions offered	1,069
Number filled by US seniors	595
Percent filled by US seniors	55.7
Total positions filled	1,013
Percent total positions filled	94.8

GY2	
Number of positions offered	4
Number filled by US seniors	2
Percent filled by US seniors	50
Total positions filled	2
Percent total positions filled	50

All	
Total Positions*	1,086
Preferred by US Seniors*	617
Preferred Positions per US Senior	1.8
Preferred by Independent Applicants†	806
Preferred Positions per IA	1.3

Source: National Resident Matching Program 2008 Match Data
* Includes all positions offered in a specialty, except preliminary positions.
† Preferred means the number of applicants for whom the specialty was the only or first choice.

For more information

Professional Associations

American Academy of Child and Adolescent Psychiatry
3615 Wisconsin Avenue NW
Washington, DC 20016-3007
202 966-7300
202 966-2891 Fax
www.aacap.org

American Academy of Psychiatry and the Law
One Regency Drive
PO Box 30
Bloomfield, CT 06002
860 242-5450
860 286-0787 Fax
E-mail: exocoff@aapl.org
www.aapl.org

American Psychiatric Association
1000 Wilson Boulevard, Suite 1825
Arlington, VA 22209-3901
703 907-7300
E-mail: apa@psych.org
www.psych.org

Certification

American Board of Psychiatry and Neurology
2150 East Lake Cook Road, Suite 900
Buffalo Grove, IL 60089
847 229-6500
847 229-6600 Fax
www.abpn.com

Program Accreditation

Accreditation Council for Graduate Medical Education
Residency Review Committee for Psychiatry
Lynne Meyer, PhD, MPH, Executive Director
515 North State Street
Chicago, IL 60654
312 755-5006
E-mail: lmeyer@acgme.org
www.acgme.org

Addiction Psychiatry

Professional Description

A psychiatrist who focuses on the evaluation and treatment of individuals with alcohol, drug, or other substance-related disorders and of individuals with the dual diagnosis of substance-related and other psychiatric disorders.

Prerequisites; Length of Training

A minimum of 4 years of prior GME is required. Length of ACGME-accredited programs is 1 year.

Data

Unless otherwise noted, all data are for 2008.

Table 1. Addiction Psychiatry Programs

Number of accredited programs	43
Program Data	
length of accredited training	1
Minimum number of prior years of GME required	4
Offers graduate year 1 positions, available immediately upon medical school completion	No
Average number of interviews for program year 1 positions	3.6
Percent new program directors, 2007-2008 academic year (source: ACGME)	4.9%
Residents/Fellows	
Total number of active residents/fellows	39
Average number of residents/fellows per program	0.9
Average percent female	30.8%
Average percent international medical graduate (IMG)	35.9%

Program Faculty

Average number of full-time physician faculty	9.1
Average number of part-time physician faculty	1.7
Average percent female full-time physician faculty	27.9%
Average ratio of full-time physician faculty to resident/fellow	3.3

Table 2. Data for Addiction Psychiatry Programs Listed in FREIDA

Number of programs providing data	23
Work Schedule (Program Year 1)	
Average hours on duty per week	34.5
Average maximum consecutive hours on duty	9.9
Average days off duty per week	1.9
Moonlighting allowed within institution	91.3%
Night float system	0.0%
Offers awareness and management of fatigue in residents/fellows	87.0%
Educational Setting (Program Year 1)	
Average hours/week of regularly scheduled lectures/conferences	4.2
Average percent of training in hospital outpatient clinics	46.5%
Average percent of training in nonhospital ambulatory care community settings	22.0%
Educational Benefits	
Curriculum on management of tobacco dependence	69.6%
Program to assess/enhance medical professionalism	73.9%
Debt management/financial counseling	34.8%
Formal program to develop teaching skills	87.0%
Formal mentoring program	69.6%
Formal program to foster interdisciplinary teamwork	34.8%
Continuous quality improvement training	87.0%
International experience	4.3%
Resident/fellow retreats	39.1%
Off-campus electives	52.2%
Hospice/home care experience	0.0%
Cultural competence awareness	100.0%
Instruction in medical Spanish or other non-English language	8.7%
Alternative/complementary medicine curriculum	26.1%
Training in identifying and reporting of domestic violence/abuse	52.2%
MPH/MBA or PhD training	17.4%
Research rotation	39.1%
Educational Features	
Offers additional training or educational experience beyond accredited length	30.4%
Offers a primary care track	4.3%
Offers a rural track	4.3%
Offers a women's health track	4.3%
Offers a hospitalist track	4.3%
Offers a research track/nonaccredited fellowship	39.1%
Offers an other track	0.0%
Resident Evaluation	
Yearly specialty in-service examination required	39.2%
Patient surveys	26.1%
Portfolio system	21.7%
360 degree evaluations	82.6%
Objective structured clinical examinations (OSCE)	17.4%
Program Evaluation	
Program graduation rates	100.0%
Board certification rates	95.7%
In-training examinations	52.2%
Performance-based assessments	34.8%
Employment Policies and Benefits	
Part-time/shared positions	34.8%
On-site child care	13.0%
Subsidized child care	4.3%
Allowance/stipend for professional expenses	78.3%

Leave for educational meetings/conferences	69.0%
Moving allowance	4.3%
Housing stipend	4.3%
On-call meal allowance	26.1%
Free parking	73.9%
PDAs	0.0%
Placement assistance upon completion of program	21.7%
Cross coverage in case of illness/disability	78.3%
Compensation and Leave (Graduate Year 1)	
Average resident/fellow compensation	$55,042
Average number weeks of vacation	3.6
Sick days (paid)	29.9
Maximum number of paid days for family/medical leave	25
Maximum number of unpaid days for family/medical leave	34
Major Medical Benefits	
Major medical insurance for residents	100.0%
Major medical insurance for dependents	100.0%
Outpatient mental health insurance	100.0%
Inpatient mental health insurance	100.0%
Group life insurance	91.3%
Dental insurance	87.0%
Disability insurance	95.7%
Disability insurance for occupationally acquired HIV	73.9%
Medical insurance coverage begins when starting program	100.0%

For more information

American Society of Addiction Medicine
4601 North Park Avenue, Upper Arcade #101
Chevy Chase, MD 20815
301 656-3920
301 656-3815 Fax
E-mail: email@asam.org
www.asam.org

Child and Adolescent Psychiatry

Professional Description

A psychiatrist with additional training in the diagnosis and treatment of developmental, behavioral, emotional, and mental disorders of childhood and adolescence.

Prerequisites; Length of Training

A minimum of 3 years of prior GME is required. Length of ACGME-accredited programs is 2 years.

Data

Unless otherwise noted, all data are for 2008.

Table 1. Child and Adolescent Psychiatry Programs

Number of accredited programs	122
Program Data	
length of accredited training	2
Minimum number of prior years of GME required	3
Offers graduate year 1 positions, available immediately upon medical school completion	No
Average number of interviews for program year 1 positions	12.2
Percent new program directors, 2007-2008 academic year (source: ACGME)	9.1%
Residents/Fellows	
Total number of active residents/fellows	720
Average number of residents/fellows per program	5.9

Average percent female	57.9%
Average percent international medical graduate (IMG)	27.2%
Program Faculty	
Average number of full-time physician faculty	8.7
Average number of part-time physician faculty	3.7
Average percent female full-time physician faculty	44.7%
Average ratio of full-time physician faculty to resident/fellow	0.9

Table 2. Data for Child and Adolescent Psychiatry Programs Listed in FREIDA

Number of programs providing data	74
Work Schedule (Program Year 1)	
Average hours on duty per week	43.5
Average maximum consecutive hours on duty	15.9
Average days off duty per week	1.9
Moonlighting allowed within institution	58.1%
Night float system	2.7%
Offers awareness and management of fatigue in residents/fellows	91.9%
Educational Setting (Program Year 1)	
Average hours/week of regularly scheduled lectures/conferences	6.6
Average percent of training in hospital outpatient clinics	29.0%
Average percent of training in nonhospital ambulatory care community settings	21.0%
Educational Benefits	
Curriculum on management of tobacco dependence	24.3%
Program to assess/enhance medical professionalism	77.0%
Debt management/financial counseling	35.1%
Formal program to develop teaching skills	89.2%
Formal mentoring program	64.9%
Formal program to foster interdisciplinary teamwork	41.9%
Continuous quality improvement training	85.1%
International experience	9.5%
Resident/fellow retreats	78.4%
Off-campus electives	87.8%
Hospice/home care experience	6.8%
Cultural competence awareness	98.6%
Instruction in medical Spanish or other non-English language	18.9%
Alternative/complementary medicine curriculum	25.7%
Training in identifying and reporting of domestic violence/abuse	85.1%
MPH/MBA or PhD training	17.6%
Research rotation	36.5%
Educational Features	
Offers additional training or educational experience beyond accredited length	8.6%
Offers a primary care track	6.8%
Offers a rural track	8.1%
Offers a women's health track	0.0%
Offers a hospitalist track	0.0%
Offers a research track/nonaccredited fellowship	21.6%
Offers an other track	10.8%
Resident Evaluation	
Yearly specialty in-service examination required	98.5%
Patient surveys	37.8%
Portfolio system	41.9%
360 degree evaluations	78.4%
Objective structured clinical examinations (OSCE)	36.5%
Program Evaluation	
Program graduation rates	86.5%
Board certification rates	93.2%
In-training examinations	94.6%
Performance-based assessments	59.5%
Employment Policies and Benefits	
Part-time/shared positions	35.1%

Specialty Data

On-site child care	45.9%
Subsidized child care	5.4%
Allowance/stipend for professional expenses	86.5%
Leave for educational meetings/conferences	87.5%
Moving allowance	6.8%
Housing stipend	5.4%
On-call meal allowance	59.5%
Free parking	55.4%
PDAs	10.8%
Placement assistance upon completion of program	28.4%
Cross coverage in case of illness/disability	91.9%
Compensation and Leave (Graduate Year 1)	
Average resident/fellow compensation	$51,282
Average number weeks of vacation	3.9
Sick days (paid)	21.6
Maximum number of paid days for family/medical leave	38
Maximum number of unpaid days for family/medical leave	56
Major Medical Benefits	
Major medical insurance for residents	98.6%
Major medical insurance for dependents	94.6%
Outpatient mental health insurance	97.3%
Inpatient mental health insurance	97.3%
Group life insurance	91.9%
Dental insurance	87.8%
Disability insurance	91.9%
Disability insurance for occupationally acquired HIV	71.6%
Medical insurance coverage begins when starting program	89.2%

For more information

American Academy of Child and Adolescent Psychiatry
3615 Wisconsin Avenue, NW
Washington, DC 20016-3007
202 966-7300
202 966-2891 Fax
www.aacap.org

Forensic Psychiatry

Professional Description

A psychiatrist who focuses on the interrelationships between psychiatry and civil, criminal, and administrative law. This specialist evaluates individuals involved with the legal system and provides specialized treatment to those incarcerated in jails, prisons, and forensic psychiatry hospitals.

Prerequisites; Length of Training

A minimum of 4 years of prior GME is required. Length of ACGME-accredited programs is 1 year.

Data

Unless otherwise noted, all data are for 2008.

Table 1. Forensic Psychiatry Programs

Number of accredited programs	40
Program Data	
length of accredited training	1
Minimum number of prior years of GME required	4
Offers graduate year 1 positions, available immediately upon medical school completion	No
Average number of interviews for program year 1 positions	5.2
Percent new program directors, 2007-2008 academic year (source: ACGME)	9.8%

Residents/Fellows

Total number of active residents/fellows	58
Average number of residents/fellows per program	1.5
Average percent female	32.8%
Average percent international medical graduate (IMG)	22.4%
Program Faculty	
Average number of full-time physician faculty	5.0
Average number of part-time physician faculty	3.8
Average percent female full-time physician faculty	24.9%
Average ratio of full-time physician faculty to resident/fellow	1.4

Table 2. Data for Forensic Psychiatry Programs Listed in FREIDA

Number of programs providing data	14
Work Schedule (Program Year 1)	
Average hours on duty per week	36.6
Average maximum consecutive hours on duty	10.4
Average days off duty per week	1.9
Moonlighting allowed within institution	71.4%
Night float system	0.0%
Offers awareness and management of fatigue in residents/fellows	71.4%
Educational Setting (Program Year 1)	
Average hours/week of regularly scheduled lectures/conferences	6.1
Average percent of training in hospital outpatient clinics	21.0%
Average percent of training in nonhospital ambulatory care community settings	33.8%
Educational Benefits	
Curriculum on management of tobacco dependence	0.0%
Program to assess/enhance medical professionalism	57.1%
Debt management/financial counseling	14.3%
Formal program to develop teaching skills	57.1%
Formal mentoring program	57.1%
Formal program to foster interdisciplinary teamwork	28.6%
Continuous quality improvement training	71.4%
International experience	0.0%
Resident/fellow retreats	28.6%
Off-campus electives	57.1%
Hospice/home care experience	0.0%
Cultural competence awareness	85.7%
Instruction in medical Spanish or other non-English language	0.0%
Alternative/complementary medicine curriculum	0.0%
Training in identifying and reporting of domestic violence/abuse	71.4%
MPH/MBA or PhD training	0.0%
Research rotation	28.6%
Educational Features	
Offers additional training or educational experience beyond accredited length	2.0%
Offers a primary care track	0.0%
Offers a rural track	0.0%
Offers a women's health track	0.0%
Offers a hospitalist track	0.0%
Offers a research track/nonaccredited fellowship	7.1%
Offers an other track	28.6%
Resident Evaluation	
Yearly specialty in-service examination required	40.0%
Patient surveys	35.7%
Portfolio system	57.1%
360 degree evaluations	92.9%
Objective structured clinical examinations (OSCE)	21.4%
Program Evaluation	
Program graduation rates	92.9%
Board certification rates	92.9%
In-training examinations	71.4%
Performance-based assessments	57.1%

Employment Policies and Benefits

Part-time/shared positions	7.1%
On-site child care	21.4%
Subsidized child care	0.0%
Allowance/stipend for professional expenses	78.6%
Leave for educational meetings/conferences	83.3%
Moving allowance	0.0%
Housing stipend	0.0%
On-call meal allowance	21.4%
Free parking	64.3%
PDAs	7.1%
Placement assistance upon completion of program	35.7%
Cross coverage in case of illness/disability	64.3%

Compensation and Leave (Graduate Year 1)

Average resident/fellow compensation	$58,909
Average number weeks of vacation	3.2
Sick days (paid)	11.7
Maximum number of paid days for family/medical leave	26
Maximum number of unpaid days for family/medical leave	34

Major Medical Benefits

Major medical insurance for residents	100.0%
Major medical insurance for dependents	100.0%
Outpatient mental health insurance	100.0%
Inpatient mental health insurance	100.0%
Group life insurance	85.7%
Dental insurance	85.7%
Disability insurance	85.7%
Disability insurance for occupationally acquired HIV	57.1%
Medical insurance coverage begins when starting program	78.6%

For more information

American Psychiatric Association
1000 Wilson Boulevard, Suite 1825
Arlington, VA 22209-3901
703 907-7300
E-mail: apa@psych.org
www.psych.org

Geriatric Psychiatry

Professional Description

A psychiatrist with expertise in the prevention, evaluation, diagnosis, and treatment of mental and emotional disorders in the elderly. The geriatric psychiatrist seeks to improve the psychiatric care of the elderly both in health and in disease.

Prerequisites; Length of Training

A minimum of 4 years of prior GME is required. Length of ACGME-accredited programs is 1 year.

Data

Unless otherwise noted, all data are for 2008.

Table 1. Geriatric Psychiatry Programs

Number of accredited programs	57

Program Data

length of accredited training	1
Minimum number of prior years of GME required	4
Offers graduate year 1 positions, available immediately upon medical school completion	No
Average number of interviews for program year 1 positions	4.4

Percent new program directors, 2007-2008 academic year (source: ACGME)	10.0%

Residents/Fellows

Total number of active residents/fellows	52
Average number of residents/fellows per program	0.9
Average percent female	53.8%
Average percent international medical graduate (IMG)	55.8%

Program Faculty

Average number of full-time physician faculty	9.3
Average number of part-time physician faculty	1.9
Average percent female full-time physician faculty	29.5%
Average ratio of full-time physician faculty to resident/fellow	3.6

Table 2. Data for Geriatric Psychiatry Programs Listed in FREIDA

Number of programs providing data	31

Work Schedule (Program Year 1)

Average hours on duty per week	39.0
Average maximum consecutive hours on duty	12.5
Average days off duty per week	1.9
Moonlighting allowed within institution	74.2%
Night float system	3.2%
Offers awareness and management of fatigue in residents/fellows	71.0%

Educational Setting (Program Year 1)

Average hours/week of regularly scheduled lectures/conferences	4.2
Average percent of training in hospital outpatient clinics	39.8%
Average percent of training in nonhospital ambulatory care community settings	13.6%

Educational Benefits

Curriculum on management of tobacco dependence	19.4%
Program to assess/enhance medical professionalism	77.4%
Debt management/financial counseling	35.5%
Formal program to develop teaching skills	90.3%
Formal mentoring program	58.1%
Formal program to foster interdisciplinary teamwork	25.8%
Continuous quality improvement training	71.0%
International experience	3.2%
Resident/fellow retreats	51.6%
Off-campus electives	61.3%
Hospice/home care experience	77.4%
Cultural competence awareness	96.8%
Instruction in medical Spanish or other non-English language	16.1%
Alternative/complementary medicine curriculum	12.9%
Training in identifying and reporting of domestic violence/abuse	67.7%
MPH/MBA or PhD training	32.3%
Research rotation	35.5%

Educational Features

Offers additional training or educational experience beyond accredited length	18.8%
Offers a primary care track	6.5%
Offers a rural track	3.2%
Offers a women's health track	0.0%
Offers a hospitalist track	0.0%
Offers a research track/nonaccredited fellowship	38.7%
Offers an other track	19.4%

Resident Evaluation

Yearly specialty in-service examination required	47.1%
Patient surveys	45.2%
Portfolio system	45.2%
360 degree evaluations	80.6%
Objective structured clinical examinations (OSCE)	6.5%

Program Evaluation

Program graduation rates	83.9%
Board certification rates	83.9%

In-training examinations	38.7%
Performance-based assessments	32.3%
Employment Policies and Benefits	
Part-time/shared positions	29.0%
On-site child care	32.3%
Subsidized child care	9.7%
Allowance/stipend for professional expenses	74.2%
Leave for educational meetings/conferences	78.1%
Moving allowance	9.7%
Housing stipend	6.5%
On-call meal allowance	25.8%
Free parking	67.7%
PDAs	12.9%
Placement assistance upon completion of program	22.6%
Cross coverage in case of illness/disability	74.2%
Compensation and Leave (Graduate Year 1)	
Average resident/fellow compensation	$55,301
Average number weeks of vacation	3.5
Sick days (paid)	27.9
Maximum number of paid days for family/medical leave	39
Maximum number of unpaid days for family/medical leave	63
Major Medical Benefits	
Major medical insurance for residents	96.8%
Major medical insurance for dependents	96.8%
Outpatient mental health insurance	96.8%
Inpatient mental health insurance	96.8%
Group life insurance	83.9%
Dental insurance	87.1%
Disability insurance	87.1%
Disability insurance for occupationally acquired HIV	71.0%
Medical insurance coverage begins when starting program	90.3%

For more information

American Association for Geriatric Psychiatry
7910 Woodmont Avenue, Suite 1050
Bethesda, MD 20814-3004
301 654-7850
301 654-4137 Fax
E-mail: main@aagponline.org
www.aagpgpa.org

American Geriatrics Society
The Empire State Building
350 Fifth Avenue, Suite 801
New York, NY 10118
212 308-1414
212 832-8646 Fax
E-mail: info@americangeriatrics.org
www.americangeriatrics.org

Hospice and Palliative Medicine

See page 57.

Pain Medicine

See page 104.

Psychosomatic Medicine

Professional Description

A psychiatrist who specializes in the diagnosis and treatment of psychiatric disorders and symptoms in complex medically ill patients. This subspecialty includes treatment of patients with acute or chronic medical, neurological, obstetrical, or surgical illness in which psychiatric illness is affecting their medical care and/or quality of life; such as HIV infection, organ transplantation, heart disease, renal failure, cancer, stroke, traumatic brain injury, high-risk pregnancy, and chronic obstructive pulmonary disease, among others. Patients also may be those who have a psychiatric disorder that is the direct consequence of a primary medical condition, or a somatoform disorder or psychological factors affecting a general medical condition. Psychiatrists specializing in psychosomatic medicine provide consultation-liaison services in general medical hospitals, attend on medical psychiatry inpatient units, and provide collaborative care in primary care and other outpatient settings.

Source: American Board of Psychiatry and Neurology

Prerequisites; Length of Training

A minimum of 4 years of prior GME is required. Length of ACGME-accredited programs is 1 year.

For more information

American Psychosomatic Society
6728 Old McLean Village Drive
McLean, VA 22101-3906
703 556-9222
703 556-8729 Fax
E-mail: info@psychosomatic.org
www.psychosomatic.org

Sleep Medicine

See page 155.

Radiation Oncology

Professional Description

A radiologist who deals with the therapeutic applications of radiant energy and its modifiers and the study and management of disease, especially malignant tumors.

Prerequisites; Length of Training

Resident education in radiation oncology includes 5 years of accredited, clinically oriented GME, of which 4 years must be in radiation oncology. GY1 training must be spent in internal medicine, family medicine, obstetrics/gynecology, surgery or surgical specialties, pediatrics, a year of categorical radiation oncology, or a transitional year program. ACGME-accredited programs in radiation oncology are 4 years.

Subspecialties

Subspecialty programs accredited by the ACGME

- Hospice and palliative medicine

American Board of Radiology subspecialty certificates

- Hospice and palliative medicine

Data

Unless otherwise noted, all data are for 2008.

Table 1. Radiation Oncology Programs

Number of accredited programs	81
Program Data	
length of accredited training	4
Minimum number of prior years of GME required	1
Offers graduate year 1 positions, available immediately upon medical school completion	No
Average number of interviews for program year 1 positions	22.4
Percent new program directors, 2007-2008 academic year (source: ACGME)	15.0%
Residents/Fellows	
Total number of active residents/fellows	573
Average number of residents/fellows per program	7.1
Average percent female	32.6%
Average percent international medical graduate (IMG)	3.8%
Program Faculty	
Average number of full-time physician faculty	9.6
Average number of part-time physician faculty	0.6
Average percent female full-time physician faculty	26.7%
Average ratio of full-time physician faculty to resident/fellow	1.0

Table 2. Data for Radiation Oncology Programs Listed in FREIDA

Number of programs providing data	34
Work Schedule (Program Year 1)	
Average hours on duty per week	49.5
Average maximum consecutive hours on duty	13.3
Average days off duty per week	1.9
Moonlighting allowed within institution	32.4%
Night float system	0.0%
Offers awareness and management of fatigue in residents/fellows	85.3%
Educational Setting (Program Year 1)	
Average hours/week of regularly scheduled lectures/conferences	8.1
Average percent of training in hospital outpatient clinics	88.3%
Average percent of training in nonhospital ambulatory care community settings	10.0%

Educational Benefits

Curriculum on management of tobacco dependence	11.8%
Program to assess/enhance medical professionalism	55.9%
Debt management/financial counseling	41.2%
Formal program to develop teaching skills	58.8%
Formal mentoring program	32.4%
Formal program to foster interdisciplinary teamwork	26.5%
Continuous quality improvement training	82.4%
International experience	20.6%
Resident/fellow retreats	35.3%
Off-campus electives	76.5%
Hospice/home care experience	17.6%
Cultural competence awareness	70.6%
Instruction in medical Spanish or other non-English language	17.6%
Alternative/complementary medicine curriculum	17.6%
Training in identifying and reporting of domestic violence/abuse	35.3%
MPH/MBA or PhD training	20.6%
Research rotation	64.7%

Educational Features

Offers additional training or educational experience beyond accredited length	7.0%
Offers a primary care track	2.9%
Offers a rural track	5.9%
Offers a women's health track	2.9%
Offers a hospitalist track	2.9%
Offers a research track/nonaccredited fellowship	26.5%
Offers an other track	8.8%

Resident Evaluation

Yearly specialty in-service examination required	98.9%
Patient surveys	26.5%
Portfolio system	29.4%
360 degree evaluations	94.1%
Objective structured clinical examinations (OSCE)	8.8%

Program Evaluation

Program graduation rates	85.3%
Board certification rates	97.1%
In-training examinations	97.1%
Performance-based assessments	32.4%

Employment Policies and Benefits

Part-time/shared positions	0.0%
On-site child care	32.4%
Subsidized child care	5.9%
Allowance/stipend for professional expenses	100.0%
Leave for educational meetings/conferences	84.0%
Moving allowance	2.9%
Housing stipend	2.9%
On-call meal allowance	47.1%
Free parking	38.2%
PDAs	29.4%
Placement assistance upon completion of program	11.8%
Cross coverage in case of illness/disability	82.4%

Compensation and Leave (Graduate Year 1)

Average resident/fellow compensation	$47,029
Average number weeks of vacation	6.3
Sick days (paid)	23.7
Maximum number of paid days for family/medical leave	40
Maximum number of unpaid days for family/medical leave	59

Major Medical Benefits

Major medical insurance for residents	100.0%
Major medical insurance for dependents	97.1%
Outpatient mental health insurance	88.2%
Inpatient mental health insurance	85.3%

Specialty Data

Group life insurance	91.2%
Dental insurance	91.2%
Disability insurance	91.2%
Disability insurance for occupationally acquired HIV	76.5%
Medical insurance coverage begins when starting program	88.2%

Table 3. Radiation Oncology Match Data

GY1	2008
Number of positions offered	15
Number filled by US seniors	13
Percent filled by US seniors	86.7
Total positions filled	15
Percent total positions filled	100
GY2	
Number of positions offered	129
Number filled by US seniors	112
Percent filled by US seniors	86.8
Total positions filled	121
Percent total positions filled	93.8
All	
Total Positions*	144
Preferred by US Seniors*	159
Preferred Positions per US Senior	0.9
Preferred by Independent Applicants†	26
Preferred Positions per IA	5.5

Source: National Resident Matching Program 2008 Match Data
* Includes all positions offered in a specialty, except preliminary positions.
† Preferred means the number of applicants for whom the specialty was the only or first choice.

For more information

Professional Association

American College of Radiation Oncology
5272 River Road, Suite 630
Bethesda, MD 20816
301 718-6515
301 656-0989 Fax
www.acro.org

Certification

American Board of Radiology
5441 East Williams Circle, Suite 200
Tucson, AZ 85711
520 790-2900
520 790-3200 Fax
E-mail: information@theabr.org
www.theabr.org

Program Accreditation

Accreditation Council for Graduate Medical Education
Residency Review Committee for Radiation Oncology
Linda Thorsen, Executive Director
515 North State Street
Chicago, IL 60654
312 755-5029
E-mail: lmt@acgme.org
www.acgme.org

Hospice and Palliative Medicine

See page 57.

Radiology-Diagnostic

Professional Description

A radiologist utilizes radiologic methodologies to diagnose and treat disease. Physicians practicing in the field of radiology most often specialize in radiology, diagnostic radiology, radiation oncology, or radiologic physics.

A diagnostic radiologist utilizes x-ray, radionuclides, ultrasound, and electromagnetic radiation to diagnose and treat disease.

Prerequisites; Length of Training

Resident education in diagnostic radiology includes 5 years of clinically oriented GME, of which 4 years must be in diagnostic radiology. The clinical year must consist of ACGME, RCPSC, or equivalent accredited training in internal medicine, pediatrics, surgery or surgical specialties, obstetrics and gynecology, neurology, family medicine, emergency medicine, or any combination of these, or an ACGME- or equivalent accredited transitional year. ACGME-accredited programs in diagnostic radiology are 4 years.

Subspecialties

Subspecialty programs accredited by the ACGME

- Abdominal radiology
- Cardiothoracic radiology
- Endovascular surgical neuroradiology
- Musculoskeletal radiology
- Neuroradiology
- Nuclear radiology
- Pediatric radiology
- Vascular and interventional radiology

American Board of Radiology subspecialty certificates

- Hospice and palliative medicine
- Neuroradiology
- Nuclear radiology
- Pediatric radiology
- Vascular and interventional radiology

Data

Unless otherwise noted, all data are for 2008.

Table 1. Radiology-Diagnostic Programs

Number of accredited programs	188
Program Data	
length of accredited training	4
Minimum number of prior years of GME required	1/0
Offers graduate year 1 positions, available immediately upon medical school completion	Some
Average number of interviews for program year 1 positions	70.6
Percent new program directors, 2007-2008 academic year (source: ACGME)	17.7%
Residents/Fellows	
Total number of active residents/fellows	4,307
Average number of residents/fellows per program	22.9
Average percent female	27.9%
Average percent international medical graduate (IMG)	7.5%
Program Faculty	
Average number of full-time physician faculty	32.6
Average number of part-time physician faculty	6.4
Average percent female full-time physician faculty	23.8%
Average ratio of full-time physician faculty to resident/fellow	1.1

Table 2. Data for Radiology-Diagnostic Programs Listed in FREIDA

Number of programs providing data	129

Work Schedule (Program Year 1)

Average hours on duty per week	51.6
Average maximum consecutive hours on duty	19.0
Average days off duty per week	1.7
Moonlighting allowed within institution	56.6%
Night float system	70.5%
Offers awareness and management of fatigue in residents/fellows	94.6%

Educational Setting (Program Year 1)

Average hours/week of regularly scheduled lectures/conferences	9.4
Average percent of training in hospital outpatient clinics	36.8%
Average percent of training in nonhospital ambulatory care community settings	16.6%

Educational Benefits

Curriculum on management of tobacco dependence	8.5%
Program to assess/enhance medical professionalism	71.3%
Debt management/financial counseling	54.3%
Formal program to develop teaching skills	65.1%
Formal mentoring program	45.7%
Formal program to foster interdisciplinary teamwork	13.2%
Continuous quality improvement training	90.7%
International experience	7.0%
Resident/fellow retreats	22.5%
Off-campus electives	61.2%
Hospice/home care experience	0.8%
Cultural competence awareness	63.6%
Instruction in medical Spanish or other non-English language	11.6%
Alternative/complementary medicine curriculum	8.5%
Training in identifying and reporting of domestic violence/abuse	31.0%
MPH/MBA or PhD training	9.3%
Research rotation	27.1%

Educational Features

Offers additional training or educational experience beyond accredited length	14.6%
Offers a primary care track	1.6%
Offers a rural track	0.8%
Offers a women's health track	3.9%
Offers a hospitalist track	1.6%
Offers a research track/nonaccredited fellowship	7.8%
Offers an other track	7.0%

Resident Evaluation

Yearly specialty in-service examination required	99.1%
Patient surveys	27.9%
Portfolio system	82.2%
360 degree evaluations	95.3%
Objective structured clinical examinations (OSCE)	19.4%

Program Evaluation

Program graduation rates	87.6%
Board certification rates	100.0%
In-training examinations	96.1%
Performance-based assessments	38.0%

Employment Policies and Benefits

Part-time/shared positions	0.8%
On-site child care	34.1%
Subsidized child care	5.4%
Allowance/stipend for professional expenses	98.4%
Leave for educational meetings/conferences	88.4%
Moving allowance	6.2%
Housing stipend	10.9%
On-call meal allowance	96.1%
Free parking	62.8%

PDAs	14.0%
Placement assistance upon completion of program	22.5%
Cross coverage in case of illness/disability	72.9%

Compensation and Leave (Graduate Year 1)

Average resident/fellow compensation	$47,789
Average number weeks of vacation	4.3
Sick days (paid)	16.9
Maximum number of paid days for family/medical leave	44
Maximum number of unpaid days for family/medical leave	62

Major Medical Benefits

Major medical insurance for residents	98.4%
Major medical insurance for dependents	93.8%
Outpatient mental health insurance	88.4%
Inpatient mental health insurance	89.1%
Group life insurance	90.7%
Dental insurance	87.6%
Disability insurance	87.6%
Disability insurance for occupationally acquired HIV	68.2%
Medical insurance coverage begins when starting program	85.3%

Table 3. Radiology-Diagnostic Match Data

GY1	2008
Number of positions offered	157
Number filled by US seniors	135
Percent filled by US seniors	86
Total positions filled	154
Percent total positions filled	98.1
GY2	
Number of positions offered	928
Number filled by US seniors	758
Percent filled by US seniors	81.7
Total positions filled	909
Percent total positions filled	98
All	
Total Positions*	1,076
Preferred by US Seniors*	939
Preferred Positions per US Senior	1.1
Preferred by Independent Applicants†	386
Preferred Positions per IA	2.8

Source: National Resident Matching Program 2008 Match Data
* Includes all positions offered in a specialty, except preliminary positions.
† Preferred means the number of applicants for whom the specialty was the only or first choice.

For more information

Professional Associations

American College of Radiology
1891 Preston White Drive
Reston, VA 20191
703 648-8900
E-mail: info@acr.org
www.acr.org

American Roentgen Ray Society
44211 Slatestone Court
Leesburg, VA 20176-5109
800 438-2777
703 729-4839 Fax
www.arrs.org

American Society for Therapeutic Radiology and Oncology
8280 Willow Oaks Corporate Drive, Suite 500
Fairfax, VA 22031
703 502-1550
703 502-7852 Fax
www.astro.org

American Society of Neuroradiology
2210 Midwest Road, Suite 207
Oakbrook, IL 60523
630 574-0220
630 574-0661 Fax
www.asnr.org

Association of University Radiologists
820 Jorie Boulevard
Oakbrook, IL 60523
630 368-3730
630 571-7837 Fax
E-mail: aur@rsna.org
www.aur.org

Radiological Society of North America
820 Jorie Boulevard
Oakbrook, IL 60523-2251
630 571-2670
630 571-7837 Fax
www.rsna.org

Society of Interventional Radiology
3975 Fair Ridge Drive, Suite 400 North
Fairfax, VA 22033
703 691-1805
703 691-1855 Fax
www.sirweb.org

Society of Radiologists in Ultrasound
1891 Preston White Drive
Reston, VA 20191
703 858-9210
703 880-0295 Fax
E-mail: info@sru.org
www.sru.org

Certification

American Board of Radiology
5441 East Williams Circle, Suite 200
Tucson, AZ 85711
520 790-2900
520 790-3200 Fax
E-mail: information@theabr.org
www.theabr.org

Program Accreditation

Accreditation Council for Graduate Medical Education
Residency Review Committee for Diagnostic Radiology
Missy Fleming, MEd, PhD, Executive Director
515 North State Street
Chicago, IL 60654
312 755-5029
E-mail: mfleming@acgme.org
www.acgme.org

Abdominal Radiology

Professional Description

Abdominal radiology constitutes the application and interpretation of conventional radiology, computed tomography, ultrasonography, magnetic resonance (MR) imaging, nuclear medicine, fluoroscopy, and interventional methods customarily included within the specialty of diagnostic radiology as they apply to diseases involving the gastrointestinal tract, genitourinary tract, and the intraperitoneal and extra peritoneal abdominal organs.

Source: Abdominal Radiology Program Requirements, ACGME, www.acgme.org/acWebsite/downloads/RRC_progReq/421pr602.pdf

Prerequisites; Length of Training

Satisfactory completion of an ACGME- or RCPSC-accredited diagnostic radiology residency, or other training judged suitable by the program director, is required. Length of ACGME-accredited programs is 1 year.

Data

Unless otherwise noted, all data are for 2008.

Table 1. Abdominal Radiology Programs	
Number of accredited programs	12
Program Data	
length of accredited training	1
Minimum number of prior years of GME required	4
Offers graduate year 1 positions, available immediately upon medical school completion	No
Average number of interviews for program year 1 positions	16.0
Percent new program directors, 2007-2008 academic year (source: ACGME)	8.3%
Residents/Fellows	
Total number of active residents/fellows	41
Average number of residents/fellows per program	3.4
Average percent female	26.8%
Average percent international medical graduate (IMG)	36.6%
Program Faculty	
Average number of full-time physician faculty	11.3
Average number of part-time physician faculty	3.1
Average percent female full-time physician faculty	30.4%
Average ratio of full-time physician faculty to resident/fellow	1.6

Table 2. Data for Abdominal Radiology Programs Listed in FREIDA	
Number of programs providing data	5
Work Schedule (Program Year 1)	
Average hours on duty per week	46.3
Average maximum consecutive hours on duty	14.9
Average days off duty per week	1.8
Moonlighting allowed within institution	40.0%
Night float system	0.0%
Offers awareness and management of fatigue in residents/fellows	80.0%
Educational Setting (Program Year 1)	
Average hours/week of regularly scheduled lectures/conferences	7.2
Average percent of training in hospital outpatient clinics	50.0%
Educational Benefits	
Curriculum on management of tobacco dependence	20.0%
Program to assess/enhance medical professionalism	40.0%
Debt management/financial counseling	60.0%
Formal program to develop teaching skills	40.0%
Formal mentoring program	40.0%
Formal program to foster interdisciplinary teamwork	20.0%
Continuous quality improvement training	80.0%

International experience	20.0%
Resident/fellow retreats	40.0%
Off-campus electives	40.0%
Hospice/home care experience	20.0%
Cultural competence awareness	60.0%
Instruction in medical Spanish or other non-English language	0.0%
Alternative/complementary medicine curriculum	20.0%
Training in identifying and reporting of domestic violence/abuse	20.0%
MPH/MBA or PhD training	20.0%
Research rotation	0.0%
Educational Features	
Offers additional training or educational experience beyond accredited length	16.7%
Offers a primary care track	0.0%
Offers a rural track	0.0%
Offers a women's health track	0.0%
Offers a hospitalist track	0.0%
Offers a research track/nonaccredited fellowship	0.0%
Offers an other track	20.0%
Resident Evaluation	
Yearly specialty in-service examination required	0.0%
Patient surveys	20.0%
Portfolio system	40.0%
360 degree evaluations	80.0%
Objective structured clinical examinations (OSCE)	0.0%
Program Evaluation	
Program graduation rates	40.0%
Board certification rates	0.0%
In-training examinations	0.0%
Performance-based assessments	80.0%
Employment Policies and Benefits	
Part-time/shared positions	0.0%
On-site child care	40.0%
Subsidized child care	20.0%
Allowance/stipend for professional expenses	100.0%
Leave for educational meetings/conferences	100.0%
Moving allowance	0.0%
Housing stipend	0.0%
On-call meal allowance	60.0%
Free parking	20.0%
PDAs	0.0%
Placement assistance upon completion of program	20.0%
Cross coverage in case of illness/disability	60.0%
Compensation and Leave (Graduate Year 1)	
Average resident/fellow compensation	$58,200
Average number weeks of vacation	3.8
Sick days (paid)	32.3
Maximum number of paid days for family/medical leave	32
Maximum number of unpaid days for family/medical leave	15
Major Medical Benefits	
Major medical insurance for residents	100.0%
Major medical insurance for dependents	100.0%
Outpatient mental health insurance	80.0%
Inpatient mental health insurance	80.0%
Group life insurance	80.0%
Dental insurance	100.0%
Disability insurance	60.0%
Disability insurance for occupationally acquired HIV	40.0%
Medical insurance coverage begins when starting program	80.0%

For more information

Society of Gastrointestinal Radiologists
SGR Management Office
c/o International Meeting Managers, Inc
4550 Post Oak Place, Suite 342
Houston, TX 77027
713 965-0566
713 960-0488 Fax
www.sgr.org

Cardiothoracic Radiology

Professional Description

The cardiothoracic radiologist works as a diagnostic and therapeutic consultant and practitioner in the application and interpretation of imaging examinations and interventional procedures related to the lungs, pleura, mediastinum, chest wall, heart, pericardium, and the thoracic vascular system in the adult. The imaging methods and procedures include, but are not necessarily limited to, routine radiography, fluoroscopy, computed tomography (CT), magnetic resonance (MR) imaging, ultrasound, and interventional techniques.

Source: Cardiothoracic Radiology Program Requirements, ACGME
www.acgme.org/acWebsite/downloads/RRC_progReq/429pr602.pdf

Prerequisites; Length of Training

Satisfactory completion of an ACGME-accredited diagnostic radiology residency or its equivalent is required. Length of ACGME-accredited programs is 1 year.
Note: ACGME accreditation of cardiothoracic radiology programs will be discontinued after June 30, 2010.

For more information

American College of Radiology
1891 Preston White Drive
Reston, VA 20191
800 227-5463
E-mail: info@acr.org
www.acr.org

Endovascular Surgical Neuroradiology

Professional Description

Endovascular surgical neuroradiology is a subspecialty that uses catheter technology, radiologic imaging, and clinical expertise to diagnose and treat diseases of the central nervous system. Practitioners have training and experience in:

- Signs and symptoms of disorders amenable to diagnosis and treatment by endovascular surgical neuroradiology techniques
- Neurological examinations to evaluate patients with neurological disorders
- Pathophysiology and natural history of these disorders
- Indications and contraindications to endovascular surgical neuroradiology procedures
- Clinical and technical aspects of endovascular surgical neuroradiology procedures
- Medical and surgical alternatives
- Preoperative and postoperative management of endovascular patients
- Neurointensive care management
- Fundamentals of imaging physics and radiation biology

Specialty Data

• Interpretation of radiographic studies pertinent to the practice

Source: Endovascular Surgical Neuroradiology Program Requirements, ACGME, www.acgme.org/acWebsite/downloads/RRC_progReq/422endovascularneuroradiology01012008.pdf

Prerequisites; Length of Training

A minimum of 4 years of prior GME is required. Length of ACGME-accredited programs is 1 year.

For more information

American Society of Neuroradiology
2210 Midwest Road, Suite 207
Oakbrook, IL 60523
630 574-0220
630 574-0661 Fax
www.asnr.org

Musculoskeletal Radiology

Professional Description

Musculoskeletal radiologists use imaging examinations and procedures to analyze disorders of the musculoskeletal system, including bones, joints, and soft tissues. The imaging methods and procedures include, but are not necessarily limited to, routine radiography, computed tomography, ultrasonography, radionuclide scintigraphy, magnetic resonance, arthrography, and image-guided percutaneous biopsy techniques.

Source: Musculoskeletal Radiology Program Requirements, ACGME, www.acgme.org/acWebsite/downloads/RRC_progReq/426pr602.pdf

Prerequisites; Length of Training

Satisfactory completion of an ACGME- or RCPSC-accredited diagnostic radiology residency, or other training judged suitable by the program director, is required. Length of ACGME-accredited programs is 1 year.

Data

Table 1. Musculoskeletal Radiology Programs

Number of accredited programs	13
Program Data	
length of accredited training	1
Minimum number of prior years of GME required	4
Offers graduate year 1 positions, available immediately upon medical school completion	No
Average number of interviews for program year 1 positions	8.7
Percent new program directors, 2007-2008 academic year (source: ACGME)	0.0%
Residents/Fellows	
Total number of active residents/fellows	25
Average number of residents/fellows per program	1.9
Average percent female	16.0%
Average percent international medical graduate (IMG)	8.0%
Program Faculty	
Average number of full-time physician faculty	4.8
Average number of part-time physician faculty	0.8
Average percent female full-time physician faculty	25.9%
Average ratio of full-time physician faculty to resident/fellow	1.1

Table 2. Data for Musculoskeletal Radiology Programs Listed in FREIDA

Number of programs providing data	4
Work Schedule (Program Year 1)	
Average hours on duty per week	37.3
Average maximum consecutive hours on duty	12.1
Average days off duty per week	1.9
Moonlighting allowed within institution	50.0%
Night float system	0.0%
Offers awareness and management of fatigue in residents/fellows	100.0%
Educational Setting (Program Year 1)	
Average hours/week of regularly scheduled lectures/conferences	5.3
Average percent of training in hospital outpatient clinics	58.7%
Average percent of training in nonhospital ambulatory care community settings	25.0%
Educational Benefits	
Curriculum on management of tobacco dependence	0.0%
Program to assess/enhance medical professionalism	50.0%
Debt management/financial counseling	25.0%
Formal program to develop teaching skills	75.0%
Formal mentoring program	25.0%
Formal program to foster interdisciplinary teamwork	0.0%
Continuous quality improvement training	75.0%
International experience	0.0%
Resident/fellow retreats	25.0%
Off-campus electives	0.0%
Hospice/home care experience	0.0%
Cultural competence awareness	75.0%
Instruction in medical Spanish or other non-English language	25.0%
Alternative/complementary medicine curriculum	25.0%
Training in identifying and reporting of domestic violence/abuse	0.0%
MPH/MBA or PhD training	0.0%
Research rotation	0.0%
Educational Features	
Offers additional training or educational experience beyond accredited length	0.0%
Offers a primary care track	0.0%
Offers a rural track	0.0%
Offers a women's health track	0.0%
Offers a hospitalist track	0.0%
Offers a research track/nonaccredited fellowship	0.0%
Offers an other track	0.0%
Resident Evaluation	
Yearly specialty in-service examination required	7.1%
Patient surveys	0.0%
Portfolio system	25.0%
360 degree evaluations	75.0%
Objective structured clinical examinations (OSCE)	0.0%
Program Evaluation	
Program graduation rates	100.0%
Board certification rates	25.0%
In-training examinations	0.0%
Performance-based assessments	25.0%
Employment Policies and Benefits	
Part-time/shared positions	0.0%
On-site child care	50.0%
Subsidized child care	0.0%
Allowance/stipend for professional expenses	100.0%
Leave for educational meetings/conferences	80.0%
Moving allowance	0.0%
Housing stipend	0.0%
On-call meal allowance	25.0%

Free parking	25.0%
PDAs	0.0%
Placement assistance upon completion of program	50.0%
Cross coverage in case of illness/disability	75.0%

Compensation and Leave (Graduate Year 1)

Average resident/fellow compensation	$56,002
Average number weeks of vacation	3.5
Sick days (paid)	12.3
Maximum number of paid days for family/medical leave	21
Maximum number of unpaid days for family/medical leave	17

Major Medical Benefits

Major medical insurance for residents	100.0%
Major medical insurance for dependents	100.0%
Outpatient mental health insurance	100.0%
Inpatient mental health insurance	100.0%
Group life insurance	75.0%
Dental insurance	100.0%
Disability insurance	75.0%
Disability insurance for occupationally acquired HIV	75.0%
Medical insurance coverage begins when starting program	75.0%

For more information

Society of Skeletal Radiology
1100 East Woodfield Road, Suite 520
Schaumburg, IL 60173
847 517-3302
847 517-7229 Fax
www.skeletalrad.org

Neuroradiology

Professional Description

A radiologist who diagnoses and treats diseases utilizing imaging procedures as they relate to the brain, spine and spinal cord, head, neck, and organs of special sense in adults and children.

Prerequisites; Length of Training

Satisfactory completion of an ACGME- or RCPSC-accredited diagnostic radiology residency, or other training judged suitable by the program director, is required. Length of ACGME-accredited programs is 1 year.

Data

Unless otherwise noted, all data are for 2008.

Table 1. Neuroradiology Programs

Number of accredited programs	85

Program Data

length of accredited training	1
Minimum number of prior years of GME required	4
Offers graduate year 1 positions, available immediately upon medical school completion	No
Average number of interviews for program year 1 positions	10.7
Percent new program directors, 2007-2008 academic year (source: ACGME)	10.5%

Residents/Fellows

Total number of active residents/fellows	244
Average number of residents/fellows per program	2.9
Average percent female	20.1%
Average percent international medical graduate (IMG)	17.6%

Program Faculty

Average number of full-time physician faculty	8.2
Average number of part-time physician faculty	0.9
Average percent female full-time physician faculty	18.4%
Average ratio of full-time physician faculty to resident/fellow	1.3

Table 2. Data for Neuroradiology Programs Listed in FREIDA

Number of programs providing data	47

Work Schedule (Program Year 1)

Average hours on duty per week	47.0
Average maximum consecutive hours on duty	16.9
Average days off duty per week	1.8
Moonlighting allowed within institution	51.1%
Night float system	12.8%
Offers awareness and management of fatigue in residents/fellows	76.6%

Educational Setting (Program Year 1)

Average hours/week of regularly scheduled lectures/conferences	5.2
Average percent of training in hospital outpatient clinics	46.3%
Average percent of training in nonhospital ambulatory care community settings	6.0%

Educational Benefits

Curriculum on management of tobacco dependence	6.4%
Program to assess/enhance medical professionalism	46.8%
Debt management/financial counseling	31.9%
Formal program to develop teaching skills	66.0%
Formal mentoring program	29.8%
Formal program to foster interdisciplinary teamwork	12.8%
Continuous quality improvement training	72.3%
International experience	10.6%
Resident/fellow retreats	10.6%
Off-campus electives	31.9%
Hospice/home care experience	2.1%
Cultural competence awareness	46.8%
Instruction in medical Spanish or other non-English language	10.6%
Alternative/complementary medicine curriculum	8.5%
Training in identifying and reporting of domestic violence/abuse	19.1%
MPH/MBA or PhD training	8.5%
Research rotation	27.7%

Educational Features

Offers additional training or educational experience beyond accredited length	59.1%
Offers a primary care track	6.4%
Offers a rural track	0.0%
Offers a women's health track	0.0%
Offers a hospitalist track	0.0%
Offers a research track/nonaccredited fellowship	6.4%
Offers an other track	2.1%

Resident Evaluation

Yearly specialty in-service examination required	7.3%
Patient surveys	19.1%
Portfolio system	27.7%
360 degree evaluations	83.0%
Objective structured clinical examinations (OSCE)	4.3%

Program Evaluation

Program graduation rates	72.3%
Board certification rates	78.7%
In-training examinations	6.4%
Performance-based assessments	25.5%

Employment Policies and Benefits

Part-time/shared positions	2.1%
On-site child care	42.6%
Subsidized child care	8.5%
Allowance/stipend for professional expenses	87.2%

Specialty Data

Leave for educational meetings/conferences	84.0%
Moving allowance	4.3%
Housing stipend	0.0%
On-call meal allowance	57.4%
Free parking	51.1%
PDAs	10.6%
Placement assistance upon completion of program	17.0%
Cross coverage in case of illness/disability	63.8%

Compensation and Leave (Graduate Year 1)

Average resident/fellow compensation	$56,180
Average number weeks of vacation	3.5
Sick days (paid)	21.3
Maximum number of paid days for family/medical leave	38
Maximum number of unpaid days for family/medical leave	46

Major Medical Benefits

Major medical insurance for residents	100.0%
Major medical insurance for dependents	97.9%
Outpatient mental health insurance	89.4%
Inpatient mental health insurance	87.2%
Group life insurance	85.1%
Dental insurance	87.2%
Disability insurance	83.0%
Disability insurance for occupationally acquired HIV	68.1%
Medical insurance coverage begins when starting program	83.0%

For more information

American Society of Neuroradiology
2210 Midwest Road, Suite 207
Oakbrook, IL 60523
630 574-0220
630 574-0661 Fax
www.asnr.org

Nuclear Radiology

Professional Description

A radiologist involved in the analysis and imaging of radionuclides and radiolabeled substances in vitro and in vivo for diagnosis, and the administration of radionuclides and radiolabeled substances for the treatment of disease.

Prerequisites; Length of Training

Satisfactory completion of an ACGME- or RCPSC-accredited diagnostic radiology residency, or other training judged suitable by the program director, is required. Length of ACGME-accredited programs is 1 year.

Data

Unless otherwise noted, all data are for 2008.

Table 1. Nuclear Radiology Programs

Number of accredited programs	24

Program Data

length of accredited training	1
Minimum number of prior years of GME required	4
Offers graduate year 1 positions, available immediately upon medical school completion	No
Average number of interviews for program year 1 positions	3.3
Percent new program directors, 2007-2008 academic year (source: ACGME)	9.1%

Residents/Fellows

Total number of active residents/fellows	7
Average number of residents/fellows per program	0.3
Average percent female	28.6%
Average percent international medical graduate (IMG)	42.9%

Program Faculty

Average number of full-time physician faculty	4.9
Average number of part-time physician faculty	0.7
Average percent female full-time physician faculty	17.2%
Average ratio of full-time physician faculty to resident/fellow	3.4

Table 2. Data for Nuclear Radiology Programs Listed in FREIDA

Number of programs providing data	8

Work Schedule (Program Year 1)

Average hours on duty per week	44.2
Average maximum consecutive hours on duty	14.9
Average days off duty per week	1.9
Moonlighting allowed within institution	50.0%
Night float system	12.5%
Offers awareness and management of fatigue in residents/fellows	87.5%

Educational Setting (Program Year 1)

Average hours/week of regularly scheduled lectures/conferences	6.3
Average percent of training in hospital outpatient clinics	61.7%

Educational Benefits

Curriculum on management of tobacco dependence	25.0%
Program to assess/enhance medical professionalism	87.5%
Debt management/financial counseling	37.5%
Formal program to develop teaching skills	87.5%
Formal mentoring program	87.5%
Formal program to foster interdisciplinary teamwork	25.0%
Continuous quality improvement training	75.0%
International experience	12.5%
Resident/fellow retreats	12.5%
Off-campus electives	37.5%
Hospice/home care experience	12.5%
Cultural competence awareness	75.0%
Instruction in medical Spanish or other non-English language	37.5%
Alternative/complementary medicine curriculum	25.0%
Training in identifying and reporting of domestic violence/abuse	37.5%
MPH/MBA or PhD training	12.5%
Research rotation	50.0%

Educational Features

Offers additional training or educational experience beyond accredited length	7.4%
Offers a primary care track	25.0%
Offers a rural track	0.0%
Offers a women's health track	0.0%
Offers a hospitalist track	0.0%
Offers a research track/nonaccredited fellowship	0.0%
Offers an other track	0.0%

Resident Evaluation

Yearly specialty in-service examination required	56.1%
Patient surveys	62.5%
Portfolio system	37.5%
360 degree evaluations	62.5%
Objective structured clinical examinations (OSCE)	12.5%

Program Evaluation

Program graduation rates	100.0%
Board certification rates	87.5%
In-training examinations	25.0%
Performance-based assessments	37.5%

Employment Policies and Benefits

Part-time/shared positions	0.0%
On-site child care	37.5%
Subsidized child care	12.5%
Allowance/stipend for professional expenses	100.0%
Leave for educational meetings/conferences	50.0%
Moving allowance	0.0%
Housing stipend	0.0%
On-call meal allowance	75.0%
Free parking	50.0%
PDAs	0.0%
Placement assistance upon completion of program	37.5%
Cross coverage in case of illness/disability	75.0%

Compensation and Leave (Graduate Year 1)

Average resident/fellow compensation	$54,186
Average number weeks of vacation	3.6
Sick days (paid)	37.3
Maximum number of paid days for family/medical leave	42
Maximum number of unpaid days for family/medical leave	30

Major Medical Benefits

Major medical insurance for residents	87.5%
Major medical insurance for dependents	87.5%
Outpatient mental health insurance	100.0%
Inpatient mental health insurance	100.0%
Group life insurance	100.0%
Dental insurance	87.5%
Disability insurance	87.5%
Disability insurance for occupationally acquired HIV	75.0%
Medical insurance coverage begins when starting program	75.0%

For more information

American College of Radiology
1891 Preston White Drive
Reston, VA 20191
703 648-8900
E-mail: info@acr.org
www.acr.org

Pediatric Radiology

Professional Description

A pediatric radiologist is proficient in all forms of diagnostic imaging as it pertains to treating diseases in the newborn, infant, child, and adolescent. This specialist has knowledge of both imaging and interventional procedures related to the care and management of diseases of children. A pediatric radiologist must be highly knowledgeable of all organ systems as they relate to growth and development, congenital malformations, diseases peculiar to infants and children, and diseases that begin in childhood but cause substantial residual impairment in adulthood.

Prerequisites; Length of Training

Satisfactory completion of an ACGME- or RCPSC-accredited diagnostic radiology residency, or other training judged suitable by the program director, is required. Length of ACGME-accredited programs is 1 year.

Data

Unless otherwise noted, all data are for 2008.

Table 1. Pediatric Radiology Programs

Number of accredited programs	45
Program Data	
length of accredited training	1
Minimum number of prior years of GME required	4
Offers graduate year 1 positions, available immediately upon medical school completion	No
Average number of interviews for program year 1 positions	4.0
Percent new program directors, 2007-2008 academic year (source: ACGME)	11.4%
Residents/Fellows	
Total number of active residents/fellows	56
Average number of residents/fellows per program	1.2
Average percent female	33.9%
Average percent international medical graduate (IMG)	33.9%
Program Faculty	
Average number of full-time physician faculty	8.4
Average number of part-time physician faculty	2.6
Average percent female full-time physician faculty	36.2%
Average ratio of full-time physician faculty to resident/fellow	2.7

Table 2. Data for Pediatric Radiology Programs Listed in FREIDA

Number of programs providing data	16
Work Schedule (Program Year 1)	
Average hours on duty per week	43.9
Average maximum consecutive hours on duty	13.8
Average days off duty per week	1.8
Moonlighting allowed within institution	18.8%
Night float system	18.8%
Offers awareness and management of fatigue in residents/fellows	81.3%
Educational Setting (Program Year 1)	
Average hours/week of regularly scheduled lectures/conferences	7.4
Average percent of training in hospital outpatient clinics	21.7%
Average percent of training in nonhospital ambulatory care community settings	10.0%
Educational Benefits	
Curriculum on management of tobacco dependence	0.0%
Program to assess/enhance medical professionalism	43.8%
Debt management/financial counseling	37.5%
Formal program to develop teaching skills	75.0%
Formal mentoring program	18.8%
Formal program to foster interdisciplinary teamwork	6.3%
Continuous quality improvement training	68.8%
International experience	6.3%
Resident/fellow retreats	12.5%
Off-campus electives	12.5%
Hospice/home care experience	0.0%
Cultural competence awareness	31.3%
Instruction in medical Spanish or other non-English language	18.8%
Alternative/complementary medicine curriculum	6.3%
Training in identifying and reporting of domestic violence/abuse	18.8%
MPH/MBA or PhD training	25.0%
Research rotation	25.0%
Educational Features	
Offers additional training or educational experience beyond accredited length	37.8%
Offers a primary care track	0.0%
Offers a rural track	0.0%
Offers a women's health track	0.0%
Offers a hospitalist track	0.0%

Specialty Data

Offers a research track/nonaccredited fellowship	12.5%
Offers an other track	12.5%
Resident Evaluation	
Yearly specialty in-service examination required	7.1%
Patient surveys	43.8%
Portfolio system	37.5%
360 degree evaluations	87.5%
Objective structured clinical examinations (OSCE)	6.3%
Program Evaluation	
Program graduation rates	87.5%
Board certification rates	87.5%
In-training examinations	6.3%
Performance-based assessments	31.3%
Employment Policies and Benefits	
Part-time/shared positions	12.5%
On-site child care	37.5%
Subsidized child care	0.0%
Allowance/stipend for professional expenses	93.8%
Leave for educational meetings/conferences	74.6%
Moving allowance	18.8%
Housing stipend	0.0%
On-call meal allowance	50.0%
Free parking	37.5%
PDAs	12.5%
Placement assistance upon completion of program	0.0%
Cross coverage in case of illness/disability	43.8%
Compensation and Leave (Graduate Year 1)	
Average resident/fellow compensation	$54,048
Average number weeks of vacation	11.6
Sick days (paid)	30.7
Maximum number of paid days for family/medical leave	39
Maximum number of unpaid days for family/medical leave	31
Major Medical Benefits	
Major medical insurance for residents	100.0%
Major medical insurance for dependents	93.8%
Outpatient mental health insurance	93.8%
Inpatient mental health insurance	93.8%
Group life insurance	100.0%
Dental insurance	93.8%
Disability insurance	93.8%
Disability insurance for occupationally acquired HIV	75.0%
Medical insurance coverage begins when starting program	93.8%

For more information

Society for Pediatric Radiology
1891 Preston White Drive
Reston, VA 20191
703 648-0680
E-mail: spr@acr.org
www.pedrad.org

Vascular and Interventional Radiology

Professional Description

A radiologist who diagnoses and treats diseases by various radiologic imaging modalities. These include fluoroscopy, digital radiography, computed tomography, sonography and magnetic resonance imaging.

Prerequisites; Length of Training

Satisfactory completion of an ACGME- or RCPSC-accredited diagnostic radiology residency, or other training judged suitable by the program director, is required. Length of ACGME-accredited programs is 1 year.

Data

Unless otherwise noted, all data are for 2008.

Table 1. Vascular and Interventional Radiology Programs

Number of accredited programs	93
Program Data	
length of accredited training	1
Minimum number of prior years of GME required	4
Offers graduate year 1 positions, available immediately upon medical school completion	No
Average number of interviews for program year 1 positions	9.4
Percent new program directors, 2007-2008 academic year (source: ACGME)	19.2%
Residents/Fellows	
Total number of active residents/fellows	143
Average number of residents/fellows per program	1.5
Average percent female	10.5%
Average percent international medical graduate (IMG)	27.3%
Program Faculty	
Average number of full-time physician faculty	6.0
Average number of part-time physician faculty	0.6
Average percent female full-time physician faculty	10.7%
Average ratio of full-time physician faculty to resident/fellow	1.6

Table 2. Data for Vascular and Interventional Radiology Programs Listed in FREIDA

Number of programs providing data	37
Work Schedule (Program Year 1)	
Average hours on duty per week	50.5
Average maximum consecutive hours on duty	17.2
Average days off duty per week	1.7
Moonlighting allowed within institution	43.2%
Night float system	2.7%
Offers awareness and management of fatigue in residents/fellows	78.4%
Educational Setting (Program Year 1)	
Average hours/week of regularly scheduled lectures/conferences	4.5
Average percent of training in hospital outpatient clinics	22.8%
Average percent of training in nonhospital ambulatory care community settings	5.0%
Educational Benefits	
Curriculum on management of tobacco dependence	13.5%
Program to assess/enhance medical professionalism	48.6%
Debt management/financial counseling	48.6%
Formal program to develop teaching skills	64.9%
Formal mentoring program	29.7%
Formal program to foster interdisciplinary teamwork	16.2%
Continuous quality improvement training	83.8%
International experience	2.7%
Resident/fellow retreats	5.4%
Off-campus electives	18.9%
Hospice/home care experience	2.7%
Cultural competence awareness	54.1%
Instruction in medical Spanish or other non-English language	13.5%
Alternative/complementary medicine curriculum	13.5%
Training in identifying and reporting of domestic violence/abuse	21.6%
MPH/MBA or PhD training	8.1%
Research rotation	5.4%

Educational Features

Offers additional training or educational experience beyond accredited length	11.4%
Offers a primary care track	8.1%
Offers a rural track	0.0%
Offers a women's health track	0.0%
Offers a hospitalist track	0.0%
Offers a research track/nonaccredited fellowship	2.7%
Offers an other track	5.4%

Resident Evaluation

Yearly specialty in-service examination required	7.5%
Patient surveys	37.8%
Portfolio system	48.6%
360 degree evaluations	94.6%
Objective structured clinical examinations (OSCE)	2.7%

Program Evaluation

Program graduation rates	83.8%
Board certification rates	78.4%
In-training examinations	8.1%
Performance-based assessments	32.4%

Employment Policies and Benefits

Part-time/shared positions	0.0%
On-site child care	32.4%
Subsidized child care	8.1%
Allowance/stipend for professional expenses	94.6%
Leave for educational meetings/conferences	83.8%
Moving allowance	2.7%
Housing stipend	0.0%
On-call meal allowance	78.4%
Free parking	45.9%
PDAs	8.1%
Placement assistance upon completion of program	13.5%
Cross coverage in case of illness/disability	70.3%

Compensation and Leave (Graduate Year 1)

Average resident/fellow compensation	$55,046
Average number weeks of vacation	3.4
Sick days (paid)	26.0
Maximum number of paid days for family/medical leave	40
Maximum number of unpaid days for family/medical leave	35

Major Medical Benefits

Major medical insurance for residents	97.3%
Major medical insurance for dependents	89.2%
Outpatient mental health insurance	89.2%
Inpatient mental health insurance	83.8%
Group life insurance	78.4%
Dental insurance	86.5%
Disability insurance	86.5%
Disability insurance for occupationally acquired HIV	73.0%
Medical insurance coverage begins when starting program	83.8%

For more information

Society of Interventional Radiology
3975 Fair Ridge Drive, Suite 400 North
Fairfax, VA 22033
703 691-1805
703 691-1855 Fax
www.sirweb.org

Sleep Medicine

Professional Description

Sleep medicine is a multidiscplinary subspecialty of family medicine, internal medicine, psychiatry, pediatrics, neurology, and otolaryngology.

Sleep medicine is a discipline of medical practice in which sleep disorders are assessed, monitored, treated, and prevented by using a combination of techniques (clinical evaluation, physiologic testing, imaging, and intervention) and medication. Specialists in sleep medicine are expected to:

- Participate in an interdisciplinary care of patients of all ages that incorporates aspects of psychiatry, neurology, internal medicine, epidemiology, surgery, pediatrics and basic science
- Acquire detailed knowledge of the sleep and respiratory control centers, physiology, and neurobiology underlying sleep and wakefulness
- Diagnose and manage sleep disorder patients in outpatient and inpatient settings

Source: Sleep Medicine Program Requirements, ACGME
www.acgme.org/acWebsite/downloads/RRC_progReq/520pr604_u605.pdf

This subspecialty includes the clinical assessment, polysomnographic evaluation, and treatment of sleep disorders, including insomnias, disorders of excessive sleepiness (eg, narcolepsy), sleep-related breathing disorders (such as obstructive sleep apnea), parasomnias, circadian rhythm disorders, sleep-related movement disorders, and other conditions pertaining to the sleep-wake cycle.
Source: American Board of Psychiatry and Neurology

Prerequisites; Length of Training

Completion of an ACGME-accredited residency program in family medicine, internal medicine, pulmonology, psychiatry, pediatrics, neurology, or otolaryngology is required; ACGME-accredited programs in sleep medicine are 1 year.

For more information

American Academy of Sleep Medicine
One Westbrook Corporate Center, Suite 920
Westchester, IL 60154
708 492-0930
708 492-0943 Fax
www.aasmnet.org

Specialty Data

Surgery-General

Professional Description

The ABS considers general surgery to be a discipline encompassing the following content areas:

- Alimentary tract
- Abdomen and its contents
- Breast, skin and soft tissue
- Endocrine system
- Head and neck surgery
- Organ transplantation
- Pediatric surgery
- Surgical critical care
- Surgical oncology
- Trauma/burns and acute care surgery
- Vascular surgery

1. The expected knowledge and performance of the certified surgeon is as follows:

- Comprehensive clinical knowledge within each area listed, to include epidemiology, anatomy, physiology, clinical presentation, and pathology (including neoplasia)*
- Knowledge of the scientific foundations in all areas, including wound healing; infection; fluid management; shock and resuscitation; immunology; antibiotic usage; metabolism; and use of enteral and parenteral nutrition
- Experience and skill in the clinical evaluation, appropriate use of radiologic imaging, and management of diseases within these areas, including diagnosis; indications for surgery and nonsurgical treatment; preoperative, operative and postoperative care; and the management of comorbidities and complications
- Extensive experience in minimally invasive surgery for the diagnosis and treatment of diseases in these areas, including basic and advanced laparoscopic procedures
- Substantial experience in diagnostic and therapeutic endoscopy, including colonoscopy, esophagogastroduodenoscopy, and bronchoscopy

2. The following specialty areas are independent of general surgery; however, the certified general surgeon is expected to be familiar with their common diseases and operative techniques:

- Thoracic surgery
- Plastic and reconstructive surgery
- Urgent and emergent problems in gynecologic, neurologic, orthopaedic, and urologic surgery

It should be recognized that the experience, knowledge, and skills required in each of the content areas will not necessarily encompass the full range and complexity of procedures, particularly advanced operations and treatments of a specialized nature. This holds especially true of disciplines that have ACGME-accredited residencies and have separate processes for certification by the ABS. Specific information on the expected proficiencies is outlined in the Patient Care Curriculum Outline of the Surgical Council on Resident Education (SCORE).

3. The certified general surgeon is also expected to have knowledge of and experience in the following specific areas:

- Resuscitation of critically ill patients, including trauma victims
- Airway intubation, both urgent and elective
- Conscious sedation
- Diagnostic ultrasonography, particularly of the following areas:
  - Thyroid and parathyroid
  - Breast
  - Abdomen, including intraoperative and laparoscopic ultrasonography
  - Endorectal
  - Trauma, including Focused Assessment with Sonography in Trauma (FAST) examination
- Noninvasive diagnostic evaluation of the vascular system
- Sentinel lymph node mapping for breast cancer and melanoma

4. The certified general surgeon is also expected to have knowledge and skills in the management and team-based interdisciplinary care of the following specific patient groups:

- Terminally ill patients, to include palliative care and management of pain, weight loss, and cachexia in patients with malignant and chronic conditions
- Morbidly obese patients, to include metabolic derangements, weight-loss surgery, and counseling of patients and families
- Geriatric surgical patients, to include operative and nonoperative care, management of comorbid chronic diseases, and the counseling of patients and families.

Source: American Board of Surgery

Prerequisites; Length of Training

No prior GME is required. ACGME-accredited programs in general surgery are 5 years.

Subspecialties

Subspecialty programs accredited by the ACGME

- Hand surgery
- Hospice and palliative medicine
- Pediatric surgery
- Surgical critical care
- Vascular surgery

Other American Board of Surgery specialty certificates

- Vascular surgery

American Board of Surgery subspecialty certificates

- Hospice and palliative medicine
- Pediatric surgery
- Surgery of the hand
- Surgical critical care

Surgery residency performance data for board certification examinations

The American Board of Surgery has posted online the 5-year average pass rate of first-time examinees for all ACGME-accredited surgery residency programs on the Surgery Qualifying and Surgery Certifying Examinations, as well as a combined first-time pass rate for both examinations. These data are intended for use by medical students who are interested in surgical residencies, as one factor that may be relevant in choosing which programs to pursue.

http://home.absurgery.org/default.jsp?prog_passreport

Data

Unless otherwise noted, all data are for 2008.

Table 1. Surgery-General Programs

Number of accredited programs	249
Program Data	
length of accredited training	5
Minimum number of prior years of GME required	0
Offers graduate year 1 positions, available immediately upon medical school completion	Yes
Average number of interviews for program year 1 positions	72.1
Percent new program directors, 2007-2008 academic year (source: ACGME)	12.0%

Residents/Fellows

Total number of active residents/fellows	7,069
Average number of residents/fellows per program	28.4
Average percent female	32.0%
Average percent international medical graduate (IMG)	18.3%

Program Faculty

Average number of full-time physician faculty	29.9
Average number of part-time physician faculty	4.3
Average percent female full-time physician faculty	13.4%
Average ratio of full-time physician faculty to resident/fellow	0.7

Table 2. Data for Surgery-General Programs Listed in FREIDA

Number of programs providing data	186

Work Schedule (Program Year 1)

Average hours on duty per week	76.1
Average maximum consecutive hours on duty	27.8
Average days off duty per week	1.1
Moonlighting allowed within institution	14.5%
Night float system	54.3%
Offers awareness and management of fatigue in residents/fellows	98.9%

Educational Setting (Program Year 1)

Average hours/week of regularly scheduled lectures/conferences	5.5
Average percent of training in hospital outpatient clinics	18.3%
Average percent of training in nonhospital ambulatory care community settings	9.6%

Educational Benefits

Curriculum on management of tobacco dependence	10.8%
Program to assess/enhance medical professionalism	82.8%
Debt management/financial counseling	68.8%
Formal program to develop teaching skills	82.3%
Formal mentoring program	79.6%
Formal program to foster interdisciplinary teamwork	26.9%
Continuous quality improvement training	91.9%
International experience	19.4%
Resident/fellow retreats	41.9%
Off-campus electives	50.5%
Hospice/home care experience	11.3%
Cultural competence awareness	78.0%
Instruction in medical Spanish or other non-English language	23.1%
Alternative/complementary medicine curriculum	16.1%
Training in identifying and reporting of domestic violence/abuse	50.0%
MPH/MBA or PhD training	25.3%
Research rotation	16.1%

Educational Features

Offers additional training or educational experience beyond accredited length	51.9%
Offers a primary care track	4.3%
Offers a rural track	4.3%
Offers a women's health track	3.8%
Offers a hospitalist track	0.5%
Offers a research track/nonaccredited fellowship	30.6%
Offers an other track	5.9%

Resident Evaluation

Yearly specialty in-service examination required	99.6%
Patient surveys	45.2%
Portfolio system	53.2%
360 degree evaluations	81.7%
Objective structured clinical examinations (OSCE)	24.2%

Program Evaluation

Program graduation rates	85.5%
Board certification rates	98.9%
In-training examinations	98.9%
Performance-based assessments	64.5%

Employment Policies and Benefits

Part-time/shared positions	0.0%
On-site child care	42.5%
Subsidized child care	6.5%
Allowance/stipend for professional expenses	95.2%
Leave for educational meetings/conferences	87.2%
Moving allowance	16.7%
Housing stipend	8.6%
On-call meal allowance	97.3%
Free parking	73.7%
PDAs	34.9%
Placement assistance upon completion of program	42.5%
Cross coverage in case of illness/disability	82.3%

Compensation and Leave (Graduate Year 1)

Average resident/fellow compensation	$45,750
Average number weeks of vacation	3.3
Sick days (paid)	19.5
Maximum number of paid days for family/medical leave	43
Maximum number of unpaid days for family/medical leave	78

Major Medical Benefits

Major medical insurance for residents	100.0%
Major medical insurance for dependents	96.8%
Outpatient mental health insurance	94.6%
Inpatient mental health insurance	94.6%
Group life insurance	92.5%
Dental insurance	91.9%
Disability insurance	93.5%
Disability insurance for occupationally acquired HIV	83.9%
Medical insurance coverage begins when starting program	89.8%

Table 3. Surgery-General Match Data

GY1	2008
Number of positions offered	1,069
Number filled by US seniors	888
Percent filled by US seniors	83.1
Total positions filled	1,067
Percent total positions filled	99.8
All	
Total Positions*	1,069
Preferred by US Seniors*	1,014
Preferred Positions per US Senior	1.1
Preferred by Independent Applicants†	779
Preferred Positions per IA	1.4

For more information

Professional Associations

American College of Surgeons
633 North Saint Clair Street
Chicago, IL 60611-3211
800 621-4111
312 202-5001 Fax
E-mail: postmaster@facs.org
www.facs.org

American Pediatric Surgical Association
111 Deer Lake Road, Suite 100
Deerfield, IL 60015
847 480-9576
847 480-9282 Fax
E-mail: eapsa@eapsa.org
www.eapsa.org

Specialty Data

American Society for Surgery of the Hand
6300 North River Road, Suite 600
Rosemont, IL 60018
847 384-8300
847 384-1435 Fax
E-mail: info@assh.org
www.assh.org

Society for Surgery of the Alimentary Tract
900 Cummings Center, #221-U
Beverly, MA 01915
978 927-8330
978 524-8890 Fax
www.ssat.com

Society of American Gastrointestinal and Endoscopic Surgeons
11300 West Olympic Boulevard, Suite 600
Los Angeles, CA 90064
310 437-0544
310 437-0585 Fax
www.sages.org

Society of Surgical Oncology
85 West Algonquin Road, Suite 550
Arlington Heights, IL 60005
847 427-1400
847 427-9656 Fax
www.surgonc.org

American Association for the Surgery of Trauma
633 N Saint Clair Street, Suite 2400
Chicago, IL 60611
312 202-5252
312 202-5063 Fax
www.aast.org

Society for Vascular Surgery
633 N Saint Clair Street, Suite 2400
Chicago, IL 60611
312 334-2300
312 334-2320 Fax
www.vascularweb.org

Certification

American Board of Surgery
1617 John F Kennedy Boulevard, Suite 860
Philadelphia, PA 19103-1847
215 568-4000
215 563-5718 Fax
www.absurgery.org

Program Accreditation

Accreditation Council for Graduate Medical Education
Residency Review Committee for General Surgery
Peggy Simpson, EdD, Executive Director
515 North State Street
Chicago, IL 60654
312 755-5499
E-mail: psimpson@acgme.org
www.acgme.org

Hand Surgery

Professional Description

A surgeon with expertise in the investigation, preservation, and restoration by medical, surgical, and rehabilitative means of all

structures of the upper extremity directly affecting the form and function of the hand and wrist.

Prerequisites; Length of Training

Satisfactory completion of an ACGME- or RCPSC-accredited general surgery, orthopaedic surgery, or plastic surgery residency program is required. Length of ACGME-accredited programs is 1 year.

For more information

American Society for Surgery of the Hand
6300 North River Road, Suite 600
Rosemont, IL 60018
847 384-8300
847 384-1435 Fax
E-mail: info@assh.org
www.assh.org

Hospice and Palliative Medicine

See page 57.

Pediatric Surgery

Professional Description

Pediatric surgery is defined as the diagnostic, preoperative, operative, and postoperative surgical management of congenital and acquired abnormalities and diseases, be they developmental, inflammatory, neoplastic, or traumatic, in the neonatal and pediatric age groups. The scope of this discipline is considered to be essentially the same as general surgery, focused especially in infancy, but to include older children with those conditions customarily treated in children's hospitals and pediatric surgical divisions of large general hospitals.

Prerequisites; Length of Training

Satisfactory completion of an ACGME- or RCPSC-accredited general surgery residency is required. Length of ACGME-accredited programs is 2 years.

Data

Unless otherwise noted, all data are for 2008.

Table 1. Pediatric Surgery Programs	
Number of accredited programs	37
Program Data	
length of accredited training	2
Minimum number of prior years of GME required	5
Offers graduate year 1 positions, available immediately upon medical school completion	No
Average number of interviews for program year 1 positions	26.2
Percent new program directors, 2007-2008 academic year (source: ACGME)	8.6%
Residents/Fellows	
Total number of active residents/fellows	69
Average number of residents/fellows per program	1.9
Average percent female	36.2%
Average percent international medical graduate (IMG)	5.8%
Program Faculty	
Average number of full-time physician faculty	6.7
Average number of part-time physician faculty	0.7
Average percent female full-time physician faculty	19.7%

Average ratio of full-time physician faculty to resident/fellow	2.3

Table 2. Data for Pediatric Surgery Programs Listed in FREIDA

Number of programs providing data	14

Work Schedule (Program Year 1)

Average hours on duty per week	74.0
Average maximum consecutive hours on duty	27.2
Average days off duty per week	1.1
Moonlighting allowed within institution	0.0%
Night float system	21.4%
Offers awareness and management of fatigue in residents/fellows	85.7%

Educational Setting (Program Year 1)

Average hours/week of regularly scheduled lectures/conferences	6.0
Average percent of training in hospital outpatient clinics	21.5%
Average percent of training in nonhospital ambulatory care community settings	20.0%

Educational Benefits

Curriculum on management of tobacco dependence	7.1%
Program to assess/enhance medical professionalism	57.1%
Debt management/financial counseling	28.6%
Formal program to develop teaching skills	78.6%
Formal mentoring program	50.0%
Formal program to foster interdisciplinary teamwork	14.3%
Continuous quality improvement training	78.6%
International experience	7.1%
Resident/fellow retreats	35.7%
Off-campus electives	28.6%
Hospice/home care experience	14.3%
Cultural competence awareness	57.1%
Instruction in medical Spanish or other non-English language	7.1%
Alternative/complementary medicine curriculum	0.0%
Training in identifying and reporting of domestic violence/abuse	50.0%
MPH/MBA or PhD training	0.0%
Research rotation	0.0%

Educational Features

Offers additional training or educational experience beyond accredited length	7.9%
Offers a primary care track	0.0%
Offers a rural track	0.0%
Offers a women's health track	0.0%
Offers a hospitalist track	0.0%
Offers a research track/nonaccredited fellowship	21.4%
Offers an other track	14.3%

Resident Evaluation

Yearly specialty in-service examination required	95.0%
Patient surveys	21.4%
Portfolio system	7.1%
360 degree evaluations	78.6%
Objective structured clinical examinations (OSCE)	0.0%

Program Evaluation

Program graduation rates	92.9%
Board certification rates	100.0%
In-training examinations	100.0%
Performance-based assessments	28.6%

Employment Policies and Benefits

Part-time/shared positions	0.0%
On-site child care	57.1%
Subsidized child care	0.0%
Allowance/stipend for professional expenses	100.0%
Leave for educational meetings/conferences	92.7%
Moving allowance	7.1%
Housing stipend	0.0%
On-call meal allowance	92.9%

Free parking	85.7%
PDAs	35.7%
Placement assistance upon completion of program	35.7%
Cross coverage in case of illness/disability	71.4%

Compensation and Leave (Graduate Year 1)

Average resident/fellow compensation	$55,428
Average number weeks of vacation	3.1
Sick days (paid)	21.4
Maximum number of paid days for family/medical leave	49
Maximum number of unpaid days for family/medical leave	71

Major Medical Benefits

Major medical insurance for residents	100.0%
Major medical insurance for dependents	100.0%
Outpatient mental health insurance	92.9%
Inpatient mental health insurance	92.9%
Group life insurance	100.0%
Dental insurance	92.9%
Disability insurance	92.9%
Disability insurance for occupationally acquired HIV	71.4%
Medical insurance coverage begins when starting program	100.0%

For more information

American Pediatric Surgical Association
111 Deer Lake Road, Suite 100
Deerfield, IL 60015
847 480-9576
847 480-9282 Fax
E-mail: eapsa@eapsa.org
www.eapsa.org

Surgical Critical Care

Professional Description

Surgical critical care is a specialty of surgery and a primary component of general surgery related to the care of patients with acute, life-threatening, or potentially life-threatening surgical conditions. Surgical critical care not only incorporates knowledge and skills of nonoperative techniques for supportive care for critically ill patients but also a broad understanding of the relationship between critical surgical illness and surgical procedures. Although much of this knowledge and skills is common to critical care specialists from a variety of medical disciplines, the diplomate in surgical critical care has specialized expertise relating both to the physiologic responses to tissue injury from trauma, burns, operation, infections, acute inflammation, or ischemia and to the ways these responses interact with other disease processes.

Specialists in surgical critical care possess advanced knowledge and skills that enable them to provide comprehensive care to critically ill patients from all surgical specialties and in all age groups. Care for the critically ill surgical patient may take place in a variety of settings, eg, prehospital situations, the emergency department, the operating room, and intensive care units. Because the care of such patients involves skill in a number of disciplines, as well as an understanding of surgery, the specialist in surgical critical care must have a broad knowledge base and expertise concerning the biology of the critically ill surgical patient and the support of organ system function.

Prerequisites; Length of Training

Satisfactory completion of an ACGME- or RCPSC-accredited general surgery residency is required. Length of ACGME-accredited programs is 1 year, and may be completed while in residency.

Specialty Data

Data

Unless otherwise noted, all data are for 2008.

Table 1. Surgical Critical Care Programs

Number of accredited programs	94

Program Data

length of accredited training	1
Minimum number of prior years of GME required	5
Offers graduate year 1 positions, available immediately upon medical school completion	No
Average number of interviews for program year 1 positions	5.5
Percent new program directors, 2007-2008 academic year (source: ACGME)	10.1%

Residents/Fellows

Total number of active residents/fellows	150
Average number of residents/fellows per program	1.6
Average percent female	28.7%
Average percent international medical graduate (IMG)	14.7%

Program Faculty

Average number of full-time physician faculty	9.7
Average number of part-time physician faculty	0.8
Average percent female full-time physician faculty	17.9%
Average ratio of full-time physician faculty to resident/fellow	2.9

Table 2. Data for Surgical Critical Care Programs Listed in FREIDA

Number of programs providing data	51

Work Schedule (Program Year 1)

Average hours on duty per week	59.3
Average maximum consecutive hours on duty	22.6
Average days off duty per week	1.3
Moonlighting allowed within institution	19.6%
Night float system	15.7%
Offers awareness and management of fatigue in residents/fellows	86.3%

Educational Setting (Program Year 1)

Average hours/week of regularly scheduled lectures/conferences	6.1
Average percent of training in hospital outpatient clinics	22.2%
Average percent of training in nonhospital ambulatory care community settings	50.0%

Educational Benefits

Curriculum on management of tobacco dependence	9.8%
Program to assess/enhance medical professionalism	72.5%
Debt management/financial counseling	39.2%
Formal program to develop teaching skills	84.3%
Formal mentoring program	54.9%
Formal program to foster interdisciplinary teamwork	29.4%
Continuous quality improvement training	94.1%
International experience	5.9%
Resident/fellow retreats	17.6%
Off-campus electives	35.3%
Hospice/home care experience	2.0%
Cultural competence awareness	52.9%
Instruction in medical Spanish or other non-English language	13.7%
Alternative/complementary medicine curriculum	13.7%
Training in identifying and reporting of domestic violence/abuse	49.0%
MPH/MBA or PhD training	15.7%
Research rotation	9.8%

Educational Features

Offers additional training or educational experience beyond accredited length	52.6%
Offers a primary care track	9.8%
Offers a rural track	2.0%
Offers a women's health track	2.0%
Offers a hospitalist track	5.9%
Offers a research track/nonaccredited fellowship	19.6%
Offers an other track	7.8%

Resident Evaluation

Yearly specialty in-service examination required	61.5%
Patient surveys	9.8%
Portfolio system	25.5%
360 degree evaluations	74.5%
Objective structured clinical examinations (OSCE)	7.8%

Program Evaluation

Program graduation rates	70.6%
Board certification rates	98.0%
In-training examinations	62.7%
Performance-based assessments	29.4%

Employment Policies and Benefits

Part-time/shared positions	3.9%
On-site child care	33.3%
Subsidized child care	3.9%
Allowance/stipend for professional expenses	82.4%
Leave for educational meetings/conferences	77.7%
Moving allowance	3.9%
Housing stipend	2.0%
On-call meal allowance	88.2%
Free parking	62.7%
PDAs	13.7%
Placement assistance upon completion of program	23.5%
Cross coverage in case of illness/disability	72.5%

Compensation and Leave (Graduate Year 1)

Average resident/fellow compensation	$54,063
Average number weeks of vacation	3.3
Sick days (paid)	15.2
Maximum number of paid days for family/medical leave	33
Maximum number of unpaid days for family/medical leave	59

Major Medical Benefits

Major medical insurance for residents	94.1%
Major medical insurance for dependents	88.2%
Outpatient mental health insurance	88.2%
Inpatient mental health insurance	88.2%
Group life insurance	86.3%
Dental insurance	82.4%
Disability insurance	80.4%
Disability insurance for occupationally acquired HIV	64.7%
Medical insurance coverage begins when starting program	90.2%

For more information

American Association for the Surgery of Trauma
633 N Saint Clair Street, Suite 2400
Chicago, IL 60611
312 202-5252
312 202-5063 Fax
www.aast.org

Vascular Surgery

Professional Description

Vascular surgery encompasses the diagnosis and management of disorders of the arterial, venous, and lymphatic systems, exclusive of the intracranial vessels and the heart. In addition to experience with dissection and control of blood vessels that general surgery trainees gain, diplomates in vascular surgery, by virtue of additional training, should have significant experience with all aspects of treating patients with all types of vascular disease, including diagnosis, medical treatment, and reconstructive vascular surgical and endovascular techniques. Specialists in vascular surgery should possess the advanced knowledge and skills to provide comprehensive care to patients with vascular disease, understand the needs of these patients, teach this information to others, provide leadership within their organizations, conduct or participate in research in vascular disorders, and demonstrate self-assessment of their outcomes.

The vascular surgeon must have advanced knowledge and experience with the management of vascular problems, including:

1. All elements of clinical evaluation; noninvasive testing including plethysmography, duplex ultrasonography, magnetic resonance imaging, CT scans, angiography, and other diagnostic tests as they are utilized in the diagnosis of vascular disease.

2. Nonoperative treatment of vascular disorders including drug therapy and risk factor management.

3. Indications and techniques relating to open operative treatment of vascular disorders, to include the entire spectrum of interventions used to treat vascular disorders including occlusive, aneurysmal, and inflammatory disease involving the arteries and veins of the body except the intracranial vessels and vessels intrinsic to the heart. This includes the cerebrovascular system including intrathoracic arch branches but exclusive of the intracranial vessels, and also includes the entire descending thoracic and abdominal aorta, the venous system of the chest and abdomen, the visceral and renal arteries, and the arteries and veins of the pelvis and upper and lower extremities.

4. Indications and techniques relating to endovascular interventions including balloon angioplasty and/or stenting of all vessels (excluding the intracranial and coronary arteries), aortic and peripheral artery endovascular stent graft placement, thrombolysis, and other adjuncts for vascular reconstructions.

5. The perioperative critical care of the vascular surgery patient.

Prerequisites; Length of Training

Satisfactory completion of an ACGME- or RCPSC-accredited general surgery program is required to enter ACGME-accredited programs of 2 years. For the integrated model, which incorporates the core surgical education, the length is 5 years.

Data

Unless otherwise noted, all data are for 2008.

Table 1. Vascular Surgery Programs

Number of accredited programs	97

Program Data

length of accredited training	1/2
Minimum number of prior years of GME required	5
Offers graduate year 1 positions, available immediately upon medical school completion	No
Average number of interviews for program year 1 positions	14.6
Percent new program directors, 2007-2008 academic year (source: ACGME)	10.4%

Residents/Fellows

Total number of active residents/fellows	227
Average number of residents/fellows per program	2.3
Average percent female	12.8%
Average percent international medical graduate (IMG)	23.8%

Program Faculty

Average number of full-time physician faculty	5.4
Average number of part-time physician faculty	0.6
Average percent female full-time physician faculty	9.0%
Average ratio of full-time physician faculty to resident/fellow	1.5

Table 2. Data for Vascular Surgery Programs Listed in FREIDA

Number of programs providing data	53

Work Schedule (Program Year 1)

Average hours on duty per week	65.1
Average maximum consecutive hours on duty	21.8
Average days off duty per week	1.3
Moonlighting allowed within institution	18.9%
Night float system	15.1%
Offers awareness and management of fatigue in residents/fellows	88.7%

Educational Setting (Program Year 1)

Average hours/week of regularly scheduled lectures/conferences	4.3
Average percent of training in hospital outpatient clinics	18.6%
Average percent of training in nonhospital ambulatory care community settings	8.1%

Educational Benefits

Curriculum on management of tobacco dependence	9.4%
Program to assess/enhance medical professionalism	58.5%
Debt management/financial counseling	45.3%
Formal program to develop teaching skills	71.7%
Formal mentoring program	43.4%
Formal program to foster interdisciplinary teamwork	9.4%
Continuous quality improvement training	73.6%
International experience	5.7%
Resident/fellow retreats	22.6%
Off-campus electives	18.9%
Hospice/home care experience	0.0%
Cultural competence awareness	52.8%
Instruction in medical Spanish or other non-English language	11.3%
Alternative/complementary medicine curriculum	11.3%
Training in identifying and reporting of domestic violence/abuse	18.9%
MPH/MBA or PhD training	13.2%
Research rotation	43.4%

Educational Features

Offers additional training or educational experience beyond accredited length	9.9%
Offers a primary care track	1.9%
Offers a rural track	1.9%
Offers a women's health track	1.9%
Offers a hospitalist track	1.9%
Offers a research track/nonaccredited fellowship	5.7%
Offers an other track	5.7%

Resident Evaluation

Yearly specialty in-service examination required	58.8%
Patient surveys	24.5%
Portfolio system	18.9%
360 degree evaluations	71.7%
Objective structured clinical examinations (OSCE)	1.9%

Program Evaluation

Program graduation rates	77.4%
Board certification rates	100.0%
In-training examinations	56.6%
Performance-based assessments	22.6%

Employment Policies and Benefits

Part-time/shared positions	5.7%
On-site child care	41.5%
Subsidized child care	5.7%
Allowance/stipend for professional expenses	88.7%
Leave for educational meetings/conferences	93.2%
Moving allowance	7.5%
Housing stipend	5.7%
On-call meal allowance	71.7%
Free parking	60.4%

Specialty Data

PDAs	22.6%
Placement assistance upon completion of program	32.1%
Cross coverage in case of illness/disability	86.8%
Compensation and Leave (Graduate Year 1)	
Average resident/fellow compensation	$55,264
Average number weeks of vacation	3.2
Sick days (paid)	20.2
Maximum number of paid days for family/medical leave	36
Maximum number of unpaid days for family/medical leave	65
Major Medical Benefits	
Major medical insurance for residents	96.2%
Major medical insurance for dependents	88.7%
Outpatient mental health insurance	88.7%
Inpatient mental health insurance	88.7%
Group life insurance	88.7%
Dental insurance	86.8%
Disability insurance	88.7%
Disability insurance for occupationally acquired HIV	66.0%
Medical insurance coverage begins when starting program	84.9%

For more information

Society for Vascular Surgery
633 North Saint Clair Street, 24th Floor
Chicago, IL 60611
800 258-7188
312 334-2320 Fax
E-mail: vascular@vascularsociety.org
www.vascularweb.org

Thoracic Surgery

Professional Description

A thoracic surgeon provides the operative, perioperative, and critical care of patients with pathologic conditions within the chest. Included is the surgical care of coronary artery disease; cancers of the lung, esophagus, and chest wall; abnormalities of the trachea; abnormalities of the great vessels and heart valves; congenital anomalies; tumors of the mediastinum; and diseases of the diaphragm. Management of the airway and injuries of the chest is within the scope of the specialty.

Thoracic surgeons have the knowledge, experience, and technical skills to accurately diagnose, operate upon safely, and effectively manage patients with thoracic diseases of the chest. This requires substantial knowledge of cardiorespiratory physiology and oncology, as well as capability in the use of heart assist devices, management of abnormal heart rhythms and drainage of the chest cavity, respiratory support systems, endoscopy, and invasive and noninvasive diagnostic techniques.

Prerequisites; Length of Training

Education in thoracic surgery must be provided in one of three formats:
- *Independent Program* (traditional format): Two or 3 years of thoracic surgery education, preceded by successful completion of an ACGME- or RCPSC-accredited surgery program.
- *Joint Surgery/Thoracic Surgery Program* (4+3 program): All 7 years of the program must be completed in the same institution, and all of the years must be accredited by the ACGME. Assuming successful completion of the programs, this format provides the graduate with the ability to apply for certification in both surgery and thoracic surgery.
- *Integrated Program*: Six years of thoracic surgery education (completed in one institution) following completion of medical school.

Subspecialties

Subspecialty programs accredited by the ACGME
- Congenital cardiac surgery

American Board of Thoracic Surgery certificate of added qualifications
- Congenital cardiac surgery

Data

Unless otherwise noted, all data are for 2008.

Table 1. Thoracic Surgery Programs

Number of accredited programs	78
Program Data	
length of accredited training	2/3
Minimum number of prior years of GME required	5
Offers graduate year 1 positions, available immediately upon medical school completion	No
Average number of interviews for program year 1 positions	13.4
Percent new program directors, 2007-2008 academic year (source: ACGME)	9.9%
Residents/Fellows	
Total number of active residents/fellows	228
Average number of residents/fellows per program	2.9
Average percent female	14.0%
Average percent international medical graduate (IMG)	26.3%
Program Faculty	
Average number of full-time physician faculty	10.1

Average number of part-time physician faculty	0.4
Average percent female full-time physician faculty	4.3%
Average ratio of full-time physician faculty to resident/fellow	2.0

Table 2. Data for Thoracic Surgery Programs Listed in FREIDA

Number of programs providing data	44

Work Schedule (Program Year 1)

Average hours on duty per week	73.0
Average maximum consecutive hours on duty	25.4
Average days off duty per week	1.2
Moonlighting allowed within institution	2.3%
Night float system	15.9%
Offers awareness and management of fatigue in residents/fellows	90.9%

Educational Setting (Program Year 1)

Average hours/week of regularly scheduled lectures/conferences	5.0
Average percent of training in hospital outpatient clinics	15.1%
Average percent of training in nonhospital ambulatory care community settings	7.0%

Educational Benefits

Curriculum on management of tobacco dependence	9.1%
Program to assess/enhance medical professionalism	72.7%
Debt management/financial counseling	47.7%
Formal program to develop teaching skills	70.5%
Formal mentoring program	54.5%
Formal program to foster interdisciplinary teamwork	20.5%
Continuous quality improvement training	86.4%
International experience	9.1%
Resident/fellow retreats	27.3%
Off-campus electives	22.7%
Hospice/home care experience	2.3%
Cultural competence awareness	65.9%
Instruction in medical Spanish or other non-English language	18.2%
Alternative/complementary medicine curriculum	13.6%
Training in identifying and reporting of domestic violence/abuse	20.5%
MPH/MBA or PhD training	9.1%
Research rotation	0.0%

Educational Features

Offers additional training or educational experience beyond accredited length	15.8%
Offers a primary care track	6.8%
Offers a rural track	0.0%
Offers a women's health track	2.3%
Offers a hospitalist track	2.3%
Offers a research track/nonaccredited fellowship	11.4%
Offers an other track	6.8%

Resident Evaluation

Yearly specialty in-service examination required	100.0%
Patient surveys	15.9%
Portfolio system	27.3%
360 degree evaluations	68.2%
Objective structured clinical examinations (OSCE)	4.5%

Program Evaluation

Program graduation rates	86.4%
Board certification rates	97.7%
In-training examinations	100.0%
Performance-based assessments	31.8%

Employment Policies and Benefits

Part-time/shared positions	0.0%
On-site child care	36.4%
Subsidized child care	4.5%
Allowance/stipend for professional expenses	97.7%
Leave for educational meetings/conferences	91.0%
Moving allowance	6.8%

Housing stipend	13.6%
On-call meal allowance	93.2%
Free parking	43.2%
PDAs	25.0%
Placement assistance upon completion of program	45.5%
Cross coverage in case of illness/disability	77.3%

Compensation and Leave (Graduate Year 1)

Average resident/fellow compensation	$55,239
Average number weeks of vacation	3.3
Sick days (paid)	25.2
Maximum number of paid days for family/medical leave	38
Maximum number of unpaid days for family/medical leave	86

Major Medical Benefits

Major medical insurance for residents	97.7%
Major medical insurance for dependents	97.7%
Outpatient mental health insurance	95.5%
Inpatient mental health insurance	95.5%
Group life insurance	90.9%
Dental insurance	90.9%
Disability insurance	88.6%
Disability insurance for occupationally acquired HIV	77.3%
Medical insurance coverage begins when starting program	88.6%

Table 3. Thoracic Surgery Match Data

GY1	2008
Number of positions offered	3
Number filled by US seniors	3
Percent filled by US seniors	100
Total positions filled	3
Percent total positions filled	100
All	
Total Positions*	3
Preferred by US Seniors*	7
Preferred Positions per US Senior	0.4
Preferred by Independent Applicants†	0
Preferred Positions per IA	0

Source: National Resident Matching Program 2008 Match Data
* Includes all positions offered in a specialty, except preliminary positions.
† Preferred means the number of applicants for whom the specialty was the only or first choice.

For more information

Professional Associations

American Association for Thoracic Surgery
900 Cummings Center, Suite 221-U
Beverly, MA 01915
978 927-8330
978 524-8890 Fax
www.aats.org

American Thoracic Society
61 Broadway
New York, NY 10006-2755
212 315-8600
212 315-6498 Fax
www.thoracic.org

Society of Thoracic Surgeons
633 North Saint Clair, Suite 2320
Chicago, IL 60611
312 202-5800
312 202-5801 Fax
E-mail: sts@sts.org
www.sts.org

Specialty Data

Thoracic Surgery Directors Association
633 North Saint Clair, Suite 2320
Chicago, IL 60611
312 202-5819
312 202-5829 Fax
E-mail: tsda@tsda.org
www.tsda.org

Certification

American Board of Thoracic Surgery
633 North Saint Clair Street, Suite 2320
Chicago, IL 60611
312 202-5900
312 202-5960 Fax
E-mail: info@abts.org
www.abts.org

Program Accreditation

Accreditation Council for Graduate Medical Education
Residency Review Committee for Thoracic Surgery
Peggy Simpson, EdD, Executive Director
515 North State Street
Chicago, IL 60654
312 755-5499 5027
E-mail: psimpson@acgme.org
www.acgme.org

Congenital Cardiac Surgery

Professional Description

"Educational programs in congenital cardiac surgery must provide the educational resources appropriate for the development of proficiency in the diagnosis and treatment of diseases of congenital arterial, venous, and lymphatic circulatory systems, including those components intrinsic to the heart."

In addition, "[f]ellows must be provided with education with special diagnostic techniques for the management of congenital cardiac lesions; the methods and techniques of cardiac catheterization, and competence in the interpretation of such findings; and experience with the application, interpretation, and limitations of echocardiography and other imaging techniques."
Source: Congenital Cardiac Surgery Program Requirements, ACGME, www.acgme.org/acWebsite/downloads/RRC_progReq/466pr206.pdf

Prerequisites; Length of Training

Satisfactory completion of a thoracic surgery program accredited by the ACGME or Royal College of Physicians and Surgeons of Canada is required. Length of ACGME-accredited programs is 1 year.

For more information

Congenital Heart Surgeons' Society
900 Cummings Center, Suite 221-U
Beverly, MA 01915
978 927-8330
978 524-8890 Fax
www.chss.org

Transitional Year

Description

The objective of the transitional year is to provide a well-balanced program of GME in multiple clinical disciplines to facilitate the choice of and/or preparation for a specific specialty. The transitional year is not meant to be a complete graduate education program in preparation for the practice of medicine.
Source: Transitional Year Program Requirements, ACGME

Prerequisites; Length of Training

No prior GME is required. ACGME-accredited programs are 1 year.

Data

Unless otherwise noted, all data are for 2008.

Table 1. Transitional Year Programs

Number of accredited programs	121
Program Data	
length of accredited training	1
Minimum number of prior years of GME required	0
Offers graduate year 1 positions, available immediately upon medical school completion	Yes
Average number of interviews for program year 1 positions	74.2
Percent new program directors, 2007-2008 academic year (source: ACGME)	10.2%
Residents/Fellows	
Total number of active residents/fellows	1,087
Average number of residents/fellows per program	9.0
Average percent female	35.1%
Average percent international medical graduate (IMG)	7.1%
Program Faculty	
Average number of full-time physician faculty	64.3
Average number of part-time physician faculty	14.9
Average percent female full-time physician faculty	22.3%
Average ratio of full-time physician faculty to resident/fellow	3.4

Table 2. Data for Transitional Year Programs Listed in FREIDA

Number of programs providing data	81
Work Schedule (Program Year 1)	
Average hours on duty per week	60.9
Average maximum consecutive hours on duty	28.4
Average days off duty per week	1.3
Moonlighting allowed within institution	11.1%
Night float system	53.1%
Offers awareness and management of fatigue in residents/fellows	98.8%
Educational Setting (Program Year 1)	
Average hours/week of regularly scheduled lectures/conferences	7.1
Average percent of training in hospital outpatient clinics	16.1%
Average percent of training in nonhospital ambulatory care community settings	12.8%
Educational Benefits	
Curriculum on management of tobacco dependence	28.4%
Program to assess/enhance medical professionalism	80.2%
Debt management/financial counseling	69.1%
Formal program to develop teaching skills	67.9%
Formal mentoring program	48.1%
Formal program to foster interdisciplinary teamwork	34.6%
Continuous quality improvement training	92.6%
International experience	27.2%
Resident/fellow retreats	50.6%
Off-campus electives	87.7%

Hospice/home care experience	55.6%
Cultural competence awareness	87.7%
Instruction in medical Spanish or other non-English language	24.7%
Alternative/complementary medicine curriculum	42.0%
Training in identifying and reporting of domestic violence/abuse	76.5%
MPH/MBA or PhD training	3.7%
Research rotation	3.7%

Educational Features

Offers additional training or educational experience beyond accredited length	0.0%
Offers a primary care track	12.3%
Offers a rural track	0.0%
Offers a women's health track	1.2%
Offers a hospitalist track	3.7%
Offers a research track/nonaccredited fellowship	1.2%
Offers an other track	2.5%

Resident Evaluation

Yearly specialty in-service examination required	21.2%
Patient surveys	54.3%
Portfolio system	55.6%
360 degree evaluations	88.9%
Objective structured clinical examinations (OSCE)	25.9%

Program Evaluation

Program graduation rates	93.8%
Board certification rates	14.8%
In-training examinations	22.2%
Performance-based assessments	58.0%

Employment Policies and Benefits

Part-time/shared positions	3.7%
On-site child care	43.2%
Subsidized child care	8.6%
Allowance/stipend for professional expenses	81.5%
Leave for educational meetings/conferences	35.3%
Moving allowance	32.1%
Housing stipend	7.4%
On-call meal allowance	96.3%
Free parking	97.5%
PDAs	40.7%
Placement assistance upon completion of program	22.2%
Cross coverage in case of illness/disability	87.7%

Compensation and Leave (Graduate Year 1)

Average resident/fellow compensation	$44,885
Average number weeks of vacation	3.1
Sick days (paid)	21.4
Maximum number of paid days for family/medical leave	41
Maximum number of unpaid days for family/medical leave	67

Major Medical Benefits

Major medical insurance for residents	100.0%
Major medical insurance for dependents	100.0%
Outpatient mental health insurance	95.1%
Inpatient mental health insurance	95.1%
Group life insurance	93.8%
Dental insurance	90.1%
Disability insurance	90.1%
Disability insurance for occupationally acquired HIV	71.6%
Medical insurance coverage begins when starting program	97.5%

Table 3. Transitional Year Match Data

GY1	2008
Number of positions offered	979
Number filled by US seniors	874
Percent filled by US seniors	89.3

Total positions filled	957
Percent total positions filled	97.8

Program Accreditation

Accreditation Council for Graduate Medical Education
Transitional Year Review Committee
Linda Thorsen, Executive Director
515 North State Street
Chicago, IL 60654
312 755-5029
E-mail: lmt@acgme.org
www.acgme.org

Specialty Data

Urology

Professional Description

A urologist manages benign and malignant medical and surgical disorders of the genitourinary system and the adrenal gland. This specialist has comprehensive knowledge of, and skills in, endoscopic, percutaneous, and open surgery of congenital and acquired conditions of the urinary and reproductive systems and their contiguous structures.

Prerequisites; Length of Training

Satisfactory completion of 1 year of an ACGME-accredited general surgery residency is required. ACGME-accredited urology programs are 3 years or 4 years.

Subspecialties

Subspecialty programs accredited by the ACGME

- Pediatric urology

Data

Unless otherwise noted, all data are for 2008.

Table 1. Urology Programs

Number of accredited programs	119

Program Data

length of accredited training	4/3
Minimum number of prior years of GME required	1/2
Offers graduate year 1 positions, available immediately upon medical school completion	No
Average number of interviews for program year 1 positions	33.7
Percent new program directors, 2007-2008 academic year (source: ACGME)	12.6%

Residents/Fellows

Total number of active residents/fellows	994
Average number of residents/fellows per program	8.4
Average percent female	21.4%
Average percent international medical graduate (IMG)	4.7%

Program Faculty

Average number of full-time physician faculty	9.9
Average number of part-time physician faculty	1.5
Average percent female full-time physician faculty	8.2%
Average ratio of full-time physician faculty to resident/fellow	0.9

Table 2. Data for Urology Programs Listed in FREIDA

Number of programs providing data	47

Work Schedule (Program Year 1)

Average hours on duty per week	65.7
Average maximum consecutive hours on duty	22.7
Average days off duty per week	1.4
Moonlighting allowed within institution	21.3%
Night float system	6.4%
Offers awareness and management of fatigue in residents/fellows	89.4%

Educational Setting (Program Year 1)

Average hours/week of regularly scheduled lectures/conferences	4.4
Average percent of training in hospital outpatient clinics	28.6%
Average percent of training in nonhospital ambulatory care community settings	16.8%

Educational Benefits

Curriculum on management of tobacco dependence	12.8%
Program to assess/enhance medical professionalism	78.7%
Debt management/financial counseling	61.7%
Formal program to develop teaching skills	80.9%
Formal mentoring program	53.2%
Formal program to foster interdisciplinary teamwork	10.6%
Continuous quality improvement training	83.0%
International experience	27.7%
Resident/fellow retreats	40.4%
Off-campus electives	27.7%
Hospice/home care experience	8.5%
Cultural competence awareness	70.2%
Instruction in medical Spanish or other non-English language	14.9%
Alternative/complementary medicine curriculum	27.7%
Training in identifying and reporting of domestic violence/abuse	40.4%
MPH/MBA or PhD training	29.8%
Research rotation	53.2%

Educational Features

Offers additional training or educational experience beyond accredited length	19.7%
Offers a primary care track	4.3%
Offers a rural track	2.1%
Offers a women's health track	8.5%
Offers a hospitalist track	8.5%
Offers a research track/nonaccredited fellowship	27.7%
Offers an other track	6.4%

Resident Evaluation

Yearly specialty in-service examination required	99.2%
Patient surveys	40.4%
Portfolio system	55.3%
360 degree evaluations	89.4%
Objective structured clinical examinations (OSCE)	12.8%

Program Evaluation

Program graduation rates	78.7%
Board certification rates	95.7%
In-training examinations	95.7%
Performance-based assessments	40.4%

Employment Policies and Benefits

Part-time/shared positions	0.0%
On-site child care	38.3%
Subsidized child care	6.4%
Allowance/stipend for professional expenses	91.5%
Leave for educational meetings/conferences	92.2%
Moving allowance	2.1%
Housing stipend	8.5%
On-call meal allowance	93.6%
Free parking	57.4%
PDAs	21.3%
Placement assistance upon completion of program	17.0%
Cross coverage in case of illness/disability	87.2%

Compensation and Leave (Graduate Year 1)

Average resident/fellow compensation	$47,524
Average number weeks of vacation	3.7
Sick days (paid)	28.8
Maximum number of paid days for family/medical leave	44
Maximum number of unpaid days for family/medical leave	64

Major Medical Benefits

Major medical insurance for residents	97.9%
Major medical insurance for dependents	93.6%
Outpatient mental health insurance	91.5%
Inpatient mental health insurance	89.4%
Group life insurance	87.2%
Dental insurance	83.0%
Disability insurance	89.4%
Disability insurance for occupationally acquired HIV	74.5%
Medical insurance coverage begins when starting program	91.5%

Table 3. Urology Match Data

GY1	2008
Number of positions offered	13
Number filled by US seniors	10
Percent filled by US seniors	76.9
Total positions filled	10
Percent total positions filled	76.9
GY2	
Number of positions offered	3
Number filled by US seniors	0
Percent filled by US seniors	0
Total positions filled	0
Percent total positions filled	0
All	
Total Positions*	12
Preferred by US Seniors*	9
Preferred Positions per US Senior	1.3
Preferred by Independent Applicants†	0
Preferred Positions per IA	0

Source: National Resident Matching Program 2008 Match Data
* Includes all positions offered in a specialty, except preliminary positions.
† Preferred means the number of applicants for whom the specialty was the only or first choice.

For more information

Professional Associations

American Association of Clinical Urologists
1100 East Woodfield Road, Suite 520
Schaumburg, IL 60173
847 517-7225
847 517-7229 Fax
Email: info@aacuweb.org
www.aacuweb.org

American Urological Association
1000 Corporate Boulevard
Linthicum, MD 21090
866 746-4282
410 689-3800 Fax
www.auanet.org

Certification

American Board of Urology
2216 Ivy Road, Suite 210
Charlottesville, VA 22903
434 979-0059
434 979-0266 Fax
www.abu.org

Program Accreditation

Accreditation Council for Graduate Medical Education
Residency Review Committee for Urology
Louise King, MS, Executive Director
515 North State Street
Chicago, IL 60654
312 755-5498
E-mail: lking@acgme.org
www.acgme.org

Pediatric Urology

Professional Description

Pediatric urology involves all aspects of congenital anomalies, childhood-acquired urologic problems such as tumors and trauma, and overlapping problems of adolescence. Pediatric urologists have advanced skills in the management of congenital anomalies and pediatric urologic problems.

Source: Pediatric Urology Program Requirements, ACGME

Prerequisites; Length of Training

Satisfactory completion of an accredited urology residency program is required. Length of ACGME-accredited programs is 1 year.

For more information

Society for Pediatric Urology
900 Cummings Center, Suite 221-U
Beverly, MA 01915
978 927-8330
978 524-8890 Fax
www.spuonline.org

Special Feature » *Andis Robeznieks*

HOT COMMODITY

Survey shows doc pay keeps climbing, but raises moderating

According to at least one health-care compensation expert, because of a shrinking supply of doctors and increasing demand, some physicians may soon see their services "turn into a barrel of oil," meaning they could become a commodity being priced so high that healthcare organizations have to get creative in order to afford it or use less of that commodity.

Some data from *Modern Healthcare*'s 2008 Physician Compensation Survey seem to fuel that contention.

Alternatives to higher physician salaries have grown to include establishing joint ventures between doctors and hospital systems, "loan forgiveness" agreements for medical-school debt, research opportunities, and payment for on-call duties and administrative services.

As healthcare becomes more volatile in terms of supply and demand, stability is also becoming a valued commodity. For hospitals, it means multiyear employment commitments that keep them off the recruiting treadmill. For physicians it can mean shift work, leaving administrative hassles to someone else and giving them more control of their daily schedules.

Although there's downward pressure on reimbursement while expenses continue to rise, of the 21 specialties tracked in the annual *Modern Healthcare* Physician Compensation Survey, 10 had salary ranges that topped the $400,000 level at the high end. For purposes of *Modern Healthcare*'s annual survey, figures are for total cash compensation, including salary, signing bonuses and other incentives.

One major difference between the 2007-08 data for this year's survey and last year's survey, however, is that compensation increases overall were not as high. Last year, three specialties registered double-digit percentage increases over the previous year: oncology, 13.9%; pathology, 12.7%; and psychiatry, 10.9%. This year, that feat was achieved only by plastic surgeons,

whose compensation grew 10.9%. The second- and third-biggest increases were pathologists at 9.2% and radiologists with 6.5%. Oncologists followed with a 6.2% increase. (This year, radiation oncology was counted as a separate specialty for the first time.)

Based on survey data, the average compensation for two specialties decreased: Psychiatry saw a decline of 5.6% and obstetrics/gynecology saw a dip of 0.6%. Several specialties saw their compensation increase by less than 2%: hospitalists, 1.9%; internists, 1.6%; noninvasive cardiologists, 1.4%; orthopedic surgeons, 1.1%; dermatologists, 0.8%; and pediatricians, 0.7%.

Kim Mobley, a Detroit-based principal with Sullivan, Cotter and Associates, says she believes the significant drop for psychiatrists' compensation was probably a factor of the particular samples available and not necessarily market forces.

Phil Villacci, a principal with Weymouth,

Mass.-based healthcare consultant Beacon Partners, says there is one market force that can't be discounted. "The amount of available money is diminishing," says Villacci, who compared physician services with barrels of petroleum. "New levels of physician compensation may be unsustainable going forward."

That's where the new models of compensation come in, Villacci says. As physicians seek higher incomes—in an environment of tighter reimbursement—opportunities to enter into joint ventures, participate in research trials or receive payment for administrative services become attractive alternatives for hospital executives.

Villacci says hospitals and systems are hiring doctors as a "defensive strategy" that includes creating stability and "professional fidelity" that leads to fewer recruitment demands while keeping patient referrals in-house.

For physicians, Villacci says hospital employment means a reduction in liability risk, workload relief and, often, unambiguous productivity-based compensation formulas that allow them to be "paid for what they do." In terms of lifestyle demands, Villacci says he knows a 48-year-old hand surgeon who, in addition to six weeks of vacation, takes every Friday off—which is the equivalent of 10 weeks of vacation—meaning he takes 16 weeks off each year.

In addition to such flexible schedules and other perks, orthopedic surgeons are receiving higher financial compensation than most of the other specialties. According to the *Modern Healthcare* survey, compensation for orthopedic surgeons is between $372,400 and $512,500 annually. The only specialties in the survey having compensation with higher dollar amounts at both ends of the scale are invasive cardiologists with pay ranging between $389,000 and $561,875, and radiologists, whose pay ranges from $386,755 to $600,000.

For orthopedists and invasive cardiologists, Villacci says organizations are willing to pay more because of the revenue they earn for the system. "What hospitals look at is what comes in at the bottom line," he says. "They're willing to spend the money for the return."

Villacci: **New levels of physician pay "may be unsustainable."**

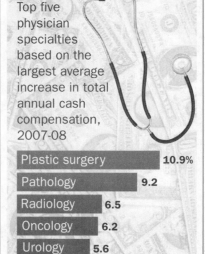

BIGGEST PAY RAISES

Top five physician specialties based on the largest average increase in total annual cash compensation, 2007-08

Plastic surgery	10.9%
Pathology	9.2
Radiology	6.5
Oncology	6.2
Urology	5.6

Note: Percentages based on data from firms that reported average salary information for that specialty for both years.

Source: Modern Healthcare's 2008 Physician Compensation Survey

See **DOC PAY** on p. 31

Salary data for the physician specialties begin on p. 28. Detailed information on the firms supplying compensation data can be found on p. 32. The complete chart is also available in the Databank/Surveys section of modernhealthcare.com.

DOC PAY >> *from p. 26*

Despite a perceived shortage of doctors and increased demand for services in primary care, family-practice physicians, internists and pediatricians saw only modest gains in compensation. Family-practice physicians, for example, saw only a 3.2% compensation increase, which puts them 10th among the specialties for the largest average pay. Their compensation pay ranged between $150,763 and $204,370.

One increasingly common way of compensating family medicine specialists has been to pay off their medical-school loans in exchange for multiyear employment commitments.

"They forgive the debt if you stay in town," says Mark Smith, president of Irving, Texas-based recruiter Merritt, Hawkins & Associates. "It's a loan you don't repay financially but you repay with time."

Merritt, Hawkins' spokesman Phil Miller says loan forgiveness, prorated over two to three years, is easier for a hospital to manage financially, but the savings is secondary. "The main point is locking the doctor into the commitment," he says. "It really is a retention strategy."

Smith: Recruiting internists brings "very few easy searches."

Internists are also in short supply, Smith says. According to the *Modern Healthcare* survey, their compensation ranges from $175,200 to $209,845 and they saw only a 1.6% increase in average compensation. But he says the demand is there. "We need more internists," Smith says. "With very few exceptions, there are very few easy searches."

In Merritt, Hawkins' own survey of healthcare compensation, Smith says the big news was pay indicated for certified registered nurse anesthetists, or CRNAs. While the *Modern Healthcare* survey shows anesthesiologists being paid between $311,600 to $446,994, the Merritt, Hawkins' survey has CRNAs earning an average of $185,000 per year—which Smith says is almost as much as his company found for psychiatrists ($189,000), and more than the compensation reported for family physicians ($172,000) and pediatricians ($159,000).

Smith says CRNAs are "beating (pediatric physicians) like a drum. In terms of real shockers out there, that was something that screamed off the pages in this general marketplace," he says.

Robert Stiefel, a physician who's an expert on anesthesiologist contract development and a principal with Brentwood, Tenn.-based consultant HealthCare Performance Strategies, says compensation for both anesthesiologists and CRNAs has led to anesthesiology departments being "decoupled" from payers. He explains that anesthesia providers receive more compensation for their services than payers will reimburse, forcing hospitals to subsidize their pay by up to 50% to keep operating rooms open.

Among other trends, Smith notes a decrease in openings for radiologists in general, but growing demand for radiology subspecialists such as pediatric, interventional and musculoskeletal radiology. He says this has led to fewer opportunities, but higher compensation offered for the subspecialist who meets an organization's specific needs.

Despite a perception that hospitalists are being used more and more extensively, Smith says the number of searches for hospitalists his company has been asked to conduct has leveled off. Merritt, Hawkins conducted 208 hospitalist searches in 2007 compared with 194 in 2006, Smith says.

"Like radiologists, places that were once asking for three are now only asking for one," Smith says.

Merritt, Hawkins' Miller says that hospitalists are still the third-most requested search the company conducts, but the market has matured and systems are now more likely to be maintaining or expanding their hospitalist program rather than starting one from scratch. "They're still in a growth mode, but the quantum leaps are kind of over," Miller says. <<

July 14, 2008 • Modern Healthcare **31**

Modern Healthcare

PHYSICIAN COMPENSATION SURVEY (1 of 4)

☐ American Medical Group Association[1]   ☐ Delta Physician Placement   ☐ Jackson & Coker

☐ Cejka Search   ☐ Hay Group   ☐ LocumTenens.com

☐ Daniel Stern & Associates   ☐ Hospital & Healthcare Compensation Service   ☐ Martin, Fletcher

Key continues on next page

ANESTHESIOLOGY
Compensation ranges from $311,600 to $446,994

HHCS	$446,994	39.6%
MGMA	$400,000	NA
Cejka	$392,000	1
Martin	$371,000	9.9
Medicus	$371,000	2.5
Pacific	$364,295	3
AMGA	$362,904	1.5
Jackson	$362,275	12.7
MDN	$350,000	4.8
Locum	$336,375	NA
Pinnacle	$336,250	(9.1)
Merritt	$336,000	12
Delta	$321,806	1.2
Hay	$311,600	(5)
Daniel	NA	NA

% change 2007-08

CARDIOLOGY (invasive)
Compensation ranges from $389,000 to $561,875

Pinnacle	$561,875	2.6%
Pacific[3]	$496,235	12.2
HHCS	$484,442	26.6
Martin	$469,000	2
Medicus	$469,000	0
MGMA	$456,901	NA
Merritt	$443,000	7.3
MDN	$427,000	4.1
AMGA	$420,106	(12.7)
Hay	$401,400	(1.7)
Cejka	$389,000	22
Daniel	NA	NA
Delta	NA	NA
Locum	NA	NA
Jackson	NA	NA

% change 2007-08

EMERGENCY MEDICINE
Compensation ranges from $216,800 to $300,000

Pinnacle	$300,000	10.1%
HHCS	$272,402	13.3
Pacific	$269,826	6.6
AMGA	$267,263	3.5
Jackson	$257,630	2.4
MGMA	$256,800	NA
MDN	$253,000	3.3
Cejka	$250,000	1
Daniel	$250,000	NA
Delta	$245,002	(6.2)
Merritt	$240,000	0
Medicus	$239,000	NA
Martin	$235,000	0
Hay	$216,800	4.4
Locum	NA	NA

% change 2007-08

FAMILY PRACTICE
Compensation ranges from $150,763 to $204,370

HHCS	$204,370	30.4%
AMGA	$201,779	3.3
Pinnacle	$177,389	(6.8)
Medicus	$176,000	1.7
MGMA	$175,918	NA
MDN	$175,000	1.2
Pacific	$173,495	2.5
Jackson	$172,556	7.8
Merritt	$172,000	6.8
Cejka	$170,000	(1.8)
Delta	$168,277	0
Martin	$165,000	13.8
Hay	$163,500	(1.2)
Locum	$150,763	NA
Daniel	NA	NA

% change 2007-08

HOSPITALIST
Compensation ranges from $174,100 to $217,052

AMGA	$217,052	7.8%
Pacific	$215,015	8
HHCS	$203,520	3
Pinnacle	$200,000	3
Cejka	$198,000	2.8
MGMA	$194,664	NA
Delta	$191,964	0
MDN	$191,000	2.1
Medicus	$191,000	1.6
Jackson	$184,289	(5.4)
Martin	$182,000	0
Merritt	$181,000	0
Hay	$174,100	(2.7)
Daniel	NA	NA
Locum	NA	NA

% change 2007-08

INTERNAL MEDICINE
Compensation ranges from $175,200 to $209,845

AMGA	$209,845	5.3%
Pinnacle	$202,500	6.3
Martin	$196,875	7.9
Pacific	$193,102	1.5
MGMA	$190,531	NA
HHCS	$189,979	(1.8)
MDN	$187,000	1.1
Medicus	$187,000	1.6
Cejka	$184,000	1.7
Delta	$183,937	0
Jackson	$181,420	(2.6)
Locum	$179,806	NA
Merritt	$176,000	1.1
Hay	$175,200	0
Daniel	NA	NA

% change 2007-08

Note: Figures represent average total annual cash compensation, which includes salary and bonuses.

[1]Company provided preliminary data.   [2]Company provided medians, not averages.   [3]Numbers for Interventional cardiology included.

Modern Healthcare

PHYSICIAN COMPENSATION SURVEY (2 of 4)

☐ MD Network   ☐ Medical Group Management Association[2]
☐ Medicus Partners   ☐ Pacific Cos.
■ Merritt, Hawkins & Associates   ☐ Pinnacle

Specialty Data

CARDIOLOGY (noninvasive)
Compensation ranges from $332,900 to $439,233

Delta	$439,233	3.9%
AMGA	$420,106	(1.9)
MGMA	$410,784	NA
MDN	$394,000	5.1
Merritt	$392,000	0
Pinnacle	$392,000	14.2
HHCS	$390,392	34.1
Pacific[4]	$380,201	(18.7)
Martin	$380,000	4.1%
Jackson	$372,600	(6.9)
Cejka	$365,000	0
Hay	$332,900	(4.3)
Daniel	NA	NA
Locum	NA	NA
Medicus	NA	NA

% change 2007-08

GASTROENTEROLOGY
Compensation ranges from $330,000 to $498,762

Pacific	$498,762	1.5%
Medicus	$482,000	4.8
AMGA	$420,898	3.4
MGMA	$418,139	NA
Martin	$410,000	1.2
MDN	$402,000	10.7
Jackson	$396,620	(10.1)
Delta	$381,404	10.3
HHCS	$379,682	33.6
Merritt	$379,000	3.8
Hay	$361,000	14.6
Pinnacle	$338,750	(15.7)
Cejka	$330,000	0
Daniel	NA	NA
Locum	NA	NA

% change 2007-08

NEUROLOGY
Compensation ranges from $203,200 to $298,503

Pacific	$298,503	(3.5)
Jackson	$264,889	20.1
Pinnacle	$252,857	(11.6)
HHCS	$252,700	27.4
AMGA	$246,924	4.1
Martin	$245,000	0
Delta	$244,326	3.1
Medicus	$241,000	(2.4)
MDN	$239,000	2.1
Merritt	$230,000	(1.7)
MGMA	$227,670	NA
Cejka	$219,000	(1.1)
Hay	$203,200	(2.9)
Daniel	NA	NA
Locum	NA	NA

% change 2007-08

DERMATOLOGY
Compensation ranges from $287,832 to $385,953

Pacific	$385,953	20%
AMGA	$371,871	3.9
Delta	$365,000	(1.8)
MGMA	$357,945	NA
Jackson	$329,267	(5.1)
Cejka	$326,000	1.9
MDN	$323,000	44.8
Merritt	$315,000	0
Hay	$294,700	4.2%
HHCS	$287,832	(3.3)
Daniel	NA	NA
Locum	NA	NA
Martin	NA	NA
Medicus	NA	NA
Pinnacle	NA	NA

% change 2007-08

GENERAL SURGERY
Compensation ranges from $271,000 to $356,938

AMGA	$356,938	2.9%
HHCS	$336,731	0
Merritt	$321,000	6.6
Martin	$318,000	5
MGMA	$316,909	NA
Medicus	$316,000	2.9
Pinnacle	$314,900	7.7
Jackson	$308,927	(3.7)
MDN	$307,000	6.2
Delta	$301,733	4.4
Pacific	$301,195	14
Hay	$286,500	6.8
Locum	$284,078	NA
Cejka	$271,000	2.9
Daniel	NA	NA

% change 2007-08

OBSTETRICS/GYNECOLOGY
Compensation ranges from $231,514 to $304,689

AMGA	$304,689	2.4%
Pacific	$287,306	(2.5)
Medicus	$286,000	0
MGMA	$280,629	NA
MDN	$279,000	1.5
Pinnacle	$265,167	2.8
Martin	$265,000	0
HHCS	$261,869	5.6
Jackson	$259,613	(4.2)
Merritt	$255,000	3.2
Delta	$253,214	(4.8)
Cejka	$243,000	5
Hay	$238,500	(3.6)
Locum	$231,514	NA
Daniel	NA	NA

% change 2007-08

Percentages rounded. Zero percentage change indicates increase or decrease of less than 1%. NA = Not available.

[4]Numbers for invasive/noninterventional included.

Source: Modern Healthcare's 2008 Physician Compensation Survey

Modern Healthcare

PHYSICIAN COMPENSATION SURVEY (3 of 4)

ONCOLOGY (including hematology)[5]
Compensation ranges from $296,500 to $410,000

Medicus	$410,000	NA
Merritt	$365,000	NA
MGMA	$363,428	NA
Cejka	$361,000	NA
HHCS	$359,158	NA
Delta	$345,833	NA
AMGA	$345,537	NA
MDN	$342,000	NA
Pinnacle	$330,000	NA
Martin	$312,500	NA
Pacific	$305,785	NA
Hay	$296,500	NA
Daniel	NA	NA
Jackson	NA	NA
Locum	NA	NA

% change 2007-08

ORTHOPEDIC SURGERY
Compensation ranges from $372,400 to $512,500

Pinnacle	$512,500	10.1%
Delta	$506,489	10.6
Medicus	$502,000	4.8
AMGA	$483,247	0
Pacific	$467,432	3.6
MDN	$463,000	8.7
HHCS	$448,148	(3.6)
MGMA	$446,303	0
Martin	$432,500	2
Jackson	$422,638	(11.2)
Merritt	$413,000	0
Cejka	$401,000	1.4
Locum	$374,200	NA
Hay	$372,400	3.7
Daniel	NA	NA

% change 2007-08

PEDIATRICS
Compensation ranges from $140,000 to $202,547

AMGA	$202,547	2.6%
Pacific	$191,908	1.9
Cejka	$184,000	9.2
MGMA	$182,727	NA
Pinnacle	$178,333	0
HHCS	$177,251	1.3
MDN	$176,000	1.7
Medicus	$174,000	(1.1)
Delta	$172,346	0
Jackson	$169,434	0
Hay	$166,800	3.1
Merritt	$159,000	0
Locum	$154,446	NA
Martin	$140,000	0
Daniel	NA	NA

% change 2007-08

PLASTIC SURGERY
Compensation ranges from $300,000 to $791,510

HHCS	$791,510	112.7%
AMGA	$390,744	1.4
Hay	$390,400	36
Delta	$387,833	NA
Jackson	$385,546	(7.9)
Pacific	$372,100	(20.5)
MGMA	$368,986	NA
MDN	$357,000	0
Cejka	$350,000	10.8
Merritt	$312,000	(8.5)
Pinnacle	$300,000	(9.1)
Daniel	NA	NA
Locum	NA	NA
Martin	NA	NA
Medicus	NA	NA

% change 2007-08

RADIATION ONCOLOGY[6]
Compensation ranges from $357,000 to $463,293

MGMA	$463,293	NA
Hay	$463,000	NA
Cejka	$454,500	NA
Pacific	$427,653	NA
AMGA	$394,034	NA
HHCS	$381,733	NA
MDN	$357,000	NA
Daniel	NA	NA
Delta	NA	NA
Jackson	NA	NA
Locum	NA	NA
Martin	NA	NA
Medicus	NA	NA
Merritt	NA	NA
Pinnacle	NA	NA

% change 2007-08

RADIOLOGY
Compensation ranges from $386,755 to $600,000

Pinnacle	$600,000	57.9%
Medicus	$491,000	6
HHCS	$487,591	38.1
Pacific	$472,804	1.1
MGMA	$466,309	NA
Jackson	$441,890	(3.9)
AMGA	$438,040	1.1
MDN	$436,000	6.3
Martin	$432,500	1.8
Delta	$429,532	(6.4)
Hay	$418,100	11.5
Cejka	$401,000	(3.7)
Merritt	$401,000	5.5
Locum	$386,755	NA
Daniel	NA	NA

% change 2007-08

Note: Figures represent average total annual cash compensation, which includes salary and bonuses.

Percentages rounded. Zero percentage change indicates increase or decrease of less than 1%. NA = Not available.

[5]Percentage-change figures not available because the specialty parameters changed for 2008.

[6]Percentage-change figures not available because the specialty is newly added for 2008.

Modern Healthcare

PHYSICIAN COMPENSATION SURVEY (4 of 4)

Specialty Data

PATHOLOGY
Compensation ranges from $239,000 to $331,842

HHCS	$331,842	65.5%
AMGA	$311,174	0
MGMA	$310,780	NA
Cejka	$298,000	16
MDN	$275,000	3
Pacific	$269,623	(4.3)
Jackson	$255,561	(14.9)
Hay	$251,700	10.7
Merritt	$239,000	(6.3)
Daniel	NA	NA
Delta	NA	NA
Locum	NA	NA
Martin	NA	NA
Medicus	NA	NA
Pinnacle	NA	NA

% change
2007-08

PSYCHIATRY
Compensation ranges from $173,800 to $248,198

Pacific	$248,198	(14%)
AMGA	$216,202	3.1
Cejka	$210,000	2.9
MDN	$208,000	10.1
Delta	$207,080	(2.4)
Medicus	$205,000	0
Jackson	$193,262	(26.5)
MGMA	$192,148	NA
HHCS	$191,828	8.2
Merritt	$189,000	1.6
Locum	$183,232	NA
Martin	$182,000	0
Pinnacle	$180,000	(22.3)
Hay	$173,800	(5.1)
Daniel	NA	NA

% change
2007-08

UROLOGY
Compensation ranges from $325,200 to $426,000

Pinnacle	$426,000	6.9%
Martin	$410,000	7.9
AMGA	$407,953	4.3
Medicus	$407,000	3
Pacific	$402,591	1
MDN	$393,000	4
MGMA	$388,125	NA
Merritt	$387,000	(3.3)
HHCS	$386,037	18.5
Delta	$383,161	(2.3)
Cejka	$382,000	15.8
Jackson	$340,616	(1.2)
Hay	$325,200	20.6
Daniel	NA	NA
Locum	NA	NA

% change
2007-08

Note: Figures represent average total annual cash compensation, which includes salary and bonuses. Percentages rounded. Zero percentage change indicates increase or decrease of less than 1%. NA = Not available.

Data trackers

Fifteen companies provided compensation data on up to 21 physician specialties

American Medical Group Association

The Alexandria, Va.-based trade group surveyed 44,600 physicians at 225 medical groups in 2007. The survey, which was conducted in partnership with RSM McGladrey, covers 215 positions/specialties and costs $550 for nonmembers. For more information contact Brad Vaudrey at 612-376-9530. Data submitted by the AMGA are preliminary and subject to change.

●●●

Cejka Search

The St. Louis-based physician and healthcare executive search firm surveyed 103 organizations and 220 physicians in 2007 covering 21 positions/specialties. Data submitted are a sample based on Cejka's proprietary database of completed searches from January to December 2007. Trend information by specialty and region is available on request. For more information contact Mary Scholz Barber at 314-236-4410.

●●●

Daniel Stern & Associates

The Pittsburgh-based physician-recruiting and consulting firm conducted its 2008 Emergency Physician Salary & Benefit Survey from January to April. Some 824 emergency medicine physicians were surveyed, and the cost for complete survey results is $395; national, regional and state-specific results are also available on request by contacting Daniel Stern at 800-438-2476.

●●●

Delta Physician Placement

The Dallas-based physician-staffing firm surveyed 639 organizations and 1,687 physicians in 50 positions/specialties from April 2007 to March 2008. Physician compensation data are compiled from both job offers and search assignments performed by the Delta Cos. nationwide on an annual basis. For more information about the company's free survey contact Mike Gianas at 800-521-5060, ext. 4113.

●●●

Hay Group

The Philadelphia-based consulting firm surveyed 108 organizations and some 14,000 physicians in 122 positions/specialties from June to August 2007. For more information on the Hay Group's physician compensation survey contact Nancy Kirby at 215-861-2828.

●●●

Hospital & Healthcare Compensation Service

The Oakland, N.J.-based consulting firm surveyed 334 organizations and 24,202 physicians in 44 positions/specialties from December 2007 to March 2008. Survey findings cost $295 and are available in Excel format as well. To order a copy call Erica Bednarz at 201-405-0075, ext. 13.

●●●

Jackson & Coker

The Alpharetta, Ga.-based physician-recruitment firm surveyed 943 physicians in 28 positions/specialties during March and April 2008. Survey findings are free of charge. For more information contact Edward McEachern at 800-272-2707.

LocumTenens.com

The Alpharetta, Ga.-based physician-recruiting agency surveyed 3,116 physicians in 49 positions/specialties during May 2008. Survey results are available free of charge by specialty. For more information call Christina Cruz at 770-643-5559.

●●●

Martin, Fletcher

The Irving, Texas-based healthcare staffing firm surveyed 1,620 organizations and 5,400 physicians in 17 positions/specialties from April 2007 to April 2008. Survey findings are available free of charge. For more information contact Christy Jones at 800-668-8822.

●●●

MD Network

The Dallas-based healthcare staffing firm surveyed 4,327 physicians and 1,276 senior-level administrative personnel in 29 specialties and subspecialties at hospitals and physician group practices in 2007. For more information contact Mark Valentine, medical director, at 800-705-7055.

●●●

Medical Group Management Association

The Englewood, Colo.-based professional membership association surveyed 1,943 organizations and 50,418 physicians in 105 positions/specialties from January to March. The full report, to be published sometime this month, can be ordered at mgma.com/physcomp. Data submitted are median figures.

●●●

Medicus Partners

The Dallas-based physician search firm surveyed 5,038 physicians in 19 positions/specialties during March. The survey was conducted via e-mail. Findings are available free of charge. For more information contact Jeff Katon at 888-260-4242, ext. 225.

●●●

Merritt, Hawkins & Associates

The Irving, Texas-based physician-recruitment firm surveyed 740 organizations and 3,146 physicians in 20 positions/specialties from April 2007 to March 2008. Survey results are available free of charge. For more information contact Stephanie Godwin at 800-876-0500.

●●●

Pacific Cos.

The Costa Mesa, Calif.-based healthcare staffing firm surveyed 948 organizations and 21,386 physicians in 26 positions/specialties from April 2007 to April 2008. For more information or to order a copy of the survey findings contact Michael Moore at 800-741-7629.

●●●

Pinnacle Health Group

The Atlanta-based physician recruitment firm surveyed 71 organizations and 150 physicians in 150 positions/specialties in 2007. Survey findings are available free of charge. For more information contact Craig Fowler at 800-492-7771, ext. 221.

Section III

Accredited Graduate Medical Education Programs

Introduction

This section of the *Directory* contains a list of graduate medical education (GME) programs accredited by the Accreditation Council for Graduate Medical Education (ACGME).

Programs are listed by specialty under the state and city of the sponsoring institution (refer to sample, below). Listed under the program name is the institution that sponsors the residency program, followed by the major participating institution(s), if any, which are recognized by at least one ACGME Residency Review Committee (RRC) as providing a major portion of required GME. Hospitals and other institutions that provide rotations of less than one-sixth of the program length or less than a total of 6 months are not listed in the *Directory*.

Listings contain the program director's name and program address, telephone and fax numbers, and e-mail address. Newly appointed program directors since the publication of last year's *Directory* are noted with an asterisk. Additional information on each program includes the ACGME-accredited length of the program and number of ACGME approved/offered positions. [*Note:* The published program length reflects the length approved by the RRC. The program may require or offer additional years; these data are included in FREIDA Online, at www.ama-assn.org/go/freida, and the *GME Library on CD-ROM*.] The program identification number appears at the bottom of each listing; the first three digits of this number indicate the specialty/subspecialty code (see "Specialties/Subspecialties with ACGME Program Requirements," p 177) and the next two the state code.

Sample Listing

Title of the Program

Sponsor: The program's sponsoring institution
The program's major participating institution(s) (if any)
Prgm Director: Name (* = new director since publication of last *Directory*)
Address
City, state, zip code
Telephone number, fax number
E-mail address
Length: Program length *ACGME Approved/Offered Positions:*
Program ID: 000-00-00-000

The Role of the ACGME

The population of programs listed in Section III is set by the ACGME, which shares with the AMA information about accreditation actions and other changes through regular electronic data transfers.

The *Directory*, as the official list of ACGME-accredited programs, generally reflects accreditation actions completed by December of the previous year. The data published in this edition were transferred from the ACGME to the AMA on January 15, 2009. *Programs with withdrawal dates after this date are included in Section III.* Readers are reminded that accreditation actions and related changes can alter the ACGME program population on a daily basis and that the *Directory* serves only as a "snapshot" of this population at a given moment. For updated information on ACGME-accredited programs, consult the ACGME Web site at www.acgme.org.

Preventive Medicine Programs

The preventive medicine programs listed in Section III include programs that offer areas of specialization in aerospace medicine, general preventive medicine, occupational medicine, and public health and general preventive medicine.

Programs

Transitional Year Programs

Transitional Year programs are available for physicians seeking broad clinical experience before entering GME in their chosen field or for physicians who have not yet decided on a medical specialty.

Combined Specialty Programs

Combined training consists of a coherent educational experience in two or more closely related specialty or subspecialty programs. The educational plan for combined training is approved by the specialty board of each of the specialties to assure that resident physicians completing combined training are eligible for board certification in each of the component specialties. Each specialty or subspecialty program is separately accredited by the ACGME through its respective Residency Review Committee (RRC). The duration of combined training is longer than any one of its component specialty programs standing alone, and shorter than all of its component specialty programs together. Applicants to combined specialty programs, listed in Appendix A, are encouraged to review requirements for admission to the certification process of each board (see Appendix B).

Restricted-entry GME Programs

Centers for Disease Control and Prevention Programs

GME programs at the Centers for Disease Control and Prevention (CDC) are usually open only to CDC physicians.

US Uniformed Services Programs

US Uniformed Services (Army, Navy, Air Force, Public Health Service) first-year GME positions are filled by graduates of accredited schools of medicine and osteopathic medicine. Only those individuals who have graduated from accredited US medical schools are eligible to apply for these first-year GME positions. The majority of the Uniformed Services' first-year GME positions are filled by individuals with an existing active duty service obligation. In most cases, only those individuals already serving in the Uniformed Services are eligible for appointment to military graduate year 2 and beyond residency positions. Graduates of non-US or non-Canadian medical schools are eligible to apply for graduate year 2 positions if they possess the standard ECFMG Certificate and have completed 1 year of GME training at an ACGME-accredited program.

It is important to note that an individual seeking to be trained in a Uniformed Services medical treatment facility must be qualified for appointment as a commissioned officer in the Uniformed Services. An active duty service obligation is required for participation in Uniformed Services GME training. Acceptance of GME applications from civilian applicants may vary among the four services. Selection priorities for Uniformed Services positions for year 2 and beyond are given to officers on active duty. For more information, interested individuals should contact their local Uniformed Services recruiting office.

In Section III, US Uniformed Services programs are identified with the text *US Uniformed Services Program*.

Programs on Probation

The *Directory* may include programs on probation. To check a program's current accreditation status, go to the ACGME Web site, www.acgme.org, click on "public," then click on "Search Through Accredited Programs and Sponsors" to look up information about programs and sponsors, including current accreditation status.

Disclaimer

It is the AMA's understanding that all institutions listed in the *Graduate Medical Education Directory* are required by law to include the phrase "EEO, M/F/D/V" on any information distributed for public view.

Sources for Additional Information

FREIDA Online (Fellowship and Residency Electronic Interactive Database Access), an Internet database available through the AMA home page at www.ama-assn.org/go/freida, offers additional information on GME programs. In addition, the *GME e-Letter*, a free monthly publication available via e-mail, offers news and updates on all facets of GME. See www.ama-assn.org/go/gmenews.

Specialties/Subspecialties With ACGME-accredited Programs

		Length(s)	GY1*	# of Prgms	
020	AI	2	N	73	Allergy and Immunology
040	AN	3 4	S	131	Anesthesiology
041	ACA	1	N	43	Adult Cardiothoracic Anesthesiology
042	PAN	1	N	45	Pediatric Anesthesiology
045	CCA	1	N	46	Critical Care Medicine
060	CRS	1	N	47	Colon and Rectal Surgery
080	D	3 4	S	111	Dermatology
081	PRD	1	N	36	Procedural Dermatology
100	DMP	1	N	54	Dermatopathology
110	EM	3 4	S	149	Emergency Medicine
114	PE	2	N	19	Pediatric Emergency Medicine
116	ESM	1	N	5	Sports Medicine
118	ETX	2	N	25	Medical Toxicology
119	UME	1	N	5	Undersea and Hyperbaric Medicine
120	FP	3	Y	456	Family Medicine
125	FPG	1	N	40	Geriatric Medicine
127	FSM	1	N	101	Sports Medicine
130	MG	2 4	S	49	Medical Genetics
131	MBG	1	N	4	Medical Biochemical Genetics
140	IM	3	Y	382	Internal Medicine
141	CD	3	N	179	Cardiovascular Disease
142	CCM	2	N	32	Critical Care Medicine
143	END	2	N	125	Endocrinology, Diabetes, and Metabolism
144	GE	3	N	154	Gastroenterology
145	HEM	2	N	8	Hematology
146	ID	2	N	143	Infectious Disease
147	ON	2	N	17	Oncology
148	NEP	2	N	141	Nephrology
149	PUD	2	N	23	Pulmonary Disease
150	RHU	2	N	109	Rheumatology
151	IMG	1	N	105	Geriatric Medicine
152	IC	1	N	133	Interventional Cardiology
154	ICE	1	N	96	Clinical Cardiac Electrophysiology
155	HO	3	N	128	Hematology and Oncology
156	PCC	3	N	133	Pulmonary Disease and Critical Care Medicine
158	THP	1	N	25	Transplant Hepatology
160	NS	5	S	99	Neurological Surgery
163	ESS	1	N	1	Endovascular Surgical Neuroradiology
180	N	3 4	S	126	Neurology
182	ENR	1	N	1	Endovascular Surgical Neuroradiology
183	NMN	1	N	21	Neuromuscular Medicine
185	CHN	3	N	69	Child Neurology
186	NDN	4	N	7	Neurodevelopmental Disabilities
187	CN	1	N	89	Clinical Neurophysiology
188	VN	1	N	60	Vascular Neurology
190	MGP	1	N	27	Molecular Genetic Pathology
200	NM	3	N	56	Nuclear Medicine
220	OBG	4	Y	249	Obstetrics and Gynecology
240	OPH	3	N	119	Ophthalmology
260	ORS	5	S	153	Orthopaedic Surgery
261	OAR	1	N	18	Adult Reconstructive Orthopaedics
262	OFA	1	N	9	Foot and Ankle Orthopaedics
263	HSO	1	N	56	Hand Surgery
265	OP	1	N	21	Pediatric Orthopaedics
267	OSS	1	N	13	Orthopaedic Surgery of the Spine
268	OSM	1	N	84	Orthopaedic Sports Medicine
269	OTR	1	N	7	Orthopaedic Trauma
270	OMO	1	N	10	Musculoskeletal Oncology
280	OTO	5	Y	103	Otolaryngology
286	NO	2	N	15	Neurotology
288	PDO	1	N	7	Pediatric Otolaryngology
300	PTH	3 4	Y	149	Pathology-Anatomic and Clinical

		Length(s)	GY1*	# of Prgms	
301	SP	1	N	59	Selective Pathology
305	BBK	1	N	47	Blood Banking/Transfusion Medicine
306	PCH	1	N	2	Chemical Pathology
307	PCP	1	N	87	Cytopathology
310	FOP	1	N	38	Forensic Pathology
311	HMP	1	N	79	Hematology
314	MM	1	N	13	Medical Microbiology
315	NP	2	N	35	Neuropathology
316	PP	1	N	25	Pediatric Pathology
320	PD	3	Y	194	Pediatrics
321	ADL	3	N	26	Adolescent Medicine
323	CCP	3	N	61	Pediatric Critical Care Medicine
324	PEM	3	N	46	Pediatric Emergency Medicine
325	PDC	3	N	49	Pediatric Cardiology
326	PDE	3	N	67	Pediatric Endocrinology
327	PHO	3	N	66	Pediatric Hematology/Oncology
328	PN	3	N	38	Pediatric Nephrology
329	NPM	3	N	97	Neonatal-Perinatal Medicine
330	PDP	3	N	47	Pediatric Pulmonology
331	PPR	3	N	28	Pediatric Rheumatology
332	PG	3	N	54	Pediatric Gastroenterology
333	PSM	1	N	9	Pediatric Sports Medicine
335	PDI	3	N	61	Pediatric Infectious Diseases
336	DBP	3	N	37	Developmental-Behavioral Pediatrics
338	PTP	1	N	4	Pediatric Transplant Hepatology
340	PM	3 4	S	79	Physical Medicine and Rehabilitation
345	SCI	1	N	19	Spinal Cord Injury Medicine
346	RPM	2	N	13	Pediatric Rehabilitation Medicine
360	PS	2 3	N	74	Plastic Surgery
361	CFS	1	N	4	Craniofacial Surgery
362	PSI	5 6	Y	29	Plastic Surgery-Integrated
363	HSP	1	N	14	Hand Surgery
380	GPM	1 2 3	S		Preventive Medicine
		1 2	N	4	Aerospace Medicine
		1 2 3	S	22	General Preventive Medicine
		1 2 3	S	28	Occupational Medicine
		1 2	S	15	Public Health and General Preventive Medicine
398	UM	1	N	1	Undersea and Hyperbaric Medicine
399	PTX	2	N	2	Medical Toxicology
400	P	4	Y	182	Psychiatry
401	ADP	1	N	42	Addiction Psychiatry
405	CHP	2	N	122	Child and Adolescent Psychiatry
406	PFP	1	N	40	Forensic Psychiatry
407	PYG	1	N	57	Geriatric Psychiatry
409	PYM	1	N	40	Psychosomatic Medicine
420	DR	4	S	188	Radiology-Diagnostic
421	AR	1	N	12	Abdominal Radiology
422	ESN	1	N	3	Endovascular Surgical Neuroradiology
423	RNR	1	N	85	Neuroradiology
424	PDR	1	N	45	Pediatric Radiology
425	NR	1	N	24	Nuclear Radiology
426	MSR	1	N	13	Musculoskeletal Radiology
427	VIR	1	N	93	Vascular and Interventional Radiology
429	CTR	1	N	2	Cardiothoracic Radiology
430	RO	4	N	81	Radiation Oncology
440	GS	5	Y	249	Surgery-General
442	CCS	1	N	95	Surgical Critical Care
443	HSS	1	N	1	Hand Surgery
445	PDS	2	N	37	Pediatric Surgery
450	VS	1 2 3	N	97	Vascular Surgery
451	VSI	5	Y	16	Vascular Surgery-Integrated
460	TS	2 3	N	76	Thoracic Surgery
461	TSI	6	Y	3	Thoracic Surgery-Integrated
466	CHS	1	N	9	Congenital Cardiac Surgery
480	U	3 4	N	119	Urology
485	UP	1	N	22	Pediatric Urology
520	SME	1	N	67	Sleep Medicine
530	PMM	1	N	93	Pain Medicine
540	HPM	1	N	48	Hospice and Palliative Medicine
700	MPD	4	Y	80	Internal Medicine/Pediatrics
999	TY	1	Y	120	Transitional Year
				8,675	**Total**

*Y = Graduate year 1 positions available
N = No GY1 positions available
S = Some programs may offer GY1 positions

Programs

Abdominal Radiology (Radiology-Diagnostic)

Georgia

Atlanta

Emory University Program
Sponsor: Emory University School of Medicine
Emory University Hospital
Grady Health System
Prgm Director: Deborah A Baumgarten, MD, MPH
1364 Clifton Road, NE
Atlanta, GA 30322
Tel: 404 778-3800   *Fax:* 404 778-3080
E-mail: deborah.baumgarten@emory.org
Length: 1 Yr   *ACGME Approved/Offered Positions:* 5
Program ID: 421-12-31-002

Illinois

Chicago

University of Chicago Program
Sponsor: University of Chicago Medical Center
Prgm Director: Abraham H Dachman, MD
5841 S Maryland Avenue, MC 2026
Chicago, IL 60637
Tel: 773 702-3550   *Fax:* 773 834-6237
E-mail: mvelligan@radiology.bsd.uchicago.edu
Length: 1 Yr   *ACGME Approved/Offered Positions:* 2
Program ID: 421-16-13-006

Massachusetts

Boston

Beth Israel Deaconess Medical Center Program
Sponsor: Beth Israel Deaconess Medical Center
Prgm Director: Jonathan B Kruskal, MD, PhD
One Deaconess Road
Boston, MA 02215
Tel: 617 667-2523   *Fax:* 617 754-2545
Length: 1 Yr   *ACGME Approved/Offered Positions:* 6
Program ID: 421-24-21-003

Brigham and Women's Hospital/Harvard Medical School Program
Sponsor: Brigham and Women's Hospital
Prgm Director: Stuart G Silverman, MD
75 Francis Street
Boston, MA 02115
Tel: 617 732-6299   *Fax:* 617 732-6317
E-mail: sgsilverman@partners.org
Length: 1 Yr   *ACGME Approved/Offered Positions:* 6
Program ID: 421-24-31-010

Minnesota

Rochester

College of Medicine, Mayo Clinic (Rochester) Program
Sponsor: College of Medicine, Mayo Clinic
Mayo Clinic (Rochester)
Rochester Methodist Hospital
Saint Marys Hospital of Rochester
Prgm Director: Grant D Schmit, MD
200 First Street, SW
Rochester, MN 55905
Tel: 507 284-0440   *Fax:* 507 266-4735
E-mail: sorenson.tammy@mayo.edu
Length: 1 Yr   *ACGME Approved/Offered Positions:* 4
Program ID: 421-26-31-004

New York

Bronx

Albert Einstein College of Medicine Program
Sponsor: Albert Einstein College of Medicine of Yeshiva
  University
Montefiore Medical Center-Weiler Division
Prgm Director: Alla Rozenblit, MD
Dept of Radiology
111 East 210th Street
Bronx, NY 10467
Tel: 718 920-4396   *Fax:* 718 920-4854
E-mail: eofrias@montefiore.org
Length: 1 Yr   *ACGME Approved/Offered Positions:* 1
Program ID: 421-35-21-001

New York

Albert Einstein College of Medicine at Beth Israel Medical Center Program
Sponsor: Beth Israel Medical Center
Prgm Director: Mitchell A Horowitz, MD
Department of Radiology
First Avenue at 16th Street
New York, NY 10003
Tel: 212 420-2546   *Fax:* 212 420-2510
E-mail: mhorowitz@chpnet.org
Length: 1 Yr   *ACGME Approved/Offered Positions:* 2
Program ID: 421-35-11-007

Stony Brook

SUNY at Stony Brook Program
Sponsor: University Hospital - SUNY at Stony Brook
Prgm Director: Harris L Cohen, MD
Department of Radiology
Health Sciences Center, Level 4 - Room 120
Stony Brook, NY 11794
Tel: 631 444-2484   *Fax:* 631 444-7538
E-mail: sbuh_radiol@notes.cc.sunysb.edu
Length: 1 Yr   *ACGME Approved/Offered Positions:* 2
Program ID: 421-35-21-009

North Carolina

Winston-Salem

Wake Forest University School of Medicine Program
Sponsor: Wake Forest University Baptist Medical Center
Prgm Director: Robert E Bechtold, MD
Department of Radiology
Medical Center Boulevard
Winston-Salem, NC 27157
Tel: 336 716-2471   *Fax:* 336 716-0555
Length: 1 Yr   *ACGME Approved/Offered Positions:* 4
Program ID: 421-36-12-005

Pennsylvania

Philadelphia

Thomas Jefferson University Program
Sponsor: Thomas Jefferson University Hospital
Prgm Director: Ethan J Halpern, MD
132 S 10th Street
763J Main Building
Philadelphia, PA 19107
Tel: 215 955-5345   *Fax:* 215 955-8549
E-mail: ethan.halpern@jefferson.edu
Length: 1 Yr   *ACGME Approved/Offered Positions:* 8
Program ID: 421-41-12-011

University of Pennsylvania Program
Sponsor: University of Pennsylvania Health System
Prgm Director: Beverly G Coleman, MD
HUP, 1 Silverstein
3400 Spruce Street
Philadelphia, PA 19104
Tel: 215 662-3466   *Fax:* 215 349-5627
Length: 1 Yr   *ACGME Approved/Offered Positions:* 8
Program ID: 421-41-13-008

Washington

Seattle

University of Washington Program
Sponsor: University of Washington School of Medicine
University of Washington Medical Center
Prgm Director: Mariam Moshiri, MD
1959 NE Pacific Street
Box 357115
Seattle, WA 98195
Tel: 206 598-0024   *Fax:* 206 598-0252
Length: 1 Yr   *ACGME Approved/Offered Positions:* 6
Program ID: 421-54-13-012

Note: * indicates a newly appointed program director

Addiction Psychiatry (Psychiatry)

Arkansas

Little Rock

University of Arkansas for Medical Sciences Program
Sponsor: University of Arkansas College of Medicine
Central Arkansas Veterans Healthcare System
UAMS Medical Center
Prgm Director: Annette S Slater, MD
4301 West Markham
Slot 550
Little Rock, AR 72205
Tel: 501 257-3131   *Fax:* 501 257-3164
E-mail: annette.slater@va.gov
Length: 1 Yr   *ACGME Approved/Offered Positions:* 1
Program ID: 401-04-13-056

California

Los Angeles

Cedars-Sinai Medical Center Program
Sponsor: Cedars-Sinai Medical Center
Los Angeles County-Harbor-UCLA Medical Center
Prgm Director: Jeffery N Wilkins, MD
8730 Alden Drive
Suite C-301
Los Angeles, CA 90048
Tel: 310 423-2600   *Fax:* 310 423-8397
E-mail: wilkinsj@cshs.org
Length: 1 Yr   *ACGME Approved/Offered Positions:* 2
Program ID: 401-05-11-051

Colorado

Aurora

University of Colorado Denver Program
Sponsor: University of Colorado Denver School of
  Medicine
Denver Health Medical Center
University of Colorado Hospital
Veterans Affairs Medical Center (Denver)
Prgm Director: Jonathan I Ritvo, MD
13001 E 17th Pl, Bldg 500, Rm E2328
Campus Box F546, PO Box 6508
Aurora, CO 80045
Tel: 720 848-3000   *Fax:* 720 848-3001
E-mail: jonathan.ritvo@uchsc.edu
Length: 1 Yr   *ACGME Approved/Offered Positions:* 3
Program ID: 401-07-21-006

Connecticut

New Haven

Yale-New Haven Medical Center Program
Sponsor: Yale-New Haven Hospital
APT Foundation, Inc Substance Abuse Treatment
Connecticut Mental Health Center
Veterans Affairs Medical Center (West Haven)
Prgm Director: Ismene L Petrakis, MD
950 Campbell Avenue
Bldg 1, 8 East
West Haven, CT 06516
Tel: 203 932-5711   *Fax:* 203 937-4791
E-mail: ismene.petrakis@yale.edu
Length: 1 Yr   *ACGME Approved/Offered Positions:* 6
Program ID: 401-08-21-016

Florida

Miami

Jackson Memorial Hospital/Jackson Health System Program
Sponsor: Jackson Memorial Hospital/Jackson Health
  System
Prgm Director: Lauren D Williams, MD
1695 NW 9th Ave
Miami, FL 33136
Tel: 305 243-4644   *Fax:* 305 243-2599
Length: 1 Yr   *ACGME Approved/Offered Positions:* 3
Program ID: 401-11-21-029

Tampa

University of South Florida Program
Sponsor: University of South Florida College of Medicine
James A Haley Veterans Hospital
Prgm Director: Elie M Francis, MD
13000 Bruce B Downs Boulevard
116A
Tampa, FL 33612
Tel: 813 631-7126   *Fax:* 813 631-7129
E-mail: Elie.Francis@va.gov
Length: 1 Yr   *ACGME Approved/Offered Positions:* 2
Program ID: 401-11-21-034

Georgia

Atlanta

Emory University Program
Sponsor: Emory University School of Medicine
Grady Health System
Veterans Affairs Medical Center (Atlanta)
Prgm Director: Karen P Drexler, MD
VAMC-Atlanta, Mental Health Service/116A
1670 Clairmont Road
Decatur, GA 30033
Tel: 404 321-6111   *Fax:* 404 329-4643
E-mail: acromwe@emory.edu
Length: 1 Yr   *ACGME Approved/Offered Positions:* 2
Program ID: 401-12-21-050

Hawaii

Honolulu

University of Hawaii Program
Sponsor: University of Hawaii John A Burns School of
  Medicine
Hawaii State Hospital
Queen's Medical Center
Tripler Army Medical Center
Prgm Director: William Haning III, MD
1356 Lusitana Street, 4th Floor
Honolulu, HI 96813
Tel: 808 586-7445   *Fax:* 808 586-2940
E-mail: iidad@dop.hawaii.edu
Length: 1 Yr   *ACGME Approved/Offered Positions:* 4
Program ID: 401-14-21-033

Illinois

Chicago

McGaw Medical Center of Northwestern University Program
Sponsor: McGaw Medical Center of Northwestern
  University
Jesse Brown Veterans Affairs Medical Center
Northwestern Memorial Hospital
Women's Treatment Center
Prgm Director: Seth Eisenberg, MD
Department of Psychiatry, Suite 7-200
446 E Ontario
Chicago, IL 60611
Tel: 312 695-5060   *Fax:* 312 926-7612
E-mail: seisenbe@nmh.org
Length: 1 Yr   *ACGME Approved/Offered Positions:* 2
Program ID: 401-16-21-009

University of Illinois College of Medicine at Chicago Program
Sponsor: University of Illinois College of Medicine at
  Chicago
Advocate Lutheran General Hospital
Jesse Brown Veterans Affairs Medical Center
University of Illinois Hospital and Clinics
Prgm Director: Rodney I Eiger, MD
Department of Psychiatry (M/C 913)
912 South Wood Street
Chicago, IL 60612
Tel: 312 213-9331
E-mail: rodney.eiger@med.va.gov
Length: 1 Yr   *ACGME Approved/Offered Positions:* 1
Program ID: 401-16-21-012

Indiana

Indianapolis

Indiana University School of Medicine Program
Sponsor: Indiana University School of Medicine
Richard L Roudebush Veterans Affairs Medical Center
William N Wishard Memorial Hospital
Prgm Director: Alan D Schmetzer, MD
Department of Psychiatry
1111 W 10th Street, PB A208
Indianapolis, IN 46202
Tel: 317 274-1224   *Fax:* 317 274-1248
E-mail: lgoudrea@iupui.edu
Length: 1 Yr   *ACGME Approved/Offered Positions:* 2
Program ID: 401-17-21-030

Kansas

Kansas City

University of Kansas School of Medicine Program

Sponsor: University of Kansas School of Medicine
Johnson County Mental Health Center
University of Kansas Medical Center
Veterans Affairs Medical Center (Kansas City)
Prgm Director: Jan L Campbell, MD
3901 Rainbow Boulevard
Kansas City, KS 66160
Tel: 913 588-6412   *Fax:* 913 588-6414
E-mail: jcampbell2@kumc.edu
Length: 1 Yr   *ACGME Approved/Offered Positions:* 1
Program ID: 401-19-31-053

Kentucky

Louisville

University of Louisville Program

Sponsor: University of Louisville School of Medicine
Central State Hospital
Seven Counties Services (Louisville)
Veterans Affairs Medical Center (Louisville)
Prgm Director: Christopher Stewart, MD*
Department of Psychiatry
c/o Chris Stewart, MD
Louisville, KY 40202
Tel: 502 296-7790   *Fax:* 502 813-6665
Length: 1 Yr   *ACGME Approved/Offered Positions:* 2
Program ID: 401-20-21-036

Maryland

Baltimore

University of Maryland/Sheppard Pratt Program

Sponsor: University of Maryland Medical System
Veterans Affairs Medical Center (Baltimore)
Prgm Director: Devang H Gandhi, MBBS, MD
Department of Psychiatry
701 W Pratt Street, Room 597
Baltimore, MD 21201
Tel: 410 328-5093   *Fax:* 410 328-1749
E-mail: dgandhi@psych.umaryland.edu
Length: 1 Yr   *ACGME Approved/Offered Positions:* 4
Program ID: 401-23-21-002

Massachusetts

Boston

Boston University Medical Center Program

Sponsor: Boston Medical Center
Brigham and Women's Hospital
Edith Nourse Rogers Memorial Veterans Hospital
   (Bedford)
Veterans Affairs Medical Center (Boston)
Prgm Director: John A Renner Jr, MD
251 Causeway Street
Boston, MA 02114
Tel: 617 248-1022   *Fax:* 617 248-1121
Length: 1 Yr   *ACGME Approved/Offered Positions:* 3
Program ID: 401-24-21-019

Massachusetts General Hospital/McLean Hospital Program

Sponsor: Massachusetts General Hospital
Brigham and Women's Hospital
Cambridge Health Alliance
McLean Hospital
Prgm Director: Shelly F Greenfield, MD, MPH
Alcohol & Drug Abuse Treatment Program
115 Mill Street, Proctor House
Belmont, MA 02478
Tel: 617 855-2241   *Fax:* 617 855-2699
E-mail: shelly_greenfield@hms.harvard.edu
Length: 1 Yr   *ACGME Approved/Offered Positions:* 3
Program ID: 401-24-31-037

Worcester

University of Massachusetts Program

Sponsor: University of Massachusetts Medical School
Community Healthlink
UMass Memorial Health Care (University Campus)
Prgm Director: Gerardo Gonzalez, MD
55 Lake Avenue North
Worcester, MA 01655
Tel: 508 856-6480   *Fax:* 508 856-8376
E-mail: Diana.Langford@umassmemorial.org
Length: 1 Yr   *ACGME Approved/Offered Positions:* 2
Program ID: 401-24-13-063

Michigan

Ann Arbor

University of Michigan Program

Sponsor: University of Michigan Hospitals and Health
   Centers
Veterans Affairs Medical Center (Ann Arbor)
Prgm Director: Iyad Alkhouri, MD*
Rachel Upjohn Building
4250 Plymouth Rd
Ann Arbor, MI 48109
Tel: 734 232-0464   *Fax:* 734 232-0244
Length: 1 Yr   *ACGME Approved/Offered Positions:* 2
Program ID: 401-25-21-022

Detroit

Wayne State University/Detroit Medical Center Program

Sponsor: Wayne State University/Detroit Medical Center
Jefferson Avenue Research Clinic
Sinai-Grace Hospital
Veterans Affairs Medical Center (Detroit)
Prgm Director: Susan M Stine, MD, PhD
Psychiatry & Behavioral Neurosciences
2761 E Jefferson Avenue
Detroit, MI 48207
Tel: 313 993-9879   *Fax:* 313 993-1372
E-mail: sstine@med.wayne.edu
Length: 1 Yr   *ACGME Approved/Offered Positions:* 2
Program ID: 401-25-21-038

Minnesota

Minneapolis

University of Minnesota Program

Sponsor: University of Minnesota Medical School
University of Minnesota Medical Center, Division of
   Fairview
Veterans Affairs Medical Center (Minneapolis)
Prgm Director: Scott L McNairy, MD
F282/2A West
2450 Riverside Avenue
Minneapolis, MN 55454
Tel: 612 467-4025   *Fax:* 612 467-1119
E-mail: scott.mcnairy@va.gov
Length: 1 Yr   *ACGME Approved/Offered Positions:* 2
Program ID: 401-26-21-003

Rochester

College of Medicine, Mayo Clinic (Rochester) Program

Sponsor: College of Medicine, Mayo Clinic
Saint Marys Hospital of Rochester
Prgm Director: Daniel K Hall-Flavin, MD
200 First Street SW
Rochester, MN 55905
Tel: 507 284-0325   *Fax:* 507 284-4345
E-mail: mgsm.roch.mn.psychiatry@mayo.edu
Length: 1 Yr   *ACGME Approved/Offered Positions:* 1
Program ID: 401-26-21-031

Nebraska

Omaha

Creighton University/University of Nebraska Program

Sponsor: Creighton University School of Medicine
Nebraska Medical Center
Veterans Affairs Medical Center (Omaha)
Prgm Director: S Pirzada Sattar, MD
4101 Woolworth Avenue, 116A
Omaha, NE 68105
Tel: 402 346-8800   *Fax:* 402 977-5684
E-mail: syed.sattar@va.gov
Length: 1 Yr   *ACGME Approved/Offered Positions:* 2
Program ID: 401-30-31-055

New Hampshire

Lebanon

Dartmouth-Hitchcock Medical Center Program

Sponsor: Mary Hitchcock Memorial Hospital
Veterans Affairs Medical Center (White River Junction)
Prgm Director: Donald A West, MD, MA
1 Medical Center Drive
Lebanon, NH 03756
Tel: 603 650-5805   *Fax:* 603 650-7820
E-mail: Donald.West@dartmouth.edu
Length: 1 Yr   *ACGME Approved/Offered Positions:* 2
Program ID: 401-32-21-024

Note: * indicates a newly appointed program director

New Mexico

Albuquerque

University of New Mexico Program
Sponsor: University of New Mexico School of Medicine
University of New Mexico Hospital
Veterans Affairs Medical Center (Albuquerque)
Prgm Director: Michael Bogenschutz, MD
MSC09 5030
1 University of New Mexico
Albuquerque, NM 87131
Tel: 505 272-8428   *Fax:* 505 272-4921
Length: 1 Yr   *ACGME Approved/Offered Positions:* 2
Program ID: 401-34-22-052

New York

Bronx

Albert Einstein College of Medicine at Bronx-Lebanon Hospital Center Program
Sponsor: Bronx-Lebanon Hospital Center
Prgm Director: John Osei-Tutu, MD
1276 Fulton Avenue
MMTP
Bronx, NY 10456
Tel: 718 901-6133   *Fax:* 718 901-6356
E-mail: joseitut@bronxleb.org
Length: 1 Yr   *ACGME Approved/Offered Positions:* 3
Program ID: 401-35-31-017

Albert Einstein College of Medicine Program
Sponsor: Albert Einstein College of Medicine of Yeshiva
   University
Bronx-Lebanon Hospital Center
Melrose-On-Track (MOT) Clinic
Montefiore Medical Center-Henry and Lucy Moses
   Division
Sound View Throgs Neck Community Mental Health
   Center
Prgm Director: Merrill Herman, MD
Department of Psychiatry and Behavioral Sciences
1300 Morris Park Ave Belfer 403
Bronx, NY 10461
Tel: 718 430-3080   *Fax:* 718 430-8987
E-mail: mherman@montefiore.org
Length: 1 Yr   *ACGME Approved/Offered Positions:* 3
Program ID: 401-35-21-023

Great Neck

NSLIJHS-North Shore University Hospital/NYU School of Medicine Program
Sponsor: North Shore-Long Island Jewish Health System
Flushing Hospital Medical Center
North Shore University Hospital
Prgm Director: Charles Jin, MD
400 Community Drive
Manhasset, NY 11030
Tel: 516 562-3010
Length: 1 Yr   *ACGME Approved/Offered Positions:* 2
Program ID: 401-35-31-007

New York

Albert Einstein College of Medicine at Beth Israel Medical Center Program
Sponsor: Beth Israel Medical Center
Prgm Director: James P Wolberg, MD, MS
1st Ave at 16th Street
8 Bernstein
New York, NY 10003
Tel: 212 420-4566   *Fax:* 212 420-2181
E-mail: jwolberg@chpnet.org
Length: 1 Yr   *ACGME Approved/Offered Positions:* 3
Program ID: 401-35-21-010

Mount Sinai School of Medicine Program
Sponsor: Mount Sinai School of Medicine
Mount Sinai Medical Center
Veterans Affairs Medical Center (Bronx)
Prgm Director: Michael M Scimeca, MD
One Gustave Levy Place
Box 1230
New York, NY 10029
Tel: 212 580-9605   *Fax:* 212 849-2809
E-mail: scimecas@aol.com
Length: 1 Yr   *ACGME Approved/Offered Positions:* 3
Program ID: 401-35-31-046

New York Presbyterian Hospital (Columbia Campus)/New York State Psychiatric Institute Program
Sponsor: New York Presbyterian Hospital
New York Presbyterian Hospital (Columbia Campus)
New York State Psychiatric Institute
Prgm Director: Frances R Levin, MD
1051 Riverside Drive, Unit 66
New York, NY 10032
Tel: 212 543-5896   *Fax:* 212 543-6018
E-mail: frl2@columbia.edu
Length: 2 Yrs   *ACGME Approved/Offered Positions:* 6
Program ID: 401-35-21-032

New York University School of Medicine Program
Sponsor: New York University School of Medicine
Bellevue Hospital Center
Prgm Director: Marc Galanter, MD
550 First Avenue
New York, NY 10016
Tel: 212 263-6960   *Fax:* 212 263-8285
Length: 1 Yr   *ACGME Approved/Offered Positions:* 4
Program ID: 401-35-21-004

Ohio

Cincinnati

University Hospital/University of Cincinnati College of Medicine Program
Sponsor: University Hospital Inc
Veterans Affairs Medical Center (Cincinnati)
Prgm Director: Shannon Miller, MD*
231 Albert Sabin Way
ML 0559
Cincinnati, OH 45267
Tel: 513 861-3100   *Fax:* 513 487-6046
E-mail: kathleen.peak@va.gov
Length: 1 Yr   *ACGME Approved/Offered Positions:* 2
Program ID: 401-38-21-013

Cleveland

University Hospitals Case Medical Center Program
Sponsor: University Hospitals Case Medical Center
Veterans Affairs Medical Center (Cleveland)
Prgm Director: Christina M Delos Reyes, MD
Department of Psychiatry - W O Walker Center
10524 Euclid Avenue
Cleveland, OH 44106
Tel: 216 844-7661   *Fax:* 216 983-5131
E-mail: kate.kilbane@UHhospitals.org
Length: 1 Yr   *ACGME Approved/Offered Positions:* 3
Program ID: 401-38-21-039

Oregon

Portland

Oregon Health & Science University Program
Sponsor: Oregon Health & Science University Hospital
Veterans Affairs Medical Center (Portland)
Prgm Director: Michael P Resnick, MD
3181 SW Sam Jackson Park Road, UHN-80
Portland, OR 97239
Tel: 503 220-8262   *Fax:* 503 494-6152
Length: 1 Yr   *ACGME Approved/Offered Positions:* 2
Program ID: 401-40-31-042

Pennsylvania

Philadelphia

University of Pennsylvania Program
Sponsor: University of Pennsylvania Health System
Prgm Director: Kyle Kampman, MD
3900 Chestnut Street
Philadelphia, PA 19104
Tel: 215 222-3200   *Fax:* 215 386-6770
E-mail: kampman_k@mail.trc.upenn.edu
Length: 1 Yr   *ACGME Approved/Offered Positions:* 4
Program ID: 401-41-21-011

Pittsburgh

University of Pittsburgh Medical Center Medical Education Program
Sponsor: Univ of Pittsburgh Medical Center Medical
   Education
UPMC Western Psychiatric Institute and Clinic
Veterans Affairs Medical Center (Pittsburgh)
Prgm Director: Antoine Douaihy, MD
3811 O'Hara Street
Room 1059
Pittsburgh, PA 15213
Tel: 412 586-9537   *Fax:* 412 246-5980
Length: 1 Yr   *ACGME Approved/Offered Positions:* 2
Program ID: 401-41-21-058

South Carolina

Charleston

Medical University of South Carolina Program
Sponsor: Medical University of South Carolina College of
   Medicine
Charleston Center of Charleston County
MUSC Medical Center
Ralph H Johnson VA Medical Center (Charleston)
Prgm Director: Tara M Wright, MD, BA*
Clinical Neuroscience Division
67 President Street, PO Box 250861
Charleston, SC 29425
Tel: 843 789-7311
E-mail: wright@musc.edu
Length: 1 Yr   *ACGME Approved/Offered Positions:* 3
Program ID: 401-45-21-014

Tennessee

Nashville

Vanderbilt University Program
Sponsor: Vanderbilt University Medical Center
Prgm Director: Peter R martin, MD
1601 21st Ave S, Ste 3068
Nashville, TN 37212
Tel: 615 322-3527   *Fax:* 615 322-0175
E-mail: peter.martin@vanderbilt.edu
Length: 1 Yr   *ACGME Approved/Offered Positions:* 2
Program ID: 401-47-21-015

Texas

Dallas

University of Texas Southwestern Medical School Program
Sponsor: University of Texas Southwestern Medical
   School
Dallas VA Medical Center
Prgm Director: Sidarth Wakhlu, MBBS
Dept of Mental Health (116A5)
4500 S Lancaster Road
Dallas, TX 75216
Tel: 214 857-0866
Length: 1 Yr   *ACGME Approved/Offered Positions:* 2
Program ID: 401-48-21-028

Houston

Baylor College of Medicine Program
Sponsor: Baylor College of Medicine
Michael E DeBakey VA Medical Center - Houston
The Menninger Clinic (Houston)
Prgm Director: Nancy Rubio, MD
2002 Holcombe Boulevard
Houston, TX 77030
Tel: 713 794-8700   *Fax:* 713 794-7917
E-mail: rubio.nancyb@med.va.gov
Length: 1 Yr   *ACGME Approved/Offered Positions:* 2
Program ID: 401-48-31-064

Washington

Seattle

University of Washington Program
Sponsor: University of Washington School of Medicine
VA Puget Sound Health Care System
Prgm Director: Andrew J Saxon, MD
1660 South Columbia Way 116ATC
Seattle, WA 98108
Tel: 206 764-2782
Length: 1 Yr   *ACGME Approved/Offered Positions:* 3
Program ID: 401-54-21-005

Wisconsin

Madison

University of Wisconsin Program
Sponsor: University of Wisconsin Hospital and Clinics
Meriter Hospital
William S Middleton Veterans Hospital
Prgm Director: Dean D Krahn, MD
Mental Health Services
2500 Overlook Terrace
Madison, WI 53705
Tel: 608 280-7015   *Fax:* 608 280-7203
E-mail: dean.krahn@va.gov
Length: 1 Yr   *ACGME Approved/Offered Positions:* 2
Program ID: 401-56-12-057

Adolescent Medicine (Pediatrics)

Alabama

Birmingham

University of Alabama Medical Center Program
Sponsor: University of Alabama Hospital
Children's Hospital of Alabama
Department of Youth Service (Chalkville)
Department of Youth Services (VACCA)
Family Court of Jefferson County
Prgm Director: Marsha S Sturdevant, MD
1616 6th Avenue South
Midtown Center, Suite 201
Birmingham, AL 35233
Tel: 205 934-5262   *Fax:* 205 975-6503
Length: 3 Yrs   *ACGME Approved/Offered Positions:* 1
Program ID: 321-01-31-028

California

Los Angeles

Childrens Hospital Los Angeles Program
Sponsor: Childrens Hospital Los Angeles
Prgm Director: Johanna L Olson, MD, BA*
4650 Sunset Blvd Mailstop #2
Los Angeles, CA 90027
Tel: 323 361-2153   *Fax:* 323 953-8116
E-mail: jolson@chla.usc.edu
Length: 3 Yrs   *ACGME Approved/Offered Positions:* 3
Program ID: 321-05-21-018

San Francisco

University of California (San Francisco) Program
Sponsor: University of California (San Francisco) School
   of Medicine
Treasure Island Job Corps
UCSF and Mount Zion Medical Centers
Prgm Director: Charles E Irwin Jr, MD
3333 California Street, Suite 245, Box 0503
San Francisco, CA 94118
Tel: 415 476-2184   *Fax:* 415 476-6106
E-mail: irwinch@peds.ucsf.edu
Length: 3 Yrs   *ACGME Approved/Offered Positions:* 6
Program ID: 321-05-11-005

Stanford

Stanford University Program
Sponsor: Stanford Hospital and Clinics
Lucile Salter Packard Children's Hospital at Stanford
Prgm Director: Neville H Golden, MD
Division of Adolescent Medicine
1174 Castro Street Suite 250-A
Mountain View, CA 94040
Tel: 650 694-0660   *Fax:* 650 694-0664
E-mail: ana.fraser@stanford.edu
Length: 3 Yrs   *ACGME Approved/Offered Positions:* 3
Program ID: 321-05-31-021

Note: * indicates a newly appointed program director

Colorado

Aurora

University of Colorado Denver Program
Sponsor: University of Colorado Denver School of
 Medicine
Children's Hospital (The)
Prgm Director: Eric J Sigel, MD
Adolescent Medicine
13123 East 16th Avenue, B025
Aurora, CO 80045
Tel: 720 777-6133   *Fax:* 720 777-7339
Length: 3 Yrs   *ACGME Approved/Offered Positions:* 3
Program ID: 321-07-21-025

District of Columbia

Washington

**Children's National Medical Center/
George Washington University Program**
Sponsor: Children's National Medical Center
Prgm Director: Tomas J Silber, MD, MA
111 Michigan Avenue NW
Washington, DC 20010
Tel: 202 476-3066   *Fax:* 202 476-3630
Length: 3 Yrs   *ACGME Approved/Offered Positions:* 5
Program ID: 321-10-21-020

Florida

Miami

Miami Children's Hospital Program
Sponsor: Miami Children's Hospital
Prgm Director: Lorena M Siqueira, MD, MSPH
3100 SW 62nd Avenue Ste 109
Miami, FL 33155
Tel: 786 624-3026   *Fax:* 786 624-3029
Length: 3 Yrs   *ACGME Approved/Offered Positions:* 3
Program ID: 321-11-22-031

Indiana

Indianapolis

**Indiana University School of Medicine
Program**
Sponsor: Indiana University School of Medicine
Clarian Riley Hospital for Children
Prgm Director: Donald P Orr, MD
Health Information & Translational Sciences, 1001
410 W 10th Street
Indianapolis, IN 46202
Tel: 317 274-8812   *Fax:* 317 274-0133
Length: 3 Yrs   *ACGME Approved/Offered Positions:* 3
Program ID: 321-17-21-006

Maryland

Baltimore

Johns Hopkins University Program
Sponsor: Johns Hopkins University School of Medicine
Johns Hopkins Hospital
Prgm Director: Jonathan M Ellen, MD
200 N Wolfe Street, Room 2065
Baltimore, MD 21287
Tel: 410 550-4115   *Fax:* 410 955-4079
E-mail: jellen@jhmi.edu
Length: 3 Yrs   *ACGME Approved/Offered Positions:* 3
Program ID: 321-23-21-007

Massachusetts

Boston

**Children's Hospital/Boston Medical
Center Program**
Sponsor: Children's Hospital
Prgm Director: S Jean Emans, MD
300 Longwood Avenue
Boston, MA 02115
Tel: 617 355-7170   *Fax:* 617 730-0185
E-mail: jean.emans@childrens.harvard.edu
Length: 3 Yrs   *ACGME Approved/Offered Positions:* 9
Program ID: 321-24-21-002

Minnesota

Minneapolis

University of Minnesota Program
Sponsor: University of Minnesota Medical School
University of Minnesota Medical Center, Division of
 Fairview
Prgm Director: Nimi Singh, MD, MPH
717 Delaware St SE
3rd Floor West
Minneapolis, MN 55414
Tel: 612 625-5497   *Fax:* 612 626-2134
Length: 3 Yrs   *ACGME Approved/Offered Positions:* 6
Program ID: 321-26-21-022

New York

Bronx

**Albert Einstein College of Medicine
Program**
Sponsor: Albert Einstein College of Medicine of Yeshiva
 University
Montefiore Medical Center-Henry and Lucy Moses
 Division
Prgm Director: Elizabeth M Alderman, MD
Department of Pediatrics
111 East 210th Street
Bronx, NY 10467
Tel: 718 920-6614   *Fax:* 718 920-5289
E-mail: ealderma@montefiore.org
Length: 3 Yrs   *ACGME Approved/Offered Positions:* 3
Program ID: 321-35-21-008

Brooklyn

**SUNY Health Science Center at Brooklyn
Program**
Sponsor: SUNY Health Science Center at Brooklyn
Kings County Hospital Center
Long Island Jewish Medical Center
University Hospital-SUNY Health Science Center at
 Brooklyn
Prgm Director: Amy L Suss, MD
450 Clarkson Avenue, Box 49, Dept of Peds
Brooklyn, NY 11203
Tel: 718 270-1006   *Fax:* 718 270-1985
E-mail: amy.suss@downstate.edu
Length: 3 Yrs   *ACGME Approved/Offered Positions:* 3
Program ID: 321-35-21-030

Great Neck

**NSLIJHS-Schneider Children's Hospital
Program**
Sponsor: North Shore-Long Island Jewish Health System
Schneider Children's Hospital at Long Island Jewish
 Med Ctr
Schneider Children's Hospital at North Shore University
 Hosp
Prgm Director: Martin M Fisher, MD
410 Lakeville Road
Suite 108
New Hyde Park, NY 11042
Tel: 516 465-3270   *Fax:* 516 465-5299
Length: 3 Yrs   *ACGME Approved/Offered Positions:* 6
Program ID: 321-35-21-010

New York

Mount Sinai School of Medicine Program
Sponsor: Mount Sinai School of Medicine
Barnard College Student Health Services
Mount Sinai Medical Center
Prgm Director: Anne Nucci-Sack, MD*
320 East 94th Street, 2nd Floor
New York, NY 10128
Tel: 212 423-2075   *Fax:* 212 423-2920
Length: 3 Yrs   *ACGME Approved/Offered Positions:* 3
Program ID: 321-35-11-012

**New York Presbyterian Hospital
(Columbia Campus) Program**
Sponsor: New York Presbyterian Hospital
Prgm Director: Karen Soren, MD
Vanderbilt Clinic 4-402
New York, NY 10032
Tel: 212 305-6227   *Fax:* 212 305-8819
Length: 3 Yrs   *ACGME Approved/Offered Positions:* 3
Program ID: 321-35-12-033

Rochester

University of Rochester Program
Sponsor: Strong Memorial Hospital of the University of
 Rochester
Rochester General Hospital
Prgm Director: Richard E Kreipe, MD*
601 Elmwood Avenue, Box 690
Rochester, NY 14642
Tel: 585 275-7844   *Fax:* 585 276-0168
E-mail: richard_kreipe@urmc.rochester.edu
Length: 3 Yrs   *ACGME Approved/Offered Positions:* 6
Program ID: 321-35-12-013

Ohio

Cincinnati

**Cincinnati Children's Hospital Medical
Center/University of Cincinnati College of
Medicine Program**
Sponsor: Cincinnati Children's Hospital Medical Center
Prgm Director: Michael G Spigarelli, MD, PhD
Division of Adolescent Medicine (ML-4000)
3333 Burnet Avenue
Cincinnati, OH 45229
Tel: 513 636-8597   *Fax:* 513 636-1129
E-mail: michael.spigarelli@cchmc.org
Length: 3 Yrs   *ACGME Approved/Offered Positions:* 6
Program ID: 321-38-21-014

Programs

Cleveland

Case Western Reserve University (MetroHealth) Program

Sponsor: MetroHealth Medical Center
University Hospitals Case Medical Center
Prgm Director: Barbara Cromer, MD
2500 MetroHealth Medical Center
Cleveland, OH 44109
Tel: 216 778-2643   *Fax:* 216 778-4223
Length: 3 Yrs   *ACGME Approved/Offered Positions:* 3
Program ID: 321-38-13-032

Pennsylvania

Philadelphia

Children's Hospital of Philadelphia Program

Sponsor: Children's Hospital of Philadelphia
Prgm Director: Nadja G Peter, MD*
11 Northwest Tower
34th Street and Civic Center Blvd
Philadelphia, PA 19104
Tel: 215 590-6864
E-mail: peter@email.chop.edu
Length: 3 Yrs   *ACGME Approved/Offered Positions:* 3
Program ID: 321-41-21-015

Pittsburgh

University of Pittsburgh Medical Center Medical Education Program

Sponsor: Univ of Pittsburgh Medical Center Medical Education
Children's Hospital of Pittsburgh of UPMC
Prgm Director: Pamela J Murray, MD
3705 Fifth Avenue
Pittsburgh, PA 15213
Tel: 412 692-8504   *Fax:* 412 692-8584
Length: 3 Yrs   *ACGME Approved/Offered Positions:* 3
Program ID: 321-41-13-026

Texas

Houston

Baylor College of Medicine Program

Sponsor: Baylor College of Medicine
Texas Children's Hospital
Prgm Director: Albert C Hergenroeder, MD
6621 Fannin St, CC1710.00
Houston, TX 77030
Tel: 832 822-3660   *Fax:* 832 825-3689
Length: 3 Yrs   *ACGME Approved/Offered Positions:* 3
Program ID: 321-48-21-016

University of Texas at Houston Program

Sponsor: University of Texas Health Science Center at Houston
Lyndon B Johnson General Hospital
Memorial Hermann Hospital
Prgm Director: William L Risser, MD, PhD
Dept of Pediatrics
PO Box 20708
Houston, TX 77225
Tel: 713 500-5755   *Fax:* 713 500-5750
Length: 3 Yrs   *ACGME Approved/Offered Positions:* 2
Program ID: 321-48-21-003

Lackland AFB

San Antonio Uniformed Services Health Education Consortium Program

Sponsor: San Antonio Uniformed Services Health Education Consortium
Brooke Army Medical Center
Wilford Hall Medical Center (AETC)
Prgm Director: Elisabeth Stafford, MD
2200 Bergquist Dr, Ste 1
Lackland AFB, TX 78236
Tel: 210 916-4017   *Fax:* 210 916-1740
E-mail: elisabeth.stafford@amedd.army.mil
Length: 3 Yrs   *ACGME Approved/Offered Positions:* 6
Program ID: 321-48-12-024
Uniformed Services Program

Washington

Seattle

University of Washington Program

Sponsor: University of Washington School of Medicine
Country Doctor Community Clinic
Department of Adult & Juvenile Detention
Group Health Cooperative
Seattle Children's Hospital
Prgm Director: Laura P Richardson, MD, MPH
4800 Sand Point Way, NE
Box 359300, W-7831
Seattle, WA 98105
Tel: 206 987-2028   *Fax:* 206 987-3939
E-mail: lpr@u.washington.edu
Length: 3 Yrs   *ACGME Approved/Offered Positions:* 3
Program ID: 321-54-21-027

Wisconsin

Milwaukee

Medical College of Wisconsin Affiliated Hospitals Program

Sponsor: Medical College of Wisconsin Affiliated Hospitals, Inc
Children's Hospital of Wisconsin
Prgm Director: Sarah Lerand, MD, MPH*
Children's Corporate Center, Suite C560
999 North 92nd Street
Milwaukee, WI 53226
Tel: 414 337-7023   *Fax:* 414 337-7020
Length: 3 Yrs   *ACGME Approved/Offered Positions:* 6
Program ID: 321-56-21-034

Adult Cardiothoracic Anesthesiology

Alabama

Birmingham

University of Alabama Medical Center Program

Sponsor: University of Alabama Hospital
Prgm Director: W Quinton Gurley, Jr, MD
1802 6th Avenue South
NP 5520
Birmingham, AL 35249
Tel: 205 996-9571   *Fax:* 205 934-0120
E-mail: qgurley@uab.edu
Length: 1 Yr   *ACGME Approved/Offered Positions:* 2
Program ID: 041-01-21-034

California

Loma Linda

Loma Linda University Program

Sponsor: Loma Linda University Medical Center
Prgm Director: Stanley Brauer, MD
11234 Anderson Street
Room 2534
Loma Linda, CA 92354
Tel: 909 558-4015   *Fax:* 909 558-0214
E-mail: cstephens@llu.edu
Length: 1 Yr   *ACGME Approved/Offered Positions:* 1
Program ID: 041-05-12-045

Los Angeles

UCLA Medical Center Program

Sponsor: UCLA David Geffen School of Medicine/UCLA Medical Center
UCLA Medical Center
Prgm Director: Aman Mahajan, MD, PhD
757 Westwood Plaza, Suite 3304
Los Angeles, CA 90095
Tel: 310 267-8655   *Fax:* 310 267-3766
Length: 1 Yr   *ACGME Approved/Offered Positions:* 3
Program ID: 041-05-12-037

University of Southern California/ LAC+USC Medical Center Program

Sponsor: University of Southern California/LAC+USC Medical Center
LAC+USC Medical Center
USC University Hospital
Prgm Director: Steven Haddy, MD
1500 San Pablo Avenue, 4th Floor
Los Angeles, CA 90033
Tel: 323 442-8900   *Fax:* 323 442-2895
Length: 1 Yr   *ACGME Approved/Offered Positions:* 1
Program ID: 041-05-31-036

Sacramento

University of California (Davis) Health System Program

Sponsor: University of California (Davis) Health System
University of California (Davis) Medical Center
Prgm Director: Amrik Singh, MBBS
PSSB Suite 1200
4150 V Street
Sacramento, CA 95817
Tel: 916 734-5394   *Fax:* 916 734-7980
E-mail: amsingh@ucdavis.edu
Length: 1 Yr   *ACGME Approved/Offered Positions:* 1
Program ID: 041-05-13-003

Note: * indicates a newly appointed program director

San Diego

University of California (San Diego) Program

Sponsor: University of California (San Diego) Medical
   Center
Veterans Affairs Medical Center (San Diego)
Prgm Director: Dalia A Banks, MD
3350 La Jolla Village Drive #125A
San Diego, CA 92161
Tel: 858 642-3340   *Fax:* 858 822-5009
E-mail: dabanks@ucsd.edu
Length: 1 Yr   *ACGME Approved/Offered Positions:* 1
Program ID: 041-05-12-041

Stanford

Stanford University Program

Sponsor: Stanford Hospital and Clinics
Prgm Director: Christina Mora Mangano, MD
300 Pasteur Drive, H3580
Stanford, CA 64305
Tel: 650 725-0376   *Fax:* 650 725-8544
E-mail: cmoraman@stanford.edu
Length: 1 Yr   *ACGME Approved/Offered Positions:* 3
Program ID: 041-05-21-026

Colorado

Aurora

University of Colorado Denver Program

Sponsor: University of Colorado Denver School of
   Medicine
Children's Hospital (The)
Exempla St Joseph Hospital
University of Colorado Hospital
Prgm Director: Tamas Seres, MD, PhD
Department of Anesthesiology
12631 E 17th Avenue, A01-8203
Aurora, CO 80045
Tel: 303 724-1758   *Fax:* 303 724-1761
Length: 1 Yr   *ACGME Approved/Offered Positions:* 1
Program ID: 041-07-13-035

Florida

Gainesville

University of Florida Program

Sponsor: University of Florida College of Medicine
North Florida/South Georgia Veterans Health System
Shands at AGH
Shands Hospital at the University of Florida
Prgm Director: Yong G Peng, MD, PhD
PO Box 100254
1600 SW Archer Rd
Gainesville, FL 32610
Tel: 352 265-0077
E-mail: ypeng@anest.ufl.edu
Length: 1 Yr   *ACGME Approved/Offered Positions:* 2
Program ID: 041-11-31-044

Miami

Jackson Memorial Hospital/Jackson Health System Program

Sponsor: Jackson Memorial Hospital/Jackson Health
   System
Prgm Director: John C Sciarra, MD
1611 NW 12th Avenue
Miami, FL 33101
Tel: 305 585-6970   *Fax:* 305 585-7169
E-mail: jsciarra@med.miami.edu
Length: 1 Yr   *ACGME Approved/Offered Positions:* 2
Program ID: 041-11-13-047

Georgia

Atlanta

Emory University Program

Sponsor: Emory University School of Medicine
Crawford Long Hospital of Emory University
Emory University Hospital
Prgm Director: Kathryn E Glas, MD, MBA
1364 Clifton Road, NE
Department of Anesthesiology
Atlanta, GA 30322
Tel: 404 778-5793   *Fax:* 404 778-3940
E-mail: kathryn.glas@emoryhealthcare.org
Length: 1 Yr   *ACGME Approved/Offered Positions:* 6
Program ID: 041-12-21-010

Illinois

Chicago

McGaw Medical Center of Northwestern University Program

Sponsor: McGaw Medical Center of Northwestern
   University
Northwestern Memorial Hospital
Prgm Director: Saadia Sherwani, MD
251 East Huron St
Feinberg 5-704
Chicago, IL 60611
Tel: 312 926-8369   *Fax:* 312 926-9206
E-mail: s-sherwani@northwestern.edu
Length: 1 Yr   *ACGME Approved/Offered Positions:* 2
Program ID: 041-16-13-039

University of Chicago Program

Sponsor: University of Chicago Medical Center
Prgm Director: Mark Chaney, MD
5841 South Maryland Avenue
MC-4028
Chicago, IL 60637
Tel: 773 702-5901   *Fax:* 773 834-0063
E-mail: tc28@airway.uchicago.edu
Length: 1 Yr   *ACGME Approved/Offered Positions:* 2
Program ID: 041-16-12-009

Maywood

Loyola University Program

Sponsor: Loyola University Medical Center
Prgm Director: Pierre LeVan, MD
2160 South First Avenue
Maywood, IL 60153
Tel: 708 216-8866   *Fax:* 708 216-1249
E-mail: mmollo@lumc.edu
Length: 1 Yr   *ACGME Approved/Offered Positions:* 1
Program ID: 041-16-21-030

Louisiana

New Orleans

Ochsner Clinic Foundation Program

Sponsor: Ochsner Clinic Foundation
Prgm Director: Donald E Harmon, MD
1514 Jefferson Highway
New Orleans, LA 70121
Tel: 504 842-3755   *Fax:* 504 842-2036
E-mail: dharmon@ochsner.org
Length: 1 Yr   *ACGME Approved/Offered Positions:* 1
Program ID: 041-21-12-033

Maryland

Baltimore

Johns Hopkins University Program

Sponsor: Johns Hopkins University School of Medicine
Johns Hopkins Hospital
Prgm Director: Daniel Nyhan, MD*
Tower 711
600 N Wolfe Street
Baltimore, MD 21287
Tel: 410 955-6192   *Fax:* 410 955-0994
E-mail: dnyhan@jhmi.edu
Length: 1 Yr   *ACGME Approved/Offered Positions:* 2
Program ID: 041-23-12-017

University of Maryland Program

Sponsor: University of Maryland Medical System
Prgm Director: Wendy K Bernstein, MD
22 South Greene Street
Baltimore, MD 21201
Tel: 410 328-6120   *Fax:* 410 328-5531
Length: 1 Yr   *ACGME Approved/Offered Positions:* 2
Program ID: 041-23-21-022

Massachusetts

Boston

Beth Israel Deaconess Medical Center Program

Sponsor: Beth Israel Deaconess Medical Center
Prgm Director: Sugantha Sundar, MD
Dept of Anesthesia, Critical Care & Pain Medicine
One Deaconess Road, CC-470
Boston, MA 02215
Tel: 617 754-2670   *Fax:* 617 754-2735
E-mail: ssundar@bidmc.harvard.edu
Length: 1 Yr   *ACGME Approved/Offered Positions:* 2
Program ID: 041-24-21-014

Brigham and Women's Hospital Program

Sponsor: Brigham and Women's Hospital
Prgm Director: Douglas C Shook, MD
Department of Anesthesiology
75 Francis Street
Boston, MA 02115
Tel: 617 732-8219   *Fax:* 617 732-6798
E-mail: dshook@partners.org
Length: 1 Yr   *ACGME Approved/Offered Positions:* 6
Program ID: 041-24-13-007

Massachusetts General Hospital Program

Sponsor: Massachusetts General Hospital
Prgm Director: Michael G Fitzsimons, MD
Division of Cardiac Anesthesiology
55 Fruit Street
Boston, MA 02114
Tel: 617 726-3318   *Fax:* 617 726-5985
E-mail: mfitzsimons@partners.org
Length: 1 Yr   *ACGME Approved/Offered Positions:* 4
Program ID: 041-24-31-032

Tufts Medical Center Program

Sponsor: Tufts Medical Center
Prgm Director: Anastasios Triantafillou, MD
800 Washington Street
Box 298
Boston, MA 02111
Tel: 617 636-6044   *Fax:* 617 636-8384
Length: 1 Yr   *ACGME Approved/Offered Positions:* 2
Program ID: 041-24-13-031

Programs

Michigan

Ann Arbor

University of Michigan Program
Sponsor: University of Michigan Hospitals and Health Centers
Prgm Director: Matthew D Caldwell, MD
1500 East Medical Center Drive
CVC 4172
Ann Arbor, MI 48109
Tel: 734 936-9479 *Fax:* 734 232-4548
Length: 1 Yr *ACGME Approved/Offered Positions:* 4
Program ID: 041-25-31-016

Detroit

Henry Ford Hospital Program
Sponsor: Henry Ford Hospital
Prgm Director: Fathy Gabriel, MD
Department of Anesthesiology
2799 W Grand Blvd
Detroit, MI 48202
Tel: 313 916-8234 *Fax:* 313 916-9434
E-mail: jrobert1@hfhs.org
Length: 1 Yr *ACGME Approved/Offered Positions:* 1
Program ID: 041-25-31-012

Minnesota

Rochester

College of Medicine, Mayo Clinic (Rochester) Program
Sponsor: College of Medicine, Mayo Clinic
Saint Marys Hospital of Rochester
Prgm Director: David J Cook, MD
200 First Street SW
Rochester, MN 55905
Tel: 507 255-1246 *Fax:* 507 255-2939
Length: 1 Yr *ACGME Approved/Offered Positions:* 3
Program ID: 041-26-13-023

Missouri

St Louis

Washington University/B-JH/SLCH Consortium Program
Sponsor: Washington University/B-JH/SLCH Consortium
Barnes-Jewish Hospital
Prgm Director: Tatiana Jamroz, MD
660 South Euclid Ave, Box 8054
St Louis, MO 63110
Tel: 314 362-1196 *Fax:* 314 747-3977
Length: 1 Yr *ACGME Approved/Offered Positions:* 3
Program ID: 041-28-13-019

New Jersey

New Brunswick

UMDNJ-Robert Wood Johnson Medical School Program
Sponsor: UMDNJ-Robert Wood Johnson Medical School
Robert Wood Johnson University Hospital
Prgm Director: Denes Papp, MD*
Department of Anesthesia
125 Paterson Street, CAB 3100
New Brunswick, NJ 08901
Tel: 732 235-6153 *Fax:* 732 235-5100
E-mail: douglael@umdnj.edu
Length: 1 Yr *ACGME Approved/Offered Positions:* 2
Program ID: 041-33-21-046

New York

Bronx

Albert Einstein College of Medicine Program
Sponsor: Albert Einstein College of Medicine of Yeshiva University
Montefiore Medical Center-Henry and Lucy Moses Division
Montefiore Medical Center-Weiler Division
Prgm Director: Linda Shore Lesserson, MD
Department of Anesthesiology, Foreman Pav, 4th Floor
111 E 210th Street
Bronx, NY 10467
Tel: 718 920-5409 *Fax:* 718 653-2367
E-mail: anestres@montefiore.org
Length: 1 Yr *ACGME Approved/Offered Positions:* 3
Program ID: 041-35-12-029

Buffalo

University at Buffalo Program
Sponsor: University at Buffalo School of Medicine
Kaleida Health System (Buffalo General Hospital)
Kaleida Health System (Millard Fillmore Hospital)
Veterans Affairs Western New York Hospital
Prgm Director: Nader D Nader, MD, PhD
3495 Bailey Avenue
Buffalo, NY 14215
Tel: 716 829-6102 *Fax:* 716 829-3640
Length: 1 Yr *ACGME Approved/Offered Positions:* 2
Program ID: 041-35-13-015

New York

Mount Sinai School of Medicine Program
Sponsor: Mount Sinai School of Medicine
Mount Sinai Medical Center
Prgm Director: Marc E Stone, MD
Department of Anesthesiology
One Gustave L Levy Place, Box 1010
New York, NY 10029
Tel: 212 241-6426 *Fax:* 212 426-2009
E-mail: marc.stone@msnyuhealth.org
Length: 1 Yr *ACGME Approved/Offered Positions:* 5
Program ID: 041-35-21-002

New York Presbyterian Hospital (Columbia Campus) Program
Sponsor: New York Presbyterian Hospital
Prgm Director: Jack Shanewise, MD
622 West 168th Street PH 5-505
New York, NY 10032
Tel: 212 342-2210 *Fax:* 212 342-2211
Length: 1 Yr *ACGME Approved/Offered Positions:* 6
Program ID: 041-35-21-006

New York Presbyterian Hospital (Cornell Campus) Program
Sponsor: New York Presbyterian Hospital
Prgm Director: Manuel L Fontes, MD
525 East 68th Street
New York, NY 10021
Tel: 212 746-0395 *Fax:* 212 746-0319
E-mail: maf2029@med.cornell.edu
Length: 1 Yr *ACGME Approved/Offered Positions:* 2
Program ID: 041-35-12-013

New York University School of Medicine Program
Sponsor: New York University School of Medicine
Bellevue Hospital Center
NYU Hospitals Center
Prgm Director: John Ostrowski, MD
Department of Anesthesiology
550 First Avenue
New York, NY 10016
Tel: 212 263-5821 *Fax:* 212 263-3217
Length: 1 Yr *ACGME Approved/Offered Positions:* 2
Program ID: 041-35-31-024

Rochester

University of Rochester Program
Sponsor: Strong Memorial Hospital of the University of Rochester
Prgm Director: Michael P Eaton, MD
610 Elmwood Avenue, Box 604
Rochester, NY 14642
Tel: 585 275-2141 *Fax:* 585 244-7271
E-mail: michael_eaton@urmc.rochester.edu
Length: 1 Yr *ACGME Approved/Offered Positions:* 2
Program ID: 041-35-21-038

North Carolina

Durham

Duke University Hospital Program
Sponsor: Duke University Hospital
Prgm Director: Mark Stafford-Smith, MD
Department of Anesthesiology
Box 3094, Room 5688 HAFS Bldg
Durham, NC 27710
Tel: 919 681-6944 *Fax:* 919 681-8993
E-mail: staff002@mc.duke.edu
Length: 1 Yr *ACGME Approved/Offered Positions:* 8
Program ID: 041-36-12-001

Ohio

Cleveland

Cleveland Clinic Foundation Program
Sponsor: Cleveland Clinic Foundation
Prgm Director: Michelle Capdeville, MD*
9500 Euclid Avenue G30
Cleveland, OH 44195
Tel: 216 445-8135 *Fax:* 216 445-2536
E-mail: mccannj@ccf.org
Length: 1 Yr *ACGME Approved/Offered Positions:* 16
Program ID: 041-38-21-018

Note: * indicates a newly appointed program director

Pennsylvania

Philadelphia

University of Pennsylvania Program

Sponsor: University of Pennsylvania Health System
Children's Hospital of Philadelphia
Presbyterian Medical Center (UPHS)
Prgm Director: Albert T Cheung, MD
Department of Anesthesiology and Critical Care
3400 Spruce Street - 680 Dulles Building
Philadelphia, PA 19104
Tel: 215 662-3785   *Fax:* 215 349-8133
E-mail: cheunga@uphs.upenn.edu
Length: 1 Yr   *ACGME Approved/Offered Positions:* 4
Program ID: 041-41-31-008

South Carolina

Charleston

Medical University of South Carolina Program

Sponsor: Medical University of South Carolina College of
     Medicine
MUSC Medical Center
Prgm Director: James H Abernathy, III, MD, MPH
167 Ashley Avenue, MSC 912
Charleston, SC 29425
Tel: 843 792-2322   *Fax:* 843 792-9314
E-mail: abernatj@musc.edu
Length: 1 Yr   *ACGME Approved/Offered Positions:* 2
Program ID: 041-45-31-020

Tennessee

Nashville

Vanderbilt University Program

Sponsor: Vanderbilt University Medical Center
Prgm Director: Annemarie Thompson, MD
3161C Medical Center East
1211 22nd Avenue South
Nashville, TN 37232
Tel: 615 343-1926   *Fax:* 615 343-4729
E-mail: annemarie.thompson@vanderbilt.edu
Length: 1 Yr   *ACGME Approved/Offered Positions:* 2
Program ID: 041-47-12-025

Texas

Dallas

University of Texas Southwestern Medical School Program

Sponsor: University of Texas Southwestern Medical
     School
Baylor University Medical Center
Dallas VA Medical Center
University Hospitals St Paul
Prgm Director: Philip E Greilich, MD
5323 Harry Hines Boulevard
Dallas, TX 75390
Tel: 214 645-8018   *Fax:* 214 645-8088
Length: 1 Yr   *ACGME Approved/Offered Positions:* 2
Program ID: 041-48-13-011

Galveston

University of Texas Medical Branch Hospitals Program

Sponsor: University of Texas Medical Branch Hospitals
Methodist Hospital (Houston)
Prgm Director: Christopher K McQuitty, MD
Suite 2A John Sealy
Galveston, TX 77555
Tel: 409 772-0790   *Fax:* 409 772-1224
Length: 1 Yr   *ACGME Approved/Offered Positions:* 1
Program ID: 041-48-31-040

Houston

Baylor College of Medicine Program

Sponsor: Baylor College of Medicine
St Luke's Episcopal Hospital
Texas Children's Hospital
Texas Heart Institute
Prgm Director: John R Cooper, Jr, MD
Division of Cardiovascular Anesthesiology
PO Box 20345, MC 1-226
Houston, TX 77225
Tel: 832 355-2666   *Fax:* 832 355-6500
E-mail: pcarpenter@heart.thi.tmc.edu
Length: 1 Yr   *ACGME Approved/Offered Positions:* 10
Program ID: 041-48-31-004

Virginia

Richmond

Virginia Commonwealth University Health System Program

Sponsor: Virginia Commonwealth University Health
     System
Medical College of Virginia Hospitals
Prgm Director: Jeffrey A Green, MD
1200 East Broad, West Hospital 7N-102
PO Box 980695
Richmond, VA 23298
Tel: 804 628-3237   *Fax:* 804 828-8300
E-mail: jagreen2@vcu.edu
Length: 1 Yr   *ACGME Approved/Offered Positions:* 2
Program ID: 041-51-12-005

Washington

Seattle

University of Washington Program

Sponsor: University of Washington School of Medicine
University of Washington Medical Center
Prgm Director: Jorg Dziersk, MD
Department of Anesthesiology
Mail Stop 356540
Seattle, WA 98195
Tel: 206 221-6453   *Fax:* 206 543-2958
E-mail: katibell@u.washington.edu
Length: 1 Yr   *ACGME Approved/Offered Positions:* 1
Program ID: 041-54-21-042

Adult Reconstructive Orthopaedics (Orthopaedic Surgery)

California

Stanford

Stanford University Program

Sponsor: Stanford Hospital and Clinics
Veterans Affairs Palo Alto Health Care System
Prgm Director: Stuart B Goodman, MD, PhD*
300 Pasteur Drive, R144
Stanford, CA 94305
Tel: 650 725-5903   *Fax:* 650 724-3044
E-mail: kdenny@stanford.edu
Length: 1 Yr   *ACGME Approved/Offered Positions:* 1
Program ID: 261-05-21-016

Illinois

Chicago

University of Chicago Program

Sponsor: University of Chicago Medical Center
Louis A Weiss Memorial Hospital
Prgm Director: Henry A Finn, MD
Weiss Memorial Hospital
4646 N Marine Drive
Chicago, IL 60640
Tel: 773 564-5881   *Fax:* 773 564-5886
Length: 1 Yr   *ACGME Approved/Offered Positions:* 2
Program ID: 261-16-21-012

Kentucky

Louisville

University of Louisville Program

Sponsor: University of Louisville School of Medicine
Jewish Hospital
Norton Audubon Hospital
Norton Hospital
University of Louisville Hospital
Prgm Director: Arthur Malkani, MD
Orthopaedic Surgery
210 East Gray Street, Suite 1003
Louisville, KY 40202
Tel: 502 852-5319   *Fax:* 502 852-7227
E-mail: cmbing02@gwise.louisville.edu
Length: 1 Yr   *ACGME Approved/Offered Positions:* 1
Program ID: 261-20-13-029

Maryland

Baltimore

Union Memorial Hospital Program

Sponsor: Union Memorial Hospital
Prgm Director: Henry R Boucher, MD
3333 North Calvert Street
Suite 400
Baltimore, MD 21218
Tel: 410 554-6890   *Fax:* 410 554-2084
E-mail: Hboucher@gcoa.net
Length: 1 Yr   *ACGME Approved/Offered Positions:* 2
Program ID: 261-23-12-033

Programs

Michigan

Royal Oak

William Beaumont Hospital Program

Sponsor: William Beaumont Hospital
Prgm Director: James Verner, MD
Department of Orthopaedic Surgery
3535 W 13 Mile Road, Suite 744
Royal Oak, MI 48073
Tel: 248 551-3140   *Fax:* 248 551-9520
E-mail: lthompson@beaumonthospitals.com
Length: 1 Yr   *ACGME Approved/Offered Positions:* 1
Program ID: 261-25-13-034
Uniformed Services Program

Minnesota

Minneapolis

University of Minnesota Program

Sponsor: University of Minnesota Medical School
University of Minnesota Medical Center, Division of
   Fairview
Veterans Affairs Medical Center (Minneapolis)
Prgm Director: Edward Y Cheng, MD
2450 Riverside Avenue S, R200
Minneapolis, MN 55454
Tel: 612 273-7951   *Fax:* 612 273-7959
Length: 1 Yr   *ACGME Approved/Offered Positions:* 2
Program ID: 261-26-21-025

Rochester

College of Medicine, Mayo Clinic (Rochester) Program

Sponsor: College of Medicine, Mayo Clinic
Mayo Clinic (Rochester)
Rochester Methodist Hospital
Saint Marys Hospital of Rochester
Prgm Director: David G Lewallen, MD
200 First Street SW
Rochester, MN 55905
Tel: 507 284-3316   *Fax:* 507 266-4234
E-mail: Price.Natalie@mayo.edu
Length: 1 Yr   *ACGME Approved/Offered Positions:* 5
Program ID: 261-26-21-015

New York

Buffalo

University at Buffalo Program

Sponsor: University at Buffalo School of Medicine
Kaleida Health System (Buffalo General Hospital)
Prgm Director: Kenneth A Krackow, MD
Buffalo General Hospital
100 High Street, Suite B276
Buffalo, NY 14203
Tel: 716 859-1256   *Fax:* 716 859-4586
E-mail: comjanet@buffalo.edu
Length: 1 Yr   *ACGME Approved/Offered Positions:* 1
Program ID: 261-35-21-026

New York

Albert Einstein College of Medicine at Beth Israel Medical Center Program

Sponsor: Beth Israel Medical Center
Prgm Director: Frances Cuomo, MD
Phillips Ambulatory Care Center
10 Union Square East, Suite 3M
New York, NY 10003
Tel: 212 844-6938   *Fax:* 212 844-6983
Length: 1 Yr   *ACGME Approved/Offered Positions:* 1
Program ID: 261-35-22-032

Hospital for Special Surgery/Cornell Medical Center Program

Sponsor: Hospital for Special Surgery
Prgm Director: Mathias Bostrom, MD
535 East 70th Street
New York, NY 10021
Tel: 212 606-1466   *Fax:* 212 606-1477
E-mail: academictraining@hss.edu
Length: 1 Yr   *ACGME Approved/Offered Positions:* 6
Program ID: 261-35-21-003

Lenox Hill Hospital Program

Sponsor: Lenox Hill Hospital
Prgm Director: Jose A Rodriguez, MD*
130 East 77th Street
William Black Hall, 11th Floor
New York, NY 10075
Tel: 212 434-4799
E-mail: josermd@aol.com
Length: 1 Yr   *ACGME Approved/Offered Positions:* 2
Program ID: 261-35-31-024

Lenox Hill Hospital Program A

Sponsor: Lenox Hill Hospital
Prgm Director: W Norman Scott, MD
Lenox Hill Hospital
210 East 64th Street
New York, NY 10021
Tel: 212 434-4340   *Fax:* 212 434-4341
E-mail: klenhardt@iskinstitute.com
Length: 1 Yr   *ACGME Approved/Offered Positions:* 4
Program ID: 261-35-21-020

North Carolina

Durham

Duke University Hospital Program

Sponsor: Duke University Hospital
Prgm Director: Michael P Bolognesi, MD
Division of Orthopaedic Surgery
Box 3269
Durham, NC 27710
Tel: 919 684-3170   *Fax:* 919 681-7672
E-mail: wendy.thompson@duke.edu
Length: 1 Yr   *ACGME Approved/Offered Positions:* 1
Program ID: 261-36-13-031

Pennsylvania

Philadelphia

Thomas Jefferson University Program

Sponsor: Thomas Jefferson University Hospital
Prgm Director: William J Hozack, MD
111 S 11th Street
Philadelphia, PA 19107
Tel: 215 955-1500
Length: 1 Yr   *ACGME Approved/Offered Positions:* 3
Program ID: 261-41-31-008

University of Pennsylvania Program

Sponsor: University of Pennsylvania Health System
Presbyterian Medical Center (UPHS)
Prgm Director: Jonathan P Garino, MD
39th & Market Streets
2 Cupp Pavilion
Philadelphia, PA 19104
Tel: 215 349-8792   *Fax:* 215 349-5890
Length: 1 Yr   *ACGME Approved/Offered Positions:* 3
Program ID: 261-41-21-001

Texas

Houston

Methodist Hospital (Houston) Program

Sponsor: Methodist Hospital (Houston)
Prgm Director: Stephen J Incavo, MD
6550 Fannin St
Suite 2500
Houston, TX 77030
Tel: 713 441-3569   *Fax:* 713 790-6614
E-mail: jmasterson@tmhs.org
Length: 1 Yr   *ACGME Approved/Offered Positions:* 2
Program ID: 261-48-21-037

Virginia

Charlottesville

University of Virginia Program

Sponsor: University of Virginia Medical Center
Prgm Director: Khaled J Saleh, MD, MSc
PO Box 800159
Charlottesville, VA 22908
Tel: 434 243-0067   *Fax:* 434 243-0242
Length: 1 Yr   *ACGME Approved/Offered Positions:* 2
Program ID: 261-51-21-009

Richmond

Virginia Commonwealth University Health System Program

Sponsor: Virginia Commonwealth University Health
   System
Bon Secours St Mary's Hospital
Medical College of Virginia Hospitals
Prgm Director: William A Jiranek, MD
Stony Point Medical Center
9000 Stony Point Parkway
Richmond, VA 23235
Tel: 804 228-4155   *Fax:* 804 228-4174
E-mail: orthoresprog@vcu.edu
Length: 1 Yr   *ACGME Approved/Offered Positions:* 2
Program ID: 261-51-21-030

Note: * indicates a newly appointed program director

Allergy and Immunology

Alabama

Birmingham

University of Alabama Medical Center Program

Sponsor: University of Alabama Hospital
Alabama Allergy and Asthma Center
Eastern Pulmonary and Sleep Medicine
Pediatric and Adult Asthma & Allergy, PC
Veterans Affairs Medical Center (Birmingham)
Prgm Director: T Prescott Atkinson, MD, PhD
Children's Hospital, CPP 220
1600 7th Avenue South
Birmingham, AL 35233
Tel: 205 996-9121   *Fax:* 205 975-7080
E-mail: patkinso@uab.edu
Length: 2 Yrs   *ACGME Approved/Offered Positions:* 4
Program ID: 020-01-21-109

California

La Jolla

Scripps Clinic/Scripps Green Hospital Program

Sponsor: Scripps Clinic/Scripps Green Hospital
Prgm Director: Katharine M Woessner, MD
10666 North Torrey Pines Road
La Jolla, CA 92037
Tel: 858 764-9010   *Fax:* 858 554-3232
E-mail: gme@scripps.edu
Length: 2 Yrs   *ACGME Approved/Offered Positions:* 4
Program ID: 020-05-31-002

Los Angeles

Kaiser Permanente Southern California (Los Angeles) Program

Sponsor: Kaiser Permanente Southern California
Kaiser Foundation Hospital (Los Angeles)
Prgm Director: Michael S Kaplan, MD
Dept of Allergy & Clin Immunology
1515 N Vermont Avenue
Los Angeles, CA 90027
Tel: 323 783-8260   *Fax:* 323 783-4646
Length: 2 Yrs   *ACGME Approved/Offered Positions:* 3
Program ID: 020-05-12-003

UCLA Medical Center Program

Sponsor: UCLA David Geffen School of Medicine/UCLA
   Medical Center
UCLA Medical Center
Prgm Director: Sean McGhee, MD
Department of Pediatrics/Immunology, Allergy
12-430 MDCC
Los Angeles, CA 90095
Tel: 310 825-6481   *Fax:* 310 825-9832
Length: 2 Yrs   *ACGME Approved/Offered Positions:* 4
Program ID: 020-05-11-038

University of Southern California/ LAC+USC Medical Center Program

Sponsor: University of Southern California/LAC+USC
   Medical Center
LAC+USC Medical Center
Prgm Director: Kenny Y Kwong, MD
1801 E Marengo, Rm 1G1
General Labs Building
Los Angeles, CA 90033
Tel: 323 226-3813   *Fax:* 323 226-5049
E-mail: kkwongusc@yahoo.com
Length: 2 Yrs   *ACGME Approved/Offered Positions:* 2
Program ID: 020-05-21-065

VA Greater Los Angeles Healthcare System Program

Sponsor: VA Greater Los Angeles Healthcare System
Childrens Hospital Los Angeles
Prgm Director: William B Klaustermeyer, MD
11301 Wilshire Blvd
Allergy/Immunology Division (111R)
Los Angeles, CA 90073
Tel: 310 268-3011   *Fax:* 310 268-4712
E-mail: william.klaustermeyer@va.gov
Length: 2 Yrs   *ACGME Approved/Offered Positions:* 3
Program ID: 020-05-21-096

Orange

University of California (Irvine) Program

Sponsor: University of California (Irvine) Medical
   Center
University of California (Irvine) College of Medicine
VA Long Beach Healthcare System
Prgm Director: Sudhir Gupta, MD, PhD
C240 Medical Science I
Irvine, CA 92697
Tel: 949 824-5818   *Fax:* 949 824-4362
Length: 2 Yrs   *ACGME Approved/Offered Positions:* 3
Program ID: 020-05-21-064

Sacramento

University of California (Davis) Health System Program

Sponsor: University of California (Davis) Health System
University of California (Davis) Medical Center
VA Northern California Health Care System
Prgm Director: Suzanne S Teuber, MD
Div of Rheumatology, Allergy and Clinical Immunol
451 Health Sciences Drive, Sutie 6510
Davis, CA 95616
Tel: 530 752-2884   *Fax:* 530 754-6047
E-mail: ssteuber@ucdavis.edu
Length: 2 Yrs   *ACGME Approved/Offered Positions:* 4
Program ID: 020-05-21-048

San Diego

University of California (San Diego) Program

Sponsor: University of California (San Diego) Medical
   Center
Rady Children's Hospital
Veterans Affairs Medical Center (San Diego)
Prgm Director: Bruce L Zuraw, MD
9500 Gilman Drive
Mail Code 0635
La Jolla, CA 92093
Tel: 858 822-6597   *Fax:* 858 642-3791
E-mail: cmurillo@ucsd.edu
Length: 2 Yrs   *ACGME Approved/Offered Positions:* 2
Program ID: 020-05-21-066

Stanford

Stanford University Program

Sponsor: Stanford Hospital and Clinics
Lucile Salter Packard Children's Hospital at Stanford
Prgm Director: Richard Moss, MD
770 Welch Road, Suite 350
Stanford, CA 94304
Tel: 650 723-5191   *Fax:* 650 723-5201
E-mail: rmoss@stanford.edu
Length: 2 Yrs   *ACGME Approved/Offered Positions:* 8
Program ID: 020-05-21-116

Colorado

Aurora

University of Colorado Denver Program

Sponsor: University of Colorado Denver School of
   Medicine
Children's Hospital (The)
National Jewish Medical and Research Center
University of Colorado Hospital
Prgm Director: Rohit K Katial, MD
1400 Jackson Street
J-329
Denver, CO 80206
Tel: 303 270-2913   *Fax:* 303 398-1806
Length: 2 Yrs   *ACGME Approved/Offered Positions:* 8
Program ID: 020-07-31-086

University of Colorado Denver Program A

Sponsor: University of Colorado Denver School of
   Medicine
Children's Hospital (The)
National Jewish Medical and Research Center
Prgm Director: Joseph D Spahn, MD
1400 Jackson Street
Denver, CO 80206
Tel: 303 388-4461   *Fax:* 303 270-2201
Length: 2 Yrs   *ACGME Approved/Offered Positions:* 8
Program ID: 020-07-31-010

Connecticut

New Haven

Yale-New Haven Medical Center Program

Sponsor: Yale-New Haven Hospital
Prgm Director: Philip W Askenase, MD*
333 Cedar Street
PO Box 208013
New Haven, CT 06520
Tel: 203 785-4143   *Fax:* 203 785-3229
Length: 2 Yrs   *ACGME Approved/Offered Positions:* 3
Program ID: 020-08-21-099

Florida

St. Petersburg

University of South Florida (All Children's) Program

Sponsor: University of South Florida College of Medicine
All Children's Hospital
Prgm Director: Morna J Dorsey, MD, MSc
801 Sixth Street South
St Petersburg, FL 33701
Tel: 727 553-3533   *Fax:* 727 553-1295
Length: 2 Yrs   *ACGME Approved/Offered Positions:* 6
Program ID: 020-11-21-106

Tampa

University of South Florida Program

Sponsor: University of South Florida College of Medicine
All Children's Hospital
Allergy Asthma and Immunology Associates of Tampa
  Bay
H Lee Moffitt Cancer Center
James A Haley Veterans Hospital
Tampa General Hospital
Prgm Director: Richard F Lockey, MD, MS
James A Haley Veterans Hospital
13000 Bruce B Downs Blvd (111D)
Tampa, FL 33612
Tel: 813 972-7631   *Fax:* 813 910-4041
E-mail: rlockey@health.usf.edu
Length: 2 Yrs   *ACGME Approved/Offered Positions:* 4
Program ID: 020-11-21-093

Georgia

Augusta

Medical College of Georgia Program

Sponsor: Medical College of Georgia
Prgm Director: William K Dolen, MD
Allergy-Immunology Section, BG 1019
1120 15th Street
Augusta, GA 30912
Tel: 706 721-2951   *Fax:* 706 721-2527
Length: 2 Yrs   *ACGME Approved/Offered Positions:* 4
Program ID: 020-12-21-013

Illinois

Chicago

McGaw Medical Center of Northwestern University Program

Sponsor: McGaw Medical Center of Northwestern
  University
Children's Memorial Hospital
Northwestern Memorial Hospital
Prgm Director: Pedro C Avila, MD
Division of Allergy-Immunology
676 N St Clair St, #14018
Chicago, IL 60611
Tel: 312 695-4000   *Fax:* 312 695-4141
E-mail: shay-knuth@northwestern.edu
Length: 2 Yrs   *ACGME Approved/Offered Positions:* 9
Program ID: 020-16-31-016

Rush University Medical Center Program

Sponsor: Rush University Medical Center
John H Stroger Hospital of Cook County
Rush Oak Park Hospital
Prgm Director: James N Moy, MD*
Rush Medical College
1725 W Harrison Street, Suite 117
Chicago, IL 60612
Tel: 312 942-6296   *Fax:* 312 563-2201
E-mail: jmoy@rush.edu
Length: 2 Yrs   *ACGME Approved/Offered Positions:* 5
Program ID: 020-16-21-108

Iowa

Iowa City

University of Iowa Hospitals and Clinics Program

Sponsor: University of Iowa Hospitals and Clinics
Prgm Director: Mary B Fasano, MD, MSPH
Department of Internal Medicine
200 Hawkins Drive
Iowa City, IA 52242
Tel: 319 356-3692   *Fax:* 319 356-8280
E-mail: mary-fasano@uiowa.edu
Length: 2 Yrs   *ACGME Approved/Offered Positions:* 3
Program ID: 020-18-21-081

Kansas

Kansas City

University of Kansas School of Medicine Program

Sponsor: University of Kansas School of Medicine
University of Kansas Hospital
Prgm Director: Daniel J Stechschulte, MD
Room 4035 Wescoe
3901 Rainbow Boulevard
Kansas City, KS 66160
Tel: 913 588-6008   *Fax:* 913 588-3987
E-mail: khinshaw@kumc.edu
Length: 2 Yrs   *ACGME Approved/Offered Positions:* 4
Program ID: 020-19-21-117

Louisiana

New Orleans

Louisiana State University Program

Sponsor: Louisiana State University School of Medicine
Children's Hospital (New Orleans)
Medical Center of Louisiana at New Orleans
Ochsner Medical Center-Kenner
Prgm Director: Cleveland Moore, MD
Departments of Medicine & Pediatrics
200 Henry Clay Ave
New Orleans, LA 70118
Tel: 504 896-9589   *Fax:* 504 896-9311
E-mail: cmoore@lsuhsc.edu
Length: 2 Yrs   *ACGME Approved/Offered Positions:* 7
Program ID: 020-21-21-070

Tulane University Program

Sponsor: Tulane University School of Medicine
Medical Center of Louisiana at New Orleans
Ochsner Clinic Foundation
Tulane University Hospital and Clinics
Veterans Affairs Medical Center (New Orleans)
Prgm Director: Laurianne G Wild, MD
Department of Medicine
1430 Tulane Avenue SL-57
New Orleans, LA 70112
Tel: 504 988-5578   *Fax:* 504 988-3686
Length: 2 Yrs   *ACGME Approved/Offered Positions:* 4
Program ID: 020-21-31-017

Shreveport

Louisiana State University (Shreveport) Program

Sponsor: LSU Health Sciences Center-University
  Hospital
Prgm Director: Adrian M Casillas, MD*
1501 Kings Highway
PO Box 33932
Shreveport, LA 71130
Tel: 318 675-7625   *Fax:* 318 675-8815
Length: 2 Yrs   *ACGME Approved/Offered Positions:* 4
Program ID: 020-21-21-060

Maryland

Baltimore

Johns Hopkins University Program

Sponsor: Johns Hopkins University School of Medicine
Johns Hopkins Bayview Medical Center
Johns Hopkins Hospital
Prgm Director: Sarbjit S Saini, MD*
5501 Hopkins Bayview Circle
Baltimore, MD 21224
Tel: 410 550-2129   *Fax:* 410 550-2527
E-mail: ssaini@jhmi.edu
Length: 2 Yrs   *ACGME Approved/Offered Positions:* 9
Program ID: 020-23-21-094

Bethesda

National Capital Consortium Program

Sponsor: National Capital Consortium
Walter Reed Army Medical Center
Prgm Director: Michael R Nelson, MD, PhD
6900 Georgia Avenue NW
Washington, DC 20307
Tel: 202 782-9405   *Fax:* 202 782-7093
E-mail: Michael.Nelson@amedd.army.mil
Length: 2 Yrs   *ACGME Approved/Offered Positions:* 8
Program ID: 020-10-11-087
Uniformed Services Program

National Institutes of Health Clinical Center Program

Sponsor: Clinical Center at the National Institutes of
  Health
Prgm Director: Kelly D Stone, MD, PhD*
Bldg 10, Room 12C103, MSC 1899
10 Center Drive
Bethesda, MD 20892
Tel: 301 435-0993   *Fax:* 301 480-5757
Length: 2 Yrs   *ACGME Approved/Offered Positions:* 8
Program ID: 020-23-21-090

Massachusetts

Boston

Boston University Medical Center Program

Sponsor: Boston Medical Center
Prgm Director: David M Center, MD
Boston University Medical Center
715 Albany Street
Boston, MA 02118
Tel: 617 638-4860   *Fax:* 617 536-8093
E-mail: dcenter@bu.edu
Length: 2 Yrs   *ACGME Approved/Offered Positions:* 2
Program ID: 020-24-21-112

Brigham and Women's Hospital Program

Sponsor: Brigham and Women's Hospital
Children's Hospital
Prgm Director: Jonathan P Arm, MBBS, MD
Smith Building, Room 638
One Jimmy Fund Way
Boston, MA 02115
Tel: 617 525-1305   *Fax:* 617 525-1310
Length: 2 Yrs   *ACGME Approved/Offered Positions:* 6
Program ID: 020-24-21-031

Children's Hospital Program

Sponsor: Children's Hospital
Brigham and Women's Hospital
Prgm Director: Lynda C Schneider, MD
Division of Immunology
300 Longwood Avenue
Boston, MA 02115
Tel: 617 355-6180   *Fax:* 617 730-0310
Length: 2 Yrs   *ACGME Approved/Offered Positions:* 4
Program ID: 020-24-21-061

Note: * indicates a newly appointed program director

Massachusetts General Hospital Program
Sponsor: Massachusetts General Hospital
Prgm Director: Aidan A Long, MD
Immunology/Allergy Unit
Cox 201, 55 Fruit Street
Boston, MA 02114
Tel: 617 726-3850   *Fax:* 617 726-3847
E-mail: mangelo@partners.org
Length: 2 Yrs   *ACGME Approved/Offered Positions:* 4
Program ID: 020-24-21-051

Michigan

Ann Arbor

University of Michigan Program
Sponsor: University of Michigan Hospitals and Health
Centers
Prgm Director: James L Baldwin, MD
24 Frank Lloyd Wright Drive
PO Box 442, Suite H-2100
Ann Arbor, MI 48106
Tel: 734 936-5634   *Fax:* 734 647-6263
Length: 2 Yrs   *ACGME Approved/Offered Positions:* 4
Program ID: 020-25-21-045

Detroit

Henry Ford Hospital Program
Sponsor: Henry Ford Hospital
Prgm Director: Christian Nageotte, MD*
1 Ford Place, 4B
Detroit, MI 48202
Tel: 586 977-5505
Length: 2 Yrs   *ACGME Approved/Offered Positions:* 4
Program ID: 020-25-11-032

Wayne State University/Detroit Medical Center Program
Sponsor: Wayne State University/Detroit Medical Center
Children's Hospital of Michigan
Detroit Receiving Hospital and University Health Center
Prgm Director: Elizabeth Secord, MD
Division of Immunology, Allergy & Rheumatology
3901 Beaubien Blvd
Detroit, MI 48201
Tel: 313 745-4450   *Fax:* 313 993-8699
E-mail: esecord@med.wayne.edu
Length: 2 Yrs   *ACGME Approved/Offered Positions:* 3
Program ID: 020-25-21-071

Minnesota

Minneapolis

University of Minnesota Program
Sponsor: University of Minnesota Medical School
University of Minnesota Medical Center, Division of
Fairview
Prgm Director: Malcolm N Blumenthal, MD
MMC 434
420 Delaware Street, SE
Minneapolis, MN 55455
Tel: 612 624-5456   *Fax:* 612 624-9188
E-mail: paccsedu@umn.edu
Length: 2 Yrs   *ACGME Approved/Offered Positions:* 2
Program ID: 020-26-21-091

Rochester

College of Medicine, Mayo Clinic (Rochester) Program
Sponsor: College of Medicine, Mayo Clinic
Mayo Clinic (Rochester)
Prgm Director: Gerald W Volcheck, MD
200 First Street, SW
Rochester, MN 55905
Tel: 507 284-4966   *Fax:* 507 284-0902
Length: 2 Yrs   *ACGME Approved/Offered Positions:* 4
Program ID: 020-26-21-115

Mississippi

Jackson

University of Mississippi Medical Center Program
Sponsor: University of Mississippi School of Medicine
University Hospitals and Clinics
Veterans Affairs Medical Center (Jackson)
Prgm Director: Stephen F Kemp, MD
Department of Medicine, Div of Allergy/Immunology
768 Lakeland Drive, Bldg LJ
Jackson, MS 39216
Tel: 601 815-1078   *Fax:* 601 984-6994
Length: 2 Yrs   *ACGME Approved/Offered Positions:* 4
Program ID: 020-27-12-124

Missouri

Kansas City

University of Missouri at Kansas City Program
Sponsor: University of Missouri-Kansas City School of
Medicine
Allergy and Asthma Specialists of Kansas City
Children's Mercy Hospital
Truman Medical Center
Prgm Director: Paul J Dowling Jr, MD
2401 Gillham Road
Kansas City, MO 64108
Tel: 816 234-3097   *Fax:* 816 346-1301
E-mail: pdowling@cmh.edu
Length: 2 Yrs   *ACGME Approved/Offered Positions:* 4
Program ID: 020-28-21-114

St Louis

St Louis University School of Medicine Program
Sponsor: St Louis University School of Medicine
Cardinal Glennon Children's Hospital
St Louis University Hospital
Veterans Affairs Medical Center (St Louis)
Prgm Director: Mark S Dykewicz, MD
1402 S Grand Blvd - R209
St Louis, MO 63104
Tel: 314 977-8828   *Fax:* 314 977-8816
Length: 2 Yrs   *ACGME Approved/Offered Positions:* 3
Program ID: 020-28-21-019

Washington University/B-JH/SLCH Consortium Program
Sponsor: Washington University/B-JH/SLCH Consortium
Barnes-Jewish Hospital
Barnes-Jewish West County Hospital
St Louis Children's Hospital
Washington University School of Medicine
Prgm Director: H James Wedner, MD
660 South Euclid Avenue, Campus Box 8122
St Louis, MO 63110
Tel: 314 454-7937   *Fax:* 314 454-7120
E-mail: jwedner@im.wustl.edu
Length: 2 Yrs   *ACGME Approved/Offered Positions:* 8
Program ID: 020-28-21-095

Nebraska

Omaha

Creighton University Program
Sponsor: Creighton University School of Medicine
Creighton University Medical Center (Tenet - SJH)
Ehrling Bergquist Hospital
Veterans Affairs Medical Center (Omaha)
Prgm Director: Jeffrey R Stokes, MD
601 N 30th St
Suite 3M-100
Omaha, NE 68131
Tel: 402 280-3637   *Fax:* 402 280-4803
E-mail: jstokes@creighton.edu
Length: 2 Yrs   *ACGME Approved/Offered Positions:* 4
Program ID: 020-30-21-088

New Jersey

Newark

UMDNJ-New Jersey Medical School Program
Sponsor: UMDNJ-New Jersey Medical School
UMDNJ-University Hospital
Veterans Affairs New Jersey Health Care System
Prgm Director: Alan H Wolff, MD
Division of Allergy & Immunology
90 Bergen Street, Suite 4700
Newark, NJ 07103
Tel: 973 972-2762   *Fax:* 973 972-2769
Length: 2 Yrs   *ACGME Approved/Offered Positions:* 6
Program ID: 020-33-11-040

New York

Bronx

Albert Einstein College of Medicine Program
Sponsor: Albert Einstein College of Medicine of Yeshiva
University
Montefiore Medical Center-Weiler Division
Prgm Director: Arye Rubinstein, MD, PhD
Montefiore Medical Center
1525 Blondell Avenue, Suite 101
Bronx, NY 10461
Tel: 718 405-8530   *Fax:* 718 405-8532
Length: 2 Yrs   *ACGME Approved/Offered Positions:* 4
Program ID: 020-35-21-054

Brooklyn

Long Island College Hospital Program
Sponsor: Long Island College Hospital
Prgm Director: Arlene T Schneider, MD
339 Hicks Street
Brooklyn, NY 11201
Tel: 718 780-4673   *Fax:* 718 780-1493
E-mail: arschneider@chpnet.org
Length: 2 Yrs   *ACGME Approved/Offered Positions:* 4
Program ID: 020-35-11-041

SUNY Health Science Center at Brooklyn Program
Sponsor: SUNY Health Science Center at Brooklyn
Kings County Hospital Center
University Hospital-SUNY Health Science Center at
Brooklyn
Prgm Director: Rauno Joks, MD
450 Clarkson Avenue, Box 50
Brooklyn, NY 11203
Tel: 718 270-2156   *Fax:* 718 270-1831
E-mail: rauno.joks@downstate.edu
Length: 2 Yrs   *ACGME Approved/Offered Positions:* 2
Program ID: 020-35-21-092

Programs

Buffalo

University at Buffalo Program

Sponsor: University at Buffalo School of Medicine
Kaleida Health System (Buffalo General Hospital)
Kaleida Health System (Women and Children's Hospital of Buffalo)
Prgm Director: Mark Ballow, MD
219 Bryant Street
Buffalo, NY 14222
Tel: 716 878-7105   *Fax:* 716 888-3841
Length: 2 Yrs   *ACGME Approved/Offered Positions:* 4
Program ID: 020-35-21-053

Great Neck

NSLIJHS-Albert Einstein College of Medicine at Long Island Jewish Medical Center Program

Sponsor: North Shore-Long Island Jewish Health System
Long Island Jewish Medical Center
Prgm Director: Vincent R Bonagura, MD
North Shore Long Island Jewish Health Care System
865 Northern Boulevard, Suite 101
Great Neck, NY 11021
Tel: 516 622-5070   *Fax:* 516 622-5060
E-mail: bonagura@lij.edu
Length: 2 Yrs   *ACGME Approved/Offered Positions:* 6
Program ID: 020-35-21-105

Mineola

Winthrop-University Hospital Program

Sponsor: Winthrop-University Hospital
Prgm Director: Luz Fonacier, MD
120 Mineola Boulevard
Suite 410
Mineola, NY 11501
Tel: 516 663-2097   *Fax:* 516 663-2946
E-mail: lfonacier@winthrop.org
Length: 2 Yrs   *ACGME Approved/Offered Positions:* 2
Program ID: 020-35-31-126

New York

Mount Sinai School of Medicine Program

Sponsor: Mount Sinai School of Medicine
Mount Sinai Medical Center
Prgm Director: Charlotte Cunningham-Rundles, MD, PhD
East Building 11-20, Box 1089
1425 Madison Avenue
New York, NY 10029
Tel: 212 659-9268   *Fax:* 212 987-5593
E-mail: charlotte.cunningham-rundles@mssm.edu
Length: 2 Yrs   *ACGME Approved/Offered Positions:* 6
Program ID: 020-35-21-083

New York Presbyterian Hospital (Columbia Campus) Program

Sponsor: New York Presbyterian Hospital
New York Presbyterian Hospital (Columbia Campus)
Prgm Director: Rachel L Miller, MD
College of Physicians and Surgeons
630 W 168th Street
New York, NY 10032
Tel: 212 305-7759   *Fax:* 212 305-2277
E-mail: rlm14@columbia.edu
Length: 2 Yrs   *ACGME Approved/Offered Positions:* 2
Program ID: 020-35-21-082

Rochester

University of Rochester Program

Sponsor: Strong Memorial Hospital of the University of Rochester
Prgm Director: Richard J Looney, MD
601 Elmwood Avenue, Box 695
Rochester, NY 14642
Tel: 585 275-5308   *Fax:* 585 442-3214
Length: 2 Yrs   *ACGME Approved/Offered Positions:* 2
Program ID: 020-35-11-043

North Carolina

Chapel Hill

University of North Carolina Hospitals Program

Sponsor: University of North Carolina Hospitals
Prgm Director: David B Peden, MD, MS
Asthma and Lung Biology
104 Mason Farm Road, CB# 7310
Chapel Hill, NC 27599
Tel: 919 966-0768   *Fax:* 919 966-9863
E-mail: sandra_florence@med.unc.edu
Length: 2 Yrs   *ACGME Approved/Offered Positions:* 4
Program ID: 020-36-13-125

Durham

Duke University Hospital Program

Sponsor: Duke University Hospital
Prgm Director: Wesley Burks, MD
Pediatric Allergy and Immunology, Box 2644
133 Medical Sciences Research Building I
Durham, NC 27710
Tel: 919 681-2949   *Fax:* 919 668-3750
Length: 2 Yrs   *ACGME Approved/Offered Positions:* 8
Program ID: 020-36-21-022

Winston-Salem

Wake Forest University School of Medicine Program

Sponsor: Wake Forest University Baptist Medical Center
Prgm Director: Stephen P Peters, MD, PhD
Department of Medicine
Medical Center Boulevard
Winston-Salem, NC 27157
Tel: 336 713-7500   *Fax:* 336 713-7544
Length: 2 Yrs   *ACGME Approved/Offered Positions:* 2
Program ID: 020-36-11-047

Ohio

Cincinnati

University Hospital/Cincinnati Children's/University of Cincinnati College of Medicine Program

Sponsor: University Hospital Inc
Cincinnati Children's Hospital Medical Center
Veterans Affairs Medical Center (Cincinnati)
Prgm Director: Amal H Assa'ad, MD
3333 Burnet Avenue
Cincinnati, OH 45229
Tel: 513 636-6771   *Fax:* 513 636-4615
Length: 2 Yrs   *ACGME Approved/Offered Positions:* 6
Program ID: 020-38-21-113

Cleveland

Cleveland Clinic Foundation Program

Sponsor: Cleveland Clinic Foundation
Prgm Director: David M Lang, MD
9500 Euclid Avenue, Desk C22
Cleveland, OH 44195
Tel: 216 445-5810   *Fax:* 216 445-2104
Length: 2 Yrs   *ACGME Approved/Offered Positions:* 4
Program ID: 020-38-21-104

Columbus

Ohio State University Hospital Program

Sponsor: Ohio State University Hospital
Nationwide Children's Hospital
Prgm Director: Bryan L Martin, DO
2050 Kenny Road, Suite 2200
Columbus, OH 43221
Tel: 614 293-6551
E-mail: bryan.martin@osumc.edu
Length: 2 Yrs   *ACGME Approved/Offered Positions:* 4
Program ID: 020-38-21-128

Pennsylvania

Hershey

Penn State University/Milton S Hershey Medical Center Program

Sponsor: Milton S Hershey Medical Center
Prgm Director: Timothy J Craig, DO
500 University Drive, Box H041
Hershey, PA 17033
Tel: 717 531-6525   *Fax:* 717 531-5785
E-mail: rmorton@psu.edu
Length: 2 Yrs   *ACGME Approved/Offered Positions:* 6
Program ID: 020-41-21-122

Philadelphia

Children's Hospital of Philadelphia Program

Sponsor: Children's Hospital of Philadelphia
Prgm Director: Kathleen E Sullivan, MD, PhD
34th Street and Civic Center Boulevard
Allergy and Immunology
Philadelphia, PA 19104
Tel: 215 590-2549   *Fax:* 215 590-4529
E-mail: sullivak@mail.med.upenn.edu
Length: 2 Yrs   *ACGME Approved/Offered Positions:* 4
Program ID: 020-41-31-123

Thomas Jefferson University Program

Sponsor: Thomas Jefferson University Hospital
Alfred I duPont Hospital for Children
Prgm Director: Stephen J McGeady, MD
833 Chestnut St
Philadelphia, PA 19107
Tel: 302 651-4728   *Fax:* 302 651-6558
Length: 2 Yrs   *ACGME Approved/Offered Positions:* 4
Program ID: 020-41-11-034

University of Pennsylvania Program

Sponsor: University of Pennsylvania Health System
Presbyterian Medical Center (UPHS)
Prgm Director: Arnold I Levinson, MD
421 Curie Boulevard
1014 BRB II/III
Philadelphia, PA 19104
Tel: 215 898-4592   *Fax:* 215 898-0193
E-mail: fpierce@mail.med.upenn.edu
Length: 2 Yrs   *ACGME Approved/Offered Positions:* 3
Program ID: 020-41-21-075

Note: * indicates a newly appointed program director

Pittsburgh

University of Pittsburgh Medical Center Medical Education Program

Sponsor: Univ of Pittsburgh Medical Center Medical Education
Children's Hospital of Pittsburgh of UPMC
UPMC Presbyterian Shadyside
Prgm Director: Andrew J MacGinnitie, MD, PhD
3705 Fifth Avenue
Pittsburgh, PA 15213
Tel: 412 692-7489   *Fax:* 412 692-8499
E-mail: Andrew.MacGinnitie@chp.edu
Length: 2 Yrs   *ACGME Approved/Offered Positions:* 4
Program ID: 020-41-21-076

Tennessee

Memphis

University of Tennessee Program

Sponsor: University of Tennessee College of Medicine
LeBonheur Children's Medical Center
Regional Medical Center at Memphis
Veterans Affairs Medical Center (Memphis)
Prgm Director: D Betty Lew, MD
Department of Pediatrics
50 North Dunlap, Room 301-WPT
Memphis, TN 38103
Tel: 901 287-5377   *Fax:* 901 287-4478
Length: 2 Yrs   *ACGME Approved/Offered Positions:* 4
Program ID: 020-47-21-025

Nashville

Vanderbilt University Program

Sponsor: Vanderbilt University Medical Center
Veterans Affairs Medical Center (Nashville)
Prgm Director: David D Hagaman, MD
2611 West End Building, Suite 265
Nashville, TN 37203
Tel: 615 936-5705   *Fax:* 615 936-5862
E-mail: david.hagaman@vanderbilt.edu
Length: 2 Yrs   *ACGME Approved/Offered Positions:* 4
Program ID: 020-47-21-097

Texas

Dallas

University of Texas Southwestern Medical School Program

Sponsor: University of Texas Southwestern Medical School
Children's Medical Center of Dallas
Dallas County Hospital District-Parkland Memorial Hospital
University Hospitals St Paul
University Hospitals Zale Lipshy
Prgm Director: David A Khan, MD
5323 Harry Hines Boulevard
Dallas, TX 75390
Tel: 214 648-5659   *Fax:* 214 648-9102
Length: 2 Yrs   *ACGME Approved/Offered Positions:* 4
Program ID: 020-48-21-085

Galveston

University of Texas Medical Branch Hospitals Program

Sponsor: University of Texas Medical Branch Hospitals
Prgm Director: J Andrew Grant, MD
301 University Blvd
8.104 Medical Research Building
Galveston, TX 77555
Tel: 409 772-3410   *Fax:* 409 772-5841
E-mail: jagrant@utmb.edu
Length: 2 Yrs   *ACGME Approved/Offered Positions:* 6
Program ID: 020-48-11-026

Houston

Baylor College of Medicine Program

Sponsor: Baylor College of Medicine
Harris County Hospital District-Ben Taub General Hospital
Texas Children's Hospital
Prgm Director: William T Shearer, MD, PhD
Department of Pediatrics
One Baylor Plaza
Houston, TX 77030
Tel: 832 824-1274   *Fax:* 832 825-7131
E-mail: wshearer@bcm.edu
Length: 2 Yrs   *ACGME Approved/Offered Positions:* 8
Program ID: 020-48-21-063

Lackland AFB

San Antonio Uniformed Services Health Education Consortium Program

Sponsor: San Antonio Uniformed Services Health Education Consortium
Wilford Hall Medical Center (AETC)
Prgm Director: James M Quinn, MD
Allergy Clinic
2200 Bergquist Drive, Suite 1
Lackland AFB, TX 78236
Tel: 210 292-7521   *Fax:* 210 292-7033
E-mail: james.quinn@lackland.af.mil
Length: 2 Yrs   *ACGME Approved/Offered Positions:* 7
Program ID: 020-48-21-077
Uniformed Services Program

Virginia

Charlottesville

University of Virginia Program

Sponsor: University of Virginia Medical Center
Prgm Director: Thomas A Platts-Mills, MD, PhD
PO Box 801355
409 Lane Road, MR 4, Room 5086
Charlottesville, VA 22908
Tel: 434 924-5917   *Fax:* 434 924-5779
E-mail: tap2z@virginia.edu
Length: 2 Yrs   *ACGME Approved/Offered Positions:* 4
Program ID: 020-51-21-100

Richmond

Virginia Commonwealth University Health System Program

Sponsor: Virginia Commonwealth University Health System
Medical College of Virginia Hospitals
Prgm Director: Lawrence B Schwartz, MD, PhD
Box 980263
Richmond, VA 23298
Tel: 804 828-9685   *Fax:* 804 828-0283
E-mail: lbschwar@vcu.edu
Length: 2 Yrs   *ACGME Approved/Offered Positions:* 4
Program ID: 020-51-21-056

Washington

Seattle

University of Washington Program

Sponsor: University of Washington School of Medicine
Harborview Medical Center
Madigan Army Medical Center
Northwest Asthma & Allergy Center
Seattle Children's Hospital
University of Washington Medical Center
Virginia Mason Medical Center
Prgm Director: William R Henderson Jr, MD
Department of Medicine, Box 358050
815 Mercer Street
Seattle, WA 98109
Tel: 206 543-3780   *Fax:* 206 685-9318
Length: 2 Yrs   *ACGME Approved/Offered Positions:* 4
Program ID: 020-54-21-078

West Virginia

Morgantown

West Virginia University Program

Sponsor: West Virginia University School of Medicine
West Virginia University Hospitals
Prgm Director: David N Weissman, MD
Department of Pediatrics
PO Box 9214
Morgantown, WV 26505
Tel: 304 293-1201
Length: 2 Yrs   *ACGME Approved/Offered Positions:* 2
Program ID: 020-55-13-121

Wisconsin

Madison

University of Wisconsin Program

Sponsor: University of Wisconsin Hospital and Clinics
William S Middleton Veterans Hospital
Prgm Director: Mark H Moss, MD
Rm K4/910 CSC-9988
600 Highland Ave
Madison, WI 53792
Tel: 608 265-9575   *Fax:* 608 263-3104
E-mail: rlforbes@medicine.wisc.edu
Length: 2 Yrs   *ACGME Approved/Offered Positions:* 6
Program ID: 020-56-21-028

Milwaukee

Medical College of Wisconsin Affiliated Hospitals Program

Sponsor: Medical College of Wisconsin Affiliated Hospitals, Inc
Children's Hospital of Wisconsin
Clement J Zablocki Veterans Affairs Medical Center
Froedtert Memorial Lutheran Hospital
Prgm Director: Asriani M Chiu, MD
Asthma & Allergy Center
9000 W Wisconsin Avenue, Suite 440
Milwaukee, WI 53226
Tel: 414 266-6840   *Fax:* 414 266-6437
E-mail: achiu@mcw.edu
Length: 2 Yrs   *ACGME Approved/Offered Positions:* 5
Program ID: 020-56-31-037

Programs

Anesthesiology

Alabama

Birmingham

University of Alabama Medical Center Program
Sponsor: University of Alabama Hospital
Prgm Director: Susan Black, MD
619 South 19th Street
Birmingham, AL 35249
Tel: 205 934-6525   *Fax:* 205 975-0232
Length: 4 Yrs   *ACGME Approved/Offered Positions:* 63
Program ID: 040-01-21-010

Arizona

Phoenix

College of Medicine, Mayo Clinic (Arizona) Program
Sponsor: College of Medicine, Mayo Clinic
Mayo Clinic Hospital
Prgm Director: Daniel J Cole, MD
5777 East Mayo Boulevard
Phoenix, AZ 85054
Tel: 480 342-1272   *Fax:* 480 342-2027
Length: 3 Yrs   *ACGME Approved/Offered Positions:* 9
Program ID: 040-03-31-197

Tucson

University of Arizona Program
Sponsor: University of Arizona College of Medicine
University Medical Center
Prgm Director: Wayne Jacobsen, MD*
College of Medicine
1501 Campbell Avenue
Tucson, AZ 85724
Tel: 520 626-7141   *Fax:* 520 626-6943
Length: 3 Yrs   *ACGME Approved/Offered Positions:* 36
Program ID: 040-03-21-012

Arkansas

Little Rock

University of Arkansas for Medical Sciences Program
Sponsor: University of Arkansas College of Medicine
Arkansas Children's Hospital
Central Arkansas Veterans Healthcare System
UAMS Medical Center
Prgm Director: Charles Napolitano, MD, MBA*
4301 W Markham St, Slot 515
Little Rock, AR 72205
Tel: 501 686-6114   *Fax:* 501 686-7059
Length: 4 Yrs   *ACGME Approved/Offered Positions:* 42
Program ID: 040-04-21-013

California

Loma Linda

Loma Linda University Program
Sponsor: Loma Linda University Medical Center
Prgm Director: Gary R Stier, MD
Department of Anesthesiology
11234 Anderson Street, Room 2534
Loma Linda, CA 92354
Tel: 909 558-4015   *Fax:* 909 558-0214
E-mail: gstier@llu.edu
Length: 4 Yrs   *ACGME Approved/Offered Positions:* 48
Program ID: 040-05-21-016

Los Angeles

Cedars-Sinai Medical Center Program
Sponsor: Cedars-Sinai Medical Center
Prgm Director: Roya Yumul, MD, PhD
8700 Beverly Blvd
Department of Anesthesiology, Rm 4209
Los Angeles, CA 90048
Tel: 310 423-1682   *Fax:* 310 423-0387
Length: 4 Yrs   *ACGME Approved/Offered Positions:* 21
Program ID: 040-05-21-019

UCLA Medical Center Program
Sponsor: UCLA David Geffen School of Medicine/UCLA
    Medical Center
UCLA Medical Center
Prgm Director: Randolph H Steadman, MD
Center for Health Sciences
10833 Le Conte Avenue
Los Angeles, CA 90095
Tel: 310 267-8655   *Fax:* 310 267-3766
E-mail: ccamargo@mednet.ucla.edu
Length: 4 Yrs   *ACGME Approved/Offered Positions:* 66
Program ID: 040-05-21-020

University of Southern California/ LAC+USC Medical Center Program
Sponsor: University of Southern California/LAC+USC
    Medical Center
Kenneth Norris Jr Cancer Hospital and Research
    Institute
LAC+USC Medical Center
USC University Hospital
Prgm Director: Rajesh V Patel, MD, MS
Room 14-901
1200 North State Street
Los Angeles, CA 90033
Tel: 323 226-7748   *Fax:* 323 226-7872
E-mail: curtiss@usc.edu
Length: 3 Yrs   *ACGME Approved/Offered Positions:* 54
Program ID: 040-05-21-018

Orange

University of California (Irvine) Program
Sponsor: University of California (Irvine) Medical
    Center
Prgm Director: Cynthia T Anderson, MD
333 City Blvd West
Suite 2150
Orange, CA 92868
Tel: 714 456-6661   *Fax:* 714 456-7702
Length: 3 Yrs   *ACGME Approved/Offered Positions:* 24
Program ID: 040-05-21-015

Sacramento

University of California (Davis) Health System Program
Sponsor: University of California (Davis) Health System
University of California (Davis) Medical Center
Prgm Director: Brian Pitts, MD, MS
PSSB Suite 1200
4150 V Street
Sacramento, CA 95817
Tel: 916 734-5031   *Fax:* 916 734-7980
Length: 3 Yrs   *ACGME Approved/Offered Positions:* 42
Program ID: 040-05-21-014

San Diego

Naval Medical Center (San Diego) Program
Sponsor: Naval Medical Center (San Diego)
Prgm Director: Eugenio Lujan, MD, BS
Department of Anesthesiology
34800 Bob Wilson Drive
San Diego, CA 92134
Tel: 619 532-8952   *Fax:* 619 532-8945
Length: 3 Yrs   *ACGME Approved/Offered Positions:* 18
Program ID: 040-05-21-006
Uniformed Services Program

University of California (San Diego) Program
Sponsor: University of California (San Diego) Medical
    Center
Veterans Affairs Medical Center (San Diego)
Prgm Director: Benjamin I Atwater, MD, PhD
200 W Arbor Drive
San Diego, CA 92103
Tel: 619 543-5297   *Fax:* 619 543-6476
E-mail: anesthesiaresidency@ucsd.edu
Length: 3 Yrs   *ACGME Approved/Offered Positions:* 36
Program ID: 040-05-21-022

San Francisco

University of California (San Francisco) Program
Sponsor: University of California (San Francisco) School
    of Medicine
San Francisco General Hospital Medical Center
UCSF and Mount Zion Medical Centers
Prgm Director: Mark A Rosen, BA, MD
Room S-436/Box 0427
513 Parnassus Avenue
San Francisco, CA 94143
Tel: 415 476-3235   *Fax:* 415 514-0185
E-mail: rosenm@anesthesia.ucsf.edu
Length: 4 Yrs   *ACGME Approved/Offered Positions:* 94
Program ID: 040-05-21-023

Stanford

Stanford University Program
Sponsor: Stanford Hospital and Clinics
Veterans Affairs Palo Alto Health Care System
Prgm Director: Alex Macario, MD, MBA
Dept of Anesthesiology, H3589
300 Pasteur Drive
Stanford, CA 94305
Tel: 650 723-7377   *Fax:* 650 725-8544
Length: 3 Yrs   *ACGME Approved/Offered Positions:* 66
Program ID: 040-05-21-025

Note: * indicates a newly appointed program director

Torrance

Los Angeles County-Harbor-UCLA Medical Center Program
Sponsor: Los Angeles County-Harbor-UCLA Medical Center
Prgm Director: Jeanette Derdemezi, MD, MSc*
Box 10
1000 W Carson Street
Torrance, CA 90509
Tel: 310 222-3472   *Fax:* 310 782-1467
E-mail: hypnosmd@yahoo.com
Length: 3 Yrs   *ACGME Approved/Offered Positions:* 13
Program ID: 040-05-11-026

Colorado

Aurora

University of Colorado Denver Program
Sponsor: University of Colorado Denver School of Medicine
Denver Health Medical Center
University of Colorado Hospital
Prgm Director: Joy L Hawkins, MD
AO1-8203, Room 2017
12631 E 17th Avenue
Aurora, CO 80045
Tel: 303 724-1758   *Fax:* 303 724-1761
E-mail: jan.ratterree@uchsc.edu
Length: 3 Yrs   *ACGME Approved/Offered Positions:* 36
Program ID: 040-07-21-028

Connecticut

Farmington

University of Connecticut Program
Sponsor: University of Connecticut School of Medicine
Hartford Hospital
St Francis Hospital and Medical Center
Univ of Connecticut Health Center/John Dempsey Hospital
Prgm Director: Jeffrey B Gross, MD
Dept of Anesthesiology MC-2015
263 Farmington Avenue
Farmington, CT 06030
Tel: 860 679-3516
Length: 3 Yrs   *ACGME Approved/Offered Positions:* 24
Program ID: 040-08-21-172

New Haven

Yale-New Haven Medical Center Program
Sponsor: Yale-New Haven Hospital
Prgm Director: Jeffrey J Schwartz, MD, BS
Dept of Anesthesiology
20 York Street
New Haven, CT 06504
Tel: 203 785-2802   *Fax:* 203 785-6664
E-mail: jeffrey.schwartz@yale.edu
Length: 3 Yrs   *ACGME Approved/Offered Positions:* 57
Program ID: 040-08-21-030

District of Columbia

Washington

George Washington University Program
Sponsor: George Washington University School of Medicine
George Washington University Hospital (UHS)
Prgm Director: Jeffrey S Berger, MD, MBA*
900 23rd Street
Washington, DC 20037
Tel: 202 715-5296   *Fax:* 202 715-4759
Length: 3 Yrs   *ACGME Approved/Offered Positions:* 21
Program ID: 040-10-21-033

Georgetown University Hospital Program
Sponsor: Georgetown University Hospital
Washington Hospital Center
Prgm Director: Russell T Wall III, MD
Department of Anesthesia, Lower Level, CCC
3800 Reservoir Road, NW
Washington, DC 20007
Tel: 202 444-5128   *Fax:* 202 444-8854
E-mail: wallr@gunet.georgetown.edu
Length: 3 Yrs   *ACGME Approved/Offered Positions:* 21
Program ID: 040-10-21-032

Florida

Gainesville

University of Florida Program
Sponsor: University of Florida College of Medicine
North Florida/South Georgia Veterans Health System
Shands Hospital at the University of Florida
Prgm Director: Michael E Mahla, MD
1600 SW Archer Road
PO Box 100254
Gainesville, FL 32610
Tel: 352 265-0077   *Fax:* 352 265-6922
E-mail: mahla@ufl.edu
Length: 4 Yrs   *ACGME Approved/Offered Positions:* 66
Program ID: 040-11-21-035

Jacksonville

College of Medicine, Mayo Clinic (Jacksonville) Program
Sponsor: College of Medicine, Mayo Clinic
Mayo Clinic Florida Hospital
Prgm Director: Marie L De Ruyter, MD
4500 San Pablo Road
Jacksonville, FL 32224
Tel: 904 296-5285
Length: 4 Yrs   *ACGME Approved/Offered Positions:* 12
Program ID: 040-11-13-194

Miami

Jackson Memorial Hospital/Jackson Health System Program
Sponsor: Jackson Memorial Hospital/Jackson Health System
University of Miami Sylvester Comprehensive Cancer Center
Veterans Affairs Medical Center (Miami)
Prgm Director: Michael C Lewis, MD
Department of Anesthesiology R-370
1611 NW 12th Avenue
Miami, FL 33136
Tel: 305 585-6973   *Fax:* 305 585-8359
E-mail: mclewis@med.miami.edu
Length: 4 Yrs   *ACGME Approved/Offered Positions:* 93
Program ID: 040-11-21-036

Georgia

Atlanta

Emory University Program
Sponsor: Emory University School of Medicine
Emory University Hospital
Grady Health System
Prgm Director: Thomas E Philpot, MD
Department of Anesthesiology
1364 Clifton Road, NE
Atlanta, GA 30322
Tel: 404 778-3903   *Fax:* 404 778-5405
E-mail: tephilp@emory.edu
Length: 3 Yrs   *ACGME Approved/Offered Positions:* 48
Program ID: 040-12-21-037

Augusta

Medical College of Georgia Program
Sponsor: Medical College of Georgia
Prgm Director: Audrey S Alleyne, MD*
1120 Fifteenth Street, BIW 2144
Augusta, GA 30912
Tel: 706 721-4544   *Fax:* 706 721-7753
E-mail: aalleyne@mcg.edu
Length: 4 Yrs   *ACGME Approved/Offered Positions:* 27
Program ID: 040-12-11-038

Illinois

Chicago

Advocate Illinois Masonic Medical Center Program
Sponsor: Advocate Illinois Masonic Medical Center
Prgm Director: Arjang Khorasani, MD*
Department of Anesthesiology Rm 4830
836 West Wellington Avenue
Chicago, IL 60657
Tel: 773 296-7035   *Fax:* 773 296-5088
E-mail: arjangkh@yahoo.com
Length: 4 Yrs   *ACGME Approved/Offered Positions:* 24
Program ID: 040-16-21-040

John H Stroger Hospital of Cook County Program
Sponsor: John H Stroger Hospital of Cook County
Prgm Director: Gennadiy Voronov, MD*
Department of Anesthesiology and Pain Management
1901 West Harrison Street
Chicago, IL 60612
Tel: 312 864-1904   *Fax:* 312 864-9747
E-mail: gvoronov@ccbhs.org
Length: 4 Yrs   *ACGME Approved/Offered Positions:* 27
Program ID: 040-16-12-039

McGaw Medical Center of Northwestern University Program
Sponsor: McGaw Medical Center of Northwestern University
Northwestern Memorial Hospital
Prgm Director: Robert E Molloy, MD
Department of Anesthesiology
251 E Huron Street, Suite 5-704
Chicago, IL 60611
Tel: 312 926-8105   *Fax:* 312 926-9206
E-mail: czell@nmff.org
Length: 4 Yrs   *ACGME Approved/Offered Positions:* 63
Program ID: 040-16-21-042

Rush University Medical Center Program
Sponsor: Rush University Medical Center
Prgm Director: Kenneth J Tuman, MD
1653 W Congress Parkway
Chicago, IL 60612
Tel: 312 942-6504   *Fax:* 312 942-8858
E-mail: sherri_sachs@rush.edu
Length: 4 Yrs   *ACGME Approved/Offered Positions:* 58
Program ID: 040-16-21-043

University of Chicago Program
Sponsor: University of Chicago Medical Center
Prgm Director: Mohammed Minhaj, MD*
MC 4028
5841 S Maryland Avenue
Chicago, IL 60637
Tel: 773 702-1425
Length: 4 Yrs *ACGME Approved/Offered Positions:* 54
Program ID: 040-16-11-044

University of Illinois College of Medicine at Chicago Program
Sponsor: University of Illinois College of Medicine at Chicago
Jesse Brown Veterans Affairs Medical Center
University of Illinois Hospital and Clinics
Prgm Director: Timothy R Vadeboncouer, MD*
1740 W Taylor St
Suite 3200 West, M/C 515
Chicago, IL 60612
Tel: 312 996-4020 *Fax:* 312 996-4019
Length: 4 Yrs *ACGME Approved/Offered Positions:* 48
Program ID: 040-16-11-041

Maywood

Loyola University Program
Sponsor: Loyola University Medical Center
Prgm Director: Amy Murray, MD
2160 S First Avenue
Maywood, IL 60153
Tel: 708 216-0421 *Fax:* 708 216-1249
Length: 4 Yrs *ACGME Approved/Offered Positions:* 39
Program ID: 040-16-11-046

Indiana

Indianapolis

Indiana University School of Medicine Program
Sponsor: Indiana University School of Medicine
Clarian Indiana University Hospital
Clarian Riley Hospital for Children
Richard L Roudebush Veterans Affairs Medical Center
William N Wishard Memorial Hospital
Prgm Director: David A Nakata, MD, MBA
Indiana University School of Medicine
1120 South Drive, Fesler Hall 204
Indianapolis, IN 46202
Tel: 317 274-0275 *Fax:* 317 274-0256
E-mail: anesres@iupui.edu
Length: 4 Yrs *ACGME Approved/Offered Positions:* 78
Program ID: 040-17-21-048

Iowa

Iowa City

University of Iowa Hospitals and Clinics Program
Sponsor: University of Iowa Hospitals and Clinics
Prgm Director: Debra J Szeluga, MD, PhD*
Department of Anesthesiology
200 Hawkins Drive
Iowa City, IA 52242
Tel: 319 356-2633
Length: 4 Yrs *ACGME Approved/Offered Positions:* 39
Program ID: 040-18-21-049

Kansas

Kansas City

University of Kansas School of Medicine Program
Sponsor: University of Kansas School of Medicine
University of Kansas Hospital
Prgm Director: James D Kindscher, MD
3901 Rainbow Blvd
1440 KU Hospital, Mailstop 1034
Kansas City, KS 66160
Tel: 913 588-3315 *Fax:* 913 588-3365
E-mail: pcampbell@kumc.edu
Length: 3 Yrs *ACGME Approved/Offered Positions:* 24
Program ID: 040-19-11-050

Wichita

University of Kansas (Wichita) Program
Sponsor: University of Kansas School of Medicine (Wichita)
Via Christi Regional Medical Center-St Francis
Wesley Medical Center
Prgm Director: Robert McKay, MD
Department of Anesthesiology
929 N St Francis, Room 8074
Wichita, KS 67214
Tel: 316 268-6147 *Fax:* 316 291-7759
E-mail: anesthe1@kumc.edu
Length: 4 Yrs *ACGME Approved/Offered Positions:* 15
Program ID: 040-19-22-051

Kentucky

Lexington

University of Kentucky College of Medicine Program
Sponsor: University of Kentucky College of Medicine
University of Kentucky Hospital
Prgm Director: Randall M Schell, MD
University of Kentucky
800 Rose Street, N-202
Lexington, KY 40536
Tel: 859 323-5956 *Fax:* 859 323-1080
E-mail: rschell@uky.edu
Length: 4 Yrs *ACGME Approved/Offered Positions:* 36
Program ID: 040-20-21-052

Louisville

University of Louisville Program
Sponsor: University of Louisville School of Medicine
University of Louisville Hospital
Veterans Affairs Medical Center (Louisville)
Prgm Director: Laura D Clark, MD*
530 S Jackson Street Room C2A03
Louisville, KY 40202
Tel: 502 852-5851 *Fax:* 502 852-6056
E-mail: Mickai@aol.com
Length: 4 Yrs *ACGME Approved/Offered Positions:* 28
Program ID: 040-20-21-053

Louisiana

New Orleans

Louisiana State University Program
Sponsor: Louisiana State University School of Medicine
Children's Hospital (New Orleans)
East Jefferson General Hospital
Medical Center of Louisiana at New Orleans
West Jefferson Medical Center
Prgm Director: Alan D Kaye, MD
450A South Clairborne Avenue
2nd Floor, Room 231
New Orleans, LA 70112
Tel: 504 568-2319 *Fax:* 504 568-2317
Length: 4 Yrs *ACGME Approved/Offered Positions:* 9
Program ID: 040-21-31-199

Ochsner Clinic Foundation Program
Sponsor: Ochsner Clinic Foundation
Prgm Director: Robin B Stedman, MD, MPH
1514 Jefferson Highway
New Orleans, LA 70121
Tel: 504 842-3755 *Fax:* 504 842-2036
E-mail: aarseneaux@ochsner.org
Length: 4 Yrs *ACGME Approved/Offered Positions:* 21
Program ID: 040-21-12-055

Tulane University Program
Sponsor: Tulane University School of Medicine
Tulane University Hospital and Clinics
Prgm Director: Paul J Primeaux Jr, MD*
1430 Tulane Ave, SL 4
New Orleans, LA 70112
Tel: 504 988-5904 *Fax:* 504 988-1941
E-mail: pburke@tulane.edu
Length: 4 Yrs *ACGME Approved/Offered Positions:* 30
Program ID: 040-21-31-168

Shreveport

Louisiana State University (Shreveport) Program
Sponsor: LSU Health Sciences Center-University Hospital
Overton Brooks Veterans Affairs Medical Center
Prgm Director: Edwin W Herron Jr, MD*
1501 Kings Highway
PO Box 33932
Shreveport, LA 71130
Tel: 318 675-7195 *Fax:* 318 675-6681
E-mail: eherr1@lsuhsc.edu
Length: 4 Yrs *ACGME Approved/Offered Positions:* 24
Program ID: 040-21-11-056

Maine

Portland

Maine Medical Center Program
Sponsor: Maine Medical Center
Prgm Director: John W Allyn, MD
22 Bramhall Street
Portland, ME 04102
Tel: 207 662-4562 *Fax:* 207 662-6236
Length: 4 Yrs *ACGME Approved/Offered Positions:* 15
Program ID: 040-22-11-057

Note: * indicates a newly appointed program director

Maryland

Baltimore

Johns Hopkins University Program
Sponsor: Johns Hopkins University School of Medicine
Johns Hopkins Hospital
Prgm Director: Deborah A Schwengel, MD
Blalock 1412
600 North Wolfe Street
Baltimore, MD 21287
Tel: 410 955-7609   *Fax:* 410 955-5607
Length: 3 Yrs   *ACGME Approved/Offered Positions:* 75
Program ID: 040-23-21-058

University of Maryland Program
Sponsor: University of Maryland Medical System
Prgm Director: Mary J Njoku, MD
Department of Anesthesiology
22 S Greene Street, S11C00
Baltimore, MD 21201
Tel: 410 328-1239   *Fax:* 410 328-0546
E-mail: mpurcell@anes.umm.edu
Length: 4 Yrs   *ACGME Approved/Offered Positions:* 39
Program ID: 040-23-11-059

Bethesda

National Capital Consortium Program
Sponsor: National Capital Consortium
Children's National Medical Center
National Naval Medical Center (Bethesda)
Walter Reed Army Medical Center
Prgm Director: Dale F Szpisjak, MD, MPH*
Dept of Anesthesiology, USUHS
4301 Jones Bridge Rd, Attn: Dr Szpisjak
Bethesda, MD 20814
Tel: 301 295-3140   *Fax:* 301 295-2200
E-mail: dszpisjak@usuhs.mil
Length: 3 Yrs   *ACGME Approved/Offered Positions:* 45
Program ID: 040-10-21-190
Uniformed Services Program

Massachusetts

Boston

Beth Israel Deaconess Medical Center Program
Sponsor: Beth Israel Deaconess Medical Center
Prgm Director: Stephanie B Jones, MD
Dept of Anesthesia, Critical Care & Pain Medicine
One Deaconess Road, CC-470
Boston, MA 02215
Tel: 617 754-2733   *Fax:* 617 754-2735
Length: 3 Yrs   *ACGME Approved/Offered Positions:* 54
Program ID: 040-24-11-060

Boston University Medical Center Program
Sponsor: Boston Medical Center
Prgm Director: Ruben J Azocar, MD
One Boston Medical Center Place
88 East Newton Street
Boston, MA 02118
Tel: 617 638-6955   *Fax:* 617 638-6966
E-mail: ruben.azocar@bmc.org
Length: 3 Yrs   *ACGME Approved/Offered Positions:* 27
Program ID: 040-24-21-062

Brigham and Women's Hospital Program
Sponsor: Brigham and Women's Hospital
Prgm Director: Daniel F Dedrick, MD
75 Francis Street
Boston, MA 02115
Tel: 617 732-8218   *Fax:* 617 582-6131
Length: 4 Yrs   *ACGME Approved/Offered Positions:* 96
Program ID: 040-24-21-066

Caritas St Elizabeth's Medical Center Program
Sponsor: Caritas St Elizabeth's Medical Center of Boston
Lahey Clinic
Prgm Director: Mark S Shulman, MD
Department of Anesthesiology & Pain Medicine
736 Cambridge Street, CMP-2, #211
Boston, MA 02135
Tel: 617 789-2777   *Fax:* 617 254-6384
E-mail: mark.shulman@caritaschristi.org
Length: 3 Yrs   *ACGME Approved/Offered Positions:* 31
Program ID: 040-24-21-067

Massachusetts General Hospital Program
Sponsor: Massachusetts General Hospital
Newton-Wellesley Hospital
Prgm Director: Keith H Baker, MD, PhD
Department of Anesthesia
55 Fruit Street, Bigelow 4
Boston, MA 02114
Tel: 617 726-3030   *Fax:* 617 724-8500
E-mail: khbaker@partners.org
Length: 4 Yrs   *ACGME Approved/Offered Positions:* 87
Program ID: 040-24-31-064

Tufts Medical Center Program
Sponsor: Tufts Medical Center
Prgm Director: Iqbal M Ahmed, MD
Department of Anesthesia
800 Washington Street, Box 298
Boston, MA 02111
Tel: 617 636-9315   *Fax:* 617 636-8384
E-mail: lettienne@tuftsmedicalcenter.org
Length: 3 Yrs   *ACGME Approved/Offered Positions:* 18
Program ID: 040-24-21-065

Springfield

Baystate Medical Center/Tufts University School of Medicine Program
Sponsor: Baystate Medical Center
Prgm Director: Prasad R Kilaru, MD
759 Chestnut Street
Porter 2
Springfield, MA 01199
Tel: 413 794-4326   *Fax:* 413 794-5349
E-mail: maria.lopez@bhs.org
Length: 4 Yrs   *ACGME Approved/Offered Positions:* 27
Program ID: 040-24-12-069

Worcester

University of Massachusetts Program
Sponsor: University of Massachusetts Medical School
UMass Memorial Health Care (University Campus)
Prgm Director: Eleanor M Duduch, MD
55 Lake Avenue, N, Room S2-706
Worcester, MA 01655
Tel: 508 856-3821   *Fax:* 508 856-5911
E-mail: duduche@ummhc.org
Length: 4 Yrs   *ACGME Approved/Offered Positions:* 24
Program ID: 040-24-31-070

Michigan

Ann Arbor

University of Michigan Program
Sponsor: University of Michigan Hospitals and Health Centers
Prgm Director: Theodore J Sanford Jr, MD
1H247 UH 0048
1500 East Medical Center Drive
Ann Arbor, MI 48109
Tel: 734 936-4280   *Fax:* 734 936-9091
E-mail: tsanford@umich.edu
Length: 4 Yrs   *ACGME Approved/Offered Positions:* 90
Program ID: 040-25-21-071

Detroit

Henry Ford Hospital Program
Sponsor: Henry Ford Hospital
Prgm Director: William H Alarcon, MD*
Department of Anesthesiology
2799 West Grand Blvd
Detroit, MI 48202
Tel: 313 916-8234   *Fax:* 313 916-9434
E-mail: jrobert1@hfhs.org
Length: 4 Yrs   *ACGME Approved/Offered Positions:* 36
Program ID: 040-25-21-185

Wayne State University/Detroit Medical Center Program
Sponsor: Wayne State University/Detroit Medical Center
Harper-Hutzel Hospital
Prgm Director: H Michael Marsh, MBBS
DRH/UHC, 3-J
4201 St Antoine Blvd
Detroit, MI 48201
Tel: 313 745-4300   *Fax:* 313 745-4777
E-mail: mhooping@med.wayne.edu
Length: 4 Yrs   *ACGME Approved/Offered Positions:* 30
Program ID: 040-25-31-073

Minnesota

Minneapolis

University of Minnesota Program
Sponsor: University of Minnesota Medical School
Hennepin County Medical Center
University of Minnesota Medical Center, Division of Fairview
Prgm Director: David S Beebe, MD
420 Delaware Street SE
MMC 294
Minneapolis, MN 55455
Tel: 612 624-9990   *Fax:* 612 626-2363
E-mail: beebe001@umn.edu
Length: 4 Yrs   *ACGME Approved/Offered Positions:* 21
Program ID: 040-26-31-075

Rochester

College of Medicine, Mayo Clinic (Rochester) Program
Sponsor: College of Medicine, Mayo Clinic
Mayo Clinic (Rochester)
Rochester Methodist Hospital
Saint Marys Hospital of Rochester
Prgm Director: Timothy R Long, MD*
200 First St SW
Rochester, MN 55905
Tel: 507 255-6219   *Fax:* 507 255-2939
E-mail: long.timothy14@mayo.edu
Length: 4 Yrs   *ACGME Approved/Offered Positions:* 57
Program ID: 040-26-21-076

Mississippi

Jackson

University of Mississippi Medical Center Program
Sponsor: University of Mississippi School of Medicine
University Hospitals and Clinics
Prgm Director: Claude D Brunson, MD
2500 North State Street
Department of Anesthesiology
Jackson, MS 39216
Tel: 601 984-5931   *Fax:* 601 984-5915
Length: 4 Yrs   *ACGME Approved/Offered Positions:* 24
Program ID: 040-27-11-077

Programs

Missouri

Columbia

University of Missouri-Columbia Program

Sponsor: University of Missouri-Columbia School of
  Medicine
University Hospitals and Clinics
Prgm Director: Alice Landrum, MD*
3W27 Health Sciences Center
DC005.00
Columbia, MO 65212
Tel: 573 882-2568   *Fax:* 573 882-2226
E-mail: landruma@missouri.edu
Length: 4 Yrs   *ACGME Approved/Offered Positions:* 12
Program ID: 040-28-11-078

Kansas City

University of Missouri at Kansas City Program

Sponsor: University of Missouri-Kansas City School of
  Medicine
St Luke's Hospital-Kansas City
Truman Medical Center
Prgm Director: Eugene E Fibuch, MD
Department of Medical Education for Anesthesiology
4400 Wornall Road
Kansas City, MO 64111
Tel: 816 932-5132   *Fax:* 816 932-5179
Length: 4 Yrs   *ACGME Approved/Offered Positions:* 24
Program ID: 040-28-12-080

St Louis

St Louis University School of Medicine Program

Sponsor: St Louis University School of Medicine
Cardinal Glennon Children's Hospital
St Louis University Hospital
Prgm Director: Dean F Connors, MD, PhD*
Department of Anesthesiology and Critical Care
3635 Vista Avenue at Grand Blvd, FDT-3
St Louis, MO 63110
Tel: 314 577-8750   *Fax:* 314 268-5102
Length: 4 Yrs   *ACGME Approved/Offered Positions:* 30
Program ID: 040-28-21-166

Washington University/B-JH/SLCH Consortium Program

Sponsor: Washington University/B-JH/SLCH Consortium
Barnes-Jewish Hospital
Prgm Director: Thomas E Cox, MD
Box 8054
660 South Euclid Avenue
St Louis, MO 63110
Tel: 800 329-5971   *Fax:* 314 747-4284
E-mail: coxt@anest.wustl.edu
Length: 4 Yrs   *ACGME Approved/Offered Positions:* 54
Program ID: 040-28-11-081

Nebraska

Omaha

University of Nebraska Medical Center College of Medicine Program

Sponsor: University of Nebraska Medical Center College
  of Medicine
Creighton University Medical Center (Tenet - SJH)
Nebraska Medical Center
Prgm Director: Jean Simonson, MD*
984455 Nebraska Medical Center
Omaha, NE 68198
Tel: 402 559-4081   *Fax:* 402 559-7372
E-mail: jsimonso@unmc.edu
Length: 3 Yrs   *ACGME Approved/Offered Positions:* 35
Program ID: 040-30-11-082

New Hampshire

Lebanon

Dartmouth-Hitchcock Medical Center Program

Sponsor: Mary Hitchcock Memorial Hospital
Prgm Director: Lisabeth L Maloney, MD, MS*
B2 L4
One Medical Center Drive
Lebanon, NH 03756
Tel: 603 650-4356   *Fax:* 603 650-8980
Length: 4 Yrs   *ACGME Approved/Offered Positions:* 30
Program ID: 040-32-11-083

New Jersey

Camden

UMDNJ-Robert Wood Johnson Medical School (Camden) Program

Sponsor: Cooper Hospital-University Medical Center
Prgm Director: Irwin Gratz, DO
Department of Anesthesiology
1 Cooper Plaza
Camden, NJ 08103
Tel: 856 968-7330   *Fax:* 856 968-8326
E-mail: nichols-michele@cooperhealth.edu
Length: 3 Yrs   *ACGME Approved/Offered Positions:* 9
Program ID: 040-33-11-195

Livingston

St Barnabas Medical Center Program

Sponsor: St Barnabas Medical Center
Prgm Director: Robert S Dorian, MD
94 Old Short Hills Road
Livingston, NJ 07039
Tel: 973 322-5512   *Fax:* 973 322-8165
E-mail: anmiller@sbhcs.com
Length: 4 Yrs   *ACGME Approved/Offered Positions:* 12
Program ID: 040-33-12-085

New Brunswick

UMDNJ-Robert Wood Johnson Medical School Program

Sponsor: UMDNJ-Robert Wood Johnson Medical School
Robert Wood Johnson University Hospital
Prgm Director: Vincent N Cirella, MD
Clinical Academic Bldg Suite 3100
125 Paterson Street
New Brunswick, NJ 08901
Tel: 732 235-6153   *Fax:* 732 235-5100
E-mail: douglael@umdnj.edu
Length: 4 Yrs   *ACGME Approved/Offered Positions:* 30
Program ID: 040-33-21-180

Newark

UMDNJ-New Jersey Medical School Program

Sponsor: UMDNJ-New Jersey Medical School
Hackensack University Medical Center
UMDNJ-University Hospital
Prgm Director: Melissa Davidson, MD
MSB E-538
185 South Orange Avenue
Newark, NJ 07103
Tel: 973 972-0470   *Fax:* 973 972-4172
Length: 3 Yrs   *ACGME Approved/Offered Positions:* 27
Program ID: 040-33-21-087

Paterson

Mount Sinai School of Medicine (St Joseph's Regional Medical Center) Program

Sponsor: Mount Sinai School of Medicine
St Joseph's Regional Medical Center
St Michael's Medical Center (A Member of Catholic
  Health East)
Prgm Director: Stephen P Winikoff, MD
703 Main Street
Paterson, NJ 07503
Tel: 973 754-2323   *Fax:* 973 977-9455
E-mail: runoj@sjhmc.org
Length: 3 Yrs   *ACGME Approved/Offered Positions:* 19
Program ID: 040-33-21-089

New Mexico

Albuquerque

University of New Mexico Program

Sponsor: University of New Mexico School of Medicine
University of New Mexico Hospital
Prgm Director: James S Harding, MD
2701 Frontier NE MSC 11-6120
Surge Building, Room 110
Albuquerque, NM 87131
Tel: 505 272-2610   *Fax:* 505 272-1300
E-mail: anesthesiology@salud.unm.edu
Length: 4 Yrs   *ACGME Approved/Offered Positions:* 22
Program ID: 040-34-21-183

New York

Albany

Albany Medical Center Program

Sponsor: Albany Medical Center
Prgm Director: Michael R Sandison, MD*
47 New Scotland Avenue
Mail Code 131
Albany, NY 12208
Tel: 518 262-4302   *Fax:* 518 262-4736
E-mail: sandism@mail.amc.edu
Length: 4 Yrs   *ACGME Approved/Offered Positions:* 18
Program ID: 040-35-21-167

Note: * indicates a newly appointed program director

Bronx

Albert Einstein College of Medicine Program

Sponsor: Albert Einstein College of Medicine of Yeshiva University
Montefiore Medical Center-Henry and Lucy Moses Division
Montefiore Medical Center-Weiler Division
Prgm Director: Albert J Saubermann, MD
Montefiore Medical Center - Foreman Pavilion 4th
111 E 210th Street
Bronx, NY 10467
Tel: 718 920-2802   *Fax:* 718 653-2367
E-mail: anestres@montefiore.org
Length: 3 Yrs   *ACGME Approved/Offered Positions:* 45
Program ID: 040-35-21-181

Brooklyn

Brookdale University Hospital and Medical Center Program

Sponsor: Brookdale University Hospital and Medical Center
Staten Island University Hospital
Prgm Director: Adel R Abadir, MD
One Brookdale Plaza
Brooklyn, NY 11212
Tel: 718 240-5356   *Fax:* 718 240-5367
Length: 3 Yrs   *ACGME Approved/Offered Positions:* 30
Program ID: 040-35-31-097

Maimonides Medical Center Program

Sponsor: Maimonides Medical Center
Prgm Director: Kalpana Tyagaraj, MD
Department of Anesthesiology
4802 Tenth Avenue
Brooklyn, NY 11219
Tel: 718 283-7599   *Fax:* 718 283-8377
E-mail: droman@maimonidesmed.org
Length: 3 Yrs   *ACGME Approved/Offered Positions:* 25
Program ID: 040-35-11-101

New York Methodist Hospital Program

Sponsor: New York Methodist Hospital
Prgm Director: Joel M Yarmush, MD
New York Methodist Hospital
506 Sixth Street
Brooklyn, NY 11215
Tel: 718 780-3279   *Fax:* 718 780-3281
E-mail: JMY@aol.com
Length: 4 Yrs   *ACGME Approved/Offered Positions:* 13
Program ID: 040-35-11-102

SUNY Health Science Center at Brooklyn Program

Sponsor: SUNY Health Science Center at Brooklyn
Kings County Hospital Center
Long Island College Hospital
University Hospital-SUNY Health Science Center at Brooklyn
Prgm Director: Audree A Bendo, MD, MS
450 Clarkson Avenue, Box 6
Brooklyn, NY 11203
Tel: 718 270-3764   *Fax:* 718 270-3977
E-mail: dawn.grant@downstate.edu
Length: 4 Yrs   *ACGME Approved/Offered Positions:* 60
Program ID: 040-35-21-110

Buffalo

University at Buffalo Program

Sponsor: University at Buffalo School of Medicine
Erie County Medical Center
Kaleida Health System (Buffalo General Hospital)
Kaleida Health System (Millard Fillmore Hospital)
Kaleida Health System (Women and Children's Hospital of Buffalo)
Roswell Park Cancer Institute
Veterans Affairs Western New York Hospital
Prgm Director: Mark J Lema, MD, PhD
Hayes Annex A
3435 Main St
Buffalo, NY 14214
Tel: 716 829-6102   *Fax:* 716 829-3640
Length: 4 Yrs   *ACGME Approved/Offered Positions:* 36
Program ID: 040-35-21-093

East Meadow

Nassau University Medical Center Program

Sponsor: Nassau University Medical Center
Winthrop-University Hospital
Prgm Director: Paul Weinberg, MD
2201 Hempstead Turnpike
East Meadow, NY 11554
Tel: 516 572-6813   *Fax:* 516 572-5019
Length: 3 Yrs   *ACGME Approved/Offered Positions:* 15
Program ID: 040-35-11-094

New York

Mount Sinai School of Medicine Program

Sponsor: Mount Sinai School of Medicine
Mount Sinai Medical Center
Prgm Director: Adam I Levine, MD
Box 1010
One Gustave L Levy Place
New York, NY 10029
Tel: 212 241-1518   *Fax:* 212 426-2009
Length: 3 Yrs   *ACGME Approved/Offered Positions:* 54
Program ID: 040-35-21-104

New York Medical College at St Vincent's Hospital and Medical Center of New York Program

Sponsor: New York Medical College
St Vincent Catholic Medical Centers (Manhattan)
Prgm Director: Donald M Mathews, MD
170 West 12th Street, Suite NR408
New York, NY 10011
Tel: 212 604-7566   *Fax:* 212 604-2637
Length: 4 Yrs   *ACGME Approved/Offered Positions:* 18
Program ID: 040-35-12-109

New York Presbyterian Hospital (Columbia Campus) Program

Sponsor: New York Presbyterian Hospital
New York Presbyterian Hospital (Columbia Campus)
Prgm Director: Leila Mei Pang, MD
622 W 168th Street
PH5-505
New York, NY 10032
Tel: 212 305-3226   *Fax:* 212 305-3204
E-mail: lmp1@columbia.edu
Length: 4 Yrs   *ACGME Approved/Offered Positions:* 72
Program ID: 040-35-11-107

New York Presbyterian Hospital (Cornell Campus) Program

Sponsor: New York Presbyterian Hospital
Memorial Sloan-Kettering Cancer Center
New York Presbyterian Hospital (Cornell Campus)
Prgm Director: John J Savarese, MD
525 E 68th Street
New York, NY 10065
Tel: 212 746-2941   *Fax:* 212 746-8713
Length: 4 Yrs   *ACGME Approved/Offered Positions:* 60
Program ID: 040-35-21-098

New York University School of Medicine Program

Sponsor: New York University School of Medicine
Bellevue Hospital Center
NYU Hospitals Center
Prgm Director: Michael Wajda, MD
550 First Avenue, Rm IRM-607
New York, NY 10016
Tel: 212 263-3894   *Fax:* 212 263-7254
Length: 3 Yrs   *ACGME Approved/Offered Positions:* 58
Program ID: 040-35-21-106

St Luke's-Roosevelt Hospital Center Program

Sponsor: St Luke's-Roosevelt Hospital Center
St Luke's-Roosevelt Hospital Center-St Luke's Division
Prgm Director: John Wasnick, MD, MPH*
Department of Anesthesiology
1111 Amsterdam Avenue
New York, NY 10025
Tel: 212 523-2500   *Fax:* 212 523-3930
E-mail: jwasnick@chpnet.org
Length: 4 Yrs   *ACGME Approved/Offered Positions:* 36
Program ID: 040-35-11-108

Rochester

University of Rochester Program

Sponsor: Strong Memorial Hospital of the University of Rochester
Prgm Director: Suzanne B Karan, MD*
Department of Anesthesiology, Box 604
601 Elmwood Avenue
Rochester, NY 14642
Tel: 585 275-5161   *Fax:* 585 276-0122
Length: 4 Yrs   *ACGME Approved/Offered Positions:* 42
Program ID: 040-35-11-111

Stony Brook

SUNY at Stony Brook Program

Sponsor: University Hospital - SUNY at Stony Brook
Prgm Director: Christopher J Gallagher, MD*
Department of Anesthesiology
HSC L-4, 060
Stony Brook, NY 11794
Tel: 631 444-2975
E-mail: christopher.gallagher@stonybrook.edu
Length: 3 Yrs   *ACGME Approved/Offered Positions:* 30
Program ID: 040-35-21-170

Syracuse

SUNY Upstate Medical University Program

Sponsor: SUNY Upstate Medical University
Prgm Director: Carlos J Lopez III, MD
750 E Adams Street
Syracuse, NY 13210
Tel: 315 464-4899   *Fax:* 315 464-4866
E-mail: spottekk@upstate.edu
Length: 3 Yrs   *ACGME Approved/Offered Positions:* 33
Program ID: 040-35-21-113

Valhalla

New York Medical College at Westchester Medical Center Program

Sponsor: New York Medical College
Danbury Hospital
Metropolitan Hospital Center
Westchester Medical Center
Prgm Director: Kathryn E McGoldrick, MD
Macy Pavilion West, Room 2389
Valhalla, NY 10595
Tel: 914 493-7693   *Fax:* 914 493-7927
E-mail: kemcgoldrick@aol.com
Length: 3 Yrs   *ACGME Approved/Offered Positions:* 28
Program ID: 040-35-21-105

North Carolina

Chapel Hill

University of North Carolina Hospitals Program
Sponsor: University of North Carolina Hospitals
Prgm Director: David C Mayer, MD
Dept of Anesthesiology, UNC School of Medicine
CB 7010 N2201 UNC Hospitals
Chapel Hill, NC 27599
Tel: 919 966-5136   *Fax:* 919 966-4873
E-mail: UNCAnesthesiology-Residency@aims.unc.edu
Length: 4 Yrs   *ACGME Approved/Offered Positions:* 42
Program ID: 040-36-21-114

Durham

Duke University Hospital Program
Sponsor: Duke University Hospital
Veterans Affairs Medical Center (Durham)
Prgm Director: Catherine M Kuhn, MD
Department of Anesthesiology
DUMC 3094
Durham, NC 27710
Tel: 919 681-2924   *Fax:* 919 681-7893
E-mail: lineb001@mc.duke.edu
Length: 4 Yrs   *ACGME Approved/Offered Positions:* 42
Program ID: 040-36-31-115

Winston-Salem

Wake Forest University School of Medicine Program
Sponsor: Wake Forest University Baptist Medical Center
Prgm Director: Pamela C Nagle, MD*
Department of Anesthesiology
Medical Center Boulevard
Winston-Salem, NC 27157
Tel: 338 716-4498   *Fax:* 336 716-8190
E-mail: anesres@wfubmc.edu
Length: 4 Yrs   *ACGME Approved/Offered Positions:* 48
Program ID: 040-36-21-116

Ohio

Cincinnati

University Hospital/University of Cincinnati College of Medicine Program
Sponsor: University Hospital Inc
Prgm Director: John P Lawrence, MD
231 Albert Sabin Way
PO Box 670531
Cincinnati, OH 45267
Tel: 513 558-6356   *Fax:* 513 558-0995
E-mail: donna.benesch@uc.edu
Length: 4 Yrs   *ACGME Approved/Offered Positions:* 18
Program ID: 040-38-21-118

Cleveland

Case Western Reserve University (MetroHealth) Program
Sponsor: MetroHealth Medical Center
Prgm Director: Samuel DeJoy, MD, DMD
2500 MetroHealth Drive
Cleveland, OH 44109
Tel: 216 778-4809   *Fax:* 216 778-5378
Length: 3 Yrs   *ACGME Approved/Offered Positions:* 21
Program ID: 040-38-21-174

Note: * indicates a newly appointed program director

Cleveland Clinic Foundation Program
Sponsor: Cleveland Clinic Foundation
Prgm Director: John E Tetzlaff, MD
9500 Euclid Avenue
Cleveland, OH 44195
Tel: 216 445-2115   *Fax:* 216 445-0605
E-mail: aned@ccf.org
Length: 4 Yrs   *ACGME Approved/Offered Positions:* 90
Program ID: 040-38-22-120

University Hospitals Case Medical Center Program
Sponsor: University Hospitals Case Medical Center
Prgm Director: Matthew P Norcia, MD
11100 Euclid Avenue
Cleveland, OH 44106
Tel: 216 844-7335   *Fax:* 216 844-3781
Length: 4 Yrs   *ACGME Approved/Offered Positions:* 36
Program ID: 040-38-21-119

Columbus

Ohio State University Hospital Program
Sponsor: Ohio State University Hospital
Prgm Director: Ronald L Harter, MD
N-416 Doan Hall
410 West Tenth Avenue
Columbus, OH 43210
Tel: 614 293-2506   *Fax:* 614 293-8153
E-mail: denise.mcmaster@osumc.edu
Length: 4 Yrs   *ACGME Approved/Offered Positions:* 36
Program ID: 040-38-11-123

Toledo

University of Toledo Program
Sponsor: University of Toledo
Prgm Director: Alan P Marco, MD
3000 Arlington Avenue - Mailstop 1137
Toledo, OH 43614
Tel: 419 383-3556   *Fax:* 419 383-3550
Length: 4 Yrs   *ACGME Approved/Offered Positions:* 15
Program ID: 040-38-21-125

Oklahoma

Oklahoma City

University of Oklahoma Health Sciences Center Program
Sponsor: University of Oklahoma College of Medicine
Integris Baptist Medical Center
OU Medical Center
OU Medical Center - Children's Hospital
Prgm Director: Jane K Fitch, MD
Department of Anesthesiology
750 NE 13th Street, Suite 200, OAC Bldg
Oklahoma City, OK 73104
Tel: 405 271-4351   *Fax:* 405 271-8695
E-mail: brent-ross@ouhsc.edu
Length: 4 Yrs   *ACGME Approved/Offered Positions:* 24
Program ID: 040-39-21-128

Oregon

Portland

Oregon Health & Science University Program
Sponsor: Oregon Health & Science University Hospital
Veterans Affairs Medical Center (Portland)
Prgm Director: Christopher E Swide, MD
Department of Anesthesiology, UHS-2
3181 SW Sam Jackson Park Road
Portland, OR 97239
Tel: 503 494-7641   *Fax:* 503 418-1389
Length: 3 Yrs   *ACGME Approved/Offered Positions:* 36
Program ID: 040-40-21-129

Pennsylvania

Hershey

Penn State University/Milton S Hershey Medical Center Program
Sponsor: Milton S Hershey Medical Center
Prgm Director: Stephen J Kimatian, MD
500 University Drive
PO Box 850
Hershey, PA 17033
Tel: 717 531-5522   *Fax:* 717 531-0826
E-mail: jverbos@psu.edu
Length: 4 Yrs   *ACGME Approved/Offered Positions:* 51
Program ID: 040-41-11-130

Philadelphia

Drexel University College of Medicine/Hahnemann University Hospital Program
Sponsor: Drexel University College of
   Medicine/Hahnemann University
Hahnemann University Hospital (Tenet Health System)
Prgm Director: Jay C Horrow, MD, MS
Mail Stop 310
245 N 15th Street
Philadelphia, PA 19102
Tel: 215 762-7922   *Fax:* 215 762-8656
Length: 3 Yrs   *ACGME Approved/Offered Positions:* 25
Program ID: 040-41-21-133

Temple University Hospital Program
Sponsor: Temple University Hospital
Prgm Director: Scott A Schartel, DO
3401 N Broad Street (502-00)
Philadelphia, PA 19140
Tel: 215 707-3326   *Fax:* 215 707-8028
E-mail: anesres@temple.edu
Length: 3 Yrs   *ACGME Approved/Offered Positions:* 24
Program ID: 040-41-31-136

Thomas Jefferson University Program
Sponsor: Thomas Jefferson University Hospital
Prgm Director: Stephen E McNulty, DO
111 S 11th Street, Suite G8490
Philadelphia, PA 19107
Tel: 215 955-6161   *Fax:* 215 923-5507
Length: 3 Yrs   *ACGME Approved/Offered Positions:* 45
Program ID: 040-41-21-137

University of Pennsylvania Program
Sponsor: University of Pennsylvania Health System
Children's Hospital of Philadelphia
Presbyterian Medical Center (UPHS)
Veterans Affairs Medical Center (Philadelphia)
Prgm Director: Robert R Gaiser, MD
6 Dulles Building
3400 Spruce Street
Philadelphia, PA 19104
Tel: 215 662-3773   *Fax:* 215 615-3898
Length: 4 Yrs   *ACGME Approved/Offered Positions:* 72
Program ID: 040-41-21-134

Pittsburgh

University of Pittsburgh Medical Center Medical Education (Mercy) Program
Sponsor: Univ of Pittsburgh Medical Center Medical
   Education
Mercy Hospital of Pittsburgh
Prgm Director: Amy L Kemp, MD
Department of Anesthesiology
1400 Locust Street
Pittsburgh, PA 15219
Tel: 412 232-8009   *Fax:* 412 232-7960
E-mail: picciafocod@upmc.edu
Length: 3 Yrs   *ACGME Approved/Offered Positions:* 15
Program ID: 040-41-12-140

University of Pittsburgh Medical Center Medical Education Program

Sponsor: Univ of Pittsburgh Medical Center Medical Education
UPMC Presbyterian Shadyside
Prgm Director: David G Metro, MD
Department of Anesthesiology
3471 Fifth Avenue, Suite 910
Pittsburgh, PA 15213
Tel: 412 692-4503   *Fax:* 412 692-4515
E-mail: wetmoreal@anes.upmc.edu
Length: 4 Yrs   *ACGME Approved/Offered Positions:* 45
Program ID: 040-41-21-139

Western Pennsylvania Hospital/Temple University Program

Sponsor: Western Pennsylvania Hospital
Allegheny General Hospital
Prgm Director: Christopher A Troianos, MD
4800 Friendship Avenue
Pittsburgh, PA 15224
Tel: 412 578-5323   *Fax:* 412 578-4981
E-mail: jrandal@wpahs.org
Length: 3 Yrs   *ACGME Approved/Offered Positions:* 33
Program ID: 040-41-32-141

Puerto Rico

San Juan

University of Puerto Rico Program

Sponsor: University of Puerto Rico School of Medicine
Cardiovascular Center of Puerto Rico and the Caribbean
University Hospital
University of Puerto Rico Hospital at Carolina
University Pediatric Hospital
VA Caribbean Healthcare System
Prgm Director: Miguel A Marrero-Rivera, MD
School of Medicine, Department of Anesthesiology
PO Box 365067
San Juan, PR 00936
Tel: 787 758-0640   *Fax:* 787 758-1327
Length: 4 Yrs   *ACGME Approved/Offered Positions:* 9
Program ID: 040-42-21-142

South Carolina

Charleston

Medical University of South Carolina Program

Sponsor: Medical University of South Carolina College of Medicine
MUSC Medical Center
Prgm Director: Rebecca L Cain, MD*
167 Ashley Avenue Suite 301
MSC 912
Charleston, SC 29425
Tel: 843 876-5753   *Fax:* 843 792-9314
Length: 4 Yrs   *ACGME Approved/Offered Positions:* 27
Program ID: 040-45-22-143

Tennessee

Knoxville

University of Tennessee Medical Center at Knoxville Program

Sponsor: University of Tennessee Graduate School of Medicine
University of Tennessee Memorial Hospital
Prgm Director: Robert M Craft, MD*
Room U109
1924 Alcoa Highway
Knoxville, TN 37920
Tel: 865 305-9220   *Fax:* 865 637-5518
E-mail: rcraft@utmck.edu
Length: 3 Yrs   *ACGME Approved/Offered Positions:* 21
Program ID: 040-47-11-144

Nashville

Vanderbilt University Program

Sponsor: Vanderbilt University Medical Center
Prgm Director: John T Algren, MD
1211 21st Avenue South
Medical Arts Building, Ste 711
Nashville, TN 37212
Tel: 615 936-1830   *Fax:* 615 936-3412
E-mail: Marsha.K.Moore@Vanderbilt.edu
Length: 4 Yrs   *ACGME Approved/Offered Positions:* 45
Program ID: 040-47-11-146

Texas

Dallas

University of Texas Southwestern Medical School Program

Sponsor: University of Texas Southwestern Medical School
Dallas County Hospital District-Parkland Memorial Hospital
Dallas VA Medical Center
Methodist Health System Dallas
University Hospitals Zale Lipshy
Prgm Director: Charles W Whitten, MD
5323 Harry Hines Blvd
Dallas, TX 75390
Tel: 214 648-0434   *Fax:* 214 648-7660
Length: 4 Yrs   *ACGME Approved/Offered Positions:* 58
Program ID: 040-48-21-147

Galveston

University of Texas Medical Branch Hospitals Program

Sponsor: University of Texas Medical Branch Hospitals
Prgm Director: S Lynn Knox, MD
Department of Anesthesiology
301 University Blvd
Galveston, TX 77555
Tel: 409 772-1221   *Fax:* 409 772-4166
E-mail: cjbreish@utmb.edu
Length: 4 Yrs   *ACGME Approved/Offered Positions:* 54
Program ID: 040-48-11-149

Houston

Baylor College of Medicine Program

Sponsor: Baylor College of Medicine
Harris County Hospital District-Ben Taub General Hospital
Michael E DeBakey VA Medical Center - Houston
St Luke's Episcopal Hospital
Prgm Director: Maya Suresh, MBBS
Baylor Faculty Center (MS: BCM 120)
1709 Dryden Road, Suite 1700
Houston, TX 77030
Tel: 713 798-7356   *Fax:* 713 798-7345
E-mail: juliew@bcm.edu
Length: 4 Yrs   *ACGME Approved/Offered Positions:* 60
Program ID: 040-48-31-150

University of Texas at Houston Program

Sponsor: University of Texas Health Science Center at Houston
Memorial Hermann Hospital
University of Texas M D Anderson Cancer Center
Prgm Director: Mary Rabb, MD
6431 Fannin Street, MSB 5.020
Houston, TX 77030
Tel: 713 500-6253   *Fax:* 713 500-6270
Length: 4 Yrs   *ACGME Approved/Offered Positions:* 66
Program ID: 040-48-31-152

Lackland AFB

San Antonio Uniformed Services Health Education Consortium Program

Sponsor: San Antonio Uniformed Services Health Education Consortium
Brooke Army Medical Center
Wilford Hall Medical Center (AETC)
Prgm Director: Rocky R Reston, MD, PhD
3851 Roger Brooke Drive
Bldg 3600
Fort Sam Houston, TX 78234
Tel: 210 916-4512   *Fax:* 210 916-3769
E-mail: AnesthesiaPD@saushec.org
Length: 3 Yrs   *ACGME Approved/Offered Positions:* 42
Program ID: 040-48-21-091
Uniformed Services Program

Lubbock

Texas Tech University (Lubbock) Program

Sponsor: Texas Tech University Health Sciences Center at Lubbock
Covenant Medical Center
Lubbock Heart Hospital
University Medical Center
Prgm Director: John Hall, MD, JD
Department of Anesthesiology
3601 4th Street, Stop 8182
Lubbock, TX 79430
Tel: 806 743-2981   *Fax:* 806 743-2984
E-mail: john.hall@ttuhsc.edu
Length: 4 Yrs   *ACGME Approved/Offered Positions:* 13
Program ID: 040-48-11-153

San Antonio

University of Texas Health Science Center at San Antonio Program

Sponsor: University of Texas School of Medicine at San Antonio
Audie L Murphy Memorial Veterans Hospital (San Antonio)
University Health System
Prgm Director: Rosemary Hickey, MD
7703 Floyd Curl Drive, MSC 7838
San Antonio, TX 78229
Tel: 210 567-4506   *Fax:* 210 567-6135
E-mail: franklina@uthscsa.edu
Length: 4 Yrs   *ACGME Approved/Offered Positions:* 42
Program ID: 040-48-21-155

Programs

Temple

Texas A&M College of Medicine-Scott and White Program

Sponsor: Scott and White Memorial Hospital
Prgm Director: Russell K McAllister, MD*
Deprtment of Anesthesiology
2401 S 31st Street
Temple, TX 76508
Tel: 254 724-4008   *Fax:* 254 724-2504
Length: 4 Yrs   *ACGME Approved/Offered Positions:* 24
Program ID: 040-48-21-156

Utah

Salt Lake City

University of Utah Program

Sponsor: University of Utah Medical Center
Prgm Director: Lazarre Ogden, MD
30 North 1900 East
3C-444 SOM
Salt Lake City, UT 84132
Tel: 801 581-6393   *Fax:* 801 581-4367
E-mail: katija.snow@hsc.utah.edu
Length: 3 Yrs   *ACGME Approved/Offered Positions:* 39
Program ID: 040-49-31-157

Vermont

Burlington

University of Vermont Program

Sponsor: Fletcher Allen Health Care
Prgm Director: Ralph W Yarnell, MD
MCHV Campus
111 Colchester Avenue
Burlington, VT 05401
Tel: 802 847-0231   *Fax:* 802 847-5324
Length: 4 Yrs   *ACGME Approved/Offered Positions:* 18
Program ID: 040-50-11-158

Virginia

Charlottesville

University of Virginia Program

Sponsor: University of Virginia Medical Center
Prgm Director: Edward C Nemergut, MD
Department of Anesthesiology
PO Box 800710
Charlottesville, VA 22908
Tel: 434 924-2283   *Fax:* 434 982-0019
E-mail: en3x@virginia.edu
Length: 4 Yrs   *ACGME Approved/Offered Positions:* 48
Program ID: 040-51-11-159

Portsmouth

Naval Medical Center (Portsmouth) Program

Sponsor: Naval Medical Center (Portsmouth)
Prgm Director: William A Beckman Jr, MD
620 John Paul Jones Circle
Dept of Anesthesiology
Portsmouth, VA 23708
Tel: 757 953-3270   *Fax:* 757 953-4595
E-mail: William.Beckman@med.navy.mil
Length: 3 Yrs   *ACGME Approved/Offered Positions:* 18
Program ID: 040-51-21-008
Uniformed Services Program

Richmond

Virginia Commonwealth University Health System Program

Sponsor: Virginia Commonwealth University Health
System
Hunter Holmes McGuire VA Medical Center (Richmond)
Medical College of Virginia Hospitals
Prgm Director: Jay H Shapiro, MD
MCV Hospitals and Physicians
PO Box 980459
Richmond, VA 23298
Tel: 804 828-0733   *Fax:* 804 828-8682
E-mail: ehandel@vcu.edu
Length: 4 Yrs   *ACGME Approved/Offered Positions:* 36
Program ID: 040-51-11-160

Washington

Seattle

University of Washington Program

Sponsor: University of Washington School of Medicine
Harborview Medical Center
University of Washington Medical Center
Prgm Director: Karen J Souter, MB, BS
1959 NE Pacific Street
Box 356540
Seattle, WA 98195
Tel: 206 543-2773   *Fax:* 206 543-2958
E-mail: anesuwa@u.washington.edu
Length: 4 Yrs   *ACGME Approved/Offered Positions:* 72
Program ID: 040-54-21-161

Virginia Mason Medical Center Program

Sponsor: Virginia Mason Medical Center
Prgm Director: Stephen M Rupp, MD
Graduate Medical Education, H8-GME
925 Seneca Street
Seattle, WA 98111
Tel: 206 583-6079   *Fax:* 206 223-6982
Length: 4 Yrs   *ACGME Approved/Offered Positions:* 24
Program ID: 040-54-12-162

West Virginia

Morgantown

West Virginia University Program

Sponsor: West Virginia University School of Medicine
West Virginia University Hospitals
Prgm Director: Richard Driver Jr, MD, MS
1 Medical Center Drive
PO Box 8255
Morgantown, WV 26506
Tel: 304 598-6148   *Fax:* 304 598-4930
E-mail: rowanja@wvuh.com
Length: 4 Yrs   *ACGME Approved/Offered Positions:* 15
Program ID: 040-55-11-163

Wisconsin

Madison

University of Wisconsin Program

Sponsor: University of Wisconsin Hospital and Clinics
Prgm Director: Paul W Kranner, MD
B6/319 Clinical Science Center
600 Highland Avenue
Madison, WI 53792
Tel: 608 263-8114   *Fax:* 608 262-1061
E-mail: mussehl@wisc.edu
Length: 4 Yrs   *ACGME Approved/Offered Positions:* 39
Program ID: 040-56-21-164

Milwaukee

Medical College of Wisconsin Affiliated Hospitals Program

Sponsor: Medical College of Wisconsin Affiliated
Hospitals, Inc
Froedtert Memorial Lutheran Hospital
Prgm Director: Thomas J Ebert, MD, PhD
9200 W Wisconsin Avenue
Milwaukee, WI 53226
Tel: 414 384-2000   *Fax:* 414 384-2939
E-mail: tjebert@mcw.edu
Length: 4 Yrs   *ACGME Approved/Offered Positions:* 66
Program ID: 040-56-21-165

Note: * indicates a newly appointed program director

Blood Banking/ Transfusion Medicine (Pathology)

Alabama

Birmingham

University of Alabama Medical Center Program
Sponsor: University of Alabama Hospital
American Red Cross Blood Services-Alabama Region
Prgm Director: Marisa B Marques, MD
619 19th Street South
West Pavilion, P230G
Birmingham, AL 35249
Tel: 205 934-7774   *Fax:* 205 975-4468
E-mail: LMB3785@uab.edu
Length: 1 Yr   *ACGME Approved/Offered Positions:* 1
Program ID: 305-01-21-041

Arkansas

Little Rock

University of Arkansas for Medical Sciences Program
Sponsor: University of Arkansas College of Medicine
American Red Cross Blood Services
Arkansas Children's Hospital
UAMS Medical Center
Prgm Director: Douglas P Blackall, MD
Department of Pathology
800 Marshall Street
Little Rock, AR 72202
Tel: 501 364-1316   *Fax:* 501 364-3155
E-mail: blackalldouglasp@uams.edu
Length: 1 Yr   *ACGME Approved/Offered Positions:* 1
Program ID: 305-04-12-084

California

Los Angeles

Cedars-Sinai Medical Center Program
Sponsor: Cedars-Sinai Medical Center
Prgm Director: Ellen B Klapper, MD
8700 Beverly Boulevard
Los Angeles, CA 90048
Tel: 310 423-7469
Length: 1 Yr   *ACGME Approved/Offered Positions:* 1
Program ID: 305-05-21-015

UCLA Medical Center Program
Sponsor: UCLA David Geffen School of Medicine/UCLA
   Medical Center
UCLA Medical Center
Prgm Director: Alyssa Ziman, MD
10833 Le Conte Avenue
Box 951713
Los Angeles, CA 90095
Tel: 310 794-1924   *Fax:* 310 206-3707
E-mail: aziman@mednet.ucla.edu
Length: 1 Yr   *ACGME Approved/Offered Positions:* 1
Program ID: 305-05-11-049

San Francisco

Blood Centers of the Pacific Program
Sponsor: Blood Centers of the Pacific
UCSF and Mount Zion Medical Centers
Prgm Director: Herbert A Perkins, MD
270 Masonic Avenue
San Francisco, CA 94118
Tel: 415 567-6400   *Fax:* 415 921-6184
E-mail: hperkins@bloodcenters.org
Length: 1 Yr   *ACGME Approved/Offered Positions:* 2
Program ID: 305-05-21-017

Stanford

Stanford University Program
Sponsor: Stanford Hospital and Clinics
Lucile Salter Packard Children's Hospital at Stanford
Stanford Blood Center
Prgm Director: Lawrence Tim Goodnough, MD
300 Pasteur Drive, Room H1402
M/C 5626
Stanford, CA 94305
Tel: 650 723-5848   *Fax:* 650 723-9178
Length: 1 Yr   *ACGME Approved/Offered Positions:* 1
Program ID: 305-05-13-086

Colorado

Aurora

University of Colorado Denver Program
Sponsor: University of Colorado Denver School of
   Medicine
Children's Hospital (The)
University of Colorado Hospital
Prgm Director: Mary Berg, MD*
12631 E 17th Avenue
Mail Stop 6511, Box B216
Aurora, CO 80045
Tel: 303 724-3483   *Fax:* 303 724-1105
E-mail: mary.berg@uchsc.edu
Length: 1 Yr   *ACGME Approved/Offered Positions:* 1
Program ID: 305-07-21-079

Denver

Bonfils Blood Center Program
Sponsor: Bonfils Blood Center
Prgm Director: Daniel R Ambruso, MD
717 Yosemite Street
Denver, CO 80230
Tel: 303 363-2241   *Fax:* 303 340-2616
Length: 1 Yr   *ACGME Approved/Offered Positions:* 1
Program ID: 305-07-13-078

Connecticut

New Haven

Yale-New Haven Medical Center Program
Sponsor: Yale-New Haven Hospital
Connecticut Red Cross Blood Services
Prgm Director: Yanyun Wu, MD, PhD
Blood Bank, Room CB-459
20 York Street
New Haven, CT 06510
Tel: 203 688-2441   *Fax:* 203 688-2748
E-mail: TransfusionFellowship@lab.labmed.ynhh.org
Length: 1 Yr   *ACGME Approved/Offered Positions:* 2
Program ID: 305-08-21-052

Georgia

Atlanta

Emory University Program
Sponsor: Emory University School of Medicine
Emory University Hospital
Prgm Director: Christopher D Hillyer, MD
1364 Clifton Road, NE
Room D-655
Atlanta, GA 30322
Tel: 404 712-5869   *Fax:* 404 727-2519
E-mail: chillye@emory.edu
Length: 1 Yr   *ACGME Approved/Offered Positions:* 2
Program ID: 305-12-31-056

Augusta

Medical College of Georgia Program
Sponsor: Medical College of Georgia
Prgm Director: Lloyd O Cook, MD, MBA
Department of Pathology, BI-1220
Augusta, GA 30912
Tel: 706 721-2731
E-mail: swillifo@mcg.edu
Length: 1 Yr   *ACGME Approved/Offered Positions:* 1
Program ID: 305-12-21-053

Illinois

Chicago

University of Chicago Program
Sponsor: University of Chicago Medical Center
Prgm Director: Beverly W Baron, MD
Blood Bank, MC0007
5841 South Maryland Avenue
Chicago, IL 60637
Tel: 773 702-1439
E-mail: Beverly.Baron@uchospitals.edu
Length: 1 Yr   *ACGME Approved/Offered Positions:* 1
Program ID: 305-16-21-054

University of Illinois College of Medicine at Chicago Program
Sponsor: University of Illinois College of Medicine at
   Chicago
University of Illinois Hospital and Clinics
Prgm Director: Sally A Campbell Lee, MD
Department of Pathology
840 S Wood Street, Room 130
Chicago, IL 60612
Tel: 312 996-1350   *Fax:* 312 996-7568
E-mail: scampbe@uic.edu
Length: 1 Yr   *ACGME Approved/Offered Positions:* 1
Program ID: 305-16-33-083

Indiana

Indianapolis

Indiana University School of Medicine Program
Sponsor: Indiana University School of Medicine
Central Indiana Regional Blood Center
Clarian Indiana University Hospital
Clarian Methodist Hospital of Indiana
Clarian Pathology Laboratory
Prgm Director: Daniel S Smith, MD
Transfusion Medicine, Room 5006C
350 W 11th Street
Indianapolis, IN 46202
Tel: 317 491-6888   *Fax:* 317 491-6882
E-mail: danssmit@iupui.edu
Length: 1 Yr   *ACGME Approved/Offered Positions:* 1
Program ID: 305-17-21-058

Programs

Iowa

Iowa City

University of Iowa Hospitals and Clinics Program
Sponsor: University of Iowa Hospitals and Clinics
Prgm Director: Thomas J Raife, MD
DeGowin Blood Center
200 Hawkins Drive, C250 GH
Iowa City, IA 52242
Tel: 319 356-0369   *Fax:* 319 356-0331
Length: 1 Yr   *ACGME Approved/Offered Positions:* 1
Program ID: 305-18-21-039

Kentucky

Louisville

University of Louisville Program
Sponsor: University of Louisville School of Medicine
American Red Cross Blood Services (Louisville Region)
Kosair Children's Hospital (Norton Healthcare, Inc)
Norton Hospital
University of Louisville Hospital
Prgm Director: William B Lockwood, MD, PhD
530 S Jackson Street
Suite C1R06
Louisville, KY 40202
Tel: 502 852-5857   *Fax:* 502 852-1771
Length: 1 Yr   *ACGME Approved/Offered Positions:* 1
Program ID: 305-20-21-059

Maryland

Baltimore

Johns Hopkins University Program
Sponsor: Johns Hopkins University School of Medicine
Johns Hopkins Hospital
Prgm Director: Paul M Ness, MD
Transfusion Medicine Division, Carnegie 667
600 N Wolfe St
Baltimore, MD 21287
Tel: 410 955-6583   *Fax:* 410 955-0618
Length: 1 Yr   *ACGME Approved/Offered Positions:* 2
Program ID: 305-23-21-026

Bethesda

National Institutes of Health Clinical Center Program
Sponsor: Clinical Center at the National Institutes of Health
Prgm Director: Cathy Conry-Cantilena, MD
10 Center Drive, MSC-1184
Building 10, Room 1C/711
Bethesda, MD 20892
Tel: 301 496-9702   *Fax:* 301 402-1360
E-mail: cathyc@mail.cc.nih.gov
Length: 1 Yr   *ACGME Approved/Offered Positions:* 3
Program ID: 305-23-21-001

Massachusetts

Boston

Brigham and Women's Hospital/Harvard Medical School Program
Sponsor: Brigham and Women's Hospital
Beth Israel Deaconess Medical Center
Children's Hospital
Massachusetts General Hospital
Prgm Director: Richard M Kaufman, MD
75 Francis Street
Boston, MA 02115
Tel: 617 732-5232   *Fax:* 617 277-9013
Length: 1 Yr   *ACGME Approved/Offered Positions:* 4
Program ID: 305-24-12-081

Springfield

Baystate Medical Center/Tufts University School of Medicine Program
Sponsor: Baystate Medical Center
Prgm Director: Chester Andrzejewski Jr, MD, PhD
Department of Pathology
759 Chestnut Street
Springfield, MA 01199
Tel: 413 794-5085   *Fax:* 413 794-5893
E-mail: lora.fillion@bhs.org
Length: 1 Yr   *ACGME Approved/Offered Positions:* 1
Program ID: 305-24-21-072

Michigan

Ann Arbor

University of Michigan Program
Sponsor: University of Michigan Hospitals and Health Centers
Prgm Director: Robertson D Davenport, MD
Department of Pathology, UH, 2G332
1500 East Medical Center Drive
Ann Arbor, MI 48109
Tel: 734 936-6776
E-mail: rddvnprt@umich.edu
Length: 1 Yr   *ACGME Approved/Offered Positions:* 1
Program ID: 305-25-31-077

Royal Oak

William Beaumont Hospital Program
Sponsor: William Beaumont Hospital
Prgm Director: Peter A Millward, MD*
Department of Clinical Pathology
3601 West Thirteen Mile Road
Royal Oak, MI 48073
Tel: 248 898-8013   *Fax:* 248 898-3398
Length: 1 Yr   *ACGME Approved/Offered Positions:* 1
Program ID: 305-25-32-012

Minnesota

Minneapolis

University of Minnesota Program
Sponsor: University of Minnesota Medical School
American Red Cross Blood Services-St Paul Region
University of Minnesota Medical Center, Division of Fairview
Prgm Director: Jeffrey McCullough, MD
420 Delaware Street SE, MMC 609
D242 Mayo Building
Minneapolis, MN 55455
Tel: 612 626-3272   *Fax:* 612 626-2696
E-mail: mccul001@umn.edu
Length: 1 Yr   *ACGME Approved/Offered Positions:* 2
Program ID: 305-26-21-013

Rochester

College of Medicine, Mayo Clinic (Rochester) Program
Sponsor: College of Medicine, Mayo Clinic
Mayo Clinic (Rochester)
Prgm Director: Jeffrey L Winters, MD
200 First Street, SW
Rochester, MN 55905
Tel: 507 538-1707   *Fax:* 507 284-1399
E-mail: pathologyeducation@mayo.edu
Length: 1 Yr   *ACGME Approved/Offered Positions:* 2
Program ID: 305-26-21-005

Missouri

St Louis

Washington University/B-JH/SLCH Consortium Program
Sponsor: Washington University/B-JH/SLCH Consortium
Barnes-Jewish Hospital
Prgm Director: Douglas M Lublin, MD, PhD
Department of Pathology
660 South Euclid Avenue, Box 8118
St Louis, MO 63110
Tel: 314 747-0687   *Fax:* 314 747-2663
E-mail: lublin@wustl.edu
Length: 1 Yr   *ACGME Approved/Offered Positions:* 2
Program ID: 305-28-22-006

New Hampshire

Lebanon

Dartmouth-Hitchcock Medical Center Program
Sponsor: Mary Hitchcock Memorial Hospital
Prgm Director: Zbigniew M Szczepiorkowski, MD, PhD
Department of Pathology
One Medical Center Drive
Lebanon, NH 03756
Tel: 603 653-9907   *Fax:* 603 650-4845
Length: 1 Yr   *ACGME Approved/Offered Positions:* 1
Program ID: 305-32-12-088

New Mexico

Albuquerque

University of New Mexico Program
Sponsor: University of New Mexico School of Medicine
University of New Mexico Hospital
Prgm Director: Kendall Crookston, MD, PhD
Department of Pathology
1 University of New Mexico, MSC08-4640
Albuquerque, NM 87131
Tel: 505 272-3696   *Fax:* 505 272-6726
E-mail: jlay@salud.unm.edu
Length: 1 Yr   *ACGME Approved/Offered Positions:* 1
Program ID: 305-34-22-082

Note: * indicates a newly appointed program director

New York

New York

New York Blood Center Program
Sponsor: New York Blood Center
Montefiore Medical Center-Henry and Lucy Moses Division
New York Presbyterian Hospital (Columbia Campus)
Westchester Medical Center
Prgm Director: Visalam Chandrasekaran, MD
310 East 67th Street
New York, NY 10065
Tel: 212 570-3142   *Fax:* 212 570-3092
Length: 1 Yr   *ACGME Approved/Offered Positions:* 6
Program ID: 305-35-21-019

Stony Brook

SUNY at Stony Brook Program
Sponsor: University Hospital - SUNY at Stony Brook
Prgm Director: Dennis K Galanakis, MD
Blood Bank, University Hospital
Stony Brook, NY 11794
Tel: 631 444-2625   *Fax:* 631 444-3137
E-mail: dgalanakis@notes.cc.sunysb.edu
Length: 1 Yr   *ACGME Approved/Offered Positions:* 1
Program ID: 305-35-21-051

Syracuse

SUNY Upstate Medical University/American Red Cross Blood Services Program
Sponsor: SUNY Upstate Medical University
Prgm Director: Lazaro G Rosales, MD
750 East Adams Street
Syracuse, NY 13210
Tel: 315 464-6768   *Fax:* 315 464-6707
Length: 1 Yr   *ACGME Approved/Offered Positions:* 1
Program ID: 305-35-21-034

North Carolina

Chapel Hill

University of North Carolina Hospitals Program
Sponsor: University of North Carolina Hospitals
Prgm Director: Mark E Brecher, MD
101 Manning Drive
Chapel Hill, NC 27514
Tel: 919 966-8465   *Fax:* 919 966-6407
Length: 1 Yr   *ACGME Approved/Offered Positions:* 1
Program ID: 305-36-21-020

Ohio

Cincinnati

Hoxworth Blood Center/University of Cincinnati College of Medicine Program
Sponsor: Hoxworth Blood Center
Prgm Director: Patricia M Carey, MD
3130 Highland Ave
PO Box 670055
Cincinnati, OH 45267
Tel: 513 558-1338   *Fax:* 513 588-1340
E-mail: Bernadette.Bennison@uc.edu
Length: 1 Yr   *ACGME Approved/Offered Positions:* 2
Program ID: 305-38-21-027

Cleveland

American Red Cross Northern Ohio Region Program
Sponsor: American Red Cross
Cleveland Clinic Foundation
University Hospitals Case Medical Center
Prgm Director: Gerald A Hoeltge, MD*
3747 Euclid Avenue
Cleveland, OH 44115
Tel: 216 444-2830   *Fax:* 216 445-7201
E-mail: hoeltgg@ccf.org
Length: 1 Yr   *ACGME Approved/Offered Positions:* 2
Program ID: 305-38-21-071

Columbus

Ohio State University Hospital Program
Sponsor: Ohio State University Hospital
American Red Cross-Central Ohio Region
Prgm Director: Melanie S Kennedy, MD
E-310 Doan Hall
410 West 10th Avenue
Columbus, OH 43210
Tel: 614 293-8185   *Fax:* 614 293-2075
E-mail: melanie.kennedy@osumc.edu
Length: 1 Yr   *ACGME Approved/Offered Positions:* 1
Program ID: 305-38-31-061

Pennsylvania

Hershey

Penn State University/Milton S Hershey Medical Center Program
Sponsor: Milton S Hershey Medical Center
Prgm Director: Ronald E Domen, MD
500 University Drive, H160
Hershey, PA 17033
Tel: 717 531-5116   *Fax:* 717 531-3803
Length: 1 Yr   *ACGME Approved/Offered Positions:* 1
Program ID: 305-41-31-087

Philadelphia

Thomas Jefferson University Program
Sponsor: Thomas Jefferson University Hospital
American Red Cross Blood Services-Penn-Jersey Region
Prgm Director: Jay H Herman, MD
111 S 11th Street
8220 Gibbon
Philadelphia, PA 19107
Tel: 215 955-8244   *Fax:* 215 923-9387
E-mail: carole.ayling@jeffersonhospital.org
Length: 1 Yr   *ACGME Approved/Offered Positions:* 1
Program ID: 305-41-21-037

University of Pennsylvania Program
Sponsor: University of Pennsylvania Health System
Prgm Director: Donald L Siegel, MD, PhD
Division of Transfusion Med, 3 Ravdin
3400 Spruce Street
Philadelphia, PA 19104
Tel: 215 662-3942   *Fax:* 215 573-3127
Length: 1 Yr   *ACGME Approved/Offered Positions:* 3
Program ID: 305-41-21-007

Pittsburgh

University of Pittsburgh Medical Center Medical Education/Institute for Transfusion Medicine Program
Sponsor: Univ of Pittsburgh Medical Center Medical Education
Children's Hospital of Pittsburgh of UPMC
Institute for Transfusion Medicine
UPMC Presbyterian Shadyside
Prgm Director: Darrell J Triulzi, MD
3636 Blvd of the Allies
Pittsburgh, PA 15213
Tel: 412 209-7304   *Fax:* 412 209-7325
E-mail: dtriulzi@itxm.org
Length: 1 Yr   *ACGME Approved/Offered Positions:* 1
Program ID: 305-41-21-065

Texas

Dallas

University of Texas Southwestern Medical School Program
Sponsor: University of Texas Southwestern Medical School
Carter BloodCare
Prgm Director: Ravindra Sarode, MD
5323 Harry Hines Boulevard
CS3.114
Dallas, TX 75390
Tel: 214 648-7887   *Fax:* 214 648-8037
E-mail: Ravi.Sarode@UTSouthwestern.edu
Length: 1 Yr   *ACGME Approved/Offered Positions:* 1
Program ID: 305-48-31-068

Houston

Baylor College of Medicine Program
Sponsor: Baylor College of Medicine
Harris County Hospital District-Ben Taub General Hospital
St Luke's Episcopal Hospital
Texas Children's Hospital
Prgm Director: Jun Teruya, MD, ScD
One Baylor Plaza
Houston, TX 77030
Tel: 832 824-1879   *Fax:* 832 825-1032
E-mail: jteruya@bcm.edu
Length: 1 Yr   *ACGME Approved/Offered Positions:* 1
Program ID: 305-48-31-080

Methodist Hospital (Houston) Program
Sponsor: Methodist Hospital (Houston)
Memorial Hermann Hospital
Prgm Director: Richard J Davey, MD
6565 Fannin St, M227
Houston, TX 77030
Tel: 713 441-2255   *Fax:* 713 441-3489
E-mail: ljozwiak@tmhs.org
Length: 1 Yr   *ACGME Approved/Offered Positions:* 1
Program ID: 305-48-33-085

University of Texas M D Anderson Cancer Center Program
Sponsor: University of Texas M D Anderson Cancer Center
Prgm Director: Aida B Narvios, MD, BS
1515 Holcombe Avenue, Unit 7
Houston, TX 77030
Tel: 713 792-7730   *Fax:* 713 792-6159
E-mail: anarvios@mdanderson.org
Length: 1 Yr   *ACGME Approved/Offered Positions:* 2
Program ID: 305-48-21-044

Programs

San Antonio

University of Texas Health Science Center at San Antonio Program

Sponsor: University of Texas School of Medicine at San Antonio
University Health System
Prgm Director: Chantal R Harrison, MD
Department of Pathology
7703 Floyd Curl Drive
San Antonio, TX 78229
Tel: 210 567-4090   *Fax:* 210 567-2367
Length: 1 Yr   *ACGME Approved/Offered Positions:* 2
Program ID: 305-48-21-045

Virginia

Charlottesville

University of Virginia Program

Sponsor: University of Virginia Medical Center
Prgm Director: Pamela Clark, MD, JD
PO Box 800286
Charlottesville, VA 22908
Tel: 434 982-0145   *Fax:* 434 982-0140
E-mail: bun4n@virginia.edu
Length: 1 Yr   *ACGME Approved/Offered Positions:* 1
Program ID: 305-51-21-074

Washington

Seattle

Puget Sound Blood Center Program

Sponsor: Puget Sound Blood Center
University of Washington Medical Center
Prgm Director: Terry Gernsheimer, MD
921 Terry Avenue
Seattle, WA 98104
Tel: 206 292-6521   *Fax:* 206 343-1774
Length: 1 Yr   *ACGME Approved/Offered Positions:* 2
Program ID: 305-54-21-066

Wisconsin

Madison

University of Wisconsin Program

Sponsor: University of Wisconsin Hospital and Clinics
Prgm Director: A J (Alice Jane) Hibbard, MD*
Room C5/253 Clinical Science Center
600 Highland Avenue
Madison, WI 53792
Tel: 608 262-7158   *Fax:* 608 263-1568
Length: 1 Yr   *ACGME Approved/Offered Positions:* 2
Program ID: 305-56-21-048

Milwaukee

Medical College of Wisconsin Affiliated Hospitals Program

Sponsor: Medical College of Wisconsin Affiliated Hospitals, Inc
BloodCenter of Wisconsin
Children's Hospital of Wisconsin
Froedtert Memorial Lutheran Hospital
Prgm Director: Jerome L Gottschall, MD
638 N 18th Street
PO Box 2178
Milwaukee, WI 53201
Tel: 414 937-6231   *Fax:* 414 933-6803
Length: 1 Yr   *ACGME Approved/Offered Positions:* 1
Program ID: 305-56-21-023

Cardiothoracic Radiology (Radiology-Diagnostic)

Massachusetts

Boston

Brigham and Women's Hospital Program

Sponsor: Brigham and Women's Hospital
Prgm Director: Beatrice Trotman-Dickenson, MBBS
75 Francis Street
Boston, MA 02115
Tel: 617 732-6285   *Fax:* 617 264-6802
E-mail: btrotmandickenson@partners.org
Length: 1 Yr   *ACGME Approved/Offered Positions:* 1
Program ID: 429-24-13-002

Pennsylvania

Philadelphia

University of Pennsylvania Program

Sponsor: University of Pennsylvania Health System
Prgm Director: Warren B Gefter, MD
HUP, 1 Silverstein
3400 Spruce Street
Philadelphia, PA 19104
Tel: 215 662-6724   *Fax:* 215 614-0033
Length: 1 Yr   *ACGME Approved/Offered Positions:* 2
Program ID: 429-41-21-001

Cardiovascular Disease (Internal Medicine)

Alabama

Birmingham

University of Alabama Medical Center Program

Sponsor: University of Alabama Hospital
Veterans Affairs Medical Center (Birmingham)
Prgm Director: Vera A Bittner, MD, MSPH
Cardiology Fellowship Program
701 19th Street South, LHRB 306
Birmingham, AL 35294
Tel: 205 934-0820   *Fax:* 205 975-8568
E-mail: mveazey@cardmail.dom.uab.edu
Length: 3 Yrs   *ACGME Approved/Offered Positions:* 15
Program ID: 141-01-21-151

Mobile

University of South Alabama Program

Sponsor: University of South Alabama Hospitals
Infirmary West
University of South Alabama Medical Center
Prgm Director: Clara V Massey, MD
2451 Fillingim Street
Suite 10B - USAMC
Mobile, AL 36617
Tel: 251 471-7923   *Fax:* 251 470-5888
E-mail: cschnell@usouthal.edu
Length: 3 Yrs   *ACGME Approved/Offered Positions:* 5
Program ID: 141-01-11-060

Arizona

Phoenix

Banner Good Samaritan Medical Center Program

Sponsor: Banner Good Samaritan Medical Center
Carl T Hayden VA Medical Center
Prgm Director: Kenneth B Desser, MD
1111 E McDowell Road, Room WT4
Phoenix, AZ 85006
Tel: 602 239-6743   *Fax:* 602 239-5094
Length: 3 Yrs   *ACGME Approved/Offered Positions:* 9
Program ID: 141-03-21-039

Scottsdale

College of Medicine, Mayo Clinic (Arizona) Program

Sponsor: College of Medicine, Mayo Clinic
Mayo Clinic (Arizona)
Mayo Clinic Hospital
Prgm Director: Susan Wilansky, MD
13400 East Shea Boulevard
Scottsdale, AZ 85259
Tel: 480 301-4072   *Fax:* 480 301-9160
Length: 3 Yrs   *ACGME Approved/Offered Positions:* 9
Program ID: 141-03-21-261

Note: * indicates a newly appointed program director

Tucson

University of Arizona Program
Sponsor: University of Arizona College of Medicine
Southern Arizona VA Health Care Center (Tucson)
University Medical Center
Prgm Director: Gordon A Ewy, MD
1501 North Campbell, Sarver Heart Center
PO Box 245037
Tucson, AZ 85724
Tel: 520 626-6221 *Fax:* 520 626-0967
E-mail: pabrams@email.arizona.edu
Length: 3 Yrs *ACGME Approved/Offered Positions:* 15
Program ID: 141-03-21-131

Arkansas

Little Rock

University of Arkansas for Medical Sciences Program
Sponsor: University of Arkansas College of Medicine
Central Arkansas Veterans Healthcare System
UAMS Medical Center
Prgm Director: Eugene S Smith III, MD
4301 West Markham, #532
Little Rock, AR 72205
Tel: 501 686-7882 *Fax:* 501 686-8319
E-mail: mjmorrisbisbee@uams.edu
Length: 3 Yrs *ACGME Approved/Offered Positions:* 12
Program ID: 141-04-21-132

California

Fresno

University of California (San Francisco)/Fresno Program
Sponsor: UCSF Fresno Medical Education Program
Community Medical Centers (Fresno)
VA Central California Health Care System
Prgm Director: John A Ambrose, MD
155 N Fresno Street
Fresno, CA 93701
Tel: 559 459-3872 *Fax:* 559 459-5157
E-mail: mpatten@fresno.ucsf.edu
Length: 3 Yrs *ACGME Approved/Offered Positions:* 9
Program ID: 141-05-21-279

La Jolla

Scripps Clinic/Scripps Green Hospital Program
Sponsor: Scripps Clinic/Scripps Green Hospital
Prgm Director: Guy P Curtis, MD, PhD
Dept of Graduate Med Education 403C
10666 N Torrey Pines Road
La Jolla, CA 92037
Tel: 858 554-3234 *Fax:* 858 554-3232
E-mail: gme@scripps.edu
Length: 3 Yrs *ACGME Approved/Offered Positions:* 9
Program ID: 141-05-21-086

Loma Linda

Loma Linda University Program
Sponsor: Loma Linda University Medical Center
Jerry L Pettis Memorial Veterans Hospital
Prgm Director: Kenneth R Jutzy, MD
Department of Cardiology
11234 Anderson Street, Suite 2426
Loma Linda, CA 92354
Tel: 909 558-7674 *Fax:* 909 651-5938
E-mail: cwitters@llu.edu
Length: 3 Yrs *ACGME Approved/Offered Positions:* 9
Program ID: 141-05-21-153

Los Angeles

Cedars-Sinai Medical Center Program
Sponsor: Cedars-Sinai Medical Center
VA Greater Los Angeles Healthcare System
Prgm Director: Sanjay Kaul, MD
8700 Beverly Blvd, 5th Fl, South Tower
Los Angeles, CA 90048
Tel: 310 423-4876 *Fax:* 310 423-0245
Length: 3 Yrs *ACGME Approved/Offered Positions:* 21
Program ID: 141-05-11-134

Kaiser Permanente Southern California (Los Angeles) Program
Sponsor: Kaiser Permanente Southern California
Kaiser Foundation Hospital (Los Angeles)
Prgm Director: Yuh-Jer A Shen, MD, MS
1526 N Edgemont St
2nd floor, Cardiology
Los Angeles, CA 90027
Tel: 323 783-1420 *Fax:* 323 783-1422
Length: 3 Yrs *ACGME Approved/Offered Positions:* 9
Program ID: 141-05-12-041

UCLA Medical Center Program
Sponsor: UCLA David Geffen School of Medicine/UCLA Medical Center
Olive View/UCLA Medical Center
UCLA Medical Center
Prgm Director: Robb Maclellan, MD
BH307- Center for the Health Sciences
650 Charles E Young Dr, South
Los Angeles, CA 90095
Tel: 310 825-2554 *Fax:* 310 206-5777
Length: 3 Yrs *ACGME Approved/Offered Positions:* 15
Program ID: 141-05-11-155

UCLA-VA Greater Los Angeles Program
Sponsor: VA Greater Los Angeles Healthcare System
Cedars-Sinai Medical Center
Prgm Director: Donald S Chang, MD, MPH
Division of Cardiology (111E)
11301 Wilshire Boulevard
Los Angeles, CA 90073
Tel: 310 268-3643 *Fax:* 310 268-4288
E-mail: Donald.Chang@va.gov
Length: 3 Yrs *ACGME Approved/Offered Positions:* 12
Program ID: 141-05-31-073

University of Southern California/ LAC+USC Medical Center Program
Sponsor: University of Southern California/LAC+USC Medical Center
LAC+USC Medical Center
Prgm Director: Ray V Matthews, MD*
1510 San Pablo Street Suite 322
Los Angeles, CA 90033
Tel: 323 442-6130 *Fax:* 323 442-6133
Length: 3 Yrs *ACGME Approved/Offered Positions:* 15
Program ID: 141-05-21-061

Orange

University of California (Irvine) Program
Sponsor: University of California (Irvine) Medical Center
Long Beach Memorial Medical Center
VA Long Beach Healthcare System
Prgm Director: Harold Olson, MD
Department of Internal Medicine
101 The City Drive South
Orange, CA 92868
Tel: 714 456-7945 *Fax:* 714 456-8895
E-mail: epwestbe@uci.edu
Length: 3 Yrs *ACGME Approved/Offered Positions:* 12
Program ID: 141-05-21-180

Sacramento

University of California (Davis) Health System Program
Sponsor: University of California (Davis) Health System
University of California (Davis) Medical Center
Prgm Director: William J Bommer, MD
4860 Y Street, Suite 2820
Division of Cardiovascular Disease
Sacramento, CA 95817
Tel: 916 734-3764 *Fax:* 916 734-8394
E-mail: cardiofellow@ucdavis.edu
Length: 3 Yrs *ACGME Approved/Offered Positions:* 12
Program ID: 141-05-21-111

San Diego

Naval Medical Center (San Diego) Program
Sponsor: Naval Medical Center (San Diego)
Prgm Director: CAPT Lisa A Gleason, MD
Cardiology Department
34730 Bob Wilson Drive Suite 303
San Diego, CA 92134
Tel: 619 532-7403 *Fax:* 619 532-9863
Length: 3 Yrs *ACGME Approved/Offered Positions:* 9
Program ID: 141-05-12-181
Uniformed Services Program

University of California (San Diego) Program
Sponsor: University of California (San Diego) Medical Center
Veterans Affairs Medical Center (San Diego)
Prgm Director: Daniel G Blanchard, MD
225 Dickinson Street
San Diego, CA 92103
Tel: 619 543-8213 *Fax:* 619 543-5576
Length: 3 Yrs *ACGME Approved/Offered Positions:* 15
Program ID: 141-05-21-209

San Francisco

California Pacific Medical Center Program
Sponsor: California Pacific Medical Center
Prgm Director: Andrew Rosenblatt, MD
Division of Cardiology
PO Box 7999
San Francisco, CA 94120
Tel: 415 600-5966 *Fax:* 415 563-5939
E-mail: Martinaz@sutterhealth.org
Length: 3 Yrs *ACGME Approved/Offered Positions:* 9
Program ID: 141-05-12-183

Kaiser Permanente Medical Group (Northern California)/San Francisco Program
Sponsor: Kaiser Permanente Medical Group (Northern California)
Kaiser Permanente Medical Center (San Francisco)
Prgm Director: Robert Lundstrom, MD
2425 Geary Boulevard
Room M160
San Francisco, CA 94115
Tel: 415 833-3034 *Fax:* 415 833-4983
E-mail: robert.lundstrom@kp.org
Length: 3 Yrs *ACGME Approved/Offered Positions:* 6
Program ID: 141-05-12-286

University of California (San Francisco) Program

Sponsor: University of California (San Francisco) School of Medicine
San Francisco General Hospital Medical Center
UCSF and Mount Zion Medical Centers
Veterans Affairs Medical Center (San Francisco)
Prgm Director: Michael H Crawford, MD
505 Parnassus Avenue, M1180
San Francisco, CA 94143
Tel: 415 502-8584 *Fax:* 415 353-9190
E-mail: crawfordm@medicine.ucsf.edu
Length: 3 Yrs *ACGME Approved/Offered Positions:* 21
Program ID: 141-05-21-184

Stanford

Stanford University Program

Sponsor: Stanford Hospital and Clinics
Veterans Affairs Palo Alto Health Care System
Prgm Director: John C Giacomini, MD
Falk CVRC
300 Pasteur Drive
Stanford, CA 94305
Tel: 650 725-3798 *Fax:* 650 725-1599
Length: 3 Yrs *ACGME Approved/Offered Positions:* 18
Program ID: 141-05-21-025

Torrance

Los Angeles County-Harbor-UCLA Medical Center Program

Sponsor: Los Angeles County-Harbor-UCLA Medical Center
Prgm Director: Matthew J Budoff, MD
Division of Cardiology
1000 W Carson Street, Box 405
Torrance, CA 90509
Tel: 310 222-4107 *Fax:* 310 787-0448
Length: 3 Yrs *ACGME Approved/Offered Positions:* 15
Program ID: 141-05-11-210

Colorado

Aurora

University of Colorado Denver Program

Sponsor: University of Colorado Denver School of Medicine
Denver Health Medical Center
University of Colorado Hospital
Veterans Affairs Medical Center (Denver)
Prgm Director: Brian D Lowes, MD
12631 E 17th Avenue
B130
Aurora, CO 80045
Tel: 303 724-2089
E-mail: Brian.Lowes@ucdenver.edu
Length: 3 Yrs *ACGME Approved/Offered Positions:* 16
Program ID: 141-07-21-074

Connecticut

Bridgeport

Bridgeport Hospital/Yale University Program

Sponsor: Bridgeport Hospital
Prgm Director: Craig A McPherson, MD
Department of Medicine
267 Grant Street
Bridgeport, CT 06610
Tel: 203 384-3442 *Fax:* 203 384-3443
E-mail: bbgras@bpthosp.org
Length: 3 Yrs *ACGME Approved/Offered Positions:* 4
Program ID: 141-08-11-211

Danbury

Danbury Hospital Program

Sponsor: Danbury Hospital
Prgm Director: Mark K Warshofsky, MD
24 Hospital Avenue
Danbury, CT 06810
Tel: 203 739-7600
Length: 3 Yrs *ACGME Approved/Offered Positions:* 6
Program ID: 141-08-13-272

Farmington

University of Connecticut Program

Sponsor: University of Connecticut School of Medicine
St Francis Hospital and Medical Center
Univ of Connecticut Health Center/John Dempsey Hospital
Prgm Director: Peter Schulman, MD
Calhoun Cardiology Center
263 Farmington Avenue
Farmington, CT 06030
Tel: 860 679-2771 *Fax:* 860 679-3346
E-mail: barta@adp.uchc.edu
Length: 3 Yrs *ACGME Approved/Offered Positions:* 9
Program ID: 141-08-31-001

University of Connecticut Program A

Sponsor: University of Connecticut School of Medicine
Hartford Hospital
Prgm Director: Gary V Heller, MD, PhD
80 Seymour Street
Hartford, CT 06102
Tel: 860 545-5020 *Fax:* 860 545-5631
Length: 3 Yrs *ACGME Approved/Offered Positions:* 15
Program ID: 141-08-31-253

New Haven

Hospital of St Raphael Program

Sponsor: Hospital of St Raphael
Prgm Director: Eugene Caracciolo, MD
1450 Chapel Street
New Haven, CT 06511
Tel: 203 789-6044 *Fax:* 203 789-6046
Length: 3 Yrs *ACGME Approved/Offered Positions:* 6
Program ID: 141-08-21-266

Yale-New Haven Medical Center Program

Sponsor: Yale-New Haven Hospital
Veterans Affairs Medical Center (West Haven)
Prgm Director: Robert L McNamara, MD, MHSc
Int Med, Section of Cardiovascular Medicine
333 Cedar Street, PO Box 208017
New Haven, CT 06520
Tel: 203 785-6484 *Fax:* 203 785-2715
Length: 3 Yrs *ACGME Approved/Offered Positions:* 15
Program ID: 141-08-21-026

Delaware

Wilmington

Jefferson Medical College/Christiana Care Health Services Program

Sponsor: Jefferson Medical College
Christiana Care Health Services Inc
Prgm Director: William Weintraub, MD
PO Box 6001
4755 Ogletown-Stanton Road
Newark, DE 19718
Tel: 302 733-1200 *Fax:* 302 733-4998
E-mail: cardiology.fellowship@christianacare.org
Length: 3 Yrs *ACGME Approved/Offered Positions:* 12
Program ID: 141-09-21-275

District of Columbia

Washington

George Washington University Program

Sponsor: George Washington University School of Medicine
George Washington University Hospital (UHS)
Prgm Director: Allen J Solomon, MD
Division of Cardiology
2150 Pennsylvania Ave NW, Suite 4-414
Washington, DC 20037
Tel: 202 741-2323 *Fax:* 202 741-2324
E-mail: asolomon@mfa.gwu.edu
Length: 3 Yrs *ACGME Approved/Offered Positions:* 9
Program ID: 141-10-21-136

Georgetown University Hospital/Washington Hospital Center Program

Sponsor: Washington Hospital Center
Georgetown University Hospital
Veterans Affairs Medical Center (Washington, DC)
Prgm Director: Julio A Panza, MD
110 Irving Street, NW
Washington, DC 20010
Tel: 202 877-9090 *Fax:* 202 877-9034
E-mail: julio.a.panza@medstar.net
Length: 3 Yrs *ACGME Approved/Offered Positions:* 18
Program ID: 141-10-11-160

Howard University Program

Sponsor: Howard University Hospital
Prgm Director: James A Diggs, MD*
2041 Georgia Avenue, NW
Suite 6C-03
Washington, DC 20060
Tel: 202 865-6792 *Fax:* 202 865-4449
Length: 3 Yrs *ACGME Approved/Offered Positions:* 6
Program ID: 141-10-21-158

Florida

Gainesville

University of Florida Program

Sponsor: University of Florida College of Medicine
Shands Hospital at the University of Florida
Prgm Director: Jamie B Conti, MD
Box 100277
1600 SW Archer Road, Room M-436
Gainesville, FL 32610
Tel: 352 846-0620 *Fax:* 352 392-3606
E-mail: lepanrl@medicine.ufl.edu
Length: 3 Yrs *ACGME Approved/Offered Positions:* 15
Program ID: 141-11-21-045

Note: * indicates a newly appointed program director

Jacksonville

College of Medicine, Mayo Clinic (Jacksonville) Program

Sponsor: College of Medicine, Mayo Clinic
Mayo Clinic (Jacksonville)
Mayo Clinic Florida Hospital
Prgm Director: Keith R Oken, MD
4500 San Pablo Road
Jacksonville, FL 32224
Tel: 904 953-0487   *Fax:* 904 953-0430
E-mail: spier.lori@mayo.edu
Length: 3 Yrs   *ACGME Approved/Offered Positions:* 6
Program ID: 141-11-13-284

University of Florida College of Medicine Jacksonville Program

Sponsor: University of Florida College of Medicine
   Jacksonville
Shands Jacksonville Medical Center
Prgm Director: Steven J Lavine, MD
Dept of Cardiology, ACC 5th Fl
655 West Eighth Street, Box C35
Jacksonville, FL 32209
Tel: 904 244-3066   *Fax:* 904 244-3102
E-mail: cardiology.gme@jax.ufl.edu
Length: 3 Yrs   *ACGME Approved/Offered Positions:* 15
Program ID: 141-11-21-027

Miami

Jackson Memorial Hospital/Jackson Health System Program

Sponsor: Jackson Memorial Hospital/Jackson Health
   System
University of Miami Hospital
Veterans Affairs Medical Center (Miami)
Prgm Director: Gervasio A Lamas, MD*
Cardiology
PO Box 016960 (R-60)
Miami, FL 33101
Tel: 305 585-5540
E-mail: nmelendr@med.miami.edu
Length: 3 Yrs   *ACGME Approved/Offered Positions:* 18
Program ID: 141-11-21-212

Miami Beach

Mount Sinai Medical Center of Florida Program

Sponsor: Mount Sinai Medical Center of Florida, Inc
Prgm Director: Cesar Conde, MD*
4300 Alton Road
Butler Building
Miami Beach, FL 33140
Tel: 305 534-4464   *Fax:* 305 674-2164
Length: 3 Yrs   *ACGME Approved/Offered Positions:* 12
Program ID: 141-11-12-076

Tampa

University of South Florida Program

Sponsor: University of South Florida College of Medicine
James A Haley Veterans Hospital
Tampa General Hospital
Prgm Director: Anne B Curtis, MD
South Tampa Center for Advanced Healthcare
2 Tampa General Circle, 5th Floor Cardiology
Tampa, FL 33606
Tel: 813 396-9156   *Fax:* 813 259-0669
E-mail: gszaltel@health.usf.edu
Length: 3 Yrs   *ACGME Approved/Offered Positions:* 15
Program ID: 141-11-21-046

Weston

Cleveland Clinic (Florida) Program

Sponsor: Cleveland Clinic Florida
Prgm Director: Craig Asher, MD
2950 Cleveland Clinic Boulevard
Weston, FL 33331
Tel: 954 659-5290   *Fax:* 954 659-5292
Length: 3 Yrs   *ACGME Approved/Offered Positions:* 6
Program ID: 141-11-31-270

Georgia

Atlanta

Emory University Program

Sponsor: Emory University School of Medicine
Crawford Long Hospital of Emory University
Emory University Hospital
Grady Health System
Veterans Affairs Medical Center (Atlanta)
Prgm Director: A Maziar Zafari, MD, PhD
Division of Cardiology
1639 Pierce Drive, WMB Suite 319
Atlanta, GA 30322
Tel: 404 727-4724   *Fax:* 404 712-8335
E-mail: cardiology@emory.edu
Length: 3 Yrs   *ACGME Approved/Offered Positions:* 34
Program ID: 141-12-21-161

Augusta

Medical College of Georgia Program

Sponsor: Medical College of Georgia
Veterans Affairs Medical Center (Augusta)
Prgm Director: Vincent J B Robinson, MD
1120 15th Street, BBR 6518
Augusta, GA 30912
Tel: 706 721-2736   *Fax:* 706 721-5150
E-mail: cardiology_fellowship_program@mail.mcg.edu
Length: 3 Yrs   *ACGME Approved/Offered Positions:* 12
Program ID: 141-12-21-004

Illinois

Chicago

Advocate Illinois Masonic Medical Center Program

Sponsor: Advocate Illinois Masonic Medical Center
Prgm Director: Cesar J Herrera, MD
836 W Wellington Avenue
Room 1247
Chicago, IL 60657
Tel: 773 296-8260   *Fax:* 773 296-5940
E-mail: paul.engelhardt@advocatehealth.com
Length: 3 Yrs   *ACGME Approved/Offered Positions:* 9
Program ID: 141-16-11-220

John H Stroger Hospital of Cook County Program

Sponsor: John H Stroger Hospital of Cook County
Rush University Medical Center
Prgm Director: Russell F Kelly, MD
Division of Adult Cardiology
1901 West Harrison Street
Chicago, IL 60612
Tel: 312 864-3413   *Fax:* 312 864-9529
E-mail: rstubbs@ccbhs.org
Length: 3 Yrs   *ACGME Approved/Offered Positions:* 9
Program ID: 141-16-12-047

McGaw Medical Center of Northwestern University Program

Sponsor: McGaw Medical Center of Northwestern
   University
Northwestern Memorial Hospital
Prgm Director: Thomas A Holly, MD*
676 N Saint Clair St Ste 600
Chicago, IL 60611
Tel: 312 926-2398   *Fax:* 312 926-8250
Length: 3 Yrs   *ACGME Approved/Offered Positions:* 21
Program ID: 141-16-21-090

Rush University Medical Center Program

Sponsor: Rush University Medical Center
Prgm Director: Clifford J Kavinsky, MD
1653 W Congress Parkway
Chicago, IL 60612
Tel: 312 942-4833   *Fax:* 312 942-5829
Length: 3 Yrs   *ACGME Approved/Offered Positions:* 18
Program ID: 141-16-11-162

University of Chicago Program

Sponsor: University of Chicago Medical Center
Prgm Director: Parker Ward, MD
5841 S Maryland Avenue
MC6080
Chicago, IL 60637
Tel: 773 702-5211   *Fax:* 773 702-8875
E-mail: card-app@medicine.bsd.uchicago.edu
Length: 3 Yrs   *ACGME Approved/Offered Positions:* 18
Program ID: 141-16-11-077

University of Illinois College of Medicine at Chicago Program

Sponsor: University of Illinois College of Medicine at
   Chicago
Advocate Christ Medical Center
Jesse Brown Veterans Affairs Medical Center
University of Illinois Hospital and Clinics
Prgm Director: Thomas D Stamos, MD
Section of Cardiology M/C 715
840 S Wood Street
Chicago, IL 60612
Tel: 312 996-0856   *Fax:* 312 413-2948
E-mail: tstamos@uic.edu
Length: 3 Yrs   *ACGME Approved/Offered Positions:* 15
Program ID: 141-16-21-163

Maywood

Loyola University Program

Sponsor: Loyola University Medical Center
Edward Hines, Jr Veterans Affairs Hospital
Prgm Director: Keith A McLean, MD
2160 South First Avenue
Dept of Medicine, Bldg 110/Room 6231
Maywood, IL 60153
Tel: 708 327-2748   *Fax:* 708 327-2770
Length: 3 Yrs   *ACGME Approved/Offered Positions:* 18
Program ID: 141-16-21-005

North Chicago

The Chicago Medical School at Rosalind Franklin University of Medicine and Science Program

Sponsor: Chicago Medical School/Rosalind Franklin
   Univ of Med & Sci
Mount Sinai Hospital Medical Center of Chicago
Veterans Affairs Medical Center (North Chicago)
Prgm Director: Sandeep Khosla, MD
L629, Mount Sinai Hospital
1500 S California Avenue
Chicago, IL 60608
Tel: 773 257-6452   *Fax:* 773 257-6726
E-mail: anita.abron@rosalindfranklin.edu
Length: 3 Yrs   *ACGME Approved/Offered Positions:* 6
Program ID: 141-16-21-062

Programs

Park Ridge

Advocate Lutheran General Hospital Program

Sponsor: Advocate Lutheran General Hospital
Prgm Director: Parag V Patel, DO
1775 W Dempster Street
Suite B-01
Park Ridge, IL 60068
Tel: 847 723-7997   *Fax:* 847 723-2131
Length: 3 Yrs   *ACGME Approved/Offered Positions:* 9
Program ID: 141-16-21-255

Indiana

Indianapolis

Indiana University School of Medicine Program

Sponsor: Indiana University School of Medicine
Clarian Methodist Hospital of Indiana
Prgm Director: Eric S Williams, MD
Krannert Institute of Cardiology
1800 N Capitol Avenue, Suite E480
Indianapolis, IN 46202
Tel: 317 962-0551   *Fax:* 317 962-0113
Length: 3 Yrs   *ACGME Approved/Offered Positions:* 15
Program ID: 141-17-21-185

St Vincent Hospital and Health Care Center Program

Sponsor: St Vincent Hospitals and Health Care Center
Prgm Director: Eric N Prystowsky, MD
8333 Naab Road
Indianapolis, IN 46260
Tel: 317 338-6024   *Fax:* 317 338-9259
E-mail: lpogue@thecaregroup.com
Length: 3 Yrs   *ACGME Approved/Offered Positions:* 6
Program ID: 141-17-13-267

Iowa

Iowa City

University of Iowa Hospitals and Clinics Program

Sponsor: University of Iowa Hospitals and Clinics
Prgm Director: Paul Lindower, MD
Department of Medicine
200 Hawkins Drive
Iowa City, IA 52242
Tel: 319 353-6777
Length: 3 Yrs   *ACGME Approved/Offered Positions:* 21
Program ID: 141-18-21-112

Kansas

Kansas City

University of Kansas School of Medicine Program

Sponsor: University of Kansas School of Medicine
University of Kansas Hospital
Veterans Affairs Medical Center (Kansas City)
Prgm Director: David Wilson, MD
Department of Internal Medicine
3901 Rainbow Blvd
Kansas City, KS 66160
Tel: 913 588-6015   *Fax:* 913 588-6010
E-mail: lblalock@kumc.edu
Length: 3 Yrs   *ACGME Approved/Offered Positions:* 9
Program ID: 141-19-21-137

Kentucky

Lexington

University of Kentucky College of Medicine Program

Sponsor: University of Kentucky College of Medicine
University of Kentucky Hospital
Veterans Affairs Medical Center (Lexington)
Prgm Director: Charles Campbell, MD*
Room 326 CTW Building
900 South Limestone
Lexington, KY 40536
Tel: 859 323-8040   *Fax:* 859 323-6475
Length: 3 Yrs   *ACGME Approved/Offered Positions:* 18
Program ID: 141-20-21-213

Louisville

University of Louisville Program

Sponsor: University of Louisville School of Medicine
Jewish Hospital
University of Louisville Hospital
Veterans Affairs Medical Center (Louisville)
Prgm Director: Stephen Wagner, MD
Department of Medicine - Division of Cardiology
Ambulatory Care Building, 3rd Floor
Louisville, KY 40292
Tel: 502 852-7959   *Fax:* 502 852-7147
Length: 3 Yrs   *ACGME Approved/Offered Positions:* 18
Program ID: 141-20-31-215

Louisiana

New Orleans

Louisiana State University Program

Sponsor: Louisiana State University School of Medicine
Medical Center of Louisiana at New Orleans
Touro Infirmary
Prgm Director: Neeraj Jain, MD*
2020 Gravier Street
7th Floor, Suite D (Cardiology)
New Orleans, LA 70112
Tel: 504 568-7878   *Fax:* 504 568-2127
Length: 3 Yrs   *ACGME Approved/Offered Positions:* 12
Program ID: 141-21-21-246

Ochsner Clinic Foundation Program

Sponsor: Ochsner Clinic Foundation
Prgm Director: Hector O Ventura, MD
1514 Jefferson Highway
New Orleans, LA 70121
Tel: 504 842-6281   *Fax:* 504 842-5960
E-mail: ptodesco@ochsner.org
Length: 3 Yrs   *ACGME Approved/Offered Positions:* 30
Program ID: 141-21-22-123

Tulane University Program

Sponsor: Tulane University School of Medicine
Medical Center of Louisiana at New Orleans
Tulane University Hospital and Clinics
Veterans Affairs Medical Center (New Orleans)
Prgm Director: Thierry H LeJemtel, MD*
1430 Tulane Avenue, SL-48
New Orleans, LA 70112
Tel: 504 988-6139   *Fax:* 504 988-4237
E-mail: jsonnier@tulane.edu
Length: 3 Yrs   *ACGME Approved/Offered Positions:* 18
Program ID: 141-21-21-130

Shreveport

Louisiana State University (Shreveport) Program

Sponsor: LSU Health Sciences Center-University
   Hospital
Overton Brooks Veterans Affairs Medical Center
Prgm Director: Pratap Reddy, MD
Cardiology Section, Room 243
1501 Kings Highway
Shreveport, LA 71130
Tel: 318 675-5941   *Fax:* 318 675-5686
Length: 3 Yrs   *ACGME Approved/Offered Positions:* 10
Program ID: 141-21-21-078

Maine

Portland

Maine Medical Center Program

Sponsor: Maine Medical Center
Prgm Director: John R O'Meara, MD
22 Bramhall Street
Portland, ME 04102
Tel: 207 662-2671   *Fax:* 207 662-6038
E-mail: omearj@mmc.org
Length: 3 Yrs   *ACGME Approved/Offered Positions:* 6
Program ID: 141-22-11-092

Maryland

Baltimore

Johns Hopkins University Program

Sponsor: Johns Hopkins University School of Medicine
Johns Hopkins Hospital
Prgm Director: James L Weiss, MD
600 N Wolfe St, Carnegie 591
Baltimore, MD 21287
Tel: 410 955-6834   *Fax:* 410 614-9422
E-mail: jlweiss@jhmi.edu
Length: 3 Yrs   *ACGME Approved/Offered Positions:* 27
Program ID: 141-23-11-093

University of Maryland Program

Sponsor: University of Maryland Medical System
Veterans Affairs Medical Center (Baltimore)
Prgm Director: R Michael Benitez, MD
Department of Medicine - Division of Cardiology
22 S Greene Street, Room G3K18
Baltimore, MD 21201
Tel: 410 328-8706   *Fax:* 410 328-3530
E-mail: mbileck@medicine.umaryland.edu
Length: 3 Yrs   *ACGME Approved/Offered Positions:* 15
Program ID: 141-23-21-049

Bethesda

National Capital Consortium (Walter Reed) Program

Sponsor: National Capital Consortium
National Naval Medical Center (Bethesda)
Walter Reed Army Medical Center
Prgm Director: John E Atwood, MD
Department of Medicine
6900 Georgia Avenue, NW, Building 2, Room 4A
Washington, DC 20307
Tel: 202 782-2908
E-mail: john.atwood@na.amedd.army.mil
Length: 3 Yrs   *ACGME Approved/Offered Positions:* 18
Program ID: 141-10-11-159
Uniformed Services Program

Note: * indicates a newly appointed program director

Massachusetts

Boston

Beth Israel Deaconess Medical Center Program
Sponsor: Beth Israel Deaconess Medical Center
Prgm Director: Duane S Pinto, MD
Division of Cardiology
One Deaconess Road, Baker 4
Boston, MA 02215
Tel: 617 632-7828   *Fax:* 617 632-7460
E-mail: dpinto@bidmc.harvard.edu
Length: 3 Yrs   *ACGME Approved/Offered Positions:* 25
Program ID: 141-24-21-006

Boston University Medical Center Program
Sponsor: Boston Medical Center
Veterans Affairs Medical Center (Boston)
Prgm Director: Donald A Weiner, MD
Dept of Medicine, Cardiology
88 E Newton Street
Boston, MA 02118
Tel: 617 638-8968   *Fax:* 617 638-8969
Length: 3 Yrs   *ACGME Approved/Offered Positions:* 18
Program ID: 141-24-21-187

Brigham and Women's Hospital Program
Sponsor: Brigham and Women's Hospital
Massachusetts General Hospital
Prgm Director: Joshua A Beckman, MD, MS
75 Francis Street
Boston, MA 02115
Tel: 617 732-7367   *Fax:* 617 232-2749
E-mail: pallen@partners.org
Length: 3 Yrs   *ACGME Approved/Offered Positions:* 18
Program ID: 141-24-21-007

Caritas St Elizabeth's Medical Center Program
Sponsor: Caritas St Elizabeth's Medical Center of Boston
Prgm Director: Michael T Johnstone, MD*
736 Cambridge Street
CCP 4C
Boston, MA 02135
Tel: 617 789-3047   *Fax:* 617 789-5029
E-mail: michael.johnstone@caritaschristi.org
Length: 3 Yrs   *ACGME Approved/Offered Positions:* 9
Program ID: 141-24-21-063

Massachusetts General Hospital Program
Sponsor: Massachusetts General Hospital
Prgm Director: Calum MacRae, MD, PhD
Cardiac Unit Fellowship, GRB 8
55 Fruit Street
Boston, MA 02114
Tel: 617 643-3238   *Fax:* 617 726-7855
E-mail: ldefabritiis1@partners.org
Length: 3 Yrs   *ACGME Approved/Offered Positions:* 18
Program ID: 141-24-11-079

Tufts Medical Center Program
Sponsor: Tufts Medical Center
Prgm Director: Jeffrey T Kuvin, MD
800 Washington Street
Box 315
Boston, MA 02111
Tel: 617 636-5846   *Fax:* 617 636-4769
E-mail: jkuvin@tuftsmedicalcenter.org
Length: 3 Yrs   *ACGME Approved/Offered Positions:* 16
Program ID: 141-24-21-010

Burlington

Lahey Clinic Program
Sponsor: Lahey Clinic
Prgm Director: Sherif B Labib, MD
41 Mall Road
Burlington, MA 01805
Tel: 781 744-8002   *Fax:* 781 744-5261
E-mail: karen.maltais@lahey.org
Length: 3 Yrs   *ACGME Approved/Offered Positions:* 9
Program ID: 141-24-21-222

Springfield

Baystate Medical Center/Tufts University School of Medicine Program
Sponsor: Baystate Medical Center
Prgm Director: Mara T Slawsky, MD, PhD
759 Chestnut Street, S4658
Springfield, MA 01199
Tel: 413 794-8722   *Fax:* 413 794-0198
Length: 3 Yrs   *ACGME Approved/Offered Positions:* 9
Program ID: 141-24-11-095

Worcester

St Vincent Hospital Program
Sponsor: St Vincent Hospital
Prgm Director: Bonnie Weiner, MD, MBA
Division of Cardiology
123 Summer Street
Worcester, MA 01608
Tel: 508 363-6162   *Fax:* 508 363-6225
Length: 3 Yrs   *ACGME Approved/Offered Positions:* 9
Program ID: 141-24-21-239

University of Massachusetts Program
Sponsor: University of Massachusetts Medical School
Boston VA Healthcare System (Brockton-West Roxbury)
UMass Memorial Health Care (University Campus)
Prgm Director: Gerard P Aurigemma, MD
Division of Cardiology
55 Lake Avenue North
Worcester, MA 01655
Tel: 508 856-2919   *Fax:* 508 856-4571
Length: 3 Yrs   *ACGME Approved/Offered Positions:* 18
Program ID: 141-24-21-011

Michigan

Ann Arbor

University of Michigan Program
Sponsor: University of Michigan Hospitals and Health Centers
Veterans Affairs Medical Center (Ann Arbor)
Prgm Director: Peter G Hagan, MB
CVC Cardiovascular Medicine SPC 5853
1500 E Medical Center Drive
Ann Arbor, MI 48109
Tel: 734 936-8214   *Fax:* 734 615-3326
E-mail: gahollow@umich.edu
Length: 3 Yrs   *ACGME Approved/Offered Positions:* 21
Program ID: 141-25-21-096

Detroit

Henry Ford Hospital Program
Sponsor: Henry Ford Hospital
Prgm Director: Henry E Kim, MD, MPH
Div of Cardiology, K-14
2799 West Grand Blvd
Detroit, MI 48202
Tel: 313 916-2871   *Fax:* 313 916-4513
Length: 3 Yrs   *ACGME Approved/Offered Positions:* 18
Program ID: 141-25-11-164

St John Hospital and Medical Center Program
Sponsor: St John Hospital and Medical Center
Prgm Director: Howard S Rosman, MD
22101 Moross Rd
2nd Floor VEP, Cath Lab
Detroit, MI 48236
Tel: 313 343-4612   *Fax:* 313 343-3730
Length: 3 Yrs   *ACGME Approved/Offered Positions:* 12
Program ID: 141-25-31-258

Wayne State University/Detroit Medical Center Program
Sponsor: Wayne State University/Detroit Medical Center
Harper-Hutzel Hospital
Prgm Director: Luis C Afonso, MD
Division of Cardiology
3990 John R Street, 1 Brush North
Detroit, MI 48201
Tel: 313 745-2620   *Fax:* 313 745-8643
E-mail: lafonso@med.wayne.edu
Length: 3 Yrs   *ACGME Approved/Offered Positions:* 12
Program ID: 141-25-21-057

Lansing

Michigan State University Program
Sponsor: Michigan State University College of Human Medicine
Sparrow Hospital
Prgm Director: George S Abela, MD, MBA
A-205 Clinical Center
138 Service Road
East Lansing, MI 48824
Tel: 517 353-4832   *Fax:* 517 432-1326
E-mail: powellm7@msu.edu
Length: 3 Yrs   *ACGME Approved/Offered Positions:* 9
Program ID: 141-25-11-259

Royal Oak

William Beaumont Hospital Program
Sponsor: William Beaumont Hospital
Prgm Director: Robert Safian, MD
3601 West 13 Mile Road
Royal Oak, MI 48073
Tel: 248 898-4176   *Fax:* 248 898-7239
Length: 3 Yrs   *ACGME Approved/Offered Positions:* 12
Program ID: 141-25-12-216

Southfield

Providence Hospital and Medical Centers Program
Sponsor: Providence Hospital and Medical Centers
Prgm Director: Christian E Machado, MD
16001 West Nine Mile Road
PO Box 2043
Southfield, MI 48075
Tel: 248 849-7129   *Fax:* 248 849-5324
E-mail: Katherine.McCaskell@providence-stjohnhealth.org
Length: 3 Yrs   *ACGME Approved/Offered Positions:* 9
Program ID: 141-25-11-214

Minnesota

Minneapolis

University of Minnesota Program

Sponsor: University of Minnesota Medical School
Abbott-Northwestern Hospital/Allina Health System
University of Minnesota Medical Center, Division of
    Fairview
Prgm Director: Marc R Pritzker, MD
Cardiology Division, MMC 508
420 Delaware Street, SE
Minneapolis, MN 55455
Tel: 612 626-2178   *Fax:* 612 626-4411
E-mail: cvfellow@umn.edu
Length: 3 Yrs   *ACGME Approved/Offered Positions:* 22
Program ID: 141-26-21-139

Rochester

College of Medicine, Mayo Clinic (Rochester) Program

Sponsor: College of Medicine, Mayo Clinic
Mayo Clinic (Rochester)
Saint Marys Hospital of Rochester
Prgm Director: Guy S Reeder, MD
200 First Street SW
Rochester, MN 55905
Tel: 507 284-3304   *Fax:* 507 266-3594
Length: 3 Yrs   *ACGME Approved/Offered Positions:* 30
Program ID: 141-26-21-066

Mississippi

Jackson

University of Mississippi Medical Center Program

Sponsor: University of Mississippi School of Medicine
University Hospitals and Clinics
Veterans Affairs Medical Center (Jackson)
Prgm Director: Thomas N Skelton, MD
Division of Cardiovascular Diseases
2500 N State St
Jackson, MS 39216
Tel: 601 984-5678   *Fax:* 601 984-5638
Length: 3 Yrs   *ACGME Approved/Offered Positions:* 12
Program ID: 141-27-21-097

Missouri

Columbia

University of Missouri-Columbia Program

Sponsor: University of Missouri-Columbia School of
    Medicine
Harry S Truman Memorial Veterans Hospital
University Hospitals and Clinics
Prgm Director: Gregory C Flaker, MD
1 Hospital Drive
CE306
Columbia, MO 65212
Tel: 573 882-2296   *Fax:* 573 884-7743
Length: 3 Yrs   *ACGME Approved/Offered Positions:* 12
Program ID: 141-28-21-098

Kansas City

University of Missouri at Kansas City Program

Sponsor: University of Missouri-Kansas City School of
    Medicine
St Luke's Hospital-Kansas City
Truman Medical Center
Prgm Director: James A Grantham, MD*
CV Education Office
4401 Wornall Road
Kansas City, MO 64111
Tel: 816 932-5475   *Fax:* 816 932-5613
E-mail: jwheeler@saint-lukes.org
Length: 3 Yrs   *ACGME Approved/Offered Positions:* 12
Program ID: 141-28-31-140

St Louis

St Louis University School of Medicine Program

Sponsor: St Louis University School of Medicine
St Louis University Hospital
Veterans Affairs Medical Center (St Louis)
Prgm Director: Arthur Labovitz, MD*
3635 Vista Ave at Grand Blvd
PO Box 15250
St Louis, MO 63110
Tel: 314 577-8890   *Fax:* 314 268-5172
Length: 3 Yrs   *ACGME Approved/Offered Positions:* 12
Program ID: 141-28-21-108

Washington University/B-JH/SLCH Consortium Program

Sponsor: Washington University/B-JH/SLCH Consortium
Barnes-Jewish Hospital
Washington University School of Medicine
Prgm Director: Benico Barzilai, MD
4989 Barnes-Jewish Hospital Plaza
St Louis, MO 63110
Tel: 314 362-1297   *Fax:* 314 362-9982
E-mail: aysaguir@im.wustl.edu
Length: 3 Yrs   *ACGME Approved/Offered Positions:* 36
Program ID: 141-28-21-188

Nebraska

Omaha

Creighton University Program

Sponsor: Creighton University School of Medicine
Creighton University Medical Center (Tenet - SJH)
Prgm Director: Claire B Hunter, MD
The Cardiac Center
3006 Webster Street
Omaha, NE 68131
Tel: 402 280-4626   *Fax:* 402 280-5967
E-mail: claire.hunter@cardiac.creighton.edu
Length: 3 Yrs   *ACGME Approved/Offered Positions:* 12
Program ID: 141-30-21-190

University of Nebraska Medical Center College of Medicine Program

Sponsor: University of Nebraska Medical Center College
    of Medicine
Nebraska Medical Center
Veterans Affairs Medical Center (Omaha)
Prgm Director: Edward L O'Leary, MD
982265 Nebraska Medical Center
Omaha, NE 68198
Tel: 402 559-5151   *Fax:* 402 559-8355
Length: 3 Yrs   *ACGME Approved/Offered Positions:* 12
Program ID: 141-30-21-191

New Hampshire

Lebanon

Dartmouth-Hitchcock Medical Center Program

Sponsor: Mary Hitchcock Memorial Hospital
Prgm Director: Edward Catherwood, MD, MS
One Medical Center Drive
Lebanon, NH 03756
Tel: 603 650-5077   *Fax:* 603 650-0523
E-mail: Jan.L.Willey@hitchcock.org
Length: 3 Yrs   *ACGME Approved/Offered Positions:* 12
Program ID: 141-32-21-178

New Jersey

Camden

UMDNJ-Robert Wood Johnson Medical School (Camden) Program

Sponsor: Cooper Hospital-University Medical Center
Prgm Director: Steven M Hollenberg, MD
One Cooper Plaza
3rd Floor Dorrance
Camden, NJ 08103
Tel: 856 968-2624   *Fax:* 856 968-7420
E-mail: jones-jerry@cooperhealth.edu
Length: 3 Yrs   *ACGME Approved/Offered Positions:* 15
Program ID: 141-33-21-240

New Brunswick

UMDNJ-Robert Wood Johnson Medical School Program

Sponsor: UMDNJ-Robert Wood Johnson Medical School
Deborah Heart and Lung Center
Robert Wood Johnson University Hospital
Prgm Director: Abel E Moreyra, MD
Dept of Medicine
One Robert Wood Johnson Pl
New Brunswick, NJ 08901
Tel: 732 235-7851   *Fax:* 732 235-8722
Length: 3 Yrs   *ACGME Approved/Offered Positions:* 12
Program ID: 141-33-21-029

Newark

Newark Beth Israel Medical Center Program

Sponsor: Newark Beth Israel Medical Center
Prgm Director: Marc Cohen, MD
201 Lyons Avenue at Osborne Terrace
Cath Lab Adm Suite, 2nd floor bridge
Newark, NJ 07112
Tel: 973 926-7852   *Fax:* 973 282-0839
E-mail: lcrapps@sbhcs.com
Length: 3 Yrs   *ACGME Approved/Offered Positions:* 6
Program ID: 141-33-31-263

UMDNJ-New Jersey Medical School Program

Sponsor: UMDNJ-New Jersey Medical School
Hackensack University Medical Center
UMDNJ-University Hospital
Veterans Affairs New Jersey Health Care System
Prgm Director: Marc Klapholz, MD
Department of Medicine, Division of Cardiology
185 South Orange Avenue, MSB-I-538
Newark, NJ 07103
Tel: 973 972-4731   *Fax:* 973 972-8927
E-mail: cooperca@umdnj.edu
Length: 3 Yrs   *ACGME Approved/Offered Positions:* 11
Program ID: 141-33-21-237

Note: * indicates a newly appointed program director

South Orange

Seton Hall University School of Health and Medical Sciences Program

Sponsor: Seton Hall University School of Health and Medical Sciences
St Joseph's Regional Medical Center
St Michael's Medical Center (A Member of Catholic Health East)
Prgm Director: Fayez Shamoon, MD
Department of Medicine
111 Central Avenue
Newark, NJ 07102
Tel: 973 877-5163   *Fax:* 973 877-5124
Length: 3 Yrs   *ACGME Approved/Offered Positions:* 11
Program ID: 141-33-11-223

New Mexico

Albuquerque

University of New Mexico Program

Sponsor: University of New Mexico School of Medicine
University of New Mexico Hospital
Veterans Affairs Medical Center (Albuquerque)
Prgm Director: Gerald A Charlton, MD
School of Medicine, One University of New Mexico
2211 Lomas Blvd, NE, ACC 5, MSC10-5550
Albuquerque, NM 87131
Tel: 505 272-6020   *Fax:* 505 272-4356
E-mail: gcharlton@salud.unm.edu
Length: 3 Yrs   *ACGME Approved/Offered Positions:* 12
Program ID: 141-34-21-165

New York

Albany

Albany Medical Center Program

Sponsor: Albany Medical Center
Veterans Affairs Medical Center (Albany)
Prgm Director: Robert D Millar, MD
Division of Cardiology, Mail Code 44
47 New Scotland Avenue
Albany, NY 12208
Tel: 518 262-5076   *Fax:* 518 262-5082
E-mail: brozowml@mail.amc.edu
Length: 3 Yrs   *ACGME Approved/Offered Positions:* 12
Program ID: 141-35-31-030

Bronx

Albert Einstein College of Medicine (Montefiore) Program

Sponsor: Albert Einstein College of Medicine of Yeshiva University
Montefiore Medical Center-Henry and Lucy Moses Division
Montefiore Medical Center-Weiler Division
Prgm Director: E Scott Monrad, MD
1825 Eastchester Road
Suite W1-120
Bronx, NY 10461
Tel: 718 904-2471   *Fax:* 718 918-1984
E-mail: nlloyd@montefiore.org
Length: 3 Yrs   *ACGME Approved/Offered Positions:* 21
Program ID: 141-35-21-124

Albert Einstein College of Medicine (Montefiore-Bronx Lebanon) Program

Sponsor: Albert Einstein College of Medicine of Yeshiva University
Bronx-Lebanon Hospital Center
Prgm Director: Kevin Ferrick, MD
111 E 210th Street
Bronx, NY 10467
Tel: 718 920-4148   *Fax:* 718 547-2111
E-mail: jacsmith@montefiore.org
Length: 3 Yrs   *ACGME Approved/Offered Positions:* 9
Program ID: 141-35-12-262

Brooklyn

Maimonides Medical Center Program

Sponsor: Maimonides Medical Center
Coney Island Hospital
Prgm Director: Jacob Shani, MD
4802 Tenth Avenue
Brooklyn, NY 11219
Tel: 718 283-6892   *Fax:* 718 635-7436
Length: 3 Yrs   *ACGME Approved/Offered Positions:* 21
Program ID: 141-35-11-192

New York Methodist Hospital Program

Sponsor: New York Methodist Hospital
Prgm Director: Terrence J Sacchi, MD
Division of Cardiology
506 6th St
Brooklyn, NY 11215
Tel: 718 780-5612   *Fax:* 718 780-3930
E-mail: tjs9002@nyp.org
Length: 3 Yrs   *ACGME Approved/Offered Positions:* 9
Program ID: 141-35-21-273

SUNY Health Science Center at Brooklyn Program

Sponsor: SUNY Health Science Center at Brooklyn
Brookdale University Hospital and Medical Center
Kings County Hospital Center
Staten Island University Hospital
University Hospital-SUNY Health Science Center at Brooklyn
Veterans Affairs Medical Center (Brooklyn)
Prgm Director: Jason M Lazar, MD
450 Clarkson Ave
Box 1199
Brooklyn, NY 11203
Tel: 718 221-5222   *Fax:* 718 270-2917
E-mail: jason.lazar@downstate.edu
Length: 3 Yrs   *ACGME Approved/Offered Positions:* 23
Program ID: 141-35-21-013

Buffalo

University at Buffalo Program

Sponsor: University at Buffalo School of Medicine
Erie County Medical Center
Kaleida Health System (Millard Fillmore Hospital)
Veterans Affairs Western New York Hospital
Prgm Director: Joseph A Paris, MD*
3495 Bailey Avenue
Buffalo, NY 14215
Tel: 716 859-1784   *Fax:* 716 859-3765
Length: 3 Yrs   *ACGME Approved/Offered Positions:* 12
Program ID: 141-35-31-051

Flushing

New York Hospital Medical Center of Queens/Cornell University Medical College Program

Sponsor: New York Hospital Medical Center of Queens
Prgm Director: Chong H Park, MD*
Division of Cardiology
56-45 Main Street
Flushing, NY 11355
Tel: 718 670-2087
Length: 3 Yrs   *ACGME Approved/Offered Positions:* 6
Program ID: 141-35-12-269

Great Neck

NSLIJHS-Albert Einstein College of Medicine at Long Island Jewish Medical Center Program

Sponsor: North Shore-Long Island Jewish Health System
Long Island Jewish Medical Center
North Shore University Hospital
Prgm Director: Stacey Rosen, MD
270-05 76th Avenue
New Hyde Park, NY 11040
Tel: 718 470-4330   *Fax:* 718 343-9762
Length: 3 Yrs   *ACGME Approved/Offered Positions:* 10
Program ID: 141-35-21-167

NSLIJHS-North Shore University Hospital/NYU School of Medicine Program

Sponsor: North Shore-Long Island Jewish Health System
Long Island Jewish Medical Center
North Shore University Hospital
Prgm Director: Donna Marchant, MD
Department of Medicine
300 Community Drive
Manhasset, NY 11030
Tel: 516 562-2342   *Fax:* 516 562-3990
Length: 3 Yrs   *ACGME Approved/Offered Positions:* 15
Program ID: 141-35-21-201

Mineola

Winthrop-University Hospital Program

Sponsor: Winthrop-University Hospital
Prgm Director: Joshua R DeLeon, MD
120 Mineola Blvd
Ste 500
Mineola, NY 11501
Tel: 516 663-4482   *Fax:* 516 663-2926
E-mail: dfulton@winthrop.org
Length: 3 Yrs   *ACGME Approved/Offered Positions:* 9
Program ID: 141-35-11-100

New York

Albert Einstein College of Medicine at Beth Israel (Long Island College Hospital) Program

Sponsor: Beth Israel Medical Center
Long Island College Hospital
Prgm Director: Deepika Misra, MD
First Avenue at 16th Street
New York, NY 10003
Tel: 212 844-8823   *Fax:* 212 844-8653
Length: 3 Yrs   *ACGME Approved/Offered Positions:* 12
Program ID: 141-35-32-265

Albert Einstein College of Medicine at Beth Israel Medical Center Program

Sponsor: Beth Israel Medical Center
Prgm Director: Paul Schweitzer, MD
Department of Medicine
First Avenue at 16th Street
New York, NY 10003
Tel: 212 420-2806   *Fax:* 212 420-2406
Length: 3 Yrs   *ACGME Approved/Offered Positions:* 12
Program ID: 141-35-11-080

Lenox Hill Hospital Program

Sponsor: Lenox Hill Hospital
Prgm Director: Neil L Coplan, MD
100 East 77th Street
New York, NY 10021
Tel: 212 434-2172   *Fax:* 212 434-2111
Length: 3 Yrs   *ACGME Approved/Offered Positions:* 12
Program ID: 141-35-11-231

Programs

Mount Sinai School of Medicine (Urban Community) Program

Sponsor: Mount Sinai School of Medicine
Elmhurst Hospital Center-Mount Sinai Services
Mount Sinai Medical Center
Prgm Director: Jonathan Halperin, MD
One Gustave L Levy Place
Box 1030
New York, NY 10029
Tel: 212 241-7243 *Fax:* 212 831-2195
E-mail: jonathan.halperin@mssm.edu
Length: 3 Yrs *ACGME Approved/Offered Positions:* 12
Program ID: 141-35-12-264

Mount Sinai School of Medicine Program

Sponsor: Mount Sinai School of Medicine
Mount Sinai Medical Center
Veterans Affairs Medical Center (Bronx)
Prgm Director: Eric Stern, MD
Box 1030
One Gustave L Levy Place
New York, NY 10029
Tel: 212 241-4025 *Fax:* 212 426-6376
E-mail: eric.stern@mssm.edu
Length: 3 Yrs *ACGME Approved/Offered Positions:* 19
Program ID: 141-35-31-193

New York Medical College at St Vincent's Hospital and Medical Center of New York Program

Sponsor: New York Medical College
St Vincent Catholic Medical Centers (Manhattan)
Caritas Health Care (Brooklyn-Queens)
Montefiore Medical Center - North Division
Richmond University Medical Center
Prgm Director: James T Mazzara, MD
153 W 11th St, Nurses' Residence 1205
New York, NY 10011
Tel: 212 604-2224 *Fax:* 212 604-7828
E-mail: mhernandez@svcmcny.org
Length: 3 Yrs *ACGME Approved/Offered Positions:* 22
Program ID: 141-35-11-033

New York Presbyterian Hospital (Columbia Campus) Program

Sponsor: New York Presbyterian Hospital
New York Presbyterian Hospital (Columbia Campus)
Prgm Director: Steven O Marx, MD*
622 W 168th Street
Division of Cardiology - PH 3-342
New York, NY 10032
Tel: 212 305-0271 *Fax:* 212 342-0475
E-mail: cg257@columbia.edu
Length: 3 Yrs *ACGME Approved/Offered Positions:* 18
Program ID: 141-35-11-081

New York Presbyterian Hospital (Cornell Campus) Program

Sponsor: New York Presbyterian Hospital
New York Presbyterian Hospital (Cornell Campus)
Prgm Director: Sei Iwai, MD*
525 East 68th Street
New York, NY 10021
Tel: 212 746-2158 *Fax:* 212 746-6951
Length: 3 Yrs *ACGME Approved/Offered Positions:* 19
Program ID: 141-35-21-202

New York Presbyterian Hospital (Cornell Campus)/Brooklyn Hospital Center Program

Sponsor: New York Presbyterian Hospital
Brooklyn Hospital Center
New York Presbyterian Hospital (Cornell Campus)
Prgm Director: Frank M Iacovone, MD*
525 E 68th Street, Starr 437
New York, NY 10021
Tel: 718 250-8265 *Fax:* 718 250-6216
Length: 3 Yrs *ACGME Approved/Offered Positions:* 6
Program ID: 141-35-31-268

New York University School of Medicine Program

Sponsor: New York University School of Medicine
Bellevue Hospital Center
Manhattan VA Harbor Health Care System
NYU Hospitals Center
Prgm Director: Barry P Rosenzweig, MD
550 First Avenue
Cardiology, NB 17 South 5
New York, NY 10016
Tel: 212 263-6554 *Fax:* 212 263-7060
E-mail: shari.smith@nyumc.org
Length: 3 Yrs *ACGME Approved/Offered Positions:* 21
Program ID: 141-35-21-143

St Luke's-Roosevelt Hospital Center Program

Sponsor: St Luke's-Roosevelt Hospital Center
Prgm Director: Alan Rozanski, MD
Division of Cardiology
1111 Amsterdam Avenue
New York, NY 10025
Tel: 212 523-2887 *Fax:* 212 523-2764
Length: 3 Yrs *ACGME Approved/Offered Positions:* 15
Program ID: 141-35-21-251

Rochester

University of Rochester Program

Sponsor: Strong Memorial Hospital of the University of Rochester
Prgm Director: Richard M Pomerantz, MD
601 Elmwood Avenue, Box 679A
Rochester, NY 14642
Tel: 585 275-7736 *Fax:* 585 473-1573
Length: 3 Yrs *ACGME Approved/Offered Positions:* 15
Program ID: 141-35-11-232

Staten Island

Staten Island University Hospital Program

Sponsor: Staten Island University Hospital
Prgm Director: James C Lafferty, MD
475 Seaview Avenue
Staten Island, NY 10305
Tel: 718 663-7000 *Fax:* 718 663-7094
Length: 3 Yrs *ACGME Approved/Offered Positions:* 6
Program ID: 141-35-13-276

Stony Brook

SUNY at Stony Brook Program

Sponsor: University Hospital - SUNY at Stony Brook
Prgm Director: Noelle Mann, MD
Division of Cardiology
HSC T-16-080
Stony Brook, NY 11794
Tel: 631 444-1066 *Fax:* 631 444-1054
Length: 3 Yrs *ACGME Approved/Offered Positions:* 12
Program ID: 141-35-21-014

Syracuse

SUNY Upstate Medical University Program

Sponsor: SUNY Upstate Medical University
Veterans Affairs Medical Center (Syracuse)
Prgm Director: Robert L Carhart Jr, MD
750 East Adams Street
Syracuse, NY 13210
Tel: 315 464-9572 *Fax:* 315 464-5985
E-mail: schirtzl@upstate.edu
Length: 3 Yrs *ACGME Approved/Offered Positions:* 9
Program ID: 141-35-21-128

Valhalla

New York Medical College at Westchester Medical Center Program

Sponsor: New York Medical College
Sound Shore Medical Center of Westchester
Westchester Medical Center
Prgm Director: John A McClung, MD
Westchester County Medical Ctr
Division of Cardiology
Valhalla, NY 10595
Tel: 914 493-7199 *Fax:* 914 493-1854
Length: 3 Yrs *ACGME Approved/Offered Positions:* 13
Program ID: 141-35-11-015

North Carolina

Chapel Hill

University of North Carolina Hospitals Program

Sponsor: University of North Carolina Hospitals
Prgm Director: Park W Willis IV, MD
Burnett-Womack Building, 6th Floor
CB 7075
Chapel Hill, NC 27599
Tel: 919 966-5205 *Fax:* 919 966-1743
E-mail: keith_lander@med.unc.edu
Length: 3 Yrs *ACGME Approved/Offered Positions:* 18
Program ID: 141-36-21-171

Durham

Duke University Hospital Program

Sponsor: Duke University Hospital
Prgm Director: Andrew Wang, MD
DUMC 3428
Durham, NC 27710
Tel: 919 681-6197 *Fax:* 919 681-7917
Length: 3 Yrs *ACGME Approved/Offered Positions:* 33
Program ID: 141-36-21-172

Greenville

Pitt County Memorial Hospital/East Carolina University Program

Sponsor: Pitt County Memorial Hospital
Brody School of Medicine at East Carolina University
Prgm Director: John D Rose, MD
600 Moye Blvd
ECHI Room 2245
Greenville, NC 27834
Tel: 252 744-5964 *Fax:* 252 744-7724
E-mail: cardiologyfellowship@ecu.edu
Length: 3 Yrs *ACGME Approved/Offered Positions:* 9
Program ID: 141-36-11-245

Winston-Salem

Wake Forest University School of Medicine Program

Sponsor: Wake Forest University Baptist Medical Center
Prgm Director: Robert J Applegate, MD
Medical Center Boulevard
Winston-Salem, NC 27157
Tel: 336 716-2718 *Fax:* 336 716-5324
Length: 3 Yrs *ACGME Approved/Offered Positions:* 15
Program ID: 141-36-21-016

Note: * indicates a newly appointed program director

Ohio

Cincinnati

University Hospital/University of Cincinnati College of Medicine Program

Sponsor: University Hospital Inc
Veterans Affairs Medical Center (Cincinnati)
Prgm Director: Neal L Weintraub, MD
Division of Cardiology
231 Albert B Sabin Way
Cincinnati, OH 45267
Tel: 513 558-1067 *Fax:* 513 558-2002
E-mail: janet.rosing@uc.edu
Length: 3 Yrs *ACGME Approved/Offered Positions:* 14
Program ID: 141-38-21-102

Cleveland

Case Western Reserve University (MetroHealth) Program

Sponsor: MetroHealth Medical Center
Cleveland Clinic Foundation
Prgm Director: Kara J Quan, MD
2500 MetroHealth Drive
Cleveland, OH 44109
Tel: 216 778-3925 *Fax:* 216 778-3927
Length: 3 Yrs *ACGME Approved/Offered Positions:* 12
Program ID: 141-38-11-196

Cleveland Clinic Foundation Program

Sponsor: Cleveland Clinic Foundation
Prgm Director: Brian Griffin, MD
9500 Euclid Avenue
Desk F25
Cleveland, OH 44195
Tel: 216 444-3925
Length: 3 Yrs *ACGME Approved/Offered Positions:* 39
Program ID: 141-38-12-197

University Hospitals Case Medical Center Program

Sponsor: University Hospitals Case Medical Center
Veterans Affairs Medical Center (Cleveland)
Prgm Director: Brian D Hoit, MD
11100 Euclid Avenue, Mailstop LKS5038
Cleveland, OH 44106
Tel: 216 844-3855 *Fax:* 216 844-8954
E-mail: cvfellow@case.edu
Length: 3 Yrs *ACGME Approved/Offered Positions:* 15
Program ID: 141-38-21-194

Columbus

Ohio State University Hospital Program

Sponsor: Ohio State University Hospital
Prgm Director: Albert J Kolibash Jr, MD
473 W 12th Avenue, 200 HLRI
Columbus, OH 43210
Tel: 614 293-8962 *Fax:* 614 293-5614
Length: 3 Yrs *ACGME Approved/Offered Positions:* 17
Program ID: 141-38-11-179

Kettering

Kettering Medical Center Program

Sponsor: Kettering Medical Center
Veterans Affairs Medical Center (Dayton)
Prgm Director: Harvey S Hahn, MD
3535 Southern Boulevard
Kettering, OH 45429
Tel: 937 395-8609 *Fax:* 937 395-8023
E-mail: harvey.hahn@khnetwork.org
Length: 3 Yrs *ACGME Approved/Offered Positions:* 6
Program ID: 141-38-31-281

Toledo

University of Toledo Program

Sponsor: University of Toledo
University Medical Center (Toledo)
Prgm Director: Peter Temesy-Armos, MD*
Health Sciences Campus
3000 Arlington Avenue, Suite 1192
Toledo, OH 43614
Tel: 419 383-3697 *Fax:* 419 383-3041
E-mail: teri.diehl@utoledo.edu
Length: 3 Yrs *ACGME Approved/Offered Positions:* 6
Program ID: 141-38-21-068

Oklahoma

Oklahoma City

University of Oklahoma Health Sciences Center Program

Sponsor: University of Oklahoma College of Medicine
OU Medical Center
Veterans Affairs Medical Center (Oklahoma City)
Prgm Director: Chittur A Sivaram, MD
PO Box 26901
Williams Pavilion - 3010 - Department of Medicine
Oklahoma City, OK 73104
Tel: 405 271-4742 *Fax:* 405 271-2619
E-mail: linda-turner@ouhsc.edu
Length: 3 Yrs *ACGME Approved/Offered Positions:* 12
Program ID: 141-39-21-103

Oregon

Portland

Oregon Health & Science University Program

Sponsor: Oregon Health & Science University Hospital
Veterans Affairs Medical Center (Portland)
Prgm Director: Jonathan R Lindner, MD
Division of Cardiovascular Medicine/UHN62
3181 SW Sam Jackson Park Road
Portland, OR 97239
Tel: 503 494-8750 *Fax:* 503 494-8550
E-mail: diamonds@ohsu.edu
Length: 3 Yrs *ACGME Approved/Offered Positions:* 15
Program ID: 141-40-31-198

Pennsylvania

Allentown

Lehigh Valley Hospital Network/Pennsylvania State University Program

Sponsor: Lehigh Valley Hospital Network
Lehigh Valley Hospital-Muhlenberg
Prgm Director: Larry E Jacobs, MD
Cardiology Fellowship
Suite 410, 1240 S Cedar Crest Boulevard
Allentown, PA 18103
Tel: 610 402-8275 *Fax:* 610 402-1675
E-mail: Larry.Jacobs@lvh.com
Length: 3 Yrs *ACGME Approved/Offered Positions:* 12
Program ID: 141-41-13-280

Danville

Geisinger Health System Program

Sponsor: Geisinger Health System
Geisinger Medical Center
Prgm Director: Jamshid Shirani, MD
Department of Medicine, MC 21-60
100 Academy Avenue
Danville, PA 17822
Tel: 570 271-6423 *Fax:* 570 271-8056
E-mail: tkalejta@geisinger.edu
Length: 3 Yrs *ACGME Approved/Offered Positions:* 12
Program ID: 141-41-11-173

Hershey

Penn State University/Milton S Hershey Medical Center Program

Sponsor: Milton S Hershey Medical Center
Prgm Director: Joseph A Gascho, MD
University Hospital
PO Box 850
Hershey, PA 17033
Tel: 717 531-6746 *Fax:* 717 531-0099
E-mail: gascho@psu.edu
Length: 3 Yrs *ACGME Approved/Offered Positions:* 15
Program ID: 141-41-11-017

Philadelphia

Albert Einstein Healthcare Network Program

Sponsor: Albert Einstein Medical Center
Prgm Director: Vincent M Figueredo, MD
5401 Old York Rd
Klein Building, Suite 363
Philadelphia, PA 19141
Tel: 215 456-8819 *Fax:* 215 456-3533
E-mail: walshp@einstein.edu
Length: 3 Yrs *ACGME Approved/Offered Positions:* 15
Program ID: 141-41-11-082

Drexel University College of Medicine/Hahnemann University Hospital Program

Sponsor: Drexel University College of Medicine/Hahnemann University
Hahnemann University Hospital (Tenet Health System)
Prgm Director: John M Fontaine, MD
245 N 15th St, Mailstop 470
Philadelphia, PA 19102
Tel: 215 762-4641 *Fax:* 215 762-3028
Length: 3 Yrs *ACGME Approved/Offered Positions:* 24
Program ID: 141-41-21-145

Temple University Hospital Program

Sponsor: Temple University Hospital
Prgm Director: William A VanDecker, MD
Cardiology Section
3401 N Broad Street
Philadelphia, PA 19140
Tel: 215 707-9587 *Fax:* 215 707-3946
E-mail: vandecwa@tuhs.temple.edu
Length: 3 Yrs *ACGME Approved/Offered Positions:* 12
Program ID: 141-41-21-036

Thomas Jefferson University Program

Sponsor: Thomas Jefferson University Hospital
Prgm Director: Arnold J Greenspon, MD
Division of Cardiology
111 South 11th Street
Philadelphia, PA 19107
Tel: 215 955-8659 *Fax:* 215 503-5976
Length: 3 Yrs *ACGME Approved/Offered Positions:* 18
Program ID: 141-41-21-037

University of Pennsylvania Program

Sponsor: University of Pennsylvania Health System
Prgm Director: Martin G St John Sutton, MD
Gates Building, 9th Floor
3400 Spruce Street
Philadelphia, PA 19104
Tel: 215 662-2285 *Fax:* 215 349-8190
E-mail: martin.sutton@uphs.upenn.edu
Length: 3 Yrs *ACGME Approved/Offered Positions:* 24
Program ID: 141-41-21-023

Pittsburgh

Allegheny General Hospital Program

Sponsor: Allegheny General Hospital
Prgm Director: Jerome E Granato, MD*
Department of Medicine
320 E North Avenue
Pittsburgh, PA 15212
Tel: 412 359-4997 *Fax:* 412 359-6544
E-mail: jgranato@wpahs.org
Length: 3 Yrs *ACGME Approved/Offered Positions:* 13
Program ID: 141-41-11-053

University of Pittsburgh Medical Center Medical Education Program

Sponsor: Univ of Pittsburgh Medical Center Medical
    Education
UPMC Presbyterian Shadyside
Prgm Director: Michael A Mathier, MD
200 Lothrop Street
S555 Scaife Hall
Pittsburgh, PA 15213
Tel: 412 647-3429 *Fax:* 412 647-0481
Length: 3 Yrs *ACGME Approved/Offered Positions:* 30
Program ID: 141-41-21-054

Western Pennsylvania Hospital/Temple University Program

Sponsor: Western Pennsylvania Hospital
Prgm Director: Alan H Gradman, MD
4800 Friendship Ave
NT 3411
Pittsburgh, PA 15224
Tel: 412 578-6902 *Fax:* 412 578-6804
Length: 3 Yrs *ACGME Approved/Offered Positions:* 6
Program ID: 141-41-11-083

Wynnewood

Lankenau Hospital Program

Sponsor: Lankenau Hospital
Prgm Director: James Burke, MD
100 Lancaster Avenue
Wynnewood, PA 19096
Tel: 610 645-2682 *Fax:* 610 896-0643
Length: 3 Yrs *ACGME Approved/Offered Positions:* 12
Program ID: 141-41-11-035

Puerto Rico

San Juan

University of Puerto Rico Program

Sponsor: University of Puerto Rico School of Medicine
Cardiovascular Center of Puerto Rico and the Caribbean
University Hospital
Prgm Director: Mario R Garcia-Palmieri, MD
University Hospital
Box 5067
San Juan, PR 00936
Tel: 787 767-8499 *Fax:* 787 754-1739
Length: 3 Yrs *ACGME Approved/Offered Positions:* 12
Program ID: 141-42-21-148

VA Caribbean Healthcare System Program

Sponsor: VA Caribbean Healthcare System
Prgm Director: Luis F Rodriguez-Ospina, MD
10 Casia Street
San Juan, PR 00921
Tel: 787 641-2966 *Fax:* 787 641-9392
Length: 3 Yrs *ACGME Approved/Offered Positions:* 6
Program ID: 141-42-31-147

Rhode Island

Providence

Brown University Program

Sponsor: Rhode Island Hospital-Lifespan
Miriam Hospital-Lifespan
Veterans Affairs Medical Center (Providence)
Prgm Director: James A Arrighi, MD
Department of Medicine
593 Eddy Street, Main Bldg, Rm 209
Providence, RI 02903
Tel: 401 444-8041 *Fax:* 401 444-5124
Length: 3 Yrs *ACGME Approved/Offered Positions:* 18
Program ID: 141-43-11-149

South Carolina

Charleston

Medical University of South Carolina Program

Sponsor: Medical University of South Carolina College of
    Medicine
MUSC Medical Center
Ralph H Johnson VA Medical Center (Charleston)
Prgm Director: Bruce W Usher Sr, MD
25 Courtenay Drive, 7ART, Rm 7063
MSC592
Charleston, SC 29425
Tel: 843 876-4807 *Fax:* 843 876-4809
E-mail: usherb@musc.edu
Length: 3 Yrs *ACGME Approved/Offered Positions:* 18
Program ID: 141-45-21-129

Tennessee

Johnson City

East Tennessee State University Program

Sponsor: James H Quillen College of Medicine
Johnson City Medical Center/Mountain States Health
    Alliance
Veterans Affairs Medical Center (Mountain Home)
Prgm Director: Christopher J Downs, MD
2 Professional Park Drive, Suite 15
Johnson City, TN 37604
Tel: 423 232-4860 *Fax:* 423 722-0002
E-mail: hilber@etsu.edu
Length: 3 Yrs *ACGME Approved/Offered Positions:* 8
Program ID: 141-47-21-104

Knoxville

University of Tennessee Medical Center at Knoxville Program

Sponsor: University of Tennessee Graduate School of
    Medicine
University of Tennessee Memorial Hospital
Prgm Director: Dale C Wortham, MD
1924 Alcoa Highway
Mailbox U114
Knoxville, TN 37920
Tel: 865 305-6324 *Fax:* 865 305-9144
E-mail: ptrentha@utmck.edu
Length: 3 Yrs *ACGME Approved/Offered Positions:* 6
Program ID: 141-47-12-278

Memphis

University of Tennessee Program

Sponsor: University of Tennessee College of Medicine
Methodist Healthcare - Memphis Hospitals
Regional Medical Center at Memphis
Veterans Affairs Medical Center (Memphis)
Prgm Director: Karl T Weber, MD
Department of Medicine
956 Court Avenue, Suite A312
Memphis, TN 38163
Tel: 901 448-5759 *Fax:* 901 448-8084
Length: 3 Yrs *ACGME Approved/Offered Positions:* 12
Program ID: 141-47-21-175

Nashville

Vanderbilt University Program

Sponsor: Vanderbilt University Medical Center
Prgm Director: Douglas B Sawyer, MD, PhD
383 PRB
2220 Pierce Avenue
Nashville, TN 37232
Tel: 615 936-1720 *Fax:* 615 936-1872
Length: 3 Yrs *ACGME Approved/Offered Positions:* 30
Program ID: 141-47-31-018

Texas

Dallas

Baylor University Medical Center Program

Sponsor: Baylor University Medical Center
Prgm Director: Peter J Wells, MD
3500 Gaston Avenue
Roberts 1st Floor, Medical Education
Dallas, TX 75246
Tel: 214 820-2234 *Fax:* 214 820-7272
Length: 3 Yrs *ACGME Approved/Offered Positions:* 9
Program ID: 141-48-31-176

University of Texas Southwestern Medical School Program

Sponsor: University of Texas Southwestern Medical
    School
Dallas County Hospital District-Parkland Memorial
    Hospital
Dallas VA Medical Center
Prgm Director: James A De Lemos, MD
Division of Cardiology, HA9133
5323 Harry Hines Boulevard
Dallas, TX 75390
Tel: 214 645-7521 *Fax:* 214 645-7501
E-mail: james.delemos@utsouthwestern.edu
Length: 3 Yrs *ACGME Approved/Offered Positions:* 27
Program ID: 141-48-21-119

Fort Sam Houston

San Antonio Uniformed Services Health Education Consortium Program

Sponsor: San Antonio Uniformed Services Health
    Education Consortium
Brooke Army Medical Center
Wilford Hall Medical Center (AETC)
Prgm Director: James L Furgerson, MD
3851 Roger Brooke Drive
Fort Sam Houston, TX 78234
Tel: 210 916-4536 *Fax:* 210 916-3218
E-mail: karen.luera2@amedd.army.mil
Length: 3 Yrs *ACGME Approved/Offered Positions:* 24
Program ID: 141-48-12-177
Uniformed Services Program

Note: * indicates a newly appointed program director

Galveston

University of Texas Medical Branch Hospitals Program

Sponsor: University of Texas Medical Branch Hospitals
Methodist Hospital (Houston)
Prgm Director: David L Ware, MD
5106 John Sealy Annex, Route 0553
301 University Boulevard
Galveston, TX 77550
Tel: 409 772-1533   *Fax:* 409 772-4982
E-mail: fellowship@cardiology.utmb.edu
Length: 3 Yrs   *ACGME Approved/Offered Positions:* 18
Program ID: 141-48-21-070

Houston

Baylor College of Medicine Program

Sponsor: Baylor College of Medicine
Harris County Hospital District-Ben Taub General
  Hospital
Michael E DeBakey VA Medical Center - Houston
St Luke's Episcopal Hospital
Prgm Director: Nasser Lakkis, MD
1709 Dryden, MS-BCM620
Ste 9.92
Houston, TX 77030
Tel: 713 798-0284   *Fax:* 713 798-0277
Length: 3 Yrs   *ACGME Approved/Offered Positions:* 31
Program ID: 141-48-21-106

Baylor College of Medicine/St Luke's Episcopal Hospital Program

Sponsor: Baylor College of Medicine
St Luke's Episcopal Hospital
Prgm Director: James M Wilson, MD
Department of Cardiology
6720 Bertner M/C 1-133
Houston, TX 77030
Tel: 832 355-4135   *Fax:* 832 355-8374
E-mail: mjones@sleh.com
Length: 3 Yrs   *ACGME Approved/Offered Positions:* 19
Program ID: 141-48-21-120

University of Texas at Houston Program

Sponsor: University of Texas Health Science Center at
  Houston
Memorial Hermann Hospital
University of Texas M D Anderson Cancer Center
Prgm Director: Francisco Fuentes, MD
6431 Fannin St
MSB 1.247
Houston, TX 77030
Tel: 713 500-6577   *Fax:* 713 500-6556
E-mail: carol.mateo@uth.tmc.edu
Length: 3 Yrs   *ACGME Approved/Offered Positions:* 21
Program ID: 141-48-31-019

Lubbock

Texas Tech University (Lubbock) Program

Sponsor: Texas Tech University Health Sciences Center
  at Lubbock
University Medical Center
Prgm Director: Leigh A Jenkins, MD
Division of Cardiology/Department of Medicine
3601 4th Street, Stop 9410
Lubbock, TX 79430
Tel: 806 743-3155   *Fax:* 806 743-3148
E-mail: lisa.teutsch@ttuhsc.edu
Length: 3 Yrs   *ACGME Approved/Offered Positions:* 6
Program ID: 141-48-21-121

San Antonio

University of Texas Health Science Center at San Antonio Program

Sponsor: University of Texas School of Medicine at San
  Antonio
Audie L Murphy Memorial Veterans Hospital (San
  Antonio)
University Health System
Prgm Director: John M Erikson, MD, PhD
Department of Medicine, MC 7872
7703 Floyd Curl Drive
San Antonio, TX 78229
Tel: 210 567-4602   *Fax:* 210 567-6960
E-mail: ramirezv0@uthscsa.edu
Length: 3 Yrs   *ACGME Approved/Offered Positions:* 15
Program ID: 141-48-21-084

Temple

Texas A&M College of Medicine-Scott and White Program

Sponsor: Scott and White Memorial Hospital
Prgm Director: David S Gantt, DO
2401 S 31st Street
Temple, TX 76508
Tel: 254 724-0108   *Fax:* 254 724-8067
E-mail: mwheeler@swmail.sw.org
Length: 3 Yrs   *ACGME Approved/Offered Positions:* 12
Program ID: 141-48-21-020

Utah

Salt Lake City

University of Utah Program

Sponsor: University of Utah Medical Center
Veterans Affairs Medical Center (Salt Lake City)
Prgm Director: Sheldon E Litwin, MD
30 North 1900 East
4A100
Salt Lake City, UT 84132
Tel: 801 585-1686   *Fax:* 801 581-7735
E-mail: katie.goodyear@hsc.utah.edu
Length: 3 Yrs   *ACGME Approved/Offered Positions:* 12
Program ID: 141-49-21-199

Vermont

Burlington

University of Vermont Program

Sponsor: Fletcher Allen Health Care
Prgm Director: Mark Capeless, MD
Cardiology Department
Fletcher Allen Health Care
Burlington, VT 05401
Tel: 802 847-2005   *Fax:* 802 847-4016
E-mail: roberta.frohock@vtmednet.org
Length: 3 Yrs   *ACGME Approved/Offered Positions:* 12
Program ID: 141-50-21-200

Virginia

Charlottesville

University of Virginia Program

Sponsor: University of Virginia Medical Center
Prgm Director: John M Dent, MD
Department of Medicine
PO Box 800662
Charlottesville, VA 22908
Tel: 434 982-1414   *Fax:* 434 924-1692
E-mail: cardiofellows@virginia.edu
Length: 3 Yrs   *ACGME Approved/Offered Positions:* 18
Program ID: 141-51-21-021

Richmond

Virginia Commonwealth University Health System Program

Sponsor: Virginia Commonwealth University Health
  System
Hunter Holmes McGuire VA Medical Center (Richmond)
Medical College of Virginia Hospitals
Prgm Director: Anthony J Minisi, MD
PO Box 980051
Cardiology Fellowship Program
Richmond, VA 23298
Tel: 804 828-9989   *Fax:* 804 828-3544
Length: 3 Yrs   *ACGME Approved/Offered Positions:* 15
Program ID: 141-51-21-022

Washington

Seattle

University of Washington Program

Sponsor: University of Washington School of Medicine
University of Washington Medical Center
Prgm Director: Catherine M Otto, MD
Division of Cardiology - Box 356422
1959 NE Pacific Street
Seattle, WA 98195
Tel: 206 685-1397   *Fax:* 206 685-9394
E-mail: uwcard@u.washington.edu
Length: 3 Yrs   *ACGME Approved/Offered Positions:* 18
Program ID: 141-54-21-105

West Virginia

Huntington

Marshall University School of Medicine Program

Sponsor: Marshall University School of Medicine
Cabell Huntington Hospital
St Mary's Hospital
Veterans Affairs Medical Center (Huntington)
Prgm Director: Paulette S Wehner, MD
Department of Medicine
1249 15th Street, Suite 4000
Huntington, WV 25701
Tel: 304 691-8534   *Fax:* 304 691-8530
Length: 3 Yrs   *ACGME Approved/Offered Positions:* 11
Program ID: 141-55-21-038

Morgantown

West Virginia University Program

Sponsor: West Virginia University School of Medicine
West Virginia University Hospitals
Prgm Director: Bradford E Warden, MD
4073 Robert C Byrd Health Sciences Center
PO Box 9168
Morgantown, WV 26506
Tel: 304 293-2801   *Fax:* 304 293-3651
E-mail: dhamilton@hsc.wvu.edu
Length: 3 Yrs   *ACGME Approved/Offered Positions:* 9
Program ID: 141-55-11-219

Programs

Wisconsin

Madison

University of Wisconsin Program

Sponsor: University of Wisconsin Hospital and Clinics
William S Middleton Veterans Hospital
Prgm Director: Ford Ballantyne III, MD
600 Highland Avenue
Room H6/319
Madison, WI 53792
Tel: 608 263-1535   *Fax:* 608 263-0405
E-mail: fellowship@medicine.wisc.edu
Length: 3 Yrs   *ACGME Approved/Offered Positions:* 9
Program ID: 141-56-21-150

Milwaukee

Aurora Health Care Program

Sponsor: Aurora Health Care
Aurora Sinai Medical Center
St Luke's Medical Center
Prgm Director: Masood Akhtar, MD
Aurora Sinai Medical Center
945 N 12th St, PO Box 342
Milwaukee, WI 53201
Tel: 414 219-7190   *Fax:* 414 219-7676
E-mail: jruffin@hrtcare.com
Length: 3 Yrs   *ACGME Approved/Offered Positions:* 18
Program ID: 141-56-21-072

Medical College of Wisconsin Affiliated Hospitals Program

Sponsor: Medical College of Wisconsin Affiliated
   Hospitals, Inc
Clement J Zablocki Veterans Affairs Medical Center
Froedtert Memorial Lutheran Hospital
Prgm Director: James F Kleczka, MD*
Cardiovascular Medicine
9200 W Wisconsin Avenue, Ste 5100
Milwaukee, WI 53226
Tel: 414 805-0009   *Fax:* 414 456-6203
Length: 3 Yrs   *ACGME Approved/Offered Positions:* 15
Program ID: 141-56-31-056

Chemical Pathology (Pathology)

Michigan

Royal Oak

William Beaumont Hospital Program

Sponsor: William Beaumont Hospital
Prgm Director: Elizabeth Sykes, MD
Clinical Pathology
3601 W Thirteen Mile Rd
Royal Oak, MI 48073
Tel: 248 551-2935   *Fax:* 248 551-3694
Length: 1 Yr   *ACGME Approved/Offered Positions:* 1
Program ID: 306-25-21-008

Texas

Houston

University of Texas M D Anderson Cancer Center Program

Sponsor: University of Texas M D Anderson Cancer
   Center
Prgm Director: Beverly C Handy, MD, JD
Div of Laboratory Medicine, Box 037
1515 Holcombe Boulevard
Houston, TX 77030
Tel: 713 792-4690   *Fax:* 713 792-4793
Length: 1 Yr   *ACGME Approved/Offered Positions:* 2
Program ID: 306-48-21-004

Child and Adolescent Psychiatry (Psychiatry)

Alabama

Birmingham

University of Alabama Medical Center Program

Sponsor: University of Alabama Hospital
Children's Hospital of Alabama
Glenwood Mental Health Services, Inc
Prgm Director: Lee I Ascherman, MD, MPH
Smolian Building - 3rd Floor
1700 7th Avenue South
Birmingham, AL 35294
Tel: 205 934-5156   *Fax:* 205 975-7406
E-mail: jweatherly@uabmc.edu
Length: 2 Yrs   *ACGME Approved/Offered Positions:* 6
Program ID: 405-01-21-172

Arizona

Phoenix

Maricopa Medical Center Program

Sponsor: Maricopa Medical Center
Prgm Director: Shayne Tomisato, MD
Desert Vista Behavioral Health
570 W Brown Road
Mesa, AZ 85201
Tel: 480 344-2026   *Fax:* 480 344-0219
Length: 2 Yrs   *ACGME Approved/Offered Positions:* 6
Program ID: 405-03-11-179

Tucson

University of Arizona Program

Sponsor: University of Arizona College of Medicine
University Medical Center
Prgm Director: Harinder Ghuman, MD
1501 North Campbell Avenue
PO Box 245002
Tucson, AZ 85724
Tel: 520 626-2566   *Fax:* 520 626-6050
Length: 2 Yrs   *ACGME Approved/Offered Positions:* 5
Program ID: 405-03-21-142

Arkansas

Little Rock

University of Arkansas for Medical Sciences Program

Sponsor: University of Arkansas College of Medicine
Arkansas Children's Hospital
Arkansas State Hospital (DBHS)
UAMS Medical Center
Prgm Director: Brian M Kubacak, MD
1120 Marshall Street
Slot 654
Little Rock, AR 72202
Tel: 501 364-4670   *Fax:* 501 364-1592
E-mail: kubacakbrianm@uams.edu
Length: 2 Yrs   *ACGME Approved/Offered Positions:* 5
Program ID: 405-04-21-146

Note: * indicates a newly appointed program director

California

Bakersfield

UCLA-Kern Medical Center Program
Sponsor: Kern Medical Center
Good Samaritan Hospital Southwest
Kern County Mental Health Department
UCLA Neuropsychiatric Hospital
Prgm Director: Elizabeth M Tully, MD
1830 Flower Street
Bakersfield, CA 93305
Tel: 661 326-2248   *Fax:* 661 862-7682
Length: 2 Yrs   *ACGME Approved/Offered Positions:* 6
Program ID: 405-05-31-191

Los Angeles

Cedars-Sinai Medical Center Program
Sponsor: Cedars-Sinai Medical Center
Five Acres - The Boys & Girls Aid Society LA
Hathaway-Sycamores Child & Family Services
Vista Del Mar Child & Family Services
Prgm Director: Roxy Szeftel, MD
8730 Alden Drive
Thalians W128
Los Angeles, CA 90048
Tel: 310 423-3566   *Fax:* 310 423-0114
Length: 2 Yrs   *ACGME Approved/Offered Positions:* 6
Program ID: 405-05-11-008

UCLA Medical Center Program
Sponsor: UCLA David Geffen School of Medicine/UCLA
   Medical Center
UCLA Neuropsychiatric Hospital
Prgm Director: Sheryl H Kataoka, MD, MS*
c/o Alicja Cziao, Program Coordinator
760 Westwood Plaza, C8-225
Los Angeles, CA 90024
Tel: 310 794-9333
E-mail: acziao@mednet.ucla.edu
Length: 2 Yrs   *ACGME Approved/Offered Positions:* 12
Program ID: 405-05-12-012

University of Southern California/ LAC+USC Medical Center Program
Sponsor: University of Southern California/LAC+USC
   Medical Center
LAC+USC Medical Center
Prgm Director: Erica Shoemaker, MD*
Division of Child & Adolescent Psychiatry
2250 Alcazar Street, CSC 2200
Los Angeles, CA 90033
Tel: 323 442-4033   *Fax:* 323 442-4003
E-mail: erica.shoemaker@keck.usc.edu
Length: 2 Yrs   *ACGME Approved/Offered Positions:* 14
Program ID: 405-05-11-010

Orange

University of California (Irvine) Program
Sponsor: University of California (Irvine) Medical
   Center
Prgm Director: Gail E Fernandez, MD
101 City Drive South, Route 88
Building 3, UCIMC
Orange, CA 92868
Tel: 714 456-5770   *Fax:* 714 456-7615
Length: 2 Yrs   *ACGME Approved/Offered Positions:* 6
Program ID: 405-05-11-007

Sacramento

University of California (Davis) Health System Program
Sponsor: University of California (Davis) Health System
Sacramento County Health and Human Services
University of California (Davis) Medical Center
Prgm Director: Malia McCarthy, MD
Department of Psychiatry and Behavioral Sciences
2230 Stockton Blvd
Sacramento, CA 95817
Tel: 916 703-0299   *Fax:* 916 703-0244
E-mail: marilyn.clark@ucdmc.ucdavis.edu
Length: 2 Yrs   *ACGME Approved/Offered Positions:* 6
Program ID: 405-05-11-005

San Diego

University of California (San Diego) Program
Sponsor: University of California (San Diego) Medical
   Center
Rady Children's Hospital
Prgm Director: Ellen K Heyneman, MD
3665 Kearny Villa Road Suite 101
San Diego, CA 92123
Tel: 858 966-4935   *Fax:* 858 966-6733
Length: 2 Yrs   *ACGME Approved/Offered Positions:* 8
Program ID: 405-05-21-014

San Francisco

University of California (San Francisco) Program
Sponsor: University of California (San Francisco) School
   of Medicine
Department of Public Health (San Francisco)
Edgewood Center for Children & Families
Prgm Director: Stuart L Lustig, MD, MPH
401 Parnassus Avenue, Box 0984-CAS
San Francisco, CA 94143
Tel: 415 476-7225   *Fax:* 415 476-7163
Length: 2 Yrs   *ACGME Approved/Offered Positions:* 10
Program ID: 405-05-21-018

Stanford

Stanford University Program
Sponsor: Stanford Hospital and Clinics
Kaiser Permanente Medical Center (Santa Clara)
Kaiser Santa Teresa
Lucile Salter Packard Children's Hospital at Stanford
Prgm Director: Shashank V Joshi, MD
401 Quarry Road
Room 2206
Stanford, CA 94305
Tel: 650 725-0957   *Fax:* 650 721-3954
Length: 2 Yrs   *ACGME Approved/Offered Positions:* 14
Program ID: 405-05-21-019

Torrance

Los Angeles County-Harbor-UCLA Medical Center Program
Sponsor: Los Angeles County-Harbor-UCLA Medical
   Center
Metropolitan State Hospital
Prgm Director: Kathleen McKenna, MD*
Child Psychiatry Division, Box 498
1000 West Carson Street
Torrance, CA 90509
Tel: 310 222-3160   *Fax:* 310 328-7217
E-mail: kmckenna@dmh.lacounty.gov
Length: 2 Yrs   *ACGME Approved/Offered Positions:* 8
Program ID: 405-05-21-020

Colorado

Aurora

University of Colorado Denver Program
Sponsor: University of Colorado Denver School of
   Medicine
Children's Hospital (The)
Colorado Mental Health Institute at Fort Logan
Denver Health Medical Center
University of Colorado Hospital
Prgm Director: Debbie R Carter, MD, BS
13001 E 17th Pl, Bldg 500, Rm E2328
Campus Box F546, PO Box 6508
Aurora, CO 80045
Tel: 303 724-6022   *Fax:* 303 724-4963
E-mail: tammy.samuels@uchsc.edu
Length: 2 Yrs   *ACGME Approved/Offered Positions:* 12
Program ID: 405-07-11-021

Connecticut

Farmington

University of Connecticut Program
Sponsor: University of Connecticut School of Medicine
Capital Region Education Council Polaris Center
Connecticut Children's Medical Center
Connecticut, Dept of Corrections: Manson Youth Facility
Riverview Hospital for Children
Univ of Connecticut Health Center/John Dempsey
   Hospital
Wheeler Clinic
Prgm Director: Daniel F Connor, MD
263 Farmington Avenue
MC 1410
Farmington, CT 06030
Tel: 860 679-8348   *Fax:* 860 679-1296
Length: 2 Yrs   *ACGME Approved/Offered Positions:* 4
Program ID: 405-08-13-186

Hartford

Institute of Living/Hartford Hospital Program
Sponsor: Hartford Hospital
Connecticut Children's Medical Center
Institute of Living
Prgm Director: Robert Sahl, MD*
200 Retreat Avenue
Braceland Building
Hartford, CT 06106
Tel: 860 545-7647   *Fax:* 860 545-7650
E-mail: rsahl@harthosp.org
Length: 2 Yrs   *ACGME Approved/Offered Positions:* 6
Program ID: 405-08-21-022

New Haven

Yale-New Haven Medical Center Program
Sponsor: Yale-New Haven Hospital
Riverview Hospital for Children
Prgm Director: Dorothy E Stubbe, MD
230 S Frontage Road
PO Box 207900
New Haven, CT 06520
Tel: 203 785-2516   *Fax:* 203 785-7400
E-mail: kathleen.czarniak@yale.edu
Length: 2 Yrs   *ACGME Approved/Offered Positions:* 14
Program ID: 405-08-11-023

District of Columbia

Washington

Children's National Medical Center/ George Washington University Program

Sponsor: Children's National Medical Center
Prgm Director: Peter T Daniolos, MD, BS
Psychiatry and Behavioral Sciences
111 Michigan Avenue, NW
Washington, DC 20010
Tel: 202 476-3932   *Fax:* 202 476-2368
E-mail: pdaniolo@cnmc.org
Length: 2 Yrs   *ACGME Approved/Offered Positions:* 12
Program ID: 405-10-21-024

Florida

Gainesville

University of Florida Program

Sponsor: University of Florida College of Medicine
Shands Hospital at the University of Florida
Prgm Director: Ayesha S Lall, MD*
1600 SW Archer Road
PO Box 100234
Gainesville, FL 32610
Tel: 352 392-8373
Length: 2 Yrs   *ACGME Approved/Offered Positions:* 8
Program ID: 405-11-11-026

Miami

Jackson Memorial Hospital/Jackson Health System Program

Sponsor: Jackson Memorial Hospital/Jackson Health System
Prgm Director: Lourdes Illa, MD
Department of Psychiatry (D-29)
PO Box 016960
Miami, FL 33101
Tel: 305 355-7010   *Fax:* 305 355-9012
E-mail: srichards2@med.miami.edu
Length: 2 Yrs   *ACGME Approved/Offered Positions:* 10
Program ID: 405-11-21-027

Tampa

University of South Florida Program

Sponsor: University of South Florida College of Medicine
All Children's Hospital
Manatee Glens
Tampa General Hospital
University Psychiatry Center
Prgm Director: Saundra Stock, MD
University Psychiatry Center
3515 East Fletcher Avenue
Tampa, FL 33613
Tel: 813 974-2805   *Fax:* 813 974-2478
E-mail: kisaac@health.usf.edu
Length: 2 Yrs   *ACGME Approved/Offered Positions:* 6
Program ID: 405-11-21-140

Georgia

Atlanta

Emory University Program

Sponsor: Emory University School of Medicine
Emory University School of Medicine (Briarcliff)
Grady Health System
Prgm Director: Arden D Dingle, MD
Child & Adolescent Psychiatry
1256 Briarcliff Rd, Suite 317S
Atlanta, GA 30306
Tel: 404 727-3886   *Fax:* 404 712-9890
E-mail: adingle@emory.edu
Length: 2 Yrs   *ACGME Approved/Offered Positions:* 12
Program ID: 405-12-21-028

Augusta

Medical College of Georgia Program

Sponsor: Medical College of Georgia
Prgm Director: Sandra B Sexson, MD
997 St Sebastian Way
Augusta, GA 30912
Tel: 706 721-6698   *Fax:* 706 721-1793
E-mail: ssexson@mail.mcg.edu
Length: 2 Yrs   *ACGME Approved/Offered Positions:* 6
Program ID: 405-12-21-148

Hawaii

Honolulu

University of Hawaii Program

Sponsor: University of Hawaii John A Burns School of Medicine
DOH CAMHD FCLB at HYCF
Kapiolani Medical Center for Women and Children
Queen's Medical Center
Prgm Director: Cathy K Bell, MD
Child & Adolescent Psychiatry
1356 Lusitana St, 4th Floor
Honolulu, HI 96813
Tel: 808 586-2939   *Fax:* 808 586-2940
Length: 2 Yrs   *ACGME Approved/Offered Positions:* 6
Program ID: 405-14-31-029

Tripler AMC

Tripler Army Medical Center Program

Sponsor: Tripler Army Medical Center
Kahi Mohala Hospital
Prgm Director: Scott D Uithol, MD
Child and Adolescent Psychiatry, Attn: MCHK-PSC
1 Jarrett White Road
Tripler AMC, HI 96859
Tel: 808 433-6418   *Fax:* 808 433-4890
E-mail: scott.uithol@us.army.mil
Length: 2 Yrs   *ACGME Approved/Offered Positions:* 8
Program ID: 405-14-21-143
Uniformed Services Program

Illinois

Chicago

McGaw Medical Center of Northwestern University Program

Sponsor: McGaw Medical Center of Northwestern University
Children's Memorial Hospital
Prgm Director: MaryBeth Lake, MD
2300 Children's Plaza, Box 10
Chicago, IL 60614
Tel: 773 880-4833   *Fax:* 773 880-4066
E-mail: amarcoux@childrensmemorial.org
Length: 2 Yrs   *ACGME Approved/Offered Positions:* 8
Program ID: 405-16-31-032

Rush University Medical Center Program

Sponsor: Rush University Medical Center
University of Illinois Hospital and Clinics
Prgm Director: Adrienne Adams, MD
Rush West Campus
2150 W Harrison Street
Chicago, IL 60612
Tel: 312 942-6673   *Fax:* 312 942-3186
Length: 2 Yrs   *ACGME Approved/Offered Positions:* 4
Program ID: 405-16-21-153

University of Chicago Program

Sponsor: University of Chicago Medical Center
HCA Chicago Lakeshore Hospital
Prgm Director: Sharon Hirsch, MD
5841 S Maryland Avenue, MC 3077
Chicago, IL 60637
Tel: 773 834-0373   *Fax:* 773 702-4297
E-mail: education@yoda.bsd.uchicago.edu
Length: 2 Yrs   *ACGME Approved/Offered Positions:* 6
Program ID: 405-16-21-034

University of Illinois College of Medicine at Chicago Program

Sponsor: University of Illinois College of Medicine at Chicago
Rush University Medical Center
University of Illinois Hospital and Clinics
Prgm Director: Kathleen Kelley, MD
Dept of Psychiatry, M/C 747
1747 W Roosevelt Road
Chicago, IL 60608
Tel: 312 355-1402   *Fax:* 312 966-9534
E-mail: bp@psych.uic.edu
Length: 2 Yrs   *ACGME Approved/Offered Positions:* 8
Program ID: 405-16-21-030

Springfield

Southern Illinois University Program

Sponsor: Southern Illinois University School of Medicine
Memorial Medical Center
St John's Hospital
Prgm Director: Ayame Takahashi, MD
5220 S 6th St Road, Suite 1200
Springfield, IL 62703
Tel: 217 545-7644   *Fax:* 217 585-6890
E-mail: rstark@siumed.edu
Length: 2 Yrs   *ACGME Approved/Offered Positions:* 4
Program ID: 405-16-21-189

Indiana

Indianapolis

Indiana University School of Medicine Program

Sponsor: Indiana University School of Medicine
Clarian Riley Hospital for Children
Larue D Carter Memorial Hospital
Prgm Director: David Dunn, MD
Clarian Riley Hospital for Children
ROC 4300
Indianapolis, IN 46202
Tel: 317 274-8162   *Fax:* 317 278-0609
E-mail: lgoudrea@iupui.edu
Length: 2 Yrs   *ACGME Approved/Offered Positions:* 8
Program ID: 405-17-21-038

Note: * indicates a newly appointed program director

Iowa

Iowa City

University of Iowa Hospitals and Clinics Program

Sponsor: University of Iowa Hospitals and Clinics
Prgm Director: Anne F Kolar, MD, BS
200 Hawkins Drive
1882 JPP
Iowa City, IA 52242
Tel: 319 356-0472   *Fax:* 319 384-8843
E-mail: anne-kolar@uiowa.edu
Length: 2 Yrs   *ACGME Approved/Offered Positions:* 6
Program ID: 405-18-11-039

Kansas

Kansas City

University of Kansas School of Medicine Program

Sponsor: University of Kansas School of Medicine
KVC Psychiatric Hospital
University of Kansas Hospital
Prgm Director: Sharon E Cain, MD
3901 Rainbow Boulevard, Mail Stop 4015
Division of Child and Adolescent Psychiatry
Kansas City, KS 66160
Tel: 913 588-6492   *Fax:* 913 588-6404
E-mail: snothstine@kumc.edu
Length: 2 Yrs   *ACGME Approved/Offered Positions:* 6
Program ID: 405-19-11-040

Kentucky

Lexington

University of Kentucky College of Medicine Program

Sponsor: University of Kentucky College of Medicine
University of Kentucky Hospital
Prgm Director: Allen Brenzel, MD, MBA*
3470 Blazer Parkway
Lexington, KY 40509
Tel: 859 323-6021   *Fax:* 859 323-1194
Length: 2 Yrs   *ACGME Approved/Offered Positions:* 6
Program ID: 405-20-21-042

Louisville

University of Louisville Program

Sponsor: University of Louisville School of Medicine
Caritas Medical Center
Child Psychiatric Services (Bingham Child Guidance Clinic)
Kosair Children's Hospital (Norton Healthcare, Inc)
Seven Counties Services (Louisville)
Prgm Director: Christopher K Peters, MD*
200 East Chestnut Street
Louisville, KY 40202
Tel: 502 852-7548   *Fax:* 502 852-1055
E-mail: jescho04@louisville.edu
Length: 2 Yrs   *ACGME Approved/Offered Positions:* 6
Program ID: 405-20-21-043

Louisiana

New Orleans

Louisiana State University Program

Sponsor: Louisiana State University School of Medicine
Children's Hospital (New Orleans)
LSU Health Science Center Juvenile Justice Program
Mercy Family Center (Metairie)
New Orleans Adolescent Hospital
Prgm Director: Humberto Quintana, MD
Department of Psychiatry
210 State Street
New Orleans, LA 70115
Tel: 504 897-4673   *Fax:* 504 897-4781
E-mail: Hquint@lsuhsc.edu
Length: 2 Yrs   *ACGME Approved/Offered Positions:* 6
Program ID: 405-21-21-159

Tulane University Program

Sponsor: Tulane University School of Medicine
Medical Center of Louisiana at New Orleans
Southeast Louisiana Hospital
Tulane University Hospital and Clinics
Prgm Director: Cecile Many, MD
Child Psychiatry Residency Program
1440 Canal St, TB52
New Orleans, LA 70112
Tel: 504 988-7829   *Fax:* 504 988-4264
E-mail: lconners@tulane.edu
Length: 2 Yrs   *ACGME Approved/Offered Positions:* 6
Program ID: 405-21-21-045

Shreveport

Louisiana State University (Shreveport) Program

Sponsor: LSU Health Sciences Center-University Hospital
Brentwood Behavioral Health Company
Prgm Director: Rita Horton, MD
1501 Kings Highway
Shreveport, LA 71130
Tel: 318 813-2451   *Fax:* 318 813-2464
Length: 2 Yrs   *ACGME Approved/Offered Positions:* 4
Program ID: 405-21-12-188

Maine

Portland

Maine Medical Center Program

Sponsor: Maine Medical Center
Spring Harbor Hospital
Prgm Director: Sandra L Fritsch, MD*
22 Bramhall Street
Portland, ME 04102
Tel: 207 662-4377   *Fax:* 207 662-6957
Length: 2 Yrs   *ACGME Approved/Offered Positions:* 6
Program ID: 405-22-11-046

Maryland

Baltimore

Johns Hopkins University Program

Sponsor: Johns Hopkins University School of Medicine
Johns Hopkins Hospital
Prgm Director: Emily J Frosch, MD
600 North Wolfe Street
CMSC 346
Baltimore, MD 21287
Tel: 410 955-7858   *Fax:* 410 955-8691
Length: 2 Yrs   *ACGME Approved/Offered Positions:* 12
Program ID: 405-23-11-047

University of Maryland Program

Sponsor: University of Maryland Medical System
Sheppard Pratt Health System
Prgm Director: Kenneth M Rogers, MD, MSPH
701 West Pratt Street, Room 422
Baltimore, MD 21201
Tel: 410 328-3522   *Fax:* 410 328-8479
Length: 2 Yrs   *ACGME Approved/Offered Positions:* 12
Program ID: 405-23-21-048

Bethesda

National Capital Consortium Program

Sponsor: National Capital Consortium
Walter Reed Army Medical Center
Prgm Director: Nancy B Black, MD
Borden Pavilion (Building 6)
6900 Georgia Avenue NW
Washington, DC 20307
Tel: 202 782-5969   *Fax:* 202 782-8387
Length: 2 Yrs   *ACGME Approved/Offered Positions:* 10
Program ID: 405-10-12-002
Uniformed Services Program

Massachusetts

Boston

Children's Hospital Program

Sponsor: Children's Hospital
Prgm Director: Enrico Mezzacappa, MD
300 Longwood Avenue
Boston, MA 02115
Tel: 617 355-7605   *Fax:* 617 730-0428
E-mail: enrico.mezzacappa@childrens.harvard.edu
Length: 2 Yrs   *ACGME Approved/Offered Positions:* 10
Program ID: 405-24-21-053

Massachusetts General Hospital/McLean Hospital Program

Sponsor: Massachusetts General Hospital
McLean Hospital
Prgm Director: Eugene V Beresin, MD, MA
WAC 812
Boston, MA 02114
Tel: 617 726-8471   *Fax:* 617 726-9136
Length: 2 Yrs   *ACGME Approved/Offered Positions:* 18
Program ID: 405-24-21-167

Tufts Medical Center Program

Sponsor: Tufts Medical Center
Prgm Director: Joseph J Jankowski, MD
800 Washington Street, #1007
Boston, MA 02111
Tel: 617 636-1635   *Fax:* 617 636-1277
Length: 2 Yrs   *ACGME Approved/Offered Positions:* 8
Program ID: 405-24-21-056

Cambridge

Cambridge Health Alliance Program

Sponsor: Cambridge Health Alliance
Prgm Director: Cynthia J Telingator, MD
1493 Cambridge Street
Cambridge, MA 02139
Tel: 617 665-1587   *Fax:* 617 665-3449
Length: 2 Yrs   *ACGME Approved/Offered Positions:* 10
Program ID: 405-24-21-057

Worcester

University of Massachusetts Program

Sponsor: University of Massachusetts Medical School
UMass Memorial Health Care (University Campus)
Westboro State Hospital
Prgm Director: W Peter Metz, MD
55 Lake Avenue North
Worcester, MA 01655
Tel: 508 856-1256
Length: 2 Yrs   *ACGME Approved/Offered Positions:* 4
Program ID: 405-24-21-156

Michigan

Ann Arbor

University of Michigan Program

Sponsor: University of Michigan Hospitals and Health
   Centers
Prgm Director: Mohammad Ghaziuddin, MD
Child & Adolescent Psychiatry
4250 Plymouth Rd
Ann Arbor, MI 48109
Tel: 734 936-6335   *Fax:* 734 936-8907
E-mail: ksk@umich.edu
Length: 2 Yrs   *ACGME Approved/Offered Positions:* 12
Program ID: 405-25-11-060

Detroit

Wayne State University/Detroit Medical Center Program

Sponsor: Wayne State University/Detroit Medical Center
Children's Hospital of Michigan
Hawthorn Center Hospital
University Psychiatric Centers - Livonia
Prgm Director: Beth Ann Brooks, MD
2751 E Jefferson
Suite 400
Detroit, MI 48207
Tel: 313 993-7019   *Fax:* 313 577-2233
Length: 2 Yrs   *ACGME Approved/Offered Positions:* 12
Program ID: 405-25-21-173

Lansing

Michigan State University Program

Sponsor: Michigan State University College of Human
   Medicine
Prgm Director: Madhvi Richards, MD
Department of Psychiatry
A-233 East Fee Hall
East Lansing, MI 48824
Tel: 517 353-4362   *Fax:* 517 432-0927
Length: 2 Yrs   *ACGME Approved/Offered Positions:* 6
Program ID: 405-25-21-185

Minnesota

Minneapolis

University of Minnesota Program

Sponsor: University of Minnesota Medical School
Hennepin County Home School
KDWB University Pediatrics Family Center
University of Minnesota Medical Center, Division of
   Fairview
Wilder Child Guidance
William Mitchell College of Law
Prgm Director: Jonathan B Jensen, MD
F256/2B West
2450 Riverside Avenue
Minneapolis, MN 55454
Tel: 612 273-9714   *Fax:* 612 273-9779
E-mail: fallx004@umn.edu
Length: 2 Yrs   *ACGME Approved/Offered Positions:* 10
Program ID: 405-26-11-066

Rochester

College of Medicine, Mayo Clinic (Rochester) Program

Sponsor: College of Medicine, Mayo Clinic
Mayo Clinic (Rochester)
Saint Marys Hospital of Rochester
Prgm Director: Cosima C Swintak, MD*
200 First Street SW
Rochester, MN 55905
Tel: 507 284-0325   *Fax:* 507 284-4345
Length: 2 Yrs   *ACGME Approved/Offered Positions:* 6
Program ID: 405-26-21-067

Mississippi

Jackson

University of Mississippi Medical Center Program

Sponsor: University of Mississippi School of Medicine
University Hospitals and Clinics
Prgm Director: Faiza N Qureshi, MD*
2500 North State Street
Box 139
Jackson, MS 39216
Tel: 601 815-1368   *Fax:* 601 815-7623
E-mail: lcporter@psychiatry.umsmed.edu
Length: 2 Yrs   *ACGME Approved/Offered Positions:* 4
Program ID: 405-27-21-176

Missouri

Columbia

University of Missouri-Columbia Program

Sponsor: University of Missouri-Columbia School of
   Medicine
Royal Oaks Hospital
University Hospitals and Clinics
Prgm Director: Syed Arshad Husain, MD
Department of Psychiatry, DC067.00
One Hospital Drive
Columbia, MO 65212
Tel: 573 882-8006   *Fax:* 573 884-5396
Length: 2 Yrs   *ACGME Approved/Offered Positions:* 6
Program ID: 405-28-21-068

St Louis

Washington University/B-JH/SLCH Consortium Program

Sponsor: Washington University/B-JH/SLCH Consortium
Barnes-Jewish Center Behavioral Health
Hawthorn Children's Psychiatric Hospital
St Louis Children's Hospital
Prgm Director: Anne L Glowinski, MD, MPE
Box 8134
660 South Euclid Avenue
St Louis, MO 63110
Tel: 314 286-2217   *Fax:* 314 286-2213
E-mail: glowinsa@wustl.edu
Length: 2 Yrs   *ACGME Approved/Offered Positions:* 8
Program ID: 405-28-21-070

Nebraska

Omaha

Creighton University/University of Nebraska Program

Sponsor: Creighton University School of Medicine
Alegent Health Immanuel Medical Center
Creighton Psychiatric Clinic
Nebraska Medical Center
Prgm Director: Jamie L Snyder, MD
Creighton University School of Medicine
3528 Dodge Street
Omaha, NE 68131
Tel: 402 345-7100   *Fax:* 402 345-8815
E-mail: ChristaHorst@creighton.edu
Length: 2 Yrs   *ACGME Approved/Offered Positions:* 8
Program ID: 405-30-31-071

Nevada

Reno

University of Nevada School of Medicine Program

Sponsor: University of Nevada School of Medicine
Jan Evans Juvenile Justice Center
MEDSchool Associates North (Reno)
Northern Nevada Child and Adolescent Services
Renown Medical Center
Washoe County School District
West Hills Hospital
Willow Springs Center
Prgm Director: Erika Ryst, MD
Department of Psychiatry and Behavioral Sciences
401 West Second Street, #216
Reno, NV 89503
Tel: 775 682-8446   *Fax:* 775 784-1428
E-mail: eryst@medicine.nevada.edu
Length: 2 Yrs   *ACGME Approved/Offered Positions:* 4
Program ID: 405-31-31-183

New Hampshire

Lebanon

Dartmouth-Hitchcock Medical Center Program

Sponsor: Mary Hitchcock Memorial Hospital
New Hampshire Hospital
Prgm Director: Robert J Racusin, MD
Section of Child & Adolescent Psych
1 Medical Center Drive
Lebanon, NH 03756
Tel: 603 650-5835   *Fax:* 603 650-0819
Length: 2 Yrs   *ACGME Approved/Offered Positions:* 6
Program ID: 405-32-21-073

Note: * indicates a newly appointed program director

New Jersey

Newark

UMDNJ-New Jersey Medical School Program

Sponsor: UMDNJ-New Jersey Medical School
Newark Beth Israel Medical Center
UMDNJ-University Behavioral Health Care
UMDNJ-University Hospital
Prgm Director: Tolga Taneli, MD
183 South Orange Avenue
BHSB, Room F1416
Newark, NJ 07101
Tel: 973 972-1604   *Fax:* 973 972-8305
E-mail: tanelito@umdnj.edu
Length: 2 Yrs   *ACGME Approved/Offered Positions:* 5
Program ID: 405-33-21-150

Piscataway

UMDNJ-Robert Wood Johnson Medical School Program

Sponsor: UMDNJ-Robert Wood Johnson Medical School
UMDNJ-University Behavioral HealthCare
Prgm Director: Theodore A Petti, MD, MPH
671 Hoes Lane - Room D409
Piscataway, NJ 08854
Tel: 732 235-4295   *Fax:* 732 235-3923
Length: 2 Yrs   *ACGME Approved/Offered Positions:* 8
Program ID: 405-33-21-074

New Mexico

Albuquerque

University of New Mexico Program

Sponsor: University of New Mexico School of Medicine
University of New Mexico Hospital
Prgm Director: Jeanne A Bereiter, MD
MSC09 5030
1 University of New Mexico
Albuquerque, NM 87131
Tel: 505 272-5002   *Fax:* 505 272-0535
E-mail: jbereiter@salud.unm.edu
Length: 2 Yrs   *ACGME Approved/Offered Positions:* 8
Program ID: 405-34-21-144

New York

Bronx

Albert Einstein College of Medicine at Bronx-Lebanon Hospital Center Program

Sponsor: Bronx-Lebanon Hospital Center
Prgm Director: Francis F Hayden, MD
1276 Fulton Avenue
Bronx, NY 10456
Tel: 718 901-8756   *Fax:* 718 466-7288
E-mail: fhayden@bronxleb.org
Length: 2 Yrs   *ACGME Approved/Offered Positions:* 8
Program ID: 405-35-21-177

Albert Einstein College of Medicine Program

Sponsor: Albert Einstein College of Medicine of Yeshiva University
Bronx Children's Psychiatric Center
Montefiore Medical Center-Henry and Lucy Moses Division
Prgm Director: Audrey M Walker, MD
Department of Psychiatry
3331 Bainbridge Avenue
Bronx, NY 10467
Tel: 718 920-7967   *Fax:* 718 882-3185
Length: 2 Yrs   *ACGME Approved/Offered Positions:* 12
Program ID: 405-35-21-077

Brooklyn

Brookdale University Hospital and Medical Center Program

Sponsor: Brookdale University Hospital and Medical Center
Prgm Director: Pierre Jean-Noel, MD, MBA
One Brookdale Plaza
Brooklyn, NY 11212
Tel: 718 240-5469   *Fax:* 718 240-5451
E-mail: pjeannoel@aol.com
Length: 2 Yrs   *ACGME Approved/Offered Positions:* 6
Program ID: 405-35-31-078

SUNY Health Science Center at Brooklyn Program

Sponsor: SUNY Health Science Center at Brooklyn
Brooklyn Children's Center
Kings County Hospital Center
Prgm Director: Lenore Engel, MD
450 Clarkson Avenue Box 1203
Brooklyn, NY 11203
Tel: 718 245-2507   *Fax:* 718 245-2517
E-mail: lengelmd@aol.com
Length: 2 Yrs   *ACGME Approved/Offered Positions:* 6
Program ID: 405-35-21-094

Buffalo

University at Buffalo Program

Sponsor: University at Buffalo School of Medicine
Kaleida Health System (Women and Children's Hosp of Buffalo)
Western New York Children's Psychiatric Center
Prgm Director: David L Kaye, MD
Millard Fillmore Hospital
3 Gates Circle
Buffalo, NY 14209
Tel: 716 887-5775   *Fax:* 716 887-5801
Length: 2 Yrs   *ACGME Approved/Offered Positions:* 6
Program ID: 405-35-21-161

Elmhurst

Mount Sinai School of Medicine (Elmhurst) Program

Sponsor: Mount Sinai School of Medicine
Elmhurst Hospital Center-Mount Sinai Services
Prgm Director: Douglas Beer, MD*
79-01 Broadway, D10-41
Elmhurst, NY 11373
Tel: 718 334-1331   *Fax:* 718 334-3441
E-mail: beerd@nychhc.org
Length: 2 Yrs   *ACGME Approved/Offered Positions:* 6
Program ID: 405-35-11-079

Great Neck

NSLIJHS-Albert Einstein College of Medicine at Long Island Jewish Medical Center Program

Sponsor: North Shore-Long Island Jewish Health System
Long Island Jewish Medical Center
Prgm Director: Richard R Pleak, MD
Division of Child and Adolescent Psychiatry
Zucker Hillside Hospital, ACP
Glen Oaks, NY 11004
Tel: 718 470-4834   *Fax:* 718 470-4678
E-mail: rpleak@lij.edu
Length: 2 Yrs   *ACGME Approved/Offered Positions:* 18
Program ID: 405-35-11-082

New York

Harlem Hospital Center Program

Sponsor: Harlem Hospital Center
Rockland Children's Psychiatric Center
Prgm Director: Sady Sultan, MD
506 Lenox Avenue
K Building, 5th Floor
New York, NY 10037
Tel: 212 939-3365   *Fax:* 212 939-3399
E-mail: ss61@columbia.edu
Length: 2 Yrs   *ACGME Approved/Offered Positions:* 4
Program ID: 405-35-21-081

Mount Sinai School of Medicine Program

Sponsor: Mount Sinai School of Medicine
Mount Sinai Medical Center
Prgm Director: John D O'Brien, MD
1 Gustave L Levy Plaza, #1230
New York, NY 10029
Tel: 212 241-0487
E-mail: john.o'brien@mssm.edu
Length: 2 Yrs   *ACGME Approved/Offered Positions:* 4
Program ID: 405-35-11-085

New York Medical College at St Vincent's Hospital and Medical Center of New York Program

Sponsor: New York Medical College
St Vincent Catholic Medical Centers (Manhattan)
South Beach Psychiatric Center
Prgm Director: A Reese Abright, MD
144 West 12th Street, Room 431
New York, NY 10011
Tel: 212 604-8213   *Fax:* 212 604-8212
Length: 2 Yrs   *ACGME Approved/Offered Positions:* 6
Program ID: 405-35-22-092

New York Presbyterian Hospital Program

Sponsor: New York Presbyterian Hospital
New York Presbyterian Hospital (Cornell Campus)
New York Presbyterian Hospital (Westchester Division)
Prgm Director: Elisabeth Guthrie, MD
1051 Riverside Drive
Unit 78
New York, NY 10032
Tel: 212 543-1831   *Fax:* 212 543-5966
Length: 2 Yrs   *ACGME Approved/Offered Positions:* 28
Program ID: 405-35-21-182

New York University School of Medicine Program

Sponsor: New York University School of Medicine
Bellevue Hospital Center
Prgm Director: Jess P Shatkin, MD, MPH
550 First Avenue, NBV 21S6
New York, NY 10016
Tel: 212 263-4769   *Fax:* 212 263-0990
E-mail: jess.shatkin@nyumc.org
Length: 2 Yrs   *ACGME Approved/Offered Positions:* 20
Program ID: 405-35-21-088

St Luke's-Roosevelt Hospital Center Program

Sponsor: St Luke's-Roosevelt Hospital Center
Holliswood Hospital
St Luke's-Roosevelt Hospital Center-Roosevelt Division
St Luke's-Roosevelt Hospital Center-St Luke's Division
Prgm Director: Ramon Solhkhah, MD
1090 Amsterdam Ave 17th Floor
Division of Child and Adolescent Psychiatry
New York, NY 10025
Tel: 212 523-3069   *Fax:* 212 523-3642
Length: 2 Yrs   *ACGME Approved/Offered Positions:* 10
Program ID: 405-35-31-166

Programs

Rochester

University of Rochester Program

Sponsor: Strong Memorial Hospital of the University of Rochester
Prgm Director: Michael A Scharf, MD
300 Crittenden Boulevard
Rochester, NY 14642
Tel: 585 275-3556   *Fax:* 585 276-2292
E-mail: michael_scharf@urmc.rochester.edu
Length: 2 Yrs   *ACGME Approved/Offered Positions:* 6
Program ID: 405-35-11-095

Stony Brook

SUNY at Stony Brook Program

Sponsor: University Hospital - SUNY at Stony Brook
Prgm Director: Judith C Crowell, MD
Putnam Hall, South Campus
Stony Brook, NY 11794
Tel: 631 632-8840   *Fax:* 631 632-8953
E-mail: jcrowell@notes.cc.sunysb.edu
Length: 2 Yrs   *ACGME Approved/Offered Positions:* 6
Program ID: 405-35-21-158

Syracuse

SUNY Upstate Medical University Program

Sponsor: SUNY Upstate Medical University
Prgm Director: Wanda P Fremont, MD
750 Adams Street
Syracuse, NY 13210
Tel: 315 464-3175   *Fax:* 315 464-3202
E-mail: anthonsb@upstate.edu
Length: 2 Yrs   *ACGME Approved/Offered Positions:* 6
Program ID: 405-35-13-178

Valhalla

New York Medical College at Westchester Medical Center Program

Sponsor: New York Medical College
Children's Village (Dobbs Ferry)
Danbury Hospital
Westchester Medical Center
Prgm Director: Steven G Dickstein, MD
Behavioral Health Center
Room B102
Valhalla, NY 10595
Tel: 914 493-1829   *Fax:* 914 493-1076
E-mail: strianoj@wcmc.com
Length: 2 Yrs   *ACGME Approved/Offered Positions:* 7
Program ID: 405-35-21-097

North Carolina

Chapel Hill

University of North Carolina Hospitals Program

Sponsor: University of North Carolina Hospitals
Central Regional Hospital (Raleigh Campus)
Prgm Director: Karen K Poulos, MD
1025 Neurosciences Hospital, CB 7160
101 Manning Drive
Chapel Hill, NC 27599
Tel: 919 733-5344   *Fax:* 919 966-2220
E-mail: karlina_matthews@med.unc.edu
Length: 2 Yrs   *ACGME Approved/Offered Positions:* 10
Program ID: 405-36-21-100

Durham

Duke University Hospital Program

Sponsor: Duke University Hospital
John Umstead Hospital
Prgm Director: Allan K Chrisman, MD
Box 3484
Durham, NC 27710
Tel: 919 416-2402   *Fax:* 919 416-9789
E-mail: chris014@mc.duke.edu
Length: 2 Yrs   *ACGME Approved/Offered Positions:* 8
Program ID: 405-36-31-101

Greenville

Pitt County Memorial Hospital/East Carolina University Program

Sponsor: Pitt County Memorial Hospital
Brody School of Medicine at East Carolina University
Prgm Director: Kaye L McGinty, MD
Brody School of Medicine
600 Moye Blvd
Greenville, NC 27834
Tel: 252 744-2673   *Fax:* 252 744-3815
Length: 2 Yrs   *ACGME Approved/Offered Positions:* 4
Program ID: 405-36-21-162

Winston-Salem

Wake Forest University School of Medicine Program

Sponsor: Wake Forest University Baptist Medical Center
Prgm Director: Guy K Palmes, MD
Medical Center Boulevard
Winston-Salem, NC 27157
Tel: 336 716-5089   *Fax:* 336 716-9642
Length: 2 Yrs   *ACGME Approved/Offered Positions:* 6
Program ID: 405-36-31-163

Ohio

Akron

Children's Hospital Medical Center of Akron/NEOUCOM Program

Sponsor: Children's Hospital Medical Center of Akron
Child Guidance and Family Solutions
Prgm Director: John F Bober, MD
388 S Main St
Suite 207
Akron, OH 44311
Tel: 330 543-8590   *Fax:* 330 543-3856
E-mail: jbober@chmca.org
Length: 2 Yrs   *ACGME Approved/Offered Positions:* 4
Program ID: 405-38-12-184

Cincinnati

Cincinnati Children's Hospital Medical Center/University of Cincinnati College of Medicine Program

Sponsor: Cincinnati Children's Hospital Medical Center
Prgm Director: Suzanne Sampang, MD
3333 Burnet Avenue
ML 6015
Cincinnati, OH 45229
Tel: 513 636-7331   *Fax:* 513 803-0571
Length: 2 Yrs   *ACGME Approved/Offered Positions:* 8
Program ID: 405-38-21-102

Cleveland

Cleveland Clinic Foundation Program

Sponsor: Cleveland Clinic Foundation
Prgm Director: Kathleen M Quinn, MD
9500 Euclid Avenue
Cleveland, OH 44195
Tel: 216 444-5950   *Fax:* 216 444-9054
E-mail: psyched@ccf.org
Length: 2 Yrs   *ACGME Approved/Offered Positions:* 4
Program ID: 405-38-21-171

University Hospitals Case Medical Center Program

Sponsor: University Hospitals Case Medical Center
Prgm Director: Maryellen Davis, MD
Department of Psychiatry - W O Walker Center
10524 Euclid Avenue
Cleveland, OH 44106
Tel: 216 844-3289   *Fax:* 216 983-5131
E-mail: maryellen.davis@UHHospitals.org
Length: 2 Yrs   *ACGME Approved/Offered Positions:* 10
Program ID: 405-38-11-103

Columbus

Ohio State University Hospital Program

Sponsor: Ohio State University Hospital
Nationwide Children's Hospital
Prgm Director: Mary Ann Murphy, MD
Neuro Sciences Facility
1670 Upham Drive, Suite 140
Columbus, OH 43210
Tel: 614 293-6852   *Fax:* 614 293-8230
Length: 2 Yrs   *ACGME Approved/Offered Positions:* 4
Program ID: 405-38-21-104

Dayton

Wright State University Program

Sponsor: Wright State University Boonshoft School of Medicine
Good Samaritan Hospital and Health Center
Kettering Medical Center
Prgm Director: William M Klykylo, MD
Elizabeth Place, E Med Plaza, 1st Floor, 627 Edwin C Mose
Dayton, OH 45408
Tel: 937 223-8840   *Fax:* 937 223-0758
E-mail: william.klykylo@wright.edu
Length: 2 Yrs   *ACGME Approved/Offered Positions:* 6
Program ID: 405-38-21-169

Toledo

University of Toledo Program

Sponsor: University of Toledo
University Medical Center (Toledo)
Prgm Director: Theodor B Rais, MD
Division of Child and Adolescent Psychiatry
3000 Arlington Avenue, Mail Stop 1161
Toledo, OH 43614
Tel: 419 383-5491   *Fax:* 419 383-3098
E-mail: Jacki.McBee@utoledo.edu
Length: 2 Yrs   *ACGME Approved/Offered Positions:* 4
Program ID: 405-38-11-105

Note: * indicates a newly appointed program director

Oklahoma

Oklahoma City

University of Oklahoma Health Sciences Center Program

Sponsor: University of Oklahoma College of Medicine
Integris Mental Health Center - Spencer
North Care Center (Oklahoma City)
OU Medical Center - Children's Hospital
Prgm Director: James R Allen, MD, MPH
Williams Pavilion, 3rd Floor
920 S L Young Blvd
Oklahoma City, OK 73104
Tel: 405 271-4219 *Fax:* 405 271-3808
E-mail: joan-willard@ouhsc.edu
Length: 2 Yrs *ACGME Approved/Offered Positions:* 6
Program ID: 405-39-11-106

Oregon

Portland

Oregon Health & Science University Program

Sponsor: Oregon Health & Science University Hospital
Prgm Director: Ajit N Jetmalani, MD
3181 SW Sam Jackson Park Road DC7P
Portland, OR 97239
Tel: 503 228-5909 *Fax:* 503 226-4186
Length: 2 Yrs *ACGME Approved/Offered Positions:* 6
Program ID: 405-40-21-107

Pennsylvania

Hershey

Penn State University/Milton S Hershey Medical Center Program

Sponsor: Milton S Hershey Medical Center
Prgm Director: Leonora K Petty, MD
Dept of Psychiatry, H073
500 University Drive
Hershey, PA 17033
Tel: 717 531-7137 *Fax:* 717 531-6491
E-mail: lpetty1@hmc.psu.edu
Length: 2 Yrs *ACGME Approved/Offered Positions:* 6
Program ID: 405-41-21-147

Philadelphia

Children's Hospital of Philadelphia Program

Sponsor: Children's Hospital of Philadelphia
Devereux Beneto Center
Prgm Director: Tami D Benton, MD
CHOP Behavioral Center
3440 Market St, Ste 200
Philadelphia, PA 19104
Tel: 215 590-7530 *Fax:* 215 590-7540
E-mail: Bentont@email.chop.edu
Length: 2 Yrs *ACGME Approved/Offered Positions:* 12
Program ID: 405-41-11-111

Drexel University College of Medicine/Hahnemann University Hospital Program

Sponsor: Drexel University College of Medicine/Hahnemann University
Brooke Glen Behavioral Hospital
Friends Hospital
Northwestern Human Services of Philadelphia
St Christopher's Hospital for Children (Tenet Health System)
Prgm Director: William A Sonis, MD
4641 Roosevelt Boulevard
PO Box 45358
Philadelphia, PA 19124
Tel: 215 831-5389 *Fax:* 215 831-4020
E-mail: wsonis@drexelmed.edu
Length: 2 Yrs *ACGME Approved/Offered Positions:* 8
Program ID: 405-41-21-110

Thomas Jefferson University Program

Sponsor: Thomas Jefferson University Hospital
Albert Einstein Medical Center
Belmont Center for Comprehensive Treatment
Prgm Director: James F Luebbert, MD
833 Chestnut St Suite 210
Philadelphia, PA 19107
Tel: 215 955-8180 *Fax:* 215 503-2853
Length: 2 Yrs *ACGME Approved/Offered Positions:* 7
Program ID: 405-41-11-113

Pittsburgh

Allegheny General Hospital Program

Sponsor: Allegheny General Hospital
Prgm Director: Lisa A Jamnback, MD
320 East North Avenue
Pittsburgh, PA 15212
Tel: 412 330-4242 *Fax:* 412 330-4010
Length: 2 Yrs *ACGME Approved/Offered Positions:* 4
Program ID: 405-41-21-174

University of Pittsburgh Medical Center Medical Education Program

Sponsor: Univ of Pittsburgh Medical Center Medical Education
UPMC Western Psychiatric Institute and Clinic
Prgm Director: Erin E Malley, MD
3811 O'Hara Street
E500
Pittsburgh, PA 15213
Tel: 412 586-9179 *Fax:* 412 246-5335
Length: 2 Yrs *ACGME Approved/Offered Positions:* 16
Program ID: 405-41-31-114

Puerto Rico

Ponce

Ponce School of Medicine Program

Sponsor: Ponce School of Medicine
ASSMCA (Mayaguez)
First Hospital Panamericano
Hospital Episcopal San Lucas
Prgm Director: Victor Sierra, MD, MS
Department of Psychiatry
PO Box 7004
Ponce, PR 00732
Tel: 787 806-1262 *Fax:* 787 806-1262
E-mail: sierrajimenezmd@aol.com
Length: 2 Yrs *ACGME Approved/Offered Positions:* 4
Program ID: 405-42-13-190

San Juan

University of Puerto Rico Program

Sponsor: University of Puerto Rico School of Medicine
First Hospital Panamericano
University of Puerto Rico Hospital at Carolina
University Pediatric Hospital
Prgm Director: Lelis L Nazario, MD
PO Box 365067
San Juan, PR 00936
Tel: 787 777-3535 *Fax:* 787 764-7004
E-mail: lnazario@rcm.upr.edu
Length: 2 Yrs *ACGME Approved/Offered Positions:* 4
Program ID: 405-42-21-116

Rhode Island

Providence

Brown University Program

Sponsor: Rhode Island Hospital-Lifespan
Emma Pendleton Bradley Hospital
Prgm Director: Jeffrey I Hunt, MD
Child & Family Psychiatry
593 Eddy Street
Providence, RI 02903
Tel: 401 444-3762 *Fax:* 401 444-8879
E-mail: Jeffrey_hunt@brown.edu
Length: 2 Yrs *ACGME Approved/Offered Positions:* 10
Program ID: 405-43-21-117

South Carolina

Charleston

Medical University of South Carolina Program

Sponsor: Medical University of South Carolina College of Medicine
Dee Norton Lowcountry Children's Center
MUSC Medical Center
Prgm Director: Markus J Kruesi, MD
67 President Street
PO Box 250861
Charleston, SC 29425
Tel: 843 792-0135 *Fax:* 843 792-5598
E-mail: kruesi@musc.edu
Length: 2 Yrs *ACGME Approved/Offered Positions:* 20
Program ID: 405-45-21-118

Columbia

Palmetto Health/University of South Carolina School of Medicine Program

Sponsor: Palmetto Health
University of South Carolina School of Medicine
Prgm Director: Craig A Stuck, MD
15 Medical Park, Suite 141
Columbia, SC 29203
Tel: 803 434-1422 *Fax:* 803 434-4062
E-mail: angelia.powell@palmettohealth.org
Length: 2 Yrs *ACGME Approved/Offered Positions:* 8
Program ID: 405-45-21-119

South Dakota

Sioux Falls

University of South Dakota Program
Sponsor: University of South Dakota School of Medicine
Avera McKennan Hospital and University Health Center
Children's Home Society
Sioux Valley Hospital University of SD Medical Center
Prgm Director: Tamara L Vik, MD*
4400 West 69th Street
Suite 1500
Sioux Falls, SD 57108
Tel: 605 322-5735   *Fax:* 605 322-5736
E-mail: tvik@usd.edu
Length: 2 Yrs   *ACGME Approved/Offered Positions:* 4
Program ID: 405-46-21-164

Tennessee

Memphis

University of Tennessee Program
Sponsor: University of Tennessee College of Medicine
LeBonheur Children's Medical Center
St Francis Hospital
University of Tennessee Medical Center
Prgm Director: Linda B Snyder, MD
711 Jefferson Avenue
Memphis, TN 38105
Tel: 901 448-5944   *Fax:* 901 448-5089
E-mail: lsnyder2@utmem.edu
Length: 2 Yrs   *ACGME Approved/Offered Positions:* 4
Program ID: 405-47-12-192

Nashville

Vanderbilt University Program
Sponsor: Vanderbilt University Medical Center
Prgm Director: D Catherine Fuchs, MD
Division of Child and Adolescent Psychiatry
1601 23rd Avenue, South, Suite 301
Nashville, TN 37212
Tel: 615 327-7264   *Fax:* 615 327-7136
E-mail: catherine.fuchs@vanderbilt.edu
Length: 2 Yrs   *ACGME Approved/Offered Positions:* 6
Program ID: 405-47-21-121

Texas

Austin

Austin Medical Education Programs of Seton Healthcare Network Program
Sponsor: Austin Medical Education Program of Seton
   Healthcare Network
Austin State Hospital
Specially For Children-Neurology
Prgm Director: Beverly J Sutton, MD
3501 Mills Avenue
6th Floor
Austin, TX 78731
Tel: 512 324-2036   *Fax:* 512 324-2084
E-mail: tpowell@seton.org
Length: 2 Yrs   *ACGME Approved/Offered Positions:* 10
Program ID: 405-48-13-181

Dallas

University of Texas Southwestern Medical School Program
Sponsor: University of Texas Southwestern Medical
   School
Children's Medical Center of Dallas
Prgm Director: Maryam Rezai, MD
5323 Harry Hines Boulevard
Dallas, TX 75390
Tel: 214 648-5302   *Fax:* 214 648-5229
E-mail: Maryam.Rezai@UTSouthwestern.edu
Length: 2 Yrs   *ACGME Approved/Offered Positions:* 12
Program ID: 405-48-21-123

Galveston

University of Texas Medical Branch Hospitals Program
Sponsor: University of Texas Medical Branch Hospitals
Prgm Director: Christopher R Thomas, MD
301 University Blvd
Galveston, TX 77555
Tel: 409 747-9667   *Fax:* 409 747-9669
E-mail: tawaggon@utmb.edu
Length: 2 Yrs   *ACGME Approved/Offered Positions:* 10
Program ID: 405-48-11-124

Houston

Baylor College of Medicine Program
Sponsor: Baylor College of Medicine
Texas Children's Hospital
The Menninger Clinic (Houston)
Prgm Director: Florence F Eddins, MD
One Baylor Plaza, MS350
6655 Travis St, Suite 700
Houston, TX 77030
Tel: 713 798-4068   *Fax:* 713 796-9718
Length: 2 Yrs   *ACGME Approved/Offered Positions:* 8
Program ID: 405-48-21-125

University of Texas at Houston Program
Sponsor: University of Texas Health Science Center at
   Houston
Harris County Psychiatric Center
Memorial Hermann Hospital
University of Texas Mental Sciences Institute
Prgm Director: Cynthia W Santos, MD
1300 Moursund, Room 267A
Houston, TX 77030
Tel: 713 500-2570   *Fax:* 713 500-2565
E-mail: Carol.Shelby@uth.tmc.edu
Length: 2 Yrs   *ACGME Approved/Offered Positions:* 10
Program ID: 405-48-21-139

San Antonio

University of Texas Health Science Center at San Antonio Program
Sponsor: University of Texas School of Medicine at San
   Antonio
Child Guidance Center
Prgm Director: Thomas L Matthews, MD
Mail Code 7792
7703 Floyd Curl Drive
San Antonio, TX 78229
Tel: 210 567-5430   *Fax:* 210 567-0817
E-mail: cardenasy@uthscsa.edu
Length: 2 Yrs   *ACGME Approved/Offered Positions:* 8
Program ID: 405-48-21-126

Temple

Texas A&M College of Medicine-Scott and White Program
Sponsor: Scott and White Memorial Hospital
Metroplex Pavilion Hospital
Prgm Director: Jane Ripperger-Suhler, MD
Child and Adolescent Psychiatry
2401 South 31st Street
Temple, TX 76508
Tel: 254 724-7842   *Fax:* 254 724-2979
E-mail: dwinkler@swmail.sw.org
Length: 2 Yrs   *ACGME Approved/Offered Positions:* 4
Program ID: 405-48-21-175

Utah

Salt Lake City

University of Utah Program
Sponsor: University of Utah Medical Center
Primary Children's Medical Center
University of Utah Neuropsychiatric Institute
Prgm Director: Doug Gray, MD
650 S Komas, Ste 208
Salt Lake City, UT 84108
Tel: 801 581-3936   *Fax:* 801 585-9096
E-mail: glenda.evans@hsc.utah.edu
Length: 2 Yrs   *ACGME Approved/Offered Positions:* 4
Program ID: 405-49-21-127

Vermont

Burlington

University of Vermont Program
Sponsor: Fletcher Allen Health Care
Prgm Director: David C Rettew, MD
1 South Prospect Street, Arnold 3
Burlington, VT 05401
Tel: 802 656-8125   *Fax:* 802 656-0987
E-mail: david.rettew@uvm.edu
Length: 2 Yrs   *ACGME Approved/Offered Positions:* 4
Program ID: 405-50-31-195

Virginia

Charlottesville

University of Virginia Program
Sponsor: University of Virginia Medical Center
Commonwealth Center for Children & Adolescents
Prgm Director: Roger C Burket, MD
PO Box 801076
Division of Child and Family Psychiatry
Charlottesville, VA 22908
Tel: 434 243-6950   *Fax:* 434 243-6970
E-mail: rcb8n@virginia.edu
Length: 2 Yrs   *ACGME Approved/Offered Positions:* 6
Program ID: 405-51-11-130

Richmond

Virginia Commonwealth University Health System Program
Sponsor: Virginia Commonwealth University Health
   System
MCV-Virginia Treatment Center for Children
Medical College of Virginia Hospitals
Prgm Director: Aradhana A Sood, MD
Box 980489
515 North 10th Street
Richmond, VA 23298
Tel: 804 828-4058   *Fax:* 804 827-3731
Length: 2 Yrs   *ACGME Approved/Offered Positions:* 6
Program ID: 405-51-11-131

Note: * indicates a newly appointed program director

Roanoke

Carilion Clinic Program
Sponsor: Carilion Clinic
Blue Ridge Behavioral Healthcare
Prgm Director: Mark D Kilgus, MD, PhD
2017 South Jefferson Street
Roanoke, VA 24014
Tel: 540 981-7695   *Fax:* 540 982-3442
E-mail: tmaddy@carilion.com
Length: 2 Yrs   *ACGME Approved/Offered Positions:* 4
Program ID: 405-51-21-193

Washington

Seattle

University of Washington Program
Sponsor: University of Washington School of Medicine
Seattle Children's Hospital
University of Washington Medical Center
Prgm Director: Christopher K Varley, MD
4800 Sand Point Way NE
Mailstop W3636
Seattle, WA 98105
Tel: 206 987-3236   *Fax:* 206 987-2246
E-mail: cvarley@u.washington.edu
Length: 2 Yrs   *ACGME Approved/Offered Positions:* 10
Program ID: 405-54-21-132

West Virginia

Morgantown

West Virginia University Program
Sponsor: West Virginia University School of Medicine
West Virginia University Hospitals
Prgm Director: Bharati S Desai, MD
Department of Behavioral Science
930 Chestnut Ridge Road
Morgantown, WV 26505
Tel: 304 293-5312   *Fax:* 304 293-8724
E-mail: bdesai@hsc.wvu.edu
Length: 2 Yrs   *ACGME Approved/Offered Positions:* 4
Program ID: 405-55-31-187

Wisconsin

Madison

University of Wisconsin Program
Sponsor: University of Wisconsin Hospital and Clinics
Meriter Hospital
Prgm Director: David V Skripka, MD
6001 Research Park Blvd
Madison, WI 53719
Tel: 608 263-6106   *Fax:* 608 261-5653
E-mail: dskripka@wisc.edu
Length: 2 Yrs   *ACGME Approved/Offered Positions:* 6
Program ID: 405-56-21-134

Milwaukee

Medical College of Wisconsin Affiliated Hospitals Program
Sponsor: Medical College of Wisconsin Affiliated
  Hospitals, Inc
Children's Hospital of Wisconsin
Rogers Memorial Hospital
Prgm Director: Jennifer Derenne, MD*
Medical College of Wisconsin
8701 Watertown Plank Road
Milwaukee, WI 53226
Tel: 414 266-6794   *Fax:* 414 266-3735
Length: 2 Yrs   *ACGME Approved/Offered Positions:* 8
Program ID: 405-56-21-135

Child Neurology (Neurology)

Alabama

Birmingham

University of Alabama Medical Center Program
Sponsor: University of Alabama Hospital
Children's Hospital of Alabama
Prgm Director: Tony M McGrath, MD*
1600 7th Avenue South
Children's Harbor Building 314
Birmingham, AL 35233
Tel: 205 996-7850   *Fax:* 205 996-7867
Length: 3 Yrs   *ACGME Approved/Offered Positions:* 3
Program ID: 185-01-21-008

Arizona

Phoenix

St Joseph's Hospital and Medical Center Program
Sponsor: St Joseph's Hospital and Medical Center
Prgm Director: Kara S Lewis, MD
MOB, Suite 400
350 West Thomas Road
Phoenix, AZ 85013
Tel: 602 406-3800   *Fax:* 602 406-3810
E-mail: ann.chowdhury@chw.edu
Length: 3 Yrs   *ACGME Approved/Offered Positions:* 3
Program ID: 185-03-21-024

Arkansas

Little Rock

University of Arkansas for Medical Sciences Program
Sponsor: University of Arkansas College of Medicine
Arkansas Children's Hospital
UAMS Medical Center
Prgm Director: Rolla M Shbarou, MD
Department of Pediatrics, Slot 512-15
800 Marshall Street
Little Rock, AR 72202
Tel: 501 364-1850   *Fax:* 501 364-6077
E-mail: shbarourollam@uams.edu
Length: 3 Yrs   *ACGME Approved/Offered Positions:* 2
Program ID: 185-04-21-085

California

Loma Linda

Loma Linda University Program
Sponsor: Loma Linda University Medical Center
Prgm Director: David J Michelson, MD
11175 Campus Street
Coleman Pavilion Rm A1120F
Loma Linda, CA 92354
Tel: 909 558-8242   *Fax:* 909 824-0479
E-mail: dmichels@llu.edu
Length: 3 Yrs   *ACGME Approved/Offered Positions:* 6
Program ID: 185-05-21-075

Los Angeles

Childrens Hospital Los Angeles Program
Sponsor: Childrens Hospital Los Angeles
LAC+USC Medical Center
Prgm Director: Wendy G Mitchell, MD
4650 Sunset Boulevard
Mail Stop 82
Los Angeles, CA 90027
Tel: 323 361-2498   *Fax:* 323 361-1109
Length: 3 Yrs   *ACGME Approved/Offered Positions:* 3
Program ID: 185-05-21-065

UCLA Medical Center Program
Sponsor: UCLA David Geffen School of Medicine/UCLA
  Medical Center
Kern Medical Center
UCLA Medical Center
Prgm Director: William D Shields, MD
Division of Pediatric Neurology
22-474 MDCC, UCLA Medical Center
Los Angeles, CA 90095
Tel: 310 794-4271
E-mail: wshields@mednet.ucla.edu
Length: 3 Yrs   *ACGME Approved/Offered Positions:* 6
Program ID: 185-05-21-062

Orange

University of California (Irvine) Program
Sponsor: University of California (Irvine) Medical
  Center
Children's Hospital of Orange County
Prgm Director: Ira T Lott, MD
101 City Drive South, ZOT 4482
The City Tower, Suite 800
Orange, CA 92868
Tel: 714 456-5333   *Fax:* 714 456-8466
E-mail: itlott@uci.edu
Length: 3 Yrs   *ACGME Approved/Offered Positions:* 3
Program ID: 185-05-21-006

San Diego

University of California (San Diego) Program
Sponsor: University of California (San Diego) Medical
  Center
Rady Children's Hospital
Veterans Affairs Medical Center (San Diego)
Prgm Director: Doris A Trauner, MD, MS
9500 Gilman Drive
Department of Neurosciences 0935
La Jolla, CA 92093
Tel: 858 822-6700   *Fax:* 858 822-6707
Length: 3 Yrs   *ACGME Approved/Offered Positions:* 6
Program ID: 185-05-21-020

San Francisco

University of California (San Francisco) Program
Sponsor: University of California (San Francisco) School
  of Medicine
UCSF and Mount Zion Medical Centers
Prgm Director: Yvonne W Wu, MD, MPH
Department of Neurology, Box 0137
350 Parnassus Avenue, Suite 609
San Francisco, CA 94143
Tel: 415 353-3678   *Fax:* 415 353-2400
Length: 3 Yrs   *ACGME Approved/Offered Positions:* 6
Program ID: 185-05-21-069

Programs

Stanford

Stanford University Program

Sponsor: Stanford Hospital and Clinics
Lucile Salter Packard Children's Hospital at Stanford
Santa Clara Valley Medical Center
Veterans Affairs Palo Alto Health Care System
Prgm Director: Paul G Fisher, MD*
Division of Child Neurology
300 Pasteur Drive, A343
Stanford, CA 94305
Tel: 650 725-8630 *Fax:* 650 498-4686
Length: 3 Yrs *ACGME Approved/Offered Positions:* 6
Program ID: 185-05-21-061

Torrance

Los Angeles County-Harbor-UCLA Medical Center Program

Sponsor: Los Angeles County-Harbor-UCLA Medical Center
Prgm Director: Kenneth R Huff, MD
Department of Child Neurology, Box 468
1000 West Carson Street
Torrance, CA 90509
Tel: 310 222-4168 *Fax:* 310 320-2271
E-mail: khuff@labiomed.org
Length: 3 Yrs *ACGME Approved/Offered Positions:* 3
Program ID: 185-05-21-017

Colorado

Aurora

University of Colorado Denver Program

Sponsor: University of Colorado Denver School of Medicine
Children's Hospital (The)
University of Colorado Hospital
Prgm Director: Julie Parsons, MD, MS
The Children's Hospital/Department of Neurology
13123 East 16th Ave, Box B 155
Aurora, CO 80045
Tel: 720 777-6895 *Fax:* 720 777-7285
Length: 3 Yrs *ACGME Approved/Offered Positions:* 6
Program ID: 185-07-21-023

District of Columbia

Washington

Children's National Medical Center/ George Washington University Program

Sponsor: Children's National Medical Center
George Washington University Hospital (UHS)
Georgetown University Hospital
Prgm Director: Phillip L Pearl, MD
111 Michigan Avenue NW
Washington, DC 20010
Tel: 202 476-2120 *Fax:* 202 476-5226
Length: 3 Yrs *ACGME Approved/Offered Positions:* 7
Program ID: 185-10-21-048

Florida

Jacksonville

College of Medicine, Mayo Clinic (Jacksonville) Program

Sponsor: College of Medicine, Mayo Clinic
Nemours Children's Clinic
Mayo Clinic (Jacksonville)
Mayo Clinic Florida Hospital
Wolfson Children's Hospital
Prgm Director: David N Hammond, MD*
807 Children's Way
Jacksonville, FL 32207
Tel: 904 390-3665 *Fax:* 904 390-3470
E-mail: jramey@nemours.org
Length: 3 Yrs *ACGME Approved/Offered Positions:* 3
Program ID: 185-11-13-100

Georgia

Atlanta

Emory University Program

Sponsor: Emory University School of Medicine
Children's Healthcare of Atlanta at Egleston
Emory University Hospital
Grady Health System
Prgm Director: John T Sladky, MD
2015 Uppergate Drive
Atlanta, GA 30322
Tel: 404 778-2400 *Fax:* 404 727-1981
E-mail: jsladky@emory.edu
Length: 3 Yrs *ACGME Approved/Offered Positions:* 3
Program ID: 185-12-21-058

Augusta

Medical College of Georgia Program

Sponsor: Medical College of Georgia
Prgm Director: James E Carroll, MD
Dept of Neurology / Section of Child Neurology
BG 2000H
Augusta, GA 30912
Tel: 706 721-3376 *Fax:* 706 721-3377
Length: 3 Yrs *ACGME Approved/Offered Positions:* 3
Program ID: 185-12-21-019

Illinois

Chicago

McGaw Medical Center of Northwestern University Program

Sponsor: McGaw Medical Center of Northwestern University
Children's Memorial Hospital
Northwestern Memorial Hospital
Prgm Director: Joshua L Goldstein, MD
Division of Neurology, Box 51
2300 N Children's Plaza
Chicago, IL 60614
Tel: 773 880-6630 *Fax:* 773 880-3374
E-mail: jgoldstein@childrensmemorial.org
Length: 3 Yrs *ACGME Approved/Offered Positions:* 6
Program ID: 185-16-21-021

University of Chicago Program

Sponsor: University of Chicago Medical Center
Prgm Director: Kenneth Silver, MD
5841 South Maryland Avenue
MC 3055
Chicago, IL 60637
Tel: 773 702-6487 *Fax:* 773 702-4786
E-mail: ksilver@peds.bsd.uchicago.edu
Length: 3 Yrs *ACGME Approved/Offered Positions:* 6
Program ID: 185-16-21-001

Indiana

Indianapolis

Indiana University School of Medicine Program

Sponsor: Indiana University School of Medicine
Clarian Indiana University Hospital
Clarian Riley Hospital for Children
Prgm Director: Laurence E Walsh, MD
575 West Dr
Room XE040
Indianapolis, IN 46202
Tel: 317 278-2229 *Fax:* 317 274-3622
Length: 3 Yrs *ACGME Approved/Offered Positions:* 3
Program ID: 185-17-21-050

Iowa

Iowa City

University of Iowa Hospitals and Clinics Program

Sponsor: University of Iowa Hospitals and Clinics
Prgm Director: Daniel J Bonthius, MD, PhD
2504 JCP
200 Hawkins Drive
Iowa City, IA 52242
Tel: 319 356-7727 *Fax:* 319 356-4855
Length: 3 Yrs *ACGME Approved/Offered Positions:* 3
Program ID: 185-18-31-106

Kentucky

Lexington

University of Kentucky College of Medicine Program

Sponsor: University of Kentucky College of Medicine
University of Kentucky Hospital
Prgm Director: Robert J Baumann, MD
Kentucky Clinic
740 South Limestone, Room L-445
Lexington, KY 40536
Tel: 859 218-5011 *Fax:* 859 323-5943
E-mail: candace.allen@uky.edu
Length: 3 Yrs *ACGME Approved/Offered Positions:* 3
Program ID: 185-20-21-099

Louisville

University of Louisville Program

Sponsor: University of Louisville School of Medicine
Kosair Children's Hospital (Norton Healthcare, Inc)
University Neurologists, PSC
University of Louisville Hospital
Prgm Director: Michael K Sowell, MD
500 S Preston Street
HSC-A, Rm 113
Louisville, KY 40292
Tel: 502 852-7981 *Fax:* 502 852-6344
E-mail: mksowe01@louisville.edu
Length: 3 Yrs *ACGME Approved/Offered Positions:* 3
Program ID: 185-20-21-103

Note: * indicates a newly appointed program director

Louisiana

New Orleans

Louisiana State University Program
Sponsor: Louisiana State University School of Medicine
Children's Hospital (New Orleans)
Medical Center of Louisiana at New Orleans
Prgm Director: Ann Henderson-Tilton, MD
Children's Hospital
200 Henry Clay Avenue
New Orleans, LA 70118
Tel: 504 891-8851   *Fax:* 504 896-9547
E-mail: atilto@aol.com
Length: 3 Yrs   *ACGME Approved/Offered Positions:* 3
Program ID: 185-21-21-022

Maryland

Baltimore

Johns Hopkins University Program
Sponsor: Johns Hopkins University School of Medicine
Johns Hopkins Hospital
Prgm Director: Harvey Singer, MD
Pediatric Neurology, 123 Jefferson Bldg
600 North Wolfe Street
Baltimore, MD 21287
Tel: 410 955-7212   *Fax:* 410 614-2297
Length: 3 Yrs   *ACGME Approved/Offered Positions:* 6
Program ID: 185-23-21-027

Bethesda

National Capital Consortium Program
Sponsor: National Capital Consortium
Walter Reed Army Medical Center
Prgm Director: Michael H Mitchell, MD
6825 16th Street NW
Department of Neurology
Washington, DC 20307
Tel: 202 782-0830   *Fax:* 202 782-4337
Length: 3 Yrs   *ACGME Approved/Offered Positions:* 5
Program ID: 185-10-11-010
Uniformed Services Program

Massachusetts

Boston

Boston University Medical Center Program
Sponsor: Boston Medical Center
Prgm Director: Karl C Kuban, MD, MS
One Boston Medical Center Place
Dowling Building, Room 3314
Boston, MA 02118
Tel: 617 414-4521   *Fax:* 617 414-4502
E-mail: karl.kuban@bmc.org
Length: 3 Yrs   *ACGME Approved/Offered Positions:* 6
Program ID: 185-24-13-102

Children's Hospital/Beth Israel Deaconess Medical Center/Harvard Medical School Program
Sponsor: Children's Hospital
Beth Israel Deaconess Medical Center
Prgm Director: Basil T Darras, MD
300 Longwood Ave
Fegan 11
Boston, MA 02115
Tel: 617 355-8735   *Fax:* 617 730-0279
Length: 3 Yrs   *ACGME Approved/Offered Positions:* 15
Program ID: 185-24-21-051

Massachusetts General Hospital Program
Sponsor: Massachusetts General Hospital
Prgm Director: Katherine B Sims, MD
CPZN-5-238
185 Cambridge St
Boston, MA 02114
Tel: 617 726-5718   *Fax:* 617 724-9620
Length: 3 Yrs   *ACGME Approved/Offered Positions:* 6
Program ID: 185-24-31-067

Tufts Medical Center Program
Sponsor: Tufts Medical Center
Prgm Director: Linda A Specht, MD, PhD
800 Washington Street
Division of Pediatric Neurology
Boston, MA 02111
Tel: 617 636-5356   *Fax:* 617 636-8375
E-mail: lspecht@tuftsmedicalcenter.org
Length: 3 Yrs   *ACGME Approved/Offered Positions:* 6
Program ID: 185-24-21-028

Michigan

Ann Arbor

University of Michigan Program
Sponsor: University of Michigan Hospitals and Health Centers
Prgm Director: Faye S Silverstein, MD
MSRB III, Box 0646, Room 8301
Ann Arbor, MI 48109
Tel: 734 763-4097   *Fax:* 734 764-4279
Length: 3 Yrs   *ACGME Approved/Offered Positions:* 3
Program ID: 185-25-21-030

Detroit

Wayne State University/Detroit Medical Center Program
Sponsor: Wayne State University/Detroit Medical Center
Children's Hospital of Michigan
Detroit Receiving Hospital and University Health Center
Harper-Hutzel Hospital
Prgm Director: Lalitha Sivaswamy, MD
Children's Hospital of Michigan
3901 Beaubien Blvd
Detroit, MI 48201
Tel: 313 745-5906   *Fax:* 313 745-0955
E-mail: lsivaswamy@med.wayne.edu
Length: 3 Yrs   *ACGME Approved/Offered Positions:* 7
Program ID: 185-25-21-052

Minnesota

Rochester

College of Medicine, Mayo Clinic (Rochester) Program
Sponsor: College of Medicine, Mayo Clinic
Mayo Clinic (Rochester)
Saint Marys Hospital of Rochester
Prgm Director: Marc C Patterson, MD*
Division of Pediatric Neurology
200 First Street SW
Rochester, MN 55905
Tel: 507 284-4333   *Fax:* 507 284-0727
Length: 3 Yrs   *ACGME Approved/Offered Positions:* 6
Program ID: 185-26-21-053

Mississippi

Jackson

University of Mississippi Medical Center Program
Sponsor: University of Mississippi School of Medicine
University Hospitals and Clinics
Prgm Director: Colette C Parker, MD
2500 North State Street
Jackson, MS 39216
Tel: 601 984-5210   *Fax:* 601 815-4942
Length: 3 Yrs   *ACGME Approved/Offered Positions:* 3
Program ID: 185-27-12-095

Missouri

Kansas City

University of Kansas Medical Center/Children's Mercy Hospital and Clinics Program
Sponsor: Children's Mercy Hospital
University of Kansas Medical Center
Prgm Director: William D Graf, MD
University of Kansas Medical Center
2401 Gillham Road
Kansas City, MO 64108
Tel: 816 234-3090   *Fax:* 816 234-3589
E-mail: wdgraf@cmh.edu
Length: 3 Yrs   *ACGME Approved/Offered Positions:* 3
Program ID: 185-19-22-096

St Louis

St Louis University School of Medicine Program
Sponsor: St Louis University School of Medicine
Cardinal Glennon Children's Hospital
St Louis University Hospital
Prgm Director: Thomas J Geller, MD
1465 South Grand
Child Neurology
St Louis, MO 63104
Tel: 314 577-5338   *Fax:* 314 268-6411
Length: 3 Yrs   *ACGME Approved/Offered Positions:* 3
Program ID: 185-28-21-033

Washington University/B-JH/SLCH Consortium Program
Sponsor: Washington University/B-JH/SLCH Consortium
Barnes-Jewish Hospital
St Louis Children's Hospital
Prgm Director: Bradley L Schlaggar, MD, PhD
660 S Euclid Ave
Campus Box 8111
St Louis, MO 63110
Tel: 314 454-6042   *Fax:* 314 454-6142
E-mail: schlaggarb@neuro.wustl.edu
Length: 3 Yrs   *ACGME Approved/Offered Positions:* 12
Program ID: 185-28-21-034

New Jersey

Newark

UMDNJ-New Jersey Medical School Program
Sponsor: UMDNJ-New Jersey Medical School
UMDNJ-University Hospital
Prgm Director: Caroline Hayes-Rosen, MD
185 South Orange Avenue MSB H-506
Newark, NJ 07103
Tel: 973 972-2922   *Fax:* 973 972-9960
E-mail: hayesrca@umdnj.edu
Length: 3 Yrs   *ACGME Approved/Offered Positions:* 3
Program ID: 185-33-21-011

New Mexico

Albuquerque

University of New Mexico Program
Sponsor: University of New Mexico School of Medicine
University of New Mexico Hospital
Veterans Affairs Medical Center (Albuquerque)
Prgm Director: Mary I Johnson, MD
1 University of New Mexico
Albuquerque, NM 87131
Tel: 505 272-3342   *Fax:* 505 272-6692
Length: 3 Yrs   *ACGME Approved/Offered Positions:* 3
Program ID: 185-34-13-105

New York

Bronx

Albert Einstein College of Medicine Program
Sponsor: Albert Einstein College of Medicine of Yeshiva
University
Montefiore Medical Center-Henry and Lucy Moses
Division
Montefiore Medical Center-Weiler Division
North Bronx Healthcare Network-Jacobi Medical Center
Prgm Director: Karen Ballaban-Gil, MD
Rose F Kennedy Building, Room 316
1300 Morris Park Avenue
Bronx, NY 10461
Tel: 718 430-2464   *Fax:* 718 430-8899
Length: 3 Yrs   *ACGME Approved/Offered Positions:* 6
Program ID: 185-35-21-002

Brooklyn

SUNY Health Science Center at Brooklyn Program
Sponsor: SUNY Health Science Center at Brooklyn
Kings County Hospital Center
University Hospital-SUNY Health Science Center at
Brooklyn
Prgm Director: Joan B Cracco, MD
450 Clarkson Avenue, Box 118
Brooklyn, NY 11203
Tel: 718 270-2042   *Fax:* 718 270-3748
Length: 3 Yrs   *ACGME Approved/Offered Positions:* 6
Program ID: 185-35-21-054

Buffalo

University at Buffalo Program
Sponsor: University at Buffalo School of Medicine
Kaleida Health System (Women and Children's Hospital
of Buffalo)
Prgm Director: Thomas J Langan, MD
Dept of Child Neurology, The Jacobs Neurological
Institute
100 High Street
Buffalo, NY 14203
Tel: 716 878-7848   *Fax:* 716 878-7326
E-mail: ejtamoga@buffalo.edu
Length: 3 Yrs   *ACGME Approved/Offered Positions:* 3
Program ID: 185-35-21-035

Note: * indicates a newly appointed program director

Great Neck

NSLIJHS-Albert Einstein College of Medicine at Long Island Jewish Medical Center Program
Sponsor: North Shore-Long Island Jewish Health System
Long Island Jewish Medical Center
Schneider Children's Hospital at Long Island Jewish
Med Ctr
Prgm Director: Robin E Smith, MBChB
Schneider Children's Hospital
410 Lakeville Road, Suite 105
New Hyde Park, NY 11042
Tel: 516 465-5351   *Fax:* 718 347-2240
Length: 3 Yrs   *ACGME Approved/Offered Positions:* 5
Program ID: 185-35-21-055

New York

New York Presbyterian Hospital (Columbia Campus) Program
Sponsor: New York Presbyterian Hospital
New York Presbyterian Hospital (Columbia Campus)
Prgm Director: Claudia A Chiriboga, MD, MPH
Harkness Pavilion, Suite 544
180 Fort Washington Avenue
New York, NY 10032
Tel: 212 305-8549   *Fax:* 212 305-1253
Length: 3 Yrs   *ACGME Approved/Offered Positions:* 6
Program ID: 185-35-21-059

New York Presbyterian Hospital (Cornell Campus) Program
Sponsor: New York Presbyterian Hospital
New York Presbyterian Hospital (Cornell Campus)
Prgm Director: Kaleb Yohay, MD
Division of Pediatric Neurology
525 East 68th Street, Box 91
New York, NY 10021
Tel: 212 746-5054   *Fax:* 212 746-4001
E-mail: kay2003@med.cornell.edu
Length: 3 Yrs   *ACGME Approved/Offered Positions:* 3
Program ID: 185-35-21-015

New York University School of Medicine Program
Sponsor: New York University School of Medicine
Bellevue Hospital Center
NYU Hospitals Center
Prgm Director: Ruth Nass, MD
550 First Avenue
New York, NY 10016
Tel: 212 263-7753   *Fax:* 212 263-7721
E-mail: ruth.nass@med.nyu.edu
Length: 3 Yrs   *ACGME Approved/Offered Positions:* 5
Program ID: 185-35-21-057

Rochester

University of Rochester Program
Sponsor: Strong Memorial Hospital of the University of
Rochester
Prgm Director: Jonathan W Mink, MD, PhD
601 Elmwood Avenue, Box 631
Rochester, NY 14642
Tel: 585 275-3669   *Fax:* 585 275-3683
E-mail: Anna_Stevenson@urmc.rochester.edu
Length: 3 Yrs   *ACGME Approved/Offered Positions:* 6
Program ID: 185-35-12-094

Stony Brook

SUNY at Stony Brook Program
Sponsor: University Hospital - SUNY at Stony Brook
Prgm Director: Mary R Andriola, MD
Department of Neurology
HSC T12-020
Stony Brook, NY 11794
Tel: 631 444-7878   *Fax:* 631 632-2451
Length: 3 Yrs   *ACGME Approved/Offered Positions:* 3
Program ID: 185-35-21-081

North Carolina

Chapel Hill

University of North Carolina Hospitals Program
Sponsor: University of North Carolina Hospitals
Prgm Director: Robert S Greenwood, MD
Department of Neurology
170 Physician's Office Bldg
Chapel Hill, NC 27599
Tel: 919 966-8160   *Fax:* 919 966-2922
E-mail: greenwor@neurology.unc.edu
Length: 3 Yrs   *ACGME Approved/Offered Positions:* 3
Program ID: 185-36-21-003

Durham

Duke University Hospital Program
Sponsor: Duke University Hospital
Prgm Director: William B Gallentine, DO*
Division of Pediatric Neurology
Box 3936
Durham, NC 27710
Tel: 919 668-0477   *Fax:* 919 681-8943
E-mail: william.gallentine@duke.edu
Length: 3 Yrs   *ACGME Approved/Offered Positions:* 3
Program ID: 185-36-21-080

Winston-Salem

Wake Forest University School of Medicine Program
Sponsor: Wake Forest University Baptist Medical Center
Prgm Director: Annette Grefe, MD*
300 South Hawthorne Road
Winston-Salem, NC 27103
Tel: 336 716-2317   *Fax:* 336 716-9489
E-mail: dholland@wfubmc.edu
Length: 3 Yrs   *ACGME Approved/Offered Positions:* 3
Program ID: 185-36-21-037

Ohio

Cincinnati

Cincinnati Children's Hospital Medical Center/University of Cincinnati College of Medicine Program
Sponsor: Cincinnati Children's Hospital Medical Center
University Hospital Inc
Prgm Director: Mark B Schapiro, MD, BA
3333 Burnet Avenue
ML 2015
Cincinnati, OH 45229
Tel: 513 636-7558   *Fax:* 513 636-1888
Length: 3 Yrs   *ACGME Approved/Offered Positions:* 12
Program ID: 185-38-21-038

Cleveland

Cleveland Clinic Foundation Program
Sponsor: Cleveland Clinic Foundation
Prgm Director: Gary E Hsich, MD*
Department of Pediatric Neurology, S71
9500 Euclid Avenue
Cleveland, OH 44195
Tel: 216 444-2945   *Fax:* 216 444-0230
E-mail: dillj@ccf.org
Length: 3 Yrs   *ACGME Approved/Offered Positions:* 6
Program ID: 185-38-21-004

University Hospitals Case Medical Center Program

Sponsor: University Hospitals Case Medical Center
Prgm Director: Nancy E Bass, MD
11100 Euclid Avenue, MS 6090
Cleveland, OH 44106
Tel: 216 844-3691   *Fax:* 216 844-8966
E-mail: nancy.bass@UHhospitals.org
Length: 3 Yrs   *ACGME Approved/Offered Positions:* 3
Program ID: 185-38-13-091

Columbus

Nationwide Children's Hospital/Ohio State University Program

Sponsor: Nationwide Children's Hospital
Ohio State University Hospital
Prgm Director: Pedro Weisleder, MD, PhD*
Division of Neurology, ED 5th Floor
700 Children's Drive
Columbus, OH 43205
Tel: 614 722-4641   *Fax:* 614 722-4633
E-mail: pedro.weisleder@nationwidechildrens.org
Length: 3 Yrs   *ACGME Approved/Offered Positions:* 6
Program ID: 185-38-21-092

Oregon

Portland

Oregon Health & Science University Program

Sponsor: Oregon Health & Science University Hospital
Prgm Director: Joseph D Pinter, MD*
Pediatric Neurology
707 SW Gaines St, CDRC-P
Portland, OR 97239
Tel: 503 494-9113   *Fax:* 503 494-2370
E-mail: pinterj@ohsu.edu
Length: 3 Yrs   *ACGME Approved/Offered Positions:* 3
Program ID: 185-40-23-048

Pennsylvania

Philadelphia

Children's Hospital of Philadelphia Program

Sponsor: Children's Hospital of Philadelphia
University of Pennsylvania Health System
Prgm Director: Donald P Younkin, MD
One Children's Center
34th St and Civic Center Blvd
Philadelphia, PA 19104
Tel: 215 590-1710   *Fax:* 215 590-2950
Length: 3 Yrs   *ACGME Approved/Offered Positions:* 9
Program ID: 185-41-21-041

St Christopher's Hospital for Children Program

Sponsor: St Christopher's Hospital for Children (Tenet Health System)
Hahnemann University Hospital (Tenet Health System)
Prgm Director: Ignacio Valencia, MD*
Erie Avenue at Front St
Philadelphia, PA 19134
Tel: 215 427-8975   *Fax:* 215 427-4393
E-mail: ignacio.valencia@drexelmed.edu
Length: 3 Yrs   *ACGME Approved/Offered Positions:* 3
Program ID: 185-41-21-040

Pittsburgh

University of Pittsburgh Medical Center Medical Education Program

Sponsor: Univ of Pittsburgh Medical Center Medical Education
Children's Hospital of Pittsburgh of UPMC
UPMC Presbyterian Shadyside
Prgm Director: Patricia K Crumrine, MD
Medical Arts Building, Suite 503
Pittsburgh, PA 15213
Tel: 412 692-5524   *Fax:* 412 692-6787
E-mail: machele.maus@chp.edu
Length: 3 Yrs   *ACGME Approved/Offered Positions:* 9
Program ID: 185-41-21-012

Puerto Rico

San Juan

University of Puerto Rico Program

Sponsor: University of Puerto Rico School of Medicine
San Juan City Hospital
University Hospital
University Pediatric Hospital
Prgm Director: Marisel Vazquez-Correa, MD
Medical Science Campus, Department of Pediatrics-GPO Box 365067
San Juan, PR 00936
Tel: 787 756-4020   *Fax:* 787 751-3911
E-mail: mariselvcvc@yahoo.com
Length: 3 Yrs   *ACGME Approved/Offered Positions:* 3
Program ID: 185-42-12-101

Tennessee

Memphis

University of Tennessee Program

Sponsor: University of Tennessee College of Medicine
LeBonheur Children's Medical Center
Methodist Healthcare - Memphis Hospitals
Regional Medical Center at Memphis
St Jude Children's Research Hospital
Veterans Affairs Medical Center (Memphis)
Prgm Director: F Fred Perkins, MD
777 Washington Ave
Suite 335
Memphis, TN 38105
Tel: 901 287-5208   *Fax:* 901 287-5325
E-mail: fperkins@utmem.edu
Length: 3 Yrs   *ACGME Approved/Offered Positions:* 6
Program ID: 185-47-12-104

Nashville

Vanderbilt University Program

Sponsor: Vanderbilt University Medical Center
Prgm Director: Jesus Eric Pina-Garza, MD*
2200 Children's way
11244 Doctors' Office Tower
Nashville, TN 37232
Tel: 615 936-5437   *Fax:* 615 936-2848
Length: 3 Yrs   *ACGME Approved/Offered Positions:* 6
Program ID: 185-47-21-042

Texas

Dallas

University of Texas Southwestern Medical School Program

Sponsor: University of Texas Southwestern Medical School
Children's Medical Center of Dallas
Dallas County Hospital District-Parkland Memorial Hospital
University Hospitals Zale Lipshy
Prgm Director: Rana R Said, MD
5323 Harry Hines Blvd
Dallas, TX 75390
Tel: 214 456-8242   *Fax:* 214 456-8990
E-mail: rana.said@utsouthwestern.edu
Length: 3 Yrs   *ACGME Approved/Offered Positions:* 9
Program ID: 185-48-21-043

Houston

Baylor College of Medicine Program

Sponsor: Baylor College of Medicine
Texas Children's Hospital
Prgm Director: Timothy E Lotze, MD
One Baylor Plaza
Houston, TX 77030
Tel: 832 822-1779   *Fax:* 832 825-1717
E-mail: telotze@texaschildrenshospital.org
Length: 3 Yrs   *ACGME Approved/Offered Positions:* 9
Program ID: 185-48-21-018

University of Texas at Houston Program

Sponsor: University of Texas Health Science Center at Houston
Memorial Hermann Hospital
Prgm Director: Ian J Butler, MD
Department of Pediatrics 3.153/MSB
6431 Fannin Street
Houston, TX 77030
Tel: 713 500-7113   *Fax:* 713 500-7101
E-mail: ian.j.butler@uth.tmc.edu
Length: 3 Yrs   *ACGME Approved/Offered Positions:* 6
Program ID: 185-48-31-078

Utah

Salt Lake City

University of Utah Program

Sponsor: University of Utah Medical Center
Primary Children's Medical Center
Veterans Affairs Medical Center (Salt Lake City)
Prgm Director: Francis M Filloux, MD
Primary Children's Medical Center
100 N Medical Drive
Salt Lake City, UT 84113
Tel: 801 587-7575   *Fax:* 801 587-7471
E-mail: neuro.residency@hsc.utah.edu
Length: 3 Yrs   *ACGME Approved/Offered Positions:* 3
Program ID: 185-49-21-044

Virginia

Charlottesville

University of Virginia Program

Sponsor: University of Virginia Medical Center
Prgm Director: Robert S Rust, MA, MD
Department of Neurology
Box 800394
Charlottesville, VA 22908
Tel: 434 924-5538   *Fax:* 434 982-1726
Length: 3 Yrs   *ACGME Approved/Offered Positions:* 3
Program ID: 185-51-31-097

Richmond

Virginia Commonwealth University Health System Program

Sponsor: Virginia Commonwealth University Health System
Hunter Holmes McGuire VA Medical Center (Richmond)
Prgm Director: Steven M Shapiro, MD
Sanger Hall, Room 6-005
1101 East Marshall Street
Richmond, VA 23298
Tel: 804 828-9940   *Fax:* 804 828-6373
Length: 3 Yrs   *ACGME Approved/Offered Positions:* 3
Program ID: 185-51-21-060

Washington

Seattle

University of Washington Program

Sponsor: University of Washington School of Medicine
Seattle Children's Hospital
University of Washington Medical Center
Prgm Director: Sidney M Gospe Jr, MD, PhD
4800 Sand Point Way NE
Neurology, B-5552
Seattle, WA 98105
Tel: 206 987-2078   *Fax:* 206 987-2649
E-mail: sgospe@u.washington.edu
Length: 3 Yrs   *ACGME Approved/Offered Positions:* 6
Program ID: 185-54-21-047

Wisconsin

Milwaukee

Medical College of Wisconsin Affiliated Hospitals Program

Sponsor: Medical College of Wisconsin Affiliated Hospitals, Inc
Children's Hospital of Wisconsin
Froedtert Memorial Lutheran Hospital
Prgm Director: Suja Anne Joseph, MD
8701 Watertown Plank Road
Milwaukee, WI 53226
Tel: 414 805-5254   *Fax:* 414 259-0469
E-mail: jdavies@mcw.edu
Length: 3 Yrs   *ACGME Approved/Offered Positions:* 6
Program ID: 185-56-21-070

Clinical Cardiac Electrophysiology (Internal Medicine)

Alabama

Birmingham

University of Alabama Medical Center Program

Sponsor: University of Alabama Hospital
Prgm Director: G Neal Kay, MD
321-J Tinsley Harrison Tower
1530 3rd Avenue South
Birmingham, AL 35294
Tel: 205 934-1335   *Fax:* 205 934-1279
Length: 1 Yr   *ACGME Approved/Offered Positions:* 2
Program ID: 154-01-21-001

Arizona

Phoenix

College of Medicine, Mayo Clinic (Arizona) Program

Sponsor: College of Medicine, Mayo Clinic
Mayo Clinic Hospital
Prgm Director: Luis Scott, MD
Mayo Clinic Hospital
5777 East Mayo Boulevard
Phoenix, AZ 85054
Tel: 480 301-0239   *Fax:* 480 301-1606
E-mail: scott.luis@mayo.edu
Length: 1 Yr   *ACGME Approved/Offered Positions:* 1
Program ID: 154-03-13-114

Arkansas

Little Rock

University of Arkansas for Medical Sciences Program

Sponsor: University of Arkansas College of Medicine
Central Arkansas Veterans Healthcare System
UAMS Medical Center
Prgm Director: Joe K Bissett, MD
4301 W Markham, Slot 532
Little Rock, AR 72205
Tel: 501 686-5880   *Fax:* 501 686-8319
E-mail: mjmorrisbisbee@uams.edu
Length: 1 Yr   *ACGME Approved/Offered Positions:* 1
Program ID: 154-04-12-104

California

Los Angeles

Cedars-Sinai Medical Center Program

Sponsor: Cedars-Sinai Medical Center
Prgm Director: Sumeet S Chugh, MD*
Cardiology, Rm 5535
8700 Beverly Boulevard
Los Angeles, CA 90048
Tel: 310 423-3300   *Fax:* 310 423-3522
E-mail: lebowitze@cshs.org
Length: 1 Yr   *ACGME Approved/Offered Positions:* 3
Program ID: 154-05-21-002

Kaiser Permanente Southern California (Los Angeles) Program

Sponsor: Kaiser Permanente Southern California
Kaiser Foundation Hospital (Los Angeles)
Prgm Director: Maged Nageh, MD
Kaiser Permanente Medical Center
4733 Sunset Blvd, 3rd Floor
Los Angeles, CA 90027
Tel: 323 783-5850   *Fax:* 323 783-8974
Length: 1 Yr   *ACGME Approved/Offered Positions:* 2
Program ID: 154-05-12-116

UCLA Medical Center Program

Sponsor: UCLA David Geffen School of Medicine/UCLA Medical Center
UCLA Medical Center
VA Greater Los Angeles Healthcare System
Prgm Director: Kalyanam Shivkumar, MD, PhD
BH-307 CHS
10833 Le Conte Ave
Los Angeles, CA 90095
Tel: 310 206-6433   *Fax:* 310 794-6492
E-mail: mbetwarda@mednet.ucla.edu
Length: 1 Yr   *ACGME Approved/Offered Positions:* 2
Program ID: 154-05-31-103

UCLA-VA Greater Los Angeles Program

Sponsor: VA Greater Los Angeles Healthcare System
UCLA Medical Center
Prgm Director: Zenaida Feliciano, MD
Cardiology 111E
11301 Wilshire Boulevard
Los Angeles, CA 90073
Tel: 310 268-3643   *Fax:* 310 268-4288
E-mail: Zenaida.Feliciano@med.va.gov
Length: 1 Yr   *ACGME Approved/Offered Positions:* 1
Program ID: 154-05-13-006

University of Southern California/ LAC+USC Medical Center Program

Sponsor: University of Southern California/LAC+USC Medical Center
LAC+USC Medical Center
USC University Hospital
Prgm Director: Leslie A Saxon, MD
1510 San Pablo Street, Suite 322
Los Angeles, CA 90033
Tel: 323 442-6130   *Fax:* 323 442-6133
E-mail: sarahlun@usc.edu
Length: 1 Yr   *ACGME Approved/Offered Positions:* 2
Program ID: 154-05-21-106

San Diego

University of California (San Diego) Program

Sponsor: University of California (San Diego) Medical Center
Veterans Affairs Medical Center (San Diego)
Prgm Director: Gregory K Feld, MD
4168 Front St
San Diego, CA 92103
Tel: 619 543-8205   *Fax:* 619 471-0221
Length: 1 Yr   *ACGME Approved/Offered Positions:* 3
Program ID: 154-05-22-007

San Francisco

University of California (San Francisco) Program

Sponsor: University of California (San Francisco) School of Medicine
UCSF and Mount Zion Medical Centers
Prgm Director: Jeffrey E Olgin, MD
500 Parnassus Avenue
Room MU 433 Box 1354
San Francisco, CA 94143
Tel: 415 476-5706   *Fax:* 415 476-6260
Length: 1 Yr   *ACGME Approved/Offered Positions:* 3
Program ID: 154-05-23-008

Note: * indicates a newly appointed program director

Stanford

Stanford University Program

Sponsor: Stanford Hospital and Clinics
Prgm Director: Paul J Wang, MD
Cardiac Arrhythmia Service
300 Pasteur Dr Rm H2146
Stanford, CA 94305
Tel: 650 723-7111 *Fax:* 650 725-7568
Length: 1 Yr *ACGME Approved/Offered Positions:* 4
Program ID: 154-05-32-009

Torrance

Los Angeles County-Harbor-UCLA Medical Center Program

Sponsor: Los Angeles County-Harbor-UCLA Medical Center
Hospital of the Good Samaritan
Prgm Director: Anil K Bhandari, MD
1225 Wilshire Boulevard
Los Angeles, CA 90017
Tel: 213 977-2239 *Fax:* 213 977-2209
Length: 1 Yr *ACGME Approved/Offered Positions:* 2
Program ID: 154-05-31-003

Colorado

Aurora

University of Colorado Denver Program

Sponsor: University of Colorado Denver School of Medicine
Denver Health Medical Center
Exempla St Joseph Hospital
University of Colorado Hospital
Prgm Director: Laurent Lewkowiez, MD
12631 E 17th Ave, Box B130
PO Box 6511
Aurora, CO 80045
Tel: 303 436-8908 *Fax:* 303 436-7739
E-mail: laurent.lewkowiez@uchsc.edu
Length: 1 Yr *ACGME Approved/Offered Positions:* 1
Program ID: 154-07-21-010

Connecticut

New Haven

Yale-New Haven Medical Center Program

Sponsor: Yale-New Haven Hospital
Prgm Director: Lynda E Rosenfeld, MD
Department of Cardiovascular Medicine, 3 FMP
333 Cedar Street, PO Box 208017
New Haven, CT 06520
Tel: 203 737-4068 *Fax:* 203 785-6506
Length: 1 Yr *ACGME Approved/Offered Positions:* 1
Program ID: 154-08-21-087

District of Columbia

Washington

George Washington University Program

Sponsor: George Washington University School of Medicine
George Washington University Hospital (UHS)
Veterans Affairs Medical Center (Washington, DC)
Washington Adventist Hospital
Prgm Director: Cynthia M Tracy, MD
2150 Pennsylvania Avenue, NW
Washington, DC 20037
Tel: 202 741-2668 *Fax:* 202 741-2324
E-mail: ctracy@mfa.gwu.edu
Length: 1 Yr *ACGME Approved/Offered Positions:* 3
Program ID: 154-10-31-012

Georgetown University Hospital/Washington Hospital Center Program

Sponsor: Washington Hospital Center
Georgetown University Hospital
Veterans Affairs Medical Center (Washington, DC)
Prgm Director: Susan O'Donoghue, MD
110 Irving Street, NW
Division of Cardiology
Washington, DC 20010
Tel: 202 877-7685 *Fax:* 202 877-2125
E-mail: denise.b.moore@medstar.net
Length: 1 Yr *ACGME Approved/Offered Positions:* 2
Program ID: 154-10-21-011

Florida

Gainesville

University of Florida Program

Sponsor: University of Florida College of Medicine
Shands Hospital at the University of Florida
Prgm Director: William M Miles, MD*
Box 100277
1600 SW Archer Road, Room M-436
Gainesville, FL 32610
Tel: 352 392-2469 *Fax:* 352 846-0314
Length: 1 Yr *ACGME Approved/Offered Positions:* 2
Program ID: 154-11-21-081

Jacksonville

University of Florida College of Medicine Jacksonville Program

Sponsor: University of Florida College of Medicine Jacksonville
Shands Jacksonville Medical Center
Prgm Director: Steve S Hsu, MD
655 West 8th Street
Jacksonville, FL 32209
Tel: 904 244-7214 *Fax:* 904 244-5902
Length: 1 Yr *ACGME Approved/Offered Positions:* 2
Program ID: 154-11-31-127

Miami

Jackson Memorial Hospital/Jackson Health System Program

Sponsor: Jackson Memorial Hospital/Jackson Health System
Mercy Hospital
University of Miami Hospital
Veterans Affairs Medical Center (Miami)
Prgm Director: Vivek Y Reddy, MD*
University of Miami Hospital
1400 NW 12 Ave, Cardiology, 4th Floor Suite 4062
Miami, FL 33136
Tel: 305 243-5060 *Fax:* 305 547-6602
E-mail: Jmendez@med.miami.edu
Length: 1 Yr *ACGME Approved/Offered Positions:* 2
Program ID: 154-11-21-014

Tampa

University of South Florida Program

Sponsor: University of South Florida College of Medicine
Tampa General Hospital
Prgm Director: Anne B Curtis, MD*
South Tampa Center for Advanced Healthcare
2 Tampa General Circle, 5th Floor Cardiology
Tampa, FL 33606
Tel: 813 396-9156 *Fax:* 813 259-0669
E-mail: gszaltel@health.usf.edu
Length: 1 Yr *ACGME Approved/Offered Positions:* 1
Program ID: 154-11-13-110

Georgia

Atlanta

Emory University Program

Sponsor: Emory University School of Medicine
Crawford Long Hospital of Emory University
Emory University Hospital
Prgm Director: Jonathan J Langberg, MD
1364 Clifton Road, NE Suite F-424
Atlanta, GA 30322
Tel: 404 712-4070 *Fax:* 404 712-4374
Length: 1 Yr *ACGME Approved/Offered Positions:* 3
Program ID: 154-12-21-015

Augusta

Medical College of Georgia Program

Sponsor: Medical College of Georgia
Medical College of Georgia Cardiovascular Center
Prgm Director: Robert A Sorrentino, MD
1120 15th Street, BBR 6518
Augusta, GA 30912
Tel: 706 721-7815 *Fax:* 706 721-5150
Length: 1 Yr *ACGME Approved/Offered Positions:* 1
Program ID: 154-12-21-125

Illinois

Chicago

Advocate Illinois Masonic Medical Center/North Side Health Network Program

Sponsor: Advocate Illinois Masonic Medical Center
Prgm Director: Richard F Kehoe, MD
836 W Wellington Ave
Chicago, IL 60657
Tel: 773 296-7135 *Fax:* 773 296-7982
E-mail: richard.kehoe-md@advocatehealth.com
Length: 1 Yr *ACGME Approved/Offered Positions:* 2
Program ID: 154-16-21-016

McGaw Medical Center of Northwestern University Program

Sponsor: McGaw Medical Center of Northwestern University
Northwestern Memorial Hospital
Prgm Director: Jeffrey J Goldberger, MD, MBA
251 East Huron Street
Feinberg School of Medicine
Chicago, IL 60611
Tel: 312 926-2148 *Fax:* 312 926-2707
Length: 1 Yr *ACGME Approved/Offered Positions:* 3
Program ID: 154-16-31-017

Rush University Medical Center Program

Sponsor: Rush University Medical Center
Prgm Director: Kousik Krishnan, MD
1653 West Congress Parkway
Chicago, IL 60612
Tel: 312 942-8771 *Fax:* 312 942-5829
Length: 1 Yr *ACGME Approved/Offered Positions:* 1
Program ID: 154-16-11-018

University of Chicago Program

Sponsor: University of Chicago Medical Center
Prgm Director: Bradley P Knight, MD
University of Chicago
5758 S Maryland Avenue
Chicago, IL 60637
Tel: 773 702-5988 *Fax:* 773 702-4666
Length: 1 Yr *ACGME Approved/Offered Positions:* 3
Program ID: 154-16-12-019

Maywood

Loyola University Program

Sponsor: Loyola University Medical Center
Prgm Director: Peter Santucci, MD
Building 110 Room 6286
2160 South First Avenue
Maywood, IL 60153
Tel: 708 216-2653   *Fax:* 708 216-6829
Length: 1 Yr   *ACGME Approved/Offered Positions:* 4
Program ID: 154-16-13-020

Indiana

Indianapolis

Indiana University School of Medicine Program

Sponsor: Indiana University School of Medicine
Clarian Methodist Hospital of Indiana
Richard L Roudebush Veterans Affairs Medical Center
Prgm Director: John M Miller, MD
Krannert Institute of Cardiology
1800 North Capitol Avenue Suite E488
Indianapolis, IN 46202
Tel: 317 962-0560   *Fax:* 317 962-0113
Length: 1 Yr   *ACGME Approved/Offered Positions:* 3
Program ID: 154-17-21-021

St Vincent Hospital and Health Care Center Program

Sponsor: St Vincent Hospitals and Health Care Center
Prgm Director: Eric N Prystowsky, MD
8333 Naab Road
Indianapolis, IN 46260
Tel: 317 338-6024   *Fax:* 317 338-9259
E-mail: lpogue@thecaregroup.com
Length: 1 Yr   *ACGME Approved/Offered Positions:* 2
Program ID: 154-17-21-094

Iowa

Iowa City

University of Iowa Hospitals and Clinics Program

Sponsor: University of Iowa Hospitals and Clinics
Prgm Director: James B Martins, MD
Cardiology E316-1 GH
200 Hawkins Drive
Iowa City, IA 52242
Tel: 319 356-2740
E-mail: james-martins@uiowa.edu
Length: 1 Yr   *ACGME Approved/Offered Positions:* 1
Program ID: 154-18-21-022

Kansas

Kansas City

University of Kansas School of Medicine Program

Sponsor: University of Kansas School of Medicine
University of Kansas Hospital
Prgm Director: Loren D Berenbom, MD*
3901 Rainbow Boulevard
1001 Eaton, MS 3006
Kansas City, KS 66160
Tel: 913 588-6015   *Fax:* 913 588-6010
E-mail: rshadduck@kumc.edu
Length: 1 Yr   *ACGME Approved/Offered Positions:* 1
Program ID: 154-19-12-108

Kentucky

Louisville

University of Louisville Program

Sponsor: University of Louisville School of Medicine
Jewish Hospital
University of Louisville Hospital
Veterans Affairs Medical Center (Louisville)
Prgm Director: A G Deam, MD
Third Floor Ambulatory Care Bldg
550 South Jackson Street
Louisville, KY 40292
Tel: 502 852-7959   *Fax:* 502 852-7147
Length: 1 Yr   *ACGME Approved/Offered Positions:* 2
Program ID: 154-20-21-023

Maryland

Baltimore

Johns Hopkins University Program

Sponsor: Johns Hopkins University School of Medicine
Johns Hopkins Bayview Medical Center
Johns Hopkins Hospital
Prgm Director: Ronald D Berger, MD, PhD
Carnegie 592
600 N Wolfe Street
Baltimore, MD 21287
Tel: 410 614-2751   *Fax:* 410 502-4854
E-mail: rberger@jhmi.edu
Length: 1 Yr   *ACGME Approved/Offered Positions:* 4
Program ID: 154-23-21-024

University of Maryland Program

Sponsor: University of Maryland Medical System
Prgm Director: Stephen R Shorofsky, MD, PhD
22 S Greene Street
S3B06
Baltimore, MD 21201
Tel: 410 328-6056   *Fax:* 410 328-2062
E-mail: mbileck@medicine.umaryland.edu
Length: 1 Yr   *ACGME Approved/Offered Positions:* 3
Program ID: 154-23-31-025

Massachusetts

Boston

Beth Israel Deaconess Medical Center Program

Sponsor: Beth Israel Deaconess Medical Center
Prgm Director: William Maisel, MD, MPH
Harvard Thorndike Electrophysiology Institute
One Deaconess Road, Baker 4
Boston, MA 02215
Tel: 617 632-7828
E-mail: wmaisel@bidmc.harvard.edu
Length: 1 Yr   *ACGME Approved/Offered Positions:* 4
Program ID: 154-24-21-026

Boston University Medical Center Program

Sponsor: Boston Medical Center
Prgm Director: Kevin M Monahan, MD
Section of Cardiology
88 East Newton Street
Boston, MA 02118
Tel: 617 638-8734   *Fax:* 617 638-8784
E-mail: paul.lelorier@bmc.org
Length: 1 Yr   *ACGME Approved/Offered Positions:* 2
Program ID: 154-24-12-089

Brigham and Women's Hospital/West Roxbury Veterans Affairs Medical Center Program

Sponsor: Brigham and Women's Hospital
Boston VA Healthcare System (Brockton-West Roxbury)
Prgm Director: Laurence Epstein, MD*
75 Francis Street
Boston, MA 02115
Tel: 857 307-1945   *Fax:* 857 307-1944
E-mail: lmepstein@partners.org
Length: 1 Yr   *ACGME Approved/Offered Positions:* 4
Program ID: 154-24-11-028

Caritas St Elizabeth's Medical Center Program

Sponsor: Caritas St Elizabeth's Medical Center of Boston
Prgm Director: Michael Orlov, MD, PhD*
736 Cambridge Street
Boston, MA 02135
Tel: 617 789-3187   *Fax:* 617 789-5029
Length: 1 Yr   *ACGME Approved/Offered Positions:* 2
Program ID: 154-24-31-119

Massachusetts General Hospital Program

Sponsor: Massachusetts General Hospital
Prgm Director: Jeremy N Ruskin, MD
32 Fruit Street
Boston, MA 02114
Tel: 617 726-8514
Length: 1 Yr   *ACGME Approved/Offered Positions:* 4
Program ID: 154-24-12-029

Tufts Medical Center Program

Sponsor: Tufts Medical Center
Prgm Director: Munther K Homoud, MD
800 Washington Street, Box 197
Boston, MA 02111
Tel: 617 636-5902   *Fax:* 617 636-4586
Length: 1 Yr   *ACGME Approved/Offered Positions:* 2
Program ID: 154-24-13-030

Burlington

Lahey Clinic Program

Sponsor: Lahey Clinic
Prgm Director: David T Martin, MD
41 Mall Road
Burlington, MA 01805
Tel: 781 744-8863   *Fax:* 781 744-5577
Length: 1 Yr   *ACGME Approved/Offered Positions:* 2
Program ID: 154-24-23-032

Springfield

Baystate Medical Center/Tufts University School of Medicine Program

Sponsor: Baystate Medical Center
Prgm Director: James R Cook, MD, MPH
759 Chestnut Street, S4658
Springfield, MA 01199
Tel: 413 794-8722   *Fax:* 413 794-0198
E-mail: nancy.lois@bhs.org
Length: 1 Yr   *ACGME Approved/Offered Positions:* 1
Program ID: 154-24-32-033

Worcester

University of Massachusetts Program

Sponsor: University of Massachusetts Medical School
UMass Memorial Health Care (University Campus)
Prgm Director: Lawrence Rosenthal, MD, PhD
55 Lake Avenue, North
Division of Cardiology
Worcester, MA 01655
Tel: 508 856-2931   *Fax:* 508 856-6959
Length: 1 Yr   *ACGME Approved/Offered Positions:* 2
Program ID: 154-24-33-034

Note: * indicates a newly appointed program director

Michigan

Ann Arbor

University of Michigan Program
Sponsor: University of Michigan Hospitals and Health
Centers
Prgm Director: Frank Pelosi Jr, MD
1500 E Medical Center Drive
CVC Cardiovascular Medicine SPC 5853
Ann Arbor, MI 48109
Tel: 734 763-7141   *Fax:* 734 936-7026
E-mail: robewilc@umich.edu
Length: 1 Yr   *ACGME Approved/Offered Positions:* 6
Program ID: 154-25-21-035

Detroit

Henry Ford Hospital Program
Sponsor: Henry Ford Hospital
Prgm Director: Claudio D Schuger, MD
2799 W Grand Boulevard
K-2, Room E235
Detroit, MI 48202
Tel: 313 916-2417   *Fax:* 313 916-8416
Length: 1 Yr   *ACGME Approved/Offered Positions:* 2
Program ID: 154-25-31-090

Lansing

Michigan State University Program
Sponsor: Michigan State University College of Human
Medicine
Ingham Regional Medical Center
Sparrow Hospital
Prgm Director: RK Thakur, MD
138 Service Road
A205 Clinical Center
East Lansing, MI 48824
Tel: 517 353-4832   *Fax:* 517 355-2134
E-mail: thakur@msu.edu
Length: 1 Yr   *ACGME Approved/Offered Positions:* 2
Program ID: 154-25-13-118

Royal Oak

William Beaumont Hospital Program
Sponsor: William Beaumont Hospital
Prgm Director: David Haines, MD
3601 West 13 Mile Road
Royal Oak, MI 48073
Tel: 248 898-4176   *Fax:* 248 898-7239
E-mail: THaggerty@beaumont.edu
Length: 1 Yr   *ACGME Approved/Offered Positions:* 1
Program ID: 154-25-31-111
Uniformed Services Program

Minnesota

Minneapolis

University of Minnesota Program
Sponsor: University of Minnesota Medical School
University of Minnesota Medical Center, Division of
Fairview
Veterans Affairs Medical Center (Minneapolis)
Prgm Director: Scott Sakaguchi, MD
Mayo Mail Code 508
420 Delaware Street, SE
Minneapolis, MN 55455
Tel: 612 625-4401   *Fax:* 612 626-4411
E-mail: cvfellow@umn.edu
Length: 1 Yr   *ACGME Approved/Offered Positions:* 3
Program ID: 154-26-21-037

Rochester

College of Medicine, Mayo Clinic (Rochester) Program
Sponsor: College of Medicine, Mayo Clinic
Mayo Clinic (Rochester)
Saint Marys Hospital of Rochester
Prgm Director: Samuel J Asirvatham, MD
200 First Street SW
Rochester, MN 55905
Tel: 507 284-3304   *Fax:* 507 266-3594
E-mail: asirvatham.samuel@mayo.edu
Length: 1 Yr   *ACGME Approved/Offered Positions:* 4
Program ID: 154-26-31-038

Missouri

Kansas City

University of Missouri at Kansas City Program
Sponsor: University of Missouri-Kansas City School of
Medicine
St Luke's Hospital-Kansas City
Prgm Director: Brian Ramza, MD, PhD
University of Missouri-Kansas City
4401 Wornall Road/MAHI-5
Kansas City, MO 64111
Tel: 816 932-5475   *Fax:* 816 932-5613
E-mail: jwheeler@saint-lukes.org
Length: 1 Yr   *ACGME Approved/Offered Positions:* 2
Program ID: 154-28-21-039

St Louis

St Louis University School of Medicine Program
Sponsor: St Louis University School of Medicine
St Louis University Hospital
Prgm Director: Lisa Schiller, MD
3635 Vista Ave at Grand Blvd
St Louis, MO 63110
Tel: 314 577-8894   *Fax:* 314 268-5141
Length: 1 Yr   *ACGME Approved/Offered Positions:* 1
Program ID: 154-28-12-102

Washington University/B-JH/SLCH Consortium Program
Sponsor: Washington University/B-JH/SLCH Consortium
Barnes-Jewish Hospital
Prgm Director: Jane Chen, MD
660 S Euclid Avenue, Box 8086
St Louis, MO 63110
Tel: 314 454-7834   *Fax:* 314 454-8250
E-mail: janechen@im.wustl.edu
Length: 1 Yr   *ACGME Approved/Offered Positions:* 3
Program ID: 154-28-31-040

Nebraska

Omaha

University of Nebraska Medical Center College of Medicine Program
Sponsor: University of Nebraska Medical Center College
of Medicine
Nebraska Medical Center
Veterans Affairs Medical Center (Omaha)
Prgm Director: Arthur R Easley Jr, MD
982265 Nebraska Medical Center
Omaha, NE 68198
Tel: 402 559-8122   *Fax:* 402 559-8355
E-mail: aeasley@unmc.edu
Length: 1 Yr   *ACGME Approved/Offered Positions:* 1
Program ID: 154-30-11-092

New Hampshire

Lebanon

Dartmouth-Hitchcock Medical Center Program
Sponsor: Mary Hitchcock Memorial Hospital
Prgm Director: Mark L Greenberg, MD, BS
One Medical Center Drive
Lebanon, NH 03756
Tel: 603 650-5077   *Fax:* 603 650-0523
E-mail: Jan.L.Willey@hitchcock.org
Length: 1 Yr   *ACGME Approved/Offered Positions:* 2
Program ID: 154-32-21-041

New Jersey

Camden

UMDNJ-Robert Wood Johnson Medical School (Camden) Program
Sponsor: Cooper Hospital-University Medical Center
Prgm Director: Lawrence Gessman, MD
One Cooper Plaza
3rd Floor Dorrance
Camden, NJ 08103
Tel: 856 342-2619   *Fax:* 856 968-7420
E-mail: jones-jerry@cooperhealth.edu
Length: 1 Yr   *ACGME Approved/Offered Positions:* 1
Program ID: 154-33-11-096

New York

Bronx

Albert Einstein College of Medicine Program
Sponsor: Albert Einstein College of Medicine of Yeshiva
University
Montefiore Medical Center-Henry and Lucy Moses
Division
Prgm Director: John D Fisher, MD
111 East 210th Street
Bronx, NY 10467
Tel: 718 920-4292   *Fax:* 718 547-2111
Length: 1 Yr   *ACGME Approved/Offered Positions:* 2
Program ID: 154-35-21-042

Brooklyn

SUNY Health Science Center at Brooklyn Program
Sponsor: SUNY Health Science Center at Brooklyn
Brookdale University Hospital and Medical Center
University Hospital-SUNY Health Science Center at
Brooklyn
Prgm Director: John Kassotis, MD, PhD
450 Clarkson Avenue, Box 1199
Brooklyn, NY 11203
Tel: 718 270-4147   *Fax:* 718 270-4106
E-mail: john.kassotis@downstate.edu
Length: 1 Yr   *ACGME Approved/Offered Positions:* 2
Program ID: 154-35-31-043

New York

Albert Einstein College of Medicine at Beth Israel Medical Center Program
Sponsor: Beth Israel Medical Center
Prgm Director: Steven J Evans, MD
1st Avenue at 16th Street
Baird Hall, 5th Floor
New York, NY 10003
Tel: 212 844-1261   *Fax:* 212 844-1260
E-mail: cclopez@chpnet.org
Length: 1 Yr   *ACGME Approved/Offered Positions:* 1
Program ID: 154-35-21-121

Programs

Mount Sinai School of Medicine Program

Sponsor: Mount Sinai School of Medicine
Mount Sinai Medical Center
Prgm Director: Davendra Mehta, MD, PhD
Department of Electrophysiology - Box 1054
One Gustave L Levy Place
New York, NY 10029
Tel: 212 241-7272   *Fax:* 212 534-2776
E-mail: davendra.mehta@msnyuhealth.org
Length: 1 Yr   *ACGME Approved/Offered Positions:* 2
Program ID: 154-35-22-047

New York Presbyterian Hospital (Columbia Campus) Program

Sponsor: New York Presbyterian Hospital
New York Presbyterian Hospital (Columbia Campus)
Prgm Director: Hasan Garan, MD, MS
Department of Medicine, Cardiology Division
177 Fort Washington Avenue, 5-435
New York, NY 10032
Tel: 212 305-8559   *Fax:* 212 342-3591
Length: 1 Yr   *ACGME Approved/Offered Positions:* 2
Program ID: 154-35-33-050

New York Presbyterian Hospital (Cornell Campus) Program

Sponsor: New York Presbyterian Hospital
New York Presbyterian Hospital (Cornell Campus)
Prgm Director: Steven M Markowitz, MD
525 E 68th Street, Starr 4
New York, NY 10021
Tel: 212 746-2655   *Fax:* 212 746-6951
Length: 1 Yr   *ACGME Approved/Offered Positions:* 3
Program ID: 154-35-23-048

New York University School of Medicine Program

Sponsor: New York University School of Medicine
Bellevue Hospital Center
Manhattan VA Harbor Health Care System
NYU Hospitals Center
Prgm Director: Larry A Chinitz, MD
560 First Avenue
TH 576
New York, NY 10016
Tel: 212 263-5656   *Fax:* 212 263-8534
E-mail: larry.chinitz@med.nyu.edu
Length: 1 Yr   *ACGME Approved/Offered Positions:* 3
Program ID: 154-35-32-049

St Luke's-Roosevelt Hospital Center Program

Sponsor: St Luke's-Roosevelt Hospital Center
Prgm Director: Suneet Mittal, MD
1111 Amsterdam Avenue
New York, NY 10025
Tel: 212 523-2887   *Fax:* 212 523-3915
Length: 1 Yr   *ACGME Approved/Offered Positions:* 2
Program ID: 154-35-42-051

Rochester

University of Rochester Program

Sponsor: Strong Memorial Hospital of the University of Rochester
Prgm Director: James P Daubert, MD, BA
Box 679
601 Elmwood Avenue
Rochester, NY 14642
Tel: 585 273-1147   *Fax:* 585 242-9549
Length: 1 Yr   *ACGME Approved/Offered Positions:* 2
Program ID: 154-35-43-052

North Carolina

Durham

Duke University Hospital Program

Sponsor: Duke University Hospital
Veterans Affairs Medical Center (Durham)
Prgm Director: Patrick M Hranitzky, MD
Box 3174
Durham, NC 27710
Tel: 919 681-6859   *Fax:* 919 681-9842
Length: 1 Yr   *ACGME Approved/Offered Positions:* 3
Program ID: 154-36-31-054

Winston-Salem

Wake Forest University School of Medicine Program

Sponsor: Wake Forest University Baptist Medical Center
Prgm Director: David M Fitzgerald, MD
Cardiology Section
Medical Center Blvd
Winston-Salem, NC 27157
Tel: 336 716-4838   *Fax:* 336 716-7771
Length: 1 Yr   *ACGME Approved/Offered Positions:* 2
Program ID: 154-36-11-055

Ohio

Cleveland

Case Western Reserve University (MetroHealth) Program

Sponsor: MetroHealth Medical Center
Prgm Director: Kara J Quan, MD
2500 MetroHealth Drive H330
Cleveland, OH 44109
Tel: 216 778-3925   *Fax:* 216 778-3927
Length: 1 Yr   *ACGME Approved/Offered Positions:* 2
Program ID: 154-38-13-095

Cleveland Clinic Foundation Program

Sponsor: Cleveland Clinic Foundation
Prgm Director: Mina K Chung, MD*
Dept of Cardiovascular Medicine F15
9500 Euclid Avenue
Cleveland, OH 44195
Tel: 216 444-2290   *Fax:* 216 445-6156
E-mail: chungm@ccf.org
Length: 1 Yr   *ACGME Approved/Offered Positions:* 4
Program ID: 154-38-21-083

University Hospitals Case Medical Center Program

Sponsor: University Hospitals Case Medical Center
Veterans Affairs Medical Center (Cleveland)
Prgm Director: Mauricio F Hong, MD
11100 Euclid Avenue, Mailstop LKS5038
Cleveland, OH 44106
Tel: 216 844-7603   *Fax:* 216 844-8954
E-mail: mfh20@case.edu
Length: 1 Yr   *ACGME Approved/Offered Positions:* 3
Program ID: 154-38-21-056

Columbus

Ohio State University Hospital Program

Sponsor: Ohio State University Hospital
Prgm Director: Raul Weiss, MD
2nd Floor, Davis Heart & Lung Research Institute
473 W 12th Avenue, #200
Columbus, OH 43210
Tel: 614 293-4967   *Fax:* 614 293-5614
E-mail: raul.weiss@osumc.edu
Length: 1 Yr   *ACGME Approved/Offered Positions:* 2
Program ID: 154-38-31-101

Toledo

University of Toledo Program

Sponsor: University of Toledo
University Medical Center (Toledo)
Prgm Director: Mohammed Yousuf Kanjwal, MD
Health Sciences Campus
3000 Arlington Avenue, Suite 1192
Toledo, OH 43614
Tel: 419 383-3697   *Fax:* 419 383-3041
E-mail: teri.diehl@utoledo.edu
Length: 1 Yr   *ACGME Approved/Offered Positions:* 1
Program ID: 154-38-31-123

Oklahoma

Oklahoma City

University of Oklahoma Health Sciences Center Program

Sponsor: University of Oklahoma College of Medicine
OU Medical Center
Veterans Affairs Medical Center (Oklahoma City)
Prgm Director: Karen J Beckman, MD
Biomedical Sciences Building, Room 357
PO Box 26901
Oklahoma City, OK 73190
Tel: 405 271-9696   *Fax:* 405 271-7455
E-mail: karen-beckman@ouhsc.edu
Length: 1 Yr   *ACGME Approved/Offered Positions:* 3
Program ID: 154-39-21-059

Oregon

Portland

Oregon Health & Science University Program

Sponsor: Oregon Health & Science University Hospital
Veterans Affairs Medical Center (Portland)
Prgm Director: Karl Stajduhar, MD*
Division of Cardiovascular Medicine/UHN-62
3181 SW Sam Jackson Park Road
Portland, OR 97239
Tel: 503 494-8750   *Fax:* 503 494-8550
E-mail: diamonds@ohsu.edu
Length: 1 Yr   *ACGME Approved/Offered Positions:* 2
Program ID: 154-40-21-060

Pennsylvania

Danville

Geisinger Health System Program

Sponsor: Geisinger Health System
Geisinger Medical Center
Prgm Director: Pugazhendhi Vijayaraman, MD*
100 N Academy Ave
Danville, PA 17822
Tel: 570 271-6423
E-mail: tkalejta@geisinger.edu
Length: 1 Yr   *ACGME Approved/Offered Positions:* 1
Program ID: 154-41-12-112

Hershey

Penn State University/Milton S Hershey Medical Center Program

Sponsor: Milton S Hershey Medical Center
Prgm Director: Deborah L Wolbrette, MD
500 University Drive, Room H1511
PO Box 850, MC H047
Hershey, PA 17033
Tel: 717 531-3907   *Fax:* 717 531-4077
E-mail: rgage@hmc.psu.edu
Length: 1 Yr   *ACGME Approved/Offered Positions:* 2
Program ID: 154-41-21-084

Note: * indicates a newly appointed program director

Philadelphia

Drexel University College of Medicine/Hahnemann University Hospital Program

Sponsor: Drexel University College of Medicine/Hahnemann University
Abington Memorial Hospital
Hahnemann University Hospital (Tenet Health System)
Prgm Director: Steven P Kutalek, MD
245 N 15th Street
Philadelphia, PA 19102
Tel: 215 762-3457   *Fax:* 215 762-3028
E-mail: skutalek@drexelmed.edu
Length: 1 Yr   *ACGME Approved/Offered Positions:* 4
Program ID: 154-41-31-062

Temple University Hospital Program

Sponsor: Temple University Hospital
Prgm Director: Richard M Greenberg, MD
9th Floor Parkinson Pavilion
3401 N Broad Street
Philadelphia, PA 19140
Tel: 215 707-9261   *Fax:* 215 707-7718
Length: 1 Yr   *ACGME Approved/Offered Positions:* 2
Program ID: 154-41-12-064

Thomas Jefferson University Program

Sponsor: Thomas Jefferson University Hospital
Prgm Director: Behzad B Pavri, MD
925 Chestnut Street
Mezzanine Level
Philadelphia, PA 19107
Tel: 215 955-8882   *Fax:* 215 503-3976
Length: 1 Yr   *ACGME Approved/Offered Positions:* 2
Program ID: 154-41-21-088

University of Pennsylvania Program

Sponsor: University of Pennsylvania Health System
Presbyterian Medical Center (UPHS)
Veterans Affairs Medical Center (Philadelphia)
Prgm Director: Ralph J Verdino, MD
Hospital of the U of Pennsylvania
9 Founders, 3400 Spruce Street
Philadelphia, PA 19104
Tel: 215 614-1889   *Fax:* 215 615-5235
E-mail: ralph.verdino@uphs.upenn.edu
Length: 1 Yr   *ACGME Approved/Offered Positions:* 6
Program ID: 154-41-22-065

Pittsburgh

University of Pittsburgh Medical Center Medical Education Program

Sponsor: Univ of Pittsburgh Medical Center Medical Education
UPMC Presbyterian Shadyside
Prgm Director: William W Barrington, MD
Presbyterian University Hospital RM B535
200 Lothrop Street
Pittsburgh, PA 15213
Tel: 412 647-6272   *Fax:* 412 647-7979
E-mail: barringtonww@upmc.edu
Length: 1 Yr   *ACGME Approved/Offered Positions:* 2
Program ID: 154-41-22-066

Wynnewood

Lankenau Hospital Program

Sponsor: Lankenau Hospital
Prgm Director: Douglas Esberg, MD
558 Lankenau MOB East
100 Lancaster Avenue
Wynnewood, PA 19096
Tel: 610 645-2682   *Fax:* 610 896-0643
Length: 1 Yr   *ACGME Approved/Offered Positions:* 2
Program ID: 154-41-23-067

Rhode Island

Providence

Brown University Program

Sponsor: Rhode Island Hospital-Lifespan
Prgm Director: Alfred Buxton, MD
Brown University School of Medicine
2 Dudley Street, Suite 360
Providence, RI 02905
Tel: 401 444-5328   *Fax:* 401 444-4652
Length: 1 Yr   *ACGME Approved/Offered Positions:* 4
Program ID: 154-43-21-068

South Carolina

Charleston

Medical University of South Carolina Program

Sponsor: Medical University of South Carolina College of Medicine
MUSC Medical Center
Prgm Director: J Marcus Wharton, MD
25 Courtenay Drive, 7ART, Rm 7063
Charleston, SC 29425
Tel: 843 876-4807   *Fax:* 843 876-4809
Length: 1 Yr   *ACGME Approved/Offered Positions:* 3
Program ID: 154-45-31-099

Tennessee

Nashville

Vanderbilt University Program

Sponsor: Vanderbilt University Medical Center
Veterans Affairs Medical Center (Nashville)
Prgm Director: Jeffrey N Rottman, MD*
383 PRB
2220 Pierce Avenue
Nashville, TN 37232
Tel: 615 936-1720   *Fax:* 615 936-1872
Length: 1 Yr   *ACGME Approved/Offered Positions:* 3
Program ID: 154-47-21-069

Texas

Dallas

Baylor University Medical Center Program

Sponsor: Baylor University Medical Center
Prgm Director: Manish D Assar, MD*
3500 Gaston Avenue
Roberts 1st Floor, Medical Education
Dallas, TX 75246
Tel: 214 841-2030   *Fax:* 214 841-2015
E-mail: mdassar1@yahoo.com
Length: 1 Yr   *ACGME Approved/Offered Positions:* 1
Program ID: 154-48-12-100

University of Texas Southwestern Medical School Program

Sponsor: University of Texas Southwestern Medical School
Dallas County Hospital District-Parkland Memorial Hospital
Dallas VA Medical Center
University Hospitals St Paul
Prgm Director: Jose A Joglar, MD
5323 Harry Hines Boulevard
Cardiology Division, HA9.133
Dallas, TX 75390
Tel: 214 590-5055   *Fax:* 214 590-0402
Length: 1 Yr   *ACGME Approved/Offered Positions:* 2
Program ID: 154-48-21-070

Houston

Baylor College of Medicine/St Luke's Episcopal Hospital Program

Sponsor: Baylor College of Medicine
St Luke's Episcopal Hospital
Prgm Director: Ali Massumi, MD
St. Luke's Episcopal Hospital Program
6720 Bertner (MC-1-133)
Houston, TX 77030
Tel: 832 355-6676   *Fax:* 832 355-8374
E-mail: mjones@sleh.com
Length: 1 Yr   *ACGME Approved/Offered Positions:* 2
Program ID: 154-48-13-073

University of Texas at Houston Program

Sponsor: University of Texas Health Science Center at Houston
Memorial Hermann Hospital
UTHSC at Houston Physician Practices
Prgm Director: Bharat K Kantharia, MD
6431 Fannin St, MSB 1.247
Houston, TX 77030
Tel: 713 500-6590   *Fax:* 713 500-6556
Length: 1 Yr   *ACGME Approved/Offered Positions:* 2
Program ID: 154-48-21-082

Temple

Texas A&M College of Medicine-Scott and White Program

Sponsor: Scott and White Memorial Hospital
Prgm Director: Stephen Huang, MD
2401 S 31st Street
Temple, TX 76508
Tel: 254 724-9184   *Fax:* 254 724-5561
E-mail: mwheeler@swmail.sw.org
Length: 1 Yr   *ACGME Approved/Offered Positions:* 1
Program ID: 154-48-21-113

Utah

Salt Lake City

University of Utah Program

Sponsor: University of Utah Medical Center
Veterans Affairs Medical Center (Salt Lake City)
Prgm Director: Mohamed H Hamdan, MD
30 North 1900 East
Division of Cardiology, 4A100
Salt Lake City, UT 84132
Tel: 801 581-7715   *Fax:* 801 581-7735
E-mail: katie.goodyear@hsc.utah.edu
Length: 1 Yr   *ACGME Approved/Offered Positions:* 2
Program ID: 154-49-21-075

Vermont

Burlington

University of Vermont Program

Sponsor: Fletcher Allen Health Care
Prgm Director: Mark A Capeless, MD
111 Colchester Avenue
Burlington, VT 05401
Tel: 802 847-2005   *Fax:* 802 847-4016
Length: 1 Yr   *ACGME Approved/Offered Positions:* 2
Program ID: 154-50-12-098

Programs

Virginia

Charlottesville

University of Virginia Program
Sponsor: University of Virginia Medical Center
Prgm Director: J Michael Mangrum, MD
Department of Internal Medicine
PO Box 800158
Charlottesville, VA 22908
Tel: 434 924-9001   *Fax:* 434 924-1692
E-mail: cardiofellows@virginia.edu
Length: 1 Yr   *ACGME Approved/Offered Positions:* 2
Program ID: 154-51-21-076

Richmond

Virginia Commonwealth University Health System Program
Sponsor: Virginia Commonwealth University Health
   System
Hunter Holmes McGuire VA Medical Center (Richmond)
Medical College of Virginia Hospitals
Prgm Director: Kenneth A Ellenbogen, MD
PO Box 980053
Richmond, VA 23298
Tel: 804 828-7565   *Fax:* 804 828-6082
E-mail: kellenbogen@mcvh-vcu.edu
Length: 1 Yr   *ACGME Approved/Offered Positions:* 2
Program ID: 154-51-31-077

Washington

Seattle

University of Washington Program
Sponsor: University of Washington School of Medicine
University of Washington Medical Center
Prgm Director: Jeanne E Poole, MD
Division of Cardiology-Arrhythmia Service, Box 356422
1959 NE Pacific Street
Seattle, WA 98195
Tel: 206 685-4176   *Fax:* 206 616-1022
Length: 1 Yr   *ACGME Approved/Offered Positions:* 2
Program ID: 154-54-21-078

Wisconsin

Madison

University of Wisconsin Program
Sponsor: University of Wisconsin Hospital and Clinics
William S Middleton Veterans Hospital
Prgm Director: Douglas Kopp, MD
600 Highland Avenue
H6/349 CSC, MC 3248
Madison, WI 53792
Tel: 608 265-4188   *Fax:* 608 263-0405
E-mail: dek@medicine.wisc.edu
Length: 1 Yr   *ACGME Approved/Offered Positions:* 1
Program ID: 154-56-21-117

Milwaukee

Aurora Health Care Program
Sponsor: Aurora Health Care
Aurora Sinai Medical Center
St Luke's Medical Center
Prgm Director: Masood Akhtar, MD
Aurora Sinai Medical Center
945 N 12th St, PO Box 342
Milwaukee, WI 53201
Tel: 414 219-7190   *Fax:* 414 219-7676
E-mail: jruffin@hrtcare.com
Length: 1 Yr   *ACGME Approved/Offered Positions:* 3
Program ID: 154-56-21-079

Clinical Neurophysiology (Neurology)

Alabama

Birmingham

University of Alabama Medical Center Program
Sponsor: University of Alabama Hospital
Veterans Affairs Medical Center (Birmingham)
Prgm Director: Shin J Oh, MD
619 South 19th Street
Birmingham, AL 35249
Tel: 205 934-2120   *Fax:* 205 975-6758
E-mail: shinjoh@uab.edu
Length: 1 Yr   *ACGME Approved/Offered Positions:* 4
Program ID: 187-01-21-038

Arizona

Phoenix

College of Medicine, Mayo Clinic (Arizona) Program
Sponsor: College of Medicine, Mayo Clinic
Mayo Clinic Hospital
Mayo Clinic (Arizona)
Prgm Director: Joseph Drazkowski, MD
5777 East Mayo Boulevard
Phoenix, AZ 85059
Tel: 480 342-2581   *Fax:* 480 342-2544
E-mail: glickler.peggy@mayo.edu
Length: 1 Yr   *ACGME Approved/Offered Positions:* 2
Program ID: 187-03-13-114

St Joseph's Hospital and Medical Center Program
Sponsor: St Joseph's Hospital and Medical Center
Prgm Director: David M Treiman, MD
Barrow Neurological Institute
350 West Thomas Road
Phoenix, AZ 85013
Tel: 602 406-6921   *Fax:* 602 798-0467
E-mail: ann.chowdhury@chw.edu
Length: 1 Yr   *ACGME Approved/Offered Positions:* 2
Program ID: 187-03-21-094

California

Loma Linda

Loma Linda University Program
Sponsor: Loma Linda University Medical Center
Prgm Director: Gordon W Peterson, MD
11175 Campus Street
Coleman Pavilion, Suite 11108
Loma Linda, CA 92354
Tel: 909 558-4907   *Fax:* 909 558-0207
E-mail: GPeterson@llu.edu
Length: 1 Yr   *ACGME Approved/Offered Positions:* 1
Program ID: 187-05-21-040

Note: * indicates a newly appointed program director

Los Angeles

UCLA Medical Center Program

Sponsor: UCLA David Geffen School of Medicine/UCLA
Medical Center
Cedars-Sinai Medical Center
Santa Monica-UCLA Medical Center
UCLA Medical Center
VA Greater Los Angeles Healthcare System
Prgm Director: Marc R Nuwer, MD, PhD
710 Westwood Plaza
Reed Building 1-194
Los Angeles, CA 90095
Tel: 310 206-3093   *Fax:* 310 267-1157
Length: 1 Yr   *ACGME Approved/Offered Positions:* 6
Program ID: 187-05-21-004

University of Southern California/ LAC+USC Medical Center Program

Sponsor: University of Southern California/LAC+USC
Medical Center
LAC+USC Medical Center
USC University Hospital
Prgm Director: Said R Beydoun, MD
1450 San Pablo St
Suite 2500, Neurophysiology Dept
Los Angeles, CA 90033
Tel: 323 442-8852   *Fax:* 323 442-8934
Length: 1 Yr   *ACGME Approved/Offered Positions:* 2
Program ID: 187-05-21-059

Orange

University of California (Irvine) Program

Sponsor: University of California (Irvine) Medical
Center
Prgm Director: Jack J Lin, MD
UCIMC Building 22C, Neurodiagnostic Laboratory
101 The City Drive South
Orange, CA 92868
Tel: 714 456-6203   *Fax:* 714 456-8805
E-mail: linjj@uci.edu
Length: 1 Yr   *ACGME Approved/Offered Positions:* 1
Program ID: 187-05-31-108

Sacramento

University of California (Davis) Health System Program

Sponsor: University of California (Davis) Health System
University of California (Davis) Medical Center
VA Northern California Health Care System
Prgm Director: Masud Seyal, MD
2315 Stockton Boulevard, Room 5308
Sacramento, CA 95817
Tel: 916 734-3514   *Fax:* 916 452-2739
Length: 1 Yr   *ACGME Approved/Offered Positions:* 2
Program ID: 187-05-31-005

San Diego

University of California (San Diego) Program

Sponsor: University of California (San Diego) Medical
Center
Prgm Director: Vincente Iragui, MD, PhD
9300 Campus Point Drive (7740)
La Jolla, CA 92037
Tel: 858 657-6080   *Fax:* 858 657-6987
E-mail: epicenter@ucsd.edu
Length: 1 Yr   *ACGME Approved/Offered Positions:* 2
Program ID: 187-05-13-110

San Francisco

University of California (San Francisco) Program

Sponsor: University of California (San Francisco) School
of Medicine
UCSF and Mount Zion Medical Centers
Veterans Affairs Medical Center (San Francisco)
Prgm Director: Catherine Lomen-Hoerth, MD, PhD
505 Parnassus Avenue
San Francisco, CA 94143
Tel: 415 514-0490   *Fax:* 415 514-0491
E-mail: catherine.lomen-hoerth@ucsf.edu
Length: 1 Yr   *ACGME Approved/Offered Positions:* 4
Program ID: 187-05-11-006

Stanford

Stanford University Program

Sponsor: Stanford Hospital and Clinics
California Pacific Medical Center
Lucile Salter Packard Children's Hospital at Stanford
Prgm Director: Leslie Dorfman, MD
Dept of Neurology, A343
300 Pasteur Drive
Stanford, CA 94305
Tel: 650 723-6888   *Fax:* 650 725-5095
Length: 1 Yr   *ACGME Approved/Offered Positions:* 5
Program ID: 187-05-21-022

District of Columbia

Washington

George Washington University Program

Sponsor: George Washington University School of
Medicine
Prgm Director: Perry K Richardson, MD
2150 Pennsylvania Avenue, NW
Suite 7-404
Washington, DC 20037
Tel: 202 741-2719   *Fax:* 202 741-2721
E-mail: prichardson@mfa.gwu.edu
Length: 1 Yr   *ACGME Approved/Offered Positions:* 1
Program ID: 187-10-12-113

Georgetown University Hospital Program

Sponsor: Georgetown University Hospital
Prgm Director: Gholam K Motamedi, MD
3800 Reservoir Road NW
PHC 7
Washington, DC 20007
Tel: 202 444-4565   *Fax:* 202 444-2661
E-mail: motamedi@georgetown.edu
Length: 1 Yr   *ACGME Approved/Offered Positions:* 2
Program ID: 187-10-21-111

Florida

Gainesville

University of Florida Program

Sponsor: University of Florida College of Medicine
North Florida/South Georgia Veterans Health System
Shands Hospital at the University of Florida
Prgm Director: Edward Valenstein, MD
Box 100236, UFHSC
Gainesville, FL 32610
Tel: 352 273-5550   *Fax:* 352 273-5575
Length: 1 Yr   *ACGME Approved/Offered Positions:* 2
Program ID: 187-11-21-025

Jacksonville

College of Medicine, Mayo Clinic (Jacksonville) Program

Sponsor: College of Medicine, Mayo Clinic
Mayo Clinic (Jacksonville)
Prgm Director: Devon I Rubin, MD
4500 San Pablo Road
Jacksonville, FL 32224
Tel: 904 953-2903   *Fax:* 904 953-0757
E-mail: rubin.devon@mayo.edu
Length: 1 Yr   *ACGME Approved/Offered Positions:* 1
Program ID: 187-11-21-103

Weston

Miami Children's Hospital/Cleveland Clinic Foundation Program

Sponsor: Miami Children's Hospital
Cleveland Clinic Florida
Prgm Director: Michael Duchowny, MD
3100 SW 62nd Avenue
Miami, FL 33155
Tel: 305 662-8342   *Fax:* 305 669-6472
Length: 1 Yr   *ACGME Approved/Offered Positions:* 2
Program ID: 187-11-13-098

Georgia

Atlanta

Emory University Program

Sponsor: Emory University School of Medicine
Emory University Hospital
Grady Health System
Wesley Woods Geriatric Hospital
Prgm Director: Jaffar Khan, MD
101 Woodruff Memorial Circle
WMRB 6009 c/o Charlotte Whitehead
Atlanta, GA 30322
Tel: 404 727-5004   *Fax:* 404 727-3157
E-mail: neuro_res@emory.edu
Length: 1 Yr   *ACGME Approved/Offered Positions:* 8
Program ID: 187-12-21-080

Augusta

Medical College of Georgia Program

Sponsor: Medical College of Georgia
Prgm Director: Michael H Rivner, MD
1120 15th Street, EMG Lab
Augusta, GA 30912
Tel: 706 721-2681   *Fax:* 706 721-8701
E-mail: mrivner@mail.mcg.edu
Length: 1 Yr   *ACGME Approved/Offered Positions:* 3
Program ID: 187-12-21-070

Illinois

Chicago

McGaw Medical Center of Northwestern University Program

Sponsor: McGaw Medical Center of Northwestern
University
Northwestern Memorial Hospital
Prgm Director: Stephan Schuele, MD, MPH
710 N Lake Shore Drive
Suite 1424
Chicago, IL 60611
Tel: 312 926-1673
Length: 1 Yr   *ACGME Approved/Offered Positions:* 3
Program ID: 187-16-21-041

Programs

Rush University Medical Center Program
Sponsor: Rush University Medical Center
John H Stroger Hospital of Cook County
Prgm Director: Madhu Soni, MD*
1725 W Harrison St
Suite 1106
Chicago, IL 60612
Tel: 312 942-4500   *Fax:* 312 942-2380
E-mail: madhu_soni@rush.edu
Length: 1 Yr   *ACGME Approved/Offered Positions:* 4
Program ID: 187-16-21-026

University of Chicago Program
Sponsor: University of Chicago Medical Center
Prgm Director: John S Ebersole, MD
5841 South Maryland Avenue, MC 2030
Chicago, IL 60637
Tel: 773 834-4702   *Fax:* 773 702-9076
E-mail: mscofiel@neurology.bsd.uchicago.edu
Length: 1 Yr   *ACGME Approved/Offered Positions:* 4
Program ID: 187-16-21-086

University of Illinois College of Medicine at Chicago Program
Sponsor: University of Illinois College of Medicine at Chicago
University of Illinois Hospital and Clinics
Prgm Director: Matthew N Meriggioli, MD
912 South Wood Street, M/C 796
Chicago, IL 60612
Tel: 312 355-1528   *Fax:* 312 996-4169
Length: 1 Yr   *ACGME Approved/Offered Positions:* 2
Program ID: 187-16-21-001

Maywood

Loyola University Program
Sponsor: Loyola University Medical Center
Prgm Director: Jorge Asconape, MD
Department of Neurology
2160 S First Avenue
Maywood, IL 60153
Tel: 708 216-3407   *Fax:* 708 216-5617
E-mail: jasconape@lumc.edu
Length: 1 Yr   *ACGME Approved/Offered Positions:* 2
Program ID: 187-16-21-051

Indiana

Indianapolis

Indiana University School of Medicine Program
Sponsor: Indiana University School of Medicine
Clarian Indiana University Hospital
Clarian Riley Hospital for Children
Prgm Director: John C Kincaid, MD
Department of Neurology, UH 1711
550 North University Boulevard
Indianapolis, IN 46202
Tel: 317 274-0311   *Fax:* 317 274-6973
E-mail: ahelton@iupui.edu
Length: 1 Yr   *ACGME Approved/Offered Positions:* 3
Program ID: 187-17-21-003

Note: * indicates a newly appointed program director

Iowa

Iowa City

University of Iowa Hospitals and Clinics Program
Sponsor: University of Iowa Hospitals and Clinics
Prgm Director: Mark E Dyken, MD
200 Hawkins Drive
Iowa City, IA 52242
Tel: 319 356-3059   *Fax:* 319 356-4505
E-mail: EricDyken@aol.com
Length: 1 Yr   *ACGME Approved/Offered Positions:* 1
Program ID: 187-18-21-054

Kansas

Kansas City

University of Kansas School of Medicine Program
Sponsor: University of Kansas School of Medicine
University of Kansas Hospital
Veterans Affairs Medical Center (Kansas City)
Prgm Director: Mazen Dimachkie, MD
Department of Neurology
3599 Rainbow Boulevard
Kansas City, KS 66160
Tel: 913 588-6970   *Fax:* 913 588-0673
Length: 1 Yr   *ACGME Approved/Offered Positions:* 3
Program ID: 187-19-13-102

Louisiana

New Orleans

Louisiana State University Program
Sponsor: Louisiana State University School of Medicine
Medical Center of Louisiana at New Orleans
Prgm Director: Piotr W Olejniczak, MD
450A S Claiborne
New Orleans, LA 70112
Tel: 504 568-4090   *Fax:* 504 568-7130
Length: 1 Yr   *ACGME Approved/Offered Positions:* 4
Program ID: 187-21-21-078

Maryland

Baltimore

Johns Hopkins University Program
Sponsor: Johns Hopkins University School of Medicine
Johns Hopkins Hospital
Prgm Director: Ronald P Lesser, MD
Department of Neurology
600 North Wolfe Street
Baltimore, MD 21287
Tel: 410 955-1270   *Fax:* 410 955-0751
Length: 1 Yr   *ACGME Approved/Offered Positions:* 5
Program ID: 187-23-21-027

University of Maryland Program
Sponsor: University of Maryland Medical System
Prgm Director: Allan Krumholz, MD
22 South Greene Street
Department of Neurology Room N4W46
Baltimore, MD 21201
Tel: 410 328-6267   *Fax:* 410 328-0697
E-mail: akrumholz@som.umaryland.edu
Length: 1 Yr   *ACGME Approved/Offered Positions:* 4
Program ID: 187-23-21-016

Bethesda

National Capital Consortium (Bethesda) Program
Sponsor: National Capital Consortium
Children's National Medical Center
Clinical Center at the National Institutes of Health
Walter Reed Army Medical Center
Prgm Director: Susumu Sato, MD
EEG Section, Office of Clinical Director, NINDS
10 Center Drive, Bldg 10 CRC, Rm 7-5680, MSC-1404
Bethesda, MD 20892
Tel: 301 496-5121   *Fax:* 301 402-8796
Length: 1 Yr   *ACGME Approved/Offered Positions:* 2
Program ID: 187-10-31-028
Uniformed Services Program

National Capital Consortium Program
Sponsor: National Capital Consortium
Walter Reed Army Medical Center
Prgm Director: Kristen C Barner, MD
Department of Neurology
4301 Jones Bridge Road
Bethesda, MD 20814
Tel: 202 782-4969
E-mail: kristen.barner@na.amedd.army.mil
Length: 1 Yr   *ACGME Approved/Offered Positions:* 2
Program ID: 187-10-31-024
Uniformed Services Program

Massachusetts

Boston

Brigham and Women's Hospital/Children's Hospital/Harvard Medical School Program
Sponsor: Brigham and Women's Hospital
Prgm Director: Barbara Dworetzky, MD
Children's Hospital
75 Francis Street
Boston, MA 02115
Tel: 617 732-7547   *Fax:* 617 730-2885
Length: 1 Yr   *ACGME Approved/Offered Positions:* 3
Program ID: 187-24-21-101

Children's Hospital/Beth Israel Deaconess Medical Center/Harvard Medical School Program
Sponsor: Children's Hospital
Beth Israel Deaconess Medical Center
Prgm Director: Elizabeth Raynor, MD*
330 Brookline Avenue, TCC-810
Boston, MA 02215
Tel: 617 667-8130   *Fax:* 617 667-8747
Length: 1 Yr   *ACGME Approved/Offered Positions:* 8
Program ID: 187-24-21-071

Massachusetts General Hospital Program
Sponsor: Massachusetts General Hospital
Prgm Director: Andrew J Cole, MD
Epilepsy Service
WAC 739 L Fruit Street
Boston, MA 02114
Tel: 617 726-3311   *Fax:* 617 726-9250
Length: 1 Yr   *ACGME Approved/Offered Positions:* 5
Program ID: 187-24-21-117

Tufts Medical Center Program
Sponsor: Tufts Medical Center
Lahey Clinic
Prgm Director: James A Russell, DO, MS
Department of Neurology
41 Mall Road
Burlington, MA 01805
Tel: 781 744-7273   *Fax:* 781 744-3049
E-mail: Karen.G.Moloney@lahey.org
Length: 1 Yr   *ACGME Approved/Offered Positions:* 1
Program ID: 187-24-21-096

Worcester

University of Massachusetts Program

Sponsor: University of Massachusetts Medical School
UMass Memorial Health Care (University Campus)
UMASS Memorial Medical Group Sleep Disorders Center
Prgm Director: Jaishree Narayanan, MD, PhD*
55 Lake Avenue North
Worcester, MA 01655
Tel: 508 856-2527   *Fax:* 508 856-6778
Length: 1 Yr   *ACGME Approved/Offered Positions:* 1
Program ID: 187-24-21-009

Michigan

Ann Arbor

University of Michigan Program

Sponsor: University of Michigan Hospitals and Health
   Centers
Prgm Director: Linda M Selwa, MD
1500 E Medical Center Drive
1914 Taubman SPC 5316
Ann Arbor, MI 48109
Tel: 734 936-9030   *Fax:* 734 936-5520
E-mail: aaltizer@umich.edu
Length: 1 Yr   *ACGME Approved/Offered Positions:* 7
Program ID: 187-25-21-010

Detroit

Henry Ford Hospital Program

Sponsor: Henry Ford Hospital
Prgm Director: Brien J Smith, MD
2799 West Grand Boulevard
K-11
Detroit, MI 48202
Tel: 313 916-2451   *Fax:* 313 916-5083
E-mail: smith@neuro.hfh.edu
Length: 1 Yr   *ACGME Approved/Offered Positions:* 5
Program ID: 187-25-21-057

Wayne State University/Detroit Medical Center Program

Sponsor: Wayne State University/Detroit Medical Center
Children's Hospital of Michigan
Prgm Director: Aashit Shah, MD
Neurology, 8D-UHC
4201 St Antoine
Detroit, MI 48201
Tel: 313 577-1244   *Fax:* 313 745-4216
Length: 1 Yr   *ACGME Approved/Offered Positions:* 6
Program ID: 187-25-21-042

Minnesota

Minneapolis

University of Minnesota Program

Sponsor: University of Minnesota Medical School
Hennepin County Medical Center
United Hospital
University of Minnesota Medical Center, Division of
   Fairview
Veterans Affairs Medical Center (Minneapolis)
Prgm Director: John W Tulloch, MD
Department of Neurology
420 Delaware Street SE, MMC 295
Minneapolis, MN 55455
Tel: 612 626-6519   *Fax:* 612 625-7950
E-mail: tullo001@umn.edu
Length: 1 Yr   *ACGME Approved/Offered Positions:* 5
Program ID: 187-26-21-030

Rochester

College of Medicine, Mayo Clinic (Rochester) Program

Sponsor: College of Medicine, Mayo Clinic
Mayo Clinic (Rochester)
Saint Marys Hospital of Rochester
Prgm Director: Eric J Sorenson, MD, MS
200 First Street, SW
Rochester, MN 55905
Tel: 507 538-1037   *Fax:* 507 266-4752
Length: 1 Yr   *ACGME Approved/Offered Positions:* 6
Program ID: 187-26-21-011

Mississippi

Jackson

University of Mississippi Medical Center Program

Sponsor: University of Mississippi School of Medicine
University Hospitals and Clinics
Prgm Director: Mecheri Sundaram, MD
Neurology, EEG/EMG
2500 North State Street
Jackson, MS 39216
Tel: 601 984-4760   *Fax:* 601 984-4895
Length: 1 Yr   *ACGME Approved/Offered Positions:* 3
Program ID: 187-27-21-043

Missouri

St Louis

St Louis University School of Medicine Program

Sponsor: St Louis University School of Medicine
St Louis University Hospital
Veterans Affairs Medical Center (St Louis)
Prgm Director: Ghazala Hayat, MD
1438 S Grand Blvd
1st Floor
St Louis, MO 63104
Tel: 314 977-4853   *Fax:* 314 977-4876
Length: 1 Yr   *ACGME Approved/Offered Positions:* 3
Program ID: 187-28-21-031

Washington University/B-JH/SLCH Consortium Program

Sponsor: Washington University/B-JH/SLCH Consortium
Barnes-Jewish Hospital
Prgm Director: Lawrence Eisenman, MD, PhD
660 S Euclid Avenue, Box 8111
St Louis, MO 63110
Tel: 314 362-3888   *Fax:* 314 362-2826
Length: 1 Yr   *ACGME Approved/Offered Positions:* 7
Program ID: 187-28-21-072

New Hampshire

Lebanon

Dartmouth-Hitchcock Medical Center Program

Sponsor: Mary Hitchcock Memorial Hospital
Prgm Director: Jeffrey A Cohen, MD
One Medical Center Drive
Lebanon, NH 03756
Tel: 603 650-5458   *Fax:* 603 650-6233
Length: 1 Yr   *ACGME Approved/Offered Positions:* 2
Program ID: 187-32-31-112

New Jersey

Edison

Seton Hall University School of Health and Medical Sciences Program

Sponsor: Seton Hall University School of Health and
   Medical Sciences
JFK Medical Center
Prgm Director: Sudhansu Chokroverty, MD
65 James Street
PO Box 3059
Edison, NJ 08818
Tel: 732 321-7950   *Fax:* 732 632-1584
Length: 1 Yr   *ACGME Approved/Offered Positions:* 1
Program ID: 187-33-21-106

New Mexico

Albuquerque

University of New Mexico Program

Sponsor: University of New Mexico School of Medicine
University of New Mexico Hospital
Prgm Director: Madeleine M Grigg-Damberger, MD
MSC10 5620
1 University of New Mexico
Albuquerque, NM 87131
Tel: 505 272-3342   *Fax:* 505 272-6692
Length: 1 Yr   *ACGME Approved/Offered Positions:* 1
Program ID: 187-34-21-061

New York

Albany

Albany Medical Center Program

Sponsor: Albany Medical Center
Prgm Director: Timothy Lynch, MD
Department of Neurology
MC 70
Albany, NY 12208
Tel: 518 262-5226   *Fax:* 518 262-6261
Length: 1 Yr   *ACGME Approved/Offered Positions:* 2
Program ID: 187-35-13-118

Bronx

Albert Einstein College of Medicine Program

Sponsor: Albert Einstein College of Medicine of Yeshiva
   University
Montefiore Medical Center-Henry and Lucy Moses
   Division
Prgm Director: Alan D Legatt, MD, PhD
Dept of Neurology, Kennedy - 311
1410 Pelham Parkway South
Bronx, NY 10461
Tel: 718 920-6530   *Fax:* 718 920-8509
E-mail: swilliam@aecom.yu.edu
Length: 1 Yr   *ACGME Approved/Offered Positions:* 5
Program ID: 187-35-21-012

Brooklyn

SUNY Health Science Center at Brooklyn Program

Sponsor: SUNY Health Science Center at Brooklyn
Kings County Hospital Center
University Hospital-SUNY Health Science Center at
   Brooklyn
Prgm Director: Geetha Chari, MD
450 Clarkson Avenue
Box 1213
Brooklyn, NY 11203
Tel: 718 270-2042   *Fax:* 718 270-3748
Length: 1 Yr   *ACGME Approved/Offered Positions:* 3
Program ID: 187-35-21-062

Programs

Buffalo

University at Buffalo Program

Sponsor: University at Buffalo School of Medicine
Kaleida Health System (Millard Fillmore Hospital)
Kaleida Health System (Women and Children's Hospital of Buffalo)
Veterans Affairs Western New York Hospital
Prgm Director: Edward J Fine, MD
The Jacobs Neurological Institute
100 High Street
Buffalo, NY 14203
Tel: 716 859-3496   *Fax:* 716 859-7573
Length: 1 Yr   *ACGME Approved/Offered Positions:* 3
Program ID: 187-35-21-032

Great Neck

NSLIJHS-Albert Einstein College of Medicine at Long Island Jewish Medical Center Program

Sponsor: North Shore-Long Island Jewish Health System
Long Island Jewish Medical Center
North Shore University Hospital
Prgm Director: Suryanarayan Murthy Vishnubhakat, MD
300 Community Drive
9th Floor Tower Pavilion
Manhasset, NY 11030
Tel: 516 562-4300   *Fax:* 516 562-2635
E-mail: svishnub@nshs.edu
Length: 1 Yr   *ACGME Approved/Offered Positions:* 2
Program ID: 187-35-31-119

New York

Mount Sinai School of Medicine Program

Sponsor: Mount Sinai School of Medicine
Mount Sinai Medical Center
Prgm Director: David M Simpson, MD
One Gustave L Levy Place
Box 1052
New York, NY 10029
Tel: 212 241-8748   *Fax:* 212 987-3301
E-mail: david.simpson@mssm.edu
Length: 1 Yr   *ACGME Approved/Offered Positions:* 1
Program ID: 187-35-21-092

New York Presbyterian Hospital (Columbia Campus) Program

Sponsor: New York Presbyterian Hospital
New York Presbyterian Hospital (Columbia Campus)
Prgm Director: Ronald G Emerson, MD
Neurological Institute
710 West 168th Street
New York, NY 10032
Tel: 212 305-2121   *Fax:* 212 305-1450
Length: 1 Yr   *ACGME Approved/Offered Positions:* 6
Program ID: 187-35-31-033

New York Presbyterian Hospital (Cornell Campus) Program

Sponsor: New York Presbyterian Hospital
Memorial Sloan-Kettering Cancer Center
New York Presbyterian Hospital (Cornell Campus)
Prgm Director: Douglas R Labar, MD, PhD*
525 East 68th Street
New York, NY 10065
Tel: 212 746-2359   *Fax:* 212 746-8845
E-mail: drlabar@med.cornell.edu
Length: 1 Yr   *ACGME Approved/Offered Positions:* 4
Program ID: 187-35-11-034

New York University School of Medicine Program

Sponsor: New York University School of Medicine
Lenox Hill Hospital
NYU Hospital for Joint Diseases
Prgm Director: Siddhartha S Nadkarni, MD
225 East 34th Street
First Floor, Comprehensive Epilepsy Center
New York, NY 10016
Tel: 212 263-8872   *Fax:* 212 263-8342
E-mail: nadkas01@med.nyu.edu
Length: 1 Yr   *ACGME Approved/Offered Positions:* 6
Program ID: 187-35-31-063

Rochester

University of Rochester Program

Sponsor: Strong Memorial Hospital of the University of Rochester
Prgm Director: Eric L Logigian, MD
601 Elmwood Avenue, Box 673
Rochester, NY 14642
Tel: 585 275-4568   *Fax:* 585 273-1254
E-mail: gail_alexander@urmc.rochester.edu
Length: 1 Yr   *ACGME Approved/Offered Positions:* 3
Program ID: 187-35-21-045

Stony Brook

SUNY at Stony Brook Program

Sponsor: University Hospital - SUNY at Stony Brook
Veterans Affairs Medical Center (Northport)
Prgm Director: Mary R Andriola, MD
Health Sciences Center, T12-020
Stony Brook, NY 11794
Tel: 631 444-1450   *Fax:* 631 632-2451
Length: 1 Yr   *ACGME Approved/Offered Positions:* 2
Program ID: 187-35-11-064

Syracuse

SUNY Upstate Medical University Program

Sponsor: SUNY Upstate Medical University
Veterans Affairs Medical Center (Syracuse)
Prgm Director: Jeremy M Shefner, MD, PhD
750 East Adams Street
Syracuse, NY 13210
Tel: 315 464-5302   *Fax:* 315 464-5303
E-mail: shefnerj@upstate.edu
Length: 1 Yr   *ACGME Approved/Offered Positions:* 3
Program ID: 187-35-21-085

North Carolina

Durham

Duke University Hospital Program

Sponsor: Duke University Hospital
Prgm Director: Aatif M Husain, MD
DUMC 3678 - 202 Bell Building
Durham, NC 27710
Tel: 919 684-8485   *Fax:* 919 684-8955
Length: 1 Yr   *ACGME Approved/Offered Positions:* 5
Program ID: 187-36-21-088

Winston-Salem

Wake Forest University School of Medicine Program

Sponsor: Wake Forest University Baptist Medical Center
Prgm Director: William L Bell, MD
Department of Neurology
Medical Center Boulevard
Winston-Salem, NC 27157
Tel: 336 716-7548   *Fax:* 336 716-7794
E-mail: wbell@wfubmc.edu
Length: 1 Yr   *ACGME Approved/Offered Positions:* 4
Program ID: 187-36-13-104

Ohio

Cincinnati

Cincinnati Children's Hospital Medical Center/University of Cincinnati College of Medicine Program

Sponsor: Cincinnati Children's Hospital Medical Center
University Hospital Inc
Prgm Director: Katherine Holland, MD, PhD
3333 Burnet Avenue, ML 2015
Department of Neurology
Cincinnati, OH 45229
Tel: 513 636-4222   *Fax:* 513 636-1888
E-mail: katherine.holland@cchmc.org
Length: 1 Yr   *ACGME Approved/Offered Positions:* 2
Program ID: 187-38-31-115

University Hospital/University of Cincinnati College of Medicine Program

Sponsor: University Hospital Inc
Prgm Director: David M Ficker, MD
260 Stetson Street, Suite 2300
PO Box 670525 ML0525
Cincinnati, OH 45267
Tel: 513 558-5475   *Fax:* 513 558-0412
Length: 1 Yr   *ACGME Approved/Offered Positions:* 2
Program ID: 187-38-21-083

Cleveland

Cleveland Clinic Foundation Program

Sponsor: Cleveland Clinic Foundation
Prgm Director: Dileep Nair, MD
9500 Euclid Avenue
Epilepsy Center/S51
Cleveland, OH 44195
Tel: 216 444-2560   *Fax:* 216 445-4378
E-mail: naird@ccf.org
Length: 1 Yr   *ACGME Approved/Offered Positions:* 6
Program ID: 187-38-31-047

University Hospitals Case Medical Center Program

Sponsor: University Hospitals Case Medical Center
Prgm Director: Monisha A Goyal, MD
11100 Euclid Avenue
Cleveland, OH 44106
Tel: 216 844-3691   *Fax:* 216 844-8966
Length: 1 Yr   *ACGME Approved/Offered Positions:* 4
Program ID: 187-38-21-046

Columbus

Ohio State University Hospital Program

Sponsor: Ohio State University Hospital
Nationwide Children's Hospital
Prgm Director: Miriam L Freimer, MD
425 Means Hall
1654 Upham Drive
Columbus, OH 43210
Tel: 614 293-7715   *Fax:* 614 293-4688
Length: 1 Yr   *ACGME Approved/Offered Positions:* 3
Program ID: 187-38-12-105

Pennsylvania

Hershey

Penn State University/Milton S Hershey Medical Center Program

Sponsor: Milton S Hershey Medical Center
Prgm Director: Kevin Scott, MD*
30 Hope Drive
Department of Neurolgy, EC037
Hershey, PA 17033
Tel: 717 531-1377   *Fax:* 717 531-0384
Length: 1 Yr   *ACGME Approved/Offered Positions:* 1
Program ID: 187-41-21-035

Note: * indicates a newly appointed program director

Philadelphia

Drexel University College of Medicine/Hahnemann University Hospital Program
Sponsor: Drexel University College of Medicine/Hahnemann University
Crozer-Chester Medical Center
Hahnemann University Hospital (Tenet Health System)
Prgm Director: Anahita F Deboo, MD
Broad and Vine Street, MS 308
Philadelphia, PA 19102
Tel: 215 762-7037   *Fax:* 215 762-8613
Length: 1 Yr   *ACGME Approved/Offered Positions:* 3
Program ID: 187-41-21-048

Temple University Hospital Program
Sponsor: Temple University Hospital
Prgm Director: Mercedes P Jacobson, MD
Suite C525
3401 North Broad Street
Philadelphia, PA 19140
Tel: 215 707-8910   *Fax:* 215 707-8235
E-mail: neurology@tuhs.temple.edu
Length: 1 Yr   *ACGME Approved/Offered Positions:* 2
Program ID: 187-41-31-049

Thomas Jefferson University Program
Sponsor: Thomas Jefferson University Hospital
Prgm Director: Michael R Sperling, MD
900 Walnut Street
Suite 200
Philadelphia, PA 19107
Tel: 215 955-1222   *Fax:* 215 955-0606
Length: 1 Yr   *ACGME Approved/Offered Positions:* 3
Program ID: 187-41-31-036

University of Pennsylvania Program
Sponsor: University of Pennsylvania Health System
Prgm Director: Shawn J Bird, MD
3400 Spruce Street, 3 Gates
Philadelphia, PA 19104
Tel: 215 662-6551   *Fax:* 215 349-5579
Length: 1 Yr   *ACGME Approved/Offered Positions:* 3
Program ID: 187-41-21-087

Pittsburgh

Allegheny General Hospital Program
Sponsor: Allegheny General Hospital
Prgm Director: George Small, MD
420 East North Avenue
Suite 206 East Wing Office Building
Pittsburgh, PA 15212
Tel: 412 359-8845   *Fax:* 412 359-8878
E-mail: mcardamo@wpahs.org
Length: 1 Yr   *ACGME Approved/Offered Positions:* 1
Program ID: 187-41-22-109

University of Pittsburgh Medical Center Medical Education Program
Sponsor: Univ of Pittsburgh Medical Center Medical Education
UPMC Presbyterian Shadyside
Prgm Director: David Lacomis, MD
UPMC Presbyterian
200 Lothrop Street, F 878
Pittsburgh, PA 15213
Tel: 412 648-2022   *Fax:* 412 624-3661
Length: 1 Yr   *ACGME Approved/Offered Positions:* 3
Program ID: 187-41-21-065

Rhode Island

Providence

Brown University Program
Sponsor: Rhode Island Hospital-Lifespan
Prgm Director: James M Gilchrist, MD
593 Eddy Street - APC 689
Providence, RI 02903
Tel: 401 444-8761   *Fax:* 401 444-5929
Length: 1 Yr   *ACGME Approved/Offered Positions:* 3
Program ID: 187-43-21-015

South Carolina

Charleston

Medical University of South Carolina Program
Sponsor: Medical University of South Carolina College of Medicine
MUSC Medical Center
Prgm Director: Paul B Pritchard, III, MD
96 Jonathan Lucas Street 307
PO Box 250606
Charleston, SC 29425
Tel: 843 792-3222   *Fax:* 843 792-8626
Length: 1 Yr   *ACGME Approved/Offered Positions:* 1
Program ID: 187-45-12-116

Tennessee

Memphis

University of Tennessee Program
Sponsor: University of Tennessee College of Medicine
LeBonheur Children's Medical Center
Methodist Healthcare - Memphis Hospitals
Regional Medical Center at Memphis
Veterans Affairs Medical Center (Memphis)
Prgm Director: Tulio E Bertorini, MD
855 Monroe Avenue, Room 415
Memphis, TN 38163
Tel: 901 448-6661   *Fax:* 901 448-7440
E-mail: tbertorini@aol.com
Length: 1 Yr   *ACGME Approved/Offered Positions:* 2
Program ID: 187-47-21-084

Nashville

Vanderbilt University Program
Sponsor: Vanderbilt University Medical Center
Prgm Director: Bassel W Abou-Khalil, MD
1161 21st Avenue South
A-1106 MCN
Nashville, TN 37232
Tel: 615 936-1567   *Fax:* 615 936-2675
Length: 1 Yr   *ACGME Approved/Offered Positions:* 8
Program ID: 187-47-21-073

Texas

Dallas

University of Texas Southwestern Medical School Program
Sponsor: University of Texas Southwestern Medical School
Children's Medical Center of Dallas
Dallas County Hospital District-Parkland Memorial Hospital
Prgm Director: Jaya R Trivedi, MD
5323 Harry Hines Boulevard
Dallas, TX 75390
Tel: 214 648-9518   *Fax:* 214 648-9311
E-mail: jaya.trivedi@utsouthwestern.edu
Length: 1 Yr   *ACGME Approved/Offered Positions:* 4
Program ID: 187-48-21-074

Houston

Baylor College of Medicine Program
Sponsor: Baylor College of Medicine
Methodist Hospital (Houston)
Michael E DeBakey VA Medical Center - Houston
St Luke's Episcopal Hospital
Texas Children's Hospital
Prgm Director: Richard A Hrachovy, MD*
One Baylor Plaza
Houston, TX 77030
Tel: 713 798-0980   *Fax:* 713 798-0984
Length: 1 Yr   *ACGME Approved/Offered Positions:* 4
Program ID: 187-48-21-037

University of Texas at Houston Program
Sponsor: University of Texas Health Science Center at Houston
Lyndon B Johnson General Hospital
Memorial Hermann Hospital
UTHSC at Houston Physician Practices
Prgm Director: Parveen Athar, MD
Department of Neurology 7.044/MSB
6431 Fannin Street
Houston, TX 77030
Tel: 713 500-7131   *Fax:* 713 500-7019
Length: 1 Yr   *ACGME Approved/Offered Positions:* 4
Program ID: 187-48-21-066

San Antonio

University of Texas Health Science Center at San Antonio Program
Sponsor: University of Texas School of Medicine at San Antonio
Audie L Murphy Memorial Veterans Hospital (San Antonio)
Brooke Army Medical Center
University Health System
Wilford Hall Medical Center (AETC)
Prgm Director: Jose E Cavazos, MD, PhD
7703 Floyd Curl Drive MSC 7883
San Antonio, TX 78229
Tel: 210 617-5161   *Fax:* 210 567-4659
Length: 1 Yr   *ACGME Approved/Offered Positions:* 2
Program ID: 187-48-31-077

Utah

Salt Lake City

University of Utah Program

Sponsor: University of Utah Medical Center
Prgm Director: Mark B Bromberg, MD, PhD
Department of Neurology, CNC
175 North Medical Drive East
Salt Lake City, UT 84132
Tel: 801 581-5405   *Fax:* 801 581-4192
E-mail: neuro.residency@hsc.utah.edu
Length: 1 Yr   *ACGME Approved/Offered Positions:* 2
Program ID: 187-49-21-075

Vermont

Burlington

University of Vermont Program

Sponsor: Fletcher Allen Health Care
Prgm Director: Keith J Nagle, MD
Clinical Neurophysiology Laboratory
111 Colchester Avenue, Patrick 5
Burlington, VT 05401
Tel: 802 847-2788   *Fax:* 802 847-5679
Length: 1 Yr   *ACGME Approved/Offered Positions:* 1
Program ID: 187-50-21-081

Virginia

Charlottesville

University of Virginia Program

Sponsor: University of Virginia Medical Center
Prgm Director: Ted M Burns, MD
PO Box 800394
Charlottesville, VA 22908
Tel: 434 982-0170   *Fax:* 434 982-1850
Length: 1 Yr   *ACGME Approved/Offered Positions:* 4
Program ID: 187-51-21-050

Richmond

Virginia Commonwealth University Health System Program

Sponsor: Virginia Commonwealth University Health
  System
Hunter Holmes McGuire VA Medical Center (Richmond)
Medical College of Virginia Hospitals
Prgm Director: Lawrence D Morton, MD
PO Box 980599
Richmond, VA 23298
Tel: 804 828-9940   *Fax:* 804 828-6373
E-mail: neurores@vcu.edu
Length: 1 Yr   *ACGME Approved/Offered Positions:* 4
Program ID: 187-51-31-053

Washington

Seattle

University of Washington Program

Sponsor: University of Washington School of Medicine
Harborview Medical Center
University of Washington Medical Center
Prgm Director: John Miller, MD, PhD
1959 Pacific Avenue, Box 356115
Seattle, WA 98195
Tel: 206 731-3576
Length: 1 Yr   *ACGME Approved/Offered Positions:* 2
Program ID: 187-54-13-100

West Virginia

Morgantown

West Virginia University Program

Sponsor: West Virginia University School of Medicine
West Virginia University Hospitals
Prgm Director: Laurie Gutmann, MD
Department of Neurology
PO Box 9180
Morgantown, WV 26506
Tel: 304 293-3527   *Fax:* 304 293-3352
Length: 1 Yr   *ACGME Approved/Offered Positions:* 2
Program ID: 187-55-21-002

Wisconsin

Madison

University of Wisconsin Program

Sponsor: University of Wisconsin Hospital and Clinics
William S Middleton Veterans Hospital
Prgm Director: Paul A Rutecki, MD*
H6/574-5132 Clinical Science Center
600 Highland Avenue
Madison, WI 53792
Tel: 608 261-1470   *Fax:* 608 263-0412
E-mail: rutecki@neurology.wisc.edu
Length: 1 Yr   *ACGME Approved/Offered Positions:* 2
Program ID: 187-56-21-091

Milwaukee

Medical College of Wisconsin Affiliated Hospitals Program

Sponsor: Medical College of Wisconsin Affiliated
  Hospitals, Inc
Children's Hospital of Wisconsin
Clement J Zablocki Veterans Affairs Medical Center
Froedtert Memorial Lutheran Hospital
Prgm Director: Paul E Barkhaus, MD
9200 W Wisconsin Avenue
Milwaukee, WI 53226
Tel: 414 805-5254   *Fax:* 414 259-0469
E-mail: pbarkhaus@mcw.edu
Length: 1 Yr   *ACGME Approved/Offered Positions:* 3
Program ID: 187-56-12-107

Colon and Rectal Surgery

California

Los Angeles

Cedars-Sinai Medical Center Program

Sponsor: Cedars-Sinai Medical Center
Prgm Director: Phillip Fleshner, MD
8737 Beverly Boulevard, Suite 101
Los Angeles, CA 90048
Tel: 310 289-9224   *Fax:* 310 289-8995
E-mail: PFleshner@aol.com
Length: 1 Yr   *ACGME Approved/Offered Positions:* 1
Program ID: 060-05-31-052

University of Southern California/ LAC+USC Medical Center Program

Sponsor: University of Southern California/LAC+USC
  Medical Center
Glendale Memorial Hospital and Health Center
Kenneth Norris Jr Cancer Hospital and Research
  Institute
LAC+USC Medical Center
USC University Hospital
Prgm Director: Glenn T Ault, MD, MEd
1441 Eastlake Avenue, Suite 7418
Los Angeles, CA 90033
Tel: 323 865-3690   *Fax:* 323 865-3671
E-mail: ault@usc.edu
Length: 1 Yr   *ACGME Approved/Offered Positions:* 3
Program ID: 060-05-21-042

San Francisco

University of California (San Francisco) Program

Sponsor: University of California (San Francisco) School
  of Medicine
San Francisco General Hospital Medical Center
UCSF and Mount Zion Medical Centers
Prgm Director: Julio Garcia-Aguilar, MD, PhD
2330 Post Street
Suite 260
San Francisco, CA 94115
Tel: 415 885-3625   *Fax:* 415 885-3886
E-mail: EducationOffice@ucsfmedctr.org
Length: 1 Yr   *ACGME Approved/Offered Positions:* 1
Program ID: 060-05-13-061

Connecticut

Hartford

St Francis Hospital and Medical Center Program

Sponsor: St Francis Hospital and Medical Center
Prgm Director: William P Pennoyer, MD*
Graduate Medical Education Attn: Piloo Mistry
114 Woodland Street
Hartford, CT 06105
Tel: 860 242-8591   *Fax:* 860 242-2511
Length: 1 Yr   *ACGME Approved/Offered Positions:* 1
Program ID: 060-08-21-032

Note: * indicates a newly appointed program director

District of Columbia

Washington

Washington Hospital Center Program
Sponsor: Washington Hospital Center
Prgm Director: Thomas J Stahl, MD
106 Irving Street, NW
Suite 2100 North
Washington, DC 20010
Tel: 202 877-8484   *Fax:* 202 877-8483
E-mail: rhoda.montgomery@medstar.net
Length: 1 Yr   *ACGME Approved/Offered Positions:* 1
Program ID: 060-10-21-045

Florida

Miami

Jackson Memorial Hospital/Jackson Health System Program
Sponsor: Jackson Memorial Hospital/Jackson Health System
Prgm Director: Floriano Marchetti, MD*
Univ of Miami/Sylvester Comprehensive Cancer Ctr (310-T)
1475 NW 12th Avenue, Room 3550
Miami, FL 33136
Tel: 305 243-3527   *Fax:* 305 243-7498
Length: 1 Yr   *ACGME Approved/Offered Positions:* 1
Program ID: 060-11-13-049

Orlando

Orlando Health Program
Sponsor: Orlando Health
Florida Hospital Medical Center
Orlando Regional Medical Center
Prgm Director: Andrea Ferrara, MD
c/o Nancy Joiner, C&R Coordinator
110 W Underwood St #A
Orlando, FL 32806
Tel: 407 422-3790   *Fax:* 407 841-5058
E-mail: NJoiner@CRCOrlando.com
Length: 1 Yr   *ACGME Approved/Offered Positions:* 3
Program ID: 060-11-21-037

Weston

Cleveland Clinic (Florida) Program
Sponsor: Cleveland Clinic Florida
Physicians Regional Medical Center (Naples)
Prgm Director: Eric G Weiss, MD
Department of Colorectal Surgery
2950 Cleveland Clinic Boulevard
Weston, FL 33331
Tel: 954 659-5240   *Fax:* 954 659-5757
E-mail: diazw@ccf.org
Length: 1 Yr   *ACGME Approved/Offered Positions:* 5
Program ID: 060-11-13-051

Georgia

Atlanta

Georgia Colon and Rectal Surgical Clinic Program
Sponsor: Georgia Colon & Rectal Surgical Clinic
Dekalb Medical Center
Gwinnett Medical Center
Northside Hospital
Saint Joseph's Hospital of Atlanta
Prgm Director: David N Armstrong, MD
5555 Peachtree Dunwoody Road
Suite 206
Atlanta, GA 30342
Tel: 770 822-0921   *Fax:* 770 995-5742
E-mail: DArmstrong@gcrsa.com
Length: 1 Yr   *ACGME Approved/Offered Positions:* 2
Program ID: 060-12-31-047

Illinois

Chicago

John H Stroger Hospital of Cook County Program
Sponsor: John H Stroger Hospital of Cook County
Advocate Lutheran General Hospital
University of Illinois Hospital and Clinics
Prgm Director: Amir L Bastawrous, MD*
1900 W Polk Street
Suite 402
Chicago, IL 60612
Tel: 312 864-5276   *Fax:* 312 864-9642
E-mail: bastawro@uic.edu
Length: 1 Yr   *ACGME Approved/Offered Positions:* 3
Program ID: 060-16-12-001

University of Chicago Program
Sponsor: University of Chicago Medical Center
McGaw Medical Center of Northwestern University
Prgm Director: Alessandro Fichera, MD
5841 South Maryland Avenue, MC 5095
Chicago, IL 60637
Tel: 773 702-6142   *Fax:* 773 834-1995
E-mail: afichera@surgery.bsd.uchicago.edu
Length: 1 Yr   *ACGME Approved/Offered Positions:* 1
Program ID: 060-16-31-066

Springfield

Southern Illinois University Program
Sponsor: Southern Illinois University School of Medicine
Memorial Medical Center
Springfield Clinic Outpatient Facility
St John's Hospital
Prgm Director: Jan Rakinic, MD
PO Box 19638
Springfield, IL 62794
Tel: 217 545-7230   *Fax:* 217 545-7762
E-mail: jrakinic@siumed.edu
Length: 1 Yr   *ACGME Approved/Offered Positions:* 1
Program ID: 060-16-21-068

Indiana

Indianapolis

Indiana University School of Medicine Program
Sponsor: Indiana University School of Medicine
St Francis Hospital - Beech Grove
St Francis Hospital - Indianapolis
St Francis Hospital - Mooresville
Prgm Director: Olaf B Johansen, MD*
1215 Hadley Road, Suite 201
Mooresville, IN 46158
Tel: 317 834-9618   *Fax:* 317 834-9467
E-mail: cindy.c@kendrickcenter.com
Length: 1 Yr   *ACGME Approved/Offered Positions:* 1
Program ID: 060-17-13-065

Kentucky

Louisville

University of Louisville Program
Sponsor: University of Louisville School of Medicine
Jewish Hospital
Norton Hospital
University of Louisville Hospital
Veterans Affairs Medical Center (Louisville)
Prgm Director: Susan Galandiuk, MD
Department of Surgery
550 South Jackson Street
Louisville, KY 40202
Tel: 502 852-4568   *Fax:* 502 852-8915
E-mail: julie.watkins@louisville.edu
Length: 1 Yr   *ACGME Approved/Offered Positions:* 1
Program ID: 060-20-12-048

Louisiana

New Orleans

Ochsner Clinic Foundation Program
Sponsor: Ochsner Clinic Foundation
Prgm Director: Charles B Whitlow, MD
1514 Jefferson Highway
New Orleans, LA 70121
Tel: 504 842-4060   *Fax:* 504 842-3964
E-mail: kcaccioppi@ochsner.org
Length: 1 Yr   *ACGME Approved/Offered Positions:* 2
Program ID: 060-21-12-003

Shreveport

Louisiana State University (Shreveport) Program
Sponsor: LSU Health Sciences Center-University Hospital
Christus Schumpert Health System
Willis-Knighton Medical Center
Prgm Director: Philip A Cole, MD
1501 Kings Highway
PO Box 33932
Shreveport, LA 71130
Tel: 318 424-8373   *Fax:* 318 424-6477
E-mail: offman@colonandrectalassociates.com
Length: 1 Yr   *ACGME Approved/Offered Positions:* 2
Program ID: 060-21-21-004

Programs

Maryland

Baltimore

Greater Baltimore Medical Center Program

Sponsor: Greater Baltimore Medical Center
Prgm Director: George Y Apostolides, MD
6535 N Charles Street, Suite 445
Towson, MD 21204
Tel: 443 849-6910   *Fax:* 443 849-6945
E-mail: gapostol@gbmc.org
Length: 1 Yr   *ACGME Approved/Offered Positions:* 1
Program ID: 060-23-12-005

Massachusetts

Burlington

Lahey Clinic Program

Sponsor: Lahey Clinic
Prgm Director: Thomas Read, MD*
Dept of Colon and Rectal Surgery
41 Mall Road
Burlington, MA 01805
Tel: 781 744-8971   *Fax:* 781 744-2945
E-mail: thomas.read@lahey.org
Length: 1 Yr   *ACGME Approved/Offered Positions:* 2
Program ID: 060-24-12-007

Michigan

Detroit

Henry Ford Hospital Program

Sponsor: Henry Ford Hospital
Prgm Director: Eric J Szilagy, MD
2799 West Grand Boulevard
Detroit, MI 48202
Tel: 313 916-2498   *Fax:* 313 916-4032
Length: 1 Yr   *ACGME Approved/Offered Positions:* 1
Program ID: 060-25-31-043

Grand Rapids

Grand Rapids Medical Education and Research Center/Michigan State University Program

Sponsor: Grand Rapids Medical Education and Research
  Center
Saint Mary's Health Care (Grand Rapids)
Spectrum Health-Blodgett Hospital
Spectrum Health-Butterworth Hospital
Prgm Director: Martin A Luchtefeld, MD
1000 Monroe Ave NW
Grand Rapids, MI 49503
Tel: 616 726-8508
Length: 1 Yr   *ACGME Approved/Offered Positions:* 2
Program ID: 060-25-12-009

Royal Oak

William Beaumont Hospital Program

Sponsor: William Beaumont Hospital
Prgm Director: Donald C Barkel, MD
3601 West 13 Mile Road
Royal Oak, MI 48073
Tel: 248 551-8235   *Fax:* 248 551-8880
Length: 1 Yr   *ACGME Approved/Offered Positions:* 1
Program ID: 060-25-12-010

Minnesota

Minneapolis

University of Minnesota Program

Sponsor: University of Minnesota Medical School
Abbott-Northwestern Hospital/Allina Health System
North Memorial Health Care
United Hospital
University of Minnesota Medical Center, Division of
  Fairview
Veterans Affairs Medical Center (Minneapolis)
Prgm Director: Judith L Trudel, MD
Dept of Colon and Rectal Surgery
1055 Westgate Drive #190
St Paul, MN 55114
Tel: 651 312-1500   *Fax:* 651 312-1595
E-mail: jltrudel@hotmail.com
Length: 1 Yr   *ACGME Approved/Offered Positions:* 5
Program ID: 060-26-21-011

Rochester

College of Medicine, Mayo Clinic (Rochester) Program

Sponsor: College of Medicine, Mayo Clinic
Mayo Clinic (Rochester)
Rochester Methodist Hospital
Saint Marys Hospital of Rochester
Prgm Director: Eric J Dozois, MD
Division of Colon and Rectal Surgery
200 First Street, SW
Rochester, MN 55905
Tel: 507 266-1149   *Fax:* 507 284-1794
E-mail: williams.rebecca@mayo.edu
Length: 1 Yr   *ACGME Approved/Offered Positions:* 3
Program ID: 060-26-21-012

Missouri

St Louis

Washington University/B-JH/SLCH Consortium Program

Sponsor: Washington University/B-JH/SLCH Consortium
Barnes-Jewish Hospital
Barnes-Jewish West County Hospital
Prgm Director: Matthew G Mutch, MD
Section of Colon and Rectal Surgery
660 S Euclid Ave, Campus Box 8109
St Louis, MO 63110
Tel: 314 454-7204   *Fax:* 314 454-5249
E-mail: mutchm@wustl.edu
Length: 1 Yr   *ACGME Approved/Offered Positions:* 3
Program ID: 060-28-21-025

Nebraska

Omaha

Creighton University Program

Sponsor: Creighton University School of Medicine
Prgm Director: Alan G Thorson, MD
9850 Nicholas Street, Suite 100
Omaha, NE 68114
Tel: 402 343-1122   *Fax:* 402 343-1177
E-mail: crspecialists@msn.com
Length: 1 Yr   *ACGME Approved/Offered Positions:* 1
Program ID: 060-30-21-035

New Jersey

New Brunswick

UMDNJ-Robert Wood Johnson Medical School Program

Sponsor: UMDNJ-Robert Wood Johnson Medical School
JFK Medical Center
Overlook Hospital
Prgm Director: Bertram T Chinn, MD
3900 Park Avenue
Edison, NJ 08820
Tel: 732 494-6640   *Fax:* 732 549-8204
Length: 1 Yr   *ACGME Approved/Offered Positions:* 3
Program ID: 060-33-12-013

New York

Buffalo

University at Buffalo Program

Sponsor: University at Buffalo School of Medicine
Kaleida Health System (Buffalo General Hospital)
Prgm Director: Amarjit Singh, MD
100 High Street
Suite B-451
Buffalo, NY 14203
Tel: 716 857-8606   *Fax:* 716 857-8735
E-mail: wrscales@buffalo.edu
Length: 1 Yr   *ACGME Approved/Offered Positions:* 1
Program ID: 060-35-12-014

Great Neck

NSLIJHS Program

Sponsor: North Shore-Long Island Jewish Health System
Long Island Jewish Medical Center
North Shore University Hospital
Prgm Director: John A Procaccino, MD
900 Northern Boulevard, Suite 100
Great Neck, NY 11021
Tel: 516 730-2100   *Fax:* 516 730-2121
E-mail: jprocacc@nshs.edu
Length: 1 Yr   *ACGME Approved/Offered Positions:* 1
Program ID: 060-35-12-053

New York

Mount Sinai School of Medicine Program

Sponsor: Mount Sinai School of Medicine
Mount Sinai Medical Center
Prgm Director: Randolph Steinhagen, MD
Department of Surgery
1 Gustave Levy Place, Box 1259
New York, NY 10029
Tel: 212 241-9289   *Fax:* 212 534-2654
E-mail: juliet.arthur-ince@mountsinai.org
Length: 1 Yr   *ACGME Approved/Offered Positions:* 1
Program ID: 060-35-21-046

New York Presbyterian Hospital (Cornell Campus) Program

Sponsor: New York Presbyterian Hospital
New York Presbyterian Hospital (Columbia Campus)
New York Presbyterian Hospital (Cornell Campus)
Prgm Director: Jeffrey W Milsom, MD
Dept of Surgery, 525 East 68th Street
P-720A, Box 172
New York, NY 10065
Tel: 212 746-6591   *Fax:* 212 746-8802
E-mail: mat9052@med.cornell.edu
Length: 1 Yr   *ACGME Approved/Offered Positions:* 2
Program ID: 060-35-21-050

Note: * indicates a newly appointed program director

St Luke's-Roosevelt Hospital Center Program
Sponsor: St Luke's-Roosevelt Hospital Center
St Luke's-Roosevelt Hospital Center-Roosevelt Division
Prgm Director: Mitchell Bernstein, MD*
Department of Surgery
1000 10th Avenue, 2nd Floor
New York, NY 10019
Tel: 212 523-8417   *Fax:* 212 523-8186
Length: 1 Yr   *ACGME Approved/Offered Positions:* 1
Program ID: 060-35-21-034

Stony Brook

SUNY Stony Brook University Hospital & Medical Center/Winthrop University Hospital Program
Sponsor: University Hospital - SUNY at Stony Brook
Winthrop-University Hospital
Prgm Director: Marvin L Corman, MD
HSC T 18-060
Stony Brook, NY 11794
Tel: 631 444-3431   *Fax:* 631 444-6348
E-mail: marvin.corman@stonybrook.edu
Length: 1 Yr   *ACGME Approved/Offered Positions:* 1
Program ID: 060-35-31-062

Ohio

Cleveland

Cleveland Clinic Foundation Program
Sponsor: Cleveland Clinic Foundation
Prgm Director: Jon D Vogel, MD
9500 Euclid Avenue, Desk A-30
Cleveland, OH 44195
Tel: 216 445-4631   *Fax:* 216 445-1079
Length: 1 Yr   *ACGME Approved/Offered Positions:* 4
Program ID: 060-38-12-016

Columbus

Grant Medical Center (OhioHealth) Program
Sponsor: Grant Medical Center (OhioHealth)
Mount Carmel
Ohio State University Hospital
Prgm Director: Pedro S Aguilar, MD
Medical Education Dept - Colon and Rectal Surgery
285 E State Street, Suite 670
Columbus, OH 43215
Tel: 614 566-9699   *Fax:* 614 566-8073
Length: 1 Yr   *ACGME Approved/Offered Positions:* 2
Program ID: 060-38-12-017

Pennsylvania

Allentown

Lehigh Valley Hospital Network/Pennsylvania State University Program
Sponsor: Lehigh Valley Hospital Network
Prgm Director: Robert J Sinnott, DO
Department of Surgery
Cedar Crest & I-78, PO Box 689
Allentown, PA 18105
Tel: 610 402-8966   *Fax:* 610 402-1667
E-mail: robert_j.sinnott@lvh.com
Length: 1 Yr   *ACGME Approved/Offered Positions:* 2
Program ID: 060-41-21-029

Erie

St Vincent Health Center Program
Sponsor: St Vincent Health Center
Hamot Medical Center
Prgm Director: John C Reilly, MD
Dept of Colon and Rectal Surgery
232 West 25th Street
Erie, PA 16544
Tel: 814 452-5100   *Fax:* 814 452-5097
E-mail: Racsurg@aol.com
Length: 1 Yr   *ACGME Approved/Offered Positions:* 2
Program ID: 060-41-12-019

Hershey

Penn State University/Milton S Hershey Medical Center Program
Sponsor: Milton S Hershey Medical Center
Prgm Director: Lisa S Poritz, MD
500 University Drive
H137
Hershey, PA 17033
Tel: 717 531-5164   *Fax:* 717 531-0646
E-mail: lporitz@psu.edu
Length: 1 Yr   *ACGME Approved/Offered Positions:* 1
Program ID: 060-41-12-063

Philadelphia

Thomas Jefferson University Program
Sponsor: Thomas Jefferson University Hospital
Prgm Director: Gerald A Isenberg, MD
Division of Colon and Rectal Surgery
1100 Walnut Street, Suite 702
Philadelphia, PA 19107
Tel: 215 955-5877   *Fax:* 215 955-2404
Length: 1 Yr   *ACGME Approved/Offered Positions:* 1
Program ID: 060-41-21-031

University of Pennsylvania Program
Sponsor: University of Pennsylvania Health System
Pennsylvania Hospital (UPHS)
Prgm Director: David J Maron, MD, MBA*
301 S 8th Street
Suite 4D
Philadelphia, PA 19106
Tel: 215 829-5047   *Fax:* 215 829-5350
Length: 1 Yr   *ACGME Approved/Offered Positions:* 1
Program ID: 060-41-33-054

Rhode Island

Pawtucket

Rhode Island Colorectal Clinic Program
Sponsor: Rhode Island Foundation for Colon and Rectal Diseases
Miriam Hospital-Lifespan
Roger Williams Medical Center
Prgm Director: Jorge A Lagares-Garcia, MD
334 East Avenue
Pawtucket, RI 02860
Tel: 401 725-4888   *Fax:* 401 725-3336
E-mail: jlagares@lifespan.org
Length: 1 Yr   *ACGME Approved/Offered Positions:* 1
Program ID: 060-43-13-054

Providence

Brown University Program
Sponsor: Rhode Island Hospital-Lifespan
Women and Infants Hospital of Rhode Island
Prgm Director: Thomas E Cataldo, MD
2 Dudley Street, Suite 370
Providence, RI 02905
Tel: 401 454-4773   *Fax:* 401 868-2330
E-mail: TCataldo@usasurg.org
Length: 1 Yr   *ACGME Approved/Offered Positions:* 1
Program ID: 060-43-12-058

Texas

Dallas

Baylor University Medical Center Program
Sponsor: Baylor University Medical Center
Prgm Director: Warren E Lichliter, MD
Dept of Colon and Rectal Surgery
3500 Gaston Avenue
Dallas, TX 75246
Tel: 214 820-4543   *Fax:* 214 820-4538
E-mail: peggypa@baylorhealth.edu
Length: 1 Yr   *ACGME Approved/Offered Positions:* 2
Program ID: 060-48-21-021

Texas Health Presbyterian Dallas Program
Sponsor: Texas Health Presbyterian Dallas
Dallas County Hospital District-Parkland Memorial Hospital
Prgm Director: J Marcus Downs, MD
8200 Walnut Hill Lane
Dallas, TX 75231
Tel: 214 363-6123   *Fax:* 214 750-1512
Length: 1 Yr   *ACGME Approved/Offered Positions:* 1
Program ID: 060-48-21-022

Houston

University of Texas at Houston Program
Sponsor: University of Texas Health Science Center at Houston
Houston Northwest Medical Center
Memorial Hermann Northwest Hospital
Methodist Hospital (Houston)
Prgm Director: Michael J Snyder, MD
6550 Fannin St
Ste 2307
Houston, TX 77030
Tel: 713 790-9250   *Fax:* 713 790-9251
E-mail: tlynchard@crchouston.com
Length: 1 Yr   *ACGME Approved/Offered Positions:* 4
Program ID: 060-48-21-023

San Antonio

Christus Santa Rosa Health Care Program
Sponsor: Christus Santa Rosa Health Care Corporation
Baptist Memorial Healthcare System
Methodist Healthcare
Prgm Director: Jaime L Mayoral, MD
333 North Santa Rosa Street
San Antonio, TX 78207
Tel: 210 212-4114   *Fax:* 210 212-4012
Length: 1 Yr   *ACGME Approved/Offered Positions:* 1
Program ID: 060-48-13-057

Utah

Salt Lake City

St Mark's Health Care Foundation Program
Sponsor: St Mark's Health Care Foundation
Intermountain Medical Center
LDS Hospital
St Mark's Hospital
Prgm Director: John A Griffin, MD*
1250 East 3900 South
Suite 260
Salt Lake City, UT 84124
Tel: 801 265-9139   *Fax:* 801 265-9478
E-mail: jgriffin@centralutahclinic.com
Length: 1 Yr   *ACGME Approved/Offered Positions:* 1
Program ID: 060-49-12-060

Washington

Seattle

Northwest Colon and Rectal Clinic Program

Sponsor: Northwest Colon and Rectal Clinic, PS
Northwest Hospital
Swedish Medical Center
Prgm Director: Richard P Billingham, MD
1101 Madison Street, Suite 500
Seattle, WA 98104
Tel: 206 386-6600   *Fax:* 206 386-2452
E-mail: rbham@u.washington.edu
Length: 1 Yr   *ACGME Approved/Offered Positions:* 1
Program ID: 060-54-21-040

Congenital Cardiac Surgery (Thoracic Surgery)

California

Los Angeles

University of Southern California/Children's Hospital Los Angeles Program

Sponsor: Childrens Hospital Los Angeles
Prgm Director: Cynthia S Herrington, MD*
4650 Sunset Boulevard
Mailbox 66
Los Angeles, CA 90027
Tel: 323 361-4218   *Fax:* 323 361-3668
E-mail: cherrington@chla.usc.edu
Length: 1 Yr   *ACGME Approved/Offered Positions:* 1
Program ID: 466-05-12-001

Colorado

Aurora

University of Colorado Denver Program

Sponsor: University of Colorado Denver School of
  Medicine
Children's Hospital (The)
Prgm Director: David N Campbell, MD
Health Sciences Center
12631 E 17th Ave, MS C310, Room 6602
Aurora, CO 80045
Tel: 720 777-6624   *Fax:* 720 777-7271
Length: 1 Yr   *ACGME Approved/Offered Positions:* 1
Program ID: 466-07-21-006

Georgia

Atlanta

Emory University Program

Sponsor: Emory University School of Medicine
Children's Healthcare of Atlanta at Egleston
Emory University Hospital
Prgm Director: Brian Kogon, MD
1405 Clifton Road, NE
Atlanta, GA 30322
Tel: 404 785-6330   *Fax:* 404 785-6266
Length: 1 Yr   *ACGME Approved/Offered Positions:* 1
Program ID: 466-12-31-008

Illinois

Chicago

McGaw Medical Center of Northwestern University/Children's Memorial Hospital Program

Sponsor: McGaw Medical Center of Northwestern
  University
Children's Memorial Hospital
Prgm Director: Carl Backer, MD*
2300 Children's Plaza, M/C 22
Chicago, IL 60614
Tel: 773 880-4378   *Fax:* 773 880-3054
Length: 1 Yr   *ACGME Approved/Offered Positions:* 1
Program ID: 466-16-12-009

Michigan

Ann Arbor

University of Michigan Program

Sponsor: University of Michigan Hospitals and Health
  Centers
Prgm Director: Richard G Ohye, MD
5144 CVC/SPC 5864
1500 East Medical Center Drive
Ann Arbor, MI 48109
Tel: 734 936-4978   *Fax:* 734 763-7353
E-mail: janiced@med.umich.edu
Length: 1 Yr   *ACGME Approved/Offered Positions:* 1
Program ID: 466-25-12-005

Ohio

Columbus

Nationwide Children's Hospital/Ohio State University Program

Sponsor: Nationwide Children's Hospital
Prgm Director: Mark E Galantowicz, MD
700 Children's Drive
Columbus, OH 43205
Tel: 614 722-3103   *Fax:* 614 722-3111
E-mail: mark.galantowicz@nationwidechildrens.org
Length: 1 Yr   *ACGME Approved/Offered Positions:* 1
Program ID: 466-38-31-004

Pennsylvania

Philadelphia

University of Pennsylvania/Children's Hospital of Philadelphia Program

Sponsor: Children's Hospital of Philadelphia
Prgm Director: Thomas L Spray, MD
8527 Main Building
34th Street and Civic Center Boulevard
Philadelphia, PA 19104
Tel: 215 590-2708   *Fax:* 215 590-2715
Length: 1 Yr   *ACGME Approved/Offered Positions:* 1
Program ID: 466-41-21-002

Texas

Houston

Texas Heart Institute/Baylor College of Medicine Program

Sponsor: Baylor College of Medicine
St Luke's Episcopal Hospital
Texas Children's Hospital
Prgm Director: Charles D Fraser, Jr, MD
6621 Fannin St, MC WT 19345H
Houston, TX 77030
Tel: 832 826-1929   *Fax:* 832 825-1905
Length: 1 Yr   *ACGME Approved/Offered Positions:* 1
Program ID: 466-48-13-007

Note: * indicates a newly appointed program director

Washington

Seattle

University of Washington Program
Sponsor: University of Washington School of Medicine
Seattle Children's Hospital
Prgm Director: Lester C Permut, MD
4800 Sand Point Way, NE
Seattle, WA 98105
Tel: 206 987-5607   *Fax:* 206 987-3839
E-mail: lester.permut@seattlechildrens.org
Length: 1 Yr   *ACGME Approved/Offered Positions:* 1
Program ID: 466-54-13-003

Craniofacial Surgery (Plastic Surgery)

Indiana

Indianapolis

Indiana University School of Medicine Program
Sponsor: Indiana University School of Medicine
Clarian Indiana University Hospital
Clarian Riley Hospital for Children
William N Wishard Memorial Hospital
Prgm Director: Robert J Havlik, MD
702 Barnhill Drive
Room 3538
Indianapolis, IN 46202
Tel: 317 274-2430   *Fax:* 317 274-7262
E-mail: pseverns@iupui.edu
Length: 1 Yr   *ACGME Approved/Offered Positions:* 1
Program ID: 361-17-22-005

Maryland

Baltimore

Johns Hopkins University/University of Maryland Program
Sponsor: Johns Hopkins University School of Medicine
Johns Hopkins Hospital
University of Maryland Medical System
Prgm Director: Eduardo Rodriguez, MD, DDS
601 N Caroline Street
McElderry Bldg, 8th Floor, Plastic Surgery
Baltimore, MD 21287
Tel: 410 328-3058   *Fax:* 410 328-8862
E-mail: edrodrig@bellsouth.net
Length: 1 Yr   *ACGME Approved/Offered Positions:* 1
Program ID: 361-23-21-001

Texas

Dallas

World Craniofacial Foundation Program
Sponsor: World Craniofacial Foundation
Prgm Director: DAVID G GENECOV, MD*
7777 Forest Lane, Suite C-717
Dallas, TX 75230
Tel: 972 566-6555   *Fax:* 972 566-6017
Length: 1 Yr   *ACGME Approved/Offered Positions:* 2
Program ID: 361-48-21-002

Wisconsin

Milwaukee

Medical College of Wisconsin Affiliated Hospitals Program
Sponsor: Medical College of Wisconsin Affiliated
    Hospitals, Inc
Children's Hospital of Wisconsin
Prgm Director: Arlen D Denny, MD
9000 W Wisconsin Avenue
Milwaukee, WI 53226
Tel: 414 266-2825   *Fax:* 414 266-2957
E-mail: adenny@chw.org
Length: 1 Yr   *ACGME Approved/Offered Positions:* 1
Program ID: 361-56-21-004

Critical Care Medicine (Anesthesiology)

Alabama

Birmingham

University of Alabama Medical Center Program
Sponsor: University of Alabama Hospital
Prgm Director: Mali Mathru, MD
619 S 19th Street, JT 845
Birmingham, AL 35249
Tel: 205 975-4699   *Fax:* 205 996-5368
E-mail: kamara@uab.edu
Length: 1 Yr   *ACGME Approved/Offered Positions:* 1
Program ID: 045-01-12-067

California

Loma Linda

Loma Linda University Program
Sponsor: Loma Linda University Medical Center
Arrowhead Regional Medical Center
Prgm Director: Gary Stier, MD
Department of Anesthesiology/Critical Care
11234 Anderson Street
Loma Linda, CA 92354
Tel: 909 558-4015   *Fax:* 909 558-4012
E-mail: cstephens@llu.edu
Length: 1 Yr
Program ID: 045-05-31-079

San Francisco

University of California (San Francisco) Program
Sponsor: University of California (San Francisco) School
    of Medicine
UCSF and Mount Zion Medical Centers
Prgm Director: Linda Liu, MD
Box 0624
505 Parnassus Avenue, M917
San Francisco, CA 94143
Tel: 415 353-1116   *Fax:* 415 353-1990
E-mail: lewc@anesthesia.ucsf.edu
Length: 1 Yr   *ACGME Approved/Offered Positions:* 6
Program ID: 045-05-21-021

Stanford

Stanford University Program
Sponsor: Stanford Hospital and Clinics
Veterans Affairs Palo Alto Health Care System
Prgm Director: Fred Mihm, MD
Department of Anesthesia, H 3580
300 Pasteur Drive
Stanford, CA 94305
Tel: 650 723-6415   *Fax:* 650 725-8544
E-mail: fmihm@stanford.edu
Length: 1 Yr   *ACGME Approved/Offered Positions:* 6
Program ID: 045-05-21-002

Connecticut

New Haven

Yale-New Haven Medical Center Program
Sponsor: Yale-New Haven Hospital
Prgm Director: Stanley H Rosenbaum, MD
333 Cedar Street
PO Box 208051
New Haven, CT 06520
Tel: 203 785-2802   *Fax:* 203 785-6664
Length: 1 Yr   *ACGME Approved/Offered Positions:* 1
Program ID: 045-08-21-058

District of Columbia

Washington

George Washington University Program
Sponsor: George Washington University School of
  Medicine
George Washington University Hospital (UHS)
Prgm Director: Christopher D Junker, MD
900 23rd Street, NW
Washington, DC 20037
Tel: 202 715-4710   *Fax:* 202 715-4759
Length: 1 Yr   *ACGME Approved/Offered Positions:* 1
Program ID: 045-10-21-039

Florida

Gainesville

University of Florida Program
Sponsor: University of Florida College of Medicine
Shands Hospital at the University of Florida
Prgm Director: A Joseph Layon, MD
PO Box 100254
1600 SW Archer Road, PSB 2536
Gainesville, FL 32610
Tel: 352 265-0486   *Fax:* 352 265-1062
E-mail: pmeehan@anest.ufl.edu
Length: 1 Yr   *ACGME Approved/Offered Positions:* 6
Program ID: 045-11-21-009

Miami

Jackson Memorial Hospital/Jackson Health System Program
Sponsor: Jackson Memorial Hospital/Jackson Health
  System
Veterans Affairs Medical Center (Miami)
Prgm Director: Ricardo Martinez-Ruiz, MD
Division of Trauma Anesthesia and Critical Care
PO Box 016370 (M820)
Miami, FL 33101
Tel: 305 575-3150
E-mail: martinez4@med.miami.edu
Length: 1 Yr   *ACGME Approved/Offered Positions:* 3
Program ID: 045-11-21-004

Georgia

Atlanta

Emory University Program
Sponsor: Emory University School of Medicine
Emory University Hospital
Grady Health System
Prgm Director: Christine Lallos, MD
1364 Clifton Road, NE
Atlanta, GA 30322
Tel: 404 778-5793
E-mail: christine.lallos@emoryhealthcare.org
Length: 1 Yr   *ACGME Approved/Offered Positions:* 1
Program ID: 045-12-21-059

Illinois

Chicago

McGaw Medical Center of Northwestern University Program
Sponsor: McGaw Medical Center of Northwestern
  University
Northwestern Memorial Hospital
Prgm Director: Sherif Afifi, MD
Department of Anesthesiology
251 E Huron Street, Suite 5-704
Chicago, IL 60611
Tel: 312 926-2537   *Fax:* 312 926-4949
E-mail: agipson@nmff.org
Length: 1 Yr   *ACGME Approved/Offered Positions:* 3
Program ID: 045-16-21-014

University of Chicago Program
Sponsor: University of Chicago Medical Center
Prgm Director: Michael O'Connor, MD
5841 S Maryland Avenue, MC 4028
Chicago, IL 60637
Tel: 773 702-6842   *Fax:* 773 834-0063
Length: 1 Yr   *ACGME Approved/Offered Positions:* 0
Program ID: 045-16-21-068

Iowa

Iowa City

University of Iowa Hospitals and Clinics Program
Sponsor: University of Iowa Hospitals and Clinics
Prgm Director: J Steven Hata, MD, MSc
200 Hawkins Drive
Iowa City, IA 52242
Tel: 319 356-0772   *Fax:* 319 356-1120
Length: 1 Yr   *ACGME Approved/Offered Positions:* 4
Program ID: 045-18-21-003

Maryland

Baltimore

Johns Hopkins University Program
Sponsor: Johns Hopkins University School of Medicine
Johns Hopkins Hospital
Prgm Director: Theresa Hartsell, MD, PhD
Meyer 297A
600 North Wolfe Street
Baltimore, MD 21287
Tel: 410 955-9080   *Fax:* 410 955-8978
E-mail: thartse1@jhmi.edu
Length: 1 Yr   *ACGME Approved/Offered Positions:* 7
Program ID: 045-23-21-034

University of Maryland Program
Sponsor: University of Maryland Medical System
Clinical Center at the National Institutes of Health
Prgm Director: Vadivelu Sivaraman, MBBS
22 South Greene Street
Suite S11C00
Baltimore, MD 21201
Tel: 410 328-6120   *Fax:* 410 328-5531
E-mail: mpurcell@anes.umm.edu
Length: 1 Yr   *ACGME Approved/Offered Positions:* 2
Program ID: 045-23-21-029

Bethesda

National Capital Consortium Program
Sponsor: National Capital Consortium
Walter Reed Army Medical Center
Prgm Director: Christian Popa, MD, BS
Critical Care Medicine
6900 Georgia Avenue NW
Washington, DC 20307
Tel: 202 782-2063   *Fax:* 202 782-5043
E-mail: christian.popa@na.amedd.army.mil
Length: 1 Yr   *ACGME Approved/Offered Positions:* 1
Program ID: 045-10-21-042
Uniformed Services Program

Massachusetts

Boston

Beth Israel Deaconess Medical Center Program
Sponsor: Beth Israel Deaconess Medical Center
Prgm Director: Todd W Sarge, MD*
Dept of Anesthesia, Critical Care & Pain Medicine
One Deaconess Road, Suite CC-470
Boston, MA 02215
Tel: 617 754-2670   *Fax:* 617 754-2735
Length: 1 Yr   *ACGME Approved/Offered Positions:* 4
Program ID: 045-24-11-001

Brigham and Women's Hospital Program
Sponsor: Brigham and Women's Hospital
Prgm Director: Nicholas Sadovnikoff, MD
75 Francis Street
Boston, MA 02115
Tel: 617 732-8280   *Fax:* 617 264-5230
E-mail: nsadovnikoff@partners.org
Length: 1 Yr   *ACGME Approved/Offered Positions:* 4
Program ID: 045-24-31-069

Massachusetts General Hospital Program
Sponsor: Massachusetts General Hospital
Prgm Director: Edward Bittner, MD, PhD
Anesthesia - Critical Care
55 Fruit Street, White 434A
Boston, MA 02114
Tel: 617 726-2273   *Fax:* 617 724-8511
Length: 1 Yr   *ACGME Approved/Offered Positions:* 7
Program ID: 045-24-31-015

Springfield

Baystate Medical Center/Tufts University School of Medicine Program
Sponsor: Baystate Medical Center
Prgm Director: Paul G Jodka, MD
759 Chestnut Street
Springfield, MA 01199
Tel: 413 794-5439   *Fax:* 413 794-5389
Length: 1 Yr   *ACGME Approved/Offered Positions:* 2
Program ID: 045-24-21-063

Note: * indicates a newly appointed program director

Worcester

University of Massachusetts Program
Sponsor: University of Massachusetts Medical School
St Vincent Hospital
UMass Memorial Health Care (University Campus)
Prgm Director: Khaldoun Faris, MD
55 Lake Avenue North
Worcester, MA 01655
Tel: 508 856-3266   *Fax:* 508 856-3921
E-mail: lisa.nicholson@umassmed.edu
Length: 1 Yr   *ACGME Approved/Offered Positions:* 2
Program ID: 045-24-31-017

Michigan

Ann Arbor

University of Michigan Program
Sponsor: University of Michigan Hospitals and Health Centers
Prgm Director: Andrew L Rosenberg, MD
4172 Cardiovascular Center
1500 East Medical Center Drive/SPC 5861
Ann Arbor, MI 48109
Tel: 734 936-7241   *Fax:* 734 232-4548
E-mail: aenadeau@umich.edu
Length: 1 Yr   *ACGME Approved/Offered Positions:* 2
Program ID: 045-25-21-060

Minnesota

Rochester

College of Medicine, Mayo Clinic (Rochester) Program
Sponsor: College of Medicine, Mayo Clinic
Mayo Clinic (Arizona)
Mayo Clinic (Jacksonville)
Mayo Clinic (Rochester)
Mayo Clinic Florida Hospital
Mayo Clinic Hospital
Rochester Methodist Hospital
Saint Marys Hospital of Rochester
Prgm Director: Bhargavi Gali, MD
Siebens, 5th Floor
200 First Street SW
Rochester, MN 55905
Tel: 507 255-7000   *Fax:* 507 255-4267
E-mail: mgsm.roch.mnanesthesiology@mayo.edu
Length: 1 Yr   *ACGME Approved/Offered Positions:* 7
Program ID: 045-26-21-024

Missouri

St Louis

St Louis University School of Medicine Program
Sponsor: St Louis University School of Medicine
Cardinal Glennon Children's Hospital
Prgm Director: Nahel N Saied, MD
Department of Anesthesiology and Critical Care
3635 Vista Avenue at Grand Boulevard
St Louis, MO 63110
Tel: 314 577-8750   *Fax:* 314 268-5102
E-mail: myersdj2@slu.edu
Length: 1 Yr   *ACGME Approved/Offered Positions:* 1
Program ID: 045-28-13-078

Washington University/B-JH/SLCH Consortium Program
Sponsor: Washington University/B-JH/SLCH Consortium
Barnes-Jewish Hospital
Prgm Director: Walter A Boyle III, MD
Campus Box 8054
600 S Euclid Avenue
St Louis, MO 63110
Tel: 314 362-8543   *Fax:* 314 747-1710
Length: 1 Yr   *ACGME Approved/Offered Positions:* 2
Program ID: 045-28-21-056

New Hampshire

Lebanon

Dartmouth-Hitchcock Medical Center Program
Sponsor: Mary Hitchcock Memorial Hospital
Prgm Director: Athos J Rassias, MD
One Medical Center Drive
Lebanon, NH 03756
Tel: 603 650-4642   *Fax:* 603 650-0614
Length: 1 Yr   *ACGME Approved/Offered Positions:* 4
Program ID: 045-32-21-030

New York

Brooklyn

SUNY Health Science Center at Brooklyn Program
Sponsor: SUNY Health Science Center at Brooklyn
University Hospital-SUNY Health Science Center at Brooklyn
Prgm Director: Jean Charchaflieh, MD
450 Clarkson Avenue
Box 6
Brooklyn, NY 11203
Tel: 718 270-3290   *Fax:* 718 270-3928
E-mail: jean.charchaflieh@downstate.edu
Length: 1 Yr   *ACGME Approved/Offered Positions:* 1
Program ID: 045-35-11-054

New York

Mount Sinai School of Medicine Program
Sponsor: Mount Sinai School of Medicine
Englewood Hospital and Medical Center
Mount Sinai Medical Center
Prgm Director: Andrew B Leibowitz, MD
Box 1264
One Gustave L Levy Place
New York, NY 10029
Tel: 212 241-8867   *Fax:* 212 860-3669
E-mail: andrew.leibowitz@mountsinai.org
Length: 1 Yr   *ACGME Approved/Offered Positions:* 0
Program ID: 045-35-21-020

New York Presbyterian Hospital (Columbia Campus) Program
Sponsor: New York Presbyterian Hospital
New York Presbyterian Hospital (Columbia Campus)
Prgm Director: Robert N Sladen, MBChB
630 West 168th Street, PH 527-B
New York, NY 10032
Tel: 212 305-8633   *Fax:* 212 305-8287
E-mail: rs543@columbia.edu
Length: 1 Yr   *ACGME Approved/Offered Positions:* 7
Program ID: 045-35-11-007

New York University School of Medicine Program
Sponsor: New York University School of Medicine
Bellevue Hospital Center
NYU Hospitals Center
Prgm Director: Brian S Kaufman, MD
550 First Avenue
New York, NY 10016
Tel: 212 263-5072   *Fax:* 212 263-7254
Length: 1 Yr   *ACGME Approved/Offered Positions:* 1
Program ID: 045-35-21-016

Rochester

University of Rochester Program
Sponsor: Strong Memorial Hospital of the University of Rochester
Prgm Director: Peter J Papadakos, MD
Department of Anesthesiology, Box 604
601 Elmwood Avenue
Rochester, NY 14642
Tel: 585 273-4750   *Fax:* 585 244-7271
Length: 1 Yr   *ACGME Approved/Offered Positions:* 1
Program ID: 045-35-11-022

North Carolina

Durham

Duke University Hospital Program
Sponsor: Duke University Hospital
Veterans Affairs Medical Center (Durham)
Prgm Director: Christopher C Young, MD
Department of Anesthesiology, #3094
Room 5673
Durham, NC 27710
Tel: 919 668-3400   *Fax:* 919 681-7893
E-mail: grosm001@mc.duke.edu
Length: 1 Yr   *ACGME Approved/Offered Positions:* 3
Program ID: 045-36-21-052

Winston-Salem

Wake Forest University School of Medicine Program
Sponsor: Wake Forest University Baptist Medical Center
Prgm Director: Jeffrey S Kelly, MD*
Department of Anesthesiology
Medical Center Boulevard
Winston-Salem, NC 27157
Tel: 336 716-6839   *Fax:* 336 716-8190
Length: 1 Yr   *ACGME Approved/Offered Positions:* 0
Program ID: 045-36-21-023

Ohio

Cincinnati

University Hospital/University of Cincinnati College of Medicine Program
Sponsor: University Hospital Inc
Prgm Director: Steven J Lisco, MD
231 Albert Sabin Way
PO Box 670531
Cincinnati, OH 45267
Tel: 513 584-5688   *Fax:* 513 584-4003
E-mail: rohrmejm@ucmail.uc.edu
Length: 1 Yr   *ACGME Approved/Offered Positions:* 2
Program ID: 045-38-13-075

Cleveland

Cleveland Clinic Foundation Program
Sponsor: Cleveland Clinic Foundation
Prgm Director: Marc J Popovich, MD
9500 Euclid Avenue
Cleveland, OH 44195
Tel: 216 444-3877   *Fax:* 216 444-7360
E-mail: aned@ccf.org
Length: 1 Yr   *ACGME Approved/Offered Positions:* 5
Program ID: 045-38-21-031

University Hospitals Case Medical Center Program
Sponsor: University Hospitals Case Medical Center
Prgm Director: Howard S Nearman, MD, MBA
11100 Euclid Ave
LKSD 2514
Cleveland, OH 44106
Tel: 216 844-7330   *Fax:* 216 844-3781
E-mail: howard.nearman@uhhospitals.org
Length: 1 Yr   *ACGME Approved/Offered Positions:* 0
Program ID: 045-38-21-012

Oregon

Portland

Oregon Health & Science University Program
Sponsor: Oregon Health & Science University Hospital
Prgm Director: Per Thorborg, MD, PhD
3181 SW Sam Jackson Park Road, UHS-2
Portland, OR 97239
Tel: 503 494-6895   *Fax:* 503 494-3092
Length: 1 Yr
Program ID: 045-40-12-077

Pennsylvania

Philadelphia

University of Pennsylvania Program
Sponsor: University of Pennsylvania Health System
Prgm Director: Benjamin Kohl, MD*
Dulles Building, Ste 680-6006
3400 Spruce Street
Philadelphia, PA 19104
Tel: 215 662-3751   *Fax:* 215 662-7451
E-mail: kohlbe@uphs.upenn.edu
Length: 1 Yr   *ACGME Approved/Offered Positions:* 3
Program ID: 045-41-21-005

Pittsburgh

University of Pittsburgh Medical Center Medical Education Program
Sponsor: Univ of Pittsburgh Medical Center Medical Education
UPMC Presbyterian Shadyside
Veterans Affairs Medical Center (Pittsburgh)
Prgm Director: Ata M Kaynar, MD
655 Scaife Hall
3550 Terrace Street
Pittsburgh, PA 15261
Tel: 412 647-8410   *Fax:* 412 647-8060
Length: 1 Yr   *ACGME Approved/Offered Positions:* 4
Program ID: 045-41-21-028

Tennessee

Nashville

Vanderbilt University Program
Sponsor: Vanderbilt University Medical Center
Prgm Director: Liza M Weavind, MD
1211 21st Avenue South
526 Medical Art Building
Nashville, TN 37212
Tel: 615 343-6268   *Fax:* 615 343-6272
E-mail: liza.weavind@vanderbilt.edu
Length: 1 Yr   *ACGME Approved/Offered Positions:* 6
Program ID: 045-47-21-057

Texas

Dallas

University of Texas Southwestern Medical School Program
Sponsor: University of Texas Southwestern Medical School
Children's Medical Center of Dallas
Dallas County Hospital District-Parkland Memorial Hospital
Dallas VA Medical Center
Prgm Director: Adebola Adesanya, MD
5323 Harry Hines Boulevard
Dallas, TX 75390
Tel: 214 648-7834   *Fax:* 214 648-7660
E-mail: leslie.noe@utsouthwestern.edu
Length: 1 Yr   *ACGME Approved/Offered Positions:* 1
Program ID: 045-48-31-073

Galveston

University of Texas Medical Branch Hospitals Program
Sponsor: University of Texas Medical Branch Hospitals
Prgm Director: Aristides P Koutrouvelis, MD
301 University Boulevard
Galveston, TX 77555
Tel: 409 772-0119   *Fax:* 409 772-1224
E-mail: arkoutro@utmb.edu
Length: 1 Yr   *ACGME Approved/Offered Positions:* 2
Program ID: 045-48-21-048

Houston

University of Texas at Houston Program
Sponsor: University of Texas Health Science Center at Houston
Memorial Hermann Hospital
Methodist Hospital (Houston)
University of Texas M D Anderson Cancer Center
Prgm Director: Thomas Feeley, MD
1515 Holcombe, Unit 112
B7.4320
Houston, TX 77030
Tel: 713 792-5040   *Fax:* 713 745-1869
E-mail: gbotz@mdanderson.org
Length: 1 Yr   *ACGME Approved/Offered Positions:* 6
Program ID: 045-48-21-032

Lackland AFB

San Antonio Uniformed Services Health Education Consortium (WHMC) Program
Sponsor: San Antonio Uniformed Services Health Education Consortium
Wilford Hall Medical Center (AETC)
Brooke Army Medical Center
University of Texas Health Science Center
Prgm Director: (LTC) Kurt W Grathwohl, MD
2200 Bergquist Drive, Suite 1
Lackland AFB, TX 78236
Tel: 210 916-4512   *Fax:* 210 916-3769
E-mail: kurt.grathwohl@amedd.army.mil
Length: 1 Yr   *ACGME Approved/Offered Positions:* 1
Program ID: 045-48-21-033
Uniformed Services Program

Washington

Seattle

University of Washington Program
Sponsor: University of Washington School of Medicine
Harborview Medical Center
University of Washington Medical Center
Prgm Director: Steven Deem, MD
Box 359724
325 9th Avenue
Seattle, WA 98104
Tel: 206 731-2848   *Fax:* 206 731-8090
Length: 1 Yr   *ACGME Approved/Offered Positions:* 3
Program ID: 045-54-22-072

Wisconsin

Madison

University of Wisconsin Program
Sponsor: University of Wisconsin Hospital and Clinics
Prgm Director: Jonathan T Ketzler, MD
B6/319 CSC
600 Highland Avenue
Madison, WI 53792
Tel: 608 263-8114   *Fax:* 608 262-1061
E-mail: info@anesthesia.wisc.edu
Length: 1 Yr   *ACGME Approved/Offered Positions:* 1
Program ID: 045-56-21-008

Milwaukee

Medical College of Wisconsin Affiliated Hospitals Program
Sponsor: Medical College of Wisconsin Affiliated Hospitals, Inc
Clement J Zablocki Veterans Affairs Medical Center
Froedtert Memorial Lutheran Hospital
Prgm Director: Sylvia Y Dolinski, MD
9200 W Wisconsin Avenue
Milwaukee, WI 53226
Tel: 414 805-2715   *Fax:* 414 259-1522
Length: 1 Yr   *ACGME Approved/Offered Positions:* 0
Program ID: 045-56-21-025

Note: * indicates a newly appointed program director

Critical Care Medicine (Internal Medicine)

California

Los Angeles

Cedars-Sinai Medical Center Program
Sponsor: Cedars-Sinai Medical Center
VA Greater Los Angeles Healthcare System
Prgm Director: Lawrence S Maldonado, MD
8700 Beverly Blvd
Los Angeles, CA 90048
Tel: 310 423-4684   *Fax:* 310 423-0436
Length: 2 Yrs   *ACGME Approved/Offered Positions:* 2
Program ID: 142-05-11-005

San Francisco

University of California (San Francisco) Program
Sponsor: University of California (San Francisco) School of Medicine
UCSF and Mount Zion Medical Centers
Prgm Director: Michael A Matthay, MD
Department of Medicine
Box 0624
San Francisco, CA 94143
Tel: 415 353-1206   *Fax:* 415 353-1990
Length: 2 Yrs   *ACGME Approved/Offered Positions:* 4
Program ID: 142-05-21-011

Stanford

Stanford University Program
Sponsor: Stanford Hospital and Clinics
Veterans Affairs Palo Alto Health Care System
Prgm Director: Norman W Rizk, MD
300 Pasteur Drive, Room M121-L
Stanford, CA 94305
Tel: 650 723-6381   *Fax:* 650 725-5489
Length: 2 Yrs   *ACGME Approved/Offered Positions:* 8
Program ID: 142-05-21-013

District of Columbia

Washington

George Washington University Program
Sponsor: George Washington University School of Medicine
George Washington University Hospital (UHS)
Prgm Director: Michael G Seneff, MD
900 23rd Street, NW
Washington, DC 20037
Tel: 202 715-4591   *Fax:* 202 715-4759
E-mail: mseneff@mfa.gwu.edu
Length: 2 Yrs   *ACGME Approved/Offered Positions:* 3
Program ID: 142-10-21-103

Florida

Miami

Jackson Memorial Hospital/Jackson Health System Program
Sponsor: Jackson Memorial Hospital/Jackson Health System
Veterans Affairs Medical Center (Miami)
Prgm Director: Roland M Schein, MD*
Dept of Medicine D-26
PO Box 016760
Miami, FL 33136
Tel: 305 575-3227   *Fax:* 305 575-3366
Length: 2 Yrs   *ACGME Approved/Offered Positions:* 2
Program ID: 142-11-21-020

Louisiana

Shreveport

Louisiana State University (Shreveport) Program
Sponsor: LSU Health Sciences Center-University Hospital
Prgm Director: L Keith Scott, MD
1501 Kings Highway
Shreveport, LA 71130
Tel: 318 675-8361   *Fax:* 318 675-5988
Length: 2 Yrs   *ACGME Approved/Offered Positions:* 4
Program ID: 142-21-21-032

Maryland

Bethesda

National Capital Consortium (Walter Reed) Program
Sponsor: National Capital Consortium
Walter Reed Army Medical Center
Prgm Director: Lawrence S Lepler, MD
6900 Georgia Avenue NW
Washington, DC 20307
Tel: 202 782-3891   *Fax:* 202 782-9032
E-mail: lawrence.lepler@na.amedd.army.mil
Length: 2 Yrs   *ACGME Approved/Offered Positions:* 4
Program ID: 142-10-21-125
Uniformed Services Program

National Institutes of Health Clinical Center Program
Sponsor: Clinical Center at the National Institutes of Health
Washington Hospital Center
Prgm Director: Dorothea R McAreavey, MD
10 Center Drive
Room 2C145
Bethesda, MD 20892
Tel: 301 496-9320   *Fax:* 301 402-1213
Length: 2 Yrs   *ACGME Approved/Offered Positions:* 8
Program ID: 142-23-21-128

Massachusetts

Springfield

Baystate Medical Center/Tufts University School of Medicine Program
Sponsor: Baystate Medical Center
Prgm Director: Mark Tidswell, MD*
759 Chestnut Street
Springfield, MA 01199
Tel: 413 794-5439   *Fax:* 413 794-5389
E-mail: suzanne.gallup@bhs.org
Length: 2 Yrs   *ACGME Approved/Offered Positions:* 3
Program ID: 142-24-21-161

Michigan

Detroit

Henry Ford Hospital Program
Sponsor: Henry Ford Hospital
Prgm Director: Michael Eichenhorn, MD*
2799 West Grand Boulevard, K-17
Detroit, MI 48202
Tel: 313 916-2436
Length: 2 Yrs   *ACGME Approved/Offered Positions:* 8
Program ID: 142-25-12-160

Minnesota

Minneapolis

Hennepin County Medical Center Program
Sponsor: Hennepin County Medical Center
Methodist Hospital
Prgm Director: Robert S Shapiro, MD
701 Park Avenue South
Pulmonary Division - G5
Minneapolis, MN 55415
Tel: 612 873-2625   *Fax:* 612 904-4680
E-mail: wendy.yates@hcmed.org
Length: 2 Yrs   *ACGME Approved/Offered Positions:* 5
Program ID: 142-26-21-118

Rochester

College of Medicine, Mayo Clinic (Rochester) Program
Sponsor: College of Medicine, Mayo Clinic
Mayo Clinic (Rochester)
Saint Marys Hospital of Rochester
Prgm Director: J Christopher Farmer, MD
200 First Street SW
Rochester, MN 55905
Tel: 507 255-6276   *Fax:* 507 255-4267
E-mail: schmidt.rachel@mayo.edu
Length: 2 Yrs   *ACGME Approved/Offered Positions:* 20
Program ID: 142-26-21-100

Missouri

Kansas City

University of Missouri at Kansas City Program
Sponsor: University of Missouri-Kansas City School of Medicine
St Luke's Hospital-Kansas City
Truman Medical Center
Prgm Director: Diana S Dark, MD
Medical Education Department
4401 Wornall Road
Kansas City, MO 64111
Tel: 816 932-8232   *Fax:* 816 932-5179
E-mail: mvanderliest@saint-lukes.org
Length: 2 Yrs   *ACGME Approved/Offered Positions:* 2
Program ID: 142-28-13-158

St Louis

St Louis University School of Medicine Program

Sponsor: St Louis University School of Medicine
St John's Mercy Medical Center
St Louis University Hospital
Prgm Director: Robert W Taylor, MD
621 S New Ballas Road
Suite 4006B
St Louis, MO 63141
Tel: 314 251-6486   *Fax:* 314 251-4155
E-mail: taylrw@stlo.mercy.net
Length: 2 Yrs   *ACGME Approved/Offered Positions:* 9
Program ID: 142-28-21-048

New Hampshire

Lebanon

Dartmouth-Hitchcock Medical Center Program

Sponsor: Mary Hitchcock Memorial Hospital
Prgm Director: Harold L Manning, MD
Critical Care Medicine
1 Medical Center Drive
Lebanon, NH 03756
Tel: 603 650-5533   *Fax:* 603 650-0580
E-mail: Harold.L.Manning@hitchcock.org
Length: 2 Yrs   *ACGME Approved/Offered Positions:* 5
Program ID: 142-32-21-140

New Jersey

Camden

UMDNJ-Robert Wood Johnson Medical School (Camden) Program

Sponsor: Cooper Hospital-University Medical Center
Prgm Director: Richard P Dellinger, MD
One Cooper Plaza
3rd Floor, Dorrance
Camden, NJ 08103
Tel: 856 342-2657   *Fax:* 856 968-7420
Length: 2 Yrs   *ACGME Approved/Offered Positions:* 10
Program ID: 142-33-21-051

South Orange

Seton Hall University School of Health and Medical Sciences Program

Sponsor: Seton Hall University School of Health and
   Medical Sciences
JFK Medical Center
St Michael's Medical Center (A Member of Catholic
   Health East)
Prgm Director: Marc R Adelman, MD
111 Central Avenue
Newark, NJ 07102
Tel: 973 877-5090   *Fax:* 973 877-2737
E-mail: angies@chhsnj.org
Length: 2 Yrs   *ACGME Approved/Offered Positions:* 3
Program ID: 142-33-11-050

New Mexico

Albuquerque

University of New Mexico Program

Sponsor: University of New Mexico School of Medicine
University of New Mexico Hospital
Veterans Affairs Medical Center (Albuquerque)
Prgm Director: Helen K Busby, MD
1 University of New Mexico
MSC 10-5550
Albuquerque, NM 87131
Tel: 505 272-4751   *Fax:* 505 272-8700
E-mail: afinkenhoefer@salud.unm.edu
Length: 2 Yrs   *ACGME Approved/Offered Positions:* 4
Program ID: 142-34-21-053

New York

Bronx

Albert Einstein College of Medicine Program

Sponsor: Albert Einstein College of Medicine of Yeshiva
   University
Montefiore Medical Center-Henry and Lucy Moses
   Division
Montefiore Medical Center-Weiler Division
Prgm Director: Vladimir Kvetan, MD
111 East 210th Street
Bronx, NY 10467
Tel: 718 920-5440   *Fax:* 718 652-2464
E-mail: vkvetan@montefiore.org
Length: 2 Yrs   *ACGME Approved/Offered Positions:* 11
Program ID: 142-35-21-067

Brooklyn

Maimonides Medical Center Program

Sponsor: Maimonides Medical Center
Prgm Director: Sidney Tessler, MD
4802 Tenth Avenue
Brooklyn, NY 11219
Tel: 718 283-8380   *Fax:* 718 283-7884
Length: 2 Yrs   *ACGME Approved/Offered Positions:* 6
Program ID: 142-35-11-056

New York

Memorial Sloan-Kettering Cancer Center/New York Presbyterian Hospital (Cornell Campus) Program

Sponsor: Memorial Sloan-Kettering Cancer Center
Prgm Director: Stephen M Pastores, MD
1275 York Avenue
C-1179
New York, NY 10021
Tel: 212 639-6396   *Fax:* 212 794-4333
Length: 2 Yrs   *ACGME Approved/Offered Positions:* 8
Program ID: 142-35-21-064

Mount Sinai School of Medicine Program

Sponsor: Mount Sinai School of Medicine
Englewood Hospital and Medical Center
Mount Sinai Medical Center
Veterans Affairs Medical Center (Bronx)
Prgm Director: John M Oropello, MD
Box 1264
One Gustave L Levy Place
New York, NY 10029
Tel: 212 241-8867   *Fax:* 212 860-3669
E-mail: john.oropello@mountsinai.org
Length: 2 Yrs   *ACGME Approved/Offered Positions:* 17
Program ID: 142-35-31-060

New York Medical College at St Vincent's Hospital and Medical Center of New York Program

Sponsor: New York Medical College
St Vincent Catholic Medical Centers (Manhattan)
Prgm Director: Mark E Astiz, MD
170 West 12th Street
New York, NY 10011
Tel: 212 604-8336   *Fax:* 212 604-8061
Length: 2 Yrs   *ACGME Approved/Offered Positions:* 5
Program ID: 142-35-11-058

Rochester

University of Rochester Program

Sponsor: Strong Memorial Hospital of the University of
   Rochester
Highland Hospital of Rochester
Prgm Director: Michael J Apostolakos, MD
Pulmonary & Critical Care Division
601 Elmwood Avenue Box 692
Rochester, NY 14642
Tel: 585 275-2050   *Fax:* 585 273-1126
Length: 2 Yrs   *ACGME Approved/Offered Positions:* 3
Program ID: 142-35-21-141

North Carolina

Winston-Salem

Wake Forest University School of Medicine Program

Sponsor: Wake Forest University Baptist Medical Center
Prgm Director: Drew A MacGregor, MD
Medical Center Blvd
Winston Salem, NC 27157
Tel: 336 716-6653   *Fax:* 336 716-9534
E-mail: dsinglet@wfubmc.edu
Length: 2 Yrs   *ACGME Approved/Offered Positions:* 4
Program ID: 142-36-21-069

Oregon

Portland

Oregon Health & Science University Program

Sponsor: Oregon Health & Science University Hospital
Prgm Director: Dane J Nichols, MD
3181 SW Sam Jackson Park Road
Mailcode UHN 67
Portland, OR 97239
Tel: 503 494-0611   *Fax:* 503 494-6670
Length: 2 Yrs   *ACGME Approved/Offered Positions:* 10
Program ID: 142-40-31-156

Pennsylvania

Danville

Geisinger Health System Program

Sponsor: Geisinger Health System
Geisinger Medical Center
Geisinger Wyoming Valley Medical Center
Prgm Director: Marilyn T Haupt, MD
100 North Academy Avenue
Danville, PA 17822
Tel: 570 271-6389   *Fax:* 570 271-6021
Length: 2 Yrs   *ACGME Approved/Offered Positions:* 4
Program ID: 142-41-12-164

Note: * indicates a newly appointed program director

Pittsburgh

University of Pittsburgh Medical Center Medical Education Program

Sponsor: Univ of Pittsburgh Medical Center Medical Education
UPMC Presbyterian Shadyside
Veterans Affairs Medical Center (Pittsburgh)
Prgm Director: Paul L Rogers, MD
Department of Critical Care Medicine
655 Scaife Hall, 3550 Terrace Street
Pittsburgh, PA 15261
Tel: 412 647-3135   *Fax:* 412 647-8060
E-mail: rogerspl@ccm.upmc.edu
Length: 2 Yrs   *ACGME Approved/Offered Positions:* 22
Program ID: 142-41-21-114

Puerto Rico

San Juan

VA Caribbean Healthcare System Program

Sponsor: VA Caribbean Healthcare System
Prgm Director: William Rodriguez, MD
111-E, OPA Building
10 Casia Street
San Juan, PR 00921
Tel: 787 641-7582   *Fax:* 787 641-9541
E-mail: william.rodriguez@med.va.gov
Length: 2 Yrs   *ACGME Approved/Offered Positions:* 2
Program ID: 142-42-12-157

Rhode Island

Providence

Brown University Program

Sponsor: Rhode Island Hospital-Lifespan
Miriam Hospital-Lifespan
Prgm Director: Mitchell Levy, MD
164 Summit Avenue, Suite 221
Providence, RI 02906
Tel: 401 444-5518   *Fax:* 401 444-3002
E-mail: mitchell_levy@brown.edu
Length: 2 Yrs   *ACGME Approved/Offered Positions:* 4
Program ID: 142-43-11-083

Texas

Houston

Baylor College of Medicine Program

Sponsor: Baylor College of Medicine
Harris County Hospital District-Ben Taub General Hospital
Prgm Director: Kalpalatha K Guntupalli, MD
Pulmonary & Critical Care Medicine Section
1709 Dryden, Ste 900
Houston, TX 77030
Tel: 713 798-5840   *Fax:* 713 798-0198
E-mail: kkg@bcm.tmc.edu
Length: 2 Yrs   *ACGME Approved/Offered Positions:* 6
Program ID: 142-48-21-091

Washington

Seattle

University of Washington Program

Sponsor: University of Washington School of Medicine
Harborview Medical Center
Prgm Director: Mark R Tonelli, MD, MA
Box 356522, BB1361 HSB, Pulmonary & Crit Care Med
1959 NE Pacific St
Seattle, WA 98195
Tel: 206 543-3166   *Fax:* 206 685-8673
E-mail: pccmfelo@u.washington.edu
Length: 2 Yrs   *ACGME Approved/Offered Positions:* 2
Program ID: 142-54-21-094

Cytopathology (Pathology)

Alabama

Birmingham

University of Alabama Medical Center Program

Sponsor: University of Alabama Hospital
Prgm Director: Isam-eldin A Eltoum, MD, MBA
Kracke Bldg/Rm 609
619 South 19th Street
Birmingham, AL 35233
Tel: 205 934-4333   *Fax:* 205 934-7094
Length: 1 Yr   *ACGME Approved/Offered Positions:* 2
Program ID: 307-01-21-041

Arkansas

Little Rock

University of Arkansas for Medical Sciences Program

Sponsor: University of Arkansas College of Medicine
Central Arkansas Veterans Healthcare System
UAMS Medical Center
Prgm Director: Murat Gokden, MD
4301 West Markham, Slot 517
Little Rock, AR 72205
Tel: 501 526-7746   *Fax:* 501 686-8381
E-mail: gordonreneen@uams.edu
Length: 1 Yr   *ACGME Approved/Offered Positions:* 1
Program ID: 307-04-21-034

California

Los Angeles

UCLA Medical Center Program

Sponsor: UCLA David Geffen School of Medicine/UCLA Medical Center
UCLA Medical Center
Prgm Director: Jianyu Rao, MD
650 Charles Young Drive South
A3-231L, CHS
Los Angeles, CA 90095
Tel: 310 794-1567   *Fax:* 310 206-8108
E-mail: jrao@mednet.ucla.edu
Length: 1 Yr   *ACGME Approved/Offered Positions:* 2
Program ID: 307-05-21-013

University of Southern California/ LAC+USC Medical Center Program

Sponsor: University of Southern California/LAC+USC Medical Center
LAC+USC Medical Center
Prgm Director: Juan C Felix, MD
1100 North State Street
Los Angeles, CA 90033
Tel: 323 409-3001   *Fax:* 323 226-3535
Length: 1 Yr   *ACGME Approved/Offered Positions:* 4
Program ID: 307-05-21-063

Programs

Orange

University of California (Irvine) Program
Sponsor: University of California (Irvine) Medical
    Center
Prgm Director: Fritz Lin, MD
101 The City Drive South
Orange, CA 92868
Tel: 714 456-6141   *Fax:* 714 456-5873
E-mail: flin@uci.edu
Length: 1 Yr   *ACGME Approved/Offered Positions:* 2
Program ID: 307-05-31-098

Sacramento

University of California (Davis) Health System Program
Sponsor: University of California (Davis) Health System
University of California (Davis) Medical Center
Prgm Director: Alaa Afify, MD
4400 V Street, Pathology Building
Sacramento, CA 95817
Tel: 916 734-8370   *Fax:* 916 734-6468
E-mail: penny.young@ucdmc.ucdavis.edu
Length: 1 Yr   *ACGME Approved/Offered Positions:* 1
Program ID: 307-05-21-081

San Francisco

University of California (San Francisco) Program
Sponsor: University of California (San Francisco) School
    of Medicine
San Francisco General Hospital Medical Center
Prgm Director: Britt-Marie Ljung, MD
1600 Divisadero Street
Cytopathology, R-200
San Francisco, CA 94115
Tel: 415 353-7048   *Fax:* 415 885-7588
E-mail: britt-marie.ljung@ucsf.edu
Length: 1 Yr   *ACGME Approved/Offered Positions:* 2
Program ID: 307-05-21-075

Stanford

Stanford University Program
Sponsor: Stanford Hospital and Clinics
Veterans Affairs Palo Alto Health Care System
Prgm Director: Christina S Kong, MD
Department of Pathology
300 Pasteur Drive, L235
Stanford, CA 94305
Tel: 650 723-9016   *Fax:* 650 725-6902
E-mail: ckong@stanford.edu
Length: 1 Yr   *ACGME Approved/Offered Positions:* 2
Program ID: 307-05-13-096

Connecticut

Hartford

Hartford Hospital Program
Sponsor: Hartford Hospital
Prgm Director: Theresa M Voytek, MD
80 Seymour Street
PO Box 5037
Hartford, CT 06102
Tel: 860 545-2249
Length: 1 Yr   *ACGME Approved/Offered Positions:* 1
Program ID: 307-08-21-053

New Haven

Yale-New Haven Medical Center Program
Sponsor: Yale-New Haven Hospital
Prgm Director: Diane P Kowalski, MD*
310 Cedar Street
PO Box 208023
New Haven, CT 06520
Tel: 203 785-2774   *Fax:* 203 737-2922
Length: 1 Yr   *ACGME Approved/Offered Positions:* 1
Program ID: 307-08-21-078

District of Columbia

Washington

George Washington University Program
Sponsor: George Washington University School of
    Medicine
George Washington University Hospital (UHS)
Prgm Director: Sana O Tabbara, MD*
Ross Hall, Room 502
2300 Eye Street, NW
Washington, DC 20037
Tel: 202 994-3391   *Fax:* 202 994-2618
E-mail: stabbara@mfa.gwu.edu
Length: 1 Yr   *ACGME Approved/Offered Positions:* 1
Program ID: 307-10-21-005

Georgetown University Hospital Program
Sponsor: Georgetown University Hospital
Prgm Director: Mary K Sidawy, MD
3900 Reservoir Road, NW
Room 210 SW, Med Dent Building
Washington, DC 20007
Tel: 202 687-8053   *Fax:* 202 687-8934
Length: 1 Yr   *ACGME Approved/Offered Positions:* 1
Program ID: 307-10-13-102

Florida

Gainesville

University of Florida Program
Sponsor: University of Florida College of Medicine
Shands Hospital at the University of Florida
Prgm Director: Edward J Wilkinson, MD
1600 SW Archer Road
Box 100275
Gainesville, FL 32610
Tel: 352 265-0238   *Fax:* 352 265-0437
E-mail: wilkinso@pathology.ufl.edu
Length: 1 Yr   *ACGME Approved/Offered Positions:* 2
Program ID: 307-11-21-047

Jacksonville

University of Florida College of Medicine Jacksonville Program
Sponsor: University of Florida College of Medicine
    Jacksonville
Shands Jacksonville Medical Center
Prgm Director: Shahla Masood, MD
655 West Eighth Street, Box C505
Jacksonville, FL 32209
Tel: 904 244-4889   *Fax:* 904 244-4060
E-mail: rebel.jones@jax.ufl.edu
Length: 1 Yr   *ACGME Approved/Offered Positions:* 2
Program ID: 307-11-21-014

Miami

Jackson Memorial Hospital/Jackson Health System Program
Sponsor: Jackson Memorial Hospital/Jackson Health
    System
University of Miami Hospital and Clinics
Prgm Director: Parvin Ganjei-Azar, MD
PO Box 016960 (R-1)
1611 NW 12th Ave
Miami, FL 33101
Tel: 305 585-6055   *Fax:* 305 585-2598
Length: 1 Yr   *ACGME Approved/Offered Positions:* 2
Program ID: 307-11-21-024

Tampa

University of South Florida Program
Sponsor: University of South Florida College of Medicine
H Lee Moffitt Cancer Center
James A Haley Veterans Hospital
Prgm Director: Barbara Centeno, MD
12901 Bruce B Downs Blvd
MDC Box 11
Tampa, FL 33612
Tel: 813 974-0535   *Fax:* 813 974-5536
E-mail: sbeacham@health.usf.edu
Length: 1 Yr   *ACGME Approved/Offered Positions:* 1
Program ID: 307-11-21-068

Georgia

Atlanta

Emory University Program
Sponsor: Emory University School of Medicine
Emory University Hospital
Grady Health System
Prgm Director: Momin T Siddiqui, MD
Anatomic Pathology, Room H-185A
1364 Clifton Road, NE
Atlanta, GA 30332
Tel: 404 712-4188   *Fax:* 404 712-0714
E-mail: momin.siddiqui@emoryhealthcare.org
Length: 1 Yr   *ACGME Approved/Offered Positions:* 2
Program ID: 307-12-21-058

Illinois

Chicago

McGaw Medical Center of Northwestern University Program
Sponsor: McGaw Medical Center of Northwestern
    University
Northwestern Memorial Hospital
Prgm Director: Ritu Nayar, MD
251 East Huron Street
Feinberg Pavilion 7-210
Chicago, IL 60611
Tel: 312 926-7017   *Fax:* 312 926-6037
Length: 1 Yr   *ACGME Approved/Offered Positions:* 2
Program ID: 307-16-21-037

University of Chicago Program
Sponsor: University of Chicago Medical Center
Prgm Director: Richard M DeMay, MD
5841 S Maryland Avenue
MC 2050
Chicago, IL 60637
Tel: 773 702-6569   *Fax:* 773 702-6570
E-mail: rdemay@uchicago.edu
Length: 1 Yr   *ACGME Approved/Offered Positions:* 1
Program ID: 307-16-21-061

Note: * indicates a newly appointed program director

Maywood

Loyola University Program
Sponsor: Loyola University Medical Center
Prgm Director: Eva M Wojcik, MD
2160 South First Avenue
Maywood, IL 60153
Tel: 708 216-8106   *Fax:* 708 216-8225
E-mail: vbaertschi@lumc.edu
Length: 1 Yr   *ACGME Approved/Offered Positions:* 2
Program ID: 307-16-21-001

Indiana

Indianapolis

Indiana University School of Medicine Program
Sponsor: Indiana University School of Medicine
Clarian Indiana University Hospital
Clarian Methodist Hospital of Indiana
Clarian Pathology Laboratory
William N Wishard Memorial Hospital
Prgm Director: Harvey M Cramer, MD
350 W 11th Street
Room 4026
Indianapolis, IN 46202
Tel: 317 491-6353   *Fax:* 317 491-6334
E-mail: hcramer@iupui.edu
Length: 1 Yr   *ACGME Approved/Offered Positions:* 3
Program ID: 307-17-21-002

Iowa

Iowa City

University of Iowa Hospitals and Clinics Program
Sponsor: University of Iowa Hospitals and Clinics
Prgm Director: Chris S Jensen, MD
200 Hawkins Drive
Iowa City, IA 52242
Tel: 319 356-4434
Length: 1 Yr   *ACGME Approved/Offered Positions:* 2
Program ID: 307-18-21-025

Kansas

Kansas City

University of Kansas School of Medicine Program
Sponsor: University of Kansas School of Medicine
University of Kansas Hospital
Prgm Director: Patricia A Thomas, MD, MA
Department of Pathology-2017 Wahl West
3901 Rainbow Boulevard
Kansas City, KS 66160
Tel: 913 588-7070   *Fax:* 913 588-7073
Length: 1 Yr   *ACGME Approved/Offered Positions:* 3
Program ID: 307-19-21-079

Kentucky

Lexington

University of Kentucky College of Medicine Program
Sponsor: University of Kentucky College of Medicine
University of Kentucky Hospital
Veterans Affairs Medical Center (Lexington)
Prgm Director: Luis M Samayoa, MD
Department of Pathology & Laboratory Medicine
800 Rose Street MS-117
Lexington, KY 40536
Tel: 859 323-1798
Length: 1 Yr   *ACGME Approved/Offered Positions:* 2
Program ID: 307-20-21-008

Louisville

University of Louisville Program
Sponsor: University of Louisville School of Medicine
University of Louisville Hospital
Prgm Director: Sunati Sahoo, MD
530 S Jackson St
Basement, Room COF19
Louisville, KY 40202
Tel: 502 852-1762   *Fax:* 502 852-1761
Length: 1 Yr   *ACGME Approved/Offered Positions:* 1
Program ID: 307-20-21-036

Louisiana

New Orleans

Tulane University Program
Sponsor: Tulane University School of Medicine
Ochsner Clinic Foundation
Tulane University Hospital and Clinics
Prgm Director: Krzysztof Moroz, MD
1430 Tulane Ave, SL79
Room 6519
New Orleans, LA 70112
Tel: 504 988-6199   *Fax:* 504 988-7862
E-mail: bdelucc@tulane.edu
Length: 1 Yr   *ACGME Approved/Offered Positions:* 1
Program ID: 307-21-21-080

Shreveport

Louisiana State University (Shreveport) Program
Sponsor: LSU Health Sciences Center-University Hospital
Prgm Director: Fleurette W Abreo, MD
1501 Kings Highway
PO Box 33932
Shreveport, LA 71130
Tel: 318 675-5895   *Fax:* 318 675-4568
E-mail: fabreo@lsuhsc.edu
Length: 1 Yr   *ACGME Approved/Offered Positions:* 2
Program ID: 307-21-21-074

Maryland

Baltimore

Johns Hopkins University Program
Sponsor: Johns Hopkins University School of Medicine
Johns Hopkins Hospital
Prgm Director: Syed Z Ali, MD
600 North Wolfe Street
Pathology 406
Baltimore, MD 21287
Tel: 410 955-1180   *Fax:* 410 614-9556
E-mail: sali@jhmi.edu
Length: 1 Yr   *ACGME Approved/Offered Positions:* 3
Program ID: 307-23-21-065

University of Maryland Program
Sponsor: University of Maryland Medical System
Prgm Director: Chen-Chih Sun, MD*
Department of Pathology
22 South Greene Street
Baltimore, MD 21201
Tel: 410 328-5555   *Fax:* 410 328-5508
Length: 1 Yr   *ACGME Approved/Offered Positions:* 1
Program ID: 307-23-12-088

Bethesda

National Institutes of Health Clinical Center Program
Sponsor: Clinical Center at the National Institutes of Health
Prgm Director: Armando C Filie, MD
Building 10, Room 2A19
9000 Rockville Pike
Bethesda, MD 20892
Tel: 301 496-6355   *Fax:* 301 402-2585
Length: 1 Yr   *ACGME Approved/Offered Positions:* 1
Program ID: 307-23-21-032

Massachusetts

Boston

Beth Israel Deaconess Medical Center Program
Sponsor: Beth Israel Deaconess Medical Center
Prgm Director: Helen H Wang, MD
330 Brookline Avenue
Boston, MA 02215
Tel: 617 667-2629
Length: 1 Yr   *ACGME Approved/Offered Positions:* 2
Program ID: 307-24-21-030

Boston University Medical Center Program
Sponsor: Boston Medical Center
Prgm Director: Antonio de las Morenas, MD
670 Albany St, 3rd Floor
Boston, MA 02118
Tel: 617 414-5059   *Fax:* 617 414-7027
Length: 1 Yr   *ACGME Approved/Offered Positions:* 2
Program ID: 307-24-21-003

Brigham and Women's Hospital Program
Sponsor: Brigham and Women's Hospital
Prgm Director: Edmund S Cibas, MD
75 Francis Street
Boston, MA 02115
Tel: 617 732-6797   *Fax:* 617 739-6192
E-mail: ecibas@partners.org
Length: 1 Yr   *ACGME Approved/Offered Positions:* 3
Program ID: 307-24-21-029

Massachusetts General Hospital Program
Sponsor: Massachusetts General Hospital
Prgm Director: Rosemary Tambouret, MD
55 Fruit Street
Boston, MA 02114
Tel: 617 724-3862   *Fax:* 617 724-6564
E-mail: rtambouret@partners.org
Length: 1 Yr   *ACGME Approved/Offered Positions:* 3
Program ID: 307-24-21-016

Springfield

Baystate Medical Center/Tufts University School of Medicine Program

Sponsor: Baystate Medical Center
Prgm Director: Robert A Goulart, MD
Department of Pathology
759 Chestnut Street
Springfield, MA 01199
Tel: 413 794-4512   *Fax:* 413 794-5893
E-mail: robert.goulart@bhs.org
Length: 1 Yr   *ACGME Approved/Offered Positions:* 1
Program ID: 307-24-21-071

Worcester

University of Massachusetts Program

Sponsor: University of Massachusetts Medical School
UMass Memorial Health Care (Memorial Campus)
UMass Memorial Health Care (University Campus)
Prgm Director: Andrew H Fischer, MD
One Innovation Drive
Three Biotech, Second Floor
Worcester, MA 01605
Tel: 508 793-6140   *Fax:* 508 793-6110
Length: 1 Yr   *ACGME Approved/Offered Positions:* 1
Program ID: 307-24-11-092

Michigan

Ann Arbor

University of Michigan Program

Sponsor: University of Michigan Hospitals and Health
  Centers
Prgm Director: Claire W Michael, MD
Department of Pathology, 2G332 UH
1500 E Medical Center Drive
Ann Arbor, MI 48109
Tel: 734 936-6776   *Fax:* 734 763-4095
Length: 1 Yr   *ACGME Approved/Offered Positions:* 2
Program ID: 307-25-31-019

Detroit

Henry Ford Hospital Program

Sponsor: Henry Ford Hospital
Prgm Director: Chad H Stone, MD
Department of Pathology
2799 West Grand Boulevard
Detroit, MI 48202
Tel: 313 916-2356   *Fax:* 313 916-2385
Length: 1 Yr   *ACGME Approved/Offered Positions:* 2
Program ID: 307-25-21-020

Wayne State University/Detroit Medical Center Program

Sponsor: Wayne State University/Detroit Medical Center
Prgm Director: Mujtaba Husain, MD
4707 St Antoine Boulevard
Detroit, MI 48201
Tel: 313 745-0831   *Fax:* 313 745-7158
E-mail: krost@dmc.org
Length: 1 Yr   *ACGME Approved/Offered Positions:* 2
Program ID: 307-25-21-046

Royal Oak

William Beaumont Hospital Program

Sponsor: William Beaumont Hospital
Prgm Director: Tomi J Kuntzman, DO
3601 West 13 Mile Road
Royal Oak, MI 48073
Tel: 248 898-1256   *Fax:* 248 898-1257
Length: 1 Yr   *ACGME Approved/Offered Positions:* 1
Program ID: 307-25-21-015

Minnesota

Minneapolis

University of Minnesota Program

Sponsor: University of Minnesota Medical School
Abbott-Northwestern Hospital/Allina Health System
Hennepin County Medical Center
University of Minnesota Medical Center, Division of
  Fairview
Prgm Director: Stefan E Pambuccian, MD
Department of Lab Medicine & Pathology
420 Delaware St SE
Minneapolis, MN 55455
Tel: 612 273-4934   *Fax:* 612 625-3976
Length: 1 Yr   *ACGME Approved/Offered Positions:* 2
Program ID: 307-26-12-100

Rochester

College of Medicine, Mayo Clinic (Rochester) Program

Sponsor: College of Medicine, Mayo Clinic
Saint Marys Hospital of Rochester
Prgm Director: Aziza Nassar, MD
200 First Street, SW
Rochester, MN 55905
Tel: 507 284-1196   *Fax:* 507 538-3267
Length: 1 Yr   *ACGME Approved/Offered Positions:* 1
Program ID: 307-26-12-104

Mississippi

Jackson

University of Mississippi Medical Center Program

Sponsor: University of Mississippi School of Medicine
University Hospitals and Clinics
Prgm Director: Mithra Baliga, MD
2500 North State Street
Jackson, MS 39216
Tel: 601 984-1897   *Fax:* 601 984-4967
Length: 1 Yr   *ACGME Approved/Offered Positions:* 2
Program ID: 307-27-21-057

Missouri

St Louis

St Louis University School of Medicine Program

Sponsor: St Louis University School of Medicine
Quest Diagnostics, Inc
St Louis University Hospital
Prgm Director: Ritu Bhalla, MD*
1402 South Grand Boulevard
St Louis, MO 63104
Tel: 314 577-8782
Length: 1 Yr   *ACGME Approved/Offered Positions:* 1
Program ID: 307-28-21-040

Washington University/B-JH/SLCH Consortium Program

Sponsor: Washington University/B-JH/SLCH Consortium
Barnes-Jewish Hospital
St Louis Children's Hospital
Prgm Director: Lourdes Ylagan, MD*
One Barnes Hospital Plaza
St Louis, MO 63110
Tel: 314 362-0115
Length: 1 Yr   *ACGME Approved/Offered Positions:* 2
Program ID: 307-28-21-062

New Hampshire

Lebanon

Dartmouth-Hitchcock Medical Center Program

Sponsor: Mary Hitchcock Memorial Hospital
Prgm Director: Vijayalakshmi Padmanabhan, MBBS, MD
One Medical Center Drive
Lebanon, NH 03756
Tel: 603 650-4807   *Fax:* 603 650-4845
E-mail: viju@hitchcock.org
Length: 1 Yr   *ACGME Approved/Offered Positions:* 2
Program ID: 307-32-21-101

New Mexico

Albuquerque

University of New Mexico Program

Sponsor: University of New Mexico School of Medicine
Presbyterian Healthcare Services
Prgm Director: Therese Bocklage, MD
Department of Pathology, MSC08 4640
1 University of New Mexico
Albuquerque, NM 87131
Tel: 505 272-8071   *Fax:* 505 272-2963
Length: 1 Yr   *ACGME Approved/Offered Positions:* 1
Program ID: 307-34-12-091

New York

Bronx

Albert Einstein College of Medicine Program

Sponsor: Albert Einstein College of Medicine of Yeshiva
  University
Montefiore Medical Center-Henry and Lucy Moses
  Division
Prgm Director: Mark J Suhrland, MD
111 East 210th Street
Bronx, NY 10467
Tel: 718 920-4269   *Fax:* 718 515-5315
E-mail: msuhrlan@montefiore.org
Length: 1 Yr   *ACGME Approved/Offered Positions:* 3
Program ID: 307-35-31-027

Great Neck

NSLIJHS-Albert Einstein College of Medicine at Long Island Jewish Medical Center Program

Sponsor: North Shore-Long Island Jewish Health System
Long Island Jewish Medical Center
Prgm Director: Patricia G Tiscornia-Wasserman, MD
Dept of Pathology, Rm B67
270-05 76th Avenue
New Hyde Park, NY 11040
Tel: 718 470-7592   *Fax:* 718 347-4866
E-mail: sullivan@lij.edu
Length: 1 Yr   *ACGME Approved/Offered Positions:* 1
Program ID: 307-35-21-066

New York

Memorial Sloan-Kettering Cancer Center Program

Sponsor: Memorial Sloan-Kettering Cancer Center
Prgm Director: Maureen F Zakowski, MD
1275 York Avenue
Bobst Building, 5th Floor
New York, NY 10065
Tel: 212 639-5900   *Fax:* 212 639-6318
E-mail: zakowskm@mskcc.org
Length: 1 Yr   *ACGME Approved/Offered Positions:* 3
Program ID: 307-35-21-006

Note: * indicates a newly appointed program director

Mount Sinai School of Medicine Program
Sponsor: Mount Sinai School of Medicine
Mount Sinai Medical Center
Prgm Director: Arnold H Szporn, MD
1 Gustave L Levy Place
Department of Pathology - Box 1194
New York, NY 10029
Tel: 212 241-9160   *Fax:* 212 289-2899
E-mail: arnold.szporn@mountsinai.org
Length: 1 Yr   *ACGME Approved/Offered Positions:* 2
Program ID: 307-35-31-048

New York Presbyterian Hospital (Cornell Campus) Program
Sponsor: New York Presbyterian Hospital
New York Presbyterian Hospital (Cornell Campus)
Prgm Director: John P Crapanzano, MD
525 East 68th Street, F766A
New York, NY 10021
Tel: 212 746-4208   *Fax:* 212 746-8359
E-mail: joc2034@med.cornell.edu
Length: 1 Yr   *ACGME Approved/Offered Positions:* 1
Program ID: 307-35-21-042

New York University School of Medicine Program
Sponsor: New York University School of Medicine
Bellevue Hospital Center
Prgm Director: Pascale Levine, MD
Suite 10U West Tower
550 First Avenue
New York, NY 10016
Tel: 212 731-5115   *Fax:* 212 731-5535
E-mail: pascale.levine@med.nyu.edu
Length: 1 Yr   *ACGME Approved/Offered Positions:* 2
Program ID: 307-35-21-070

Rochester

University of Rochester Program
Sponsor: Strong Memorial Hospital of the University of Rochester
Prgm Director: Ellen Giampoli, MD*
Department of Pathology
601 Elmwood Avenue Box 626
Rochester, NY 14642
Tel: 585 273-4580   *Fax:* 585 273-1027
E-mail: betsy_mcdonald@urmc.rochester.edu
Length: 1 Yr   *ACGME Approved/Offered Positions:* 2
Program ID: 307-35-21-031

Syracuse

SUNY Upstate Medical University Program
Sponsor: SUNY Upstate Medical University
Prgm Director: Kamal K Khurana, MD
750 East Adams Street
Syracuse, NY 13210
Tel: 315 464-4270   *Fax:* 315 464-4267
Length: 1 Yr   *ACGME Approved/Offered Positions:* 1
Program ID: 307-35-21-022

North Carolina

Chapel Hill

University of North Carolina Hospitals Program
Sponsor: University of North Carolina Hospitals
Prgm Director: Susan J Maygarden, MD
CB 7525
Department of Pathology and Laboratory Medicine
Chapel Hill, NC 27599
Tel: 919 843-1071   *Fax:* 919 966-6417
Length: 1 Yr   *ACGME Approved/Offered Positions:* 2
Program ID: 307-36-21-044

Durham

Duke University Hospital Program
Sponsor: Duke University Hospital
Prgm Director: Rajesh C Dash, MD
Box 3712
Durham, NC 27710
Tel: 919 668-3352   *Fax:* 919 668-2937
E-mail: r.dash@duke.edu
Length: 1 Yr   *ACGME Approved/Offered Positions:* 2
Program ID: 307-36-21-039

Greenville

Pitt County Memorial Hospital/East Carolina University Program
Sponsor: Pitt County Memorial Hospital
Prgm Director: James L Finley, MD
2100 Stantonsburg Rd
Pitt County Memorial Hospital
Greenville, NC 27834
Tel: 252 744-5912   *Fax:* 252 744-1889
E-mail: jfinley@pcmh.com
Length: 1 Yr   *ACGME Approved/Offered Positions:* 1
Program ID: 307-36-21-021

Winston-Salem

Wake Forest University School of Medicine Program
Sponsor: Wake Forest University Baptist Medical Center
Prgm Director: James O Cappellari IV, MD
Medical Center Boulevard
Winston-Salem, NC 27157
Tel: 336 716-2650   *Fax:* 336 716-7595
Length: 1 Yr   *ACGME Approved/Offered Positions:* 1
Program ID: 307-36-21-082

Ohio

Cleveland

Case Western Reserve University (MetroHealth) Program
Sponsor: MetroHealth Medical Center
Prgm Director: Amer Khiyami, MD
2500 MetroHealth Drive
Department of Pathology
Cleveland, OH 44109
Tel: 216 778-3879   *Fax:* 216 778-7112
E-mail: akhiyami@metrohealth.org
Length: 1 Yr   *ACGME Approved/Offered Positions:* 1
Program ID: 307-38-21-038

Cleveland Clinic Foundation Program
Sponsor: Cleveland Clinic Foundation
Prgm Director: Jennifer A Brainard, MD
Department of Anatomic Pathology/L25
9500 Euclid Avenue
Cleveland, OH 44195
Tel: 216 445-8474   *Fax:* 216 445-6967
Length: 1 Yr   *ACGME Approved/Offered Positions:* 2
Program ID: 307-38-21-097

University Hospitals Case Medical Center Program
Sponsor: University Hospitals Case Medical Center
Prgm Director: Fadi W Abdul-Karim, MD
Department of Pathology
11100 Euclid Avenue
Cleveland, OH 44106
Tel: 216 844-1807   *Fax:* 216 844-1810
Length: 1 Yr   *ACGME Approved/Offered Positions:* 1
Program ID: 307-38-21-072

Columbus

Ohio State University Hospital Program
Sponsor: Ohio State University Hospital
Prgm Director: Rulong Shen, MD
S305 Rhodes Hall
450 West 10th Avenue
Columbus, OH 43210
Tel: 614 293-8946   *Fax:* 614 293-8747
Length: 1 Yr   *ACGME Approved/Offered Positions:* 2
Program ID: 307-38-31-077

Oregon

Portland

Oregon Health & Science University Program
Sponsor: Oregon Health & Science University Hospital
Prgm Director: Terry Morgan, MD, PhD
Department of Pathology, L113
3181 SW Sam Jackson Park Road
Portland, OR 97239
Tel: 503 494-8276   *Fax:* 503 494-8148
Length: 1 Yr   *ACGME Approved/Offered Positions:* 1
Program ID: 307-40-21-083

Pennsylvania

Danville

Geisinger Health System Program
Sponsor: Geisinger Health System
Geisinger Medical Center
Prgm Director: Steven C Meschter, MD
100 North Academy Avenue
Danville, PA 17822
Tel: 570 271-5385
E-mail: smeschter@geisinger.edu
Length: 1 Yr   *ACGME Approved/Offered Positions:* 1
Program ID: 307-41-21-059

Philadelphia

Drexel University College of Medicine/Hahnemann University Hospital Program
Sponsor: Drexel University College of Medicine/Hahnemann University
Hahnemann University Hospital (Tenet Health System)
Prgm Director: Xiaoli Chen, MD*
245 N 15th Street, Mail Stop 435
Philadelphia, PA 19129
Tel: 215 762-4698   *Fax:* 215 762-3274
Length: 1 Yr   *ACGME Approved/Offered Positions:* 2
Program ID: 307-41-21-028

Thomas Jefferson University Program
Sponsor: Thomas Jefferson University Hospital
Prgm Director: Moira D Wood, MD
260 Main Building
132 S 10th Street
Philadelphia, PA 19107
Tel: 215 955-7752   *Fax:* 215 955-2426
E-mail: moira.wood@mail.tju.edu
Length: 1 Yr   *ACGME Approved/Offered Positions:* 1
Program ID: 307-41-31-009

University of Pennsylvania Program
Sponsor: University of Pennsylvania Health System
Prgm Director: Prabodh K Gupta, MD
6 Founders Pavilion
3400 Spruce Street
Philadelphia, PA 19104
Tel: 215 662-3238   *Fax:* 215 662-6518
Length: 1 Yr   *ACGME Approved/Offered Positions:* 3
Program ID: 307-41-21-004

Programs

Pittsburgh

Allegheny General Hospital Program

Sponsor: Allegheny General Hospital
Prgm Director: Jan F Silverman, MD
320 East North Avenue
Pittsburgh, PA 15212
Tel: 412 359-6886   *Fax:* 412 359-3598
Length: 1 Yr   *ACGME Approved/Offered Positions:* 2
Program ID: 307-41-21-076

University of Pittsburgh Medical Center Medical Education Program

Sponsor: Univ of Pittsburgh Medical Center Medical
   Education
Magee-Womens Hospital of UPMC
UPMC Presbyterian Shadyside
Prgm Director: Walid E Khalbuss, MD, PhD*
Department of Pathology
5150 Centre Avenue POB2 Suite 201
Pittsburgh, PA 15232
Tel: 412 623-3765   *Fax:* 412 623-4779
E-mail: khalbussw2@upmc.edu
Length: 1 Yr   *ACGME Approved/Offered Positions:* 3
Program ID: 307-41-31-049

South Carolina

Charleston

Medical University of South Carolina Program

Sponsor: Medical University of South Carolina College of
   Medicine
MUSC Medical Center
Prgm Director: Jack Yang, MD*
165 Ashley Avenue, Suite 309
PO Box 250908
Charleston, SC 29425
Tel: 843 792-3121   *Fax:* 843 792-0555
E-mail: yanja@musc.edu
Length: 1 Yr   *ACGME Approved/Offered Positions:* 2
Program ID: 307-45-21-012

Tennessee

Knoxville

University of Tennessee Medical Center at Knoxville Program

Sponsor: University of Tennessee Graduate School of
   Medicine
University of Tennessee Memorial Hospital
Prgm Director: Elizabeth W Hubbard, MD
1924 Alcoa Highway
Box 108
Knoxville, TN 37920
Tel: 865 305-9080   *Fax:* 865 305-6866
E-mail: ehubbard@utmck.edu
Length: 1 Yr   *ACGME Approved/Offered Positions:* 1
Program ID: 307-47-21-095

Texas

Dallas

University of Texas Southwestern Medical School Program

Sponsor: University of Texas Southwestern Medical
   School
Dallas County Hospital District-Parkland Memorial
   Hospital
Prgm Director: Wareef Kabbani, MD*
5323 Harry Hines Boulevard
Dallas, TX 75235
Tel: 214 590-8176   *Fax:* 214 590-1473
E-mail: wareef.kabbani@utsouthwestern.edu
Length: 1 Yr   *ACGME Approved/Offered Positions:* 2
Program ID: 307-48-21-060

Galveston

University of Texas Medical Branch Hospitals Program

Sponsor: University of Texas Medical Branch Hospitals
Prgm Director: Vicki J Schnadig, MD
301 University Boulevard
Galveston, TX 77555
Tel: 409 772-6655   *Fax:* 409 772-8437
E-mail: eeshipwa@utmb.edu
Length: 1 Yr   *ACGME Approved/Offered Positions:* 1
Program ID: 307-48-13-093

Houston

Baylor College of Medicine Program

Sponsor: Baylor College of Medicine
Harris County Hospital District-Ben Taub General
   Hospital
Michael E DeBakey VA Medical Center - Houston
Prgm Director: Rodolfo Laucirica, MD
One Baylor Plaza
Department of Pathology
Houston, TX 77030
Tel: 713 873-3216   *Fax:* 713 873-3214
Length: 1 Yr   *ACGME Approved/Offered Positions:* 3
Program ID: 307-48-21-023

Methodist Hospital (Houston) Program

Sponsor: Methodist Hospital (Houston)
Lyndon B Johnson General Hospital
University of Texas M D Anderson Cancer Center
Prgm Director: Dina R Mody, MD
6565 Fannin St, M227
Houston, TX 77030
Tel: 713 441-6483   *Fax:* 713 441-3489
E-mail: ljozwiak@tmhs.org
Length: 1 Yr   *ACGME Approved/Offered Positions:* 2
Program ID: 307-48-31-099

University of Texas M D Anderson Cancer Center Program

Sponsor: University of Texas M D Anderson Cancer
   Center
Prgm Director: Nancy P Caraway, MD*
1515 Holcombe Boulevard, Unit 53
Houston, TX 77030
Tel: 713 792-2068   *Fax:* 713 792-2067
E-mail: crconner@mdanderson.org
Length: 1 Yr   *ACGME Approved/Offered Positions:* 6
Program ID: 307-48-21-054

Lackland AFB

San Antonio Uniformed Services Health Education Consortium Program

Sponsor: San Antonio Uniformed Services Health
   Education Consortium
Brooke Army Medical Center
Wilford Hall Medical Center (AETC)
Prgm Director: Karen K Nauschuetz, MD*
Department of Pathology
3851 Roger Brooke Drive
Fort Sam Houston, TX 78234
Tel: 210 916-3307   *Fax:* 210 916-4530
E-mail: karen.nauschuetz@amedd.army.mil
Length: 1 Yr   *ACGME Approved/Offered Positions:* 2
Program ID: 307-48-21-011
Uniformed Services Program

San Antonio

University of Texas Health Science Center at San Antonio Program

Sponsor: University of Texas School of Medicine at San
   Antonio
Audie L Murphy Memorial Veterans Hospital (San
   Antonio)
University Health System
Prgm Director: Philip T Valente, MD
7703 Floyd Curl Drive
San Antonio, TX 78229
Tel: 210 567-6731   *Fax:* 210 567-2478
Length: 1 Yr   *ACGME Approved/Offered Positions:* 2
Program ID: 307-48-11-018

Temple

Texas A&M College of Medicine-Scott and White Program

Sponsor: Scott and White Memorial Hospital
Prgm Director: Lubna H Sayage-Rabie, MD
2401 South 31st Street
Temple, TX 76508
Tel: 254 724-3691   *Fax:* 254 724-4391
E-mail: cdixon@swmail.sw.org
Length: 1 Yr   *ACGME Approved/Offered Positions:* 2
Program ID: 307-48-21-086

Utah

Salt Lake City

University of Utah Program

Sponsor: University of Utah Medical Center
Prgm Director: Brian T Collins, MD
Room 3860
1950 Circle of Hope
Salt Lake City, UT 84112
Tel: 801 587-4608   *Fax:* 801 581-7035
E-mail: brian.collins@path.utah.edu
Length: 1 Yr   *ACGME Approved/Offered Positions:* 1
Program ID: 307-49-31-103

Vermont

Burlington

University of Vermont Program

Sponsor: Fletcher Allen Health Care
Prgm Director: Scott Anderson, MD*
ACC-East Pavilion Level 2
111 Colchester Avenue
Burlington, VT 05401
Tel: 802 847-2172   *Fax:* 802 847-9644
Length: 1 Yr   *ACGME Approved/Offered Positions:* 1
Program ID: 307-50-21-056

Note: * indicates a newly appointed program director

Virginia

Charlottesville

University of Virginia Program
Sponsor: University of Virginia Medical Center
Prgm Director: Kristen A Atkins, MD
PO Box 800214
Charlottesville, VA 22908
Tel: 434 924-9498   *Fax:* 434 924-9492
E-mail: kaa2p@virginia.edu
Length: 1 Yr   *ACGME Approved/Offered Positions:* 2
Program ID: 307-51-21-069

Richmond

Virginia Commonwealth University Health System Program
Sponsor: Virginia Commonwealth University Health System
Medical College of Virginia Hospitals
Prgm Director: Celeste N Powers, MD, PhD
Box 980139
Richmond, VA 23298
Tel: 804 628-0142   *Fax:* 804 828-5055
E-mail: cpowers@mcvh-vcu.edu
Length: 1 Yr   *ACGME Approved/Offered Positions:* 2
Program ID: 307-51-21-055

Washington

Seattle

University of Washington Program
Sponsor: University of Washington School of Medicine
Harborview Medical Center
Prgm Director: Annette Peck-Sabath, MD*
325 9th Avenue
Box 359791
Seattle, WA 98104
Tel: 206 744-4271   *Fax:* 206 744-8240
E-mail: residency@pathology.washington.edu
Length: 1 Yr   *ACGME Approved/Offered Positions:* 1
Program ID: 307-54-21-084

Wisconsin

Madison

University of Wisconsin Program
Sponsor: University of Wisconsin Hospital and Clinics
Prgm Director: Suzanne M Selvaggi, MD
University of Wisconsin Hospital and Clinics
600 Highland Ave
Madison, WI 53792
Tel: 608 265-9160   *Fax:* 608 263-6453
E-mail: SSelvaggi@uwhealth.org
Length: 1 Yr   *ACGME Approved/Offered Positions:* 2
Program ID: 307-56-21-052

Milwaukee

Medical College of Wisconsin Affiliated Hospitals Program
Sponsor: Medical College of Wisconsin Affiliated Hospitals, Inc
Froedtert Memorial Lutheran Hospital
Prgm Director: Vinod B Shidham, MD
Department of Pathology
9200 West Wisconsin Avenue
Milwaukee, WI 53226
Tel: 414 805-8452   *Fax:* 414 805-8444
E-mail: vshidham@hotmail.com
Length: 1 Yr   *ACGME Approved/Offered Positions:* 2
Program ID: 307-56-21-085

Dermatology

Alabama

Birmingham

University of Alabama Medical Center Program
Sponsor: University of Alabama Hospital
Veterans Affairs Medical Center (Birmingham)
Prgm Director: Boni E Elewski, MD
EFH 414
1720 University Blvd
Birmingham, AL 35294
Tel: 205 934-5189   *Fax:* 205 934-5766
E-mail: beelewski@aol.com
Length: 3 Yrs   *ACGME Approved/Offered Positions:* 15
Program ID: 080-01-21-010

Arizona

Scottsdale

College of Medicine, Mayo Clinic (Arizona) Program
Sponsor: College of Medicine, Mayo Clinic
Mayo Clinic (Arizona)
Maricopa Medical Center
Mayo Clinic Hospital
Phoenix Children's Hospital
Prgm Director: Karen E Warschaw, MD
13400 E Shea Boulevard
Scottsdale, AZ 85259
Tel: 480 301-4898   *Fax:* 480 301-9272
Length: 3 Yrs   *ACGME Approved/Offered Positions:* 6
Program ID: 080-03-21-127

Arkansas

Little Rock

University of Arkansas for Medical Sciences Program
Sponsor: University of Arkansas College of Medicine
Central Arkansas Veterans Healthcare System
UAMS Medical Center
Prgm Director: Cheryl A Armstrong, MD*
Department of Dermatology
4301 West Markham St, #576
Little Rock, AR 72205
Tel: 501 686-8259   *Fax:* 501 686-7264
E-mail: carmstrong@uams.edu
Length: 4 Yrs   *ACGME Approved/Offered Positions:* 12
Program ID: 080-04-21-013

California

Loma Linda

Loma Linda University Program
Sponsor: Loma Linda University Medical Center
Jerry L Pettis Memorial Veterans Hospital
Riverside County Regional Medical Center
Prgm Director: Nancy J Anderson, MD
Dept of Dermatology, Suite 2600
11370 Anderson Street
Loma Linda, CA 92354
Tel: 909 558-2842   *Fax:* 909 558-2442
Length: 3 Yrs   *ACGME Approved/Offered Positions:* 6
Program ID: 080-05-21-111

Los Angeles

UCLA Medical Center Program
Sponsor: UCLA David Geffen School of Medicine/UCLA Medical Center
Olive View/UCLA Medical Center
UCLA Medical Center
VA Greater Los Angeles Healthcare System
Prgm Director: Robert L Modlin, MD
52-121 CHS
10833 Le Conte Ave
Los Angeles, CA 90095
Tel: 310 825-6214   *Fax:* 310 206-9878
Length: 3 Yrs   *ACGME Approved/Offered Positions:* 11
Program ID: 080-05-21-017

University of Southern California/LAC+USC Medical Center Program
Sponsor: University of Southern California/LAC+USC Medical Center
LAC+USC Medical Center
Prgm Director: David H Peng, MD, MPH*
1200 N State Street, Room 8440
Los Angeles, CA 90033
Tel: 323 865-0983   *Fax:* 323 226-2654
Length: 3 Yrs   *ACGME Approved/Offered Positions:* 9
Program ID: 080-05-11-015

Orange

University of California (Irvine) Program
Sponsor: University of California (Irvine) Medical Center
Kaiser Foundation Hospitals (Anaheim)
VA Long Beach Healthcare System
Prgm Director: Kristen M Kelly, MD
101 The City Drive South
Bldg 53, Rm 302A
Orange, CA 92868
Tel: 714 456-8381   *Fax:* 714 456-8313
E-mail: kmkelly@uci.edu
Length: 3 Yrs   *ACGME Approved/Offered Positions:* 12
Program ID: 080-05-21-014

Sacramento

University of California (Davis) Health System Program
Sponsor: University of California (Davis) Health System
University of California (Davis) Medical Center
VA Northern California Health Care System
Prgm Director: Nasim Fazel, MD, DDS*
3301 C Street, Suite 1400
Sacramento, CA 95816
Tel: 916 734-6876   *Fax:* 916 442-5702
E-mail: nasim.fazel@ucdmc.ucdavis.edu
Length: 3 Yrs   *ACGME Approved/Offered Positions:* 9
Program ID: 080-05-21-101

San Diego

Naval Medical Center (San Diego) Program
Sponsor: Naval Medical Center (San Diego)
Prgm Director: Neil F Gibbs, MD
34520 Bob Wilson Drive, Suite 300
San Diego, CA 92134
Tel: 619 532-9666   *Fax:* 619 532-9458
E-mail: marianne.mccaskill@med.navy.mil
Length: 3 Yrs   *ACGME Approved/Offered Positions:* 15
Program ID: 080-05-31-006
Uniformed Services Program

Programs

University of California (San Diego) Program

Sponsor: University of California (San Diego) Medical Center
Veterans Affairs Medical Center (San Diego)
Prgm Director: Richard L Gallo, MD, PhD*
Division of Dermatology
200 West Arbor Drive
San Diego, CA 92103
Tel: 619 543-3626   *Fax:* 619 543-2144
Length: 3 Yrs   *ACGME Approved/Offered Positions:* 9
Program ID: 080-05-21-018

San Francisco

University of California (San Francisco) Program

Sponsor: University of California (San Francisco) School of Medicine
San Francisco General Hospital Medical Center
UCSF and Mount Zion Medical Centers
Veterans Affairs Medical Center (San Francisco)
Prgm Director: Jack S Resneck Jr, MD
1701 Divisadero Street
3rd Floor
San Francisco, CA 94143
Tel: 415 353-9610
E-mail: resneckj@derm.ucsf.edu
Length: 3 Yrs   *ACGME Approved/Offered Positions:* 18
Program ID: 080-05-21-019

Stanford

Stanford University Program

Sponsor: Stanford Hospital and Clinics
Santa Clara Valley Medical Center
Veterans Affairs Palo Alto Health Care System
Prgm Director: Alfred T Lane, MD
Department of Dermatology
900 Blake Wilbur Drive, Room W0069
Stanford, CA 94305
Tel: 650 723-6105   *Fax:* 650 723-7796
Length: 3 Yrs   *ACGME Approved/Offered Positions:* 16
Program ID: 080-05-21-020

Torrance

Los Angeles County-Harbor-UCLA Medical Center Program

Sponsor: Los Angeles County-Harbor-UCLA Medical Center
Willow Medical Center
Prgm Director: Michael S Kolodney, MD, PhD
LA Biomedical Research Institute
1124 W Carson Street, Bldg, HH-1, Rm 210
Torrance, CA 90502
Tel: 310 222-1845   *Fax:* 310 222-1847
E-mail: harborucladerm@yahoo.com
Length: 3 Yrs   *ACGME Approved/Offered Positions:* 3
Program ID: 080-05-12-137

Colorado

Aurora

University of Colorado Denver Program

Sponsor: University of Colorado Denver School of Medicine
Denver Health Medical Center
University of Colorado Hospital
Veterans Affairs Medical Center (Denver)
Prgm Director: Sylvia L Brice, MD
PO Box 6510
Campus Stop F703
Aurora, CO 80045
Tel: 720 848-0510   *Fax:* 720 848-0530
E-mail: kemp.weston@uchsc.edu
Length: 3 Yrs   *ACGME Approved/Offered Positions:* 15
Program ID: 080-07-21-022

Connecticut

Farmington

University of Connecticut Program

Sponsor: University of Connecticut School of Medicine
St Francis Hospital and Medical Center
VA Connecticut-Newington
Prgm Director: Jane M Grant-Kels, MD
Dermatology MC-6230, Dowling South Suite 300
263 Farmington Avenue
Farmington, CT 06030
Tel: 860 679-6759   *Fax:* 860 679-1267
E-mail: ciwanik@uchc.edu
Length: 3 Yrs   *ACGME Approved/Offered Positions:* 6
Program ID: 080-08-31-138

New Haven

Yale-New Haven Medical Center Program

Sponsor: Yale-New Haven Hospital
Prgm Director: Michael Girardi, MD
333 Cedar Street
Bldg LCI, Rm 501 PO Box 208059
New Haven, CT 06520
Tel: 203 785-4092   *Fax:* 203 785-7637
Length: 3 Yrs   *ACGME Approved/Offered Positions:* 12
Program ID: 080-08-21-023

District of Columbia

Washington

Howard University Program

Sponsor: Howard University Hospital
Children's National Medical Center
Veterans Affairs Medical Center (Washington, DC)
Prgm Director: Rebat M Halder, MD
2041 Georgia Avenue, NW
Washington, DC 20060
Tel: 202 865-6725   *Fax:* 202 865-1757
Length: 3 Yrs   *ACGME Approved/Offered Positions:* 7
Program ID: 080-10-21-025

Washington Hospital Center Program

Sponsor: Washington Hospital Center
Children's National Medical Center
Prgm Director: Alan N Moshell, MD
110 Irving Street, NW, 2B-44
Washington, DC 20010
Tel: 202 877-6654   *Fax:* 202 877-3288
Length: 3 Yrs   *ACGME Approved/Offered Positions:* 6
Program ID: 080-10-21-106

Florida

Gainesville

University of Florida Program

Sponsor: University of Florida College of Medicine
North Florida/South Georgia Veterans Health System
Shands Hospital at the University of Florida
Prgm Director: Stanton K Wesson, MD
PO Box 100277
Division of Dermatology & Cutaneous Surgery
Gainesville, FL 32610
Tel: 352 392-4984   *Fax:* 352 392-5376
Length: 3 Yrs   *ACGME Approved/Offered Positions:* 6
Program ID: 080-11-21-115

Jacksonville

College of Medicine, Mayo Clinic (Jacksonville) Program

Sponsor: College of Medicine, Mayo Clinic
Mayo Clinic (Jacksonville)
Prgm Director: James H Keeling, MD
4500 San Pablo Road
Jacksonville, FL 32224
Tel: 904 953-0429   *Fax:* 904 953-0430
E-mail: hammer.linda@mayo.edu
Length: 3 Yrs   *ACGME Approved/Offered Positions:* 6
Program ID: 080-11-31-125

Miami

Jackson Memorial Hospital/Jackson Health System Program

Sponsor: Jackson Memorial Hospital/Jackson Health System
University of Miami Sylvester Comprehensive Cancer Center
Veterans Affairs Medical Center (Miami)
Prgm Director: Lawrence A Schachner, MD
PO Box 016250 (R-250)
Miami, FL 33101
Tel: 305 243-6742   *Fax:* 305 243-6191
Length: 3 Yrs   *ACGME Approved/Offered Positions:* 21
Program ID: 080-11-21-026

Tampa

University of South Florida Program

Sponsor: University of South Florida College of Medicine
H Lee Moffitt Cancer Center
James A Haley Veterans Hospital
Tampa General Hospital
Prgm Director: Neil A Fenske, MD
MDC Box 79
12901 Bruce B Downs Blvd
Tampa, FL 33612
Tel: 813 974-3070   *Fax:* 813 974-4272
E-mail: slamar@health.usf.edu
Length: 3 Yrs   *ACGME Approved/Offered Positions:* 12
Program ID: 080-11-21-096

Georgia

Atlanta

Emory University Program

Sponsor: Emory University School of Medicine
Emory University Hospital
Grady Health System
Veterans Affairs Medical Center (Atlanta)
Prgm Director: Robert A Swerlick, MD
Department of Dermatology- WMRB Building
101 Woodruff Circle, Suite 5001
Atlanta, GA 30322
Tel: 404 727-3669   *Fax:* 404 727-5874
Length: 3 Yrs   *ACGME Approved/Offered Positions:* 16
Program ID: 080-12-21-028

Note: * indicates a newly appointed program director

Augusta

Medical College of Georgia Program
Sponsor: Medical College of Georgia
Veterans Affairs Medical Center (Augusta)
Prgm Director: Jack L Lesher Jr, MD
1004 Chafee Avenue
Division of Dermatology
Augusta, GA 30904
Tel: 706 721-6231   *Fax:* 706 721-6220
Length: 3 Yrs   *ACGME Approved/Offered Positions:* 9
Program ID: 080-12-11-029

Illinois

Chicago

John H Stroger Hospital of Cook County Program
Sponsor: John H Stroger Hospital of Cook County
Prgm Director: Warren W Piette, MD
Administration Bldg, 5th Floor, Room 519
1900 W Polk Street
Chicago, IL 60612
Tel: 312 864-4478   *Fax:* 312 864-9663
Length: 3 Yrs   *ACGME Approved/Offered Positions:* 9
Program ID: 080-16-12-030

McGaw Medical Center of Northwestern University Program
Sponsor: McGaw Medical Center of Northwestern
  University
Evanston Hospital
Northwestern Memorial Hospital
Prgm Director: Amy S Paller, MD
676 North St Clair Street
Suite 1600
Chicago, IL 60611
Tel: 312 695-3721   *Fax:* 312 695-0664
E-mail: msferruz@nmff.org
Length: 3 Yrs   *ACGME Approved/Offered Positions:* 11
Program ID: 080-16-21-031

Rush University Medical Center Program
Sponsor: Rush University Medical Center
Prgm Director: Michael D Tharp, MD
1653 W Congress Parkway
220 Annex Building
Chicago, IL 60612
Tel: 312 942-6096   *Fax:* 312 942-7778
E-mail: derm@rush.edu
Length: 3 Yrs   *ACGME Approved/Offered Positions:* 5
Program ID: 080-16-11-032

University of Chicago Program
Sponsor: University of Chicago Medical Center
Prgm Director: Christopher R Shea, MD
Section of Dermatology
5841 S Maryland Avenue, MC 5067
Chicago, IL 60637
Tel: 773 702-6559   *Fax:* 773 702-8398
E-mail: nsimweny@medicine.bsd.uchicago.edu
Length: 3 Yrs   *ACGME Approved/Offered Positions:* 10
Program ID: 080-16-11-033

University of Illinois College of Medicine at Chicago Program
Sponsor: University of Illinois College of Medicine at
  Chicago
Jesse Brown Veterans Affairs Medical Center
University of Illinois Hospital and Clinics
Prgm Director: Lawrence S Chan, MD
840 S Wood Street, M/C 624, Room 380 CME
Chicago, IL 60612
Tel: 312 996-6966   *Fax:* 312 996-1188
Length: 3 Yrs   *ACGME Approved/Offered Positions:* 12
Program ID: 080-16-21-034

Maywood

Loyola University Program
Sponsor: Loyola University Medical Center
Edward Hines, Jr Veterans Affairs Hospital
Prgm Director: James W Swan, MD
2160 S First Avenue
Bldg 54, Room 101
Maywood, IL 60153
Tel: 708 216-4962   *Fax:* 708 327-3385
E-mail: jswan@lumc.edu
Length: 3 Yrs   *ACGME Approved/Offered Positions:* 6
Program ID: 080-16-12-135

Springfield

Southern Illinois University Program
Sponsor: Southern Illinois University School of Medicine
Memorial Medical Center
St John's Hospital
Prgm Director: Lucinda S Buescher, MD
PO Box 19644
Springfield, IL 62794
Tel: 217 545-5465   *Fax:* 217 545-4485
E-mail: smiller@siumed.edu
Length: 3 Yrs   *ACGME Approved/Offered Positions:* 6
Program ID: 080-16-21-118

Indiana

Indianapolis

Indiana University School of Medicine Program
Sponsor: Indiana University School of Medicine
Clarian Indiana University Hospital
Clarian Riley Hospital for Children
Richard L Roudebush Veterans Affairs Medical Center
William N Wishard Memorial Hospital
Prgm Director: Jeffrey B Travers, MD, PhD
550 N University Blvd, Suite 3240
Indianapolis, IN 46202
Tel: 317 274-7705   *Fax:* 317 274-7051
Length: 4 Yrs   *ACGME Approved/Offered Positions:* 11
Program ID: 080-17-21-035

Iowa

Iowa City

University of Iowa Hospitals and Clinics Program
Sponsor: University of Iowa Hospitals and Clinics
Veterans Affairs Medical Center (Iowa City)
Prgm Director: Christopher J Arpey, MD
Department of Dermatology, 40025Z PFP
200 Hawkins Drive
Iowa City, IA 52242
Tel: 319 356-1694   *Fax:* 319 356-0349
E-mail: christopher-arpey@uiowa.edu
Length: 3 Yrs   *ACGME Approved/Offered Positions:* 13
Program ID: 080-18-21-036

Kansas

Kansas City

University of Kansas School of Medicine Program
Sponsor: University of Kansas School of Medicine
Children's Mercy Hospital
University of Kansas Hospital
Veterans Affairs Medical Center (Kansas City)
Prgm Director: Daniel J Aires, MD
3901 Rainbow Boulevard
Room 40009 Wescoe
Kansas City, KS 66160
Tel: 913 588-3840   *Fax:* 913 588-8300
E-mail: skovash@kumc.edu
Length: 3 Yrs   *ACGME Approved/Offered Positions:* 9
Program ID: 080-19-11-037

Kentucky

Louisville

University of Louisville Program
Sponsor: University of Louisville School of Medicine
University of Louisville Hospital
Veterans Affairs Medical Center (Louisville)
Prgm Director: Jeffrey P Callen, MD
310 East Broadway
Louisville, KY 40292
Tel: 502 852-7287   *Fax:* 502 852-4720
Length: 3 Yrs   *ACGME Approved/Offered Positions:* 7
Program ID: 080-20-21-038

Louisiana

New Orleans

Louisiana State University Program
Sponsor: Louisiana State University School of Medicine
Earl K Long Medical Center
Medical Center of Louisiana at New Orleans
Veterans Affairs Medical Center (New Orleans)
Prgm Director: Brian D Lee, MD
Department of Dermatology
1542 Tulane Ave, Ste 639
New Orleans, LA 70112
Tel: 504 568-7110   *Fax:* 504 568-2170
Length: 3 Yrs   *ACGME Approved/Offered Positions:* 16
Program ID: 080-21-21-109

Tulane University Program
Sponsor: Tulane University School of Medicine
Medical Center of Louisiana at New Orleans
Ochsner Clinic Foundation
Tulane University Hospital and Clinics
Prgm Director: Joseph P Shrum, MD
1430 Tulane Avenue, TB-36
New Orleans, LA 70112
Tel: 504 988-5114   *Fax:* 504 988-7382
E-mail: jshrum@tulane.edu
Length: 3 Yrs   *ACGME Approved/Offered Positions:* 12
Program ID: 080-21-21-108

Maryland

Baltimore

Johns Hopkins University Program
Sponsor: Johns Hopkins University School of Medicine
Johns Hopkins Bayview Medical Center
Johns Hopkins Hospital
Prgm Director: Rhoda M Alani, MD
601 North Caroline Street, JHOPC, 6th Fl
Baltimore, MD 21287
Tel: 410 614-6204   *Fax:* 410 614-5015
Length: 3 Yrs   *ACGME Approved/Offered Positions:* 10
Program ID: 080-23-21-040

University of Maryland Program
Sponsor: University of Maryland Medical System
Veterans Affairs Medical Center (Baltimore)
Prgm Director: Anthony A Gaspari, MD
405 West Redwood Street
6th Floor
Baltimore, MD 21201
Tel: 410 328-5766   *Fax:* 410 328-0098
Length: 3 Yrs   *ACGME Approved/Offered Positions:* 6
Program ID: 080-23-21-041

Bethesda

National Capital Consortium Program
Sponsor: National Capital Consortium
National Naval Medical Center (Bethesda)
Walter Reed Army Medical Center
Prgm Director: George W Turiansky, MD
Dermatology Service, Clinic 1J
6900 Georgia Avenue NW
Washington, DC 20307
Tel: 202 782-9464   *Fax:* 202 782-4698
Length: 3 Yrs   *ACGME Approved/Offered Positions:* 15
Program ID: 080-10-21-123
Uniformed Services Program

National Institutes of Health Clinical Center Program
Sponsor: Clinical Center at the National Institutes of Health
Prgm Director: Mark C Udey, MD, PhD
Building 10, Room 12N238
10 Center Drive MSC 1908
Bethesda, MD 20892
Tel: 301 496-2481   *Fax:* 301 496-5370
Length: 1 Yr   *ACGME Approved/Offered Positions:* 4
Program ID: 080-23-12-008

Massachusetts

Boston

Boston University Medical Center Program
Sponsor: Boston Medical Center
Tufts Medical Center
Veterans Affairs Medical Center (Boston)
Prgm Director: Mina Yaar, MD*
609 Albany Street
Boston, MA 02118
Tel: 617 638-5534   *Fax:* 617 638-5515
Length: 3 Yrs   *ACGME Approved/Offered Positions:* 15
Program ID: 080-24-21-044

Massachusetts General Hospital/Harvard Medical School Program
Sponsor: Massachusetts General Hospital
Beth Israel Deaconess Medical Center
Prgm Director: Joseph Kvedar, MD
Bartlett 616
55 Fruit Street
Boston, MA 02114
Tel: 617 726-5254   *Fax:* 617 726-1875
E-mail: dkovacev@partners.org
Length: 3 Yrs   *ACGME Approved/Offered Positions:* 20
Program ID: 080-24-31-043

Tufts Medical Center Program
Sponsor: Tufts Medical Center
Veterans Affairs Medical Center (Boston)
Prgm Director: Daniel S Loo, MD
800 Washington Street, #114
Boston, MA 02111
Tel: 617 636-6430   *Fax:* 617 636-9169
Length: 3 Yrs   *ACGME Approved/Offered Positions:* 9
Program ID: 080-24-21-141

Worcester

University of Massachusetts Program
Sponsor: University of Massachusetts Medical School
UMass Memorial Health Care (Hahnemann Campus)
UMass Memorial Health Care (University Campus)
Veterans Affairs Medical Center (Boston)
Prgm Director: Karen Wiss, MD*
Division of Dermatology
281 Lincoln St, Hahnemann Campus
Worcester, MA 01605
Tel: 508 334-5978   *Fax:* 508 334-5981
E-mail: wissk@ummhc.org
Length: 3 Yrs   *ACGME Approved/Offered Positions:* 9
Program ID: 080-24-21-114

Michigan

Ann Arbor

University of Michigan Program
Sponsor: University of Michigan Hospitals and Health Centers
Prgm Director: Charles N Ellis, MD
1910 Taubman Center 0314 - Residency
1500 E Medical Center Drive
Ann Arbor, MI 48109
Tel: 734 936-6674   *Fax:* 734 936-6395
E-mail: Derm.Res.App@umich.edu
Length: 4 Yrs   *ACGME Approved/Offered Positions:* 24
Program ID: 080-25-31-045

Detroit

Henry Ford Hospital Program
Sponsor: Henry Ford Hospital
Prgm Director: Alice C Watson, MD
3031 West Grand Blvd
Suite 800
Detroit, MI 48202
Tel: 313 916-2171
Length: 3 Yrs   *ACGME Approved/Offered Positions:* 18
Program ID: 080-25-12-046

Wayne State University Program
Sponsor: Wayne State University School of Medicine
Oakwood Heritage Hospital
Veterans Affairs Medical Center (Detroit)
Prgm Director: David A Mehregan, MD
Graduate Medical Education
540 E Canfield, Rm 1241
Detroit, MI 48201
Tel: 313 429-7843   *Fax:* 313 429-7931
E-mail: pnelson@med.wayne.edu
Length: 3 Yrs   *ACGME Approved/Offered Positions:* 12
Program ID: 080-25-13-139

Minnesota

Minneapolis

University of Minnesota Program
Sponsor: University of Minnesota Medical School
Hennepin County Medical Center
University of Minnesota Medical Center, Division of Fairview
Veterans Affairs Medical Center (Minneapolis)
Prgm Director: Neal A Foman, MD, MS*
MMC 98 Dermatology
420 Delaware Street SE
Minneapolis, MN 55455
Tel: 612 624-9964
E-mail: dermapp@umn.edu
Length: 3 Yrs   *ACGME Approved/Offered Positions:* 18
Program ID: 080-26-31-048

Rochester

College of Medicine, Mayo Clinic (Rochester) Program
Sponsor: College of Medicine, Mayo Clinic
Mayo Clinic (Rochester)
Prgm Director: Amer N Kalaaji, MD
200 First St SW
Rochester, MN 55905
Tel: 507 284-5997   *Fax:* 507 284-2072
E-mail: mayo.derm@mayo.edu
Length: 3 Yrs   *ACGME Approved/Offered Positions:* 25
Program ID: 080-26-21-049

Missouri

Columbia

University of Missouri-Columbia Program
Sponsor: University of Missouri-Columbia School of Medicine
Harry S Truman Memorial Veterans Hospital
University Hospitals and Clinics
Prgm Director: Dana S Ward, MD
Department of Dermatology
1 Hospital Drive MA111
Columbia, MO 65212
Tel: 573 882-8578   *Fax:* 573 884-5947
Length: 3 Yrs   *ACGME Approved/Offered Positions:* 9
Program ID: 080-28-21-050

St Louis

St Louis University School of Medicine Program
Sponsor: St Louis University School of Medicine
Anheuser-Busch Institute
Prgm Director: Scott W Fosko, MD
1402 South Grand Boulevard
St Louis, MO 63104
Tel: 314 256-3433   *Fax:* 314 256-3431
Length: 3 Yrs   *ACGME Approved/Offered Positions:* 12
Program ID: 080-28-21-116

Washington University/B-JH/SLCH Consortium Program
Sponsor: Washington University/B-JH/SLCH Consortium
Barnes-Jewish Hospital
Prgm Director: Susan J Bayliss, MD
Division of Dermatology
660 South Euclid Avenue, Box 8123
St Louis, MO 63110
Tel: 314 454-2714   *Fax:* 314 454-5928
E-mail: rbrannan@dom.wustl.edu
Length: 3 Yrs   *ACGME Approved/Offered Positions:* 16
Program ID: 080-28-21-051

Note: * indicates a newly appointed program director

New Hampshire

Lebanon

Dartmouth-Hitchcock Medical Center Program

Sponsor: Mary Hitchcock Memorial Hospital
Veterans Affairs Medical Center (White River Junction)
Prgm Director: James G Dinulos, MD, DPM
One Medical Center Drive
Lebanon, NH 03756
Tel: 603 653-9400   *Fax:* 603 650-0921
E-mail: elaine.r.danyew@hitchcock.org
Length: 3 Yrs   *ACGME Approved/Offered Positions:* 6
Program ID: 080-32-21-053

New Jersey

Camden

UMDNJ-Robert Wood Johnson Medical School (Camden) Program

Sponsor: Cooper Hospital-University Medical Center
Prgm Director: Justin J Green, MD
Three Cooper Plaza
Suite 220
Camden, NJ 08103
Tel: 856 342-2014   *Fax:* 856 966-0735
E-mail: lanzilotta-elaine@cooperhealth.edu
Length: 3 Yrs   *ACGME Approved/Offered Positions:* 3
Program ID: 080-33-21-117

New Brunswick

UMDNJ-Robert Wood Johnson Medical School Program A

Sponsor: UMDNJ-Robert Wood Johnson Medical School
Robert Wood Johnson University Hospital
Prgm Director: Amy S Pappert, MD
Department of Dermatology
1 World's Fair Drive, Suite 2400
Somerset, NJ 08873
Tel: 732 235-7765   *Fax:* 732 235-6568
E-mail: gallinvk@umdnj.edu
Length: 3 Yrs   *ACGME Approved/Offered Positions:* 3
Program ID: 080-33-31-128

Newark

UMDNJ-New Jersey Medical School Program

Sponsor: UMDNJ-New Jersey Medical School
UMDNJ-University Hospital
Veterans Affairs New Jersey Health Care System
Prgm Director: Robert A Schwartz, MD, MPH
185 South Orange Avenue
MSB-H576
Newark, NJ 07103
Tel: 973 972-6884
Length: 3 Yrs   *ACGME Approved/Offered Positions:* 6
Program ID: 080-33-21-107

New Mexico

Albuquerque

University of New Mexico Program

Sponsor: University of New Mexico School of Medicine
University of New Mexico Hospital
Veterans Affairs Medical Center (Albuquerque)
Prgm Director: R Steven Padilla, MD, MBA
Department of Dermatology - MSC 07 4240
1021 Medical Arts Avenue, NE
Albuquerque, NM 87131
Tel: 505 272-6000   *Fax:* 505 272-6003
E-mail: dermatology@salud.unm.edu
Length: 3 Yrs   *ACGME Approved/Offered Positions:* 6
Program ID: 080-34-21-054

New York

Bronx

Albert Einstein College of Medicine Program

Sponsor: Albert Einstein College of Medicine of Yeshiva
University
Montefiore Medical Center-Henry and Lucy Moses
Division
Montefiore Medical Center-Weiler Division
North Bronx Healthcare Network-Jacobi Medical Center
North Bronx Healthcare Network-North Central Bronx
Hospital
Prgm Director: Steven R Cohen, MD, MPH
Division of Dermatology
111 East 210th Street
Bronx, NY 10467
Tel: 718 920-2176   *Fax:* 718 944-4219
E-mail: srcohen@montefiore.org
Length: 3 Yrs   *ACGME Approved/Offered Positions:* 13
Program ID: 080-35-31-058

Brooklyn

SUNY Health Science Center at Brooklyn Program

Sponsor: SUNY Health Science Center at Brooklyn
Kings County Hospital Center
University Hospital-SUNY Health Science Center at
Brooklyn
Veterans Affairs Medical Center (Brooklyn)
Prgm Director: Alan R Shalita, MD
450 Clarkson Avenue
Brooklyn, NY 11203
Tel: 718 270-1229   *Fax:* 718 270-2794
Length: 3 Yrs   *ACGME Approved/Offered Positions:* 18
Program ID: 080-35-21-065

Buffalo

University at Buffalo Program

Sponsor: University at Buffalo School of Medicine
Kaleida Health System (Women and Children's Hosp of
Buffalo)
Roswell Park Cancer Institute
Veterans Affairs Western New York Hospital
Prgm Director: Craig Miller, MD, PhD
Roswell Park Cancer Institute - Dermatology - MRC
Elm and Carlton Streets
Buffalo, NY 14263
Tel: 716 845-8527   *Fax:* 716 845-3056
E-mail: Dianne.Wolff@roswellpark.org
Length: 3 Yrs   *ACGME Approved/Offered Positions:* 7
Program ID: 080-35-21-057

New York

Mount Sinai School of Medicine Program

Sponsor: Mount Sinai School of Medicine
Elmhurst Hospital Center-Mount Sinai Services
Mount Sinai Medical Center
Queens Hospital Center
Prgm Director: Mark G Lebwohl, MD*
One Gustave L Levy Place, Box 1047
New York, NY 10029
Tel: 212 241-9778   *Fax:* 212 876-5661
Length: 3 Yrs   *ACGME Approved/Offered Positions:* 12
Program ID: 080-35-21-061

New York Medical College (Metropolitan) Program

Sponsor: New York Medical College
Metropolitan Hospital Center
Montefiore Medical Center - North Division
Prgm Director: Bijan Safai, MD, ScD
Department of Dermatology
Metropolitan Hospital Center,1901 First Avenue
New York, NY 10029
Tel: 212 423-6602   *Fax:* 212 423-8464
E-mail: nymcdermatology@gmail.com
Length: 3 Yrs   *ACGME Approved/Offered Positions:* 8
Program ID: 080-35-21-063

New York Presbyterian Hospital (Columbia Campus) Program

Sponsor: New York Presbyterian Hospital
New York Presbyterian Hospital (Columbia Campus)
Prgm Director: David R Bickers, MD
161 Fort Washington Avenue
12th Floor
New York, NY 10032
Tel: 212 305-5565   *Fax:* 212 305-4571
E-mail: bcw2112@columbia.edu
Length: 3 Yrs   *ACGME Approved/Offered Positions:* 11
Program ID: 080-35-21-104

New York Presbyterian Hospital (Cornell Campus) Program

Sponsor: New York Presbyterian Hospital
Lincoln Medical and Mental Health Center
New York Presbyterian Hospital (Cornell Campus)
Prgm Director: John A Carucci, MD, PhD
1305 York Avenue, 9th Floor
New York, NY 10065
Tel: 646 962-7948   *Fax:* 646 962-0040
E-mail: cym2004@med.cornell.edu
Length: 3 Yrs   *ACGME Approved/Offered Positions:* 13
Program ID: 080-35-21-062

New York University School of Medicine Program

Sponsor: New York University School of Medicine
Bellevue Hospital Center
Manhattan VA Harbor Health Care System
NYU Hospitals Center
Prgm Director: David Polsky, MD, PhD
550 First Avenue, Room H100
New York, NY 10016
Tel: 212 263-3722   *Fax:* 212 263-8752
E-mail: dermprogdir@med.nyu.edu
Length: 3 Yrs   *ACGME Approved/Offered Positions:* 23
Program ID: 080-35-21-064

St Luke's-Roosevelt Hospital Center Program

Sponsor: St Luke's-Roosevelt Hospital Center
Beth Israel Medical Center
Prgm Director: Vincent A Deleo, MD
1090 Amsterdam Avenue
Suite 11B
New York, NY 10025
Tel: 212 523-3814   *Fax:* 212 523-3808
E-mail: vdeleo@chpnet.org
Length: 3 Yrs   *ACGME Approved/Offered Positions:* 9
Program ID: 080-35-21-124

Programs

Rochester

University of Rochester Program
Sponsor: Strong Memorial Hospital of the University of Rochester
Prgm Director: Mary Gail Mercurio, MD*
601 Elmwood Avenue, Box 697
Rochester, NY 14642
Tel: 585 275-0193   *Fax:* 585 275-0022
Length: 3 Yrs   *ACGME Approved/Offered Positions:* 9
Program ID: 080-35-21-102

Stony Brook

SUNY at Stony Brook Program
Sponsor: University Hospital - SUNY at Stony Brook
Memorial Sloan-Kettering Cancer Center
Veterans Affairs Medical Center (Northport)
Prgm Director: Peter Klein, MD
Dept of Dermatology
HSC T-16, Room 060
Stony Brook, NY 11794
Tel: 631 444-3843
E-mail: Peter.Klein@stonybrook.edu
Length: 3 Yrs   *ACGME Approved/Offered Positions:* 7
Program ID: 080-35-21-113

North Carolina

Chapel Hill

University of North Carolina Hospitals Program
Sponsor: University of North Carolina Hospitals
Prgm Director: Dean S Morrell, MD
Department of Dermatology, CB 7287
3100 Thurston-Bowles Bldg
Chapel Hill, NC 27599
Tel: 919 966-0785   *Fax:* 919 966-3898
E-mail: cherie_ezuka@med.unc.edu
Length: 3 Yrs   *ACGME Approved/Offered Positions:* 13
Program ID: 080-36-11-066

Durham

Duke University Hospital Program
Sponsor: Duke University Hospital
Veterans Affairs Medical Center (Durham)
Prgm Director: Navjeet Sidhu-Malik, MD
Division of Dermatology
Box 3643, DUMC
Durham, NC 27710
Tel: 919 684-6973   *Fax:* 919 684-9577
E-mail: sidhu003@mc.duke.edu
Length: 3 Yrs   *ACGME Approved/Offered Positions:* 11
Program ID: 080-36-21-067

Greenville

Pitt County Memorial Hospital/East Carolina University Program
Sponsor: Pitt County Memorial Hospital
Brody School of Medicine at East Carolina University
Prgm Director: William A Burke, MD
600 Moye Boulevard, Brody 3E-117
Greenville, NC 27834
Tel: 252 744-2555   *Fax:* 252 744-3047
Length: 3 Yrs   *ACGME Approved/Offered Positions:* 6
Program ID: 080-36-13-132

Note: * indicates a newly appointed program director

Winston-Salem

Wake Forest University School of Medicine Program
Sponsor: Wake Forest University Baptist Medical Center
Prgm Director: Amy J McMichael, MD
Medical Center Boulevard
Winston-Salem, NC 27157
Tel: 336 716-2768   *Fax:* 336 716-7732
E-mail: amcmicha@wfubmc.edu
Length: 3 Yrs   *ACGME Approved/Offered Positions:* 9
Program ID: 080-36-21-110

Ohio

Cincinnati

University Hospital/University of Cincinnati College of Medicine Program
Sponsor: University Hospital Inc
Prgm Director: Diya F Mutasim, MD
Department of Dermatology
231 Albert Sabin Way, PO Box 670592
Cincinnati, OH 45267
Tel: 513 558-6242   *Fax:* 513 558-0198
Length: 3 Yrs   *ACGME Approved/Offered Positions:* 12
Program ID: 080-38-21-068

Cleveland

Cleveland Clinic Foundation Program
Sponsor: Cleveland Clinic Foundation
Prgm Director: Jonelle K McDonnell, MD
9500 Euclid Avenue, Desk A61
Cleveland, OH 44195
Tel: 216 444-5772   *Fax:* 216 636-0435
Length: 4 Yrs   *ACGME Approved/Offered Positions:* 16
Program ID: 080-38-12-070

University Hospitals Case Medical Center Program
Sponsor: University Hospitals Case Medical Center
MetroHealth Medical Center
Veterans Affairs Medical Center (Cleveland)
Prgm Director: Susan T Nedorost, MD
11100 Euclid Avenue
Cleveland, OH 44106
Tel: 216 844-5794   *Fax:* 216 844-8993
E-mail: kristina.myers@uhhospitals.org
Length: 3 Yrs   *ACGME Approved/Offered Positions:* 18
Program ID: 080-38-21-120

Columbus

Ohio State University Hospital Program
Sponsor: Ohio State University Hospital
Veterans Affairs Medical Center (Columbus)
Prgm Director: Matthew Zirwas, MD*
130 Doan Hall
410 West 10th Avenue
Columbus, OH 43210
Tel: 614 293-4434   *Fax:* 614 293-8090
E-mail: beata.sandefur@osumc.edu
Length: 4 Yrs   *ACGME Approved/Offered Positions:* 9
Program ID: 080-38-11-072

Dayton

Wright State University Program
Sponsor: Wright State University Boonshoft School of Medicine
Veterans Affairs Medical Center (Dayton)
Wright State Dermatology (Elizabeth Place)
Prgm Director: Julian J Trevino, MD*
Department of Dermatology
PO Box 927
Dayton, OH 45401
Tel: 937 268-6511   *Fax:* 937 267-5310
Length: 3 Yrs   *ACGME Approved/Offered Positions:* 6
Program ID: 080-38-21-073

Oklahoma

Oklahoma City

University of Oklahoma Health Sciences Center Program
Sponsor: University of Oklahoma College of Medicine
OU Medical Center
Veterans Affairs Medical Center (Oklahoma City)
Prgm Director: Richard D Sontheimer, MD
Department of Dermatology
619 Northeast 13th Street
Oklahoma City, OK 73104
Tel: 405 271-4662   *Fax:* 405 271-7216
E-mail: goldie-wall@ouhsc.edu
Length: 3 Yrs   *ACGME Approved/Offered Positions:* 9
Program ID: 080-39-21-074

Oregon

Portland

Oregon Health & Science University Program
Sponsor: Oregon Health & Science University Hospital
Veterans Affairs Medical Center (Portland)
Prgm Director: Theresa S Devere, MD*
3303 SW Bond Avenue
CH16D
Portland, OR 97239
Tel: 503 494-4713   *Fax:* 503 494-6844
E-mail: andeshel@ohsu.edu
Length: 3 Yrs   *ACGME Approved/Offered Positions:* 12
Program ID: 080-40-21-075

Pennsylvania

Danville

Geisinger Health System Program
Sponsor: Geisinger Health System
Geisinger Medical Center
Prgm Director: Michele S Maroon, MD
115 Woodbine Lane
Danville, PA 17822
Tel: 570 271-8074   *Fax:* 570 271-5940
Length: 3 Yrs   *ACGME Approved/Offered Positions:* 12
Program ID: 080-41-12-076

Hershey

Penn State University/Milton S Hershey Medical Center Program
Sponsor: Milton S Hershey Medical Center
Prgm Director: Bryan Anderson, MD*
Department of Dermatology, HU14
500 University Drive, UPC II Suite 4300
Hershey, PA 17033
Tel: 717 531-6049   *Fax:* 717 531-6516
E-mail: banderson@hmc.psu.edu
Length: 3 Yrs   *ACGME Approved/Offered Positions:* 9
Program ID: 080-41-21-103

Philadelphia

Drexel University College of Medicine/Hahnemann University Hospital Program
Sponsor: Drexel University College of Medicine/Hahnemann University
Hahnemann University Hospital (Tenet Health System)
Prgm Director: Herbert Allen, MD
219 N Broad Street
Mail Stop 401 HUH
Philadelphia, PA 19107
Tel: 215 762-5550   *Fax:* 215 762-5570
E-mail: lmurria@drexelmed.edu
Length: 4 Yrs   *ACGME Approved/Offered Positions:* 12
Program ID: 080-41-21-077

Thomas Jefferson University Program
Sponsor: Thomas Jefferson University Hospital
Prgm Director: Jason B Lee, MD
Bluemle Life Sciences Bldg, Ste 450
233 S 10th Street
Philadelphia, PA 19107
Tel: 215 955-5785   *Fax:* 215 503-5788
Length: 3 Yrs   *ACGME Approved/Offered Positions:* 12
Program ID: 080-41-11-079

University of Pennsylvania Program
Sponsor: University of Pennsylvania Health System
Veterans Affairs Medical Center (Philadelphia)
Prgm Director: William D James, MD
Department of Dermatology
3600 Spruce Street, 2 Maloney Building
Philadelphia, PA 19104
Tel: 215 662-7883   *Fax:* 215 662-7884
Length: 3 Yrs   *ACGME Approved/Offered Positions:* 20
Program ID: 080-41-21-080

Pittsburgh

University of Pittsburgh Medical Center Medical Education Program
Sponsor: Univ of Pittsburgh Medical Center Medical Education
UPMC Presbyterian Shadyside
Veterans Affairs Medical Center (Pittsburgh)
Prgm Director: Larisa Geskin, MD*
190 Lothrop Street
Suite 145 Lothrop Hall
Pittsburgh, PA 15213
Tel: 412 647-4279   *Fax:* 412 647-4788
Length: 3 Yrs   *ACGME Approved/Offered Positions:* 15
Program ID: 080-41-11-081

Puerto Rico

San Juan

University of Puerto Rico Program
Sponsor: University of Puerto Rico School of Medicine
University Hospital
Prgm Director: Nestor P Sanchez, MD
University District Hospital
PO Box 365067
San Juan, PR 00936
Tel: 787 765-7950   *Fax:* 787 767-0467
E-mail: rcmdermatol@rcm.upr.edu
Length: 3 Yrs   *ACGME Approved/Offered Positions:* 9
Program ID: 080-42-21-082

Rhode Island

Providence

Brown University Program
Sponsor: Rhode Island Hospital-Lifespan
Veterans Affairs Medical Center (Providence)
Prgm Director: Charles McDonald, MD*
Dermatology Foundation
593 Eddy Street
Providence, RI 02903
Tel: 401 444-7137   *Fax:* 401 444-7105
Length: 3 Yrs   *ACGME Approved/Offered Positions:* 11
Program ID: 080-43-21-122

Roger Williams Medical Center Program
Sponsor: Roger Williams Medical Center
Providence Community Health Center
Prgm Director: Vincent Falanga, MD
50 Maude Street
Providence, RI 02908
Tel: 401 456-2521   *Fax:* 401 456-6449
Length: 3 Yrs   *ACGME Approved/Offered Positions:* 7
Program ID: 080-43-21-083

South Carolina

Charleston

Medical University of South Carolina Program
Sponsor: Medical University of South Carolina College of Medicine
MUSC Medical Center
Ralph H Johnson VA Medical Center (Charleston)
Prgm Director: Ross B Pollack, MD
135 Rutledge Avenue, 11th Floor
POB 250578
Charleston, SC 29425
Tel: 843 792-5858   *Fax:* 843 792-9804
E-mail: pollack@musc.edu
Length: 3 Yrs   *ACGME Approved/Offered Positions:* 9
Program ID: 080-45-21-099

Tennessee

Memphis

University of Tennessee Program
Sponsor: University of Tennessee College of Medicine
Methodist Healthcare - Memphis Hospitals
Regional Medical Center at Memphis
Veterans Affairs Medical Center (Memphis)
Prgm Director: E William Rosenberg, MD
Department of Medicine
956 Court Avenue - Room D662
Memphis, TN 38163
Tel: 901 448-5795   *Fax:* 901 448-8284
Length: 3 Yrs   *ACGME Approved/Offered Positions:* 6
Program ID: 080-47-21-084

Nashville

Vanderbilt University Program
Sponsor: Vanderbilt University Medical Center
Veterans Affairs Medical Center (Nashville)
Prgm Director: Darrel L Ellis, MD
1301 Medical Center Drive
Suite 3903, The Vanderbilt Clinic
Nashville, TN 37232
Tel: 615 322-0845   *Fax:* 615 343-3947
Length: 3 Yrs   *ACGME Approved/Offered Positions:* 12
Program ID: 080-47-21-098

Texas

Dallas

University of Texas Southwestern Medical School Program
Sponsor: University of Texas Southwestern Medical School
Children's Medical Center of Dallas
Dallas County Hospital District-Parkland Memorial Hospital
Dallas VA Medical Center
Prgm Director: Ponciano D Cruz Jr, MD
5323 Harry Hines Boulevard
Dallas, TX 75390
Tel: 214 648-8806   *Fax:* 214 648-7678
E-mail: Jo.Urquhart@UTSouthwestern.edu
Length: 3 Yrs   *ACGME Approved/Offered Positions:* 18
Program ID: 080-48-21-085

Galveston

University of Texas Medical Branch Hospitals (Austin) Program
Sponsor: University of Texas Medical Branch Hospitals
University Medical Center at Brackenridge
Central Texas Veterans Hlth Care System Facilities (Austin)
Prgm Director: Dayna Diven, MD
UTMB Austin Program
601 East 15th Street
Austin, TX 78701
Tel: 512 324-9699   *Fax:* 512 324-9657
Length: 3 Yrs   *ACGME Approved/Offered Positions:* 3
Program ID: 080-48-12-140

University of Texas Medical Branch Hospitals Program
Sponsor: University of Texas Medical Branch Hospitals
Prgm Director: Richard F Wagner Jr, MD, JD
4112 McCullough Bldg
301 University Blvd
Galveston, TX 77555
Tel: 409 772-1911   *Fax:* 409 772-1943
Length: 3 Yrs   *ACGME Approved/Offered Positions:* 9
Program ID: 080-48-11-086

Houston

Baylor College of Medicine Program
Sponsor: Baylor College of Medicine
Baylor Clinic
Harris County Hospital District-Ben Taub General Hospital
Michael E DeBakey VA Medical Center - Houston
Prgm Director: John E Wolf Jr, MD
Department of Dermatology
1709 Dryden, Suite 1050
Houston, TX 77030
Tel: 713 798-7620   *Fax:* 713 798-6923
E-mail: dermatology@bcm.tmc.edu
Length: 3 Yrs   *ACGME Approved/Offered Positions:* 10
Program ID: 080-48-21-087

University of Texas at Houston Program
Sponsor: University of Texas Health Science Center at Houston
Lyndon B Johnson General Hospital
Memorial Hermann Hospital
University of Texas M D Anderson Cancer Center
Prgm Director: Ronald P Rapini, MD
Department of Dermatology
6655 Travis St, Suite 980
Houston, TX 77030
Tel: 713 500-8334   *Fax:* 713 500-8323
E-mail: Ronald P. Rapini@uth.tmc.edu
Length: 3 Yrs   *ACGME Approved/Offered Positions:* 15
Program ID: 080-48-21-100

Lackland AFB

San Antonio Uniformed Services Health Education Consortium Program

Sponsor: San Antonio Uniformed Services Health Education Consortium
Wilford Hall Medical Center (AETC)
Prgm Director: Robert T Gilson, MD
59 MDW/SGO5D
2200 Bergquist Drive, Ste 1
Lackland AFB, TX 78236
Tel: 210 292-5371   *Fax:* 210 292-3781
Length: 3 Yrs   *ACGME Approved/Offered Positions:* 21
Program ID: 080-48-21-121
Uniformed Services Program

Lubbock

Texas Tech University (Lubbock) Program

Sponsor: Texas Tech University Health Sciences Center at Lubbock
Veterans Affairs Medical Center (Amarillo)
Prgm Director: Cloyce L Stetson, MD
4A-100 Stop 9400
3601 Fourth Street
Lubbock, TX 79430
Tel: 806 743-2456   *Fax:* 806 743-1105
Length: 3 Yrs   *ACGME Approved/Offered Positions:* 7
Program ID: 080-48-21-105

San Antonio

University of Texas Health Science Center at San Antonio Program

Sponsor: University of Texas School of Medicine at San Antonio
Audie L Murphy Memorial Veterans Hospital (San Antonio)
Christus Santa Rosa Health Care Corporation
University Health System
Prgm Director: Eric W Kraus, MD
Medicine/Dermatology, MSC 7876
7703 Floyd Curl Drive
San Antonio, TX 78229
Tel: 210 567-1510   *Fax:* 210 567-6679
E-mail: derm@uthscsa.edu
Length: 3 Yrs   *ACGME Approved/Offered Positions:* 5
Program ID: 080-48-22-088

Temple

Texas A&M College of Medicine-Scott and White Program

Sponsor: Scott and White Memorial Hospital
Prgm Director: David F Butler, MD
Department of Dermatology
409 W Adams
Temple, TX 76501
Tel: 254 742-3775   *Fax:* 254 742-3789
E-mail: dfbutler@swmail.sw.org
Length: 3 Yrs   *ACGME Approved/Offered Positions:* 6
Program ID: 080-48-21-133

Utah

Salt Lake City

University of Utah Program

Sponsor: University of Utah Medical Center
Primary Children's Medical Center
Veterans Affairs Medical Center (Salt Lake City)
Prgm Director: Marta J Petersen, MD
4A330 School of Medicine
30 North 1900 East
Salt Lake City, UT 84132
Tel: 801 585-9624   *Fax:* 801 581-5972
Length: 3 Yrs   *ACGME Approved/Offered Positions:* 9
Program ID: 080-49-21-112

Vermont

Burlington

University of Vermont Program

Sponsor: Fletcher Allen Health Care
Prgm Director: Kathryn Schwarzenberger, MD
89 Beaumont Ave, D208
Burlington, VT 05405
Tel: 802 847-4570   *Fax:* 802 847-3364
E-mail: kathryn.schwarzenberger@vtmednet.org
Length: 3 Yrs   *ACGME Approved/Offered Positions:* 6
Program ID: 080-50-13-129

Virginia

Charlottesville

University of Virginia Program

Sponsor: University of Virginia Medical Center
Prgm Director: Thomas G Cropley, MD*
PO Box 800718
Charlottesville, VA 22908
Tel: 434 924-1958
Length: 3 Yrs   *ACGME Approved/Offered Positions:* 6
Program ID: 080-51-11-089

Norfolk

Eastern Virginia Medical School Program

Sponsor: Eastern Virginia Medical School
Children's Hospital of the King's Daughters
Naval Medical Center (Portsmouth)
Sentara Norfolk General Hospital
Veterans Affairs Medical Center (Hampton)
Prgm Director: Antoinette F Hood, MD
721 Fairfax Ave, Suite 200
Norfolk, VA 23507
Tel: 757 446-5629
Length: 3 Yrs   *ACGME Approved/Offered Positions:* 6
Program ID: 080-51-21-130

Richmond

Virginia Commonwealth University Health System Program

Sponsor: Virginia Commonwealth University Health System
Hunter Holmes McGuire VA Medical Center (Richmond)
Medical College of Virginia Hospitals
Prgm Director: Julia R Nunley, MD
401 North 11th Street
PO Box 980164
Richmond, VA 23298
Tel: 804 628-3156   *Fax:* 804 828-9596
E-mail: ssmith6@mcvh-vcu.edu
Length: 3 Yrs   *ACGME Approved/Offered Positions:* 6
Program ID: 080-51-21-090

Washington

Seattle

University of Washington Program

Sponsor: University of Washington School of Medicine
University of Washington Medical Center
Prgm Director: Roy Colven, MD
Division of Dermatology, Box 356524
1959 NE Pacific St
Seattle, WA 98195
Tel: 206 543-5290   *Fax:* 206 543-2489
E-mail: rcolven@u.washington.edu
Length: 3 Yrs   *ACGME Approved/Offered Positions:* 10
Program ID: 080-54-31-091

West Virginia

Morgantown

West Virginia University Program

Sponsor: West Virginia University School of Medicine
West Virginia University Hospitals
Prgm Director: Rodney F Kovach, MD
Health Sciences Center North
PO Box 9158
Morgantown, WV 26506
Tel: 304 293-6618   *Fax:* 304 293-3724
E-mail: agoff@hsc.wvu.edu
Length: 3 Yrs   *ACGME Approved/Offered Positions:* 3
Program ID: 080-55-11-092

Wisconsin

Madison

University of Wisconsin Program

Sponsor: University of Wisconsin Hospital and Clinics
Marshfield Clinic-St Joseph's Hospital
William S Middleton Veterans Hospital
Prgm Director: William D Aughenbaugh, MD
University of Wisconsin
One South Park St, 7th Floor
Madison, WI 53715
Tel: 608 287-2620   *Fax:* 608 287-2676
E-mail: waughenbaugh@dermatology.wisc.edu
Length: 3 Yrs   *ACGME Approved/Offered Positions:* 7
Program ID: 080-56-21-093

Marshfield

Marshfield Clinic-St Joseph's Hospital Program

Sponsor: Marshfield Clinic-St Joseph's Hospital
Prgm Director: Donald J Miech, MD
1000 North Oak Avenue
Marshfield, WI 54449
Tel: 715 387-5311   *Fax:* 715 389-4141
Length: 3 Yrs   *ACGME Approved/Offered Positions:* 6
Program ID: 080-56-22-131

Milwaukee

Medical College of Wisconsin Affiliated Hospitals Program

Sponsor: Medical College of Wisconsin Affiliated Hospitals, Inc
Children's Hospital of Wisconsin
Clement J Zablocki Veterans Affairs Medical Center
Froedtert Memorial Lutheran Hospital
Prgm Director: Barbara D Wilson, MD
Department of Dermatology
9200 West Wisconsin Avenue
Milwaukee, WI 53226
Tel: 414 805-9859   *Fax:* 414 258-8085
E-mail: bwilson@mcw.edu
Length: 3 Yrs   *ACGME Approved/Offered Positions:* 12
Program ID: 080-56-21-095

Note: * indicates a newly appointed program director

Dermatopathology (Dermatology)

Alabama

Birmingham

University of Alabama Medical Center Program
Sponsor: University of Alabama Hospital
Dermatopathology Services, PC
Veterans Affairs Medical Center (Birmingham)
Prgm Director: Aleodor A Andea, MD*
Dept of Dermatology 149 PD6A, Suite 149
619 19th Street South
Birmingham, AL 35249
Tel: 205 975-6941 *Fax:* 205 975-6922
E-mail: aandea@uab.edu
Length: 1 Yr *ACGME Approved/Offered Positions:* 2
Program ID: 100-01-21-024

Arkansas

Little Rock

University of Arkansas for Medical Sciences Program
Sponsor: University of Arkansas College of Medicine
UAMS Medical Center
Prgm Director: Kim M Hiatt, MD, MS
4301 West Markham
Department of Pathology, Slot 517
Little Rock, AR 72205
Tel: 501 686-8007 *Fax:* 501 603-1479
E-mail: HiattKimM@uams.edu
Length: 1 Yr *ACGME Approved/Offered Positions:* 1
Program ID: 100-04-21-062

California

Los Angeles

UCLA Medical Center Program
Sponsor: UCLA David Geffen School of Medicine/UCLA Medical Center
UCLA Medical Center
Prgm Director: Scott W Binder, MD
10833 Le Conte Avenue
13-186 Center for Health Sciences
Los Angeles, CA 90095
Tel: 310 267-2680 *Fax:* 310 267-2058
E-mail: sbinder@mednet.ucla.edu
Length: 1 Yr *ACGME Approved/Offered Positions:* 3
Program ID: 100-05-21-071

San Francisco

University of California (San Francisco) Program
Sponsor: University of California (San Francisco) School of Medicine
San Francisco General Hospital Medical Center
UCSF and Mount Zion Medical Centers
Veterans Affairs Medical Center (San Francisco)
Prgm Director: Philip E LeBoit, MD
Dermatopathology Section (UCSF Box 1790)
1701 Divisadero Street, Room 350
San Francisco, CA 94115
Tel: 415 353-7550 *Fax:* 415 353-7553
E-mail: philip.leboit@ucsf.edu
Length: 1 Yr *ACGME Approved/Offered Positions:* 2
Program ID: 100-05-21-035

Stanford

Stanford University Program
Sponsor: Stanford Hospital and Clinics
Prgm Director: Uma Sundram, MD, PhD*
300 Pasteur Drive, Room L235
Stanford, CA 94305
Tel: 650 498-4401 *Fax:* 650 725-7409
Length: 1 Yr *ACGME Approved/Offered Positions:* 2
Program ID: 100-05-21-041

Colorado

Aurora

University of Colorado Denver Program
Sponsor: University of Colorado Denver School of Medicine
Dermatopathology Services LLC
University of Colorado Hospital
Veterans Affairs Medical Center (Denver)
Prgm Director: Loren E Golitz, MD
Department of Pathology B216
4200 East Ninth Avenue
Denver, CO 80262
Tel: 303 355-0600 *Fax:* 303 355-5744
E-mail: patricia.braund@uchsc.edu
Length: 1 Yr *ACGME Approved/Offered Positions:* 2
Program ID: 100-07-13-067

Connecticut

New Haven

Yale-New Haven Medical Center Program
Sponsor: Yale-New Haven Hospital
Prgm Director: Rossitza Lazova, MD
PO Box 208059
15 York Street
New Haven, CT 06520
Tel: 203 785-6476 *Fax:* 203 785-6869
E-mail: wendy.rollinson@yale.edu
Length: 1 Yr *ACGME Approved/Offered Positions:* 1
Program ID: 100-08-21-045

Florida

Gainesville

University of Florida Program
Sponsor: University of Florida College of Medicine
Shands Hospital at the University of Florida
Prgm Director: Vladimir Vincek, MD, PhD
PO Box 100275
4800 SW 35th Drive
Gainesville, FL 32608
Tel: 352 265-9900 *Fax:* 352 265-9918
E-mail: vincek26@pathology.ufl.edu
Length: 1 Yr *ACGME Approved/Offered Positions:* 1
Program ID: 100-11-31-065

Tampa

University of South Florida Program
Sponsor: University of South Florida College of Medicine
H Lee Moffitt Cancer Center
James A Haley Veterans Hospital
Prgm Director: L Frank Glass, MD
12901 Bruce B Downs Boulevard, MDC 11
Tampa, FL 33612
Tel: 813 974-3744 *Fax:* 813 974-4272
E-mail: mcrochunis@umsa.usf.edu
Length: 1 Yr *ACGME Approved/Offered Positions:* 1
Program ID: 100-11-12-077

Georgia

Atlanta

Emory University Program
Sponsor: Emory University School of Medicine
Emory University Hospital
Prgm Director: Douglas C Parker, MD*
Rm H-185A Pathology, Emory University Hospital
1364 Clifton Road, NE
Atlanta, GA 30322
Tel: 404 616-7433 *Fax:* 404 616-9804
E-mail: dpark02@emory.edu
Length: 1 Yr *ACGME Approved/Offered Positions:* 1
Program ID: 100-12-21-044

Illinois

Chicago

McGaw Medical Center of Northwestern University Program
Sponsor: McGaw Medical Center of Northwestern University
Northwestern Memorial Hospital
Prgm Director: Joan Guitart, MD
676 North St Clair Street
Suite 1600
Chicago, IL 60611
Tel: 312 695-7932 *Fax:* 312 695-0664
E-mail: MSferruz@nmff.org
Length: 1 Yr *ACGME Approved/Offered Positions:* 1
Program ID: 100-16-21-064

University of Chicago Program
Sponsor: University of Chicago Medical Center
Prgm Director: Christopher R Shea, MD
5841 S Maryland Avenue, MC 5067
Room L-502
Chicago, IL 60637
Tel: 773 702-6559 *Fax:* 773 702-8398
E-mail: nsimweny@medicine.bsd.uchicago.edu
Length: 1 Yr *ACGME Approved/Offered Positions:* 2
Program ID: 100-16-31-001

Indiana

Indianapolis

Indiana University School of Medicine Program
Sponsor: Indiana University School of Medicine
Clarian Indiana University Hospital
MAPS/Dermatology Inc
Richard L Roudebush Veterans Affairs Medical Center
William N Wishard Memorial Hospital
Prgm Director: William B Moores, MD
350 W 11th Street
Suite 4018A
Indianapolis, IN 46202
Tel: 317 491-6423 *Fax:* 317 491-6424
E-mail: shamrick@iupui.edu
Length: 1 Yr *ACGME Approved/Offered Positions:* 2
Program ID: 100-17-21-020

Louisiana

New Orleans

Tulane University Program

Sponsor: Tulane University School of Medicine
Medical Center of Louisiana at New Orleans
Tulane University Hospital and Clinics
Prgm Director: Alun R Wang, MD, PhD
1430 Tulane Ave, SL79
New Orleans, LA 70112
Tel: 504 988-2436   *Fax:* 504 988-7389
Length: 1 Yr   *ACGME Approved/Offered Positions:* 1
Program ID: 100-21-21-052

Maryland

Baltimore

Johns Hopkins University Program

Sponsor: Johns Hopkins University School of Medicine
Johns Hopkins Hospital
Prgm Director: Jacqueline M Junkins-Hopkins, MD*
Blalock 907
600 North Wolfe Street
Baltimore, MD 21287
Tel: 410 955-3484   *Fax:* 410 955-2445
Length: 1 Yr   *ACGME Approved/Offered Positions:* 2
Program ID: 100-23-21-026

Massachusetts

Boston

Beth Israel Deaconess Medical Center/Harvard Medical School Program

Sponsor: Beth Israel Deaconess Medical Center
Brigham and Women's Hospital
Massachusetts General Hospital
Prgm Director: Steven R Tahan, MD
Department of Pathology
330 Brookline Ave
Boston, MA 02215
Tel: 617 667-4344   *Fax:* 617 975-5499
E-mail: stahan@bidmc.harvard.edu
Length: 1 Yr   *ACGME Approved/Offered Positions:* 4
Program ID: 100-24-31-002

Boston University Medical Center Program

Sponsor: Boston Medical Center
Prgm Director: Jag Bhawan, MD
609 Albany J-308
Boston, MA 02118
Tel: 617 638-5570   *Fax:* 617 638-5575
Length: 1 Yr   *ACGME Approved/Offered Positions:* 2
Program ID: 100-24-21-033

Tufts Medical Center Program

Sponsor: Tufts Medical Center
Caris Cohen Dx
Prgm Director: Thomas D Horn, MD, MBA
320 Needham Street
Suite 200
Newton, MA 02464
Tel: 617 969-4100   *Fax:* 617 969-3393
E-mail: thorn@cariscohendx.com
Length: 1 Yr   *ACGME Approved/Offered Positions:* 2
Program ID: 100-24-31-091

Worcester

University of Massachusetts Program

Sponsor: University of Massachusetts Medical School
UMass Memorial Health Care (Hahnemann Campus)
Prgm Director: April Chunling Deng, MD, PhD
Three Biotech, One Innovation Drive
Department of Pathology
Worcester, MA 01605
Tel: 508 793-6188   *Fax:* 508 493-6110
Length: 1 Yr   *ACGME Approved/Offered Positions:* 1
Program ID: 100-24-21-089

Michigan

Ann Arbor

University of Michigan Program

Sponsor: University of Michigan Hospitals and Health
  Centers
Prgm Director: Douglas R Fullen, MD
1301 Catherine Street
M3261-Med Sci I
Ann Arbor, MI 48109
Tel: 734 764-4460   *Fax:* 734 764-4690
E-mail: dfullen@med.umich.edu
Length: 1 Yr   *ACGME Approved/Offered Positions:* 2
Program ID: 100-25-12-080

Minnesota

Rochester

College of Medicine, Mayo Clinic (Rochester) Program

Sponsor: College of Medicine, Mayo Clinic
Mayo Clinic (Rochester)
Prgm Director: Lawrence E Gibson, MD
200 First Street, SW
Rochester, MN 55905
Tel: 507 284-3736   *Fax:* 507 284-2072
E-mail: mayodermfellows@mayo.edu
Length: 1 Yr   *ACGME Approved/Offered Positions:* 2
Program ID: 100-26-21-004

Missouri

St Louis

St Louis University School of Medicine Program

Sponsor: St Louis University School of Medicine
Anheuser-Busch Institute
Cardinal Glennon Children's Hospital
St Louis University Hospital
Prgm Director: M Yadira Hurley, MD
1402 South Grand Boulevard
St Louis, MO 63104
Tel: 314 256-3430   *Fax:* 314 256-3431
Length: 1 Yr   *ACGME Approved/Offered Positions:* 1
Program ID: 100-28-12-088

Washington University/B-JH/SLCH Consortium Program

Sponsor: Washington University/B-JH/SLCH Consortium
Barnes-Jewish Hospital
Prgm Director: Anne C Lind, MD
660 South Euclid Avenue
Campus Box 8118
St Louis, MO 63110
Tel: 314 362-0117   *Fax:* 314 362-8950
Length: 1 Yr   *ACGME Approved/Offered Positions:* 1
Program ID: 100-28-21-036

New Hampshire

Lebanon

Dartmouth-Hitchcock Medical Center Program

Sponsor: Mary Hitchcock Memorial Hospital
Prgm Director: Jeoffry B Brennick, MD
One Medical Center Drive
Lebanon, NH 03756
Tel: 603 650-7226   *Fax:* 603 650-4845
Length: 1 Yr   *ACGME Approved/Offered Positions:* 2
Program ID: 100-32-31-083

New Jersey

Newark

UMDNJ-New Jersey Medical School Program

Sponsor: UMDNJ-New Jersey Medical School
UMDNJ-University Hospital
Prgm Director: W Clark Lambert, MD, PhD
Room C-520, Medical Sciences Building
185 South Orange Avenue
Newark, NJ 07103
Tel: 973 972-6255   *Fax:* 973 972-5877
E-mail: lamberwc@umdnj.edu
Length: 1 Yr   *ACGME Approved/Offered Positions:* 1
Program ID: 100-33-21-034

New York

Bronx

Albert Einstein College of Medicine Program

Sponsor: Albert Einstein College of Medicine of Yeshiva
  University
Montefiore Medical Center-Henry and Lucy Moses
  Division
Montefiore Medical Center-Weiler Division
Pathology Associates
Prgm Director: Mark Jacobson, MD
Henry and Lucy Moses Division
111 E 210th Street
Bronx, NY 10467
Tel: 718 920-6573   *Fax:* 718 547-8349
Length: 1 Yr   *ACGME Approved/Offered Positions:* 2
Program ID: 100-35-31-079

Brooklyn

SUNY Health Science Center at Brooklyn Program

Sponsor: SUNY Health Science Center at Brooklyn
Academy of Dermatopathology
Kings County Hospital Center
University Hospital-SUNY Health Science Center at
  Brooklyn
Prgm Director: Edward R Heilman, MD
145 East 32nd Street, 10th Floor
New York, NY 10016
Tel: 718 270-1229
Length: 1 Yr   *ACGME Approved/Offered Positions:* 7
Program ID: 100-35-31-074

Note: * indicates a newly appointed program director

New York

Memorial Sloan-Kettering Cancer Center Program
Sponsor: Memorial Sloan-Kettering Cancer Center
Prgm Director: Klaus J Busam, MD
1275 York Avenue
New York, NY 10065
Tel: 212 639-5679   *Fax:* 212 717-3203
Length: 1 Yr   *ACGME Approved/Offered Positions:* 2
Program ID: 100-35-31-087

Mount Sinai School of Medicine Program
Sponsor: Mount Sinai School of Medicine
Mount Sinai Medical Center
Prgm Director: Miriam B Birge, MD*
One Gustave L Levy Place, Box 1194
New York, NY 10029
Tel: 212 241-6064   *Fax:* 212 241-7832
E-mail: miriam.birge@mssm.edu
Length: 1 Yr   *ACGME Approved/Offered Positions:* 1
Program ID: 100-35-21-056

New York University School of Medicine Program
Sponsor: New York University School of Medicine
Bellevue Hospital Center
Manhattan VA Harbor Health Care System
NYU Hospitals Center
Prgm Director: Shane A Meehan, MD
530 First Avenue, Suite 7J
New York, NY 10016
Tel: 212 263-7250   *Fax:* 212 684-2991
E-mail: shane.meehan@nyumc.org
Length: 1 Yr   *ACGME Approved/Offered Positions:* 5
Program ID: 100-35-21-005

North Carolina

Durham

Duke University Hospital Program
Sponsor: Duke University Hospital
Veterans Affairs Medical Center (Durham)
Prgm Director: M Angelica Selim, MD
Box 3712
Durham, NC 27710
Tel: 919 681-4632   *Fax:* 919 684-4445
Length: 1 Yr   *ACGME Approved/Offered Positions:* 2
Program ID: 100-36-21-006

Winston-Salem

Wake Forest University School of Medicine Program
Sponsor: Wake Forest University Baptist Medical Center
Prgm Director: Omar P Sangueza, MD
Medical Center Boulevard
Winston-Salem, NC 27157
Tel: 336 716-4096   *Fax:* 336 716-7595
Length: 1 Yr   *ACGME Approved/Offered Positions:* 1
Program ID: 100-36-21-039

Ohio

Cincinnati

University Hospital/University of Cincinnati College of Medicine Program
Sponsor: University Hospital Inc
Prgm Director: Diya F Mutasim, MD
231 Albert Sabin Way, Room 7409
PO Box 670592
Cincinnati, OH 45267
Tel: 513 558-6242   *Fax:* 513 558-0198
E-mail: diya.mutasim@uc.edu
Length: 1 Yr   *ACGME Approved/Offered Positions:* 1
Program ID: 100-38-12-070

Cleveland

Cleveland Clinic Foundation Program
Sponsor: Cleveland Clinic Foundation
Prgm Director: Wilma F Bergfeld, MD
9500 Euclid Avenue
Cleveland, OH 44195
Tel: 216 444-2168   *Fax:* 216 445-6967
Length: 1 Yr   *ACGME Approved/Offered Positions:* 2
Program ID: 100-38-12-009

University Hospitals Case Medical Center Program
Sponsor: University Hospitals Case Medical Center
Prgm Director: Kimberly J Hollandsworth, MD
3100 Bolwell Health Center, 11100 Euclid Avenue
Cleveland, OH 44106
Tel: 216 368-0533   *Fax:* 216 368-0212
Length: 1 Yr   *ACGME Approved/Offered Positions:* 1
Program ID: 100-38-31-069

Columbus

Ohio State University Hospital Program
Sponsor: Ohio State University Hospital
Prgm Director: Sara B Peters, MD, PhD
N-305 Doan Hall, 410 West 10th Avenue
Columbus, OH 43210
Tel: 614 293-5292   *Fax:* 614 293-7634
E-mail: Gretchen.Staschiak@osumc.edu
Length: 1 Yr   *ACGME Approved/Offered Positions:* 2
Program ID: 100-38-12-084

Oregon

Portland

Oregon Health & Science University Program
Sponsor: Oregon Health & Science University Hospital
Prgm Director: Clifton R White Jr, MD
3303 SW Bond Avenue
CH 5D
Portland, OR 97239
Tel: 503 418-9169   *Fax:* 503 494-4957
E-mail: ricee@ohsu.edu
Length: 1 Yr   *ACGME Approved/Offered Positions:* 1
Program ID: 100-40-13-090

Pennsylvania

Danville

Geisinger Health System Program
Sponsor: Geisinger Health System
Geisinger Medical Center
Prgm Director: Dirk M Elston, MD
Department of Dermatology
115 Woodbine Lane
Danville, PA 17822
Tel: 570 271-8074   *Fax:* 570 271-5940
Length: 1 Yr   *ACGME Approved/Offered Positions:* 2
Program ID: 100-41-31-076

Hershey

Penn State University/Milton S Hershey Medical Center Program
Sponsor: Milton S Hershey Medical Center
Prgm Director: Klaus F Helm, MD
Department of Pathology H179
500 University Drive
Hershey, PA 17033
Tel: 717 531-1677   *Fax:* 717 531-7741
Length: 1 Yr   *ACGME Approved/Offered Positions:* 1
Program ID: 100-41-21-085

Philadelphia

Drexel University College of Medicine/Hahnemann University Hospital Program
Sponsor: Drexel University College of
    Medicine/Hahnemann University
Hahnemann University Hospital (Tenet Health System)
Institute for Dermatopathology
Prgm Director: Herbert B Allen, MD
219 North Broad Street
4th Floor
Philadelphia, PA 19107
Tel: 215 762-5557   *Fax:* 215 762-5570
E-mail: Herbert.Allen@drexelmed.edu
Length: 1 Yr   *ACGME Approved/Offered Positions:* 1
Program ID: 100-41-21-047

Thomas Jefferson University Program
Sponsor: Thomas Jefferson University Hospital
Prgm Director: Jason B Lee, MD
833 Chestnut Street
Suite 704
Philadelphia, PA 19107
Tel: 215 503-4257   *Fax:* 215 503-4317
Length: 1 Yr   *ACGME Approved/Offered Positions:* 1
Program ID: 100-41-13-086

University of Pennsylvania Program
Sponsor: University of Pennsylvania Health System
Veterans Affairs Medical Center (Philadelphia)
Prgm Director: Rosalie Elenitsas, MD
3600 Spruce Street, 2nd Floor, Maloney Bldg
Philadelphia, PA 19104
Tel: 215 662-4497   *Fax:* 215 349-5615
Length: 1 Yr   *ACGME Approved/Offered Positions:* 2
Program ID: 100-41-11-012

Pittsburgh

University of Pittsburgh Medical Center Medical Education Program
Sponsor: Univ of Pittsburgh Medical Center Medical
    Education
UPMC Presbyterian Shadyside
Prgm Director: Drazen M Jukic, MD, PhD
UPMC Shadyside Place
580 S Aiken Avenue, Suite 510
Pittsburgh, PA 15232
Tel: 412 623-2614   *Fax:* 412 623-3417
E-mail: dermpathed@upmc.edu
Length: 1 Yr   *ACGME Approved/Offered Positions:* 2
Program ID: 100-41-21-028

Rhode Island

Providence

Roger Williams Medical Center Program
Sponsor: Roger Williams Medical Center
Prgm Director: Caroline S Wilkel, MD
825 Chalkstone Avenue
Providence, RI 02908
Tel: 401 456-2662   *Fax:* 401 456-2131
E-mail: lmulzer@rwmc.org
Length: 1 Yr   *ACGME Approved/Offered Positions:* 1
Program ID: 100-43-21-031

Programs

South Carolina

Charleston

Medical University of South Carolina Program

Sponsor: Medical University of South Carolina College of Medicine
MUSC Medical Center
Prgm Director: John S Metcalf, MD
165 Ashley Avenue
Charleston, SC 29425
Tel: 843 792-3491   *Fax:* 843 792-8974
E-mail: metcalfj@musc.edu
Length: 1 Yr   *ACGME Approved/Offered Positions:* 2
Program ID: 100-45-21-023

Tennessee

Memphis

University of Tennessee Program

Sponsor: University of Tennessee College of Medicine
Baptist Memorial Hospital
Methodist Healthcare - Memphis Hospitals
Regional Medical Center at Memphis
University of Tennessee Department of Pathology
Prgm Director: Andrzej Slominski, MD, PhD
930 Madison Avenue 5th Floor
Memphis, TN 38163
Tel: 901 448-3741   *Fax:* 901 448-2435
Length: 1 Yr   *ACGME Approved/Offered Positions:* 1
Program ID: 100-47-21-040

Texas

Dallas

University of Texas Southwestern Medical School Program

Sponsor: University of Texas Southwestern Medical School
Dallas County Hospital District-Parkland Memorial Hospital
Dallas VA Medical Center
Prgm Director: Clay J Cockerell, MD
2330 Butler Street, Suite 115
Dallas, TX 75235
Tel: 214 530-5200   *Fax:* 214 530-5232
E-mail: ccockerell@ameripath.com
Length: 1 Yr   *ACGME Approved/Offered Positions:* 5
Program ID: 100-48-21-013

Galveston

University of Texas Medical Branch Hospitals Program

Sponsor: University of Texas Medical Branch Hospitals
Prgm Director: Ramon L Sanchez, MD, PhD
Department of Dermatology
301 University Blvd
Galveston, TX 77555
Tel: 409 772-1911   *Fax:* 409 772-1943
Length: 1 Yr   *ACGME Approved/Offered Positions:* 2
Program ID: 100-48-21-048

Houston

Baylor College of Medicine Program

Sponsor: Baylor College of Medicine
Baylor Clinic
Harris County Hospital District-Ben Taub General Hospital
Prgm Director: Jon A Reed, MD, MS
One Baylor Plaza
Department of Pathology
Houston, TX 77030
Tel: 713 798-4083   *Fax:* 713 798-3665
E-mail: yboney@bcm.edu
Length: 1 Yr   *ACGME Approved/Offered Positions:* 1
Program ID: 100-48-21-057

University of Texas at Houston Program

Sponsor: University of Texas Health Science Center at Houston
Memorial Hermann Hospital
Methodist Hospital (Houston)
UTHSC at Houston Physician Practices
Prgm Director: Ronald P Rapini, MD
Department of Dermatology
6655 Travis Street, Suite 980
Houston, TX 77030
Tel: 713 500-8334   *Fax:* 713 500-8323
E-mail: Irene.M.Morales@uth.tmc.edu
Length: 1 Yr   *ACGME Approved/Offered Positions:* 1
Program ID: 100-48-21-081

University of Texas M D Anderson Cancer Center Program

Sponsor: University of Texas M D Anderson Cancer Center
Harris County Hospital District-Ben Taub General Hospital
Prgm Director: Victor G Prieto, MD, PhD
Department of Pathology Box 85
1515 Holcombe Boulevard
Houston, TX 77030
Tel: 713 792-3187   *Fax:* 713 745-3740
Length: 1 Yr   *ACGME Approved/Offered Positions:* 2
Program ID: 100-48-13-072

Vermont

Burlington

University of Vermont Program

Sponsor: Fletcher Allen Health Care
Prgm Director: Deborah L Cook, MD
111 Colchester Avenue
Burlington, VT 05401
Tel: 802 847-5186   *Fax:* 802 847-4155
E-mail: deborah.l.cook@vtmednet.org
Length: 1 Yr   *ACGME Approved/Offered Positions:* 1
Program ID: 100-50-13-078

Virginia

Charlottesville

University of Virginia Program

Sponsor: University of Virginia Medical Center
Prgm Director: James W Patterson, MD
Department of Pathology
PO Box 800214
Charlottesville, VA 22908
Tel: 434 982-4402   *Fax:* 434 243-6757
E-mail: tsm3e@virginia.edu
Length: 1 Yr   *ACGME Approved/Offered Positions:* 2
Program ID: 100-51-21-061

Washington

Seattle

University of Washington Program

Sponsor: University of Washington School of Medicine
University of Washington Medical Center
Prgm Director: Zsolt B Argenyi, MD
1959 NE Pacific Street
Box 356100
Seattle, WA 98195
Tel: 206 598-2119   *Fax:* 206 598-4928
E-mail: residency@pathology.washington.edu
Length: 1 Yr   *ACGME Approved/Offered Positions:* 1
Program ID: 100-54-11-073

Note: * indicates a newly appointed program director

Developmental-Behavioral Pediatrics (Pediatrics)

Arkansas

Little Rock

University of Arkansas for Medical Sciences Program
Sponsor: University of Arkansas College of Medicine
Arkansas Children's Hospital
Dennis Developmental Center
Prgm Director: Jill J Fussell, MD
800 Marshall Street
Slot 512-41
Little Rock, AR 72202
Tel: 501 364-3866   *Fax:* 501 364-2151
E-mail: fusselljillj@uams.edu
Length: 3 Yrs   *ACGME Approved/Offered Positions:* 3
Program ID: 336-04-21-002

California

Los Angeles

Childrens Hospital Los Angeles Program
Sponsor: Childrens Hospital Los Angeles
Prgm Director: Douglas Vanderbilt, MD
4650 Sunset Boulevard
Mailstop 76
Los Angeles, CA 90027
Tel: 323 660-2450   *Fax:* 323 361-8566
E-mail: dvanderbilt@chla.usc.edu
Length: 3 Yrs
Program ID: 336-05-31-044

UCLA Medical Center Program
Sponsor: UCLA David Geffen School of Medicine/UCLA
  Medical Center
Santa Monica-UCLA Medical Center
Prgm Director: Judy Howard, MD
David Geffen School of Medicine at UCLA
300 UCLA Medical Plaza, Suite 3300
Los Angeles, CA 90095
Tel: 310 794-1456   *Fax:* 310 206-4215
Length: 3 Yrs   *ACGME Approved/Offered Positions:* 1
Program ID: 336-05-13-003

Sacramento

University of California (Davis) Health System Program
Sponsor: University of California (Davis) Health System
University of California (Davis) Medical Center
Prgm Director: Robin L Hansen, MD
MIND Institute
2825 50th Street
Sacramento, CA 95817
Tel: 916 703-0248   *Fax:* 916 703-0243
E-mail: robin.hansen@ucdmc.ucdavis.edu
Length: 3 Yrs   *ACGME Approved/Offered Positions:* 6
Program ID: 336-05-22-018

Stanford

Stanford University Program
Sponsor: Stanford Hospital and Clinics
Lucile Salter Packard Children's Hospital at Stanford
Prgm Director: Heidi M Feldman, MD, PhD
750 Welch Road
Suite 315
Palo Alto, CA 94303
Tel: 650 723-5711   *Fax:* 650 725-8351
Length: 3 Yrs   *ACGME Approved/Offered Positions:* 6
Program ID: 336-05-12-041

Connecticut

New Haven

Yale-New Haven Medical Center Program
Sponsor: Yale-New Haven Hospital
Prgm Director: Carol C Weitzman, MD
333 Cedar Street
PO Box 208064
New Haven, CT 06520
Tel: 203 688-4548   *Fax:* 203 785-3932
E-mail: carol.weitzman@yale.edu
Length: 3 Yrs   *ACGME Approved/Offered Positions:* 3
Program ID: 336-08-11-001

Hawaii

Honolulu

University of Hawaii Program
Sponsor: University of Hawaii John A Burns School of
  Medicine
Kapiolani Medical Center for Women and Children
Shriners Hospitals for Children (Honolulu)
Tripler Army Medical Center
Prgm Director: Jeffrey K Okamoto, MD
1319 Punahou Street, Room 757
Honolulu, HI 96826
Tel: 808 983-8387   *Fax:* 808 945-1570
E-mail: jokamoto@hawaii.edu
Length: 3 Yrs   *ACGME Approved/Offered Positions:* 1
Program ID: 336-14-21-034

Illinois

Chicago

University of Chicago Program
Sponsor: University of Chicago Medical Center
Advocate Illinois Masonic Medical Center
LaRabida Children's Hospital and Research Center
University of Illinois Hospital and Clinics
Prgm Director: Peter J Smith, MD, MA
950 East 61st - SSC 207
Chicago, IL 60637
Tel: 773 702-3095   *Fax:* 773 702-0208
E-mail: psmith2@peds.bsd.uchicago.edu
Length: 3 Yrs   *ACGME Approved/Offered Positions:* 6
Program ID: 336-16-21-028

Iowa

Iowa City

University of Iowa Hospitals and Clinics Program
Sponsor: University of Iowa Hospitals and Clinics
Prgm Director: Deborah C Lin-Dyken, MD
100 Hawkins Drive
Room 213 CDD
Iowa City, IA 52242
Tel: 319 353-6132   *Fax:* 319 356-8284
E-mail: deborah-lin-dyken@uiowa.edu
Length: 3 Yrs   *ACGME Approved/Offered Positions:* 1
Program ID: 336-18-31-021

Kansas

Kansas City

University of Kansas School of Medicine Program
Sponsor: University of Kansas School of Medicine
University of Kansas Hospital
Prgm Director: Kathryn Ellerbeck, MD, MPH
Center for Child Health and Development
3901 Rainbow Blvd, MSN 4003
Kansas City, KS 66160
Tel: 913 588-5781   *Fax:* 913 588-5916
E-mail: swaqiah@kumc.edu
Length: 3 Yrs   *ACGME Approved/Offered Positions:* 3
Program ID: 336-19-31-027

Maryland

Baltimore

University of Maryland Program
Sponsor: University of Maryland Medical System
Prgm Director: Anna Maria Wilms Floet, MD*
Department of Pediatrics
737 West Lombard St, Suite 130
Baltimore, MD 21201
Tel: 410 706-3543   *Fax:* 410 706-5770
Length: 3 Yrs   *ACGME Approved/Offered Positions:* 6
Program ID: 336-23-31-004

Massachusetts

Boston

Children's Hospital/Boston Medical Center Program
Sponsor: Children's Hospital
Prgm Director: Leonard Rappaport, MD, MS
300 Longwood Avenue
Boston, MA 02115
Tel: 617 355-7030   *Fax:* 617 730-0252
Length: 3 Yrs   *ACGME Approved/Offered Positions:* 6
Program ID: 336-24-31-019

Children's Hospital/Boston Medical Center Program A
Sponsor: Children's Hospital
Boston Medical Center
Prgm Director: Steven Parker, MD
One Boston Medical Center Place, Mat 5
Boston, MA 02118
Tel: 617 414-4788   *Fax:* 617 414-7915
E-mail: augustyn@bu.edu
Length: 3 Yrs   *ACGME Approved/Offered Positions:* 5
Program ID: 336-24-11-011

Programs

Tufts Medical Center Program
Sponsor: Tufts Medical Center
Prgm Director: Karen J Miller, MD
Floating Hospital, Tufts Medical Center
800 Washington Street, Box 334
Boston, MA 02111
Tel: 617 636-5309   *Fax:* 617 636-5621
E-mail: kmiller7@tuftsmedicalcenter.org
Length: 3 Yrs   *ACGME Approved/Offered Positions:* 3
Program ID: 336-24-13-033

Michigan

Ann Arbor

University of Michigan Program
Sponsor: University of Michigan Hospitals and Health
  Centers
Prgm Director: Barbara T Felt, MD*
1924 TC, 1500 E Medical Center Drive
Ann Arbor, MI 48109
Tel: 734 936-9777   *Fax:* 734 936-6897
Length: 3 Yrs   *ACGME Approved/Offered Positions:* 3
Program ID: 336-25-12-045

Minnesota

Minneapolis

University of Minnesota Program
Sponsor: University of Minnesota Medical School
Hennepin County Medical Center
Park Nicollet Clinic-Alexander Center
University of Minnesota Medical Center, Division of
  Fairview
Prgm Director: Daniel P Kohen, MD
McNamara Alumni Center, Suite 160
200 Oak Street, SE
Minneapolis, MN 55455
Tel: 612 626-4260   *Fax:* 612 624-0997
E-mail: dpkohen@umn.edu
Length: 3 Yrs   *ACGME Approved/Offered Positions:* 1
Program ID: 336-26-31-023

Rochester

**College of Medicine, Mayo Clinic
(Rochester) Program**
Sponsor: College of Medicine, Mayo Clinic
Mayo Clinic (Rochester)
Prgm Director: Robert G Voigt, MD
200 First Street SW
Rochester, MN 55905
Tel: 507 538-0154   *Fax:* 507 284-0160
E-mail: voigt.robert@mayo.edu
Length: 3 Yrs   *ACGME Approved/Offered Positions:* 1
Program ID: 336-26-21-042

Missouri

Kansas City

**University of Missouri at Kansas City
Program**
Sponsor: University of Missouri-Kansas City School of
  Medicine
Children's Mercy Hospital
Prgm Director: Carol B Garrison, MD
2401 Gillham Road
Kansas City, MO 64108
Tel: 816 234-3213   *Fax:* 816 983-6320
E-mail: cgarrison@cmh.edu
Length: 3 Yrs   *ACGME Approved/Offered Positions:* 3
Program ID: 336-28-12-032

Note: * indicates a newly appointed program director

New York

Bronx

**Albert Einstein College of Medicine
Program**
Sponsor: Albert Einstein College of Medicine of Yeshiva
  University
Prgm Director: Maris D Rosenberg, MD
1410 Pelham Parkway South
Bronx, NY 10461
Tel: 718 430-8504   *Fax:* 718 892-2296
Length: 3 Yrs   *ACGME Approved/Offered Positions:* 6
Program ID: 336-35-21-015

Great Neck

**NSLIJHS-Schneider Children's Hospital
Program**
Sponsor: North Shore-Long Island Jewish Health System
Schneider Children's Hospital at Long Island Jewish
  Med Ctr
Prgm Director: David L Meryash, MD
1983 Marcus Avenue, Suite 130
Lake Success, NY 11040
Tel: 516 802-6113   *Fax:* 516 616-5801
E-mail: dmeryash@lij.edu
Length: 3 Yrs   *ACGME Approved/Offered Positions:* 1
Program ID: 336-35-12-037

New York

**New York University School of Medicine
Program**
Sponsor: New York University School of Medicine
Bellevue Hospital Center
Prgm Director: Alan L Mendelsohn, MD
Department of Pediatrics
550 First Avenue, NBV 8 South 4-11
New York, NY 10016
Tel: 212 562-6342   *Fax:* 212 562-2474
E-mail: alm5@nyu.edu
Length: 3 Yrs   *ACGME Approved/Offered Positions:* 2
Program ID: 336-35-21-005

Rochester

University of Rochester Program
Sponsor: Strong Memorial Hospital of the University of
  Rochester
Prgm Director: Stephen B Sulkes, MD
Box 671
601 Elmwood Avenue
Rochester, NY 14642
Tel: 585 275-0355   *Fax:* 585 275-3366
E-mail: Phyllis_Ives@urmc.rochester.edu
Length: 3 Yrs   *ACGME Approved/Offered Positions:* 3
Program ID: 336-35-31-040

North Carolina

Chapel Hill

**University of North Carolina Hospitals
Program**
Sponsor: University of North Carolina Hospitals
Prgm Director: Daniel L Moran, MD
Center for Development and Learning
CB 7255
Chapel Hill, NC 27599
Tel: 919 966-5171   *Fax:* 919 966-2230
E-mail: daniel.moran@cdl.unc.edu
Length: 3 Yrs   *ACGME Approved/Offered Positions:* 6
Program ID: 336-36-31-036

Ohio

Akron

**Children's Hospital Medical Center of
Akron/NEOUCOM Program**
Sponsor: Children's Hospital Medical Center of Akron
Prgm Director: Diane Langkamp, MD, EdD
Akron Children's Hospital
One Perkins Square
Akron, OH 44308
Tel: 330 543-8952   *Fax:* 330 543-6045
E-mail: dlangkamp@chmca.org
Length: 3 Yrs   *ACGME Approved/Offered Positions:* 6
Program ID: 336-38-13-043

Cincinnati

**Cincinnati Children's Hospital Medical
Center/University of Cincinnati College of
Medicine Program**
Sponsor: Cincinnati Children's Hospital Medical Center
Prgm Director: Susan E Wiley, MD*
3333 Burnet Avenue
MLC 4002
Cincinnati, OH 45229
Tel: 513 636-8375   *Fax:* 513 803-0072
Length: 3 Yrs   *ACGME Approved/Offered Positions:* 6
Program ID: 336-38-31-006

Cleveland

**University Hospitals Case Medical
Center Program**
Sponsor: University Hospitals Case Medical Center
Prgm Director: Nancy Roizen, MD*
Rainbow Babies & Children's Hospital, WLK 6038
10524 Euclid Ave Suite 3150
Cleveland, OH 44106
Tel: 216 844-3230   *Fax:* 216 844-7601
Length: 3 Yrs   *ACGME Approved/Offered Positions:* 2
Program ID: 336-38-12-030

Columbus

**Nationwide Children's Hospital/Ohio
State University Program**
Sponsor: Nationwide Children's Hospital
Ohio State University Hospital
Prgm Director: Daniel L Coury, MD
700 Children's Drive
Columbus, OH 43205
Tel: 614 722-2435   *Fax:* 614 722-4966
E-mail: Daniel.Coury@NationwideChildrens.org
Length: 3 Yrs   *ACGME Approved/Offered Positions:* 3
Program ID: 336-38-13-013

Oklahoma

Oklahoma City

**University of Oklahoma Health Sciences
Center Program**
Sponsor: University of Oklahoma College of Medicine
OU Medical Center - Children's Hospital
Prgm Director: Laura J McGuinn, MD
Child Study Center
1100 NE 13th Street
Oklahoma City, OK 73117
Tel: 405 271-6824   *Fax:* 405 271-8835
E-mail: laura-mcguinn@ouhsc.edu
Length: 3 Yrs   *ACGME Approved/Offered Positions:* 3
Program ID: 336-39-21-038

Pennsylvania

Philadelphia

Children's Hospital of Philadelphia Program

Sponsor: Children's Hospital of Philadelphia
Prgm Director: Nathan J Blum, MD*
Behavioral-Development Pediatrics Training Program
3550 Market Street 3rd Floor
Philadelphia, PA 19104
Tel: 215 590-7681
E-mail: blum@email.chop.edu
Length: 3 Yrs   *ACGME Approved/Offered Positions:* 6
Program ID: 336-41-13-007

Pittsburgh

University of Pittsburgh Medical Center Medical Education Program

Sponsor: Univ of Pittsburgh Medical Center Medical Education
Children's Hospital of Pittsburgh of UPMC
Prgm Director: William I Cohen, MD
3705 Fifth Avenue
Pittsburgh, PA 15213
Tel: 412 692-6546   *Fax:* 412 692-8729
Length: 3 Yrs   *ACGME Approved/Offered Positions:* 2
Program ID: 336-41-13-008

Rhode Island

Providence

Brown University Program

Sponsor: Rhode Island Hospital-Lifespan
Memorial Hospital of Rhode Island
Prgm Director: Pamela C High, MD, MS
Division of Developmental-Behavioral Pediatrics
593 Eddy Street
Providence, RI 02903
Tel: 401 444-5440   *Fax:* 401 444-8488
E-mail: phigh@lifespan.org
Length: 3 Yrs   *ACGME Approved/Offered Positions:* 4
Program ID: 336-43-21-012

South Carolina

Charleston

Medical University of South Carolina Program

Sponsor: Medical University of South Carolina College of Medicine
MUSC Medical Center
Prgm Director: Michelle M Macias, MD
135 Rutledge Avenue
MSC 567
Charleston, SC 29425
Tel: 843 876-1505   *Fax:* 843 876-1518
E-mail: courvoic@musc.edu
Length: 3 Yrs   *ACGME Approved/Offered Positions:* 3
Program ID: 336-45-12-020

Greenville

Greenville Hospital System/University of South Carolina School of Medicine Program

Sponsor: Greenville Hospital System/University of South Carolina
Prgm Director: Desmond P Kelly, MD
Division of Developmental-Behavioral Pediatrics
200 Patewood Avenue, Suite A200
Greenville, SC 29615
Tel: 864 454-5156   *Fax:* 864 454-5111
E-mail: dkelly@ghs.org
Length: 3 Yrs   *ACGME Approved/Offered Positions:* 3
Program ID: 336-45-13-035

Tennessee

Nashville

Vanderbilt University Program

Sponsor: Vanderbilt University Medical Center
Prgm Director: Tyler Reimschisel, MD*
3401 West End Avenue, Suite 460 West
Nashville, TN 37203
Tel: 615 936-0269   *Fax:* 615 936-0256
E-mail: tyler.reimschisel@vanderbilt.edu
Length: 3 Yrs   *ACGME Approved/Offered Positions:* 1
Program ID: 336-47-13-031

Virginia

Charlottesville

University of Virginia Program

Sponsor: University of Virginia Medical Center
Prgm Director: James A Blackman, MD, MPH
2270 Ivy Road
PO Box 800232
Charlottesville, VA 22903
Tel: 434 982-1676   *Fax:* 434 924-2780
E-mail: JAB5U@virginia.edu
Length: 3 Yrs   *ACGME Approved/Offered Positions:* 2
Program ID: 336-51-22-014

Washington

Seattle

University of Washington Program

Sponsor: University of Washington School of Medicine
Seattle Children's Hospital
University of Washington Medical Center
Prgm Director: William O Walker Jr, MD
Div of Genetics and Developmental Med
4800 Sand Point Way NE, A 7938
Seattle, WA 98105
Tel: 206 987-3664   *Fax:* 206 987-3824
Length: 3 Yrs   *ACGME Approved/Offered Positions:* 3
Program ID: 336-54-12-026

Tacoma

Madigan Army Medical Center Program

Sponsor: Madigan Army Medical Center
Seattle Children's Hospital
University of Washington Center on Human Development (CHDD)
Prgm Director: Beth E Davis, MD, MPH
Department of Pediatrics
Attn: MCHJ-P
Tacoma, WA 98431
Tel: 263 968-1330   *Fax:* 263 968-0384
Length: 3 Yrs   *ACGME Approved/Offered Positions:* 6
Program ID: 336-54-12-009
Uniformed Services Program

Emergency Medicine

Alabama

Birmingham

University of Alabama Medical Center Program

Sponsor: University of Alabama Hospital
Prgm Director: Andrew R Edwards, MD
619 19th Street, Jefferson Tower N266
Birmingham, AL 35249
Tel: 205 975-5071   *Fax:* 205 996-9590
E-mail: emresidency@uabmc.edu
Length: 3 Yrs   *ACGME Approved/Offered Positions:* 24
Program ID: 110-01-31-165

Arizona

Phoenix

Maricopa Medical Center Program

Sponsor: Maricopa Medical Center
Prgm Director: Eric D Katz, MD
2601 East Roosevelt Street
Phoenix, AZ 85010
Tel: 602 344-5808   *Fax:* 602 344-5907
E-mail: eric_katz@medprodoctors.com
Length: 3 Yrs   *ACGME Approved/Offered Positions:* 42
Program ID: 110-03-21-082

Tucson

University of Arizona Program

Sponsor: University of Arizona College of Medicine
University Medical Center
Prgm Director: Samuel M Keim, MD
1501 North Campbell Avenue
Tucson, AZ 85724
Tel: 520 626-7233   *Fax:* 520 626-1633
Length: 3 Yrs   *ACGME Approved/Offered Positions:* 48
Program ID: 110-03-12-056

Arkansas

Little Rock

University of Arkansas for Medical Sciences Program

Sponsor: University of Arkansas College of Medicine
Arkansas Children's Hospital
UAMS Medical Center
Prgm Director: Christopher D Melton, MD
4301 West Markham, Slot 584
Little Rock, AR 72205
Tel: 501 686-5516   *Fax:* 501 686-8586
E-mail: meltonchristopher@uams.edu
Length: 3 Yrs   *ACGME Approved/Offered Positions:* 30
Program ID: 110-04-21-071

California

Bakersfield

Kern Medical Center Program

Sponsor: Kern Medical Center
Prgm Director: Rick A McPheeters, DO
Department of Emergency Medicine
1830 Flower Street
Bakersfield, CA 93305
Tel: 661 326-2160   *Fax:* 661 326-2165
E-mail: barnards@kernmedctr.com
Length: 3 Yrs   *ACGME Approved/Offered Positions:* 24
Program ID: 110-05-12-001

Fresno

University of California (San Francisco)/Fresno Program

Sponsor: UCSF Fresno Medical Education Program
Community Medical Centers (Fresno)
Prgm Director: James A Comes, MD
Emergency Medicine Residency Program
155 N Fresno Street
Fresno, CA 93701
Tel: 559 499-6440   *Fax:* 559 499-6441
Length: 4 Yrs   *ACGME Approved/Offered Positions:* 40
Program ID: 110-05-12-002

Loma Linda

Loma Linda University Program

Sponsor: Loma Linda University Medical Center
Riverside County Regional Medical Center
Prgm Director: Dustin D Smith, MD
11234 Anderson Street, Room A-108
Loma Linda, CA 92354
Tel: 909 824-4085
E-mail: ddsmith@llu.edu
Length: 3 Yrs   *ACGME Approved/Offered Positions:* 39
Program ID: 110-05-12-068

Los Angeles

UCLA Medical Center/Olive View Program

Sponsor: UCLA David Geffen School of Medicine/UCLA
   Medical Center
Olive View/UCLA Medical Center
UCLA Medical Center
Prgm Director: Scott R Votey, MD*
Emergency Medicine Center
924 Westwood Blvd, Suite 300
Los Angeles, CA 90095
Tel: 310 794-0585   *Fax:* 310 794-0599
E-mail: svotey@ucla.edu
Length: 4 Yrs   *ACGME Approved/Offered Positions:* 48
Program ID: 110-05-12-003

University of Southern California/ LAC+USC Medical Center Program

Sponsor: University of Southern California/LAC+USC
   Medical Center
LAC+USC Medical Center
Prgm Director: Stuart Swadron, MD
1200 North State Street
Room 1011 GH
Los Angeles, CA 90033
Tel: 323 226-6937   *Fax:* 323 226-8101
Length: 3 Yrs   *ACGME Approved/Offered Positions:* 54
Program ID: 110-05-12-005

Oakland

Alameda County Medical Center Program

Sponsor: Alameda County Medical Center
UCSF and Mount Zion Medical Centers
Prgm Director: Eric R Snoey, MD
1411 East 31st Street #22123
Oakland, CA 94602
Tel: 510 437-4564   *Fax:* 510 437-8322
Length: 4 Yrs   *ACGME Approved/Offered Positions:* 40
Program ID: 110-05-12-006

Orange

University of California (Irvine) Program

Sponsor: University of California (Irvine) Medical
   Center
Long Beach Memorial Medical Center
Prgm Director: Jennifer A Oman, MD
101 The City Drive South, Route 128
Orange, CA 92868
Tel: 714 456-5239   *Fax:* 714 456-5390
E-mail: jkrawczy@uci.edu
Length: 3 Yrs   *ACGME Approved/Offered Positions:* 21
Program ID: 110-05-21-078

Sacramento

University of California (Davis) Health System Program

Sponsor: University of California (Davis) Health System
Kaiser Foundation Hospital (South Sacramento)
University of California (Davis) Medical Center
Prgm Director: Peter E Sokolove, MD
4150 V Street
PSSB, Suite 2100
Sacramento, CA 95817
Tel: 916 734-8571   *Fax:* 916 734-7950
E-mail: emres@ucdmc.ucdavis.edu
Length: 3 Yrs   *ACGME Approved/Offered Positions:* 36
Program ID: 110-05-21-097

San Diego

Naval Medical Center (San Diego) Program

Sponsor: Naval Medical Center (San Diego)
Prgm Director: David A Tanen, MD
Department of Emergency Medicine
Suite 118
San Diego, CA 92134
Tel: 619 532-7498   *Fax:* 619 532-5307
E-mail: david.tanen@med.navy.mil
Length: 3 Yrs   *ACGME Approved/Offered Positions:* 30
Program ID: 110-05-12-067
Uniformed Services Program

University of California (San Diego) Program

Sponsor: University of California (San Diego) Medical
   Center
Prgm Director: Binh T Ly, MD*
200 W Arbor Drive
San Diego, CA 92103
Tel: 619 543-6236   *Fax:* 619 543-7598
E-mail: kmrichardson@ucsd.edu
Length: 3 Yrs   *ACGME Approved/Offered Positions:* 24
Program ID: 110-05-21-080

San Francisco

University of California (San Francisco)/San Francisco General Hospital Program

Sponsor: University of California (San Francisco) School
   of Medicine
San Francisco General Hospital Medical Center
UCSF Med Ctr/Langley Porter Psychiatric Hosp and
   Clinics
Prgm Director: Susan B Promes, MD
505 Parnassus Avenue, M-24
UCSF Emergency Medicine
San Francisco, CA 94143
Tel: 415 353-1529   *Fax:* 415 353-8499
E-mail: emresidency@ucsf.edu
Length: 4 Yrs   *ACGME Approved/Offered Positions:* 48
Program ID: 110-05-13-192

Stanford

Stanford University Hospital/Kaiser Permanente Medical Center Program

Sponsor: Stanford Hospital and Clinics
Kaiser Permanente Medical Center (Santa Clara)
Prgm Director: Phillip M Harter, MD
Division of Emergency Medicine
701 Welch Rd, Bldg C
Palo Alto, CA 94304
Tel: 650 723-9215   *Fax:* 650 723-0121
E-mail: em.residency@med.stanford.edu
Length: 3 Yrs   *ACGME Approved/Offered Positions:* 36
Program ID: 110-05-21-098

Torrance

Los Angeles County-Harbor-UCLA Medical Center Program

Sponsor: Los Angeles County-Harbor-UCLA Medical
   Center
Prgm Director: David B Burbulys, MD
1000 West Carson Street, D9
Harbor Mail Box 21, PO Box 2910
Torrance, CA 90502
Tel: 310 222-3500   *Fax:* 310 782-1763
E-mail: burbulys@emedharbor.edu
Length: 3 Yrs   *ACGME Approved/Offered Positions:* 45
Program ID: 110-05-12-008

Colorado

Denver

Denver Health Medical Center Program

Sponsor: Denver Health Medical Center
University of Colorado Hospital
Prgm Director: Stephen Wolf, MD
Mail Code 0108
777 Bannock Street
Denver, CO 80204
Tel: 303 436-7142   *Fax:* 303 436-7541
Length: 4 Yrs   *ACGME Approved/Offered Positions:* 56
Program ID: 110-07-12-009

Connecticut

Farmington

University of Connecticut Program

Sponsor: University of Connecticut School of Medicine
Connecticut Children's Medical Center
Hartford Hospital
Prgm Director: Susan E Dufel, MD, FACEP
Dept of Traumatology/Emergency Medicine
80 Seymour Street
Hartford, CT 06102
Tel: 860 545-1457   *Fax:* 860 545-1461
Length: 3 Yrs   *ACGME Approved/Offered Positions:* 36
Program ID: 110-08-21-120

New Haven

Yale-New Haven Medical Center Program

Sponsor: Yale-New Haven Hospital
Bridgeport Hospital
Prgm Director: Laura J Bontempo, MD
Emergency Medicine Residency
464 Congress Avenue, Suite 260
New Haven, CT 06519
Tel: 203 785-5174   *Fax:* 203 785-4580
E-mail: laura.bontempo@yale.edu
Length: 4 Yrs   *ACGME Approved/Offered Positions:* 52
Program ID: 110-08-21-139

Note: * indicates a newly appointed program director

Delaware

Wilmington

Christiana Care Health Services Program
Sponsor: Christiana Care Health Services Inc
Prgm Director: Neil B Jasani, MD
4755 Ogletown-Stanton Road
PO Box 6001
Newark, DE 19718
Tel: 302 733-4176   *Fax:* 302 733-1633
E-mail: llafontaine@christianacare.org
Length: 3 Yrs   *ACGME Approved/Offered Positions:* 45
Program ID: 110-09-12-057

District of Columbia

Washington

George Washington University Program
Sponsor: George Washington University School of
   Medicine
George Washington University Hospital (UHS)
Inova Fairfax Hospital
Prgm Director: Raymond Lucas, MD
2150 Pennsylvania Avenue, NW
Suite 2B-421
Washington, DC 20037
Tel: 202 741-2911   *Fax:* 202 741-2921
E-mail: rlucas@mfa.gwu.edu
Length: 4 Yrs   *ACGME Approved/Offered Positions:* 40
Program ID: 110-10-12-011

Georgetown University Hospital/Washington Hospital Center Program
Sponsor: Washington Hospital Center
Georgetown University Hospital
Prgm Director: Jeffrey N Love, MD, MS
Department of Emergency Medicine
110 Irving Street, NW, Suite NA1177
Washington, DC 20010
Tel: 202 877-8282   *Fax:* 202 877-7633
E-mail: jeffrey.n.love@medstar.net
Length: 3 Yrs   *ACGME Approved/Offered Positions:* 30
Program ID: 110-10-12-181

Florida

Gainesville

University of Florida Program
Sponsor: University of Florida College of Medicine
Shands Hospital at the University of Florida
Prgm Director: Richard W Stair, MD, FACEP
Department of Emergency Medicine
1329 SW 16th Street, Room 4270
Gainesville, FL 32610
Tel: 352 265-5911   *Fax:* 352 265-5606
Length: 3 Yrs   *ACGME Approved/Offered Positions:* 24
Program ID: 110-11-31-186

Jacksonville

University of Florida College of Medicine Jacksonville Program
Sponsor: University of Florida College of Medicine
   Jacksonville
Shands Jacksonville Medical Center
Prgm Director: David A Caro, MD, FACEP
655 West 8th Street, Box C506
Jacksonville, FL 32209
Tel: 904 244-4837   *Fax:* 904 244-4508
Length: 3 Yrs   *ACGME Approved/Offered Positions:* 45
Program ID: 110-11-12-058

Orlando

Florida Hospital Medical Center Program
Sponsor: Florida Hospital Medical Center
Prgm Director: Dale S Birenbaum, MD
7727 Lake Underhill Road
Orlando, FL 32822
Tel: 407 303-6413   *Fax:* 407 303-6414
Length: 3 Yrs   *ACGME Approved/Offered Positions:* 24
Program ID: 110-11-12-190

Orlando Health Program
Sponsor: Orlando Health
Orlando Regional Medical Center
Prgm Director: Salvatore Silvestri, MD
1414 South Kuhl Avenue
Orlando, FL 32806
Tel: 407 237-6329   *Fax:* 407 649-3083
E-mail: Sal.Silvestri@orlandohealth.com
Length: 3 Yrs   *ACGME Approved/Offered Positions:* 42
Program ID: 110-11-21-072

Tampa

University of South Florida Program
Sponsor: University of South Florida College of Medicine
Tampa General Hospital
Prgm Director: Kelly P O'Keefe, MD, FACEP
1 Davis Blvd, Suite 504
Tampa, FL 33606
Tel: 813 627-5931   *Fax:* 813 254-6440
Length: 3 Yrs   *ACGME Approved/Offered Positions:* 30
Program ID: 110-11-21-167

Georgia

Atlanta

Emory University Program
Sponsor: Emory University School of Medicine
Grady Health System
Prgm Director: Philip Shayne, MD
49 Jesse Hill Jr Drive, SE
Atlanta, GA 30303
Tel: 404 616-6673   *Fax:* 404 616-0191
E-mail: emres@emory.edu
Length: 3 Yrs   *ACGME Approved/Offered Positions:* 66
Program ID: 110-12-12-012

Augusta

Medical College of Georgia Program
Sponsor: Medical College of Georgia
Prgm Director: Stephen A Shiver, MD*
1120 15th Street
AF-1026
Augusta, GA 30912
Tel: 706 721-2613   *Fax:* 706 721-9081
E-mail: sshiver@mcg.edu
Length: 3 Yrs   *ACGME Approved/Offered Positions:* 30
Program ID: 110-12-21-090

Illinois

Chicago

John H Stroger Hospital of Cook County Program
Sponsor: John H Stroger Hospital of Cook County
Prgm Director: Steven H Bowman, MD
Department of Emergency Medicine
1900 West Polk Street, 10th Floor
Chicago, IL 60612
Tel: 312 864-0060   *Fax:* 312 864-9656
E-mail: elee@ccbh.org
Length: 4 Yrs   *ACGME Approved/Offered Positions:* 80
Program ID: 110-16-21-083

McGaw Medical Center of Northwestern University Program
Sponsor: McGaw Medical Center of Northwestern
   University
Evanston Hospital
Northwestern Memorial Hospital
Prgm Director: Jamie L Collings, MD
259 E Erie
Suite 100
Chicago, IL 60611
Tel: 312 694-9620   *Fax:* 312 926-6274
E-mail: emedres@northwestern.edu
Length: 4 Yrs   *ACGME Approved/Offered Positions:* 48
Program ID: 110-16-12-015

Resurrection Medical Center Program
Sponsor: Resurrection Medical Center
St Francis Hospital
Prgm Director: Marc A Dorfman, MD
Emergency Medicine Residency Program
7435 West Talcott Avenue
Chicago, IL 60631
Tel: 773 792-7921   *Fax:* 773 594-7805
E-mail: dtoriani@reshealthcare.org
Length: 3 Yrs   *ACGME Approved/Offered Positions:* 39
Program ID: 110-16-31-146

University of Chicago Program
Sponsor: University of Chicago Medical Center
Advocate Lutheran General Hospital
Prgm Director: David S Howes, MD
5841 South Maryland Avenue, MC 5068
Chicago, IL 60637
Tel: 773 702-2887   *Fax:* 773 702-3135
Length: 3 Yrs   *ACGME Approved/Offered Positions:* 48
Program ID: 110-16-12-014

University of Illinois College of Medicine at Chicago Program
Sponsor: University of Illinois College of Medicine at
   Chicago
Advocate Illinois Masonic Medical Center
Mercy Hospital and Medical Center
University of Illinois Hospital and Clinics
Prgm Director: Edward B Bunney, MD
Suite 471 College of Medicine, East, M/C 724
808 S Wood Street
Chicago, IL 60612
Tel: 312 413-7484   *Fax:* 312 413-0289
Length: 3 Yrs   *ACGME Approved/Offered Positions:* 39
Program ID: 110-16-12-016

Oak Lawn

Advocate Christ Medical Center Program
Sponsor: Advocate Christ Medical Center
Prgm Director: Robert C Harwood, MD, MPH
4440 West 95th Street
Dept of Emergency Medicine Rm 185W
Oak Lawn, IL 60453
Tel: 708 684-5375   *Fax:* 708 684-1028
E-mail: rosemary.zelinski@advocatehealth.com
Length: 3 Yrs   *ACGME Approved/Offered Positions:* 42
Program ID: 110-16-12-017

Peoria

University of Illinois College of Medicine at Peoria Program
Sponsor: University of Illinois College of Medicine at
   Peoria
OSF St Francis Medical Center
Prgm Director: Marc D Squillante, DO
530 NE Glen Oak Avenue
Peoria, IL 61637
Tel: 309 655-6710   *Fax:* 309 624-9887
E-mail: glendah@uic.edu
Length: 3 Yrs   *ACGME Approved/Offered Positions:* 30
Program ID: 110-16-12-069

Indiana

Indianapolis

Indiana University School of Medicine Program

Sponsor: Indiana University School of Medicine
Clarian Methodist Hospital of Indiana
William N Wishard Memorial Hospital
Prgm Director: Carey D Chisholm, MD
I-65 at 21st Street
PO Box 1367
Indianapolis, IN 46206
Tel: 317 962-5975   *Fax:* 317 963-5394
Length: 3 Yrs   *ACGME Approved/Offered Positions:* 59
Program ID: 110-17-12-018

Iowa

Iowa City

University of Iowa Hospitals and Clinics Program

Sponsor: University of Iowa Hospitals and Clinics
St Luke's Methodist Hospital
Prgm Director: Hans R House, MD
200 Hawkins Drive
C43 GH
Iowa City, IA 52242
Tel: 319 384-6511   *Fax:* 319 356-1138
E-mail: hans-house@uiowa.edu
Length: 3 Yrs   *ACGME Approved/Offered Positions:* 24
Program ID: 110-18-12-174

Kentucky

Lexington

University of Kentucky College of Medicine Program

Sponsor: University of Kentucky College of Medicine
University of Kentucky Hospital
Prgm Director: Rebecca C Bowers, MD
Department of Emergency Medicine
800 Rose Street, Room M-53
Lexington, KY 40536
Tel: 859 323-5083   *Fax:* 859 323-8056
E-mail: raweinb@uky.edu
Length: 3 Yrs   *ACGME Approved/Offered Positions:* 24
Program ID: 110-20-21-129

Louisville

University of Louisville Program

Sponsor: University of Louisville School of Medicine
Kosair Children's Hospital (Norton Healthcare, Inc)
University of Louisville Hospital
Prgm Director: Mary Nan Mallory, MD
530 South Jackson St
Louisville, KY 40202
Tel: 502 852-7633   *Fax:* 502 852-0066
Length: 3 Yrs   *ACGME Approved/Offered Positions:* 30
Program ID: 110-20-12-020

Louisiana

Baton Rouge

Louisiana State University (Baton Rouge) Program

Sponsor: Earl K Long Medical Center
Baton Rouge General Medical Center
Our Lady of the Lake Regional Medical Center
Prgm Director: Cris V Mandry, MD
Emergency Medicine Residency Program
5825 Airline Highway
Baton Rouge, LA 70805
Tel: 225 358-3940   *Fax:* 225 358-3939
E-mail: emrpbr@lsuhsc.edu
Length: 3 Yrs   *ACGME Approved/Offered Positions:* 45
Program ID: 110-21-21-117

New Orleans

Louisiana State University Program

Sponsor: Louisiana State University School of Medicine
Medical Center of Louisiana at New Orleans
Prgm Director: Micelle J Haydel, MD
2020 Gravier 7th Floor Suite D
New Orleans, LA 70112
Tel: 504 903-3594   *Fax:* 504 903-4569
E-mail: micellehaydel@yahoo.com
Length: 4 Yrs   *ACGME Approved/Offered Positions:* 52
Program ID: 110-21-12-021

Shreveport

Louisiana State University (Shreveport) Program

Sponsor: LSU Health Sciences Center-University
  Hospital
Prgm Director: Thomas K Swoboda, MD, MS
1541 Kings Highway
PO Box 33932
Shreveport, LA 71130
Tel: 318 675-6632   *Fax:* 318 675-6878
E-mail: eking@lsuhsc.edu
Length: 3 Yrs   *ACGME Approved/Offered Positions:* 21
Program ID: 110-21-22-170

Maine

Portland

Maine Medical Center Program

Sponsor: Maine Medical Center
Prgm Director: Andrew D Perron, MD, FACEP
22 Bramhall Street
Residency Office, 321 Bramhall Street
Portland, ME 04102
Tel: 207 662-7050   *Fax:* 207 662-7054
E-mail: kanej@mmc.org
Length: 3 Yrs   *ACGME Approved/Offered Positions:* 24
Program ID: 110-22-21-142

Maryland

Baltimore

Johns Hopkins University Program

Sponsor: Johns Hopkins University School of Medicine
Johns Hopkins Bayview Medical Center
Johns Hopkins Hospital
Prgm Director: Gabor D Kelen, MD
1830 E Monument Street
Suite 6-100
Baltimore, MD 21287
Tel: 410 955-5107   *Fax:* 410 502-5146
E-mail: emresidency@jhmi.edu
Length: 4 Yrs   *ACGME Approved/Offered Positions:* 48
Program ID: 110-23-12-022

University of Maryland Program

Sponsor: University of Maryland Medical System
Prgm Director: Amal Mattu, MD
110 S Paca St
Sixth Floor, Suite 200
Baltimore, MD 21201
Tel: 410 328-8025   *Fax:* 410 328-8028
E-mail: amalmattu@comcast.net
Length: 3 Yrs   *ACGME Approved/Offered Positions:* 40
Program ID: 110-23-21-101

Massachusetts

Boston

Beth Israel Deaconess Medical Center/Harvard Medical School Program

Sponsor: Beth Israel Deaconess Medical Center
Prgm Director: Carlo Rosen, MD
Department of Emergency Medicine
One Deaconess Road, West/CC2
Boston, MA 02215
Tel: 617 754-2339   *Fax:* 617 754-2350
Length: 3 Yrs   *ACGME Approved/Offered Positions:* 36
Program ID: 110-24-31-163

Boston University Medical Center Program

Sponsor: Boston Medical Center
Prgm Director: Jeffrey I Schneider, MD*
One Boston Medical Center Place
Dowling 1 South Room 1321
Boston, MA 02118
Tel: 617 414-4064   *Fax:* 617 414-7759
E-mail: jeffrey.schneider@bmc.org
Length: 4 Yrs   *ACGME Approved/Offered Positions:* 48
Program ID: 110-24-21-084

Brigham and Women's Hospital/Harvard Medical School Program

Sponsor: Brigham and Women's Hospital
Massachusetts General Hospital
Prgm Director: Eric Nadel, MD
Department of Emergency Medicine
75 Francis Street - Neville House
Boston, MA 02115
Tel: 617 732-8070   *Fax:* 617 582-6038
E-mail: mmorgan3@partners.org
Length: 4 Yrs   *ACGME Approved/Offered Positions:* 60
Program ID: 110-24-21-150

Springfield

Baystate Medical Center/Tufts University School of Medicine Program

Sponsor: Baystate Medical Center
Prgm Director: Joseph Schmidt, MD
759 Chestnut Street
Springfield, MA 01199
Tel: 413 794-5999   *Fax:* 413 794-8070
E-mail: peg.lynch@bhs.org
Length: 3 Yrs   *ACGME Approved/Offered Positions:* 36
Program ID: 110-24-21-116

Worcester

University of Massachusetts Program

Sponsor: University of Massachusetts Medical School
UMass Memorial Health Care (University Campus)
Prgm Director: Jeffrey M Cukor, MD
55 Lake Avenue North
Worcester, MA 01655
Tel: 508 421-1418   *Fax:* 508 334-7411
Length: 3 Yrs   *ACGME Approved/Offered Positions:* 36
Program ID: 110-24-21-074

Note: * indicates a newly appointed program director

Michigan

Ann Arbor

University of Michigan Program
Sponsor: University of Michigan Hospitals and Health
  Centers
St Joseph Mercy Hospital
Prgm Director: Terry Kowalenko, MD
1500 E Medical Center Drive SPC 5305
B1-380 Taubman Center
Ann Arbor, MI 48109
Tel: 734 763-7919   *Fax:* 734 763-9298
E-mail: Emresidency@umich.edu
Length: 4 Yrs   *ACGME Approved/Offered Positions:* 56
Program ID: 110-25-21-106

Detroit

Henry Ford Hospital Program
Sponsor: Henry Ford Hospital
Prgm Director: Christopher A Lewandowski, MD
2799 West Grand Boulevard, CFP-260
Detroit, MI 48202
Tel: 313 916-1553   *Fax:* 313 916-7437
E-mail: jowens1@hfhs.org
Length: 3 Yrs   *ACGME Approved/Offered Positions:* 55
Program ID: 110-25-12-025

St John Hospital and Medical Center Program
Sponsor: St John Hospital and Medical Center
Prgm Director: Don M Benson, DO
22101 Moross Road
Detroit, MI 48236
Tel: 313 343-8797   *Fax:* 313 343-7620
Length: 3 Yrs   *ACGME Approved/Offered Positions:* 36
Program ID: 110-25-21-132

Wayne State University/Detroit Medical Center (Detroit Receiving Hospital) Program
Sponsor: Wayne State University/Detroit Medical Center
Detroit Receiving Hospital and University Health Center
Prgm Director: Robert P Wahl, MD
6G University Health Center
4201 St Antoine
Detroit, MI 48201
Tel: 313 993-2530   *Fax:* 313 993-7703
E-mail: rwahl@med.wayne.edu
Length: 3 Yrs   *ACGME Approved/Offered Positions:* 36
Program ID: 110-25-12-024

Wayne State University/Detroit Medical Center (Sinai-Grace Hospital) Program
Sponsor: Wayne State University/Detroit Medical Center
Sinai-Grace Hospital
Prgm Director: Matthew J Griffin, MD
6071 West Outer Drive
Detroit, MI 48235
Tel: 313 966-1020   *Fax:* 313 966-1024
Length: 3 Yrs   *ACGME Approved/Offered Positions:* 36
Program ID: 110-25-12-059

Grand Blanc

Genesys Regional Medical Center Program
Sponsor: Genesys Regional Medical Center
Prgm Director: Alan Janssen, DO
One Genesys Parkway
Grand Blanc, MI 48439
Tel: 810 606-6372   *Fax:* 810 606-5990
E-mail: mlarocque@genesys.org
Length: 4 Yrs   *ACGME Approved/Offered Positions:* 28
Program ID: 110-25-13-196

Grand Rapids

Grand Rapids Medical Education and Research Center/Michigan State University Program
Sponsor: Grand Rapids Medical Education and Research
  Center
Spectrum Health-Butterworth Hospital
Prgm Director: Michael D Brown, MD, MSc
1000 Monroe, NW, MC-49
Grand Rapids, MI 49503
Tel: 616 391-3588   *Fax:* 616 391-3674
Length: 3 Yrs   *ACGME Approved/Offered Positions:* 30
Program ID: 110-25-12-026

Kalamazoo

Kalamazoo Center for Medical Studies/Michigan State University Program
Sponsor: Michigan State Univ/Kalamazoo Center for
  Medical Studies
Borgess Medical Center
Bronson Methodist Hospital
Prgm Director: David T Overton, MD, MBA
1000 Oakland Drive
Kalamazoo, MI 49008
Tel: 269 337-6600   *Fax:* 269 337-6475
E-mail: emergmed@kcms.msu.edu
Length: 3 Yrs   *ACGME Approved/Offered Positions:* 60
Program ID: 110-25-21-124

Lansing

Sparrow Hospital/Michigan State University Program
Sponsor: Sparrow Hospital
Ingham Regional Medical Center
Prgm Director: Ted Glynn, MD
PO Box 30480
Lansing, MI 48909
Tel: 517 364-2583   *Fax:* 517 364-3002
E-mail: anne.irvine@sparrow.org
Length: 3 Yrs   *ACGME Approved/Offered Positions:* 30
Program ID: 110-25-12-027

Royal Oak

William Beaumont Hospital Program
Sponsor: William Beaumont Hospital
William Beaumont Hospital - Troy
Prgm Director: Ryan C Fringer, MD
Department of Emergency Medicine
3601 West Thirteen Mile Road
Royal Oak, MI 48073
Tel: 248 898-9174   *Fax:* 248 898-2017
E-mail: rfringer@beaumont.edu
Length: 3 Yrs   *ACGME Approved/Offered Positions:* 36
Program ID: 110-25-12-065

Saginaw

Synergy Medical Education Alliance/Michigan State University Program
Sponsor: Synergy Medical Education Alliance
Covenant HealthCare System-Cooper Campus
St Mary's of Michigan
Prgm Director: Mary Jo Wagner, MD
1000 Houghton Avenue
Saginaw, MI 48602
Tel: 989 583-6817   *Fax:* 989 583-7436
E-mail: mjwagner@synergymedical.org
Length: 3 Yrs   *ACGME Approved/Offered Positions:* 24
Program ID: 110-25-11-138

Minnesota

Minneapolis

Hennepin County Medical Center Program
Sponsor: Hennepin County Medical Center
Prgm Director: Marc Martel, MD
701 Park Avenue South
Department of Emergency Medicine
Minneapolis, MN 55415
Tel: 612 873-5683   *Fax:* 612 904-4241
E-mail: mary.hirschboeck@hcmed.org
Length: 3 Yrs   *ACGME Approved/Offered Positions:* 36
Program ID: 110-26-12-028

Rochester

College of Medicine, Mayo Clinic (Rochester) Program
Sponsor: College of Medicine, Mayo Clinic
Saint Marys Hospital of Rochester
Prgm Director: Annie T Sadosty, MD
Generose G-410
1216 Second Street, SW
Rochester, MN 55902
Tel: 507 255-2192   *Fax:* 507 293-0584
E-mail: emres@mayo.edu
Length: 3 Yrs   *ACGME Approved/Offered Positions:* 24
Program ID: 110-26-21-161

St. Paul

HealthPartners Institute for Medical Education Program
Sponsor: HealthPartners Institute for Medical
  Education
Regions Hospital
Prgm Director: Felix K Ankel, MD
640 Jackson St
Mail Stop 11102F
St Paul, MN 55101
Tel: 651 254-3666   *Fax:* 651 254-5216
Length: 3 Yrs   *ACGME Approved/Offered Positions:* 30
Program ID: 110-26-21-144

Mississippi

Jackson

University of Mississippi Medical Center Program
Sponsor: University of Mississippi School of Medicine
University Hospitals and Clinics
Prgm Director: William Phillips, MD*
2500 North State Street
Jackson, MS 39216
Tel: 601 984-5582   *Fax:* 601 984-5583
Length: 3 Yrs   *ACGME Approved/Offered Positions:* 30
Program ID: 110-27-21-073

Missouri

Kansas City

University of Missouri at Kansas City Program
Sponsor: University of Missouri-Kansas City School of
  Medicine
Truman Medical Center
Prgm Director: Christine Sullivan, MD
2301 Holmes Street
Kansas City, MO 64108
Tel: 816 404-1536   *Fax:* 816 404-5094
Length: 3 Yrs   *ACGME Approved/Offered Positions:* 36
Program ID: 110-28-12-029

Programs

St Louis

St Louis University School of Medicine Program
Sponsor: St Louis University School of Medicine
Cardinal Glennon Children's Hospital
St John's Mercy Medical Center
St Mary's Health Center
Prgm Director: Vijai Chauhan, MD
3635 Vista Ave at Grand Blvd
St Louis, MO 63110
Tel: 314 577-8776   *Fax:* 314 268-5697
Length: 3 Yrs   *ACGME Approved/Offered Positions:* 18
Program ID: 110-28-31-201

Washington University/B-JH/SLCH Consortium Program
Sponsor: Washington University/B-JH/SLCH Consortium
Barnes-Jewish Hospital
St Louis Children's Hospital
Prgm Director: Douglas M Char, MD
660 South Euclid Avenue, Box 8072
St Louis, MO 63110
Tel: 314 362-9177   *Fax:* 314 362-0478
Length: 4 Yrs   *ACGME Approved/Offered Positions:* 56
Program ID: 110-28-21-154

Nebraska

Omaha

University of Nebraska Medical Center Program
Sponsor: University of Nebraska Medical Center College of Medicine
Nebraska Medical Center
Prgm Director: Michael C Wadman, MD
981150 Nebraska Medical Center
Omaha, NE 68198
Tel: 402 559-6802   *Fax:* 402 559-9659
E-mail: terickson@unmc.edu
Length: 3 Yrs   *ACGME Approved/Offered Positions:* 24
Program ID: 110-30-31-168

Nevada

Reno

University of Nevada School of Medicine Program
Sponsor: University of Nevada School of Medicine
University Medical Center of Southern Nevada
Prgm Director: Michael L Epter, DO
Suite 135
Las Vegas, NV 89106
Tel: 702 383-7885   *Fax:* 702 383-8235
E-mail: mepter@medicine.nevada.edu
Length: 3 Yrs   *ACGME Approved/Offered Positions:* 30
Program ID: 110-31-31-189

New Jersey

Camden

UMDNJ-Robert Wood Johnson Medical School (Camden) Program
Sponsor: Cooper Hospital-University Medical Center
Prgm Director: Andrew L Nyce, MD
One Cooper Plaza
Camden, NJ 08103
Tel: 856 342-2351   *Fax:* 856 968-8272
Length: 3 Yrs   *ACGME Approved/Offered Positions:* 33
Program ID: 110-33-21-118

Morristown

Atlantic Health (Morristown) Program
Sponsor: Atlantic Health
Morristown Memorial Hospital
Prgm Director: Richard D Shih, MD
100 Madison Avenue Box 8
Morristown, NJ 07960
Tel: 973 971-7926   *Fax:* 973 290-7202
E-mail: mmh_em@yahoo.com
Length: 3 Yrs   *ACGME Approved/Offered Positions:* 24
Program ID: 110-33-12-060

Newark

Newark Beth Israel Medical Center Program
Sponsor: Newark Beth Israel Medical Center
Prgm Director: Marc Borenstein, MD, FACEP
201 Lyons Ave at Osborne Terrace
Newark, NJ 07112
Tel: 973 926-6671   *Fax:* 973 282-0562
Length: 3 Yrs   *ACGME Approved/Offered Positions:* 36
Program ID: 110-33-21-158

UMDNJ-New Jersey Medical School Program
Sponsor: UMDNJ-New Jersey Medical School
UMDNJ-University Hospital
Prgm Director: Joseph Rella, MD
30 Bergen Street
ADMC 11 Room 1110
Newark, NJ 07103
Tel: 973 972-9219   *Fax:* 973 972-9268
E-mail: rellajg@umdnj.edu
Length: 4 Yrs   *ACGME Approved/Offered Positions:* 32
Program ID: 110-33-31-177

New Mexico

Albuquerque

University of New Mexico Program
Sponsor: University of New Mexico School of Medicine
University of New Mexico Hospital
Prgm Director: Steven A McLaughlin, MD
Department of Emergency Medicine
MSC10 5560
Albuquerque, NM 87131
Tel: 505 272-5062   *Fax:* 505 272-6503
Length: 3 Yrs   *ACGME Approved/Offered Positions:* 30
Program ID: 110-34-21-075

New York

Albany

Albany Medical Center Program
Sponsor: Albany Medical Center
Prgm Director: John H Burton, MD
47 New Scotland Avenue
MC-139
Albany, NY 12208
Tel: 518 262-4050   *Fax:* 518 262-5362
E-mail: burtonj@mail.amc.edu
Length: 3 Yrs   *ACGME Approved/Offered Positions:* 30
Program ID: 110-35-21-086

Bronx

Albert Einstein College of Medicine (Jacobi/Montefiore) Program
Sponsor: Albert Einstein College of Medicine of Yeshiva University
Montefiore Medical Center-Henry and Lucy Moses Division
North Bronx Healthcare Network-Jacobi Medical Center
Prgm Director: Thomas B Perera, MD
Jacobi - 1-W-20
1400 Pelham Parkway South
Bronx, NY 10461
Tel: 718 918-5814   *Fax:* 718 918-7459
E-mail: thomas.perera@nbhn.net
Length: 4 Yrs   *ACGME Approved/Offered Positions:* 72
Program ID: 110-35-12-030

Lincoln Medical and Mental Health Center Program
Sponsor: Lincoln Medical and Mental Health Center
Prgm Director: Joan E McInerney, MD, MBA*
234 East 149th Street
Bronx, NY 10451
Tel: 718 579-5431   *Fax:* 718 579-4822
Length: 3 Yrs   *ACGME Approved/Offered Positions:* 33
Program ID: 110-35-12-053

Brooklyn

Brooklyn Hospital Center Program
Sponsor: Brooklyn Hospital Center
Prgm Director: Benson Yeh, MD
121 DeKalb Avenue
Dept Emergency Medicine
Brooklyn, NY 11201
Tel: 718 250-8369   *Fax:* 718 250-6528
E-mail: yeh@BrooklynEM.org
Length: 4 Yrs   *ACGME Approved/Offered Positions:* 24
Program ID: 110-35-21-093

Maimonides Medical Center Program
Sponsor: Maimonides Medical Center
Prgm Director: John P Marshall, MD
4802 Tenth Avenue
Brooklyn, NY 11219
Tel: 718 283-6029   *Fax:* 718 635-7228
E-mail: phainke@maimonidesmed.org
Length: 3 Yrs   *ACGME Approved/Offered Positions:* 39
Program ID: 110-35-21-164

New York Methodist Hospital Program
Sponsor: New York Methodist Hospital
Prgm Director: Theodore J Gaeta, DO, MPH
506 Sixth Street
Brooklyn, NY 11215
Tel: 718 780-5040   *Fax:* 718 780-3153
E-mail: thg9001@nyp.org
Length: 3 Yrs   *ACGME Approved/Offered Positions:* 30
Program ID: 110-35-21-147

SUNY Health Science Center at Brooklyn Program
Sponsor: SUNY Health Science Center at Brooklyn
Kings County Hospital Center
University Hospital-SUNY Health Science Center at Brooklyn
Prgm Director: Christopher I Doty, MD
450 Clarkson Avenue, Box 1228
Department of Emergency Medicine
Brooklyn, NY 11203
Tel: 718 245-3318
E-mail: christopher.doty@downstate.edu
Length: 4 Yrs   *ACGME Approved/Offered Positions:* 64
Program ID: 110-35-31-135

Note: * indicates a newly appointed program director

Buffalo

University at Buffalo Program
Sponsor: University at Buffalo School of Medicine
Erie County Medical Center
Kaleida Health System (Buffalo General Hospital)
Kaleida Health System (Women and Children's Hosp of Buffalo)
Prgm Director: Christian DeFazio, MD*
Dept of Emergency Medicine
100 High Street A-143
Buffalo, NY 14203
Tel: 716 859-1993   *Fax:* 716 859-1555
Length: 3 Yrs   *ACGME Approved/Offered Positions:* 36
Program ID: 110-35-31-127

Flushing

New York Hospital Medical Center of Queens/Cornell University Medical College Program
Sponsor: New York Hospital Medical Center of Queens
Prgm Director: James G Ryan, MD
56-45 Main Street
Department of Emergency Medicine
Flushing, NY 11355
Tel: 718 661-7305   *Fax:* 718 661-7679
E-mail: Lik9007@nyp.org
Length: 3 Yrs   *ACGME Approved/Offered Positions:* 30
Program ID: 110-35-31-173

Great Neck

NSLIJHS-Albert Einstein College of Medicine at Long Island Jewish Medical Center Program
Sponsor: North Shore-Long Island Jewish Health System
Long Island Jewish Medical Center
Prgm Director: Gino A Farina, MD
270-05 76th Avenue
New Hyde Park, NY 11040
Tel: 718 470-7873   *Fax:* 718 962-7728
E-mail: gfarina@lij.edu
Length: 4 Yrs   *ACGME Approved/Offered Positions:* 44
Program ID: 110-35-12-062

NSLIJHS-North Shore University Hospital/NYU School of Medicine Program
Sponsor: North Shore-Long Island Jewish Health System
North Shore University Hospital
Prgm Director: Joseph LaMantia, MD
300 Community Drive
Manhasset, NY 11030
Tel: 516 562-1244   *Fax:* 516 562-3569
Length: 3 Yrs   *ACGME Approved/Offered Positions:* 30
Program ID: 110-35-21-141

New York

Albert Einstein College of Medicine at Beth Israel Medical Center Program
Sponsor: Beth Israel Medical Center
Prgm Director: Saadia Akhtar, MD
First Avenue at 16th Street
New York, NY 10003
Tel: 212 420-4253   *Fax:* 212 420-2863
E-mail: sakhtar@chpnet.org
Length: 3 Yrs   *ACGME Approved/Offered Positions:* 36
Program ID: 110-35-11-149

Mount Sinai School of Medicine Program
Sponsor: Mount Sinai School of Medicine
Elmhurst Hospital Center-Mount Sinai Services
Mount Sinai Medical Center
Prgm Director: Peter L Shearer, MD
One Gustave L Levy Place, Box 1149
New York, NY 10029
Tel: 212 241-0748   *Fax:* 212 241-4366
E-mail: claribel.velasquez@mssm.edu
Length: 4 Yrs   *ACGME Approved/Offered Positions:* 60
Program ID: 110-35-21-087

New York Medical College (Metropolitan) Program
Sponsor: New York Medical College
Metropolitan Hospital Center
Westchester Medical Center
Prgm Director: Lorraine Giordano, MD
1901 First Avenue
Room 2A20
New York, NY 10029
Tel: 212 423-6390   *Fax:* 212 423-6383
E-mail: lmgmd@hotmail.com
Length: 3 Yrs   *ACGME Approved/Offered Positions:* 24
Program ID: 110-35-12-031

New York Presbyterian Hospital Program
Sponsor: New York Presbyterian Hospital
New York Presbyterian Hospital (Columbia Campus)
New York Presbyterian Hospital (Cornell Campus)
Prgm Director: Wallace A Carter Jr, MD
Columbia University College of Physicians and Surgeons
525 East 68th Street, Mailbox 301
New York, NY 10021
Tel: 212 746-0433   *Fax:* 212 746-0887
Length: 4 Yrs   *ACGME Approved/Offered Positions:* 48
Program ID: 110-35-13-169

New York University School of Medicine Program
Sponsor: New York University School of Medicine
Bellevue Hospital Center
NYU Hospitals Center
Prgm Director: Jeffrey Manko, MD*
Department of Emergency Medicine, Room A340A
462 First Avenue
New York, NY 10016
Tel: 212 562-4317   *Fax:* 212 263-6826
E-mail: Jeffrey.Manko@nyumc.org
Length: 4 Yrs   *ACGME Approved/Offered Positions:* 64
Program ID: 110-35-21-092

St Luke's-Roosevelt Hospital Center Program
Sponsor: St Luke's-Roosevelt Hospital Center
St Luke's-Roosevelt Hospital Center-Roosevelt Division
St Luke's-Roosevelt Hospital Center-St Luke's Division
Prgm Director: Richard Lanoix, MD
St Luke's-Roosevelt Hospital Center
1000 Tenth Avenue
New York, NY 10019
Tel: 212 523-6752   *Fax:* 212 523-8000
E-mail: rlanoix@chpnet.org
Length: 3 Yrs   *ACGME Approved/Offered Positions:* 42
Program ID: 110-35-21-109

Rochester

University of Rochester Program
Sponsor: Strong Memorial Hospital of the University of Rochester
Prgm Director: Flavia Nobay, MD*
Strong Memorial Hospital-Emergency Medicine Dept
601 Elmwood Avenue Box 655
Rochester, NY 14642
Tel: 585 463-2940   *Fax:* 585 473-3516
E-mail: michelle_abraham@urmc.rochester.edu
Length: 3 Yrs   *ACGME Approved/Offered Positions:* 36
Program ID: 110-35-21-131

Stony Brook

SUNY at Stony Brook Program
Sponsor: University Hospital - SUNY at Stony Brook
Prgm Director: Gregory P Garra, DO
Department of Emergency Medicine
Health Sciences Center Level 4, Room 080
Stony Brook, NY 11794
Tel: 631 444-3880   *Fax:* 631 444-3919
Length: 3 Yrs   *ACGME Approved/Offered Positions:* 30
Program ID: 110-35-21-091

Syracuse

SUNY Upstate Medical University Program
Sponsor: SUNY Upstate Medical University
Prgm Director: Gary Johnson, MD
750 East Adams Street
Syracuse, NY 13210
Tel: 315 464-4363   *Fax:* 315 464-4854
E-mail: resapp@upstate.edu
Length: 3 Yrs   *ACGME Approved/Offered Positions:* 30
Program ID: 110-35-21-121

North Carolina

Chapel Hill

University of North Carolina Hospitals Program
Sponsor: University of North Carolina Hospitals
Wake Medical Center
Prgm Director: Douglas R Trocinski, MD
Department of Emergency Medicine
CB 7594
Chapel Hill, NC 27599
Tel: 919 966-6440   *Fax:* 919 966-3049
E-mail: dtrocin@med.unc.edu
Length: 3 Yrs   *ACGME Approved/Offered Positions:* 30
Program ID: 110-36-21-130

Charlotte

Carolinas Medical Center Program
Sponsor: Carolinas Medical Center
Prgm Director: E Parker Hays Jr, MD
1000 Blythe Blvd, PO Box 32861
3rd Floor MEB
Charlotte, NC 28232
Tel: 704 355-3799   *Fax:* 704 355-7047
E-mail: mary.fiorillo@carolinashealthcare.org
Length: 3 Yrs   *ACGME Approved/Offered Positions:* 36
Program ID: 110-36-12-032

Durham

Duke University Hospital Program
Sponsor: Duke University Hospital
Prgm Director: Sarah A Stahmer, MD
Box 3935
Durham, OR 27710
Tel: 919 681-2247   *Fax:* 919 668-6115
Length: 3 Yrs   *ACGME Approved/Offered Positions:* 24
Program ID: 110-36-13-166

Greenville

Pitt County Memorial Hospital/East Carolina University Program
Sponsor: Pitt County Memorial Hospital
Prgm Director: Leigh A Patterson, MD
Department of Emergency Medicine
600 Moye Boulevard
Greenville, NC 27834
Tel: 252 744-4184   *Fax:* 252 744-4125
Length: 3 Yrs   *ACGME Approved/Offered Positions:* 40
Program ID: 110-36-12-063

Programs

Winston-Salem

Wake Forest University School of Medicine Program

Sponsor: Wake Forest University Baptist Medical Center
Prgm Director: Mitchell C Sokolosky, MD
Medical Center Boulevard
Winston-Salem, NC 27157
Tel: 336 716-4625   *Fax:* 336 716-5438
E-mail: emedres@wfubmc.edu
Length: 3 Yrs   *ACGME Approved/Offered Positions:* 39
Program ID: 110-36-12-033

Ohio

Akron

Akron General Medical Center/NEOUCOM Program

Sponsor: Akron General Medical Center
Prgm Director: Christ G Kyriakedes, DO
400 Wabash Avenue
Akron, OH 44307
Tel: 330 344-6326   *Fax:* 330 253-8293
Length: 3 Yrs   *ACGME Approved/Offered Positions:* 24
Program ID: 110-38-12-035

Summa Health System/NEOUCOM Program

Sponsor: Summa Health System
Akron City Hospital (Summa Health System)
Prgm Director: Michael S Beeson, MD, MBA
525 East Market Street
PO Box 2090
Akron, OH 44304
Tel: 330 375-4021   *Fax:* 330 375-4052
Length: 3 Yrs   *ACGME Approved/Offered Positions:* 30
Program ID: 110-38-12-034

Cincinnati

University Hospital/University of Cincinnati College of Medicine Program

Sponsor: University Hospital Inc
Prgm Director: Brian A Stettler, MD*
231 Albert Sabin Way
Mail Location 0769
Cincinnati, OH 45267
Tel: 513 558-6349   *Fax:* 513 558-6434
E-mail: stettlba@ucmail.uc.edu
Length: 4 Yrs   *ACGME Approved/Offered Positions:* 48
Program ID: 110-38-12-036

Cleveland

Case Western Reserve University (MetroHealth) Program

Sponsor: MetroHealth Medical Center
Cleveland Clinic Foundation
University Hospitals Case Medical Center
Prgm Director: Jeffrey Pennington, MD
2500 MetroHealth Drive
BG-3
Cleveland, OH 44109
Tel: 216 778-5088   *Fax:* 216 778-5349
E-mail: emresidency@metrohealth.org
Length: 3 Yrs   *ACGME Approved/Offered Positions:* 39
Program ID: 110-38-21-110

University Hospitals Case Medical Center Program

Sponsor: University Hospitals Case Medical Center
MetroHealth Medical Center
Prgm Director: Barry E Brenner, MD
11100 Euclid Avenue
Cleveland, OH 44106
Tel: 216 844-3631   *Fax:* 216 844-7783
Length: 3 Yrs   *ACGME Approved/Offered Positions:* 24
Program ID: 110-38-13-200

Columbus

Ohio State University Hospital Program

Sponsor: Ohio State University Hospital
Nationwide Children's Hospital
Prgm Director: Daniel R Martin, MD, FACEP
167 Means Hall
1654 Upham Dr
Columbus, OH 43210
Tel: 614 293-3551   *Fax:* 614 293-3124
E-mail: Ellen.Harr-Weatherby@osumc.edu
Length: 3 Yrs   *ACGME Approved/Offered Positions:* 36
Program ID: 110-38-12-038

Dayton

Wright State University Program

Sponsor: Wright State University Boonshoft School of
   Medicine
Good Samaritan Hospital and Health Center
Kettering Medical Center
Miami Valley Hospital
Prgm Director: James E Brown Jr, MD
3525 Southern Boulevard
Kettering, OH 45429
Tel: 937 395-8839   *Fax:* 937 395-8387
E-mail: som_em@wright.edu
Length: 3 Yrs   *ACGME Approved/Offered Positions:* 42
Program ID: 110-38-12-039

Toledo

Mercy Health Partners/St Vincent Mercy Medical Center Program

Sponsor: St Vincent Mercy Medical Center
Prgm Director: Randall W King, MD
2213 Cherry Street
c/o Emergency Medicine Residency DEC/Grd Fl
Toledo, OH 43608
Tel: 419 251-4723   *Fax:* 419 251-2698
E-mail: kinr20@mhsnr.org
Length: 3 Yrs   *ACGME Approved/Offered Positions:* 42
Program ID: 110-38-12-040

University of Toledo Program

Sponsor: University of Toledo
St Luke's Hospital
University Medical Center (Toledo)
Prgm Director: Catherine A Marco, MD, FACEP
3000 Arlington Avenue
Toledo, OH 43614
Tel: 419 383-6343   *Fax:* 419 383-3105
E-mail: catherine.marco@utoledo.edu
Length: 3 Yrs   *ACGME Approved/Offered Positions:* 24
Program ID: 110-38-12-198

Oklahoma

Tulsa

University of Oklahoma College of Medicine-Tulsa Program

Sponsor: University of Oklahoma College of
   Medicine-Tulsa
Hillcrest Medical Center
Saint Francis Health System
St John Medical Center
Prgm Director: Carolyn K Synovitz, MD, MPH*
Schusterman Center, Department of Emergency Medici
4502 East 41st Street
Tulsa, OK 74135
Tel: 918 660-3823   *Fax:* 918 660-3821
Length: 3 Yrs   *ACGME Approved/Offered Positions:* 18
Program ID: 110-39-31-193

Oregon

Portland

Oregon Health & Science University Program

Sponsor: Oregon Health & Science University Hospital
St Vincent Hospital and Medical Center
Prgm Director: Patrick Brunett, MD
3181 SW Sam Jackson Park Road
Portland, OR 97239
Tel: 503 494-9590   *Fax:* 503 494-8237
E-mail: palmerci@ohsu.edu
Length: 3 Yrs   *ACGME Approved/Offered Positions:* 30
Program ID: 110-40-12-042

Pennsylvania

Allentown

Lehigh Valley Hospital Network/Pennsylvania State University Hospital Program

Sponsor: Lehigh Valley Hospital Network
Lehigh Valley Hospital (Muhlenberg)
Prgm Director: Gary Bonfante, DO
2545 Schoenersville Road
5th Floor Residency Suite
Bethlehem, PA 18017
Tel: 484 884-2888   *Fax:* 484 884-2885
E-mail: gary.bonfante@lvh.com
Length: 4 Yrs   *ACGME Approved/Offered Positions:* 56
Program ID: 110-41-21-199

Bethlehem

St Luke's Hospital Program

Sponsor: St Luke's Hospital
Prgm Director: Scott W Melanson, MD
801 Ostrum Street
Bethlehem, PA 18015
Tel: 610 954-4903   *Fax:* 610 954-2153
E-mail: melanss@slhn.org
Length: 3 Yrs   *ACGME Approved/Offered Positions:* 24
Program ID: 110-41-21-111

Danville

Geisinger Health System Program

Sponsor: Geisinger Health System
Geisinger Medical Center
Prgm Director: Thomas F Payton, MD, MBA*
Department of Emergency Medicine
100 North Academy Avenue
Danville, PA 17822
Tel: 570 271-6812
Length: 3 Yrs   *ACGME Approved/Offered Positions:* 27
Program ID: 110-41-12-043

Note: * indicates a newly appointed program director

Hershey

Penn State University/Milton S Hershey Medical Center Program

Sponsor: Milton S Hershey Medical Center
Prgm Director: Lawrence E Kass, MD
500 University Drive, H-043
Hershey, PA 17033
Tel: 717 531-1443   *Fax:* 717 531-4441
Length: 3 Yrs   *ACGME Approved/Offered Positions:* 24
Program ID: 110-41-33-171

Philadelphia

Albert Einstein Healthcare Network Program

Sponsor: Albert Einstein Medical Center
Prgm Director: Merle Carter, MD*
5501 Old York Road
Korman B-14
Philadelphia, PA 19141
Tel: 215 456-3480   *Fax:* 215 456-6601
Length: 4 Yrs   *ACGME Approved/Offered Positions:* 60
Program ID: 110-41-21-122

Drexel University College of Medicine/Hahnemann University Hospital Program

Sponsor: Drexel University College of
  Medicine/Hahnemann University
Hahnemann University Hospital (Tenet Health System)
Mercy Philadelphia Hospital
Prgm Director: Edward A Ramoska, MD, MPH
Hahnemann University Hospital
245 North 15th Street
Philadelphia, PA 19102
Tel: 215 762-2365   *Fax:* 215 762-1307
E-mail: edward.ramoska@drexelmed.edu
Length: 3 Yrs   *ACGME Approved/Offered Positions:* 45
Program ID: 110-41-12-045

Temple University Hospital Program

Sponsor: Temple University Hospital
Prgm Director: Jacob W Ufberg, MD
Jones Hall, Tenth Floor
Park Avenue & Ontario Street
Philadelphia, PA 19140
Tel: 215 707-5308   *Fax:* 215 707-3494
Length: 3 Yrs   *ACGME Approved/Offered Positions:* 36
Program ID: 110-41-21-155

Thomas Jefferson University Program

Sponsor: Thomas Jefferson University Hospital
Methodist Hospital
Prgm Director: Bernard L Lopez, MD, MS
1020 Sansom Street
Room 1651 B Thompson Building
Philadelphia, PA 19107
Tel: 215 955-9837   *Fax:* 215 955-9870
E-mail: lori.berryman@jefferson.edu
Length: 3 Yrs   *ACGME Approved/Offered Positions:* 36
Program ID: 110-41-12-064

University of Pennsylvania Program

Sponsor: University of Pennsylvania Health System
Children's Hospital of Philadelphia
Prgm Director: Francis De Roos, MD
3400 Spruce Street
Ground Ravdin
Philadelphia, PA 19104
Tel: 215 662-6305   *Fax:* 215 662-3953
E-mail: clement.mackiewicz@uphs.upenn.edu
Length: 4 Yrs   *ACGME Approved/Offered Positions:* 40
Program ID: 110-41-21-148

Pittsburgh

Allegheny General Hospital Program

Sponsor: Allegheny General Hospital
Prgm Director: Mara S Aloi, MD
320 East North Avenue
Pittsburgh, PA 15212
Tel: 412 359-4905   *Fax:* 412 359-4963
E-mail: aghemres@wpahs.org
Length: 3 Yrs   *ACGME Approved/Offered Positions:* 24
Program ID: 110-41-12-054

University of Pittsburgh Medical Center Medical Education Program

Sponsor: Univ of Pittsburgh Medical Center Medical
  Education
Mercy Hospital of Pittsburgh
UPMC Presbyterian Shadyside
Prgm Director: Allan B Wolfson, MD
230 McKee Place
Suite 500
Pittsburgh, PA 15213
Tel: 412 647-8283   *Fax:* 412 647-8225
Length: 3 Yrs   *ACGME Approved/Offered Positions:* 48
Program ID: 110-41-12-055

York

York Hospital Program

Sponsor: York Hospital
Prgm Director: David A Kramer, MD
1001 South George Street
York, PA 17405
Tel: 717 851-3070   *Fax:* 717 851-3469
E-mail: dkramer@yorkhospital.edu
Length: 3 Yrs   *ACGME Approved/Offered Positions:* 36
Program ID: 110-41-21-089

Puerto Rico

Ponce

Hospital Episcopal San Lucas/Ponce School of Medicine Program

Sponsor: Hospital Episcopal San Lucas
Prgm Director: Carlos F Garcia-Gubern, MD
PO Box 336810
Ponce, PR 00733
Tel: 787 843-3031   *Fax:* 787 841-7165
E-mail: ponce.emergencymedicine@gmail.com
Length: 3 Yrs   *ACGME Approved/Offered Positions:* 18
Program ID: 110-42-12-187

San Juan

University of Puerto Rico Program

Sponsor: University of Puerto Rico School of Medicine
University of Puerto Rico Hospital at Carolina
Prgm Director: Juan A González-Sánchez, MD, FACEP
PO Box 29207
San Juan, PR 00929
Tel: 787 757-1800   *Fax:* 787 750-0930
E-mail: juagonzalez@rcm.upr.edu
Length: 3 Yrs   *ACGME Approved/Offered Positions:* 30
Program ID: 110-42-12-046

Rhode Island

Providence

Brown University Program

Sponsor: Rhode Island Hospital-Lifespan
Miriam Hospital-Lifespan
Prgm Director: Brian Clyne, MD
593 Eddy Street
Claverick 274
Providence, RI 02903
Tel: 401 444-4247   *Fax:* 401 444-6662
E-mail: emresidency@lifespan.org
Length: 4 Yrs   *ACGME Approved/Offered Positions:* 48
Program ID: 110-43-21-114

South Carolina

Charleston

Medical University of South Carolina Program

Sponsor: Medical University of South Carolina College of
  Medicine
MUSC Medical Center
Prgm Director: Sarvotham Kini, MD
169 Ashley Avenue
PO Box 250300
Charleston, SC 29425
Tel: 843 876-8023   *Fax:* 843 792-9616
E-mail: kinis@musc.edu
Length: 3 Yrs   *ACGME Approved/Offered Positions:* 18
Program ID: 110-45-12-183

Columbia

Palmetto Health/University of South Carolina School of Medicine Program

Sponsor: Palmetto Health
Palmetto Health Richland
Prgm Director: Thomas P Cook, MD, PhD
Five Richland Medical Park Drive
Suite 350
Columbia, SC 29203
Tel: 803 434-3790   *Fax:* 803 434-3946
E-mail: tpcookmd@hotmail.com
Length: 3 Yrs   *ACGME Approved/Offered Positions:* 30
Program ID: 110-45-12-047

Tennessee

Chattanooga

University of Tennessee College of Medicine at Chattanooga Program

Sponsor: University of Tennessee College of
  Medicine-Chattanooga
Erlanger Medical Center
Prgm Director: James H Creel, Jr, MD, FACEP
Division of Emergency Medicine
975 East Third Street
Chattanooga, TN 37403
Tel: 423 778-7628   *Fax:* 423 778-7677
Length: 3 Yrs   *ACGME Approved/Offered Positions:* 24
Program ID: 110-47-21-195

Nashville

Vanderbilt University Program

Sponsor: Vanderbilt University Medical Center
Prgm Director: Keith D Wrenn, MD
703 Oxford House
1313 21st Avenue South
Nashville, TN 37232
Tel: 615 936-1157   *Fax:* 615 936-1316
E-mail: keith.wrenn@vanderbilt.edu
Length: 3 Yrs   *ACGME Approved/Offered Positions:* 36
Program ID: 110-47-21-113

Programs

Texas

Corpus Christi

Christus Spohn Memorial Hospital Program
Sponsor: Christus Spohn Memorial Hospital
Prgm Director: Thomas J McLaughlin, DO
2606 Hospital Boulevard
Corpus Christi, TX 78405
Tel: 361 902-6570 *Fax:* 361 881-1467
E-mail: belinda.flores@christushealth.org
Length: 3 Yrs *ACGME Approved/Offered Positions:* 24
Program ID: 110-48-13-188

Dallas

University of Texas Southwestern Medical School Program
Sponsor: University of Texas Southwestern Medical School
Dallas County Hospital District-Parkland Memorial Hospital
Prgm Director: Michael P Wainscott, MD
Emergency Medicine Residency Program
5323 Harry Hines Boulevard
Dallas, TX 75390
Tel: 214 590-1352 *Fax:* 214 590-4079
E-mail: michael.wainscott@utsouthwestern.edu
Length: 3 Yrs *ACGME Approved/Offered Positions:* 57
Program ID: 110-48-21-153

El Paso

Texas Tech University Health Sciences Center Paul L Foster School of Medicine Program
Sponsor: Texas Tech University Hlth Sci Ctr Paul L Foster Sch of Med
R E Thomason General Hospital / Texas Tech University HSC
Prgm Director: Veronica L Greer, MD*
4801 Alberta Dr
Suite B3200
El Paso, TX 79905
Tel: 915 545-7333 *Fax:* 915 545-7338
E-mail: veronica.greer@ttuhsc.edu
Length: 3 Yrs *ACGME Approved/Offered Positions:* 30
Program ID: 110-48-12-070

Fort Hood

Darnall Army Medical Center Program
Sponsor: Carl R Darnall Army Medical Center
Prgm Director: Melissa L Givens, MD, MPH
Emergency Medicine Residency Program
36000 Darnall Loop, Box 32
Fort Hood, TX 76544
Tel: 254 288-8303 *Fax:* 254 286-7055
Length: 3 Yrs *ACGME Approved/Offered Positions:* 25
Program ID: 110-48-12-048
Uniformed Services Program

Galveston

University of Texas Medical Branch Hospitals Program
Sponsor: University of Texas Medical Branch Hospitals
Prgm Director: Brian Zachariah, MD, MBA
301 University Boulevard
Galveston, TX 77555
Tel: 409 772-0531 *Fax:* 409 772-0557
E-mail: bszachar@utmb.edu
Length: 3 Yrs *ACGME Approved/Offered Positions:* 24
Program ID: 110-48-21-191

Houston

University of Texas at Houston Program
Sponsor: University of Texas Health Science Center at Houston
Memorial Hermann Hospital
Prgm Director: Eric F Reichman, PhD, MD
6431 Fannin St, JJL 447
Houston, TX 77030
Tel: 713 500-7834 *Fax:* 713 500-0758
E-mail: Eric.F.Reichman@uth.tmc.edu
Length: 3 Yrs *ACGME Approved/Offered Positions:* 36
Program ID: 110-48-21-096

Lackland AFB

San Antonio Uniformed Services Health Education Consortium Program
Sponsor: San Antonio Uniformed Services Health Education Consortium
Brooke Army Medical Center
Wilford Hall Medical Center (AETC)
Prgm Director: Robert Kacprowicz, MD
Department of Emergency Medicine
3851 Roger Brooke Drive
Fort Sam Houston, TX 78234
Tel: 210 916-1006 *Fax:* 210 916-2265
Length: 3 Yrs *ACGME Approved/Offered Positions:* 48
Program ID: 110-48-21-085
Uniformed Services Program

Temple

Texas A&M College of Medicine-Scott and White Program
Sponsor: Scott and White Memorial Hospital
Prgm Director: Timothy C Stallard, MD, FACEP
2401 South 31st Street
Temple, TX 76508
Tel: 254 724-5815 *Fax:* 254 724-1044
E-mail: crush@swmail.sw.org
Length: 3 Yrs *ACGME Approved/Offered Positions:* 36
Program ID: 110-48-21-102

Utah

Salt Lake City

University of Utah Program
Sponsor: University of Utah Medical Center
Intermountain Medical Center
Prgm Director: Susan Stroud, MD*
30 North 1900 East Room 1C026
Salt Lake City, UT 84132
Tel: 801 587-7653 *Fax:* 801 585-0603
Length: 3 Yrs *ACGME Approved/Offered Positions:* 24
Program ID: 110-49-21-178

Virginia

Charlottesville

University of Virginia Program
Sponsor: University of Virginia Medical Center
Prgm Director: Chris A Ghaemmaghami, MD
Department of Emergency Medicine
Box 800699
Charlottesville, VA 22908
Tel: 434 982-1800 *Fax:* 434 982-4118
E-mail: cg3n@virginia.edu
Length: 3 Yrs *ACGME Approved/Offered Positions:* 30
Program ID: 110-51-21-125

Norfolk

Eastern Virginia Medical School Program
Sponsor: Eastern Virginia Medical School
Sentara Norfolk General Hospital
Sentara Virginia Beach General Hospital
Prgm Director: Francis L Counselman, MD
Raleigh Building Room 304
600 Gresham Drive
Norfolk, VA 23507
Tel: 757 388-3397 *Fax:* 757 388-2885
Length: 3 Yrs *ACGME Approved/Offered Positions:* 27
Program ID: 110-51-12-050

Portsmouth

Naval Medical Center (Portsmouth) Program
Sponsor: Naval Medical Center (Portsmouth)
Prgm Director: James V Ritchie, MD
620 John Paul Jones Circle
Portsmouth, VA 23708
Tel: 757 953-1408 *Fax:* 757 953-0808
E-mail: james.ritchie@med.navy.mil
Length: 3 Yrs *ACGME Approved/Offered Positions:* 30
Program ID: 110-51-21-105
Uniformed Services Program

Richmond

Virginia Commonwealth University Health System Program
Sponsor: Virginia Commonwealth University Health System
Medical College of Virginia Hospitals
Prgm Director: Timothy C Evans, MD
1201 East Marshall Street
PO Box 980401
Richmond, VA 23298
Tel: 804 628-0392 *Fax:* 804 828-4603
E-mail: tevans@mcvh-vcu.edu
Length: 3 Yrs *ACGME Approved/Offered Positions:* 30
Program ID: 110-51-21-160

Washington

Tacoma

Madigan Army Medical Center/University of Washington Program
Sponsor: Madigan Army Medical Center
Prgm Director: Benjamin P Harrison, MD
Department of Emergency Medicine
MCHJ-EM
Tacoma, WA 98431
Tel: 253 968-1250 *Fax:* 253 968-2550
E-mail: benjamin.harrison@amedd.army.mil
Length: 3 Yrs *ACGME Approved/Offered Positions:* 36
Program ID: 110-54-12-051
Uniformed Services Program

West Virginia

Morgantown

West Virginia University Program
Sponsor: West Virginia University School of Medicine
West Virginia University Hospitals
Prgm Director: Hollynn Larrabee, MD*
Robert C Byrd Health Sciences Center, North
PO Box 9149
Morgantown, WV 26506
Tel: 304 293-7215 *Fax:* 304 293-6702
E-mail: hlarrabee@hsc.wvu.edu
Length: 3 Yrs *ACGME Approved/Offered Positions:* 21
Program ID: 110-55-21-128

Note: * indicates a newly appointed program director

Wisconsin

Madison

University of Wisconsin Program

Sponsor: University of Wisconsin Hospital and Clinics
Prgm Director: Mark P Bogner, MD
F2/214 Clinical Sciences Center, MC3280
600 Highland Avenue
Madison, WI 53792
Tel: 608 890-8682   *Fax:* 608 262-2641
Length: 3 Yrs   *ACGME Approved/Offered Positions:* 24
Program ID: 110-56-13-184

Milwaukee

Medical College of Wisconsin Affiliated Hospitals Program

Sponsor: Medical College of Wisconsin Affiliated
    Hospitals, Inc
Children's Hospital of Wisconsin
Froedtert Memorial Lutheran Hospital
Prgm Director: Edward P Callahan, MD, MS
9200 West Wisconsin Avenue
Pavilion, 1P
Milwaukee, WI 53226
Tel: 414 805-6460   *Fax:* 414 805-6464
E-mail: fmlhem@mcw.edu
Length: 3 Yrs   *ACGME Approved/Offered Positions:* 24
Program ID: 110-56-12-052

Endocrinology, Diabetes, and Metabolism (Internal Medicine)

Alabama

Birmingham

University of Alabama Medical Center Program

Sponsor: University of Alabama Hospital
Veterans Affairs Medical Center (Birmingham)
Prgm Director: Fernando Ovalle, MD
510 20th Street South
FOT Suite 702
Birmingham, AL 35294
Tel: 205 934-4171   *Fax:* 205 975-9304
E-mail: fovalle@uab.edu
Length: 2 Yrs   *ACGME Approved/Offered Positions:* 3
Program ID: 143-01-21-103

Arizona

Phoenix

Banner Good Samaritan Medical Center Program

Sponsor: Banner Good Samaritan Medical Center
Carl T Hayden VA Medical Center
Prgm Director: B Sylvia Vela, MD
Phoenix VA Health Care System
650 E Indian School Road
Phoenix, AZ 85012
Tel: 602 277-5551   *Fax:* 602 200-6005
E-mail: sylvia.vela@va.gov
Length: 2 Yrs   *ACGME Approved/Offered Positions:* 4
Program ID: 143-03-21-169

Tucson

University of Arizona Program

Sponsor: University of Arizona College of Medicine
Southern Arizona VA Health Care Center (Tucson)
University Medical Center
University of Arizona/UPHK Graduate Medical Ed
    Consortium
Prgm Director: Stephen Thomson, MD*
Department of Medicine, Arizona Health Sciences
Center
1501 N Campbell Avenue
Tucson, AZ 85724
Tel: 520 626-3709   *Fax:* 520 626-3644
E-mail: sthomson@deptofmed.arizona.edu
Length: 2 Yrs   *ACGME Approved/Offered Positions:* 5
Program ID: 143-03-21-185

Arkansas

Little Rock

University of Arkansas for Medical Sciences Program

Sponsor: University of Arkansas College of Medicine
Central Arkansas Veterans Healthcare System
UAMS Medical Center
Prgm Director: Debra L Simmons, MD, MS
4301 W Markham Street, Slot 587
Little Rock, AR 72205
Tel: 501 686-5130   *Fax:* 501 686-8148
E-mail: newmankennethal@uams.edu
Length: 2 Yrs   *ACGME Approved/Offered Positions:* 6
Program ID: 143-04-21-165

California

La Jolla

Scripps Clinic/Scripps Green Hospital Program

Sponsor: Scripps Clinic/Scripps Green Hospital
Prgm Director: James D McCallum, MBChB
10666 North Torrey Pines Road
La Jolla, CA 92037
Tel: 858 554-3200   *Fax:* 858 554-3232
E-mail: gme@scripps.edu
Length: 2 Yrs   *ACGME Approved/Offered Positions:* 2
Program ID: 143-05-21-057

Los Angeles

Cedars-Sinai Medical Center Program

Sponsor: Cedars-Sinai Medical Center
VA Greater Los Angeles Healthcare System
Prgm Director: Glenn D Braunstein, MD*
8700 Beverly Blvd
Becker Bldg B-131
Los Angeles, CA 90048
Tel: 310 423-5140   *Fax:* 310 423-0437
E-mail: braunstein@cshs.org
Length: 2 Yrs   *ACGME Approved/Offered Positions:* 8
Program ID: 143-05-11-092

UCLA Medical Center Program

Sponsor: UCLA David Geffen School of Medicine/UCLA
    Medical Center
UCLA Medical Center
Prgm Director: Dorothy S Martinez, MD*
900 Veteran Ave
Warren Hall 24130
Los Angeles, CA 90095
Tel: 310 794-7555   *Fax:* 310 794-7654
E-mail: dmartinez@mednet.ucla.edu
Length: 2 Yrs   *ACGME Approved/Offered Positions:* 6
Program ID: 143-05-11-105

UCLA-VA Greater Los Angeles Program

Sponsor: VA Greater Los Angeles Healthcare System
Prgm Director: Gregory Brent, MD*
11301 Wilshire Blvd, 111D
Los Angeles, CA 90073
Tel: 310 268-3735
Length: 2 Yrs   *ACGME Approved/Offered Positions:* 4
Program ID: 143-05-31-049

University of Southern California/ LAC+USC Medical Center Program

Sponsor: University of Southern California/LAC+USC
    Medical Center
LAC+USC Medical Center
USC University Hospital
Prgm Director: Jonathan S LoPresti, MD, PhD
1333 San Pablo Street BMT-B11
Los Angeles, CA 90033
Tel: 323 442-2806   *Fax:* 323 442-2809
Length: 2 Yrs   *ACGME Approved/Offered Positions:* 8
Program ID: 143-05-21-041

Programs

Orange

University of California (Irvine) Program

Sponsor: University of California (Irvine) Medical Center
Children's Hospital of Orange County
VA Long Beach Healthcare System
Prgm Director: Andersen Bogi, MD, PhD
Medical Sciences I, Room C240
Irvine, CA 92697
Tel: 949 824-9093   *Fax:* 949 824-2200
Length: 2 Yrs   *ACGME Approved/Offered Positions:* 3
Program ID: 143-05-21-122

Sacramento

University of California (Davis) Health System Program

Sponsor: University of California (Davis) Health System
University of California (Davis) Medical Center
VA Northern California Health Care System
Prgm Director: Sidika E Kasim-Karakas, MD
Department of Medicine
4150 V Street, PSSB Suite G400
Sacramento, CA 95817
Tel: 916 734-3730   *Fax:* 916 734-7953
Length: 2 Yrs   *ACGME Approved/Offered Positions:* 3
Program ID: 143-05-21-078

San Diego

University of California (San Diego) Program

Sponsor: University of California (San Diego) Medical Center
Veterans Affairs Medical Center (San Diego)
Prgm Director: Nai-Wen Chi, MD, PhD
MC-0673
9500 Gilman Dr
La Jolla, CA 92093
Tel: 858 534-6274   *Fax:* 858 534-6653
Length: 2 Yrs   *ACGME Approved/Offered Positions:* 6
Program ID: 143-05-21-139

San Francisco

University of California (San Francisco) Program

Sponsor: University of California (San Francisco) School of Medicine
San Francisco General Hospital Medical Center
UCSF and Mount Zion Medical Centers
Veterans Affairs Medical Center (San Francisco)
Prgm Director: Michael S German, MD*
500 Parnassus Ave
San Francisco, CA 94143
Tel: 415 476-9262   *Fax:* 415 731-3612
Length: 2 Yrs   *ACGME Approved/Offered Positions:* 6
Program ID: 143-05-21-124

Stanford

Stanford University Program

Sponsor: Stanford Hospital and Clinics
Santa Clara Valley Medical Center
Veterans Affairs Palo Alto Health Care System
Prgm Director: Laurence Katznelson, MD
Department of Medicine, Division of Endocrinology
300 Pasteur Drive, Room S025
Stanford, CA 94305
Tel: 650 498-4353   *Fax:* 650 725-7085
Length: 2 Yrs   *ACGME Approved/Offered Positions:* 6
Program ID: 143-05-21-022

Torrance

Los Angeles County-Harbor-UCLA Medical Center Program

Sponsor: Los Angeles County-Harbor-UCLA Medical Center
City of Hope National Medical Center
Prgm Director: Ronald S Swerdloff, MD
1000 W Carson Street, Bin 446
Torrance, CA 90509
Tel: 310 222-1867   *Fax:* 310 533-0627
E-mail: humcendocrine@labiomed.org
Length: 2 Yrs   *ACGME Approved/Offered Positions:* 8
Program ID: 143-05-11-140

Colorado

Aurora

University of Colorado Denver Program

Sponsor: University of Colorado Denver School of Medicine
University of Colorado Hospital
Prgm Director: Daniel H Bessesen, MD
PO Box 6511 - MS 8106
Aurora, CO 80045
Tel: 303 724-3921   *Fax:* 303 724-3920
E-mail: daniel.bessesen@uchsc.edu
Length: 2 Yrs   *ACGME Approved/Offered Positions:* 6
Program ID: 143-07-21-050

Connecticut

Farmington

University of Connecticut Program

Sponsor: University of Connecticut School of Medicine
Hartford Hospital
Hospital for Central Connecticut
St Francis Hospital and Medical Center
Univ of Connecticut Health Center/John Dempsey Hospital
Prgm Director: Pamela Taxel, MD, MA
263 Farmington Avenue
Farmington, CT 06030
Tel: 860 679-4743   *Fax:* 860 679-1040
E-mail: cusati@nso.uchc.edu
Length: 2 Yrs   *ACGME Approved/Offered Positions:* 4
Program ID: 143-08-31-001

New Haven

Yale-New Haven Medical Center Program

Sponsor: Yale-New Haven Hospital
Veterans Affairs Medical Center (West Haven)
Prgm Director: Silvio E Inzucchi, MD
333 Cedar St, LLCI 101
PO Box 208020
New Haven, CT 06520
Tel: 203 785-2479   *Fax:* 203 737-2999
E-mail: tracy.crosby@yale.edu
Length: 2 Yrs   *ACGME Approved/Offered Positions:* 6
Program ID: 143-08-21-023

District of Columbia

Washington

George Washington University Program

Sponsor: George Washington University School of Medicine
George Washington University Hospital (UHS)
Veterans Affairs Medical Center (Washington, DC)
Prgm Director: Kenneth L Becker, MD, PhD
2150 Pennsylvania Avenue, NW
Endocrinology, 3rd Floor
Washington, DC 20037
Tel: 202 745-8300   *Fax:* 202 745-8302
E-mail: drkbecker@gmail.com
Length: 2 Yrs   *ACGME Approved/Offered Positions:* 6
Program ID: 143-10-21-093

Georgetown University Hospital Program

Sponsor: Georgetown University Hospital
Washington Hospital Center
Prgm Director: Kenneth D Burman, MD
Division of Endocrinology (#232 Bldg D)
4000 Reservoir Road NW
Washington, DC 20007
Tel: 202 877-9137   *Fax:* 202 877-6588
E-mail: steelewe@gunet.georgetown.edu
Length: 2 Yrs   *ACGME Approved/Offered Positions:* 5
Program ID: 143-10-21-072

Howard University Program

Sponsor: Howard University Hospital
Prgm Director: James T Williams Jr, MD
2041 Georgia Avenue, NW
Washington, DC 20060
Tel: 202 865-1920   *Fax:* 202 865-7199
E-mail: james.t.williams@verizon.net
Length: 2 Yrs   *ACGME Approved/Offered Positions:* 3
Program ID: 143-10-21-107

Florida

Gainesville

University of Florida Program

Sponsor: University of Florida College of Medicine
North Florida/South Georgia Veterans Health System
Shands Hospital at the University of Florida
Prgm Director: Suzanne L Quinn, MD
Department of Medicine
PO Box 100226, JHMHC
Gainesville, FL 32610
Tel: 352 392-2612   *Fax:* 352 846-2231
Length: 2 Yrs   *ACGME Approved/Offered Positions:* 2
Program ID: 143-11-21-033

Jacksonville

College of Medicine, Mayo Clinic (Jacksonville) Program

Sponsor: College of Medicine, Mayo Clinic
Mayo Clinic (Jacksonville)
Mayo Clinic Florida Hospital
Prgm Director: Shon E Meek, MD
4500 San Pablo Road
Jacksonville, FL 32224
Tel: 904 953-0421   *Fax:* 904 953-0430
E-mail: paglia.melissa@mayo.edu
Length: 2 Yrs   *ACGME Approved/Offered Positions:* 2
Program ID: 143-11-12-177

Note: * indicates a newly appointed program director

University of Florida College of Medicine Jacksonville Program

Sponsor: University of Florida College of Medicine Jacksonville
Shands Jacksonville Medical Center
Prgm Director: Kent R Wehmeier, MD
653-1 West 8th Street, L-14
Jacksonville, FL 32209
Tel: 904 244-4704   *Fax:* 904 244-5650
E-mail: teena.wyatt@jax.ufl.edu
Length: 2 Yrs   *ACGME Approved/Offered Positions:* 4
Program ID: 143-11-45-188

Miami

Jackson Memorial Hospital/Jackson Health System Program

Sponsor: Jackson Memorial Hospital/Jackson Health System
Veterans Affairs Medical Center (Miami)
Prgm Director: Jennifer B Marks, MD
Dept of Medicine D-110
1450 NW 10th Avenue, DRI Bldg, Rm 3054
Miami, FL 33136
Tel: 305 243-6433   *Fax:* 305 243-3313
Length: 2 Yrs   *ACGME Approved/Offered Positions:* 8
Program ID: 143-11-21-141

Tampa

University of South Florida Program

Sponsor: University of South Florida College of Medicine
H Lee Moffitt Cancer Center
James A Haley Veterans Hospital
Tampa General Hospital
Prgm Director: Joaquin Gomez-Daspet, MD*
12901 N 30th St, Box 19
Tampa, FL 33612
Tel: 813 972-7624   *Fax:* 813 972-7623
E-mail: karen.murphy@va.gov
Length: 2 Yrs   *ACGME Approved/Offered Positions:* 3
Program ID: 143-11-21-034

Georgia

Atlanta

Emory University Program

Sponsor: Emory University School of Medicine
Emory University Hospital
Grady Health System
Veterans Affairs Medical Center (Atlanta)
Prgm Director: Peter M Thule, MD
Endocrinology, MC 111
1670 Clairmont Rd
Decatur, GA 30033
Tel: 404 321-6111   *Fax:* 404 417-2943
E-mail: lsdanie@emory.edu
Length: 2 Yrs   *ACGME Approved/Offered Positions:* 6
Program ID: 143-12-21-109

Augusta

Medical College of Georgia Program

Sponsor: Medical College of Georgia
Veterans Affairs Medical Center (Augusta)
Prgm Director: Anthony L Mulloy, DO
Department of Medicine
1467 Harper Street, HB 5025
Augusta, GA 30912
Tel: 706 721-2131   *Fax:* 706 721-6892
E-mail: amulloy@mail.mcg.edu
Length: 2 Yrs   *ACGME Approved/Offered Positions:* 2
Program ID: 143-12-21-002

Illinois

Chicago

McGaw Medical Center of Northwestern University Program

Sponsor: McGaw Medical Center of Northwestern University
Jesse Brown Veterans Affairs Medical Center
Northwestern Memorial Hospital
Prgm Director: Peter A Kopp, MD
Tarry 15
303 East Chicago Avenue
Chicago, IL 60611
Tel: 312 503-1394   *Fax:* 312 908-9032
E-mail: endocrine-fellowship@northwestern.edu
Length: 2 Yrs   *ACGME Approved/Offered Positions:* 4
Program ID: 143-16-21-060

Rush University Medical Center Program

Sponsor: Rush University Medical Center
John H Stroger Hospital of Cook County
Prgm Director: Leon Fogelfeld, MD
John H Stroger Hospital of Cook County
1900 W Harrison Street, Room 811
Chicago, IL 60612
Tel: 312 864-0531   *Fax:* 312 864-9734
E-mail: lfreeman@cchil.org
Length: 2 Yrs   *ACGME Approved/Offered Positions:* 4
Program ID: 143-16-31-174

University of Chicago Program

Sponsor: University of Chicago Medical Center
Prgm Director: Roy E Weiss, MD, PhD
5841 S Maryland Avenue
AMB MC1027 M267
Chicago, IL 60637
Tel: 773 834-7555   *Fax:* 773 834-0486
E-mail: rweiss@medicine.bsd.uchicago.edu
Length: 2 Yrs   *ACGME Approved/Offered Positions:* 10
Program ID: 143-16-21-157

University of Illinois College of Medicine at Chicago Program

Sponsor: University of Illinois College of Medicine at Chicago
Advocate Christ Medical Center
Jesse Brown Veterans Affairs Medical Center
University of Illinois Hospital and Clinics
Prgm Director: Elena Barengolts, MD
Section of Endocrinology (M/C 640)
1819 West Polk Street
Chicago, IL 60612
Tel: 312 996-6060   *Fax:* 312 413-0437
E-mail: sat@uic.edu
Length: 2 Yrs   *ACGME Approved/Offered Positions:* 6
Program ID: 143-16-21-170

Maywood

Loyola University Program

Sponsor: Loyola University Medical Center
Edward Hines, Jr Veterans Affairs Hospital
Prgm Director: Pauline Camacho, MD*
2160 S First Ave
Building 54, Room 137
Maywood, IL 60153
Tel: 708 216-6435   *Fax:* 708 216-5936
E-mail: pcamach@lumc.edu
Length: 2 Yrs   *ACGME Approved/Offered Positions:* 3
Program ID: 143-16-21-003

North Chicago

The Chicago Medical School at Rosalind Franklin University of Medicine and Science Program

Sponsor: Chicago Medical School/Rosalind Franklin University of Medicine & Science
Mount Sinai Hospital Medical Center of Chicago
Veterans Affairs Medical Center (North Chicago)
Prgm Director: Sant P Singh, MD
Department of Medicine-Division of Endocrinology
3333 Green Bay Road
North Chicago, IL 60064
Tel: 847 688-1900   *Fax:* 224 610-3818
E-mail: sant.singh@rosalindfranklin.edu
Length: 2 Yrs   *ACGME Approved/Offered Positions:* 4
Program ID: 143-16-21-042

Springfield

Southern Illinois University Program

Sponsor: Southern Illinois University School of Medicine
Memorial Medical Center
St John's Hospital
Prgm Director: Romesh Khardori, MD, PhD
701 North First Street, D405
PO Box 19636
Springfield, IL 62794
Tel: 217 545-0166   *Fax:* 217 545-1229
Length: 2 Yrs   *ACGME Approved/Offered Positions:* 4
Program ID: 143-16-21-164

Indiana

Indianapolis

Indiana University School of Medicine Program

Sponsor: Indiana University School of Medicine
Clarian Indiana University Hospital
Richard L Roudebush Veterans Affairs Medical Center
William N Wishard Memorial Hospital
Prgm Director: Paris Roach, MD
Dept of Medicine, Emerson Hall 421
545 Barnhill Drive
Indianapolis, IN 46202
Tel: 317 274-0550   *Fax:* 317 274-4311
E-mail: paroach@iupui.edu
Length: 2 Yrs   *ACGME Approved/Offered Positions:* 6
Program ID: 143-17-21-125

Iowa

Iowa City

University of Iowa Hospitals and Clinics Program

Sponsor: University of Iowa Hospitals and Clinics
Prgm Director: Joseph S Dillon, MBChB
Department of Medicine
200 Hawkins Drive
Iowa City, IA 52242
Tel: 319 353-7812   *Fax:* 319 353-7850
Length: 2 Yrs   *ACGME Approved/Offered Positions:* 4
Program ID: 143-18-21-079

Kansas

Kansas City

University of Kansas School of Medicine Program
Sponsor: University of Kansas School of Medicine
University of Kansas Hospital
Veterans Affairs Medical Center (Kansas City)
Prgm Director: Leland Graves III, MD
Mail Stop 2024
3901 Rainbow Boulevard
Kansas City, KS 66160
Tel: 913 588-6022   *Fax:* 913 588-4060
Length: 2 Yrs   *ACGME Approved/Offered Positions:* 2
Program ID: 143-19-12-181

Kentucky

Lexington

University of Kentucky College of Medicine Program
Sponsor: University of Kentucky College of Medicine
University of Kentucky Hospital
Prgm Director: L Raymond Reynolds, MD
800 Rose Street, UKMC MN524
Lexington, KY 40536
Tel: 859 323-5821   *Fax:* 859 323-5707
Length: 2 Yrs   *ACGME Approved/Offered Positions:* 4
Program ID: 143-20-12-184

Louisville

University of Louisville Program
Sponsor: University of Louisville School of Medicine
Jewish Hospital
Norton Hospital
University of Louisville Hospital
Veterans Affairs Medical Center (Louisville)
Prgm Director: Stephen J Winters, MD
Department of Medicine
550 South Jackson Street, ACB, A3G11
Louisville, KY 40202
Tel: 502 852-5237   *Fax:* 502 852-4978
E-mail: sjwint01@louisville.edu
Length: 2 Yrs   *ACGME Approved/Offered Positions:* 3
Program ID: 143-20-31-073

Louisiana

New Orleans

Ochsner Clinic Foundation Program
Sponsor: Ochsner Clinic Foundation
Prgm Director: Ramona Granda-Rodriguez, MD
1514 Jefferson Highway
New Orleans, LA 70121
Tel: 504 542-4023   *Fax:* 504 842-3419
E-mail: vstamant@ochsner.org
Length: 2 Yrs   *ACGME Approved/Offered Positions:* 4
Program ID: 143-21-22-118

Tulane University Program
Sponsor: Tulane University School of Medicine
Medical Center of Louisiana at New Orleans
Tulane University Hospital and Clinics
Veterans Affairs Medical Center (New Orleans)
Prgm Director: Vivian A Fonseca, MD
SL 53
New Orleans, LA 70112
Tel: 504 988-4026
E-mail: gafner@tulane.edu
Length: 2 Yrs   *ACGME Approved/Offered Positions:* 5
Program ID: 143-21-21-089

Shreveport

Louisiana State University (Shreveport) Program
Sponsor: LSU Health Sciences Center-University Hospital
Overton Brooks Veterans Affairs Medical Center
Prgm Director: Steven N Levine, MD
Department of Medicine
1501 Kings Highway
Shreveport, LA 71103
Tel: 318 675-5960   *Fax:* 318 675-5984
Length: 2 Yrs   *ACGME Approved/Offered Positions:* 3
Program ID: 143-21-21-074

Maryland

Baltimore

Johns Hopkins University Program
Sponsor: Johns Hopkins University School of Medicine
Johns Hopkins Hospital
Prgm Director: Gary Wand, MD
School of Medicine
1830 E Monument Street, Suite 333
Baltimore, MD 21287
Tel: 410 955-7225   *Fax:* 410 955-0841
Length: 2 Yrs   *ACGME Approved/Offered Positions:* 6
Program ID: 143-23-11-061

Union Memorial Hospital Program
Sponsor: Union Memorial Hospital
Prgm Director: Mansur E Shomali, MD
201 East University Parkway
33rd Street Professional Building, Suite 501
Baltimore, MD 21218
Tel: 410 554-4511   *Fax:* 410 554-6490
Length: 2 Yrs   *ACGME Approved/Offered Positions:* 2
Program ID: 143-23-31-187

University of Maryland Program
Sponsor: University of Maryland Medical System
Veterans Affairs Medical Center (Baltimore)
Prgm Director: Kristi D Silver, MD*
660 West Redwood St
Room 498
Baltimore, MD 21201
Tel: 410 706-1628   *Fax:* 410 706-6146
E-mail: ksilver@medicine.umaryland.edu
Length: 2 Yrs   *ACGME Approved/Offered Positions:* 6
Program ID: 143-23-21-036

Bethesda

National Capital Consortium (Bethesda) Program
Sponsor: National Capital Consortium
National Naval Medical Center (Bethesda)
Walter Reed Army Medical Center
Prgm Director: Victor J Bernet, MD
8901 Wisconsin Avenue
Bethesda, MD 20889
Tel: 202 782-6770   *Fax:* 202 782-0187
Length: 2 Yrs   *ACGME Approved/Offered Positions:* 8
Program ID: 143-23-11-126
Uniformed Services Program

National Institutes of Health Clinical Center Program
Sponsor: Clinical Center at the National Institutes of Health
Prgm Director: Monica C Skarulis, MD
10 Center Drive MSC 1613
Bldg 10 CRC Rm 6-3940
Bethesda, MD 20892
Tel: 301 496-1913   *Fax:* 301 480-4517
E-mail: monicas@mail.nih.gov
Length: 2 Yrs   *ACGME Approved/Offered Positions:* 12
Program ID: 143-23-21-161

Massachusetts

Boston

Beth Israel Deaconess Medical Center Program
Sponsor: Beth Israel Deaconess Medical Center
Prgm Director: Evan Rosen, MD, PhD
Endocrinology, Diabetes and Metabolism
330 Brookline Ave, Division of Endocrinology
Boston, MA 02215
Tel: 617 735-3221   *Fax:* 617 735-3323
E-mail: erosen@bidmc.harvard.edu
Length: 2 Yrs   *ACGME Approved/Offered Positions:* 6
Program ID: 143-24-21-004

Boston University Medical Center Program
Sponsor: Boston Medical Center
Prgm Director: Joshua D Safer, MD
88 East Newton Street, E-201
Boston, MA 02118
Tel: 617 638-8530   *Fax:* 617 638-8882
E-mail: jsafer@bu.edu
Length: 2 Yrs   *ACGME Approved/Offered Positions:* 6
Program ID: 143-24-21-127

Brigham and Women's Hospital Program
Sponsor: Brigham and Women's Hospital
Children's Hospital
Prgm Director: Robert G Dluhy, MD
221 Longwood Avenue
Boston, MA 02115
Tel: 617 732-5011   *Fax:* 617 732-5764
Length: 2 Yrs   *ACGME Approved/Offered Positions:* 6
Program ID: 143-24-21-005

Massachusetts General Hospital Program
Sponsor: Massachusetts General Hospital
Prgm Director: Beverly M K Biller, MD
Department of Medicine
55 Fruit Street, BUL 457B
Boston, MA 02114
Tel: 617 726-3870   *Fax:* 617 726-5072
E-mail: kminyard@partners.org
Length: 2 Yrs   *ACGME Approved/Offered Positions:* 8
Program ID: 143-24-11-052

Tufts Medical Center Program
Sponsor: Tufts Medical Center
Prgm Director: Ronald M Lechan, MD, PhD
800 Washington Street, #268
Boston, MA 02111
Tel: 617 636-5689   *Fax:* 617 636-4719
Length: 2 Yrs   *ACGME Approved/Offered Positions:* 4
Program ID: 143-24-21-006

Burlington

Lahey Clinic Program
Sponsor: Lahey Clinic
Prgm Director: Mary Beth Hodge, MD
41 Mall Road
Burlington, MA 01805
Tel: 781 744-8493   *Fax:* 781 744-5348
Length: 2 Yrs   *ACGME Approved/Offered Positions:* 2
Program ID: 143-24-21-119

Note: * indicates a newly appointed program director

Springfield

Baystate Medical Center/Tufts University School of Medicine Program
Sponsor: Baystate Medical Center
Prgm Director: Kamal C Shoukri, MD
759 Chestnut Street
Room S2620
Springfield, MA 01199
Tel: 413 794-0207   *Fax:* 413 794-9329
E-mail: kamal.shoukri@bhs.org
Length: 2 Yrs   *ACGME Approved/Offered Positions:* 2
Program ID: 143-24-11-062

Worcester

University of Massachusetts Program
Sponsor: University of Massachusetts Medical School
UMass Memorial Health Care (Memorial Campus)
UMass Memorial Health Care (University Campus)
Prgm Director: Neil Aronin, MD
55 Lake Avenue, North
Worcester, MA 01655
Tel: 508 856-3536   *Fax:* 508 856-6950
Length: 2 Yrs   *ACGME Approved/Offered Positions:* 5
Program ID: 143-24-21-007

Michigan

Ann Arbor

University of Michigan Program
Sponsor: University of Michigan Hospitals and Health Centers
Veterans Affairs Medical Center (Ann Arbor)
Prgm Director: Ariel L Barkan, MD
1500 W Medical Center Drive
3920 Taubman Center, Box 0354
Ann Arbor, MI 48109
Tel: 734 615-6964   *Fax:* 734 936-9240
Length: 2 Yrs   *ACGME Approved/Offered Positions:* 8
Program ID: 143-25-21-063

Detroit

Henry Ford Hospital Program
Sponsor: Henry Ford Hospital
Prgm Director: Abraham Thomas, MD, MPH*
3031 W Grand Blvd
Suite 800
Detroit, MI 48202
Tel: 313 916-3761   *Fax:* 313 916-6992
E-mail: cjones3@hfhs.org
Length: 2 Yrs   *ACGME Approved/Offered Positions:* 4
Program ID: 143-25-11-112

Wayne State University/Detroit Medical Center Program
Sponsor: Wayne State University/Detroit Medical Center
Detroit Receiving Hospital and University Health Center
Harper-Hutzel Hospital
Prgm Director: Abdul Abou-Samra, MD, PhD
Division of Endocrinology, UHC-4H
4201 St Antoine
Detroit, MI 48201
Tel: 313 745-4008   *Fax:* 313 993-0903
Length: 2 Yrs   *ACGME Approved/Offered Positions:* 6
Program ID: 143-25-21-040

Lansing

Michigan State University Program
Sponsor: Michigan State University College of Human Medicine
Michigan State University Clinical Center
Mid Michigan Physicians PC
Sparrow Hospital
Prgm Director: Ved V Gossain, MBBS, MD
Department of Medicine
B323 Clinical Center
East Lansing, MI 48824
Tel: 517 353-3730   *Fax:* 517 432-1326
E-mail: ved.gossain@ht.msu.edu
Length: 2 Yrs   *ACGME Approved/Offered Positions:* 2
Program ID: 143-25-13-182

Minnesota

Minneapolis

University of Minnesota Program
Sponsor: University of Minnesota Medical School
Hennepin County Medical Center
University of Minnesota Medical Center, Division of Fairview
Veterans Affairs Medical Center (Minneapolis)
Prgm Director: J Bruce Redmon, MD*
Department of Medicine, MMC 101
420 Delaware St SE
Minneapolis, MN 55455
Tel: 612 625-2154   *Fax:* 612 626-3133
Length: 2 Yrs   *ACGME Approved/Offered Positions:* 6
Program ID: 143-26-21-096

Rochester

College of Medicine, Mayo Clinic (Rochester) Program
Sponsor: College of Medicine, Mayo Clinic
Mayo Clinic (Rochester)
Saint Marys Hospital of Rochester
Prgm Director: Neena Natt, MD
200 First Street, SW
Rochester, MN 55905
Tel: 507 284-2476   *Fax:* 507 284-5745
E-mail: bargsten.denise@mayo.edu
Length: 2 Yrs   *ACGME Approved/Offered Positions:* 10
Program ID: 143-26-21-043

Mississippi

Jackson

University of Mississippi Medical Center Program
Sponsor: University of Mississippi School of Medicine
University Hospitals and Clinics
Veterans Affairs Medical Center (Jackson)
Prgm Director: Jose S Subauste, MD
Division of Endocrinology/Metabolism
2500 North State Street
Jackson, MS 39216
Tel: 601 984-5525   *Fax:* 601 984-5769
Length: 2 Yrs   *ACGME Approved/Offered Positions:* 4
Program ID: 143-27-21-171

Missouri

Columbia

University of Missouri-Columbia Program
Sponsor: University of Missouri-Columbia School of Medicine
Harry S Truman Memorial Veterans Hospital
University Hospitals and Clinics
Prgm Director: David W Gardner, MD
D109 Diabetes & Endocrinology Center UMHC
One Hospital Drive
Columbia, MO 65212
Tel: 573 882-2273   *Fax:* 573 884-5530
Length: 2 Yrs   *ACGME Approved/Offered Positions:* 6
Program ID: 143-28-21-064

St Louis

St Louis University School of Medicine Program
Sponsor: St Louis University School of Medicine
St Louis University Hospital
Veterans Affairs Medical Center (St Louis)
Prgm Director: Stewart G Albert, MD
Division of Endocrinology
1402 S Grand Blvd
St Louis, MO 63104
Tel: 314 977-8458   *Fax:* 314 977-6797
E-mail: albertsg@slu.edu
Length: 2 Yrs   *ACGME Approved/Offered Positions:* 4
Program ID: 143-28-21-080

Washington University/B-JH/SLCH Consortium Program
Sponsor: Washington University/B-JH/SLCH Consortium
Barnes-Jewish Hospital
Veterans Affairs Medical Center (St Louis)
Prgm Director: Clay F Semenkovich, MD
4989 Barnes Hospital Plaza
Campus Box 8127
St Louis, MO 63110
Tel: 314 362-7617   *Fax:* 314 362-7641
E-mail: kmuehlha@dom.wustl.edu
Length: 2 Yrs   *ACGME Approved/Offered Positions:* 8
Program ID: 143-28-21-159

Nebraska

Omaha

Creighton University Program
Sponsor: Creighton University School of Medicine
Creighton University Medical Center (Tenet - SJH)
Prgm Director: Andjela Drincic, MD*
601 North 30th Street, Suite 5766
Omaha, NE 68131
Tel: 402 449-4479   *Fax:* 402 280-5256
E-mail: vickiereid@creighton.edu
Length: 2 Yrs   *ACGME Approved/Offered Positions:* 3
Program ID: 143-30-21-179

University of Nebraska Medical Center College of Medicine Program
Sponsor: University of Nebraska Medical Center College of Medicine
Nebraska Medical Center
Veterans Affairs Medical Center (Omaha)
Prgm Director: James T Lane, MD
DEM-Diabetes, Endocrinology Metabolism
983020 Nebraska Medical Center
Omaha, NE 68198
Tel: 402 559-6205   *Fax:* 402 559-9504
E-mail: jtlane1@unmc.edu
Length: 2 Yrs   *ACGME Approved/Offered Positions:* 4
Program ID: 143-30-21-160

New Hampshire

Lebanon

Dartmouth-Hitchcock Medical Center Program
Sponsor: Mary Hitchcock Memorial Hospital
Prgm Director: Donald L St Germain, MD
One Medical Center Drive
Lebanon, NH 03756
Tel: 603 650-7910   *Fax:* 603 650-6130
Length: 2 Yrs   *ACGME Approved/Offered Positions:* 4
Program ID: 143-32-31-183

New Jersey

New Brunswick

UMDNJ-Robert Wood Johnson Medical School Program
Sponsor: UMDNJ-Robert Wood Johnson Medical School
Jersey Shore University Medical Center
Robert Wood Johnson University Hospital
Prgm Director: Louis F Amorosa, MD
One Robert Wood Johnson Place, MEB 384
PO Box 19
New Brunswick, NJ 08903
Tel: 732 235-7748   *Fax:* 732 235-7096
Length: 2 Yrs   *ACGME Approved/Offered Positions:* 4
Program ID: 143-33-21-026

Newark

UMDNJ-New Jersey Medical School Program
Sponsor: UMDNJ-New Jersey Medical School
UMDNJ-University Hospital
Veterans Affairs New Jersey Health Care System
Prgm Director: David Bleich, MD
185 S Orange Avenue, MSB I-588
Newark, NJ 07103
Tel: 973 972-6170   *Fax:* 973 972-5185
Length: 2 Yrs   *ACGME Approved/Offered Positions:* 2
Program ID: 143-33-21-148

New Mexico

Albuquerque

University of New Mexico Program
Sponsor: University of New Mexico School of Medicine
University of New Mexico Hospital
Veterans Affairs Medical Center (Albuquerque)
Prgm Director: Patricia Kapsner, MD*
MSC10 5550
1 University of New Mexico
Albuquerque, NM 87131
Tel: 505 272-4658   *Fax:* 505 272-5155
E-mail: pkapsner@salud.unm.edu
Length: 2 Yrs   *ACGME Approved/Offered Positions:* 4
Program ID: 143-34-21-113

New York

Albany

Albany Medical Center Program
Sponsor: Albany Medical Center
Prgm Director: Matthew C Leinung, MD
Department of Medicine
43 New Scotland Avenue, MC-140
Albany, NY 12208
Tel: 518 262-5185   *Fax:* 518 262-6303
E-mail: brozowml@mail.amc.edu
Length: 2 Yrs   *ACGME Approved/Offered Positions:* 3
Program ID: 143-35-31-027

Bronx

Albert Einstein College of Medicine Program
Sponsor: Albert Einstein College of Medicine of Yeshiva University
Montefiore Medical Center-Henry and Lucy Moses Division
North Bronx Healthcare Network-Jacobi Medical Center
North Bronx Healthcare Network-North Central Bronx Hospital
Prgm Director: Martin Surks, MD
Montefiore Medical Center
111 East 210th Street
Bronx, NY 10467
Tel: 718 920-2017   *Fax:* 718 920-5202
E-mail: msurks@montefiore.org
Length: 2 Yrs   *ACGME Approved/Offered Positions:* 8
Program ID: 143-35-21-097

Brooklyn

SUNY Health Science Center at Brooklyn Program
Sponsor: SUNY Health Science Center at Brooklyn
Kings County Hospital Center
University Hospital-SUNY Health Science Center at Brooklyn
Veterans Affairs Medical Center (Brooklyn)
Woodhull Medical and Mental Health Center
Prgm Director: Agnieszka Gliwa, MD*
450 Clarkson Ave, Box 1205
Brooklyn, NY 11203
Tel: 718 270-1698   *Fax:* 718 270-1699
E-mail: Agnes.Gliwa@downstate.edu
Length: 2 Yrs   *ACGME Approved/Offered Positions:* 5
Program ID: 143-35-21-010

Buffalo

University at Buffalo Program
Sponsor: University at Buffalo School of Medicine
Erie County Medical Center
Kaleida Health System (Millard Fillmore Hospital)
Veterans Affairs Western New York Hospital
Prgm Director: Ajay Chaudhuri, MD
3 Gates Circle
Buffalo, NY 14209
Tel: 716 887-4069   *Fax:* 716 887-4773
Length: 2 Yrs   *ACGME Approved/Offered Positions:* 5
Program ID: 143-35-31-008

East Meadow

Nassau University Medical Center Program
Sponsor: Nassau University Medical Center
Prgm Director: Kenneth H Hupart, MD
2201 Hempstead Turnpike
East Meadow, NY 11554
Tel: 516 572-6504   *Fax:* 516 572-0082
Length: 2 Yrs   *ACGME Approved/Offered Positions:* 2
Program ID: 143-35-21-081

Great Neck

NSLIJHS-Albert Einstein College of Medicine at Long Island Jewish Medical Center Program
Sponsor: North Shore-Long Island Jewish Health System
Long Island Jewish Medical Center
North Shore University Hospital
Prgm Director: Stuart A Weinerman, MD
2800 Marcus Ave, Suite 200
New Hyde Park, NY 11042
Tel: 516 708-2542   *Fax:* 516 708-2573
E-mail: sweinerm@nshs.edu
Length: 2 Yrs   *ACGME Approved/Offered Positions:* 2
Program ID: 143-35-31-178

Mineola

Winthrop-University Hospital Program
Sponsor: Winthrop-University Hospital
Prgm Director: Lawrence E Shapiro, MD
222 Station Plaza North, #350
Mineola, NY 11501
Tel: 516 663-4775   *Fax:* 516 663-4780
E-mail: dpalma@winthrop.org
Length: 2 Yrs   *ACGME Approved/Offered Positions:* 3
Program ID: 143-35-11-065

New York

Albert Einstein College of Medicine at Beth Israel Medical Center Program
Sponsor: Beth Israel Medical Center
Prgm Director: Leonid Poretsky, MD
Division of Endocrinology and Metabolism
317 East 17th Street, Room 7F05
New York, NY 10003
Tel: 212 420-4666   *Fax:* 212 420-2224
Length: 2 Yrs   *ACGME Approved/Offered Positions:* 4
Program ID: 143-35-11-009

Mount Sinai School of Medicine Program
Sponsor: Mount Sinai School of Medicine
Mount Sinai Medical Center
Prgm Director: Robert T Yanagisawa, MD
One Gustave L Levy Place
Box 1055
New York, NY 10029
Tel: 212 241-1500   *Fax:* 212 241-4218
Length: 2 Yrs   *ACGME Approved/Offered Positions:* 8
Program ID: 143-35-31-130

New York Medical College at St Vincent's Hospital and Medical Center of New York Program
Sponsor: New York Medical College
St Vincent Catholic Medical Centers (Manhattan)
Cabrini Medical Center
Prgm Director: Vincent Yen, MD
170 W 12th Street
New York, NY 10011
Tel: 212 604-8781   *Fax:* 212 604-2128
E-mail: vyen@svcmcny.org
Length: 2 Yrs   *ACGME Approved/Offered Positions:* 2
Program ID: 143-35-21-162

New York Presbyterian Hospital (Columbia Campus) Program
Sponsor: New York Presbyterian Hospital
New York Presbyterian Hospital (Columbia Campus)
Prgm Director: John P Bilezikian, MD, BA
622 W 168th Street, PH 8 West - 864
New York, NY 10032
Tel: 212 305-6238   *Fax:* 212 305-6486
Length: 2 Yrs   *ACGME Approved/Offered Positions:* 6
Program ID: 143-35-11-053

Note: * indicates a newly appointed program director

New York Presbyterian Hospital (Cornell Campus) Program
Sponsor: New York Presbyterian Hospital
Memorial Sloan-Kettering Cancer Center
New York Presbyterian Hospital (Cornell Campus)
Prgm Director: David J Brillon, MD
525 East 68th Street
Room Payson 220
New York, NY 10065
Tel: 212 746-6318   *Fax:* 212 746-8527
Length: 2 Yrs   *ACGME Approved/Offered Positions:* 4
Program ID: 143-35-21-136

New York University School of Medicine Program
Sponsor: New York University School of Medicine
Bellevue Hospital Center
Prgm Director: Ann Danoff, MD
Department of Medicine
550 First Avenue
New York, NY 10016
Tel: 212 263-8060   *Fax:* 212 263-2593
E-mail: ysa.romero@med.nyu.edu
Length: 2 Yrs   *ACGME Approved/Offered Positions:* 8
Program ID: 143-35-21-098

St Luke's-Roosevelt Hospital Center Program
Sponsor: St Luke's-Roosevelt Hospital Center
Prgm Director: F Xavier Pi-Sunyer, MD, MPH
1111 Amsterdam Avenue
New York, NY 10025
Tel: 212 523-4161   *Fax:* 212 523-4830
E-mail: nbirbals@chpnet.org
Length: 2 Yrs   *ACGME Approved/Offered Positions:* 2
Program ID: 143-35-21-086

Rochester

University of Rochester Program
Sponsor: Strong Memorial Hospital of the University of Rochester
Prgm Director: Laura M Calvi, MD
601 Elmwood Avenue Box 693
Rochester, NY 14642
Tel: 585 275-5011   *Fax:* 585 273-1288
E-mail: laura_calvi@urmc.rochester.edu
Length: 2 Yrs   *ACGME Approved/Offered Positions:* 4
Program ID: 143-35-11-145

Stony Brook

SUNY at Stony Brook Program
Sponsor: University Hospital - SUNY at Stony Brook
Veterans Affairs Medical Center (Northport)
Prgm Director: Harold E Carlson, MD
T-15, Room 060
Stony Brook, NY 11794
Tel: 631 444-1038   *Fax:* 631 444-9092
Length: 2 Yrs   *ACGME Approved/Offered Positions:* 4
Program ID: 143-35-21-011

Syracuse

SUNY Upstate Medical University Program
Sponsor: SUNY Upstate Medical University
Veterans Affairs Medical Center (Syracuse)
Prgm Director: Ruth S Weinstock, MD, PhD
750 E Adams Street
CWB 353
Syracuse, NY 13210
Tel: 315 473-5740
E-mail: haightm@upstate.edu
Length: 2 Yrs   *ACGME Approved/Offered Positions:* 4
Program ID: 143-35-21-087

Valhalla

New York Medical College at Westchester Medical Center Program
Sponsor: New York Medical College
Sound Shore Medical Center of Westchester
Westchester Medical Center
Prgm Director: Irene A Weiss, MD
Westchester Medical Center
Valhalla, NY 10595
Tel: 914 594-4429   *Fax:* 914 594-4380
Length: 2 Yrs   *ACGME Approved/Offered Positions:* 3
Program ID: 143-35-21-172

North Carolina
Chapel Hill

University of North Carolina Hospitals Program
Sponsor: University of North Carolina Hospitals
Prgm Director: Jean M Dostou, MD
8026 Burnett Womack CB 7172
Chapel Hill, NC 27599
Tel: 919 966-0134   *Fax:* 919 966-8146
Length: 2 Yrs   *ACGME Approved/Offered Positions:* 4
Program ID: 143-36-21-115

Durham

Duke University Hospital Program
Sponsor: Duke University Hospital
Veterans Affairs Medical Center (Durham)
Prgm Director: Thomas J Weber, MD
Box 3470
Durham, NC 27710
Tel: 919 688-4289   *Fax:* 919 668-1366
Length: 2 Yrs   *ACGME Approved/Offered Positions:* 8
Program ID: 143-36-21-116

Winston-Salem

Wake Forest University School of Medicine Program
Sponsor: Wake Forest University Baptist Medical Center
Prgm Director: K Patrick Ober, MD
Medical Center Boulevard
Winston-Salem, NC 27157
Tel: 336 713-7251   *Fax:* 336 713-7255
Length: 2 Yrs   *ACGME Approved/Offered Positions:* 2
Program ID: 143-36-21-013

Ohio
Cincinnati

University Hospital/University of Cincinnati College of Medicine Program
Sponsor: University Hospital Inc
Veterans Affairs Medical Center (Cincinnati)
Prgm Director: David D'Alessio, MD
Mail Location 0547
PO Box 670547
Cincinnati, OH 45267
Tel: 513 558-4444   *Fax:* 513 558-8581
Length: 2 Yrs   *ACGME Approved/Offered Positions:* 5
Program ID: 143-38-21-066

Cleveland

Cleveland Clinic Foundation Program
Sponsor: Cleveland Clinic Foundation
Prgm Director: Robert Zimmerman, MD, BS
Dept of Endocrinology, A 53
9500 Euclid Avenue
Cleveland, OH 44195
Tel: 216 444-9428   *Fax:* 216 445-1656
E-mail: zimmerr@ccf.org
Length: 2 Yrs   *ACGME Approved/Offered Positions:* 6
Program ID: 143-38-12-132

University Hospitals Case Medical Center Program
Sponsor: University Hospitals Case Medical Center
Veterans Affairs Medical Center (Cleveland)
Prgm Director: Baha M Arafah, MD
School of Medicine, BRB 433
10900 Euclid Avenue
Cleveland, OH 44106
Tel: 216 844-3144   *Fax:* 216 844-3120
E-mail: bxa@case.edu
Length: 2 Yrs   *ACGME Approved/Offered Positions:* 4
Program ID: 143-38-21-131

Columbus

Ohio State University Hospital Program
Sponsor: Ohio State University Hospital
Prgm Director: Matthew D Ringel, MD*
1581 Dodd Drive
445D McCampbell Hall
Columbus, OH 43210
Tel: 614 292-3800   *Fax:* 614 292-1550
Length: 2 Yrs   *ACGME Approved/Offered Positions:* 4
Program ID: 143-38-11-121

Oklahoma
Oklahoma City

University of Oklahoma Health Sciences Center Program
Sponsor: University of Oklahoma College of Medicine
OU Medical Center
Veterans Affairs Medical Center (Oklahoma City)
Prgm Director: Hal Scofield, MD
PO Box 26901
WP 1345
Oklahoma City, OK 73190
Tel: 405 271-5896   *Fax:* 405 271-7522
E-mail: carla-deal@ouhsc.edu
Length: 2 Yrs   *ACGME Approved/Offered Positions:* 6
Program ID: 143-39-21-067

Oregon
Portland

Oregon Health & Science University Program
Sponsor: Oregon Health & Science University Hospital
Veterans Affairs Medical Center (Portland)
Prgm Director: Robert F Klein, MD
3181 SW Sam Jackson Park Road
Division of Endocrinology, L607
Portland, OR 97239
Tel: 503 494-7450   *Fax:* 503 494-3707
E-mail: bisaccip@ohsu.edu
Length: 2 Yrs   *ACGME Approved/Offered Positions:* 4
Program ID: 143-40-31-147

Pennsylvania

Hershey

Penn State University/Milton S Hershey Medical Center Program

Sponsor: Milton S Hershey Medical Center
Prgm Director: Andrea Manni, MD
500 University Drive
PO Box 850
Hershey, PA 17033
Tel: 717 531-8395   *Fax:* 717 531-5726
Length: 2 Yrs   *ACGME Approved/Offered Positions:* 4
Program ID: 143-41-11-015

Philadelphia

Temple University Hospital Program

Sponsor: Temple University Hospital
Prgm Director: Elias S Siraj, MD
3322 North Broad St
MOB 2nd Floor
Philadelphia, PA 19140
Tel: 215 707-4746   *Fax:* 215 707-5599
Length: 2 Yrs   *ACGME Approved/Offered Positions:* 2
Program ID: 143-41-21-029

Thomas Jefferson University Program

Sponsor: Thomas Jefferson University Hospital
Prgm Director: Intekhab Ahmed, MD
211 S 9th Street
Suite 600
Philadelphia, PA 19107
Tel: 215 955-5104   *Fax:* 215 928-3160
E-mail: intekhab.ahmed@jefferson.edu
Length: 2 Yrs   *ACGME Approved/Offered Positions:* 4
Program ID: 143-41-21-166

University of Pennsylvania Program

Sponsor: University of Pennsylvania Health System
Veterans Affairs Medical Center (Philadelphia)
Prgm Director: Susan J Mandel, MD, MPH
415 Curie Blvd
700 Clinical Research Building
Philadelphia, PA 19104
Tel: 215 746-6391   *Fax:* 215 898-5408
E-mail: sherardg@mail.med.upenn.edu
Length: 2 Yrs   *ACGME Approved/Offered Positions:* 6
Program ID: 143-41-21-021

Pittsburgh

University of Pittsburgh Medical Center Medical Education Program

Sponsor: Univ of Pittsburgh Medical Center Medical Education
UPMC Presbyterian Shadyside
Prgm Director: R Harsha Rao, MD, MRCP
503 Medical Arts Building
3708 Fifth Avenue
Pittsburgh, PA 15213
Tel: 412 648-9317   *Fax:* 412 648-3290
Length: 2 Yrs   *ACGME Approved/Offered Positions:* 10
Program ID: 143-41-21-037

Puerto Rico

San Juan

University of Puerto Rico Program

Sponsor: University of Puerto Rico School of Medicine
University Hospital
Prgm Director: Margarita Ramirez-Vick, MD
University Hospital
PO Box 365067
San Juan, PR 00936
Tel: 787 754-0101   *Fax:* 787 294-3622
Length: 2 Yrs   *ACGME Approved/Offered Positions:* 3
Program ID: 143-42-21-100

Rhode Island

Providence

Brown University Program

Sponsor: Rhode Island Hospital-Lifespan
Roger Williams Medical Center
Veterans Affairs Medical Center (Providence)
Prgm Director: Robert J Smith, MD
Rhode Island Hospital
593 Eddy Street
Providence, RI 02903
Tel: 401 444-3420   *Fax:* 401 444-4921
Length: 2 Yrs   *ACGME Approved/Offered Positions:* 4
Program ID: 143-43-11-101

South Carolina

Charleston

Medical University of South Carolina Program

Sponsor: Medical University of South Carolina College of Medicine
MUSC Medical Center
Ralph H Johnson VA Medical Center (Charleston)
Prgm Director: Louis M Luttrell, MD, PhD
96 Jonathan Lucas Street, Ste 816
MSC 624
Charleston, SC 29425
Tel: 843 792-2529   *Fax:* 843 792-4114
E-mail: gunnellm@musc.edu
Length: 2 Yrs   *ACGME Approved/Offered Positions:* 5
Program ID: 143-45-21-088

Columbia

Palmetto Health/University of South Carolina School of Medicine Program

Sponsor: Palmetto Health
Palmetto Health Richland
William Jennings Bryan Dorn Veterans Hospital
Prgm Director: Tu Lin, MD
Department of Medicine
Two Medical Park, Suite 502
Columbia, SC 29203
Tel: 803 540-1000   *Fax:* 803 540-1050
E-mail: Tu.Lin@uscmed.sc.edu
Length: 2 Yrs   *ACGME Approved/Offered Positions:* 3
Program ID: 143-45-21-077

Tennessee

Memphis

University of Tennessee Program

Sponsor: University of Tennessee College of Medicine
Methodist Healthcare - Memphis Hospitals
Regional Medical Center at Memphis
Veterans Affairs Medical Center (Memphis)
Prgm Director: Samuel Dagogo-Jack, MD, MBBS
Division of Endocrinology
920 Madison Ave, #300A
Memphis, TN 38163
Tel: 901 448-2608
E-mail: mblake4@utmem.edu
Length: 2 Yrs   *ACGME Approved/Offered Positions:* 6
Program ID: 143-47-21-117

Nashville

Vanderbilt University Program

Sponsor: Vanderbilt University Medical Center
Veterans Affairs Medical Center (Nashville)
Prgm Director: James M May, MD
7465 Medical Research Building IV
2213 Garland Avenue
Nashville, TN 37232
Tel: 615 936-1653   *Fax:* 615 936-1667
Length: 2 Yrs   *ACGME Approved/Offered Positions:* 4
Program ID: 143-47-31-016

Texas

Dallas

University of Texas Southwestern Medical School Program

Sponsor: University of Texas Southwestern Medical School
Dallas County Hospital District-Parkland Memorial Hospital
Dallas VA Medical Center
Prgm Director: William J Kovacs, MD
5323 Harry Hines Blvd
Room Y5.318
Dallas, TX 75390
Tel: 214 648-3494   *Fax:* 214 648-8917
E-mail: Endocrine.Fellowship@UTSouthwestern.edu
Length: 2 Yrs   *ACGME Approved/Offered Positions:* 8
Program ID: 143-48-21-083

Galveston

University of Texas Medical Branch Hospitals Program

Sponsor: University of Texas Medical Branch Hospitals
University of Texas Medical School at Galveston
Prgm Director: Kevin H McKinney, MD
8138 Medical Research Building
301 University Boulevard
Galveston, TX 77555
Tel: 409 772-1922   *Fax:* 409 772-8709
E-mail: khmckinn@utmb.edu
Length: 2 Yrs   *ACGME Approved/Offered Positions:* 4
Program ID: 143-48-21-163

Note: * indicates a newly appointed program director

Houston

Baylor College of Medicine Program
Sponsor: Baylor College of Medicine
Harris County Hospital District-Ben Taub General Hospital
Michael E DeBakey VA Medical Center - Houston
St Luke's Episcopal Hospital
Texas Children's Hospital
University of Texas M D Anderson Cancer Center
Prgm Director: Ashok Balasubramanyam, MD
One Baylor Plaza, Room ABBR R607
Section of Endocrinology
Houston, TX 77030
Tel: 713 798-8654 *Fax:* 713 798-3810
E-mail: ashokb@bcm.tmc.edu
Length: 2 Yrs *ACGME Approved/Offered Positions:* 10
Program ID: 143-48-21-070

University of Texas at Houston Program
Sponsor: University of Texas Health Science Center at Houston
Lyndon B Johnson General Hospital
Memorial Hermann Hospital
Prgm Director: Philip R Orlander, MD
Internal Medicine - Endocrinology Division
6431 Fannin St, MSB 4.202
Houston, TX 77030
Tel: 713 500-6650 *Fax:* 713 500-6647
Length: 2 Yrs *ACGME Approved/Offered Positions:* 4
Program ID: 143-48-31-017

Lackland AFB

San Antonio Uniformed Services Health Education Consortium Program
Sponsor: San Antonio Uniformed Services Health Education Consortium
Wilford Hall Medical Center (AETC)
Prgm Director: (LtCol) Tom J Sauerwein, MD, MS
59th MDOS/SGO5E
2200 Bergquist Drive, Suite 1
Lackland AFB, TX 78236
Tel: 210 292-6475 *Fax:* 210 292-3748
E-mail: tom.sauerwein@lackland.af.mil
Length: 2 Yrs *ACGME Approved/Offered Positions:* 4
Program ID: 143-48-12-048
Uniformed Services Program

San Antonio

University of Texas Health Science Center at San Antonio Program
Sponsor: University of Texas School of Medicine at San Antonio
Audie L Murphy Memorial Veterans Hospital (San Antonio)
University Health System
Prgm Director: Jan M Bruder, MD
7703 Floyd Curl Drive MSC 7877
San Antonio, TX 78229
Tel: 210 567-4900 *Fax:* 210 567-6693
Length: 2 Yrs *ACGME Approved/Offered Positions:* 4
Program ID: 143-48-21-055

Utah

Salt Lake City

University of Utah Program
Sponsor: University of Utah Medical Center
Primary Children's Medical Center
Veterans Affairs Medical Center (Salt Lake City)
Prgm Director: Donald A McClain, MD, PhD
30 North 1900 East Rm 1C412
Salt Lake City, UT 84132
Tel: 801 585-0954 *Fax:* 801 585-0956
E-mail: susan.brown@hsc.utah.edu
Length: 2 Yrs *ACGME Approved/Offered Positions:* 2
Program ID: 143-49-21-175

Vermont

Burlington

University of Vermont Program
Sponsor: Fletcher Allen Health Care
Prgm Director: Rose Christian, MD*
Rm 110
208 South Park Drive
Colchester, VT 05446
Tel: 802 656-2530 *Fax:* 802 656-8031
E-mail: rose.christian@vtmednet.org
Length: 2 Yrs *ACGME Approved/Offered Positions:* 2
Program ID: 143-50-21-134

Virginia

Charlottesville

University of Virginia Program
Sponsor: University of Virginia Medical Center
Prgm Director: Alan C Dalkin, MD
Department of Internal Medicine
PO Box 801412
Charlottesville, VA 22908
Tel: 434 243-2603 *Fax:* 434 243-9143
Length: 2 Yrs *ACGME Approved/Offered Positions:* 8
Program ID: 143-51-21-019

Norfolk

Eastern Virginia Medical School Program
Sponsor: Eastern Virginia Medical School
Sentara Norfolk General Hospital
Prgm Director: John T O'Brian, MD
855 West Brambleton Avenue
Norfolk, VA 23510
Tel: 757 446-5974 *Fax:* 757 446-5970
Length: 2 Yrs *ACGME Approved/Offered Positions:* 2
Program ID: 143-51-12-176

Richmond

Virginia Commonwealth University Health System Program
Sponsor: Virginia Commonwealth University Health System
Hunter Holmes McGuire VA Medical Center (Richmond)
Medical College of Virginia Hospitals
Prgm Director: Diane M Biskobing, MD
Medical College of Virginia
PO Box 980111
Richmond, VA 23298
Tel: 804 828-9696 *Fax:* 804 828-8389
E-mail: dbiskobing@mcvh-vcu.edu
Length: 2 Yrs *ACGME Approved/Offered Positions:* 5
Program ID: 143-51-21-020

Washington

Seattle

University of Washington Program
Sponsor: University of Washington School of Medicine
Harborview Medical Center
Seattle Children's Hospital
University of Washington Medical Center
VA Puget Sound Health Care System
Prgm Director: Dace L Trence, MD
1959 NE Pacific Street
Box 356426 Medicine/Endocrinology
Seattle, WA 98195
Tel: 206 598-4882 *Fax:* 206 598-4976
Length: 2 Yrs *ACGME Approved/Offered Positions:* 8
Program ID: 143-54-21-071

West Virginia

Huntington

Marshall University School of Medicine Program
Sponsor: Marshall University School of Medicine
Cabell Huntington Hospital
St Mary's Hospital
Veterans Affairs Medical Center (Huntington)
Prgm Director: John W Leidy Jr, MD, PhD
Department of Medicine
1249 15th Street
Huntington, WV 25701
Tel: 304 691-1095 *Fax:* 304 691-8630
E-mail: muendo@marshall.edu
Length: 2 Yrs *ACGME Approved/Offered Positions:* 4
Program ID: 143-55-21-031

Wisconsin

Madison

University of Wisconsin Program
Sponsor: University of Wisconsin Hospital and Clinics
Prgm Director: Yoram Shenker, MD
H4/568 Clinical Science Ctr (5148)
600 Highland Avenue
Madison, WI 53792
Tel: 608 263-7780 *Fax:* 608 263-9983
E-mail: yxs@medicine.wisc.edu
Length: 2 Yrs *ACGME Approved/Offered Positions:* 6
Program ID: 143-56-21-102

Milwaukee

Medical College of Wisconsin Affiliated Hospitals Program
Sponsor: Medical College of Wisconsin Affiliated Hospitals, Inc
Clement J Zablocki Veterans Affairs Medical Center
Froedtert Memorial Lutheran Hospital
Prgm Director: Albert L Jochen, MD
9200 W Wisconsin Ave
Milwaukee, WI 53226
Tel: 414 805-0438 *Fax:* 414 456-6210
Length: 2 Yrs *ACGME Approved/Offered Positions:* 4
Program ID: 143-56-31-039

Endovascular Surgical Neuroradiology (Neurological Surgery)

Arizona

Phoenix

St Joseph's Hospital and Medical Center Program

Sponsor: St Joseph's Hospital and Medical Center
Prgm Director: Cameron McDougall, MD
2910 N 3rd Avenue
Phoenix, AZ 85013
Tel: 602 406-3964   *Fax:* 602 406-4161
Length: 1 Yr   *ACGME Approved/Offered Positions:* 2
Program ID: 163-03-12-002

Endovascular Surgical Neuroradiology (Neurology)

Minnesota

Minneapolis

University of Minnesota Program

Sponsor: University of Minnesota Medical School
Hennepin County Medical Center
University of Minnesota Medical Center, Division of
   Fairview
Prgm Director: Adnan I Qureshi, MD
420 Delaware Street SE
MMC 295
Minneapolis, MN 55455
Tel: 612 625-9622   *Fax:* 612 625-7950
Length: 1 Yr   *ACGME Approved/Offered Positions:* 3
Program ID: 182-26-12-001

Endovascular Surgical Neuroradiology (Radiology)

Maryland

Baltimore

Johns Hopkins University Program

Sponsor: Johns Hopkins University School of Medicine
Johns Hopkins Hospital
Prgm Director: Philippe Gailloud, MD
600 N Wolfe Street, Nelson B-100
Baltimore, MD 21287
Tel: 410 955-8525   *Fax:* 410 614-8238
Length: 1 Yr   *ACGME Approved/Offered Positions:* 2
Program ID: 422-23-31-006

Missouri

St Louis

Washington University/B-JH/SLCH Consortium Program

Sponsor: Washington University/B-JH/SLCH Consortium
Barnes-Jewish Hospital
Prgm Director: Colin P Derdeyn, MD
510 South Kingshighway, WUSM Box 8131
Campus Box 8131
St Louis, MO 63110
Tel: 314 362-2560   *Fax:* 314 362-4886
E-mail: derdeync@wustl.edu
Length: 1 Yr   *ACGME Approved/Offered Positions:* 2
Program ID: 422-28-12-003

Ohio

Cleveland

Cleveland Clinic Foundation Program

Sponsor: Cleveland Clinic Foundation
Prgm Director: Thomas J Masaryk, MD
9500 Euclid Avenue, L10
Cleveland, OH 44195
Tel: 216 444-6653   *Fax:* 216 444-3466
Length: 1 Yr   *ACGME Approved/Offered Positions:* 2
Program ID: 422-38-13-004

Note: * indicates a newly appointed program director

Family Medicine

Alabama

Birmingham

St Vincent's East Program

Sponsor: St Vincent's East
Prgm Director: Marion H Sims, MD
2152 Old Springville Road
Birmingham, AL 35215
Tel: 205 838-6926   *Fax:* 205 838-6999
E-mail: kathy.graves@stvhs.com
Length: 3 Yrs   *ACGME Approved/Offered Positions:* 15
Program ID: 120-01-31-020

Huntsville

University of Alabama Medical Center (Huntsville) Program

Sponsor: University of Alabama Hospital
Huntsville Hospital
Prgm Director: Allan J Wilke, MD, MA
301 Governors Drive, SW
Huntsville, AL 35801
Tel: 256 551-4632   *Fax:* 256 551-4633
E-mail: francisp@uasomh.uab.edu
Length: 3 Yrs   *ACGME Approved/Offered Positions:* 39
Program ID: 120-01-11-023

Mobile

University of South Alabama Program

Sponsor: University of South Alabama Hospitals
University of South Alabama Medical Center
USA Children's and Women's Hospital
Prgm Director: Allen Perkins, MD, MPH
1504 Springhill Avenue
Suite 3414
Mobile, AL 36604
Tel: 251 434-3480   *Fax:* 251 434-3573
E-mail: fmres@usouthal.edu
Length: 3 Yrs   *ACGME Approved/Offered Positions:* 18
Program ID: 120-01-11-024

Montgomery

Baptist Outreach Services (Montgomery) Program

Sponsor: Baptist Outreach Services
Baptist Medical Center South
Prgm Director: Thomas G Kincer, MD
4371 Narrow Lane Rd #100
Montgomery, AL 36116
Tel: 334 613-3680   *Fax:* 334 613-3685
E-mail: lnorred@baptistfirst.org
Length: 3 Yrs   *ACGME Approved/Offered Positions:* 18
Program ID: 120-01-21-624

Selma

University of Alabama Medical Center (Selma Dallas County) Program

Sponsor: University of Alabama Hospital
Vaughan Regional Medical Center
Prgm Director: Boyd L Bailey, MD
1023 Medical Center Parkway
Suite 200
Selma, AL 36701
Tel: 334 875-4184   *Fax:* 334 874-3511
E-mail: shunter@uabsfm.org
Length: 3 Yrs   *ACGME Approved/Offered Positions:* 15
Program ID: 120-01-21-026

Tuscaloosa

Tuscaloosa College of Community Health Science Program

Sponsor: Tuscaloosa College of Community Health
   Sciences
DCH Regional Medical Center
Prgm Director: John B Waits, MD
Box 870377
Tuscaloosa, AL 35487
Tel: 205 348-1373   *Fax:* 205 348-2695
E-mail: jwaits@cchs.ua.edu
Length: 3 Yrs   *ACGME Approved/Offered Positions:* 36
Program ID: 120-01-21-027

Alaska

Anchorage

Alaska Family Medicine/Providence Hospital Program

Sponsor: Providence Hospital
Prgm Director: Harold Johnston, MD
1201 East 36th Avenue
Anchorage, AK 99508
Tel: 907 561-4500   *Fax:* 907 561-4806
Length: 3 Yrs   *ACGME Approved/Offered Positions:* 36
Program ID: 120-02-21-596

Arizona

Phoenix

Banner Good Samaritan Medical Center Program

Sponsor: Banner Good Samaritan Medical Center
Prgm Director: Jeffrey D Wolfrey, MD
1300 North 12th Street, Suite 605
Phoenix, AZ 85006
Tel: 602 239-2668   *Fax:* 602 239-2067
E-mail: lori.logan@bannerhealth.com
Length: 3 Yrs   *ACGME Approved/Offered Positions:* 24
Program ID: 120-03-12-028

Phoenix Baptist Hospital and Medical Center Program

Sponsor: Phoenix Baptist Hospital and Med
   Ctr/Vanguard Health System
Prgm Director: Wendy Orm, MD
Family Practice Residency Program
2000 West Bethany Home Road
Phoenix, AZ 85015
Tel: 602 246-5521   *Fax:* 602 433-6641
E-mail: ssjackson@abrazohealth.com
Length: 3 Yrs   *ACGME Approved/Offered Positions:* 21
Program ID: 120-03-21-029

St Joseph's Hospital and Medical Center Program

Sponsor: St Joseph's Hospital and Medical Center
Prgm Director: Paul R Steinberg, MD, MSW
2927 North 7th Avenue
Phoenix, AZ 85013
Tel: 602 406-3591   *Fax:* 602 406-4122
Length: 3 Yrs   *ACGME Approved/Offered Positions:* 24
Program ID: 120-03-12-030

Scottsdale

College of Medicine, Mayo Clinic (Arizona) Program

Sponsor: College of Medicine, Mayo Clinic
Scottsdale Healthcare - Shea
Mayo Clinic Hospital
Prgm Director: Andrea Darby-Stewart, MD
13737 North 92nd Street
Scottsdale, AZ 85260
Tel: 480 860-4868
E-mail: darbystewart.andrea@mayo.edu
Length: 3 Yrs   *ACGME Approved/Offered Positions:* 12
Program ID: 120-03-21-570

Scottsdale Healthcare-Osborn Program

Sponsor: Scottsdale Healthcare-Osborn
Prgm Director: Robert J Creager, MD, MEd
Family Medicine Center
7301 E Second Street, Suite 210
Scottsdale, AZ 85251
Tel: 480 882-4890   *Fax:* 480 882-6801
E-mail: fpres@shc.org
Length: 3 Yrs   *ACGME Approved/Offered Positions:* 24
Program ID: 120-03-32-031

Tucson

University of Arizona Program

Sponsor: University of Arizona College of Medicine
University Medical Center
University of Arizona/UPHK Graduate Medical Ed
   Consortium
Prgm Director: Edward Paul, MD
Family Practice Office
707 North Alvernon, Ste 101
Tucson, AZ 85711
Tel: 520 694-1615   *Fax:* 520 694-1428
Length: 3 Yrs   *ACGME Approved/Offered Positions:* 24
Program ID: 120-03-12-032

Arkansas

El Dorado

University of Arkansas for Medical Sciences AHEC (South Arkansas) Program

Sponsor: UAMS-Area Health Education Centers
Medical Center of South Arkansas (Union Medical
   Center)
Central Arkansas Veterans Healthcare System
Prgm Director: Stephen P King, MD*
460 West Oak, 3rd Floor East
El Dorado, AR 71730
Tel: 870 881-4450   *Fax:* 870 881-4497
Length: 3 Yrs   *ACGME Approved/Offered Positions:* 15
Program ID: 120-04-21-405

Fort Smith

University of Arkansas for Medical Sciences AHEC (Fort Smith) Program

Sponsor: UAMS-Area Health Education Centers
Sparks Regional Medical Center
Prgm Director: Jimmy D Acklin, MD
AHEC-Family Medical Center
612 South 12th Street
Fort Smith, AR 72901
Tel: 479 785-2431   *Fax:* 479 242-4311
E-mail: csmith@ahecfs.uams.edu
Length: 3 Yrs   *ACGME Approved/Offered Positions:* 24
Program ID: 120-04-21-034

Programs

Jonesboro

University of Arkansas for Medical Sciences AHEC (Northeast) Program

Sponsor: UAMS-Area Health Education Centers
St Bernards Regional Medical Center
Prgm Director: Joe H Stallings, MD
223 East Jackson
Jonesboro, AR 72401
Tel: 870 972-0063   *Fax:* 870 910-0024
E-mail: robin@ahecne.uams.edu
Length: 3 Yrs   *ACGME Approved/Offered Positions:* 18
Program ID: 120-04-21-406

Little Rock

University of Arkansas for Medical Sciences Program

Sponsor: University of Arkansas College of Medicine
UAMS Medical Center
Prgm Director: Daniel A Knight, MD
521 Jack Stephens Drive
Little Rock, AR 72205
Tel: 501 686-6563   *Fax:* 501 686-8421
E-mail: familymedicine@uams.edu
Length: 3 Yrs   *ACGME Approved/Offered Positions:* 18
Program ID: 120-04-21-035

Pine Bluff

University of Arkansas for Medical Sciences AHEC (Pine Bluff) Program

Sponsor: UAMS-Area Health Education Centers
Jefferson Regional Medical Center
Prgm Director: Harvie M Attwood, MD, BS
4010 S Mulberry Street
Pine Bluff, AR 71603
Tel: 870 541-7611   *Fax:* 870 541-7602
E-mail: resdirector@ahecpb.uams.edu
Length: 3 Yrs   *ACGME Approved/Offered Positions:* 30
Program ID: 120-04-11-037

Springdale

University of Arkansas for Medical Sciences AHEC (Northwest) Program

Sponsor: UAMS-Area Health Education Centers
Northwest Medical Center
Washington Regional Medical Center
Prgm Director: F Allan Martin, MD*
Family Medical Center
2907 East Joyce Blvd
Fayetteville, AR 72703
Tel: 479 521-0263   *Fax:* 479 521-8723
E-mail: amartin@ahecnw.uams.edu
Length: 3 Yrs   *ACGME Approved/Offered Positions:* 27
Program ID: 120-04-21-033

Texarkana

University of Arkansas for Medical Sciences AHEC (Southwest) Program

Sponsor: UAMS-Area Health Education Centers
Christus St Michael Health System
Wadley Regional Medical Center (Texarkana, TX)
Prgm Director: Russell Mayo, MD
300 East 6th Street
Texarkana, AR 71854
Tel: 870 779-6080   *Fax:* 870 779-6093
E-mail: gillespiebeckyl@uams.edu
Length: 3 Yrs   *ACGME Approved/Offered Positions:* 21
Program ID: 120-04-21-527

California

Anaheim

Kaiser Permanente Southern California (Anaheim) Program

Sponsor: Kaiser Permanente Southern California
Kaiser Foundation Hospitals (Anaheim)
Prgm Director: Timothy A Munzing, MD
1900 E 4th Street
Santa Ana, CA 92705
Tel: 714 967-4766   *Fax:* 714 967-4548
E-mail: tim.a.munzing@kp.org
Length: 3 Yrs   *ACGME Approved/Offered Positions:* 18
Program ID: 120-05-31-515

Bakersfield

Kern Medical Center Program

Sponsor: Kern Medical Center
Prgm Director: David M Moore, MD
1830 Flower Street
Bakersfield, CA 93305
Tel: 661 326-5050   *Fax:* 661 862-7635
E-mail: mooredavi@kernmedctr.com
Length: 3 Yrs   *ACGME Approved/Offered Positions:* 18
Program ID: 120-05-11-038

Camp Pendleton

Naval Hospital (Camp Pendleton) Program

Sponsor: Naval Hospital (Camp Pendleton)
Prgm Director: John R Holman, MD, MPH
Family Medicine
Box 555191
Camp Pendleton, CA 92055
Tel: 760 725-0406   *Fax:* 760 725-1101
E-mail: john.holman@med.navy.mil
Length: 3 Yrs   *ACGME Approved/Offered Positions:* 36
Program ID: 120-05-12-014
Uniformed Services Program

Chula Vista

Scripps Mercy Hospital (Chula Vista) Program

Sponsor: Scripps Mercy Hospital (Chula Vista)
Prgm Director: Marianne McKennett, MD
435 H Street
CV-112
Chula Vista, CA 91910
Tel: 619 691-7587   *Fax:* 619 691-7120
Length: 3 Yrs   *ACGME Approved/Offered Positions:* 18
Program ID: 120-05-21-632

Colton

Arrowhead Regional Medical Center Program

Sponsor: Arrowhead Regional Medical Center
Prgm Director: Niren A Raval, DO
Family Medicine Department
400 N Pepper Avenue
Colton, CA 92324
Tel: 909 580-6230   *Fax:* 909 580-6308
E-mail: corrosl@armc.sbcounty.gov
Length: 3 Yrs   *ACGME Approved/Offered Positions:* 50
Program ID: 120-05-11-057

Fontana

Kaiser Permanente Southern California (Fontana) Program

Sponsor: Kaiser Permanente Southern California
Kaiser Foundation Hospital (Fontana)
Prgm Director: Kendall G Scott, MD
9961 Sierra Avenue
Fontana, CA 92335
Tel: 909 427-5083   *Fax:* 909 427-5619
Length: 3 Yrs   *ACGME Approved/Offered Positions:* 27
Program ID: 120-05-12-040

French Camp

San Joaquin General Hospital Program

Sponsor: San Joaquin General Hospital
Prgm Director: Ramiro Zuniga, MD*
500 W Hospital Road
French Camp, CA 95231
Tel: 209 468-7102   *Fax:* 209 468-6747
E-mail: rzuniga@sjgh.org
Length: 3 Yrs   *ACGME Approved/Offered Positions:* 21
Program ID: 120-05-31-066

Fresno

University of California (San Francisco)/Fresno Program

Sponsor: UCSF Fresno Medical Education Program
Community Medical Centers (Fresno)
Prgm Director: Ivan Gomez, MD
155 N Fresno Street
Fresno, CA 93701
Tel: 559 499-6450   *Fax:* 559 499-6451
E-mail: family@fresno.ucsf.edu
Length: 3 Yrs   *ACGME Approved/Offered Positions:* 39
Program ID: 120-05-21-041

Glendale

Glendale Adventist Medical Center Program

Sponsor: Glendale Adventist Medical Center
Prgm Director: Janet A Cunningham MD, MBA, MPH
Family Medicine Center, Suite 201
801 South Chevy Chase Drive
Glendale, CA 91205
Tel: 818 500-5594   *Fax:* 818 500-5550
E-mail: MartinAT@ah.org
Length: 3 Yrs   *ACGME Approved/Offered Positions:* 24
Program ID: 120-05-21-372

Hanford

Loma Linda University (Hanford) Rural Program

Sponsor: Loma Linda University Medical Center
Hanford Community Medical Center
Central Valley General Hospital
Prgm Director: Daniel Engeberg, MD
1025 N Douty St, #105
Hanford, CA 93230
Tel: 559 583-2106   *Fax:* 559 583-2120
E-mail: EngebeDL@ah.org
Length: 3 Yrs   *ACGME Approved/Offered Positions:* 12
Program ID: 120-05-13-685

Loma Linda

Loma Linda University Program

Sponsor: Loma Linda University Medical Center
Jerry L Pettis Memorial Veterans Hospital
Prgm Director: Jamie S Osborn, MD
Family Medicine Center
25455 Barton Road, Suite 209-B
Loma Linda, CA 92354
Tel: 909 558-6688   *Fax:* 909 558-6656
E-mail: sreile@llu.edu
Length: 3 Yrs   *ACGME Approved/Offered Positions:* 24
Program ID: 120-05-21-471

Long Beach

Long Beach Memorial Medical Center Program

Sponsor: Long Beach Memorial Medical Center
Prgm Director: Susan Y Melvin, DO
450 East Spring Street, #1
Long Beach, CA 90806
Tel: 562 933-0055   *Fax:* 562 933-0079
E-mail: cneal@memorialcare.org
Length: 3 Yrs   *ACGME Approved/Offered Positions:* 24
Program ID: 120-05-21-044

Los Angeles

Kaiser Permanente Southern California (Los Angeles) Program

Sponsor: Kaiser Permanente Southern California
Kaiser Foundation Hospital (Los Angeles)
Kaiser Permanente Panorama City Medical Center
Prgm Director: Jimmy H Hara, MD
4950 Sunset Boulevard, 4th Floor
Los Angeles, CA 90027
Tel: 323 783-4516   *Fax:* 323 783-4030
Length: 3 Yrs   *ACGME Approved/Offered Positions:* 27
Program ID: 120-05-11-047

UCLA Medical Center Program

Sponsor: UCLA David Geffen School of Medicine/UCLA
    Medical Center
Olive View/UCLA Medical Center
Santa Monica-UCLA Medical Center
Prgm Director: Denise K Sur, MD
1920 Colorado Ave
Santa Monica, CA 90404
Tel: 310 319-4709   *Fax:* 310 453-5106
Length: 3 Yrs   *ACGME Approved/Offered Positions:* 36
Program ID: 120-05-11-049

University of Southern California/California Hospital Medical Center (Los Angeles) Program

Sponsor: California Hospital Medical Center
Prgm Director: Maureen P Strohm, MD
1400 South Grand Ave Suite 101
Los Angeles, CA 90015
Tel: 213 744-0801   *Fax:* 213 741-1434
E-mail: mstrohm@usc.edu
Length: 3 Yrs   *ACGME Approved/Offered Positions:* 18
Program ID: 120-05-21-458

White Memorial Medical Center Program

Sponsor: White Memorial Medical Center
Prgm Director: Luis Samaniego, MD
1720 Cesar E Chavez Avenue
Los Angeles, CA 90033
Tel: 323 260-5789   *Fax:* 323 881-8641
E-mail: wmmcfprp@ah.org
Length: 3 Yrs   *ACGME Approved/Offered Positions:* 21
Program ID: 120-05-21-480

Martinez

Contra Costa County Health Services Program

Sponsor: Contra Costa Regional Medical Center
Prgm Director: Jeremy Fish, MD
2500 Alhambra Avenue
Martinez, CA 94553
Tel: 925 370-5117   *Fax:* 925 370-5052
E-mail: jfish@ccfamilymed.com
Length: 3 Yrs   *ACGME Approved/Offered Positions:* 39
Program ID: 120-05-31-050

Merced

Mercy Medical Center (Merced) Program

Sponsor: Mercy Medical Center Merced
Prgm Director: John Paik-tesch, MD*
Family Medicine Residency Program
315 East 13th Street
Merced, CA 95340
Tel: 209 385-7175   *Fax:* 209 385-7893
Length: 3 Yrs   *ACGME Approved/Offered Positions:* 24
Program ID: 120-05-21-459

Modesto

Stanislaus Residency Program

Sponsor: Stanislaus County Health Services
Doctors Medical Center
Prgm Director: Peter W Broderick, MD, MEd
830 Scenic Drive
Modesto, CA 95350
Tel: 209 576-3528   *Fax:* 209 576-3597
E-mail: madelaine.riel@tenethealth.com
Length: 3 Yrs   *ACGME Approved/Offered Positions:* 27
Program ID: 120-05-11-052

Moreno Valley

Riverside County Regional Medical Center Program

Sponsor: Riverside County Regional Medical Center
Prgm Director: Asma B Jafri, MD
26520 Cactus Avenue
Moreno Valley, CA 92555
Tel: 951 486-5611   *Fax:* 951 486-5620
Length: 3 Yrs   *ACGME Approved/Offered Positions:* 27
Program ID: 120-05-21-421

Northridge

Northridge Hospital Medical Center Program

Sponsor: Northridge Hospital Medical Center
Prgm Director: Pamela M Davis, MD
Northridge Family Practice Center
18406 Roscoe Blvd
Northridge, CA 91325
Tel: 818 993-4054   *Fax:* 818 727-0793
E-mail: pamela.davis@chw.edu
Length: 3 Yrs   *ACGME Approved/Offered Positions:* 21
Program ID: 120-05-11-053

Orange

University of California (Irvine) Program

Sponsor: University of California (Irvine) Medical
    Center
Western Medical Center
Prgm Director: Charles P Vega, MD
Department of Family Medicine
Bldg 200, Rte 81, Suite 512
Orange, CA 92868
Tel: 714 456-8298   *Fax:* 714 456-7984
E-mail: apalega@uci.edu
Length: 3 Yrs   *ACGME Approved/Offered Positions:* 30
Program ID: 120-05-21-042

Pasadena

Kaiser Permanente Southern California (Woodland Hills) Program

Sponsor: Kaiser Permanente Southern California
Kaiser Foundation Hospital (Woodland Hills)
Prgm Director: Ted X O'Connell, MD
5601 De Soto Avenue
North 6, 3rd Floor
Woodland Hills, CA 91365
Tel: 818 719-4828   *Fax:* 818 719-3344
Length: 3 Yrs   *ACGME Approved/Offered Positions:* 18
Program ID: 120-05-21-514

Pomona

Pomona Valley Hospital Medical Center Program

Sponsor: Pomona Valley Hospital Medical Center
Prgm Director: Gregory E Dahlquist, MD
1770 N Orange Grove, Suite 201
Pomona, CA 91767
Tel: 909 469-9493   *Fax:* 909 865-2982
E-mail: greg.dahlquist@pvhmc.org
Length: 3 Yrs   *ACGME Approved/Offered Positions:* 18
Program ID: 120-05-21-610

Redding

Mercy Medical Center (Redding) Program

Sponsor: Mercy Medical Center
Prgm Director: Duane D Bland, MD, BS
2175 Rosaline Avenue
PO Box 496009
Redding, CA 96049
Tel: 530 225-6090   *Fax:* 530 225-6093
E-mail: duane.bland@chw.edu
Length: 3 Yrs   *ACGME Approved/Offered Positions:* 19
Program ID: 120-05-31-054

Riverside

Kaiser Permanente Southern California (Riverside) Program

Sponsor: Kaiser Permanente Southern California
Kaiser Foundation Hospital (Riverside)
Prgm Director: Walter C Morgan PD, MD
10800 Magnolia Avenue RMC-2G
Family Medicine Residency
Riverside, CA 92505
Tel: 951 353-4364   *Fax:* 951 353-3608
Length: 3 Yrs   *ACGME Approved/Offered Positions:* 18
Program ID: 120-05-21-509

Sacramento

Methodist Hospital of Sacramento Program

Sponsor: Methodist Hospital of Sacramento
Mercy General Hospital (Mercy Healthcare Sacramento)
Prgm Director: Amir Sweha, MD
7500 Hospital Drive
Sacramento, CA 95823
Tel: 916 423-6009   *Fax:* 916 688-0225
Length: 3 Yrs   *ACGME Approved/Offered Positions:* 21
Program ID: 120-05-21-564

Sutter Health Program

Sponsor: Sutter Health
Sutter Davis Hospital
Sutter General Hospital
Prgm Director: Marion Leff, MD
1201 Alhambra Blvd, Suite 340
Sacramento, CA 95816
Tel: 916 731-7866   *Fax:* 916 731-7867
E-mail: sutterfmrp@sutterhealth.org
Length: 3 Yrs   *ACGME Approved/Offered Positions:* 18
Program ID: 120-05-31-556

University of California (Davis) Health System Program

Sponsor: University of California (Davis) Health System
University of California (Davis) Medical Center
VA Northern California Health Care System
Prgm Director: Thomas Balsbaugh, MD
Department of Family and Community Medicine
4860 Y Street, Suite 2300
Sacramento, CA 95817
Tel: 916 734-3615   *Fax:* 916 734-5641
Length: 3 Yrs   *ACGME Approved/Offered Positions:* 40
Program ID: 120-05-11-039

Programs

Salinas

Natividad Medical Center Program

Sponsor: Natividad Medical Center
Prgm Director: Gary R Gray, DO
1441 Constitution Blvd, Bldg 300
PO Box 81611
Salinas, CA 93912
Tel: 831 755-4201   *Fax:* 831 755-6315
E-mail: nmcfpres@co.monterey.ca.us
Length: 3 Yrs   *ACGME Approved/Offered Positions:* 24
Program ID: 120-05-21-056

San Diego

University of California (San Diego) Program

Sponsor: University of California (San Diego) Medical Center
Naval Medical Center (San Diego)
Prgm Director: Tyson Ikeda, MD
200 West Arbor Drive, #8809
San Diego, CA 92103
Tel: 619 543-5776   *Fax:* 619 543-5996
E-mail: tikeda@ucsd.edu
Length: 3 Yrs   *ACGME Approved/Offered Positions:* 21
Program ID: 120-05-21-058

San Francisco

University of California (San Francisco) Program

Sponsor: University of California (San Francisco) School of Medicine
San Francisco General Hospital Medical Center
Prgm Director: Teresa J Villela, MD
Building 80-83
1001 Potrero Avenue
San Francisco, CA 94110
Tel: 415 206-6881   *Fax:* 415 206-8387
E-mail: sfghfcm@fcm.ucsf.edu
Length: 3 Yrs   *ACGME Approved/Offered Positions:* 39
Program ID: 120-05-11-059

San Jose

San Jose-O'Connor Hospital Program

Sponsor: O'Connor Hospital
Prgm Director: Robert M Norman, MD
455 O'Connor Drive #250
San Jose, CA 95128
Tel: 408 283-7767   *Fax:* 408 283-7608
E-mail: MichaelStevens@dochs.org
Length: 3 Yrs   *ACGME Approved/Offered Positions:* 24
Program ID: 120-05-12-684

Santa Rose

Santa Rosa Consortium/University of California (San Francisco) Program

Sponsor: Santa Rosa Consortium
Sutter Medical Center of Santa Rosa
Prgm Director: Colin P Kopes-Kerr, MD, MPH
3324 Chanate Road
Santa Rosa, CA 95404
Tel: 707 576-4081   *Fax:* 707 576-4087
E-mail: KopesC@sutterhealth.org
Length: 3 Yrs   *ACGME Approved/Offered Positions:* 36
Program ID: 120-05-11-065

Torrance

Los Angeles County-Harbor-UCLA Medical Center Program

Sponsor: Los Angeles County-Harbor-UCLA Medical Center
Prgm Director: Daniel B Castro, MD
Department of Family Medicine
1403 W Lomita Boulevard, 2nd floor
Harbor City, CA 90710
Tel: 310 534-6221   *Fax:* 310 326-7205
Length: 3 Yrs   *ACGME Approved/Offered Positions:* 36
Program ID: 120-05-21-478

Travis AFB

David Grant Medical Center Program

Sponsor: David Grant Medical Center
Prgm Director: Kathryn K Holder, MD
60th Medical Operations Sqd SGOF
101 Bodin Circle
Travis AFB, CA 94535
Tel: 707 423-5349   *Fax:* 707 423-9193
Length: 3 Yrs   *ACGME Approved/Offered Positions:* 48
Program ID: 120-05-11-001
Uniformed Services Program

Ventura

Ventura County Medical Center Program

Sponsor: Ventura County Medical Center
Prgm Director: David Araujo, MD*
Medical Education Office
3291 Loma Vista Road
Ventura, CA 93003
Tel: 805 652-6228   *Fax:* 805 652-6606
Length: 3 Yrs   *ACGME Approved/Offered Positions:* 39
Program ID: 120-05-11-068

Whittier

Presbyterian Intercommunity Hospital Program

Sponsor: Presbyterian Intercommunity Hospital
Prgm Director: Virag Y Shah, MD
12291 Washington Blvd
Suite 500
Whittier, CA 90606
Tel: 562 698-0811   *Fax:* 562 698-3541
E-mail: virayshah@yahoo.com
Length: 3 Yrs   *ACGME Approved/Offered Positions:* 21
Program ID: 120-05-21-352

Colorado

Aurora

University of Colorado Denver (HealthONE Rose Medical Center) Program

Sponsor: University of Colorado Denver School of Medicine
HealthONE Rose Medical Center
Prgm Director: Brian S Bacak, MD
4545 East 9th Avenue, Suite 010
Denver, CO 80220
Tel: 303 584-7900
E-mail: pam.sullivan@rfmr.com
Length: 3 Yrs   *ACGME Approved/Offered Positions:* 18
Program ID: 120-07-21-071

University of Colorado Denver (University Hospital) Program

Sponsor: University of Colorado Denver School of Medicine
Denver Health Medical Center
University of Colorado Hospital
Prgm Director: Daniel J Burke, MD
3055 Roslyn Street, Suite 100
Denver, CO 80238
Tel: 720 848-9096   *Fax:* 720 848-9050
E-mail: alice.skram@uchsc.edu
Length: 3 Yrs   *ACGME Approved/Offered Positions:* 24
Program ID: 120-07-21-619

Denver

Exempla St Joseph Hospital Program

Sponsor: Exempla St Joseph Hospital
Prgm Director: Warren G Thompson, MD
2005 Franklin Street
Midtown II, Suite 350
Denver, CO 80205
Tel: 303 318-2008   *Fax:* 303 318-2003
E-mail: thompsong@exempla.org
Length: 3 Yrs   *ACGME Approved/Offered Positions:* 24
Program ID: 120-07-12-070

Englewood

University of Colorado Denver (HealthONE Swedish Medical Center) Program

Sponsor: University of Colorado Denver School of Medicine
HealthONE Swedish Medical Center
Prgm Director: Bradford T Winslow, MD
191 E Orchard Road, #200
Littleton, CO 80121
Tel: 303 795-5247   *Fax:* 303 795-2912
E-mail: brad.winslow@sfmr.com
Length: 3 Yrs   *ACGME Approved/Offered Positions:* 18
Program ID: 120-07-21-544

Fort Collins

Fort Collins Family Medicine Program

Sponsor: Poudre Valley Hospital
Prgm Director: Austin G Bailey Jr, MD
Fort Collins Family Medicine Residency Program
1025 Pennock Place
Fort Collins, CO 80524
Tel: 970 495-8803   *Fax:* 970 495-8891
E-mail: rrw@pvhs.org
Length: 3 Yrs   *ACGME Approved/Offered Positions:* 18
Program ID: 120-07-31-072

Grand Junction

St Mary's Hospital and Medical Center Program

Sponsor: St Mary's Hospital and Medical Center
Prgm Director: Sherman Straw, MD*
1160 Patterson Road
Grand Junction, CO 81506
Tel: 970 244-2195   *Fax:* 970 244-7522
E-mail: joan.cox@stmarygj.org
Length: 3 Yrs   *ACGME Approved/Offered Positions:* 24
Program ID: 120-07-31-073

Greeley

North Colorado Medical Center Program

Sponsor: North Colorado Medical Center
Prgm Director: Mark E Wallace, MD, MPH
Residency Training Program
1600 23rd Avenue
Greeley, CO 80634
Tel: 970 346-2855   *Fax:* 970 346-2828
E-mail: residency@bannerhealth.com
Length: 3 Yrs   *ACGME Approved/Offered Positions:* 24
Program ID: 120-07-11-074

Note: * indicates a newly appointed program director

Pueblo

Southern Colorado Family Medicine Program

Sponsor: St Mary-Corwin Medical Center
Prgm Director: Charles H Raye, MD
1008 Minnequa Avenue
Suite 1124
Pueblo, CO 81004
Tel: 719 557-5872   *Fax:* 719 557-4780
E-mail: nhamilto@centura.org
Length: 3 Yrs   *ACGME Approved/Offered Positions:* 18
Program ID: 120-07-21-075

Westminster

St Anthony Hospital Program

Sponsor: St Anthony Hospital North
St Anthony Hospital Central
Prgm Director: Ned R Nixon Jr, MD*
2551 West 84th Avenue
Westminster, CO 80031
Tel: 303 430-6002   *Fax:* 303 430-6001
E-mail: nednixon@centura.org
Length: 3 Yrs   *ACGME Approved/Offered Positions:* 27
Program ID: 120-07-12-069

Wray

North Colorado Medical Center Rural Program

Sponsor: North Colorado Medical Center
Wray Community District Hospital
Prgm Director: Mark E Wallace, MD, MPH
1600 23rd Avenue
Greeley, CO 80634
Tel: 970 346-2855   *Fax:* 970 346-2828
E-mail: residency@bannerhealth.com
Length: 3 Yrs   *ACGME Approved/Offered Positions:* 3
Program ID: 120-07-31-524

Connecticut

Hartford

University of Connecticut Program

Sponsor: University of Connecticut School of Medicine
St Francis Hospital and Medical Center
Prgm Director: Eugene Orientale Jr, MD
Family Medicine at Asylum Hill
99 Woodland Street
Hartford, CT 06105
Tel: 860 714-6738   *Fax:* 860 714-8079
E-mail: wwiggles@stfranciscare.org
Length: 3 Yrs   *ACGME Approved/Offered Positions:* 20
Program ID: 120-08-21-076

Middletown

Middlesex Hospital Program

Sponsor: Middlesex Hospital
Prgm Director: Michael A Stehney, MD, MPH
90 South Main Street
Middletown, CT 06457
Tel: 860 358-6418   *Fax:* 860 358-6650
Length: 3 Yrs   *ACGME Approved/Offered Positions:* 24
Program ID: 120-08-21-077

Stamford

Stamford Hospital/Columbia University College of Physicians and Surgeons Program

Sponsor: Stamford Hospital
Prgm Director: Joseph V Connelly, MD
30 Shelburne Road
PO Box 9317
Stamford, CT 06904
Tel: 203 276-2270   *Fax:* 203 276-2413
Length: 3 Yrs   *ACGME Approved/Offered Positions:* 15
Program ID: 120-08-11-078

Delaware

Wilmington

Christiana Care Health Services Program

Sponsor: Christiana Care Health Services Inc
Prgm Director: Lisa Maxwell, MD*
Family Medicine Center
1401 Foulk Road, Ste 100
Wilmington, DE 19803
Tel: 302 477-3318   *Fax:* 302 477-3162
Length: 3 Yrs   *ACGME Approved/Offered Positions:* 24
Program ID: 120-09-11-079

St Francis Hospital Program

Sponsor: St Francis Hospital
Prgm Director: Paul M Eberts, MD
Medical Services Bldg, Level II
PO Box 2500
Wilmington, DE 19805
Tel: 302 575-8046   *Fax:* 302 575-8050
Length: 3 Yrs   *ACGME Approved/Offered Positions:* 18
Program ID: 120-09-21-415

District of Columbia

Washington

Howard University Program

Sponsor: Howard University Hospital
Prgm Director: Babafemi Adenuga, MD
2139 Georgia Avenue, NW
Suite 3B
Washington, DC 20001
Tel: 202 865-1452   *Fax:* 202 865-7202
E-mail: atgordon@huhosp.org
Length: 3 Yrs   *ACGME Approved/Offered Positions:* 18
Program ID: 120-10-21-081

Providence Hospital/Georgetown University Hospital Program

Sponsor: Providence Hospital
Prgm Director: Patricia Evans, MD, MA
4151 Bladensburg Road
Colmar Manor, MD 20722
Tel: 301 699-7707   *Fax:* 301 779-9001
E-mail: wallacab@georgetown.edu
Length: 3 Yrs   *ACGME Approved/Offered Positions:* 21
Program ID: 120-10-21-080

Florida

Clearwater

University of South Florida (Morton Plant Mease Health Care) Program

Sponsor: University of South Florida College of Medicine
Morton Plant Hospital
Prgm Director: Sean T Bryan, MD*
807 N Myrtle Avenue
Clearwater, FL 33755
Tel: 727 467-2501   *Fax:* 727 467-2471
E-mail: Sean.Bryan@baycare.org
Length: 3 Yrs   *ACGME Approved/Offered Positions:* 24
Program ID: 120-11-21-625

Daytona Beach

Halifax Medical Center Program

Sponsor: Halifax Medical Center
Prgm Director: Edwin E Prevatte Jr, MD
PO Box 2830
303 N Clyde Morris Blvd
Daytona Beach, FL 32120
Tel: 386 254-4167   *Fax:* 386 258-4867
E-mail: residency.coordinator@halifax.org
Length: 3 Yrs   *ACGME Approved/Offered Positions:* 24
Program ID: 120-11-11-083

Eglin AFB

Headquarters Air Armament Center (AFMC) Program

Sponsor: US Air Force Regional Hospital
Prgm Director: James Haynes, MD, BS
96 MDOS/SGOF
307 Boatner Road, Suite 114
Eglin AFB, FL 32542
Tel: 850 883-9360   *Fax:* 850 883-8192
E-mail: james.haynes@eglin.af.mil
Length: 3 Yrs   *ACGME Approved/Offered Positions:* 30
Program ID: 120-11-12-003
Uniformed Services Program

Gainesville

University of Florida Program

Sponsor: University of Florida College of Medicine
Shands at AGH
Prgm Director: Karen L Hall, MD
Shands at AGH
625 SW 4th Avenue
Gainesville, FL 32601
Tel: 352 392-4541   *Fax:* 352 392-7766
E-mail: zinkel@ufl.edu
Length: 3 Yrs   *ACGME Approved/Offered Positions:* 24
Program ID: 120-11-21-084

Jacksonville

College of Medicine, Mayo Clinic (Jacksonville) Program

Sponsor: College of Medicine, Mayo Clinic
Mayo Clinic (Jacksonville)
Mayo Clinic Florida Hospital
Prgm Director: Walter Taylor, MD
4500 San Pablo Rd
Jacksonville, FL 32224
Tel: 904 953-0427   *Fax:* 904 953-0430
E-mail: sayward.jennifer@mayo.edu
Length: 3 Yrs   *ACGME Approved/Offered Positions:* 18
Program ID: 120-11-21-545

Programs

Naval Hospital (Jacksonville) Program

Sponsor: Naval Hospital (Jacksonville)
Prgm Director: Richard W Sams II, MD, MA
Department of Family Medicine
2080 Child Street
Jacksonville, FL 32214
Tel: 904 542-7970 *Fax:* 904 542-7836
E-mail: richard.sams@med.navy.mil
Length: 3 Yrs *ACGME Approved/Offered Positions:* 39
Program ID: 120-11-21-015
Uniformed Services Program

St Vincent's Medical Center Program

Sponsor: St Vincent's Medical Center
Prgm Director: David A McInnes, MD, MEd
2627 Riverside Avenue
Jacksonville, FL 32204
Tel: 904 308-7374 *Fax:* 904 308-2998
E-mail: Fammed@fdn.com
Length: 3 Yrs *ACGME Approved/Offered Positions:* 30
Program ID: 120-11-11-085

Miami

Jackson Memorial Hospital/Jackson Health System Program

Sponsor: Jackson Memorial Hospital/Jackson Health
  System
Prgm Director: Penny Tenzer, MD
Department of Family Medicine & Community Health
PO Box 016700 (R-700)
Miami, FL 33101
Tel: 305 243-2951 *Fax:* 305 243-1251
Length: 3 Yrs *ACGME Approved/Offered Positions:* 24
Program ID: 120-11-21-087

Orlando

Florida Hospital Medical Center Program

Sponsor: Florida Hospital Medical Center
Prgm Director: Kristen D Gray, MD
2501 N Orange Avenue, Suite 235
Orlando, FL 32804
Tel: 407 303-2814 *Fax:* 407 303-2885
E-mail: fh.familymedicinemd@flhosp.org
Length: 3 Yrs *ACGME Approved/Offered Positions:* 48
Program ID: 120-11-11-088

Pensacola

Naval Hospital (Pensacola) Program

Sponsor: Naval Hospital (Pensacola)
Prgm Director: Timothy F Mott, MD*
Code 55
6000 Highway 98 West
Pensacola, FL 32512
Tel: 850 505-6472 *Fax:* 850 505-6501
Length: 3 Yrs *ACGME Approved/Offered Positions:* 21
Program ID: 120-11-12-016
Uniformed Services Program

St. Petersburg

Bayfront Medical Center Program

Sponsor: Bayfront Medical Center
Prgm Director: David O Parrish, MD
700 Sixth Street South
St Petersburg, FL 33701
Tel: 727 893-6156 *Fax:* 727 553-7340
E-mail: fp.web@bayfront.org
Length: 3 Yrs *ACGME Approved/Offered Positions:* 24
Program ID: 120-11-11-090

Tallahassee

Tallahassee Family Medicine Program

Sponsor: Tallahassee Memorial HealthCare
Prgm Director: Donald A Zorn, MD
Family Medicine Residency Program
1301 Hodges Drive
Tallahassee, FL 32308
Tel: 850 431-3452 *Fax:* 850 431-6403
Length: 3 Yrs *ACGME Approved/Offered Positions:* 30
Program ID: 120-11-11-086

Georgia

Albany

Phoebe Putney Memorial Hospital (Southwest Georgia) Program

Sponsor: Phoebe Putney Memorial Hospital
Prgm Director: George T Fredrick, MD*
2336 Dawson Road, Suite 2200
Albany, GA 31707
Tel: 229 312-8797
Length: 3 Yrs *ACGME Approved/Offered Positions:* 15
Program ID: 120-12-21-525

Atlanta

Atlanta Medical Center Program

Sponsor: Atlanta Medical Center
Prgm Director: Frank R Don Diego, MD
1000 Corporate Center Drive
Suite 200
Morrow, GA 30260
Tel: 770 968-6460 *Fax:* 770 968-6465
E-mail: tammy.hamm@tenethealth.com
Length: 3 Yrs *ACGME Approved/Offered Positions:* 18
Program ID: 120-12-21-536

Emory University Program

Sponsor: Emory University School of Medicine
Emory Johns Creek Hospital
Grady Health System
Prgm Director: Eddie Needham, MD
4555 North Shallowford Road
Suite 100
Atlanta, GA 30338
Tel: 404 727-8868 *Fax:* 404 727-1174
E-mail: jneedha@learnlink.emory.edu
Length: 3 Yrs *ACGME Approved/Offered Positions:* 30
Program ID: 120-12-21-562

Morehouse School of Medicine Program

Sponsor: Morehouse School of Medicine
Grady Health System
Tenet-South Fulton Medical Center
Prgm Director: Folashade Omole, MD
720 Westview Drive, SW
Atlanta, GA 30310
Tel: 404 756-1230 *Fax:* 404 756-1206
E-mail: cclarke@msm.edu
Length: 3 Yrs *ACGME Approved/Offered Positions:* 15
Program ID: 120-12-21-439

Augusta

Medical College of Georgia Program

Sponsor: Medical College of Georgia
Prgm Director: Paul D Forney, MD
Department of Family Medicine
HB3020
Augusta, GA 30912
Tel: 706 721-3157 *Fax:* 706 721-6123
E-mail: residency@mail.mcg.edu
Length: 3 Yrs *ACGME Approved/Offered Positions:* 24
Program ID: 120-12-21-091

Columbus

The Medical Center Program (Columbus)

Sponsor: The Medical Center Inc
Prgm Director: John R Bucholtz, DO
1900 10th Avenue
Suite 100
Columbus, GA 31902
Tel: 706 571-1430 *Fax:* 706 571-1604
E-mail: john.bucholtz@crhs.net
Length: 3 Yrs *ACGME Approved/Offered Positions:* 36
Program ID: 120-12-11-092

Fort Benning

Martin Army Community Hospital Program

Sponsor: Martin Army Community Hospital
Prgm Director: Mark L Higdon, DO
MEDDAC (Attn: MCXB-FRT)
7950 Martin Loop
Fort Benning, GA 31905
Tel: 706 544-1556 *Fax:* 706 544-3234
E-mail: mark.higdon@us.army.mil
Length: 3 Yrs *ACGME Approved/Offered Positions:* 21
Program ID: 120-12-11-008
Uniformed Services Program

Fort Gordon

Dwight David Eisenhower Army Medical Center Program

Sponsor: Dwight David Eisenhower Army Medical
  Center
Prgm Director: Michael S Friedman, MD
Dept of Family & Community Medicine
Dwight David Eisenhower Army Medical Center
Fort Gordon, GA 30905
Tel: 706 787-9358 *Fax:* 706 787-9356
E-mail: mike.friedman@us.army.mil
Length: 3 Yrs *ACGME Approved/Offered Positions:* 30
Program ID: 120-12-21-009
Uniformed Services Program

Macon

Mercer University School of Medicine Program

Sponsor: Medical Center of Central Georgia
Prgm Director: Roberta J Weintraut, MD
Family Health Center
3780 Eisenhower Parkway
Macon, GA 31206
Tel: 478 633-5550 *Fax:* 478 784-5496
E-mail: fp.residency@mccg.edu
Length: 3 Yrs *ACGME Approved/Offered Positions:* 24
Program ID: 120-12-12-093

Rome

Floyd Medical Center Program

Sponsor: Floyd Medical Center
Prgm Director: Randy G Robinson, MD
304 Shorter Ave
Suite 201
Rome, GA 30165
Tel: 706 509-3358 *Fax:* 706 509-4709
E-mail: rrobinson@floyd.org
Length: 3 Yrs *ACGME Approved/Offered Positions:* 21
Program ID: 120-12-31-094

Note: * indicates a newly appointed program director

Savannah

Mercer University School of Medicine (Savannah) Program

Sponsor: Memorial Health-University Medical Center
Prgm Director: Robert Pallay, MD
Family Medicine
1107 East 66th Street
Savannah, GA 31404
Tel: 912 350-3785   *Fax:* 912 350-5118
E-mail: pallaro1@memorialhealth.com
Length: 3 Yrs   *ACGME Approved/Offered Positions:* 18
Program ID: 120-12-11-095

Waycross

Medical College of Georgia/Satilla Regional Medical Center Program

Sponsor: Medical College of Georgia
Satilla Regional Medical Center
Prgm Director: Paul D Forney, MD
Department of Family Medicine
1120 15th Street
Augusta, GA 30912
Tel: 706 721-4675   *Fax:* 706 721-6123
E-mail: residency@satilla.org
Length: 3 Yrs   *ACGME Approved/Offered Positions:* 6
Program ID: 120-12-21-637

Hawaii

Tripler AMC

Tripler Army Medical Center Program

Sponsor: Tripler Army Medical Center
Prgm Director: Robert Oh, MD, MPH
Attn: MCHK-FMR (Residency Director)
1 Jarrett White Road
Honolulu, HI 96859
Tel: 808 433-1117   *Fax:* 808 433-1153
E-mail: robert.oh@us.army.mil
Length: 3 Yrs   *ACGME Approved/Offered Positions:* 24
Program ID: 120-14-21-502
Uniformed Services Program

Wahiawa

University of Hawaii Program

Sponsor: University of Hawaii John A Burns School of Medicine
Wahiawa General Hospital
Prgm Director: Lee Buenconsejo-Lum, MD
A Family Practice Clinic
95-390 Kuahelani Avenue
Mililani, HI 96789
Tel: 808 627-3230   *Fax:* 808 627-3265
E-mail: lbuencon@hawaii.edu
Length: 3 Yrs   *ACGME Approved/Offered Positions:* 18
Program ID: 120-14-21-541

Idaho

Boise

Family Medicine Residency of Idaho Program

Sponsor: Family Medicine Residency of Idaho
St Alphonsus Regional Medical Center
St Luke's Regional Medical Center
Prgm Director: Ted Epperly, MD
777 North Raymond Street
Boise, ID 83704
Tel: 208 367-6040   *Fax:* 208 367-6123
E-mail: info@fmridaho.org
Length: 3 Yrs   *ACGME Approved/Offered Positions:* 30
Program ID: 120-15-11-097

Caldwell

Family Medicine Residency of Idaho Rural Program

Sponsor: Family Medicine Residency of Idaho
West Valley Medical Center
Saint Alphonsus Medical Group
St Luke's Regional Medical Center
Prgm Director: Ted D Epperly, MD
777 North Raymond Street
Boise, ID 83704
Tel: 208 367-6040   *Fax:* 208 367-6123
E-mail: info@fmridaho.org
Length: 3 Yrs   *ACGME Approved/Offered Positions:* 6
Program ID: 120-15-21-588

Pocatello

Idaho State University Program

Sponsor: Idaho State University
Portneuf Regional Medical Center
Prgm Director: Jonathan Cree, MD, MA
Department of Family Medicine
465 Memorial Drive
Pocatello, ID 83201
Tel: 208 282-3253   *Fax:* 208 282-4818
E-mail: fammed@fmed.isu.edu
Length: 3 Yrs   *ACGME Approved/Offered Positions:* 18
Program ID: 120-15-21-521

Illinois

Aurora

Rush University Medical Center/Copley Memorial Hospital Program

Sponsor: Rush University Medical Center
Rush-Copley Medical Center
Prgm Director: Carrie Nelson, MD, MS
2020 Ogden Avenue, Suite 325
Aurora, IL 60504
Tel: 630 898-3635   *Fax:* 630 375-2812
E-mail: carrie_e_nelson@rsh.net
Length: 3 Yrs   *ACGME Approved/Offered Positions:* 12
Program ID: 120-16-21-604

Belleville

St Louis University School of Medicine (Belleville) Program

Sponsor: St Louis University School of Medicine
St Elizabeth's Hospital
Prgm Director: E Charles Robacker, MD
180 South Third Street, Suite 400
Belleville, IL 62220
Tel: 618 233-7880   *Fax:* 618 222-4792
Length: 3 Yrs   *ACGME Approved/Offered Positions:* 42
Program ID: 120-16-21-427

Berwyn

MacNeal Hospital Program

Sponsor: MacNeal Hospital
Prgm Director: Donna Lawlor, MD
3231 South Euclid Avenue
5th Floor
Berwyn, IL 60402
Tel: 708 783-3094   *Fax:* 708 783-3656
E-mail: fammed@macneal.com
Length: 3 Yrs   *ACGME Approved/Offered Positions:* 36
Program ID: 120-16-11-098

Carbondale

Southern Illinois University (Carbondale) Program

Sponsor: Southern Illinois University School of Medicine
Memorial Hospital of Carbondale
Prgm Director: Penelope K Tippy, MD
305 West Jackson Street, Suite 200
Carbondale, IL 62901
Tel: 618 536-6621   *Fax:* 618 453-1102
Length: 3 Yrs   *ACGME Approved/Offered Positions:* 18
Program ID: 120-16-11-099

Chicago

Jackson Park Hospital Program

Sponsor: Jackson Park Hospital
Prgm Director: Lakshmi P Dodda, MD
7501 Stony Island Avenue
Chicago, IL 60649
Tel: 773 947-7310   *Fax:* 773 947-7721
Length: 3 Yrs   *ACGME Approved/Offered Positions:* 15
Program ID: 120-16-12-363

Mount Sinai Hospital Medical Center of Chicago Program

Sponsor: Mount Sinai Hospital Medical Center of Chicago
Prgm Director: Ihab Aziz, MD
Dept of Family Medicine & Community Health
California Avenue at 15th Street
Chicago, IL 60608
Tel: 773 257-6025   *Fax:* 773 257-6045
E-mail: azii@sinai.org
Length: 3 Yrs   *ACGME Approved/Offered Positions:* 18
Program ID: 120-16-31-618

Resurrection Medical Center Program

Sponsor: Resurrection Medical Center
Prgm Director: Timothy R McCurry, MD
7447 W Talcott Avenue
Suite 182
Chicago, IL 60631
Tel: 773 990-7625   *Fax:* 773 594-7975
Length: 3 Yrs   *ACGME Approved/Offered Positions:* 18
Program ID: 120-16-11-102

Saints Mary and Elizabeth Medical Center Program

Sponsor: Saints Mary and Elizabeth Medical Center
Prgm Director: Michael H Friedman, MD
1431 N Western Ave
Suite 406
Chicago, IL 60622
Tel: 312 633-5842   *Fax:* 312 633-5936
E-mail: smefmr@reshealthcare.org
Length: 3 Yrs   *ACGME Approved/Offered Positions:* 36
Program ID: 120-16-12-693

St Joseph Hospital Program

Sponsor: St Joseph Hospital
Prgm Director: Luis T Garcia, MD
2900 North Lake Shore Drive
Chicago, IL 60657
Tel: 773 665-3300   *Fax:* 773 665-3228
Length: 3 Yrs   *ACGME Approved/Offered Positions:* 18
Program ID: 120-16-11-103

Swedish Covenant Hospital Program

Sponsor: Swedish Covenant Hospital
Prgm Director: Walten I Baba, MD, PhD
5145 North California Avenue
Chicago, IL 60625
Tel: 773 989-3808   *Fax:* 773 989-1648
E-mail: meded@schosp.org
Length: 3 Yrs   *ACGME Approved/Offered Positions:* 19
Program ID: 120-16-31-106

Programs

University of Illinois College of Medicine at Chicago Program

Sponsor: University of Illinois College of Medicine at Chicago
University of Illinois Hospital and Clinics
Prgm Director: Mark C Potter, MD
Dept of Family Medicine Residency (M/C 663)
1919 West Taylor Street
Chicago, IL 60612
Tel: 312 355-1706   *Fax:* 312 996-2579
Length: 3 Yrs   *ACGME Approved/Offered Positions:* 18
Program ID: 120-16-21-488

University of Illinois College of Medicine at Chicago/Advocate Illinois Masonic Med Ctr Program

Sponsor: University of Illinois College of Medicine at Chicago
Advocate Illinois Masonic Medical Center
Prgm Director: Margaret Wiedmann, MD
Family Medicine Residency Program
836 West Wellington Avenue
Chicago, IL 60657
Tel: 773 296-8248   *Fax:* 773 296-8249
E-mail: ILMasonicFPR@advocatehealth.com
Length: 3 Yrs   *ACGME Approved/Offered Positions:* 24
Program ID: 120-16-21-467

Decatur

Southern Illinois University (Decatur) Program

Sponsor: Southern Illinois University School of Medicine
Decatur Memorial Hospital
Prgm Director: John G Bradley, MD
250 West Kenwood Avenue
Decatur, IL 62526
Tel: 217 872-0850   *Fax:* 217 872-0851
E-mail: decaturfpinfo@siumed.edu
Length: 3 Yrs   *ACGME Approved/Offered Positions:* 15
Program ID: 120-16-21-354

Evanston

McGaw Medical Center of Northwestern University (Evanston) Program

Sponsor: McGaw Medical Center of Northwestern University
Evanston Hospital
Glenbrook Hospital
Prgm Director: David C Holub, MD*
2050 Pfingsten Road, Suite 200
Glenview, IL 60026
Tel: 847 657-1820   *Fax:* 847 657-1823
Length: 3 Yrs   *ACGME Approved/Offered Positions:* 15
Program ID: 120-16-21-654

Hinsdale

Adventist Hinsdale Hospital Program

Sponsor: Adventist Hinsdale Hospital
Prgm Director: Clara L Carls, DO
135 North Oak Street
Hinsdale, IL 60521
Tel: 630 856-8950   *Fax:* 630 856-8923
Length: 3 Yrs   *ACGME Approved/Offered Positions:* 27
Program ID: 120-16-21-109

LaGrange

Adventist LaGrange Memorial Hospital Program

Sponsor: Adventist La Grange Memorial Hospital
Prgm Director: William J Nelson, MD
Family Medicine Residency
5101 S Willow Springs Road
La Grange, IL 60525
Tel: 708 245-8900   *Fax:* 708 245-5615
Length: 3 Yrs   *ACGME Approved/Offered Positions:* 21
Program ID: 120-16-11-110

Maywood

Loyola University/Cook County Hospital Program

Sponsor: Loyola University Medical Center
John H Stroger Hospital of Cook County
Provident Hospital of Cook County
Prgm Director: Gail Y Floyd, MD
Department of Family Medicine
500 E 51st Street, 7th Floor
Chicago, IL 60615
Tel: 312 572-2643   *Fax:* 312 572-2669
E-mail: gyfloyd@msn.com
Length: 3 Yrs   *ACGME Approved/Offered Positions:* 36
Program ID: 120-16-11-100

Oak Lawn

Advocate Christ Medical Center Program

Sponsor: Advocate Christ Medical Center
Prgm Director: Stephen G Bennett, MD
4140 Southwest Highway
Hometown, IL 60456
Tel: 708 857-5905   *Fax:* 708 422-9535
E-mail: stephen.bennett@advocatehealth.com
Length: 3 Yrs   *ACGME Approved/Offered Positions:* 24
Program ID: 120-16-21-364

Oak Park

West Suburban Medical Center Program

Sponsor: West Suburban Medical Center
Prgm Director: Scott Levin A, MD
Family Medicine Center
1 Erie Court, Suite 4110 Professional Office Bldg
Oak Park, IL 60302
Tel: 708 763-2369   *Fax:* 708 763-2162
E-mail: westsubfmresidencyprogram@reshealthcare.org
Length: 3 Yrs   *ACGME Approved/Offered Positions:* 24
Program ID: 120-16-31-112

Park Ridge

Advocate Lutheran General Hospital Program

Sponsor: Advocate Lutheran General Hospital
Prgm Director: Judith A Gravdal, MD
1775 Dempster Street, 6 South
Park Ridge, IL 60068
Tel: 847 723-7979   *Fax:* 847 723-5615
Length: 3 Yrs   *ACGME Approved/Offered Positions:* 27
Program ID: 120-16-11-107

Peoria

University of Illinois College of Medicine at Peoria Program

Sponsor: University of Illinois College of Medicine at Peoria
Methodist Medical Center of Illinois
Prgm Director: Thomas B Golemon, MD
Family Medical Center
815 Main Street, Suite C
Peoria, IL 61602
Tel: 309 672-5908   *Fax:* 309 672-4790
E-mail: tgleason@mmci.org
Length: 3 Yrs   *ACGME Approved/Offered Positions:* 30
Program ID: 120-16-11-113

Quincy

Southern Illinois University (Quincy) Program

Sponsor: Southern Illinois University School of Medicine
Blessing Hospital
Prgm Director: Thomas H Miller, MD
612 N 11th Street, Suite B
Quincy, IL 62301
Tel: 217 224-8957   *Fax:* 217 224-7950
Length: 3 Yrs   *ACGME Approved/Offered Positions:* 18
Program ID: 120-16-21-365

Rockford

University of Illinois College of Medicine (Rockford) Rural Program

Sponsor: University of Illinois College of Medicine at Rockford
Katherine Shaw Bethea Hospital
Swedish American Hospital
Prgm Director: Farion R Williams, MD
1221 East State Street
Rockford, IL 61101
Tel: 815 972-1030   *Fax:* 815 972-1092
E-mail: dixonrtt@ksbhospital.com
Length: 3 Yrs   *ACGME Approved/Offered Positions:* 6
Program ID: 120-16-11-675

University of Illinois College of Medicine at Rockford Program

Sponsor: University of Illinois College of Medicine at Rockford
Swedish American Hospital
Prgm Director: Richard Londo, MD*
1221 East State Street
Rockford, IL 61104
Tel: 815 972-1000
E-mail: rlondo@uic.edu
Length: 3 Yrs   *ACGME Approved/Offered Positions:* 27
Program ID: 120-16-31-115

Springfield

Southern Illinois University Program

Sponsor: Southern Illinois University School of Medicine
Memorial Medical Center
St John's Hospital
Prgm Director: Janet R Albers, MD
520 N 4th Street
PO Box 19670
Springfield, IL 62794
Tel: 217 757-8197   *Fax:* 217 747-1351
Length: 3 Yrs   *ACGME Approved/Offered Positions:* 24
Program ID: 120-16-21-117

Urbana

Carle Foundation Hospital Program

Sponsor: Carle Foundation Hospital
Prgm Director: Bharat Gopal, MD
602 West University Avenue
South Clinic 2
Urbana, IL 61801
Tel: 217 383-5798
E-mail: fmrp@carle.com
Length: 3 Yrs   *ACGME Approved/Offered Positions:* 15
Program ID: 120-16-21-492

Note: * indicates a newly appointed program director

Indiana

Evansville

Deaconess Hospital Program
Sponsor: Deaconess Hospital
Prgm Director: Kim A Volz, MD
Wallace M Adye Center
515 Read Street
Evansville, IN 47710
Tel: 812 450-5027   *Fax:* 812 450-5052
E-mail: residents@deaconess.com
Length: 3 Yrs   *ACGME Approved/Offered Positions:* 18
Program ID: 120-17-21-119

Fort Wayne

Fort Wayne Medical Education Program
Sponsor: Fort Wayne Medical Education Program
Lutheran Hospital of Indiana
Parkview Memorial Hospital
St Joseph Hospital
Prgm Director: Brenda S O'Hara, MD
750 Broadway, Suite 250
Fort Wayne, IN 46802
Tel: 260 422-6573   *Fax:* 260 423-6621
E-mail: Hein@fwmep.edu
Length: 3 Yrs   *ACGME Approved/Offered Positions:* 30
Program ID: 120-17-21-121

Indianapolis

Community Hospitals of Indianapolis Program
Sponsor: Community Hospitals of Indianapolis
Community Hospital North
Prgm Director: Diana Burtea, MD
10122 East 10th Street, Suite 100
Indianapolis, IN 46229
Tel: 317 355-5829   *Fax:* 317 898-9760
E-mail: fpres@ecommunity.com
Length: 3 Yrs   *ACGME Approved/Offered Positions:* 21
Program ID: 120-17-11-123

Indiana University School of Medicine Program
Sponsor: Indiana University School of Medicine
Clarian Methodist Hospital of Indiana
Prgm Director: Sharron P Grannis, MD
1520 North Senate Avenue
Indianapolis, IN 46202
Tel: 317 962-1044   *Fax:* 317 962-1048
E-mail: sgrannis@clarian.org
Length: 3 Yrs   *ACGME Approved/Offered Positions:* 30
Program ID: 120-17-11-126

St Francis Hospital and Health Centers Program
Sponsor: St Francis Hospital - Beech Grove
Prgm Director: Richard D Feldman, MD
8111 S Emerson Ave
Indianapolis, IN 46237
Tel: 317 783-8641   *Fax:* 317 782-6872
E-mail: nancy.miller@ssfhs.org
Length: 3 Yrs   *ACGME Approved/Offered Positions:* 21
Program ID: 120-17-11-125

St Vincent Hospital and Health Care Center Program
Sponsor: St Vincent Hospitals and Health Care Center
Prgm Director: David M Harsha, MD
8414 Naab Road, Suite 160
Indianapolis, IN 46260
Tel: 317 338-7600   *Fax:* 317 338-7606
Length: 3 Yrs   *ACGME Approved/Offered Positions:* 24
Program ID: 120-17-11-127

Muncie

Ball Memorial Hospital Program
Sponsor: Ball Memorial Hospital
Prgm Director: Stewart C Brown, MD
Edmund F Ball Medical Education Bldg
221 North Celia Avenue
Muncie, IN 47303
Tel: 765 747-4454   *Fax:* 765 741-1983
E-mail: dstephens@chsmail.org
Length: 3 Yrs   *ACGME Approved/Offered Positions:* 24
Program ID: 120-17-11-128

South Bend

Memorial Hospital of South Bend Program
Sponsor: Memorial Hospital of South Bend
Prgm Director: Robert J Riley, MD, MS
714 North Michigan Street
South Bend, IN 46601
Tel: 574 647-7913   *Fax:* 574 647-6819
E-mail: familymedicine@memorialsb.org
Length: 3 Yrs   *ACGME Approved/Offered Positions:* 27
Program ID: 120-17-11-129

St Joseph's Regional Medical Center (South Bend) Program
Sponsor: St Joseph's Regional Medical Center (South Bend)
Prgm Director: Martin F Wieschhaus, MD
801 E LaSalle Street
PO Box 1935
South Bend, IN 46634
Tel: 574 239-6152   *Fax:* 574 472-6088
E-mail: moenm@sjrmc.com
Length: 3 Yrs   *ACGME Approved/Offered Positions:* 27
Program ID: 120-17-11-130

Terre Haute

Union Hospital Program
Sponsor: Union Hospital, Inc
Prgm Director: Paul L Daluga, MD
1513 North 6 1/2 Street
Terre Haute, IN 47807
Tel: 812 238-7631   *Fax:* 812 238-7003
Length: 3 Yrs   *ACGME Approved/Offered Positions:* 21
Program ID: 120-17-11-131

Iowa

Cedar Rapids

Cedar Rapids Medical Education Foundation Program
Sponsor: Cedar Rapids Medical Education Foundation
Mercy Medical Center
St Luke's Methodist Hospital
Prgm Director: Gordon H Baustian, MD
1026 A Avenue, NE
Cedar Rapids, IA 52402
Tel: 319 369-7393   *Fax:* 319 369-8351
Length: 3 Yrs   *ACGME Approved/Offered Positions:* 21
Program ID: 120-18-22-132

Davenport

Genesis Quad Cities Program
Sponsor: Genesis Health System
Genesis Medical Center
Prgm Director: Andrew A Andresen, MD
1345 W Central Park
Davenport, IA 52804
Tel: 563 421-4455   *Fax:* 563 421-4449
E-mail: halligant@genesishealth.com
Length: 3 Yrs   *ACGME Approved/Offered Positions:* 18
Program ID: 120-18-21-133

Des Moines

Broadlawns Medical Center Program
Sponsor: Broadlawns Medical Center
Prgm Director: Larry A Severidt, MD
1801 Hickman Road
Des Moines, IA 50314
Tel: 515 282-2565   *Fax:* 515 282-2332
E-mail: lseveridt@broadlawns.org
Length: 3 Yrs   *ACGME Approved/Offered Positions:* 30
Program ID: 120-18-11-134

Central Iowa Health System (Iowa Lutheran Hospital) Program
Sponsor: Central Iowa Health System (Iowa Methodist/Iowa Lutheran)
Prgm Director: Corrine M Ganske, MD
840 East University Avenue
Des Moines, IA 50316
Tel: 515 265-1050
Length: 3 Yrs   *ACGME Approved/Offered Positions:* 24
Program ID: 120-18-31-135

Mercy Medical Center (Des Moines) Program
Sponsor: Mercy Hospital Medical Center
Prgm Director: Charles H Korte, MD
Mercy Family Medicine Residency Program
250 Laurel St
Des Moines, IA 50314
Tel: 515 643-4610   *Fax:* 515 643-4662
Length: 3 Yrs   *ACGME Approved/Offered Positions:* 24
Program ID: 120-18-21-598

Iowa City

University of Iowa Hospitals and Clinics Program
Sponsor: University of Iowa Hospitals and Clinics
Prgm Director: Michael K Maharry, MD
Department of Family Medicine
200 Hawkins Dr
Iowa City, IA 52242
Tel: 319 384-7767   *Fax:* 319 384-7822
E-mail: fp-residency@uiowa.edu
Length: 3 Yrs   *ACGME Approved/Offered Positions:* 18
Program ID: 120-18-11-136

Mason City

Mercy Medical Center (Mason City) Program
Sponsor: Mercy Medical Center-North Iowa
Prgm Director: Scott T Henderson, MD
1000 4th Street SW
Mason City, IA 50401
Tel: 641 422-7779   *Fax:* 641 422-7125
Length: 3 Yrs   *ACGME Approved/Offered Positions:* 18
Program ID: 120-18-21-373

Pella

University of Iowa Hospitals and Clinics Rural (Pella) Program
Sponsor: University of Iowa Hospitals and Clinics
Pella Regional Health Center
Prgm Director: Michael K Maharry, MD
200 Hawkins Drive
Iowa City, IA 52242
Tel: 319 384-7767   *Fax:* 319 384-7822
E-mail: fp-rural@uiowa.edu
Length: 3 Yrs   *ACGME Approved/Offered Positions:* 3
Program ID: 120-18-31-666

Sioux City

Siouxland Medical Education Foundation Program

Sponsor: Siouxland Medical Education Foundation
Mercy Medical Center (Sioux City)
St Luke's Regional Medical Center
Prgm Director: Kurt A Rosenkrans, MD
2501 Pierce Street
Sioux City, IA 51104
Tel: 712 294-5000   *Fax:* 712 294-5091
E-mail: s.leonard@slmef.org
Length: 3 Yrs   *ACGME Approved/Offered Positions:* 18
Program ID: 120-18-21-137

Waterloo

Northeast Iowa Medical Education Foundation Program

Sponsor: Northeast Iowa Medical Education Foundation
Allen Memorial Hospital
Covenant Medical Center
Prgm Director: Anthony A Day, MD
2055 Kimball Avenue
Waterloo, IA 50702
Tel: 319 272-2525   *Fax:* 319 272-2527
E-mail: residency@neimef.org
Length: 3 Yrs   *ACGME Approved/Offered Positions:* 18
Program ID: 120-18-21-138

Kansas

Kansas City

University of Kansas School of Medicine (Junction City) Rural Program

Sponsor: University of Kansas School of Medicine
Geary Community Hospital
University of Kansas Hospital
Prgm Director: Belinda A Vail, MD, MS
3901 Rainbow Boulevard
1060 Delp, MS4010
Kansas City, KS 66160
Tel: 913 588-1902   *Fax:* 913 588-1951
E-mail: kestrada@kumc.edu
Length: 3 Yrs   *ACGME Approved/Offered Positions:* 3
Program ID: 120-19-21-553

University of Kansas School of Medicine Program

Sponsor: University of Kansas School of Medicine
University of Kansas Hospital
Prgm Director: Belinda Vail, MD
3901 Rainbow Blvd
1060 Delp, MS1040
Kansas City, KS 66160
Tel: 913 588-1902   *Fax:* 913 588-1951
Length: 3 Yrs   *ACGME Approved/Offered Positions:* 27
Program ID: 120-19-11-139

Salina

University of Kansas (Wichita)/Salina Program

Sponsor: University of Kansas School of Medicine
(Wichita)
Salina Regional Health Center
Prgm Director: Robert S Freelove, MD
Salina Health Education Foundation
651 E Prescott
Salina, KS 67401
Tel: 785 825-7251   *Fax:* 785 825-1605
E-mail: rfreelove@salinahealth.org
Length: 3 Yrs   *ACGME Approved/Offered Positions:* 12
Program ID: 120-19-21-366

Wichita

University of Kansas (Wichita)/Via Christi Regional Medical Center Program

Sponsor: University of Kansas School of Medicine
(Wichita)
Via Christi Regional Medical Center-St Francis
Via Christi Regional Medical Center-St Joseph
Prgm Director: Richard H Leu, MD
707 N Emporia
Wichita, KS 67214
Tel: 316 858-3571   *Fax:* 316 858-3495
E-mail: Marcia_Beasley@Via-Christi.org
Length: 3 Yrs   *ACGME Approved/Offered Positions:* 54
Program ID: 120-19-21-630

University of Kansas (Wichita)/Wesley Program

Sponsor: University of Kansas School of Medicine
(Wichita)
Wesley Medical Center
Prgm Director: Paul A Callaway, MD
850 N Hillside
Wichita, KS 67214
Tel: 316 962-3976   *Fax:* 316 962-7184
Length: 3 Yrs   *ACGME Approved/Offered Positions:* 27
Program ID: 120-19-11-142

Kentucky

Edgewood

St Elizabeth Medical Center Program

Sponsor: St Elizabeth Medical Center
Prgm Director: Donald J Swikert, MD
413 South Loop Road
Edgewood, KY 41017
Tel: 859 301-3841   *Fax:* 859 301-3820
E-mail: KWard@StElizabeth.com
Length: 3 Yrs   *ACGME Approved/Offered Positions:* 24
Program ID: 120-20-11-143

Glasgow

University of Louisville (Glasgow) Program

Sponsor: University of Louisville School of Medicine
T J Samson Community Hospital
Prgm Director: Brent Wright, MD
1325 North Race Street
Glasgow, KY 42141
Tel: 270 651-4865   *Fax:* 270 651-4751
E-mail: bwrightmd@hotmail.com
Length: 3 Yrs   *ACGME Approved/Offered Positions:* 12
Program ID: 120-20-21-613

Hazard

University of Kentucky College of Medicine (Hazard) Program

Sponsor: University of Kentucky College of Medicine
ARH Regional Medical Center (Hazard)
Prgm Director: Angela Rice, DO*
Room B440
750 Morton Blvd
Hazard, KY 41701
Tel: 606 439-1559   *Fax:* 606 439-1131
Length: 3 Yrs   *ACGME Approved/Offered Positions:* 12
Program ID: 120-20-21-512

Lexington

University of Kentucky College of Medicine (Morehead) Rural Program

Sponsor: University of Kentucky College of Medicine
University of Kentucky Hospital
Prgm Director: Michael King, MD*
K302 Kentucky Clinic
Lexington, KY 40536
Tel: 859 323-6371
E-mail: clterry@st-claire.org
Length: 3 Yrs   *ACGME Approved/Offered Positions:* 6
Program ID: 120-20-31-663

University of Kentucky College of Medicine Program

Sponsor: University of Kentucky College of Medicine
University of Kentucky Hospital
Prgm Director: Michael King, MD*
University of Kentucky Family & Community Medicine
Lexington, KY 40536
Tel: 859 323-6371
E-mail: jthoma2@email.uky.edu
Length: 3 Yrs   *ACGME Approved/Offered Positions:* 18
Program ID: 120-20-21-144

Louisville

University of Louisville Program

Sponsor: University of Louisville School of Medicine
Jewish Hospital
University of Louisville Hospital
Prgm Director: Michael Ostapchuk, MD, MS*
201 Abraham Flexner Way, Suite 690
Louisville, KY 40292
Tel: 502 852-5499   *Fax:* 502 852-4944
Length: 3 Yrs   *ACGME Approved/Offered Positions:* 24
Program ID: 120-20-21-145

Madisonville

Trover Clinic Foundation Program

Sponsor: Trover Clinic Foundation
Regional Medical Center of Hopkins County
Prgm Director: Robert L Wood, MD
200 Clinic Drive
Madisonville, KY 42431
Tel: 270 825-6690   *Fax:* 270 825-6696
E-mail: famdoc@trover.org
Length: 3 Yrs   *ACGME Approved/Offered Positions:* 18
Program ID: 120-20-31-146

Louisiana

Alexandria

Louisiana State University (Shreveport)/Rapides Regional Medical Center Program

Sponsor: LSU Health Sciences Center-University
Hospital
Rapides Regional Medical Center
Prgm Director: Brian Elkins, MD
821 Elliott Street
Alexandria, LA 71301
Tel: 318 441-1041   *Fax:* 318 441-1066
E-mail: kburna@lsuhsc.edu
Length: 3 Yrs   *ACGME Approved/Offered Positions:* 18
Program ID: 120-21-31-566

Note: * indicates a newly appointed program director

Baton Rouge

Baton Rouge General Medical Center Program
Sponsor: Baton Rouge General Medical Center
Prgm Director: Robert Chasuk, MD
3801 North Boulevard
Baton Rouge, LA 70806
Tel: 225 387-7899 *Fax:* 225 381-2579
E-mail: fmrp@brgeneral.org
Length: 3 Yrs *ACGME Approved/Offered Positions:* 24
Program ID: 120-21-21-560

Bogalusa

Louisiana State University (Bogalusa) Program
Sponsor: Louisiana State University School of Medicine
LSU Health Science Center-Bogalusa Medical Center
Prgm Director: Richard D Friend, MD
420 Avenue F
Bogalusa, LA 70427
Tel: 985 735-6735 *Fax:* 985 732-6688
Length: 3 Yrs *ACGME Approved/Offered Positions:* 12
Program ID: 120-21-13-695

Kenner

Louisiana State University (Kenner) Program
Sponsor: Louisiana State University School of Medicine
Ochsner Medical Center-Kenner
Leonard J Chabert Medical Center
Prgm Director: James S Campbell, MD
Department of Family Medicine
200 West Esplanade Avenue, Suite 409
Kenner, LA 70065
Tel: 504 471-2757 *Fax:* 504 471-2764
E-mail: sgelpi@lsuhsc.edu
Length: 3 Yrs *ACGME Approved/Offered Positions:* 18
Program ID: 120-21-21-641

Lafayette

Louisiana State University (Lafayette) Program
Sponsor: University Medical Center (Lafayette)
Prgm Director: Alan P Boussard, MD
2390 West Congress Street
Lafayette, LA 70506
Tel: 337 261-6690 *Fax:* 337 261-6662
E-mail: abrou1@lsuhsc.edu
Length: 3 Yrs *ACGME Approved/Offered Positions:* 24
Program ID: 120-21-11-149

Lake Charles

Louisiana State University (Lake Charles) Program
Sponsor: Louisiana State University School of Medicine
Lake Charles Memorial Hospital
Prgm Director: Alan LeBato, MD
1525 Oak Park Boulevard
Lake Charles, LA 70601
Tel: 337 494-2023 *Fax:* 337 430-6966
Length: 3 Yrs *ACGME Approved/Offered Positions:* 24
Program ID: 120-21-21-594

Metairie

East Jefferson General Hospital Program
Sponsor: East Jefferson General Hospital
Prgm Director: David W Euans, MD
Family Practice Center
4228 Houma Boulevard, Suite 230
Metairie, LA 70006
Tel: 504 883-3722 *Fax:* 504 883-3723
Length: 3 Yrs *ACGME Approved/Offered Positions:* 21
Program ID: 120-21-21-631

Monroe

Louisiana State University (Shreveport)/Monroe Program
Sponsor: E A Conway Medical Center
Prgm Director: Euil E Luther, MD
4864 Jackson Street
PO Box 1881
Monroe, LA 71210
Tel: 318 330-7650 *Fax:* 318 330-7613
Length: 3 Yrs *ACGME Approved/Offered Positions:* 24
Program ID: 120-21-21-440

Shreveport

Louisiana State University (Shreveport) Program
Sponsor: LSU Health Sciences Center-University Hospital
Christus Schumpert Health System
Prgm Director: Michael B Harper, MD
PO Box 33932
1501 Kings Highway
Shreveport, LA 71130
Tel: 318 675-5815 *Fax:* 318 675-7950
E-mail: nbrice@lsuhsc.edu
Length: 3 Yrs *ACGME Approved/Offered Positions:* 24
Program ID: 120-21-21-150

Vivian

Louisiana State University (Shreveport) Rural Program
Sponsor: LSU Health Sciences Center-University Hospital
North Caddo Medical Center
Prgm Director: Michael B Harper, MD
PO Box 33932
1501 Kings Highway
Shreveport, LA 71130
Tel: 318 675-5815 *Fax:* 318 675-7950
E-mail: nbrice@lsuhsc.edu
Length: 3 Yrs *ACGME Approved/Offered Positions:* 6
Program ID: 120-21-11-567

Maine

Augusta

Maine-Dartmouth Family Medicine Program
Sponsor: Maine-Dartmouth Family Medicine Residency
Maine General Medical Center
Prgm Director: Henry Colt, MD
15 E Chestnut Street
Augusta, ME 04330
Tel: 207 626-1893 *Fax:* 207 626-1902
Length: 3 Yrs *ACGME Approved/Offered Positions:* 30
Program ID: 120-22-22-151

Bangor

Eastern Maine Medical Center Program
Sponsor: Eastern Maine Medical Center
Prgm Director: James W Jarvis, MD*
Center for Family Medicine
895 Union Street, Suite 12
Bangor, ME 04401
Tel: 207 973-7973 *Fax:* 207 973-7684
E-mail: jjarvis@emh.org
Length: 3 Yrs *ACGME Approved/Offered Positions:* 27
Program ID: 120-22-12-152

Lewiston

Central Maine Medical Center Program
Sponsor: Central Maine Medical Center
Prgm Director: Edmund Claxton Jr, MD
76 High Street
Lewiston, ME 04240
Tel: 207 795-2803 *Fax:* 207 795-2190
Length: 3 Yrs *ACGME Approved/Offered Positions:* 21
Program ID: 120-22-11-153

Portland

Maine Medical Center Program
Sponsor: Maine Medical Center
Prgm Director: Alison M Samitt, MD
22 Bramhall Street
Portland, ME 04102
Tel: 207 662-2875 *Fax:* 207 662-6055
Length: 3 Yrs *ACGME Approved/Offered Positions:* 22
Program ID: 120-22-31-154

Maryland

Andrews AFB

National Capital Consortium Program
Sponsor: National Capital Consortium
Malcolm Grow Medical Center
Prgm Director: Robert E Manaker, MD
79 MDOS/SGOL
1075 W Perimeter Road
Andrews AFB, MD 20762
Tel: 240 857-3956 *Fax:* 240 857-3011
Length: 3 Yrs *ACGME Approved/Offered Positions:* 18
Program ID: 120-23-21-002
Uniformed Services Program

Baltimore

Franklin Square Hospital Center Program
Sponsor: Franklin Square Hospital Center
Prgm Director: Sallie Rixey, MD, MEd
9000 Franklin Square Drive
Baltimore, MD 21237
Tel: 443 777-6545 *Fax:* 443 777-8489
E-mail: sallie.rixey@medstar.net
Length: 3 Yrs *ACGME Approved/Offered Positions:* 24
Program ID: 120-23-12-155

University of Maryland Program
Sponsor: University of Maryland Medical System
Union Memorial Hospital
Prgm Director: Yvette L Rooks, MD
Department of Family Medicine
29 South Paca Street, Lower Level
Baltimore, MD 21201
Tel: 410 328-4282 *Fax:* 410 328-0639
E-mail: yrooks-worrell@som.umaryland.edu
Length: 3 Yrs *ACGME Approved/Offered Positions:* 24
Program ID: 120-23-21-156

Massachusetts

Boston

Boston University Medical Center Program
Sponsor: Boston Medical Center
Prgm Director: Thomas C Hines, MD
Dowling 5 South
One Boston Medical Center Place
Boston, MA 02118
Tel: 617 414-4465 *Fax:* 617 414-3345
E-mail: family.medicine@bmc.org
Length: 3 Yrs *ACGME Approved/Offered Positions:* 18
Program ID: 120-24-21-644

Cambridge

Tufts University at Cambridge Health Alliance Program

Sponsor: Cambridge Health Alliance
Prgm Director: Joseph W Gravel Jr, MD
195 Canal Street
Malden, MA 02148
Tel: 781 338-0550   *Fax:* 781 338-0150
E-mail: tuftsfmr@tufts.edu
Length: 3 Yrs   *ACGME Approved/Offered Positions:* 24
Program ID: 120-24-31-687

Lawrence

Greater Lawrence Family Health Center Program

Sponsor: Greater Lawrence Family Health Center Inc
Lawrence General Hospital
Prgm Director: Scott C Early, MD
34 Haverhill Street
Lawrence, MA 01841
Tel: 978 725-7410   *Fax:* 978 687-2106
E-mail: residency@glfhc.org
Length: 3 Yrs   *ACGME Approved/Offered Positions:* 24
Program ID: 120-24-21-528

Leominster

University of Massachusetts (Fitchburg) Program

Sponsor: University of Massachusetts Medical School
Health Alliance Hospital-Leominster
Prgm Director: James J Ledwith Jr, MD*
Fitchburg Family Medicine Residency Program
275 Nichols Road
Fitchburg, MA 01420
Tel: 978 878-8374   *Fax:* 978 343-5687
Length: 3 Yrs   *ACGME Approved/Offered Positions:* 18
Program ID: 120-24-31-159

Worcester

University of Massachusetts Program

Sponsor: University of Massachusetts Medical School
UMass Memorial Health Care (Memorial Campus)
Prgm Director: Stacy E Potts, MD*
Memorial Campus
119 Belmont Street, Jaquith 2
Worcester, MA 01605
Tel: 508 334-6141   *Fax:* 508 334-6404
E-mail: pottss@ummhc.org
Length: 3 Yrs   *ACGME Approved/Offered Positions:* 36
Program ID: 120-24-21-160

Michigan

Ann Arbor

University of Michigan Program

Sponsor: University of Michigan Hospitals and Health
   Centers
Chelsea Community Hospital
Prgm Director: James M Cooke, MD
1500 E Medical Center Drive
Room L2003, SCP 5239
Ann Arbor, MI 48109
Tel: 734 615-2690   *Fax:* 734 615-2687
E-mail: fammed-residency@med.umich.edu
Length: 3 Yrs   *ACGME Approved/Offered Positions:* 30
Program ID: 120-25-21-425

Detroit

Henry Ford Hospital Program

Sponsor: Henry Ford Hospital
Prgm Director: Maria E Shreve-Nicolai, MD*
Department of Family Medicine
One Ford Place 2E
Detroit, MI 48202
Tel: 313 874-5475   *Fax:* 313 874-5381
Length: 3 Yrs   *ACGME Approved/Offered Positions:* 24
Program ID: 120-25-21-484

St John Hospital and Medical Center Program

Sponsor: St John Hospital and Medical Center
Prgm Director: Mark R Paschall, MD
24911 Little Mack
St Clair Shores, MI 48080
Tel: 586 447-9064   *Fax:* 586 447-9081
Length: 3 Yrs   *ACGME Approved/Offered Positions:* 24
Program ID: 120-25-11-163

Flint

McLaren Regional Medical Center Program

Sponsor: McLaren Regional Medical Center
Prgm Director: Paul A Lazar, MD
Family Practice Education
401 S Ballenger Highway
Flint, MI 48532
Tel: 810 733-9654   *Fax:* 810 733-9690
Length: 3 Yrs   *ACGME Approved/Offered Positions:* 18
Program ID: 120-25-21-573

Grand Blanc

Genesys Regional Medical Center Program

Sponsor: Genesys Regional Medical Center
Prgm Director: Kenneth E Yokosawa, MD
One Genesys Parkway
Grand Blanc, MI 48439
Tel: 810 606-5981   *Fax:* 810 606-5636
Length: 3 Yrs   *ACGME Approved/Offered Positions:* 39
Program ID: 120-25-31-166

Grand Rapids

Grand Rapids Medical Education and Research Center/Michigan State University Program

Sponsor: Grand Rapids Medical Education and Research
   Center
Saint Mary's Health Care (Grand Rapids)
Prgm Director: John E vanSchagen, MD
300 Lafayette SE #3400
Grand Rapids, MI 49503
Tel: 616 685-6741   *Fax:* 616 685-3033
E-mail: crispina@trinity-health.org
Length: 3 Yrs   *ACGME Approved/Offered Positions:* 30
Program ID: 120-25-21-167

Grosse Pointe

William Beaumont Hospital-Grosse Pointe Program

Sponsor: William Beaumont Hospital
William Beaumont Hospital-Grosse Pointe
Prgm Director: Peter Tucker, MD*
468 Cadieux Road
Grosse Pointe, MI 48230
Tel: 586 498-4400
E-mail: peter.tucker@beaumont.edu
Length: 3 Yrs   *ACGME Approved/Offered Positions:* 24
Program ID: 120-25-21-168

Howell

St Joseph Mercy (Livingston) Hospital Program

Sponsor: St Joseph Mercy (Livingston) Hospital
Prgm Director: Kevin G Deighton, MD
7575 Grand River
Suite 209
Brighton, MI 48114
Tel: 810 844-7940   *Fax:* 810 844-7955
E-mail: kingl@trinity-health.org
Length: 3 Yrs   *ACGME Approved/Offered Positions:* 24
Program ID: 120-25-21-690

Kalamazoo

Kalamazoo Center for Medical Studies/Michigan State University Program

Sponsor: Michigan State Univ/Kalamazoo Center for
   Medical Studies
Borgess Medical Center
Bronson Methodist Hospital
Prgm Director: William W Allen, MD
Family Medicine
1000 Oakland Drive
Kalamazoo, MI 49008
Tel: 269 337-6554   *Fax:* 269 337-6565
E-mail: famprac@kcms.msu.edu
Length: 3 Yrs   *ACGME Approved/Offered Positions:* 18
Program ID: 120-25-21-169

Lansing

Sparrow Hospital/Michigan State University Program

Sponsor: Sparrow Hospital
Prgm Director: George F Smith, MD
1200 E Michigan Ave
Suite 245-C
Lansing, MI 48912
Tel: 517 364-5762   *Fax:* 517 364-5764
Length: 3 Yrs   *ACGME Approved/Offered Positions:* 30
Program ID: 120-25-21-170

Marquette

Marquette General Hospital Program

Sponsor: Marquette General Hospital
Prgm Director: William M Short, MD
1414 W Fair Ave, Suite 36
Marquette, MI 49855
Tel: 906 225-3867   *Fax:* 906 225-7667
E-mail: residency@mgh.org
Length: 3 Yrs   *ACGME Approved/Offered Positions:* 18
Program ID: 120-25-21-370

Midland

MidMichigan Medical Center-Midland Program

Sponsor: MidMichigan Medical Center-Midland
Prgm Director: William H Dery, MD
Office of Medical Education
4005 Orchard Drive
Midland, MI 48670
Tel: 989 839-3320   *Fax:* 989 839-1949
E-mail: fpresidency@midmichigan.org
Length: 3 Yrs   *ACGME Approved/Offered Positions:* 18
Program ID: 120-25-31-171

Note: * indicates a newly appointed program director

Pontiac

Oakland Physicians Medical Center Program
Sponsor: Oakland Physicians Medical Center
St Joseph Mercy-Oakland
Prgm Director: Nikhil Hemady, MD
Family Medicine Center
461 West Huron
Pontiac, MI 48341
Tel: 248 857-6700
E-mail: fpr@nomc.org
Length: 3 Yrs   *ACGME Approved/Offered Positions:* 18
Program ID: 120-25-12-172

Rochester

Wayne State University/Crittenton Program
Sponsor: Wayne State University School of Medicine
Crittenton Hospital Medical Center
Prgm Director: Tsveti Markova, MD
1101 W University Drive
3-North
Rochester, MI 48307
Tel: 248 601-4900   *Fax:* 248 601-4994
E-mail: lrang@med.wayne.edu
Length: 3 Yrs   *ACGME Approved/Offered Positions:* 24
Program ID: 120-25-21-694

Royal Oak

William Beaumont Hospital Program
Sponsor: William Beaumont Hospital
William Beaumont Hospital - Troy
Prgm Director: Cynthia L Fisher, MD
Family Medicine Residency Program
44300 Dequindre Road
Sterling Heights, MI 48314
Tel: 248 964-0430   *Fax:* 248 964-1830
E-mail: fm@beaumont.edu
Length: 3 Yrs   *ACGME Approved/Offered Positions:* 24
Program ID: 120-25-21-374

Saginaw

Synergy Medical Education Alliance Program
Sponsor: Synergy Medical Education Alliance
Covenant HealthCare System-Cooper Campus
Covenant HealthCare System-Harrison Campus
Prgm Director: Edward A Jackson, MD
1000 Houghton Avenue
Saginaw, MI 48602
Tel: 989 583-7917   *Fax:* 989 583-7919
Length: 3 Yrs   *ACGME Approved/Offered Positions:* 18
Program ID: 120-25-31-174

Southfield

Providence Hospital and Medical Centers Program
Sponsor: Providence Hospital and Medical Centers
Prgm Director: Karen Mitchell, MD*
Murray N Deighton Fam Prac Ctr
22250 Providence Dr, Ste 557
Southfield, MI 48075
Tel: 248 849-3447   *Fax:* 248 849-8277
Length: 3 Yrs   *ACGME Approved/Offered Positions:* 27
Program ID: 120-25-21-175

Traverse City

Munson Medical Center Program
Sponsor: Munson Medical Center
Prgm Director: Daniel M Webster, MD
Graduate Medical Education Office
1400 Medical Campus Drive
Traverse City, MI 49684
Tel: 231 935-8012   *Fax:* 231 935-8098
E-mail: residency@mhc.net
Length: 3 Yrs   *ACGME Approved/Offered Positions:* 15
Program ID: 120-25-21-602

Wayne

Oakwood Annapolis Hospital Program
Sponsor: Oakwood Annapolis Hospital
Oakwood Hospital
Prgm Director: Karen L Weaver, MD*
33155 Annapolis Avenue
Wayne, MI 48184
Tel: 734 467-2483   *Fax:* 734 467-2485
E-mail: karen.weaver@oakwood.org
Length: 3 Yrs   *ACGME Approved/Offered Positions:* 30
Program ID: 120-25-31-678

Minnesota

Duluth

Duluth Graduate Medical Education Council Program
Sponsor: Duluth Graduate Medical Education Council
St Luke's Hospital
St Mary's Medical Center
Prgm Director: Thomas W Day, MD
330 North Eighth Avenue East
Duluth, MN 55805
Tel: 218 529-9105   *Fax:* 218 529-9120
Length: 3 Yrs   *ACGME Approved/Offered Positions:* 30
Program ID: 120-26-21-176

Mankato

University of Minnesota (Mankato) Program
Sponsor: University of Minnesota Medical School
Immanuel St Joseph's-Mayo Health System
Prgm Director: John C McCabe III, MD
101 Martin Luther King Jr Dr
Mankato, MN 56001
Tel: 507 385-6572   *Fax:* 507 385-6511
E-mail: nowak.wendy@mayo.edu
Length: 3 Yrs   *ACGME Approved/Offered Positions:* 15
Program ID: 120-26-21-568

Minneapolis

Hennepin County Medical Center Program
Sponsor: Hennepin County Medical Center
Prgm Director: Allyson R Brotherson, MD, MS
Family Medical Center
5 West Lake Street
Minneapolis, MN 55408
Tel: 612 545-9222   *Fax:* 612 545-9259
Length: 3 Yrs   *ACGME Approved/Offered Positions:* 36
Program ID: 120-26-11-177

University of Minnesota Program
Sponsor: University of Minnesota Medical School
University of Minnesota Medical Center, Division of Fairview
Prgm Director: Patricia Adam, MD, MPH*
Smiley's Clinic
2020 East 28th Street
Minneapolis, MN 55407
Tel: 612 333-0774   *Fax:* 612 359-0475
Length: 3 Yrs   *ACGME Approved/Offered Positions:* 24
Program ID: 120-26-21-650

Robbinsdale

University of Minnesota/North Memorial Health Care Program
Sponsor: University of Minnesota Medical School
North Memorial Health Care
Prgm Director: Mark R Bixby, MD
1020 West Broadway
Minneapolis, MN 55411
Tel: 612 302-8200   *Fax:* 612 302-8275
E-mail: pcoppa@umphysicians.umn.edu
Length: 3 Yrs   *ACGME Approved/Offered Positions:* 30
Program ID: 120-26-31-651

Rochester

College of Medicine, Mayo Clinic (Rochester) Program
Sponsor: College of Medicine, Mayo Clinic
Mayo Clinic (Rochester)
Rochester Methodist Hospital
Saint Marys Hospital of Rochester
Prgm Director: Robert T Flinchbaugh, DO
Department of Family Medicine
200 First Street SW
Rochester, MN 55905
Tel: 507 266-0251   *Fax:* 507 266-0216
E-mail: younge.tamara@mayo.edu
Length: 3 Yrs   *ACGME Approved/Offered Positions:* 24
Program ID: 120-26-21-179

St Cloud

University of Minnesota (St Cloud) Program
Sponsor: University of Minnesota Medical School
St Cloud Hospital
CentraCare Clinic (River Campus)
Prgm Director: Joseph M Blonski, MD
1520 Whitney Court, Suite 200
St Cloud, MN 56303
Tel: 320 240-3181   *Fax:* 320 240-3165
Length: 3 Yrs   *ACGME Approved/Offered Positions:* 12
Program ID: 120-26-21-586

St Louis Park

University of Minnesota/Methodist Hospital Program
Sponsor: University of Minnesota Medical School
Methodist Hospital
Park Nicollet Clinic
Prgm Director: Jeremy S Springer, MD
6600 Excelsior Blvd
Ste 160
St Louis Park, MN 55426
Tel: 952 993-7706   *Fax:* 952 993-6798
E-mail: sprin019@umn.edu
Length: 3 Yrs   *ACGME Approved/Offered Positions:* 18
Program ID: 120-26-21-617

St Paul

Allina Hospitals & Clinics Program
Sponsor: Allina Hospitals & Clinics
United Hospital
Children's Hospitals and Clinics of Minnesota - St Paul
Prgm Director: Kathleen M Macken, MD
545 West Seventh Street
St Paul, MN 55102
Tel: 651 241-1001   *Fax:* 651 241-1116
E-mail: Joy.Gray@allina.com
Length: 3 Yrs   *ACGME Approved/Offered Positions:* 18
Program ID: 120-26-21-526

St. Paul

University of Minnesota/HealthEast St Joseph's Hospital Program

Sponsor: University of Minnesota Medical School
HealthEast St Joseph's Hospital
Prgm Director: Casey S Martin, MD*
580 Rice Street
St Paul, MN 55103
Tel: 651 223-7343   *Fax:* 651 665-0684
E-mail: marti176@umn.edu
Length: 3 Yrs   *ACGME Approved/Offered Positions:* 24
Program ID: 120-26-12-653

University of Minnesota/St John's Hospital Program

Sponsor: University of Minnesota Medical School
HealthEast St John's Hospital
Prgm Director: William O Roberts, MD, MS
Phalen Village Clinic
1414 Maryland Avenue East
St Paul, MN 55106
Tel: 651 793-5603   *Fax:* 651 495-0499
E-mail: johnfp@umn.edu
Length: 3 Yrs   *ACGME Approved/Offered Positions:* 18
Program ID: 120-26-11-652

Mississippi

Jackson

University of Mississippi Medical Center Program

Sponsor: University of Mississippi School of Medicine
Mississippi Baptist Medical Center
University Hospitals and Clinics
Prgm Director: Shannon D Pittman, MD
Department of Family Medicine
2500 North State Street
Jackson, MS 39216
Tel: 601 984-5426   *Fax:* 601 984-6889
E-mail: sdpittman@familymed.umsmed.edu
Length: 3 Yrs   *ACGME Approved/Offered Positions:* 30
Program ID: 120-27-21-181

Tupelo

North Mississippi Medical Center (Tupelo) Program

Sponsor: North Mississippi Medical Center
Prgm Director: Michael O'Dell, MD, MHA
1665 South Green Street
Tupelo, MS 38804
Tel: 662 377-2261   *Fax:* 662 377-2263
Length: 3 Yrs   *ACGME Approved/Offered Positions:* 18
Program ID: 120-27-21-558

Missouri

Columbia

University of Missouri-Columbia Program

Sponsor: University of Missouri-Columbia School of
   Medicine
University Hospitals and Clinics
Prgm Director: Erika N Ringdahl, MD
Dept of Family & Community Med
MA303 Medical Sciences Building; DCO32.00
Columbia, MO 65212
Tel: 573 882-9099   *Fax:* 573 884-4122
E-mail: resident@health.missouri.edu
Length: 3 Yrs   *ACGME Approved/Offered Positions:* 36
Program ID: 120-28-11-182

Kansas City

Research Medical Center Program

Sponsor: Research Medical Center
Prgm Director: Stephen C Salanski, MD
6650 Troost, Suite 305
Kansas City, MO 64131
Tel: 816 276-7650   *Fax:* 816 276-7090
E-mail: stephen.salanski@hcamidwest.com
Length: 3 Yrs   *ACGME Approved/Offered Positions:* 36
Program ID: 120-28-21-183

University of Missouri at Kansas City Program

Sponsor: University of Missouri-Kansas City School of
   Medicine
Truman Medical Center-Lakewood
Prgm Director: Todd D Shaffer, MD, MBA
7900 Lee's Summit Road
Kansas City, MO 64139
Tel: 816 404-7751   *Fax:* 816 404-7756
E-mail: info@umkcfm.org
Length: 3 Yrs   *ACGME Approved/Offered Positions:* 36
Program ID: 120-28-21-422

Springfield

Cox Medical Center Program

Sponsor: Cox Medical Center
Prgm Director: Mary Jo Fisher, MD*
Family Medicine Residency Program
1423 N Jefferson Ave, Suite A100
Springfield, MO 65802
Tel: 417 269-8787   *Fax:* 417 269-8750
E-mail: vickie.greenwood@coxhealth.com
Length: 3 Yrs   *ACGME Approved/Offered Positions:* 24
Program ID: 120-28-21-476

St Louis

St John's Mercy Medical Center Program

Sponsor: St John's Mercy Medical Center
Prgm Director: Grant Hoekzema, MD
12680 Olive Blvd
Suite 300
Creve Couer, MO 63141
Tel: 314 251-8950   *Fax:* 314 251-8889
E-mail: shimali.premaratne@mercy.net
Length: 3 Yrs   *ACGME Approved/Offered Positions:* 19
Program ID: 120-28-21-186

Montana

Billings

Montana Family Medicine Residency Program

Sponsor: Montana Family Medicine Residency
Billings Clinic
St Vincent Healthcare
Prgm Director: Roxanne Fahrenwald, MD, MS
123 South 27th Street
Suite B
Billings, MT 59101
Tel: 406 247-3306   *Fax:* 406 247-3307
E-mail: info@mfmr.fammed.washington.edu
Length: 3 Yrs   *ACGME Approved/Offered Positions:* 18
Program ID: 120-29-21-590

Nebraska

Kearney

University of Nebraska Medical Center College of Medicine Rural Program

Sponsor: University of Nebraska Medical Center College
   of Medicine
Good Samaritan Hospital (Kearney)
Faith Regional Health Services
Great Plains Regional Medical Center
Regional West Medical Center
St Francis Medical Center (Grand Island)
Prgm Director: Jeffrey D Harrison, MD, BS
Department of Family Medicine
983075 Nebraska Medical Center
Omaha, NE 68198
Tel: 402 559-5641   *Fax:* 402 559-6501
Length: 3 Yrs   *ACGME Approved/Offered Positions:* 30
Program ID: 120-30-21-517

Lincoln

Lincoln Medical Education Partnership Program

Sponsor: Lincoln Medical Education Partnership
BryanLGH Medical Center East
BryanLGH Medical Center West
St Elizabeth Regional Medical Center
Prgm Director: Michael A Myers, MD
Family Medicine Program
4600 Valley Road, Suite 210
Lincoln, NE 68510
Tel: 402 483-4591   *Fax:* 402 483-5079
E-mail: mmyers@lmep.com
Length: 3 Yrs   *ACGME Approved/Offered Positions:* 24
Program ID: 120-30-31-187

Omaha

Clarkson Regional Health Service Program

Sponsor: Nebraska Medical Center
Prgm Director: Richard H Hurd, MD
987400 Nebraska Medical Center
Omaha, NE 68198
Tel: 402 552-2050   *Fax:* 402 552-2186
E-mail: bhilburn@nebraskamed.com
Length: 3 Yrs   *ACGME Approved/Offered Positions:* 18
Program ID: 120-30-21-498

Creighton University Program

Sponsor: Creighton University School of Medicine
Creighton University Medical Center (Tenet - SJH)
Prgm Director: Thomas J Hansen, MD, MDiv
Department of Family Medicine
601 North 30th Street, Suite 6720
Omaha, NE 68131
Tel: 402 280-4111   *Fax:* 402 280-5165
E-mail: maureens@creighton.edu
Length: 3 Yrs   *ACGME Approved/Offered Positions:* 30
Program ID: 120-30-31-188

University of Nebraska Medical Center College of Medicine Program

Sponsor: University of Nebraska Medical Center College
   of Medicine
Ehrling Bergquist Hospital
Prgm Director: Jeffrey D Harrison, MD
Department of Family Medicine
983075 Nebraska Medical Center
Omaha, NE 68198
Tel: 402 559-7249   *Fax:* 402 559-6501
Length: 3 Yrs   *ACGME Approved/Offered Positions:* 48
Program ID: 120-30-21-189

Note: * indicates a newly appointed program director

Nevada

Las Vegas

University of Nevada School of Medicine (Las Vegas) Program

Sponsor: University of Nevada School of Medicine
University Medical Center of Southern Nevada
Prgm Director: Aron F Rogers, DO
Family Medicine Center
2410 Fire Mesa St, Suite 180
Las Vegas, NV 89128
Tel: 702 992-6873   *Fax:* 702 992-6878
E-mail: karaymond@medicine.nevada.edu
Length: 3 Yrs   *ACGME Approved/Offered Positions:* 12
Program ID: 120-31-21-481

Reno

University of Nevada School of Medicine Program

Sponsor: University of Nevada School of Medicine
Ioannis A Lougaris Veterans Affairs Medical Center
Renown Medical Center
Prgm Director: Richard D Williams, MD
Dept of Family & Community Medicine, Reno
Brigham Building (316) UNSOM
Reno, NV 89557
Tel: 775 784-6180   *Fax:* 775 784-4473
E-mail: kselbach@medicine.nevada.edu
Length: 3 Yrs   *ACGME Approved/Offered Positions:* 18
Program ID: 120-31-21-482

New Hampshire

Concord

New Hampshire-Dartmouth Family Medicine Program

Sponsor: Concord Hospital
Prgm Director: Gail B Fayre, MD
Concord Hospital
250 Pleasant Street
Concord, NH 03301
Tel: 603 227-7000   *Fax:* 603 228-7173
E-mail: nhdfpr@crhc.org
Length: 3 Yrs   *ACGME Approved/Offered Positions:* 24
Program ID: 120-32-31-557

New Jersey

Edison

JFK Medical Center Program

Sponsor: JFK Medical Center
Prgm Director: Robin O Winter, MD
65 James Street
Edison, NJ 08820
Tel: 732 321-7493   *Fax:* 732 906-4986
Length: 3 Yrs   *ACGME Approved/Offered Positions:* 18
Program ID: 120-33-11-190

Flemington

Hunterdon Medical Center Program

Sponsor: Hunterdon Medical Center
Prgm Director: Stanley M Kozakowski, MD
2100 Wescott Drive
Flemington, NJ 08822
Tel: 908 788-6160   *Fax:* 908 788-6422
E-mail: kozakowski@hunterdonhealthcare.org
Length: 3 Yrs   *ACGME Approved/Offered Positions:* 18
Program ID: 120-33-11-191

Freehold

UMDNJ-Robert Wood Johnson at CentraState Program

Sponsor: UMDNJ-Robert Wood Johnson Medical School
CentraState Medical Center
Prgm Director: Kenneth W Faistl, MD
1001 West Main Street
Suite B
Freehold, NJ 07728
Tel: 732 294-2540   *Fax:* 732 409-2621
Length: 3 Yrs   *ACGME Approved/Offered Positions:* 18
Program ID: 120-33-12-679

Hoboken

UMDNJ/Hoboken Municipal Hospital Program

Sponsor: UMDNJ-New Jersey Medical School
Hoboken Municipal Hospital
Prgm Director: Abbie Jacobs, MD
308 Willow Avenue
Hoboken, NJ 07030
Tel: 201 418-3125   *Fax:* 201 418-3148
E-mail: ajacobs@hobokenumc.com
Length: 3 Yrs   *ACGME Approved/Offered Positions:* 24
Program ID: 120-33-11-192

Marlton

West Jersey-Memorial Hospital at Virtua Program

Sponsor: West Jersey Health System
Virtua-Memorial Hospital Burlington County
Virtua-West Jersey Hospital Voorhees
Prgm Director: Mary Willard, MD
2225 Evesham Road, Suite 101
Voorhees, NJ 08043
Tel: 856 795-7075   *Fax:* 856 325-3705
Length: 3 Yrs   *ACGME Approved/Offered Positions:* 24
Program ID: 120-33-12-667

Montclair

Mountainside Hospital Program

Sponsor: Mountainside Hospital
Prgm Director: Richard Cirello, MD, BA
799 Bloomfield Avenue - Suite 201
Verona, NJ 07044
Tel: 973 746-7050   *Fax:* 973 259-3569
E-mail: annmarie.jones@mountainsidehosp.com
Length: 3 Yrs   *ACGME Approved/Offered Positions:* 18
Program ID: 120-33-11-193

New Brunswick

UMDNJ-Robert Wood Johnson Medical School Program

Sponsor: UMDNJ-Robert Wood Johnson Medical School
Robert Wood Johnson University Hospital
Prgm Director: Karen W Lin, MD, MS
Dept of Family Medicine, MEB, Room 278
One Robert Wood Johnson Place, PO Box 19
New Brunswick, NJ 08903
Tel: 732 235-7667   *Fax:* 732 235-6095
E-mail: fmrwjuh@umdnj.edu
Length: 3 Yrs   *ACGME Approved/Offered Positions:* 12
Program ID: 120-33-21-419

UMDNJ-Robert Wood Johnson Medical School/Capital Health System-Fuld Campus Program

Sponsor: UMDNJ-Robert Wood Johnson Medical School
Capital Health System - Mercer Campus
Capital Health System-Fuld Campus
Prgm Director: Martha H Lansing, MD
4056 Quakerbridge Road, Suite 101
Trenton, NJ 08619
Tel: 609 528-9145   *Fax:* 609 528-9146
E-mail: fprchs@chsnj.org
Length: 3 Yrs   *ACGME Approved/Offered Positions:* 12
Program ID: 120-33-21-559

Paterson

Mount Sinai School of Medicine/St Joseph's Program

Sponsor: Mount Sinai School of Medicine
St Joseph's Regional Medical Center
Prgm Director: Michael D DeLisi, MD
1135 Broad Street
Suite 201
Clifton, NJ 07013
Tel: 973 754-4121   *Fax:* 973 754-4190
E-mail: sjfm@sjhmc.org
Length: 3 Yrs   *ACGME Approved/Offered Positions:* 12
Program ID: 120-35-31-681

Phillipsburg

Warren Hospital Program

Sponsor: Warren Hospital
Prgm Director: Raymond Buch, MD
755 Memorial Parkway
Suite 300
Phillipsburg, NJ 08865
Tel: 908 859-6785   *Fax:* 908 454-9889
Length: 3 Yrs   *ACGME Approved/Offered Positions:* 21
Program ID: 120-33-21-436

Somerville

Somerset Medical Center Program

Sponsor: Somerset Medical Center
Prgm Director: John L Bucek, MD
110 Rehill Avenue
Somerville, NJ 08876
Tel: 908 685-2899   *Fax:* 908 704-0083
E-mail: fpresidency@somerset-healthcare.com
Length: 3 Yrs   *ACGME Approved/Offered Positions:* 21
Program ID: 120-33-11-194

Summit

Atlantic Health (Overlook) Program

Sponsor: Atlantic Health
Overlook Hospital
Prgm Director: Joseph Tribuna, MD
33 Overlook Road
Suite L-01
Summit, NJ 07901
Tel: 908 522-5289   *Fax:* 908 273-8014
Length: 3 Yrs   *ACGME Approved/Offered Positions:* 21
Program ID: 120-33-11-195

Woodbury

Underwood-Memorial Hospital Program

Sponsor: Underwood-Memorial Hospital
Prgm Director: Gregory E Herman, MD
c/o Family Medicine Center
75 W Red Bank Avenue
Woodbury, NJ 08096
Tel: 856 853-2056   *Fax:* 856 686-5218
E-mail: kempd@umhospital.org
Length: 3 Yrs   *ACGME Approved/Offered Positions:* 12
Program ID: 120-33-21-445

Programs

New Mexico

Albuquerque

University of New Mexico Program
Sponsor: University of New Mexico School of Medicine
University of New Mexico Hospital
Prgm Director: Sally Bachofer, MD
MSC 09-5040
1 University of New Mexico (FPC)
Albuquerque, NM 87131
Tel: 505 272-6607   *Fax:* 505 272-1348
E-mail: FMResidency@salud.unm.edu
Length: 3 Yrs   *ACGME Approved/Offered Positions:* 36
Program ID: 120-34-21-197

Las Cruces

Memorial Medical Center (Las Cruces) Program
Sponsor: Memorial Medical Center
Prgm Director: Bert D Garrett, MD
2450 S Telshor Boulevard
Las Cruces, NM 88011
Tel: 505 521-5378   *Fax:* 505 521-5568
Length: 3 Yrs   *ACGME Approved/Offered Positions:* 18
Program ID: 120-34-21-577

Roswell

University of New Mexico (Roswell) Rural Program
Sponsor: University of New Mexico School of Medicine
Eastern New Mexico Medical Center
University of New Mexico Hospital
Prgm Director: Karen E Vaillant, MD
350 W Country Club Road Suite 101
Roswell, NM 88201
Tel: 575 624-5625   *Fax:* 575 624-5630
E-mail: familypractice_residency@chs.net
Length: 3 Yrs   *ACGME Approved/Offered Positions:* 12
Program ID: 120-34-21-608

Santa Fe

University of New Mexico (Santa Fe) Rural Program
Sponsor: University of New Mexico School of Medicine
St Vincent Hospital
University of New Mexico Hospital
Prgm Director: Mario Pacheco, MD
455 St Michaels Drive
Santa Fe, NM 87505
Tel: 505 995-3985   *Fax:* 505 946-3129
E-mail: deborah.weiss@stvin.org
Length: 3 Yrs   *ACGME Approved/Offered Positions:* 12
Program ID: 120-34-21-595

New York

Albany

Albany Medical Center Program
Sponsor: Albany Medical Center
St Peter's Hospital
Prgm Director: Neil C Mitnick, DO
Department of Family Medicine
2 Clara Barton Drive, Suite 110
Albany, NY 12208
Tel: 518 213-0336   *Fax:* 518 213-0334
E-mail: wagnerc@mail.amc.edu
Length: 3 Yrs   *ACGME Approved/Offered Positions:* 18
Program ID: 120-35-21-198

Bay Shore

NSLIJHS-Southside Hospital Program
Sponsor: North Shore-Long Island Jewish Health System
Southside Hospital
Prgm Director: Richard J Bonanno, MD
301 E Main Street
Bay Shore, NY 11706
Tel: 631 968-3295   *Fax:* 631 968-4241
E-mail: mmanzari@nshs.edu
Length: 3 Yrs   *ACGME Approved/Offered Positions:* 27
Program ID: 120-35-21-199

Bronx

Albert Einstein College of Medicine Program
Sponsor: Albert Einstein College of Medicine of Yeshiva
   University
Montefiore Medical Center-Henry and Lucy Moses
   Division
Prgm Director: Mary Duggan, MD
Albert Einstein College of Medicine
3544 Jerome Avenue
Bronx, NY 10467
Tel: 718 920-5521   *Fax:* 718 515-5416
E-mail: nlewis@montefiore.org
Length: 3 Yrs   *ACGME Approved/Offered Positions:* 30
Program ID: 120-35-21-209

Bronx-Lebanon Hospital Center Program
Sponsor: Bronx-Lebanon Hospital Center
Prgm Director: Douglas J Reich, MD
1276 Fulton Aveune - Third Floor
Bronx, NY 10456
Tel: 718 901-8781   *Fax:* 718 901-8704
Length: 3 Yrs   *ACGME Approved/Offered Positions:* 30
Program ID: 120-35-21-465

Brooklyn

Brooklyn Hospital Center Program
Sponsor: Brooklyn Hospital Center
Prgm Director: Vasantha Kondamudi, MD
121 DeKalb Avenue
Brooklyn, NY 11201
Tel: 718 250-8817   *Fax:* 718 250-6609
E-mail: vkk9001@nyp.org
Length: 3 Yrs   *ACGME Approved/Offered Positions:* 21
Program ID: 120-35-21-530

Lutheran Medical Center Program
Sponsor: Lutheran Medical Center
Prgm Director: Claudia Lyon, DO
Department of Family Medicine
5616 Sixth Avenue
Brooklyn, NY 11220
Tel: 718 630-6813   *Fax:* 718 630-8697
E-mail: clyon@lmcmc.com
Length: 3 Yrs   *ACGME Approved/Offered Positions:* 24
Program ID: 120-35-11-207

SUNY Health Science Center at Brooklyn Program
Sponsor: SUNY Health Science Center at Brooklyn
Kings County Hospital Center
University Hospital-SUNY Health Science Center at
   Brooklyn
Prgm Director: Margaret Donat, MD
Department of Family Practice
450 Clarkson Avenue, Box 67
Brooklyn, NY 11203
Tel: 718 270-2546   *Fax:* 718 270-2125
E-mail: margaret.donat@downstate.edu
Length: 3 Yrs   *ACGME Approved/Offered Positions:* 18
Program ID: 120-35-21-210

Wyckoff Heights Medical Center Program
Sponsor: Wyckoff Heights Medical Center
Prgm Director: Farideh Zonouzi-Zadeh, MD
374 Stockholm Street
Room 413-C
Brooklyn, NY 11237
Tel: 718 963-6768   *Fax:* 718 906-3926
E-mail: fzonouzi@bqhcny.org
Length: 3 Yrs   *ACGME Approved/Offered Positions:* 18
Program ID: 120-35-21-507

Buffalo

University at Buffalo Program
Sponsor: University at Buffalo School of Medicine
Erie County Medical Center
Kaleida Health System (Buffalo General Hospital)
Kaleida Health System (Millard Fillmore Hospital)
University at Buffalo Affiliated Physician Practices
   (UBAPP)
Prgm Director: Michael E Zionts, MD
462 Grider Street - CC102
Buffalo, NY 14215
Tel: 716 898-5972   *Fax:* 716 898-4750
Length: 3 Yrs   *ACGME Approved/Offered Positions:* 42
Program ID: 120-35-21-489

University at Buffalo Rural Program
Sponsor: University at Buffalo School of Medicine
Kaleida Health System (Buffalo General Hospital)
Olean General Hospital
University at Buffalo Physician Practices (UBPP)
Prgm Director: Michael Zionts, MD
462 Grider Street
Buffalo, NY 14215
Tel: 716 898-5972   *Fax:* 716 898-3164
E-mail: psm4@buffalo.edu
Length: 3 Yrs   *ACGME Approved/Offered Positions:* 6
Program ID: 120-35-21-516

Glen Cove

NSLIJHS-North Shore University Hospital/Glen Cove Program
Sponsor: North Shore-Long Island Jewish Health System
North Shore University Hospital at Glen Cove
Prgm Director: William J Bennett, MD
101 St Andrews Lane
Glen Cove, NY 11542
Tel: 516 674-7637   *Fax:* 516 674-7639
Length: 3 Yrs   *ACGME Approved/Offered Positions:* 21
Program ID: 120-35-11-202

Jamaica

Mount Sinai School of Medicine/Jamaica Hospital Medical Center Program
Sponsor: Jamaica Hospital Medical Center
Prgm Director: Gina M Basello, DO*
Department of Family Medicine
8900 Van Wyck Expressway
Jamaica, NY 11418
Tel: 718 206-6748   *Fax:* 718 206-8716
E-mail: gbasello@jhmc.org
Length: 3 Yrs   *ACGME Approved/Offered Positions:* 30
Program ID: 120-35-11-206

New York Medical College (Brooklyn-Queens) Program
Sponsor: New York Medical College
Caritas Health Care (Brooklyn-Queens)
Prgm Director: Montgomery B Douglas, MD*
Caritas Health Care, INC
114-49 Sutphin Blvd
Jamaica, NY 11434
Tel: 718 322-2903   *Fax:* 718 322-6152
Length: 3 Yrs   *ACGME Approved/Offered Positions:* 30
Program ID: 120-35-21-420

Note: * indicates a newly appointed program director

Johnson City

United Health Services Hospitals Program

Sponsor: United Health Services Hospitals
Wilson Medical Center (United Health System)
Prgm Director: Richard R Terry, DO
33-57 Harrison Street
Johnson City, NY 13790
Tel: 607 763-5334   *Fax:* 607 763-5415
E-mail: medical_education@uhs.org
Length: 3 Yrs   *ACGME Approved/Offered Positions:* 27
Program ID: 120-35-11-203

New York

Albert Einstein College of Medicine at Beth Israel Medical Center Program

Sponsor: Beth Israel Medical Center
Prgm Director: Andreas Cohrssen, MD
Beth Israel Medical Center
16 East 16th Street, 5th Floor
New York, NY 10003
Tel: 212 206-5255   *Fax:* 212 206-5251
E-mail: zlopez@institute2000.org
Length: 3 Yrs   *ACGME Approved/Offered Positions:* 24
Program ID: 120-35-32-538

Mid-Hudson Family Health Institute Program

Sponsor: Mid-Hudson Family Health Inst/The Inst for
   Fam Health
Kingston Hospital
Prgm Director: Mark A Josefski, MD
Residency Administrative Offices
396 Broadway
Kingston, NY 12401
Tel: 845 334-2700   *Fax:* 845 338-0307
Length: 3 Yrs   *ACGME Approved/Offered Positions:* 18
Program ID: 120-35-21-204

New York Presbyterian Hospital (Columbia Campus) Program

Sponsor: New York Presbyterian Hospital
New York Presbyterian Hospital (Columbia Campus)
Prgm Director: Carmen M Dominguez-Rafer, MD, MPH
Family Medicine Residency Program
610 West 158th Street
New York, NY 10032
Tel: 212 544-1880   *Fax:* 212 544-1870
E-mail: rub9004@nyp.org
Length: 3 Yrs   *ACGME Approved/Offered Positions:* 18
Program ID: 120-35-21-581

Niagara Falls

University at Buffalo (Niagara Falls) Program

Sponsor: University at Buffalo School of Medicine
Niagara Falls Memorial Medical Center
Prgm Director: Laurence R Plumb, MD
Hamilton B Mizer-Primary Care Ctr
501 Tenth Street
Niagara Falls, NY 14301
Tel: 716 278-4618   *Fax:* 716 285-8992
E-mail: laurence.plumb@nfmmc.org
Length: 3 Yrs   *ACGME Approved/Offered Positions:* 12
Program ID: 120-35-12-211

Oceanside

South Nassau Communities Hospital Program

Sponsor: South Nassau Communities Hospital
Prgm Director: Samuel A Sandowski, MD
196 Merrick Road
Oceanside, NY 11572
Tel: 516 255-8415   *Fax:* 516 255-8453
Length: 3 Yrs   *ACGME Approved/Offered Positions:* 18
Program ID: 120-35-11-212

Rochester

University of Rochester/Highland Hospital of Rochester Program

Sponsor: Strong Memorial Hospital of the University of
   Rochester
Highland Hospital of Rochester
Prgm Director: Stephen H Schultz, MD
777 Clinton Avenue South
Rochester, NY 14620
Tel: 585 279-4831   *Fax:* 585 442-8319
E-mail: fmres@urmc.rochester.edu
Length: 3 Yrs   *ACGME Approved/Offered Positions:* 30
Program ID: 120-35-21-214

Schenectady

Ellis Hospital of Schenectady Program

Sponsor: Ellis Hospital
Prgm Director: Gary R Dunkerley, MD
Family Health Cntr, Attn: Residency Office
600 Mc Clellan St
Schenectady, NY 12304
Tel: 518 347-5293   *Fax:* 518 347-5196
E-mail: dunkerleyg@ellishospital.org
Length: 3 Yrs   *ACGME Approved/Offered Positions:* 30
Program ID: 120-35-12-215

Stony Brook

SUNY at Stony Brook Program

Sponsor: University Hospital - SUNY at Stony Brook
Prgm Director: Donna I Meltzer, MD
Department of Family Practice
Level 4 Room 50 HSC
Stony Brook, NY 11794
Tel: 631 444-8430   *Fax:* 631 444-7552
E-mail: SBUH_FamMed_Residency@sunysb.edu
Length: 3 Yrs   *ACGME Approved/Offered Positions:* 21
Program ID: 120-35-21-408

Syracuse

SUNY Health Science Center at Syracuse/St Joseph's Hospital Health Center Program

Sponsor: St Joseph's Hospital Health Center
Prgm Director: James B Tucker, MD
301 Prospect Avenue
Syracuse, NY 13203
Tel: 315 448-5537   *Fax:* 315 448-6313
E-mail: anne.louise@sjhsyr.org
Length: 3 Yrs   *ACGME Approved/Offered Positions:* 39
Program ID: 120-35-21-216

Utica

St Elizabeth Medical Center (Utica) Program

Sponsor: St Elizabeth Hospital
Prgm Director: William A Jorgensen, DO
Family Medicine Residency Program
120 Hobart Street
Utica, NY 13501
Tel: 315 734-3571   *Fax:* 315 734-3572
Length: 3 Yrs   *ACGME Approved/Offered Positions:* 26
Program ID: 120-35-11-217

Yonkers

New York Medical College at St Joseph's Medical Center Program

Sponsor: New York Medical College
St Josephs Medical Center
Prgm Director: Sonia A Velez, MD, JD
127 South Broadway
Yonkers, NY 10701
Tel: 914 378-7586   *Fax:* 914 378-1071
E-mail: stjosfp@saintjosephs.org
Length: 3 Yrs   *ACGME Approved/Offered Positions:* 31
Program ID: 120-35-11-218

North Carolina

Asheville

Mountain Area Health Education Center Program

Sponsor: Mountain Area Health Education Center
Mission Hospitals - Memorial Campus
Prgm Director: Blake Fagan, MD*
118 W T Weaver Boulevard
Asheville, NC 28804
Tel: 828 258-0670   *Fax:* 828 257-4738
Length: 3 Yrs   *ACGME Approved/Offered Positions:* 27
Program ID: 120-36-11-219

Camp Lejeune

Naval Hospital (Camp Lejeune) Program

Sponsor: Naval Hospital-Camp Lejeune
Prgm Director: Steven A Kewish, MD
100 Brewster Boulevard
Camp Lejeune, NC 28547
Tel: 910 450-3138   *Fax:* 910 450-4649
E-mail: NHCLGMECoordinator@med.navy.mil
Length: 3 Yrs   *ACGME Approved/Offered Positions:* 18
Program ID: 120-36-12-665
Uniformed Services Program

Chapel Hill

University of North Carolina Hospitals Program

Sponsor: University of North Carolina Hospitals
Prgm Director: Clark R Denniston, MD
Department of Family Medicine
Manning Drive, Campus Box 7595
Chapel Hill, NC 27599
Tel: 919 966-3456   *Fax:* 919 966-6125
E-mail: uncfpr@med.unc.edu
Length: 3 Yrs   *ACGME Approved/Offered Positions:* 24
Program ID: 120-36-31-220

Charlotte

Carolinas Medical Center Program

Sponsor: Carolinas Medical Center
Carolinas Medical Center: Mercy
Prgm Director: Vanessa McPherson, MD
Family Medicine Residency Program
PO Box 32861
Charlotte, NC 28232
Tel: 704 446-7700   *Fax:* 704 446-7795
E-mail: Vanessa.McPherson@carolinashealthcare.org
Length: 3 Yrs   *ACGME Approved/Offered Positions:* 24
Program ID: 120-36-11-221

Concord

Carolinas Medical Center (Northeast-Cabarrus) Program

Sponsor: Carolinas Medical Center-Northeast
Prgm Director: Mark D Robinson, MD
270 Copperfield Blvd, Suite 201
Concord, NC 28025
Tel: 704 721-2060   *Fax:* 704 721-2077
E-mail: residency@northeastmedical.org
Length: 3 Yrs   *ACGME Approved/Offered Positions:* 24
Program ID: 120-36-21-580

Durham

Duke University Hospital Program

Sponsor: Duke University Hospital
Prgm Director: Brian H Halstater, MD
Dept of Community/Family Medicine
Box 3886
Durham, NC 27710
Tel: 919 681-3028   *Fax:* 919 668-1785
Length: 3 Yrs   *ACGME Approved/Offered Positions:* 12
Program ID: 120-36-21-222

Programs

Fayetteville

Duke University Hospital/Southern Regional Area Health Education Center Program
Sponsor: Southern Regional Area Health Education Center
Cape Fear Valley Medical Center
Prgm Director: Sandra M Carr, MD
Southern Regional AHEC
1601 Owen Drive
Fayetteville, NC 28304
Tel: 910 678-7259   *Fax:* 910 678-0115
E-mail: sandra.carr@SR-ahec.org
Length: 3 Yrs   *ACGME Approved/Offered Positions:* 18
Program ID: 120-36-31-223

Fort Bragg

Womack Army Medical Center Program
Sponsor: Womack Army Medical Center
Prgm Director: James Liffrig, MD, MPH
Department of Family Medicine
Family Medicine Residency Program
Fort Bragg, NC 28310
Tel: 910 907-8251
E-mail: james.liffrig@us.army.mil
Length: 3 Yrs   *ACGME Approved/Offered Positions:* 27
Program ID: 120-36-21-011
Uniformed Services Program

Greensboro

Moses H Cone Memorial Hospital Program
Sponsor: Moses H Cone Memorial Hospital
Prgm Director: William A Hensel, MD
Family Practice Center
1125 North Church Street
Greensboro, NC 27401
Tel: 336 832-8132   *Fax:* 336 832-7078
Length: 3 Yrs   *ACGME Approved/Offered Positions:* 24
Program ID: 120-36-11-224

Greenville

Pitt County Memorial Hospital/East Carolina University Program
Sponsor: Pitt County Memorial Hospital
Brody School of Medicine at East Carolina University
Prgm Director: Gary Levine, MD
Department of Family Medicine
Family Medicine Center
Greenville, NC 27834
Tel: 252 744-4616   *Fax:* 252 744-4614
E-mail: ecufammedres@ecu.edu
Length: 3 Yrs   *ACGME Approved/Offered Positions:* 30
Program ID: 120-36-11-225

Hendersonville

Mountain Area Health Education Center Rural Program
Sponsor: Mountain Area Health Education Center
Margaret R Pardee Memorial Hospital
Prgm Director: Geoffrey L Jones, MD*
709 N Justice St, Suite B
Hendersonville, NC 28791
Tel: 828 696-1255   *Fax:* 828 696-1257
Length: 3 Yrs   *ACGME Approved/Offered Positions:* 6
Program ID: 120-36-21-575

Monroe

Carolinas Medical Center Rural Program
Sponsor: Carolinas Medical Center
Carolinas Medical Center Union
Prgm Director: James M Wetter, MD
PO Box 5003
600 Hospital Drive
Monroe, NC 28111
Tel: 704 226-5013   *Fax:* 704 296-4172
E-mail: james.wetter@carolinashealthcare.org
Length: 3 Yrs   *ACGME Approved/Offered Positions:* 6
Program ID: 120-36-21-634

Wilmington

New Hanover Regional Medical Center Program
Sponsor: New Hanover Regional Medical Center
Prgm Director: Janalynn F Beste, MD
Residency in Family Medicine
2523 Delaney Ave
Wilmington, NC 28403
Tel: 910 343-1122   *Fax:* 910 343-1999
Length: 3 Yrs   *ACGME Approved/Offered Positions:* 12
Program ID: 120-36-21-611

Winston-Salem

Wake Forest University School of Medicine Program
Sponsor: Wake Forest University Baptist Medical Center
Forsyth Memorial Hospital
Prgm Director: Mark Andrews, MD
Family and Community Medicine
Medical Center Blvd
Winston-Salem, NC 27157
Tel: 336 716-2832   *Fax:* 336 716-9126
E-mail: mlocke@wfubmc.edu
Length: 3 Yrs   *ACGME Approved/Offered Positions:* 30
Program ID: 120-36-31-226

North Dakota

Bismarck

University of North Dakota (Bismarck) Program
Sponsor: Univ of North Dakota School of Medicine and Health Sciences
Medcenter One Hospital
St Alexius Medical Center
Prgm Director: Jeffrey E Hostetter, MD, MS
Center for Family Medicine
515 East Broadway Avenue
Bismarck, ND 58501
Tel: 701 751-9500   *Fax:* 701 751-9508
E-mail: jhostett@medicine.nodak.edu
Length: 3 Yrs   *ACGME Approved/Offered Positions:* 15
Program ID: 120-37-21-227

Grand Forks

Altru Health System (Grand Forks) Program
Sponsor: Altru Health System Hospital
Prgm Director: Greg D Greek, MD
Grand Forks Family Medicine Residency
725 Hamline Street
Grand Forks, ND 58203
Tel: 701 780-6810   *Fax:* 701 780-6860
Length: 3 Yrs   *ACGME Approved/Offered Positions:* 18
Program ID: 120-37-31-229

Minot

University of North Dakota (Minot) Program
Sponsor: Univ of North Dakota School of Medicine and Health Sciences
Trinity Health
Prgm Director: Kimberly T Krohn, MD, MPH
Center for Family Medicine - Minot
1201 11th Ave SW
Minot, ND 58701
Tel: 701 858-6700   *Fax:* 701 858-6749
E-mail: karenru@medicine.nodak.edu
Length: 3 Yrs   *ACGME Approved/Offered Positions:* 15
Program ID: 120-37-31-230

Ohio

Akron

Akron General Medical Center/NEOUCOM Program
Sponsor: Akron General Medical Center
Prgm Director: Elliot B Davidson, MD*
400 Wabash Avenue
Akron, OH 44307
Tel: 330 344-7671   *Fax:* 330 344-6852
Length: 3 Yrs   *ACGME Approved/Offered Positions:* 15
Program ID: 120-38-31-232

Summa Health System/NEOUCOM Program
Sponsor: Summa Health System
Akron City Hospital (Summa Health System)
Prgm Director: Richard M Hines, MD
55 Arch Street Suite 3A
Akron, OH 44304
Tel: 330 375-3144   *Fax:* 330 375-4291
Length: 3 Yrs   *ACGME Approved/Offered Positions:* 24
Program ID: 120-38-21-231

Barberton

Barberton Citizens Hospital/NEOUCOM Program
Sponsor: Barberton Citizens Hospital
Prgm Director: James R Richard, MD
155 Fifth Street, NE
Barberton, OH 44203
Tel: 330 615-3224   *Fax:* 330 615-3221
Length: 3 Yrs   *ACGME Approved/Offered Positions:* 18
Program ID: 120-38-21-437

Bellefontaine

Ohio State University Hospital Rural Program
Sponsor: Ohio State University Hospital
Mary Rutan Hospital
Prgm Director: Randall L Longenecker, MD
4879 US Route 68 South
West Liberty, OH 43357
Tel: 937 465-0080   *Fax:* 937 465-9945
E-mail: residency@madriverfamilypractice.org
Length: 3 Yrs   *ACGME Approved/Offered Positions:* 6
Program ID: 120-38-21-640

Canton

Aultman Hospital/NEOUCOM Program
Sponsor: Aultman Hospital
Prgm Director: S David Wakulchik, MD
2600 7th Street, SW
Canton, OH 44710
Tel: 330 363-6250   *Fax:* 330 580-5509
Length: 3 Yrs   *ACGME Approved/Offered Positions:* 21
Program ID: 120-38-11-234

Note: * indicates a newly appointed program director

Cincinnati

Christ Hospital/University of Cincinnati College of Medicine Program

Sponsor: Christ Hospital
Prgm Director: Philip Diller, MD, PhD
Department of Family Medicine
2123 Auburn Avenue, Suite 340
Cincinnati, OH 45219
Tel: 513 721-2221   *Fax:* 513 345-6665
E-mail: mullensf@fammed.uc.edu
Length: 3 Yrs   *ACGME Approved/Offered Positions:* 15
Program ID: 120-38-21-235

TriHealth (Bethesda North Hospital) Program

Sponsor: TriHealth
TriHealth - Bethesda North Hospital
Prgm Director: Lorraine Stephens, MD
Family Medicine Residency Program
4411 Montgomery Road, Suite 206
Cincinnati, OH 45212
Tel: 513 557-4450   *Fax:* 513 631-0796
E-mail: patty_smith@trihealth.com
Length: 3 Yrs   *ACGME Approved/Offered Positions:* 18
Program ID: 120-38-21-474

Cleveland

Case Western Reserve University (MetroHealth) Program

Sponsor: MetroHealth Medical Center
Prgm Director: Aphrodite Papadakis, MD*
Department of Family Medicine
2500 MetroHealth Drive, GG39B
Cleveland, OH 44109
Tel: 216 778-3487   *Fax:* 216 778-8225
Length: 3 Yrs   *ACGME Approved/Offered Positions:* 18
Program ID: 120-38-11-237

Fairview Hospital/Cleveland Clinic Program

Sponsor: Fairview Hospital
Prgm Director: Stephen P Flynn, MD
18200 Lorain Avenue
Cleveland, OH 44111
Tel: 216 476-7085   *Fax:* 216 476-7604
E-mail: vickie.erhardt@fairviewhospital.org
Length: 3 Yrs   *ACGME Approved/Offered Positions:* 18
Program ID: 120-38-11-238

University Hospitals Case Medical Center Program

Sponsor: University Hospitals Case Medical Center
Prgm Director: Al Cadesky, MD
Department of Family Medicine
11100 Euclid Avenue, Bolwell 1200
Cleveland, OH 44106
Tel: 216 844-5483   *Fax:* 216 844-1030
Length: 3 Yrs   *ACGME Approved/Offered Positions:* 24
Program ID: 120-38-11-236

Columbus

Grant Medical Center (OhioHealth) Program

Sponsor: Grant Medical Center (OhioHealth)
Prgm Director: Robert Skully, MD
Medical Education Department
285 E State Street, Suite 670
Columbus, OH 43215
Tel: 614 566-8270   *Fax:* 614 566-8073
E-mail: GMCMedEd@ohiohealth.com
Length: 3 Yrs   *ACGME Approved/Offered Positions:* 39
Program ID: 120-38-31-239

Mount Carmel Program

Sponsor: Mount Carmel
Prgm Director: Chad M Braun, MD
477 Cooper Road
Suite 300
Westerville, OH 43081
Tel: 614 898-8711   *Fax:* 614 898-0392
Length: 3 Yrs   *ACGME Approved/Offered Positions:* 21
Program ID: 120-38-32-240

Ohio State University Hospital Program

Sponsor: Ohio State University Hospital
Nationwide Children's Hospital
Ohio State University Hospitals, East
Prgm Director: Doug Knutson, MD
Department of Family Medicine
2231 N High Street, Room 205
Columbus, OH 43201
Tel: 614 293-2655   *Fax:* 614 293-2717
E-mail: Doug.Knutson@osumc.edu
Length: 3 Yrs   *ACGME Approved/Offered Positions:* 23
Program ID: 120-38-21-241

Ohio State University Hospital Urban Program

Sponsor: Ohio State University Hospital
Ohio State University Hospitals, East
Prgm Director: Parita Patel, MD*
2231 North High Street
Room 205
Columbus, OH 43201
Tel: 614 257-3560   *Fax:* 614 257-3538
Length: 3 Yrs   *ACGME Approved/Offered Positions:* 6
Program ID: 120-38-12-673

Riverside Methodist Hospitals (OhioHealth) Program

Sponsor: Riverside Methodist Hospitals (OhioHealth)
Prgm Director: Edward T Bope, MD
Riverside Family Practice Center
697 Thomas Lane
Columbus, OH 43214
Tel: 614 566-4398   *Fax:* 614 566-6843
E-mail: ksavage@ohiohealth.com
Length: 3 Yrs   *ACGME Approved/Offered Positions:* 18
Program ID: 120-38-21-242

Dayton

Miami Valley Hospital Program

Sponsor: Miami Valley Hospital
Prgm Director: Theodore E Wymyslo, MD
101 Wyoming Street
Dayton, OH 45409
Tel: 937 208-2427   *Fax:* 937 208-4487
E-mail: mvhfpr@mvh.org
Length: 3 Yrs   *ACGME Approved/Offered Positions:* 21
Program ID: 120-38-31-244

Wright State University/Dayton Community Hospitals Program

Sponsor: Wright State University Boonshoft School of Medicine
Good Samaritan Hospital and Health Center
Prgm Director: Teresa W Zryd, MD, MSPH
2345 Philadelphia Drive
Dayton, OH 45406
Tel: 937 275-2792   *Fax:* 937 277-1140
E-mail: family_practice@shp-dayton.org
Length: 3 Yrs   *ACGME Approved/Offered Positions:* 15
Program ID: 120-38-31-243

Sylvania

Flower Hospital Program

Sponsor: Flower Hospital
Prgm Director: Jeanine Huttner, MD
Family Physicians Association
5300 Harroun Road, Suite 304
Sylvania, OH 43560
Tel: 419 824-1928   *Fax:* 419 824-1771
Length: 3 Yrs   *ACGME Approved/Offered Positions:* 18
Program ID: 120-38-11-246

Toledo

Mercy Health Partners/St Vincent Mercy Medical Center Program

Sponsor: St Vincent Mercy Medical Center
St Charles Mercy Hospital
Prgm Director: Jahangir Adil, MD
2200 Jefferson Avenue
Toledo, OH 43604
Tel: 419 251-1859   *Fax:* 419 242-9806
Length: 3 Yrs   *ACGME Approved/Offered Positions:* 24
Program ID: 120-38-31-249

St Luke's Hospital Program

Sponsor: St Luke's Hospital
University of Toledo
Prgm Director: Thomas Tafelski, DO, PhD*
6005 Monclova Road
Maumee, OH 43537
Tel: 419 383-5531   *Fax:* 419 383-5515
E-mail: cinda.bernard@utoledo.edu
Length: 3 Yrs
Program ID: 120-38-13-688

Toledo Hospital Program

Sponsor: Toledo Hospital
Prgm Director: Robert S Fredrick, MD*
2051 West Central Avenue
Toledo, OH 43606
Tel: 419 291-2342   *Fax:* 419 291-6952
E-mail: tthfpr@promedica.org
Length: 3 Yrs   *ACGME Approved/Offered Positions:* 18
Program ID: 120-38-21-250

Wilmington

Clinton Memorial Hospital/University of Cincinnati College of Medicine Program

Sponsor: Clinton Memorial Hospital
Prgm Director: Keith B Holten, MD
825 W Locust Street
Wilmington, OH 45177
Tel: 937 383-3382   *Fax:* 937 383-0610
E-mail: residency@cmhregional.com
Length: 3 Yrs   *ACGME Approved/Offered Positions:* 12
Program ID: 120-38-21-626

Youngstown

St Elizabeth Health Center/NEOUCOM Program

Sponsor: St Elizabeth Health Center
Prgm Director: Rudolph M Krafft, MD
1044 Belmont Ave
PO Box 1790
Youngstown, OH 44501
Tel: 330 744-0301   *Fax:* 330 480-2948
E-mail: rosey_hilland@hmis.org
Length: 3 Yrs   *ACGME Approved/Offered Positions:* 12
Program ID: 120-38-11-251

Programs

Western Reserve Care System/NEOUCOM Program

Sponsor: Forum Health/Western Reserve Care System (Youngstown)
Prgm Director: Lisa Weiss, MD*
Family Practice Center
500 Gypsy Lane
Youngstown, OH 44501
Tel: 330 884-3983   *Fax:* 330 884-0506
E-mail: mevanchick@forumhealth.org
Length: 3 Yrs   *ACGME Approved/Offered Positions:* 12
Program ID: 120-38-11-359

Oklahoma

Enid

University of Oklahoma/Garfield County Medical Society Rural Program

Sponsor: University of Oklahoma College of Medicine
St Mary's Regional Medical Center
Integris Bass Baptist Health Center
OU Medical Center
Prgm Director: J Michael Pontious, MD
620 S Madison, Suite 304
Enid, OK 73701
Tel: 580 242-1300   *Fax:* 580 237-7913
E-mail: tracy-bittle@ouhsc.edu
Length: 3 Yrs   *ACGME Approved/Offered Positions:* 12
Program ID: 120-39-11-253

Lawton

University of Oklahoma Health Sciences Center (Lawton) Program

Sponsor: University of Oklahoma College of Medicine
Comanche County Memorial Hospital
Southwestern Medical Center
Prgm Director: Dan F Criswell, MD
1202 NW Arlington
Lawton, OK 73507
Tel: 580 248-2288   *Fax:* 580 248-5348
Length: 3 Yrs   *ACGME Approved/Offered Positions:* 12
Program ID: 120-39-21-659

Oklahoma City

Integris Baptist Medical Center/Great Plains Medical Foundation Program

Sponsor: Integris Baptist Medical Center
Deaconess Hospital
Prgm Director: Neal D Clemenson, MD
Suite 100
Oklahoma City, OK 73112
Tel: 405 951-2623   *Fax:* 405 951-2824
Length: 3 Yrs   *ACGME Approved/Offered Positions:* 15
Program ID: 120-39-21-585

St Anthony Hospital Program

Sponsor: St Anthony Hospital
Prgm Director: Cheyn Onarecker, MD
608 NW 9th Street, Suite 1000
Oklahoma City, OK 73102
Tel: 405 272-7494   *Fax:* 405 272-6985
Length: 3 Yrs   *ACGME Approved/Offered Positions:* 27
Program ID: 120-39-21-513

University of Oklahoma Health Sciences Center Program

Sponsor: University of Oklahoma College of Medicine
OU Medical Center
Prgm Director: James Barrett, MD
900 NE 10th Street
Oklahoma City, OK 73104
Tel: 405 271-2230   *Fax:* 405 271-4366
Length: 3 Yrs   *ACGME Approved/Offered Positions:* 36
Program ID: 120-39-21-254

Tulsa

In His Image at Hillcrest Medical Center Program

Sponsor: In His Image Inc
Hillcrest Medical Center
Prgm Director: Mitchell W Duininck, MD
7600 South Lewis Avenue
Tulsa, OK 74136
Tel: 918 493-7880   *Fax:* 918 493-7888
E-mail: admin@inhisimage.org
Length: 3 Yrs   *ACGME Approved/Offered Positions:* 30
Program ID: 120-39-21-499

University of Oklahoma College of Medicine-Tulsa Program

Sponsor: University of Oklahoma College of Medicine-Tulsa
Hillcrest Medical Center
Prgm Director: Andrew Donnelly, MD*
Department of Family Medicine
1111 S Saint Louis Ave
Tulsa, OK 74120
Tel: 918 619-4764   *Fax:* 918 619-4707
Length: 3 Yrs   *ACGME Approved/Offered Positions:* 42
Program ID: 120-39-21-256

University of Oklahoma College of Medicine-Tulsa Rural Program

Sponsor: University of Oklahoma College of Medicine-Tulsa
Hillcrest Medical Center
Jane Phillips Episcopal-Memorial Medical Center
Prgm Director: W M Woods, MD
400 Wyandotte Place
PO Box 420
Ramona, OK 74061
Tel: 918 536-2104   *Fax:* 918 536-2203
E-mail: sharon-tennant@ouhsc.edu
Length: 3 Yrs   *ACGME Approved/Offered Positions:* 6
Program ID: 120-39-21-600

Oregon

Klamath Falls

Oregon Health & Science University (Cascades East) Program

Sponsor: Oregon Health & Science University Hospital
Sky Lakes Medical Center
Prgm Director: Robert G Ross, MD, MEd
Cascades East Family Medicine Residency
2801 Daggett Avenue
Klamath Falls, OR 97601
Tel: 541 274-4612   *Fax:* 541 885-0328
Length: 3 Yrs   *ACGME Approved/Offered Positions:* 24
Program ID: 120-40-21-540

Portland

Oregon Health & Science University Program

Sponsor: Oregon Health & Science University Hospital
Prgm Director: Roger D Garvin, MD
Department of Family Medicine
3181 SW Sam Jackson Park Road
Portland, OR 97239
Tel: 503 494-3367   *Fax:* 503 494-7659
E-mail: fmres@ohsu.edu
Length: 3 Yrs   *ACGME Approved/Offered Positions:* 36
Program ID: 120-40-21-371

Providence Health System/Milwaukie Hospital Program

Sponsor: Providence Health System, Portland Service Area
Providence Milwaukie Hospital
Prgm Director: William R Gillanders, MD
10150 SE 32nd Avenue
Milwaukie, OR 97222
Tel: 503 513-8930   *Fax:* 503 513-8953
Length: 3 Yrs   *ACGME Approved/Offered Positions:* 21
Program ID: 120-40-21-656

Pennsylvania

Abington

Abington Memorial Hospital Program

Sponsor: Abington Memorial Hospital
Prgm Director: Gerald J Hansen III, MD
Abington Family Medicine Residency Program
500 Old York Road Suite 108
Jenkintown, PA 19046
Tel: 215 481-2729   *Fax:* 215 481-7446
Length: 3 Yrs   *ACGME Approved/Offered Positions:* 21
Program ID: 120-41-11-258

Allentown

Lehigh Valley Hospital Network/Pennsylvania State University Program

Sponsor: Lehigh Valley Hospital Network
Prgm Director: Julie A Dostal, MD
1628 West Chew Street
School of Nursing, First Floor
Allentown, PA 18105
Tel: 610 969-4970   *Fax:* 610 969-4912
Length: 3 Yrs   *ACGME Approved/Offered Positions:* 18
Program ID: 120-41-21-572

Sacred Heart Hospital/Temple University (Allentown) Program

Sponsor: Sacred Heart Hospital
Prgm Director: Richard T Martin, MD
Family Medicine Residency
450 Chew Street
Allentown, PA 18102
Tel: 610 776-5912   *Fax:* 610 663-3165
Length: 3 Yrs   *ACGME Approved/Offered Positions:* 18
Program ID: 120-41-21-259

Altoona

Altoona Regional Health System (Altoona Hospital Campus) Program

Sponsor: Altoona Regional Health System (Altoona Hospital Campus)
Prgm Director: Donald M Beckstead, MD
501 Howard Avenue, Suite F2
Altoona, PA 16601
Tel: 814 889-2020
E-mail: recruitment@altoonafp.org
Length: 3 Yrs   *ACGME Approved/Offered Positions:* 18
Program ID: 120-41-11-260

Beaver

The Medical Center (Beaver, PA) Program

Sponsor: HVHS, The Medical Center, Beaver
Prgm Director: James P McKenna, MD
918 Third Avenue
Beaver Falls, PA 15010
Tel: 724 843-6007   *Fax:* 724 847-7840
Length: 3 Yrs   *ACGME Approved/Offered Positions:* 18
Program ID: 120-41-21-409

Note: * indicates a newly appointed program director

Bethlehem

St Luke's Hospital Program
Sponsor: St Luke's Hospital
Prgm Director: Robert Langan, MD
2830 Easton Avenue
Bethlehem, PA 18017
Tel: 610 954-3550   *Fax:* 610 954-3693
E-mail: fpresidency@slhn.org
Length: 3 Yrs   *ACGME Approved/Offered Positions:* 18
Program ID: 120-41-21-603

Bryn Mawr

Bryn Mawr Hospital Program
Sponsor: Bryn Mawr Hospital
Prgm Director: Joseph A Greco, MD*
130 S Bryn Mawr Avenue
3rd Floor H Wing
Bryn Mawr, PA 19010
Tel: 610 645-1523   *Fax:* 610 325-1395
Length: 3 Yrs   *ACGME Approved/Offered Positions:* 18
Program ID: 120-41-31-261

Danville

Geisinger Health System Program
Sponsor: Geisinger Health System
Geisinger Wyoming Valley Medical Center
Prgm Director: Mary Elizabeth Roth, MD, MS
1000 East Mountain Boulevard
Wilkes Barre, PA 18711
Tel: 570 826-7864   *Fax:* 570 826-7387
E-mail: meroth@geisinger.edu
Length: 3 Yrs   *ACGME Approved/Offered Positions:* 18
Program ID: 120-41-12-689

Erie

St Vincent Health Center Program
Sponsor: St Vincent Health Center
Prgm Director: Bruce C Gebhardt, MD*
2314 Sassafras Street, 3rd Floor
Erie, PA 16502
Tel: 814 452-5120   *Fax:* 814 452-5097
E-mail: bgebhardt@svhs.org
Length: 3 Yrs   *ACGME Approved/Offered Positions:* 18
Program ID: 120-41-11-264

Johnstown

Conemaugh Valley Memorial Hospital Program
Sponsor: Conemaugh Valley Memorial Hospital
Prgm Director: Jeanne P Spencer, MD
1086 Franklin Street
Johnstown, PA 15905
Tel: 814 534-9364   *Fax:* 814 534-5599
Length: 3 Yrs   *ACGME Approved/Offered Positions:* 18
Program ID: 120-41-11-269

Lancaster

Lancaster General Hospital Program
Sponsor: Lancaster General Hospital
Prgm Director: Stephen D Ratcliffe, MD
555 N Duke Street
PO Box 3555
Lancaster, PA 17604
Tel: 717 544-4940   *Fax:* 717 544-4149
Length: 3 Yrs   *ACGME Approved/Offered Positions:* 39
Program ID: 120-41-12-270

Latrobe

Latrobe Area Hospital Program
Sponsor: Latrobe Area Hospital
Prgm Director: Carol J Fox, MD
One Mellon Way
Latrobe, PA 15650
Tel: 724 537-1485   *Fax:* 724 537-1635
E-mail: residency@excelahealth.org
Length: 3 Yrs   *ACGME Approved/Offered Positions:* 18
Program ID: 120-41-11-277

Lebanon

Penn State University/Good Samaritan Hospital Program
Sponsor: Milton S Hershey Medical Center
Good Samaritan Hospital
Prgm Director: Paul Aitken Jr, MD, MPH
PO Box 1520
Lebanon, PA 17042
Tel: 717 270-1949   *Fax:* 717 270-1958
E-mail: fpr@gshleb.org
Length: 3 Yrs   *ACGME Approved/Offered Positions:* 24
Program ID: 120-41-21-504

McKeesport

University of Pittsburgh Medical Center Medical Education (McKeesport Hospital) Program
Sponsor: Univ of Pittsburgh Medical Center Medical Education
UPMC McKeesport
Prgm Director: William H Markle, MD
Latterman Family Health Center
2347 Fifth Avenue
McKeesport, PA 15132
Tel: 412 673-5009   *Fax:* 412 673-1021
E-mail: kramersb@upmc.edu
Length: 3 Yrs   *ACGME Approved/Offered Positions:* 18
Program ID: 120-41-12-271

Monroeville

Western Pennsylvania Hospital/Forbes Regional Campus Program
Sponsor: Western Pennsylvania Hospital/Forbes Regional Campus
Prgm Director: Katherine L Neely, MD
Physicians Office Building One, Suite 216
2566 Haymaker Road
Monroeville, PA 15146
Tel: 412 828-2768   *Fax:* 412 858-4442
Length: 3 Yrs   *ACGME Approved/Offered Positions:* 18
Program ID: 120-41-22-278

Norristown

Montgomery Hospital Program
Sponsor: Montgomery Hospital
Prgm Director: Hazel M Bluestein, MD
1301 Powell Street
Norristown, PA 19401
Tel: 610 277-0964   *Fax:* 610 277-7065
Length: 3 Yrs   *ACGME Approved/Offered Positions:* 18
Program ID: 120-41-11-272

Philadelphia

Chestnut Hill Hospital Program
Sponsor: Chestnut Hill Hospital
Prgm Director: Marc W McKenna, MD
8815 Germantown Avenue, 5th Floor
Philadelphia, PA 19118
Tel: 215 248-8145   *Fax:* 215 753-2148
E-mail: marc_mckenna@chs.net
Length: 3 Yrs   *ACGME Approved/Offered Positions:* 18
Program ID: 120-41-31-275

Drexel University College of Medicine/Hahnemann University Hospital Program
Sponsor: Drexel University College of Medicine/Hahnemann University
Hahnemann University Hospital (Tenet Health System)
Prgm Director: David Berkson, MD
10 Shurs Lane
Suite 301
Philadelphia, PA 19127
Tel: 215 967-1632   *Fax:* 215 482-1095
Length: 3 Yrs   *ACGME Approved/Offered Positions:* 12
Program ID: 120-41-31-576

Thomas Jefferson University Program
Sponsor: Thomas Jefferson University Hospital
Prgm Director: Patrick McManus, MD
1015 Walnut Street, Suite 401
Philadelphia, PA 19107
Tel: 215 955-2363   *Fax:* 215 955-0640
E-mail: patrick.mcmanus@jefferson.edu
Length: 3 Yrs   *ACGME Approved/Offered Positions:* 27
Program ID: 120-41-21-276

University of Pennsylvania Program
Sponsor: University of Pennsylvania Health System
Presbyterian Medical Center (UPHS)
Prgm Director: Richard A Neill Neill, MD
Department of Family Medicine & Community Health
51 N 39th Street, 6th Floor Mutch Building
Philadelphia, PA 19104
Tel: 215 662-8949   *Fax:* 215 243-3290
E-mail: fampract@mail.med.upenn.edu
Length: 3 Yrs   *ACGME Approved/Offered Positions:* 18
Program ID: 120-41-21-633

Pittsburgh

University of Pittsburgh Medical Center Medical Education (Mercy) Program
Sponsor: Univ of Pittsburgh Medical Center Medical Education
Prgm Director: William K Johnjulio, MD
Family Medicine Residency Program
1400 Locust Street
Pittsburgh, PA 15219
Tel: 412 232-5955   *Fax:* 412 232-7827
E-mail: residencyf@upmc.edu
Length: 3 Yrs   *ACGME Approved/Offered Positions:* 12
Program ID: 120-41-11-578

University of Pittsburgh Medical Center Medical Education (Presbyterian Shadyside Hospital) Program
Sponsor: Univ of Pittsburgh Medical Center Medical Education
UPMC Presbyterian Shadyside
Prgm Director: N Randall Kolb, MD
UPMC Shadyside Family Medicine Residency
5230 Centre Avenue
Pittsburgh, PA 15232
Tel: 412 623-3030   *Fax:* 412 623-3012
E-mail: herbsterwl@upmc.edu
Length: 3 Yrs   *ACGME Approved/Offered Positions:* 27
Program ID: 120-41-12-280

University of Pittsburgh Medical Center Medical Education (St Margaret Hospital) Program
Sponsor: Univ of Pittsburgh Medical Center Medical Education
UPMC St Margaret
Prgm Director: Ted C Schaffer, MD
815 Freeport Road
Pittsburgh, PA 15215
Tel: 412 784-4232   *Fax:* 412 784-5274
E-mail: floatkm@upmc.edu
Length: 3 Yrs   *ACGME Approved/Offered Positions:* 36
Program ID: 120-41-12-279

Programs

Western Pennsylvania Hospital/Temple University Program

Sponsor: Western Pennsylvania Hospital
Prgm Director: Nancy Levine, MD
4800 Friendship Ave, Suite N221
Pittsburgh, PA 15224
Tel: 412 578-1649   *Fax:* 412 688-7711
E-mail: famprac@wpahs.org
Length: 3 Yrs   *ACGME Approved/Offered Positions:* 12
Program ID: 120-41-12-579

Sayre

Guthrie/Robert Packer Hospital Program

Sponsor: Robert Packer Hospital
Prgm Director: Robert T McClelland, MD
One Guthrie Square
Sayre, PA 18840
Tel: 570 882-3292   *Fax:* 570 882-2807
E-mail: fampract@guthrie.org
Length: 3 Yrs   *ACGME Approved/Offered Positions:* 12
Program ID: 120-41-21-518

Upland

Crozer-Chester Medical Center Program

Sponsor: Crozer-Chester Medical Center
Crozer Keystone Health System-Delaware County Mem
    Hosp
Prgm Director: William J Warning II, MD
1260 E Woodland Avenue, Suite 200
Springfield, PA 19064
Tel: 610 690-4480   *Fax:* 610 690-4474
E-mail: fmresidency@crozer.org
Length: 3 Yrs   *ACGME Approved/Offered Positions:* 21
Program ID: 120-41-21-477

Washington

Washington Hospital Program

Sponsor: Washington Hospital
Prgm Director: Paul T Cullen, MD
95 Leonard Avenue
Bldg 2, Third Floor
Washington, PA 15301
Tel: 724 223-3548   *Fax:* 724 229-2178
E-mail: dshade@washingtonhospital.org
Length: 3 Yrs   *ACGME Approved/Offered Positions:* 24
Program ID: 120-41-12-283

West Reading

Reading Hospital and Medical Center Program

Sponsor: Reading Hospital and Medical Center
Prgm Director: D Michael Baxter, MD
Doctors' Office Building - Suite 2120
301 South Seventh Avenue
West Reading, PA 19611
Tel: 610 988-8855   *Fax:* 610 988-8390
E-mail: fmres@readinghospital.org
Length: 3 Yrs   *ACGME Approved/Offered Positions:* 18
Program ID: 120-41-12-281

Wilkes-Barre

United Health and Hospital Services Program

Sponsor: Wyoming Valley Health Care System
Prgm Director: Richard B English, MD, MHA
2 Sharpe Street
Caller #3500
Kingston, PA 18704
Tel: 570 552-8900   *Fax:* 570 552-8958
Length: 3 Yrs   *ACGME Approved/Offered Positions:* 21
Program ID: 120-41-21-284

Williamsport

Williamsport Hospital and Medical Center Program

Sponsor: Susquehanna Health System
Prgm Director: David N Ambrose, MD
Family Medicine Residency Program
699 Rural Avenue
Williamsport, PA 17701
Tel: 570 321-2340   *Fax:* 570 321-2359
E-mail: wmsptfp@susquehannahealth.org
Length: 3 Yrs   *ACGME Approved/Offered Positions:* 21
Program ID: 120-41-31-285

York

York Hospital Program

Sponsor: York Hospital
Prgm Director: Bruce M Bushwick, MD
1001 South George Street
York, PA 17405
Tel: 717 851-3038   *Fax:* 717 851-5852
Length: 3 Yrs   *ACGME Approved/Offered Positions:* 24
Program ID: 120-41-11-286

Puerto Rico

Manati

Dr Alejandro Otero Lopez Hospital Program

Sponsor: Hospital Dr Alejandro Otero Lopez
Prgm Director: Luis R Rosa Toledo, MD
PO Box 1142
Manati, PR 00674
Tel: 787 621-3700   *Fax:* 787 621-3266
Length: 3 Yrs   *ACGME Approved/Offered Positions:* 18
Program ID: 120-42-21-501

Mayaguez

Bella Vista Hospital Program

Sponsor: Bella Vista Hospital
Prgm Director: Eliasin Munoz, MD
PO Box 1750
Mayaguez, PR 00681
Tel: 787 834-2350   *Fax:* 787 652-6032
E-mail: bvfamilymedicine@hotmail.com
Length: 3 Yrs   *ACGME Approved/Offered Positions:* 18
Program ID: 120-42-21-620

Ponce

Dr Pila Hospital/Ponce School of Medicine Program

Sponsor: Dr Pila Hospital
Prgm Director: Malynie Blanco, MD
Family Practice Program
PO Box 331910
Ponce, PR 00733
Tel: 787 848-5600   *Fax:* 787 651-5580
E-mail: malynieblanco@hotmail.com
Length: 3 Yrs   *ACGME Approved/Offered Positions:* 12
Program ID: 120-42-21-466

San Juan

University of Puerto Rico Program

Sponsor: University of Puerto Rico School of Medicine
University Hospital
University of Puerto Rico Hospital at Carolina
Prgm Director: Rebecca Rodriguez, MD
PO Box 509
Loíza, PR 00772
Tel: 787 876-7415   *Fax:* 787 876-7416
E-mail: facmedfam@prtc.net
Length: 3 Yrs   *ACGME Approved/Offered Positions:* 24
Program ID: 120-42-21-287

Rhode Island

Pawtucket

Memorial Hospital of Rhode Island/Brown University Program

Sponsor: Memorial Hospital of Rhode Island
Prgm Director: Gowri Anandarajah, MD*
Department of Family Medicine
111 Brewster Street
Pawtucket, RI 02860
Tel: 401 729-2236   *Fax:* 401 729-2923
Length: 3 Yrs   *ACGME Approved/Offered Positions:* 39
Program ID: 120-43-21-288

South Carolina

Anderson

AnMed Health (Anderson) Program

Sponsor: AnMed Health
Prgm Director: Stoney A Abercrombie, MD
Oglesby Center
2000 East Greenville Street, Suite 3600
Anderson, SC 29621
Tel: 864 224-8100   *Fax:* 864 512-3702
E-mail: Darlene.Norton@anmedhealth.org
Length: 3 Yrs   *ACGME Approved/Offered Positions:* 27
Program ID: 120-45-11-289

Charleston

Trident Medical Center/Medical University of South Carolina Program

Sponsor: Trident Medical Center
MUSC Medical Center
Prgm Director: Peter J Carek, MD, MS
9228 Medical Plaza Drive
Charleston, SC 29406
Tel: 843 876-7080   *Fax:* 843 876-7111
Length: 3 Yrs   *ACGME Approved/Offered Positions:* 30
Program ID: 120-45-21-290

Columbia

Palmetto Health/University of South Carolina School of Medicine Program

Sponsor: Palmetto Health
Palmetto Health Richland
William Jennings Bryan Dorn Veterans Hospital
Prgm Director: Charles J Carter, MD
Family Practice Center
3209 Colonial Drive
Columbia, SC 29203
Tel: 803 434-6116
Length: 3 Yrs   *ACGME Approved/Offered Positions:* 30
Program ID: 120-45-11-291

Florence

McLeod Regional Medical Center Program

Sponsor: McLeod Regional Medical Center
Prgm Director: William H Hester, MD
555 East Cheves Street
Florence, SC 29506
Tel: 843 777-2812   *Fax:* 843 777-2810
E-mail: dbacon@mcleodhealth.org
Length: 3 Yrs   *ACGME Approved/Offered Positions:* 24
Program ID: 120-45-21-375

Note: * indicates a newly appointed program director

Greenville

Greenville Hospital System/University of South Carolina School of Medicine Program

Sponsor: Greenville Hospital System/University of South Carolina
Prgm Director: Robert B Hanlin, MD
877 W Faris Rd
Greenville, SC 29605
Tel: 864 455-9022   *Fax:* 864 455-9015
E-mail: cfm@ghs.org
Length: 3 Yrs   *ACGME Approved/Offered Positions:* 18
Program ID: 120-45-11-292

Greenwood

Self Regional Healthcare/Greenwood Program

Sponsor: Self Regional Healthcare
Prgm Director: Gary Goforth, MD
155 Academy Avenue
Greenwood, SC 29646
Tel: 864 725-4869   *Fax:* 864 725-4883
E-mail: ggoforth@selfregional.org
Length: 3 Yrs   *ACGME Approved/Offered Positions:* 27
Program ID: 120-45-21-376

Seneca

AnMed Health (Anderson) Rural Program

Sponsor: AnMed Health
Oconee Memorial Hospital
Prgm Director: Ed Evans, MD
Seneca Medical Associates
11082 N Radio Station Rd
Seneca, SC 29678
Tel: 864 482-0027   *Fax:* 864 482-0028
E-mail: teevans@senecamed.com
Length: 3 Yrs   *ACGME Approved/Offered Positions:* 6
Program ID: 120-45-21-668

Spartanburg

Spartanburg Regional Healthcare System Program

Sponsor: Spartanburg Regional Healthcare System
Prgm Director: Otis L Baughman III, MD
Family Medicine Center
853 North Church Street, Suite 510
Spartanburg, SC 29303
Tel: 864 560-1558   *Fax:* 864 560-1565
E-mail: jhcannon@srhs.com
Length: 3 Yrs   *ACGME Approved/Offered Positions:* 36
Program ID: 120-45-11-293

South Dakota

Rapid City

Rapid City Regional Hospital Program

Sponsor: Rapid City Regional Hospital
Prgm Director: Douglas A Bright, MD
502 E Monroe
Rapid City, SD 57701
Tel: 605 719-4020   *Fax:* 605 719-4044
E-mail: tbarnes@rcrh.org
Length: 3 Yrs   *ACGME Approved/Offered Positions:* 18
Program ID: 120-46-21-547

Sioux Falls

Sioux Falls Family Medicine Program

Sponsor: Center for Family Medicine
Avera McKennan Hospital and University Health Center
Sioux Valley Hospital University of SD Medical Center
Prgm Director: Earl D Kemp, MD
1115 E 20th Street
Sioux Falls, SD 57105
Tel: 605 575-1640   *Fax:* 605 335-1006
E-mail: earl.kemp@usd.edu
Length: 3 Yrs   *ACGME Approved/Offered Positions:* 24
Program ID: 120-46-11-294

Tennessee

Bristol

East Tennessee State University (Bristol) Program

Sponsor: James H Quillen College of Medicine
Wellmont Health System - Bristol Regional Medical Center
Prgm Director: Gregory E Clarity, MD*
208 Medical Park Blvd
Bristol, TN 37620
Tel: 423 990-3012   *Fax:* 423 990-3045
Length: 3 Yrs   *ACGME Approved/Offered Positions:* 24
Program ID: 120-47-31-296

Chattanooga

University of Tennessee College of Medicine at Chattanooga Program

Sponsor: University of Tennessee College of Medicine-Chattanooga
Erlanger Medical Center
Prgm Director: Stephen M Adams, MD
Department of Family Medicine
1100 East Third Street
Chattanooga, TN 37403
Tel: 423 778-2957   *Fax:* 423 778-2959
Length: 3 Yrs   *ACGME Approved/Offered Positions:* 18
Program ID: 120-47-31-584

Jackson

University of Tennessee (Jackson) Program

Sponsor: University of Tennessee College of Medicine
Jackson-Madison County General Hospital
Prgm Director: Gregg E Mitchell, MD
294 Summar Drive
Jackson, TN 38301
Tel: 731 927-8442   *Fax:* 731 410-0369
E-mail: sjcole@utmem.edu
Length: 3 Yrs   *ACGME Approved/Offered Positions:* 24
Program ID: 120-47-21-299

Johnson City

East Tennessee State University Program

Sponsor: James H Quillen College of Medicine
Johnson City Medical Center/Mountain States Health Alliance
Prgm Director: Max M Bayard III, MD
917 W Walnut Street
Johnson City, TN 37604
Tel: 423 439-6471   *Fax:* 423 439-4320
Length: 3 Yrs   *ACGME Approved/Offered Positions:* 21
Program ID: 120-47-21-410

Kingsport

East Tennessee State University (Kingsport) Program

Sponsor: James H Quillen College of Medicine
Wellmont Health System - Holston Valley
Prgm Director: Reid Blackwelder, MD
201 Cassel Drive
Kingsport, TN 37660
Tel: 423 245-9626   *Fax:* 423 245-9634
E-mail: blackwel@mail.etsu.edu
Length: 3 Yrs   *ACGME Approved/Offered Positions:* 24
Program ID: 120-47-31-297

Knoxville

University of Tennessee Medical Center at Knoxville Program

Sponsor: University of Tennessee Graduate School of Medicine
University of Tennessee Memorial Hospital
Prgm Director: Amy Barger-Stevens, MD
1924 Alcoa Highway, Box U-67
Knoxville, TN 37920
Tel: 865 305-9352   *Fax:* 865 305-6321
E-mail: utfmrp@utmck.edu
Length: 3 Yrs   *ACGME Approved/Offered Positions:* 26
Program ID: 120-47-11-298

Memphis

University of Tennessee/Saint Francis Program

Sponsor: University of Tennessee College of Medicine
St Francis Hospital
Prgm Director: Steven D Schrock, MD*
1301 Primacy Parkway
Memphis, TN 38119
Tel: 901 448-0276   *Fax:* 901 448-0404
E-mail: pgriffit@utmem.edu
Length: 3 Yrs   *ACGME Approved/Offered Positions:* 24
Program ID: 120-47-21-453

Nashville

Meharry Medical College Program

Sponsor: Meharry Medical College School of Medicine
Metropolitan Nashville General Hospital
Prgm Director: Millard D Collins Jr, MD
Department of Family Medicine
1005 Dr D B Todd Jr, Blvd
Nashville, TN 37208
Tel: 615 327-6935   *Fax:* 615 327-5634
E-mail: lhairston@mmc.edu
Length: 3 Yrs   *ACGME Approved/Offered Positions:* 18
Program ID: 120-47-21-463

Texas

Abilene

Texas Tech University (Lubbock) Rural Program at Abilene

Sponsor: Texas Tech University Health Sciences Center at Lubbock
Hendrick Medical Center/Health System
University Medical Center
Prgm Director: Ronald L Cook, DO
3601 4th Street
Lubbock, TX 79430
Tel: 806 743-2770   *Fax:* 806 743-3955
E-mail: jeanna.glenn@ttuhsc.edu
Length: 3 Yrs   *ACGME Approved/Offered Positions:* 6
Program ID: 120-48-11-660

Programs

Amarillo

Texas Tech University (Amarillo) Program

Sponsor: Texas Tech University Health Sciences Center at Amarillo
Baptist-St Anthony's Health System
Northwest Texas Health Care System
Prgm Director: Timothy J Benton, MD*
Department of Family Medicine
1400 Wallace Blvd
Amarillo, TX 79106
Tel: 806 212-3500   *Fax:* 806 212-3559
Length: 3 Yrs   *ACGME Approved/Offered Positions:* 18
Program ID: 120-48-21-511

Austin

Austin Medical Education Programs of Seton Healthcare Network Program

Sponsor: Austin Medical Education Program of Seton Healthcare Network
University Medical Center at Brackenridge
Prgm Director: Samuel B Adkins III, MD
1313 Red River St
Suite 100
Austin, TX 78701
Tel: 512 324-7318   *Fax:* 512 324-8018
Length: 3 Yrs   *ACGME Approved/Offered Positions:* 21
Program ID: 120-48-11-302

Baytown

San Jacinto Methodist Hospital Program

Sponsor: San Jacinto Methodist Hospital
Prgm Director: Clare Hawkins, MD
Family Medicine Residency
4301 Garth Road, Suite 400
Baytown, TX 77521
Tel: 281 420-8841   *Fax:* 281 420-8480
E-mail: CHawkins@tmhs.org
Length: 3 Yrs   *ACGME Approved/Offered Positions:* 24
Program ID: 120-48-21-432

Bryan

Family Medicine Foundation of Brazos Valley Program

Sponsor: Family Practice Foundation of the Brazos Valley
St Joseph Regional Health Center
Prgm Director: David A McClellan, MD
1301 Memorial Drive
Suite 200
Bryan, TX 77802
Tel: 979 862-4465   *Fax:* 979 774-6603
E-mail: rmartinez@medicine.tamhsc.edu
Length: 3 Yrs   *ACGME Approved/Offered Positions:* 21
Program ID: 120-48-31-605

Conroe

Conroe Medical Education Foundation Program

Sponsor: Conroe Medical Education Foundation
Conroe Regional Medical Center
Prgm Director: Stephen L McKernan, DO, BS
704 Old Montgomery Road
Conroe, TX 77301
Tel: 936 523-5242   *Fax:* 936 539-3635
E-mail: jennie.faulkner@lonestarfamily.org
Length: 3 Yrs   *ACGME Approved/Offered Positions:* 24
Program ID: 120-48-21-454

Corpus Christi

Christus Spohn Memorial Hospital Program

Sponsor: Christus Spohn Memorial Hospital
Prgm Director: Jose R Hinojosa, MD*
Corpus Christi Family Practice Residency Program
2606 Hospital Boulevard
Corpus Christi, TX 78405
Tel: 361 902-4473   *Fax:* 361 881-1467
E-mail: belinda.flores@christushealth.org
Length: 3 Yrs   *ACGME Approved/Offered Positions:* 36
Program ID: 120-48-22-303

Dallas

Methodist Health System Dallas/University of Texas Southwestern Medical School Program

Sponsor: Methodist Health System Dallas
Methodist Charlton Medical Center
Prgm Director: Brett A Johnson, MD
Charlton Methodist Hospital
3500 West Wheatland Road
Dallas, TX 75237
Tel: 214 947-5420   *Fax:* 214 947-5425
E-mail: brettjohnson@mhd.com
Length: 3 Yrs   *ACGME Approved/Offered Positions:* 18
Program ID: 120-48-21-433

University of Texas Southwestern Medical School Program

Sponsor: University of Texas Southwestern Medical School
Dallas County Hospital District-Parkland Memorial Hospital
University Hospitals St Paul
Prgm Director: Madelyn P Pollock, MD
6263 Harry Hines Blvd
Dallas, TX 75390
Tel: 214 648-1079   *Fax:* 214 648-1085
E-mail: madelyn.pollock@utsouthwestern.edu
Length: 3 Yrs   *ACGME Approved/Offered Positions:* 24
Program ID: 120-48-21-361

El Paso

Texas Tech University Health Sciences Center Paul L Foster School of Medicine Program

Sponsor: Texas Tech University Hlth Sci Ctr Paul L Foster Sch of Med
R E Thomason General Hospital / Texas Tech University HSC
Prgm Director: Oscar A Noriega, MD*
9849 Kenworthy Street
El Paso, TX 79924
Tel: 915 757-3178   *Fax:* 915 751-4378
Length: 3 Yrs   *ACGME Approved/Offered Positions:* 24
Program ID: 120-48-11-309

Fort Hood

Darnall Army Medical Center Program

Sponsor: Carl R Darnall Army Medical Center
Prgm Director: Douglas M Maurer, DO, MPH
36000 Darnall Loop (Box 12)
Fort Hood, TX 76544
Tel: 254 288-8234   *Fax:* 254 286-7196
E-mail: april.arrington@amedd.army.mil
Length: 3 Yrs   *ACGME Approved/Offered Positions:* 18
Program ID: 120-48-21-657
Uniformed Services Program

Fort Worth

John Peter Smith Hospital (Tarrant County Hospital District) Program

Sponsor: John Peter Smith Hospital (Tarrant County Hospital District)
Prgm Director: Daniel Casey, MD
1500 South Main Street
Fort Worth, TX 76104
Tel: 817 927-1200   *Fax:* 817 927-1691
E-mail: dcasey@jpshealth.org
Length: 3 Yrs   *ACGME Approved/Offered Positions:* 72
Program ID: 120-48-31-304

Galveston

University of Texas Medical Branch Hospitals Program

Sponsor: University of Texas Medical Branch Hospitals
Colorado-Fayette Medical Center
Columbus Community Hospital
Prgm Director: Lisa R Nash, DO
301 University Boulevard
Route 1123
Galveston, TX 77555
Tel: 409 772-0641   *Fax:* 409 772-0635
E-mail: lrnash@utmb.edu
Length: 3 Yrs   *ACGME Approved/Offered Positions:* 24
Program ID: 120-48-21-305

Garland

Baylor Medical Center at Garland Program

Sponsor: Baylor Medical Center at Garland
Prgm Director: Leslie E Tingle, MD
601 Clara Barton Blvd, Ste 340
Garland, TX 75042
Tel: 972 272-5935   *Fax:* 972 272-9137
E-mail: lest@baylorhealth.edu
Length: 3 Yrs   *ACGME Approved/Offered Positions:* 18
Program ID: 120-48-21-574

Harlingen

Valley Baptist Medical Center Program

Sponsor: Valley Baptist Medical Center
Prgm Director: Bruce A Leibert, MD
2222 Benwood Street
Harlingen, TX 78550
Tel: 956 389-2448   *Fax:* 956 389-2498
E-mail: familypractice@valleybaptist.net
Length: 3 Yrs   *ACGME Approved/Offered Positions:* 15
Program ID: 120-48-21-593

Houston

Baylor College of Medicine (Kelsey-Seybold) Program

Sponsor: Baylor College of Medicine
Harris County Hospital District-Ben Taub General Hospital
Kelsey-Seybold Main Campus
St Luke's Episcopal Hospital
Prgm Director: Tricia Elliott, MD*
2727 W Holcombe
Houston, TX 77025
Tel: 713 442-4620
E-mail: tricia.elliott@kelsey-seybold.com
Length: 3 Yrs   *ACGME Approved/Offered Positions:* 18
Program ID: 120-48-12-682

Note: * indicates a newly appointed program director

Baylor College of Medicine Program

Sponsor: Baylor College of Medicine
Harris County Hospital District-Ben Taub General
 Hospital
HCPHES Antoine Health Clinic
St Luke's Episcopal Hospital
Prgm Director: Fareed Khan, MBBS
Dept of Family & Community Med
3701 Kirby Drive, Suite 600
Houston, TX 77098
Tel: 713 867-8281   *Fax:* 713 867-7819
Length: 3 Yrs   *ACGME Approved/Offered Positions:* 18
Program ID: 120-48-11-306

Memorial Hermann Hospital System Program

Sponsor: Memorial Hermann Hospital System
Memorial Hermann Southwest Hospital
Prgm Director: David W Bauer, MD, PhD
14023 Southwest Freeway
Sugar Land, TX 77478
Tel: 281 325-4251   *Fax:* 281 325-4292
E-mail: memfpadmit@memorialhermann.org
Length: 3 Yrs   *ACGME Approved/Offered Positions:* 46
Program ID: 120-48-21-307

Methodist Hospital (Houston) Program

Sponsor: Methodist Hospital (Houston)
Prgm Director: Donald Briscoe, MD
424 Hahlo St.
Houston, TX 77020
Tel: 713 674-3326   *Fax:* 713 343-5488
E-mail: dabriscoe@tmhs.org
Length: 3 Yrs   *ACGME Approved/Offered Positions:* 24
Program ID: 120-48-21-565

University of Texas at Houston Program

Sponsor: University of Texas Health Science Center at
 Houston
Lyndon B Johnson General Hospital
Memorial Hermann Hospital
Prgm Director: Rolf O Montalvo-Chen, MD*
6431 Fannin St
Ste JJL 308
Houston, TX 77030
Tel: 713 500-7610   *Fax:* 713 500-7619
Length: 3 Yrs   *ACGME Approved/Offered Positions:* 36
Program ID: 120-48-21-490

Lubbock

Texas Tech University (Lubbock) Program

Sponsor: Texas Tech University Health Sciences Center
 at Lubbock
Covenant Medical Center
University Medical Center
Prgm Director: Ronald L Cook, DO, MBA
Department of Family and Community Medicine
3601 4th Street, Stop 8143
Lubbock, TX 79430
Tel: 806 743-2770   *Fax:* 806 743-3955
E-mail: family.medicine@ttuhsc.edu
Length: 3 Yrs   *ACGME Approved/Offered Positions:* 27
Program ID: 120-48-21-310

McAllen

University of Texas Health Science Center at San Antonio (McAllen) Program

Sponsor: University of Texas School of Medicine at San
 Antonio
McAllen Medical Center
Prgm Director: Jesus J Naranjo, MD
205 E Toronto Avenue
McAllen, TX 78503
Tel: 956 687-6155   *Fax:* 956 618-0451
E-mail: bakers@mfprp.com
Length: 3 Yrs   *ACGME Approved/Offered Positions:* 18
Program ID: 120-48-11-311

Odessa

Texas Tech University (Permian Basin) Program

Sponsor: Texas Tech University Health Sciences Center
 (Permian Basin)
Medical Center Hospital
Parks Methodist Retirement Village
Seabury Center NCU
Prgm Director: Rosa I Vizcarra, MD*
Department of Family and Community Medicine
701 W 5th Street
Odessa, TX 79763
Tel: 432 335-5311   *Fax:* 432 335-5316
Length: 3 Yrs   *ACGME Approved/Offered Positions:* 18
Program ID: 120-48-21-457

San Antonio

Christus Santa Rosa Health Care Program

Sponsor: Christus Santa Rosa Health Care Corporation
Prgm Director: Todd A Thames, MD*
Center for Children & Families, Suite F-4703
333 N Santa Rosa Street
San Antonio, TX 78207
Tel: 210 704-3753   *Fax:* 210 704-2545
E-mail: todd.thames@christushealth.org
Length: 3 Yrs   *ACGME Approved/Offered Positions:* 23
Program ID: 120-48-21-616

University of Texas Health Science Center at San Antonio Program

Sponsor: University of Texas School of Medicine at San
 Antonio
University Health System
Prgm Director: Mark T Nadeau, MD, MBA
Department of Family and Community Medicine
7703 Floyd Curl Drive, Mailstop 7795
San Antonio, TX 78229
Tel: 210 358-3931   *Fax:* 210 220-3763
E-mail: sananfprp@uthscsa.edu
Length: 3 Yrs   *ACGME Approved/Offered Positions:* 36
Program ID: 120-48-21-312

Temple

Texas A&M College of Medicine-Scott and White Program

Sponsor: Scott and White Memorial Hospital
Carl R Darnall Army Medical Center
Central Texas Veterans Affairs Healthcare System
Prgm Director: John L Manning, MD
1402 West Avenue H
Temple, TX 76504
Tel: 254 771-8401   *Fax:* 254 771-8493
E-mail: jmanning@swmail.sw.org
Length: 3 Yrs   *ACGME Approved/Offered Positions:* 18
Program ID: 120-48-21-469

Tyler

University of Texas Health Center at Tyler Program

Sponsor: University of Texas Health Center at Tyler
Mother Frances Hospital Regional Health Care Center
Prgm Director: Jonathan E MacClements, MD
11937 US Highway 271
Tyler, TX 75708
Tel: 903 877-7204   *Fax:* 903 877-7778
E-mail: kaye.dennis@uthct.edu
Length: 3 Yrs   *ACGME Approved/Offered Positions:* 21
Program ID: 120-48-21-464

Waco

McLennan County Medical Education and Research Foundation Program

Sponsor: McLennan County Medical Education and
 Research Foundation
Hillcrest Baptist Medical Center
Providence Health Center
Prgm Director: Lynda J Barry, MD
1600 Providence Drive
PO Box 3276
Waco, TX 76707
Tel: 254 750-8240   *Fax:* 254 759-3549
E-mail: lbarry@wacofpc.org
Length: 3 Yrs   *ACGME Approved/Offered Positions:* 36
Program ID: 120-48-11-313

Wichita Falls

North Central Texas Medical Foundation Program

Sponsor: North Central Texas Medical Foundation
United Regional Health Care System (URHCS)
Prgm Director: Ahmed A Mattar, MD*
1301 Third Street, Suite 200
Wichita Falls, TX 76301
Tel: 940 767-5145   *Fax:* 940 767-3027
Length: 3 Yrs   *ACGME Approved/Offered Positions:* 24
Program ID: 120-48-21-435

Utah

Ogden

McKay-Dee Hospital Center Program

Sponsor: McKay-Dee Hospital Center
Prgm Director: Gregory L Gochnour, MD
4403 Harrison Boulevard, Suite A-700
Ogden, UT 84403
Tel: 801 387-5324   *Fax:* 801 387-5335
Length: 3 Yrs   *ACGME Approved/Offered Positions:* 18
Program ID: 120-49-21-495

Provo

Utah Valley Regional Medical Center Program

Sponsor: Utah Valley Regional Medical Center
Prgm Director: Michael L Rhodes, MD
475 West 940 North
Provo, UT 84604
Tel: 801 357-7940   *Fax:* 801 357-7927
Length: 3 Yrs   *ACGME Approved/Offered Positions:* 21
Program ID: 120-49-21-583

Salt Lake City

St Mark's Health Care Foundation Program

Sponsor: St Mark's Health Care Foundation
St Mark's Hospital
Prgm Director: John Berneike, MD
1250 E 3900 S
Suite 260
Salt Lake City, UT 84124
Tel: 801 265-2000   *Fax:* 801 265-2008
E-mail: residency@utahhealthcare.org
Length: 3 Yrs   *ACGME Approved/Offered Positions:* 12
Program ID: 120-49-21-529

University of Utah Program

Sponsor: University of Utah Medical Center
Salt Lake Regional Medical Center
Prgm Director: Sonja Van Hala, MD, MPH
Family & Preventive Medicine
375 Chipeta Way, Ste A
Salt Lake City, UT 84108
Tel: 801 587-3411   *Fax:* 801 581-2771
E-mail: fp.residency@hsc.utah.edu
Length: 3 Yrs   *ACGME Approved/Offered Positions:* 24
Program ID: 120-49-21-315

Vermont

Burlington

University of Vermont Program

Sponsor: Fletcher Allen Health Care
Prgm Director: John G King, MD, MPH
Milton Family Practice Center
28 Centre Drive
Milton, VT 05468
Tel: 802 847-8547   *Fax:* 802 847-1570
E-mail: jennifer.wilson@vtmednet.org
Length: 3 Yrs   *ACGME Approved/Offered Positions:* 18
Program ID: 120-50-21-316

Virginia

Charlottesville

University of Virginia Program

Sponsor: University of Virginia Medical Center
Prgm Director: John Gazewood, MD, MSPH
Department of Family Medicine
PO Box 800729
Charlottesville, VA 22908
Tel: 434 243-6638   *Fax:* 434 243-2916
Length: 3 Yrs   *ACGME Approved/Offered Positions:* 24
Program ID: 120-51-11-317

Falls Church

Virginia Commonwealth University Health System (Falls Church) Program

Sponsor: Virginia Commonwealth University Health
   System
Inova Fairfax Hospital
Inova Fair Oaks Hospital
Prgm Director: Samuel M Jones, MD
3650 Joseph Siewick Drive
4th Floor
Fairfax, VA 22033
Tel: 703 391-2020   *Fax:* 703 391-1211
Length: 3 Yrs   *ACGME Approved/Offered Positions:* 24
Program ID: 120-51-11-322

Fort Belvoir

National Capital Consortium (DeWitt Healthcare Network) Program

Sponsor: National Capital Consortium
Dewitt Healthcare Network
Inova Fairfax Hospital
Prgm Director: Kevin E Moore, MD
Family Medicine Residency
9501 Farrell Road
Fort Belvoir, VA 22060
Tel: 703 805-0146   *Fax:* 703 805-0284
E-mail: kevin.e.moore@amedd.army.mil
Length: 3 Yrs   *ACGME Approved/Offered Positions:* 24
Program ID: 120-51-12-012
Uniformed Services Program

Front Royal

Medical College of Virginia/Virginia Commonwealth University-Valley Health System Program

Sponsor: Valley Health System
Warren Memorial Hospital
Winchester Medical Center
Prgm Director: Francis X Dennehy Jr, MD
140 West Eleventh Street
Front Royal, VA 22630
Tel: 540 636-2028   *Fax:* 540 636-2062
E-mail: mharris@valleyhealthlink.com
Length: 3 Yrs   *ACGME Approved/Offered Positions:* 15
Program ID: 120-51-21-627

Lynchburg

Centra Health Program

Sponsor: Centra Health Inc
Prgm Director: Charles E Driscoll, MD, MEd
2097 Langhorne Road
Lynchburg, VA 24501
Tel: 434 947-5210   *Fax:* 434 947-5213
E-mail: charles.driscoll@centrahealth.com
Length: 3 Yrs   *ACGME Approved/Offered Positions:* 18
Program ID: 120-51-21-318

Midlothian

Virginia Commonwealth University-Bon Secours (St Francis) Program

Sponsor: Bon Secours Richmond Health System
Prgm Director: Paul V Jackson, MD
13540 Hull Street Road
Midlothian, VA 23112
Tel: 804 595-1414   *Fax:* 804 739-8923
E-mail: Paul_Jackson@bshsi.org
Length: 3 Yrs   *ACGME Approved/Offered Positions:* 18
Program ID: 120-51-31-683

Newport News

VCU/Riverside Regional Medical Center Program

Sponsor: Riverside Regional Medical Center
Prgm Director: Steven S Leblang, MD
Riverside Brentwood Medical Center
10510 Jefferson Avenue, Suite B
Newport News, VA 23601
Tel: 757 594-3878   *Fax:* 757 591-9021
Length: 3 Yrs   *ACGME Approved/Offered Positions:* 36
Program ID: 120-51-31-323

Norfolk

Eastern Virginia Medical School Program

Sponsor: Eastern Virginia Medical School
Sentara Norfolk General Hospital
Prgm Director: Sahira A Humadi, MD
825 Fairfax Avenue
Norfolk, VA 23507
Tel: 757 446-5738   *Fax:* 757 446-8450
E-mail: humadisa@evms.edu
Length: 3 Yrs   *ACGME Approved/Offered Positions:* 24
Program ID: 120-51-21-319

Portsmouth

Eastern Virginia Medical School (Portsmouth) Program

Sponsor: Eastern Virginia Medical School
Maryview Medical Center
Prgm Director: Anne L Donnelly, MD
600 Crawford St
Portsmouth, VA 23704
Tel: 757 606-1188   *Fax:* 757 606-1185
Length: 3 Yrs   *ACGME Approved/Offered Positions:* 18
Program ID: 120-51-21-442

Richmond

Virginia Commonwealth University Health System (Chesterfield) Program

Sponsor: Virginia Commonwealth University Health
   System
Chippenham and Johnston-Willis Hospitals
   (Chippenham Campus)
Prgm Director: Richard H Hoffman, MD
2500 Pocoshock Place
Suite 104
Richmond, VA 23235
Tel: 804 276-2150   *Fax:* 804 674-4145
E-mail: adaubenspeck@chesterfieldfp.com
Length: 3 Yrs   *ACGME Approved/Offered Positions:* 18
Program ID: 120-51-11-320

Roanoke

Carilion Clinic Program

Sponsor: Carilion Clinic
Carilion Roanoke Memorial Hospital
Prgm Director: Roger A Hofford, MD
1314 Peters Creek Road, NW
Roanoke, VA 24017
Tel: 540 562-5702   *Fax:* 540 562-4258
E-mail: rhofford@carilion.com
Length: 3 Yrs   *ACGME Approved/Offered Positions:* 33
Program ID: 120-51-11-325

Washington

Bremerton

Naval Hospital (Bremerton) Program

Sponsor: Naval Hospital (Bremerton)
Prgm Director: David R Congdon, MD*
Puget Sound Family Medicine Program
One Boone Road, Code 03FP-GME
Bremerton, WA 98312
Tel: 360 475-5368   *Fax:* 360 475-4512
Length: 3 Yrs   *ACGME Approved/Offered Positions:* 18
Program ID: 120-54-21-494
Uniformed Services Program

Olympia

St Peter Hospital Program

Sponsor: St Peter Hospital
Prgm Director: Kevin Haughton, MD
525 Lilly Road NE
PBP09
Olympia, WA 98506
Tel: 360 493-7525   *Fax:* 360 493-5524
E-mail: lisa-ann.roura@providence.org
Length: 3 Yrs   *ACGME Approved/Offered Positions:* 18
Program ID: 120-54-21-497

Renton

Valley Medical Center Program

Sponsor: Valley Medical Center
Prgm Director: Antonio Pedroza, MD
3915 Talbot Rd South, Suite 401
Renton, WA 98055
Tel: 425 656-4287   *Fax:* 425 656-5395
E-mail: carly_dosremedios@valleymed.org
Length: 3 Yrs   *ACGME Approved/Offered Positions:* 24
Program ID: 120-54-21-470

Note: * indicates a newly appointed program director

Seattle

Group Health Cooperative Program
Sponsor: Group Health Cooperative
Virginia Mason Medical Center
Prgm Director: Sara D Thompson, MD
Family Medicine Residency
125 16th Avenue East, CSB160
Seattle, WA 98112
Tel: 206 326-3585   *Fax:* 206 326-3543
E-mail: ghcfpr@ghc.org
Length: 3 Yrs   *ACGME Approved/Offered Positions:* 15
Program ID: 120-54-21-327

Swedish Medical Center/Cherry Hill Program
Sponsor: Swedish Medical Center
Prgm Director: Samuel W Cullison, MD
550 16th Avenue, Suite 100
Seattle, WA 98122
Tel: 206 320-2233   *Fax:* 206 320-8173
Length: 3 Yrs   *ACGME Approved/Offered Positions:* 30
Program ID: 120-54-21-328

Swedish Medical Center/First Hill Program
Sponsor: Swedish Medical Center
Prgm Director: Michael L Tuggy, MD
1401 Madison Street
Suite 100
Seattle, WA 98104
Tel: 206 386-6054   *Fax:* 206 215-6027
Length: 3 Yrs   *ACGME Approved/Offered Positions:* 30
Program ID: 120-54-31-326

University of Washington Program
Sponsor: University of Washington School of Medicine
University of Washington Medical Center
Prgm Director: Judith Pauwels, MD
4245 Roosevelt Way NE
Box 354775
Seattle, WA 98105
Tel: 206 598-2883   *Fax:* 206 598-5769
E-mail: residency@fammed.washington.edu
Length: 3 Yrs   *ACGME Approved/Offered Positions:* 24
Program ID: 120-54-31-329

Spokane

Spokane Medical Centers/University of Washington School of Medicine Program
Sponsor: Inland Empire Hospital Services Association
Deaconess Medical Center
Sacred Heart Medical Center
Prgm Director: Gary R Newkirk, MD
104 West Fifth Avenue
Suite 200 W
Spokane, WA 99204
Tel: 509 624-2313   *Fax:* 509 459-0686
E-mail: info@fammedspokane.org
Length: 3 Yrs   *ACGME Approved/Offered Positions:* 22
Program ID: 120-54-21-330

Spokane Medical Centers/University of Washington School of Medicine Rural Program
Sponsor: Inland Empire Hospital Services Association
Mount Carmel Hospital
Sacred Heart Medical Center
Prgm Director: Gary R Newkirk, MD
104 West Fifth Avenue
Suite 200 W
Spokane, WA 99204
Tel: 509 624-2313   *Fax:* 509 459-0686
E-mail: info@fammedspokane.org
Length: 3 Yrs   *ACGME Approved/Offered Positions:* 6
Program ID: 120-54-21-552

Tacoma

Madigan Army Medical Center Program
Sponsor: Madigan Army Medical Center
Prgm Director: Ross E Colt, MD, MBA
Department of Family Medicine
MCHJ-FP
Tacoma, WA 98431
Tel: 253 968-1335   *Fax:* 253 968-2608
Length: 3 Yrs   *ACGME Approved/Offered Positions:* 18
Program ID: 120-54-21-013
Uniformed Services Program

Multicare Medical Center Program
Sponsor: MultiCare Medical Center
Tacoma General Hospital
Prgm Director: Kevin F Murray, MD
521 Martin Luther King, Jr Way
Tacoma, WA 98405
Tel: 253 403-2938   *Fax:* 253 403-2968
Length: 3 Yrs   *ACGME Approved/Offered Positions:* 24
Program ID: 120-54-31-331

Vancouver

Southwest Washington Medical Center Program
Sponsor: Southwest Washington Medical Center
Prgm Director: David R Ruiz, MD
PO Box 1600
100 E 33rd Stret, Suite 100
Vancouver, WA 98668
Tel: 360 514-7560   *Fax:* 360 514-7587
E-mail: nmoyer@swmedicalcenter.org
Length: 3 Yrs   *ACGME Approved/Offered Positions:* 21
Program ID: 120-54-21-546

Yakima

Yakima Valley Memorial Hospital Program
Sponsor: Yakima Valley Memorial Hospital
Yakima Regional Medical and Heart Center
Prgm Director: Russell G Maier, MD
1806 W Lincoln Ave
Yakima, WA 98902
Tel: 509 452-4946   *Fax:* 509 457-3989
E-mail: info@cwfm.fammed.washington.edu
Length: 3 Yrs   *ACGME Approved/Offered Positions:* 18
Program ID: 120-54-21-522

West Virginia

Charleston

Charleston Area Medical Center/West Virginia University (Charleston Division) Program
Sponsor: Charleston Area Medical Center/West Virginia University
Prgm Director: Andy R Tanner, DO
Robert C Byrd Clinical Teaching Center
3200 MacCorkle Avenue, 5th Floor
Charleston, WV 25304
Tel: 304 388-4620   *Fax:* 304 388-4621
E-mail: familymed@camc.org
Length: 3 Yrs   *ACGME Approved/Offered Positions:* 18
Program ID: 120-55-11-337

Clarksburg

United Hospital Center Program
Sponsor: United Hospital Center
Prgm Director: Eric Radcliffe, MD
One Hospital Plaza
PO Box 2308
Clarksburg, WV 26302
Tel: 304 624-2224   *Fax:* 304 624-2787
Length: 3 Yrs   *ACGME Approved/Offered Positions:* 24
Program ID: 120-55-22-334

Huntington

Marshall University School of Medicine Program
Sponsor: Marshall University School of Medicine
Cabell Huntington Hospital
Prgm Director: Warren M Shaver, MD
Dept of Family and Community Health
1600 Medical Center Dr, Suite 1500
Huntington, WV 25701
Tel: 304 691-1165   *Fax:* 304 691-1153
E-mail: badkins@marshall.edu
Length: 3 Yrs   *ACGME Approved/Offered Positions:* 24
Program ID: 120-55-21-335

Morgantown

West Virginia University Program
Sponsor: West Virginia University School of Medicine
West Virginia University Hospitals
Prgm Director: Robert Carlisle, MD, MPH*
Robert C Byrd Health Sciences Ctr
Box 9152
Morgantown, WV 26506
Tel: 304 598-6907   *Fax:* 304 598-6908
Length: 3 Yrs   *ACGME Approved/Offered Positions:* 18
Program ID: 120-55-11-336

Ranson

West Virginia University Rural Program
Sponsor: West Virginia University School of Medicine
Jefferson Memorial Hospital
City Hospital
Veterans Affairs Medical Center (Martinsburg)
Prgm Director: David A Baltierra, MD
Harpers Ferry Family Medicine
171 Taylor Street
Harpers Ferry, WV 25425
Tel: 304 535-6343   *Fax:* 304 535-6618
E-mail: therrienc@rcbhsc.wvu.edu
Length: 3 Yrs   *ACGME Approved/Offered Positions:* 12
Program ID: 120-55-21-569

Wheeling

Wheeling Hospital Program
Sponsor: Wheeling Hospital
Prgm Director: Edward R Marks III, MD
Family Health Center
40 Medical Park, Suite 406
Wheeling, WV 26003
Tel: 304 243-7853   *Fax:* 304 243-3891
E-mail: wheelingfpr@wheelinghospital.org
Length: 3 Yrs   *ACGME Approved/Offered Positions:* 24
Program ID: 120-55-22-338

Wisconsin

Appleton

University of Wisconsin (Fox Valley) Program
Sponsor: University of Wisconsin School of Medicine and Public Health
Appleton Medical Center
St Elizabeth Hospital
Prgm Director: Lee M Vogel, MD*
229 S Morrison Street
Appleton, WI 54911
Tel: 920 832-2783   *Fax:* 920 832-2797
Length: 3 Yrs   *ACGME Approved/Offered Positions:* 18
Program ID: 120-56-31-368

Baraboo

University of Wisconsin (Baraboo) Rural Program

Sponsor: University of Wisconsin School of Medicine and Public Health
St Clare Hospital and Health Services
St Mary's Hospital
Prgm Director: James R Damos, MD
1700 Tuttle Street
Baraboo, WI 53913
Tel: 608 355-7244   *Fax:* 608 355-7001
E-mail: jdamos@wisc.edu
Length: 3 Yrs   *ACGME Approved/Offered Positions:* 6
Program ID: 120-56-21-609

Eau Claire

University of Wisconsin (Eau Claire) Program

Sponsor: University of Wisconsin School of Medicine and Public Health
Luther Hospital
Sacred Heart Hospital
Prgm Director: Richard R McClaflin, MD
617 W Clairemont
Eau Claire, WI 54701
Tel: 715 839-5177   *Fax:* 715 839-4733
Length: 3 Yrs   *ACGME Approved/Offered Positions:* 19
Program ID: 120-56-31-342

Janesville

Mercy Health System Program

Sponsor: Mercy Health System
Prgm Director: James G Horton, MD, MPH
849 Kellogg Avenue
Janesville, WI 53546
Tel: 608 758-7811   *Fax:* 608 758-7801
Length: 3 Yrs   *ACGME Approved/Offered Positions:* 18
Program ID: 120-56-21-503

La Crosse

Franciscan Skemp Healthcare Program

Sponsor: Franciscan Skemp Healthcare-La Crosse Campus
Prgm Director: Thomas J Grau, MD, MA
700 West Avenue South
La Crosse, WI 54601
Tel: 608 392-9775   *Fax:* 608 392-4168
E-mail: grau.thomas@mayo.edu
Length: 3 Yrs   *ACGME Approved/Offered Positions:* 18
Program ID: 120-56-11-339

Madison

University of Wisconsin (Madison) Program

Sponsor: University of Wisconsin School of Medicine and Public Health
St Mary's Hospital
Prgm Director: Kathleen A Oriel, MD, MS*
Department of Family Medicine
777 South Mills Street
Madison, WI 53715
Tel: 608 263-4550   *Fax:* 608 263-5813
Length: 3 Yrs   *ACGME Approved/Offered Positions:* 42
Program ID: 120-56-11-343

Milwaukee

Aurora Health Care Program

Sponsor: Aurora Health Care
St Luke's Medical Center
Prgm Director: Jacob L Bidwell, MD*
Physician Office Building Ste 175
2801 W Kinnickinnic River Parkway
Milwaukee, WI 53215
Tel: 414 649-6723   *Fax:* 414 649-3361
Length: 3 Yrs   *ACGME Approved/Offered Positions:* 30
Program ID: 120-56-21-348

Medical College of Wisconsin Affiliated Hospitals (Columbia-St Mary's) Program

Sponsor: Medical College of Wisconsin Affiliated Hospitals, Inc
Columbia St Mary's Hospitals
Prgm Director: William J Geiger, MD
1121 East North Avenue
Milwaukee, WI 53212
Tel: 414 267-6502   *Fax:* 414 267-3892
Length: 3 Yrs   *ACGME Approved/Offered Positions:* 18
Program ID: 120-56-21-670

Medical College of Wisconsin Affiliated Hospitals (St Joseph) Program

Sponsor: Medical College of Wisconsin Affiliated Hospitals, Inc
Wheaton Franciscan Healthcare-St Joseph
Prgm Director: Beth A Damitz, MD
2400 W Villard Avenue
Milwaukee, WI 53209
Tel: 414 527-8348   *Fax:* 414 527-8046
E-mail: stjoefp@mcw.edu
Length: 3 Yrs   *ACGME Approved/Offered Positions:* 18
Program ID: 120-56-31-349

Racine

Medical College of Wisconsin Affiliated Hospitals (Racine) Program

Sponsor: Medical College of Wisconsin Affiliated Hospitals, Inc
Wheaton Franciscan Healthcare - All Saints (Racine) Campus
Prgm Director: Allen R Last, MD
1320 Wisconsin Avenue
Racine, WI 53403
Tel: 262 687-5689   *Fax:* 262 687-5657
E-mail: racinefp@mcw.edu
Length: 3 Yrs   *ACGME Approved/Offered Positions:* 18
Program ID: 120-56-21-438

Waukesha

Medical College of Wisconsin Affiliated Hospitals (Waukesha) Program

Sponsor: Medical College of Wisconsin Affiliated Hospitals, Inc
Waukesha Memorial Hospital
Prgm Director: Michael F Mazzone, MD
210 NW Barstow Ste 201
Waukesha, WI 53188
Tel: 262 548-6907   *Fax:* 262 928-4075
Length: 3 Yrs   *ACGME Approved/Offered Positions:* 18
Program ID: 120-56-21-345

Wausau

University of Wisconsin (Wausau) Program

Sponsor: University of Wisconsin School of Medicine and Public Health
Wausau Hospital
Prgm Director: Kevin J O'Connell, MD
425 Wind Ridge Drive
Wausau, WI 54401
Tel: 715 675-3391   *Fax:* 715 675-5262
E-mail: mary.zaglifa@fammed.wisc.edu
Length: 3 Yrs   *ACGME Approved/Offered Positions:* 18
Program ID: 120-56-21-350

Wyoming

Casper

University of Wyoming (Casper) Program

Sponsor: University of Wyoming College of Health Sciences
Wyoming Medical Center
Prgm Director: Stephan N Trent, DO
1522 East A Street
Casper, WY 82601
Tel: 307 233-6003   *Fax:* 307 473-1284
E-mail: uwfp@uwyo.edu
Length: 3 Yrs   *ACGME Approved/Offered Positions:* 24
Program ID: 120-57-12-351

Cheyenne

University of Wyoming (Cheyenne) Program

Sponsor: University of Wyoming College of Health Sciences
Cheyenne Regional Medical Center
Prgm Director: James F Broomfield, MD
821 East 18th Street
Cheyenne, WY 82001
Tel: 307 777-7911   *Fax:* 307 638-3616
Length: 3 Yrs   *ACGME Approved/Offered Positions:* 18
Program ID: 120-57-12-369

Note: * indicates a newly appointed program director

Foot and Ankle Orthopaedics (Orthopaedic Surgery)

Alabama

Birmingham

American Sports Medicine Institute Program

Sponsor: American Sports Medicine Institute
St Vincent's Hospital
University of Alabama at Birmingham/Highlands
Prgm Director: Angus M McBryde, MD
2660 10th Avenue South, Suite 505
Birmingham, AL 35205
Tel: 205 918-2146
E-mail: janf@asmi.org
Length: 1 Yr   *ACGME Approved/Offered Positions:* 3
Program ID: 262-01-21-004

Arkansas

Little Rock

University of Arkansas for Medical Sciences Program

Sponsor: University of Arkansas College of Medicine
Central Arkansas Veterans Healthcare System
UAMS Medical Center
Prgm Director: Ruth L Thomas, MD
4301 W Markham, Slot 531
Little Rock, AR 72205
Tel: 501 686-5673   *Fax:* 501 603-1549
E-mail: ThomasRuthL@uams.edu
Length: 1 Yr   *ACGME Approved/Offered Positions:* 1
Program ID: 262-04-31-003

Maryland

Baltimore

Mercy Medical Center (Baltimore) Program

Sponsor: Mercy Medical Center
Prgm Director: Mark S Myerson, MD
301 St Paul Place
Baltimore, MD 21202
Tel: 410 659-2800   *Fax:* 410 659-2999
E-mail: bcawley@mdmercy.com
Length: 1 Yr   *ACGME Approved/Offered Positions:* 3
Program ID: 262-23-11-005

Union Memorial Hospital Program

Sponsor: Union Memorial Hospital
Prgm Director: Lew C Schon, MD
3333 North Calvert Street, Suite 400
Baltimore, MD 21218
Tel: 410 554-2891   *Fax:* 410 554-2030
Length: 1 Yr   *ACGME Approved/Offered Positions:* 3
Program ID: 262-23-21-007

New York

New York

Hospital for Special Surgery Program

Sponsor: Hospital for Special Surgery
St Luke's-Roosevelt Hospital Center-Roosevelt Division
Prgm Director: Jonathan Deland, MD
535 East 70th Street
New York, NY 10021
Tel: 212 606-1466   *Fax:* 212 606-1477
E-mail: academictraining@hss.edu
Length: 1 Yr   *ACGME Approved/Offered Positions:* 3
Program ID: 262-35-31-009

Rochester

University of Rochester Program

Sponsor: Strong Memorial Hospital of the University of
Rochester
Prgm Director: Benedict DiGiovanni, MD*
Department of Orthopaedic Surgery
601 Elmwood Avenue, Box 665
Rochester, NY 14642
Tel: 585 275-5168   *Fax:* 585 756-4721
Length: 1 Yr   *ACGME Approved/Offered Positions:* 1
Program ID: 262-35-21-011

North Carolina

Durham

Duke University Hospital Program

Sponsor: Duke University Hospital
Prgm Director: James A Nunley II, MD
Division of Orthopaedic Surgery
Box 2923
Durham, NC 27710
Tel: 919 684-3170   *Fax:* 919 681-7672
E-mail: wendy.thompson@duke.edu
Length: 1 Yr   *ACGME Approved/Offered Positions:* 2
Program ID: 262-36-13-008

Pennsylvania

Hershey

Penn State University/Milton S Hershey Medical Center Program

Sponsor: Milton S Hershey Medical Center
Prgm Director: Paul J Juliano, MD
30 Hope Drive
EC089
Hershey, PA 17033
Tel: 717 531-4833   *Fax:* 717 531-0498
E-mail: OrthoResidency@hmc.psu.edu
Length: 1 Yr   *ACGME Approved/Offered Positions:* 1
Program ID: 262-41-13-012

Texas

Dallas

Baylor University Medical Center Program

Sponsor: Baylor University Medical Center
Medical City Hospital of Dallas
Texas Health Presbyterian Dallas
Prgm Director: James W Brodsky, MD
Suite 7000
Dallas, TX 75246
Tel: 214 823-7090   *Fax:* 214 818-1225
Length: 1 Yr   *ACGME Approved/Offered Positions:* 3
Program ID: 262-48-12-010

Forensic Pathology (Pathology)

Alabama

Birmingham

University of Alabama Medical Center Program

Sponsor: University of Alabama Hospital
Jefferson County Coroner/Medical Examiner's Office
Prgm Director: Gregory G Davis, MD, MPH
1515 Sixth Avenue South, Room 220
Birmingham, AL 35233
Tel: 205 930-3603   *Fax:* 205 930-3595
E-mail: gdavis@uab.edu
Length: 1 Yr   *ACGME Approved/Offered Positions:* 1
Program ID: 310-01-21-049

California

Los Angeles

County of Los Angeles-Department of Coroner Program

Sponsor: County of Los Angeles-Department of Coroner
Prgm Director: Lakshmanan Sathyavagiswaran, MD
1104 North Mission Road
Los Angeles, CA 90033
Tel: 323 343-0522   *Fax:* 323 225-2235
Length: 1 Yr   *ACGME Approved/Offered Positions:* 6
Program ID: 310-05-12-002

San Diego

San Diego County Medical Examiner Program

Sponsor: San Diego County Medical Examiner
Prgm Director: Christina Stanley, MD
5555 Overland Avenue
Suite 1411
San Diego, CA 92123
Tel: 858 694-2899
Length: 1 Yr   *ACGME Approved/Offered Positions:* 2
Program ID: 310-05-21-059

Colorado

Aurora

University of Colorado Denver Program

Sponsor: University of Colorado Denver School of
Medicine
Denver Office of the Medical Examiner
Prgm Director: Amy Martin, MD
660 Bannock Street
Denver, CO 80204
Tel: 303 436-7001   *Fax:* 303 436-7709
E-mail: amy.martin@denvergov.org
Length: 1 Yr   *ACGME Approved/Offered Positions:* 1
Program ID: 310-07-31-097

Programs

Florida

Fort Lauderdale

Broward County Medical Examiner's Office Program
Sponsor: Broward County Medical Examiner's Office
Prgm Director: Stephen J Cina, MD
5301 SW 31st Avenue
Fort Lauderdale, FL 33312
Tel: 954 327-6513
E-mail: cinasj@pol.net
Length: 1 Yr   *ACGME Approved/Offered Positions:* 2
Program ID: 310-11-21-056

Miami

Miami-Dade County Office of Medical Examiner Program
Sponsor: Miami-Dade County Office of Medical
   Examiner
Prgm Director: Bruce A Hyma, MD
Number One on Bob Hope Road
Miami, FL 33136
Tel: 305 545-2425   *Fax:* 305 545-2412
Length: 1 Yr   *ACGME Approved/Offered Positions:* 4
Program ID: 310-11-21-055

Tampa

University of South Florida Program
Sponsor: University of South Florida College of Medicine
Hillsborough County Medical Examiner Department
Prgm Director: Vernard I Adams, MD
11025 North 46th Street
Tampa, FL 33617
Tel: 813 272-5342
Length: 1 Yr   *ACGME Approved/Offered Positions:* 2
Program ID: 310-11-31-066

Georgia

Atlanta

Emory University Program
Sponsor: Emory University School of Medicine
Fulton County Medical Examiner's Office
Prgm Director: Randy L Hanzlick, MD
430 Pryor St, SW
Atlanta, GA 30312
Tel: 404 730-4400   *Fax:* 404 332-0386
E-mail: mmojonn@emory.edu
Length: 1 Yr   *ACGME Approved/Offered Positions:* 2
Program ID: 310-12-21-052

Illinois

Chicago

Office of the Medical Examiner of Cook County Program
Sponsor: Office of the Medical Examiner of Cook County
Prgm Director: Nancy L Jones, MD*
2121 West Harrison Street
Chicago, IL 60612
Tel: 312 997-4500   *Fax:* 312 997-3024
Length: 1 Yr   *ACGME Approved/Offered Positions:* 4
Program ID: 310-16-21-035

Indiana

Indianapolis

Indiana University School of Medicine Program
Sponsor: Indiana University School of Medicine
Prgm Director: Joye M Carter, MD
Department of Pathology and Laboratory Medicine
635 Barnhill Drive, MS128
Indianapolis, IN 46202
Tel: 317 327-4744   *Fax:* 317 327-4563
E-mail: jcarter@indygov.org
Length: 1 Yr   *ACGME Approved/Offered Positions:* 1
Program ID: 310-17-21-076

Kentucky

Louisville

University of Louisville Program
Sponsor: University of Louisville School of Medicine
Office of Chief Medical Examiner
Prgm Director: Tracey S Corey, MD
810 Barret Avenue
Louisville, KY 40204
Tel: 502 852-5587   *Fax:* 502 852-1767
Length: 1 Yr   *ACGME Approved/Offered Positions:* 2
Program ID: 310-20-21-048

Maryland

Baltimore

Office of the Chief Medical Examiner/State of Maryland Program
Sponsor: Office of the Chief Medical Examiner
Prgm Director: David R Fowler, MD
111 Penn Street
Baltimore, MD 21201
Tel: 410 333-3225   *Fax:* 410 333-3063
Length: 1 Yr   *ACGME Approved/Offered Positions:* 4
Program ID: 310-23-11-012

Bethesda

National Capital Consortium Program
Sponsor: National Capital Consortium
Armed Forces Institute of Pathology
Office of the Chief Medical Examiner
Prgm Director: Craig T Mallak, JD, MD
1413 Research Boulevard
Building 102
Rockville, MD 20850
Tel: 301 319-0145   *Fax:* 301 319-3544
E-mail: craig.mallak@afip.osd.mil
Length: 1 Yr   *ACGME Approved/Offered Positions:* 4
Program ID: 310-10-32-001
Uniformed Services Program

Massachusetts

Boston

Office of the Chief Medical Examiner, Commonwealth of Massachusetts Program
Sponsor: Office of the Chief Medical Examiner
Prgm Director: Henry M Nields, MD, PhD*
720 Albany Street
Boston, MA 02118
Tel: 617 267-6767   *Fax:* 617 267-4931
Length: 1 Yr   *ACGME Approved/Offered Positions:* 4
Program ID: 310-24-12-093

Michigan

Detroit

Wayne County Medical Examiner's Office Program
Sponsor: Wayne County Medical Examiner's Office
Prgm Director: Cheryl Loewe, MD
1300 East Warren Avenue
Detroit, MI 48207
Tel: 313 833-2543   *Fax:* 313 833-2534
Length: 1 Yr   *ACGME Approved/Offered Positions:* 2
Program ID: 310-25-11-013

Minnesota

Minneapolis

Hennepin County Medical Examiner Program
Sponsor: Hennepin County Medical Examiner
Prgm Director: Andrew M Baker, MD
530 Chicago Avenue
Minneapolis, MN 55415
Tel: 612 215-6300   *Fax:* 612 215-6330
E-mail: david.eggen@co.hennepin.mn.us
Length: 1 Yr   *ACGME Approved/Offered Positions:* 1
Program ID: 310-26-12-014

Missouri

Kansas City

Office of the Jackson County Medical Examiner Program
Sponsor: Office of the Jackson County Medical
   Examiner
Prgm Director: Mary H Dudley, MD
660 E 24th Street
Kansas City, MO 64108
Tel: 816 881-6600   *Fax:* 816 404-1345
Length: 1 Yr   *ACGME Approved/Offered Positions:* 1
Program ID: 310-28-11-086

St Louis

St Louis University School of Medicine Program
Sponsor: St Louis University School of Medicine
St Louis City Medical Examiner Office
St Louis County Medical Examiner's Office
Prgm Director: Jane W Turner, MD, PhD
3556 Caroline Street, Room C305
St Louis, MO 63104
Tel: 314 613-7091
E-mail: turnerjw@slu.edu
Length: 1 Yr   *ACGME Approved/Offered Positions:* 1
Program ID: 310-28-21-075

New Jersey

Newark

Newark Regional Medical Examiner Office Program
Sponsor: Newark Regional Medical Examiner Office
Prgm Director: Lyla E Perez, MD*
325 Norfolk Street
Newark, NJ 07103
Tel: 973 648-7258   *Fax:* 973 648-3692
Length: 1 Yr   *ACGME Approved/Offered Positions:* 1
Program ID: 310-33-31-088

Note: * indicates a newly appointed program director

New Mexico

Albuquerque

University of New Mexico Program
Sponsor: University of New Mexico School of Medicine
Office of the Medical Investigator
Prgm Director: Jeffrey S Nine, MD
Office of the Medical Investigator - MSC11 6030
1 University of New Mexico
Albuquerque, NM 87131
Tel: 505 272-8011   *Fax:* 505 272-0727
Length: 1 Yr   *ACGME Approved/Offered Positions:* 4
Program ID: 310-34-21-015

New York

New York

Office of the Chief Medical Examiner-City of New York Program
Sponsor: Office of Chief Medical Examiner - City of New York
Prgm Director: Barbara A Sampson, MD, PhD
520 First Avenue
New York, NY 10016
Tel: 212 447-2335   *Fax:* 212 447-2334
E-mail: sampson@ocme.nyc.gov
Length: 1 Yr   *ACGME Approved/Offered Positions:* 4
Program ID: 310-35-21-063

North Carolina

Chapel Hill

University of North Carolina Hospitals Program
Sponsor: University of North Carolina Hospitals
Office of the Chief Medical Examiner
Prgm Director: John D Butts, MD
CB 7580
Chapel Hill, NC 27599
Tel: 919 966-2253
Length: 1 Yr   *ACGME Approved/Offered Positions:* 2
Program ID: 310-36-21-019

Winston-Salem

Wake Forest University School of Medicine Program
Sponsor: Wake Forest University Baptist Medical Center
Prgm Director: Donald R Jason, MD, JD
Department of Pathology
Medical Center Boulevard
Winston-Salem, NC 27157
Tel: 336 716-2634   *Fax:* 336 716-7595
E-mail: djason@wfubmc.edu
Length: 1 Yr   *ACGME Approved/Offered Positions:* 1
Program ID: 310-36-12-085

Ohio

Cleveland

Cuyahoga County Coroner's Office Program
Sponsor: Cuyahoga County Coroner's Office
Prgm Director: Joseph A Felo, DO
11001 Cedar Avenue
Cleveland, OH 44106
Tel: 216 721-5610   *Fax:* 216 707-3186
E-mail: jfelo@hotmail.com
Length: 1 Yr   *ACGME Approved/Offered Positions:* 3
Program ID: 310-38-11-021

Dayton

Office of the Montgomery County Coroner Program
Sponsor: Office of the Montgomery County Coroner
Prgm Director: Lee Lehman, MD, PhD
361 West Third Street
Dayton, OH 45402
Tel: 937 225-4156   *Fax:* 937 496-7916
Length: 1 Yr   *ACGME Approved/Offered Positions:* 1
Program ID: 310-38-21-067

Oklahoma

Oklahoma City

Office of the Chief Medical Examiner - State of Oklahoma Program
Sponsor: Office of the Chief Medical Examiner-State of Oklahoma
Prgm Director: Jeffery J Gofton, MD
901 N Stonewall
Oklahoma City, OK 73117
Tel: 405 239-7141   *Fax:* 405 232-0073
E-mail: medical_examiner@ocmeokc.state.ok.us
Length: 1 Yr   *ACGME Approved/Offered Positions:* 1
Program ID: 310-39-21-092

Pennsylvania

Pittsburgh

Medical Examiner's Office of Allegheny County Program
Sponsor: Allegheny County Medical Examiner's Office
Prgm Director: Abdulrezzak Shakir, MD
542 Fourth Avenue
Pittsburgh, PA 15219
Tel: 412 350-4800
Length: 1 Yr   *ACGME Approved/Offered Positions:* 2
Program ID: 310-41-21-024

Puerto Rico

San Juan

University of Puerto Rico Program
Sponsor: University of Puerto Rico School of Medicine
Institute of Forensic Sciences of Puerto Rico
Prgm Director: Irma Rivera-Diez, MD
PO Box 11878 Caparra Heights Station
San Juan, PR 00922
Tel: 787 765-0615   *Fax:* 787 759-7315
E-mail: irivera@icf.gobierno.pr
Length: 1 Yr   *ACGME Approved/Offered Positions:* 1
Program ID: 310-42-21-095

South Carolina

Charleston

Medical University of South Carolina Program
Sponsor: Medical University of South Carolina College of Medicine
MUSC Medical Center
Prgm Director: Cynthia A Schandl, MD, PhD
165 Ashley Avenue, Pathology Department
MSC 908
Charleston, SC 29425
Tel: 843 792-3500   *Fax:* 843 792-3537
E-mail: schandlc@musc.edu
Length: 1 Yr   *ACGME Approved/Offered Positions:* 1
Program ID: 310-45-21-026

Tennessee

Nashville

Office of the Chief Medical Examiner (Tennessee) Program
Sponsor: Medical Examiner's Office, TN and Nashville and Davidson Co
Prgm Director: Staci A Turner, MD*
850 R S Gass Boulevard
Nashville, TN 37216
Tel: 615 743-1800   *Fax:* 615 743-1890
Length: 1 Yr   *ACGME Approved/Offered Positions:* 2
Program ID: 310-47-21-084

Texas

Dallas

University of Texas Southwestern Medical School Program
Sponsor: University of Texas Southwestern Medical School
Prgm Director: Jeffrey J Barnard, MD
5230 Medical Center Drive
Dallas, TX 75235
Tel: 214 920-5913
Length: 1 Yr   *ACGME Approved/Offered Positions:* 3
Program ID: 310-48-11-028

Fort Worth

Tarrant County Medical Examiner Program
Sponsor: Tarrant County Medical Examiner's Office
Prgm Director: Nizam Peerwani, MD
200 Feliks Gwozds Place
Fort Worth, TX 76104
Tel: 817 920-5700   *Fax:* 817 920-5713
E-mail: npeerwani@tarrantcounty.com
Length: 1 Yr   *ACGME Approved/Offered Positions:* 1
Program ID: 310-48-22-087

Houston

Harris County Medical Examiner Department Program
Sponsor: Harris County Medical Examiner Department
Prgm Director: Luis A Sanchez, MD
1885 Old Spanish Trail
Houston, TX 77054
Tel: 713 796-6808   *Fax:* 713 799-8078
E-mail: luis.sanchez@meo.hctx.net
Length: 1 Yr   *ACGME Approved/Offered Positions:* 2
Program ID: 310-48-21-080

Lubbock

Texas Tech University (Lubbock) Program
Sponsor: Texas Tech University Health Sciences Center at Lubbock
Prgm Director: Thomas R Beaver, MD
4434 South Loop 289
Division of Forensic Pathology TTUHSC
Lubbock, TX 79414
Tel: 806 743-7755   *Fax:* 806 743-7759
E-mail: John.Omalley@ttuhsc.edu
Length: 1 Yr   *ACGME Approved/Offered Positions:* 1
Program ID: 310-48-13-091

Programs

San Antonio

Bexar County Medical Examiner's Office Program

Sponsor: Bexar County Medical Examiner's Office
Prgm Director: Randall E Frost, MD
7337 Louis Pasteur Drive
San Antonio, TX 78229
Tel: 210 335-4053   *Fax:* 210 335-4052
E-mail: frostmd@bexar.org
Length: 1 Yr   *ACGME Approved/Offered Positions:* 2
Program ID: 310-48-21-044

Virginia

Richmond

Virginia Commonwealth University Health System Program

Sponsor: Virginia Commonwealth University Health
System
Office of Chief Medical Examiner
Prgm Director: Deborah Kay, MD*
400 East Jackson Street
Richmond, VA 23219
Tel: 804 786-1033   *Fax:* 804 371-8595
Length: 1 Yr   *ACGME Approved/Offered Positions:* 3
Program ID: 310-51-21-030

Washington

Seattle

King County Medical Examiner's Office Program

Sponsor: King County Medical Examiner's Office
Prgm Director: Richard C Harruff, MD, PhD*
325 9th Avenue
HMC Box 359792
Seattle, WA 98104
Tel: 206 731-3232   *Fax:* 206 731-8555
E-mail: richard.harruff@kingcounty.gov
Length: 1 Yr   *ACGME Approved/Offered Positions:* 2
Program ID: 310-54-21-031

Wisconsin

Milwaukee

Medical College of Wisconsin Affiliated Hospitals/Milwaukee County Medical Examiner's Office Program

Sponsor: Medical College of Wisconsin Affiliated
Hospitals, Inc
Prgm Director: Christopher Happy, MD*
933 West Highland Avenue
Milwaukee, WI 53233
Tel: 414 223-1200   *Fax:* 414 223-1237
E-mail: Christopher.happy@milwcnty.com
Length: 1 Yr   *ACGME Approved/Offered Positions:* 2
Program ID: 310-56-21-053

Forensic Psychiatry (Psychiatry)

Arkansas

Little Rock

University of Arkansas for Medical Sciences Program

Sponsor: University of Arkansas College of Medicine
Arkansas State Hospital (DBHS)
UAMS Medical Center
Prgm Director: Ben Guise, MD
COM Department of Psychiatry
4301 West Markham St, Slot 589
Little Rock, AR 72205
Tel: 501 686-6196   *Fax:* 501 686-7424
E-mail: forensicpsych@uams.edu
Length: 1 Yr   *ACGME Approved/Offered Positions:* 2
Program ID: 406-04-33-046

California

Los Angeles

University of Southern California/ LAC+USC Medical Center Program

Sponsor: University of Southern California/LAC+USC
Medical Center
LAC+USC Medical Center
Twin Towers Correctional Facility-Jail Mental Health
Service
Prgm Director: Tim Botello, MPH, MD
2020 Zonal Avenue, IRD 714, Los Angeles, CA 90033
PO Box 86125
Los Angeles, CA 90086
Tel: 323 226-4942   *Fax:* 323 226-2777
E-mail: botello@usc.edu
Length: 1 Yr   *ACGME Approved/Offered Positions:* 5
Program ID: 406-05-31-002

VA Greater Los Angeles/UCLA-San Fernando Valley Program

Sponsor: VA Greater Los Angeles Healthcare System
Metropolitan State Hospital
Olive View/UCLA Medical Center
Prgm Director: Neena Sachinvala, MD
Department of Psychiatry
14445 Olive View Drive, 6D129
Sylmar, CA 91342
Tel: 818 891-7711   *Fax:* 818 895-9346
Length: 1 Yr   *ACGME Approved/Offered Positions:* 4
Program ID: 406-05-11-003

Sacramento

University of California (Davis) Health System Program

Sponsor: University of California (Davis) Health System
Napa State Hospital
Sacramento County Correctional Health Services
University of California (Davis) Medical Center
Prgm Director: Charles Scott, MD
Department of Psychiatry
2230 Stockton Boulevard
Sacramento, CA 95817
Tel: 916 734-7471   *Fax:* 916 703-5261
E-mail: david.spagnolo@ucdmc.ucdavis.edu
Length: 1 Yr   *ACGME Approved/Offered Positions:* 3
Program ID: 406-05-31-028

San Francisco

University of California (San Francisco) Program

Sponsor: University of California (San Francisco) School
of Medicine
California Department of Corrections
Center for Occupational Psychiatry
UCSF Med Ctr/Langley Porter Psychiatric Hosp and
Clinics
Prgm Director: Renee Binder, MD
401 Parnassus Avenue, Box F
San Francisco, CA 94143
Tel: 415 476-7304   *Fax:* 415 502-2206
Length: 1 Yr   *ACGME Approved/Offered Positions:* 2
Program ID: 406-05-21-037

Colorado

Aurora

University of Colorado Denver Program

Sponsor: University of Colorado Denver School of
Medicine
Colorado Department of Corrections
Colorado Mental Health Institute at Pueblo
Denver Health Medical Center
Prgm Director: Richard P Martinez, MD, MA
13001 E 17th Pl, Bldg 500, Rm E2328
Campus Box F546, PO Box 6508
Aurora, CO 80045
Tel: 303 436-3394   *Fax:* 303 436-3391
E-mail: richard.martinez@dhha.org
Length: 1 Yr   *ACGME Approved/Offered Positions:* 3
Program ID: 406-07-21-004

Connecticut

New Haven

Yale-New Haven Medical Center Program

Sponsor: Yale-New Haven Hospital
Connecticut Mental Health Center
Connecticut Valley Hospital
Riverview Hospital for Children
Yale Law School
Prgm Director: Howard V Zonana, MD
34 Park Street
Room 153
New Haven, CT 06519
Tel: 203 974-7158   *Fax:* 203 974-7177
Length: 1 Yr   *ACGME Approved/Offered Positions:* 5
Program ID: 406-08-21-005

District of Columbia

Washington

Georgetown University Hospital Program

Sponsor: Georgetown University Hospital
DMH Assessment Center
St Elizabeth's Hospital-DC Department of Mental Health
Prgm Director: Alan W Newman, MD*
Department of Psychiatry
3800 Reservoir Rd, NW, Kober Cogan, Room 614
Washington, DC 20007
Tel: 202 687-8537   *Fax:* 202 687-5494
E-mail: awn1@gunet.georgetown.edu
Length: 1 Yr   *ACGME Approved/Offered Positions:* 4
Program ID: 406-10-21-056

Note: * indicates a newly appointed program director

National Capital Consortium Program

Sponsor: National Capital Consortium
Walter Reed Army Medical Center
Clifton T Perkins Hospital Center
FBI-Center for Analysis of Violent Crime Forensic
  Psychiatry
Maryland Correctional Institute-Women
St Elizabeth's Hospital-DC Department of Mental Health
Uniformed Svcs Univ of Health Sci Hebert School of
  Medicine
Prgm Director: Christopher L Lange, MD
Bldg 6, Rm 3025
6900 Georgia Avenue, NW
Washington, DC 20307
Tel: 202 782-8056   *Fax:* 202 782-8379
E-mail: forensics@nccpsychiatry.info
Length: 1 Yr   *ACGME Approved/Offered Positions:* 2
Program ID: 406-10-21-006
Uniformed Services Program

Florida

Gainesville

University of Florida Program

Sponsor: University of Florida College of Medicine
Shands Hospital at the University of Florida
Prgm Director: Tonia L Werner, MD
PO Box 100256
1600 SW Archer Road, RM 8404
Gainesville, FL 32610
Tel: 352 265-3284   *Fax:* 352 265-3285
E-mail: twerner@ufl.edu
Length: 1 Yr   *ACGME Approved/Offered Positions:* 4
Program ID: 406-11-21-007

Miami

Jackson Memorial Hospital/Jackson Health System Program

Sponsor: Jackson Memorial Hospital/Jackson Health
  System
South Florida Evaluation and Treatment Center
Prgm Director: Joseph W Poitier Jr, MD
1695 NW 9th Avenue (D-29)
Room 2101
Miami, FL 33136
Tel: 305 355-8260   *Fax:* 305 355-7266
E-mail: jpoitier@jhsmiami.org
Length: 1 Yr   *ACGME Approved/Offered Positions:* 2
Program ID: 406-11-12-052

Tampa

University of South Florida Program

Sponsor: University of South Florida College of Medicine
Hernando Correctional Institution
Hillsborough County Sheriff's Office
Tampa General Hospital
University Psychiatry Center
Zephyrhills Correctional Institution
Prgm Director: Wade C Myers, MD
Department of Psychiatry & Behavioral Medicine
3515 E Fletcher Avenue
Tampa, FL 33613
Tel: 813 974-0311   *Fax:* 813 974-1130
E-mail: kisaac@health.usf.edu
Length: 1 Yr   *ACGME Approved/Offered Positions:* 2
Program ID: 406-11-12-055

Georgia

Atlanta

Emory University Program

Sponsor: Emory University School of Medicine
Georgia Regional Hospital at Atlanta
Grady Health System
Prgm Director: Peter Ash, MD
Faculty Office Building, Psychiatry, Room 325
49 Jesse Hill Jr Drive SE
Atlanta, GA 30303
Tel: 404 778-1482   *Fax:* 404 727-3155
E-mail: pash01@emory.edu
Length: 1 Yr   *ACGME Approved/Offered Positions:* 2
Program ID: 406-12-21-008

Louisiana

New Orleans

Tulane University Program

Sponsor: Tulane University School of Medicine
Eastern Louisiana Mental Health System
Tulane University Hospital and Clinics
Prgm Director: Terry LeBourgeois, MD
Dept of Psychiatry & Neurology TB 53
1440 Canal St
New Orleans, LA 70112
Tel: 504 988-2201   *Fax:* 504 988-7457
E-mail: hlebour@tulane.edu
Length: 1 Yr   *ACGME Approved/Offered Positions:* 3
Program ID: 406-21-21-010

Shreveport

Louisiana State University (Shreveport) Program

Sponsor: LSU Health Sciences Center-University
  Hospital
Caddo Correctional Center
First Judicial District Court
Pinecrest Developmental Center
Swanson Center for Youth
Prgm Director: Marc A Colon, MD
1501 Kings Highway
Shreveport, LA 71130
Tel: 318 675-6040   *Fax:* 318 675-6054
E-mail: mcolon@lsuhsc.edu
Length: 1 Yr   *ACGME Approved/Offered Positions:* 2
Program ID: 406-21-13-057

Maryland

Baltimore

University of Maryland Program

Sponsor: University of Maryland Medical System
Clifton T Perkins Hospital Center
Medical Services Div of Circuit Court for Baltimore City
Prgm Director: Annette L Hanson, MD*
8450 Dorsey Run Road
PO Box 1000
Jessup, MD 20794
Tel: 410 724-3149   *Fax:* 410 727-5148
E-mail: hansonax@dhmh.state.md.us
Length: 1 Yr   *ACGME Approved/Offered Positions:* 2
Program ID: 406-23-21-011

Massachusetts

Boston

Massachusetts General Hospital/McLean Hospital Program

Sponsor: Massachusetts General Hospital
Bridgewater State Hospital
Cambridge Court Clinic
Erich Lindemann Mental Health Center
Prgm Director: Ronald Schouten, MD, JD
15 Parkman Street
WAC 812
Boston, MA 02114
Tel: 617 726-5195   *Fax:* 617 724-2808
E-mail: rschouten@partners.org
Length: 1 Yr   *ACGME Approved/Offered Positions:* 3
Program ID: 406-24-21-012

Worcester

University of Massachusetts Program

Sponsor: University of Massachusetts Medical School
Bridgewater State Hospital
Worcester State Hospital
Prgm Director: Paul Noroian, MD*
55 Lake Avenue North
Worcester, MA 01655
Tel: 508 368-3573   *Fax:* 508 363-1512
E-mail: cara.sanford@umassmed.edu
Length: 1 Yr   *ACGME Approved/Offered Positions:* 3
Program ID: 406-24-31-013

Michigan

Saline

University of Michigan Program

Sponsor: University of Michigan Hospitals and Health
  Centers
Center for Forensic Psychiatry
Prgm Director: Craig A Lemmen, MD
8303 Platt Road
PO Box 2060
Ann Arbor, MI 48106
Tel: 734 295-4301   *Fax:* 734 944-2359
E-mail: lemmenc@michigan.gov
Length: 1 Yr   *ACGME Approved/Offered Positions:* 3
Program ID: 406-25-21-014

Missouri

Columbia

University of Missouri-Columbia Program

Sponsor: University of Missouri-Columbia School of
  Medicine
Fulton State Hospital
Prgm Director: Bruce Harry, MD
Division of Psychiatry, DC067.00
One Hospital Drive
Columbia, MO 65212
Tel: 573 592-2700   *Fax:* 573 592-2863
E-mail: harryb@health.missouri.edu
Length: 1 Yr   *ACGME Approved/Offered Positions:* 2
Program ID: 406-28-31-054

New York

Bronx

Albert Einstein College of Medicine Program
Sponsor: Albert Einstein College of Medicine of Yeshiva University
Bronx Psychiatric Center
Prgm Director: Merrill Rotter, MD
1500 Waters Place
Bronx, NY 10461
Tel: 718 862-4745   *Fax:* 718 862-4856
Length: 1 Yr   *ACGME Approved/Offered Positions:* 3
Program ID: 406-35-21-015

New York

New York Medical College at St Vincent's Hospital and Medical Center of New York Program
Sponsor: New York Medical College
St Vincent Catholic Medical Centers (Manhattan)
Prgm Director: Spencer Eth, MD
144 West 12th Street, Reiss 175
New York, NY 10011
Tel: 212 604-8196   *Fax:* 212 604-8197
Length: 1 Yr   *ACGME Approved/Offered Positions:* 3
Program ID: 406-35-31-027

New York Presbyterian Hospital (Columbia Campus) Program
Sponsor: New York Presbyterian Hospital
Bellevue Hospital Center
Mid-Hudson Forensic Psychiatric Center
New York Presbyterian Hospital (Columbia Campus)
New York State Psychiatric Institute
Prgm Director: Steven Simring, MD
1051 Riverside Drive, Unit 115
New York, NY 10032
Tel: 212 543-5182   *Fax:* 212 543-5356
Length: 1 Yr   *ACGME Approved/Offered Positions:* 3
Program ID: 406-35-21-039

New York University School of Medicine Program
Sponsor: New York University School of Medicine
Bellevue Hospital Center
Kirby Forensic Psychiatric Center
Prgm Director: Richard Rosner, MD
100 Centre Street, Suite 500
New York, NY 10013
Tel: 212 374-2290   *Fax:* 212 374-3050
Length: 1 Yr   *ACGME Approved/Offered Positions:* 4
Program ID: 406-35-31-016

Rochester

University of Rochester Program
Sponsor: Strong Memorial Hospital of the University of Rochester
Rochester Psychiatric Center
Unity Hospital (Unity Health System)
Prgm Director: J Richard Ciccone, MD
300 Crittenden Boulevard
Rochester, NY 14642
Tel: 585 275-4986   *Fax:* 585 244-4734
Length: 1 Yr   *ACGME Approved/Offered Positions:* 2
Program ID: 406-35-11-017

Syracuse

SUNY Upstate Medical University Program
Sponsor: SUNY Upstate Medical University
Prgm Director: James L Knoll IV, MD
750 East Adams Street
Syracuse, NY 13210
Tel: 315 464-3104   *Fax:* 315 464-3141
Length: 1 Yr   *ACGME Approved/Offered Positions:* 3
Program ID: 406-35-13-036

North Carolina

Chapel Hill

University of North Carolina Hospitals Program
Sponsor: University of North Carolina Hospitals
Central Regional Hospital (Raleigh Campus)
Prgm Director: Peter N Barboriak, MD, PhD
Spruill Bldg, 820 South Boylan Ave
Mailing Address: 3601 Mail Service Center
Raleigh, NC 27699
Tel: 919 733-9187   *Fax:* 919 966-7772
Length: 1 Yr   *ACGME Approved/Offered Positions:* 2
Program ID: 406-36-21-048

Ohio

Cincinnati

University Hospital/University of Cincinnati College of Medicine Program
Sponsor: University Hospital Inc
University Institute for Psychiatry and Law
Prgm Director: John C Kennedy, MD
231 Albert Sabin Way
PO Box 0559
Cincinnati, OH 45267
Tel: 513 558-4423   *Fax:* 513 558-3823
E-mail: carrie.arb@uc.edu
Length: 1 Yr   *ACGME Approved/Offered Positions:* 2
Program ID: 406-38-21-033

Cleveland

University Hospitals Case Medical Center Program
Sponsor: University Hospitals Case Medical Center
Northcoast Behavioral Health (Cleveland)
Prgm Director: Phillip J Resnick, MD
11100 Euclid Avenue
Cleveland, OH 44106
Tel: 216 844-3415   *Fax:* 216 844-1703
E-mail: phillip.resnick@case.edu
Length: 1 Yr   *ACGME Approved/Offered Positions:* 4
Program ID: 406-38-21-019

Oregon

Portland

Oregon Health & Science University Program
Sponsor: Oregon Health & Science University Hospital
Oregon State Hospital
Prgm Director: Landy Sparr, MD, MA
Department of Psychiatry, UHN80
3181 SW Sam Jackson Park Road
Portland, OR 97239
Tel: 503 494-4044   *Fax:* 503 494-6170
Length: 1 Yr   *ACGME Approved/Offered Positions:* 2
Program ID: 406-40-31-051

Pennsylvania

Philadelphia

University of Pennsylvania Program
Sponsor: University of Pennsylvania Health System
Ann Klein Forensic Center
Norristown State Hospital
Philadelphia Prison System
Veterans Affairs Medical Center (Philadelphia)
Prgm Director: Robert L Sadoff, MD
Department of Psychiatry
305 Blockley Hall
Philadelphia, PA 19104
Tel: 215 887-6144   *Fax:* 215 887-6477
E-mail: sadoffbobsadoff@aol.com
Length: 1 Yr   *ACGME Approved/Offered Positions:* 4
Program ID: 406-41-12-059

Pittsburgh

University of Pittsburgh Medical Center Medical Education Program
Sponsor: Univ of Pittsburgh Medical Center Medical Education
Allegheny County Behavior Assessment Unit
Mayview State Hospital
UPMC Western Psychiatric Institute and Clinic
Prgm Director: Christine A Martone, MD
3811 O'Hara Street
Pittsburgh, PA 15213
Tel: 412 246-6040   *Fax:* 412 246-5880
E-mail: martoneca@upmc.edu
Length: 1 Yr   *ACGME Approved/Offered Positions:* 3
Program ID: 406-41-13-043

South Carolina

Charleston

Medical University of South Carolina Program
Sponsor: Medical University of South Carolina College of Medicine
Charleston/Dorchester Community Mental Health Center
Prgm Director: Susan J Hardesty, MD
Department of Psychiatry
67 President Street, PO Box 250861
Charleston, SC 29425
Tel: 843 792-0180   *Fax:* 843 792-0189
E-mail: hardests@musc.edu
Length: 1 Yr   *ACGME Approved/Offered Positions:* 2
Program ID: 406-45-13-053

Columbia

Palmetto Health/University of South Carolina School of Medicine Program
Sponsor: Palmetto Health
South Carolina Department of Mental Health (SCDMH)
University of South Carolina School of Medicine
Prgm Director: Richard L Frierson, MD
Dept of Neuropsychiatry & Behavioral Science
3555 Harden Street Extension, Suite 301
Columbia, SC 29203
Tel: 803 434-2808   *Fax:* 803 434-2985
E-mail: richard.frierson@uscmed.sc.edu
Length: 1 Yr   *ACGME Approved/Offered Positions:* 2
Program ID: 406-45-21-020

Note: * indicates a newly appointed program director

Texas

Dallas

University of Texas Southwestern Medical School Program
Sponsor: University of Texas Southwestern Medical School
Dallas VA Medical Center
Prgm Director: Heidi S Vermette, MD
5323 Harry Hines Boulevard
Dallas, TX 75390
Tel: 214 857-0805   *Fax:* 214 857-0917
E-mail: shaniquwa.patrick@utsouthwestern.edu
Length: 1 Yr   *ACGME Approved/Offered Positions:* 2
Program ID: 406-48-31-042

San Antonio

University of Texas Health Science Center at San Antonio Program
Sponsor: University of Texas School of Medicine at San Antonio
Audie L Murphy Memorial Veterans Hospital (San Antonio)
Bexar County District Courts
Bexar County Juvenile Probation Department
Kerrville State Hospital
University of Texas Health Science Center
Prgm Director: William H Campbell, MD, MBA
Department of Psychiatry - MC 7792
7703 Floyd Curl Drive
San Antonio, TX 78229
Tel: 210 567-5430   *Fax:* 210 567-0817
E-mail: campbellw@uthscsa.edu
Length: 1 Yr   *ACGME Approved/Offered Positions:* 3
Program ID: 406-48-12-050

Virginia

Charlottesville

University of Virginia Program
Sponsor: University of Virginia Medical Center
Western State Hospital
Prgm Director: Bruce Cohen, MD
PO Box 800623
Charlottesville, VA 22908
Tel: 434 924-2241   *Fax:* 434 924-8496
Length: 1 Yr   *ACGME Approved/Offered Positions:* 1
Program ID: 406-51-31-032

Washington

Tacoma

University of Washington Program
Sponsor: University of Washington School of Medicine
Western State Hospital
Prgm Director: Gregory B Leong, MD*
9601 Steilacoom Boulevard SW
Tacoma, WA 98498
Tel: 253 756-2974   *Fax:* 253 761-7577
E-mail: leonggb@dshs.wa.gov
Length: 1 Yr   *ACGME Approved/Offered Positions:* 1
Program ID: 406-54-21-022

West Virginia

Morgantown

West Virginia University Program
Sponsor: West Virginia University School of Medicine
West Virginia University Hospitals
William R Sharpe Jr Hospital
Prgm Director: Thomas Adamski, MD*
930 Chestnut Ridge Road
Morgantown, WV 26505
Tel: 304 293-5312   *Fax:* 304 293-8724
Length: 1 Yr   *ACGME Approved/Offered Positions:* 2
Program ID: 406-55-13-038

Wisconsin

Milwaukee

Medical College of Wisconsin Affiliated Hospitals Program
Sponsor: Medical College of Wisconsin Affiliated Hospitals, Inc
Clement J Zablocki Veterans Affairs Medical Center
Mendota Mental Health Institute
Milwaukee County Behavioral Health Division
Prgm Director: Joseph B Layde, MD, JD
8701 Watertown Plank Road
Milwaukee, WI 53226
Tel: 414 955-8992   *Fax:* 414 955-6299
E-mail: jlayde@mcw.edu
Length: 1 Yr   *ACGME Approved/Offered Positions:* 2
Program ID: 406-56-21-023

Gastroenterology (Internal Medicine)

Alabama

Birmingham

University of Alabama Medical Center Program
Sponsor: University of Alabama Hospital
Veterans Affairs Medical Center (Birmingham)
Prgm Director: Charles M Wilcox, MD
University Station
Birmingham, AL 35294
Tel: 205 975-4958   *Fax:* 205 934-1546
Length: 3 Yrs   *ACGME Approved/Offered Positions:* 9
Program ID: 144-01-21-127

Mobile

University of South Alabama Program
Sponsor: University of South Alabama Hospitals
Infirmary West
University of South Alabama Medical Center
Prgm Director: Jack A DiPalma, MD
2451 Fillingim Street
Mobile, AL 36617
Tel: 251 660-5555   *Fax:* 251 660-5558
E-mail: gastro@usouthal.edu
Length: 3 Yrs   *ACGME Approved/Offered Positions:* 6
Program ID: 144-01-21-213

Arizona

Phoenix

Banner Good Samaritan Medical Center Program
Sponsor: Banner Good Samaritan Medical Center
Carl T Hayden VA Medical Center
Prgm Director: Francisco C Ramirez, MD
650 E Indian School Road
Phoenix, AZ 85012
Tel: 602 277-5551   *Fax:* 602 222-6562
E-mail: Francisco.Ramirez2@med.va.gov
Length: 3 Yrs   *ACGME Approved/Offered Positions:* 9
Program ID: 144-03-12-225

Scottsdale

College of Medicine, Mayo Clinic (Arizona) Program
Sponsor: College of Medicine, Mayo Clinic
Mayo Clinic (Arizona)
Mayo Clinic Hospital
Prgm Director: M Edwyn Harrison, MD
13400 E Shea Boulevard, 2-A
Scottsdale, AZ 85259
Tel: 480 301-6990   *Fax:* 480 301-8673
E-mail: ruscitti.phyllis@mayo.edu
Length: 3 Yrs   *ACGME Approved/Offered Positions:* 6
Program ID: 144-03-21-224

Tucson

University of Arizona Program

Sponsor: University of Arizona College of Medicine
Southern Arizona VA Health Care Center (Tucson)
University Medical Center
University of Arizona/UPHK Graduate Medical Ed
  Consortium
Prgm Director: Steve Goldschmid, MD*
Department of Internal Medicine-Gastroenterology
1501 North Campbell Avenue, PO Box 245028
Tucson, AZ 85724
Tel: 520 626-6349 *Fax:* 520 626-2919
E-mail: lcontrer@email.arizona.edu
Length: 3 Yrs *ACGME Approved/Offered Positions:* 10
Program ID: 144-03-21-110

Arkansas

Little Rock

University of Arkansas for Medical Sciences Program

Sponsor: University of Arkansas College of Medicine
Central Arkansas Veterans Healthcare System
UAMS Medical Center
Prgm Director: Kevin W Olden, MD
4301 West Markham, Slot 567
Shorey S8/68
Little Rock, AR 72205
Tel: 501 686-7840 *Fax:* 501 686-6248
E-mail: sedavis@uams.edu
Length: 3 Yrs *ACGME Approved/Offered Positions:* 7
Program ID: 144-04-21-111

California

Fresno

University of California (San Francisco)/Fresno Program

Sponsor: UCSF Fresno Medical Education Program
Community Medical Centers (Fresno)
VA Central California Health Care System
Prgm Director: Muhammad Y Sheikh, MD
2823 Fresno Street, 1st Floor, Endoscopy
Fresno, CA 93721
Tel: 559 459-3882 *Fax:* 559 459-3887
Length: 3 Yrs *ACGME Approved/Offered Positions:* 6
Program ID: 144-05-12-235

La Jolla

Scripps Clinic/Scripps Green Hospital Program

Sponsor: Scripps Clinic/Scripps Green Hospital
Prgm Director: Walter J Coyle, MD
10666 N Torrey Pines Road
La Jolla, CA 92037
Tel: 858 554-8880 *Fax:* 858 554-8065
Length: 3 Yrs *ACGME Approved/Offered Positions:* 6
Program ID: 144-05-21-073

Loma Linda

Loma Linda University Program

Sponsor: Loma Linda University Medical Center
Jerry L Pettis Memorial Veterans Hospital
Riverside County Regional Medical Center
Prgm Director: Michael H Walter, MD
Division of Gastroenterology
11234 Anderson Street, Room 1568
Loma Linda, CA 92354
Tel: 909 558-4911 *Fax:* 909 558-0490
E-mail: mwalter@llu.edu
Length: 3 Yrs *ACGME Approved/Offered Positions:* 9
Program ID: 144-05-21-087

Los Angeles

Kaiser Permanente Southern California (Los Angeles) Program

Sponsor: Kaiser Permanente Southern California
Kaiser Foundation Hospital (Los Angeles)
Prgm Director: Harpreet Sekhon, MD
1526 North Edgemont Street
7th Floor
Los Angeles, CA 90027
Tel: 323 783-3799 *Fax:* 323 783-7056
Length: 3 Yrs *ACGME Approved/Offered Positions:* 6
Program ID: 144-05-12-037

UCLA Medical Center Program

Sponsor: UCLA David Geffen School of Medicine/UCLA
  Medical Center
Cedars-Sinai Medical Center
UCLA Medical Center
VA Greater Los Angeles Healthcare System
Prgm Director: Bennett Roth, MD*
Center for the Health Sciences, 44-138
Box 951684
Los Angeles, CA 90095
Tel: 310 825-6618 *Fax:* 310 794-9718
Length: 3 Yrs *ACGME Approved/Offered Positions:* 21
Program ID: 144-05-11-130

University of Southern California/ LAC+USC Medical Center Program

Sponsor: University of Southern California/LAC+USC
  Medical Center
LAC+USC Medical Center
USC University Hospital
Prgm Director: Michael M Kline, MD
2011 Zonal Avenue, HMR 101
Department of Medicine
Los Angeles, CA 90033
Tel: 323 442-5576 *Fax:* 323 442-5425
Length: 3 Yrs *ACGME Approved/Offered Positions:* 13
Program ID: 144-05-21-053

Orange

University of California (Irvine) Program

Sponsor: University of California (Irvine) Medical
  Center
VA Long Beach Healthcare System
Prgm Director: V Raman Muthusamy, MD*
101 The City Drive South
Building 53, Room 113
Orange, CA 92868
Tel: 714 456-5765 *Fax:* 714 456-7753
Length: 3 Yrs *ACGME Approved/Offered Positions:* 12
Program ID: 144-05-21-151

Sacramento

University of California (Davis) Health System Program

Sponsor: University of California (Davis) Health System
University of California (Davis) Medical Center
Prgm Director: Christopher L Bowlus, MD
Divison of Gastroenterology and Hepatology
4150 V Street, Suite 3500
Sacramento, CA 95817
Tel: 916 734-7183 *Fax:* 916 734-7908
Length: 3 Yrs *ACGME Approved/Offered Positions:* 9
Program ID: 144-05-21-094

San Diego

Naval Medical Center (San Diego) Program

Sponsor: Naval Medical Center (San Diego)
Prgm Director: Theodore W Schafer, MD
34800 Bob Wilson Drive
Suite 301
San Diego, CA 92134
Tel: 619 532-8983 *Fax:* 619 532-9620
Length: 3 Yrs *ACGME Approved/Offered Positions:* 6
Program ID: 144-05-12-152
Uniformed Services Program

University of California (San Diego) Program

Sponsor: University of California (San Diego) Medical
  Center
Veterans Affairs Medical Center (San Diego)
Prgm Director: Thomas J Savides, MD
9500 Gilman Drive, Bldg UC303, Rm 220
La Jolla, CA 92093
Tel: 858 534-2766 *Fax:* 858 534-3338
Length: 3 Yrs *ACGME Approved/Offered Positions:* 12
Program ID: 144-05-21-174

San Francisco

California Pacific Medical Center Program

Sponsor: California Pacific Medical Center
Prgm Director: Michael Verhille, MD
2351 Clay Street, Suite 380
San Francisco, CA 94115
Tel: 415 600-3376
Length: 3 Yrs *ACGME Approved/Offered Positions:* 4
Program ID: 144-05-12-153

University of California (San Francisco) Program

Sponsor: University of California (San Francisco) School
  of Medicine
San Francisco General Hospital Medical Center
UCSF and Mount Zion Medical Centers
Veterans Affairs Medical Center (San Francisco)
Prgm Director: Jonathan P Terdiman, MD
Division of Gastroenterology
513 Parnassus Avenue, S-357
San Francisco, CA 94143
Tel: 415 476-2776 *Fax:* 415 476-0659
Length: 3 Yrs *ACGME Approved/Offered Positions:* 18
Program ID: 144-05-21-154

Stanford

Stanford University Program

Sponsor: Stanford Hospital and Clinics
Veterans Affairs Palo Alto Health Care System
Prgm Director: Ramsey Cheung, MD
Department of Medicine/Gastroenterology
300 Pasteur Drive, MC:5187
Stanford, CA 94305
Tel: 650 493-5000 *Fax:* 650 852-3259
E-mail: rcheung@stanford.edu
Length: 3 Yrs *ACGME Approved/Offered Positions:* 12
Program ID: 144-05-21-022

Note: * indicates a newly appointed program director

Colorado

Aurora

University of Colorado Denver Program
Sponsor: University of Colorado Denver School of Medicine
University of Colorado Hospital
Prgm Director: Lisa M Forman, MD, MSCE
12631 E 17th Ave, MS B158
PO Box 6511
Aurora, CO 80045
Tel: 303 724-1858
Length: 3 Yrs *ACGME Approved/Offered Positions:* 12
Program ID: 144-07-21-065

Connecticut

Bridgeport

Bridgeport Hospital/Yale University Program
Sponsor: Bridgeport Hospital
Yale-New Haven Hospital
Prgm Director: George G Abdelsayed, MD
Division of Gastroenterology
267 Grant Street
Bridgeport, CT 06610
Tel: 203 384-3175   *Fax:* 203 336-7307
E-mail: pgabde@bpthosp.org
Length: 3 Yrs *ACGME Approved/Offered Positions:* 3
Program ID: 144-08-11-190

Farmington

University of Connecticut Program
Sponsor: University of Connecticut School of Medicine
Hartford Hospital
Hospital for Central Connecticut
St Francis Hospital and Medical Center
Univ of Connecticut Health Center/John Dempsey Hospital
Prgm Director: John W Birk, MD*
Department of Medicine/Gastroenterology Division
263 Farmington Avenue
Farmington, CT 06030
Tel: 860 679-8090   *Fax:* 860 679-3159
E-mail: cusati@nso.uchc.edu
Length: 3 Yrs *ACGME Approved/Offered Positions:* 6
Program ID: 144-08-31-001

New Haven

Yale-New Haven Medical Center Program
Sponsor: Yale-New Haven Hospital
Hospital of St Raphael
Veterans Affairs Medical Center (West Haven)
Prgm Director: Deborah D Proctor, MD
Section of Digestive Disease - 1080 LMP
PO Box 208019
New Haven, CT 06520
Tel: 203 785-7012   *Fax:* 203 737-1755
E-mail: fellowship@yale.edu
Length: 3 Yrs *ACGME Approved/Offered Positions:* 18
Program ID: 144-08-21-023

Norwalk

Norwalk Hospital Program
Sponsor: Norwalk Hospital
Yale-New Haven Hospital
Prgm Director: William Hale, MD
Department of Internal Medicine
Maple Street
Norwalk, CT 06856
Tel: 203 852-2278   *Fax:* 203 852-2738
E-mail: carrie.saviano@norwalkhealth.org
Length: 3 Yrs *ACGME Approved/Offered Positions:* 4
Program ID: 144-08-31-002

District of Columbia

Washington

George Washington University Program
Sponsor: George Washington University School of Medicine
George Washington University Hospital (UHS)
Inova Fairfax Hospital
Veterans Affairs Medical Center (Washington, DC)
Prgm Director: Marie L Borum, MD, EdD
Department of Medicine - Gastroenterology
2150 Pennsylvania Avenue, NW
Washington, DC 20037
Tel: 202 741-2160   *Fax:* 202 741-2169
Length: 3 Yrs *ACGME Approved/Offered Positions:* 6
Program ID: 144-10-21-114

Georgetown University Hospital Program
Sponsor: Georgetown University Hospital
Veterans Affairs Medical Center (Washington, DC)
Prgm Director: Nadim G Haddad, MD
Division of Gastroenterology (5 PHC)
3800 Reservoir Road, NW
Washington, DC 20007
Tel: 202 444-8761   *Fax:* 202 444-7797
E-mail: steelewe@gunet.georgetown.edu
Length: 3 Yrs *ACGME Approved/Offered Positions:* 12
Program ID: 144-10-21-088

Georgetown University Hospital/Washington Hospital Center Program
Sponsor: Washington Hospital Center
Clinical Center at the National Institutes of Health
Prgm Director: Michael S Gold, MD*
110 Irving Street, NW
Suite 3A3-A7
Washington, DC 20010
Tel: 202 877-7108   *Fax:* 202 877-8163
E-mail: diane.k.whitt@medstar.net
Length: 3 Yrs *ACGME Approved/Offered Positions:* 5
Program ID: 144-10-21-212

Howard University Program
Sponsor: Howard University Hospital
Prgm Director: Duane T Smoot, MD
2041 Georgia Avenue, NW
Washington, DC 20060
Tel: 202 865-1910   *Fax:* 202 865-7268
E-mail: dsmoot@howard.edu
Length: 3 Yrs *ACGME Approved/Offered Positions:* 6
Program ID: 144-10-21-133

Florida

Gainesville

University of Florida Program
Sponsor: University of Florida College of Medicine
North Florida/South Georgia Veterans Health System
Shands Hospital at the University of Florida
Prgm Director: Chris E Forsmark, MD
Box 100214
1600 SW Archer Rd
Gainesville, FL 32610
Tel: 352 392-2877   *Fax:* 352 392-3618
E-mail: forsmce@medicine.ufl.edu
Length: 3 Yrs *ACGME Approved/Offered Positions:* 12
Program ID: 144-11-21-039

Jacksonville

College of Medicine, Mayo Clinic (Jacksonville) Program
Sponsor: College of Medicine, Mayo Clinic
Mayo Clinic (Jacksonville)
Mayo Clinic Florida Hospital
Prgm Director: Massimo Raimondo, MD*
4500 San Pablo Road
Jacksonville, FL 32224
Tel: 904 953-0487   *Fax:* 904 953-0430
E-mail: spier.lori@mayo.edu
Length: 3 Yrs *ACGME Approved/Offered Positions:* 6
Program ID: 144-11-21-222

University of Florida College of Medicine Jacksonville Program
Sponsor: University of Florida College of Medicine Jacksonville
Shands Jacksonville Medical Center
Prgm Director: Louis R Lambiase, MD, MHA
Dept of Medicine/Gastroenterology LRC 4th Floor
653 W 8th Street
Jacksonville, FL 32209
Tel: 904 633-0089   *Fax:* 904 633-0028
E-mail: Gastroenterology.gme@jax.ufl.edu
Length: 3 Yrs *ACGME Approved/Offered Positions:* 6
Program ID: 144-11-21-024

Miami

Jackson Memorial Hospital/Jackson Health System Program
Sponsor: Jackson Memorial Hospital/Jackson Health System
Mount Sinai Medical Center of Florida, Inc
University of Miami Hospital
Veterans Affairs Medical Center (Miami)
Prgm Director: Jeffrey B Raskin, MD
PO Box 016960 (D-49)
Miami, FL 33101
Tel: 305 243-8644   *Fax:* 305 325-9476
Length: 3 Yrs *ACGME Approved/Offered Positions:* 18
Program ID: 144-11-21-176

Tampa

University of South Florida Program
Sponsor: University of South Florida College of Medicine
James A Haley Veterans Hospital
Tampa General Hospital
Prgm Director: Patrick G Brady, MD
12901 Bruce B Downs Boulevard
MDC 82
Tampa, FL 33612
Tel: 813 974-2034   *Fax:* 813 974-5333
E-mail: jpenders@health.usf.edu
Length: 3 Yrs *ACGME Approved/Offered Positions:* 9
Program ID: 144-11-21-040

Programs

Weston

Cleveland Clinic (Florida) Program
Sponsor: Cleveland Clinic Florida
Prgm Director: Fernando Castro-Pavia, MD
2950 Cleveland Clinic Boulevard
Weston, FL 33331
Tel: 954 659-5646   *Fax:* 954 659-5647
E-mail: hernang1@ccf.org
Length: 3 Yrs   *ACGME Approved/Offered Positions:* 4
Program ID: 144-11-13-228

Georgia
Atlanta

Emory University Program
Sponsor: Emory University School of Medicine
Emory University Hospital
Grady Health System
Veterans Affairs Medical Center (Atlanta)
Prgm Director: Jan-Michael A Klapproth, MD*
1364 Clifton Road, NE
Department of Medicine
Atlanta, GA 30322
Tel: 404 727-5638   *Fax:* 404 727-5767
E-mail: jklappr@emory.edu
Length: 3 Yrs   *ACGME Approved/Offered Positions:* 12
Program ID: 144-12-21-136

Augusta

Medical College of Georgia Program
Sponsor: Medical College of Georgia
Veterans Affairs Medical Center (Augusta)
Prgm Director: Robert R Schade, MD
Sect of Gastroenterology, BBR2538
1120 15th Street
Augusta, GA 30912
Tel: 706 721-2238   *Fax:* 706 721-0331
E-mail: rschade@mail.mcg.edu
Length: 3 Yrs   *ACGME Approved/Offered Positions:* 7
Program ID: 144-12-21-003

Illinois
Chicago

John H Stroger Hospital of Cook County Program
Sponsor: John H Stroger Hospital of Cook County
Prgm Director: Bashar M Attar, MD, PhD
1901 West Harrison Street
Chicago, IL 60612
Tel: 312 864-7213   *Fax:* 312 864-9624
Length: 3 Yrs   *ACGME Approved/Offered Positions:* 9
Program ID: 144-16-12-041

McGaw Medical Center of Northwestern University Program
Sponsor: McGaw Medical Center of Northwestern University
Jesse Brown Veterans Affairs Medical Center
Northwestern Memorial Hospital
Prgm Director: Ikuo Hirano, MD
Division of Gastroenterology
676 North Saint Clair Street, Suite 1400
Chicago, IL 60611
Tel: 312 695-4036   *Fax:* 312 695-3999
Length: 3 Yrs   *ACGME Approved/Offered Positions:* 9
Program ID: 144-16-21-074

Rush University Medical Center Program
Sponsor: Rush University Medical Center
Prgm Director: Michael D Brown, MD
1725 W Harrison Street
Suite 206
Chicago, IL 60612
Tel: 312 563-3875   *Fax:* 312 563-3883
E-mail: mbrowngi@ameritech.net
Length: 3 Yrs   *ACGME Approved/Offered Positions:* 9
Program ID: 144-16-11-137

University of Chicago Program
Sponsor: University of Chicago Medical Center
Prgm Director: David T Rubin, MD
MC 4076
5841 S Maryland Ave
Chicago, IL 60637
Tel: 773 702-9925   *Fax:* 773 702-2182
Length: 3 Yrs   *ACGME Approved/Offered Positions:* 12
Program ID: 144-16-11-067

University of Illinois College of Medicine at Chicago Program
Sponsor: University of Illinois College of Medicine at Chicago
Jesse Brown Veterans Affairs Medical Center
University of Illinois Hospital and Clinics
Prgm Director: Allan G Halline, MD
840 South Wood Street - MC 716
Chicago, IL 60612
Tel: 312 996-6651   *Fax:* 312 996-5103
E-mail: laurenw@uic.edu
Length: 3 Yrs   *ACGME Approved/Offered Positions:* 11
Program ID: 144-16-21-138

Maywood

Loyola University Program
Sponsor: Loyola University Medical Center
Edward Hines, Jr Veterans Affairs Hospital
Prgm Director: Claus Fimmel, MD
2160 S First Avenue
Department of Medicine
Maywood, IL 60153
Tel: 708 216-8548   *Fax:* 708 216-4113
E-mail: GI_Fellowship@lumc.edu
Length: 3 Yrs   *ACGME Approved/Offered Positions:* 12
Program ID: 144-16-21-004

Park Ridge

Advocate Lutheran General Hospital Program
Sponsor: Advocate Lutheran General Hospital
Prgm Director: Alan Shapiro, MD*
1775 Dempster Street
Park Ridge, IL 60068
Tel: 847 723-6464   *Fax:* 847 723-5615
Length: 3 Yrs   *ACGME Approved/Offered Positions:* 3
Program ID: 144-16-21-214

Indiana
Indianapolis

Indiana University School of Medicine Program
Sponsor: Indiana University School of Medicine
Clarian Indiana University Hospital
Richard L Roudebush Veterans Affairs Medical Center
William N Wishard Memorial Hospital
Prgm Director: Michael Chiorean, MD*
Department of Medicine, Regenstrief 4100
1050 Wishard Blvd
Indianapolis, IN 46202
Tel: 317 274-6474   *Fax:* 317 274-0975
Length: 3 Yrs   *ACGME Approved/Offered Positions:* 14
Program ID: 144-17-21-155

Iowa
Iowa City

University of Iowa Hospitals and Clinics Program
Sponsor: University of Iowa Hospitals and Clinics
Veterans Affairs Medical Center (Iowa City)
Prgm Director: Kyle E Brown, MD
Department of Medicine
200 Hawkins Drive
Iowa City, IA 52242
Tel: 319 384-6579   *Fax:* 319 356-7918
Length: 3 Yrs   *ACGME Approved/Offered Positions:* 9
Program ID: 144-18-21-095

Kansas
Kansas City

University of Kansas School of Medicine Program
Sponsor: University of Kansas School of Medicine
University of Kansas Hospital
Veterans Affairs Medical Center (Kansas City)
Prgm Director: Prateek Sharma, MD
Division of Gastroenterology
3901 Rainbow Boulevard
Kansas City, KS 66160
Tel: 913 588-3283   *Fax:* 913 588-3975
Length: 3 Yrs   *ACGME Approved/Offered Positions:* 9
Program ID: 144-19-21-115

Kentucky
Lexington

University of Kentucky College of Medicine Program
Sponsor: University of Kentucky College of Medicine
University of Kentucky Hospital
Veterans Affairs Medical Center (Lexington)
Prgm Director: Luis R Pena, MD
MN649
800 Rose Street
Lexington, KY 40536
Tel: 859 323-5105   *Fax:* 859 257-8860
E-mail: luis.pena@uky.edu
Length: 3 Yrs   *ACGME Approved/Offered Positions:* 9
Program ID: 144-20-21-177

Louisville

University of Louisville Program
Sponsor: University of Louisville School of Medicine
Jewish Hospital
Norton Hospital
University of Louisville Hospital
Veterans Affairs Medical Center (Louisville)
Prgm Director: Richard A Wright, MD, MBA
Division of Gastroenterology/Hepatology
University of Louisville
Louisville, KY 40292
Tel: 502 852-1384   *Fax:* 502 852-0846
E-mail: gifellow@louisville.edu
Length: 3 Yrs   *ACGME Approved/Offered Positions:* 14
Program ID: 144-20-31-089

Note: * indicates a newly appointed program director

Louisiana

New Orleans

Louisiana State University Program
Sponsor: Louisiana State University School of Medicine
Leonard J Chabert Medical Center
Medical Center of Louisiana at New Orleans
Ochsner Medical Center-Kenner
Tulane University Hospital and Clinics
Prgm Director: William A Ferrante, MD
2020 Gravier Street, 7th Floor, Suite D
New Orleans, LA 70112
Tel: 504 568-4498   *Fax:* 504 568-2127
E-mail: wferra@lsuhsc.edu
Length: 3 Yrs   *ACGME Approved/Offered Positions:* 6
Program ID: 144-21-21-139

Ochsner Clinic Foundation Program
Sponsor: Ochsner Clinic Foundation
Prgm Director: James W Smith, MD
1514 Jefferson Highway
New Orleans, LA 70121
Tel: 504 842-4015   *Fax:* 504 842-0098
E-mail: dpinkston@ochsner.org
Length: 3 Yrs   *ACGME Approved/Offered Positions:* 6
Program ID: 144-21-22-149

Tulane University Program
Sponsor: Tulane University School of Medicine
Medical Center of Louisiana at New Orleans
Tulane University Hospital and Clinics
Veterans Affairs Medical Center (New Orleans)
Prgm Director: Robert S Bulat, MD, PhD
Section of Gastroenterology SL 35
1430 Tulane Avenue Room 3548
New Orleans, LA 70112
Tel: 504 988-5763   *Fax:* 504 988-2188
E-mail: rbulat@tulane.edu
Length: 3 Yrs   *ACGME Approved/Offered Positions:* 9
Program ID: 144-21-21-108

Shreveport

Louisiana State University (Shreveport) Program
Sponsor: LSU Health Sciences Center-University Hospital
Overton Brooks Veterans Affairs Medical Center
Willis-Knighton Medical Center
Prgm Director: Kenneth J Manas, MD
1501 Kings Highway
PO Box 33932
Shreveport, LA 71130
Tel: 318 675-5982   *Fax:* 318 675-5957
Length: 3 Yrs   *ACGME Approved/Offered Positions:* 6
Program ID: 144-21-13-226

Maryland

Baltimore

Johns Hopkins University Program
Sponsor: Johns Hopkins University School of Medicine
Johns Hopkins Hospital
Prgm Director: Francis M Giardiello, MD
1830 E Monument Street
Suite 431
Baltimore, MD 21205
Tel: 410 955-2635   *Fax:* 410 614-8337
E-mail: lwelch@jhmi.edu
Length: 3 Yrs   *ACGME Approved/Offered Positions:* 15
Program ID: 144-23-11-075

University of Maryland Program
Sponsor: University of Maryland Medical System
Clinical Center at the National Institutes of Health
Veterans Affairs Medical Center (Baltimore)
Prgm Director: Bruce D Greenwald, MD
22 S Greene St
Room N3W62
Baltimore, MD 21201
Tel: 410 328-8731   *Fax:* 410 328-8315
Length: 3 Yrs   *ACGME Approved/Offered Positions:* 14
Program ID: 144-23-21-042

Bethesda

National Capital Consortium (Bethesda) Program
Sponsor: National Capital Consortium
National Naval Medical Center (Bethesda)
University of Maryland Medical System
Walter Reed Army Medical Center
Prgm Director: John D Horwhat, MD*
8901 Wisconsin Avenue
Bethesda, MD 20889
Tel: 202 390-5094   *Fax:* 202 782-4416
E-mail: john.david.horwhat@us.army.mil
Length: 3 Yrs   *ACGME Approved/Offered Positions:* 15
Program ID: 144-23-11-156
Uniformed Services Program

Massachusetts

Boston

Beth Israel Deaconess Medical Center Program
Sponsor: Beth Israel Deaconess Medical Center
Prgm Director: Ciaran P Kelly, MD
330 Brookline Avenue
Dana 601
Boston, MA 02215
Tel: 617 667-1272   *Fax:* 617 667-8144
E-mail: mjewell@bidmc.harvard.edu
Length: 3 Yrs   *ACGME Approved/Offered Positions:* 12
Program ID: 144-24-21-005

Boston University Medical Center Program
Sponsor: Boston Medical Center
Veterans Affairs Medical Center (Boston)
Prgm Director: Robert C Lowe, MD
650 Albany Street
Room 504
Boston, MA 02118
Tel: 617 638-8330   *Fax:* 617 638-7785
E-mail: robert.lowe@bmc.org
Length: 3 Yrs   *ACGME Approved/Offered Positions:* 9
Program ID: 144-24-21-157

Brigham and Women's Hospital Program
Sponsor: Brigham and Women's Hospital
Prgm Director: Frederick Makrauer, MD
75 Francis Street
Boston, MA 02115
Tel: 617 525-8818   *Fax:* 617 264-5271
Length: 3 Yrs   *ACGME Approved/Offered Positions:* 15
Program ID: 144-24-21-006

Massachusetts General Hospital Program
Sponsor: Massachusetts General Hospital
Prgm Director: Andrea E Reid, MD, MPH
GI Unit, Jackson 724
55 Fruit Street
Boston, MA 02114
Tel: 617 724-7563   *Fax:* 617 726-3673
Length: 3 Yrs   *ACGME Approved/Offered Positions:* 12
Program ID: 144-24-11-068

Tufts Medical Center Program
Sponsor: Tufts Medical Center
Caritas St Elizabeth's Medical Center of Boston
Prgm Director: Joel Weinstock, MD
Division of Gastroenterology
750 Washington Street, Box 233
Boston, MA 02111
Tel: 617 636-4593   *Fax:* 617 636-4505
Length: 3 Yrs   *ACGME Approved/Offered Positions:* 12
Program ID: 144-24-21-007

Burlington

Lahey Clinic Program
Sponsor: Lahey Clinic
Prgm Director: Stephen C Fabry, MD
41 Mall Road
Burlington, MA 01805
Tel: 781 744-8767   *Fax:* 781 744-5276
E-mail: gifellowship@lahey.org
Length: 3 Yrs   *ACGME Approved/Offered Positions:* 6
Program ID: 144-24-21-141

Worcester

University of Massachusetts Program
Sponsor: University of Massachusetts Medical School
UMass Memorial Health Care (University Campus)
Prgm Director: David R Cave, MD, PhD
Division of Gastroenterology
55 Lake Avenue North
Worcester, MA 01655
Tel: 508 856-8399   *Fax:* 508 856-3981
Length: 3 Yrs   *ACGME Approved/Offered Positions:* 9
Program ID: 144-24-21-008

Michigan

Ann Arbor

University of Michigan Program
Sponsor: University of Michigan Hospitals and Health Centers
Veterans Affairs Medical Center (Ann Arbor)
Prgm Director: Ellen M Zimmermann, MD
3912 Taubman Center, SPC 5362
Ann Arbor, MI 48109
Tel: 734 615-8468   *Fax:* 734 936-7392
E-mail: ezimmer@umich.edu
Length: 3 Yrs   *ACGME Approved/Offered Positions:* 18
Program ID: 144-25-21-077

Detroit

Henry Ford Hospital Program
Sponsor: Henry Ford Hospital
Prgm Director: Mary Ann Huang, MD*
2799 West Grand Boulevard
Detroit, MI 48202
Tel: 313 916-2408
Length: 3 Yrs   *ACGME Approved/Offered Positions:* 12
Program ID: 144-25-11-142

Wayne State University/Detroit Medical Center Program
Sponsor: Wayne State University/Detroit Medical Center
Detroit Receiving Hospital and University Health Center
Harper-Hutzel Hospital
Veterans Affairs Medical Center (Detroit)
Prgm Director: Murray N Ehrinpreis, MD
3990 John R Street
6 Hudson
Detroit, MI 48201
Tel: 313 745-8601   *Fax:* 313 745-8843
Length: 3 Yrs   *ACGME Approved/Offered Positions:* 7
Program ID: 144-25-21-049

Royal Oak

William Beaumont Hospital Program
Sponsor: William Beaumont Hospital
Prgm Director: Mitchell S Cappell, MD, PhD
3535 W 13 Mile Road, MOB 233
Royal Oak, MI 48073
Tel: 248 551-0030   *Fax:* 248 551-1163
E-mail: MCappell@beaumont.edu
Length: 3 Yrs   *ACGME Approved/Offered Positions:* 6
Program ID: 144-25-12-180

Southfield

Providence Hospital and Medical Centers Program
Sponsor: Providence Hospital and Medical Centers
St John Macomb-Oakland Hospital
Prgm Director: Michael Piper, MD
16001 West Nine Mile Road
PO Box 2043
Southfield, MI 48037
Tel: 248 849-7129   *Fax:* 248 849-5324
E-mail:
katherine.mccaskell@providence-stjohnhealth.org
Length: 3 Yrs   *ACGME Approved/Offered Positions:* 6
Program ID: 144-25-11-178

Minnesota

Minneapolis

University of Minnesota Program
Sponsor: University of Minnesota Medical School
Hennepin County Medical Center
University of Minnesota Medical Center, Division of
   Fairview
Veterans Affairs Medical Center (Minneapolis)
Prgm Director: Roger L Gebhard, MD
Gastroenterology Section (111D)
One Veterans Drive
Minneapolis, MN 55417
Tel: 612 467-4100   *Fax:* 612 725-2248
Length: 3 Yrs   *ACGME Approved/Offered Positions:* 12
Program ID: 144-26-21-117

Rochester

College of Medicine, Mayo Clinic (Rochester) Program
Sponsor: College of Medicine, Mayo Clinic
Mayo Clinic (Rochester)
Saint Marys Hospital of Rochester
Prgm Director: Darrell S Pardi, MD
200 First St SW
Rochester, MN 55905
Tel: 507 266-4056   *Fax:* 507 293-0469
Length: 3 Yrs   *ACGME Approved/Offered Positions:* 30
Program ID: 144-26-21-058

Mississippi

Jackson

University of Mississippi Medical Center Program
Sponsor: University of Mississippi School of Medicine
University Hospitals and Clinics
Veterans Affairs Medical Center (Jackson)
Prgm Director: Walter T Boone, MD
Division of Digestive Diseases
2500 N State St
Jackson, MS 39216
Tel: 601 984-4540   *Fax:* 601 984-4548
E-mail: boonemd@aol.com
Length: 3 Yrs   *ACGME Approved/Offered Positions:* 9
Program ID: 144-27-21-079

Missouri

Columbia

University of Missouri-Columbia Program
Sponsor: University of Missouri-Columbia School of
   Medicine
Harry S Truman Memorial Veterans Hospital
University Hospitals and Clinics
Prgm Director: Jamal Ibdah, MD, PhD
CE440 Div of Gastroenterology
Five Hospital Drive, DC043.00
Columbia, MO 65212
Tel: 573 882-0482   *Fax:* 573 884-4595
Length: 3 Yrs   *ACGME Approved/Offered Positions:* 9
Program ID: 144-28-21-080

Kansas City

University of Missouri at Kansas City Program
Sponsor: University of Missouri-Kansas City School of
   Medicine
St Luke's Hospital-Kansas City
Truman Medical Center
Prgm Director: Wendell K Clarkston, MD
Department of Medicine
2301 Holmes St
Kansas City, MO 64108
Tel: 816 404-5001   *Fax:* 816 404-5014
Length: 3 Yrs   *ACGME Approved/Offered Positions:* 6
Program ID: 144-28-31-118

St Louis

St Louis University School of Medicine Program
Sponsor: St Louis University School of Medicine
St Louis University Hospital
Veterans Affairs Medical Center (St Louis)
Prgm Director: Charlene M Prather, MD, MPH
3635 Vista Ave at Grand Blvd
PO Box 15250
St Louis, MO 63110
Tel: 314 577-8764   *Fax:* 314 577-8125
E-mail: neuhausj@slu.edu
Length: 3 Yrs   *ACGME Approved/Offered Positions:* 12
Program ID: 144-28-21-182

Washington University/B-JH/SLCH Consortium Program
Sponsor: Washington University/B-JH/SLCH Consortium
Barnes-Jewish Hospital
Prgm Director: Nicholas O Davidson, MD
660 S Euclid Avenue, Box 8124
St Louis, MO 63110
Tel: 314 362-2027   *Fax:* 314 362-2033
E-mail: dhoward@im.wustl.edu
Length: 3 Yrs   *ACGME Approved/Offered Positions:* 12
Program ID: 144-28-21-158

Nebraska

Omaha

University of Nebraska Medical Center College of Medicine Program
Sponsor: University of Nebraska Medical Center College
   of Medicine
Nebraska Medical Center
Veterans Affairs Medical Center (Omaha)
Prgm Director: Renee L Young, MD
Section of Gastroenterology/Hepatology
982000 Nebraska Medical Center
Omaha, NE 68198
Tel: 402 559-4356   *Fax:* 402 559-9004
Length: 3 Yrs   *ACGME Approved/Offered Positions:* 6
Program ID: 144-30-21-160

New Hampshire

Lebanon

Dartmouth-Hitchcock Medical Center Program
Sponsor: Mary Hitchcock Memorial Hospital
Veterans Affairs Medical Center (White River Junction)
Prgm Director: Arifa Toor, MD
One Medical Center Drive
Lebanon, NH 03756
Tel: 603 650-5602   *Fax:* 603 650-5225
E-mail: arifa.toor@hitchcock.org
Length: 3 Yrs   *ACGME Approved/Offered Positions:* 6
Program ID: 144-32-21-150

New Jersey

Camden

UMDNJ-Robert Wood Johnson Medical School (Camden) Program
Sponsor: Cooper Hospital-University Medical Center
Our Lady of Lourdes Medical Center
Prgm Director: Christopher W Deitch, MD
Cooper Health System
501 Fellowship Road
Mount Laurel, NJ 08054
Tel: 856 642-2133   *Fax:* 856 642-2134
Length: 3 Yrs   *ACGME Approved/Offered Positions:* 9
Program ID: 144-33-21-050

New Brunswick

UMDNJ-Robert Wood Johnson Medical School Program
Sponsor: UMDNJ-Robert Wood Johnson Medical School
Robert Wood Johnson University Hospital
Veterans Affairs New Jersey Health Care System
Prgm Director: Kiron M Das, MD, PhD
Division of Gastroenterology and Hepatology
One Robert Wood Johnson Place, MEB 478
New Brunswick, NJ 08903
Tel: 732 235-7784   *Fax:* 732 235-7792
Length: 3 Yrs   *ACGME Approved/Offered Positions:* 6
Program ID: 144-33-21-026

Note: * indicates a newly appointed program director

Newark

UMDNJ-New Jersey Medical School Program

Sponsor: UMDNJ-New Jersey Medical School
UMDNJ-University Hospital
Veterans Affairs New Jersey Health Care System
Prgm Director: Zamir S Brelvi, MD
185 South Orange Avenue
MSB H538
Newark, NJ 07103
Tel: 973 972-5252   *Fax:* 973 972-3144
Length: 3 Yrs   *ACGME Approved/Offered Positions:* 9
Program ID: 144-33-21-200

South Orange

Seton Hall University School of Health and Medical Sciences Program

Sponsor: Seton Hall University School of Health and Medical Sciences
St Joseph's Regional Medical Center
St Michael's Medical Center (A Member of Catholic Health East)
Prgm Director: Walid J Baddoura, MD
703 Main Street
Paterson, NJ 07503
Tel: 973 754-2390   *Fax:* 973 754-2382
Length: 3 Yrs   *ACGME Approved/Offered Positions:* 6
Program ID: 144-33-21-051

New Mexico

Albuquerque

University of New Mexico Program

Sponsor: University of New Mexico School of Medicine
University of New Mexico Hospital
Veterans Affairs Medical Center (Albuquerque)
Prgm Director: Martin G Kistin, MD
Department of Medicine/GI Division
1 University of New Mexico MSC10-5550 ACC 5
Albuquerque, NM 87131
Tel: 505 272-4755   *Fax:* 505 272-6839
E-mail: GIFellowship@salud.unm.edu
Length: 3 Yrs   *ACGME Approved/Offered Positions:* 12
Program ID: 144-34-21-143

New York

Albany

Albany Medical Center Program

Sponsor: Albany Medical Center
Veterans Affairs Medical Center (Albany)
Prgm Director: Seth Richter, MD
Department of Medicine
47 New Scotland Avenue, MC 48
Albany, NY 12208
Tel: 518 262-6858   *Fax:* 518 262-6873
E-mail: brozowml@mail.amc.edu
Length: 3 Yrs   *ACGME Approved/Offered Positions:* 6
Program ID: 144-35-31-027

Bronx

Albert Einstein College of Medicine Program

Sponsor: Albert Einstein College of Medicine of Yeshiva University
Montefiore Medical Center-Henry and Lucy Moses Division
North Bronx Healthcare Network-Jacobi Medical Center
Prgm Director: David A Greenwald, MD
Division of Gastroenterology
111 East 210th Street
Bronx, NY 10467
Tel: 718 920-4846   *Fax:* 718 798-6408
E-mail: dgreenwa@montefiore.org
Length: 3 Yrs   *ACGME Approved/Offered Positions:* 12
Program ID: 144-35-21-102

New York Medical College (Bronx) Program

Sponsor: New York Medical College
Montefiore Medical Center - North Division
Prgm Director: Hilary I Hertan, MD
600 E 233rd St
Bronx, NY 10466
Tel: 718 920-9692   *Fax:* 718 920-6857
E-mail: hhertan@aol.com
Length: 3 Yrs   *ACGME Approved/Offered Positions:* 3
Program ID: 144-35-21-043

Brooklyn

Brooklyn Hospital Center Program

Sponsor: Brooklyn Hospital Center
St Barnabas Hospital
Wyckoff Heights Medical Center
Prgm Director: Sury Anand, MD
121 Dekalb Avenue
Brooklyn, NY 11201
Tel: 718 250-6945   *Fax:* 718 250-6489
E-mail: ddg9001@nyp.org
Length: 3 Yrs   *ACGME Approved/Offered Positions:* 9
Program ID: 144-35-12-185

Long Island College Hospital Program

Sponsor: Long Island College Hospital
Woodhull Medical and Mental Health Center
Prgm Director: Irwin M Grosman, MD
Division of Gastroenterology
339 Hicks Street
Brooklyn, NY 11201
Tel: 718 780-1738   *Fax:* 718 780-1391
Length: 3 Yrs   *ACGME Approved/Offered Positions:* 6
Program ID: 144-35-11-069

Maimonides Medical Center Program

Sponsor: Maimonides Medical Center
Coney Island Hospital
Prgm Director: Kadirawel Iswara, MD
1025 48th Street
Brooklyn, NY 11219
Tel: 718 283-7476   *Fax:* 718 635-7383
E-mail: kiswara@maimonidesmed.org
Length: 3 Yrs   *ACGME Approved/Offered Positions:* 7
Program ID: 144-35-11-162

New York Methodist Hospital Program

Sponsor: New York Methodist Hospital
Interfaith Medical Center
Prgm Director: Maurice A Cerulli, MD*
506 Sixth Street
Brooklyn, NY 11215
Tel: 718 780-3832   *Fax:* 718 780-3413
Length: 3 Yrs   *ACGME Approved/Offered Positions:* 6
Program ID: 144-35-13-230

SUNY Health Science Center at Brooklyn Program

Sponsor: SUNY Health Science Center at Brooklyn
Brookdale University Hospital and Medical Center
Kings County Hospital Center
University Hospital-SUNY Health Science Center at Brooklyn
Veterans Affairs Medical Center (Brooklyn)
Prgm Director: Frank G Gress, MD*
Division of Digestive Diseases, Box 1196
450 Clarkson Ave
Brooklyn, NY 11203
Tel: 718 270-1113   *Fax:* 718 270-7201
E-mail: selina.adams@downstate.edu
Length: 3 Yrs   *ACGME Approved/Offered Positions:* 18
Program ID: 144-35-21-011

Buffalo

University at Buffalo Program

Sponsor: University at Buffalo School of Medicine
Erie County Medical Center
Veterans Affairs Western New York Hospital
Prgm Director: Michael D Sitrin, MD
3495 Bailey Ave
Buffalo, NY 14215
Tel: 716 862-3163   *Fax:* 716 862-6777
Length: 3 Yrs   *ACGME Approved/Offered Positions:* 9
Program ID: 144-35-31-009

East Meadow

Nassau University Medical Center Program

Sponsor: Nassau University Medical Center
Prgm Director: Paul Mustacchia, MD
2201 Hempstead Turnpike
East Meadow, NY 11554
Tel: 516 572-6501   *Fax:* 516 572-5609
E-mail: pmustacc@numc.edu
Length: 3 Yrs   *ACGME Approved/Offered Positions:* 6
Program ID: 144-35-21-090

Elmhurst

Mount Sinai School of Medicine (Elmhurst) Program

Sponsor: Mount Sinai School of Medicine
Elmhurst Hospital Center-Mount Sinai Services
Prgm Director: Vivek Gumaste, MD
79-01 Broadway
Elmhurst, NY 11373
Tel: 718 334-2288   *Fax:* 718 334-1738
E-mail: gumastev@nychhc.org
Length: 3 Yrs   *ACGME Approved/Offered Positions:* 3
Program ID: 144-35-31-234

Flushing

New York Hospital Medical Center of Queens/Cornell University Medical College Program

Sponsor: New York Hospital Medical Center of Queens
Prgm Director: Moshe Rubin, MD*
56-45 Main Street
Flushing, NY 11355
Tel: 718 670-2559   *Fax:* 718 670-2456
E-mail: mrubinmd@mac.com
Length: 3 Yrs   *ACGME Approved/Offered Positions:* 3
Program ID: 144-35-11-091

Programs

Great Neck

NSLIJHS-Albert Einstein College of Medicine at Long Island Jewish Medical Center Program
Sponsor: North Shore-Long Island Jewish Health System
Long Island Jewish Medical Center
Prgm Director: Maurice A Cerulli, MD*
270-05 76th Avenue
Room B202
New Hyde Park, NY 11040
Tel: 718 470-7281   *Fax:* 718 343-0128
E-mail: mcerulli@nshs.edu
Length: 3 Yrs   *ACGME Approved/Offered Positions:* 6
Program ID: 144-35-21-144

NSLIJHS-North Shore University Hospital/NYU School of Medicine Program
Sponsor: North Shore-Long Island Jewish Health System
North Shore University Hospital
Prgm Director: David E Bernstein, MD
Department of Medicine
300 Community Drive
Manhasset, NY 11030
Tel: 516 562-4281   *Fax:* 516 562-2683
Length: 3 Yrs   *ACGME Approved/Offered Positions:* 4
Program ID: 144-35-21-170

Mineola

Winthrop-University Hospital Program
Sponsor: Winthrop-University Hospital
Prgm Director: James Grendell, MD
222 Station Plaza N, #429
Mineola, NY 11501
Tel: 516 663-2528   *Fax:* 516 663-4617
E-mail: mkramps@winthrop.org
Length: 3 Yrs   *ACGME Approved/Offered Positions:* 6
Program ID: 144-35-11-109

New York

Albert Einstein College of Medicine at Beth Israel Medical Center Program
Sponsor: Beth Israel Medical Center
Prgm Director: Albert D Min, MD
Department of Medicine
First Avenue at 16th Street, 17 Baird Hall
New York, NY 10003
Tel: 212 420-4751   *Fax:* 212 844-4373
E-mail: amin@chpnet.org
Length: 3 Yrs   *ACGME Approved/Offered Positions:* 6
Program ID: 144-35-11-010

Harlem Hospital Center Program
Sponsor: Harlem Hospital Center
Prgm Director: Lisa A Ozick, MD*
506 Lenox Ave at 135th Street
New York, NY 10037
Tel: 212 939-1430   *Fax:* 212 939-1432
Length: 3 Yrs   *ACGME Approved/Offered Positions:* 3
Program ID: 144-35-11-172

Lenox Hill Hospital Program
Sponsor: Lenox Hill Hospital
Prgm Director: Peter J Baiocco, MD
100 East 77th Street
New York, NY 10075
Tel: 212 434-2686   *Fax:* 212 434-3396
E-mail: mhill@lenoxhill.net
Length: 3 Yrs   *ACGME Approved/Offered Positions:* 6
Program ID: 144-35-11-194

Memorial Sloan-Kettering Cancer Center/New York Presbyterian Hospital (Cornell Campus) Program
Sponsor: Memorial Sloan-Kettering Cancer Center
Prgm Director: Arnold J Markowitz, MD
1275 York Avenue
Memorial Sloan-Kettering Cancer Ctr
New York, NY 10021
Tel: 212 639-8286   *Fax:* 212 639-2766
Length: 3 Yrs   *ACGME Approved/Offered Positions:* 6
Program ID: 144-35-21-179

Mount Sinai School of Medicine Program
Sponsor: Mount Sinai School of Medicine
Mount Sinai Medical Center
Veterans Affairs Medical Center (Bronx)
Prgm Director: Steven H Itzkowitz, MD
One Gustave L Levy Place
Box 1069
New York, NY 10029
Tel: 212 659-9697   *Fax:* 212 849-2574
Length: 3 Yrs   *ACGME Approved/Offered Positions:* 18
Program ID: 144-35-31-163

New York Medical College at St Vincent's Hospital and Medical Center of New York Program
Sponsor: New York Medical College
St Vincent Catholic Medical Centers (Manhattan)
Prgm Director: James Robilotti, MD
170 West 12th Street
New York, NY 10011
Tel: 212 604-8333   *Fax:* 212 604-8446
E-mail: jamesrobilotti@hotmail.com
Length: 3 Yrs   *ACGME Approved/Offered Positions:* 6
Program ID: 144-35-11-029

New York Presbyterian Hospital (Columbia Campus) Program
Sponsor: New York Presbyterian Hospital
New York Presbyterian Hospital (Columbia Campus)
Prgm Director: Reuben J Garcia-Carrasquillo, MD
622 W 168th Street
Box 83
New York, NY 10032
Tel: 212 342-4776   *Fax:* 212 342-5759
E-mail: rjc3@columbia.edu
Length: 3 Yrs   *ACGME Approved/Offered Positions:* 10
Program ID: 144-35-11-070

New York Presbyterian Hospital (Cornell Campus) Program
Sponsor: New York Presbyterian Hospital
New York Presbyterian Hospital (Cornell Campus)
Prgm Director: Robert A Schaefer, MD
Department of Medicine
1305 York Avenue, 4th Floor
New York, NY 10021
Tel: 646 962-4000   *Fax:* 646 962-0110
E-mail: mhsu@med.cornell.edu
Length: 3 Yrs   *ACGME Approved/Offered Positions:* 9
Program ID: 144-35-21-171

New York University School of Medicine Program
Sponsor: New York University School of Medicine
Bellevue Hospital Center
Manhattan VA Harbor Health Care System
NYU Hospitals Center
Prgm Director: Michael A Poles, MD, PhD*
550 First Avenue
New York, NY 10016
Tel: 212 686-7500   *Fax:* 212 686-7500
E-mail: michael.poles@nyumc.org
Length: 3 Yrs   *ACGME Approved/Offered Positions:* 9
Program ID: 144-35-21-120

St Luke's-Roosevelt Hospital Center Program
Sponsor: St Luke's-Roosevelt Hospital Center
Mount Sinai Medical Center
Prgm Director: Donald P Kotler, MD
Gastroenterology, Service and Research 1210
1111 Amsterdam Avenue
New York, NY 10025
Tel: 212 523-3680   *Fax:* 212 523-3683
Length: 3 Yrs   *ACGME Approved/Offered Positions:* 6
Program ID: 144-35-21-105

Rochester

University of Rochester Program
Sponsor: Strong Memorial Hospital of the University of Rochester
Prgm Director: Arthur J DeCross, MD, MS
601 Elmwood Ave
PO Box 646
Rochester, NY 14642
Tel: 585 275-5139   *Fax:* 585 276-0101
Length: 3 Yrs   *ACGME Approved/Offered Positions:* 9
Program ID: 144-35-21-220

Stony Brook

SUNY at Stony Brook Program
Sponsor: University Hospital - SUNY at Stony Brook
Veterans Affairs Medical Center (Northport)
Prgm Director: Edward H Cheng, MD
T-17, Room 060
Stony Brook, NY 11794
Tel: 631 444-2119   *Fax:* 631 444-8886
Length: 3 Yrs   *ACGME Approved/Offered Positions:* 7
Program ID: 144-35-21-012

Syracuse

SUNY Upstate Medical University Program
Sponsor: SUNY Upstate Medical University
Veterans Affairs Medical Center (Syracuse)
Prgm Director: Ronald Szyjkowski, MD
750 East Adams Street
Syracuse, NY 13210
Tel: 315 464-5804   *Fax:* 315 464-5809
E-mail: krauseb@upstate.edu
Length: 3 Yrs   *ACGME Approved/Offered Positions:* 3
Program ID: 144-35-21-106

Valhalla

New York Medical College at Westchester Medical Center Program
Sponsor: New York Medical College
Metropolitan Hospital Center
Sound Shore Medical Center of Westchester
Westchester Medical Center
Prgm Director: Edward Lebovics, MD
Department of Medicine
Munger Pavilion, Suite 206
Valhalla, NY 10595
Tel: 914 493-7337   *Fax:* 914 594-4317
E-mail: Lorraine_Schwarz@nymc.edu
Length: 3 Yrs   *ACGME Approved/Offered Positions:* 10
Program ID: 144-35-11-013

Note: * indicates a newly appointed program director

North Carolina

Chapel Hill

University of North Carolina Hospitals Program
Sponsor: University of North Carolina Hospitals
Prgm Director: Nicholas J Shaheen, MD, MPH
4162F Bioinformatics Building
130 Mason Farm Road
Chapel Hill, NC 27599
Tel: 919 966-2514   *Fax:* 919 966-6842
E-mail: skennedy@med.unc.edu
Length: 3 Yrs   *ACGME Approved/Offered Positions:* 12
Program ID: 144-36-21-145

Durham

Duke University Hospital Program
Sponsor: Duke University Hospital
Veterans Affairs Medical Center (Durham)
Prgm Director: Andrew J Muir, MD
Gastroenterology Section, Box 3913
Durham, NC 27710
Tel: 919 684-2052   *Fax:* 919 684-8264
E-mail: muir0002@mc.duke.edu
Length: 3 Yrs   *ACGME Approved/Offered Positions:* 12
Program ID: 144-36-21-146

Winston-Salem

Wake Forest University School of Medicine Program
Sponsor: Wake Forest University Baptist Medical Center
Prgm Director: Girish Mishra, MD, MS
Section of Gastroenterology
Medical Center Blvd
Winston-Salem, NC 27157
Tel: 336 713-7308   *Fax:* 336 713-7322
Length: 3 Yrs   *ACGME Approved/Offered Positions:* 6
Program ID: 144-36-21-014

Ohio

Cincinnati

University Hospital/University of Cincinnati College of Medicine Program
Sponsor: University Hospital Inc
Veterans Affairs Medical Center (Cincinnati)
Prgm Director: Stephen D Zucker, MD
Mail Location 595
Cincinnati, OH 45267
Tel: 513 558-5244   *Fax:* 513 558-1744
E-mail: zuckersd@email.uc.edu
Length: 3 Yrs   *ACGME Approved/Offered Positions:* 8
Program ID: 144-38-21-081

Cleveland

Case Western Reserve University (MetroHealth) Program
Sponsor: MetroHealth Medical Center
Prgm Director: Hemangi Kale, MD
2500 MetroHealth Drive
Cleveland, OH 44109
Tel: 216 778-2245   *Fax:* 216 778-4873
Length: 3 Yrs   *ACGME Approved/Offered Positions:* 9
Program ID: 144-38-11-165

Cleveland Clinic Foundation Program
Sponsor: Cleveland Clinic Foundation
Prgm Director: Bret Lashner, MD*
9500 Euclid Avenue
Desk A30
Cleveland, OH 44195
Tel: 216 636-0122   *Fax:* 216 444-6305
Length: 3 Yrs   *ACGME Approved/Offered Positions:* 12
Program ID: 144-38-12-166

University Hospitals Case Medical Center Program
Sponsor: University Hospitals Case Medical Center
Veterans Affairs Medical Center (Cleveland)
Prgm Director: Gregory S Cooper, MD
11100 Euclid Avenue
Wearn 247
Cleveland, OH 44106
Tel: 216 844-5386   *Fax:* 216 983-0347
Length: 3 Yrs   *ACGME Approved/Offered Positions:* 10
Program ID: 144-38-21-164

Columbus

Ohio State University Hospital Program
Sponsor: Ohio State University Hospital
Prgm Director: Sheryl A Pfeil, MD
395 W 12th Ave
234 Office Tower
Columbus, OH 43210
Tel: 614 293-4262   *Fax:* 614 293-8518
E-mail: sheryl.pfeil@osumc.edu
Length: 3 Yrs   *ACGME Approved/Offered Positions:* 9
Program ID: 144-38-11-092

Dayton

Wright State University Program
Sponsor: Wright State University Boonshoft School of Medicine
Miami Valley Hospital
Veterans Affairs Medical Center (Dayton)
Prgm Director: Gregory J Beck, MD*
Department of Medicine
PO Box 927
Dayton, OH 45401
Tel: 937 320-5050   *Fax:* 937 320-5060
Length: 3 Yrs   *ACGME Approved/Offered Positions:* 4
Program ID: 144-38-21-099

Oklahoma

Oklahoma City

University of Oklahoma Health Sciences Center Program
Sponsor: University of Oklahoma College of Medicine
OU Medical Center
Veterans Affairs Medical Center (Oklahoma City)
Prgm Director: William M Tierney, MD
PO Box 26901
Oklahoma City, OK 73126
Tel: 405 271-5428   *Fax:* 405 271-5803
E-mail: helen-prince@ouhsc.edu
Length: 3 Yrs   *ACGME Approved/Offered Positions:* 9
Program ID: 144-39-21-082

Oregon

Portland

Oregon Health & Science University Program
Sponsor: Oregon Health & Science University Hospital
Kaiser Foundation Hospitals-Northwest Region
Veterans Affairs Medical Center (Portland)
Prgm Director: Kandice L Knigge, MD
3181 SW Sam Jackson Park Road
L461
Portland, OR 97239
Tel: 503 494-9276
E-mail: conwaym@ohsu.edu
Length: 3 Yrs   *ACGME Approved/Offered Positions:* 7
Program ID: 144-40-31-167

Pennsylvania

Danville

Geisinger Health System Program
Sponsor: Geisinger Health System
Geisinger Medical Center
Prgm Director: Robert E Smith, MD
Department of Gastroenterology
100 N Academy Avenue
Danville, PA 17822
Tel: 570 271-6405   *Fax:* 570 271-6852
Length: 3 Yrs   *ACGME Approved/Offered Positions:* 6
Program ID: 144-41-21-211

Hershey

Penn State University/Milton S Hershey Medical Center Program
Sponsor: Milton S Hershey Medical Center
Prgm Director: Thomas J McGarrity, MD
Gastroenterology - H045
500 University Drive, PO Box 850
Hershey, PA 17033
Tel: 717 531-3834   *Fax:* 717 531-4598
Length: 3 Yrs   *ACGME Approved/Offered Positions:* 6
Program ID: 144-41-11-015

Philadelphia

Albert Einstein Healthcare Network Program
Sponsor: Albert Einstein Medical Center
Prgm Director: Philip O Katz, MD
5401 Old York Road
Klein Building, Suite 363
Philadelphia, PA 19141
Tel: 215 456-7162   *Fax:* 215 455-1933
E-mail: walshp@einstein.edu
Length: 3 Yrs   *ACGME Approved/Offered Positions:* 9
Program ID: 144-41-31-218

Drexel University College of Medicine/Hahnemann University Hospital Program
Sponsor: Drexel University College of Medicine/Hahnemann University
Abington Memorial Hospital
Hahnemann University Hospital (Tenet Health System)
Prgm Director: Asyia S Ahmad, MD*
245 North 15th Street, Mail Stop 913
Philadelphia, PA 19102
Tel: 215 762-6072   *Fax:* 215 762-5034
E-mail: asyia.ahmad@drexelmed.edu
Length: 3 Yrs   *ACGME Approved/Offered Positions:* 6
Program ID: 144-41-21-122

Temple University Hospital Program
Sponsor: Temple University Hospital
Prgm Director: Brenda L Horwitz, MD
3401 N Broad St
Philadelphia, PA 19140
Tel: 215 707-3431   *Fax:* 215 707-2684
E-mail: horwitbl@tuhs.temple.edu
Length: 3 Yrs   *ACGME Approved/Offered Positions:* 12
Program ID: 144-41-21-033

Thomas Jefferson University Program
Sponsor: Thomas Jefferson University Hospital
Prgm Director: Anthony J DiMarino Jr, MD
Main Building, Suite 480
132 S Tenth Street
Philadelphia, PA 19107
Tel: 215 955-5793   *Fax:* 215 955-0872
Length: 3 Yrs   *ACGME Approved/Offered Positions:* 9
Program ID: 144-41-21-034

University of Pennsylvania Program

Sponsor: University of Pennsylvania Health System
Presbyterian Medical Center (UPHS)
Prgm Director: David A Katzka, MD
3 Ravdin Building
3400 Spruce Street
Philadelphia, PA 19104
Tel: 215 662-4599   *Fax:* 215 349-5915
E-mail: gifellowship@uphs.upenn.edu
Length: 3 Yrs   *ACGME Approved/Offered Positions:* 15
Program ID: 144-41-21-021

Pittsburgh

Allegheny General Hospital Program

Sponsor: Allegheny General Hospital
Western Pennsylvania Hospital
Prgm Director: Rad M Agrawal, MD
Suite 301
1307 Federal Street
Pittsburgh, PA 15212
Tel: 412 359-3846   *Fax:* 412 442-2158
E-mail: pshoemak@wpahs.org
Length: 3 Yrs   *ACGME Approved/Offered Positions:* 12
Program ID: 144-41-11-045

University of Pittsburgh Medical Center Medical Education Program

Sponsor: Univ of Pittsburgh Medical Center Medical
  Education
UPMC Presbyterian Shadyside
Veterans Affairs Medical Center (Pittsburgh)
Prgm Director: Miguel D Regueiro, MD
Department of Medicine - Level C Wing
200 Lothrop Street
Pittsburgh, PA 15213
Tel: 412 648-9241   *Fax:* 412 648-9378
Length: 3 Yrs   *ACGME Approved/Offered Positions:* 18
Program ID: 144-41-21-060

Wynnewood

Lankenau Hospital Program

Sponsor: Lankenau Hospital
Prgm Director: Giancarlo Mercogliano, MD, MBA
Department of Medicine
100 Lancaster Avenue
Wynnewood, PA 19096
Tel: 610 896-7360   *Fax:* 610 526-3731
E-mail: gibbsc@mlhs.org
Length: 3 Yrs   *ACGME Approved/Offered Positions:* 6
Program ID: 144-41-11-032

Puerto Rico

San Juan

University of Puerto Rico Program

Sponsor: University of Puerto Rico School of Medicine
University Hospital
Prgm Director: Esther A Torres, MD
Department of Medicine A-838
PO Box 365067
San Juan, PR 00936
Tel: 787 758-2525   *Fax:* 787 754-1739
E-mail: etorres@pol.net
Length: 3 Yrs   *ACGME Approved/Offered Positions:* 9
Program ID: 144-42-21-124

VA Caribbean Healthcare System Program

Sponsor: VA Caribbean Healthcare System
University Hospital
Prgm Director: Doris H Toro, MD
Medical Service (111)
10 Casia Street
San Juan, PR 00921
Tel: 787 641-3669   *Fax:* 787 641-4561
E-mail: Doris.Toro@va.gov
Length: 3 Yrs   *ACGME Approved/Offered Positions:* 6
Program ID: 144-42-31-223

Rhode Island

Providence

Brown University Program

Sponsor: Rhode Island Hospital-Lifespan
Veterans Affairs Medical Center (Providence)
Prgm Director: Steven Moss, MD
Rhode Island Hospital, 593 Eddy St, APC 406
Providence, RI 02903
Tel: 401 444-5031   *Fax:* 401 444-6194
Length: 3 Yrs   *ACGME Approved/Offered Positions:* 12
Program ID: 144-43-11-125

South Carolina

Charleston

Medical University of South Carolina Program

Sponsor: Medical University of South Carolina College of
  Medicine
MUSC Medical Center
Ralph H Johnson VA Medical Center (Charleston)
Prgm Director: Ira R Willner, MD
25 Courtney Drive
Suite 7100 A
Charleston, SC 29425
Tel: 843 792-6901   *Fax:* 843 876-4301
Length: 3 Yrs   *ACGME Approved/Offered Positions:* 12
Program ID: 144-45-21-107

Tennessee

Memphis

University of Tennessee Program

Sponsor: University of Tennessee College of Medicine
Methodist Healthcare - Memphis Hospitals
Regional Medical Center at Memphis
Veterans Affairs Medical Center (Memphis)
Prgm Director: Mohammad K Ismail, MD
920 Madison Ave, Ste 240
Memphis, TN 38163
Tel: 901 448-5813   *Fax:* 901 448-7091
E-mail: mismail@utmem.edu
Length: 3 Yrs   *ACGME Approved/Offered Positions:* 9
Program ID: 144-47-21-188

Nashville

Vanderbilt University Program

Sponsor: Vanderbilt University Medical Center
Veterans Affairs Medical Center (Nashville)
Prgm Director: Keith Wilson, MD
2215 Garland Ave
Room 1030-C MRB-IV
Nashville, TN 37232
Tel: 615 322-5200   *Fax:* 615 343-6229
E-mail: scharneitha.britton@vanderbilt.edu
Length: 3 Yrs   *ACGME Approved/Offered Positions:* 12
Program ID: 144-47-31-016

Texas

Dallas

Baylor University Medical Center Program

Sponsor: Baylor University Medical Center
Prgm Director: Lawrence R Schiller, MD
3500 Gaston Avenue
1 Roberts Medical Education
Dallas, TX 75246
Tel: 214 820-2671   *Fax:* 214 818-8179
Length: 3 Yrs   *ACGME Approved/Offered Positions:* 6
Program ID: 144-48-31-148

University of Texas Southwestern Medical School Program

Sponsor: University of Texas Southwestern Medical
  School
Dallas County Hospital District-Parkland Memorial
  Hospital
Dallas VA Medical Center
Prgm Director: Don C Rockey, MD
5323 Harry Hines Boulevard
Dallas, TX 75235
Tel: 214 648-3444   *Fax:* 214 648-0274
Length: 3 Yrs   *ACGME Approved/Offered Positions:* 18
Program ID: 144-48-21-100

Galveston

University of Texas Medical Branch Hospitals Program

Sponsor: University of Texas Medical Branch Hospitals
University of Texas M D Anderson Cancer Center
Prgm Director: Joseph H Sellin, MD*
4106 McCullough
301 University Blvd
Galveston, TX 77555
Tel: 409 772-1501   *Fax:* 409 772-4789
E-mail: jhsellin@utmb.edu
Length: 3 Yrs   *ACGME Approved/Offered Positions:* 9
Program ID: 144-48-21-062

Houston

Baylor College of Medicine Program

Sponsor: Baylor College of Medicine
Harris County Hospital District-Ben Taub General
  Hospital
Michael E DeBakey VA Medical Center - Houston
St Luke's Episcopal Hospital
Prgm Director: Yasser H Shaib, MD*
1709 Dryden Road, 5th Floor, 05.56
Houston, TX 77030
Tel: 713 794-7801   *Fax:* 713 795-4471
Length: 3 Yrs   *ACGME Approved/Offered Positions:* 15
Program ID: 144-48-21-085

University of Texas at Houston Program

Sponsor: University of Texas Health Science Center at
  Houston
Lyndon B Johnson General Hospital
Memorial Hermann Hospital
Methodist Hospital (Houston)
University of Texas M D Anderson Cancer Center
Prgm Director: Frank J Lukens, MD*
Department of Internal Medicine
6431 Fannin St, MSB 4.234
Houston, TX 77030
Tel: 713 500-6677   *Fax:* 713 500-6699
E-mail: Frank.J.Lukens@uth.tmc.edu
Length: 3 Yrs   *ACGME Approved/Offered Positions:* 10
Program ID: 144-48-31-017

Note: * indicates a newly appointed program director

Lackland AFB

San Antonio Uniformed Services Health Education Consortium Program

Sponsor: San Antonio Uniformed Services Health Education Consortium
Wilford Hall Medical Center (AETC)
Prgm Director: Lt Col Kevin J Franklin, MD
759th Medical Operations Squadron/MMIG
2200 Bergquist Drive, Ste 1
Lackland AFB, TX 78236
Tel: 210 292-6485   *Fax:* 210 292-0192
E-mail: kevin.franklin1@lackland.af.mil
Length: 3 Yrs   *ACGME Approved/Offered Positions:* 14
Program ID: 144-48-12-063
Uniformed Services Program

San Antonio

University of Texas Health Science Center at San Antonio Program

Sponsor: University of Texas School of Medicine at San Antonio
Audie L Murphy Memorial Veterans Hospital (San Antonio)
University Health System
Prgm Director: Charles Brady, MD
7703 Floyd Curl Drive
San Antonio, TX 78229
Tel: 210 567-4876   *Fax:* 210 567-1976
Length: 3 Yrs   *ACGME Approved/Offered Positions:* 6
Program ID: 144-48-21-072

Temple

Texas A&M College of Medicine-Scott and White Program

Sponsor: Scott and White Memorial Hospital
Central Texas Veterans Affairs Healthcare System
Prgm Director: Richard A Erickson, MD
2401 S 31st St
Temple, TX 76508
Tel: 254 724-2489   *Fax:* 254 724-7210
E-mail: rerickson@swmail.sw.org
Length: 3 Yrs   *ACGME Approved/Offered Positions:* 6
Program ID: 144-48-21-018

Utah

Salt Lake City

University of Utah Program

Sponsor: University of Utah Medical Center
Veterans Affairs Medical Center (Salt Lake City)
Prgm Director: Kathryn A Peterson, MD, MS*
30 North 1900 East, Room 4R118
Salt Lake City, UT 84132
Tel: 801 581-7802
Length: 3 Yrs   *ACGME Approved/Offered Positions:* 6
Program ID: 144-49-21-168

Vermont

Burlington

University of Vermont Program

Sponsor: Fletcher Allen Health Care
Prgm Director: Nicholas Ferrentino, MD
UVM/FAHC
111 Colchester Avenue, Smith 251
Burlington, VT 05405
Tel: 802 847-2554   *Fax:* 802 847-4928
Length: 3 Yrs   *ACGME Approved/Offered Positions:* 3
Program ID: 144-50-21-169

Virginia

Charlottesville

University of Virginia Program

Sponsor: University of Virginia Medical Center
Prgm Director: Carl L Berg, MD
Department of Internal Medicine
PO Box 800708
Charlottesville, VA 22908
Tel: 434 243-6400   *Fax:* 434 243-6405
Length: 3 Yrs   *ACGME Approved/Offered Positions:* 15
Program ID: 144-51-21-019

Richmond

Virginia Commonwealth University Health System Program

Sponsor: Virginia Commonwealth University Health System
Hunter Holmes McGuire VA Medical Center (Richmond)
Medical College of Virginia Hospitals
Prgm Director: Richard K Sterling, MD, MSc*
1200 East Broad Street
PO Box 980341
Richmond, VA 23298
Tel: 804 828-9034   *Fax:* 804 828-4945
Length: 3 Yrs   *ACGME Approved/Offered Positions:* 10
Program ID: 144-51-21-020

Washington

Seattle

University of Washington Program

Sponsor: University of Washington School of Medicine
Harborview Medical Center
Seattle Cancer Care Alliance
University of Washington Medical Center
VA Puget Sound Health Care System
Prgm Director: David J Kearney, MD
1959 NE Pacific Street
Box 356424
Seattle, WA 98195
Tel: 206 277-1445   *Fax:* 206 764-2232
Length: 3 Yrs   *ACGME Approved/Offered Positions:* 15
Program ID: 144-54-21-086

West Virginia

Morgantown

West Virginia University Program

Sponsor: West Virginia University School of Medicine
West Virginia University Hospitals
Prgm Director: Uma Sundaram, MD
Medical Center Drive
Box 9161
Morgantown, WV 26506
Tel: 304 293-4123   *Fax:* 304 293-2135
Length: 3 Yrs   *ACGME Approved/Offered Positions:* 6
Program ID: 144-55-31-229

Wisconsin

Madison

University of Wisconsin Program

Sponsor: University of Wisconsin Hospital and Clinics
Prgm Director: Eric A Gaumnitz, MD
600 Highland Avenue
Room H6/516 - 5124 CSC
Madison, WI 53792
Tel: 608 263-4034   *Fax:* 608 265-5677
E-mail: ps2@medicine.wisc.edu
Length: 3 Yrs   *ACGME Approved/Offered Positions:* 9
Program ID: 144-56-21-126

Milwaukee

Aurora Health Care Program

Sponsor: Aurora Health Care
Aurora Sinai Medical Center
St Luke's Medical Center
Prgm Director: Aboud Affi, MD
Aurora Sinai Medical Center
945 N 12th St, PO Box 342
Milwaukee, WI 53201
Tel: 414 219-7695
E-mail: rebecca.young@aurora.org
Length: 3 Yrs   *ACGME Approved/Offered Positions:* 3
Program ID: 144-56-21-210

Medical College of Wisconsin Affiliated Hospitals Program

Sponsor: Medical College of Wisconsin Affiliated Hospitals, Inc
Clement J Zablocki Veterans Affairs Medical Center
Froedtert Memorial Lutheran Hospital
Prgm Director: Kia Saeian, MD, MSc
9200 W Wisconsin Ave
GI Division
Milwaukee, WI 53226
Tel: 414 456-6766   *Fax:* 414 456-6214
Length: 3 Yrs   *ACGME Approved/Offered Positions:* 13
Program ID: 144-56-31-048

Programs

Geriatric Medicine (Family Medicine)

Arizona

Phoenix

St Joseph's Hospital and Medical Center Program

Sponsor: St Joseph's Hospital and Medical Center
Del E Webb Memorial Hospital
Walter O Boswell Memorial Hospital
Prgm Director: Walter J Nieri, MD
Boswell Memorial Hospital
10515 W Santa Fe Drive
Sun City, AZ 85351
Tel: 623 815-7661   *Fax:* 623 815-2981
E-mail: walter.nieri@bannerhealth.com
Length: 1 Yr   *ACGME Approved/Offered Positions:* 5
Program ID: 125-03-21-029

California

Colton

Arrowhead Regional Medical Center Program

Sponsor: Arrowhead Regional Medical Center
Prgm Director: John F Randolph, MD
Department of Family Medicine
400 N Pepper Ave
Colton, CA 92324
Tel: 909 580-6260   *Fax:* 909 580-1362
Length: 1 Yr   *ACGME Approved/Offered Positions:* 2
Program ID: 125-05-21-033

Fontana

Kaiser Permanente Southern California (Fontana) Program

Sponsor: Kaiser Permanente Southern California
Kaiser Foundation Hospital (Fontana)
Prgm Director: Israel B Coutin, MD
9961 Sierra Avenue
Fontana, CA 92335
Tel: 909 427-7322   *Fax:* 909 427-4208
Length: 1 Yr   *ACGME Approved/Offered Positions:* 2
Program ID: 125-05-12-065

Los Angeles

Kaiser Permanente Southern California (Los Angeles) Program

Sponsor: Kaiser Permanente Southern California
Kaiser Foundation Hospital (Los Angeles)
Kaiser Foundation Hospital (Woodland Hills)
Prgm Director: Peter Khang, MD, MPH
4950 Sunset Blvd
Los Angeles, CA 90027
Tel: 323 783-8553   *Fax:* 323 783-4771
E-mail: peter.s.khang@kp.org
Length: 1 Yr   *ACGME Approved/Offered Positions:* 2
Program ID: 125-05-21-025

Florida

Orlando

Florida Hospital Medical Center Program

Sponsor: Florida Hospital Medical Center
Florida Living Nursing Center Inc
Mayflower Retirement Community
Prgm Director: Ariel Cole, MD
2501 North Orange Avenue
Suite 235
Orlando, FL 32804
Tel: 407 303-2814   *Fax:* 407 303-2885
E-mail: Christine.Joseph@flhosp.org
Length: 1 Yr   *ACGME Approved/Offered Positions:* 3
Program ID: 125-11-21-032

Georgia

Macon

Mercer University School of Medicine Program

Sponsor: Medical Center of Central Georgia
Central Georgia Rehabilitation Hospital
Central Georgia Senior Health, Inc
Oaks at Peake Nursing Home
Prgm Director: Richard J Ackermann, MD
3780 Eisenhower Parkway
Macon, GA 31206
Tel: 478 633-5550   *Fax:* 478 784-5496
Length: 1 Yr   *ACGME Approved/Offered Positions:* 4
Program ID: 125-12-13-063

Illinois

Peoria

University of Illinois College of Medicine at Peoria Program

Sponsor: University of Illinois College of Medicine at Peoria
Methodist Medical Center of Illinois
Prgm Director: John J Coon, MD
815 Main, Suite C
Peoria, IL 61602
Tel: 309 672-5908   *Fax:* 309 672-4790
Length: 1 Yr   *ACGME Approved/Offered Positions:* 2
Program ID: 125-16-13-052

Urbana

Carle Foundation Hospital Program

Sponsor: Carle Foundation Hospital
Prgm Director: Suma Peter, MD
Carle Clinic Association
602 W University
Urbana, IL 61801
Tel: 217 383-5198   *Fax:* 217 383-4681
E-mail: Star.Andrews@carle.com
Length: 1 Yr   *ACGME Approved/Offered Positions:* 2
Program ID: 125-16-13-058

Indiana

Indianapolis

St Vincent Hospital and Health Care Center Program

Sponsor: St Vincent Hospitals and Health Care Center
Prgm Director: Patrick J Healey, MD
Suite 100
8220 Naab Rd
Indianapolis, IN 46260
Tel: 317 338-7780   *Fax:* 317 338-7907
Length: 1 Yr   *ACGME Approved/Offered Positions:* 1
Program ID: 125-17-31-036

Iowa

Des Moines

Mercy Medical Center (Des Moines) Program

Sponsor: Mercy Hospital Medical Center
Prgm Director: Carol L Kuhle, DO
Mercy Geriatric Fellowship Program
250 Laurel Street
Des Moines, IA 50314
Tel: 515 643-4610   *Fax:* 515 643-4662
Length: 1 Yr   *ACGME Approved/Offered Positions:* 2
Program ID: 125-18-13-056

Iowa City

University of Iowa Hospitals and Clinics Program

Sponsor: University of Iowa Hospitals and Clinics
Prgm Director: Gerald J Jogerst, MD
200 Hawkins Drive
Iowa City, IA 52242
Tel: 319 384-7704   *Fax:* 319 384-7822
E-mail: gretchen-schmuch@uiowa.edu
Length: 1 Yr   *ACGME Approved/Offered Positions:* 2
Program ID: 125-18-21-034

Kentucky

Louisville

University of Louisville Program

Sponsor: University of Louisville School of Medicine
Jewish Hospital
University of Louisville Hospital
Veterans Affairs Medical Center (Louisville)
Prgm Director: Sarah Holloman, MD*
201 Abraham Flexner Way
Suite 690
Louisville, KY 40202
Tel: 502 852-1806
E-mail: norma.thieman@louisville.edu
Length: 1 Yr   *ACGME Approved/Offered Positions:* 3
Program ID: 125-20-21-035

Note: * indicates a newly appointed program director

Louisiana

Lafayette

Louisiana State University (Lafayette) Program

Sponsor: University Medical Center (Lafayette)
Hospice of Acadiana
Lafayette General Medical Center
Oakwood of Acadiana/River Oaks Retirement Manor
Rehabilitation Hospital of Acadiana Long Term Acute Care
Prgm Director: Lainie Moncada, MD
Department of Family Medicine
2390 West Congress St
Lafayette, LA 70506
Tel: 337 261-6690   *Fax:* 337 261-6662
E-mail: lmonca@lsuhsc.edu
Length: 1 Yr   *ACGME Approved/Offered Positions:* 2
Program ID: 125-21-21-066

Maine

Augusta

Maine-Dartmouth Family Medicine Program

Sponsor: Maine-Dartmouth Family Medicine Residency
Maine General Medical Center
Prgm Director: Karen Gershman, MD
15 E Chestnut St
Augusta, ME 04330
Tel: 207 626-1893   *Fax:* 207 626-1902
Length: 1 Yr   *ACGME Approved/Offered Positions:* 4
Program ID: 125-22-11-051

Michigan

Lansing

Sparrow Hospital/Michigan State University Program

Sponsor: Sparrow Hospital
Michigan State University Clinical Center
Prgm Director: Mark D Ensberg, MD
Suite 245-C
Lansing, MI 48912
Tel: 517 364-7575   *Fax:* 517 364-7560
E-mail: ensberg@msu.edu
Length: 1 Yr   *ACGME Approved/Offered Positions:* 2
Program ID: 125-25-12-055

Missouri

Columbia

University of Missouri-Columbia Program

Sponsor: University of Missouri-Columbia School of Medicine
University Hospitals and Clinics
Prgm Director: David R Mehr, MD, MS
Dept of Family and Community Med
M224 Medical Sciences Building
Columbia, MO 65212
Tel: 573 882-3126   *Fax:* 573 884-6172
E-mail: mehrd@health.missouri.edu
Length: 1 Yr   *ACGME Approved/Offered Positions:* 3
Program ID: 125-28-21-026

Kansas City

University of Missouri at Kansas City Program

Sponsor: University of Missouri-Kansas City School of Medicine
Truman Medical Center-Lakewood
Prgm Director: Jon F Dedon, MD
7900 Lee's Summit Road
Kansas City, MO 64139
Tel: 816 404-7751   *Fax:* 816 404-7756
E-mail: kimberly.sixkiller@tmcmed.org
Length: 1 Yr   *ACGME Approved/Offered Positions:* 3
Program ID: 125-28-31-027

New Jersey

Freehold

UMDNJ-Robert Wood Johnson at CentraState Program

Sponsor: UMDNJ-Robert Wood Johnson Medical School
CentraState Medical Center
Prgm Director: Joshua Raymond, MD, MPH
1001 W Main Street
Suite B
Freehold, NJ 07728
Tel: 732 294-1989   *Fax:* 732 409-2621
E-mail: JoshuaJRaymond@hotmail.com
Length: 1 Yr   *ACGME Approved/Offered Positions:* 2
Program ID: 125-33-13-067

New Brunswick

UMDNJ-Robert Wood Johnson Medical School Program

Sponsor: UMDNJ-Robert Wood Johnson Medical School
Robert Wood Johnson University Hospital
Prgm Director: John M Heath, MD
Department of Family Medicine
One Robert Wood Johnson Place MEB 268
New Brunswick, NJ 08901
Tel: 732 235-7669   *Fax:* 732 246-8084
Length: 1 Yr   *ACGME Approved/Offered Positions:* 4
Program ID: 125-33-21-009

New York

Johnson City

United Health Services Hospitals Program

Sponsor: United Health Services Hospitals
Binghamton General Hospital
Wilson Medical Center (United Health System)
Prgm Director: James Crosby, MD
40 Arch Street
Johnson City, NY 13790
Tel: 607 763-5334   *Fax:* 607 763-5414
E-mail: james_Crosby@uhs.org
Length: 1 Yr   *ACGME Approved/Offered Positions:* 2
Program ID: 125-35-31-054

North Carolina

Asheville

Mountain Area Health Education Center Program

Sponsor: Mountain Area Health Education Center
CarePartners
Deerfield Episcopal Retirement Community, Inc
Mission Hospitals - Memorial Campus
Prgm Director: Elizabeth J Castillo, MD, PhD
118 W T Weaver Boulevard
Asheville, NC 28804
Tel: 828 545-7054   *Fax:* 828 257-4739
E-mail: gmrpinfo@mahec.net
Length: 1 Yr   *ACGME Approved/Offered Positions:* 2
Program ID: 125-36-12-059

Greenville

Pitt County Memorial Hospital/East Carolina University Program

Sponsor: Pitt County Memorial Hospital
Prgm Director: Irene M Hamrick, MD
Department of Family Medicine
4N-72 Brody Medical Sciences Bldg
Greenville, NC 27834
Tel: 252 744-2597   *Fax:* 252 744-2623
E-mail: hamricki@ecu.edu
Length: 1 Yr   *ACGME Approved/Offered Positions:* 4
Program ID: 125-36-11-011

Ohio

Cincinnati

Christ Hospital/University of Cincinnati College of Medicine Program

Sponsor: Christ Hospital
Episcopal Retirement Homes
Heritagespring of West Chester
Maple Knoll Village
University Hospital Inc
Prgm Director: Gregg Warshaw, MD
Department of Family Medicine
231 Albert Sabin Way, PO Box 670504
Cincinnati, OH 45267
Tel: 513 584-0650   *Fax:* 513 584-2809
E-mail: hardinsc@fammed.uc.edu
Length: 1 Yr   *ACGME Approved/Offered Positions:* 3
Program ID: 125-38-21-012

Cleveland

Case Western Reserve University (MetroHealth) Program

Sponsor: MetroHealth Medical Center
Prgm Director: Mary V Corrigan, MD
Senior Health & Wellness Center
4229 Pearl Road
Cleveland, OH 44109
Tel: 216 957-3528   *Fax:* 216 957-2930
E-mail: caustin1@metrohealth.org
Length: 1 Yr   *ACGME Approved/Offered Positions:* 3
Program ID: 125-38-21-031

Columbus

Riverside Methodist Hospitals (OhioHealth) Program

Sponsor: Riverside Methodist Hospitals (OhioHealth)
Prgm Director: Jeffrey W Milks, MD
Riverside Family Practice Center
697 Thomas Lane
Columbus, OH 43214
Tel: 614 566-4398   *Fax:* 614 566-6843
Length: 1 Yr   *ACGME Approved/Offered Positions:* 2
Program ID: 125-38-11-049

Dayton

Wright State University/Dayton Community Hospitals Program

Sponsor: Wright State University Boonshoft School of Medicine
Veterans Affairs Medical Center (Dayton)
Prgm Director: Steven K Swedlund, MD*
PO Box 927
Dayton, OH 45401
Tel: 937 331-9167 *Fax:* 937 331-9169
E-mail: geriflwp@wright.edu
Length: 1 Yr *ACGME Approved/Offered Positions:* 2
Program ID: 125-38-31-072

Pennsylvania

Allentown

Sacred Heart Hospital/Temple University (Allentown) Program

Sponsor: Sacred Heart Hospital
Moss Rehabilitation Hospital
Prgm Director: Daniel H Coller, MD*
450 Chew Street
Ste 101
Allentown, PA 18102
Tel: 610 776-4872 *Fax:* 610 606-4467
E-mail: dcoller@shh.org
Length: 1 Yr *ACGME Approved/Offered Positions:* 3
Program ID: 125-41-12-048

Lancaster

Lancaster General Hospital Program

Sponsor: Lancaster General Hospital
Prgm Director: Matthew J Beelen, MD
2110 Harrisburg Pk
PO Box 3200, Suite 300
Lancaster, PA 17604
Tel: 717 544-3022 *Fax:* 717 544-3021
E-mail: mjbeelen@lancastergeneral.org
Length: 1 Yr *ACGME Approved/Offered Positions:* 3
Program ID: 125-41-12-042

Philadelphia

Thomas Jefferson University Program

Sponsor: Thomas Jefferson University Hospital
Prgm Director: Susan M Parks, MD
1015 Walnut Street, Suite 401
Philadelphia, PA 19107
Tel: 215 955-5708 *Fax:* 215 955-0640
E-mail: cynthia.branch@jefferson.edu
Length: 1 Yr *ACGME Approved/Offered Positions:* 4
Program ID: 125-41-21-015

Pittsburgh

University of Pittsburgh Medical Center Medical Education (St Margaret Hospital) Program

Sponsor: Univ of Pittsburgh Medical Center Medical Education
UPMC St Margaret
Prgm Director: Vincent M Balestrino, MD
Division of Gerontology
815 Freeport Road
Pittsburgh, PA 15215
Tel: 412 784-4261 *Fax:* 412 784-5274
E-mail: elickerpj@upmc.edu
Length: 1 Yr *ACGME Approved/Offered Positions:* 2
Program ID: 125-41-12-016

Puerto Rico

San Juan

University of Puerto Rico Program

Sponsor: University of Puerto Rico School of Medicine
University of Puerto Rico Hospital at Carolina
VA Caribbean Healthcare System
Prgm Director: Ismenio Millan, MD
Carr 3 Km 83 Ave 65 de Infanteria
Call Box 6021
Carolina, PR 00984
Tel: 787 776-4420 *Fax:* 787 776-4421
E-mail: imillan@hospitalupr.org
Length: 1 Yr *ACGME Approved/Offered Positions:* 3
Program ID: 125-42-21-017

Tennessee

Chattanooga

University of Tennessee College of Medicine at Chattanooga Program

Sponsor: University of Tennessee College of Medicine-Chattanooga
Erlanger Medical Center
Prgm Director: John B Standridge, MD
1100 East 3rd Street
Chattanooga, TN 37403
Tel: 423 778-2957 *Fax:* 423 778-2959
Length: 1 Yr *ACGME Approved/Offered Positions:* 1
Program ID: 125-47-12-061

Knoxville

University of Tennessee Medical Center at Knoxville Program

Sponsor: University of Tennessee Graduate School of Medicine
University of Tennessee Memorial Hospital
Prgm Director: Ronald H Lands, MD, MFA
1924 Alcoa Highway
Knoxville, TN 37920
Tel: 865 305-9352 *Fax:* 865 305-6532
Length: 1 Yr *ACGME Approved/Offered Positions:* 2
Program ID: 125-47-13-071

Texas

Amarillo

Texas Tech University (Amarillo) Program

Sponsor: Texas Tech University Health Sciences Center at Amarillo
Baptist-St Anthony's Health System
Veterans Affairs Medical Center (Amarillo)
Prgm Director: Dennis P Zoller, MD
1400 Wallace Boulevard
Amarillo, TX 79106
Tel: 806 212-3550 *Fax:* 806 212-3554
E-mail: Gerry.Ault@ttuhsc.edu
Length: 1 Yr *ACGME Approved/Offered Positions:* 2
Program ID: 125-48-33-050

Corpus Christi

Christus Spohn Memorial Hospital Program

Sponsor: Christus Spohn Memorial Hospital
Retama Manor Nursing Center
Prgm Director: Kathleen Soch, MD
2606 Hospital Boulevard
Corpus Christi, TX 78405
Tel: 361 902-4499 *Fax:* 361 902-4588
E-mail: belinda.flores@christushealth.org
Length: 1 Yr *ACGME Approved/Offered Positions:* 1
Program ID: 125-48-13-060

Fort Worth

John Peter Smith Hospital (Tarrant County Hospital District) Program

Sponsor: John Peter Smith Hospital (Tarrant County Hospital District)
Prgm Director: Lesca Hadley, MD
1500 South Main Street
Fort Worth, TX 76104
Tel: 817 927-1200 *Fax:* 817 927-1691
Length: 1 Yr *ACGME Approved/Offered Positions:* 2
Program ID: 125-48-21-039

Odessa

Texas Tech University (Permian Basin) Program

Sponsor: Texas Tech University Health Sciences Center (Permian Basin)
Medical Center Hospital
Prgm Director: Chau M Le, MD
Department of Family Medicine
701 W 5th Street
Odessa, TX 79763
Tel: 432 335-5311 *Fax:* 432 335-5316
E-mail: Chau.Le@ttuhsc.edu
Length: 1 Yr
Program ID: 125-48-31-068

Virginia

Roanoke

Carilion Clinic Program

Sponsor: Carilion Clinic
Carilion Roanoke Memorial Hospital
Veterans Affairs Medical Center (Salem)
Prgm Director: Soheir S Boshra, MD
2118 Rosalind Avenue
Roanoke, VA 24014
Tel: 540 981-7653 *Fax:* 540 981-7469
E-mail: sboshra@carilion.com
Length: 1 Yr *ACGME Approved/Offered Positions:* 2
Program ID: 125-51-13-044

Washington

Seattle

Swedish Medical Center/First Hill Program

Sponsor: Swedish Medical Center
Prgm Director: Carroll Haymon, MD*
1401 Madison Street, #100
Seattle, WA 98104
Tel: 206 386-6054 *Fax:* 206 215-6027
Length: 1 Yr *ACGME Approved/Offered Positions:* 3
Program ID: 125-54-31-040

West Virginia

Ranson

West Virginia University Rural Program

Sponsor: West Virginia University School of Medicine
Jefferson Memorial Hospital
Veterans Affairs Medical Center (Martinsburg)
Prgm Director: Konrad C Nau, MD
171 Taylor Street
Harpers Ferry, WV 25425
Tel: 304 535-6343 *Fax:* 304 535-6618
E-mail: therrienc@rcbhsc.wvu.edu
Length: 1 Yr *ACGME Approved/Offered Positions:* 3
Program ID: 125-55-12-053

Note: * indicates a newly appointed program director

Geriatric Medicine (Internal Medicine)

Alabama

Birmingham

University of Alabama Medical Center Program
Sponsor: University of Alabama Hospital
Veterans Affairs Medical Center (Birmingham)
Prgm Director: Richard V Sims, MD
933 South 19th Street
CH19, 201
Birmingham, AL 35294
Tel: 205 934-3259   *Fax:* 205 558-7068
Length: 1 Yr   *ACGME Approved/Offered Positions:* 3
Program ID: 151-01-21-001

Arizona

Phoenix

Banner Good Samaritan Medical Center Program
Sponsor: Banner Good Samaritan Medical Center
Carl T Hayden VA Medical Center
Prgm Director: Gary H Salzman, MD
Geriatric Fellowship, WT-4
1111 E McDowell Rd
Phoenix, AZ 85006
Tel: 602 239-6950   *Fax:* 602 239-5094
Length: 1 Yr   *ACGME Approved/Offered Positions:* 2
Program ID: 151-03-21-102

Tucson

University of Arizona Program
Sponsor: University of Arizona College of Medicine
Southern Arizona VA Health Care Center (Tucson)
University Medical Center
Prgm Director: Mindy J Fain, MD
College of Medicine, Geriatrics & Gerontology
PO Box 245069
Tucson, AZ 85724
Tel: 520 626-6854   *Fax:* 520 626-8854
E-mail: mfain@aging.arizona.edu
Length: 1 Yr   *ACGME Approved/Offered Positions:* 2
Program ID: 151-03-21-122

Arkansas

Little Rock

University of Arkansas for Medical Sciences Program
Sponsor: University of Arkansas College of Medicine
Central Arkansas Veterans Healthcare System
UAMS Medical Center
Prgm Director: Carmen Arick, MD*
4301 W Markham Street #748
Little Rock, AR 72205
Tel: 501 526-6547   *Fax:* 501 686-5884
E-mail: hartmarianc@uams.edu
Length: 1 Yr   *ACGME Approved/Offered Positions:* 6
Program ID: 151-04-21-003

California

Los Angeles

UCLA Medical Center Program
Sponsor: UCLA David Geffen School of Medicine/UCLA Medical Center
VA Greater Los Angeles Healthcare System
Prgm Director: Nancy Weintraub, MD*
10945 Le Conte Ave, Suite 2339
Los Angeles, CA 90095
Tel: 818 895-9311   *Fax:* 818 895-9519
Length: 1 Yr   *ACGME Approved/Offered Positions:* 12
Program ID: 151-05-21-005

University of Southern California/LAC+USC Medical Center Program
Sponsor: University of Southern California/LAC+USC Medical Center
Hollenbeck Palms
LAC+USC Medical Center
USC University Hospital
Prgm Director: Dohwa Kim, MD
Division of GHGIM
1200 N State Street, Room 8435
Los Angeles, CA 90033
Tel: 323 226-6571   *Fax:* 323 226-2718
E-mail: boneal@usc.edu
Length: 1 Yr   *ACGME Approved/Offered Positions:* 2
Program ID: 151-05-21-114

Orange

University of California (Irvine) Program
Sponsor: University of California (Irvine) Medical Center
VA Long Beach Healthcare System
Prgm Director: Lisa M Gibbs, MD*
Bldg 200, Suite 835, Rte 81
101 The City Drive South
Orange, CA 92868
Tel: 714 456-5530
Length: 1 Yr   *ACGME Approved/Offered Positions:* 2
Program ID: 151-05-21-086

Sacramento

University of California (Davis) Health System Program
Sponsor: University of California (Davis) Health System
University of California (Davis) Medical Center
VA Northern California Health Care System
Prgm Director: Calvin H Hirsch, MD
Div of Gen Med, UC Davis Med Ctr
4150 V Street, PSSB-2400
Sacramento, CA 95817
Tel: 916 734-7004   *Fax:* 916 734-2732
E-mail: chhirsch@ucdavis.edu
Length: 1 Yr   *ACGME Approved/Offered Positions:* 4
Program ID: 151-05-21-006

San Diego

University of California (San Diego) Program
Sponsor: University of California (San Diego) Medical Center
Veterans Affairs Medical Center (San Diego)
Prgm Director: John W Daly, MD
Department of Medicine
200 West Arbor Drive
San Diego, CA 92103
Tel: 619 543-2420   *Fax:* 619 543-3383
E-mail: hdelaney@ucsd.edu
Length: 1 Yr   *ACGME Approved/Offered Positions:* 4
Program ID: 151-05-21-046

San Francisco

University of California (San Francisco) Program
Sponsor: University of California (San Francisco) School of Medicine
UCSF and Mount Zion Medical Centers
Veterans Affairs Medical Center (San Francisco)
Prgm Director: G Michael Harper, MD
VA Medical Center (181G)
4150 Clement Street
San Francisco, CA 94121
Tel: 415 221-4810   *Fax:* 415 750-6641
Length: 1 Yr   *ACGME Approved/Offered Positions:* 8
Program ID: 151-05-31-007

Stanford

Stanford University Program
Sponsor: Stanford Hospital and Clinics
Veterans Affairs Palo Alto Health Care System
Prgm Director: Mary K Goldstein, MD, MS
3801 Miranda Ave
GRECC 182B
Palo Alto, CA 94304
Tel: 650 493-5000   *Fax:* 650 496-2505
E-mail: goldstein@stanford.edu
Length: 1 Yr   *ACGME Approved/Offered Positions:* 4
Program ID: 151-05-21-053

Colorado

Aurora

University of Colorado Denver Program
Sponsor: University of Colorado Denver School of Medicine
University of Colorado Hospital
Veterans Affairs Medical Center (Denver)
Prgm Director: Laurence J Robbins, MD
Geriatrics Section (111D)
1055 Clermont Street
Denver, CO 80220
Tel: 303 393-2822
E-mail: laurence.robbins@va.gov
Length: 1 Yr   *ACGME Approved/Offered Positions:* 4
Program ID: 151-07-21-073

Connecticut

Bridgeport

Bridgeport Hospital Program
Sponsor: Bridgeport Hospital
Prgm Director: Beata Skudlarska, MD
95 Armory Road
Stratford, CT 06614
Tel: 203 384-3388   *Fax:* 203 384-4034
E-mail: pvarge@bpthosp.org
Length: 1 Yr   *ACGME Approved/Offered Positions:* 2
Program ID: 151-08-13-161

Farmington

University of Connecticut Program

Sponsor: University of Connecticut School of Medicine
Hebrew Home and Hospital
St Francis Hospital and Medical Center
Univ of Connecticut Health Center/John Dempsey
    Hospital
VA Connecticut-Newington
Prgm Director: Gail M Sullivan, MD, MPH
Center on Aging, MC-5215
263 Farmington Avenue
Farmington, CT 06030
Tel: 860 679-3956   *Fax:* 860 679-1307
E-mail: gsullivan@nso1.uchc.edu
Length: 1 Yr   *ACGME Approved/Offered Positions:* 6
Program ID: 151-08-31-008

New Haven

Hospital of St Raphael Program

Sponsor: Hospital of St Raphael
Prgm Director: Gerard J Kerins, MD, MPA
1450 Chapel Street
New Haven, CT 06511
Tel: 203 789-4150   *Fax:* 203 789-3222
Length: 1 Yr   *ACGME Approved/Offered Positions:* 1
Program ID: 151-08-13-149

Yale-New Haven Medical Center Program

Sponsor: Yale-New Haven Hospital
Veterans Affairs Medical Center (West Haven)
Prgm Director: Margaret M Drickamer, MD
Yale-New Haven Hospital
20 York Street
New Haven, CT 06510
Tel: 203 688-9423   *Fax:* 203 688-4209
E-mail: robbin.bonanno@yale.edu
Length: 1 Yr   *ACGME Approved/Offered Positions:* 4
Program ID: 151-08-21-054

District of Columbia

Washington

George Washington University Program

Sponsor: George Washington University School of
    Medicine
George Washington University Hospital (UHS)
Veterans Affairs Medical Center (Washington, DC)
Prgm Director: Elizabeth L Cobbs, MD
Department of Medicine, 2-South
2150 Pennsylvania Avenue, NW
Washington, DC 20037
Tel: 202 741-2278   *Fax:* 202 741-2791
Length: 1 Yr   *ACGME Approved/Offered Positions:* 5
Program ID: 151-10-21-055

Florida

Gainesville

University of Florida Program

Sponsor: University of Florida College of Medicine
North Florida/South Georgia Veterans Health System
Shands Hospital at the University of Florida
Prgm Director: John R Meuleman, MD
GRECC
VA Medical Center, VA 182
Gainesville, FL 32608
Tel: 352 374-6114   *Fax:* 352 374-6077
E-mail: john.meuleman@va.gov
Length: 1 Yr   *ACGME Approved/Offered Positions:* 4
Program ID: 151-11-21-009

Miami

Jackson Memorial Hospital/Jackson Health System Program

Sponsor: Jackson Memorial Hospital/Jackson Health
    System
Veterans Affairs Medical Center (Miami)
Prgm Director: Jorge G Ruiz, MD
Division of Gerontology and Geriatric Medicine
PO Box 016960 (D-503)
Miami, FL 33101
Tel: 305 575-3388   *Fax:* 305 575-3365
E-mail: jruiz2@med.miami.edu
Length: 1 Yr   *ACGME Approved/Offered Positions:* 10
Program ID: 151-11-21-010

Tampa

University of South Florida Program

Sponsor: University of South Florida College of Medicine
James A Haley Veterans Hospital
Tampa General Hospital
Veterans Affairs Medical Center (Bay Pines)
Prgm Director: Claudia Beghé, MD
College of Medicine, MDC Box 19
12901 Bruce B Downs Blvd
Tampa, FL 33612
Tel: 813 974-2460   *Fax:* 813 974-2580
E-mail: Claudia.Beghe@va.gov
Length: 1 Yr   *ACGME Approved/Offered Positions:* 5
Program ID: 151-11-21-011

Weston

Cleveland Clinic (Florida) Program

Sponsor: Cleveland Clinic Florida
Health South Sunrise Rehabilitation Hospital
Sunrise Health & Rehabilitation Center
Prgm Director: Jerry O Ciocon, MD
2950 Cleveland Clinic Boulevard
Weston, FL 33331
Tel: 954 659-5353   *Fax:* 954 659-5354
E-mail: hernang1@ccf.org
Length: 1 Yr   *ACGME Approved/Offered Positions:* 1
Program ID: 151-11-21-144

Georgia

Atlanta

Emory University Program

Sponsor: Emory University School of Medicine
Veterans Affairs Medical Center (Atlanta)
Wesley Woods Geriatric Hospital
Prgm Director: N Wilson Holland Jr, MD
Wesley Woods Geriatric Center
1841 Clifton Road, NE
Atlanta, GA 30329
Tel: 404 321-6111   *Fax:* 404 417-2912
E-mail: Wilson.Holland@va.gov
Length: 1 Yr   *ACGME Approved/Offered Positions:* 7
Program ID: 151-12-21-100

Hawaii

Honolulu

University of Hawaii Program

Sponsor: University of Hawaii John A Burns School of
    Medicine
Kuakini Medical Center
Queen's Medical Center
VA Pacific Islands Health Care System (Honolulu)
Prgm Director: Kamal H Masaki, MD
Kuakini Medical Center
347 North Kuakini Street, HPM9
Honolulu, HI 96817
Tel: 808 523-8461   *Fax:* 808 528-1897
E-mail: km1@hawaii.rr.com
Length: 1 Yr   *ACGME Approved/Offered Positions:* 12
Program ID: 151-14-21-047

Illinois

Chicago

McGaw Medical Center of Northwestern University Program

Sponsor: McGaw Medical Center of Northwestern
    University
Northwestern Memorial Hospital
Prgm Director: Adnan Arseven, MD
Division of Geriatric Medicine
645 N Michigan Avenue, Suite 630
Chicago, IL 60611
Tel: 312 695-4557   *Fax:* 312 695-0951
E-mail: LRios@nmff.org
Length: 1 Yr   *ACGME Approved/Offered Positions:* 4
Program ID: 151-16-21-079

Rush University Medical Center Program

Sponsor: Rush University Medical Center
Prgm Director: Jack Olson, MD
710 S Paulina Street
Room 423
Chicago, IL 60612
Tel: 312 942-5321   *Fax:* 312 942-8399
E-mail: Rush_Geriatrics@rush.edu
Length: 1 Yr   *ACGME Approved/Offered Positions:* 4
Program ID: 151-16-11-081

University of Chicago Program

Sponsor: University of Chicago Medical Center
Prgm Director: Stacie Levine, MD*
5841 South Maryland Avenue
(MC6098) AMB W737
Chicago, IL 60637
Tel: 773 702-8130   *Fax:* 773 702-3538
Length: 1 Yr   *ACGME Approved/Offered Positions:* 6
Program ID: 151-16-11-012

University of Illinois College of Medicine at Chicago Program

Sponsor: University of Illinois College of Medicine at
    Chicago
Jesse Brown Veterans Affairs Medical Center
University of Illinois Hospital and Clinics
Prgm Director: Felipe P Perez, MD
Department of Medicine
840 South Wood Street M/C 717
Chicago, IL 60612
Tel: 312 996-7704   *Fax:* 312 413-1343
E-mail: pbizz@uic.edu
Length: 1 Yr   *ACGME Approved/Offered Positions:* 7
Program ID: 151-16-21-091

Note: * indicates a newly appointed program director

Maywood

Loyola University Program

Sponsor: Loyola University Medical Center
Edward Hines, Jr Veterans Affairs Hospital
Prgm Director: Ileana Soneru, MD
Department of Medicine (181)
5000 S 5th Ave & Roosevelt Road
Hines, IL 60141
Tel: 708 202-2584   *Fax:* 708 202-2163
Length: 1 Yr   *ACGME Approved/Offered Positions:* 9
Program ID: 151-16-21-013

Park Ridge

Advocate Lutheran General Hospital Program

Sponsor: Advocate Lutheran General Hospital
Prgm Director: William D Rhoades III, DO
Department of Medicine
1775 West Dempster Street
Park Ridge, IL 60068
Tel: 847 723-4756   *Fax:* 847 696-3391
Length: 1 Yr   *ACGME Approved/Offered Positions:* 2
Program ID: 151-16-21-120

Indiana

Indianapolis

Indiana University School of Medicine Program

Sponsor: Indiana University School of Medicine
Richard L Roudebush Veterans Affairs Medical Center
Westpark Healthcare Center
William N Wishard Memorial Hospital
Prgm Director: Glenda R Westmoreland, MD, MPH
1001 West 10th Street
Outpatient West Building, M200
Indianapolis, IN 46202
Tel: 317 630-2219   *Fax:* 317 630-2667
E-mail: lajmars@iupui.edu
Length: 1 Yr   *ACGME Approved/Offered Positions:* 6
Program ID: 151-17-21-016

Kansas

Kansas City

University of Kansas School of Medicine Program

Sponsor: University of Kansas School of Medicine
Aberdeen Village
Kansas City Presbyterian Manor
Southview Home Care
University of Kansas Hospital
Veterans Affairs Medical Center (Kansas City)
Prgm Director: Daniel L Swagerty Jr, MD, MPH
Landon Center on Aging
3901 Rainbow Blvd, MS 1005
Kansas City, KS 66160
Tel: 913 588-1940   *Fax:* 913 588-1201
E-mail: jsullivan@kumc.edu
Length: 1 Yr   *ACGME Approved/Offered Positions:* 4
Program ID: 151-19-21-056

Maine

Portland

Maine Medical Center Program

Sponsor: Maine Medical Center
New England Rehabilitation Hospital
Prgm Director: David W Scotton, MD
22 Bramhall Street
Portland, ME 04102
Tel: 207 662-3157   *Fax:* 207 662-6434
E-mail: scottd@maine.rr.com
Length: 1 Yr   *ACGME Approved/Offered Positions:* 2
Program ID: 151-22-21-146

Maryland

Baltimore

Johns Hopkins University Program

Sponsor: Johns Hopkins University School of Medicine
Johns Hopkins Bayview Medical Center
Johns Hopkins Hospital
Prgm Director: Matthew K McNabney, MD
5505 Hopkins Bayview Circle
Baltimore, MD 21224
Tel: 410 550-5827   *Fax:* 410 550-7045
E-mail: mmcnabne@jhmi.edu
Length: 1 Yr   *ACGME Approved/Offered Positions:* 10
Program ID: 151-23-11-018

University of Maryland Program

Sponsor: University of Maryland Medical System
Franklin Woods Center
Veterans Affairs Medical Center (Baltimore)
Prgm Director: Conrad May, MD
Box 152
22 South Greene Street
Baltimore, MD 21201
Tel: 410 605-7000   *Fax:* 410 605-7913
E-mail: cmay@grecc.umaryland.edu
Length: 1 Yr   *ACGME Approved/Offered Positions:* 6
Program ID: 151-23-21-104

Massachusetts

Boston

Beth Israel Deaconess Medical Center Program

Sponsor: Beth Israel Deaconess Medical Center
Prgm Director: Alan P Abrams, MD, MPH
Gerontology Division
110 Francis St, Suite 1A
Boston, MA 02215
Tel: 617 667-1858   *Fax:* 617 632-8673
E-mail: aabrams@bidmc.harvard.edu
Length: 1 Yr   *ACGME Approved/Offered Positions:* 12
Program ID: 151-24-21-019

Boston University Medical Center Program

Sponsor: Boston Medical Center
Edith Nourse Rogers Memorial Veterans Hospital (Bedford)
Harbor Health Services, Inc
Upham's Corner Health Center
Prgm Director: Sharon Levine, MD
88 East Newton Street, Robinson 2
Boston, MA 02118
Tel: 617 638-4150   *Fax:* 617 638-5258
E-mail: laurie.dubois@bmc.org
Length: 1 Yr   *ACGME Approved/Offered Positions:* 6
Program ID: 151-24-31-020

Springfield

Baystate Medical Center/Tufts University School of Medicine Program

Sponsor: Baystate Medical Center
Prgm Director: Sandra Bellantonio, MD
759 Chestnut Street
Springfield, MA 01199
Tel: 413 794-8121   *Fax:* 413 794-4054
E-mail: jennifer.cloutier@bhs.org
Length: 1 Yr   *ACGME Approved/Offered Positions:* 2
Program ID: 151-24-21-128

Michigan

Ann Arbor

University of Michigan Program

Sponsor: University of Michigan Hospitals and Health Centers
Veterans Affairs Medical Center (Ann Arbor)
Prgm Director: Robert V Hogikyan, MD, MPH
E Ann Arbor Health & Geriatrics, 4260 Plymouth Rd
Room B1-337, SPC 5797
Ann Arbor, MI 48109
Tel: 734 936-2519   *Fax:* 734 763-2064
E-mail: mreinhol@umich.edu
Length: 1 Yr   *ACGME Approved/Offered Positions:* 8
Program ID: 151-25-21-024

Dearborn

Oakwood Hospital Program

Sponsor: Oakwood Hospital
Prgm Director: David M Sengstock, MD, MSc
18101 Oakwood Boulevard
Medical Education/Geriatric Fellowship
Dearborn, MI 48123
Tel: 313 982-5203   *Fax:* 313 436-2071
E-mail: alexandk@oakwood.org
Length: 1 Yr   *ACGME Approved/Offered Positions:* 3
Program ID: 151-25-13-143

Detroit

Wayne State University/Detroit Medical Center Program

Sponsor: Wayne State University/Detroit Medical Center
Detroit Receiving Hospital and University Health Center
Elwood Geriatric Village
Hartford Nursing and Rehabilitation Center
Veterans Affairs Medical Center (Detroit)
Village of East Harbor
Prgm Director: Joel Steinberg, MD
Dept of Medicine, 5C
4201 St Antoine
Detroit, MI 48201
Tel: 313 577-5030   *Fax:* 313 745-4710
E-mail: thunt@med.wayne.edu
Length: 1 Yr   *ACGME Approved/Offered Positions:* 6
Program ID: 151-25-21-111

Flint

Hurley Medical Center/Michigan State University Program

Sponsor: Hurley Medical Center
Prgm Director: Ghassan Bachuwa, MD
One Hurley Plaza, MOB Suite 212
Flint, MI 48503
Tel: 810 257-9682   *Fax:* 810 762-7245
Length: 1 Yr   *ACGME Approved/Offered Positions:* 1
Program ID: 151-25-31-141

Programs

Royal Oak

William Beaumont Hospital Program

Sponsor: William Beaumont Hospital
Prgm Director: John J Voytas, MD
3535 W 13 Mile Road
Suite 105
Royal Oak, MI 48073
Tel: 248 551-0622   *Fax:* 248 551-1244
E-mail: jvoytas@beaumont.edu
Length: 1 Yr   *ACGME Approved/Offered Positions:* 4
Program ID: 151-25-31-117

Minnesota

Minneapolis

Hennepin County Medical Center Program

Sponsor: Hennepin County Medical Center
Augustana Care Corporation
Benedictine Health Center of Minneapolis
Prgm Director: Lawrence J Kerzner, MD
Geriatric Medicine Division
701 Park Avenue
Minneapolis, MN 55415
Tel: 612 873-7490   *Fax:* 612 904-4243
E-mail: Lawrence.Kerzner@hcmed.org
Length: 1 Yr   *ACGME Approved/Offered Positions:* 2
Program ID: 151-26-31-050

University of Minnesota Program

Sponsor: University of Minnesota Medical School
Regions Hospital
University of Minnesota Medical Center, Division of
   Fairview
Prgm Director: Michael T Spilane, MD
401 Phalen Blvd
St Paul, MN 55130
Tel: 651 254-7622   *Fax:* 651 254-7623
E-mail: joellyn.l.pilarski@healthpartners.com
Length: 1 Yr   *ACGME Approved/Offered Positions:* 2
Program ID: 151-26-13-140

Rochester

College of Medicine, Mayo Clinic (Rochester) Program

Sponsor: College of Medicine, Mayo Clinic
Comfort Home Health Care
Mayo Clinic (Rochester)
Saint Marys Hospital of Rochester
Samaritan Bethany Heights
Samaritan Bethany Home on Eighth
Prgm Director: Gregory J Hanson, MD
Mayo Clinic College of Medicine
200 First Street SW
Rochester, MN 55905
Tel: 507 284-2511
E-mail: hanson.gregory@mayo.edu
Length: 1 Yr   *ACGME Approved/Offered Positions:* 2
Program ID: 151-26-21-085

Missouri

St Louis

St Louis University School of Medicine Program

Sponsor: St Louis University School of Medicine
St Louis University Hospital
Veterans Affairs Medical Center (St Louis)
Prgm Director: Julie K Gammack, MD
Department of Medicine
1402 S Grand Blvd, M238
St Louis, MO 63104
Tel: 314 977-8462   *Fax:* 314 771-8575
E-mail: brookssa@slu.edu
Length: 1 Yr   *ACGME Approved/Offered Positions:* 8
Program ID: 151-28-21-095

Washington University/B-JH/SLCH Consortium Program

Sponsor: Washington University/B-JH/SLCH Consortium
Barnes-Jewish Hospital
Prgm Director: David B Carr, MD
4488 Forest Park Boulevard
Box 201
St Louis, MO 63108
Tel: 314 286-2700   *Fax:* 314 286-2701
E-mail: jwilson@dom.wustl.edu
Length: 1 Yr   *ACGME Approved/Offered Positions:* 3
Program ID: 151-28-21-027

Nebraska

Omaha

University of Nebraska Medical Center College of Medicine Program

Sponsor: University of Nebraska Medical Center College
   of Medicine
Nebraska Medical Center
Prgm Director: William L Lyons, MD
981320 Nebraska Medical Center
Omaha, NE 68198
Tel: 402 559-6029   *Fax:* 402 559-3877
Length: 1 Yr   *ACGME Approved/Offered Positions:* 4
Program ID: 151-30-21-028

Nevada

Reno

University of Nevada School of Medicine Program

Sponsor: University of Nevada School of Medicine
Circle of Life Hospice, Inc
Ioannis A Lougaris Veterans Affairs Medical Center
MEDSchool Associates North (Reno)
Renown Medical Center
Prgm Director: Diane Chau, MD
1000 Locust Street, MS18
Reno, NV 89502
Tel: 775 786-7200   *Fax:* 775 328-1815
E-mail: dianechaumd@yahoo.com
Length: 1 Yr   *ACGME Approved/Offered Positions:* 3
Program ID: 151-31-31-158

New Jersey

Neptune

Jersey Shore University Medical Center Program

Sponsor: Jersey Shore University Medical Center
Prgm Director: Joshua R Shua-Haim, MD
1945 Route 33
Neptune, NJ 07754
Tel: 732 776-4420   *Fax:* 732 657-0111
E-mail: shua-haim@comcast.net
Length: 1 Yr   *ACGME Approved/Offered Positions:* 2
Program ID: 151-33-21-129

Newark

UMDNJ-New Jersey Medical School Program

Sponsor: UMDNJ-New Jersey Medical School
Hackensack University Medical Center
Prgm Director: Lisa K Tank, MD
30 Prospect Avenue
Hackensack, NJ 07601
Tel: 201 996-2503   *Fax:* 201 883-0870
E-mail: ltank@humed.com
Length: 1 Yr   *ACGME Approved/Offered Positions:* 3
Program ID: 151-33-21-103

New Mexico

Albuquerque

University of New Mexico Program

Sponsor: University of New Mexico School of Medicine
University of New Mexico Hospital
Veterans Affairs Medical Center (Albuquerque)
Prgm Director: Carla Herman, MD, MPH
Geriatric Division, MSC10 5550
1University of New Mexico
Albuquerque, NM 87131
Tel: 505 272-5630   *Fax:* 505 272-3167
Length: 1 Yr   *ACGME Approved/Offered Positions:* 4
Program ID: 151-34-21-093

New York

Bronx

Albert Einstein College of Medicine Program

Sponsor: Albert Einstein College of Medicine of Yeshiva
   University
Montefiore Medical Center-Henry and Lucy Moses
   Division
Prgm Director: Amy R Ehrlich, MD
111 East 210th Street
Bronx, NY 10467
Tel: 718 920-6722   *Fax:* 718 655-9672
E-mail: aehrlich@montefiore.org
Length: 1 Yr   *ACGME Approved/Offered Positions:* 6
Program ID: 151-35-21-083

New York Medical College (Bronx) Program

Sponsor: New York Medical College
Montefiore Medical Center - North Division
Prgm Director: T S Dharmarajan, MD, MBBS
Department of Medicine, 5th Floor
600 East 233rd Street
Bronx, NY 10466
Tel: 718 920-9889   *Fax:* 718 920-9036
E-mail: tdharmar@montefiore.org
Length: 1 Yr   *ACGME Approved/Offered Positions:* 8
Program ID: 151-35-11-107

Note: * indicates a newly appointed program director

Brooklyn

Maimonides Medical Center Program
Sponsor: Maimonides Medical Center
Prgm Director: Barbara E Paris, MD
Division of Geriatrics
4802 Tenth Avenue
Brooklyn, NY 11219
Tel: 718 283-7089   *Fax:* 718 635-6417
E-mail: bparis@maimonidesmed.org
Length: 1 Yr   *ACGME Approved/Offered Positions:* 4
Program ID: 151-35-11-126

New York Methodist Hospital Program
Sponsor: New York Methodist Hospital
Prgm Director: Thayyullathil Bharathan, MD
506 Sixth Street
Brooklyn, NY 11215
Tel: 718 780-5246   *Fax:* 718 780-3259
Length: 1 Yr   *ACGME Approved/Offered Positions:* 4
Program ID: 151-35-21-121

SUNY Health Science Center at Brooklyn Program
Sponsor: SUNY Health Science Center at Brooklyn
Kings County Hospital Center
Lutheran Medical Center
University Hospital-SUNY Health Science Center at Brooklyn
Veterans Affairs Medical Center (Brooklyn)
Prgm Director: Mohammed A Nurhussein, MD*
450 Clarkson Avenue, Box 50
Brooklyn, NY 11203
Tel: 718 270-1531   *Fax:* 718 270-1561
Length: 1 Yr   *ACGME Approved/Offered Positions:* 2
Program ID: 151-35-21-156

Buffalo

University at Buffalo Program
Sponsor: University at Buffalo School of Medicine
Kaleida Health System (Millard Fillmore Hospital)
Veterans Affairs Western New York Hospital
Prgm Director: Bruce J Naughton, MD
3 Gates Circle
Buffalo, NY 14209
Tel: 716 887-4021   *Fax:* 716 887-4437
Length: 1 Yr   *ACGME Approved/Offered Positions:* 3
Program ID: 151-35-31-030

Flushing

Flushing Hospital Medical Center Program
Sponsor: Flushing Hospital Medical Center
Prgm Director: Anthony T Vela, MD
4500 Parsons Boulevard
Flushing, NY 11355
Tel: 718 670-3121   *Fax:* 718 670-4510
E-mail: avelamd@aol.com
Length: 1 Yr   *ACGME Approved/Offered Positions:* 4
Program ID: 151-35-21-123

New York Hospital Medical Center of Queens/Cornell University Medical College Program
Sponsor: New York Hospital Medical Center of Queens
Silvercrest Extended Care Facility
Prgm Director: Zheng-Bo Huang, MD
56-45 Main Street
Flushing, NY 11355
Tel: 718 670-2939   *Fax:* 718 670-2456
E-mail: zhh9003@nyp.org
Length: 1 Yr   *ACGME Approved/Offered Positions:* 3
Program ID: 151-35-31-145

Great Neck

NSLIJHS-Albert Einstein College of Medicine at Long Island Jewish Medical Center Program
Sponsor: North Shore-Long Island Jewish Health System
Cold Spring Hills Center for Nursing and Rehabilitation
Long Island Jewish Medical Center
Prgm Director: Gisele P Wolf-Klein, MD
270-05 76th Avenue
New Hyde Park, NY 11042
Tel: 718 470-7295   *Fax:* 718 470-0827
Length: 1 Yr   *ACGME Approved/Offered Positions:* 8
Program ID: 151-35-21-031

Jamaica

New York Medical College (Brooklyn-Queens) Program
Sponsor: New York Medical College
Caritas Health Care (Brooklyn-Queens)
Prgm Director: Dharamjit N Kumar, MD
152-11 89th Avenue
Jamaica, NY 11432
Tel: 718 558-2891   *Fax:* 718 558-2476
E-mail: dkumar@bqhcny.org
Length: 1 Yr   *ACGME Approved/Offered Positions:* 4
Program ID: 151-35-31-124

Mineola

Winthrop-University Hospital Program
Sponsor: Winthrop-University Hospital
Cold Spring Hills Center for Nursing and Rehabilitation
Prgm Director: Lucy O Macina, MD
222 Station Plaza N, Room 518
Mineola, NY 11501
Tel: 516 663-2588   *Fax:* 516 663-4644
Length: 1 Yr   *ACGME Approved/Offered Positions:* 4
Program ID: 151-35-21-088

New York

Mount Sinai School of Medicine Program
Sponsor: Mount Sinai School of Medicine
Jewish Home and Hospital Lifecare System
Mount Sinai Medical Center
Prgm Director: Helen M Fernandez, MD, MPH
Box 1070
One Gustave L Levy Place
New York, NY 10029
Tel: 212 241-8910   *Fax:* 212 987-0793
Length: 1 Yr   *ACGME Approved/Offered Positions:* 14
Program ID: 151-35-31-062

New York Medical College at St Vincent's and Medical Center of New York Program
Sponsor: New York Medical College
St Vincent Catholic Medical Centers (Manhattan)
Prgm Director: Caroline A Vitale, MD*
Geriatric Medicine, NR 12-21
153 W 11th Street
New York, NY 10011
Tel: 212 604-2191   *Fax:* 212 604-2128
E-mail: ssolisberwa@svcmcny.org
Length: 1 Yr   *ACGME Approved/Offered Positions:* 2
Program ID: 151-35-21-090

New York Presbyterian Hospital (Cornell Campus) Program
Sponsor: New York Presbyterian Hospital
New York Presbyterian Hospital (Cornell Campus)
Prgm Director: Barrie L Raik, MD
Division of Geriatrics and Gerontology
525 East 68th Street, Box 39
New York, NY 10065
Tel: 212 746-1729   *Fax:* 212 746-4888
E-mail: dba2004@med.cornell.edu
Length: 1 Yr   *ACGME Approved/Offered Positions:* 4
Program ID: 151-35-12-127

New York University School of Medicine Program
Sponsor: New York University School of Medicine
Bellevue Hospital Center
Goldwater Memorial Hospital
Manhattan VA Harbor Health Care System
NYU Hospitals Center
Prgm Director: Scott E Sherman, MD, MPH*
550 First Avenue
CD 696
New York, NY 10016
Tel: 212 686-7500   *Fax:* 212 951-3269
E-mail: scott.sherman@med.nyu.edu
Length: 1 Yr   *ACGME Approved/Offered Positions:* 7
Program ID: 151-35-21-101

St Luke's-Roosevelt Hospital Center Program
Sponsor: St Luke's-Roosevelt Hospital Center
Beth Israel Medical Center
Prgm Director: Jessica Petilla, MD*
1111 Amsterdam Avenue
Department of Geriatrics-Clark 7
New York, NY 10025
Tel: 212 523-5934   *Fax:* 212 523-2842
Length: 1 Yr   *ACGME Approved/Offered Positions:* 4
Program ID: 151-35-31-132

Rochester

University of Rochester Program
Sponsor: Strong Memorial Hospital of the University of Rochester
Highland Hospital of Rochester
Monroe Community Hospital
Prgm Director: Thomas V Caprio, MD*
435 E Henrietta Road
Rochester, NY 14620
Tel: 585 760-6364   *Fax:* 585 760-6376
Length: 1 Yr   *ACGME Approved/Offered Positions:* 6
Program ID: 151-35-31-105

Staten Island

Staten Island University Hospital Program
Sponsor: Staten Island University Hospital
Prgm Director: Donna Seminara, MD
375 Seguine Avenue
Staten Island, NY 10309
Tel: 718 226-4374   *Fax:* 718 226-3995
Length: 1 Yr   *ACGME Approved/Offered Positions:* 4
Program ID: 151-35-21-110

Stony Brook

SUNY at Stony Brook Program
Sponsor: University Hospital - SUNY at Stony Brook
Gurwin Jewish Geriatric Center
Veterans Affairs Medical Center (Northport)
Prgm Director: Suzanne D Fields, MD, MS
Primary Care Center
205 N Belle Mead Rd
Setauket, NY 11733
Tel: 631 444-5273   *Fax:* 631 444-5295
Length: 1 Yr   *ACGME Approved/Offered Positions:* 5
Program ID: 151-35-22-109

Syracuse

SUNY Upstate Medical University Program
Sponsor: SUNY Upstate Medical University
Veterans Affairs Medical Center (Syracuse)
Prgm Director: Sharon A Brangman, MD
750 East Adams Street
Syracuse, NY 13210
Tel: 315 464-5167   *Fax:* 315 464-5771
Length: 1 Yr   *ACGME Approved/Offered Positions:* 3
Program ID: 151-35-21-097

Programs

North Carolina

Chapel Hill

University of North Carolina Hospitals Program

Sponsor: University of North Carolina Hospitals
Prgm Director: Debra L Bynum, MD*
CB 7550
5003 Old Clinic Bldg
Chapel Hill, NC 27599
Tel: 919 966-1456   *Fax:* 919 966-9734
Length: 1 Yr   *ACGME Approved/Offered Positions:* 3
Program ID: 151-36-21-059

Durham

Duke University Hospital Program

Sponsor: Duke University Hospital
Veterans Affairs Medical Center (Durham)
Prgm Director: Mitchell T Heflin, MD*
Box 3881
Durham, NC 27710
Tel: 919 660-7561   *Fax:* 919 684-8569
E-mail: hefli001@mc.duke.edu
Length: 1 Yr   *ACGME Approved/Offered Positions:* 4
Program ID: 151-36-21-033

Winston-Salem

Wake Forest University School of Medicine Program

Sponsor: Wake Forest University Baptist Medical Center
Prgm Director: Hal H Atkinson, MD, MS
Section on Geriatrics/Ground Floor, Sticht Center
Medical Center Boulevard
Winston-Salem, NC 27157
Tel: 336 713-8583   *Fax:* 336 713-8800
E-mail: patsmith@wfubmc.edu
Length: 1 Yr   *ACGME Approved/Offered Positions:* 4
Program ID: 151-36-21-034

Ohio

Akron

Summa Health System/NEOUCOM Program

Sponsor: Summa Health System
Akron City Hospital (Summa Health System)
Bath Manor Care Center
Windsong Care Center
Prgm Director: Kyle R Allen, DO
75 Arch Street
Suite G1
Akron, OH 44304
Tel: 330 375-3747   *Fax:* 330 375-4939
Length: 1 Yr   *ACGME Approved/Offered Positions:* 2
Program ID: 151-38-21-160

Cleveland

Cleveland Clinic Foundation Program

Sponsor: Cleveland Clinic Foundation
Prgm Director: Barbara J Messinger-Rapport, MD, PhD
9500 Euclid Avenue
Desk A91
Cleveland, OH 44195
Tel: 216 444-8091   *Fax:* 216 445-8762
E-mail: meded@ccf.org
Length: 1 Yr   *ACGME Approved/Offered Positions:* 2
Program ID: 151-38-12-037

University Hospitals Case Medical Center Program

Sponsor: University Hospitals Case Medical Center
Veterans Affairs Medical Center (Cleveland)
Prgm Director: Thomas Hornick, MD
Geriatric Medicine
11100 Euclid Avenue
Cleveland, OH 44106
Tel: 216 791-3800   *Fax:* 216 421-3027
Length: 1 Yr   *ACGME Approved/Offered Positions:* 12
Program ID: 151-38-21-035

Columbus

Ohio State University Hospital Program

Sponsor: Ohio State University Hospital
Wexner Heritage Village
Prgm Director: Robert A Murden, MD
2050 Kenny Road
Martha Morehouse Pavilion, Suite 2335
Columbus, OH 43221
Tel: 614 293-4953   *Fax:* 614 293-6890
E-mail: robert.murden@osumc.edu
Length: 1 Yr   *ACGME Approved/Offered Positions:* 1
Program ID: 151-38-31-147

Oklahoma

Oklahoma City

University of Oklahoma Health Sciences Center Program

Sponsor: University of Oklahoma College of Medicine
OU Medical Center - Presbyterian Tower
Veterans Affairs Medical Center (Oklahoma City)
Prgm Director: David O Staats, MD
PO Box 26901, VAMC 11G
Oklahoma City, OK 73190
Tel: 405 271-8558   *Fax:* 405 271-3887
E-mail: david-staats@ouhsc.edu
Length: 1 Yr   *ACGME Approved/Offered Positions:* 4
Program ID: 151-39-21-112

Oregon

Portland

Oregon Health & Science University Program

Sponsor: Oregon Health & Science University Hospital
Legacy Good Samaritan Hospital and Medical Center
Veterans Affairs Medical Center (Portland)
Prgm Director: Mark Traines, MD*
Medical Service (P3-MED)
PO Box 1034
Portland, OR 97207
Tel: 503 220-8262   *Fax:* 503 721-7807
Length: 1 Yr   *ACGME Approved/Offered Positions:* 6
Program ID: 151-40-31-038

Pennsylvania

Abington

Abington Memorial Hospital Program

Sponsor: Abington Memorial Hospital
Prgm Director: Mary T Hoffman, MD
1200 Old York Road
Abington, PA 19001
Tel: 215 481-4350   *Fax:* 215 481-4361
Length: 1 Yr   *ACGME Approved/Offered Positions:* 2
Program ID: 151-41-21-135

Philadelphia

Albert Einstein Healthcare Network Program

Sponsor: Albert Einstein Medical Center
Prgm Director: Richard Grant, MD, MPH
5501 Old York Road
Philadelphia, PA 19141
Tel: 215 456-8608   *Fax:* 215 456-7512
E-mail: grantr@einstein.edu
Length: 1 Yr   *ACGME Approved/Offered Positions:* 4
Program ID: 151-41-11-078

Temple University Hospital Program

Sponsor: Temple University Hospital
Crozer-Chester Medical Center
Prgm Director: William S Zirker, MD, MPH
Temple University Hospital
3401 N Broad St
Philadelphia, PA 19140
Tel: 610 447-2078   *Fax:* 610 447-2080
E-mail: william.zirker@crozer.org
Length: 1 Yr   *ACGME Approved/Offered Positions:* 8
Program ID: 151-41-21-118

University of Pennsylvania Program

Sponsor: University of Pennsylvania Health System
Veterans Affairs Medical Center (Philadelphia)
Prgm Director: Edna P Schwab, MD
Division of Geriatric Medicine
Ralston House, 3615 Chestnut Street
Philadelphia, PA 19104
Tel: 215 662-4416   *Fax:* 215 573-9133
Length: 1 Yr   *ACGME Approved/Offered Positions:* 5
Program ID: 151-41-21-060

Pittsburgh

University of Pittsburgh Medical Center Medical Education Program

Sponsor: Univ of Pittsburgh Medical Center Medical
   Education
Asbury Health Center
Canterbury Place
Charles Morris Center Nursing & Rehabilitation
Heritage Shadyside
UPMC Presbyterian Shadyside
Veterans Affairs Medical Center (Pittsburgh)
Prgm Director: Debra K Weiner, MD
Division of Geriatric Medicine
3471 Fifth Avenue, Suite 500
Pittsburgh, PA 15213
Tel: 412 692-2372   *Fax:* 412 692-2370
E-mail: dweiner@pitt.edu
Length: 1 Yr   *ACGME Approved/Offered Positions:* 8
Program ID: 151-41-21-077

Puerto Rico

San Juan

University of Puerto Rico Program

Sponsor: University of Puerto Rico School of Medicine
University Hospital
University of Puerto Rico Hospital at Carolina
VA Caribbean Healthcare System
Prgm Director: Ivonne Z Jimenez-Velazquez, MD
Box 365067
Medical Sciences Campus
San Juan, PR 00936
Tel: 787 758-2525   *Fax:* 787 754-1739
E-mail: ijv@prw.net
Length: 1 Yr   *ACGME Approved/Offered Positions:* 2
Program ID: 151-42-21-089

Note: * indicates a newly appointed program director

Rhode Island

Providence

Brown University Program
Sponsor: Rhode Island Hospital-Lifespan
Prgm Director: Aman Nanda, MD
593 Eddy Street
Providence, RI 02903
Tel: 401 444-5248   *Fax:* 401 444-3397
E-mail: dbethel@lifespan.org
Length: 1 Yr   *ACGME Approved/Offered Positions:* 4
Program ID: 151-43-12-139

South Carolina

Columbia

Palmetto Health/University of South Carolina School of Medicine Program
Sponsor: Palmetto Health
Palmetto Health Richland
William Jennings Bryan Dorn Veterans Hospital
Prgm Director: G Paul Eleazer, MD
15 Medical Park, Ste 211
Columbia, SC 29203
Tel: 803 434-4390   *Fax:* 803 434-4334
Length: 1 Yr   *ACGME Approved/Offered Positions:* 4
Program ID: 151-45-21-119

Tennessee

Nashville

Vanderbilt University Program
Sponsor: Vanderbilt University Medical Center
Veterans Affairs Medical Center (Nashville)
Prgm Director: James S Powers, MD
Senior Care Service
7155 Vanderbilt Medical Center East
Nashville, TN 37232
Tel: 615 936-3274   *Fax:* 615 936-3156
Length: 1 Yr   *ACGME Approved/Offered Positions:* 2
Program ID: 151-47-21-125

Texas

Dallas

University of Texas Southwestern Medical School Program
Sponsor: University of Texas Southwestern Medical
  School
Dallas County Hospital District-Parkland Memorial
  Hospital
Dallas VA Medical Center
Prgm Director: Vivyenne M Roche, MD
5323 Harry Hines Boulevard
Dallas, TX 75390
Tel: 214 648-9012   *Fax:* 214 648-2087
Length: 1 Yr   *ACGME Approved/Offered Positions:* 3
Program ID: 151-48-12-136

Galveston

University of Texas Medical Branch Hospitals Program
Sponsor: University of Texas Medical Branch Hospitals
Mainland Medical Center
Prgm Director: Mukaila Raji, MD*
Department of Medicine
301 University Boulevard
Galveston, TX 77555
Tel: 409 772-1987
E-mail: rbailes@utmb.edu
Length: 1 Yr   *ACGME Approved/Offered Positions:* 4
Program ID: 151-48-21-106

Houston

Baylor College of Medicine Program
Sponsor: Baylor College of Medicine
Methodist Hospital (Houston)
Michael E DeBakey VA Medical Center - Houston
Prgm Director: Aimee D Garcia, MD
Houston Veterans Affairs Medical Center (110)
2002 Holcombe Boulevard
Houston, TX 77030
Tel: 713 794-7121   *Fax:* 713 794-8875
E-mail: aimeeg@bcm.tmc.edu
Length: 1 Yr   *ACGME Approved/Offered Positions:* 6
Program ID: 151-48-31-040

University of Texas at Houston Program
Sponsor: University of Texas Health Science Center at
  Houston
Harris County Psychiatric Center
Lyndon B Johnson General Hospital
Prgm Director: Carmel B Dyer, MD*
6431 Fannin MSB 4.200
Houston, TX 77030
Tel: 713 500-6290   *Fax:* 713 500-0706
Length: 1 Yr   *ACGME Approved/Offered Positions:* 2
Program ID: 151-48-31-162

San Antonio

University of Texas Health Science Center at San Antonio Program
Sponsor: University of Texas School of Medicine at San
  Antonio
Audie L Murphy Memorial Veterans Hospital (San
  Antonio)
Prgm Director: Laura K Chiodo, MD, MPH
Div of Geriatrics, Gerontology & Palliative Med
San Antonio, TX 78229
Tel: 210 617-5300   *Fax:* 210 949-3060
E-mail: chiodo@uthscsa.edu
Length: 1 Yr   *ACGME Approved/Offered Positions:* 5
Program ID: 151-48-21-075

Utah

Salt Lake City

University of Utah Program
Sponsor: University of Utah Medical Center
Veterans Affairs Medical Center (Salt Lake City)
Prgm Director: Jonathan R Nebeker, MD, MS
Department of Medicine
30 North 1900 East
Salt Lake City, UT 84132
Tel: 801 584-2522   *Fax:* 801 584-5640
E-mail: Deanna.Matthews@va.gov
Length: 1 Yr   *ACGME Approved/Offered Positions:* 2
Program ID: 151-49-21-052

Virginia

Charlottesville

University of Virginia Program
Sponsor: University of Virginia Medical Center
Prgm Director: Jonathan M Evans, MD, MPH
PO Box 800901
Charlottesville, VA 22908
Tel: 434 243-9266   *Fax:* 434 243-9282
Length: 1 Yr   *ACGME Approved/Offered Positions:* 2
Program ID: 151-51-21-042

Norfolk

Eastern Virginia Medical School Program
Sponsor: Eastern Virginia Medical School
Berger Goldrich Home at Beth Sholom Village
Chesapeake Place
Harbor's Edge
Lake Taylor Transitional Care Hospital
Oakwood Rehabilitation and Nursing Center
Sentara Norfolk General Hospital
Prgm Director: Marissa C Galicia-Castillo, MD, MEd*
825 Fairfax Avenue, Suite 201
Norfolk, VA 23507
Tel: 757 446-7040   *Fax:* 757 446-7049
E-mail: galicimc@evms.edu
Length: 1 Yr   *ACGME Approved/Offered Positions:* 2
Program ID: 151-51-31-137

Richmond

Virginia Commonwealth University Health System Program
Sponsor: Virginia Commonwealth University Health
  System
Hunter Holmes McGuire VA Medical Center (Richmond)
Medical College of Virginia Hospitals
Prgm Director: Angela Gentili, MD
Geriatrics Medicine Section (181)
1201 Broad Rock Blvd
Richmond, VA 23249
Tel: 804 675-5181   *Fax:* 804 675-5551
E-mail: angela.gentili@va.gov
Length: 1 Yr   *ACGME Approved/Offered Positions:* 6
Program ID: 151-51-21-043

Washington

Seattle

University of Washington Program
Sponsor: University of Washington School of Medicine
Harborview Medical Center
University of Washington Medical Center
VA Puget Sound Health Care System
Prgm Director: Itamar B Abrass, MD
325 9th Avenue
Box 359755
Seattle, WA 98104
Tel: 206 744-9100   *Fax:* 206 744-9976
Length: 1 Yr   *ACGME Approved/Offered Positions:* 4
Program ID: 151-54-21-044

Tacoma

Madigan Army Medical Center Program
Sponsor: Madigan Army Medical Center
Veterans Affairs Medical Center (Tacoma)
Prgm Director: Sharon Falzgraf, MD
American Lake (A-182-GEC)
Tacoma, WA 98493
Tel: 253 583-2085   *Fax:* 253 589-4133
E-mail: sharon.falzgraf@med.va.gov
Length: 1 Yr   *ACGME Approved/Offered Positions:* 2
Program ID: 151-54-12-074
Uniformed Services Program

West Virginia

Charleston

Charleston Area Medical Center/West Virginia University (Charleston Division) Program

Sponsor: Charleston Area Medical Center/West Virginia University
Prgm Director: Todd H Goldberg, MD
WVU Health Sciences Center, Charleston Division, Dept of Med
3110 MacCorkle Avenue, SE
Charleston, WV 25304
Tel: 304 347-1323   *Fax:* 304 347-1344
E-mail: tgoldberg@hsc.wvu.edu
Length: 1 Yr   *ACGME Approved/Offered Positions:* 2
Program ID: 151-55-12-151

Wisconsin

Madison

University of Wisconsin Program

Sponsor: University of Wisconsin Hospital and Clinics
William S Middleton Veterans Hospital
Prgm Director: Steven R Barczi, MD
GRECC
2500 Overlook Terrace
Madison, WI 53705
Tel: 608 280-7000   *Fax:* 608 280-7291
E-mail: dls@medicine.wisc.edu
Length: 1 Yr   *ACGME Approved/Offered Positions:* 4
Program ID: 151-56-21-049

Milwaukee

Aurora Health Care Program

Sponsor: Aurora Health Care
Aurora Sinai Medical Center
Prgm Director: Michael L Malone, MD
Aurora Sinai Medical Center
945 N 12th St, PO Box 342
Milwaukee, WI 53201
Tel: 414 219-7058
E-mail: maria.salazar@aurora.org
Length: 1 Yr   *ACGME Approved/Offered Positions:* 2
Program ID: 151-56-21-076

Medical College of Wisconsin Affiliated Hospitals Program

Sponsor: Medical College of Wisconsin Affiliated Hospitals, Inc
Clement J Zablocki Veterans Affairs Medical Center
Froedtert Memorial Lutheran Hospital
Prgm Director: Kathryn Denson, MD
9200 W Wisconsin Avenue
Milwaukee, WI 53226
Tel: 414 384-2000   *Fax:* 414 382-5376
Length: 1 Yr   *ACGME Approved/Offered Positions:* 4
Program ID: 151-56-31-048

Geriatric Psychiatry (Psychiatry)

Arkansas

Little Rock

University of Arkansas for Medical Sciences Program

Sponsor: University of Arkansas College of Medicine
Arkansas Health Center
Central Arkansas Veterans Healthcare System
UAMS Medical Center
Prgm Director: Lou Ann Eads, MD
Department of Psychiatry, Slot 554
4301 West Markham Street
Little Rock, AR 72205
Tel: 501 257-3235   *Fax:* 501 257-3350
E-mail: eadslouann@uams.edu
Length: 1 Yr   *ACGME Approved/Offered Positions:* 1
Program ID: 407-04-12-070

California

Los Angeles

UCLA Medical Center Program

Sponsor: UCLA David Geffen School of Medicine/UCLA Medical Center
UCLA Neuropsychiatric Hospital
VA Greater Los Angeles Healthcare System
Prgm Director: David Sultzer, MD
Psychiatry Residency Office
760 Westwood Plaza C8-225 NPI
Los Angeles, CA 90024
Tel: 310 268-3708
E-mail: kamaya@mednet.ucla.edu
Length: 1 Yr   *ACGME Approved/Offered Positions:* 6
Program ID: 407-05-21-001

San Diego

University of California (San Diego) Program

Sponsor: University of California (San Diego) Medical Center
Veterans Affairs Medical Center (San Diego)
Prgm Director: Daniel D Sewell, MD
Department of Psychiatry
9500 Gilman Drive (9116A-1)
La Jolla, CA 92093
Tel: 619 543-3779   *Fax:* 619 543-3648
E-mail: dsewell@ucsd.edu
Length: 1 Yr   *ACGME Approved/Offered Positions:* 2
Program ID: 407-05-31-002

San Francisco

University of California (San Francisco) Program

Sponsor: University of California (San Francisco) School of Medicine
UCSF Med Ctr/Langley Porter Psychiatric Hosp and Clinics
Veterans Affairs Medical Center (San Francisco)
Prgm Director: J Craig Nelson, MD
University of California San Francisco
401 Parnassus Avenue, Box 0984-F
San Francisco, CA 94143
Tel: 415 476-7405   *Fax:* 415 476-7320
E-mail: geriatric.psychiatry@lppi.ucsf.edu
Length: 1 Yr   *ACGME Approved/Offered Positions:* 3
Program ID: 407-05-11-065

Stanford

Stanford University Program

Sponsor: Stanford Hospital and Clinics
Veterans Affairs Palo Alto Health Care System
Prgm Director: Jared R Tinklenberg, MD
401 Quarry Road Room 2204
Stanford, CA 94305
Tel: 650 858-3915   *Fax:* 650 725-3762
E-mail: jerytink@stanford.edu
Length: 1 Yr   *ACGME Approved/Offered Positions:* 4
Program ID: 407-05-11-003

Colorado

Aurora

University of Colorado Denver Program

Sponsor: University of Colorado Denver School of Medicine
Denver Health Medical Center
Veterans Affairs Medical Center (Denver)
Prgm Director: Jennifer A Osborne, MD*
1055 Clermont Street
Denver, CO 80220
Tel: 303 399-8020
E-mail: jennifer.osborne3@va.gov
Length: 1 Yr   *ACGME Approved/Offered Positions:* 2
Program ID: 407-07-21-071

Connecticut

New Haven

Yale-New Haven Medical Center Program

Sponsor: Yale-New Haven Hospital
Hamden Health Care Center
Jewish Home for the Elderly
Masonicare
Veterans Affairs Medical Center (West Haven)
Prgm Director: Paul Kirwin, MD*
184 Liberty Street
New Haven, CT 06519
Tel: 203 932-5711
Length: 1 Yr   *ACGME Approved/Offered Positions:* 3
Program ID: 407-08-21-052

Florida

Miami

Jackson Memorial Hospital/Jackson Health System Program

Sponsor: Jackson Memorial Hospital/Jackson Health System
Mount Sinai Medical Center of Florida, Inc
Veterans Affairs Medical Center (Miami)
Prgm Director: Elizabeth A Crocco, MD
1400 NW 10th Avenue, Suite 702
Miami, FL 33136
Tel: 305 674-2194   *Fax:* 305 532-5241
Length: 1 Yr   *ACGME Approved/Offered Positions:* 5
Program ID: 407-11-21-004

Note: * indicates a newly appointed program director

Tampa

University of South Florida Program
Sponsor: University of South Florida College of Medicine
James A Haley Veterans Hospital
University Psychiatry Center
Veterans Affairs Medical Center (Bay Pines)
Prgm Director: Maria T Caserta, MD, PhD*
Dept of Psychiatry & Behavioral Med
3515 E Fletcher Avenue
Tampa, FL 33613
Tel: 813 974-2805   *Fax:* 813 974-2478
E-mail: kisaac@health.usf.edu
Length: 1 Yr   *ACGME Approved/Offered Positions:* 2
Program ID: 407-11-31-005

Georgia

Atlanta

Emory University Program
Sponsor: Emory University School of Medicine
Wesley Woods Geriatric Hospital
Prgm Director: Larry E Tune, MD
1841 Clifton Road
Atlanta, GA 30329
Tel: 404 728-4969   *Fax:* 404 728-4963
E-mail: sdpfwb@emory.edu
Length: 1 Yr   *ACGME Approved/Offered Positions:* 2
Program ID: 407-12-21-006

Hawaii

Honolulu

University of Hawaii Program
Sponsor: University of Hawaii John A Burns School of
   Medicine
Hawaii Health Systems Corporation
Queen's Medical Center
VA Pacific Islands Health Care System (Honolulu)
Prgm Director: Junji Takeshita, MD
1356 Lusitana Street, 4th Floor
Honolulu, HI 96813
Tel: 808 586-2900   *Fax:* 808 596-2940
Length: 1 Yr   *ACGME Approved/Offered Positions:* 2
Program ID: 407-14-21-007

Illinois

Chicago

McGaw Medical Center of Northwestern University Program
Sponsor: McGaw Medical Center of Northwestern
   University
Northwestern Memorial Hospital
Prgm Director: Deborah A Reed, MD
446 E Ontario Ste 7-200
Chicago, IL 60611
Tel: 312 926-8058   *Fax:* 312 926-4837
E-mail: dareed@northwestern.edu
Length: 1 Yr   *ACGME Approved/Offered Positions:* 2
Program ID: 407-16-21-008

Indiana

Indianapolis

Indiana University School of Medicine Program
Sponsor: Indiana University School of Medicine
Richard L Roudebush Veterans Affairs Medical Center
Prgm Director: Valerie Smith-Gamble, MD
1111 W 10th Street, A208
Indianapolis, IN 46202
Tel: 317 274-1239   *Fax:* 317 274-1248
E-mail: lgoudrea@iupui.edu
Length: 1 Yr   *ACGME Approved/Offered Positions:* 2
Program ID: 407-17-21-009

Iowa

Iowa City

University of Iowa Hospitals and Clinics Program
Sponsor: University of Iowa Hospitals and Clinics
Prgm Director: Judith H Crossett, MD, PhD
200 Hawkins Drive
Dept of Psychiatry, 2880 JPP
Iowa City, IA 52242
Tel: 319 384-8211   *Fax:* 319 356-2587
E-mail: judith-crossett@uiowa.edu
Length: 1 Yr   *ACGME Approved/Offered Positions:* 2
Program ID: 407-18-21-057

Maryland

Baltimore

Johns Hopkins University Program
Sponsor: Johns Hopkins University School of Medicine
Johns Hopkins Bayview Medical Center
Johns Hopkins Hospital
Prgm Director: Peter V Rabins, MD, MPH
Meyer 279
600 North Wolfe Street
Baltimore, MD 21287
Tel: 410 955-6736   *Fax:* 410 614-1094
Length: 1 Yr   *ACGME Approved/Offered Positions:* 2
Program ID: 407-23-21-012

University of Maryland/Sheppard Pratt Program
Sponsor: University of Maryland Medical System
Veterans Affairs Medical Center (Baltimore)
Prgm Director: William T Regenold, MD
10 North Greene Street, 116A
Baltimore, MD 21201
Tel: 410 328-6511   *Fax:* 410 328-5584
Length: 1 Yr   *ACGME Approved/Offered Positions:* 3
Program ID: 407-23-31-013

Bethesda

National Capital Consortium Program
Sponsor: National Capital Consortium
US Soldiers' and Airmen's Home
Walter Reed Army Medical Center
Prgm Director: Charles Milliken, MD
Attn: Leslie Galloway/Geriatric Psychiatry
6900 Georgia Avenue, NW; Walter Reed Army Medical
Washington, DC 20307
Tel: 202 782-7104   *Fax:* 202 782-6480
E-mail: geriatrics@nccpsychiatry.info
Length: 1 Yr   *ACGME Approved/Offered Positions:* 2
Program ID: 407-10-21-062
Uniformed Services Program

Massachusetts

Belmont

McLean Hospital Program
Sponsor: McLean Hospital
Prgm Director: Sumer Verma, MD
115 Mill Street
Belmont, MA 02478
Tel: 617 855-3183   *Fax:* 617 855-3246
Length: 1 Yr   *ACGME Approved/Offered Positions:* 2
Program ID: 407-24-21-014

Cambridge

Cambridge Health Alliance Program
Sponsor: Cambridge Health Alliance
Hearth - Ending Elder Homelessness
Youville Hospital & Rehabilitation Center
Prgm Director: Stephen L Pinals, MD
Cambridge Hospital
1493 Cambridge Street
Cambridge, MA 02139
Tel: 617 591-6413   *Fax:* 617 591-6405
Length: 1 Yr   *ACGME Approved/Offered Positions:* 2
Program ID: 407-24-31-058

Michigan

Ann Arbor

University of Michigan Program
Sponsor: University of Michigan Hospitals and Health
   Centers
Veterans Affairs Medical Center (Ann Arbor)
Prgm Director: Susan Maixner, MD*
4250 Plymouth Road
Room 1524 RUB
Ann Arbor, MI 48109
Tel: 734 764-6879   *Fax:* 734 936-1130
E-mail: smaixner@med.umich.edu
Length: 2 Yrs   *ACGME Approved/Offered Positions:* 6
Program ID: 407-25-21-015

Detroit

Wayne State University/Lafayette Clinic Program
Sponsor: Wayne State University/Detroit Medical Center
Detroit Receiving Hospital and University Health Center
Henry Ford Center for Senior Independence
Henry Ford Village
Moroun Nursing Home
Rehabilitation Institute
Veterans Affairs Medical Center (Detroit)
Prgm Director: Shuja Haque, MD
UPC-Jefferson
2751 East Jefferson Avenue, Suite 400
Detroit, MI 48207
Tel: 313 576-3373   *Fax:* 313 577-2233
Length: 1 Yr   *ACGME Approved/Offered Positions:* 3
Program ID: 407-25-31-016

Minnesota

Minneapolis

University of Minnesota Program
Sponsor: University of Minnesota Medical School
Bethesda Hospital
HealthPartners Hospice of the Lakes & Palliative Care
Hennepin County Medical Center
Methodist Hospital
University of Minnesota Medical Center, Division of
    Fairview
Veterans Affairs Medical Center (Minneapolis)
Prgm Director: Susan E Czapiewski, MD, MS
VA Medical Center (116A)
One Veterans Drive
Minneapolis, MN 55417
Tel: 612 467-3535   *Fax:* 612 725-2292
Length: 1 Yr   *ACGME Approved/Offered Positions:* 2
Program ID: 407-26-21-017

Rochester

College of Medicine, Mayo Clinic (Rochester) Program
Sponsor: College of Medicine, Mayo Clinic
Mayo Clinic (Rochester)
Prgm Director: Jarrett W Richardson III, MD*
200 First Street SW Mayo W-11A
Rochester, MN 55905
Tel: 507 284-4159   *Fax:* 507 284-4158
E-mail: pearson.amber@mayo.edu
Length: 1 Yr   *ACGME Approved/Offered Positions:* 1
Program ID: 407-26-12-067

Missouri

St Louis

St Louis University School of Medicine Program
Sponsor: St Louis University School of Medicine
St Louis University Hospital
Veterans Affairs Medical Center (St Louis)
Prgm Director: Jothika N Manepalli, MD
Department of Neurology and Psychaitry
1438 South Grand Boulevard
St Louis, MO 63104
Tel: 314 977-4828   *Fax:* 314 977-4877
Length: 1 Yr   *ACGME Approved/Offered Positions:* 3
Program ID: 407-28-21-018

Nebraska

Omaha

Creighton University/University of Nebraska Program
Sponsor: Creighton University School of Medicine
Alegent Health Immanuel Medical Center
Nebraska Medical Center
Prgm Director: Prasad R Padala, MD
985582 Nebraska Medical Center
Omaha, NE 68198
Tel: 402 449-0621   *Fax:* 402 943-5543
E-mail: ppadala@unmc.edu
Length: 1 Yr   *ACGME Approved/Offered Positions:* 2
Program ID: 407-30-21-019

New Hampshire

Lebanon

Dartmouth-Hitchcock Medical Center Program
Sponsor: Mary Hitchcock Memorial Hospital
Veterans Affairs Medical Center (White River Junction)
Prgm Director: Thomas E Oxman, MD
1 Medical Center Drive
Lebanon, NH 03756
Tel: 603 653-3556   *Fax:* 603 650-5842
Length: 1 Yr   *ACGME Approved/Offered Positions:* 2
Program ID: 407-32-21-020

New Jersey

Piscataway

UMDNJ-Robert Wood Johnson Medical School Program
Sponsor: UMDNJ-Robert Wood Johnson Medical School
UMDNJ-University Behavioral HealthCare
University Medical Center at Princeton
Veterans Affairs New Jersey Health Care System
Prgm Director: Shailaja Shah, MD
COPSA, Institute for Alzheimer's Disease
100 Metroplex Drive, Suite 200
Edison, NJ 08817
Tel: 732 235-4295   *Fax:* 732 235-3923
Length: 1 Yr   *ACGME Approved/Offered Positions:* 3
Program ID: 407-33-21-021

New Mexico

Albuquerque

University of New Mexico Program
Sponsor: University of New Mexico School of Medicine
University of New Mexico Hospital
Veterans Affairs Medical Center (Albuquerque)
Prgm Director: William J Apfeldorf, MD, PhD
MSC09 5030
1 University of New Mexico
Albuquerque, NM 87131
Tel: 505 272-6093   *Fax:* 505 272-3497
E-mail: wapfeldort@salud.unm.edu
Length: 1 Yr   *ACGME Approved/Offered Positions:* 2
Program ID: 407-34-12-063

New York

Bronx

Albert Einstein College of Medicine Program
Sponsor: Albert Einstein College of Medicine of Yeshiva
    University
Montefiore Medical Center-Henry and Lucy Moses
    Division
Prgm Director: Gary J Kennedy, MD
111 East 210th Street
Bronx, NY 10467
Tel: 718 920-4236   *Fax:* 718 920-6538
E-mail: gjkennedy@msn.com
Length: 1 Yr   *ACGME Approved/Offered Positions:* 5
Program ID: 407-35-21-022

Brooklyn

SUNY Health Science Center at Brooklyn Program
Sponsor: SUNY Health Science Center at Brooklyn
Kingsboro Psychiatric Center
Kingsbrook Jewish Medical Center
University Hospital-SUNY Health Science Center at
    Brooklyn
Veterans Affairs Medical Center (Brooklyn)
Prgm Director: Carl I Cohen, MD
450 Clarkson Avenue
Brooklyn, NY 11203
Tel: 718 270-2907   *Fax:* 718 270-4104
Length: 1 Yr   *ACGME Approved/Offered Positions:* 3
Program ID: 407-35-31-023

Buffalo

University at Buffalo Program
Sponsor: University at Buffalo School of Medicine
Buffalo Psychiatric Center
Erie County Medical Center
Kaleida Health System (Millard Fillmore Hospital)
University at Buffalo Physician Practices (UBPP)
Veterans Affairs Western New York Hospital
Prgm Director: Marion Zucker Goldstein, MD, MS
462 Grider Street
Buffalo, NY 14215
Tel: 716 898-3630   *Fax:* 716 898-3612
Length: 1 Yr   *ACGME Approved/Offered Positions:* 2
Program ID: 407-35-31-069

Great Neck

NSLIJHS-Albert Einstein College of Medicine at Long Island Jewish Medical Center Program
Sponsor: North Shore-Long Island Jewish Health System
Hillside Hospital (Long Island Jewish Medical Center)
Long Island Jewish Medical Center
Pilgrim Psychiatric Center
Prgm Director: Blaine S Greenwald, MD
Ambulatory Care Pavilion
75-59 263rd Street
Glen Oaks, NY 11004
Tel: 718 470-8159   *Fax:* 718 962-7712
Length: 1 Yr   *ACGME Approved/Offered Positions:* 7
Program ID: 407-35-11-024

New York

Albert Einstein College of Medicine at Beth Israel Medical Center Program
Sponsor: Beth Israel Medical Center
St Luke's-Roosevelt Hospital Center
Prgm Director: Melinda S Lantz, MD
First Avenue at 16th Street #6K40
New York, NY 10003
Tel: 212 420-2457   *Fax:* 212 844-7659
E-mail: mlantz@chpnet.org
Length: 1 Yr   *ACGME Approved/Offered Positions:* 4
Program ID: 407-35-12-025

Mount Sinai School of Medicine Program
Sponsor: Mount Sinai School of Medicine
Elmhurst Hospital Center-Mount Sinai Services
Mount Sinai Medical Center
Pilgrim Psychiatric Center
Veterans Affairs Medical Center (Bronx)
Prgm Director: Judith Neugroschl, MD
One Gustave L Levy Place
Box 1230
New York, NY 10029
Tel: 212 824-8949   *Fax:* 212 987-4031
Length: 1 Yr   *ACGME Approved/Offered Positions:* 3
Program ID: 407-35-13-026

Note: * indicates a newly appointed program director

New York Medical College at St Vincent's Hospital and Medical Center of New York Program
Sponsor: New York Medical College
St Vincent Catholic Medical Centers (Manhattan)
Prgm Director: David Cordon, MD
153 West 11th Street
New York, NY 10011
Tel: 212 604-1525   *Fax:* 212 604-8197
E-mail: dcordon@svcmcny.org
Length: 1 Yr   *ACGME Approved/Offered Positions:* 2
Program ID: 407-35-23-028

New York Presbyterian Hospital (Columbia Campus) Program
Sponsor: New York Presbyterian Hospital
Binghamton Psychiatric Center
New York Presbyterian Hospital (Columbia Campus)
Rockland Psychiatric Center
Prgm Director: D Peter Birkett, MD
Columbia University Stroud Center
100 Haven Avenue, T3-30F
New York, NY 10032
Tel: 212 781-0600   *Fax:* 212 795-7696
E-mail: jat4@columbia.edu
Length: 1 Yr   *ACGME Approved/Offered Positions:* 3
Program ID: 407-35-21-042

New York University School of Medicine Program
Sponsor: New York University School of Medicine
Bellevue Hospital Center
Manhattan Psychiatric Center
NYU Hospitals Center
Rusk Institute of Rehabilitation Medicine
Prgm Director: Philip Saltiel, MD*
530 First Avenue, Suite 3D
New York, NY 10016
Tel: 212 223-2920
Length: 1 Yr   *ACGME Approved/Offered Positions:* 2
Program ID: 407-35-22-027

Rochester

University of Rochester Program
Sponsor: Strong Memorial Hospital of the University of Rochester
Rochester Psychiatric Center
Prgm Director: Jeffrey M Lyness, MD
300 Crittenden Boulevard
Box Psych
Rochester, NY 14642
Tel: 585 275-6741   *Fax:* 585 276-2292
Length: 1 Yr   *ACGME Approved/Offered Positions:* 3
Program ID: 407-35-32-029

Stony Brook

SUNY at Stony Brook Program
Sponsor: University Hospital - SUNY at Stony Brook
Prgm Director: Steven Cole, MD, MA
Department of Psychiatry and Behavioral Science
HSC, T-10, Room 040
Stony Brook, NY 11794
Tel: 631 444-2861   *Fax:* 631 444-7534
Length: 1 Yr   *ACGME Approved/Offered Positions:* 3
Program ID: 407-35-13-066

White Plains

New York Presbyterian Hospital (Cornell Campus)/Westchester Program
Sponsor: New York Presbyterian Hospital
New York Presbyterian Hospital (Westchester Division)
Prgm Director: Sibel A Klimstra, MD
21 Bloomingdale Road
White Plains, NY 10605
Tel: 914 997-5807   *Fax:* 914 682-6979
Length: 1 Yr   *ACGME Approved/Offered Positions:* 2
Program ID: 407-35-21-030

North Carolina

Durham

Duke University Hospital Program
Sponsor: Duke University Hospital
John Umstead Hospital
Veterans Affairs Medical Center (Durham)
Prgm Director: Mugdha Thakur, MD
Duke University Medical Center
Box 3903
Durham, NC 27710
Tel: 919 681-8536   *Fax:* 919 681-7668
E-mail: ridle001@mc.duke.edu
Length: 1 Yr   *ACGME Approved/Offered Positions:* 4
Program ID: 407-36-21-047

Ohio

Cleveland

University Hospitals Case Medical Center Program
Sponsor: University Hospitals Case Medical Center
Veterans Affairs Medical Center (Cleveland)
Prgm Director: Philipp L Dines, MD, PhD*
W O Walker Center
10524 Euclid Avenue
Cleveland, OH 44106
Tel: 216 844-3414   *Fax:* 216 844-1703
E-mail: philipp.dines@uhhospitals.org
Length: 1 Yr   *ACGME Approved/Offered Positions:* 2
Program ID: 407-38-21-045

Oregon

Portland

Oregon Health & Science University Program
Sponsor: Oregon Health & Science University Hospital
Veterans Affairs Medical Center (Portland)
Prgm Director: Linda K Ganzini, MD, MPH
Department of Psychiatry (UHN 80)
3181 SW Sam Jackson Park Road
Portland, OR 97239
Tel: 503 273-5315   *Fax:* 503 402-2952
E-mail: Linda.Ganzini@va.gov
Length: 1 Yr   *ACGME Approved/Offered Positions:* 2
Program ID: 407-40-21-031

Pennsylvania

Philadelphia

Albert Einstein Healthcare Network Program
Sponsor: Albert Einstein Medical Center
Belmont Center for Comprehensive Treatment
Prgm Director: Marc H Zisselman, MD
5501 Old York Road
Philadelphia, PA 19141
Tel: 215 456-9472
Length: 1 Yr   *ACGME Approved/Offered Positions:* 3
Program ID: 407-41-21-044

University of Pennsylvania Program
Sponsor: University of Pennsylvania Health System
Veterans Affairs Medical Center (Philadelphia)
Prgm Director: Joel E Streim, MD
3615 Chestnut Street
Philadelphia, PA 19104
Tel: 215 615-3086   *Fax:* 215 349-8389
E-mail: jstreim@mail.med.upenn.edu
Length: 1 Yr   *ACGME Approved/Offered Positions:* 4
Program ID: 407-41-31-033

Pittsburgh

University of Pittsburgh Medical Center Medical Education Program
Sponsor: Univ of Pittsburgh Medical Center Medical Education
UPMC Presbyterian Shadyside
UPMC Western Psychiatric Institute and Clinic
Veterans Affairs Medical Center (Pittsburgh)
Prgm Director: Jules Rosen, MD
3811 O'Hara Street, Room E720
Pittsburgh, PA 15213
Tel: 412 246-5900   *Fax:* 412 586-9300
Length: 1 Yr   *ACGME Approved/Offered Positions:* 5
Program ID: 407-41-11-034

Rhode Island

Providence

Brown University (Butler Hospital) Program
Sponsor: Butler Hospital
Miriam Hospital-Lifespan
Veterans Affairs Medical Center (Providence)
Prgm Director: Robert Kohn, MD
345 Blackstone Boulevard
Providence, RI 02906
Tel: 401 455-6277   *Fax:* 401 455-6566
E-mail: robert_kohn@brown.edu
Length: 1 Yr   *ACGME Approved/Offered Positions:* 3
Program ID: 407-43-21-048

South Carolina

Charleston

Medical University of South Carolina Program
Sponsor: Medical University of South Carolina College of Medicine
Ralph H Johnson VA Medical Center (Charleston)
Prgm Director: Edgar Weiss, MD
67 President Street
PO Box 250861
Charleston, SC 29425
Tel: 843 792-0192
E-mail: pucalm@musc.edu
Length: 1 Yr   *ACGME Approved/Offered Positions:* 2
Program ID: 407-45-21-035

Columbia

Palmetto Health/University of South Carolina School of Medicine Program
Sponsor: Palmetto Health
Palmetto Health Baptist
University of South Carolina School of Medicine
Prgm Director: James G Bouknight, MD, PhD
Clinical Education Building
15 Medical Park, Suite 141
Columbia, SC 29203
Tel: 803 296-3569   *Fax:* 803 434-4062
E-mail: James.Bouknight@palmettohealth.org
Length: 1 Yr   *ACGME Approved/Offered Positions:* 2
Program ID: 407-45-13-068

Programs

Tennessee

Memphis

University of Tennessee Program
Sponsor: University of Tennessee College of Medicine
St Francis Hospital
University of Tennessee Medical Center
Veterans Affairs Medical Center (Memphis)
Prgm Director: Kenneth Sakauye, MD
Department of Psychiatry
135 North Pauline, Suite 122
Memphis, TN 38105
Tel: 901 448-4572 *Fax:* 901 448-1684
E-mail: ksakauye@utmem.edu
Length: 1 Yr *ACGME Approved/Offered Positions:* 2
Program ID: 407-47-12-074

Texas

Dallas

University of Texas Southwestern Medical School Program
Sponsor: University of Texas Southwestern Medical
School
Dallas County Hospital District-Parkland Memorial
Hospital
Dallas VA Medical Center
Prgm Director: Mustafa M Husain, MD
5323 Harry Hines Boulevard
Dallas, TX 75390
Tel: 214 648-2806 *Fax:* 214 648-8030
Length: 1 Yr *ACGME Approved/Offered Positions:* 3
Program ID: 407-48-21-036

San Antonio

University of Texas Health Science Center at San Antonio Program
Sponsor: University of Texas School of Medicine at San
Antonio
Audie L Murphy Memorial Veterans Hospital (San
Antonio)
University of Texas Health Science Center
Prgm Director: Jeffrey A Cordes, MD
7703 Floyd Curl Drive
Mail Code 7792
San Antonio, TX 78229
Tel: 210 567-5430 *Fax:* 210 567-0817
Length: 1 Yr *ACGME Approved/Offered Positions:* 2
Program ID: 407-48-21-060

Virginia

Charlottesville

University of Virginia Program
Sponsor: University of Virginia Medical Center
Prgm Director: Suzanne Holroyd, MD
PO Box 800623
Charlottesville, VA 22901
Tel: 434 924-2241 *Fax:* 434 924-5149
Length: 1 Yr *ACGME Approved/Offered Positions:* 3
Program ID: 407-51-21-043

Roanoke

Carilion Clinic Program
Sponsor: Carilion Clinic
Veterans Affairs Medical Center (Salem)
Prgm Director: David Trinkle, MD
PO Box 13367
Roanoke, VA 24033
Tel: 540 981-7653 *Fax:* 540 981-7469
E-mail: dtrinkle@carilion.com
Length: 1 Yr *ACGME Approved/Offered Positions:* 2
Program ID: 407-51-12-055

Washington

Seattle

University of Washington Program
Sponsor: University of Washington School of Medicine
Harborview Medical Center
University of Washington Medical Center
VA Puget Sound Health Care System
Prgm Director: Marcella Pascualy, MD
Mental Health Service (S-116-MHS)
1660 South Columbian Way
Seattle, WA 98108
Tel: 206 277-1843 *Fax:* 206 764-2573
E-mail: marcella.pascualy@med.va.gov
Length: 1 Yr *ACGME Approved/Offered Positions:* 3
Program ID: 407-54-21-037

Wisconsin

Madison

University of Wisconsin Program
Sponsor: University of Wisconsin Hospital and Clinics
Mendota Mental Health Institute
William S Middleton Veterans Hospital
Prgm Director: Timothy Howell, MD, MA
Mental Health Clinic 2A
2500 Overlook Terrace
Madison, WI 53705
Tel: 608 280-7084 *Fax:* 608 280-7204
Length: 1 Yr *ACGME Approved/Offered Positions:* 2
Program ID: 407-56-21-039

Milwaukee

Medical College of Wisconsin Affiliated Hospitals Program
Sponsor: Medical College of Wisconsin Affiliated
Hospitals, Inc
Clement J Zablocki Veterans Affairs Medical Center
Froedtert Memorial Lutheran Hospital
Rogers Memorial Hospital
Village at Manor Park Continuing Care Retirement
Community
Prgm Director: Harold Harsch, MD
Department of Psychiatry and Behavioral Medicine
8701 W Watertown Plank Road
Milwaukee, WI 53226
Tel: 414 955-7240 *Fax:* 414 955-6299
Length: 1 Yr *ACGME Approved/Offered Positions:* 2
Program ID: 407-56-31-073

Hand Surgery (General Surgery)

Kentucky

Louisville

University of Louisville Program
Sponsor: University of Louisville School of Medicine
Jewish Hospital
University of Louisville Hospital
Veterans Affairs Medical Center (Louisville)
Prgm Director: Thomas W Wolff, MD
225 Abraham Flexner Way
Suite 850
Louisville, KY 40202
Tel: 502 562-0312 *Fax:* 502 562-0326
E-mail: lthompson@cmki.org
Length: 1 Yr *ACGME Approved/Offered Positions:* 8
Program ID: 443-20-21-003

Note: * indicates a newly appointed program director

Hand Surgery (Orthopaedic Surgery)

Alabama

Birmingham

University of Alabama Medical Center Program

Sponsor: University of Alabama Hospital
Brookwood Medical Center
University of Alabama at Birmingham/Highlands
Prgm Director: Thomas R Hunt III, MD
510 20th Street South, FOT 930
Birmingham, AL 35294
Tel: 205 930-8494   *Fax:* 205 930-8569
E-mail: vicki.allen@ortho.uab.edu
Length: 1 Yr   *ACGME Approved/Offered Positions:* 3
Program ID: 263-01-20-018

Arkansas

Little Rock

University of Arkansas for Medical Sciences Program

Sponsor: University of Arkansas College of Medicine
Arkansas Children's Hospital
Central Arkansas Veterans Healthcare System
UAMS Medical Center
Prgm Director: Robert M Lumsden II, MD*
Department of Orthopaedic Surgery/Hand Surgery
4301 W Markham St, Slot 531
Little Rock, AR 72205
Tel: 501 686-5595   *Fax:* 501 686-7824
Length: 1 Yr   *ACGME Approved/Offered Positions:* 1
Program ID: 263-04-21-064

California

Los Angeles

UCLA Medical Center Program

Sponsor: UCLA David Geffen School of Medicine/UCLA Medical Center
Olive View/UCLA Medical Center
Santa Monica-UCLA Medical Center
Shriners Hospitals for Children (Los Angeles)
UCLA Medical Center
Prgm Director: Prosper Benhaim, MD*
Box 956902 Room 76-143 CHS
10833 Le Conte Avenue
Los Angeles, CA 90095
Tel: 310 206-4468   *Fax:* 310 206-0063
E-mail: pbenhaim@mednet.ucla.edu
Length: 1 Yr   *ACGME Approved/Offered Positions:* 2
Program ID: 263-05-21-014

University of Southern California/ LAC+USC Medical Center Program

Sponsor: University of Southern California/LAC+USC Medical Center
LAC+USC Medical Center
USC University Hospital
Prgm Director: Stephen B Schnall, MD
1200 North State Street, GNH 3900
Dept of Orthopaedic Surgery
Los Angeles, CA 90033
Tel: 323 226-7204   *Fax:* 323 226-8205
Length: 1 Yr   *ACGME Approved/Offered Positions:* 2
Program ID: 263-05-21-039

Orange

University of California Irvine/ Kaiser Permanente Southern California (Orange County) Program

Sponsor: University of California (Irvine) Medical Center
Kaiser Foundation Hospitals (Anaheim)
Kaiser Permanente Southern California
Prgm Director: Neil F Jones, MD
101 The City Drive South
Pavilion 3, 2nd Floor
Orange, CA 92868
Tel: 714 456-5759   *Fax:* 714 456-7547
Length: 1 Yr   *ACGME Approved/Offered Positions:* 2
Program ID: 263-05-12-075

Sacramento

University of California (Davis) Health System Program

Sponsor: University of California (Davis) Health System
University of California (Davis) Medical Center
Prgm Director: Robert M Szabo, MD, MPH
Department of Orthopaedics
4860 Y Street, Suite 3800
Sacramento, CA 95817
Tel: 916 734-3678   *Fax:* 916 734-7904
E-mail: barbara.petitt@ucdmc.ucdavis.edu
Length: 1 Yr   *ACGME Approved/Offered Positions:* 1
Program ID: 263-05-21-023

San Diego

University of California (San Diego) Program

Sponsor: University of California (San Diego) Medical Center
Veterans Affairs Medical Center (San Diego)
Prgm Director: Matthew J Meunier, MD
200 West Arbor Drive, #8894
San Diego, CA 92103
Tel: 619 543-5555   *Fax:* 619 543-2540
E-mail: mmeunier@ucsd.edu
Length: 1 Yr   *ACGME Approved/Offered Positions:* 1
Program ID: 263-05-31-024

San Francisco

University of California (San Francisco) Program

Sponsor: University of California (San Francisco) School of Medicine
San Francisco General Hospital Medical Center
Shriners Hospitals for Children (Sacramento)
UCSF and Mount Zion Medical Centers
Prgm Director: Lisa L Lattanza, MD
500 Parnassus Ave MU-320W
San Francisco, CA 94143
Tel: 415 476-6043   *Fax:* 415 476-1304
E-mail: lattanza@orthosurg.ucsf.edu
Length: 1 Yr   *ACGME Approved/Offered Positions:* 1
Program ID: 263-05-21-019

Stanford

Stanford University Program

Sponsor: Stanford Hospital and Clinics
Lucile Salter Packard Children's Hospital at Stanford
Veterans Affairs Palo Alto Health Care System
Prgm Director: Amy L Ladd, MD
770 Welch Road
Suite 400
Palo Alto, CA 94304
Tel: 650 723-6796   *Fax:* 650 723-6786
E-mail: pam.rawls@stanford.edu
Length: 1 Yr   *ACGME Approved/Offered Positions:* 2
Program ID: 263-05-31-054

Colorado

Aurora

University of Colorado Denver Program

Sponsor: University of Colorado Denver School of Medicine
Children's Hospital (The)
Denver Health Medical Center
University of Colorado Hospital
Veterans Affairs Medical Center (Denver)
Prgm Director: Frank A Scott, MD
4200 East Ninth Avenue, B-202
Denver, CO 80262
Tel: 303 724-2961   *Fax:* 303 724-2978
Length: 1 Yr   *ACGME Approved/Offered Positions:* 2
Program ID: 263-07-21-076

Connecticut

Farmington

University of Connecticut Program

Sponsor: University of Connecticut School of Medicine
Connecticut Children's Medical Center
Hartford Hospital
Hartford Surgery Center, LLC
Prgm Director: H Kirk Watson, MD
85 Seymour Street, Suite 816
Hartford, CT 06106
Tel: 860 527-7161   *Fax:* 860 251-6128
E-mail: hkwatson01@aol.com
Length: 1 Yr   *ACGME Approved/Offered Positions:* 2
Program ID: 263-08-21-030

Florida

Gainesville

University of Florida Program

Sponsor: University of Florida College of Medicine
Shands Hospital at the University of Florida
Prgm Director: Paul C Dell, MD
Orthopaedic and Sports Med Institute
PO Box 112727
Gainesville, FL 32611
Tel: 352 273-7374   *Fax:* 352 273-7388
E-mail: dellpc@ortho.ufl.edu
Length: 1 Yr   *ACGME Approved/Offered Positions:* 2
Program ID: 263-11-21-011

Miami

Jackson Memorial Hospital/Jackson Health System Program

Sponsor: Jackson Memorial Hospital/Jackson Health System
Bascom Palmer Eye Institute-Anne Bates Leach Eye Hospital
Miami Children's Hospital
Veterans Affairs Medical Center (Miami)
Prgm Director: Anne E Ouellette, MD, MBA
Department of Orthopaedics (D-27)
1611 NW 12th Avenue, Suite 303
Miami, FL 33136
Tel: 305 326-6590   *Fax:* 305 326-6585
E-mail: eouellette@thehandplace.com
Length: 1 Yr   *ACGME Approved/Offered Positions:* 2
Program ID: 263-11-21-013

Programs

Illinois

Chicago

University of Chicago Program
Sponsor: University of Chicago Medical Center
Prgm Director: Daniel P Mass, MD
5841 South Maryland Ave, MC3079
Chicago, IL 60637
Tel: 773 702-6306   *Fax:* 773 702-4378
Length: 1 Yr   *ACGME Approved/Offered Positions:* 1
Program ID: 263-16-21-035

Indiana

Indianapolis

Indiana University School of Medicine Program
Sponsor: Indiana University School of Medicine
Clarian Indiana University Hospital
Indiana Hand Center
Richard L Roudebush Veterans Affairs Medical Center
St Vincent Hospitals and Health Care Center
William N Wishard Memorial Hospital
Prgm Director: Jeffrey A Greenberg, MD, MS
8501 Harcourt Road
PO Box 80434
Indianapolis, IN 46280
Tel: 317 471-4328   *Fax:* 317 872-1595
Length: 1 Yr   *ACGME Approved/Offered Positions:* 6
Program ID: 263-17-21-041

Iowa

Iowa City

University of Iowa Hospitals and Clinics Program
Sponsor: University of Iowa Hospitals and Clinics
Prgm Director: Brian D Adams, MD
Orthopedic Surgery
200 Hawkins Dr
Iowa City, IA 52242
Tel: 319 353-6222   *Fax:* 319 353-6754
Length: 1 Yr   *ACGME Approved/Offered Positions:* 1
Program ID: 263-18-21-009

Maryland

Baltimore

Union Memorial Hospital Program
Sponsor: Union Memorial Hospital
Prgm Director: Thomas J Graham, MD
The Curtis National Hand Center
3333 North Calvert Street
Baltimore, MD 21218
Tel: 410 554-6593   *Fax:* 410 554-4363
E-mail: tori.wilson@medstar.net
Length: 1 Yr   *ACGME Approved/Offered Positions:* 4
Program ID: 263-23-12-069

Bethesda

National Capital Consortium (Walter Reed) Program
Sponsor: National Capital Consortium
Union Memorial Hospital
Walter Reed Army Medical Center
Prgm Director: Martin F Baechler, MD
Department of Orthopaedics and Rehabilitation
Orthopaedic Surgery Service, 5B25
Washington, DC 20307
Tel: 202 782-5852   *Fax:* 202 782-6845
E-mail: Martin.baechler@us.army.mil
Length: 1 Yr   *ACGME Approved/Offered Positions:* 2
Program ID: 263-10-21-056
Uniformed Services Program

Massachusetts

Boston

Beth Israel Deaconess Medical Center/Harvard Medical School Program
Sponsor: Beth Israel Deaconess Medical Center
Children's Hospital
Prgm Director: Charles S Day, MD
Department of Orthopaedic Surgery
330 Brookline Avenue, Stoneman 10th Fl
Boston, MA 02215
Tel: 617 667-2140   *Fax:* 617 667-2155
Length: 1 Yr   *ACGME Approved/Offered Positions:* 1
Program ID: 263-24-21-072

Brigham and Women's Hospital/Harvard Medical School Program
Sponsor: Brigham and Women's Hospital
Boston VA Healthcare System (Brockton-West Roxbury)
Children's Hospital
Faulkner Hospital
Massachusetts General Hospital
Prgm Director: Barry P Simmons, MD
75 Francis Street
Boston, MA 02115
Tel: 617 732-8550   *Fax:* 617 732-6937
Length: 1 Yr   *ACGME Approved/Offered Positions:* 3
Program ID: 263-24-21-034

Massachusetts General Hospital/Harvard Medical School Program
Sponsor: Massachusetts General Hospital
Prgm Director: Sang-Gil Lee, MD
101 Merrimac Street 2nd Fl
Boston, MA 02114
Tel: 617 726-3822
Length: 1 Yr   *ACGME Approved/Offered Positions:* 4
Program ID: 263-24-21-057

Tufts Medical Center Program
Sponsor: Tufts Medical Center
New England Baptist Hospital
Prgm Director: Charles Cassidy, MD
Department of Orthopaedics, Box 26
800 Washington Street
Boston, MA 02111
Tel: 617 636-0592   *Fax:* 617 636-5178
E-mail: jdolph@tuftsmedicalcenter.org
Length: 1 Yr   *ACGME Approved/Offered Positions:* 2
Program ID: 263-24-21-029

Worcester

University of Massachusetts Program
Sponsor: University of Massachusetts Medical School
UMass Memorial Health Care (Hahnemann Campus)
Prgm Director: Marci Jones, MD
Hahnemann Campus
281 Lincoln Street
Worcester, MA 01605
Tel: 508 334-5183   *Fax:* 508 334-5151
E-mail: michelle.auger@umassmed.edu
Length: 1 Yr   *ACGME Approved/Offered Positions:* 2
Program ID: 263-24-31-065

Minnesota

Minneapolis

University of Minnesota Program
Sponsor: University of Minnesota Medical School
Gillette Children's Hospital
Hennepin County Medical Center
TRIA Orthopaedic Center
University of Minnesota Medical Center, Division of Fairview
Veterans Affairs Medical Center (Minneapolis)
Prgm Director: Matthew D Putnam, MD
2450 Riverside Avenue
Room R200
Minneapolis, MN 55454
Tel: 612 273-1177   *Fax:* 612 273-7959
Length: 1 Yr   *ACGME Approved/Offered Positions:* 2
Program ID: 263-26-21-037

Rochester

College of Medicine, Mayo Clinic (Rochester) Program
Sponsor: College of Medicine, Mayo Clinic
Mayo Clinic (Rochester)
Rochester Methodist Hospital
Saint Marys Hospital of Rochester
Prgm Director: Richard A Berger, MD, PhD
200 First Street, SW
Rochester, MN 55905
Tel: 507 284-3316   *Fax:* 507 266-4234
E-mail: Price.Natalie@mayo.edu
Length: 1 Yr   *ACGME Approved/Offered Positions:* 5
Program ID: 263-26-21-007

Mississippi

Jackson

University of Mississippi Medical Center Program
Sponsor: University of Mississippi School of Medicine
University Hospitals and Clinics
Veterans Affairs Medical Center (Jackson)
Prgm Director: William B Geissler, MD
2500 N State Street
Jackson, MS 39216
Tel: 601 984-5153   *Fax:* 601 984-5151
Length: 1 Yr   *ACGME Approved/Offered Positions:* 1
Program ID: 263-27-21-032

Note: * indicates a newly appointed program director

Missouri

St Louis

Washington University/B-JH/SLCH Consortium Program
Sponsor: Washington University/B-JH/SLCH Consortium
Barnes-Jewish Hospital
Prgm Director: Martin I Boyer, MD
Campus Box 8233
660 South Euclid Avenue
St Louis, MO 63110
Tel: 314 747-2813   *Fax:* 314 747-2643
E-mail: orthsurg@wudosis.wustl.edu
Length: 1 Yr   *ACGME Approved/Offered Positions:* 2
Program ID: 263-28-21-003

New Jersey

Newark

UMDNJ-New Jersey Medical School Program
Sponsor: UMDNJ-New Jersey Medical School
UMDNJ-University Hospital
Prgm Director: Virak Tan, MD
90 Bergen Street
DOC Suite 7300
Newark, NJ 07103
Tel: 973 972-0763   *Fax:* 973 972-1080
E-mail: birthwma@umdnj.edu
Length: 1 Yr   *ACGME Approved/Offered Positions:* 1
Program ID: 263-33-13-070

New Mexico

Albuquerque

University of New Mexico Program
Sponsor: University of New Mexico School of Medicine
University of New Mexico Hospital
Prgm Director: Moheb S Moneim, MD
MSC10 5600
1 University of New Mexico
Albuquerque, NM 87131
Tel: 505 272-4107   *Fax:* 505 272-8098
E-mail: jroberts@salud.unm.edu
Length: 1 Yr   *ACGME Approved/Offered Positions:* 2
Program ID: 263-34-21-027

New York

Buffalo

University at Buffalo Program
Sponsor: University at Buffalo School of Medicine
Erie County Medical Center
Kaleida Health System (Millard Fillmore Hospital)
Prgm Director: Owen J Moy, MD
Kaleida Health-Millard Fillmore
3 Gates Circle
Buffalo, NY 14209
Tel: 716 887-4040   *Fax:* 716 887-5090
Length: 1 Yr   *ACGME Approved/Offered Positions:* 3
Program ID: 263-35-21-012

New York

Albert Einstein College of Medicine at Beth Israel Medical Center Program
Sponsor: Beth Israel Medical Center
Prgm Director: Charles P Melone Jr, MD
321 East 34th Street
New York, NY 10016
Tel: 212 340-0000   *Fax:* 212 340-0038
Length: 1 Yr   *ACGME Approved/Offered Positions:* 1
Program ID: 263-35-12-066

Hospital for Special Surgery/Cornell Medical Center Program
Sponsor: Hospital for Special Surgery
Prgm Director: Scott W Wolfe, MD
535 East 70th Street
New York, NY 10021
Tel: 212 606-1466   *Fax:* 212 606-1477
E-mail: academictraining@hss.edu
Length: 1 Yr   *ACGME Approved/Offered Positions:* 3
Program ID: 263-35-21-017

Mount Sinai School of Medicine Program
Sponsor: Mount Sinai School of Medicine
Bellevue Hospital Center
NYU Hospitals Center
Prgm Director: Michael Hausman, MD
5 E 98th Street, Box 1188
Attn: Program Coordinator/Amanda Mercado
New York, NY 10029
Tel: 212 241-1621   *Fax:* 212 241-9429
E-mail: Amanda.Mercado@mountsinai.org
Length: 1 Yr   *ACGME Approved/Offered Positions:* 1
Program ID: 263-35-22-068

New York Presbyterian Hospital (Columbia Campus) Program
Sponsor: New York Presbyterian Hospital
New York Presbyterian Hospital (Columbia Campus)
Prgm Director: Melvin P Rosenwasser, MD
622 West 168th Street
11th floor
New York, NY 10032
Tel: 212 305-8036
E-mail: lf120@columbia.edu
Length: 1 Yr   *ACGME Approved/Offered Positions:* 1
Program ID: 263-35-31-008

New York University School of Medicine/Hospital for Joint Diseases Program
Sponsor: New York University School of Medicine
Bellevue Hospital Center
Elmhurst Hospital Center-Mount Sinai Services
Jamaica Hospital Medical Center
NYU Hospital for Joint Diseases
Prgm Director: Martin A Posner, MD
301 East 17th Street
Room 1402
New York, NY 10003
Tel: 212 348-6644   *Fax:* 212 369-4742
Length: 1 Yr   *ACGME Approved/Offered Positions:* 3
Program ID: 263-35-21-047

St Luke's-Roosevelt Hospital Center Program
Sponsor: St Luke's-Roosevelt Hospital Center
Prgm Director: Steven Z Glickel, MD
1000 Tenth Avenue
New York, NY 10019
Tel: 212 523-7590   *Fax:* 212 523-5579
Length: 1 Yr   *ACGME Approved/Offered Positions:* 2
Program ID: 263-35-21-055

Rochester

University of Rochester Program
Sponsor: Strong Memorial Hospital of the University of Rochester
Prgm Director: Richard J Miller, MD
Department of Orthopaedics
601 Elmwood Avenue, Box 665
Rochester, NY 14642
Tel: 585 275-7983   *Fax:* 585 273-3297
Length: 1 Yr   *ACGME Approved/Offered Positions:* 1
Program ID: 263-35-21-010

Stony Brook

SUNY at Stony Brook Program
Sponsor: University Hospital - SUNY at Stony Brook
Prgm Director: Lawrence C Hurst, MD
SUNY Stony Brook HSC T18-020
Stony Brook, NY 11794
Tel: 631 444-3145
E-mail: lmerill@notes.cc.sunysb.edu
Length: 1 Yr   *ACGME Approved/Offered Positions:* 2
Program ID: 263-35-31-026

Syracuse

SUNY Upstate Medical University Program
Sponsor: SUNY Upstate Medical University
Crouse Hospital
Prgm Director: Brian J Harley, MD
550 Harrison Street
Suite 128
Syracuse, NY 13202
Tel: 315 464-8632   *Fax:* 315 464-5222
Length: 1 Yr   *ACGME Approved/Offered Positions:* 2
Program ID: 263-35-21-021

North Carolina

Durham

Duke University Hospital Program
Sponsor: Duke University Hospital
Prgm Director: David S Ruch, MD
Division of Orthopaedic Surgery
Box 3466
Durham, NC 27710
Tel: 919 684-3170   *Fax:* 919 681-7672
E-mail: wendy.thompson@duke.edu
Length: 1 Yr   *ACGME Approved/Offered Positions:* 3
Program ID: 263-36-21-022

Winston-Salem

Wake Forest University School of Medicine Program
Sponsor: Wake Forest University Baptist Medical Center
Prgm Director: L Andrew Koman, MD
Medical Center Boulevard, #1070
Winston-Salem, NC 27517
Tel: 336 716-2878
E-mail: hermance@wfubmc.edu
Length: 1 Yr   *ACGME Approved/Offered Positions:* 2
Program ID: 263-36-21-060

Ohio

Cincinnati

University Hospital/University of Cincinnati College of Medicine Program

Sponsor: University Hospital Inc
Prgm Director: Peter J Stern, MD
538 Oak Street
Suite 200
Cincinnati, OH 45219
Tel: 513 961-4263 *Fax:* 513 699-1435
Length: 1 Yr *ACGME Approved/Offered Positions:* 3
Program ID: 263-38-21-015

Cleveland

Cleveland Clinic Foundation Program

Sponsor: Cleveland Clinic Foundation
MetroHealth Medical Center
Prgm Director: Peter J Evans, MD, PhD
Department of Orthopaedic Surgery / A40
The Cleveland Clinic Foundation, 9500 Euclid Avenue
Cleveland, OH 44195
Tel: 216 444-7973 *Fax:* 216 445-3694
E-mail: evansp2@ccf.org
Length: 1 Yr *ACGME Approved/Offered Positions:* 3
Program ID: 263-38-21-045

Oklahoma

Oklahoma City

Integris Baptist Medical Center Program

Sponsor: Integris Baptist Medical Center
OU Medical Center
Prgm Director: Ghazi M Rayan, MD
Graduate Medical Education
3300 Northwest Expressway, Room 100-4394
Oklahoma City, OK 73112
Tel: 405 945-4888 *Fax:* 405 552-5102
E-mail: annette.kezbers@integrisok.com
Length: 1 Yr *ACGME Approved/Offered Positions:* 2
Program ID: 263-39-21-049

Pennsylvania

Erie

Hamot Medical Center Program

Sponsor: Hamot Medical Center
Shriners Hospitals for Children (Erie)
Prgm Director: John D Lubahn, MD
201 State Street
Erie, PA 16550
Tel: 814 877-6257 *Fax:* 814 877-4010
E-mail: pat.rogers@hamot.org
Length: 1 Yr *ACGME Approved/Offered Positions:* 1
Program ID: 263-41-13-073

Philadelphia

Thomas Jefferson University Program

Sponsor: Thomas Jefferson University Hospital
Shriners Hospitals for Children (Philadelphia)
Prgm Director: A Lee Osterman, MD
700 S Henderson Road
Suite 200
King of Prussia, PA 19078
Tel: 610 768-4467 *Fax:* 610 768-4469
E-mail: ALOsterman@HandCenters.com
Length: 1 Yr *ACGME Approved/Offered Positions:* 6
Program ID: 263-41-21-001

University of Pennsylvania Program

Sponsor: University of Pennsylvania Health System
Presbyterian Medical Center (UPHS)
Prgm Director: David R Steinberg, MD
3400 Spruce Street, 2 Silverstein
Philadelphia, PA 19104
Tel: 215 662-3344 *Fax:* 215 349-5128
Length: 1 Yr *ACGME Approved/Offered Positions:* 1
Program ID: 263-41-21-004

Pittsburgh

Allegheny General Hospital Program

Sponsor: Allegheny General Hospital
Prgm Director: Mark E Baratz, MD
1307 Federal Street
Pittsburgh, PA 15212
Tel: 412 359-6501 *Fax:* 412 359-6265
Length: 1 Yr *ACGME Approved/Offered Positions:* 3
Program ID: 263-41-21-031

University of Pittsburgh Medical Center Medical Education Program

Sponsor: Univ of Pittsburgh Medical Center Medical Education
Children's Hospital of Pittsburgh of UPMC
Hand and UpperEx Center (Wexford Office)
Jefferson Regional Medical Center
UPMC Presbyterian Shadyside
Prgm Director: Joseph E Imbriglia, MD
Clinical Office
6001 Stonewood Drive, 2nd Floor
Wexford, PA 15090
Tel: 724 933-3850 *Fax:* 724 933-3861
E-mail: dbuyna@handupperex.com
Length: 1 Yr *ACGME Approved/Offered Positions:* 6
Program ID: 263-41-21-051

Rhode Island

Providence

Brown University Program

Sponsor: Rhode Island Hospital-Lifespan
Prgm Director: Edward Akelman, MD
2 Dudley Street, Suite 200
Providence, RI 02905
Tel: 401 457-2190 *Fax:* 401 457-2191
Length: 1 Yr *ACGME Approved/Offered Positions:* 2
Program ID: 263-43-21-028

Tennessee

Nashville

Vanderbilt University Program

Sponsor: Vanderbilt University Medical Center
Prgm Director: Donald H Lee, MD
Medical Center East, South Tower
Room 3200
Nashville, TN 37232
Tel: 615 322-4683
E-mail: karen.shelton@Vanderbilt.ddu
Length: 1 Yr *ACGME Approved/Offered Positions:* 1
Program ID: 263-47-12-071

Texas

Houston

Baylor College of Medicine Program

Sponsor: Baylor College of Medicine
Harris County Hospital District-Ben Taub General Hospital
Michael E DeBakey VA Medical Center - Houston
St Luke's Episcopal Hospital
Texas Orthopedic Hospital (Houston)
Prgm Director: Michael J Epstein, MD
Department of Orthopaedic Surgery
1709 Dryden Road, 12th Floor
Houston, TX 77030
Tel: 713 986-7390 *Fax:* 713 986-7391
E-mail: desig@bcm.edu
Length: 1 Yr *ACGME Approved/Offered Positions:* 2
Program ID: 263-48-31-002

San Antonio

University of Texas Health Science Center at San Antonio Program

Sponsor: University of Texas School of Medicine at San Antonio
Baptist Memorial Healthcare System
Center for Special Surgery at the Texas Center for Athletes
Methodist Healthcare
St Luke's Baptist Hospital
The Hand Center (San Antonio)
Prgm Director: William C Pederson, MD
21 Spurs Lane, Suite 310
San Antonio, TX 78240
Tel: 210 558-7025 *Fax:* 210 558-4664
E-mail: carlawaller@yahoo.com
Length: 1 Yr *ACGME Approved/Offered Positions:* 4
Program ID: 263-48-21-025

Utah

Salt Lake City

University of Utah Program

Sponsor: University of Utah Medical Center
Prgm Director: Douglas T Hutchinson, MD
590 Wakara Way
Salt Lake City, UT 84108
Tel: 801 587-5453 *Fax:* 801 587-5411
Length: 1 Yr *ACGME Approved/Offered Positions:* 2
Program ID: 263-49-21-048

Washington

Seattle

University of Washington Program

Sponsor: University of Washington School of Medicine
Harborview Medical Center
Seattle Children's Hospital
University of Washington Medical Center
Prgm Director: Thomas E Trumble, MD
4245 NE Roosevelt Way
Box 354743
Seattle, WA 98105
Tel: 206 598-1879 *Fax:* 206 598-9979
E-mail: tnm3@u.washington.edu
Length: 1 Yr *ACGME Approved/Offered Positions:* 4
Program ID: 263-54-21-033

Note: * indicates a newly appointed program director

Wisconsin

Milwaukee

Medical College of Wisconsin Affiliated Hospitals Program

Sponsor: Medical College of Wisconsin Affiliated Hospitals, Inc
Blount Orthopaedic Clinic Ltd
Children's Hospital of Wisconsin
Columbia St Mary's Hospitals
Froedtert Memorial Lutheran Hospital
Orthopaedic Associates of Wisconsin
Waukesha Memorial Hospital
Prgm Director: Roger A Daley, MD, PhD
Department of Orthopaedic Surgery
9200 West Wisconsin Avenue
Milwaukee, WI 53226
Tel: 414 805-7429   *Fax:* 414 805-7499
Length: 1 Yr   *ACGME Approved/Offered Positions:* 1
Program ID: 263-56-31-074

Hand Surgery (Plastic Surgery)

California

Los Angeles

University of Southern California/ LAC+USC Medical Center Program

Sponsor: University of Southern California/LAC+USC Medical Center
LAC+USC Medical Center
Southern California Orthopedic Institute
Prgm Director: Randolph Sherman, MD
1510 San Pablo Street, Suite 415
Los Angeles, CA 90033
Tel: 323 442-6482   *Fax:* 323 442-6481
Length: 1 Yr   *ACGME Approved/Offered Positions:* 2
Program ID: 363-05-21-014

San Francisco

California Pacific Medical Center/University of California (San Francisco) Program

Sponsor: California Pacific Medical Center
Prgm Director: Gregory M Buncke, MD
45 Castro Street, Suite 121
San Francisco, CA 94114
Tel: 415 565-6136   *Fax:* 415 864-1654
Length: 1 Yr   *ACGME Approved/Offered Positions:* 2
Program ID: 363-05-31-017

Connecticut

New Haven

Yale-New Haven Medical Center Program

Sponsor: Yale-New Haven Hospital
Prgm Director: J Grant Thomson, MD
PO Box 208041
New Haven, CT 06520
Tel: 203 737-5130   *Fax:* 203 785-5714
E-mail: grant.thomson@yale.edu
Length: 1 Yr   *ACGME Approved/Offered Positions:* 1
Program ID: 363-08-31-027

Illinois

Springfield

Southern Illinois University Program

Sponsor: Southern Illinois University School of Medicine
Memorial Medical Center
St John's Hospital
Prgm Director: Michael W Neumeister, MD
PO Box 19653
Springfield, IL 62794
Tel: 217 545-7018   *Fax:* 217 545-2588
Length: 1 Yr   *ACGME Approved/Offered Positions:* 1
Program ID: 363-16-21-023

Massachusetts

Boston

Beth Israel Deaconess Medical Center/Harvard Medical School Program

Sponsor: Beth Israel Deaconess Medical Center
Children's Hospital
Shriners Hospitals for Children (Boston)
Prgm Director: Joseph Upton, MD
830 Boylston Street, Suite 212
Chestnut Hill, MA 02167
Tel: 617 739-1972   *Fax:* 617 739-6624
E-mail: upton-office@earthlink.net
Length: 1 Yr   *ACGME Approved/Offered Positions:* 1
Program ID: 363-24-31-012

Mississippi

Jackson

University of Mississippi Medical Center Program

Sponsor: University of Mississippi School of Medicine
St Dominic-Jackson Memorial Hospital
University Hospitals and Clinics
Veterans Affairs Medical Center (Jackson)
Prgm Director: Michael F Angel, MD
2500 North State Street
Jackson, MS 39216
Tel: 601 984-5180   *Fax:* 601 984-5183
Length: 1 Yr   *ACGME Approved/Offered Positions:* 1
Program ID: 363-27-13-028

Missouri

St Louis

Washington University/B-JH/SLCH Consortium Program

Sponsor: Washington University/B-JH/SLCH Consortium
Barnes-Jewish Hospital
Prgm Director: Keith E Brandt, MD
660 South Euclid Avenue, 1150 NW Tower
Campus Box 8238
St Louis, MO 63110
Tel: 314 747-0541   *Fax:* 314 362-4536
Length: 1 Yr   *ACGME Approved/Offered Positions:* 2
Program ID: 363-28-21-005

New York

New York

New York University School of Medicine Program

Sponsor: New York University School of Medicine
Bellevue Hospital Center
Mount Sinai Medical Center
NYU Hospitals Center
Prgm Director: David T Chiu, MD
Institute of Reconstructive Plastic Surgery
550 First Avenue
New York, NY 10016
Tel: 212 263-8279   *Fax:* 212 263-3279
Length: 1 Yr   *ACGME Approved/Offered Positions:* 2
Program ID: 363-35-21-010

Programs

Oregon

Portland

Oregon Health & Science University Program

Sponsor: Oregon Health & Science University Hospital
Shriners Hospitals for Children (Portland)
Veterans Affairs Medical Center (Portland)
Prgm Director: Joel S Solomon, MD, PhD
3181 SW Sam Jackson Park Road
Portland, OR 97239
Tel: 503 494-7824   *Fax:* 503 494-0441
E-mail: kotsovos@ohsu.edu
Length: 1 Yr   *ACGME Approved/Offered Positions:* 1
Program ID: 363-40-21-018

Pennsylvania

Pittsburgh

University of Pittsburgh Medical Center Medical Education Program

Sponsor: Univ of Pittsburgh Medical Center Medical
Education
Hand and UpperEx Center (Wexford Office)
UPMC Presbyterian Shadyside
Prgm Director: W P Andrew Lee, MD*
3550 Terrace Street
Scaife Hall, Suite 690
Pittsburgh, PA 15261
Tel: 412 383-8080   *Fax:* 412 383-9053
E-mail: beedlend@upmc.edu
Length: 1 Yr   *ACGME Approved/Offered Positions:* 1
Program ID: 363-41-21-016

Texas

Dallas

University of Texas Southwestern Medical School Program

Sponsor: University of Texas Southwestern Medical
School
Children's Medical Center of Dallas
Dallas County Hospital District-Parkland Memorial
Hospital
Dallas VA Medical Center
University Hospitals St Paul
University Hospitals Zale Lipshy
Prgm Director: Sean Bidic, MD*
Department of Plastic Surgery
1801 Inwood Rd, WA4.224
Dallas, TX 75390
Tel: 214 645-3114   *Fax:* 214 645-3105
E-mail: kaydance.hope@utsouthwestern.edu
Length: 1 Yr   *ACGME Approved/Offered Positions:* 1
Program ID: 363-48-21-004

Houston

Baylor College of Medicine Program

Sponsor: Baylor College of Medicine
Harris County Hospital District-Ben Taub General
Hospital
Michael E DeBakey VA Medical Center - Houston
St Luke's Episcopal Hospital
Texas Children's Hospital
Prgm Director: David T Netscher, MD
Division of Plastic Surgery Education Office
6701 Fannin St, CC 610.00
Houston, TX 77030
Tel: 832 822-3140   *Fax:* 832 825-0175
E-mail: plasticprograms@bcm.tmc.edu
Length: 1 Yr   *ACGME Approved/Offered Positions:* 2
Program ID: 363-48-31-008

Virginia

Charlottesville

University of Virginia Program

Sponsor: University of Virginia Medical Center
Prgm Director: David B Drake, MD
Dept of Plastic Surgery
PO Box 800376
Charlottesville, VA 22908
Tel: 434 924-1234   *Fax:* 434 924-1333
Length: 1 Yr   *ACGME Approved/Offered Positions:* 1
Program ID: 363-51-21-013

Wisconsin

Milwaukee

Medical College of Wisconsin Affiliated Hospitals Program

Sponsor: Medical College of Wisconsin Affiliated
Hospitals, Inc
Children's Hospital of Wisconsin
Froedtert Memorial Lutheran Hospital
Prgm Director: Hani S Matloub, MD
8700 Watertown Plank Road
Milwaukee, WI 53226
Tel: 414 805-5446   *Fax:* 414 259-0901
E-mail: bruening@mcw.edu
Length: 1 Yr   *ACGME Approved/Offered Positions:* 2
Program ID: 363-56-21-007

Hematology (Internal Medicine)

California

Los Angeles

University of Southern California/ LAC+USC Medical Center Program

Sponsor: University of Southern California/LAC+USC
Medical Center
Kenneth Norris Jr Cancer Hospital and Research
Institute
LAC+USC Medical Center
USC University Hospital
Prgm Director: Howard A Liebman, MD, MA
1441 Eastlake Avenue, Rm 3466
Los Angeles, CA 90033
Tel: 323 865-3913   *Fax:* 323 865-0060
E-mail: liebman@usc.edu
Length: 2 Yrs   *ACGME Approved/Offered Positions:* 7
Program ID: 145-05-21-046

Stanford

Stanford University Program

Sponsor: Stanford Hospital and Clinics
Prgm Director: Linda M Boxer, MD, PhD
Department of Medicine/Division of Hematology
CCSR 1145, MC 5151
Stanford, CA 94305
Tel: 650 725-4036   *Fax:* 650 736-0974
E-mail: cmacklin@stanford.edu
Length: 2 Yrs   *ACGME Approved/Offered Positions:* 10
Program ID: 145-05-21-020

Connecticut

New Haven

Yale-New Haven Medical Center Program

Sponsor: Yale-New Haven Hospital
Prgm Director: Bernard G Forget, MD
Hematology Section, WWW 403
333 Cedar Street
New Haven, CT 06520
Tel: 203 785-4144   *Fax:* 203 785-7232
Length: 2 Yrs   *ACGME Approved/Offered Positions:* 6
Program ID: 145-08-21-021

District of Columbia

Washington

Howard University Program

Sponsor: Howard University Hospital
Prgm Director: Anita Aggarwal, DO, PhD*
2041 Georgia Avenue, NW
Washington, DC 20060
Tel: 202 865-1921
E-mail: aaggarwal@howard.edu
Length: 2 Yrs   *ACGME Approved/Offered Positions:* 3
Program ID: 145-10-21-114

Note: * indicates a newly appointed program director

Maryland

Bethesda

National Institutes of Health Clinical Center Program
Sponsor: Clinical Center at the National Institutes of Health
Prgm Director: Charles D Bolan Jr, MD, MS
10 Center Drive MSC 1202
Building 10, CRC Room 4E-5140
Bethesda, MD 20892
Tel: 301 451-7099   *Fax:* 301 594-1290
Length: 2 Yrs   *ACGME Approved/Offered Positions:* 8
Program ID: 145-23-21-177

New York

Buffalo

University at Buffalo Program
Sponsor: University at Buffalo School of Medicine
Erie County Medical Center
Roswell Park Cancer Institute
University at Buffalo Physician Practices (UBPP)
Veterans Affairs Western New York Hospital
Prgm Director: Zale Bernstein, MD
Dept of Hematology
462 Grider Street
Buffalo, NY 14215
Tel: 716 898-3941   *Fax:* 716 898-3279
Length: 2 Yrs   *ACGME Approved/Offered Positions:* 6
Program ID: 145-35-31-008

Puerto Rico

San Juan

San Juan City Hospital Program
Sponsor: San Juan City Hospital
VA Caribbean Healthcare System
Prgm Director: Luis Baez, MD
Department of Medicine
PO Box 21405
Rio Piedras, PR 00928
Tel: 787 758-7348   *Fax:* 787 758-7348
E-mail: sjccop@prtc.net
Length: 2 Yrs   *ACGME Approved/Offered Positions:* 4
Program ID: 145-42-11-086

Wisconsin

Madison

University of Wisconsin Program
Sponsor: University of Wisconsin Hospital and Clinics
Prgm Director: Mark B Juckett, MD
600 Highland Avenue
Room H4/534
Madison, WI 53792
Tel: 608 263-0338   *Fax:* 608 262-1982
E-mail: dsg@medicine.wisc.edu
Length: 2 Yrs   *ACGME Approved/Offered Positions:* 4
Program ID: 145-56-21-109

Hematology (Pathology)

Alabama

Birmingham

University of Alabama Medical Center Program
Sponsor: University of Alabama Hospital
Prgm Director: Vishnu V Reddy, MD
North Pavilion Bldg Rm 3549
1802 6th Ave S
Birmingham, AL 35249
Tel: 205 975-8880   *Fax:* 205 934-4418
E-mail: vreddy@uab.edu
Length: 1 Yr   *ACGME Approved/Offered Positions:* 2
Program ID: 311-01-21-056

Arizona

Tucson

University of Arizona Program
Sponsor: University of Arizona College of Medicine
University Medical Center
Prgm Director: Catherine E Spier, MD
1501 N Campbell Avenue
Tucson, AZ 85724
Tel: 520 626-6830   *Fax:* 520 626-2521
E-mail: cspier@email.arizona.edu
Length: 1 Yr   *ACGME Approved/Offered Positions:* 1
Program ID: 311-03-32-098

Arkansas

Little Rock

University of Arkansas for Medical Sciences Program
Sponsor: University of Arkansas College of Medicine
Central Arkansas Veterans Healthcare System
UAMS Medical Center
Prgm Director: Robert B Lorsbach, MD, PhD
4301 West Markham
Mail Slot 517
Little Rock, AR 72205
Tel: 501 686-8310   *Fax:* 501 603-1479
E-mail: rlorsbach@uams.edu
Length: 1 Yr   *ACGME Approved/Offered Positions:* 1
Program ID: 311-04-21-038

California

Duarte

City of Hope National Medical Center Program
Sponsor: City of Hope National Medical Center
Prgm Director: Karl Gaal, MD
Department of Pathology
1500 East Duarte Road
Duarte, CA 91010
Tel: 626 359-8111   *Fax:* 626 301-8145
Length: 1 Yr   *ACGME Approved/Offered Positions:* 3
Program ID: 311-05-21-040

La Jolla

Scripps Clinic/Scripps Green Hospital Program
Sponsor: Scripps Clinic/Scripps Green Hospital
Prgm Director: Kelly Bethel, MD
10666 N Torrey Pines Road
Mail Code 403C
La Jolla, CA 92037
Tel: 858 554-9733   *Fax:* 858 554-5452
Length: 1 Yr   *ACGME Approved/Offered Positions:* 2
Program ID: 311-05-21-088

Los Angeles

Cedars-Sinai Medical Center Program
Sponsor: Cedars-Sinai Medical Center
Prgm Director: Stephen Lee, MD
8700 Beverly Boulevard
Room 4533
Los Angeles, CA 90048
Tel: 310 423-5471
Length: 1 Yr   *ACGME Approved/Offered Positions:* 2
Program ID: 311-05-21-016

UCLA Medical Center Program
Sponsor: UCLA David Geffen School of Medicine/UCLA Medical Center
UCLA Medical Center
Prgm Director: Linda G Baum, MD, PhD
UCLA Medical Center
10833 Le Conte Avenue
Los Angeles, CA 90095
Tel: 310 206-5985   *Fax:* 310 206-0657
E-mail: lbaum@mednet.ucla.edu
Length: 1 Yr   *ACGME Approved/Offered Positions:* 2
Program ID: 311-05-21-062

University of Southern California/ LAC+USC Medical Center Program
Sponsor: University of Southern California/LAC+USC Medical Center
LAC+USC Medical Center
Prgm Director: Russell K Brynes, MD
USC-Keck School of Medicine
1200 N State Street Rm 2426
Los Angeles, CA 90033
Tel: 323 226-7067   *Fax:* 323 226-2686
E-mail: Brynes@usc.edu
Length: 1 Yr   *ACGME Approved/Offered Positions:* 2
Program ID: 311-05-21-017

Sacramento

University of California (Davis) Health System Program
Sponsor: University of California (Davis) Health System
University of California (Davis) Medical Center
Prgm Director: Denis M Dwyre, MD*
Department of Pathology
4400 V Street, Pathology Building, Suite 1118
Sacramento, CA 95817
Tel: 916 734-2340
Length: 1 Yr   *ACGME Approved/Offered Positions:* 1
Program ID: 311-05-21-009

San Francisco

University of California (San Francisco) Program
Sponsor: University of California (San Francisco) School of Medicine
UCSF and Mount Zion Medical Centers
Prgm Director: Joan E Etzell, MD
505 Parnassus Avenue
Moffitt-Long Hospital, Room M-524, Box 0100
San Francisco, CA 94143
Tel: 415 353-1750   *Fax:* 415 353-1106
E-mail: joan.etzell@ucsf.edu
Length: 1 Yr   *ACGME Approved/Offered Positions:* 2
Program ID: 311-05-21-053

Stanford

Stanford University Program
Sponsor: Stanford Hospital and Clinics
Prgm Director: Daniel A Arber, MD
300 Pasteur Drive, H1507
Stanford, CA 94305
Tel: 650 725-5604
E-mail: darber@stanfordmed.org
Length: 1 Yr *ACGME Approved/Offered Positions:* 4
Program ID: 311-05-21-073

Connecticut

Hartford

Hartford Hospital Program
Sponsor: Hartford Hospital
Prgm Director: William N Rezuke Jr, MD
80 Seymour Street
Hartford, CT 06102
Tel: 860 545-3510   *Fax:* 860 545-2204
E-mail: wrezuke@harthosp.org
Length: 1 Yr *ACGME Approved/Offered Positions:* 1
Program ID: 311-08-11-021

New Haven

Yale-New Haven Medical Center Program
Sponsor: Yale-New Haven Hospital
Veterans Affairs Medical Center (West Haven)
Prgm Director: Brian R Smith, MD
Departments of Laboratory Medicine and Pathology
20 York Street, CB 407, PO Box 208035
New Haven, CT 06504
Tel: 203 688-2286   *Fax:* 203 688-7340
E-mail: june.fisher@yale.edu
Length: 1 Yr *ACGME Approved/Offered Positions:* 2
Program ID: 311-08-13-085

District of Columbia

Washington

Georgetown University Hospital Program
Sponsor: Georgetown University Hospital
Prgm Director: Metin Ozdemirli, MD, PhD
3900 Reservoir Road, NW
Room SW209 Med Dent Building
Washington, DC 20007
Tel: 202 687-6205   *Fax:* 202 687-8935
Length: 1 Yr *ACGME Approved/Offered Positions:* 1
Program ID: 311-10-21-079

Florida

Gainesville

University of Florida Program
Sponsor: University of Florida College of Medicine
Shands Hospital at the University of Florida
Prgm Director: Ying Li, MD, PhD*
PO Box 100275
Gainesville, FL 32610
Tel: 352 265-0111   *Fax:* 352 265-1063
Length: 1 Yr *ACGME Approved/Offered Positions:* 2
Program ID: 311-11-21-051

Miami

Jackson Memorial Hospital/Jackson Health System Program
Sponsor: Jackson Memorial Hospital/Jackson Health System
Prgm Director: Gerald E Byrne Jr, MD
1611 NW 12th Avenue
Miami, FL 33136
Tel: 305 585-7242
Length: 1 Yr *ACGME Approved/Offered Positions:* 1
Program ID: 311-11-31-083

Tampa

University of South Florida Program
Sponsor: University of South Florida College of Medicine
All Children's Hospital
H Lee Moffitt Cancer Center
Prgm Director: Hernani Cualing, MD
MCC 2071
12902 Magnolia Street
Tampa, FL 33612
Tel: 813 745-3914   *Fax:* 813 745-1708
Length: 1 Yr *ACGME Approved/Offered Positions:* 1
Program ID: 311-11-21-103

Georgia

Atlanta

Emory University Program
Sponsor: Emory University School of Medicine
Emory University Hospital
Prgm Director: Shiyong Li, MD, PhD
1364 Clifton Road, NE
Atlanta, GA 30322
Tel: 404 712-5456   *Fax:* 404 712-4140
E-mail: sli2@emory.edu
Length: 1 Yr *ACGME Approved/Offered Positions:* 2
Program ID: 311-12-21-027

Illinois

Chicago

McGaw Medical Center of Northwestern University Program
Sponsor: McGaw Medical Center of Northwestern University
Northwestern Memorial Hospital
Prgm Director: LoAnn C Peterson, MD
Department of Pathology, Feinberg, Pavilion 7-205
251 E Huron Street
Chicago, IL 60611
Tel: 312 926-8504   *Fax:* 312 926-0560
E-mail: loannc@northwestern.edu
Length: 1 Yr *ACGME Approved/Offered Positions:* 2
Program ID: 311-16-21-058

University of Chicago Program
Sponsor: University of Chicago Medical Center
Prgm Director: James W Vardiman, MD
5841 South Maryland Ave, MC0008
Chicago, IL 60637
Tel: 773 702-6196   *Fax:* 773 702-1200
E-mail: james.vardiman@uchospitals.edu
Length: 1 Yr *ACGME Approved/Offered Positions:* 1
Program ID: 311-16-21-037

University of Illinois College of Medicine at Chicago Program
Sponsor: University of Illinois College of Medicine at Chicago
University of Illinois Hospital and Clinics
Prgm Director: Frederick Behm, MD
840 S Wood Street, Room 130 CSN
Chicago, IL 60612
Tel: 312 996-3150   *Fax:* 312 996-7586
E-mail: fredbehm@uic.edu
Length: 1 Yr *ACGME Approved/Offered Positions:* 1
Program ID: 311-16-21-041

Maywood

Loyola University Program
Sponsor: Loyola University Medical Center
Prgm Director: Serhan Alkan, MD
2160 South First Avenue
Maywood, IL 60153
Tel: 708 327-2610   *Fax:* 708 216-8225
E-mail: vbaertschi@lumc.edu
Length: 1 Yr *ACGME Approved/Offered Positions:* 2
Program ID: 311-16-21-018

Indiana

Indianapolis

Indiana University School of Medicine Program
Sponsor: Indiana University School of Medicine
Clarian Pathology Laboratory
Prgm Director: Magdalena Czader, MD, PhD*
Clarian Pathology Laboratory
350 West 11th Street, Room 5028
Indianapolis, IN 46202
Tel: 317 491-6564   *Fax:* 317 491-6114
Length: 1 Yr *ACGME Approved/Offered Positions:* 3
Program ID: 311-17-21-045

Iowa

Iowa City

University of Iowa Hospitals and Clinics Program
Sponsor: University of Iowa Hospitals and Clinics
Prgm Director: Nancy S Rosenthal, MD
200 Hawkins Drive, 6223 RCP
Iowa City, IA 52242
Tel: 319 384-8751   *Fax:* 319 384-8051
Length: 1 Yr *ACGME Approved/Offered Positions:* 2
Program ID: 311-18-21-023

Louisiana

New Orleans

Tulane University Program
Sponsor: Tulane University School of Medicine
Ochsner Clinic Foundation
Tulane University Hospital and Clinics
Prgm Director: John R Krause, MD
1430 Tulane Ave
Room 6519
New Orleans, LA 70112
Tel: 504 988-5210   *Fax:* 504 988-7389
E-mail: bdelucc@tulane.edu
Length: 1 Yr *ACGME Approved/Offered Positions:* 2
Program ID: 311-21-31-076

Note: * indicates a newly appointed program director

Maryland

Baltimore

Johns Hopkins University Program
Sponsor: Johns Hopkins University School of Medicine
Johns Hopkins Hospital
Prgm Director: Michael J Borowitz, MD, PhD
401 N Broadway
2335 Weinberg Building
Baltimore, MD 21231
Tel: 410 614-2889
Length: 1 Yr   *ACGME Approved/Offered Positions:* 2
Program ID: 311-23-21-072

University of Maryland Program
Sponsor: University of Maryland Medical System
Prgm Director: X Frank Zhao, MD, PhD
22 South Greene Street
Baltimore, MD 21201
Tel: 410 328-5555   *Fax:* 410 328-5508
Length: 1 Yr   *ACGME Approved/Offered Positions:* 2
Program ID: 311-23-31-106

Bethesda

National Institutes of Health Clinical Center Program
Sponsor: Clinical Center at the National Institutes of Health
Prgm Director: Stefania Pittaluga, MD, PhD
10 Center Drive, Building 10 Room 2B42
Bethesda, MD 20892
Tel: 301 496-0183   *Fax:* 301 402-2415
Length: 1 Yr   *ACGME Approved/Offered Positions:* 2
Program ID: 311-23-31-087

Massachusetts

Boston

Beth Israel Deaconess Medical Center Program
Sponsor: Beth Israel Deaconess Medical Center
Prgm Director: German A Pihan, MD
330 Brookline Avenue
Boston, MA 02215
Tel: 617 667-3603   *Fax:* 617 667-4533
Length: 1 Yr   *ACGME Approved/Offered Positions:* 2
Program ID: 311-24-21-036

Brigham and Women's Hospital Program
Sponsor: Brigham and Women's Hospital
Children's Hospital
Prgm Director: Geraldine S Pinkus, MD
75 Francis Street
Boston, MA 02115
Tel: 617 732-7520   *Fax:* 617 713-3044
Length: 1 Yr   *ACGME Approved/Offered Positions:* 4
Program ID: 311-24-21-048

Massachusetts General Hospital Program
Sponsor: Massachusetts General Hospital
Prgm Director: Robert P Hasserjian, MD
55 Fruit Street
Warren Building, Second Floor
Boston, MA 02114
Tel: 617 724-1445   *Fax:* 617 726-7474
E-mail: rhasserjian@partners.org
Length: 1 Yr   *ACGME Approved/Offered Positions:* 2
Program ID: 311-24-12-081

Worcester

University of Massachusetts Program
Sponsor: University of Massachusetts Medical School
Prgm Director: Suyang Hao, MD
One Innovation Drive
Biotech Three, Second Floor
Worcester, MA 01605
Tel: 508 793-6176   *Fax:* 508 793-6110
Length: 1 Yr   *ACGME Approved/Offered Positions:* 1
Program ID: 311-24-21-099

Michigan

Ann Arbor

University of Michigan Program
Sponsor: University of Michigan Hospitals and Health Centers
Prgm Director: Megan S Lim, MD, PhD
1301 Catherine Street
M5242 Medical Science Building I
Ann Arbor, MI 48109
Tel: 734 936-1874   *Fax:* 734 936-2756
Length: 1 Yr   *ACGME Approved/Offered Positions:* 2
Program ID: 311-25-21-026

Detroit

Wayne State University/Detroit Medical Center Program
Sponsor: Wayne State University/Detroit Medical Center
Detroit Receiving Hospital and University Health Center
Harper-Hutzel Hospital
Prgm Director: Margarita Palutke, MD
University Laboratories
4201 St Antoine Boulevard
Detroit, MI 48201
Tel: 313 993-0486   *Fax:* 313 993-0489
E-mail: mklein5@dmc.org
Length: 1 Yr   *ACGME Approved/Offered Positions:* 2
Program ID: 311-25-21-082

Royal Oak

William Beaumont Hospital Program
Sponsor: William Beaumont Hospital
Prgm Director: Vonda K Douglas-Nikitin, MD
Department of Clinical Pathology
3601 West Thirteen Mile Road
Royal Oak, MI 48073
Tel: 248 551-2935   *Fax:* 248 551-3694
Length: 1 Yr   *ACGME Approved/Offered Positions:* 2
Program ID: 311-25-21-033

Minnesota

Minneapolis

University of Minnesota Program
Sponsor: University of Minnesota Medical School
University of Minnesota Medical Center, Division of Fairview
Prgm Director: Vanessa Dayton, MD
420 Delaware Street SE
Mayo Mail Code 609
Minneapolis, MN 55455
Tel: 612 273-2166   *Fax:* 612 626-2696
Length: 1 Yr   *ACGME Approved/Offered Positions:* 2
Program ID: 311-26-11-092

Rochester

College of Medicine, Mayo Clinic (Rochester) Program
Sponsor: College of Medicine, Mayo Clinic
Mayo Clinic (Rochester)
Prgm Director: James D Hoyer, MD
200 First Street SW
Rochester, MN 55905
Tel: 507 538-6453
Length: 1 Yr   *ACGME Approved/Offered Positions:* 2
Program ID: 311-26-21-029

Missouri

St Louis

St Louis University School of Medicine Program
Sponsor: St Louis University School of Medicine
St Louis University Hospital
Prgm Director: Leonard E Grosso, MD, PhD
1402 South Grand Boulevard
St Louis, MO 63104
Tel: 314 577-8482   *Fax:* 314 268-5598
Length: 1 Yr   *ACGME Approved/Offered Positions:* 1
Program ID: 311-28-21-074

Washington University/B-JH/SLCH Consortium Program
Sponsor: Washington University/B-JH/SLCH Consortium
Barnes-Jewish Hospital
Prgm Director: Friederike Kreisel, MD
One Barnes Hospital Plaza
St Louis, MO 63110
Tel: 314 362-0346   *Fax:* 314 747-2040
Length: 1 Yr   *ACGME Approved/Offered Positions:* 2
Program ID: 311-28-21-050

Nebraska

Omaha

University of Nebraska Medical Center College of Medicine Program
Sponsor: University of Nebraska Medical Center College of Medicine
Nebraska Medical Center
Prgm Director: Dennis D Weisenburger, MD
Department of Pathology and Microbiology
983135 Nebraska Medical Center
Omaha, NE 68198
Tel: 402 559-7688   *Fax:* 402 559-6018
E-mail: dweisenb@unmc.edu
Length: 1 Yr   *ACGME Approved/Offered Positions:* 3
Program ID: 311-30-21-010

New Hampshire

Lebanon

Dartmouth-Hitchcock Medical Center Program
Sponsor: Mary Hitchcock Memorial Hospital
Prgm Director: Prabhjot Kaur, MD
One Medical Center Drive
Lebanon, NH 03756
Tel: 603 650-7269   *Fax:* 603 650-4845
Length: 1 Yr   *ACGME Approved/Offered Positions:* 1
Program ID: 311-32-12-104

New Jersey

New Brunswick

UMDNJ-Robert Wood Johnson Medical School Program

Sponsor: UMDNJ-Robert Wood Johnson Medical School
Robert Wood Johnson University Hospital
Prgm Director: Lauri Goodell, MD
One Robert Wood Johnson Place
MEB 212
New Brunswick, NJ 08903
Tel: 732 235-8121   *Fax:* 732 235-8124
Length: 1 Yr   *ACGME Approved/Offered Positions:* 1
Program ID: 311-33-21-025

New Mexico

Albuquerque

University of New Mexico Program

Sponsor: University of New Mexico School of Medicine
University of New Mexico Hospital
Prgm Director: Kathryn Foucar, MD
Hematopathology
1001 Woodward Place NE
Albuquerque, NM 87102
Tel: 505 938-8456   *Fax:* 505 938-8414
Length: 1 Yr   *ACGME Approved/Offered Positions:* 4
Program ID: 311-34-21-013

New York

Albany

Albany Medical Center Program

Sponsor: Albany Medical Center
Prgm Director: Tipu Nazeer, MD
Dept of Pathology/Hematopathology, MC 81
47 New Scotland Avenue
Albany, NY 12208
Tel: 518 262-5436   *Fax:* 518 262-5861
E-mail: pathresidency@mail.amc.edu
Length: 1 Yr   *ACGME Approved/Offered Positions:* 1
Program ID: 311-35-31-031

Bronx

Albert Einstein College of Medicine Program

Sponsor: Albert Einstein College of Medicine of Yeshiva University
Montefiore Medical Center-Henry and Lucy Moses Division
Prgm Director: Howard Ratech, MD
111 East 210th Street
Bronx, NY 10467
Tel: 718 920-7782   *Fax:* 718 920-7611
E-mail: hratech@montefiore.org
Length: 1 Yr   *ACGME Approved/Offered Positions:* 2
Program ID: 311-35-31-068

New York

Albert Einstein College of Medicine at Beth Israel Medical Center Program

Sponsor: Beth Israel Medical Center
St Luke's-Roosevelt Hospital Center
Prgm Director: Wen Fan, MD, PhD*
First Avenue at 16th Street
New York, NY 10003
Tel: 212 523-8621   *Fax:* 212 523-4829
Length: 1 Yr   *ACGME Approved/Offered Positions:* 2
Program ID: 311-35-21-006

Memorial Sloan-Kettering Cancer Center Program

Sponsor: Memorial Sloan-Kettering Cancer Center
Prgm Director: Daniel A Filippa, MD
1275 York Avenue
New York, NY 10065
Tel: 212 639-5905   *Fax:* 212 717-3203
Length: 1 Yr   *ACGME Approved/Offered Positions:* 1
Program ID: 311-35-31-102

New York Presbyterian Hospital (Columbia Campus) Program

Sponsor: New York Presbyterian Hospital
New York Presbyterian Hospital (Columbia Campus)
Prgm Director: Bachir Alobeid, MD
630 West 168th Street
Room VC 14-229
New York, NY 10032
Tel: 212 342-0545   *Fax:* 212 305-2301
E-mail: ba2024@columbia.edu
Length: 1 Yr   *ACGME Approved/Offered Positions:* 2
Program ID: 311-35-21-084

New York Presbyterian Hospital (Cornell Campus) Program

Sponsor: New York Presbyterian Hospital
Prgm Director: Amy Chadburn, MD*
525 East 68th Street
New York, NY 10065
Tel: 212 746-2442   *Fax:* 212 746-8173
Length: 1 Yr   *ACGME Approved/Offered Positions:* 2
Program ID: 311-35-21-086

New York University School of Medicine Program

Sponsor: New York University School of Medicine
Bellevue Hospital Center
NYU Hospitals Center
Prgm Director: Sherif Ibrahim, MD, PhD
560 First Avenue
New York, NY 10016
Tel: 212 263-5967   *Fax:* 212 263-7712
Length: 1 Yr   *ACGME Approved/Offered Positions:* 2
Program ID: 311-35-21-060

Rochester

University of Rochester Program

Sponsor: Strong Memorial Hospital of the University of Rochester
Prgm Director: W Richard Burack, MD, PhD
601 Elmwood Avenue, Box 626
Rm 1-6344
Rochester, NY 14642
Tel: 585 273-4580   *Fax:* 585 273-1027
E-mail: betsy_mcdonald@urmc.rochester.edu
Length: 1 Yr   *ACGME Approved/Offered Positions:* 1
Program ID: 311-35-13-105

Syracuse

SUNY Upstate Medical University Program

Sponsor: SUNY Upstate Medical University
Prgm Director: Katalin Banki, MD
750 East Adams Street
Syracuse, NY 13210
Tel: 315 464-6790   *Fax:* 315 464-4675
E-mail: bankik@upstate.edu
Length: 1 Yr   *ACGME Approved/Offered Positions:* 2
Program ID: 311-35-21-030

North Carolina

Chapel Hill

University of North Carolina Hospitals Program

Sponsor: University of North Carolina Hospitals
Prgm Director: Cherie H Dunphy, MD
Department of Pathology and Laboratory Medicine
101 Manning Drive
Chapel Hill, NC 27514
Tel: 919 843-0718   *Fax:* 919 843-0733
Length: 1 Yr   *ACGME Approved/Offered Positions:* 1
Program ID: 311-36-21-032

Durham

Duke University Hospital Program

Sponsor: Duke University Hospital
Veterans Affairs Medical Center (Durham)
Prgm Director: Patrick J Buckley, MD, PhD
Department of Pathology, Erwin Road
Box 3712
Durham, NC 27710
Tel: 919 681-6578   *Fax:* 919 684-1856
Length: 1 Yr   *ACGME Approved/Offered Positions:* 2
Program ID: 311-36-21-055

Winston-Salem

Wake Forest University School of Medicine Program

Sponsor: Wake Forest University Baptist Medical Center
Prgm Director: Michael W Beaty, MD
Medical Center Boulevard
Winston-Salem, NC 27157
Tel: 336 716-7014   *Fax:* 336 716-7595
E-mail: mbeaty@wfubmc.edu
Length: 1 Yr   *ACGME Approved/Offered Positions:* 1
Program ID: 311-36-31-100

Ohio

Cleveland

Cleveland Clinic Foundation Program

Sponsor: Cleveland Clinic Foundation
Prgm Director: Eric D Hsi, MD
9500 Euclid Avenue L11
Cleveland, OH 44195
Tel: 216 444-5230   *Fax:* 216 444-4414
Length: 1 Yr   *ACGME Approved/Offered Positions:* 2
Program ID: 311-38-21-065

University Hospitals Case Medical Center Program

Sponsor: University Hospitals Case Medical Center
Prgm Director: Howard Meyerson, MD
Department of Pathology
11100 Euclid Avenue
Cleveland, OH 44106
Tel: 216 844-1839   *Fax:* 216 844-5601
E-mail: Howard.Meyerson@uhhospitals.org
Length: 1 Yr   *ACGME Approved/Offered Positions:* 1
Program ID: 311-38-21-011

Columbus

Ohio State University Hospital Program

Sponsor: Ohio State University Hospital
Prgm Director: Frederick K Racke, MD, PhD
E-310 Doan Hall
410 West 10th Avenue
Columbus, OH 43210
Tel: 614 366-2467   *Fax:* 614 293-2075
E-mail: Frederick.Racke@osumc.edu
Length: 1 Yr   *ACGME Approved/Offered Positions:* 1
Program ID: 311-38-21-052

Note: * indicates a newly appointed program director

Oregon

Portland

Oregon Health & Science University Program
Sponsor: Oregon Health & Science University Hospital
Prgm Director: Guang Fan, MD, PhD
3181 SW Sam Jackson Park Road
Department of Pathology, L-113
Portland, OR 97201
Tel: 503 494-9439   *Fax:* 503 494-8148
Length: 1 Yr   *ACGME Approved/Offered Positions:* 2
Program ID: 311-40-21-090

Pennsylvania

Philadelphia

Drexel University College of Medicine/Hahnemann University Hospital Program
Sponsor: Drexel University College of
Medicine/Hahnemann University
Hahnemann University Hospital (Tenet Health System)
Prgm Director: J Steve Hou, MD
245 N 15th Street
Philadelphia, PA 19102
Tel: 215 762-1179   *Fax:* 215 762-1051
E-mail: J.Steve.Hou@drexelmed.edu
Length: 1 Yr   *ACGME Approved/Offered Positions:* 1
Program ID: 311-41-11-093

Thomas Jefferson University Program
Sponsor: Thomas Jefferson University Hospital
Prgm Director: William Kocher, MD
111 South 11th Street
Philadelphia, PA 19107
Tel: 215 955-6725   *Fax:* 215 955-2604
E-mail: william.kocher@jefferson.edu
Length: 1 Yr   *ACGME Approved/Offered Positions:* 1
Program ID: 311-41-21-078

University of Pennsylvania Program
Sponsor: University of Pennsylvania Health System
Children's Hospital of Philadelphia
Prgm Director: Mariusz Wasik, MD
Stellar Chance Laboratories
422 Curie Blvd 413B/Stellar Chance Labs
Philadelphia, PA 19104
Tel: 215 662-6530   *Fax:* 215 662-7529
E-mail: nger.ong@uphs.upenn.edu
Length: 1 Yr   *ACGME Approved/Offered Positions:* 2
Program ID: 311-41-21-069

Pittsburgh

University of Pittsburgh Medical Center Medical Education Program
Sponsor: Univ of Pittsburgh Medical Center Medical
Education
UPMC Presbyterian Shadyside
Prgm Director: Steven H Swerdlow, MD
UPMC-Presbyterian, Suite G-300
200 Lothrop Street
Pittsburgh, PA 15213
Tel: 412 647-5191   *Fax:* 412 647-4008
Length: 1 Yr   *ACGME Approved/Offered Positions:* 3
Program ID: 311-41-21-014

South Carolina

Charleston

Medical University of South Carolina Program
Sponsor: Medical University of South Carolina College of
Medicine
MUSC Medical Center
Prgm Director: John Lazarchick, MD
171 Ashley Avenue
Charleston, SC 29425
Tel: 843 792-3424   *Fax:* 843 792-4811
Length: 1 Yr   *ACGME Approved/Offered Positions:* 1
Program ID: 311-45-21-057

Tennessee

Memphis

University of Tennessee Program
Sponsor: University of Tennessee College of Medicine
St Jude Children's Research Hospital
Prgm Director: Nadeem Zafar, MD
930 Madison #500
Memphis, TN 38163
Tel: 901 448-6436   *Fax:* 901 448-6979
Length: 1 Yr   *ACGME Approved/Offered Positions:* 1
Program ID: 311-47-21-108

Nashville

Vanderbilt University Program
Sponsor: Vanderbilt University Medical Center
Veterans Affairs Medical Center (Nashville)
Prgm Director: Thomas L McCurley, MD
1301 Medical Center Drive
4601 TVC
Nashville, TN 37232
Tel: 615 322-0146   *Fax:* 615 343-7961
Length: 1 Yr   *ACGME Approved/Offered Positions:* 2
Program ID: 311-47-21-070

Texas

Dallas

University of Texas Southwestern Medical School Program
Sponsor: University of Texas Southwestern Medical
School
Dallas County Hospital District-Parkland Memorial
Hospital
Prgm Director: Nitin J Karandikar, MD, PhD
Department of Pathology
5323 Harry Hines Blvd
Dallas, TX 75390
Tel: 214 648-1416   *Fax:* 214 648-4070
Length: 1 Yr   *ACGME Approved/Offered Positions:* 2
Program ID: 311-48-21-064

Houston

Baylor College of Medicine Program
Sponsor: Baylor College of Medicine
Harris County Hospital District-Ben Taub General
Hospital
Methodist Hospital (Houston)
Texas Children's Hospital
Prgm Director: Eugenio Banez, MD
Department of Pathology
One Baylor Plaza
Houston, TX 77030
Tel: 713 798-4083   *Fax:* 713 798-3665
E-mail: yboney@bcm.edu
Length: 1 Yr   *ACGME Approved/Offered Positions:* 1
Program ID: 311-48-21-012

Methodist Hospital (Houston) Program
Sponsor: Methodist Hospital (Houston)
University of Texas M D Anderson Cancer Center
Prgm Director: Chung-Che Chang, MD, PhD
6565 Fannin St, MS205
Houston, TX 77030
Tel: 713 441-4458   *Fax:* 713 441-3489
E-mail: ljozwiak@tmhs.org
Length: 1 Yr   *ACGME Approved/Offered Positions:* 2
Program ID: 311-48-23-101

University of Texas M D Anderson Cancer Center Program
Sponsor: University of Texas M D Anderson Cancer
Center
Prgm Director: Jeffrey L Jorgensen, MD, PhD
Dept of Hematopathology - Box 72
1515 Holcombe Boulevard
Houston, TX 77030
Tel: 713 792-8648   *Fax:* 713 792-8438
Length: 1 Yr   *ACGME Approved/Offered Positions:* 5
Program ID: 311-48-21-019

San Antonio

University of Texas Health Science Center at San Antonio Program
Sponsor: University of Texas School of Medicine at San
Antonio
Audie L Murphy Memorial Veterans Hospital (San
Antonio)
University Health System
Prgm Director: Marsha C Kinney, MD
7703 Floyd Curl Drive
Mail Code 7750
San Antonio, TX 78229
Tel: 210 567-6731   *Fax:* 210 567-2478
Length: 1 Yr   *ACGME Approved/Offered Positions:* 2
Program ID: 311-48-21-020

Temple

Texas A&M College of Medicine-Scott and White Program
Sponsor: Scott and White Memorial Hospital
Prgm Director: William Koss, MD
2401 South 31st Street
Temple, TX 76508
Tel: 254 724-5801   *Fax:* 254 724-6329
Length: 1 Yr   *ACGME Approved/Offered Positions:* 2
Program ID: 311-48-21-044

Utah

Salt Lake City

University of Utah Program
Sponsor: University of Utah Medical Center
Prgm Director: Sherrie L Perkins, MD, PhD
500 Chipeta Way-Medical Directors
Salt Lake City, UT 84108
Tel: 801 581-5854
Length: 1 Yr   *ACGME Approved/Offered Positions:* 2
Program ID: 311-49-21-024

Virginia

Charlottesville

University of Virginia Program
Sponsor: University of Virginia Medical Center
Prgm Director: John B Cousar, MD
PO Box 800214
Charlottesville, VA 22908
Tel: 434 924-9752   *Fax:* 434 924-9492
E-mail: jbc4aj@virginia.edu
Length: 1 Yr   *ACGME Approved/Offered Positions:* 1
Program ID: 311-51-21-097

Richmond

Virginia Commonwealth University Health System Program

Sponsor: Virginia Commonwealth University Health System
Medical College of Virginia Hospitals
Prgm Director: Jonathan Ben-Ezra, MD
PO Box 980662
Richmond, VA 23298
Tel: 804 828-0902   *Fax:* 804 828-2812
E-mail: jben-ezra@mcvh-vcu.edu
Length: 1 Yr   *ACGME Approved/Offered Positions:* 2
Program ID: 311-51-13-096

Washington

Seattle

University of Washington Program

Sponsor: University of Washington School of Medicine
Seattle Cancer Care Alliance
University of Washington Medical Center
Prgm Director: Daniel E Sabath, MD, PhD
1959 NE Pacific Street, Box 357110
Seattle, WA 98195
Tel: 206 598-6833   *Fax:* 206 598-6189
E-mail: residency@pathology.washington.edu
Length: 1 Yr   *ACGME Approved/Offered Positions:* 2
Program ID: 311-54-21-067

West Virginia

Morgantown

West Virginia University Program

Sponsor: West Virginia University School of Medicine
West Virginia University Hospitals
Prgm Director: James E Coad, MD
Department of Pathology
Mail Stop 9203
Morgantown, WV 26506
Tel: 304 293-3212   *Fax:* 304 293-1627
E-mail: jcoad@hsc.wvu.edu
Length: 1 Yr   *ACGME Approved/Offered Positions:* 1
Program ID: 311-55-12-107

Wisconsin

Madison

University of Wisconsin Program

Sponsor: University of Wisconsin Hospital and Clinics
Prgm Director: Catherine Leith, MBChB
600 Highland Avenue
Madison, WI 53792
Tel: 608 262-7158   *Fax:* 608 263-1568
E-mail: pathresidency@uwhealth.org
Length: 1 Yr   *ACGME Approved/Offered Positions:* 1
Program ID: 311-56-21-061

Milwaukee

Medical College of Wisconsin Affiliated Hospitals Program

Sponsor: Medical College of Wisconsin Affiliated Hospitals, Inc
Froedtert Memorial Lutheran Hospital
Prgm Director: Steven Kroft, MD
9200 West Wisconsin Avenue
Milwaukee, WI 53226
Tel: 414 805-8449   *Fax:* 414 805-6980
E-mail: mhardy@mcw.edu
Length: 1 Yr   *ACGME Approved/Offered Positions:* 1
Program ID: 311-56-21-071

Hematology and Oncology (Internal Medicine)

Alabama

Birmingham

University of Alabama Medical Center Program

Sponsor: University of Alabama Hospital
Veterans Affairs Medical Center (Birmingham)
Prgm Director: Lisle M Nabell, MD*
1530 3rd Avenue South
NP 2540
Birmingham, AL 35294
Tel: 205 934-3061   *Fax:* 205 975-9002
E-mail: Kelly.Adamson@ccc.uab.edu
Length: 3 Yrs   *ACGME Approved/Offered Positions:* 13
Program ID: 155-01-21-001

Arizona

Scottsdale

College of Medicine, Mayo Clinic (Arizona) Program

Sponsor: College of Medicine, Mayo Clinic
Mayo Clinic (Arizona)
Mayo Clinic Hospital
Prgm Director: Donald W Northfelt, MD
Department of Hematology/Oncology
13400 E Shea Boulevard
Scottsdale, AZ 85259
Tel: 480 301-9824   *Fax:* 480 301-4171
E-mail: bell.lois@mayo.edu
Length: 3 Yrs   *ACGME Approved/Offered Positions:* 3
Program ID: 155-03-13-149

Tucson

University of Arizona Program

Sponsor: University of Arizona College of Medicine
University Medical Center
Prgm Director: Frederick R Ahmann, MD
Arizona Cancer Center
1515 N Campbell Avenue
Tucson, AZ 85724
Tel: 602 626-8096   *Fax:* 602 626-8095
Length: 3 Yrs   *ACGME Approved/Offered Positions:* 7
Program ID: 155-03-21-003

Arkansas

Little Rock

University of Arkansas for Medical Sciences Program

Sponsor: University of Arkansas College of Medicine
Central Arkansas Veterans Healthcare System
UAMS Medical Center
Prgm Director: Issam Makhoul, MD*
4301 West Markham, Slot 508
Division of Hematology/Oncology
Little Rock, AR 72205
Tel: 501 686-8511
E-mail: laray@uams.edu
Length: 3 Yrs   *ACGME Approved/Offered Positions:* 9
Program ID: 155-04-21-129

Note: * indicates a newly appointed program director

California

La Jolla

Scripps Clinic/Scripps Green Hospital Program
Sponsor: Scripps Clinic/Scripps Green Hospital
The Scripps Research Institute
Prgm Director: Michael P Kosty, MD
10666 North Torrey Pines Road, 403C
La Jolla, CA 92037
Tel: 858 554-9043   *Fax:* 858 554-3232
E-mail: gme@scripps.edu
Length: 3 Yrs   *ACGME Approved/Offered Positions:* 6
Program ID: 155-05-12-145

Los Angeles

UCLA Medical Center Program
Sponsor: UCLA David Geffen School of Medicine/UCLA
   Medical Center
UCLA Medical Center
Prgm Director: Fairooz F Kabbinavar, MD
10945 Le Conte Avenue, Suite 2333
Los Angeles, CA 90095
Tel: 310 206-3921   *Fax:* 310 267-0151
Length: 3 Yrs   *ACGME Approved/Offered Positions:* 18
Program ID: 155-05-21-123

Orange

University of California (Irvine) Program
Sponsor: University of California (Irvine) Medical
   Center
VA Long Beach Healthcare System
Prgm Director: Randall F Holcombe, MD
101 The City Drive South
Rte 81, Building 56, Room 247
Orange, CA 92868
Tel: 714 456-5153   *Fax:* 714 456-2242
Length: 3 Yrs   *ACGME Approved/Offered Positions:* 6
Program ID: 155-05-21-136

Sacramento

University of California (Davis) Health System Program
Sponsor: University of California (Davis) Health System
University of California (Davis) Medical Center
VA Northern California Health Care System
Prgm Director: Theodore Wun, MD
2315 Stockton Boulevard
Sacramento, CA 95817
Tel: 916 734-3772   *Fax:* 916 734-7946
Length: 3 Yrs   *ACGME Approved/Offered Positions:* 10
Program ID: 155-05-31-005

San Diego

University of California (San Diego) Program
Sponsor: University of California (San Diego) Medical
   Center
Veterans Affairs Medical Center (San Diego)
Prgm Director: Sanford Shattil, MD*
3855 Health Sciences Dr #0829
La Jolla, CA 92093
Tel: 858 822-6425   *Fax:* 858 822-6444
Length: 3 Yrs   *ACGME Approved/Offered Positions:* 12
Program ID: 155-05-12-007

San Francisco

University of California (San Francisco) Program
Sponsor: University of California (San Francisco) School
   of Medicine
UCSF and Mount Zion Medical Centers
Prgm Director: Emily K Bergsland, MD
1600 Divisadero St, 7th Floor, A708
Box 1770
San Francisco, CA 94143
Tel: 415 353-7065   *Fax:* 415 353-9959
E-mail: kcopeland@medicine.ucsf.edu
Length: 3 Yrs   *ACGME Approved/Offered Positions:* 18
Program ID: 155-05-21-113

Sylmar

UCLA-Olive View Program
Sponsor: Olive View/UCLA Medical Center
Cedars-Sinai Medical Center
Prgm Director: Nancy R Feldman, MD
Olive View-UCLA Medical Center
14445 Olive View Drive, Rm 2B-182
Sylmar, CA 91342
Tel: 818 364-3205   *Fax:* 818 364-4573
E-mail: hemonc@uclasfvp.org
Length: 3 Yrs   *ACGME Approved/Offered Positions:* 8
Program ID: 155-05-13-008

Torrance

Los Angeles County-Harbor-UCLA Medical Center Program 1
Sponsor: Los Angeles County-Harbor-UCLA Medical
   Center
City of Hope National Medical Center
Kaiser Foundation Hospital (Baldwin Park)
Kaiser Foundation Hospital (Bellflower)
Prgm Director: Rowan T Chlebowski, MD, PhD
1000 W Carson Street, Bldg J-3
Torrance, CA 90509
Tel: 310 222-2217   *Fax:* 310 320-2564
E-mail: vcooray@labiomed.org
Length: 3 Yrs   *ACGME Approved/Offered Positions:* 13
Program ID: 155-05-31-093

Colorado

Aurora

University of Colorado Denver Program
Sponsor: University of Colorado Denver School of
   Medicine
University of Colorado Hospital
Prgm Director: Catherine E Klein, MD
Division of Medical Oncology, Mailstop 8117
12801 East 17th
Aurora, CO 80045
Tel: 303 724-3847   *Fax:* 303 724-3889
Length: 3 Yrs   *ACGME Approved/Offered Positions:* 12
Program ID: 155-07-21-096

Connecticut

Farmington

University of Connecticut Program
Sponsor: University of Connecticut School of Medicine
Hartford Hospital
St Francis Hospital and Medical Center
Univ of Connecticut Health Center/John Dempsey
   Hospital
Prgm Director: Robert D Bona, MD
Department of Medicine, MC 1628
263 Farmington Avenue
Farmington, CT 06030
Tel: 860 679-2255   *Fax:* 860 679-4973
Length: 3 Yrs   *ACGME Approved/Offered Positions:* 6
Program ID: 155-08-21-009

District of Columbia

Washington

George Washington University Program
Sponsor: George Washington University School of
   Medicine
George Washington University Hospital (UHS)
Veterans Affairs Medical Center (Washington, DC)
Prgm Director: Imad A Tabbara, MD
Division of Hematology/Oncology, Suite 3-428
2150 Pennsylvania Avenue, NW
Washington, DC 20037
Tel: 202 741-2478   *Fax:* 202 741-2487
Length: 3 Yrs   *ACGME Approved/Offered Positions:* 6
Program ID: 155-10-21-074

Georgetown University Hospital Program
Sponsor: Georgetown University Hospital
Prgm Director: Jimmy J Hwang, MD
3800 Reservoir Road NW
5th Floor, PHC Bldg
Washington, DC 20007
Tel: 202 444-7036   *Fax:* 202 444-7797
E-mail: ah@gunet.georgetown.edu
Length: 3 Yrs   *ACGME Approved/Offered Positions:* 18
Program ID: 155-10-12-148

Georgetown University Hospital/Washington Hospital Center Program
Sponsor: Washington Hospital Center
Prgm Director: Dennis A Priebat, MD
110 Irving Street, NW
Suite C-2151
Washington, DC 20010
Tel: 202 877-2505   *Fax:* 202 877-8910
E-mail: dennis.a.priebat@medstar.net
Length: 3 Yrs   *ACGME Approved/Offered Positions:* 7
Program ID: 155-10-31-011

Florida

Gainesville

University of Florida Program
Sponsor: University of Florida College of Medicine
North Florida/South Georgia Veterans Health System
Shands Hospital at the University of Florida
Prgm Director: Carmen J Allegra, MD*
Box J100278, JHMAC
Gainesville, FL 32610
Tel: 352 273-7759   *Fax:* 352 392-8530
E-mail: shirley.ambrosino@medicine.ufl.edu
Length: 3 Yrs   *ACGME Approved/Offered Positions:* 15
Program ID: 155-11-21-104

Jacksonville

College of Medicine, Mayo Clinic (Jacksonville) Program

Sponsor: College of Medicine, Mayo Clinic
Mayo Clinic (Jacksonville)
Mayo Clinic Florida Hospital
Prgm Director: Vivek Roy, MD
4500 San Pablo Road
Jacksonville, FL 32224
Tel: 904 953-2000   *Fax:* 904 953-0430
E-mail: hammer.linda@mayo.edu
Length: 3 Yrs   *ACGME Approved/Offered Positions:* 6
Program ID: 155-11-31-108

Miami

Jackson Memorial Hospital/Jackson Health System Program

Sponsor: Jackson Memorial Hospital/Jackson Health System
Prgm Director: Pasquale W Benedetto, MD
1475 NW 12th Ave, Ste 3310
PO Box 016960 (D8-4)
Miami, FL 33136
Tel: 305 243-4909   *Fax:* 305 243-4905
E-mail: pbenedet@med.miami.edu
Length: 3 Yrs   *ACGME Approved/Offered Positions:* 12
Program ID: 155-11-21-012

Orlando

Orlando Health Program

Sponsor: Orlando Health
Orlando Regional Medical Center
Prgm Director: Said M Baidas, MD
1400 South Orange Avenue
MP 700
Orlando, FL 32806
Tel: 321 841-6608   *Fax:* 407 649-6994
E-mail: said.baidas@orlandohealth.com
Length: 3 Yrs   *ACGME Approved/Offered Positions:* 6
Program ID: 155-11-12-153

Tampa

University of South Florida Program

Sponsor: University of South Florida College of Medicine
H Lee Moffitt Cancer Center
James A Haley Veterans Hospital
Tampa General Hospital
Prgm Director: Kenneth Zuckerman, MD
H Lee Moffitt Cancer Center
12902 Magnolia Drive, SRB-HEME
Tampa, FL 33612
Tel: 813 745-2069   *Fax:* 813 745-4064
Length: 3 Yrs   *ACGME Approved/Offered Positions:* 22
Program ID: 155-11-31-013

Georgia

Atlanta

Emory University Program

Sponsor: Emory University School of Medicine
Emory University Hospital
Grady Health System
Prgm Director: Ruth O'Regan, MD
Emory Winship Cancer Institute
1365 Clifton Road, NE
Atlanta, GA 30322
Tel: 404 778-1351   *Fax:* 404 778-5530
E-mail: roregan@emory.edu
Length: 3 Yrs   *ACGME Approved/Offered Positions:* 15
Program ID: 155-12-21-014

Augusta

Medical College of Georgia Program

Sponsor: Medical College of Georgia
Veterans Affairs Medical Center (Augusta)
Prgm Director: Abdullah Kutlar, MD
Dept of Medicine-Hematology/Oncology
1120 15th Street, BAA 5407
Augusta, GA 30912
Tel: 706 721-2505   *Fax:* 706 721-5566
Length: 3 Yrs   *ACGME Approved/Offered Positions:* 6
Program ID: 155-12-31-015

Illinois

Chicago

John H Stroger Hospital of Cook County Program

Sponsor: John H Stroger Hospital of Cook County
Rush University Medical Center
Prgm Director: Margaret C Telfer, MD
1900 W Polk St
Rm 750, Admin Bldg
Chicago, IL 60612
Tel: 312 864-7250   *Fax:* 312 864-9002
E-mail: greyes@ccbhs.org
Length: 3 Yrs   *ACGME Approved/Offered Positions:* 6
Program ID: 155-16-21-106

McGaw Medical Center of Northwestern University Program

Sponsor: McGaw Medical Center of Northwestern University
Northwestern Memorial Hospital
Prgm Director: William J Gradishar, MD
676 N St Clair Street
Suite 850
Chicago, IL 60611
Tel: 312 695-4541   *Fax:* 312 695-6189
Length: 3 Yrs   *ACGME Approved/Offered Positions:* 15
Program ID: 155-16-21-016

Rush University Medical Center Program

Sponsor: Rush University Medical Center
Prgm Director: Jamile Shammo, MD
1725 W Harrison Street
Professional Building I, Suite 809
Chicago, IL 60612
Tel: 312 563-4502   *Fax:* 312 942-3192
E-mail: jamile_shammo@rush.edu
Length: 3 Yrs   *ACGME Approved/Offered Positions:* 6
Program ID: 155-16-21-085

University of Chicago Program

Sponsor: University of Chicago Medical Center
Prgm Director: Ezra Cohen, MD*
5841 South Maryland Avenue
Mail Code 2115
Chicago, IL 60637
Tel: 773 702-4137   *Fax:* 773 834-2835
Length: 3 Yrs   *ACGME Approved/Offered Positions:* 21
Program ID: 155-16-21-079

University of Illinois College of Medicine at Chicago Program

Sponsor: University of Illinois College of Medicine at Chicago
Jesse Brown Veterans Affairs Medical Center
University of Illinois Hospital and Clinics
Prgm Director: David J Peace, MD
840 S Wood Street, Suite 820-E
MC 713
Chicago, IL 60612
Tel: 312 413-9308   *Fax:* 312 413-4131
E-mail: dpeace@uic.edu
Length: 3 Yrs   *ACGME Approved/Offered Positions:* 12
Program ID: 155-16-31-017

Maywood

Loyola University Program

Sponsor: Loyola University Medical Center
Edward Hines, Jr Veterans Affairs Hospital
Prgm Director: Joseph I Clark, MD
Cardinal Bernardin Cancer Center
2160 S First Avenue
Maywood, IL 60153
Tel: 708 327-3236   *Fax:* 708 327-3218
Length: 3 Yrs   *ACGME Approved/Offered Positions:* 9
Program ID: 155-16-21-110

Park Ridge

Advocate Lutheran General Hospital Program

Sponsor: Advocate Lutheran General Hospital
Prgm Director: Jacob D Bitran, MD
1700 Luther Lane
Park Ridge, IL 60068
Tel: 847 723-5861   *Fax:* 847 723-8250
Length: 3 Yrs   *ACGME Approved/Offered Positions:* 3
Program ID: 155-16-31-147

Indiana

Indianapolis

Indiana University School of Medicine Program

Sponsor: Indiana University School of Medicine
Clarian Indiana University Hospital
Prgm Director: Michael J Robertson, MD
Indiana Cancer Pavilion
535 Barnhill Drive, Room 473
Indianapolis, IN 46202
Tel: 317 278-6942   *Fax:* 317 278-4190
Length: 3 Yrs   *ACGME Approved/Offered Positions:* 15
Program ID: 155-17-21-020

Iowa

Iowa City

University of Iowa Hospitals and Clinics Program

Sponsor: University of Iowa Hospitals and Clinics
Veterans Affairs Medical Center (Iowa City)
Prgm Director: Roger D Gingrich, MD, PhD
200 Hawkins Drive
5970 JPP
Iowa City, IA 52242
Tel: 319 356-3425   *Fax:* 319 353-8988
E-mail: hemoncfellowship@uiowa.edu
Length: 3 Yrs   *ACGME Approved/Offered Positions:* 12
Program ID: 155-18-21-021

Kansas

Kansas City

University of Kansas School of Medicine Program

Sponsor: University of Kansas School of Medicine
Veterans Affairs Medical Center (Kansas City)
Prgm Director: Sarah A Taylor, MD
Division of Hematology/Oncology
2330 Shawnee Mission Parkway, Suite 210, MS 5003
Westwood, KS 66205
Tel: 913 588-6029   *Fax:* 913 588-4085
Length: 3 Yrs   *ACGME Approved/Offered Positions:* 10
Program ID: 155-19-12-133

Note: * indicates a newly appointed program director

Kentucky

Lexington

University of Kentucky College of Medicine Program

Sponsor: University of Kentucky College of Medicine
University of Kentucky Hospital
Veterans Affairs Medical Center (Lexington)
Prgm Director: Kevin T McDonagh, MD
Department of Medicine
J511 Kentucky Clinic
Lexington, KY 40536
Tel: 859 323-1786   *Fax:* 859 257-7715
Length: 3 Yrs   *ACGME Approved/Offered Positions:* 6
Program ID: 155-20-21-103

Louisville

University of Louisville Program

Sponsor: University of Louisville School of Medicine
James Graham Brown Medical Center
University of Louisville Hospital
Veterans Affairs Medical Center (Louisville)
Prgm Director: Damian A Laber, MD
James Graham Brown Cancer Center
529 South Jackson Street, Suite 205
Louisville, KY 40202
Tel: 502 562-4359   *Fax:* 502 562-4368
E-mail: sairama@ulh.org
Length: 3 Yrs   *ACGME Approved/Offered Positions:* 9
Program ID: 155-20-21-022

Louisiana

New Orleans

Tulane University Program

Sponsor: Tulane University School of Medicine
Medical Center of Louisiana at New Orleans
Tulane University Hospital and Clinics
Veterans Affairs Medical Center (New Orleans)
Prgm Director: Hana Safah, MD
Hematology/Medical Onocology Fellowship Program
1430 Tulane Avenue SL-78
New Orleans, LA 70112
Tel: 504 988-5482   *Fax:* 504 988-5483
E-mail: swilson7@tulane.edu
Length: 3 Yrs   *ACGME Approved/Offered Positions:* 7
Program ID: 155-21-21-023

Shreveport

Louisiana State University (Shreveport) Program

Sponsor: LSU Health Sciences Center-University
  Hospital
Prgm Director: Glenn M Mills, MD
1501 Kings Highway
PO Box 33932
Shreveport, LA 71130
Tel: 318 813-1057   *Fax:* 318 813-1055
Length: 3 Yrs   *ACGME Approved/Offered Positions:* 15
Program ID: 155-21-31-024

Maryland

Baltimore

Johns Hopkins University Program

Sponsor: Johns Hopkins University School of Medicine
Johns Hopkins Hospital
Prgm Director: Ross C Donehower, MD
1650 Orleans Street, 187
Baltimore, MD 21231
Tel: 410 955-8838   *Fax:* 410 955-0125
E-mail: nrosenb@jhmi.edu
Length: 3 Yrs   *ACGME Approved/Offered Positions:* 24
Program ID: 155-23-21-154

University of Maryland Program

Sponsor: University of Maryland Medical System
National Institute on Aging (Clinical Research Branch)
Prgm Director: Ann B Zimrin, MD
Marlene & Stewart Greenebaum Cancer Center
22 S Greene Street, S9D11
Baltimore, MD 21201
Tel: 410 328-2594   *Fax:* 410 328-6896
E-mail: azimrin@umm.edu
Length: 3 Yrs   *ACGME Approved/Offered Positions:* 15
Program ID: 155-23-21-025

Bethesda

National Capital Consortium (Bethesda) Program

Sponsor: National Capital Consortium
Walter Reed Army Medical Center
Prgm Director: Christopher M Gallagher, MD
Building 2, Ward 78
6900 Georgia Avenue, NW
Washington, DC 20307
Tel: 202 782-5748   *Fax:* 202 782-3256
E-mail: christopher.gallagher@amedd.army.mil
Length: 3 Yrs   *ACGME Approved/Offered Positions:* 12
Program ID: 155-23-21-088
Uniformed Services Program

Massachusetts

Boston

Beth Israel Deaconess Medical Center Program

Sponsor: Beth Israel Deaconess Medical Center
Prgm Director: Reed E Drews, MD
330 Brookline Ave
Boston, MA 02215
Tel: 617 667-2131   *Fax:* 617 667-3915
E-mail: rdrews@bidmc.harvard.edu
Length: 3 Yrs   *ACGME Approved/Offered Positions:* 18
Program ID: 155-24-21-026

Boston University Medical Center Program

Sponsor: Boston Medical Center
Veterans Affairs Medical Center (Boston)
Prgm Director: Kevan L Hartshorn, MD
Section of Hematology/Oncology
650 Albany Street, X405
Boston, MA 02118
Tel: 617 638-7521   *Fax:* 617 638-7530
E-mail: khartsho@bu.edu
Length: 3 Yrs   *ACGME Approved/Offered Positions:* 15
Program ID: 155-24-31-027

Brigham and Women's Hospital Program

Sponsor: Brigham and Women's Hospital
Dana-Farber Cancer Institute
Massachusetts General Hospital
Prgm Director: Robert J Mayer, MD
75 Francis Street
Boston, MA 02115
Tel: 617 632-3474   *Fax:* 617 632-2260
Length: 3 Yrs   *ACGME Approved/Offered Positions:* 46
Program ID: 155-24-21-073

Caritas St Elizabeth's Medical Center Program

Sponsor: Caritas St Elizabeth's Medical Center of
  Boston
Prgm Director: Paul J Hesketh, MD
736 Cambridge Street
Boston, MA 02135
Tel: 617 789-2317   *Fax:* 617 789-2959
E-mail: sarah.francis@caritaschristi.org
Length: 3 Yrs   *ACGME Approved/Offered Positions:* 7
Program ID: 155-24-21-124

Tufts Medical Center Program

Sponsor: Tufts Medical Center
Prgm Director: Gary M Strauss, MD, MPH
800 Washington Street
Box 245
Boston, MA 02111
Tel: 617 636-5147   *Fax:* 617 636-2342
E-mail: gstrauss@tuftsmedicalcenter.org
Length: 3 Yrs   *ACGME Approved/Offered Positions:* 15
Program ID: 155-24-12-029

Springfield

Baystate Medical Center/Tufts University School of Medicine Program

Sponsor: Baystate Medical Center
Prgm Director: Grace Makari-Judson, MD
3400 Main Street
Springfield, MA 01107
Tel: 413 794-5433   *Fax:* 413 794-3613
E-mail: precious.smith@bhs.org
Length: 3 Yrs   *ACGME Approved/Offered Positions:* 3
Program ID: 155-24-13-030

Worcester

University of Massachusetts Program

Sponsor: University of Massachusetts Medical School
UMass Memorial Health Care (Memorial Campus)
UMass Memorial Health Care (University Campus)
Prgm Director: William V Walsh, MD
55 Lake Avenue North
Worcester, MA 01655
Tel: 508 334-5539   *Fax:* 508 334-6294
E-mail: walshw@ummhc.org
Length: 3 Yrs   *ACGME Approved/Offered Positions:* 6
Program ID: 155-24-21-075

Michigan

Ann Arbor

University of Michigan Program

Sponsor: University of Michigan Hospitals and Health
  Centers
Prgm Director: Scott D Gitlin, MD
C369 Med Inn, SPC 5848
1500 E Medical Center Drive
Ann Arbor, MI 48109
Tel: 734 615-1623   *Fax:* 734 615-2109
Length: 3 Yrs   *ACGME Approved/Offered Positions:* 18
Program ID: 155-25-21-098

Detroit

Henry Ford Hospital Program
Sponsor: Henry Ford Hospital
Prgm Director: Ira S Wollner, MD
Department of Medicine
2799 West Grand Boulevard
Detroit, MI 48202
Tel: 313 916-3788   *Fax:* 313 916-7911
E-mail: iwollne1@hfhs.org
Length: 3 Yrs   *ACGME Approved/Offered Positions:* 12
Program ID: 155-25-21-031

Wayne State University/Detroit Medical Center Program
Sponsor: Wayne State University/Detroit Medical Center
Harper-Hutzel Hospital
Prgm Director: Charles A Schiffer, MD
4100 John R Street - 4 HWCRC
Detroit, MI 48201
Tel: 313 576-8720   *Fax:* 313 576-8767
E-mail: schiffer@karmanos.org
Length: 3 Yrs   *ACGME Approved/Offered Positions:* 12
Program ID: 155-25-13-142

Lansing

Michigan State University Program
Sponsor: Michigan State University College of Human
   Medicine
Ingham Regional Medical Center
McLaren Regional Medical Center
Sparrow Hospital
Willowbrook Manor Nursing Home
Prgm Director: Kenneth A Schwartz, MD
Department of Medicine
B-203 Life Sciences Building
East Lansing, MI 48824
Tel: 517 353-3728   *Fax:* 517 432-1326
E-mail: schwart7@msu.edu
Length: 3 Yrs   *ACGME Approved/Offered Positions:* 6
Program ID: 155-25-21-126

Southfield

Providence Hospital and Medical Centers Program
Sponsor: Providence Hospital and Medical Centers
Karmanos Cancer Hospital
Prgm Director: Howard Terebelo, DO
16001 West Nine Mile Road, Box 2043
Southfield, MI 48037
Tel: 248 849-7129   *Fax:* 248 849-3230
E-mail:
katherine.mccaskell@providence-stjohnhealth.org
Length: 3 Yrs   *ACGME Approved/Offered Positions:* 6
Program ID: 155-25-12-140

Minnesota

Minneapolis

University of Minnesota Program
Sponsor: University of Minnesota Medical School
University of Minnesota Medical Center, Division of
   Fairview
Prgm Director: Linda J Burns, MD
420 Delaware Street SE
Minneapolis, MN 55455
Tel: 612 624-8144   *Fax:* 612 625-9988
E-mail: burns019@umn.edu
Length: 3 Yrs   *ACGME Approved/Offered Positions:* 18
Program ID: 155-26-21-032

Rochester

College of Medicine, Mayo Clinic (Rochester) Program
Sponsor: College of Medicine, Mayo Clinic
Mayo Clinic (Rochester)
Rochester Methodist Hospital
Prgm Director: Timothy J Moynihan, MD
200 First Street, SW
Siebens Building, 5th Floor
Rochester, MN 55905
Tel: 507 538-1538
E-mail: moynihan.timothy@mayo.edu
Length: 3 Yrs   *ACGME Approved/Offered Positions:* 27
Program ID: 155-26-31-033

Mississippi

Jackson

University of Mississippi Medical Center Program
Sponsor: University of Mississippi School of Medicine
University Hospitals and Clinics
Veterans Affairs Medical Center (Jackson)
Prgm Director: Stephanie L Elkins, MD
2500 North State Street
Jackson, MS 39216
Tel: 601 984-5616   *Fax:* 601 984-5689
Length: 3 Yrs   *ACGME Approved/Offered Positions:* 9
Program ID: 155-27-21-114

Missouri

Columbia

University of Missouri-Columbia Program
Sponsor: University of Missouri-Columbia School of
   Medicine
University Hospitals and Clinics
Prgm Director: Carl E Freter, MD, PhD*
Ellis Fischel Cancer Center
115 Business Loop 70 W, DC116.71
Columbia, MO 65203
Tel: 573 882-0598   *Fax:* 573 884-6050
Length: 3 Yrs   *ACGME Approved/Offered Positions:* 8
Program ID: 155-28-21-083

Kansas City

University of Missouri at Kansas City Program
Sponsor: University of Missouri-Kansas City School of
   Medicine
St Luke's Hospital-Kansas City
Truman Medical Center
Prgm Director: Jill A Moormeier, MD, MPH
2411 Holmes
Kansas City, MO 64108
Tel: 816 235-1946   *Fax:* 816 404-4377
Length: 3 Yrs   *ACGME Approved/Offered Positions:* 3
Program ID: 155-28-21-034

St Louis

St Louis University School of Medicine Program
Sponsor: St Louis University School of Medicine
St Louis University Hospital
Prgm Director: Paul J Petruska, MD
3655 Vista Avenue
3rd Floor - West Pavilion
St Louis, MO 63110
Tel: 314 577-8854   *Fax:* 314 773-1167
Length: 3 Yrs   *ACGME Approved/Offered Positions:* 6
Program ID: 155-28-11-036

Washington University/B-JH/SLCH Consortium Program
Sponsor: Washington University/B-JH/SLCH Consortium
Barnes-Jewish Hospital
Prgm Director: Joel Picus, MD
4989 Barnes Hospital Plaza
St Louis, MO 63110
Tel: 314 362-5740
Length: 3 Yrs   *ACGME Approved/Offered Positions:* 18
Program ID: 155-28-31-035

Nebraska

Omaha

University of Nebraska Medical Center College of Medicine Program
Sponsor: University of Nebraska Medical Center College
   of Medicine
Nebraska Medical Center
Veterans Affairs Medical Center (Omaha)
Prgm Director: Greg Bociek, MD, MS
Department of Medicine
987680 Nebraska Medical Center
Omaha, NE 68198
Tel: 402 559-5388   *Fax:* 402 559-6520
Length: 3 Yrs   *ACGME Approved/Offered Positions:* 6
Program ID: 155-30-21-037

New Hampshire

Lebanon

Dartmouth-Hitchcock Medical Center Program
Sponsor: Mary Hitchcock Memorial Hospital
Prgm Director: Thomas H Davis, MD
One Medical Center Drive
Lebanon, NH 03756
Tel: 603 650-8626   *Fax:* 603 650-7791
E-mail: thomas.h.davis@hitchcock.org
Length: 3 Yrs   *ACGME Approved/Offered Positions:* 9
Program ID: 155-32-21-038

New Jersey

Camden

UMDNJ-Robert Wood Johnson Medical School (Camden) Program
Sponsor: Cooper Hospital-University Medical Center
Prgm Director: Alexandre Hageboutros, MD
Three Cooper Plaza, Suite 211
Camden, NJ 08103
Tel: 856 968-7322   *Fax:* 856 338-0628
E-mail: kay-vicki@cooperhealth.edu
Length: 3 Yrs   *ACGME Approved/Offered Positions:* 6
Program ID: 155-33-21-039

New Brunswick

UMDNJ-Robert Wood Johnson Medical School Program
Sponsor: UMDNJ-Robert Wood Johnson Medical School
Robert Wood Johnson University Hospital
Prgm Director: Parvin Saidi, MD
Dept of Medicine, PO Box 19
1 Robert Wood Johnson Plaza
New Brunswick, NJ 08903
Tel: 732 235-7679   *Fax:* 732 235-7115
Length: 3 Yrs   *ACGME Approved/Offered Positions:* 12
Program ID: 155-33-21-040

Note: * indicates a newly appointed program director

Newark

Newark Beth Israel Medical Center Program
Sponsor: Newark Beth Israel Medical Center
Prgm Director: Alice J Cohen, MD
201 Lyons Avenue at Osborne Terrace
Newark, NJ 07112
Tel: 973 926-7230   *Fax:* 973 926-9568
Length: 3 Yrs   *ACGME Approved/Offered Positions:* 3
Program ID: 155-33-31-132

South Orange

Seton Hall University School of Health and Medical Sciences Program
Sponsor: Seton Hall University School of Health and Medical Sciences
St Joseph's Regional Medical Center
St Michael's Medical Center (A Member of Catholic Health East)
Prgm Director: Michael Maroules, MD
400 South Orange Avenue
South Orange, NJ 07079
Tel: 973 754-4360   *Fax:* 973 754-3734
Length: 3 Yrs   *ACGME Approved/Offered Positions:* 6
Program ID: 155-33-13-137

New Mexico

Albuquerque

University of New Mexico Program
Sponsor: University of New Mexico School of Medicine
University of New Mexico Hospital
Veterans Affairs Medical Center (Albuquerque)
Prgm Director: Ian Rabinowitz, MD
Division of Hematology/Oncology
900 Camino de Salud, NE, MSC 08-4630
Albuquerque, NM 87131
Tel: 505 272-5837   *Fax:* 505 272-2841
Length: 3 Yrs   *ACGME Approved/Offered Positions:* 4
Program ID: 155-34-21-115

New York

Bronx

Albert Einstein College of Medicine Program
Sponsor: Albert Einstein College of Medicine of Yeshiva University
Montefiore Medical Center-Henry and Lucy Moses Division
Montefiore Medical Center-Weiler Division
North Bronx Healthcare Network-Jacobi Medical Center
Prgm Director: Rasim A Gucalp, MD
111 East 210th Street
Department of Oncology
Bronx, NY 10467
Tel: 718 920-4826   *Fax:* 718 798-7474
Length: 3 Yrs   *ACGME Approved/Offered Positions:* 26
Program ID: 155-35-21-127

New York Medical College (Bronx) Program
Sponsor: New York Medical College
Montefiore Medical Center - North Division
Prgm Director: Peter H Wiernik, MD
600 East 233rd Street
Bronx, NY 10466
Tel: 718 304-7220   *Fax:* 718 304-7228
Length: 3 Yrs   *ACGME Approved/Offered Positions:* 6
Program ID: 155-35-12-131

Brooklyn

Brookdale University Hospital and Medical Center Program
Sponsor: Brookdale University Hospital and Medical Center
Prgm Director: William Steier, MD
1 Brookdale Plaza
Brooklyn, NY 11212
Tel: 718 240-5653   *Fax:* 718 240-6516
Length: 3 Yrs   *ACGME Approved/Offered Positions:* 6
Program ID: 155-35-21-041

Brooklyn Hospital Center Program
Sponsor: Brooklyn Hospital Center
Wyckoff Heights Medical Center
Prgm Director: Arunbhai G Patel, MD
Department of Medicine
121 DeKalb Avenue
Brooklyn, NY 11201
Tel: 718 250-6960   *Fax:* 718 250-6493
E-mail: arungpatelmd@gmail.com
Length: 3 Yrs   *ACGME Approved/Offered Positions:* 4
Program ID: 155-35-12-135

Maimonides Medical Center Program
Sponsor: Maimonides Medical Center
Coney Island Hospital
Prgm Director: Alan B Astrow, MD
953 49th Street, Room 502
Brooklyn, NY 11219
Tel: 718 283-8297   *Fax:* 718 635-7110
Length: 3 Yrs   *ACGME Approved/Offered Positions:* 9
Program ID: 155-35-13-139

New York Methodist Hospital Program
Sponsor: New York Methodist Hospital
Prgm Director: Muthuswamy Krishnamurthy, MD
506 Sixth Street
Brooklyn, NY 11215
Tel: 718 780-5246   *Fax:* 718 780-3259
E-mail: dockrishna@yahoo.com
Length: 3 Yrs   *ACGME Approved/Offered Positions:* 4
Program ID: 155-35-21-138

SUNY Health Science Center at Brooklyn Program
Sponsor: SUNY Health Science Center at Brooklyn
Kings County Hospital Center
Long Island College Hospital
University Hospital-SUNY Health Science Center at Brooklyn
Veterans Affairs Medical Center (Brooklyn)
Prgm Director: William B Solomon, MD
Department of Medicine, Box 50
450 Clarkson Avenue
Brooklyn, NY 11203
Tel: 718 270-2785   *Fax:* 718 270-1578
Length: 3 Yrs   *ACGME Approved/Offered Positions:* 14
Program ID: 155-35-11-043

Great Neck

NSLIJHS-Albert Einstein College of Medicine at Long Island Jewish Medical Center Program
Sponsor: North Shore-Long Island Jewish Health System
Long Island Jewish Medical Center
Prgm Director: Dilip V Patel, MD
207-05 76th Avenue
3rd Floor Institute of Oncology
New Hyde Park, NY 11040
Tel: 718 470-8931   *Fax:* 718 470-0169
Length: 3 Yrs   *ACGME Approved/Offered Positions:* 6
Program ID: 155-35-22-046

NSLIJHS-North Shore University Hospital/NYU School of Medicine Program
Sponsor: North Shore-Long Island Jewish Health System
North Shore University Hospital
Prgm Director: Thomas P Bradley, MD
300 Community Drive
Manhasset, NY 11030
Tel: 516 734-8900   *Fax:* 516 734-8950
Length: 3 Yrs   *ACGME Approved/Offered Positions:* 9
Program ID: 155-35-31-116

Mineola

Winthrop-University Hospital Program
Sponsor: Winthrop-University Hospital
Prgm Director: Harry Staszewski, MD
200 Old Country Road
Suite 450
Mineola, NY 11501
Tel: 516 663-9568   *Fax:* 516 663-9543
E-mail: afischer@winthrop.org
Length: 3 Yrs   *ACGME Approved/Offered Positions:* 4
Program ID: 155-35-13-045

New York

Albert Einstein College of Medicine at Beth Israel Medical Center Program
Sponsor: Beth Israel Medical Center
Prgm Director: Ronald Blum, MD
Department of Medicine
First Avenue at 16th Street
New York, NY 10003
Tel: 212 844-8282   *Fax:* 212 844-8299
Length: 3 Yrs   *ACGME Approved/Offered Positions:* 3
Program ID: 155-35-23-047

Lenox Hill Hospital Program
Sponsor: Lenox Hill Hospital
Prgm Director: Colette Spaccavento, MD
100 East 77th Street
4 Achelis
New York, NY 10075
Tel: 212 434-2158   *Fax:* 212 434-3396
E-mail: mhill@lenoxhill.net
Length: 3 Yrs   *ACGME Approved/Offered Positions:* 4
Program ID: 155-35-33-049

Memorial Sloan-Kettering Cancer Center/New York Presbyterian Hospital (Cornell Campus) Program
Sponsor: Memorial Sloan-Kettering Cancer Center
Prgm Director: Dean F Bajorin, MD
1275 York Avenue
Box 8
New York, NY 10065
Tel: 212 639-5809   *Fax:* 212 639-2283
Length: 3 Yrs   *ACGME Approved/Offered Positions:* 45
Program ID: 155-35-21-084

Mount Sinai School of Medicine Program
Sponsor: Mount Sinai School of Medicine
Mount Sinai Medical Center
Prgm Director: David W Sternberg, MD, PhD
One Gustave L Levy Place
Box 1079
New York, NY 10029
Tel: 212 241-5493   *Fax:* 212 996-5787
E-mail: david.sternberg@mssm.edu
Length: 3 Yrs   *ACGME Approved/Offered Positions:* 12
Program ID: 155-35-21-050

Programs

New York Medical College at St Vincent's Hospital and Medical Center of New York Program

Sponsor: New York Medical College
St Vincent Catholic Medical Centers (Manhattan)
Prgm Director: Sanford Kempin, MD
170 West 12th Street
New York, NY 10011
Tel: 212 604-6011   *Fax:* 212 604-6039
E-mail: skempin@aptiumoncology.com
Length: 3 Yrs   *ACGME Approved/Offered Positions:* 4
Program ID: 155-35-12-053

New York Presbyterian Hospital (Columbia Campus) Program

Sponsor: New York Presbyterian Hospital
New York Presbyterian Hospital (Columbia Campus)
Prgm Director: David G Savage, MD
622 W 168th Street
New York, NY 10032
Tel: 212 305-9783   *Fax:* 212 305-6798
E-mail: dgs5@columbia.edu
Length: 3 Yrs   *ACGME Approved/Offered Positions:* 15
Program ID: 155-35-11-052

New York Presbyterian Hospital (Cornell Campus) Program

Sponsor: New York Presbyterian Hospital
New York Presbyterian Hospital (Cornell Campus)
Prgm Director: Ronald J Scheff, MD
525 East 68th Street
New York, NY 10065
Tel: 212 746-2075   *Fax:* 212 746-6645
Length: 3 Yrs   *ACGME Approved/Offered Positions:* 18
Program ID: 155-35-31-051

New York University School of Medicine Program

Sponsor: New York University School of Medicine
Bellevue Hospital Center
NYU Hospitals Center
Prgm Director: Franco Muggia, MD
550 First Avenue
New York, NY 10016
Tel: 212 263-6485   *Fax:* 212 263-8210
Length: 3 Yrs   *ACGME Approved/Offered Positions:* 18
Program ID: 155-35-31-152

St Luke's-Roosevelt Hospital Center Program

Sponsor: St Luke's-Roosevelt Hospital Center
Prgm Director: Mala Varma, MD
1000 Tenth Avenue Suite 11C
New York, NY 10019
Tel: 212 523-7281   *Fax:* 212 523-2004
E-mail: mvarma@chpnet.org
Length: 3 Yrs   *ACGME Approved/Offered Positions:* 5
Program ID: 155-35-31-134

Rochester

University of Rochester Program

Sponsor: Strong Memorial Hospital of the University of Rochester
Prgm Director: Deepak Sahasrabudhe, MD
601 Elmwood Avenue, Box 704
Rochester, NY 14642
Tel: 585 275-4797   *Fax:* 585 273-1042
Length: 3 Yrs   *ACGME Approved/Offered Positions:* 12
Program ID: 155-35-21-100

Staten Island

Staten Island University Hospital Program

Sponsor: Staten Island University Hospital
Prgm Director: Frank J Forte, MD
256 Mason Avenue Building C
Staten Island, NY 10305
Tel: 718 226-6443   *Fax:* 718 226-6434
Length: 3 Yrs   *ACGME Approved/Offered Positions:* 6
Program ID: 155-35-31-144

Stony Brook

SUNY at Stony Brook Program

Sponsor: University Hospital - SUNY at Stony Brook
Veterans Affairs Medical Center (Northport)
Prgm Director: Theodore G Gabig, MD
Division of Hematology
HSC, T-15-40
Stony Brook, NY 11794
Tel: 631 444-1748   *Fax:* 631 444-7530
Length: 3 Yrs   *ACGME Approved/Offered Positions:* 8
Program ID: 155-35-13-054

Syracuse

SUNY Upstate Medical University Program

Sponsor: SUNY Upstate Medical University
Prgm Director: Ajeet Gajra, MD
750 E Adams Street
ROC 2275
Syracuse, NY 13210
Tel: 315 464-4353   *Fax:* 315 464-8279
E-mail: dartnela@upstate.edu
Length: 3 Yrs   *ACGME Approved/Offered Positions:* 6
Program ID: 155-35-31-086

Valhalla

New York Medical College at Westchester Medical Center Program

Sponsor: New York Medical College
Metropolitan Hospital Center
Richmond University Medical Center
Sound Shore Medical Center of Westchester
Westchester Medical Center
Prgm Director: Robert G Lerner, MD
Department of Medicine
Munger Pavilion
Valhalla, NY 10595
Tel: 914 594-4979   *Fax:* 914 594-4396
E-mail: robert_lerner@nymc.edu
Length: 3 Yrs   *ACGME Approved/Offered Positions:* 8
Program ID: 155-35-31-101

North Carolina

Chapel Hill

University of North Carolina Hospitals Program

Sponsor: University of North Carolina Hospitals
Prgm Director: Thomas C Shea, MD
Physicians Office Bldg
170 Manning Drive, CB 7305
Chapel Hill, NC 27599
Tel: 919 966-3856   *Fax:* 919 966-6735
Length: 3 Yrs   *ACGME Approved/Offered Positions:* 15
Program ID: 155-36-21-055

Durham

Duke University Hospital Program

Sponsor: Duke University Hospital
Prgm Director: William H Kane, MD, PhD
Box 3841
Durham, NC 27710
Tel: 919 684-8952   *Fax:* 919 681-6160
Length: 3 Yrs   *ACGME Approved/Offered Positions:* 24
Program ID: 155-36-31-056

Greenville

Pitt County Memorial Hospital/East Carolina University Program

Sponsor: Pitt County Memorial Hospital
Prgm Director: Darla K Liles, MD
Brody 3E-127, ECU SOM
Greenville, NC 27858
Tel: 252 744-2560   *Fax:* 252 744-3418
E-mail: lilesd@mail.ecu.edu
Length: 3 Yrs   *ACGME Approved/Offered Positions:* 6
Program ID: 155-36-11-141

Winston-Salem

Wake Forest University School of Medicine Program

Sponsor: Wake Forest University Baptist Medical Center
Prgm Director: John Owen, MD, MBA
Section on Hematology and Oncology
Medical Center Boulevard
Winston-Salem, NC 27157
Tel: 336 716-6777   *Fax:* 336 716-5687
Length: 3 Yrs   *ACGME Approved/Offered Positions:* 12
Program ID: 155-36-21-076

Ohio

Cincinnati

University Hospital/University of Cincinnati College of Medicine Program

Sponsor: University Hospital Inc
Veterans Affairs Medical Center (Cincinnati)
Prgm Director: Kathleen Havlin, MD*
231 Albert Sabin Way
PO Box 670562
Cincinnati, OH 45267
Tel: 513 558-3828   *Fax:* 513 558-2203
Length: 3 Yrs   *ACGME Approved/Offered Positions:* 9
Program ID: 155-38-21-102

Cleveland

Cleveland Clinic Foundation Program

Sponsor: Cleveland Clinic Foundation
Prgm Director: Timothy D Gilligan, MD
Taussig Cancer Center
9500 Euclid Avenue, Desk R35
Cleveland, OH 44195
Tel: 216 445-0624   *Fax:* 216 636-1711
E-mail: meded@ccf.org
Length: 3 Yrs   *ACGME Approved/Offered Positions:* 17
Program ID: 155-38-21-057

University Hospitals Case Medical Center Program

Sponsor: University Hospitals Case Medical Center
MetroHealth Medical Center
Prgm Director: Joseph A Bokar, MD, PhD
2103 Cornell Road
WRB 2-129
Cleveland, OH 44106
Tel: 216 368-1177   *Fax:* 216 368-1166
E-mail: joseph.bokar@case.edu
Length: 3 Yrs   *ACGME Approved/Offered Positions:* 12
Program ID: 155-38-21-117

Note: * indicates a newly appointed program director

Columbus

Ohio State University Hospital Program
Sponsor: Ohio State University Hospital
Arthur G James Cancer Hospital and Research Institute
Prgm Director: Kristie A Blum, MD*
Starling-Loving Hall
320 W Tenth Avenue
Columbus, OH 43210
Tel: 614 293-8858   *Fax:* 614 293-7484
Length: 3 Yrs   *ACGME Approved/Offered Positions:* 18
Program ID: 155-38-31-058

Dayton

Wright State University Program
Sponsor: Wright State University Boonshoft School of
   Medicine
Good Samaritan Hospital and Health Center
Veterans Affairs Medical Center (Dayton)
Prgm Director: Michael A Baumann, MD
4100 W Third Street
Dayton, OH 45428
Tel: 937 268-6511   *Fax:* 937 267-5310
E-mail: michael.baumann@wright.edu
Length: 3 Yrs   *ACGME Approved/Offered Positions:* 3
Program ID: 155-38-11-059

Oklahoma

Oklahoma City

University of Oklahoma Health Sciences Center Program
Sponsor: University of Oklahoma College of Medicine
OU Medical Center - Presbyterian Tower
Veterans Affairs Medical Center (Oklahoma City)
Prgm Director: Arafat Tfayli, MD
920 Stanton L Young Blvd, WP2040
Hematology-Oncology Section
Oklahoma City, OK 73104
Tel: 405 271-4022   *Fax:* 405 271-4221
E-mail: arafat-tfayli@ouhsc.edu
Length: 3 Yrs   *ACGME Approved/Offered Positions:* 9
Program ID: 155-39-21-060

Oregon

Portland

Oregon Health & Science University Program
Sponsor: Oregon Health & Science University Hospital
Veterans Affairs Medical Center (Portland)
Prgm Director: Charles D Lopez, MD, PhD
3181 SW Sam Jackson Park Road, l-586
Portland, OR 97239
Tel: 503 494-6525   *Fax:* 503 494-3257
Length: 3 Yrs   *ACGME Approved/Offered Positions:* 12
Program ID: 155-40-21-118

Pennsylvania

Hershey

Penn State University/Milton S Hershey Medical Center Program
Sponsor: Milton S Hershey Medical Center
Lehigh Valley Hospital Network
Prgm Director: Harold A Harvey, MD
Penn State College of Medicine
PO Box 850, 500 University Drive, H046
Hershey, PA 17033
Tel: 717 531-8678   *Fax:* 717 531-5076
E-mail: hharvey@hmc.psu.edu
Length: 3 Yrs   *ACGME Approved/Offered Positions:* 9
Program ID: 155-41-21-061

Philadelphia

Drexel University College of Medicine/Hahnemann University Hospital Program
Sponsor: Drexel University College of
   Medicine/Hahnemann University
Hahnemann University Hospital (Tenet Health System)
Prgm Director: Michael J Styler, MD
Broad and Vine Streets, MS 412
Philadelphia, PA 19102
Tel: 215 762-7026   *Fax:* 215 762-8857
E-mail: fmcmanus@drexelmed.edu
Length: 3 Yrs   *ACGME Approved/Offered Positions:* 9
Program ID: 155-41-31-062

Temple University Hospital Program
Sponsor: Temple University Hospital
Fox Chase Cancer Center
Prgm Director: Russell J Schilder, MD
Broad and Ontario Streets
Philadelphia, PA 19140
Tel: 215 728-3545   *Fax:* 215 728-3639
E-mail: russell.schilder@fccc.edu
Length: 3 Yrs   *ACGME Approved/Offered Positions:* 19
Program ID: 155-41-21-091

Thomas Jefferson University Program
Sponsor: Thomas Jefferson University Hospital
Prgm Director: Joanne Filicko-O'Hara, MD
Hematology/Medical Oncology Fellowship Program
834 Chestnut St, Suite 320 BEN Bldg
Philadelphia, PA 19107
Tel: 215 955-5822   *Fax:* 215 923-3836
E-mail: joanne.filicko@mail.jci.tju.edu
Length: 3 Yrs   *ACGME Approved/Offered Positions:* 15
Program ID: 155-41-21-130

University of Pennsylvania Program
Sponsor: University of Pennsylvania Health System
Prgm Director: Alison W Loren, MD, MS
3400 Spruce Street
16 Penn Tower
Philadelphia, PA 19104
Tel: 215 662-3681   *Fax:* 215 615-3704
E-mail: alexa.davis@uphs.upenn.edu
Length: 3 Yrs   *ACGME Approved/Offered Positions:* 27
Program ID: 155-41-21-081

Pittsburgh

University of Pittsburgh Medical Center Medical Education Program
Sponsor: Univ of Pittsburgh Medical Center Medical
   Education
UPMC Presbyterian Shadyside
Prgm Director: Robert L Redner, MD
UPMC Cancer Center
5150 Centre Avenue, Room 461
Pittsburgh, PA 15232
Tel: 412 623-3257   *Fax:* 412 623-7768
Length: 3 Yrs   *ACGME Approved/Offered Positions:* 24
Program ID: 155-41-21-122

Western Pennsylvania Hospital/Temple University Program
Sponsor: Western Pennsylvania Hospital
Allegheny General Hospital
Prgm Director: Robert B Kaplan, MD, MS
West Penn Cancer Institute
4800 Friendship Avenue
Pittsburgh, PA 15224
Tel: 412 578-4087   *Fax:* 412 578-4391
E-mail: rbkaplan@msn.com
Length: 3 Yrs   *ACGME Approved/Offered Positions:* 12
Program ID: 155-41-31-092

Wynnewood

Lankenau Hospital Program
Sponsor: Lankenau Hospital
Prgm Director: Mary Denshaw-Burke, MD
Suite 30 MOBW
100 Lancaster Avenue
Wynnewood, PA 19096
Tel: 610 645-3060   *Fax:* 610 645-2602
E-mail: Denshaw-BurkeM@mlhs.org
Length: 3 Yrs   *ACGME Approved/Offered Positions:* 4
Program ID: 155-41-31-077

Puerto Rico

San Juan

University of Puerto Rico Program
Sponsor: University of Puerto Rico School of Medicine
University Hospital
Prgm Director: Justiniano Castro, MD
Dpt of Medicine, UPR School of Medicine
PO Box 365067
San Juan, PR 00936
Tel: 787 754-0101   *Fax:* 787 756-5866
Length: 3 Yrs   *ACGME Approved/Offered Positions:* 3
Program ID: 155-42-21-080

Rhode Island

Providence

Brown University Program
Sponsor: Rhode Island Hospital-Lifespan
Miriam Hospital-Lifespan
Prgm Director: Anthony Mega, MD
164 Summit Avenue
Fain Building, 3rd Floor-Rear, Suite 390
Providence, RI 02906
Tel: 401 793-4645   *Fax:* 401 793-7132
E-mail: AMega@lifespan.org
Length: 3 Yrs   *ACGME Approved/Offered Positions:* 9
Program ID: 155-43-31-128

Roger Williams Medical Center Program
Sponsor: Roger Williams Medical Center
Rhode Island Hospital-Lifespan
Prgm Director: Frank J Cummings, MD
825 Chalkstone Avenue
Providence, RI 02908
Tel: 401 456-2070   *Fax:* 401 456-2016
Length: 3 Yrs   *ACGME Approved/Offered Positions:* 6
Program ID: 155-43-21-120

South Carolina

Charleston

Medical University of South Carolina Program
Sponsor: Medical University of South Carolina College of
   Medicine
MUSC Medical Center
Prgm Director: Lawrence B Afrin, MD
96 Jonathan Lucas Street
PO Box 250635, 903 CSB
Charleston, SC 29425
Tel: 843 792-4271   *Fax:* 843 792-0644
Length: 3 Yrs   *ACGME Approved/Offered Positions:* 10
Program ID: 155-45-21-063

Tennessee

Memphis

University of Tennessee Program

Sponsor: University of Tennessee College of Medicine
Methodist Healthcare - Memphis Hospitals
Prgm Director: Furhan Yunus, MD*
Department of Medicine
1331 Union Avenue, Suite 800
Memphis, TN 38104
Tel: 901 722-0558   *Fax:* 901 722-0445
Length: 3 Yrs   *ACGME Approved/Offered Positions:* 12
Program ID: 155-47-21-125

Nashville

Vanderbilt University Program

Sponsor: Vanderbilt University Medical Center
Meharry Medical College School of Medicine
Veterans Affairs Medical Center (Nashville)
Prgm Director: Jill Gilbert, MD*
Division of Hematology-Oncology
777 Preston Research Building
Nashville, TN 37232
Tel: 615 343-4677   *Fax:* 615 343-7602
E-mail: jill.gilbert@vanderbilt.edu
Length: 3 Yrs   *ACGME Approved/Offered Positions:* 18
Program ID: 155-47-31-065

Texas

Dallas

University of Texas Southwestern Medical School Program

Sponsor: University of Texas Southwestern Medical
School
Dallas County Hospital District-Parkland Memorial
Hospital
Dallas VA Medical Center
Prgm Director: Jonathan E Dowell, MD
5323 Harry Hines Blvd
Mail Code 8852
Dallas, TX 75390
Tel: 214 648-4180   *Fax:* 214 648-1955
E-mail: jonathan.dowell@utsouthwestern.edu
Length: 3 Yrs   *ACGME Approved/Offered Positions:* 12
Program ID: 155-48-21-066

Fort Sam Houston

San Antonio Uniformed Services Health Education Consortium Program

Sponsor: San Antonio Uniformed Services Health
Education Consortium
Brooke Army Medical Center
Wilford Hall Medical Center (AETC)
Prgm Director: Michael B Osswald, MD
2200 Bergquist Drive, Suite 1
Suite 1
Lackland AFB, TX 78236
Tel: 210 292-3820   *Fax:* 210 292-7317
Length: 3 Yrs   *ACGME Approved/Offered Positions:* 12
Program ID: 155-48-31-067
Uniformed Services Program

Houston

Baylor College of Medicine Program

Sponsor: Baylor College of Medicine
Harris County Hospital District-Ben Taub General
Hospital
Methodist Hospital (Houston)
Michael E DeBakey VA Medical Center - Houston
University of Texas M D Anderson Cancer Center
Prgm Director: Teresa G Hayes, MD, PhD
1709 Dryden Ste 650
Houston, TX 77030
Tel: 713 794-7368   *Fax:* 713 794-7733
E-mail: thayes@bcm.edu
Length: 3 Yrs   *ACGME Approved/Offered Positions:* 20
Program ID: 155-48-21-146

University of Texas at Houston/M D Anderson Cancer Center Program

Sponsor: University of Texas Health Science Center at
Houston
Harris County Hospital District-Ben Taub General
Hospital
Lyndon B Johnson General Hospital
Methodist Hospital (Houston)
University of Texas M D Anderson Cancer Center
Prgm Director: Robert A Wolff, MD
1515 Holcombe, Unit 421
Houston, TX 77030
Tel: 713 792-7246   *Fax:* 713 745-1827
E-mail: rwolff@mdanderson.org
Length: 3 Yrs   *ACGME Approved/Offered Positions:* 42
Program ID: 155-48-12-150

San Antonio

University of Texas Health Science Center at San Antonio Program

Sponsor: University of Texas School of Medicine at San
Antonio
Audie L Murphy Memorial Veterans Hospital (San
Antonio)
University Health System
Prgm Director: Anand B Karnad, MD
7979 Wurzbach Rd 4th Floor Zellar MSC 8221
San Antonio, TX 78229
Tel: 210 450-1667   *Fax:* 210 450-1666
Length: 3 Yrs   *ACGME Approved/Offered Positions:* 12
Program ID: 155-48-21-099

Utah

Salt Lake City

University of Utah Program

Sponsor: University of Utah Medical Center
Prgm Director: Martha Glenn, MD
50 North Medical Drive
Salt Lake City, UT 84132
Tel: 801 585-0255   *Fax:* 801 585-0124
Length: 3 Yrs   *ACGME Approved/Offered Positions:* 12
Program ID: 155-49-21-082

Vermont

Burlington

University of Vermont Program

Sponsor: Fletcher Allen Health Care
Prgm Director: George K Philips, MBBS, MD
Given Building E214
89 Beaumont Avenue
Burlington, VT 05405
Tel: 802 656-5487   *Fax:* 802 656-5493
E-mail: George.Philips@vtmednet.org
Length: 3 Yrs   *ACGME Approved/Offered Positions:* 6
Program ID: 155-50-21-069

Virginia

Charlottesville

University of Virginia Program

Sponsor: University of Virginia Medical Center
Prgm Director: Christiana M Brenin, MD*
PO Box 800716
Charlottesville, VA 22908
Tel: 434 924-8552   *Fax:* 434 982-4207
E-mail: cmb4z@virginia.edu
Length: 3 Yrs   *ACGME Approved/Offered Positions:* 7
Program ID: 155-51-31-078

Richmond

Virginia Commonwealth University Health System Program

Sponsor: Virginia Commonwealth University Health
System
Hunter Holmes McGuire VA Medical Center (Richmond)
Medical College of Virginia Hospitals
Prgm Director: Laurie J Lyckholm, MD
1101 E Marshall Street, Room 6-030
PO Box 980230
Richmond, VA 23298
Tel: 804 828-9723   *Fax:* 804 828-8079
E-mail: lyckholm@vcu.edu
Length: 3 Yrs   *ACGME Approved/Offered Positions:* 8
Program ID: 155-51-21-070

Washington

Seattle

University of Washington Program

Sponsor: University of Washington School of Medicine
Fred Hutchinson Cancer Research Center
Prgm Director: F Marc Stewart, MD
825 Eastlake Avenue E
Mail Stop G4-810
Seattle, WA 98109
Tel: 206 288-1192   *Fax:* 206 288-1119
E-mail: landerso@seattlecca.org
Length: 3 Yrs   *ACGME Approved/Offered Positions:* 27
Program ID: 155-54-13-151

West Virginia

Morgantown

West Virginia University Program

Sponsor: West Virginia University School of Medicine
West Virginia University Hospitals
Prgm Director: Thomas F Hogan, MD
PO Box 9162
RCB-HSC
Morgantown, WV 26506
Tel: 304 293-4229   *Fax:* 304 293-2519
E-mail: thogan@hsc.wvu.edu
Length: 3 Yrs   *ACGME Approved/Offered Positions:* 8
Program ID: 155-55-21-109

Note: * indicates a newly appointed program director

Wisconsin

Milwaukee

Medical College of Wisconsin Affiliated Hospitals Program

Sponsor: Medical College of Wisconsin Affiliated Hospitals, Inc
Clement J Zablocki Veterans Affairs Medical Center
Froedtert Memorial Lutheran Hospital
Prgm Director: Christopher R Chitambar, MD
Div of Neoplastic Diseases and Related Disorders
9200 West Wisconsin Avenue
Milwaukee, WI 53226
Tel: 414 805-4602   *Fax:* 414 805-4606
Length: 3 Yrs   *ACGME Approved/Offered Positions:* 9
Program ID: 155-56-21-119

Hospice and Palliative Medicine

Alabama

Birmingham

University of Alabama Hospital Program

Sponsor: University of Alabama Hospital
Prgm Director: Rodney O Tucker, MD
CH19 Suite 219
1530 3rd Avenue South
Birmingham, AL 35294
Tel: 205 975-8197   *Fax:* 205 975-8173
Length: 1 Yr   *ACGME Approved/Offered Positions:* 4
Program ID: 540-01-14-027

Arizona

Phoenix

College of Medicine, Mayo Clinic Program

Sponsor: College of Medicine, Mayo Clinic
Mayo Clinic Hospital
Prgm Director: Eric E Prommer, MD
5777 E Mayo Boulevard
Phoenix, AZ 85254
Tel: 480 342-2088
Length: 1 Yr   *ACGME Approved/Offered Positions:* 1
Program ID: 540-03-14-014

California

Los Angeles

Cedars-Sinai Medical Center Program

Sponsor: Cedars-Sinai Medical Center
VA Greater Los Angeles Healthcare System
Prgm Director: Kenneth E Rosenfeld, MD
Graduate Medical Education Office
8797 Beverly Blvd, Suite 250
Los Angeles, CA 90048
Tel: 310 478-3711   *Fax:* 310 268-4272
E-mail: kenneth.rosenfeld@va.gov
Length: 1 Yr   *ACGME Approved/Offered Positions:* 4
Program ID: 540-05-14-030

San Diego

Scripps Mercy Hospital Program

Sponsor: Scripps Mercy Hospital
San Diego Hospice and Palliative Care Center
Prgm Director: Gary T Buckholz, MD
4077 Fifth Avenue
San Diego, CA 92103
Tel: 619 688-1600   *Fax:* 619 298-7027
E-mail: gbuckholz@sdhospice.org
Length: 1 Yr   *ACGME Approved/Offered Positions:* 12
Program ID: 540-05-14-060

San Francisco

University of California (San Francisco) School of Medicine Program

Sponsor: University of California (San Francisco) School of Medicine
Prgm Director: Steven Pantilat, MD
521 Parnassus Ave, Suite C-126
UCSF, Box 0903
San Francisco, CA 94143
Tel: 415 476-9019   *Fax:* 415 476-5020
E-mail: stevep@medicine.ucsf.edu
Length: 1 Yr   *ACGME Approved/Offered Positions:* 4
Program ID: 540-05-14-056

Stanford

Stanford Hospital and Clinics Program

Sponsor: Stanford Hospital and Clinics
Prgm Director: V J Periyakoil, MD
300 Pastuer Drive S101
Stanford, CA 94305
Tel: 650 723-5334
E-mail: vyju1@stanford.edu
Length: 1 Yr   *ACGME Approved/Offered Positions:* 6
Program ID: 540-05-14-019

District of Columbia

Washington

George Washington University School of Medicine Program

Sponsor: George Washington University School of Medicine
Veterans Affairs Medical Center (Washington, DC)
Prgm Director: Karen Blackstone, MD
2121 Eye Street NW
Washington, DC 20052
Tel: 202 745-8000   *Fax:* 202 745-4024
E-mail: karen.blackstone@va.gov
Length: 1 Yr   *ACGME Approved/Offered Positions:* 2
Program ID: 540-10-14-044

Florida

Tampa

University of South Florida College of Medicine Program

Sponsor: University of South Florida College of Medicine
Prgm Director: Robert M Walker, MD
12901 Bruce B Downs Blvd
MDC 19
Tampa, FL 33612
Tel: 813 974-5300   *Fax:* 813 974-5460
E-mail: rowalker@health.usf.edu
Length: 1 Yr   *ACGME Approved/Offered Positions:* 6
Program ID: 540-11-14-025

Illinois

Chicago

McGaw Medical Center of Northwestern University Program

Sponsor: McGaw Medical Center of Northwestern University
Prgm Director: Jamie VonRoenn, MD
645 North Michigan Avenue
Suite 1058-A
Chicago, IL 60611
Tel: 312 695-4542   *Fax:* 312 695-6189
E-mail: j-vonroenn@northwestern.edu
Length: 1 Yr   *ACGME Approved/Offered Positions:* 3
Program ID: 540-16-14-026

Rush University Medical Center Program
Sponsor: Rush University Medical Center
Prgm Director: Martha Twaddle, MD
Department of Medicine
1653 W Congress Pkwy
Chicago, IL 60612
Tel: 847 467-7423
E-mail: www.carecenter.org
Length: 1 Yr   *ACGME Approved/Offered Positions:* 3
Program ID: 540-16-14-042

Indiana

Indianapolis

Indiana University School of Medicine Program
Sponsor: Indiana University School of Medicine
St Vincent Hospitals and Health Care Center
Prgm Director: Gregory P Gramelspacher, MD
1120 South Drive
Fesler Hall 302
Indianapolis, IN 46202
Tel: 317 630-6911   *Fax:* 317 630-7066
Length: 1 Yr   *ACGME Approved/Offered Positions:* 3
Program ID: 540-17-14-002

Iowa

Mason City

Mercy Medical Center-North Iowa Program
Sponsor: Mercy Medical Center-North Iowa
Prgm Director: William D Clark, MD
1000 4th St SW
Mason City, IA 50401
Tel: 641 422-7320   *Fax:* 641 422-7125
E-mail: clarkw@mercyhealth.com
Length: 1 Yr   *ACGME Approved/Offered Positions:* 1
Program ID: 540-18-12-012

Kansas

Kansas City

University of Kansas School of Medicine Program
Sponsor: University of Kansas School of Medicine
Prgm Director: Karin B Porter-Williamson, MD
3901 Rainbow Boulevard
Kansas City, KS 66160
Tel: 913 588-6063   *Fax:* 913 588-3877
E-mail: kporter-williamson@kumc.edu
Length: 1 Yr   *ACGME Approved/Offered Positions:* 2
Program ID: 540-19-14-036

Kentucky

Lexington

University of Kentucky College of Medicine Program
Sponsor: University of Kentucky College of Medicine
Hospice of the Bluegrass
Prgm Director: Todd Cote, MD
Department of Internal Medicine
K529 Kentucky Clinic 740 South Limestone
Lexington, KY 40536
Tel: 859 276-5344   *Fax:* 859 296-0362
E-mail: tcote@hospicebg.org
Length: 1 Yr   *ACGME Approved/Offered Positions:* 1
Program ID: 540-20-14-059

Louisville

University of Louisville School of Medicine Program
Sponsor: University of Louisville School of Medicine
Prgm Director: Christian D Furman, MD, MSPH
550 South Jackson Street, ACB-3rd Floor
Louisville, KY 40292
Tel: 502 852-7945   *Fax:* 502 852-8980
E-mail: amy.kiper@louisville.edu
Length: 1 Yr   *ACGME Approved/Offered Positions:* 2
Program ID: 540-20-14-032

Massachusetts

Boston

Massachusetts General Hospital Program
Sponsor: Massachusetts General Hospital
Children's Hospital
Dana-Farber Cancer Institute
Prgm Director: Vicki A Jackson, MD, MPH
55 Fruit Street
Founders 600
Boston, MA 02114
Tel: 617 724-9509   *Fax:* 617 724-8693
E-mail: vjackson@partners.org
Length: 1 Yr   *ACGME Approved/Offered Positions:* 9
Program ID: 540-24-14-046

Michigan

Ann Arbor

University of Michigan Hospitals and Health Centers Program
Sponsor: University of Michigan Hospitals and Health Centers
Prgm Director: Marcos L Montagnini, MD
2215 Fuller Road
Ann Arbor, MI 48105
Tel: 734 845-3072   *Fax:* 734 845-3298
E-mail: mmontag@umich.edu
Length: 1 Yr   *ACGME Approved/Offered Positions:* 3
Program ID: 540-25-14-033

Detroit

Henry Ford Hospital Program
Sponsor: Henry Ford Hospital
Prgm Director: Leslie Bricker, MD
2799 W Grand Blvd
Detroit, MI 48202
Tel: 313 916-8144
Length: 1 Yr   *ACGME Approved/Offered Positions:* 2
Program ID: 540-25-14-017

Wayne State University/Detroit Medical Center Program
Sponsor: Wayne State University/Detroit Medical Center
Prgm Director: Kevin R McDonald, MD
Graduate Medical Education
4201 St Antoine, UHC 9C
Detroit, MI 48201
Tel: 313 576-3997   *Fax:* 313 576-1092
E-mail: kevin.mcdonald@va.gov
Length: 1 Yr   *ACGME Approved/Offered Positions:* 3
Program ID: 540-25-14-058

Minnesota

Minneapolis

University of Minnesota Medical School Program
Sponsor: University of Minnesota Medical School
Prgm Director: Sandra W Gordon-Kolb, MD
MMC 293
420 Delaware Street SE
Minneapolis, MN 55455
Tel: 612 273-4861   *Fax:* 612 626-2694
E-mail: ward0192@umn.edu
Length: 1 Yr   *ACGME Approved/Offered Positions:* 2
Program ID: 540-26-12-023

Rochester

College of Medicine, Mayo Clinic Program
Sponsor: College of Medicine, Mayo Clinic
Mayo Clinic (Rochester)
Rochester Methodist Hospital
Saint Marys Hospital of Rochester
Prgm Director: Elise C Carey, MD
200 First Street SW
Rochester, MN 55905
Tel: 507 284-1450   *Fax:* 507 284-5370
Length: 1 Yr   *ACGME Approved/Offered Positions:* 2
Program ID: 540-26-14-037

New Hampshire

Lebanon

Mary Hitchcock Memorial Hospital Program
Sponsor: Mary Hitchcock Memorial Hospital
Prgm Director: Frances C Brokaw, MD, MS
1 Medical Center Dr
Lebanon, NH 03756
Tel: 603 650-5402
Length: 1 Yr   *ACGME Approved/Offered Positions:* 3
Program ID: 540-32-04-047

New York

Bronx

Albert Einstein College of Medicine of Yeshiva University Program
Sponsor: Albert Einstein College of Medicine of Yeshiva University
Montefiore Medical Center-Henry and Lucy Moses Division
Visiting Nurse Service of New York
Prgm Director: Allen C Hutcheson, MD
Montefiore Fellowship in Hospice and Palliative Me
3335 Steuben Ave
Bronx, NY 10467
Tel: 718 920-6378   *Fax:* 718 881-6054
E-mail: ahutches@montefiore.org
Length: 1 Yr   *ACGME Approved/Offered Positions:* 2
Program ID: 540-35-12-015

Note: * indicates a newly appointed program director

Buffalo

University at Buffalo School of Medicine Program

Sponsor: University at Buffalo School of Medicine
Center for Hospice and Palliative Care/Hospice Buffalo
Prgm Director: Amy A McDonald, MD
117 Cary Hall
3435 Main Street
Buffalo, NY 14214
Tel: 716 862-3282   *Fax:* 716 862-8655
E-mail: amy.mcdonald@va.gov
Length: 1 Yr   *ACGME Approved/Offered Positions:* 2
Program ID: 540-35-14-009

Great Neck

North Shore-Long Island Jewish Health System Program

Sponsor: North Shore-Long Island Jewish Health System
Prgm Director: Dana Lustbader, MD
Dana Lustbader MD, Critical Care Medicine
300 Community Drive
Manhasset, NY 11030
Tel: 516 562-1621   *Fax:* 516 562-3014
E-mail: Lustbader@nshs.edu
Length: 1 Yr   *ACGME Approved/Offered Positions:* 2
Program ID: 540-35-14-049

New York

Beth Israel Medical Center Program

Sponsor: Beth Israel Medical Center
Prgm Director: Pauline Lesage, MD, LLB
First Avenue at 16th Street
Baird Hall - 12th Floor
New York, NY 10003
Tel: 212 844-1487   *Fax:* 212 844-1503
E-mail: mglajchen@chpnet.org
Length: 1 Yr   *ACGME Approved/Offered Positions:* 6
Program ID: 540-35-12-039

Mount Sinai School of Medicine Program

Sponsor: Mount Sinai School of Medicine
Mount Sinai Medical Center
Visiting Nurse Service of New York
Prgm Director: Nathan Goldstein, MD
Department of Geriatrics - Box 1070
One Gustave Levy Place
New York, NY 10029
Tel: 212 241-1446   *Fax:* 212 860-9737
Length: 1 Yr   *ACGME Approved/Offered Positions:* 4
Program ID: 540-35-14-043

Rochester

Strong Memorial Hospital of the University of Rochester Program

Sponsor: Strong Memorial Hospital of the University of
Rochester
Prgm Director: David Korones, MD
601 Elmwood Avenue
Box 687
Rochester, NY 14642
Tel: 585 275-2981   *Fax:* 585 273-1039
E-mail: david_korones@urmc.rochester.edu
Length: 1 Yr   *ACGME Approved/Offered Positions:* 2
Program ID: 540-35-14-001

North Carolina

Durham

Duke University Hospital Program

Sponsor: Duke University Hospital
Duke HomeCare & Hospice
Veterans Affairs Medical Center (Durham)
Prgm Director: James Tulsky, MD
Duke University Medical Center, Box 3951
Durham, NC 27710
Tel: 919 668-2362   *Fax:* 919 668-1300
Length: 1 Yr   *ACGME Approved/Offered Positions:* 1
Program ID: 540-36-14-021

Ohio

Akron

Children's Hospital Medical Center of Akron Program

Sponsor: Children's Hospital Medical Center of Akron
Prgm Director: Sarah E Friebert, MD
1 Perkins Square
Akron, OH 44308
Tel: 330 543-3343   *Fax:* 330 543-3539
E-mail: sfriebert@chmca.org
Length: 1 Yr   *ACGME Approved/Offered Positions:* 1
Program ID: 540-38-32-038

Summa Health System Program

Sponsor: Summa Health System
Akron City Hospital (Summa Health System)
Prgm Director: Steven M Radwany, MD
Suite 1A
55 Arch Street
Akron, OH 44304
Tel: 330 375-3600   *Fax:* 330 375-4939
E-mail: radwanys@summa-health.org
Length: 1 Yr   *ACGME Approved/Offered Positions:* 3
Program ID: 540-38-14-005

Cleveland

Cleveland Clinic Foundation Program

Sponsor: Cleveland Clinic Foundation
Prgm Director: Susan LeGrand, MD
Taussig Cancer Institute
9500 Euclid Avenue, R35
Cleveland, OH 44195
Tel: 216 445-0624   *Fax:* 216 636-1711
E-mail: meded@ccf.org
Length: 1 Yr   *ACGME Approved/Offered Positions:* 4
Program ID: 540-38-14-006

MetroHealth Medical Center Program

Sponsor: MetroHealth Medical Center
Hospice of the Western Reserve
Prgm Director: Elizabeth O'Toole, MD
2500 MetroHealth Drive R243
Cleveland, OH 44109
Tel: 216 778-2777   *Fax:* 216 778-5935
E-mail: eeotoole@metrohealth.org
Length: 1 Yr   *ACGME Approved/Offered Positions:* 2
Program ID: 540-38-14-003

Dayton

Wright State University Boonshoft School of Medicine Program

Sponsor: Wright State University Boonshoft School of
Medicine
Prgm Director: Geetika Kumar, MBBS
PO Box 927
Dayton, OH 45401
Tel: 937 268-6511   *Fax:* 937 267-5310
E-mail: diana.ramsey@wright.edu
Length: 1 Yr   *ACGME Approved/Offered Positions:* 2
Program ID: 540-38-14-022

Oregon

Portland

Oregon Health & Science University Hospital Program

Sponsor: Oregon Health & Science University Hospital
Prgm Director: Nora Tobin, MD
3181 SW Sam Jackson Park Rd L579
Portland, OR 97239
Tel: 503 273-5015   *Fax:* 503 721-7807
Length: 1 Yr   *ACGME Approved/Offered Positions:* 2
Program ID: 540-40-14-004

Pennsylvania

Lancaster

Lancaster General Hospital Program

Sponsor: Lancaster General Hospital
Prgm Director: James A Probolus, MD
685 Good Drive
PO Box 4125
Lancaster, PA 17604
Tel: 717 295-3900
Length: 1 Yr   *ACGME Approved/Offered Positions:* 1
Program ID: 540-41-12-008

Philadelphia

Children's Hospital of Philadelphia Program

Sponsor: Children's Hospital of Philadelphia
Penn Home Care and Hospice Services
Prgm Director: Jeffrey C Klick, MD
Pediatric Advanced Care Team
4th Floor Wood Building
Philadelphia, PA 19104
Tel: 215 590-3347   *Fax:* 215 590-2180
E-mail: klick@email.chop.edu
Length: 1 Yr   *ACGME Approved/Offered Positions:* 1
Program ID: 540-41-32-013

University of Pennsylvania Health System Program

Sponsor: University of Pennsylvania Health System
Prgm Director: Jennifer Kapo, MD
3400 Spruce Street
Philadelphia, PA 19104
Tel: 215 823-4583
E-mail: jennifer.kapo@uphs.upenn.edu
Length: 1 Yr   *ACGME Approved/Offered Positions:* 2
Program ID: 540-41-14-048

Pittsburgh

Univ of Pittsburgh Medical Center Medical Education Program

Sponsor: Univ of Pittsburgh Medical Center Medical
Education
Family Hospice and Palliative Care
Prgm Director: Robert Arnold, MD
200 Lothrop Street, MUH 932 W
Pittsburgh, PA 15213
Tel: 412 802-6249   *Fax:* 412 692-4315
E-mail: rabob@pitt.edu
Length: 1 Yr   *ACGME Approved/Offered Positions:* 2
Program ID: 540-41-14-011

Programs

Tennessee

Chattanooga

University of Tennessee College of Medicine-Chattanooga Program
Sponsor: University of Tennessee College of
  Medicine-Chattanooga
Erlanger Medical Center
Hospice of Chattanooga
Prgm Director: Valencia S Clay, MD
960 East Third Street
Suite 104
Chattanooga, TN 37403
Tel: 423 892-4289   *Fax:* 423 892-8301
E-mail: Valencia_Clay@hospiceofchattanooga.org
Length: 1 Yr   *ACGME Approved/Offered Positions:* 1
Program ID: 540-47-14-051

Nashville

Vanderbilt University Medical Center Program
Sponsor: Vanderbilt University Medical Center
Prgm Director: Sumathi K Misra, MD, MPH
1211 Medical Center Drive
Nashville, TN 37232
Tel: 615 835-5338   *Fax:* 615 936-3156
E-mail: sumathi.misra@vanderbilt.edu
Length: 1 Yr   *ACGME Approved/Offered Positions:* 2
Program ID: 540-47-14-053

Texas

Houston

University of Texas M D Anderson Cancer Center Program
Sponsor: University of Texas M D Anderson Cancer
  Center
Prgm Director: Suresh K Reddy, MD
1515 Holcombe Blvd, Unit 008
Houston, TX 77030
Tel: 713 794-5362   *Fax:* 713 792-6092
E-mail: ccooley@mdanderson.org
Length: 1 Yr   *ACGME Approved/Offered Positions:* 5
Program ID: 540-48-43-034

San Antonio

University of Texas Medical School at San Antonio Program
Sponsor: University of Texas School of Medicine at San
  Antonio
Prgm Director: Sandra E Sanchez-Reilly, MD
7703 Floyd Curl Drive MC 7875
San Antonio, TX 78229
Tel: 210 617-5237   *Fax:* 210 617-5312
E-mail: sanchezreill@uthscsa.edu
Length: 1 Yr   *ACGME Approved/Offered Positions:* 4
Program ID: 540-48-14-024

Utah

Salt Lake City

University of Utah Medical Center Program
Sponsor: University of Utah Medical Center
Prgm Director: Sharon Weinstein, MD
50 North Medical Drive, Room 3C444SOM
Salt Lake City, UT 84132
Tel: 801 585-0112   *Fax:* 801 585-0159
E-mail: suzy.simmonds@hci.utah.edu
Length: 1 Yr   *ACGME Approved/Offered Positions:* 1
Program ID: 540-49-04-054

Virginia

Richmond

Virginia Commonwealth University Health System Program
Sponsor: Virginia Commonwealth University Health
  System
Hunter Holmes McGuire VA Medical Center (Richmond)
Prgm Director: Laurel J Lyckholm, MD
Box 980230
Richmond, VA 23298
Tel: 804 828-9723   *Fax:* 804 828-8079
E-mail: lyckholm@vcu.edu
Length: 1 Yr   *ACGME Approved/Offered Positions:* 4
Program ID: 540-51-14-018

Wisconsin

Madison

University of Wisconsin Hospital and Clinics Program
Sponsor: University of Wisconsin Hospital and Clinics
HospiceCare Inc.
William S Middleton Veterans Hospital
Prgm Director: Matthew D LoConte, MD
600 Highland Ave
Madison, WI 53792
Tel: 608 280-7056   *Fax:* 608 280-7140
E-mail: md.loconte@hosp.wisc.edu
Length: 1 Yr   *ACGME Approved/Offered Positions:* 4
Program ID: 540-56-14-016

Marshfield

Marshfield Clinic-St Joseph's Hospital Program
Sponsor: Marshfield Clinic-St Joseph's Hospital
Prgm Director: Tomasz R Okon, MD
1000 North Oak Avenue
Marshfield, WI 54449
Tel: 715 389-4151
Length: 1 Yr   *ACGME Approved/Offered Positions:* 1
Program ID: 540-56-14-040

Milwaukee

Medical College of Wisconsin Affiliated Hospitals, Inc Program
Sponsor: Medical College of Wisconsin Affiliated
  Hospitals, Inc
Froedtert Memorial Lutheran Hospital
Prgm Director: Drew A Rosielle, MD
Palliative Care Center
9200 W Wisconsin Avenue
Milwaukee, WI 53226
Tel: 414 805-4607   *Fax:* 414 805-4608
E-mail: drosiell@mcw.edu
Length: 1 Yr   *ACGME Approved/Offered Positions:* 2
Program ID: 540-56-14-010

Infectious Disease (Internal Medicine)

Alabama

Birmingham

University of Alabama Medical Center Program
Sponsor: University of Alabama Hospital
Cooper Green Hospital
Veterans Affairs Medical Center (Birmingham)
Prgm Director: Victoria A Johnson, MD*
1530 3rd Avenue South
Tinsley Harrison Tower 229
Birmingham, AL 35294
Tel: 205 934-5191   *Fax:* 205 934-5155
E-mail: vnoles@uab.edu
Length: 2 Yrs   *ACGME Approved/Offered Positions:* 8
Program ID: 146-01-21-121

Mobile

University of South Alabama Program
Sponsor: University of South Alabama Hospitals
Infirmary West
Mobile Infirmary Medical Center
University of South Alabama Medical Center
USA Children's and Women's Hospital
Prgm Director: John A Vande Waa, DO, PhD
Department of Medicine, Mastin 400 G
2451 Fillingim Street
Mobile, AL 36617
Tel: 251 471-7895   *Fax:* 251 471-7898
Length: 2 Yrs   *ACGME Approved/Offered Positions:* 2
Program ID: 146-01-11-089

Arizona

Tucson

University of Arizona Program
Sponsor: University of Arizona College of Medicine
Southern Arizona VA Health Care Center (Tucson)
University Medical Center
University of Arizona/UPHK Graduate Medical Ed
  Consortium
Prgm Director: Stephen A Klotz, MD
Section of Infectious Diseases
1501 N Campbell Avenue
Tucson, AZ 85724
Tel: 520 626-6887   *Fax:* 520 626-5183
E-mail: lqg@u.arizona.edu
Length: 2 Yrs   *ACGME Approved/Offered Positions:* 4
Program ID: 146-03-13-201

Arkansas

Little Rock

University of Arkansas for Medical Sciences Program
Sponsor: University of Arkansas College of Medicine
Central Arkansas Veterans Healthcare System
UAMS Medical Center
Prgm Director: Robert W Bradsher Jr, MD
4301 W Markham, #639
Little Rock, AR 72205
Tel: 501 686-5585   *Fax:* 501 686-5549
E-mail: imresident@uams.edu
Length: 2 Yrs   *ACGME Approved/Offered Positions:* 4
Program ID: 146-04-21-107

Note: * indicates a newly appointed program director

California

Fresno

University of California (San Francisco)/Fresno Program

Sponsor: UCSF Fresno Medical Education Program
Community Medical Centers (Fresno)
VA Central California Health Care System
Prgm Director: Naiel N Nassar, MD
155 North Fresno Street, Suite 307
Fresno, CA 93701
Tel: 559 499-6500   *Fax:* 559 499-6501
E-mail: judythomas@fresno.ucsf.edu
Length: 2 Yrs   *ACGME Approved/Offered Positions:* 4
Program ID: 146-05-21-211

Los Angeles

UCLA Medical Center Program

Sponsor: UCLA David Geffen School of Medicine/UCLA
   Medical Center
UCLA Medical Center
Prgm Director: David A Pegues, MD
37-121 Center for Health Science
10833 Le Conte Avenue
Los Angeles, CA 90095
Tel: 310 267-9634   *Fax:* 310 267-3840
E-mail: dpegues@mednet.ucla.edu
Length: 2 Yrs   *ACGME Approved/Offered Positions:* 4
Program ID: 146-05-11-124

UCLA-VA Greater Los Angeles Program

Sponsor: VA Greater Los Angeles Healthcare System
Cedars-Sinai Medical Center
Olive View/UCLA Medical Center
Prgm Director: Matthew B Goetz, MD
Infectious Disease Sect (111F)
11301 Wilshire Boulevard
Los Angeles, CA 90073
Tel: 310 268-3015   *Fax:* 310 268-4928
E-mail: matthew.goetz@va.gov
Length: 2 Yrs   *ACGME Approved/Offered Positions:* 9
Program ID: 146-05-21-195

University of Southern California/ LAC+USC Medical Center Program

Sponsor: University of Southern California/LAC+USC
   Medical Center
LAC+USC Medical Center
USC University Hospital
Prgm Director: Paul D Holtom, MD
1200 N State St, Room 6610
Los Angeles, CA 90033
Tel: 323 226-7504   *Fax:* 323 226-3696
E-mail: eromero@usc.edu
Length: 2 Yrs   *ACGME Approved/Offered Positions:* 6
Program ID: 146-05-21-042

Orange

University of California (Irvine) Program

Sponsor: University of California (Irvine) Medical
   Center
VA Long Beach Healthcare System
Prgm Director: Geeta K Gupta, MD
101 City Drive South
Bldg 53, Ste 215
Orange, CA 92868
Tel: 714 456-7612   *Fax:* 714 456-7169
E-mail: ggupta@uci.edu
Length: 2 Yrs   *ACGME Approved/Offered Positions:* 4
Program ID: 146-05-21-141

Sacramento

University of California (Davis) Health System Program

Sponsor: University of California (Davis) Health System
University of California (Davis) Medical Center
VA Northern California Health Care System
Prgm Director: Stuart H Cohen, MD
4150 V Street, Suite 500
Sacramento, CA 95817
Tel: 916 734-3741   *Fax:* 916 734-7766
E-mail: stcohen@ucdavis.edu
Length: 2 Yrs   *ACGME Approved/Offered Positions:* 4
Program ID: 146-05-21-095

San Diego

Naval Medical Center (San Diego) Program

Sponsor: Naval Medical Center (San Diego)
Prgm Director: Braden R Hale, MD, MPH
Department of Medicine
34800 Bob Wilson Drive
San Diego, CA 92134
Tel: 619 532-7475   *Fax:* 619 532-7478
Length: 2 Yrs   *ACGME Approved/Offered Positions:* 4
Program ID: 146-05-12-142
Uniformed Services Program

University of California (San Diego) Program

Sponsor: University of California (San Diego) Medical
   Center
Prgm Director: Constance A Benson, MD
Stein Clinical Research Bldg, Rm 401
9500 Gilman Drive, MC 0711
La Jolla, CA 92093
Tel: 858 822-0333   *Fax:* 858 822-5362
E-mail: cbenson@ucsd.edu
Length: 2 Yrs   *ACGME Approved/Offered Positions:* 8
Program ID: 146-05-21-163

San Francisco

University of California (San Francisco) Program

Sponsor: University of California (San Francisco) School
   of Medicine
San Francisco General Hospital Medical Center
UCSF and Mount Zion Medical Centers
Veterans Affairs Medical Center (San Francisco)
Prgm Director: Henry F Chambers, MD
513 Parnassus Avenue, Box 0654, Room S380
UCSF Medical Center
San Francisco, CA 94143
Tel: 415 206-5437   *Fax:* 415 648-8425
Length: 2 Yrs   *ACGME Approved/Offered Positions:* 10
Program ID: 146-05-21-144

Stanford

Stanford University Program

Sponsor: Stanford Hospital and Clinics
Prgm Director: David Relman, MD
Department of Medicine
300 Pasteur Dr
Stanford, CA 94305
Tel: 650 852-3308   *Fax:* 650 498-7011
Length: 2 Yrs   *ACGME Approved/Offered Positions:* 10
Program ID: 146-05-21-023

Torrance

Los Angeles County-Harbor-UCLA Medical Center Program

Sponsor: Los Angeles County-Harbor-UCLA Medical
   Center
Prgm Director: John E Edwards Jr, MD
1000 W Carson Street
St John's Cardiovascular Research Center
Torrance, CA 90509
Tel: 310 222-3813   *Fax:* 310 782-2016
E-mail: WRafkin@labiomed.org
Length: 2 Yrs   *ACGME Approved/Offered Positions:* 4
Program ID: 146-05-11-164

Colorado

Aurora

University of Colorado Denver Program

Sponsor: University of Colorado Denver School of
   Medicine
Denver Health Medical Center
University of Colorado Hospital
Veterans Affairs Medical Center (Denver)
Prgm Director: Nancy E Madinger, MD
Division of Infectious Diseases
4200 E 9th Ave, B168
Denver, CO 80262
Tel: 303 315-7233   *Fax:* 303 315-8681
E-mail: Nancy.Madinger@uchsc.edu
Length: 2 Yrs   *ACGME Approved/Offered Positions:* 8
Program ID: 146-07-21-050

Connecticut

Farmington

University of Connecticut Program

Sponsor: University of Connecticut School of Medicine
Hartford Hospital
Hospital for Central Connecticut
St Francis Hospital and Medical Center
Univ of Connecticut Health Center/John Dempsey
   Hospital
Prgm Director: Kevin Dieckhaus, MD*
Division of Infectious Diseases
263 Farmington Avenue
Farmington, CT 06030
Tel: 860 679-4745   *Fax:* 860 679-4701
E-mail: dieckhaus@up.uchc.edu
Length: 2 Yrs   *ACGME Approved/Offered Positions:* 4
Program ID: 146-08-31-001

New Haven

Yale-New Haven Medical Center Program

Sponsor: Yale-New Haven Hospital
Hospital of St Raphael
Veterans Affairs Medical Center (West Haven)
Prgm Director: Vincent J Quagliarello, MD
Internal Medicine, Infectious Diseases
PO Box 20822
New Haven, CT 06520
Tel: 203 785-7571   *Fax:* 203 785-3864
E-mail: marilyn.a.powers@yale.edu
Length: 2 Yrs   *ACGME Approved/Offered Positions:* 8
Program ID: 146-08-21-024

District of Columbia

Washington

George Washington University Program
Sponsor: George Washington University School of Medicine
George Washington University Hospital (UHS)
Veterans Affairs Medical Center (Washington, DC)
Prgm Director: Afsoon Roberts, MD*
Department of Medicine
2150 Pennsylvania Ave, NW, 5th Floor
Washington, DC 20037
Tel: 202 741-2234   *Fax:* 202 741-2241
Length: 2 Yrs   *ACGME Approved/Offered Positions:* 5
Program ID: 146-10-21-109

Georgetown University Hospital Program
Sponsor: Georgetown University Hospital
Prgm Director: Princy N Kumar, MD
Department of Medicine
3800 Reservoir Road, NW
Washington, DC 20007
Tel: 202 687-8514   *Fax:* 202 687-6476
E-mail: steelewe@gunet.georgetown.edu
Length: 2 Yrs   *ACGME Approved/Offered Positions:* 3
Program ID: 146-10-21-090

Georgetown University Hospital/Washington Hospital Center Program
Sponsor: Washington Hospital Center
Prgm Director: Margo Smith, MD
110 Irving Street, NW
Washington, DC 20010
Tel: 202 877-7164   *Fax:* 202 877-0341
Length: 2 Yrs   *ACGME Approved/Offered Positions:* 4
Program ID: 146-10-11-179

Howard University Program
Sponsor: Howard University Hospital
Prgm Director: Imtiaz Choudhary, MD
2041 Georgia Avenue, NW
Division of Infectious Diseases
Washington, DC 20060
Tel: 202 865-1873   *Fax:* 202 865-4607
E-mail: ichoudhary@hotmail.com
Length: 2 Yrs   *ACGME Approved/Offered Positions:* 2
Program ID: 146-10-21-091

Florida

Gainesville

University of Florida Program
Sponsor: University of Florida College of Medicine
North Florida/South Georgia Veterans Health System
Shands Hospital at the University of Florida
Prgm Director: Frederick S Southwick, MD
Box 100277
Gainesville, FL 32610
Tel: 352 392-4058   *Fax:* 352 392-6481
Length: 2 Yrs   *ACGME Approved/Offered Positions:* 5
Program ID: 146-11-21-033

Jacksonville

College of Medicine, Mayo Clinic (Jacksonville) Program
Sponsor: College of Medicine, Mayo Clinic
Mayo Clinic (Jacksonville)
Mayo Clinic Florida Hospital
Prgm Director: Michael R Keating, MD
4500 San Pablo Road
Jacksonville, FL 32224
Tel: 904 953-0421   *Fax:* 904 953-0430
E-mail: paglia.melissa@mayo.edu
Length: 2 Yrs   *ACGME Approved/Offered Positions:* 2
Program ID: 146-11-21-207

University of Florida College of Medicine Jacksonville Program
Sponsor: University of Florida College of Medicine Jacksonville
Shands Jacksonville Medical Center
Duval County Health Department
Prgm Director: Michael Sands, MD, MPH
Duval County Health Department
1833 Boulevard Suite 500
Jacksonville, FL 32206
Tel: 904 253-1326   *Fax:* 904 798-2784
E-mail: nancy.culpepper@jax.ufl.edu
Length: 2 Yrs   *ACGME Approved/Offered Positions:* 2
Program ID: 146-11-21-186

Miami

Jackson Memorial Hospital/Jackson Health System Program
Sponsor: Jackson Memorial Hospital/Jackson Health System
Prgm Director: Gio J Baracco, MD
Miami VA Medical Center / Infectious Disease (111)
1201 NW 16th Street
Miami, FL 33125
Tel: 305 575-3193   *Fax:* 305 575-3300
E-mail: gbaracco@med.miami.edu
Length: 2 Yrs   *ACGME Approved/Offered Positions:* 9
Program ID: 146-11-21-165

Orlando

Orlando Health Program
Sponsor: Orlando Health
Orlando Regional Medical Center
Prgm Director: Mark R Wallace, MD
77 West Underwood Street
4th Floor, Suite B
Orlando, FL 32806
Tel: 321 841-7750   *Fax:* 321 841-8160
Length: 2 Yrs   *ACGME Approved/Offered Positions:* 4
Program ID: 146-11-12-210

Tampa

University of South Florida Program
Sponsor: University of South Florida College of Medicine
H Lee Moffitt Cancer Center
James A Haley Veterans Hospital
Tampa General Hospital
Prgm Director: John T Sinnott IV, MD
Tampa General Hospital
Davis Island
Tampa, FL 33606
Tel: 813 844-4187   *Fax:* 813 844-7605
Length: 2 Yrs   *ACGME Approved/Offered Positions:* 10
Program ID: 146-11-21-034

Georgia

Atlanta

Emory University Program
Sponsor: Emory University School of Medicine
Emory University Hospital
Prgm Director: Wendy S Armstrong, MD*
Emory University School of Medicine
49 Jesse Hill Jr Drive SE
Atlanta, GA 30303
Tel: 404 616-0673   *Fax:* 404 880-9305
E-mail: wsarmst@emory.edu
Length: 2 Yrs   *ACGME Approved/Offered Positions:* 12
Program ID: 146-12-21-129

Augusta

Medical College of Georgia Program
Sponsor: Medical College of Georgia
Veterans Affairs Medical Center (Augusta)
Prgm Director: John F Fisher, MD
Department of Medicine
Room BA-5300
Augusta, GA 30912
Tel: 706 721-2236   *Fax:* 706 721-2000
Length: 2 Yrs   *ACGME Approved/Offered Positions:* 2
Program ID: 146-12-21-003

Illinois

Chicago

McGaw Medical Center of Northwestern University Program
Sponsor: McGaw Medical Center of Northwestern University
Northwestern Memorial Hospital
Prgm Director: John P Flaherty, MD
645 N Michigan Avenue
Suite 900
Chicago, IL 60611
Tel: 312 695-5090   *Fax:* 312 695-5088
E-mail: j-flaherty4@northwestern.edu
Length: 2 Yrs   *ACGME Approved/Offered Positions:* 6
Program ID: 146-16-21-059

Rush University Medical Center Program
Sponsor: Rush University Medical Center
John H Stroger Hospital of Cook County
Prgm Director: Gordon M Trenholme, MD
Section of Infectious Diseases
1750 West Harrison St, 140-143 AAC
Chicago, IL 60612
Tel: 312 942-5865   *Fax:* 312 942-2184
Length: 2 Yrs   *ACGME Approved/Offered Positions:* 10
Program ID: 146-16-11-130

University of Chicago Program
Sponsor: University of Chicago Medical Center
Prgm Director: Jean-Luc Benoit, MD
5841 S Maryland Avenue, MC5065
Chicago, IL 60637
Tel: 773 702-2710   *Fax:* 773 702-8998
E-mail: jbenoit@medicine.bsd.uchicago.edu
Length: 2 Yrs   *ACGME Approved/Offered Positions:* 4
Program ID: 146-16-21-202

Note: * indicates a newly appointed program director

University of Illinois College of Medicine at Chicago Program

Sponsor: University of Illinois College of Medicine at Chicago
Jesse Brown Veterans Affairs Medical Center
University of Chicago Medical Center
University of Illinois Hospital and Clinics
Prgm Director: Maximo O Brito, MD
Section of Infectious Diseases, (M/C 735)
808 S Wood Street, Rm 888
Chicago, IL 60612
Tel: 312 569-7448   *Fax:* 312 569-8114
E-mail: mbrito@uic.edu
Length: 2 Yrs   *ACGME Approved/Offered Positions:* 6
Program ID: 146-16-21-131

Maywood

Loyola University Program

Sponsor: Loyola University Medical Center
Edward Hines, Jr Veterans Affairs Hospital
Prgm Director: Joseph R Lentino, MD, PhD
Department of Medicine
2160 S First Ave - Bldg 54 - Room 149
Maywood, IL 60153
Tel: 708 216-3232   *Fax:* 708 202-2410
Length: 2 Yrs   *ACGME Approved/Offered Positions:* 4
Program ID: 146-16-21-004

North Chicago

The Chicago Medical School at Rosalind Franklin University of Medicine and Science Program

Sponsor: Chicago Medical School/Rosalind Franklin Univ of Med & Sci
Mount Sinai Hospital Medical Center of Chicago
Veterans Affairs Medical Center (North Chicago)
Prgm Director: Walid F Khayr, MD
Department of Medicine-Division of Infectious Disease
3333 Green Bay Road
North Chicago, IL 60064
Tel: 847 688-1900   *Fax:* 847 578-8647
E-mail: anita.abron@rosalindfranklin.edu
Length: 2 Yrs   *ACGME Approved/Offered Positions:* 3
Program ID: 146-16-21-044

Springfield

Southern Illinois University Program

Sponsor: Southern Illinois University School of Medicine
Memorial Medical Center
St John's Hospital
Prgm Director: Nancy Khardori, MD, PhD
PO Box 19636
Springfield, IL 62794
Tel: 217 545-0181   *Fax:* 217 545-8025
E-mail: nkhardori@siumed.edu
Length: 2 Yrs   *ACGME Approved/Offered Positions:* 2
Program ID: 146-16-21-180

Indiana

Indianapolis

Indiana University School of Medicine Program

Sponsor: Indiana University School of Medicine
Clarian Indiana University Hospital
Prgm Director: Mitchell Goldman, MD
Wishard Memorial Hosp OPW-430
1001 West 10th Street
Indianapolis, IN 46202
Tel: 317 630-6119   *Fax:* 317 630-7522
Length: 2 Yrs   *ACGME Approved/Offered Positions:* 5
Program ID: 146-17-21-146

Iowa

Iowa City

University of Iowa Hospitals and Clinics Program

Sponsor: University of Iowa Hospitals and Clinics
Prgm Director: Daniel J Diekema, MD, MS*
Department of Medicine
200 Hawkins Drive
Iowa City, IA 52242
Tel: 319 384-5626   *Fax:* 319 356-4600
E-mail: daniel-diekema@uiowa.edu
Length: 2 Yrs   *ACGME Approved/Offered Positions:* 4
Program ID: 146-18-21-096

Kansas

Kansas City

University of Kansas School of Medicine Program

Sponsor: University of Kansas School of Medicine
Research Medical Center
University of Kansas Hospital
Veterans Affairs Medical Center (Kansas City)
Prgm Director: Daniel R Hinthorn, MD
Department of Internal Medicine
3901 Rainbow Boulevard
Kansas City, KS 66160
Tel: 913 588-6035   *Fax:* 913 588-6024
Length: 2 Yrs   *ACGME Approved/Offered Positions:* 6
Program ID: 146-19-21-110

Kentucky

Lexington

University of Kentucky College of Medicine Program

Sponsor: University of Kentucky College of Medicine
University of Kentucky Hospital
Veterans Affairs Medical Center (Lexington)
Prgm Director: Ardis Hoven, MD*
Division of Infectious Diseases, Room MN672
800 Rose Street
Lexington, KY 40536
Tel: 859 323-8178
Length: 2 Yrs   *ACGME Approved/Offered Positions:* 2
Program ID: 146-20-21-196

Louisville

University of Louisville Program

Sponsor: University of Louisville School of Medicine
University of Louisville Hospital
Veterans Affairs Medical Center (Louisville)
Prgm Director: Julio A Ramirez, MD
627 South Preston Street
Suite 104
Louisville, KY 40202
Tel: 502 852-5131   *Fax:* 502 852-1147
Length: 2 Yrs   *ACGME Approved/Offered Positions:* 5
Program ID: 146-20-31-092

Louisiana

New Orleans

Louisiana State University Program

Sponsor: Louisiana State University School of Medicine
Medical Center of Louisiana at New Orleans
Ochsner Medical Center-Kenner
Touro Infirmary
Prgm Director: Julio E Figueroa Jr, MD
533 Bolivar Street, Room 701
Section of Infectious Diseases
New Orleans, LA 70112
Tel: 504 568-5031   *Fax:* 504 568-5553
Length: 2 Yrs   *ACGME Approved/Offered Positions:* 6
Program ID: 146-21-21-051

Ochsner Clinic Foundation Program

Sponsor: Ochsner Clinic Foundation
Prgm Director: Julia B Garcia-Diaz, MD, MS
1514 Jefferson Highway
New Orleans, LA 70121
Tel: 504 842-4005   *Fax:* 504 842-4631
E-mail: gamiller@ochsner.org
Length: 2 Yrs   *ACGME Approved/Offered Positions:* 2
Program ID: 146-21-22-100

Tulane University Program

Sponsor: Tulane University School of Medicine
Medical Center of Louisiana at New Orleans
Tulane University Hospital and Clinics
Prgm Director: David M Mushatt, MD, MPH
Infectious Diseases Section, SL-87
1430 Tulane Ave
New Orleans, LA 70112
Tel: 504 988-7316   *Fax:* 504 988-3644
E-mail: infdis@tulane.edu
Length: 2 Yrs   *ACGME Approved/Offered Positions:* 4
Program ID: 146-21-21-105

Shreveport

Louisiana State University (Shreveport) Program

Sponsor: LSU Health Sciences Center-University Hospital
Overton Brooks Veterans Affairs Medical Center
Prgm Director: Robert L Penn, MD
1501 Kings Highway
Shreveport, LA 71130
Tel: 318 675-5900   *Fax:* 318 675-5907
Length: 2 Yrs   *ACGME Approved/Offered Positions:* 3
Program ID: 146-21-21-052

Maine

Portland

Maine Medical Center Program

Sponsor: Maine Medical Center
Prgm Director: Robert P Smith Jr, MD, MPH
22 Bramhall Street
Portland, ME 04102
Tel: 207 662-2099   *Fax:* 207 662-6116
Length: 2 Yrs   *ACGME Approved/Offered Positions:* 2
Program ID: 146-22-21-182

Programs

Maryland

Baltimore

Johns Hopkins University Program
Sponsor: Johns Hopkins University School of Medicine
Johns Hopkins Hospital
Prgm Director: Kelly Gebo, MD, MPH
Dept of Medicine, Div of Infectious Diseases
1830 E Monument St, Room 457
Baltimore, MD 21205
Tel: 410 502-2325   *Fax:* 410 955-7889
Length: 2 Yrs   *ACGME Approved/Offered Positions:* 12
Program ID: 146-23-11-060

University of Maryland Program
Sponsor: University of Maryland Medical System
Veterans Affairs Medical Center (Baltimore)
Prgm Director: Bruce L Gilliam, MD
Division of Infectious Diseases
725 West Lombard St, Room N550
Baltimore, MD 21201
Tel: 410 706-7560   *Fax:* 410 706-1992
Length: 2 Yrs   *ACGME Approved/Offered Positions:* 10
Program ID: 146-23-21-036

Bethesda

National Capital Consortium (Walter Reed) Program
Sponsor: National Capital Consortium
National Naval Medical Center (Bethesda)
Walter Reed Army Medical Center
Prgm Director: Glenn W Wortmann, MD
Infectious Disease Clinic, WARD 63
6900 Georgia Ave NW
Washington, DC 20307
Tel: 202 782-6740   *Fax:* 202 782-3765
E-mail: glenn.wortmann@amedd.army.mil
Length: 2 Yrs   *ACGME Approved/Offered Positions:* 10
Program ID: 146-10-11-127
Uniformed Services Program

National Institutes of Health Clinical Center Program
Sponsor: Clinical Center at the National Institutes of Health
Prgm Director: John Bennett, MD
9000 Rockville Pike
Bldg 10 Rm 11N234
Bethesda, MD 20892
Tel: 301 496-3461   *Fax:* 301 480-0050
Length: 2 Yrs   *ACGME Approved/Offered Positions:* 9
Program ID: 146-23-21-184

Massachusetts

Boston

Beth Israel Deaconess Medical Center Program
Sponsor: Beth Israel Deaconess Medical Center
Prgm Director: George M Eliopoulos, MD*
Division of Infectious Diseases
110 Francis Street, Suite GB
Boston, MA 02215
Tel: 617 632-7434   *Fax:* 617 632-0766
E-mail: geliopou@bidmc.harvard.edu
Length: 2 Yrs   *ACGME Approved/Offered Positions:* 10
Program ID: 146-24-21-132

Boston University Medical Center Program
Sponsor: Boston Medical Center
Veterans Affairs Medical Center (Boston)
Prgm Director: Paul R Skolnik, MD
650 Albany Street, EBRC 6
Boston, MA 02118
Tel: 617 414-3520   *Fax:* 617 414-5218
E-mail: paul.skolnik@bmc.org
Length: 2 Yrs   *ACGME Approved/Offered Positions:* 6
Program ID: 146-24-21-148

Massachusetts General Hospital/Brigham and Women's Hospital Program
Sponsor: Massachusetts General Hospital
Brigham and Women's Hospital
Children's Hospital
Prgm Director: Benjamin Davis, MD*
55 Fruit Street, GRJ 504
Boston, MA 02114
Tel: 617 724-1930   *Fax:* 617 726-7653
Length: 2 Yrs   *ACGME Approved/Offered Positions:* 20
Program ID: 146-24-21-021

Tufts Medical Center Program
Sponsor: Tufts Medical Center
Prgm Director: Helen W Boucher, MD
800 Washington Street
Box 41
Boston, MA 02111
Tel: 617 636-7001   *Fax:* 617 636-8525
Length: 2 Yrs   *ACGME Approved/Offered Positions:* 12
Program ID: 146-24-21-006

Springfield

Baystate Medical Center/Tufts University School of Medicine Program
Sponsor: Baystate Medical Center
Prgm Director: Eric V Granowitz, MD
759 Chestnut Street
Springfield, MA 01199
Tel: 413 794-5376   *Fax:* 413 794-4199
E-mail: pauline.blair@bhs.org
Length: 2 Yrs   *ACGME Approved/Offered Positions:* 2
Program ID: 146-24-11-061

Worcester

University of Massachusetts Program
Sponsor: University of Massachusetts Medical School
UMass Memorial Health Care (Memorial Campus)
UMass Memorial Health Care (University Campus)
Prgm Director: William L Marshall, MD
55 Lake Avenue, North
Worcester, MA 01655
Tel: 508 856-7513   *Fax:* 508 856-7525
Length: 2 Yrs   *ACGME Approved/Offered Positions:* 7
Program ID: 146-24-21-007

Michigan

Ann Arbor

University of Michigan Program
Sponsor: University of Michigan Hospitals and Health Centers
Veterans Affairs Medical Center (Ann Arbor)
Prgm Director: Daniel R Kaul, MD*
3119 Taubman Center
1500 E Medical Center Drive
Ann Arbor, MI 48109
Tel: 734 936-8183   *Fax:* 734 936-2737
E-mail: franciss@umich.edu
Length: 2 Yrs   *ACGME Approved/Offered Positions:* 4
Program ID: 146-25-21-062

Detroit

Henry Ford Hospital Program
Sponsor: Henry Ford Hospital
Prgm Director: Indira Brar, MD
Department of Medicine
2799 W Grand Boulevard
Detroit, MI 48202
Tel: 313 916-2573   *Fax:* 313 916-2993
Length: 2 Yrs   *ACGME Approved/Offered Positions:* 4
Program ID: 146-25-11-133

St John Hospital and Medical Center Program
Sponsor: St John Hospital and Medical Center
Prgm Director: Leonard B Johnson, MD
19251 Mack Avenue
Suite 340
Grosse Pointe Woods, MI 48236
Tel: 313 343-8823   *Fax:* 313 343-7840
E-mail: leonard.johnson@stjohn.org
Length: 2 Yrs   *ACGME Approved/Offered Positions:* 3
Program ID: 146-25-21-191

Wayne State University/Detroit Medical Center Program
Sponsor: Wayne State University/Detroit Medical Center
Detroit Receiving Hospital and University Health Center
Harper-Hutzel Hospital
Prgm Director: Pranatharthi H Chandrasekar, MD
Division of Infectious Diseases
3990 John R St, 5-Hudson, Room 5910
Detroit, MI 48201
Tel: 313 745-9649
Length: 2 Yrs   *ACGME Approved/Offered Positions:* 8
Program ID: 146-25-21-040

Lansing

Michigan State University Program
Sponsor: Michigan State University College of Human Medicine
Ingham County Health Department
Michigan State University Clinical Center
Sparrow Hospital
Prgm Director: Daniel Havlichek Jr, MD
B-417 Clinical Center
East Lansing, MI 48824
Tel: 517 353-3747   *Fax:* 517 432-9471
E-mail: daniel.havlichek@ht.msu.edu
Length: 2 Yrs   *ACGME Approved/Offered Positions:* 4
Program ID: 146-25-31-203

Royal Oak

William Beaumont Hospital Program
Sponsor: William Beaumont Hospital
Prgm Director: Christopher F Carpenter, MD
3601 West 13 Mile Road
Royal Oak, MI 48073
Tel: 248 551-7941   *Fax:* 248 551-3838
Length: 2 Yrs   *ACGME Approved/Offered Positions:* 4
Program ID: 146-25-12-102

Note: * indicates a newly appointed program director

Minnesota

Minneapolis

University of Minnesota Program

Sponsor: University of Minnesota Medical School
University of Minnesota Medical Center, Division of Fairview
Veterans Affairs Medical Center (Minneapolis)
Prgm Director: James R Johnson, MD
MMC 250
420 Delaware Street SE
Minneapolis, MN 55455
Tel: 612 626-9943   *Fax:* 612 625-4410
E-mail: belve003@umn.edu
Length: 2 Yrs   *ACGME Approved/Offered Positions:* 6
Program ID: 146-26-21-112

Rochester

College of Medicine, Mayo Clinic (Rochester) Program

Sponsor: College of Medicine, Mayo Clinic
Federal Medical Center (Federal Bureau of Prisons)
Mayo Clinic (Rochester)
Rochester Methodist Hospital
Saint Marys Hospital of Rochester
Prgm Director: Abinash Virk, MD
Department of Medicine
200 First Street, SW
Rochester, MN 55905
Tel: 507 255-1980   *Fax:* 507 255-7767
E-mail: parsons.kathy@mayo.edu
Length: 2 Yrs   *ACGME Approved/Offered Positions:* 8
Program ID: 146-26-21-045

Mississippi

Jackson

University of Mississippi Medical Center Program

Sponsor: University of Mississippi School of Medicine
University Hospitals and Clinics
Veterans Affairs Medical Center (Jackson)
Prgm Director: Leandro A Mena, MD, MPH
Division of Infectious Diseases
2500 N State Street, N-502
Jackson, MS 39216
Tel: 601 984-5560   *Fax:* 601 815-4014
E-mail: LMena@medicine.umsmed.edu
Length: 2 Yrs   *ACGME Approved/Offered Positions:* 4
Program ID: 146-27-21-063

Missouri

Columbia

University of Missouri-Columbia Program

Sponsor: University of Missouri-Columbia School of Medicine
Harry S Truman Memorial Veterans Hospital
University Hospitals and Clinics
Prgm Director: William Salzer, MD
CE309, Clinical Support & Education Building
Five Hospital Drive
Columbia, MO 65212
Tel: 573 882-3107   *Fax:* 573 884-5790
Length: 2 Yrs   *ACGME Approved/Offered Positions:* 3
Program ID: 146-28-21-064

Kansas City

University of Missouri at Kansas City Program

Sponsor: University of Missouri-Kansas City School of Medicine
St Luke's Hospital-Kansas City
Truman Medical Center
Prgm Director: Alan R Salkind, MD
Green 4 Unit
2411 Holmes Street, Green 4 Unit
Kansas City, MO 64108
Tel: 816 235-1935   *Fax:* 816 235-5538
Length: 2 Yrs   *ACGME Approved/Offered Positions:* 2
Program ID: 146-28-31-113

St Louis

St Louis University School of Medicine Program

Sponsor: St Louis University School of Medicine
St Louis University Hospital
Prgm Director: Donald J Kennedy, MD
1100 S Grand Blvd, DRC-8th Fl
St Louis, MO 63104
Tel: 314 977-5500   *Fax:* 314 771-3816
E-mail: novotnce@slu.edu
Length: 2 Yrs   *ACGME Approved/Offered Positions:* 4
Program ID: 146-28-21-177

Washington University/B-JH/SLCH Consortium Program

Sponsor: Washington University/B-JH/SLCH Consortium
Barnes-Jewish Hospital
Prgm Director: Nigar Kirmani, MD
660 South Euclid Avenue, Box 8051
St Louis, MO 63110
Tel: 314 454-8214   *Fax:* 314 454-8687
Length: 2 Yrs   *ACGME Approved/Offered Positions:* 10
Program ID: 146-28-21-149

Nebraska

Omaha

Creighton University Program

Sponsor: Creighton University School of Medicine
Creighton University Medical Center (Tenet - SJH)
Douglas County Hospital
Nebraska Medical Center
Veterans Affairs Medical Center (Omaha)
Prgm Director: Gary L Gorby, MD
c/o Omaha VA Medical Center
4101 Woolworth Avenue (111D)
Omaha, NE 68105
Tel: 402 995-5219   *Fax:* 402 977-5601
E-mail: dona.goodrich@va.gov
Length: 2 Yrs   *ACGME Approved/Offered Positions:* 4
Program ID: 146-30-21-151

New Hampshire

Lebanon

Dartmouth-Hitchcock Medical Center Program

Sponsor: Mary Hitchcock Memorial Hospital
Prgm Director: Jeffrey Parsonnet, MD
One Medical Center Drive
Lebanon, NH 03756
Tel: 603 650-6060   *Fax:* 603 650-6110
E-mail: jeffrey.parsonnet@hitchcock.org
Length: 2 Yrs   *ACGME Approved/Offered Positions:* 3
Program ID: 146-32-21-187

New Jersey

Camden

UMDNJ-Robert Wood Johnson Medical School (Camden) Program

Sponsor: Cooper Hospital-University Medical Center
Prgm Director: Daniel K Meyer, MD
Education & Research Bldg, Rm 272
401 Haddon Avenue
Camden, NJ 08103
Tel: 856 757-7767   *Fax:* 856 757-7803
E-mail: conners-deanne@cooperhealth.edu
Length: 2 Yrs   *ACGME Approved/Offered Positions:* 4
Program ID: 146-33-21-173

New Brunswick

UMDNJ-Robert Wood Johnson Medical School Program

Sponsor: UMDNJ-Robert Wood Johnson Medical School
Jersey Shore University Medical Center
Robert Wood Johnson University Hospital
Prgm Director: Melvin P Weinstein, MD
Dept of Medicine, MEB 362
One Robert Wood Johnson Place
New Brunswick, NJ 08903
Tel: 732 235-7713   *Fax:* 732 235-7951
E-mail: lindseei@umdnj.edu
Length: 2 Yrs   *ACGME Approved/Offered Positions:* 4
Program ID: 146-33-21-026

Newark

Newark Beth Israel Medical Center Program

Sponsor: Newark Beth Israel Medical Center
Prgm Director: Eliahu Bishburg, MD
201 Lyons Avenue
Newark, NJ 07112
Tel: 973 926-5212
E-mail: ebishburg@sbhcs.com
Length: 2 Yrs   *ACGME Approved/Offered Positions:* 2
Program ID: 146-33-21-204

UMDNJ-New Jersey Medical School Program

Sponsor: UMDNJ-New Jersey Medical School
Hackensack University Medical Center
UMDNJ-University Hospital
Veterans Affairs New Jersey Health Care System
Prgm Director: Lisa L Dever, MD
185 South Orange Avenue MSB I-689
University Heights
Newark, NJ 07103
Tel: 973 972-4830   *Fax:* 973 972-1141
E-mail: infectiousdiseases@umdnj.edu
Length: 2 Yrs   *ACGME Approved/Offered Positions:* 8
Program ID: 146-33-21-172

South Orange

Seton Hall University School of Health and Medical Sciences Program

Sponsor: Seton Hall University School of Health and Medical Sciences
St Michael's Medical Center (A Member of Catholic Hlth East)
Prgm Director: George Perez, MD*
111 Central Avenue
Newark, NJ 07102
Tel: 973 877-5487
Length: 2 Yrs   *ACGME Approved/Offered Positions:* 6
Program ID: 146-33-11-152

Programs

New Mexico

Albuquerque

University of New Mexico Program

Sponsor: University of New Mexico School of Medicine
University of New Mexico Hospital
Veterans Affairs Medical Center (Albuquerque)
Prgm Director: Corey Tancik, MD
MSC10 5550
1 University of New Mexico, MSC10 5550
Albuquerque, NM 87131
Tel: 505 272-1670   *Fax:* 505 272-4435
E-mail: hmedina@salud.unm.edu
Length: 2 Yrs   *ACGME Approved/Offered Positions:* 4
Program ID: 146-34-21-134

New York

Bronx

Albert Einstein College of Medicine Program

Sponsor: Albert Einstein College of Medicine of Yeshiva
   University
Montefiore Medical Center-Henry and Lucy Moses
   Division
Prgm Director: Ira M Leviton, MD
Division of Infectious Diseases
111 East 210th Street
Bronx, NY 10467
Tel: 718 920-7791   *Fax:* 718 920-2746
E-mail: ileviton@montefiore.org
Length: 2 Yrs   *ACGME Approved/Offered Positions:* 10
Program ID: 146-35-21-101

Brooklyn

Maimonides Medical Center Program

Sponsor: Maimonides Medical Center
Coney Island Hospital
Long Island College Hospital
Prgm Director: Monica Ghitan, MD
Department of Medicine
4802 Tenth Avenue
Brooklyn, NY 11219
Tel: 718 283-6017   *Fax:* 718 283-8813
E-mail: mghitan@maimonidesmed.org
Length: 2 Yrs   *ACGME Approved/Offered Positions:* 5
Program ID: 146-35-11-171

SUNY Health Science Center at Brooklyn Program

Sponsor: SUNY Health Science Center at Brooklyn
University Hospital-SUNY Health Science Center at
   Brooklyn
Prgm Director: William M McCormack, MD
450 Clarkson Ave
Box 56
Brooklyn, NY 11203
Tel: 718 270-1432   *Fax:* 718 270-4123
E-mail: william.mccormack@downstate.edu
Length: 2 Yrs   *ACGME Approved/Offered Positions:* 8
Program ID: 146-35-21-011

Buffalo

University at Buffalo Program

Sponsor: University at Buffalo School of Medicine
Erie County Medical Center
Roswell Park Cancer Institute
Veterans Affairs Western New York Hospital
Prgm Director: Charles S Berenson, MD
3495 Bailey Avenue
Buffalo, NY 14215
Tel: 716 862-6529   *Fax:* 716 862-6526
E-mail: berenson@acsu.buffalo.edu
Length: 2 Yrs   *ACGME Approved/Offered Positions:* 4
Program ID: 146-35-31-009

Flushing

New York Hospital Medical Center of Queens/Cornell University Medical College Program

Sponsor: New York Hospital Medical Center of Queens
Prgm Director: James J Rahal, MD
56-45 Main Street
Flushing, NY 11355
Tel: 718 670-1525   *Fax:* 718 661-7899
E-mail: jjr9002@nyp.org
Length: 2 Yrs   *ACGME Approved/Offered Positions:* 3
Program ID: 146-35-21-178

Great Neck

NSLIJHS-Albert Einstein College of Medicine at Long Island Jewish Medical Center Program

Sponsor: North Shore-Long Island Jewish Health System
Long Island Jewish Medical Center
Prgm Director: Carol Singer, MD
270-05 76th Avenue
Staff House, Suite 226
New Hyde Park, NY 11040
Tel: 718 470-7290   *Fax:* 718 470-0637
E-mail: csinger@lij.edu
Length: 2 Yrs   *ACGME Approved/Offered Positions:* 3
Program ID: 146-35-21-135

NSLIJHS-North Shore University Hospital/NYU School of Medicine Program

Sponsor: North Shore-Long Island Jewish Health System
North Shore University Hospital
Prgm Director: Marcia E Epstein, MD
Department of Medicine
300 Community Drive
Manhasset, NY 11030
Tel: 516 562-4280   *Fax:* 516 562-2626
E-mail: mepstein@nshs.edu
Length: 2 Yrs   *ACGME Approved/Offered Positions:* 3
Program ID: 146-35-21-160

Jamaica

New York Medical College (Brooklyn-Queens) Program

Sponsor: New York Medical College
Caritas Health Care (Brooklyn-Queens)
Prgm Director: Kenneth Roistacher, MD
Mary Immaculate Hospital
152-11 89th Avenue
Jamaica, NY 11432
Tel: 718 558-6391   *Fax:* 718 558-2257
E-mail: kroistacher@bqhcny.org
Length: 2 Yrs   *ACGME Approved/Offered Positions:* 5
Program ID: 146-35-22-041

Mineola

Winthrop-University Hospital Program

Sponsor: Winthrop-University Hospital
Prgm Director: Diane H Johnson, MD*
222 Station Plaza North
Suite 432
Mineola, NY 11501
Tel: 516 663-2505   *Fax:* 516 663-2753
Length: 2 Yrs   *ACGME Approved/Offered Positions:* 3
Program ID: 146-35-11-065

New York

Albert Einstein College of Medicine at Beth Israel Medical Center Program

Sponsor: Beth Israel Medical Center
Prgm Director: Stanley R Yancovitz, MD
Division of Infectious Disease
First Avenue at 16th Street, 19BH14
New York, NY 10003
Tel: 212 844-1292
E-mail: syancovi@chpnet.org
Length: 2 Yrs   *ACGME Approved/Offered Positions:* 4
Program ID: 146-35-11-010

Harlem Hospital Center Program

Sponsor: Harlem Hospital Center
Prgm Director: Vel Sivapalan, MD
Room 3101 A
506 Lenox Avenue
New York, NY 10037
Tel: 212 939-2942   *Fax:* 212 939-2968
E-mail: vs10@columbia.edu
Length: 2 Yrs   *ACGME Approved/Offered Positions:* 5
Program ID: 146-35-11-162

Memorial Sloan-Kettering Cancer Center/New York Presbyterian Hospital (Cornell Campus) Program

Sponsor: Memorial Sloan-Kettering Cancer Center
Prgm Director: Susan Seo, MD
1275 York Avenue
New York, NY 10065
Tel: 212 639-3151   *Fax:* 212 717-3021
Length: 2 Yrs   *ACGME Approved/Offered Positions:* 6
Program ID: 146-35-21-167

Mount Sinai School of Medicine Program

Sponsor: Mount Sinai School of Medicine
Elmhurst Hospital Center-Mount Sinai Services
Mount Sinai Medical Center
Prgm Director: Shirish Huprikar, MD*
Box 1090
One Gustave L Levy Place
New York, NY 10029
Tel: 212 241-6885   *Fax:* 212 534-3240
Length: 2 Yrs   *ACGME Approved/Offered Positions:* 7
Program ID: 146-35-31-153

New York Medical College at St Vincent's Hospital and Medical Center of New York Program

Sponsor: New York Medical College
St Vincent Catholic Medical Centers (Manhattan)
Prgm Director: Glenn S Turett, MD
170 W 12th Street
New York, NY 10011
Tel: 212 604-8328   *Fax:* 212 604-2738
Length: 2 Yrs   *ACGME Approved/Offered Positions:* 2
Program ID: 146-35-11-174

New York Presbyterian Hospital (Columbia Campus) Program

Sponsor: New York Presbyterian Hospital
New York Presbyterian Hospital (Columbia Campus)
Prgm Director: Scott M Hammer, MD
622 W 168th Street
New York, NY 10032
Tel: 212 305-7185   *Fax:* 212 305-7290
Length: 2 Yrs   *ACGME Approved/Offered Positions:* 6
Program ID: 146-35-11-054

Note: * indicates a newly appointed program director

New York Presbyterian Hospital (Cornell Campus) Program
Sponsor: New York Presbyterian Hospital
New York Presbyterian Hospital (Cornell Campus)
Prgm Director: Linnie M Golightly, MD
525 East 68th Street
Room A-421
New York, NY 10021
Tel: 212 746-6303   *Fax:* 212 746-8675
E-mail: glr2007@med.cornell.edu
Length: 2 Yrs   *ACGME Approved/Offered Positions:* 6
Program ID: 146-35-21-161

New York University School of Medicine Program
Sponsor: New York University School of Medicine
Bellevue Hospital Center
Manhattan VA Harbor Health Care System
Prgm Director: Joel Ernst, MD
Department of Medicine
550 First Avenue
New York, NY 10016
Tel: 212 263-5182   *Fax:* 212 263-9230
E-mail: joel.ernst@med.nyu.edu
Length: 2 Yrs   *ACGME Approved/Offered Positions:* 8
Program ID: 146-35-21-114

St Luke's-Roosevelt Hospital Center Program
Sponsor: St Luke's-Roosevelt Hospital Center
Prgm Director: Bruce Polsky, MD
1111 Amsterdam Avenue
New York, NY 10025
Tel: 212 523-2525   *Fax:* 212 523-3931
E-mail: bpolsky@chpnet.org
Length: 2 Yrs   *ACGME Approved/Offered Positions:* 3
Program ID: 146-35-21-103

Rochester

University of Rochester Program
Sponsor: Strong Memorial Hospital of the University of Rochester
Prgm Director: Christine M Hay, MD
601 Elmwood Avenue
Box 689
Rochester, NY 14642
Tel: 585 275-5871   *Fax:* 585 442-9328
E-mail: christine_hay@urmc.rochester.edu
Length: 2 Yrs   *ACGME Approved/Offered Positions:* 6
Program ID: 146-35-11-170

Stony Brook

SUNY at Stony Brook Program
Sponsor: University Hospital - SUNY at Stony Brook
Veterans Affairs Medical Center (Northport)
Prgm Director: Victor Jimenez, MD
Division of Infectious Disease
HSC T15, 080
Stony Brook, NY 11794
Tel: 631 444-3490   *Fax:* 631 444-7518
E-mail: Victor.Jimenez@va.gov
Length: 2 Yrs   *ACGME Approved/Offered Positions:* 5
Program ID: 146-35-21-012

Syracuse

SUNY Upstate Medical University Program
Sponsor: SUNY Upstate Medical University
Crouse Hospital
Veterans Affairs Medical Center (Syracuse)
Prgm Director: Timothy Endy, MD, MPH
750 East Adams Street
Syracuse, NY 13210
Tel: 315 464-5533   *Fax:* 315 464-5579
Length: 2 Yrs   *ACGME Approved/Offered Positions:* 3
Program ID: 146-35-21-140

Valhalla

New York Medical College at Westchester Medical Center Program
Sponsor: New York Medical College
Metropolitan Hospital Center
Westchester Medical Center
Prgm Director: Gary P Wormser, MD
Division of Infectious Diseases
Munger Pavillion, Room 245
Valhalla, NY 10595
Tel: 914 493-8865   *Fax:* 914 594-4673
Length: 2 Yrs   *ACGME Approved/Offered Positions:* 4
Program ID: 146-35-11-013

North Carolina

Chapel Hill

University of North Carolina Hospitals Program
Sponsor: University of North Carolina Hospitals
Prgm Director: Charles M van der Horst, MD
CB 7030, 130 Mason Farm Rd, Bioinformatics Bldg
Division of Infectious Diseases
Chapel Hill, NC 27599
Tel: 919 966-2536   *Fax:* 919 966-6714
E-mail: cvdh@med.unc.edu
Length: 2 Yrs   *ACGME Approved/Offered Positions:* 8
Program ID: 146-36-21-136

Durham

Duke University Hospital Program
Sponsor: Duke University Hospital
Veterans Affairs Medical Center (Durham)
Prgm Director: Gary M Cox, MD
Box 3867
Durham, NC 27710
Tel: 919 684-2660   *Fax:* 919 684-8902
Length: 2 Yrs   *ACGME Approved/Offered Positions:* 8
Program ID: 146-36-21-137

Greenville

Pitt County Memorial Hospital/East Carolina University Program
Sponsor: Pitt County Memorial Hospital
Brody School of Medicine at East Carolina University
Prgm Director: Paul P Cook, MD
Division of Infectious Diseases
Doctors Park 6A
Greenville, NC 27834
Tel: 252 744-5725   *Fax:* 252 744-3472
Length: 2 Yrs   *ACGME Approved/Offered Positions:* 3
Program ID: 146-36-21-100

Winston-Salem

Wake Forest University School of Medicine Program
Sponsor: Wake Forest University Baptist Medical Center
Prgm Director: James E Peacock Jr, MD
Section on Infectious Diseases
Medical Center Boulevard
Winston-Salem, NC 27157
Tel: 336 716-4507   *Fax:* 336 716-3825
E-mail: jpeacock@wfubmc.edu
Length: 2 Yrs   *ACGME Approved/Offered Positions:* 6
Program ID: 146-36-21-014

Ohio

Cincinnati

University Hospital/University of Cincinnati College of Medicine Program
Sponsor: University Hospital Inc
Veterans Affairs Medical Center (Cincinnati)
Prgm Director: Lisa Haglund, MD
PO Box 670560
Cincinnati, OH 45267
Tel: 513 558-4704   *Fax:* 513 558-2089
E-mail: buchanj@uc.edu
Length: 2 Yrs   *ACGME Approved/Offered Positions:* 4
Program ID: 146-38-21-066

Cleveland

Cleveland Clinic Foundation Program
Sponsor: Cleveland Clinic Foundation
Prgm Director: Carlos M Isada, MD
Desk S-32
9500 Euclid Avenue
Cleveland, OH 44195
Tel: 216 444-2762   *Fax:* 216 445-9446
E-mail: isadac@ccf.org
Length: 2 Yrs   *ACGME Approved/Offered Positions:* 6
Program ID: 146-38-12-156

University Hospitals Case Medical Center Program
Sponsor: University Hospitals Case Medical Center
MetroHealth Medical Center
Veterans Affairs Medical Center (Cleveland)
Prgm Director: Robert A Salata, MD
Division of Infectious Diseases & HIV Medicine
11100 Euclid Avenue
Cleveland, OH 44106
Tel: 216 844-3287   *Fax:* 216 844-1632
E-mail: ras7@case.edu
Length: 2 Yrs   *ACGME Approved/Offered Positions:* 6
Program ID: 146-38-21-154

Columbus

Ohio State University Hospital Program
Sponsor: Ohio State University Hospital
Prgm Director: Susan L Koletar, MD
Department of Internal Medicine
410 W 10th Avenue
Columbus, OH 43210
Tel: 614 293-5667   *Fax:* 614 293-4556
E-mail: koletar.1@osu.edu
Length: 2 Yrs   *ACGME Approved/Offered Positions:* 6
Program ID: 146-38-11-094

Dayton

Wright State University Program
Sponsor: Wright State University Boonshoft School of Medicine
Good Samaritan Hospital and Health Center
Miami Valley Hospital
Veterans Affairs Medical Center (Dayton)
Prgm Director: Jack M Bernstein, MD
4100 W Third Street
Dayton, OH 45428
Tel: 937 262-3393
E-mail: jack.bernstein@wright.edu
Length: 2 Yrs   *ACGME Approved/Offered Positions:* 2
Program ID: 146-38-31-189

Toledo

University of Toledo Program
Sponsor: University of Toledo
St Vincent Mercy Medical Center
University Medical Center (Toledo)
Prgm Director: Joan M Duggan, MD
3120 Glendale Ave
Toledo, OH 43614
Tel: 419 383-4328   *Fax:* 419 383-2847
Length: 2 Yrs   *ACGME Approved/Offered Positions:* 4
Program ID: 146-38-21-015

Oklahoma

Oklahoma City

University of Oklahoma Health Sciences Center Program
Sponsor: University of Oklahoma College of Medicine
OU Medical Center
Veterans Affairs Medical Center (Oklahoma City)
Prgm Director: Douglas A Drevets, MD
PO Box 26901
Oklahoma City, OK 73126
Tel: 405 456-3284   *Fax:* 405 297-5934
E-mail: douglas-drevets@ouhsc.edu
Length: 2 Yrs   *ACGME Approved/Offered Positions:* 3
Program ID: 146-39-21-067

Oregon

Portland

Oregon Health & Science University Program
Sponsor: Oregon Health & Science University Hospital
Veterans Affairs Medical Center (Portland)
Prgm Director: Thomas T Ward, MD
Infectious Diseases, L457
3181 SW Sam Jackson Park Road
Portland, OR 97239
Tel: 503 494-0591   *Fax:* 503 494-4264
E-mail: wardt@ohsu.edu
Length: 2 Yrs   *ACGME Approved/Offered Positions:* 4
Program ID: 146-40-31-157

Pennsylvania

Hershey

Penn State University/Milton S Hershey Medical Center Program
Sponsor: Milton S Hershey Medical Center
Prgm Director: John Zurlo, MD
500 University Drive
Mail Code H-036
Hershey, PA 17033
Tel: 717 531-8881   *Fax:* 717 531-4633
Length: 2 Yrs   *ACGME Approved/Offered Positions:* 4
Program ID: 146-41-11-016

Philadelphia

Albert Einstein Healthcare Network Program
Sponsor: Albert Einstein Medical Center
Prgm Director: Bartholomew R Bono, MD*
5401 Old York Road, Klein 363
Philadelphia, PA 19141
Tel: 215 456-6948   *Fax:* 215 456-7926
E-mail: bonob@einstein.edu
Length: 2 Yrs   *ACGME Approved/Offered Positions:* 2
Program ID: 146-41-13-208

Drexel University College of Medicine/Hahnemann University Hospital Program
Sponsor: Drexel University College of
  Medicine/Hahnemann University
Abington Memorial Hospital
Hahnemann University Hospital (Tenet Health System)
Prgm Director: Jeffrey M Jacobson, MD
Division of Infectious Diseases
245 North 15th Street, Room 6302 NCB, MS 461
Philadelphia, PA 19102
Tel: 215 762-6555   *Fax:* 215 762-3031
E-mail: sgarrett@drexelmed.edu
Length: 2 Yrs   *ACGME Approved/Offered Positions:* 5
Program ID: 146-41-21-046

Temple University Hospital Program
Sponsor: Temple University Hospital
Prgm Director: Rafik Samuel, MD
3401 N Broad St
Philadelphia, PA 19140
Tel: 215 707-1982   *Fax:* 215 707-4414
Length: 2 Yrs   *ACGME Approved/Offered Positions:* 5
Program ID: 146-41-21-029

Thomas Jefferson University Program
Sponsor: Thomas Jefferson University Hospital
Lankenau Hospital
Prgm Director: Joseph A DeSimone Jr, MD
Division of Infectious Diseases
211 South 9th St, Suite 210
Philadelphia, PA 19107
Tel: 215 955-7785   *Fax:* 215 955-9362
E-mail: joseph.desimone@jefferson.edu
Length: 2 Yrs   *ACGME Approved/Offered Positions:* 4
Program ID: 146-41-21-056

University of Pennsylvania Program
Sponsor: University of Pennsylvania Health System
Prgm Director: Emily Blumberg, MD
3400 Spruce St
Infectious Disease, 3 Silverstein, Suite E
Philadelphia, PA 19104
Tel: 215 662-7066   *Fax:* 215 662-7611
E-mail: blumbere@mail.med.upenn.edu
Length: 2 Yrs   *ACGME Approved/Offered Positions:* 8
Program ID: 146-41-21-022

Pittsburgh

University of Pittsburgh Medical Center Medical Education Program
Sponsor: Univ of Pittsburgh Medical Center Medical
  Education
UPMC Presbyterian Shadyside
Prgm Director: Emanuel N Vergis, MD, MPH
Infectious Disease, Suite 3A Falk Med Bldg
3601 Fifth Avenue
Pittsburgh, PA 15213
Tel: 412 648-6108   *Fax:* 412 648-6399
Length: 2 Yrs   *ACGME Approved/Offered Positions:* 6
Program ID: 146-41-21-037

Puerto Rico

San Juan

University of Puerto Rico Program
Sponsor: University of Puerto Rico School of Medicine
University Hospital
VA Caribbean Healthcare System
Prgm Director: Jorge Bertran, MD
Department of Medicine UPR School of Medicine
PO Box 365067
San Juan, PR 00936
Tel: 787 758-2525   *Fax:* 787 754-1739
E-mail: jbertran@rcm.upr.edu
Length: 2 Yrs   *ACGME Approved/Offered Positions:* 4
Program ID: 146-42-21-118

VA Caribbean Healthcare System Program
Sponsor: VA Caribbean Healthcare System
University Hospital
Prgm Director: Glenda M Gonzalez-Claudio, MD
10 Casia Street (111)
San Juan, PR 00921
Tel: 787 641-7582   *Fax:* 787 641-4561
Length: 2 Yrs   *ACGME Approved/Offered Positions:* 4
Program ID: 146-42-31-117

Rhode Island

Providence

Brown University Program
Sponsor: Rhode Island Hospital-Lifespan
Memorial Hospital of Rhode Island
Miriam Hospital-Lifespan
Prgm Director: Karen T Tashima, MD
The Miriam Hospital
164 Summit Ave
Providence, RI 02906
Tel: 401 793-4979   *Fax:* 401 793-4323
Length: 2 Yrs   *ACGME Approved/Offered Positions:* 5
Program ID: 146-43-21-197

Roger Williams Medical Center Program
Sponsor: Roger Williams Medical Center
Rhode Island Hospital-Lifespan
Prgm Director: Gail Skowron, MD
825 Chalkstone Avenue
Providence, RI 02908
Tel: 401 456-2437   *Fax:* 401 456-6839
E-mail: gail_skowron@brown.edu
Length: 2 Yrs   *ACGME Approved/Offered Positions:* 2
Program ID: 146-43-31-038

South Carolina

Charleston

Medical University of South Carolina Program
Sponsor: Medical University of South Carolina College of
  Medicine
MUSC Medical Center
Ralph H Johnson VA Medical Center (Charleston)
Prgm Director: Cassandra D Salgado, MD, MS*
135 Rutledge Avenue, 12th Floor Rutledge Tower
MSC752
Charleston, SC 29425
Tel: 843 792-4541   *Fax:* 843 792-6680
E-mail: nelsonsh@musc.edu
Length: 2 Yrs   *ACGME Approved/Offered Positions:* 5
Program ID: 146-45-21-104

Tennessee

Johnson City

East Tennessee State University Program
Sponsor: James H Quillen College of Medicine
Johnson City Medical Center/Mountain States Health
  Alliance
Veterans Affairs Medical Center (Mountain Home)
Prgm Director: James W Myers, MD*
Department of Internal Medicine
Box 70622
Johnson City, TN 37614
Tel: 423 439-6380   *Fax:* 423 439-7010
E-mail: myersj@etsu.edu
Length: 2 Yrs   *ACGME Approved/Offered Positions:* 6
Program ID: 146-47-21-047

Note: * indicates a newly appointed program director

Memphis

University of Tennessee Program

Sponsor: University of Tennessee College of Medicine
Methodist Healthcare - Memphis Hospitals
Regional Medical Center at Memphis
Veterans Affairs Medical Center (Memphis)
Prgm Director: James M Fleckenstein, MD
Department of Medicine
956 Court Street
Memphis, TN 38163
Tel: 901 448-5770   *Fax:* 901 448-5940
E-mail: jflecke1@tennessee.edu
Length: 2 Yrs   *ACGME Approved/Offered Positions:* 4
Program ID: 146-47-21-138

Nashville

Vanderbilt University Program

Sponsor: Vanderbilt University Medical Center
Comprehensive Care Center
Prgm Director: Patty W Wright, MD
A-2200 Medical Center North
1161 21st Avenue South
Nashville, TN 37232
Tel: 615 322-2035   *Fax:* 615 343-6160
E-mail: patty.w.wright@vanderbilt.edu
Length: 2 Yrs   *ACGME Approved/Offered Positions:* 10
Program ID: 146-47-31-017

Texas

Dallas

University of Texas Southwestern Medical School Program

Sponsor: University of Texas Southwestern Medical
School
Dallas County Hospital District-Parkland Memorial
Hospital
Dallas VA Medical Center
Prgm Director: Roger J Bedimo, MD, MS
Attn: Tricia Cox
5323 Harry Hines Blvd
Dallas, TX 75390
Tel: 214 648-9914   *Fax:* 214 648-2741
E-mail: tricia.cox@utsouthwestern.edu
Length: 2 Yrs   *ACGME Approved/Offered Positions:* 7
Program ID: 146-48-21-098

Galveston

University of Texas Medical Branch Hospitals Program

Sponsor: University of Texas Medical Branch Hospitals
Prgm Director: Juan C Sarria, MD*
Div of Infectious Disease, 0435
301 University Boulevard
Galveston, TX 77555
Tel: 409 747-1856   *Fax:* 409 772-6527
E-mail: jcsarria@utmb.edu
Length: 2 Yrs   *ACGME Approved/Offered Positions:* 5
Program ID: 146-48-21-048

Houston

Baylor College of Medicine Program

Sponsor: Baylor College of Medicine
Prgm Director: Barbara W Trautner, MD, PhD
1709 Dryden, Suite 625
Houston, TX 77030
Tel: 713 798-8918   *Fax:* 713 798-8948
Length: 2 Yrs   *ACGME Approved/Offered Positions:* 8
Program ID: 146-48-21-070

University of Texas at Houston Program

Sponsor: University of Texas Health Science Center at
Houston
Lyndon B Johnson General Hospital
University of Texas M D Anderson Cancer Center
Prgm Director: Pablo C Okhuysen, MD
6431 Fannin St
MSB 2.112
Houston, TX 77030
Tel: 713 500-6765   *Fax:* 713 500-5495
E-mail: Lakecia.Quinney@uth.tmc.edu
Length: 2 Yrs   *ACGME Approved/Offered Positions:* 10
Program ID: 146-48-31-018

Lackland AFB

San Antonio Uniformed Services Health Education Consortium Program

Sponsor: San Antonio Uniformed Services Health
Education Consortium
Wilford Hall Medical Center (AETC)
Brooke Army Medical Center
University of Texas Health Science Center
Prgm Director: (LTC) Clinton K Murray, MD
Infectious Disease Service (MCHE-MDI)
3851 Roger Brooke Drive
Fort Sam Houston, TX 78234
Tel: 210 916-4355   *Fax:* 210 916-0388
E-mail: clinton.murray@amedd.army.mil
Length: 2 Yrs   *ACGME Approved/Offered Positions:* 12
Program ID: 146-48-12-049
Uniformed Services Program

San Antonio

University of Texas Health Science Center at San Antonio Program

Sponsor: University of Texas School of Medicine at San
Antonio
Audie L Murphy Memorial Veterans Hospital (San
Antonio)
University Health System
Prgm Director: Thomas F Patterson, MD
Medicine/Infectious Diseases, MSC: 7881
7703 Floyd Curl Drive
San Antonio, TX 78229
Tel: 210 567-4823   *Fax:* 210 567-4670
Length: 2 Yrs   *ACGME Approved/Offered Positions:* 4
Program ID: 146-48-21-057

Temple

Texas A&M College of Medicine-Scott and White Program

Sponsor: Scott and White Memorial Hospital
Prgm Director: John L Carpenter, MD
2401 S 31st Street
Temple, TX 76508
Tel: 254 724-2111   *Fax:* 254 724-9280
Length: 2 Yrs   *ACGME Approved/Offered Positions:* 2
Program ID: 146-48-21-198

Utah

Salt Lake City

University of Utah Program

Sponsor: University of Utah Medical Center
LDS Hospital
Prgm Director: Harry Rosado Santos, MD
30 North 1900 East, Room 4B319
Salt Lake City, UT 84132
Tel: 801 581-8812   *Fax:* 801 585-3377
E-mail: harry.rosado@hsc.utah.edu
Length: 2 Yrs   *ACGME Approved/Offered Positions:* 4
Program ID: 146-49-21-158

Vermont

Burlington

University of Vermont Program

Sponsor: Fletcher Allen Health Care
Prgm Director: Christopher J Grace, MD
Smith 275
Burlington, VT 05401
Tel: 802 847-4836   *Fax:* 802 847-5322
E-mail: christopher.grace@vtmednet.org
Length: 2 Yrs   *ACGME Approved/Offered Positions:* 2
Program ID: 146-50-21-194

Virginia

Charlottesville

University of Virginia Program

Sponsor: University of Virginia Medical Center
Prgm Director: Brian Wispelwey, MD, MS*
Department of Medicine
PO Box 801340
Charlottesville, VA 22908
Tel: 434 982-1699   *Fax:* 434 924-0075
Length: 2 Yrs   *ACGME Approved/Offered Positions:* 5
Program ID: 146-51-21-019

Norfolk

Eastern Virginia Medical School Program

Sponsor: Eastern Virginia Medical School
Sentara Norfolk General Hospital
Prgm Director: Edward C Oldfield III, MD
825 Fairfax Avenue, Hofheimer Hall
Norfolk, VA 23507
Tel: 757 446-8910   *Fax:* 757 446-5242
E-mail: oldfieec@evms.edu
Length: 2 Yrs   *ACGME Approved/Offered Positions:* 2
Program ID: 146-51-12-199

Richmond

Virginia Commonwealth University Health System Program

Sponsor: Virginia Commonwealth University Health
System
Hunter Holmes McGuire VA Medical Center (Richmond)
Medical College of Virginia Hospitals
Prgm Director: Sara G Monroe, MD
1101 E Marshall St, Room 7-082
PO Box 980049
Richmond, VA 23298
Tel: 804 828-9711   *Fax:* 804 828-3097
Length: 2 Yrs   *ACGME Approved/Offered Positions:* 4
Program ID: 146-51-21-020

Washington

Seattle

University of Washington Program

Sponsor: University of Washington School of Medicine
University of Washington Medical Center
Prgm Director: Wesley C Van Voorhis, MD, PhD
Allergy & Infectious Disease Dept - Box 355330
1959 NE Pacific Street
Seattle, WA 98195
Tel: 206 543-2447   *Fax:* 206 616-4898
E-mail: eya@u.washington.edu
Length: 2 Yrs   *ACGME Approved/Offered Positions:* 20
Program ID: 146-54-21-071

Programs

West Virginia

Morgantown

West Virginia University Program

Sponsor: West Virginia University School of Medicine
West Virginia University Hospitals
Prgm Director: Rashida Khakoo, MD
Medical Center Drive
PO Box 9163
Morgantown, WV 26506
Tel: 304 293-3306   *Fax:* 304 293-8677
Length: 2 Yrs   *ACGME Approved/Offered Positions:* 2
Program ID: 146-55-21-188

Wisconsin

Madison

University of Wisconsin Program

Sponsor: University of Wisconsin Hospital and Clinics
William S Middleton Veterans Hospital
Prgm Director: David R Andes, MD
Room H4/574
600 Highland Avenue
Madison, WI 53792
Tel: 608 263-1545   *Fax:* 608 263-4464
Length: 2 Yrs   *ACGME Approved/Offered Positions:* 4
Program ID: 146-56-21-120

Milwaukee

Medical College of Wisconsin Affiliated Hospitals Program

Sponsor: Medical College of Wisconsin Affiliated
    Hospitals, Inc
AIDS Resource Center of Wisconsin
Clement J Zablocki Veterans Affairs Medical Center
Froedtert Memorial Lutheran Hospital
Wheaton Franciscan Healthcare-St Joseph
Prgm Director: Mary Beth Graham, MD
Infectious Disease Division
9200 W Wisconsin Ave
Milwaukee, WI 53226
Tel: 414 456-7000   *Fax:* 414 456-6206
E-mail: mbgraham@mcw.edu
Length: 2 Yrs   *ACGME Approved/Offered Positions:* 5
Program ID: 146-56-31-039

Internal Medicine

Alabama

Birmingham

Baptist Health System Program

Sponsor: Baptist Health System Inc
Baptist Medical Center-Princeton
Trinity Medical Center
Prgm Director: Robert A Kreisberg, MD*
701 Princeton Ave SW
Birmingham, AL 35211
Tel: 205 592-5745   *Fax:* 205 599-4702
E-mail: robert.kreisberg@bhsala.com
Length: 3 Yrs   *ACGME Approved/Offered Positions:* 34
Program ID: 140-01-21-020

University of Alabama Medical Center Program

Sponsor: University of Alabama Hospital
Veterans Affairs Medical Center (Birmingham)
Prgm Director: Gustavo R Heudebert, MD
1530 3rd Avenue South
Boshell Diabetes Building 327
Birmingham, AL 35294
Tel: 205 934-2490   *Fax:* 205 975-6424
E-mail: medres@uab.edu
Length: 3 Yrs   *ACGME Approved/Offered Positions:* 123
Program ID: 140-01-21-022

Mobile

University of South Alabama Program

Sponsor: University of South Alabama Hospitals
University of South Alabama Medical Center
Prgm Director: Thomas B Montgomery, MD
2451 Fillingim Street
Mastin 400-L
Mobile, AL 36617
Tel: 251 471-7891   *Fax:* 251 471-1291
E-mail: pgreen@usouthal.edu
Length: 3 Yrs   *ACGME Approved/Offered Positions:* 48
Program ID: 140-01-11-024

Montgomery

University of Alabama Medical Center (Montgomery) Program

Sponsor: University of Alabama Hospital
Baptist Medical Center South
Prgm Director: W J Many Jr, MD
4371 Narrow Lane Road
Suite 200
Montgomery, AL 36116
Tel: 334 284-5211   *Fax:* 334 284-9020
E-mail: jbrown@uabmontgomery.com
Length: 3 Yrs   *ACGME Approved/Offered Positions:* 24
Program ID: 140-01-21-447

Arizona

Phoenix

Banner Good Samaritan Medical Center Program

Sponsor: Banner Good Samaritan Medical Center
Carl T Hayden VA Medical Center
Prgm Director: Cheryl W O'Malley, MD*
Department of Medicine
1111 E McDowell Road, LL-2
Phoenix, AZ 85006
Tel: 602 239-2296   *Fax:* 602 239-2084
E-mail: cheryl.OMalley@bannerhealth.com
Length: 3 Yrs   *ACGME Approved/Offered Positions:* 71
Program ID: 140-03-21-025

Maricopa Medical Center Program

Sponsor: Maricopa Medical Center
Prgm Director: Shannon E Skinner, MD*
Department of Medicine
2601 E Roosevelt St, #0D10
Phoenix, AZ 85008
Tel: 602 344-1218   *Fax:* 602 344-1488
E-mail: karen_boettcher@medprodoctors.com
Length: 3 Yrs   *ACGME Approved/Offered Positions:* 61
Program ID: 140-03-11-026

St Joseph's Hospital and Medical Center Program

Sponsor: St Joseph's Hospital and Medical Center
Prgm Director: Jaya M Raj, MD*
Department of Medicine
350 West Thomas Road
Phoenix, AZ 85013
Tel: 602 406-3545   *Fax:* 602 406-4974
Length: 3 Yrs   *ACGME Approved/Offered Positions:* 35
Program ID: 140-03-11-027

Scottsdale

College of Medicine, Mayo Clinic (Arizona) Program

Sponsor: College of Medicine, Mayo Clinic
Mayo Clinic (Arizona)
Mayo Clinic Hospital
Prgm Director: Keith J Cannon, MD
Department of Medicine
13400 E Shea Boulevard
Scottsdale, AZ 85259
Tel: 480 301-9824   *Fax:* 480 301-4171
E-mail: bell.lois@mayo.edu
Length: 3 Yrs   *ACGME Approved/Offered Positions:* 30
Program ID: 140-03-21-512

Tucson

University of Arizona Program

Sponsor: University of Arizona College of Medicine
Southern Arizona VA Health Care Center (Tucson)
Tucson Medical Center
University Medical Center
Prgm Director: William P Johnson, MD
Department of Medicine-Medicine Education Office
1501 N Campbell Avenue, Box 245040, Rm 6336
Tucson, AZ 85724
Tel: 520 626-2761   *Fax:* 520 626-6020
Length: 3 Yrs   *ACGME Approved/Offered Positions:* 81
Program ID: 140-03-21-029

University of Arizona/UPHK Graduate Medical Education Consortium Program

Sponsor: University of Arizona/UPHK Graduate Medical
    Ed Consortium
University Medical Center
Prgm Director: Thomas Boyer, MD
GME
2800 East Ajo Way
Tucson, AZ 85713
Tel: 520 874-4502   *Fax:* 520 874-4510
E-mail: sherri@email.arizona.edu
Length: 3 Yrs   *ACGME Approved/Offered Positions:* 15
Program ID: 140-03-12-536

Note: * indicates a newly appointed program director

Arkansas

Little Rock

University of Arkansas for Medical Sciences Program

Sponsor: University of Arkansas College of Medicine
Central Arkansas Veterans Healthcare System
UAMS Medical Center
Prgm Director: Michael Saccente, MD
4301 W Markham Street
Internal Medicine Residency Office, #634
Little Rock, AR 72205
Tel: 501 686-7592   *Fax:* 501 686-6001
E-mail: imresident@uams.edu
Length: 3 Yrs   *ACGME Approved/Offered Positions:* 66
Program ID: 140-04-21-030

California

Bakersfield

Kern Medical Center Program

Sponsor: Kern Medical Center
Prgm Director: Alan S Ragland, DO
Department of Medicine
1830 Flower Street
Bakersfield, CA 93305
Tel: 661 326-2202   *Fax:* 661 862-7612
Length: 3 Yrs   *ACGME Approved/Offered Positions:* 24
Program ID: 140-05-31-031

French Camp

San Joaquin General Hospital Program

Sponsor: San Joaquin General Hospital
Prgm Director: Sheela S Kapre, MD
Department of Medicine
Box 1020, 500 W Hospital Road
French Camp, CA 95231
Tel: 209 468-6624   *Fax:* 209 468-6246
E-mail: skapre@sjgh.org
Length: 3 Yrs   *ACGME Approved/Offered Positions:* 21
Program ID: 140-05-12-069

Fresno

University of California (San Francisco)/Fresno Program

Sponsor: UCSF Fresno Medical Education Program
Community Medical Centers (Fresno)
VA Central California Health Care System
Prgm Director: Ivy L Darden, MD
Department of Medicine
155 North Fresno Street
Fresno, CA 93701
Tel: 559 499-6500   *Fax:* 559 499-6501
E-mail: internal.medicine@fresno.ucsf.edu
Length: 3 Yrs   *ACGME Approved/Offered Positions:* 64
Program ID: 140-05-31-033

La Jolla

Scripps Clinic/Scripps Green Hospital Program

Sponsor: Scripps Clinic/Scripps Green Hospital
Prgm Director: Joel C Diamant, MD
Dept of Grad Med Ed, Suite 403C
10666 N Torrey Pines Road
La Jolla, CA 92037
Tel: 858 554-3200   *Fax:* 858 554-3232
E-mail: gme@scripps.edu
Length: 3 Yrs   *ACGME Approved/Offered Positions:* 24
Program ID: 140-05-21-490

Loma Linda

Loma Linda University Program

Sponsor: Loma Linda University Medical Center
Jerry L Pettis Memorial Veterans Hospital
Riverside County Regional Medical Center
Prgm Director: Daniel I Kim, MD, MBA
11234 Anderson Street, Room 1503
PO Box 2000
Loma Linda, CA 92354
Tel: 909 558-7263   *Fax:* 909 558-0427
E-mail: mhallas@llu.edu
Length: 3 Yrs   *ACGME Approved/Offered Positions:* 99
Program ID: 140-05-21-038

Long Beach

St Mary Medical Center Program

Sponsor: St Mary Medical Center
Los Angeles County-Harbor-UCLA Medical Center
Prgm Director: Chester Choi, MD
Department of Medical Education
1050 Linden Avenue
Long Beach, CA 90813
Tel: 562 491-9350   *Fax:* 562 491-9146
E-mail: cchoi@chw.edu
Length: 3 Yrs   *ACGME Approved/Offered Positions:* 30
Program ID: 140-05-31-039

Los Angeles

Cedars-Sinai Medical Center Program

Sponsor: Cedars-Sinai Medical Center
VA Greater Los Angeles Healthcare System
Prgm Director: Mark S Noah, MD
Department of Medicine
8700 Beverly Blvd, Suite B-115
Los Angeles, CA 90048
Tel: 310 423-5161   *Fax:* 310 423-0436
Length: 3 Yrs   *ACGME Approved/Offered Positions:* 136
Program ID: 140-05-11-040

Kaiser Permanente Southern California (Los Angeles) Program

Sponsor: Kaiser Permanente Southern California
Kaiser Foundation Hospital (Los Angeles)
Prgm Director: Thomas Y Tom, MD
Internal Medicine
4950 Sunset Blvd, 6th Floor
Los Angeles, CA 90027
Tel: 323 783-4892   *Fax:* 323 783-1187
Length: 3 Yrs   *ACGME Approved/Offered Positions:* 46
Program ID: 140-05-12-042

UCLA Medical Center Program

Sponsor: UCLA David Geffen School of Medicine/UCLA Medical Center
UCLA Medical Center
Prgm Director: Jodi L Friedman, MD
757 Westwood Plaza
Suite 7501
Los Angeles, CA 90095
Tel: 310 825-7375   *Fax:* 310 825-3537
Length: 3 Yrs   *ACGME Approved/Offered Positions:* 92
Program ID: 140-05-11-046

UCLA-VA Greater Los Angeles Program

Sponsor: VA Greater Los Angeles Healthcare System
Prgm Director: Neil Paige, MD
Wadsworth Division, 691/111 A
11301 Wilshire Blvd
Los Angeles, CA 90073
Tel: 310 268-3034   *Fax:* 310 268-4818
Length: 3 Yrs   *ACGME Approved/Offered Positions:* 76
Program ID: 140-05-31-048

University of Southern California/ LAC+USC Medical Center Program

Sponsor: University of Southern California/LAC+USC Medical Center
LAC+USC Medical Center
Prgm Director: Ron Ben-Ari, MD
2020 Zonal Avenue
IRD, Rm 620
Los Angeles, CA 90033
Tel: 323 226-7556   *Fax:* 323 226-2657
E-mail: uscgme@usc.edu
Length: 3 Yrs   *ACGME Approved/Offered Positions:* 165
Program ID: 140-05-21-044

White Memorial Medical Center Program

Sponsor: White Memorial Medical Center
Prgm Director: Juan C Barrio, MD
Department of Internal Medicine
1720 E Cesar E Chavez Avenue
Los Angeles, CA 90033
Tel: 323 268-5000   *Fax:* 323 881-8702
E-mail: florespi@ah.org
Length: 3 Yrs   *ACGME Approved/Offered Positions:* 20
Program ID: 140-05-11-049

Oakland

Alameda County Medical Center Program

Sponsor: Alameda County Medical Center
Prgm Director: Theodore G Rose Jr, MD
Department of Medicine
1411 E 31st Street
Oakland, CA 94602
Tel: 510 437-4172   *Fax:* 510 536-2270
Length: 3 Yrs   *ACGME Approved/Offered Positions:* 61
Program ID: 140-05-31-051

Kaiser Permanente Medical Group (Northern California/Oakland) Program

Sponsor: Kaiser Permanente Medical Group (Northern California)
Kaiser Permanente Medical Center (Oakland)
Prgm Director: Michael J Clement, MD
Medical Education Department
280 West MacArthur Boulevard
Oakland, CA 94611
Tel: 510 752-7867   *Fax:* 510 752-1571
E-mail: medicine.oakmeded@kp.org
Length: 3 Yrs   *ACGME Approved/Offered Positions:* 39
Program ID: 140-05-12-052

Orange

University of California (Irvine) Program

Sponsor: University of California (Irvine) Medical Center
Long Beach Memorial Medical Center
VA Long Beach Healthcare System
Prgm Director: Lloyd Rucker, MD
Medical Center
101 The City Drive S, Bldg 200, Suite 720, Rte 1
Orange, CA 92868
Tel: 714 456-5691   *Fax:* 714 456-8874
E-mail: nhardgro@uci.edu
Length: 3 Yrs   *ACGME Approved/Offered Positions:* 85
Program ID: 140-05-21-036

Pasadena

Huntington Memorial Hospital Program

Sponsor: Huntington Memorial Hospital
Prgm Director: Anthony G Koerner, MD
Graduate Medical Education
100 California Boulevard
Pasadena, CA 91105
Tel: 626 397-5160   *Fax:* 626 397-2914
Length: 3 Yrs   *ACGME Approved/Offered Positions:* 23
Program ID: 140-05-11-056

Sacramento

University of California (Davis) Health System Program

Sponsor: University of California (Davis) Health System
University of California (Davis) Medical Center
Prgm Director: Mark C Henderson, MD
Department of Medicine
4150 V Street #3116
Sacramento, CA 95817
Tel: 916 734-7080   *Fax:* 916 734-1150
Length: 3 Yrs   *ACGME Approved/Offered Positions:* 93
Program ID: 140-05-21-032

San Diego

Naval Medical Center (San Diego) Program

Sponsor: Naval Medical Center (San Diego)
Prgm Director: Patricia V Pepper, MD, MSc
Department of Internal Medicine, Suite 300
34730 Bob Wilson Drive
San Diego, CA 92134
Tel: 619 532-7507   *Fax:* 619 532-7508
Length: 3 Yrs   *ACGME Approved/Offered Positions:* 44
Program ID: 140-05-12-012
Uniformed Services Program

Scripps Mercy Hospital Program

Sponsor: Scripps Mercy Hospital
Prgm Director: Stanley A Amundson, MD
Dept of Medical Education
4077 5th Avenue, MER 35
San Diego, CA 92103
Tel: 619 260-7215   *Fax:* 619 260-7305
E-mail: Amundson.Stan@scrippshealth.org
Length: 3 Yrs   *ACGME Approved/Offered Positions:* 36
Program ID: 140-05-11-057

University of California (San Diego) Program

Sponsor: University of California (San Diego) Medical
   Center
Veterans Affairs Medical Center (San Diego)
Prgm Director: Elaine A Muchmore, MD*
402 Dickinson Street, MPF 380
San Diego, CA 92103
Tel: 858 642-3356   *Fax:* 858 552-7485
Length: 3 Yrs   *ACGME Approved/Offered Positions:* 92
Program ID: 140-05-21-058

San Francisco

California Pacific Medical Center Program

Sponsor: California Pacific Medical Center
Prgm Director: Paul Aronowitz, MD
2351 Clay Street, Suite 380
Pacific Campus
San Francisco, CA 94115
Tel: 415 600-1133   *Fax:* 415 775-7437
E-mail: meded@sutterhealth.org
Length: 3 Yrs   *ACGME Approved/Offered Positions:* 59
Program ID: 140-05-12-062

Kaiser Permanente Medical Group (Northern California)/San Francisco Program

Sponsor: Kaiser Permanente Medical Group (Northern
   California)
Kaiser Permanente Medical Center (San Francisco)
Prgm Director: Michael L Coppolino, MD, MSc*
2425 Geary Boulevard, Room M-160
San Francisco, CA 94115
Tel: 415 833-9182
E-mail: Michael.Coppolino@kp.org
Length: 3 Yrs   *ACGME Approved/Offered Positions:* 38
Program ID: 140-05-12-060

St Mary's Hospital and Medical Center Program

Sponsor: St Mary's Hospital and Medical Center
Prgm Director: Terrie Mendelson, MD
Department of Medicine
450 Stanyan Street
San Francisco, CA 94117
Tel: 415 750-5781   *Fax:* 415 750-8149
E-mail: Kathy.Banks@chw.edu
Length: 3 Yrs   *ACGME Approved/Offered Positions:* 39
Program ID: 140-05-22-063

University of California (San Francisco) Program

Sponsor: University of California (San Francisco) School
   of Medicine
San Francisco General Hospital Medical Center
UCSF and Mount Zion Medical Centers
Veterans Affairs Medical Center (San Francisco)
Prgm Director: Harry Hollander, MD
Department of Internal Medicine
505 Parnassus Ave Box 0119
San Francisco, CA 94143
Tel: 415 476-1528   *Fax:* 415 502-1976
E-mail: aforseth@medicine.ucsf.edu
Length: 3 Yrs   *ACGME Approved/Offered Positions:* 175
Program ID: 140-05-21-064

San Jose

Santa Clara Valley Medical Center Program

Sponsor: Santa Clara Valley Medical Center
Prgm Director: Steven C Roey, MD, MEd*
Department of Medicine
751 S Bascom Avenue
San Jose, CA 95128
Tel: 408 885-6036   *Fax:* 408 885-4046
Length: 3 Yrs   *ACGME Approved/Offered Positions:* 60
Program ID: 140-05-31-065

Santa Barbara

Santa Barbara Cottage Hospital Program

Sponsor: Santa Barbara Cottage Hospital
Prgm Director: Andrew S Gersoff, MD
Medical Education Office
Box 689
Santa Barbara, CA 93102
Tel: 805 569-7315   *Fax:* 805 569-8358
Length: 3 Yrs   *ACGME Approved/Offered Positions:* 25
Program ID: 140-05-22-066

Santa Clara

Kaiser Permanente Medical Group (Northern California)/Santa Clara Program

Sponsor: Kaiser Permanente Medical Group (Northern
   California)
Kaiser Permanente Medical Center (Santa Clara)
Prgm Director: Danny Sam, MD
Graduate Medical Education Office
710 Lawrence Expressway, Dept 384
Santa Clara, CA 95051
Tel: 408 851-3830   *Fax:* 408 851-3839
Length: 3 Yrs   *ACGME Approved/Offered Positions:* 42
Program ID: 140-05-21-067

Stanford

Stanford University Program

Sponsor: Stanford Hospital and Clinics
Veterans Affairs Palo Alto Health Care System
Prgm Director: Kelley M Skeff, MD, PhD
300 Pasteur Drive, S101
Stanford, CA 94305
Tel: 650 723-5334   *Fax:* 650 498-6205
Length: 3 Yrs   *ACGME Approved/Offered Positions:* 112
Program ID: 140-05-21-068

Sylmar

UCLA-Olive View Program

Sponsor: Olive View/UCLA Medical Center
Prgm Director: Soma Wali, MD
14445 Olive View Drive, #2B182
Los Angeles, CA 91342
Tel: 818 364-3205   *Fax:* 818 364-4573
E-mail: soma.wali@uclaoliveview.org
Length: 3 Yrs   *ACGME Approved/Offered Positions:* 72
Program ID: 140-05-21-047

Torrance

Los Angeles County-Harbor-UCLA Medical Center Program

Sponsor: Los Angeles County-Harbor-UCLA Medical
   Center
Prgm Director: Darryl Y Sue, MD
1000 W Carson Street, Box 400
Torrance, CA 90509
Tel: 310 222-2409   *Fax:* 310 320-9688
E-mail: dysue49@gmail.com
Length: 3 Yrs   *ACGME Approved/Offered Positions:* 56
Program ID: 140-05-11-070

Colorado

Aurora

University of Colorado Denver Program

Sponsor: University of Colorado Denver School of
   Medicine
Denver Health Medical Center
University of Colorado Hospital
Veterans Affairs Medical Center (Denver)
Prgm Director: Suzanne L Brandenburg, MD
PO Box 6511
Academic Office One, 8th Fl, Room 8602
Aurora, CO 80045
Tel: 303 724-1784   *Fax:* 303 724-1799
E-mail: Sherrry.Berka@ucdenver.edu
Length: 3 Yrs   *ACGME Approved/Offered Positions:* 152
Program ID: 140-07-21-073

Denver

Exempla St Joseph Hospital Program

Sponsor: Exempla St Joseph Hospital
Prgm Director: Robert B Gibbons, MD
Department of Medicine
1835 Franklin Street
Denver, CO 80218
Tel: 303 837-7836   *Fax:* 303 866-8044
Length: 3 Yrs   *ACGME Approved/Offered Positions:* 38
Program ID: 140-07-31-072

Connecticut

Bridgeport

Bridgeport Hospital/Yale University Program

Sponsor: Bridgeport Hospital
Prgm Director: Constantine A Manthous, MD
267 Grant Street
PO Box 5000
Bridgeport, CT 06610
Tel: 203 384-3792   *Fax:* 203 384-4294
E-mail: bericc@bpthosp.org
Length: 3 Yrs   *ACGME Approved/Offered Positions:* 40
Program ID: 140-08-11-074

Note: * indicates a newly appointed program director

St Vincent's Medical Center Program

Sponsor: St Vincent's Medical Center
Prgm Director: Ingram M Roberts, MD, MBA
Department of Medicine
2800 Main Street
Bridgeport, CT 06606
Tel: 203 576-5576   *Fax:* 203 576-5022
E-mail: mededucation@stvincents.org
Length: 3 Yrs   *ACGME Approved/Offered Positions:* 30
Program ID: 140-08-11-075

Danbury

Danbury Hospital Program

Sponsor: Danbury Hospital
Yale-New Haven Hospital
Prgm Director: Winston Y Shih, MD, BS
Department of Medicine
24 Hospital Avenue
Danbury, CT 06810
Tel: 203 797-7104   *Fax:* 203 830-2047
Length: 3 Yrs   *ACGME Approved/Offered Positions:* 42
Program ID: 140-08-11-076

Derby

Griffin Hospital Program

Sponsor: Griffin Hospital
Prgm Director: Seema D'souza, MD*
Department of Internal Medicine
130 Division Street
Derby, CT 06418
Tel: 203 732-7327   *Fax:* 203 732-7185
E-mail: mbliga@griffinhealth.org
Length: 3 Yrs   *ACGME Approved/Offered Positions:* 23
Program ID: 140-08-31-077

Farmington

University of Connecticut (New Britain) Program

Sponsor: University of Connecticut School of Medicine
Hospital for Central Connecticut
Univ of Connecticut Health Center/John Dempsey Hospital
Prgm Director: Scott R Allen, MD
Primary Care Internal Medicine Residency Program
263 Farmington Avenue
Farmington, CT 06030
Tel: 860 679-4017   *Fax:* 860 679-1621
Length: 3 Yrs   *ACGME Approved/Offered Positions:* 52
Program ID: 140-08-21-499

University of Connecticut Program

Sponsor: University of Connecticut School of Medicine
Hartford Hospital
St Francis Hospital and Medical Center
Univ of Connecticut Health Center/John Dempsey Hospital
Prgm Director: Steven Angus, MD
263 Farmington Avenue
Dept of Medicine, Room L2104
Farmington, CT 06030
Tel: 860 679-2437   *Fax:* 860 679-4613
E-mail: angus@uchc.edu
Length: 3 Yrs   *ACGME Approved/Offered Positions:* 122
Program ID: 140-08-31-078

Greenwich

Greenwich Hospital Association Program

Sponsor: Greenwich Hospital
Prgm Director: Charles B Seelig, MD, MS
Room 1-3217
Five Perryridge Road
Greenwich, CT 06830
Tel: 203 863-3913   *Fax:* 203 863-3924
Length: 3 Yrs   *ACGME Approved/Offered Positions:* 21
Program ID: 140-08-21-079

New Haven

Hospital of St Raphael Program

Sponsor: Hospital of St Raphael
Prgm Director: Robert J Nardino, MD
Department of Medicine
1450 Chapel Street
New Haven, CT 06511
Tel: 203 789-3358   *Fax:* 203 789-3222
Length: 3 Yrs   *ACGME Approved/Offered Positions:* 61
Program ID: 140-08-31-084

Yale-New Haven Medical Center (Waterbury) Program

Sponsor: Yale-New Haven Hospital
Waterbury Hospital Health Center
Prgm Director: Stephen J Huot, MD, PhD
Department of Medicine
20 York Street
New Haven, CT 06520
Tel: 203 785-5644   *Fax:* 203 785-7258
E-mail: stephen.huot@yale.edu
Length: 3 Yrs   *ACGME Approved/Offered Positions:* 50
Program ID: 140-08-21-496

Yale-New Haven Medical Center Program

Sponsor: Yale-New Haven Hospital
Veterans Affairs Medical Center (West Haven)
Prgm Director: Cyrus R Kapadia, MBBS, MD
1074 LMP
PO Box 208030
New Haven, CT 06520
Tel: 203 785-7113   *Fax:* 203 785-7030
Length: 3 Yrs   *ACGME Approved/Offered Positions:* 109
Program ID: 140-08-21-085

Norwalk

Norwalk Hospital Program

Sponsor: Norwalk Hospital
Prgm Director: Mark Kulaga, MD
Department of Medicine
Maple Street
Norwalk, CT 06856
Tel: 203 852-2248   *Fax:* 203 855-3589
E-mail: mark.kulaga@norwalkhealth.org
Length: 3 Yrs   *ACGME Approved/Offered Positions:* 44
Program ID: 140-08-31-086

Stamford

Stamford Hospital/Columbia University College of Physicians and Surgeons Program

Sponsor: Stamford Hospital
Prgm Director: Noel I Robin, MD
PO Box 9317
Shelburne & W Broad Street
Stamford, CT 06904
Tel: 203 276-7485   *Fax:* 203 276-7368
Length: 3 Yrs   *ACGME Approved/Offered Positions:* 20
Program ID: 140-08-11-087

Waterbury

St Mary's Hospital (Waterbury) Program

Sponsor: St Mary's Hospital
Veterans Affairs Medical Center (West Haven)
Prgm Director: Gregory Buller, MD
Department of Medicine
56 Franklin Street
Waterbury, CT 06706
Tel: 203 709-8685   *Fax:* 203 709-3518
E-mail: laronin@stmh.org
Length: 3 Yrs   *ACGME Approved/Offered Positions:* 34
Program ID: 140-08-13-530

Delaware

Wilmington

Jefferson Medical College/Christiana Care Health Services Program

Sponsor: Jefferson Medical College
Christiana Care Health Services Inc
Prgm Director: Brian M Aboff, MD
Department of Medicine
PO Box 6001
Newark, DE 19718
Tel: 302 733-6344   *Fax:* 302 733-6386
E-mail: medicine.residency@christianacare.org
Length: 3 Yrs   *ACGME Approved/Offered Positions:* 50
Program ID: 140-09-11-090

District of Columbia

Washington

George Washington University Program

Sponsor: George Washington University School of Medicine
George Washington University Hospital (UHS)
Veterans Affairs Medical Center (Washington, DC)
Prgm Director: Jehan El-Bayoumi, MD*
Department of Medicine
2150 Pennsylvania Avenue, NW, 5-411
Washington, DC 20037
Tel: 202 741-2235   *Fax:* 202 741-2241
Length: 3 Yrs   *ACGME Approved/Offered Positions:* 97
Program ID: 140-10-21-093

Georgetown University Hospital Program

Sponsor: Georgetown University Hospital
Prgm Director: Michael Adams, MD
Department of Medicine
3800 Reservoir Road, NW
Washington, DC 20007
Tel: 202 444-2895   *Fax:* 202 444-1096
E-mail: adamsm@gunet.georgetown.edu
Length: 3 Yrs   *ACGME Approved/Offered Positions:* 97
Program ID: 140-10-21-091

Georgetown University Hospital/Washington Hospital Center Program

Sponsor: Washington Hospital Center
Prgm Director: Sailaja Pindiprolu, MD*
Department of Medicine
110 Irving Street, NW
Washington, DC 20010
Tel: 202 877-6749   *Fax:* 202 877-6292
Length: 3 Yrs   *ACGME Approved/Offered Positions:* 90
Program ID: 140-10-11-097

Howard University Program

Sponsor: Howard University Hospital
Prgm Director: Peter L Sealy, MD
Department of Medicine
2041 Georgia Avenue NW
Washington, DC 20060
Tel: 202 865-1989   *Fax:* 202 865-7199
E-mail: psealy@howard.edu
Length: 3 Yrs   *ACGME Approved/Offered Positions:* 81
Program ID: 140-10-21-461

Providence Hospital Program

Sponsor: Providence Hospital
Prgm Director: Junette C Gibbons, MD
1150 Varnum Street, NE
Washington, DC 20017
Tel: 202 269-7747   *Fax:* 202 269-7892
Length: 3 Yrs   *ACGME Approved/Offered Positions:* 21
Program ID: 140-10-21-095

Programs

Florida

Atlantis

University of Miami School of Medicine at Florida Atlantic University Program

Sponsor: University of Miami Hospital and Clinics
JFK Medical Center
West Palm Beach VA Medical Center
Prgm Director: Charles Posternack, MD
5301 Congress Avenue
Atlantis, FL 33462
Tel: 561 548-1273   *Fax:* 561 548-1254
Length: 3 Yrs   *ACGME Approved/Offered Positions:* 66
Program ID: 140-11-31-535

Gainesville

University of Florida Program

Sponsor: University of Florida College of Medicine
North Florida/South Georgia Veterans Health System
Shands Hospital at the University of Florida
Prgm Director: N Lawrence Edwards, MD
Box 100277
1600 SW Archer Rd
Gainesville, FL 32610
Tel: 352 265-0239   *Fax:* 352 265-1103
Length: 3 Yrs   *ACGME Approved/Offered Positions:* 93
Program ID: 140-11-21-098

Jacksonville

College of Medicine, Mayo Clinic (Jacksonville) Program

Sponsor: College of Medicine, Mayo Clinic
Mayo Clinic (Jacksonville)
Mayo Clinic Florida Hospital
Prgm Director: Kenneth G Nix Jr, MD*
Education Services
4500 San Pablo Road
Jacksonville, FL 32224
Tel: 904 953-0428   *Fax:* 904 953-0430
E-mail: nix.kenneth@mayo.edu
Length: 3 Yrs   *ACGME Approved/Offered Positions:* 30
Program ID: 140-11-21-509

University of Florida College of Medicine Jacksonville Program

Sponsor: University of Florida College of Medicine
 Jacksonville
Shands Jacksonville Medical Center
Prgm Director: N S Nahman Jr, MD
Department of Medicine, LRC 4th floor
653-1 West 8th St, GME Box L18
Jacksonville, FL 32209
Tel: 904 244-3094   *Fax:* 904 244-3634
E-mail: lorna.matos@jax.ufl.edu
Length: 3 Yrs   *ACGME Approved/Offered Positions:* 44
Program ID: 140-11-21-099

Miami

Jackson Memorial Hospital/Jackson Health System Program

Sponsor: Jackson Memorial Hospital/Jackson Health
 System
Veterans Affairs Medical Center (Miami)
Prgm Director: Stephen N Symes, MD
Department of Medicine
PO Box 016960 (R-60)
Miami, FL 33101
Tel: 305 585-5215
E-mail: ssymes@med.miami.edu
Length: 3 Yrs   *ACGME Approved/Offered Positions:* 138
Program ID: 140-11-21-100

Miami Beach

Mount Sinai Medical Center of Florida Program

Sponsor: Mount Sinai Medical Center of Florida, Inc
Prgm Director: Allen Young, MD
4300 Alton Road
Lowenstein Building
Miami Beach, FL 33140
Tel: 305 674-2053   *Fax:* 305 674-2057
Length: 3 Yrs   *ACGME Approved/Offered Positions:* 37
Program ID: 140-11-12-101

Orlando

Florida Hospital Medical Center Program

Sponsor: Florida Hospital Medical Center
Prgm Director: George Everett, MD, MS
2501 North Orange Avenue, Suite 235
Orlando, FL 32804
Tel: 407 303-3275   *Fax:* 407 303-7285
E-mail: george.everett.md@flhosp.org
Length: 3 Yrs   *ACGME Approved/Offered Positions:* 24
Program ID: 140-11-31-539

Orlando Health Program

Sponsor: Orlando Health
Orlando Regional Medical Center
Prgm Director: Mario J Madruga, MD
Department of Medicine
86 W Underwood Street, Suite 102
Orlando, FL 32806
Tel: 407 841-5145   *Fax:* 407 841-5101
E-mail: immp@orhs.org
Length: 3 Yrs   *ACGME Approved/Offered Positions:* 46
Program ID: 140-11-31-102

Tampa

University of South Florida Program

Sponsor: University of South Florida College of Medicine
James A Haley Veterans Hospital
Tampa General Hospital
Prgm Director: Michael T Flannery, MD
2A Columbia Drive, Sixth Floor
Tampa, FL 33606
Tel: 813 259-0670   *Fax:* 813 259-0679
E-mail: jwaterma@hsc.usf.edu
Length: 3 Yrs   *ACGME Approved/Offered Positions:* 87
Program ID: 140-11-21-104

Weston

Cleveland Clinic (Florida) Program

Sponsor: Cleveland Clinic Florida
Prgm Director: Jose M Muniz, MD
2950 Cleveland Clinic Boulevard
Weston, FL 33331
Tel: 954 659-5884   *Fax:* 954 659-5515
E-mail: imprg@ccf.org
Length: 3 Yrs   *ACGME Approved/Offered Positions:* 30
Program ID: 140-11-21-528

Georgia

Atlanta

Atlanta Medical Center Program

Sponsor: Atlanta Medical Center
Prgm Director: Miriam Parker, MD
GME Department - Internal Medicine
303 Parkway Drive NE, Box 423
Atlanta, GA 30312
Tel: 404 265-4919   *Fax:* 404 265-4989
E-mail: Miriam.Parker@tenethealth.com
Length: 3 Yrs   *ACGME Approved/Offered Positions:* 30
Program ID: 140-12-12-106

Emory University Program

Sponsor: Emory University School of Medicine
Emory University Hospital
Grady Health System
Veterans Affairs Medical Center (Atlanta)
Prgm Director: Carlos del Rio, MD*
69 Jesse Hill Jr Dr SE
Department of Medicine
Atlanta, GA 30303
Tel: 404 616-6779   *Fax:* 404 525-2957
Length: 3 Yrs   *ACGME Approved/Offered Positions:* 177
Program ID: 140-12-21-105

Morehouse School of Medicine Program

Sponsor: Morehouse School of Medicine
Grady Health System
Prgm Director: Myra E Rose, MD
Department of Medicine
720 Westview Drive, SW
Atlanta, GA 30310
Tel: 404 756-1325   *Fax:* 404 756-1313
Length: 3 Yrs   *ACGME Approved/Offered Positions:* 49
Program ID: 140-12-21-502

Augusta

Medical College of Georgia Program

Sponsor: Medical College of Georgia
Veterans Affairs Medical Center (Augusta)
Prgm Director: David R Haburchak, MD
Department of Medicine
1120 15th Street, BI-5070
Augusta, GA 30912
Tel: 706 721-2423   *Fax:* 706 721-6918
Length: 3 Yrs   *ACGME Approved/Offered Positions:* 63
Program ID: 140-12-21-107

Fort Gordon

Dwight David Eisenhower Army Medical Center Program

Sponsor: Dwight David Eisenhower Army Medical
 Center
Prgm Director: Peter J Skidmore, MD
Army Medical Center
Department of Medicine
Fort Gordon, GA 30905
Tel: 706 787-0674   *Fax:* 706 787-0987
Length: 3 Yrs   *ACGME Approved/Offered Positions:* 24
Program ID: 140-12-22-458
Uniformed Services Program

Macon

Mercer University School of Medicine Program

Sponsor: Medical Center of Central Georgia
Prgm Director: Edwin W Grimsley, MD
Department of Medicine
707 Pine St
Macon, GA 31207
Tel: 478 301-5820   *Fax:* 478 301-5825
E-mail: mccgintmed@mercer.edu
Length: 3 Yrs   *ACGME Approved/Offered Positions:* 29
Program ID: 140-12-21-491

Savannah

Mercer University School of Medicine (Savannah) Program

Sponsor: Memorial Health-University Medical Center
Prgm Director: Steven L Carpenter, MD
4700 Waters Ave
Savannah, GA 31404
Tel: 912 350-8350   *Fax:* 912 350-7270
E-mail: KrzmaLy1@memorialhealth.com
Length: 3 Yrs   *ACGME Approved/Offered Positions:* 35
Program ID: 140-12-12-108

Note: * indicates a newly appointed program director

Hawaii

Honolulu

University of Hawaii Program

Sponsor: University of Hawaii John A Burns School of
  Medicine
Queen's Medical Center
Prgm Director: Erlaine F Bello, MD
1356 Lusitana Street, 7th Floor
Honolulu, HI 96813
Tel: 808 586-2910   *Fax:* 808 586-7486
Length: 3 Yrs   *ACGME Approved/Offered Positions:* 72
Program ID: 140-14-21-109

Tripler AMC

Tripler Army Medical Center Program

Sponsor: Tripler Army Medical Center
Prgm Director: Stephen M Salerno, MD, MPH
1 Jarrett White Road
Tripler AMC, HI 96859
Tel: 808 433-4049   *Fax:* 808 433-1555
E-mail: stephen.salerno@us.army.mil
Length: 3 Yrs   *ACGME Approved/Offered Positions:* 30
Program ID: 140-14-11-007
Uniformed Services Program

Illinois

Chicago

Advocate Illinois Masonic Medical Center/North Side Health Network Program

Sponsor: Advocate Illinois Masonic Medical Center
Prgm Director: Teresa Ramos, MD
836 W Wellington Avenue
Room 7304
Chicago, IL 60657
Tel: 773 296-7046   *Fax:* 773 296-7486
E-mail: Teresa.Ramos-MD@advocatehealth.com
Length: 3 Yrs   *ACGME Approved/Offered Positions:* 56
Program ID: 140-16-11-114

John H Stroger Hospital of Cook County Program

Sponsor: John H Stroger Hospital of Cook County
Prgm Director: Suja M Mathew, MD*
Department of Medicine
1900 W Polk St, 15th Floor
Chicago, IL 60612
Tel: 312 864-7229   *Fax:* 312 864-9725
Length: 3 Yrs   *ACGME Approved/Offered Positions:* 144
Program ID: 140-16-12-113

Louis A Weiss Memorial Hospital Program

Sponsor: Louis A Weiss Memorial Hospital
Prgm Director: Shehzad Ali, MD
4646 N Marine Drive
Chicago, IL 60640
Tel: 773 564-5225   *Fax:* 773 564-5226
Length: 3 Yrs   *ACGME Approved/Offered Positions:* 39
Program ID: 140-16-11-115

McGaw Medical Center of Northwestern University Program

Sponsor: McGaw Medical Center of Northwestern
  University
Jesse Brown Veterans Affairs Medical Center
Northwestern Memorial Hospital
Prgm Director: Diane B Wayne, MD
251 East Huron St
Galter Pavilion Suite 3-150
Chicago, IL 60611
Tel: 312 926-4227   *Fax:* 312 926-6905
Length: 3 Yrs   *ACGME Approved/Offered Positions:* 128
Program ID: 140-16-21-119

Mercy Hospital and Medical Center Program

Sponsor: Mercy Hospital and Medical Center
Prgm Director: Steven R Potts, DO
2525 South Michigan Avenue
Chicago, IL 60616
Tel: 312 567-2053   *Fax:* 312 567-2695
Length: 3 Yrs   *ACGME Approved/Offered Positions:* 48
Program ID: 140-16-11-116

Rush University Medical Center Program

Sponsor: Rush University Medical Center
Prgm Director: Richard I Abrams, MD
Department of Internal Medicine
1653 W Congress Parkway - 301 Jones Building
Chicago, IL 60612
Tel: 312 942-5269   *Fax:* 312 942-5271
E-mail: Richard_I_Abrams@rush.edu
Length: 3 Yrs   *ACGME Approved/Offered Positions:* 124
Program ID: 140-16-11-121

St Joseph Hospital Program

Sponsor: St Joseph Hospital
Prgm Director: Joel B Spear, MD
Department of Medicine
2900 Lake Shore Drive
Chicago, IL 60657
Tel: 773 665-3022   *Fax:* 773 665-3384
E-mail: hhayes01@reshealthcare.org
Length: 3 Yrs   *ACGME Approved/Offered Positions:* 72
Program ID: 140-16-11-122

University of Chicago Program

Sponsor: University of Chicago Medical Center
Prgm Director: James N Woodruff, MD
Medicine, MC 7082 / AMB A-23
5841 S Maryland Avenue
Chicago, IL 60637
Tel: 773 702-1455   *Fax:* 773 834-0464
E-mail: imr@medicine.bsd.uchicago.edu
Length: 3 Yrs   *ACGME Approved/Offered Positions:* 108
Program ID: 140-16-11-123

University of Illinois College of Medicine at Chicago Program

Sponsor: University of Illinois College of Medicine at
  Chicago
Jesse Brown Veterans Affairs Medical Center
University of Illinois Hospital and Clinics
Prgm Director: Fred A Zar, MD
Department of Medicine
840 S Wood Street, 440 CSN, M/C 718
Chicago, IL 60612
Tel: 312 996-5014   *Fax:* 312 413-1343
E-mail: fazar@uic.edu
Length: 3 Yrs   *ACGME Approved/Offered Positions:* 112
Program ID: 140-16-21-124

Evanston

McGaw Medical Center of Northwestern University (Evanston) Program

Sponsor: McGaw Medical Center of Northwestern
  University
Evanston Hospital
Glenbrook Hospital
Prgm Director: Ruric C Anderson III, MD, MBA
Department of Medicine
2650 Ridge Avenue
Evanston, IL 60201
Tel: 847 570-2509   *Fax:* 847 570-2905
E-mail: aanderson2@enh.org
Length: 3 Yrs   *ACGME Approved/Offered Positions:* 66
Program ID: 140-16-31-125

St Francis Hospital of Evanston Program

Sponsor: St Francis Hospital
Prgm Director: Harvey J Friedman, MD
Department of Medicine
355 Ridge Avenue
Evanston, IL 60202
Tel: 847 316-3109   *Fax:* 847 316-3307
Length: 3 Yrs   *ACGME Approved/Offered Positions:* 54
Program ID: 140-16-11-126

Maywood

Loyola University Program

Sponsor: Loyola University Medical Center
Edward Hines, Jr Veterans Affairs Hospital
Prgm Director: Kevin P Simpson, MD
Room 7609, Building 102
2160 S First Avenue
Maywood, IL 60153
Tel: 708 216-5368   *Fax:* 708 216-9456
Length: 3 Yrs   *ACGME Approved/Offered Positions:* 107
Program ID: 140-16-21-128

Melrose Park

Resurrection Medical Center (Westlake) Program

Sponsor: Resurrection Medical Center
Westlake Community Hospital
Prgm Director: Vijay V Yeldandi, MD
1225 Lake Street
Melrose Park, IL 60160
Tel: 708 938-7350   *Fax:* 708 938-7098
E-mail: ResurrectionWestlake@reshealthcare.org
Length: 3 Yrs   *ACGME Approved/Offered Positions:* 42
Program ID: 140-16-11-454

North Chicago

The Chicago Medical School at Rosalind Franklin University of Medicine and Science Program

Sponsor: Chicago Medical School/Rosalind Franklin
  Univ of Med & Sci
Mount Sinai Hospital Medical Center of Chicago
Veterans Affairs Medical Center (North Chicago)
Prgm Director: Jeanette L Morrison, MD*
Chicago Medical School
3333 Green Bay Road
North Chicago, IL 60064
Tel: 847 578-8646
Length: 3 Yrs   *ACGME Approved/Offered Positions:* 63
Program ID: 140-16-21-111

Oak Lawn

University of Illinois College of Medicine at Chicago/Advocate Christ Medical Center Program

Sponsor: University of Illinois College of Medicine at
  Chicago
Advocate Christ Medical Center
Prgm Director: Lee W Tai, MD
Department of Medicine
4440 West 95th Street, 131-NO
Oak Lawn, IL 60453
Tel: 708 684-5673   *Fax:* 708 684-2500
E-mail: lee.tai@advocatehealth.com
Length: 3 Yrs   *ACGME Approved/Offered Positions:* 72
Program ID: 140-16-21-129

Programs

Oak Park

West Suburban Medical Center Program
Sponsor: West Suburban Medical Center
Prgm Director: Max L Harris, MD
3 Erie Court, Suite L-700
Oak Park, IL 60302
Tel: 708 763-6908   *Fax:* 708 763-6655
E-mail: imtyws@reshealthcare.org
Length: 3 Yrs   *ACGME Approved/Offered Positions:* 24
Program ID: 140-16-21-467

Park Ridge

Advocate Lutheran General Hospital Program
Sponsor: Advocate Lutheran General Hospital
Prgm Director: William D Rhoades, DO*
Department of Medicine - 6 South
1775 West Dempster Street
Park Ridge, IL 60068
Tel: 847 723-7194   *Fax:* 847 696-3391
Length: 3 Yrs   *ACGME Approved/Offered Positions:* 67
Program ID: 140-16-21-130

Peoria

University of Illinois College of Medicine at Peoria Program
Sponsor: University of Illinois College of Medicine at
Peoria
OSF St Francis Medical Center
Prgm Director: John D Rogers, MD
Department of Internal Medicine
530 NE Glen Oak Ave
Peoria, IL 61637
Tel: 309 655-2730   *Fax:* 309 655-7732
E-mail: imres@uic.edu
Length: 3 Yrs   *ACGME Approved/Offered Positions:* 34
Program ID: 140-16-31-131

Springfield

Southern Illinois University Program
Sponsor: Southern Illinois University School of Medicine
Memorial Medical Center
St John's Hospital
Prgm Director: Andrew J Varney, MD
701 N First Street, Room D442
Department of Medicine
Springfield, IL 62794
Tel: 217 545-0193   *Fax:* 217 545-8156
Length: 3 Yrs   *ACGME Approved/Offered Positions:* 57
Program ID: 140-16-21-132

Urbana

University of Illinois College of Medicine at Urbana Program
Sponsor: University of Illinois College of Medicine at
Urbana
Carle Foundation Hospital
Provena Covenant Medical Center
Veterans Affairs Medical Center (Danville)
Prgm Director: Robert M Healy, MD
611 W Park Street
Urbana, IL 61801
Tel: 217 383-3110   *Fax:* 217 244-0621
E-mail: imrp@illinois.edu
Length: 3 Yrs   *ACGME Approved/Offered Positions:* 54
Program ID: 140-16-21-456

Indiana

Indianapolis

Indiana University School of Medicine Program
Sponsor: Indiana University School of Medicine
Clarian Indiana University Hospital
Clarian Methodist Hospital of Indiana
Clarian Riley Hospital for Children
Richard L Roudebush Veterans Affairs Medical Center
William N Wishard Memorial Hospital
Prgm Director: Lia S Logio, MD
WD OPW M200
1001 West 10th Street
Indianapolis, IN 46202
Tel: 317 656-4260   *Fax:* 317 630-2667
E-mail: iureside@iupui.edu
Length: 3 Yrs   *ACGME Approved/Offered Positions:* 120
Program ID: 140-17-21-133

St Vincent Hospital and Health Care Center Program
Sponsor: St Vincent Hospitals and Health Care Center
Prgm Director: Craig J Wilson, MD, MSc
2001 W 86th Street
Indianapolis, IN 46260
Tel: 317 338-6728   *Fax:* 317 338-6359
E-mail: srbruen@stvincent.org
Length: 3 Yrs   *ACGME Approved/Offered Positions:* 54
Program ID: 140-17-11-135

Muncie

Ball Memorial Hospital Program
Sponsor: Ball Memorial Hospital
Prgm Director: J Matthew Neal, MD, MBA
Internal Medicine Residency
2401 University Avenue
Muncie, IN 47303
Tel: 765 747-3367   *Fax:* 765 751-1451
Length: 3 Yrs   *ACGME Approved/Offered Positions:* 18
Program ID: 140-17-11-136

Iowa

Des Moines

University of Iowa (Des Moines) Program
Sponsor: Central Iowa Health System (Iowa
Methodist/Iowa Lutheran)
Veterans Affairs Central Iowa Health Care System
Prgm Director: William J Yost, MD
Internal Medicine Residency Program
1415 Woodland Avenue, Suite 140
Des Moines, IA 50309
Tel: 515 241-6636   *Fax:* 515 241-6576
E-mail: intmedres@ihs.org
Length: 3 Yrs   *ACGME Approved/Offered Positions:* 26
Program ID: 140-18-31-137

Iowa City

University of Iowa Hospitals and Clinics Program
Sponsor: University of Iowa Hospitals and Clinics
Prgm Director: Scott A Vogelgesang, MD
Department of Internal Medicine, E323 GH
200 Hawkins Drive
Iowa City, IA 52242
Tel: 319 384-9668   *Fax:* 319 384-8955
E-mail: intmedres@uiowa.edu
Length: 3 Yrs   *ACGME Approved/Offered Positions:* 77
Program ID: 140-18-21-138

Kansas

Kansas City

University of Kansas School of Medicine Program
Sponsor: University of Kansas School of Medicine
University of Kansas Hospital
Veterans Affairs Medical Center (Kansas City)
Prgm Director: Lisa M Vansaghi, MD*
3901 Rainbow Blvd, MS 2027
1011 Wescoe
Kansas City, KS 66160
Tel: 913 588-6051   *Fax:* 913 588-0890
E-mail: lvansaghi@kumc.edu
Length: 3 Yrs   *ACGME Approved/Offered Positions:* 103
Program ID: 140-19-21-139

Wichita

University of Kansas (Wichita) Program
Sponsor: University of Kansas School of Medicine
(Wichita)
Veterans Affairs Medical Center (Wichita)
Via Christi Regional Medical Center-St Francis
Wesley Medical Center
Prgm Director: Garold O Minns, MD
Department of Internal Medicine
1010 N Kansas
Wichita, KS 67214
Tel: 316 293-2650   *Fax:* 316 293-1878
E-mail: internalmed-wichita@kumc.edu
Length: 3 Yrs   *ACGME Approved/Offered Positions:* 36
Program ID: 140-19-21-140

Kentucky

Lexington

University of Kentucky College of Medicine Program
Sponsor: University of Kentucky College of Medicine
University of Kentucky Hospital
Veterans Affairs Medical Center (Lexington)
Prgm Director: Charles Griffith III, MD, MSPH*
Department of Medicine
K506 Kentucky Clinic, 740 S Limestone St
Lexington, KY 40536
Tel: 859 323-6642   *Fax:* 859 323-1197
Length: 3 Yrs   *ACGME Approved/Offered Positions:* 73
Program ID: 140-20-21-141

Louisville

University of Louisville Program
Sponsor: University of Louisville School of Medicine
University of Louisville Hospital
Veterans Affairs Medical Center (Louisville)
Prgm Director: Barbara R Casper, MD
3rd Floor ACB
550 S Jackson St
Louisville, KY 40202
Tel: 502 852-7040   *Fax:* 502 852-0936
Length: 3 Yrs   *ACGME Approved/Offered Positions:* 78
Program ID: 140-20-31-142

Note: * indicates a newly appointed program director

Louisiana

Baton Rouge

Louisiana State University (Baton Rouge) Program

Sponsor: Earl K Long Medical Center
Prgm Director: George H Karam, MD
Department of Medicine
5825 Airline Highway
Baton Rouge, LA 70805
Tel: 225 358-1065
Length: 3 Yrs   *ACGME Approved/Offered Positions:* 36
Program ID: 140-21-21-507

Houma

Leonard J Chabert Medical Center Program

Sponsor: Leonard J Chabert Medical Center
Prgm Director: Dayton Daberkow II, MD
1978 Industrial Boulevard
Houma, LA 70363
Tel: 985 873-2710   *Fax:* 985 873-2722
E-mail: mdrury@lsuhsc.edu
Length: 3 Yrs   *ACGME Approved/Offered Positions:* 24
Program ID: 140-21-21-537

Lafayette

Louisiana State University (Lafayette) Program

Sponsor: University Medical Center (Lafayette)
Prgm Director: Leela Lakshmiprasad, MD
PO Box 69300
2390 W Congress Street
Lafayette, LA 70596
Tel: 337 261-6789   *Fax:* 337 261-6791
E-mail: tlatio@lsuhsc.edu
Length: 3 Yrs   *ACGME Approved/Offered Positions:* 26
Program ID: 140-21-11-144

New Orleans

Louisiana State University Program

Sponsor: Louisiana State University School of Medicine
Medical Center of Louisiana at New Orleans
Ochsner Medical Center-Kenner
Touro Infirmary
Prgm Director: Jorge A Martinez, MD, JD
2020 Gravier St
7th Floor Suite D, Box E7-20
New Orleans, LA 70112
Tel: 504 568-4713   *Fax:* 504 568-7884
E-mail: jmarti4@lsuhsc.edu
Length: 3 Yrs   *ACGME Approved/Offered Positions:* 73
Program ID: 140-21-21-143

Ochsner Clinic Foundation Program

Sponsor: Ochsner Clinic Foundation
Prgm Director: William Davis, MD
Department of Medicine
1514 Jefferson Highway
New Orleans, LA 70121
Tel: 504 842-4096   *Fax:* 504 842-3327
E-mail: ecarter@ochsner.org
Length: 3 Yrs   *ACGME Approved/Offered Positions:* 56
Program ID: 140-21-22-146

Tulane University Program

Sponsor: Tulane University School of Medicine
Medical Center of Louisiana at New Orleans
Tulane University Hospital and Clinics
Veterans Affairs Medical Center (New Orleans)
Prgm Director: Jeffrey G Wiese, MD
Department of Medicine
1430 Tulane Avenue, SL-50
New Orleans, LA 70112
Tel: 504 988-7809   *Fax:* 504 988-3971
E-mail: imres@tulane.edu
Length: 3 Yrs   *ACGME Approved/Offered Positions:* 88
Program ID: 140-21-21-147

Shreveport

Louisiana State University (Shreveport) Program

Sponsor: LSU Health Sciences Center-University Hospital
Overton Brooks Veterans Affairs Medical Center
Prgm Director: Larry E Slay, MD
1501 Kings Highway
Shreveport, LA 71130
Tel: 318 675-5915   *Fax:* 318 675-5958
Length: 3 Yrs   *ACGME Approved/Offered Positions:* 77
Program ID: 140-21-21-148

Maine

Portland

Maine Medical Center Program

Sponsor: Maine Medical Center
Prgm Director: Jane Pringle, MD*
Department of Medicine
22 Bramhall Street
Portland, ME 04102
Tel: 207 662-6836   *Fax:* 207 662-6308
E-mail: kuchac@mmc.org
Length: 3 Yrs   *ACGME Approved/Offered Positions:* 47
Program ID: 140-22-11-149

Maryland

Baltimore

Franklin Square Hospital Center Program

Sponsor: Franklin Square Hospital Center
Prgm Director: Philip F Panzarella, MD, MPH*
Department of Medicine
9000 Franklin Square Drive
Baltimore, MD 21237
Tel: 443 777-8340   *Fax:* 443 777-8340
Length: 3 Yrs   *ACGME Approved/Offered Positions:* 35
Program ID: 140-23-12-151

Good Samaritan Hospital of Maryland Program

Sponsor: Good Samaritan Hospital of Maryland
Prgm Director: Robert D Chow, MD
5601 Loch Raven Boulevard
RMB 502
Baltimore, MD 21239
Tel: 443 444-4863   *Fax:* 443 444-4997
E-mail: robert.dobbin.chow@medstar.net
Length: 3 Yrs   *ACGME Approved/Offered Positions:* 40
Program ID: 140-23-21-489

Greater Baltimore Medical Center Program

Sponsor: Greater Baltimore Medical Center
Prgm Director: Paul N Foster, MD
6565 North Charles Street
Pavilion East, Suite 203
Baltimore, MD 21204
Tel: 443 849-2654   *Fax:* 443 849-8030
E-mail: medres@gbmc.org
Length: 3 Yrs   *ACGME Approved/Offered Positions:* 44
Program ID: 140-23-31-152

Harbor Hospital Center Program

Sponsor: Harbor Hospital Center
Prgm Director: Richard B Williams, MD
Department of Medicine
3001 S Hanover Street
Baltimore, MD 21225
Tel: 410 350-3565   *Fax:* 410 354-0186
E-mail: terry.kus@medstar.net
Length: 3 Yrs   *ACGME Approved/Offered Positions:* 38
Program ID: 140-23-31-158

Johns Hopkins University Program

Sponsor: Johns Hopkins University School of Medicine
Johns Hopkins Hospital
Prgm Director: Charles Wiener, MD
Department of Medicine, 9th Floor
1830 E Monument Street
Baltimore, MD 21287
Tel: 410 955-7910   *Fax:* 410 614-8510
Length: 3 Yrs   *ACGME Approved/Offered Positions:* 110
Program ID: 140-23-11-153

Johns Hopkins University/Bayview Medical Center Program

Sponsor: Johns Hopkins University School of Medicine
Johns Hopkins Bayview Medical Center
Prgm Director: Colleen Christmas, MD
4940 Eastern Ave
A-1-W Room 102
Baltimore, MD 21224
Tel: 410 550-4453   *Fax:* 410 550-1094
E-mail: cchris16@jhmi.edu
Length: 3 Yrs   *ACGME Approved/Offered Positions:* 51
Program ID: 140-23-11-150

Johns Hopkins University/Sinai Hospital of Baltimore Program

Sponsor: Johns Hopkins University School of Medicine
Sinai Hospital of Baltimore
Prgm Director: Steven R Gambert, MD
2401 W Belvedere Avenue
Hoffberger Prof Bldg, Suite 56
Baltimore, MD 21215
Tel: 410 601-7068   *Fax:* 410 601-5285
E-mail: taanders@lifebridgehealth.org
Length: 3 Yrs   *ACGME Approved/Offered Positions:* 57
Program ID: 140-23-12-157

Maryland General Hospital Program

Sponsor: Maryland General Hospital
Prgm Director: William C Anthony, MD, MBA
Department of Medicine, Suite 3B
827 Linden Avenue
Baltimore, MD 21201
Tel: 410 225-8790   *Fax:* 410 225-8910
Length: 3 Yrs   *ACGME Approved/Offered Positions:* 21
Program ID: 140-23-11-154

St Agnes HealthCare Program

Sponsor: St Agnes Hospital
Prgm Director: Norman M Dy, MD
900 Caton Avenue Box 198
Baltimore, MD 21229
Tel: 410 368-8858   *Fax:* 410 368-3525
Length: 3 Yrs   *ACGME Approved/Offered Positions:* 40
Program ID: 140-23-12-156

Programs

Union Memorial Hospital Program

Sponsor: Union Memorial Hospital
Prgm Director: Robert P Ferguson, MD
Department of Medicine
201 E University Parkway
Baltimore, MD 21218
Tel: 410 554-2284   *Fax:* 410 554-2184
Length: 3 Yrs   *ACGME Approved/Offered Positions:* 36
Program ID: 140-23-12-159

University of Maryland Program

Sponsor: University of Maryland Medical System
Veterans Affairs Medical Center (Baltimore)
Prgm Director: Susan D Wolfsthal, MD
Department of Medicine - Univ of Maryland Med Ctr
22 S Greene St, Room N3E09
Baltimore, MD 21201
Tel: 410 328-2388   *Fax:* 410 328-0267
Length: 3 Yrs   *ACGME Approved/Offered Positions:* 123
Program ID: 140-23-21-160

Bethesda

National Capital Consortium (Bethesda) Program

Sponsor: National Capital Consortium
National Naval Medical Center (Bethesda)
Prgm Director: Terrence X Dwyer, MD
Office of Program Director for Internal Medicine
8901 Wisconsin Ave
Bethesda, MD 20889
Tel: 301 319-8361   *Fax:* 301 319-8660
Length: 3 Yrs   *ACGME Approved/Offered Positions:* 40
Program ID: 140-23-11-013
Uniformed Services Program

National Capital Consortium (Walter Reed) Program

Sponsor: National Capital Consortium
Walter Reed Army Medical Center
Prgm Director: Brian M Cuneo, MD
Department of Medicine
6900 Georgia Avenue, NW
Washington, DC 20307
Tel: 202 782-5731   *Fax:* 202 782-5388
Length: 3 Yrs   *ACGME Approved/Offered Positions:* 53
Program ID: 140-10-11-006
Uniformed Services Program

Cheverly

Prince George's Hospital Center Program

Sponsor: Prince George's Hospital Center
Prgm Director: Kimberly B Valenti, MD, PhD
3001 Hospital Drive
Department of Medicine, 5th Floor
Cheverly, MD 20785
Tel: 301 618-3783   *Fax:* 301 618-2986
E-mail: kim.valenti@dimensionshealth.org
Length: 3 Yrs   *ACGME Approved/Offered Positions:* 42
Program ID: 140-23-21-161

Massachusetts

Boston

Beth Israel Deaconess Medical Center Program

Sponsor: Beth Israel Deaconess Medical Center
Prgm Director: Eileen E Reynolds, MD
One Deaconess Road
Deaconess 306
Boston, MA 02215
Tel: 617 632-8264   *Fax:* 617 632-8261
Length: 3 Yrs   *ACGME Approved/Offered Positions:* 158
Program ID: 140-24-21-162

Boston University Medical Center Program

Sponsor: Boston Medical Center
Veterans Affairs Medical Center (Boston)
Prgm Director: Steven C Borkan, MD*
Internal Medicine Residency Program
80 E Concord Street, Evans 124
Boston, MA 02118
Tel: 617 638-6500   *Fax:* 617 638-6501
E-mail: steven.borkan@bmc.org
Length: 3 Yrs   *ACGME Approved/Offered Positions:* 151
Program ID: 140-24-31-164

Brigham and Women's Hospital Program

Sponsor: Brigham and Women's Hospital
Prgm Director: Joel T Katz, MD
Department of Medicine
75 Francis Street
Boston, MA 02115
Tel: 617 732-5775   *Fax:* 617 264-6346
E-mail: bwhresinfo@partners.org
Length: 3 Yrs   *ACGME Approved/Offered Positions:* 174
Program ID: 140-24-21-172

Caritas Carney Hospital Program

Sponsor: Caritas Carney Hospital
Prgm Director: Michael Barza, MD
Department of Medicine
2100 Dorchester Avenue
Boston, MA 02124
Tel: 617 506-2723   *Fax:* 617 474-3855
Length: 3 Yrs   *ACGME Approved/Offered Positions:* 42
Program ID: 140-24-11-166

Caritas St Elizabeth's Medical Center Program

Sponsor: Caritas St Elizabeth's Medical Center of Boston
Prgm Director: John N Unterborn, MD
Department of Medicine
736 Cambridge Street
Boston, MA 02135
Tel: 617 562-7502   *Fax:* 617 562-7797
Length: 3 Yrs   *ACGME Approved/Offered Positions:* 58
Program ID: 140-24-21-173

Massachusetts General Hospital Program

Sponsor: Massachusetts General Hospital
Prgm Director: Hasan Bazari, MD
Medical Services, Bigelow 740
55 Fruit Street
Boston, MA 02114
Tel: 617 726-2862   *Fax:* 617 724-7441
E-mail: mghimresidency@partners.org
Length: 3 Yrs   *ACGME Approved/Offered Positions:* 162
Program ID: 140-24-11-169

Tufts Medical Center Program

Sponsor: Tufts Medical Center
Prgm Director: Richard I Kopelman, MD
Department of Medicine
750 Washington Street, Box 21
Boston, MA 02111
Tel: 617 636-5246   *Fax:* 617 636-7119
Length: 3 Yrs   *ACGME Approved/Offered Positions:* 72
Program ID: 140-24-21-171

Burlington

Lahey Clinic Program

Sponsor: Lahey Clinic
Prgm Director: Gerry Orfanos, MD
Department of Medicine
41 Mall Road
Burlington, MA 01805
Tel: 781 744-5700   *Fax:* 781 744-5358
E-mail: gerry.orfanos@lahey.org
Length: 3 Yrs   *ACGME Approved/Offered Positions:* 42
Program ID: 140-24-21-511

Cambridge

Cambridge Health Alliance Program

Sponsor: Cambridge Health Alliance
Prgm Director: Richard J Pels, MD
1493 Cambridge Street
Cambridge, MA 02139
Tel: 617 665-1021   *Fax:* 617 665-2151
Length: 3 Yrs   *ACGME Approved/Offered Positions:* 24
Program ID: 140-24-11-175

Mount Auburn Hospital Program

Sponsor: Mount Auburn Hospital
Prgm Director: Eric M Flint, MD
Department of Medicine
330 Mount Auburn Street
Cambridge, MA 02138
Tel: 617 499-5160   *Fax:* 617 499-5593
E-mail: mmcglone@mah.harvard.edu
Length: 3 Yrs   *ACGME Approved/Offered Positions:* 42
Program ID: 140-24-11-176

Framingham

MetroWest Medical Center Program

Sponsor: MetroWest Medical Center-Framingham Union Hospital
Prgm Director: Thomas L Treadwell, MD
115 Lincoln Street
Framingham, MA 01702
Tel: 508 383-1572   *Fax:* 508 872-4794
E-mail: thomas.treadwell@mwmc.com
Length: 3 Yrs   *ACGME Approved/Offered Positions:* 24
Program ID: 140-24-21-177

Pittsfield

Berkshire Medical Center Program

Sponsor: Berkshire Medical Center
Prgm Director: A Gray Ellrodt, MD
Department of Medicine
725 North Street
Pittsfield, MA 01201
Tel: 413 447-2839   *Fax:* 413 447-2088
Length: 3 Yrs   *ACGME Approved/Offered Positions:* 37
Program ID: 140-24-11-179

Salem

Salem Hospital Program

Sponsor: Salem Hospital
Prgm Director: Wayne M Trebbin, MD
Department of Medicine
81 Highland Avenue
Salem, MA 01970
Tel: 978 825-6490   *Fax:* 978 825-6312
E-mail: WTrebbin@partners.org
Length: 3 Yrs   *ACGME Approved/Offered Positions:* 20
Program ID: 140-24-12-180

Springfield

Baystate Medical Center/Tufts University School of Medicine Program

Sponsor: Baystate Medical Center
Prgm Director: Kevin T Hinchey, MD
Department of Medicine
759 Chestnut Street S2570
Springfield, MA 01199
Tel: 413 794-4143   *Fax:* 413 794-8075
E-mail: kevin.hinchey@bhs.org
Length: 3 Yrs   *ACGME Approved/Offered Positions:* 56
Program ID: 140-24-11-181

Note: * indicates a newly appointed program director

Worcester

St Vincent Hospital Program
Sponsor: St Vincent Hospital
Prgm Director: Jane A Lochrie, MD
Worcester Medical Center
123 Summer Street
Worcester, MA 01608
Tel: 508 363-5587   *Fax:* 508 363-9798
Length: 3 Yrs   *ACGME Approved/Offered Positions:* 75
Program ID: 140-24-11-183

University of Massachusetts Program
Sponsor: University of Massachusetts Medical School
UMass Memorial Health Care (Memorial Campus)
UMass Memorial Health Care (University Campus)
Prgm Director: Richard M Forster, MD
University Campus, Department of Medicine Residency
Office
55 Lake Avenue, North
Worcester, MA 01655
Tel: 508 856-2173   *Fax:* 508 856-6781
E-mail: snellM@ummhc.org
Length: 3 Yrs   *ACGME Approved/Offered Positions:* 95
Program ID: 140-24-21-184

Michigan

Ann Arbor

St Joseph Mercy Hospital Program
Sponsor: St Joseph Mercy Hospital
Prgm Director: John A Hopper, MD*
5333 McAuley Dr Reichert Health Buidling #3009
PO Box 995
Ann Arbor, MI 48106
Tel: 734 712-3935   *Fax:* 734 712-5583
Length: 3 Yrs   *ACGME Approved/Offered Positions:* 49
Program ID: 140-25-12-186

University of Michigan Program
Sponsor: University of Michigan Hospitals and Health
  Centers
Veterans Affairs Medical Center (Ann Arbor)
Prgm Director: John Del Valle, MD
3116 Taubman Center, SPC 5368
1500 E Medical Center Drive
Ann Arbor, MI 48109
Tel: 734 936-4385   *Fax:* 734 936-3654
Length: 3 Yrs   *ACGME Approved/Offered Positions:* 128
Program ID: 140-25-21-187

Dearborn

Oakwood Hospital Program
Sponsor: Oakwood Hospital
Prgm Director: Jonathan Zimmerman, MD, MBA
18101 Oakwood Boulevard
Dearborn, MI 48124
Tel: 313 436-2578   *Fax:* 313 436-2071
E-mail: medres@oakwood.org
Length: 3 Yrs   *ACGME Approved/Offered Positions:* 30
Program ID: 140-25-31-188

Detroit

Detroit Medical Center (Grace Hospital) Program
Sponsor: Detroit Medical Center Corporation
Sinai-Grace Hospital
Prgm Director: Mohamed S Siddique, MD
Department of Medicine
6071 West Outer Drive
Detroit, MI 48235
Tel: 313 966-4970   *Fax:* 313 966-1738
Length: 3 Yrs   *ACGME Approved/Offered Positions:* 60
Program ID: 140-25-21-506

Henry Ford Hospital Program
Sponsor: Henry Ford Hospital
Prgm Director: Kimberly M Baker-Genaw, MD
Department of Medicine CFP-1
2799 W Grand Blvd
Detroit, MI 48202
Tel: 313 916-3829   *Fax:* 313 916-1394
E-mail: kgenaw1@hfhs.org
Length: 3 Yrs   *ACGME Approved/Offered Positions:* 116
Program ID: 140-25-11-189

St John Hospital and Medical Center Program
Sponsor: St John Hospital and Medical Center
Prgm Director: Louis D Saravolatz, MD
19251 Mack Ave
Suite 335
Grosse Pointe Woods, MI 48236
Tel: 313 343-3362   *Fax:* 313 343-7784
Length: 3 Yrs   *ACGME Approved/Offered Positions:* 50
Program ID: 140-25-11-191

Wayne State University/Detroit Medical Center Program
Sponsor: Wayne State University/Detroit Medical Center
Prgm Director: Therese Vettese, MD*
Detroit Medical Center
4201 St Antoine Blvd, UHC Suite 2E
Detroit, MI 48201
Tel: 313 745-2223
Length: 3 Yrs   *ACGME Approved/Offered Positions:* 104
Program ID: 140-25-21-194

Flint

Hurley Medical Center/Michigan State University Program
Sponsor: Hurley Medical Center
Prgm Director: Hemant T Thawani, MD*
Department of Medicine
One Hurley Plaza
Flint, MI 48502
Tel: 810 257-9682   *Fax:* 810 762-7245
Length: 3 Yrs   *ACGME Approved/Offered Positions:* 30
Program ID: 140-25-31-196

McLaren Regional Medical Center/Michigan State University Program
Sponsor: McLaren Regional Medical Center
Prgm Director: Susan J Smith, MD
Department of Medicine
401 S Ballenger Highway
Flint, MI 48532
Tel: 810 342-2968   *Fax:* 810 342-4976
E-mail: susans@mclaren.org
Length: 3 Yrs   *ACGME Approved/Offered Positions:* 36
Program ID: 140-25-21-471

Grand Rapids

Grand Rapids Medical Education and Research Center/Michigan State University Program
Sponsor: Grand Rapids Medical Education and Research
  Center
Saint Mary's Health Care (Grand Rapids)
Spectrum Health-Butterworth Hospital
Prgm Director: Mark Spoolstra, MD
25 Michigan Street NE, Suite 2200
Grand Rapids, MI 49503
Tel: 616 391-3775
E-mail: laura.mohr@spectrum-health.org
Length: 3 Yrs   *ACGME Approved/Offered Positions:* 48
Program ID: 140-25-31-198

Kalamazoo

Kalamazoo Center for Medical Studies/Michigan State University Program
Sponsor: Michigan State Univ/Kalamazoo Center for
  Medical Studies
Borgess Medical Center
Bronson Methodist Hospital
Prgm Director: Mark E Loehrke, MD
Internal Medicine Department
1000 Oakland Drive
Kalamazoo, MI 49008
Tel: 269 337-6356   *Fax:* 269 337-6380
E-mail: loehrke@kcms.msu.edu
Length: 3 Yrs   *ACGME Approved/Offered Positions:* 30
Program ID: 140-25-21-199

Lansing

Michigan State University Program
Sponsor: Michigan State University College of Human
  Medicine
Sparrow Hospital
Prgm Director: Heather S Laird-Fick, MD, MPH
B-301 Clinical Center - MSU
138 Service Rd
East Lansing, MI 48824
Tel: 517 353-5100   *Fax:* 517 432-2759
Length: 3 Yrs   *ACGME Approved/Offered Positions:* 36
Program ID: 140-25-21-195

Pontiac

St Joseph Mercy-Oakland Program
Sponsor: St Joseph Mercy-Oakland
Prgm Director: Ben Diaczok, MD
Department of Medicine
44405 Woodward Avenue
Pontiac, MI 48341
Tel: 248 858-6233   *Fax:* 248 858-3244
Length: 3 Yrs   *ACGME Approved/Offered Positions:* 50
Program ID: 140-25-11-200

Royal Oak

William Beaumont Hospital Program
Sponsor: William Beaumont Hospital
Prgm Director: Michael A Barnes, MD
Department of Medicine
3601 West Thirteen Mile Road
Royal Oak, MI 48073
Tel: 248 551-0406   *Fax:* 248 551-8880
Length: 3 Yrs   *ACGME Approved/Offered Positions:* 64
Program ID: 140-25-12-201

Saginaw

Synergy Medical Education Alliance Program
Sponsor: Synergy Medical Education Alliance
Covenant HealthCare System-Cooper Campus
Covenant HealthCare System-Harrison Campus
St Mary's of Michigan
Prgm Director: Suhasini Gudipati, MD
Department of Internal Medicine
1000 Houghton Avenue, Suite 1100
Saginaw, MI 48602
Tel: 989 583-6826   *Fax:* 989 583-6840
E-mail: sduby@synergymedical.org
Length: 3 Yrs   *ACGME Approved/Offered Positions:* 18
Program ID: 140-25-31-202

Programs

Southfield

Providence Hospital and Medical Centers Program
Sponsor: Providence Hospital and Medical Centers
Prgm Director: Neil A Basmaji, MD
16001 West Nine Mile Road
Southfield, MI 48075
Tel: 248 849-3151   *Fax:* 248 849-3230
E-mail: im@providence-stjohnhealth.org
Length: 3 Yrs   *ACGME Approved/Offered Positions:* 33
Program ID: 140-25-11-203

Minnesota

Minneapolis

Abbott-Northwestern Hospital Program
Sponsor: Abbott-Northwestern Hospital/Allina Health System
Prgm Director: Robert J Miner, MD
Medical Education-11135
800 E 28th Street
Minneapolis, MN 55407
Tel: 612 863-6766   *Fax:* 612 863-4144
E-mail: anne.m.klinkhammer@allina.com
Length: 3 Yrs   *ACGME Approved/Offered Positions:* 39
Program ID: 140-26-31-204

Hennepin County Medical Center Program
Sponsor: Hennepin County Medical Center
Prgm Director: Anne G Pereira, MD, MPH
Department of Medicine
701 Park Avenue South, Med Ed G5
Minneapolis, MN 55415
Tel: 612 873-4733   *Fax:* 612 904-4263
Length: 3 Yrs   *ACGME Approved/Offered Positions:* 65
Program ID: 140-26-31-207

University of Minnesota Program
Sponsor: University of Minnesota Medical School
Regions Hospital
University of Minnesota Medical Center, Division of Fairview
Veterans Affairs Medical Center (Minneapolis)
Prgm Director: William T Browne, MD
MMC 284
420 Delaware Street, SE
Minneapolis, MN 55455
Tel: 612 626-5031
Length: 3 Yrs   *ACGME Approved/Offered Positions:* 90
Program ID: 140-26-21-205

Rochester

College of Medicine, Mayo Clinic (Rochester) Program
Sponsor: College of Medicine, Mayo Clinic
Mayo Clinic (Rochester)
Saint Marys Hospital of Rochester
Prgm Director: Furman S McDonald, MD, MPH
Department of Medicine
200 First Street SW
Rochester, MN 55905
Tel: 507 284-2630   *Fax:* 507 284-1249
E-mail: res-IM@mayo.edu
Length: 3 Yrs   *ACGME Approved/Offered Positions:* 169
Program ID: 140-26-21-208

Mississippi

Jackson

University of Mississippi Medical Center Program
Sponsor: University of Mississippi School of Medicine
University Hospitals and Clinics
Veterans Affairs Medical Center (Jackson)
Prgm Director: Vincent E Herrin, MD
Department of Medicine
2500 N State Street
Jackson, MS 39216
Tel: 601 984-5601   *Fax:* 601 984-6665
Length: 3 Yrs   *ACGME Approved/Offered Positions:* 71
Program ID: 140-27-21-209

Keesler AFB

Keesler Medical Center Program
Sponsor: Keesler Medical Center
University Hospitals and Clinics
Prgm Director: Michael A Forgione, MD*
81 MDG/SGOMI
301 Fisher St
Keesler AFB, MS 39534
Tel: 228 376-3632   *Fax:* 228 376-0103
E-mail: michael.forgione@keesler.af.mil
Length: 3 Yrs   *ACGME Approved/Offered Positions:* 24
Program ID: 140-27-12-001
Uniformed Services Program

Missouri

Chesterfield

St Luke's Hospital Program
Sponsor: St Luke's Hospital
St Louis ConnectCare
Prgm Director: Leon R Robison, MD
222 S Woods Mill Road
Suite 760 North
St Louis, MO 63017
Tel: 314 205-6050   *Fax:* 314 434-5939
Length: 3 Yrs   *ACGME Approved/Offered Positions:* 40
Program ID: 140-28-21-219

Columbia

University of Missouri-Columbia Program
Sponsor: University of Missouri-Columbia School of Medicine
Harry S Truman Memorial Veterans Hospital
University Hospitals and Clinics
Prgm Director: Stephen A Brietzke, MD
MA 406 Internal Medicine
One Hospital Drive
Columbia, MO 65212
Tel: 573 884-1606   *Fax:* 573 884-5690
E-mail: im_house@health.missouri.edu
Length: 3 Yrs   *ACGME Approved/Offered Positions:* 60
Program ID: 140-28-21-210

Kansas City

University of Missouri at Kansas City Program
Sponsor: University of Missouri-Kansas City School of Medicine
St Luke's Hospital-Kansas City
Truman Medical Center
Prgm Director: Brent W Beasley, MD
Internal Medicine Residency
2411 Holmes St
Kansas City, MO 64108
Tel: 816 932-3409   *Fax:* 816 932-5179
Length: 3 Yrs   *ACGME Approved/Offered Positions:* 56
Program ID: 140-28-31-214

St Louis

St John's Mercy Medical Center Program
Sponsor: St John's Mercy Medical Center
Prgm Director: Bernard J McGuire, MD
Department of Medicine
615 S New Ballas Road
St Louis, MO 63141
Tel: 314 251-5834   *Fax:* 314 251-6272
E-mail: Michelle.Kempf@mercy.net
Length: 3 Yrs   *ACGME Approved/Offered Positions:* 21
Program ID: 140-28-31-217

St Louis University School of Medicine Program
Sponsor: St Louis University School of Medicine
St Louis University Hospital
Veterans Affairs Medical Center (St Louis)
Prgm Director: M Louay Omran, MD
Department of Medicine
1402 S Grand Boulevard
St Louis, MO 63104
Tel: 314 577-8762   *Fax:* 314 577-8100
Length: 3 Yrs   *ACGME Approved/Offered Positions:* 81
Program ID: 140-28-21-218

St Mary's Health Center Program
Sponsor: St Mary's Health Center
Prgm Director: Morey Gardner, MD
Department of Medicine
6420 Clayton Road
St Louis, MO 63117
Tel: 314 768-8778   *Fax:* 314 768-7101
E-mail: marilyn_martin@ssmhc.com
Length: 3 Yrs   *ACGME Approved/Offered Positions:* 28
Program ID: 140-28-11-220

Washington University/B-JH/SLCH Consortium Program
Sponsor: Washington University/B-JH/SLCH Consortium
Barnes-Jewish Hospital
Prgm Director: Melvin S Blanchard, MD
660 Euclid Avenue
Box 8121
St Louis, MO 63110
Tel: 314 362-8065   *Fax:* 314 747-1080
E-mail: wuintmed@im.wustl.edu
Length: 3 Yrs   *ACGME Approved/Offered Positions:* 162
Program ID: 140-28-21-215

Nebraska

Omaha

Creighton University Program
Sponsor: Creighton University School of Medicine
Creighton University Medical Center (Tenet - SJH)
Veterans Affairs Medical Center (Omaha)
Prgm Director: Robert W Dunlay, MD
Department of Medicine
601 N 30th St, Suite 5850
Omaha, NE 68131
Tel: 402 280-4392   *Fax:* 402 280-4158
E-mail: resapp@creighton.edu
Length: 3 Yrs   *ACGME Approved/Offered Positions:* 65
Program ID: 140-30-21-222

University of Nebraska Medical Center College of Medicine Program
Sponsor: University of Nebraska Medical Center College of Medicine
Veterans Affairs Medical Center (Omaha)
Prgm Director: James R O'Dell, MD
Department of Internal Medicine
982055 Nebraska Medical Center
Omaha, NE 68198
Tel: 402 559-6488   *Fax:* 402 559-6114
E-mail: sseina@unmc.edu
Length: 3 Yrs   *ACGME Approved/Offered Positions:* 60
Program ID: 140-30-21-224

Note: * indicates a newly appointed program director

Nevada

Las Vegas

University of Nevada School of Medicine (Las Vegas) Program

Sponsor: University of Nevada School of Medicine
University Medical Center of Southern Nevada
Nevada Cancer Institute
Prgm Director: Sandhya Wahi-Gururaj, MD, MPH*
2040 West Charleston Boulevard
Suite 300
Las Vegas, NV 89102
Tel: 702 671-2345   *Fax:* 702 671-2376
Length: 3 Yrs   *ACGME Approved/Offered Positions:* 49
Program ID: 140-31-21-497

Reno

University of Nevada School of Medicine Program

Sponsor: University of Nevada School of Medicine
Ioannis A Lougaris Veterans Affairs Medical Center
Renown Medical Center
Prgm Director: Beverly M Parker, MD
Department of Medicine
1000 Locust Street (111)
Reno, NV 89502
Tel: 775 328-1429   *Fax:* 775 337-2271
E-mail: intmedreno@unr.edu
Length: 3 Yrs   *ACGME Approved/Offered Positions:* 38
Program ID: 140-31-21-483

New Hampshire

Lebanon

Dartmouth-Hitchcock Medical Center Program

Sponsor: Mary Hitchcock Memorial Hospital
Veterans Affairs Medical Center (White River Junction)
Prgm Director: Harley P Friedman, MD
Department of Medicine
One Medical Center Drive
Lebanon, NH 03756
Tel: 603 650-9480   *Fax:* 603 650-6122
E-mail: mindy.f.pickett@hitchcock.org
Length: 3 Yrs   *ACGME Approved/Offered Positions:* 67
Program ID: 140-32-21-225

New Jersey

Atlantic City

AtlantiCare Regional Medical Center Program

Sponsor: AtlantiCare Regional Medical Center
Prgm Director: Zia Salam, MD
Office of Medical Education
1925 Pacific Avenue
Atlantic City, NJ 08401
Tel: 609 441-8074   *Fax:* 609 441-8907
E-mail: imresidency@atlanticare.org
Length: 3 Yrs   *ACGME Approved/Offered Positions:* 40
Program ID: 140-33-31-226

Camden

UMDNJ-Robert Wood Johnson Medical School (Camden) Program

Sponsor: Cooper Hospital-University Medical Center
Prgm Director: Vijay Rajput, MD
401 Haddon Ave
Third Floor
Camden, NJ 08103
Tel: 856 757-7722   *Fax:* 856 968-9587
E-mail: cooper-med-residency@umdnj.edu
Length: 3 Yrs   *ACGME Approved/Offered Positions:* 54
Program ID: 140-33-21-227

Englewood

Mount Sinai School of Medicine (Englewood) Program

Sponsor: Mount Sinai School of Medicine
Englewood Hospital and Medical Center
Prgm Director: Alexandra H Gottdiener, MD
Department of Medicine
350 Engle Street
Englewood, NJ 07631
Tel: 201 894-3312   *Fax:* 201 894-0839
E-mail: kimberly.farrish@ehmc.com
Length: 3 Yrs   *ACGME Approved/Offered Positions:* 39
Program ID: 140-33-21-228

Jersey City

Mount Sinai School of Medicine (Jersey City) Program

Sponsor: Mount Sinai School of Medicine
Jersey City Medical Center
Prgm Director: Douglas Ratner, MD
Department of Medicine
355 Grand Street
Jersey City, NJ 07302
Tel: 201 915-2431   *Fax:* 201 915-2219
E-mail: dratner@libertyhcs.org
Length: 3 Yrs   *ACGME Approved/Offered Positions:* 51
Program ID: 140-33-21-232

Livingston

St Barnabas Medical Center Program

Sponsor: St Barnabas Medical Center
Prgm Director: Richard S Panush, MD
Department of Medicine
94 Old Short Hills Road
Livingston, NJ 07039
Tel: 973 322-5645   *Fax:* 973 322-8215
E-mail: rspanush@sbhcs.com
Length: 3 Yrs   *ACGME Approved/Offered Positions:* 36
Program ID: 140-33-12-457

Long Branch

Monmouth Medical Center Program

Sponsor: Monmouth Medical Center
Prgm Director: Sara Wallach, MD
300 Second Avenue
Long Branch, NJ 07740
Tel: 732 923-6540   *Fax:* 732 923-6536
E-mail: mmcmedicine@sbhcs.com
Length: 3 Yrs   *ACGME Approved/Offered Positions:* 36
Program ID: 140-33-11-233

Montclair

Mountainside Hospital Program

Sponsor: Mountainside Hospital
Prgm Director: Ruth C Wong-Liang, MD
1 Bay Avenue
Montclair, NJ 07042
Tel: 973 429-6195   *Fax:* 973 429-6575
E-mail: ruth.wong-liang@mountainsidehosp.com
Length: 3 Yrs   *ACGME Approved/Offered Positions:* 24
Program ID: 140-33-11-234

Morristown

Atlantic Health (Morristown) Program

Sponsor: Atlantic Health
Morristown Memorial Hospital
Prgm Director: Donna J Astiz, MD
Department of Medicine
100 Madison Avenue
Morristown, NJ 07962
Tel: 973 971-5912   *Fax:* 973 290-8325
E-mail: mmh.imresidency@atlantichealth.org
Length: 3 Yrs   *ACGME Approved/Offered Positions:* 45
Program ID: 140-33-11-235

Neptune

Jersey Shore University Medical Center Program

Sponsor: Jersey Shore University Medical Center
Prgm Director: Elliot Frank, MD, MBA
Department of Medicine
1945 State, Route 33
Neptune, NJ 07754
Tel: 732 776-4420   *Fax:* 732 776-3795
Length: 3 Yrs   *ACGME Approved/Offered Positions:* 50
Program ID: 140-33-12-236

New Brunswick

Drexel University College of Medicine/St Peter's University Hospital Program

Sponsor: St Peter's University Hospital
Prgm Director: Nayan K Kothari, MD
254 Easton Avenue
New Brunswick, NJ 08901
Tel: 732 745-8585   *Fax:* 732 745-3847
E-mail: kdemarest@saintpetersuh.com
Length: 3 Yrs   *ACGME Approved/Offered Positions:* 45
Program ID: 140-33-21-531

UMDNJ-Robert Wood Johnson Medical School Program

Sponsor: UMDNJ-Robert Wood Johnson Medical School
Robert Wood Johnson University Hospital
University Medical Center at Princeton
Prgm Director: Ranita Sharma, MD
Department of Medicine
One Robert Wood Johnson Pl, PO Box 19
New Brunswick, NJ 08903
Tel: 732 235-7742   *Fax:* 732 235-7427
E-mail: sharmar1@umdnj.edu
Length: 3 Yrs   *ACGME Approved/Offered Positions:* 78
Program ID: 140-33-21-243

Newark

Newark Beth Israel Medical Center Program

Sponsor: Newark Beth Israel Medical Center
Prgm Director: Ellen Cohen, MD
Department of Medicine - C4
201 Lyons Avenue
Newark, NJ 07112
Tel: 973 926-7425   *Fax:* 973 926-6130
Length: 3 Yrs   *ACGME Approved/Offered Positions:* 52
Program ID: 140-33-21-518

UMDNJ-New Jersey Medical School Program

Sponsor: UMDNJ-New Jersey Medical School
Hackensack University Medical Center
UMDNJ-University Hospital
Veterans Affairs New Jersey Health Care System
Prgm Director: Jo-Ann Reteguiz, MD
150 Bergen Street
Level I, Room 248
Newark, NJ 07103
Tel: 973 972-6055   *Fax:* 973 972-3129
E-mail: kilgorle@umdnj.edu
Length: 3 Yrs   *ACGME Approved/Offered Positions:* 107
Program ID: 140-33-21-237

Programs

Paterson

Mount Sinai School of Medicine (St Joseph's Regional Medical Center) Program

Sponsor: Mount Sinai School of Medicine
St Joseph's Regional Medical Center
Prgm Director: M Anees Khan, MD
703 Main Street
Paterson, NJ 07503
Tel: 973 754-2431   *Fax:* 973 754-3376
E-mail: mccoym@sjhmc.org
Length: 3 Yrs   *ACGME Approved/Offered Positions:* 51
Program ID: 140-33-21-522

Perth Amboy

Raritan Bay Medical Center Program

Sponsor: Raritan Bay Medical Center-Perth Amboy
   Division
Prgm Director: Constante Gil, MD
Internal Medicine Residency Department
530 New Brunswick Avenue
Perth Amboy, NJ 08861
Tel: 732 324-5080   *Fax:* 732 324-4669
E-mail: ovargas@rbmc.org
Length: 3 Yrs   *ACGME Approved/Offered Positions:* 27
Program ID: 140-33-21-466

Plainfield

Muhlenberg Regional Medical Center Program

Sponsor: Muhlenberg Regional Medical Center
Prgm Director: Francis L Griffin, MD
Department of Medicine
Park Avenue & Randolph Road
Plainfield, NJ 07061
Tel: 908 668-2985   *Fax:* 908 226-4543
Length: 3 Yrs   *ACGME Approved/Offered Positions:* 27
Program ID: 140-33-11-244

South Orange

Seton Hall University School of Health and Medical Sciences (St Francis) Program

Sponsor: Seton Hall University School of Health and
   Medical Sciences
St Francis Medical Center
Prgm Director: Dennis J Cleri, MD
601 Hamilton Avenue
Graduate Medical Education - Room B 158
Trenton, NJ 08629
Tel: 609 599-6291   *Fax:* 609 599-6232
E-mail: esmith@StFrancisMedical.org
Length: 3 Yrs   *ACGME Approved/Offered Positions:* 28
Program ID: 140-33-13-523

Seton Hall University School of Health and Medical Sciences Program

Sponsor: Seton Hall University School of Health and
   Medical Sciences
St Michael's Medical Center (A Member of Catholic Hlth
   East)
Trinitas Hospital
Prgm Director: Ernest E Federici, MD
Department of Medicine
400 S Orange Avenue
South Orange, NJ 07079
Tel: 908 994-5257   *Fax:* 908 351-7930
E-mail: intmed@trinitas.org
Length: 3 Yrs   *ACGME Approved/Offered Positions:* 85
Program ID: 140-33-21-498

Summit

Atlantic Health (Overlook) Program

Sponsor: Atlantic Health
Overlook Hospital
Prgm Director: Jeffrey Brensilver M, MD
99 Beauvoir Avenue
Summit, NJ 07902
Tel: 908 522-2898   *Fax:* 908 522-0804
Length: 3 Yrs   *ACGME Approved/Offered Positions:* 33
Program ID: 140-33-11-245

Trenton

Capital Health System-Fuld Campus Program

Sponsor: Capital Health System-Fuld Campus
Prgm Director: Saba A Hasan, MBBS
Department of Medicine
750 Brunswick Avenue
Trenton, NJ 08638
Tel: 609 394-6031   *Fax:* 609 394-6028
E-mail: imres@chsnj.org
Length: 3 Yrs   *ACGME Approved/Offered Positions:* 28
Program ID: 140-33-21-246

New Mexico

Albuquerque

University of New Mexico Program

Sponsor: University of New Mexico School of Medicine
University of New Mexico Hospital
Veterans Affairs Medical Center (Albuquerque)
Prgm Director: Ann Gateley, MD, MSW
Dept of Internal Medicine, MSC10 5550
1 University of New Mexico
Albuquerque, NM 87131
Tel: 505 272-6331   *Fax:* 505 272-4628
E-mail: IMResidency@salud.unm.edu
Length: 3 Yrs   *ACGME Approved/Offered Positions:* 74
Program ID: 140-34-21-247

New York

Albany

Albany Medical Center Program

Sponsor: Albany Medical Center
Veterans Affairs Medical Center (Albany)
Prgm Director: Alwin F Steinmann, MD
Medical Education Office (MC-17)
47 New Scotland Avenue
Albany, NY 12208
Tel: 518 262-5377   *Fax:* 518 262-6873
Length: 3 Yrs   *ACGME Approved/Offered Positions:* 67
Program ID: 140-35-31-248

Bronx

Albert Einstein College of Medicine (Jacobi) Program

Sponsor: Albert Einstein College of Medicine of Yeshiva
   University
North Bronx Healthcare Network-Jacobi Medical Center
Prgm Director: William D Rifkin, MD*
Department of Medicine - 3N21
1400 Pelham Parkway South
Bronx, NY 10461
Tel: 718 918-5640   *Fax:* 718 918-7460
Length: 3 Yrs   *ACGME Approved/Offered Positions:* 98
Program ID: 140-35-31-521

Albert Einstein College of Medicine (Montefiore) Program

Sponsor: Albert Einstein College of Medicine of Yeshiva
   University
Montefiore Medical Center-Henry and Lucy Moses
   Division
Prgm Director: Sharon Silbiger, MD
Department of Medicine
111 East 210th Street
Bronx, NY 10467
Tel: 718 920-6098   *Fax:* 718 920-8375
Length: 3 Yrs   *ACGME Approved/Offered Positions:* 161
Program ID: 140-35-21-287

Bronx-Lebanon Hospital Center Program

Sponsor: Bronx-Lebanon Hospital Center
Prgm Director: Sridhar S Chilimuri, MD
Department of Medicine
1650 Selwyn Ave
Bronx, NY 10457
Tel: 718 960-1026   *Fax:* 718 960-2055
Length: 3 Yrs   *ACGME Approved/Offered Positions:* 102
Program ID: 140-35-11-263

Lincoln Medical and Mental Health Center Program

Sponsor: Lincoln Medical and Mental Health Center
Prgm Director: Vihren G Dimitrov, MD
234 East 149th Street
Bronx, NY 10451
Tel: 718 579-5000   *Fax:* 718 579-4836
E-mail: linmed@linmed.org
Length: 3 Yrs   *ACGME Approved/Offered Positions:* 90
Program ID: 140-35-21-470

Mount Sinai School of Medicine (Bronx) Program

Sponsor: Mount Sinai School of Medicine
Veterans Affairs Medical Center (Bronx)
North Bronx Healthcare Network-North Central Bronx
   Hospital
Prgm Director: Mark A Korsten, MD
130 W Kingsbridge Road
Room 7A11
Bronx, NY 10468
Tel: 718 584-9000   *Fax:* 718 741-4233
Length: 3 Yrs   *ACGME Approved/Offered Positions:* 56
Program ID: 140-35-31-517

New York Medical College (Bronx) Program

Sponsor: New York Medical College
Montefiore Medical Center - North Division
Prgm Director: Barry J Fomberstein, MD
600 E 233rd St
Bronx, NY 10466
Tel: 718 920-9168   *Fax:* 718 920-9036
Length: 3 Yrs   *ACGME Approved/Offered Positions:* 71
Program ID: 140-35-21-285

St Barnabas Hospital Program

Sponsor: St Barnabas Hospital
Prgm Director: James G Hellerman, MD
Department of Medicine
Third Avenue and 183rd St
Bronx, NY 10457
Tel: 718 960-6202   *Fax:* 718 960-3486
E-mail: jhellerman@pol.net
Length: 3 Yrs   *ACGME Approved/Offered Positions:* 102
Program ID: 140-35-21-485

Note: * indicates a newly appointed program director

Brooklyn

Brookdale University Hospital and Medical Center Program

Sponsor: Brookdale University Hospital and Medical Center
Prgm Director: Barbara J Berger, MD
One Brookdale Plaza
Brooklyn, NY 11212
Tel: 718 240-6205   *Fax:* 718 240-6516
E-mail: bberger@brookdale.edu
Length: 3 Yrs   *ACGME Approved/Offered Positions:* 73
Program ID: 140-35-11-264

Brooklyn Hospital Center Program

Sponsor: Brooklyn Hospital Center
Prgm Director: Kenneth Ong, MD
Department of Medicine
121 DeKalb Avenue
Brooklyn, NY 11201
Tel: 718 250-6925   *Fax:* 718 250-8120
E-mail: keo9002@nyp.org
Length: 3 Yrs   *ACGME Approved/Offered Positions:* 89
Program ID: 140-35-12-265

Coney Island Hospital Program

Sponsor: Coney Island Hospital
Prgm Director: Selvanayagam Niranjan, MD
2601 Ocean Parkway
Department of Medicine, Suite 4N98
Brooklyn, NY 11235
Tel: 718 616-3779   *Fax:* 718 616-3797
E-mail: walders@nychhc.org
Length: 3 Yrs   *ACGME Approved/Offered Positions:* 63
Program ID: 140-35-11-269

Interfaith Medical Center Program

Sponsor: Interfaith Medical Center
Prgm Director: Eric A Jaffe, MD
Department of Medicine
1545 Atlantic Avenue, Room S120
Brooklyn, NY 11213
Tel: 718 613-4063   *Fax:* 718 613-4893
E-mail: dmedicine@interfaithmedical.com
Length: 3 Yrs   *ACGME Approved/Offered Positions:* 75
Program ID: 140-35-21-276

Kingsbrook Jewish Medical Center Program

Sponsor: Kingsbrook Jewish Medical Center
Prgm Director: Mohammad Zahir, MD
Department of Medicine
585 Schenectady Ave
Brooklyn, NY 11203
Tel: 718 604-5401   *Fax:* 718 604-5450
Length: 3 Yrs   *ACGME Approved/Offered Positions:* 48
Program ID: 140-35-11-277

Long Island College Hospital Program

Sponsor: Long Island College Hospital
Prgm Director: Jeffrey Vieira, MD
339 Hicks Street
Brooklyn, NY 11201
Tel: 718 780-1881   *Fax:* 718 780-1300
E-mail: jvieira@chpnet.org
Length: 3 Yrs   *ACGME Approved/Offered Positions:* 78
Program ID: 140-35-11-280

Lutheran Medical Center Program

Sponsor: Lutheran Medical Center
Prgm Director: Daniel J Giaccio, MD
Department of Medicine
150 55th St
Brooklyn, NY 11220
Tel: 718 630-6373   *Fax:* 718 210-1093
Length: 3 Yrs   *ACGME Approved/Offered Positions:* 66
Program ID: 140-35-11-282

Maimonides Medical Center Program

Sponsor: Maimonides Medical Center
Prgm Director: Andrew C Yacht, MD
Department of Medicine
4802 10th Avenue
Brooklyn, NY 11219
Tel: 718 283-8343   *Fax:* 718 283-8498
Length: 3 Yrs   *ACGME Approved/Offered Positions:* 85
Program ID: 140-35-11-283

New York Methodist Hospital Program

Sponsor: New York Methodist Hospital
Prgm Director: Harvey Dosik, MD
Department of Medicine
506 Sixth Street
Brooklyn, NY 11215
Tel: 718 780-5240   *Fax:* 718 780-3259
E-mail: had9003@nyp.org
Length: 3 Yrs   *ACGME Approved/Offered Positions:* 104
Program ID: 140-35-11-284

SUNY Health Science Center at Brooklyn Program

Sponsor: SUNY Health Science Center at Brooklyn
Kings County Hospital Center
University Hospital-SUNY Health Science Center at Brooklyn
Veterans Affairs Medical Center (Brooklyn)
Prgm Director: Jeanne Macrae, MD
450 Clarkson Avenue, Box 50
Brooklyn, NY 11203
Tel: 718 270-6707   *Fax:* 718 270-4488
E-mail: Resmed@downstate.edu
Length: 3 Yrs   *ACGME Approved/Offered Positions:* 138
Program ID: 140-35-21-305

Woodhull Medical and Mental Health Center Program

Sponsor: Woodhull Medical and Mental Health Center
Prgm Director: Gregorio Hidalgo, MD
760 Broadway
Brooklyn, NY 11206
Tel: 718 963-5808   *Fax:* 718 963-8753
E-mail: yolanda.dawson@woodhullhc.nychhc.org
Length: 3 Yrs   *ACGME Approved/Offered Positions:* 57
Program ID: 140-35-21-487

Wyckoff Heights Medical Center Program

Sponsor: Wyckoff Heights Medical Center
Prgm Director: Mark K Adler, MD
Department of Medicine
374 Stockholm Street
Brooklyn, NY 11237
Tel: 718 963-7586   *Fax:* 718 486-4270
E-mail: nnunez@bqhcny.org
Length: 3 Yrs   *ACGME Approved/Offered Positions:* 54
Program ID: 140-35-21-520

Buffalo

University at Buffalo (Catholic Health System—Sisters of Charity) Program

Sponsor: University at Buffalo School of Medicine
Mercy Hospital of Buffalo
Sisters of Charity Hospital
Prgm Director: Khalid J Qazi, MD
Department of Medicine
2157 Main St
Buffalo, NY 14214
Tel: 716 862-1420   *Fax:* 716 862-1867
E-mail: mwahl@chsbuffalo.org
Length: 3 Yrs   *ACGME Approved/Offered Positions:* 40
Program ID: 140-35-21-251

University at Buffalo Program

Sponsor: University at Buffalo School of Medicine
Erie County Medical Center
Kaleida Health System (Buffalo General Hospital)
Veterans Affairs Western New York Hospital
Prgm Director: Ellen P Rich, MD
Department of Medicine
462 Grider Street
Buffalo, NY 14215
Tel: 716 898-3941   *Fax:* 716 898-3279
E-mail: ubintmda@buffalo.edu
Length: 3 Yrs   *ACGME Approved/Offered Positions:* 127
Program ID: 140-35-31-252

Cooperstown

Bassett Healthcare Program

Sponsor: Bassett Healthcare
Mary Imogene Bassett Hospital
Prgm Director: William W LeCates, MD
One Atwell Road
Cooperstown, NY 13326
Tel: 607 547-6522   *Fax:* 607 547-6612
E-mail: charlotte.hoag@bassett.org
Length: 3 Yrs   *ACGME Approved/Offered Positions:* 31
Program ID: 140-35-11-253

East Meadow

Nassau University Medical Center Program

Sponsor: Nassau University Medical Center
Prgm Director: Aloysius B Cuyjet, MD, MPH
Department of Medicine
2201 Hempstead Turnpike
East Meadow, NY 11554
Tel: 516 572-6501   *Fax:* 516 572-5609
E-mail: sbunting@numc.edu
Length: 3 Yrs   *ACGME Approved/Offered Positions:* 68
Program ID: 140-35-21-254

Elmhurst

Mount Sinai School of Medicine (Elmhurst) Program

Sponsor: Mount Sinai School of Medicine
Elmhurst Hospital Center-Mount Sinai Services
Prgm Director: Rand David, MD
79-01 Broadway
Suite A1-16
Elmhurst, NY 11373
Tel: 718 334-2490   *Fax:* 718 334-5845
Length: 3 Yrs   *ACGME Approved/Offered Positions:* 54
Program ID: 140-35-11-268

Far Rockaway

St John's Episcopal Hospital-South Shore Program

Sponsor: St John's Episcopal Hospital-South Shore
University Hospital-SUNY Health Science Center at Brooklyn
Prgm Director: Sheldon Markowitz, MD
Department of Medicine
327 Beach 19th St
Far Rockaway, NY 11691
Tel: 718 869-7672   *Fax:* 718 869-8530
E-mail: splasket@ehs.org
Length: 3 Yrs   *ACGME Approved/Offered Positions:* 51
Program ID: 140-35-21-486

Programs

Flushing

Flushing Hospital Medical Center Program

Sponsor: Flushing Hospital Medical Center
Prgm Director: Karen Beekman, MD
4500 Parsons Boulevard
Flushing, NY 11355
Tel: 718 670-5218   *Fax:* 718 670-4510
Length: 3 Yrs   *ACGME Approved/Offered Positions:* 52
Program ID: 140-35-11-272

New York Hospital Medical Center of Queens/Cornell University Medical College Program

Sponsor: New York Hospital Medical Center of Queens
Prgm Director: Steven F Reichert, MD
56-45 Main St
Flushing, NY 11355
Tel: 718 670-1347   *Fax:* 718 670-2456
E-mail: str9023@nyp.org
Length: 3 Yrs   *ACGME Approved/Offered Positions:* 78
Program ID: 140-35-11-262

Forest Hills

NSLIJHS-Forest Hills Hospital Program

Sponsor: North Shore-Long Island Jewish Health System
Forest Hills Hospital
Prgm Director: Mohammad H Sheikhai, MD
102-01 66th Road
Department of Medicine
Forest Hills, NY 11375
Tel: 718 830-1018   *Fax:* 718 830-1015
Length: 3 Yrs   *ACGME Approved/Offered Positions:* 38
Program ID: 140-35-21-468

Great Neck

NSLIJHS-Albert Einstein College of Medicine at Long Island Jewish Medical Center Program

Sponsor: North Shore-Long Island Jewish Health System
Long Island Jewish Medical Center
Prgm Director: Alan S Multz, MD
Department of Medicine
270-05 76th Avenue
New Hyde Park, NY 11042
Tel: 718 470-7270   *Fax:* 718 470-0827
E-mail: amultz@lij.edu
Length: 3 Yrs   *ACGME Approved/Offered Positions:* 72
Program ID: 140-35-21-281

NSLIJHS-North Shore University Hospital/NYU School of Medicine Program

Sponsor: North Shore-Long Island Jewish Health System
North Shore University Hospital
Prgm Director: Saima Chaudhry, MD, MS*
Department of Medicine
300 Community Drive
Manhasset, NY 11030
Tel: 516 562-4764   *Fax:* 516 562-3555
E-mail: ddimisa@nshs.edu
Length: 3 Yrs   *ACGME Approved/Offered Positions:* 85
Program ID: 140-35-21-271

Jamaica

Jamaica Hospital Medical Center Program

Sponsor: Jamaica Hospital Medical Center
Prgm Director: Richard W Pinsker, MD
8900 Van Wyck Expressway
Jamaica, NY 11418
Tel: 718 206-6768   *Fax:* 718 206-6651
Length: 3 Yrs   *ACGME Approved/Offered Positions:* 66
Program ID: 140-35-12-275

Mount Sinai School of Medicine (Queens Hospital Center) Program

Sponsor: Mount Sinai School of Medicine
Queens Hospital Center
Prgm Director: Debra J Brennessel, MD
Department of Medicine
82-68 164th Street
Jamaica, NY 11432
Tel: 718 883-4847   *Fax:* 718 883-6197
Length: 3 Yrs   *ACGME Approved/Offered Positions:* 51
Program ID: 140-35-21-510

New York Medical College (Brooklyn-Queens) Program

Sponsor: New York Medical College
Caritas Health Care (Brooklyn-Queens)
Prgm Director: Frantz Duffoo, MD
Department of Medicine
152-11 89th Avenue
Jamaica, NY 11432
Tel: 718 558-4004   *Fax:* 718 558-6971
Length: 3 Yrs   *ACGME Approved/Offered Positions:* 72
Program ID: 140-35-22-267

Johnson City

United Health Services Hospitals Program

Sponsor: United Health Services Hospitals
Binghamton General Hospital
Wilson Medical Center (United Health System)
Prgm Director: James R Jewell, MD
Wilson Memorial Regional Medical Center
33-57 Harrison Street
Johnson City, NY 13790
Tel: 607 763-6674   *Fax:* 607 798-1629
E-mail: James_Jewell@uhs.org
Length: 3 Yrs   *ACGME Approved/Offered Positions:* 26
Program ID: 140-35-31-255

Mineola

Winthrop-University Hospital Program

Sponsor: Winthrop-University Hospital
Prgm Director: Mark J Corapi, MD
Department of Medicine
222 Station Plaza North, Suite 509
Mineola, NY 11501
Tel: 516 663-2781   *Fax:* 516 663-8796
E-mail: Lwade@winthrop.org
Length: 3 Yrs   *ACGME Approved/Offered Positions:* 81
Program ID: 140-35-11-256

Mount Vernon

Mount Vernon Hospital Program

Sponsor: Mount Vernon Hospital
Prgm Director: Zev Carrey, MD
Department of Medicine
12 North 7th Avenue - Room 501
Mount Vernon, NY 10550
Tel: 914 361-6441   *Fax:* 914 664-2416
Length: 3 Yrs   *ACGME Approved/Offered Positions:* 24
Program ID: 140-35-21-482

New Rochelle

New York Medical College (Sound Shore) Program

Sponsor: New York Medical College
Sound Shore Medical Center of Westchester
Prgm Director: Stephen Jesmajian, MD
16 Guion Place
New Rochelle, NY 10802
Tel: 914 365-3681   *Fax:* 914 365-5489
E-mail: medicine@sshsw.org
Length: 3 Yrs   *ACGME Approved/Offered Positions:* 41
Program ID: 140-35-11-258

New York

Albert Einstein College of Medicine at Beth Israel Medical Center Program

Sponsor: Beth Israel Medical Center
Prgm Director: Adrienne M Fleckman, MD
Department of Medicine
First Avenue at 16th Street
New York, NY 10003
Tel: 212 420-4012   *Fax:* 212 420-4615
Length: 3 Yrs   *ACGME Approved/Offered Positions:* 119
Program ID: 140-35-11-261

Harlem Hospital Center Program

Sponsor: Harlem Hospital Center
Prgm Director: Linnea Capps, MD, MPH
Department of Medicine
506 Lenox Avenue at 135th Street
New York, NY 10037
Tel: 212 939-1423   *Fax:* 212 939-2429
E-mail: dl95@columbia.edu
Length: 3 Yrs   *ACGME Approved/Offered Positions:* 75
Program ID: 140-35-11-273

Lenox Hill Hospital Program

Sponsor: Lenox Hill Hospital
Prgm Director: Robin Dibner, MD
Department of Medicine
100 E 77th Street
New York, NY 10021
Tel: 212 434-2140   *Fax:* 212 434-2246
E-mail: intmed@lenoxhill.net
Length: 3 Yrs   *ACGME Approved/Offered Positions:* 94
Program ID: 140-35-11-278

Mount Sinai School of Medicine (North General) Program

Sponsor: Mount Sinai School of Medicine
North General Hospital
Prgm Director: Ronald K Cobbs, MD*
1879 Madison Avenue
New York, NY 10035
Tel: 212 423-4482   *Fax:* 212 423-4399
E-mail: ronald.cobbs@ngsc.org
Length: 3 Yrs   *ACGME Approved/Offered Positions:* 30
Program ID: 140-35-11-274

Mount Sinai School of Medicine Program

Sponsor: Mount Sinai School of Medicine
Mount Sinai Medical Center
Prgm Director: Mark W Babyatsky, MD
Department of Medicine
One Gustave L Levy Place, Box 1118
New York, NY 10029
Tel: 212 241-8140   *Fax:* 212 241-8445
Length: 3 Yrs   *ACGME Approved/Offered Positions:* 124
Program ID: 140-35-31-288

New York Downtown Hospital Program

Sponsor: New York Downtown Hospital
Prgm Director: Candido J Anaya, MD
Department of Medicine
170 William Street
New York, NY 10038
Tel: 212 312-5760   *Fax:* 212 312-5735
Length: 3 Yrs   *ACGME Approved/Offered Positions:* 51
Program ID: 140-35-31-289

New York Medical College (Metropolitan) Program

Sponsor: New York Medical College
Metropolitan Hospital Center
Prgm Director: Shobhana A Chaudhari, MD
Department of Medicine
1901 First Avenue
New York, NY 10029
Tel: 212 423-6771   *Fax:* 212 423-8099
Length: 3 Yrs   *ACGME Approved/Offered Positions:* 60
Program ID: 140-35-31-290

Note: * indicates a newly appointed program director

New York Medical College at St Vincent's Hospital and Medical Center of New York Program

Sponsor: New York Medical College
St Vincent Catholic Medical Centers (Manhattan)
Prgm Director: Margaret D Smith, MD
170 W 12th Street
New York, NY 10011
Tel: 212 604-2124   *Fax:* 212 604-3225
Length: 3 Yrs   *ACGME Approved/Offered Positions:* 78
Program ID: 140-35-11-302

New York Presbyterian Hospital (Columbia Campus) Program

Sponsor: New York Presbyterian Hospital
New York Presbyterian Hospital (Columbia Campus)
Prgm Director: Joseph Tenenbaum, MD*
622 W 168th Street
New York, NY 10032
Tel: 212 305-2913   *Fax:* 212 305-9213
Length: 3 Yrs   *ACGME Approved/Offered Positions:* 141
Program ID: 140-35-11-297

New York Presbyterian Hospital (Cornell Campus) Program

Sponsor: New York Presbyterian Hospital
New York Presbyterian Hospital (Cornell Campus)
Prgm Director: Mark S Pecker, MD
Department of Medicine, Box 130
1300 York Avenue, Rm M-528
New York, NY 10065
Tel: 212 746-4749   *Fax:* 212 746-6692
Length: 3 Yrs   *ACGME Approved/Offered Positions:* 133
Program ID: 140-35-21-270

New York University School of Medicine Program

Sponsor: New York University School of Medicine
Bellevue Hospital Center
Manhattan VA Harbor Health Care System
NYU Hospitals Center
Prgm Director: R Ellen Pearlman, MD
550 First Avenue
NBV 16 N 27
New York, NY 10016
Tel: 212 263-6887   *Fax:* 212 263-2913
Length: 3 Yrs   *ACGME Approved/Offered Positions:* 164
Program ID: 140-35-21-292

St Luke's-Roosevelt Hospital Center Program

Sponsor: St Luke's-Roosevelt Hospital Center
Ryan Chelsea Clinton Community Health Center
University Medical Practice Associates
Westside Pulmonary
Prgm Director: Ethan D Fried, MD, MS
Department of Medicine
1000 Tenth Ave
New York, NY 10019
Tel: 212 523-3314   *Fax:* 212 523-3948
E-mail: edfried@chpnet.org
Length: 3 Yrs   *ACGME Approved/Offered Positions:* 158
Program ID: 140-35-21-301

Rochester

Rochester General Hospital Program

Sponsor: Rochester General Hospital
Prgm Director: Paul L Bernstein, MD
1425 Portland Avenue
Box 240
Rochester, NY 14621
Tel: 585 922-4365   *Fax:* 585 922-4440
E-mail: paul.bernstein@viahealth.org
Length: 3 Yrs   *ACGME Approved/Offered Positions:* 57
Program ID: 140-35-31-314

Unity Health System (Rochester) Program

Sponsor: Unity St Mary's Campus (Unity Health System)
Unity Hospital (Unity Health System)
Prgm Director: Michael DiSalle, MD
Department of Medicine
1555 Long Pond Road
Rochester, NY 14626
Tel: 585 723-7797   *Fax:* 585 723-7834
E-mail: respro@unityhealth.org
Length: 3 Yrs   *ACGME Approved/Offered Positions:* 41
Program ID: 140-35-31-527

University of Rochester Program

Sponsor: Strong Memorial Hospital of the University of Rochester
Highland Hospital of Rochester
Prgm Director: Donald R Bordley, MD
Department of Medicine
601 Elmwood Avenue, Box MED
Rochester, NY 14642
Tel: 585 275-2874   *Fax:* 585 756-5111
Length: 3 Yrs   *ACGME Approved/Offered Positions:* 81
Program ID: 140-35-11-313

Staten Island

New York Medical College (Richmond) Program

Sponsor: New York Medical College
Richmond University Medical Center
Prgm Director: Susan D Grossman, MD
335 Bard Avenue
Staten Island, NY 10310
Tel: 718 818-4355   *Fax:* 718 818-3225
Length: 3 Yrs   *ACGME Approved/Offered Positions:* 58
Program ID: 140-35-11-303

Staten Island University Hospital Program

Sponsor: Staten Island University Hospital
Prgm Director: Robert V Wetz, MD
475 Seaview Avenue
Staten Island, NY 10305
Tel: 718 226-6905   *Fax:* 718 226-9271
Length: 3 Yrs   *ACGME Approved/Offered Positions:* 100
Program ID: 140-35-11-304

Stony Brook

SUNY at Stony Brook Program

Sponsor: University Hospital - SUNY at Stony Brook
Veterans Affairs Medical Center (Northport)
Prgm Director: William Wertheim, MD
Department of Medicine
T-16, Room 020
Stony Brook, NY 11794
Tel: 631 444-2065   *Fax:* 631 444-2493
Length: 3 Yrs   *ACGME Approved/Offered Positions:* 91
Program ID: 140-35-21-315

Syracuse

SUNY Upstate Medical University Program

Sponsor: SUNY Upstate Medical University
Prgm Director: Stephen J Knohl, MD*
750 E Adams Street
Room 6602
Syracuse, NY 13210
Tel: 315 464-4506   *Fax:* 315 464-4484
E-mail: knohls@upstate.edu
Length: 3 Yrs   *ACGME Approved/Offered Positions:* 73
Program ID: 140-35-21-316

Valhalla

New York Medical College at Westchester Medical Center Program

Sponsor: New York Medical College
Westchester Medical Center
Prgm Director: Andrew H Gutwein, MD
Department of Medicine
Munger Pavillion, Room 256
Valhalla, NY 10595
Tel: 914 493-8373
Length: 3 Yrs   *ACGME Approved/Offered Positions:* 62
Program ID: 140-35-11-317

North Carolina

Chapel Hill

University of North Carolina Hospitals Program

Sponsor: University of North Carolina Hospitals
Prgm Director: Lee R Berkowitz, MD
126 Macnider Hall
CB 7005
Chapel Hill, NC 27599
Tel: 919 843-8075   *Fax:* 919 843-2356
E-mail: lee_berkowitz@med.unc.edu
Length: 3 Yrs   *ACGME Approved/Offered Positions:* 75
Program ID: 140-36-21-318

Charlotte

Carolinas Medical Center Program

Sponsor: Carolinas Medical Center
Prgm Director: Beth E Susi, MD
Department of Medicine
PO Box 32861
Charlotte, NC 28232
Tel: 704 355-3165   *Fax:* 704 355-7626
E-mail: intmed@carolinashealthcare.org
Length: 3 Yrs   *ACGME Approved/Offered Positions:* 36
Program ID: 140-36-11-319

Durham

Duke University Hospital Program

Sponsor: Duke University Hospital
Veterans Affairs Medical Center (Durham)
Prgm Director: Diana B McNeill, MD
Department of Medicine
Erwin Rd, 8th Floor, Rm 8254 Duke North-Box 3182
Durham, NC 27710
Tel: 919 684-3841   *Fax:* 919 681-6448
E-mail: medres@mc.duke.edu
Length: 3 Yrs   *ACGME Approved/Offered Positions:* 146
Program ID: 140-36-21-320

Greensboro

Moses H Cone Memorial Hospital Program

Sponsor: Moses H Cone Memorial Hospital
Prgm Director: Samuel Cykert, MD*
Department of Internal Medicine
1200 N Elm Street
Greensboro, NC 27401
Tel: 336 832-8062   *Fax:* 336 832-8026
E-mail: linda.newman@mosescone.com
Length: 3 Yrs   *ACGME Approved/Offered Positions:* 22
Program ID: 140-36-11-321

Greenville

Pitt County Memorial Hospital/East Carolina University Program

Sponsor: Pitt County Memorial Hospital
Prgm Director: Suzanne Kraemer, MD, MS
Brody School of Medicine
PCMH-TA, Room 340
Greenville, NC 27858
Tel: 252 744-3682   *Fax:* 252 744-2280
Length: 3 Yrs   *ACGME Approved/Offered Positions:* 52
Program ID: 140-36-11-323

Wilmington

New Hanover Regional Medical Center Program

Sponsor: New Hanover Regional Medical Center
Prgm Director: Charles J Schleupner, MSc, MD
SEAHEC Internal Medicine
2131 South 17th Street, PO Box 9025
Wilmington, NC 28402
Tel: 910 343-2516   *Fax:* 910 762-6800
E-mail: charles.schleupner@seahec.net
Length: 3 Yrs   *ACGME Approved/Offered Positions:* 23
Program ID: 140-36-11-324

Winston-Salem

Wake Forest University School of Medicine Program

Sponsor: Wake Forest University Baptist Medical Center
Prgm Director: Peter R Lichstein, MD
Medical Center Blvd
Winston-Salem, NC 27157
Tel: 336 716-4490   *Fax:* 336 716-2273
E-mail: plichste@wfubmc.edu
Length: 3 Yrs   *ACGME Approved/Offered Positions:* 94
Program ID: 140-36-21-325

North Dakota

Fargo

University of North Dakota Program

Sponsor: Univ of North Dakota School of Medicine and
  Health Sciences
Veterans Affairs Medical and Regional Office Center
  (Fargo)
MeritCare Health System
Prgm Director: David J Theige, MD
1919 North Elm Street
Fargo, ND 58102
Tel: 701 234-6353   *Fax:* 701 234-7230
Length: 3 Yrs   *ACGME Approved/Offered Positions:* 25
Program ID: 140-37-21-326

Ohio

Akron

Akron General Medical Center/NEOUCOM Program

Sponsor: Akron General Medical Center
Prgm Director: Titus G Sheers, MD
Department of Medicine
400 Wabash Avenue
Akron, OH 44307
Tel: 330 344-6140   *Fax:* 330 535-9270
E-mail: kstith@agmc.org
Length: 3 Yrs   *ACGME Approved/Offered Positions:* 34
Program ID: 140-38-11-328

Summa Health System/NEOUCOM Program

Sponsor: Summa Health System
Akron City Hospital (Summa Health System)
Prgm Director: David B Sweet, MD
Internal Medicine/Mary Yanik
525 E Market Street
Akron, OH 44304
Tel: 330 375-3742   *Fax:* 330 375-3760
E-mail: yanikm@summa-health.org
Length: 3 Yrs   *ACGME Approved/Offered Positions:* 56
Program ID: 140-38-11-327

Canton

Canton Medical Education Foundation/NEOUCOM Program

Sponsor: Canton Medical Education Foundation
Aultman Hospital
Mercy Medical Center (Canton)
Prgm Director: Kathleen A Senger, MD
Internal Medicine Residency
2600 6th Street, SW
Canton, OH 44710
Tel: 330 363-6293   *Fax:* 330 588-2605
Length: 3 Yrs   *ACGME Approved/Offered Positions:* 36
Program ID: 140-38-21-330

Cincinnati

Christ Hospital Program

Sponsor: Christ Hospital
Maple Knoll Village
Prgm Director: John R Schroder, MD, MHA
Department of Medicine
2139 Auburn Avenue
Cincinnati, OH 45219
Tel: 513 585-2808   *Fax:* 513 585-2673
Length: 3 Yrs   *ACGME Approved/Offered Positions:* 42
Program ID: 140-38-11-331

Jewish Hospital of Cincinnati Program

Sponsor: Jewish Hospital of Cincinnati
Prgm Director: Stephen J Goldberg, MD, MBA
Department of Internal Medicine
4777 E Galbraith Road
Cincinnati, OH 45236
Tel: 513 686-5446   *Fax:* 513 686-5443
E-mail: jewishhospcincinnati@gmail.com
Length: 3 Yrs   *ACGME Approved/Offered Positions:* 32
Program ID: 140-38-11-333

TriHealth (Good Samaritan Hospital) Program

Sponsor: TriHealth
TriHealth - Good Samaritan Hospital
Prgm Director: Helen K Koselka, MD
Department of Medicine
375 Dixmyth Avenue
Cincinnati, OH 45220
Tel: 513 862-3229   *Fax:* 513 221-5865
E-mail: Candice_Larkins@trihealth.com
Length: 3 Yrs   *ACGME Approved/Offered Positions:* 27
Program ID: 140-38-31-332

University Hospital/University of Cincinnati College of Medicine Program

Sponsor: University Hospital Inc
Veterans Affairs Medical Center (Cincinnati)
Prgm Director: Gregory W Rouan, MD
Department of Medicine
PO Box 670557
Cincinnati, OH 45267
Tel: 513 558-2590   *Fax:* 513 558-3878
E-mail: ucintmed@uc.edu
Length: 3 Yrs   *ACGME Approved/Offered Positions:* 84
Program ID: 140-38-21-334

Cleveland

Case Western Reserve University (MetroHealth) Program

Sponsor: MetroHealth Medical Center
Prgm Director: Michael J McFarlane, MD
Office of Academic Programs (G573)
2500 MetroHealth Drive
Cleveland, OH 44109
Tel: 216 778-3592   *Fax:* 216 778-5823
E-mail: medres@metrohealth.org
Length: 3 Yrs   *ACGME Approved/Offered Positions:* 79
Program ID: 140-38-11-336

Case Western Reserve University (St Vincent Charity/St Luke's) Program

Sponsor: St Vincent Charity Hospital/St Luke's Medical
  Center
Prgm Director: Richard E Christie, MD
2351 E 22nd Street
Cleveland, OH 44115
Tel: 216 363-2543   *Fax:* 216 363-2721
Length: 3 Yrs   *ACGME Approved/Offered Positions:* 44
Program ID: 140-38-11-338

Cleveland Clinic Foundation Program

Sponsor: Cleveland Clinic Foundation
Prgm Director: Craig Nielsen, MD
Internal Medicine Residency Office, NA-10
9500 Euclid Avenue
Cleveland, OH 44195
Tel: 216 444-2336   *Fax:* 216 445-6290
E-mail: imed@ccf.org
Length: 3 Yrs   *ACGME Approved/Offered Positions:* 120
Program ID: 140-38-12-339

Fairview Hospital Program

Sponsor: Fairview Hospital
Prgm Director: K V Gopalakrishna, MD
Internal Medicine Residency Program
18101 Lorain Avenue
Cleveland, OH 44111
Tel: 216 476-7106   *Fax:* 216 476-2944
E-mail: linda.armagno@fairviewhospital.org
Length: 3 Yrs   *ACGME Approved/Offered Positions:* 38
Program ID: 140-38-21-340

Huron Hospital Program

Sponsor: Huron Hospital
Hillcrest Hospital
Prgm Director: Andrei Brateanu, MD
Department of Medicine
13951 Terrace Road
East Cleveland, OH 44112
Tel: 216 761-7394   *Fax:* 216 761-7579
E-mail: abrateanu@hotmail.com
Length: 3 Yrs   *ACGME Approved/Offered Positions:* 55
Program ID: 140-38-21-476

University Hospitals Case Medical Center Program

Sponsor: University Hospitals Case Medical Center
Veterans Affairs Medical Center (Cleveland)
Prgm Director: Keith B Armitage, MD
Department of Medicine
11100 Euclid Avenue
Cleveland, OH 44106
Tel: 216 844-3833   *Fax:* 216 844-8216
E-mail: keith.armitage@case.edu
Length: 3 Yrs   *ACGME Approved/Offered Positions:* 113
Program ID: 140-38-21-335

Note: * indicates a newly appointed program director

Columbus

Mount Carmel Program
Sponsor: Mount Carmel
Prgm Director: John C Weiss, MD
Department of Medicine
793 W State Street
Columbus, OH 43222
Tel: 614 234-1052   *Fax:* 614 234-2772
Length: 3 Yrs   *ACGME Approved/Offered Positions:* 30
Program ID: 140-38-12-341

Ohio State University Hospital Program
Sponsor: Ohio State University Hospital
Prgm Director: David A Wininger, MD
378 North Doan Office Tower
395 W 12th Avenue
Columbus, OH 43210
Tel: 614 293-3989   *Fax:* 614 293-9789
Length: 3 Yrs   *ACGME Approved/Offered Positions:* 82
Program ID: 140-38-11-342

Riverside Methodist Hospitals (OhioHealth) Program
Sponsor: Riverside Methodist Hospitals (OhioHealth)
Prgm Director: Thomas J Boes, MD
3535 Olentangy River Road
Columbus, OH 43214
Tel: 614 566-5468   *Fax:* 614 566-6852
Length: 3 Yrs   *ACGME Approved/Offered Positions:* 54
Program ID: 140-38-12-343

Dayton

Wright State University Program
Sponsor: Wright State University Boonshoft School of Medicine
Good Samaritan Hospital and Health Center
Miami Valley Hospital
Veterans Affairs Medical Center (Dayton)
Wright - Patterson Medical Center
Prgm Director: Virginia C Wood, MD
PO Box 927
Dayton, OH 45401
Tel: 937 208-2867   *Fax:* 937 208-2621
Length: 3 Yrs   *ACGME Approved/Offered Positions:* 84
Program ID: 140-38-21-345

Kettering

Kettering Medical Center Program
Sponsor: Kettering Medical Center
Prgm Director: Stephen D McDonald, MD
Internal Medicine Residency
3535 Southern Blvd
Kettering, OH 45429
Tel: 937 395-8693   *Fax:* 937 395-8399
Length: 3 Yrs   *ACGME Approved/Offered Positions:* 30
Program ID: 140-38-21-347

Toledo

Mercy Health Partners/St Vincent Mercy Medical Center Program
Sponsor: St Vincent Mercy Medical Center
University Medical Center (Toledo)
Prgm Director: Vijay Mahajan, MD, EdD
2213 Cherry Street
Toledo, OH 43608
Tel: 419 251-4554   *Fax:* 419 251-6750
Length: 3 Yrs   *ACGME Approved/Offered Positions:* 24
Program ID: 140-38-12-533

University of Toledo Program
Sponsor: University of Toledo
University Medical Center (Toledo)
Prgm Director: Ragheb Assaly, MD*
3000 Arlington Avenue, Room 4143
Mail Stop 1150
Toledo, OH 43614
Tel: 419 383-3687   *Fax:* 419 383-6180
Length: 3 Yrs   *ACGME Approved/Offered Positions:* 48
Program ID: 140-38-21-348

Youngstown

St Elizabeth Health Center/NEOUCOM Program
Sponsor: St Elizabeth Health Center
Prgm Director: Thomas P Marnejon, DO
Internal Medicine Residency Program
1044 Belmont Ave
Youngstown, OH 44501
Tel: 330 480-3344   *Fax:* 330 480-3777
E-mail: gwendolyn_brown@hmis.org
Length: 3 Yrs   *ACGME Approved/Offered Positions:* 24
Program ID: 140-38-11-349

Western Reserve Care System/NEOUCOM Program
Sponsor: Forum Health/Western Reserve Care System (Youngstown)
Northside Medical Center
Prgm Director: Rebecca S Bailey, MD
2nd Floor RRC
500 Gypsy Lane
Youngstown, OH 44501
Tel: 330 884-5812   *Fax:* 330 884-5688
E-mail: P007146@forumhealth.org
Length: 3 Yrs   *ACGME Approved/Offered Positions:* 35
Program ID: 140-38-31-350

Oklahoma

Oklahoma City

University of Oklahoma Health Sciences Center Program
Sponsor: University of Oklahoma College of Medicine
OU Medical Center
Veterans Affairs Medical Center (Oklahoma City)
Prgm Director: Brent R Brown, MD
Department of Medicine, Room WP-1130
PO Box 26901
Oklahoma City, OK 73190
Tel: 405 271-5963   *Fax:* 405 271-7186
E-mail: patti-levin@ouhsc.edu
Length: 3 Yrs   *ACGME Approved/Offered Positions:* 62
Program ID: 140-39-21-351

Tulsa

University of Oklahoma College of Medicine-Tulsa Program
Sponsor: University of Oklahoma College of Medicine-Tulsa
St John Medical Center
Prgm Director: Sherri L Sanders, MD
Department of Internal Medicine
4502 E 41st Street
Tulsa, OK 74135
Tel: 918 744-2548   *Fax:* 918 744-2531
E-mail: barbara-mccoy@ouhsc.edu
Length: 3 Yrs   *ACGME Approved/Offered Positions:* 51
Program ID: 140-39-21-352

Oregon

Portland

Legacy Emanuel Hospital and Health Center Program
Sponsor: Legacy Emanuel Hospital and Health Center
Legacy Good Samaritan Hospital and Medical Center
Prgm Director: Stephen R Jones, MD
1015 NW 22nd Avenue, R-200
Portland, OR 97210
Tel: 503 413-8258   *Fax:* 503 413-7361
Length: 3 Yrs   *ACGME Approved/Offered Positions:* 44
Program ID: 140-40-11-353

Oregon Health & Science University Program
Sponsor: Oregon Health & Science University Hospital
Veterans Affairs Medical Center (Portland)
Prgm Director: Thomas G Cooney, MD
Department of Medicine, OP-30
3181 SW Sam Jackson Park Road
Portland, OR 97239
Tel: 503 494-8530   *Fax:* 503 494-5636
Length: 3 Yrs   *ACGME Approved/Offered Positions:* 92
Program ID: 140-40-31-357

Providence Health System/Providence Medical Center Program
Sponsor: Providence Health System, Portland Service Area
Providence Portland Medical Center
Prgm Director: Mark R Rosenberg, MD
Department of Medical Education
5050 NE Hoyt St, Suite 540
Portland, OR 97213
Tel: 503 215-6123   *Fax:* 503 215-6857
E-mail: imresprog@providence.org
Length: 3 Yrs   *ACGME Approved/Offered Positions:* 30
Program ID: 140-40-31-355

Providence Health System/St Vincent Hospital and Medical Center Program
Sponsor: Providence Health System, Portland Service Area
St Vincent Hospital and Medical Center
Prgm Director: Steven D Freer, MD
Department of Medicine
9205 SW Barnes Road, Suite 20
Portland, OR 97225
Tel: 503 216-2229   *Fax:* 503 216-4041
Length: 3 Yrs   *ACGME Approved/Offered Positions:* 27
Program ID: 140-40-31-356

Pennsylvania

Abington

Abington Memorial Hospital Program
Sponsor: Abington Memorial Hospital
Prgm Director: David G Smith, MD
Department of Medicine
1200 Old York Road, Suite 2B
Abington, PA 19001
Tel: 215 481-4105   *Fax:* 215 481-4361
E-mail: amh-imresidents@amh.org
Length: 3 Yrs   *ACGME Approved/Offered Positions:* 62
Program ID: 140-41-12-358

Allentown

Lehigh Valley Hospital Network/Pennsylvania State University Program

Sponsor: Lehigh Valley Hospital Network
Prgm Director: Marc Shalaby, MD
CC & I-78, PO Box 689
Department of Medicine
Allentown, PA 18105
Tel: 610 402-8048   *Fax:* 610 402-1675
Length: 3 Yrs   *ACGME Approved/Offered Positions:* 48
Program ID: 140-41-21-359

Bethlehem

St Luke's Hospital Program

Sponsor: St Luke's Hospital
Prgm Director: Gloria Fioravanti, DO
Department of Medicine
801 Ostrum Street
Bethlehem, PA 18015
Tel: 610 954-4644   *Fax:* 610 954-4920
E-mail: imresidency@slhn.org
Length: 3 Yrs   *ACGME Approved/Offered Positions:* 24
Program ID: 140-41-31-360

Danville

Geisinger Health System Program

Sponsor: Geisinger Health System
Geisinger Medical Center
Prgm Director: Mary E O'Keefe, MD
Department of Medicine - MC 01-39
100 North Academy Avenue
Danville, PA 17822
Tel: 570 271-6787   *Fax:* 570 271-5734
Length: 3 Yrs   *ACGME Approved/Offered Positions:* 51
Program ID: 140-41-11-362

Darby

Mercy Catholic Medical Center Program

Sponsor: Mercy Catholic Medical Center Inc
Mercy Fitzgerald Hospital
Mercy Philadelphia Hospital
Prgm Director: Arnold R Eiser, MD
1500 Lansdowne Avenue
Darby, PA 19023
Tel: 610 237-4553   *Fax:* 610 237-5022
E-mail: erogers@mercyhealth.org
Length: 3 Yrs   *ACGME Approved/Offered Positions:* 67
Program ID: 140-41-11-375

Easton

Easton Hospital Program

Sponsor: Easton Hospital (Northampton Hospital Corporation)
Prgm Director: Susan P Sloan, MD
Department of Medicine
250 South 21st Street
Easton, PA 18042
Tel: 610 250-4518   *Fax:* 610 250-4833
Length: 3 Yrs   *ACGME Approved/Offered Positions:* 24
Program ID: 140-41-11-363

Harrisburg

PinnacleHealth Hospitals Program

Sponsor: PinnacleHealth Hospitals
Prgm Director: John Goldman, MD
Department of Medicine
PO Box 8700
Harrisburg, PA 17105
Tel: 717 231-8508   *Fax:* 717 231-8535
E-mail: jbeck@pinnaclehealth.org
Length: 3 Yrs   *ACGME Approved/Offered Positions:* 38
Program ID: 140-41-11-365

Hershey

Penn State University/Milton S Hershey Medical Center Program

Sponsor: Milton S Hershey Medical Center
Prgm Director: Edward R Bollard, MD, DDS
Internal Medicine Residency Training Program-H039
Mail Code H176/500 University Drive
Hershey, PA 17033
Tel: 717 531-8390   *Fax:* 717 531-5831
E-mail: ebollard@psu.edu
Length: 3 Yrs   *ACGME Approved/Offered Positions:* 70
Program ID: 140-41-11-366

Johnstown

Conemaugh Valley Memorial Hospital Program

Sponsor: Conemaugh Valley Memorial Hospital
Prgm Director: Martin J Glynn, MD, MBA*
Department of Medicine E-3
1086 Franklin Street
Johnstown, PA 15905
Tel: 814 534-9408   *Fax:* 814 534-3290
E-mail: mglynn@conemaugh.org
Length: 3 Yrs   *ACGME Approved/Offered Positions:* 27
Program ID: 140-41-31-367

McKeesport

University of Pittsburgh Medical Center Medical Education (McKeesport Hospital) Program

Sponsor: Univ of Pittsburgh Medical Center Medical Education
UPMC McKeesport
Prgm Director: Stasia L Miaskiewicz, MD
Department of Medicine
1500 5th Avenue
McKeesport, PA 15132
Tel: 412 664-2167   *Fax:* 412 664-2164
Length: 3 Yrs   *ACGME Approved/Offered Positions:* 36
Program ID: 140-41-21-368

Philadelphia

Albert Einstein Healthcare Network Program

Sponsor: Albert Einstein Medical Center
Prgm Director: Glenn Eiger, MD
5401 Old York Road
Klein 363
Philadelphia, PA 19141
Tel: 215 456-6940   *Fax:* 215 456-7926
E-mail: medicine@einstein.edu
Length: 3 Yrs   *ACGME Approved/Offered Positions:* 90
Program ID: 140-41-11-369

Drexel University College of Medicine/Hahnemann University Hospital Program

Sponsor: Drexel University College of Medicine/Hahnemann University
Hahnemann University Hospital (Tenet Health System)
Prgm Director: Richard G Paluzzi, MD
245 N 15th Street
Mail Stop 427
Philadelphia, PA 19102
Tel: 215 762-7916   *Fax:* 215 762-7765
E-mail: I.M.5@drexel.edu
Length: 3 Yrs   *ACGME Approved/Offered Positions:* 146
Program ID: 140-41-21-374

Pennsylvania Hospital of the University of Pennsylvania Health System Program

Sponsor: Pennsylvania Hospital (UPHS)
Prgm Director: Dennis C Policastro, MD
Department of Medicine
800 Spruce Street, 1 Pine West
Philadelphia, PA 19107
Tel: 215 829-5410   *Fax:* 215 829-7129
Length: 3 Yrs   *ACGME Approved/Offered Positions:* 50
Program ID: 140-41-11-376

Temple University Hospital Program

Sponsor: Temple University Hospital
Prgm Director: Darilyn V Moyer, MD
Temple University Hospital
3401 North Broad Street
Philadelphia, PA 19140
Tel: 215 707-3397   *Fax:* 215 707-5978
E-mail: mcruz@temple.edu
Length: 3 Yrs   *ACGME Approved/Offered Positions:* 112
Program ID: 140-41-21-378

Thomas Jefferson University Program

Sponsor: Thomas Jefferson University Hospital
Prgm Director: Gregory C Kane, MD
1025 Walnut Street
Room 805
Philadelphia, PA 19107
Tel: 215 955-3892   *Fax:* 215 955-3890
Length: 3 Yrs   *ACGME Approved/Offered Positions:* 125
Program ID: 140-41-21-379

University of Pennsylvania Program

Sponsor: University of Pennsylvania Health System
Prgm Director: Lisa M Bellini, MD
100 Centrex
3400 Spruce Street
Philadelphia, PA 19104
Tel: 215 662-3924   *Fax:* 215 662-7919
E-mail: mededu@uphs.upenn.edu
Length: 3 Yrs   *ACGME Approved/Offered Positions:* 162
Program ID: 140-41-21-380

Pittsburgh

Allegheny General Hospital Program

Sponsor: Allegheny General Hospital
Prgm Director: James J Reilly, MD
320 East North Avenue
Pittsburgh, PA 15212
Tel: 412 359-4971   *Fax:* 412 359-4983
E-mail: jreilly@wpahs.org
Length: 3 Yrs   *ACGME Approved/Offered Positions:* 57
Program ID: 140-41-11-381

University of Pittsburgh Medical Center Medical Education (Mercy) Program

Sponsor: Univ of Pittsburgh Medical Center Medical Education
Prgm Director: Anthony J Pinevich, MD, MBA*
1400 Locust Street
Pittsburgh, PA 15219
Tel: 412 232-8080
Length: 3 Yrs   *ACGME Approved/Offered Positions:* 51
Program ID: 140-41-11-385

Note: * indicates a newly appointed program director

University of Pittsburgh Medical Center Medical Education Program
Sponsor: Univ of Pittsburgh Medical Center Medical Education
UPMC Presbyterian Shadyside
Veterans Affairs Medical Center (Pittsburgh)
Prgm Director: Raquel A Buranosky, MD, MPH
UPMC Montefiore, N713
200 Lothrop Street
Pittsburgh, PA 15213
Tel: 412 692-4700   *Fax:* 412 692-4944
Length: 3 Yrs   *ACGME Approved/Offered Positions:* 179
Program ID: 140-41-21-504

Western Pennsylvania Hospital/Temple University Program
Sponsor: Western Pennsylvania Hospital
Prgm Director: Mary Lynn Sealey, MD*
Department of Medicine
4800 Friendship Avenue
Pittsburgh, PA 15224
Tel: 412 578-6902   *Fax:* 412 578-7212
Length: 3 Yrs   *ACGME Approved/Offered Positions:* 45
Program ID: 140-41-11-387

Sayre

Guthrie/Robert Packer Hospital Program
Sponsor: Robert Packer Hospital
Prgm Director: Felix J DeSio, MD
Internal Medicine Residency Program
Guthrie Square
Sayre, PA 18840
Tel: 570 882-4559   *Fax:* 570 882-5352
Length: 3 Yrs   *ACGME Approved/Offered Positions:* 27
Program ID: 140-41-12-389

Scranton

Scranton-Temple Residency Program
Sponsor: Scranton-Temple Residency Program Inc
Mercy Hospital
Moses Taylor Hospital
Prgm Director: Linda Thomas, MD
Department of Medicine
746 Jefferson Avenue
Scranton, PA 18510
Tel: 570 343-2383   *Fax:* 570 963-6133
E-mail: strp@strpweb.org
Length: 3 Yrs   *ACGME Approved/Offered Positions:* 30
Program ID: 140-41-21-390

Upland

Crozer-Chester Medical Center Program
Sponsor: Crozer-Chester Medical Center
Prgm Director: Ashish Rana, MD
One Medical Center Blvd
Department of Medicine, 3 East
Upland, PA 19013
Tel: 610 874-6114   *Fax:* 610 447-6373
E-mail: ccmcdom@crozer.org
Length: 3 Yrs   *ACGME Approved/Offered Positions:* 24
Program ID: 140-41-31-514

West Reading

Reading Hospital and Medical Center Program
Sponsor: Reading Hospital and Medical Center
Prgm Director: David L George, MD, MBA
Department of Medicine
Sixth Avenue and Spruce Streets
West Reading, PA 19611
Tel: 610 988-8133   *Fax:* 610 988-9003
Length: 3 Yrs   *ACGME Approved/Offered Positions:* 20
Program ID: 140-41-21-388

Wynnewood

Lankenau Hospital Program
Sponsor: Lankenau Hospital
Prgm Director: Cynthia D Smith, MD
100 Lancaster Avenue
Annenberg Conference Center G10
Wynnewood, PA 19096
Tel: 610 645-3305   *Fax:* 610 645-8141
E-mail: diresol@mlhs.org
Length: 3 Yrs   *ACGME Approved/Offered Positions:* 52
Program ID: 140-41-11-373

York

York Hospital Program
Sponsor: York Hospital
Prgm Director: Kevin Muzzio, MD*
Department of Medicine
1001 S George Street
York, PA 17405
Tel: 717 851-2164   *Fax:* 717 851-2843
Length: 3 Yrs   *ACGME Approved/Offered Positions:* 30
Program ID: 140-41-11-392

Puerto Rico

Bayamon

Universidad Central del Caribe Program
Sponsor: Universidad Central del Caribe School of Medicine
Hospital Universitario Dr Ramon Ruiz Arnau
Prgm Director: Luis M Reyes-Ortiz, MD
Dept of Medicine
PO Box 60327
Bayamon, PR 00956
Tel: 787 740-4295   *Fax:* 787 269-0050
E-mail: lrodriguez@uccaribe.edu
Length: 3 Yrs   *ACGME Approved/Offered Positions:* 36
Program ID: 140-42-12-452

Mayaguez

Ramon Betances Hospital-Mayaguez Medical Center/Ponce School of Medicine Consortium Program
Sponsor: Dr Ramon E Betances Hospital-Mayaguez Medical Center
Advanced Cardiology Center Corp/Ponce SOM Consortium
Prgm Director: Milton D Carrero, MD
410 Hostos Avenue
Mayaguez, PR 00681
Tel: 787 833-3695   *Fax:* 787 833-9060
E-mail: MiltonDCarrero@aol.com
Length: 3 Yrs   *ACGME Approved/Offered Positions:* 15
Program ID: 140-42-31-525

Ponce

Damas Hospital/Ponce School of Medicine Program
Sponsor: Damas Hospital
Prgm Director: Miguel A Magraner, MD*
Medical Education, Edif Parra
2225 Ponce BYP, Ste 407
Ponce, PR 00717
Tel: 787 840-8686   *Fax:* 787 984-2986
E-mail: damasmed@coqui.net
Length: 3 Yrs   *ACGME Approved/Offered Positions:* 21
Program ID: 140-42-11-453

Hospital Episcopal San Lucas/Ponce School of Medicine Program
Sponsor: Hospital Episcopal San Lucas
Playa Medical Center
Ponce School of Medicine
Prgm Director: Orlando L Vazquez-Torres, MD
Department of Medicine
PO Box 336810
Ponce, PR 00733
Tel: 787 844-1271   *Fax:* 787 844-1271
E-mail: imresidency@hotmail.com
Length: 3 Yrs   *ACGME Approved/Offered Positions:* 18
Program ID: 140-42-11-395

San German

Hospital de la Concepcion Program
Sponsor: Hospital de la Concepcion
Prgm Director: Francisco Jaume, MD
Oficina Educacion Medica
PO Box 285
San German, PR 00683
Tel: 787 892-1860   *Fax:* 787 264-7916
E-mail: resmedica@hospitalconcepcion.org
Length: 3 Yrs   *ACGME Approved/Offered Positions:* 15
Program ID: 140-42-21-488

San Juan

San Juan City Hospital Program
Sponsor: San Juan City Hospital
Prgm Director: Maria de Lourdes Miranda, MD
PMB 79
PO Box 70344
San Juan, PR 00936
Tel: 787 766-2222   *Fax:* 787 765-5147
Length: 3 Yrs   *ACGME Approved/Offered Positions:* 30
Program ID: 140-42-11-396

University of Puerto Rico Program
Sponsor: University of Puerto Rico School of Medicine
University Hospital
University of Puerto Rico Hospital at Carolina
Prgm Director: Carlos A Gonzalez-Oppenheimer, MD
Internal Medicine Residency Program
Box 365067
San Juan, PR 00936
Tel: 787 759-8252   *Fax:* 787 754-1739
E-mail: glcolon@rcm.upr.edu
Length: 3 Yrs   *ACGME Approved/Offered Positions:* 49
Program ID: 140-42-21-397

VA Caribbean Healthcare System Program
Sponsor: VA Caribbean Healthcare System
University Hospital
Prgm Director: Jose J Gutierrez-Nunez, MD
Medical Service (111)
10 Casia Street
San Juan, PR 00921
Tel: 787 641-3669   *Fax:* 787 641-4561
E-mail: gutiej@aol.com
Length: 3 Yrs   *ACGME Approved/Offered Positions:* 62
Program ID: 140-42-31-398

Rhode Island

Pawtucket

Memorial Hospital of Rhode Island/Brown University Program
Sponsor: Memorial Hospital of Rhode Island
Prgm Director: Eleanor Summerhill, MD
Department of Medicine
111 Brewster Street
Pawtucket, RI 02860
Tel: 401 729-2221   *Fax:* 401 729-2202
E-mail: im@mhri.org
Length: 3 Yrs   *ACGME Approved/Offered Positions:* 32
Program ID: 140-43-21-473

Providence

Brown University Program
Sponsor: Rhode Island Hospital-Lifespan
Miriam Hospital-Lifespan
Prgm Director: Dominick Tammaro, MD*
Department of Medicine
593 Eddy Street
Providence, RI 02902
Tel: 401 444-4083   *Fax:* 401 444-3056
E-mail: imrp_rih@brown.edu
Length: 3 Yrs   *ACGME Approved/Offered Positions:* 132
Program ID: 140-43-11-400

Roger Williams Medical Center Program
Sponsor: Roger Williams Medical Center
Prgm Director: Alan B Weitberg, MD
Department of Medicine
825 Chalkstone Avenue
Providence, RI 02908
Tel: 401 456-2070   *Fax:* 401 456-2016
Length: 3 Yrs   *ACGME Approved/Offered Positions:* 43
Program ID: 140-43-31-401

South Carolina

Charleston

Medical University of South Carolina Program
Sponsor: Medical University of South Carolina College of
   Medicine
MUSC Medical Center
Ralph H Johnson VA Medical Center (Charleston)
Prgm Director: E Benjamin Clyburn, MD
Department of Internal Medicine
96 Jonathan Lucas Street, PO Box 250623
Charleston, SC 29425
Tel: 843 792-4074   *Fax:* 843 792-0448
E-mail: resmed@musc.edu
Length: 3 Yrs   *ACGME Approved/Offered Positions:* 85
Program ID: 140-45-21-403

Columbia

Palmetto Health/University of South Carolina School of Medicine Program
Sponsor: Palmetto Health
Palmetto Health Richland
William Jennings Bryan Dorn Veterans Hospital
Prgm Director: Stephen H Greenberg, MD
USC School of Medicine
Two Medical Park, Suite 502
Columbia, SC 29203
Tel: 803 540-1090   *Fax:* 803 540-1050
E-mail: astevens@gw.mp.sc.edu
Length: 3 Yrs   *ACGME Approved/Offered Positions:* 38
Program ID: 140-45-21-404

Greenville

Greenville Hospital System/University of South Carolina School of Medicine Program
Sponsor: Greenville Hospital System/University of South
   Carolina
Prgm Director: Bruce B Latham, MD
Department of Internal Medicine
701 Grove Road
Greenville, SC 29605
Tel: 864 455-7882   *Fax:* 864 455-5008
E-mail: kstone@ghs.org
Length: 3 Yrs   *ACGME Approved/Offered Positions:* 34
Program ID: 140-45-11-405

Note: * indicates a newly appointed program director

South Dakota

Sioux Falls

University of South Dakota Program
Sponsor: University of South Dakota School of Medicine
Avera McKennan Hospital and University Health Center
Royal C Johnson Veterans Affairs Medical Center
Sioux Valley Hospital University of SD Medical Center
Prgm Director: Turi A McNamee, MD*
Department of Medicine
1400 W 22nd Street
Sioux Falls, SD 57105
Tel: 605 357-1352   *Fax:* 605 357-1365
Length: 3 Yrs   *ACGME Approved/Offered Positions:* 26
Program ID: 140-46-21-406

Tennessee

Chattanooga

University of Tennessee College of Medicine at Chattanooga Program
Sponsor: University of Tennessee College of
   Medicine-Chattanooga
Erlanger Medical Center
Prgm Director: Lisa J Staton, MD*
975 East Third Street
Box 94
Chattanooga, TN 37403
Tel: 423 778-2998   *Fax:* 423 778-2611
Length: 3 Yrs   *ACGME Approved/Offered Positions:* 30
Program ID: 140-47-11-407

Johnson City

East Tennessee State University Program
Sponsor: James H Quillen College of Medicine
Johnson City Medical Center/Mountain States Health
   Alliance
Veterans Affairs Medical Center (Mountain Home)
Wellmont Health System - Holston Valley
Prgm Director: Stephen Loyd, MD*
Internal Medicine
Box 70622
Johnson City, TN 37614
Tel: 423 439-8082   *Fax:* 423 439-6386
E-mail: loyds@etsu.edu
Length: 3 Yrs   *ACGME Approved/Offered Positions:* 79
Program ID: 140-47-21-408

Knoxville

University of Tennessee Medical Center at Knoxville Program
Sponsor: University of Tennessee Graduate School of
   Medicine
University of Tennessee Memorial Hospital
Prgm Director: Mark S Rasnake, MD*
1924 Alcoa Highway
Knoxville, TN 37920
Tel: 865 305-9340   *Fax:* 865 305-6849
Length: 3 Yrs   *ACGME Approved/Offered Positions:* 27
Program ID: 140-47-11-409

Memphis

University of Tennessee Program
Sponsor: University of Tennessee College of Medicine
Methodist Healthcare - Memphis Hospitals
Regional Medical Center at Memphis
Veterans Affairs Medical Center (Memphis)
Prgm Director: Kim M Huch, MD*
Department of Medicine
956 Court Avenue, Room H314
Memphis, TN 38103
Tel: 901 448-5814   *Fax:* 901 448-7836
Length: 3 Yrs   *ACGME Approved/Offered Positions:* 104
Program ID: 140-47-21-412

Nashville

Meharry Medical College Program
Sponsor: Meharry Medical College School of Medicine
Alvin C York Veterans Affairs Medical Center
Metropolitan Nashville General Hospital
Prgm Director: David S Trochtenberg, MD, MS
Department of Medicine
1005 Dr D B Todd Jr, Blvd
Nashville, TN 37208
Tel: 615 327-5825   *Fax:* 615 327-6417
E-mail: dtrochtenberg@mmc.edu
Length: 3 Yrs   *ACGME Approved/Offered Positions:* 36
Program ID: 140-47-11-413

University of Tennessee (Nashville) Program
Sponsor: University of Tennessee College of Medicine
Baptist Hospital
Prgm Director: Tracey E Doering, MD
Department of Medicine, Box 94
2000 Church Street
Nashville, TN 37236
Tel: 615 284-5663   *Fax:* 615 284-5984
E-mail: tracey.doering@baptisthospital.com
Length: 3 Yrs   *ACGME Approved/Offered Positions:* 16
Program ID: 140-47-21-478

Vanderbilt University Program
Sponsor: Vanderbilt University Medical Center
Veterans Affairs Medical Center (Nashville)
Prgm Director: John S Sergent, MD
D-3100 Medical Center N
21st and Garland Streets
Nashville, TN 37232
Tel: 615 322-2036   *Fax:* 615 343-6119
Length: 3 Yrs   *ACGME Approved/Offered Positions:* 115
Program ID: 140-47-31-414

Texas

Amarillo

Texas Tech University (Amarillo) Program
Sponsor: Texas Tech University Health Sciences Center
   at Amarillo
Northwest Texas Health Care System
Veterans Affairs Medical Center (Amarillo)
Prgm Director: Brian C Weis, MD, PhD
1400 Coulter
Amarillo, TX 79106
Tel: 806 354-5489   *Fax:* 806 354-5765
E-mail: Brian.Weis@ttuhsc.edu
Length: 3 Yrs   *ACGME Approved/Offered Positions:* 37
Program ID: 140-48-21-477

Austin

University of Texas Medical Branch (Austin) Program
Sponsor: University of Texas Medical Branch Hospitals
University Medical Center at Brackenridge
Central Texas Veterans Hlth Care System Facilities
   (Austin)
Prgm Director: Beth W Miller, MD
Brackenridge Annex - 601 E 15th Street
Austin, TX 78701
Tel: 512 324-7889   *Fax:* 512 477-8933
Length: 3 Yrs   *ACGME Approved/Offered Positions:* 49
Program ID: 140-48-12-415

Dallas

Baylor University Medical Center Program
Sponsor: Baylor University Medical Center
Prgm Director: Michael Emmett, MD
Department of Medicine
3500 Gaston Avenue, H-102
Dallas, TX 75246
Tel: 214 820-6202   *Fax:* 214 820-6385
E-mail: bumcimre@baylorhealth.edu
Length: 3 Yrs   *ACGME Approved/Offered Positions:* 30
Program ID: 140-48-31-416

Methodist Health System Dallas Program
Sponsor: Methodist Health System Dallas
Prgm Director: Leigh K Hunter, MD
Department of Medicine
PO Box 655999
Dallas, TX 75265
Tel: 214 947-2306   *Fax:* 214 947-2358
E-mail: amypark@mhd.com
Length: 3 Yrs   *ACGME Approved/Offered Positions:* 27
Program ID: 140-48-12-417

Texas Health Presbyterian Dallas Program
Sponsor: Texas Health Presbyterian Dallas
Prgm Director: Mark Feldman, MD
Department of Internal Medicine
8200 Walnut Hill Lane
Dallas, TX 75231
Tel: 214 345-7881   *Fax:* 214 345-5167
E-mail: graceannbodin@texashealth.org
Length: 3 Yrs   *ACGME Approved/Offered Positions:* 24
Program ID: 140-48-11-420

University of Texas Southwestern Medical School Program
Sponsor: University of Texas Southwestern Medical
    School
Dallas County Hospital District-Parkland Memorial
    Hospital
Dallas VA Medical Center
University Hospitals St Paul
Prgm Director: Carol L Croft, MD
Department of Medicine
5323 Harry Hines Blvd
Dallas, TX 75390
Tel: 214 648-9511   *Fax:* 214 648-7550
Length: 3 Yrs   *ACGME Approved/Offered Positions:* 161
Program ID: 140-48-21-419

El Paso

Texas Tech University Health Sciences Center Paul L Foster School of Medicine Program
Sponsor: Texas Tech University Hlth Sci Ctr Paul L
    Foster Sch of Med
R E Thomason General Hospital / Texas Tech University
    HSC
Prgm Director: Armando D Meza, MD
4800 Alberta Avenue
El Paso, TX 79905
Tel: 915 545-6626
Length: 3 Yrs   *ACGME Approved/Offered Positions:* 45
Program ID: 140-48-11-424

William Beaumont Army Medical Center Program
Sponsor: William Beaumont Army Medical Center
Prgm Director: Kent J DeZee, MD, MPH
Department of Medicine
5005 N Piedras Street
El Paso, TX 79920
Tel: 915 569-3397   *Fax:* 915 569-1943
E-mail: kent.dezee@amedd.army.mil
Length: 3 Yrs   *ACGME Approved/Offered Positions:* 27
Program ID: 140-48-12-008
Uniformed Services Program

Galveston

University of Texas Medical Branch Hospitals Program
Sponsor: University of Texas Medical Branch Hospitals
Prgm Director: Richard W Goodgame, MD*
Department of Medicine
301 University Blvd
Galveston, TX 77550
Tel: 409 772-2263   *Fax:* 409 772-5462
E-mail: rwgoodga@utmb.edu
Length: 3 Yrs   *ACGME Approved/Offered Positions:* 92
Program ID: 140-48-21-421

Harlingen

University of Texas Health Science Center at San Antonio Lower Rio Grande Valley RAHC Program
Sponsor: University of Texas School of Medicine at San
    Antonio
Valley Baptist Medical Center
Prgm Director: James F Hanley, MD
Rio Grande Valley Regional Academic Health Center
2102 Treasure Hills Blvd
Harlingen, TX 78550
Tel: 956 365-8807   *Fax:* 956 365-8806
E-mail: RAHCResidency@uthscsa.edu
Length: 3 Yrs   *ACGME Approved/Offered Positions:* 15
Program ID: 140-48-21-524

Houston

Baylor College of Medicine Program
Sponsor: Baylor College of Medicine
Prgm Director: Richard J Hamill, MD
Department of Medicine - BCM 620
1709 Dryden Road, Suite 550
Houston, TX 77030
Tel: 713 798-0206   *Fax:* 713 798-0207
Length: 3 Yrs   *ACGME Approved/Offered Positions:* 150
Program ID: 140-48-21-422

Methodist Hospital Program
Sponsor: Methodist Hospital (Houston)
Prgm Director: Jose A Perez Jr, MD, MBA
6550 Fannin St, SM 1001
Houston, TX 77030
Tel: 713 441-6729   *Fax:* 713 790-3026
Length: 3 Yrs   *ACGME Approved/Offered Positions:* 30
Program ID: 140-48-13-534

University of Texas at Houston Program
Sponsor: University of Texas Health Science Center at
    Houston
Lyndon B Johnson General Hospital
Memorial Hermann Hospital
Prgm Director: Mark A Farnie, MD
Department of Medicine
6431 Fannin St, MSB 1.134
Houston, TX 77030
Tel: 713 500-6525   *Fax:* 713 500-6530
E-mail: vera.s.jones@uth.tmc.edu
Length: 3 Yrs   *ACGME Approved/Offered Positions:* 125
Program ID: 140-48-31-423

Lackland AFB

San Antonio Uniformed Services Health Education Consortium Program
Sponsor: San Antonio Uniformed Services Health
    Education Consortium
Brooke Army Medical Center
Wilford Hall Medical Center (AETC)
Prgm Director: William N Hannah Jr, MD*
Department of Medicine MCHE-MDX
3851 Roger Brooke Drive
Fort Sam Houston, TX 78234
Tel: 210 916-3856   *Fax:* 210 916-4721
E-mail: Carmen.Vargas@amedd.army.mil
Length: 3 Yrs   *ACGME Approved/Offered Positions:* 96
Program ID: 140-48-12-009
Uniformed Services Program

Lubbock

Texas Tech University (Lubbock) Program
Sponsor: Texas Tech University Health Sciences Center
    at Lubbock
University Medical Center
Prgm Director: Kenneth M Nugent, MD
Department of Internal Medicine
3601 Fourth Street
Lubbock, TX 79430
Tel: 806 743-3155   *Fax:* 806 743-3143
E-mail: brandi.mckinnon@ttuhsc.edu
Length: 3 Yrs   *ACGME Approved/Offered Positions:* 34
Program ID: 140-48-21-459

Odessa

Texas Tech University (Permian Basin) Program
Sponsor: Texas Tech University Health Sciences Center
    (Permian Basin)
Medical Center Hospital
Midland Memorial Hospital
Prgm Director: James K Burks, MD
701 W 5th Street
Odessa, TX 79763
Tel: 432 335-5250   *Fax:* 432 335-5262
E-mail: james.burks@ttuhsc.edu
Length: 3 Yrs   *ACGME Approved/Offered Positions:* 36
Program ID: 140-48-21-519

San Antonio

University of Texas Health Science Center at San Antonio Program
Sponsor: University of Texas School of Medicine at San
    Antonio
Audie L Murphy Memorial Veterans Hospital (San
    Antonio)
University Health System
Prgm Director: George E Crawford, MD
Department of Medicine
7703 Floyd Curl Drive MC 7871
San Antonio, TX 78229
Tel: 210 567-6685   *Fax:* 210 567-1739
E-mail: crawfordg@uthscsa.edu
Length: 3 Yrs   *ACGME Approved/Offered Positions:* 98
Program ID: 140-48-21-425

Temple

Texas A&M College of Medicine-Scott and White Program
Sponsor: Scott and White Memorial Hospital
Prgm Director: John D Myers, MD*
Department of Medicine
2401 S 31st Street
Temple, TX 76508
Tel: 254 724-2364   *Fax:* 254 724-4709
E-mail: bedwards@swmail.sw.org
Length: 3 Yrs   *ACGME Approved/Offered Positions:* 54
Program ID: 140-48-21-426

Utah

Salt Lake City

University of Utah Program
Sponsor: University of Utah Medical Center
LDS Hospital
Veterans Affairs Medical Center (Salt Lake City)
Prgm Director: Caroline K Milne, MD
Department of Internal Medicine
30 North 1900 East, 4C104
Salt Lake City, UT 84132
Tel: 801 581-7899   *Fax:* 801 585-0418
E-mail: improg.dir@hsc.utah.edu
Length: 3 Yrs   *ACGME Approved/Offered Positions:* 109
Program ID: 140-49-21-427

Vermont

Burlington

University of Vermont Program
Sponsor: Fletcher Allen Health Care
Prgm Director: Mark Levine, MD
Department of Medicine
111 Colchester Ave, Smith 244
Burlington, VT 05401
Tel: 802 847-4959   *Fax:* 802 847-5927
Length: 3 Yrs   *ACGME Approved/Offered Positions:* 44
Program ID: 140-50-21-429

Virginia

Charlottesville

University of Virginia Program
Sponsor: University of Virginia Medical Center
Prgm Director: Gerald R Donowitz, MD
PO Box 800696
Room 6558, Outpatient Clinics West, Hospital Drive
Charlottesville, VA 22908
Tel: 434 924-1918   *Fax:* 434 243-0399
E-mail: grd@virginia.edu
Length: 3 Yrs   *ACGME Approved/Offered Positions:* 101
Program ID: 140-51-21-430

Norfolk

Eastern Virginia Medical School Program
Sponsor: Eastern Virginia Medical School
DePaul Medical Center
Sentara Norfolk General Hospital
Veterans Affairs Medical Center (Hampton)
Prgm Director: David J Castaldo, MD
Hofheimer Hall
825 Fairfax Avenue, Suite 410
Norfolk, VA 23507
Tel: 757 446-8910   *Fax:* 757 446-7921
E-mail: intmedres@evms.edu
Length: 3 Yrs   *ACGME Approved/Offered Positions:* 56
Program ID: 140-51-21-432

Portsmouth

Naval Medical Center (Portsmouth) Program
Sponsor: Naval Medical Center (Portsmouth)
Prgm Director: Lisa S Inouye, MD, MPH
Charette Health Care Center
620 John Paul Jones Circle
Portsmouth, VA 23708
Tel: 757 953-2268   *Fax:* 757 953-9666
E-mail: lisa.inouye@med.navy.mil
Length: 3 Yrs   *ACGME Approved/Offered Positions:* 40
Program ID: 140-51-11-014
Uniformed Services Program

Richmond

Virginia Commonwealth University Health System Program
Sponsor: Virginia Commonwealth University Health System
Hunter Holmes McGuire VA Medical Center (Richmond)
Medical College of Virginia Hospitals
Prgm Director: Stephanie A Call, MD, MSPH
Dept of Internal Med, West Hospital, Rm 6-202
1200 East Broad Street, PO Box 980509
Richmond, VA 23298
Tel: 804 828-9726   *Fax:* 804 828-4926
E-mail: imea@vcu.edu
Length: 3 Yrs   *ACGME Approved/Offered Positions:* 111
Program ID: 140-51-21-433

Roanoke

Carilion Clinic Program
Sponsor: Carilion Clinic
Veterans Affairs Medical Center (Salem)
Prgm Director: Jon M Sweet, MD
Department of Medicine
PO Box 13367
Roanoke, VA 24033
Tel: 540 981-7120   *Fax:* 540 983-1133
E-mail: imresidency@carilion.com
Length: 3 Yrs   *ACGME Approved/Offered Positions:* 47
Program ID: 140-51-31-431

Washington

Seattle

University of Washington Program
Sponsor: University of Washington School of Medicine
Harborview Medical Center
University of Washington Medical Center
VA Puget Sound Health Care System
Veterans Affairs Medical Center (Boise)
Prgm Director: Kenneth P Steinberg, MD
Department of Medicine
Box 356421
Seattle, WA 98195
Tel: 206 543-3605   *Fax:* 206 685-8652
E-mail: medres@u.washington.edu
Length: 3 Yrs   *ACGME Approved/Offered Positions:* 174
Program ID: 140-54-21-434

Virginia Mason Medical Center Program
Sponsor: Virginia Mason Medical Center
Prgm Director: Alvin S Calderon, MD, PhD
925 Seneca Street, Mailstop H8-GME
Seattle, WA 98101
Tel: 206 583-6079   *Fax:* 206 583-2307
Length: 3 Yrs   *ACGME Approved/Offered Positions:* 36
Program ID: 140-54-12-435

Spokane

Spokane Medical Centers/University of Washington School of Medicine Program
Sponsor: Inland Empire Hospital Services Association
Deaconess Medical Center
Sacred Heart Medical Center
Prgm Director: Judy A Benson, MD
West 101-8th Avenue
PO Box 2555
Spokane, WA 99220
Tel: 509 474-3022   *Fax:* 509 474-5316
E-mail: yaegert@intmedspokane.org
Length: 3 Yrs   *ACGME Approved/Offered Positions:* 22
Program ID: 140-54-31-436

Tacoma

Madigan Army Medical Center Program
Sponsor: Madigan Army Medical Center
Prgm Director: Cecily K Peterson, MD
Department of Medicine
9040 Jackson Ave
Tacoma, WA 98431
Tel: 253 968-0208   *Fax:* 253 968-1168
E-mail: cecily.peterson@us.army.mil
Length: 3 Yrs   *ACGME Approved/Offered Positions:* 33
Program ID: 140-54-12-010
Uniformed Services Program

West Virginia

Charleston

Charleston Area Medical Center/West Virginia University (Charleston Division) Program
Sponsor: Charleston Area Medical Center/West Virginia University
Prgm Director: Greg D Clarke, MD
3110 Mac Corkle Avenue
Charleston, WV 25304
Tel: 304 347-1220   *Fax:* 304 347-1344
Length: 3 Yrs   *ACGME Approved/Offered Positions:* 34
Program ID: 140-55-11-438

Huntington

Marshall University School of Medicine Program
Sponsor: Marshall University School of Medicine
Cabell Huntington Hospital
St Mary's Hospital
Veterans Affairs Medical Center (Huntington)
Prgm Director: Larry D Dial Jr, MD*
Department of Medicine
1249 15th Street, Suite 2000
Huntington, WV 25701
Tel: 304 691-1084
E-mail: muimres@marshall.edu
Length: 3 Yrs   *ACGME Approved/Offered Positions:* 44
Program ID: 140-55-21-439

Morgantown

West Virginia University Program
Sponsor: West Virginia University School of Medicine
West Virginia University Hospitals
Prgm Director: Michelle A Nuss, MD
RCB Health Sciences Ctr
1 Medical Ctr Dr, PO Box 9168
Morgantown, WV 26506
Tel: 304 293-4239   *Fax:* 304 293-3651
E-mail: chenry@hsc.wvu.edu
Length: 3 Yrs   *ACGME Approved/Offered Positions:* 59
Program ID: 140-55-11-440

Note: * indicates a newly appointed program director

Wisconsin

La Crosse

Gundersen Lutheran Medical Foundation Program

Sponsor: Gundersen Lutheran Medical Foundation
Gundersen Clinic Ltd
Gundersen Lutheran Medical Center
Prgm Director: Steven B Pearson, MD
Lutheran Hospital-LaCrosse
1836 South Avenue/C03-006A
La Crosse, WI 54601
Tel: 608 775-2923   *Fax:* 608 775-1548
Length: 3 Yrs   *ACGME Approved/Offered Positions:* 24
Program ID: 140-56-12-442

Madison

University of Wisconsin Program

Sponsor: University of Wisconsin Hospital and Clinics
William S Middleton Veterans Hospital
Prgm Director: Bennett Vogelman, MD
J5/230 CSC-2454
600 Highland Avenue
Madison, WI 53792
Tel: 608 263-7352   *Fax:* 608 262-6743
E-mail: bsv@medicine.wisc.edu
Length: 3 Yrs   *ACGME Approved/Offered Positions:* 85
Program ID: 140-56-21-443

Marshfield

Marshfield Clinic-St Joseph's Hospital Program

Sponsor: Marshfield Clinic-St Joseph's Hospital
Prgm Director: Mark R Hennick, MD
Department of Medicine
1000 N Oak Ave
Marshfield, WI 54449
Tel: 715 387-5260   *Fax:* 715 387-5163
E-mail: hennick.mark@marshfieldclinic.org
Length: 3 Yrs   *ACGME Approved/Offered Positions:* 18
Program ID: 140-56-31-444

Milwaukee

Aurora Health Care Program

Sponsor: Aurora Health Care
Aurora Sinai Medical Center
St Luke's Medical Center
Prgm Director: Mark A Gennis, MD
Aurora Sinai Medical Center
945 N 12th St, PO Box 342
Milwaukee, WI 53201
Tel: 414 219-7635   *Fax:* 414 219-4539
E-mail: rebecca.young@aurora.org
Length: 3 Yrs   *ACGME Approved/Offered Positions:* 39
Program ID: 140-56-21-446

Medical College of Wisconsin Affiliated Hospitals Program

Sponsor: Medical College of Wisconsin Affiliated
   Hospitals, Inc
Clement J Zablocki Veterans Affairs Medical Center
Froedtert Memorial Lutheran Hospital
Prgm Director: Michael Frank, MD
Department of Medicine/CLCC 5113
9200 W Wisconsin Avenue
Milwaukee, WI 53226
Tel: 414 805-0531   *Fax:* 414 805-0535
E-mail: immcw@mcw.edu
Length: 3 Yrs   *ACGME Approved/Offered Positions:* 99
Program ID: 140-56-31-445

Internal Medicine/Pediatrics

Alabama

Birmingham

University of Alabama Medical Center Program

Sponsor: University of Alabama Hospital
Children's Hospital of Alabama
Prgm Director: Jason R Hartig, MD
1600 7th Avenue South
Bldg ACC604
Birmingham, AL 35233
Tel: 205 934-0669   *Fax:* 205 975-6403
Length: 4 Yrs   *ACGME Approved/Offered Positions:* 16
Program ID: 700-01-32-115

Mobile

University of South Alabama Program

Sponsor: University of South Alabama Hospitals
University of South Alabama Medical Center
USA Children's and Women's Hospital
Prgm Director: Judy Blair-Elortegui, MD
Medicine-Pediatrics Residency Program
1700 Center Street
Mobile, AL 36604
Tel: 251 415-1087   *Fax:* 251 415-1387
E-mail: dhcobb@jaguar1.usouthal.edu
Length: 4 Yrs   *ACGME Approved/Offered Positions:* 11
Program ID: 700-01-32-085

Arizona

Phoenix

Banner Good Samaritan Medical Center Program

Sponsor: Banner Good Samaritan Medical Center
Carl T Hayden VA Medical Center
Maricopa Medical Center
Phoenix Children's Hospital
Prgm Director: Donna L Holland, MD
Dept of Medicine
1111 E McDowell Rd
Phoenix, AZ 85006
Tel: 602 239-2296   *Fax:* 602 239-2084
Length: 4 Yrs   *ACGME Approved/Offered Positions:* 24
Program ID: 700-03-14-001

Arkansas

Little Rock

University of Arkansas for Medical Sciences Program

Sponsor: University of Arkansas College of Medicine
Arkansas Children's Hospital
Central Arkansas Veterans Healthcare System
UAMS Medical Center
Prgm Director: Robert H Hopkins Jr, MD
4301 W Markham St
Internal Medicine Residency Office, #634
Little Rock, AR 72205
Tel: 501 686-5162   *Fax:* 501 686-6001
E-mail: imresident@uams.edu
Length: 4 Yrs   *ACGME Approved/Offered Positions:* 19
Program ID: 700-04-14-002

California

Loma Linda

Loma Linda University Program

Sponsor: Loma Linda University Medical Center
Jerry L Pettis Memorial Veterans Hospital
Riverside County Regional Medical Center
Prgm Director: Sonny Lee, MD*
Int Med/Peds Combined Program
PO Box 2000
Loma Linda, CA 92354
Tel: 909 558-4174
E-mail: MedPeds@llu.edu
Length: 4 Yrs   *ACGME Approved/Offered Positions:* 16
Program ID: 700-05-32-003

Los Angeles

UCLA Medical Center Program

Sponsor: UCLA David Geffen School of Medicine/UCLA
   Medical Center
UCLA Medical Center
Prgm Director: Alice Kuo, MD, PhD
757 Westwood Plaza
Suite 7501
Los Angeles, CA 90024
Tel: 310 794-2583   *Fax:* 310 312-9210
Length: 4 Yrs   *ACGME Approved/Offered Positions:* 16
Program ID: 700-05-32-130

University of Southern California/ LAC+USC Medical Center Program

Sponsor: University of Southern California/LAC+USC
   Medical Center
LAC+USC Medical Center
Prgm Director: Breck R Nichols, MD, MPH
Women's and Children's Hospital
1240 N Mission Road, Rm L-902
Los Angeles, CA 90033
Tel: 323 226-3691   *Fax:* 323 226-4380
E-mail: brn@usc.edu
Length: 4 Yrs   *ACGME Approved/Offered Positions:* 24
Program ID: 700-05-32-005

San Diego

University of California (San Diego) Program

Sponsor: University of California (San Diego) Medical
   Center
Rady Children's Hospital
Veterans Affairs Medical Center (San Diego)
Prgm Director: Lori Wan, MD
Combined Med/Peds
200 W Arbor Dr #8425
San Diego, CA 92103
Tel: 619 471-0434   *Fax:* 619 543-6529
E-mail: heejinkim@ucsd.edu
Length: 4 Yrs   *ACGME Approved/Offered Positions:* 16
Program ID: 700-05-14-099

Connecticut

New Haven

Yale-New Haven Medical Center Program

Sponsor: Yale-New Haven Hospital
Prgm Director: Benjamin R Doolittle, MD, MDiv*
PO Box 208086
New Haven, CT 06520
Tel: 203 785-7941   *Fax:* 203 785-7030
Length: 4 Yrs   *ACGME Approved/Offered Positions:* 16
Program ID: 700-08-14-127

Programs

Delaware

Wilmington

Jefferson Medical College/Christiana Care Health Services Program
Sponsor: Jefferson Medical College
Christiana Care Health Services Inc
Alfred I duPont Hospital for Children
Prgm Director: Allen R Friedland, MD
4755 Ogletown-Stanton Rd
PO Box 6001, Room 4B00
Newark, DE 19718
Tel: 302 733-2313   *Fax:* 302 733-4339
Length: 4 Yrs   *ACGME Approved/Offered Positions:* 24
Program ID: 700-09-14-009

District of Columbia

Washington

Georgetown University Hospital Program
Sponsor: Georgetown University Hospital
Virginia Hospital Center-Arlington
Prgm Director: Amy L Burke, MD, MPH
3800 Reservoir Rd NW
5th Floor PHC Building
Washington, DC 20007
Tel: 202 444-6239   *Fax:* 202 444-5208
E-mail: burkeal@gunet.georgetown.edu
Length: 4 Yrs   *ACGME Approved/Offered Positions:* 16
Program ID: 700-10-14-129

Florida

Miami

Jackson Memorial Hospital/Jackson Health System Program
Sponsor: Jackson Memorial Hospital/Jackson Health System
Prgm Director: Stefanie R Brown, MD*
1611 NW 12th Avenue
Central 600
Miami, FL 33136
Tel: 305 585-5954   *Fax:* 305 585-7381
Length: 4 Yrs   *ACGME Approved/Offered Positions:* 17
Program ID: 700-11-14-086

Tampa

University of South Florida Program
Sponsor: University of South Florida College of Medicine
All Children's Hospital
James A Haley Veterans Hospital
Tampa General Hospital
Prgm Director: Lynn Ringenberg, MD
USF Health South Tampa Center
2 Tampa General Circle, Suite 5008
Tampa, FL 33606
Tel: 813 259-8752   *Fax:* 813 259-8749
E-mail: lringenb@health.usf.edu
Length: 4 Yrs   *ACGME Approved/Offered Positions:* 16
Program ID: 700-11-32-125

Illinois

Chicago

Rush University Medical Center Program
Sponsor: Rush University Medical Center
Prgm Director: James B McAuley, MD, MPH*
Rush Med-Peds Program
1653 West Congress Parkway
Chicago, IL 60612
Tel: 312 942-4071   *Fax:* 312 942-4168
Length: 4 Yrs   *ACGME Approved/Offered Positions:* 16
Program ID: 700-16-32-103

University of Chicago Program
Sponsor: University of Chicago Medical Center
Prgm Director: Rita M Rossi-Foulkes, MD, MS
5841 South Maryland Ave MC7082
Chicago, IL 60637
Tel: 773 702-0309   *Fax:* 773 702-2230
E-mail: rrossifo@medicine.bsd.uchicago.edu
Length: 4 Yrs   *ACGME Approved/Offered Positions:* 16
Program ID: 700-16-14-012

University of Illinois College of Medicine at Chicago Program
Sponsor: University of Illinois College of Medicine at Chicago
University of Illinois Hospital and Clinics
Prgm Director: Saul J Weiner, MD
840 S Wood St
M/C 856
Chicago, IL 60612
Tel: 312 413-5454   *Fax:* 312 413-8283
E-mail: cbrown@uic.edu
Length: 4 Yrs   *ACGME Approved/Offered Positions:* 16
Program ID: 700-16-14-013

Maywood

Loyola University Program
Sponsor: Loyola University Medical Center
Edward Hines, Jr Veterans Affairs Hospital
Prgm Director: Gregory Ozark, MD
2160 S First Ave
Bldg 101, Room 1740
Maywood, IL 60153
Tel: 708 216-3151   *Fax:* 708 216-9033
E-mail: MedPEDSresidencyLUMC@lumc.edu
Length: 4 Yrs   *ACGME Approved/Offered Positions:* 16
Program ID: 700-16-14-014

Peoria

University of Illinois College of Medicine at Peoria Program
Sponsor: University of Illinois College of Medicine at Peoria
OSF St Francis Medical Center
Prgm Director: Christina B Nulty, MD
OSF Saint Francis Med Ctr
530 NE Glen Oak Ave
Peoria, IL 61637
Tel: 309 655-3863   *Fax:* 309 655-4161
E-mail: cnulty@uic.edu
Length: 4 Yrs   *ACGME Approved/Offered Positions:* 32
Program ID: 700-16-32-015

Indiana

Indianapolis

Indiana University School of Medicine Program
Sponsor: Indiana University School of Medicine
Clarian Indiana University Hospital
Clarian Methodist Hospital of Indiana
Clarian Riley Hospital for Children
Richard L Roudebush Veterans Affairs Medical Center
William N Wishard Memorial Hospital
Prgm Director: Alexander M Djuricich, MD
702 Barnhill Dr/Rm 5867
Indianapolis, IN 46202
Tel: 317 274-4034   *Fax:* 317 274-1476
E-mail: mprp@iupui.edu
Length: 4 Yrs   *ACGME Approved/Offered Positions:* 56
Program ID: 700-17-14-018

Kansas

Wichita

University of Kansas (Wichita) Program
Sponsor: University of Kansas School of Medicine (Wichita)
Veterans Affairs Medical Center (Wichita)
Via Christi Regional Medical Center-St Francis
Wesley Medical Center
Prgm Director: Katherine J Melhorn, MD
1010 North Kansas
Wichita, KS 67214
Tel: 316 293-2631   *Fax:* 316 293-2689
E-mail: pediatrics@kumc.edu
Length: 4 Yrs   *ACGME Approved/Offered Positions:* 12
Program ID: 700-19-32-124

Kentucky

Lexington

University of Kentucky College of Medicine Program
Sponsor: University of Kentucky College of Medicine
University of Kentucky Hospital
Veterans Affairs Medical Center (Lexington)
Prgm Director: Christopher A Feddock, MD, MS
Kentucky Clinic Rm K506
740 S Limestone St
Lexington, KY 40536
Tel: 859 323-6561   *Fax:* 859 323-1197
E-mail: ukmedpeds@uky.edu
Length: 4 Yrs   *ACGME Approved/Offered Positions:* 24
Program ID: 700-20-14-019

Louisville

University of Louisville Program
Sponsor: University of Louisville School of Medicine
Kosair Children's Hospital (Norton Healthcare, Inc)
University of Louisville Hospital
Veterans Affairs Medical Center (Louisville)
Prgm Director: Christopher L Sweeney, MD*
Combined Internal Medicine/Pediatrics Residency
550 South Jackson Street A3K00
Louisville, KY 40202
Tel: 502 852-4277   *Fax:* 502 852-8980
E-mail: medpeds@louisville.edu
Length: 4 Yrs   *ACGME Approved/Offered Positions:* 20
Program ID: 700-20-32-020

Note: * indicates a newly appointed program director

Louisiana

New Orleans

Louisiana State University Program
Sponsor: Louisiana State University School of Medicine
Children's Hospital (New Orleans)
Medical Center of Louisiana at New Orleans
Ochsner Medical Center-Kenner
Prgm Director: Betty Lo-Blais, MD
2020 Gravier St
7th Floor Suite D box E7-20
New Orleans, LA 70112
Tel: 504 415-8498   *Fax:* 504 568-7884
E-mail: blo@lsuhsc.edu
Length: 4 Yrs   *ACGME Approved/Offered Positions:* 26
Program ID: 700-21-14-022

Tulane University Program
Sponsor: Tulane University School of Medicine
Medical Center of Louisiana at New Orleans
Ochsner Clinic Foundation
Tulane Hospital for Children
Tulane University Hospital and Clinics
Veterans Affairs Medical Center (New Orleans)
Prgm Director: Tracy L Conrad, DO
1430 Tulane Ave
Box SL 37
New Orleans, LA 70112
Tel: 504 988-5458   *Fax:* 504 988-6808
Length: 4 Yrs   *ACGME Approved/Offered Positions:* 24
Program ID: 700-21-32-023

Shreveport

Louisiana State University (Shreveport) Program
Sponsor: LSU Health Sciences Center-University
Hospital
Prgm Director: Pat F Bass III, MD, MS
Med Educ - Med/Peds
1501 Kings Hwy
Shreveport, LA 71130
Tel: 318 675-5940   *Fax:* 318 675-5958
E-mail: pmitch@lsuhsc.edu
Length: 4 Yrs   *ACGME Approved/Offered Positions:* 16
Program ID: 700-21-32-101

Maine

Portland

Maine Medical Center Program
Sponsor: Maine Medical Center
Prgm Director: Patrice M Thibodeau, MD
22 Bramhall Street
Portland, ME 04102
Tel: 207 662-2405   *Fax:* 207 662-6701
E-mail: medpeds@mmc.org
Length: 4 Yrs   *ACGME Approved/Offered Positions:* 12
Program ID: 700-22-32-128

Maryland

Baltimore

University of Maryland Program
Sponsor: University of Maryland Medical System
Veterans Affairs Medical Center (Baltimore)
Prgm Director: Susan D Wolfsthal, MD
22 S Greene St, Rm N3E09
Baltimore, MD 21201
Tel: 410 328-2388   *Fax:* 410 328-0267
Length: 4 Yrs   *ACGME Approved/Offered Positions:* 16
Program ID: 700-23-32-095

Massachusetts

Boston

Brigham and Women's Hospital/Children's Hospital/Harvard Medical School Program
Sponsor: Brigham and Women's Hospital
Children's Hospital
Prgm Director: Niraj Sharma, MD, MPH
75 Francis Street
Boston, MA 02115
Tel: 617 525-7278   *Fax:* 617 264-6346
E-mail: bwhresinfo@partners.org
Length: 4 Yrs   *ACGME Approved/Offered Positions:* 16
Program ID: 700-24-14-084

Massachusetts General Hospital/Harvard Medical School Program
Sponsor: Massachusetts General Hospital
Prgm Director: David Y Ting, MD
175 Cambridge St
5th Floor
Boston, MA 02114
Tel: 617 726-7782   *Fax:* 617 724-9068
Length: 4 Yrs   *ACGME Approved/Offered Positions:* 32
Program ID: 700-24-14-097

Springfield

Baystate Medical Center/Tufts University School of Medicine Program
Sponsor: Baystate Medical Center
Prgm Director: Samuel H Borden, MD
759 Chestnut St
Room S2580
Springfield, MA 01107
Tel: 413 794-3998   *Fax:* 413 794-4588
Length: 4 Yrs   *ACGME Approved/Offered Positions:* 32
Program ID: 700-24-32-024

Worcester

University of Massachusetts Program
Sponsor: University of Massachusetts Medical School
UMass Memorial Health Care (University Campus)
Prgm Director: John M Solomonides, MD
Dept of Pediatrics
55 Lake Ave N
Worcester, MA 01655
Tel: 508 856-3590   *Fax:* 508 856-3779
E-mail: gretchen.jones@umassmed.edu
Length: 4 Yrs   *ACGME Approved/Offered Positions:* 16
Program ID: 700-24-32-111

Michigan

Ann Arbor

University of Michigan Program
Sponsor: University of Michigan Hospitals and Health
Centers
Veterans Affairs Medical Center (Ann Arbor)
Prgm Director: Michael P Lukela, MD
3116 Taubman Ctr Box 5368
1500 E Medical Center Dr
Ann Arbor, MI 48109
Tel: 734 936-4385   *Fax:* 734 936-3654
E-mail: medpeds@umich.edu
Length: 4 Yrs   *ACGME Approved/Offered Positions:* 32
Program ID: 700-25-14-025

Detroit

Wayne State University Program
Sponsor: Wayne State University/Detroit Medical Center
Children's Hospital of Michigan
Detroit Receiving Hospital and University Health Center
Harper-Hutzel Hospital
Prgm Director: Renato Roxas Jr, MD
4201 St Antoine UHC 5C Box 258
Detroit, MI 48201
Tel: 313 577-4342
E-mail: medpeds@med.wayne.edu
Length: 4 Yrs   *ACGME Approved/Offered Positions:* 28
Program ID: 700-25-14-029

Flint

Hurley Medical Center/Michigan State University Program
Sponsor: Hurley Medical Center
Hamilton Community Health Network
Prgm Director: Laura A Carravallah, MD
Combined Internal Medicine/Pediatrics - 3AW
One Hurley Plaza
Flint, MI 48503
Tel: 810 257-9283   *Fax:* 810 257-9736
E-mail: lcarrav1@hurleymc.com
Length: 4 Yrs   *ACGME Approved/Offered Positions:* 16
Program ID: 700-25-32-030

Grand Rapids

Grand Rapids Medical Education and Research Center/Michigan State University Program
Sponsor: Grand Rapids Medical Education and Research
Center
Spectrum Health-Butterworth Hospital
Prgm Director: Richard A Switzer, MD
Suite 2200
Grand Rapids, MI 49503
Tel: 616 391-3776   *Fax:* 616 391-3130
Length: 4 Yrs   *ACGME Approved/Offered Positions:* 16
Program ID: 700-25-14-098

Kalamazoo

Kalamazoo Center for Medical Studies/Michigan State University Program
Sponsor: Michigan State Univ/Kalamazoo Center for
Medical Studies
Borgess Medical Center
Bronson Methodist Hospital
Prgm Director: Joseph A D'Ambrosio, MD, DMD
Medicine-Pediatrics Program
1000 Oakland Dr
Kalamazoo, MI 49008
Tel: 269 337-6371   *Fax:* 269 337-6380
Length: 4 Yrs   *ACGME Approved/Offered Positions:* 16
Program ID: 700-25-14-089

Royal Oak

William Beaumont Hospital Program
Sponsor: William Beaumont Hospital
Prgm Director: Jeffrey D Haller, MD
3601 West 13 Mile Road
Royal Oak, MI 48073
Tel: 248 551-4469   *Fax:* 248 551-8880
E-mail: jaanderson@beaumont.edu
Length: 4 Yrs   *ACGME Approved/Offered Positions:* 16
Program ID: 700-25-32-033

Minnesota

Minneapolis

University of Minnesota Program

Sponsor: University of Minnesota Medical School
Children's Hospitals and Clinics of Minnesota - St Paul
Hennepin County Medical Center
Regions Hospital
University of Minnesota Medical Center, Division of
    Fairview
Veterans Affairs Medical Center (Minneapolis)
Prgm Director: Bradley J Benson, MD
420 Delaware St SE
MMC 391
Minneapolis, MN 55455
Tel: 612 624-0990   *Fax:* 612 625-3238
E-mail: benso040@umn.edu
Length: 4 Yrs   *ACGME Approved/Offered Positions:* 48
Program ID: 700-26-14-034

Mississippi

Jackson

University of Mississippi Medical Center Program

Sponsor: University of Mississippi School of Medicine
University Hospitals and Clinics
Veterans Affairs Medical Center (Jackson)
Prgm Director: Jimmy L Stewart, MD
Department of Medicine
2500 N State St
Jackson, MS 39216
Tel: 601 984-5604   *Fax:* 601 984-6665
E-mail: jstewart@medicine.umsmed.edu
Length: 4 Yrs   *ACGME Approved/Offered Positions:* 10
Program ID: 700-27-14-035

Missouri

Columbia

University of Missouri-Columbia Program

Sponsor: University of Missouri-Columbia School of
    Medicine
Harry S Truman Memorial Veterans Hospital
University Hospitals and Clinics
Prgm Director: Robert W Lancey, MD
Dept of Child Health
One Hospital Dr/Rm N725
Columbia, MO 65212
Tel: 573 882-4438   *Fax:* 573 884-5226
E-mail: adamskrausp@health.missouri.edu
Length: 4 Yrs   *ACGME Approved/Offered Positions:* 16
Program ID: 700-28-32-126

Kansas City

University of Missouri at Kansas City Program

Sponsor: University of Missouri-Kansas City School of
    Medicine
Children's Mercy Hospital
St Luke's Hospital-Kansas City
Truman Medical Center
Prgm Director: Brenda Rogers, MD
Combined Int Med/Peds
2411 Holmes St
Kansas City, MO 64108
Tel: 816 404-0950   *Fax:* 816 404-0959
Length: 4 Yrs   *ACGME Approved/Offered Positions:* 24
Program ID: 700-28-32-036

St Louis

St Louis University School of Medicine Program

Sponsor: St Louis University School of Medicine
Cardinal Glennon Children's Hospital
St Louis University Hospital
Prgm Director: Marilyn Maxwell, MD
Dept of Internal Medicine
1402 S Grand Blvd
St Louis, MO 63104
Tel: 314 577-8762   *Fax:* 314 577-8100
Length: 4 Yrs   *ACGME Approved/Offered Positions:* 16
Program ID: 700-28-14-037

Nebraska

Omaha

University of Nebraska Medical Center College of Medicine Program

Sponsor: University of Nebraska Medical Center College
    of Medicine
Children's Hospital
Nebraska Medical Center
Veterans Affairs Medical Center (Omaha)
Prgm Director: Jennifer Parker, MD
Department of Internal Medicine Education
982055 Nebraska Medical Center - Internal Medicine
Office
Omaha, NE 68198
Tel: 402 559-7268   *Fax:* 402 559-6114
E-mail: eblaszak@unmc.edu
Length: 4 Yrs   *ACGME Approved/Offered Positions:* 8
Program ID: 700-30-14-136

New Jersey

Newark

Newark Beth Israel Medical Center Program

Sponsor: Newark Beth Israel Medical Center
Prgm Director: Jon F Sicat, DO
201 Lyons Ave
Newark, NJ 07112
Tel: 973 926-4949   *Fax:* 973 923-2441
E-mail: Jsicat@sbhcs.com
Length: 4 Yrs   *ACGME Approved/Offered Positions:* 12
Program ID: 700-33-32-041

UMDNJ-New Jersey Medical School Program

Sponsor: UMDNJ-New Jersey Medical School
Hackensack University Medical Center
UMDNJ-University Hospital
Prgm Director: Mary Cantey, MD*
Dept of Pediatrics
185 S Orange Ave, F603
Newark, NJ 07103
Tel: 973 972-6015   *Fax:* 973 972-1019
Length: 4 Yrs   *ACGME Approved/Offered Positions:* 16
Program ID: 700-33-32-040

New York

Albany

Albany Medical Center Program

Sponsor: Albany Medical Center
Veterans Affairs Medical Center (Albany)
Prgm Director: Hamish A Kerr, MBChB, MS
Divison of Combined Medicine/Pediatrics
724 Watervliet-Shaker Rd
Latham, NY 12110
Tel: 518 262-7500   *Fax:* 518 262-7505
E-mail: kerrh@mail.amc.edu
Length: 4 Yrs   *ACGME Approved/Offered Positions:* 16
Program ID: 700-35-14-044

Buffalo

University at Buffalo Program

Sponsor: University at Buffalo School of Medicine
Erie County Medical Center
Kaleida Health System (Buffalo General Hospital)
Kaleida Health System (Women and Children's Hosp of
    Buffalo)
Prgm Director: Michael J Aronica, MD, MS
300 Linwood Avenue
Buffalo, NY 14209
Tel: 716 961-9412   *Fax:* 716 961-9403
E-mail: aronica@buffalo.edu
Length: 4 Yrs   *ACGME Approved/Offered Positions:* 16
Program ID: 700-35-32-049

New York

Mount Sinai School of Medicine Program

Sponsor: Mount Sinai School of Medicine
Elmhurst Hospital Center-Mount Sinai Services
Mount Sinai Medical Center
Prgm Director: Eva Waite, MD
One Gustave L Levy Pl
Box 1512
New York, NY 10029
Tel: 212 241-6934   *Fax:* 212 241-4309
E-mail: eva.waite@mssm.edu
Length: 4 Yrs   *ACGME Approved/Offered Positions:* 16
Program ID: 700-35-32-105

Rochester

University of Rochester Program

Sponsor: Strong Memorial Hospital of the University of
    Rochester
Highland Hospital of Rochester
Rochester General Hospital
Prgm Director: Brett W Robbins, MD
601 Elmwood Ave Box 777R
Rochester, NY 14642
Tel: 585 273-1044   *Fax:* 585 442-6580
E-mail: medped@urmc.rochester.edu
Length: 4 Yrs   *ACGME Approved/Offered Positions:* 32
Program ID: 700-35-32-054

Stony Brook

SUNY at Stony Brook Program

Sponsor: University Hospital - SUNY at Stony Brook
Prgm Director: Frederick J Reindl, MD
School of Medicine
HSC T-11, Rm 040
Stony Brook, NY 11794
Tel: 631 444-2020   *Fax:* 631 444-2894
Length: 4 Yrs   *ACGME Approved/Offered Positions:* 12
Program ID: 700-35-32-093

Note: * indicates a newly appointed program director

North Carolina

Chapel Hill

University of North Carolina Hospitals Program
Sponsor: University of North Carolina Hospitals
Prgm Director: Edmund A Liles Jr, MD
Med Sch Wing D
CB 7593
Chapel Hill, NC 27599
Tel: 919 966-6770   *Fax:* 919 966-8419
Length: 4 Yrs   *ACGME Approved/Offered Positions:* 24
Program ID: 700-36-32-055

Durham

Duke University Hospital Program
Sponsor: Duke University Hospital
Prgm Director: Suzanne K Woods, MD
Dept of Medicine-Pediatrics
Box 3127
Durham, NC 27710
Tel: 919 681-3009   *Fax:* 919 681-5825
E-mail: phillis.scott@duke.edu
Length: 4 Yrs   *ACGME Approved/Offered Positions:* 24
Program ID: 700-36-14-056

Greenville

Pitt County Memorial Hospital/East Carolina University Program
Sponsor: Pitt County Memorial Hospital
Brody School of Medicine at East Carolina University
Prgm Director: Gregg M Talente, MD, MS
Division of General Internal Medicine
PCMH-TA 389
Greenville, NC 27834
Tel: 252 744-4633   *Fax:* 252 744-4688
Length: 4 Yrs   *ACGME Approved/Offered Positions:* 24
Program ID: 700-36-32-057

Ohio

Cincinnati

University Hospital/University of Cincinnati College of Medicine Program
Sponsor: University Hospital Inc
Cincinnati Children's Hospital Medical Center
Prgm Director: Caroline V Mueller, MD, MS
Dept of Internal Medicine
PO Box 670557
Cincinnati, OH 45267
Tel: 513 584-0397   *Fax:* 513 584-0369
Length: 4 Yrs   *ACGME Approved/Offered Positions:* 28
Program ID: 700-38-14-082

Cleveland

Case Western Reserve University (MetroHealth) Program
Sponsor: MetroHealth Medical Center
Prgm Director: David J Mansour, MD, MA
Internal Medicine-Pediatrics
2500 MetroHealth Dr, H574
Cleveland, OH 44109
Tel: 216 778-2882   *Fax:* 216 778-1384
E-mail: dmansour@metrohealth.org
Length: 4 Yrs   *ACGME Approved/Offered Positions:* 24
Program ID: 700-38-32-061

University Hospitals Case Medical Center Program
Sponsor: University Hospitals Case Medical Center
Prgm Director: Katie E Machanda, MD
Internal Medicine/Pediatrics Office
11100 Euclid Ave, Mailstop LKS 5029
Cleveland, OH 44106
Tel: 216 844-7555   *Fax:* 216 844-8216
E-mail: Katie.Machanda@uhhospitals.org
Length: 4 Yrs   *ACGME Approved/Offered Positions:* 16
Program ID: 700-38-32-121

Columbus

Ohio State University Hospital Program
Sponsor: Ohio State University Hospital
Nationwide Children's Hospital
Prgm Director: Scott A Holliday, MD
OSU IM/Peds Program
700 Children's Dr - ED650A
Columbus, OH 43205
Tel: 614 722-0417   *Fax:* 614 722-6132
Length: 4 Yrs   *ACGME Approved/Offered Positions:* 32
Program ID: 700-38-14-063

Dayton

Wright State University Program
Sponsor: Wright State University Boonshoft School of Medicine
Children's Medical Center
Miami Valley Hospital
Veterans Affairs Medical Center (Dayton)
Prgm Director: Marc A Raslich, MD
Medicine-Pediatrics Residency Program
PO Box 927
Dayton, OH 45401
Tel: 937 224-3078   *Fax:* 937 224-3112
E-mail: som_medpeds@wright.edu
Length: 4 Yrs   *ACGME Approved/Offered Positions:* 16
Program ID: 700-38-32-064

Oklahoma

Oklahoma City

University of Oklahoma Health Sciences Center Program
Sponsor: University of Oklahoma College of Medicine
OU Medical Center - Children's Hospital
OU Medical Center - Presbyterian Tower
Veterans Affairs Medical Center (Oklahoma City)
Prgm Director: Stacie E Rougas, MD
The Children's Hospital
1200 Everett Drive, 10th Floor East
Oklahoma City, OK 73104
Tel: 405 271-4417   *Fax:* 405 271-2920
Length: 4 Yrs   *ACGME Approved/Offered Positions:* 12
Program ID: 700-39-32-090

Tulsa

University of Oklahoma College of Medicine-Tulsa Program
Sponsor: University of Oklahoma College of Medicine-Tulsa
Saint Francis Health System
St John Medical Center
Prgm Director: Brian J Yount, MD
Room 3G08
4502 E 41st Street
Tulsa, OK 74135
Tel: 918 660-3395   *Fax:* 918 660-3396
E-mail: med-peds@ouhsc.edu
Length: 4 Yrs   *ACGME Approved/Offered Positions:* 12
Program ID: 700-39-32-067

Pennsylvania

Danville

Geisinger Health System Program
Sponsor: Geisinger Health System
Geisinger Medical Center
Prgm Director: Michelle Thompson, MD
Geisinger Medical Center
100 North Academy Avenue
Danville, PA 17822
Tel: 570 271-6520   *Fax:* 570 214-6354
Length: 4 Yrs   *ACGME Approved/Offered Positions:* 20
Program ID: 700-41-14-068

Hershey

Penn State University/Milton S Hershey Medical Center Program
Sponsor: Milton S Hershey Medical Center
Prgm Director: Ronald J Williams, MD
PO Box 850
500 University Dr
Hershey, PA 17033
Tel: 717 531-5385   *Fax:* 717 531-0856
E-mail: PennStateMedPeds@hmc.psu.edu
Length: 4 Yrs   *ACGME Approved/Offered Positions:* 16
Program ID: 700-41-32-081

Philadelphia

University of Pennsylvania Program
Sponsor: University of Pennsylvania Health System
Children's Hospital of Philadelphia
Presbyterian Medical Center (UPHS)
Prgm Director: Todd Barton, MD
3400 Spruce Street
Philadelphia, PA 19104
Tel: 215 662-3924   *Fax:* 215 662-7919
E-mail: mededu@uphs.upenn.edu
Length: 4 Yrs   *ACGME Approved/Offered Positions:* 16
Program ID: 700-41-14-129

Pittsburgh

University of Pittsburgh Medical Center Medical Education Program
Sponsor: Univ of Pittsburgh Medical Center Medical Education
Children's Hospital of Pittsburgh of UPMC
UPMC Presbyterian Shadyside
Prgm Director: Alda Maria R Gonzaga, MD, MS*
200 Lothrop Street
Suite 9S
Pittsburgh, PA 15213
Tel: 412 802-6578   *Fax:* 412 692-4499
E-mail: gonzagaa@upmc.edu
Length: 4 Yrs   *ACGME Approved/Offered Positions:* 16
Program ID: 700-41-14-128

Rhode Island

Providence

Brown University Program
Sponsor: Rhode Island Hospital-Lifespan
Prgm Director: Suzanne McLaughlin, MD, MSc*
Dept of Medicine
593 Eddy Street
Providence, RI 02903
Tel: 401 444-7486   *Fax:* 401 444-8804
E-mail: smclaughlin1@lifespan.org
Length: 4 Yrs   *ACGME Approved/Offered Positions:* 16
Program ID: 700-43-14-108

South Carolina

Charleston

Medical University of South Carolina Program

Sponsor: Medical University of South Carolina College of Medicine
MUSC Medical Center
Prgm Director: Cassandra Salgado, MD, MS
165 Ashley Ave
PO Box 250561
Charleston, SC 29425
Tel: 843 792-0435   *Fax:* 843 792-6680
E-mail: hasegawa@musc.edu
Length: 4 Yrs   *ACGME Approved/Offered Positions:* 8
Program ID: 700-45-32-127

Columbia

Palmetto Health/University of South Carolina School of Medicine Program

Sponsor: Palmetto Health
Palmetto Health Richland
William Jennings Bryan Dorn Veterans Hospital
Prgm Director: Kathryn A Stephenson, MD
14 Medical Park Ste 400
Columbia, SC 29203
Tel: 803 434-7606   *Fax:* 803 434-3855
E-mail: ashley.lynn@palmettohealth.org
Length: 4 Yrs   *ACGME Approved/Offered Positions:* 8
Program ID: 700-45-32-137

Greenville

Greenville Hospital System/University of South Carolina School of Medicine Program

Sponsor: Greenville Hospital System/University of South Carolina
Prgm Director: Russell Kolarik, MD*
701 Grove Rd
Greenville, SC 29605
Tel: 864 455-7844   *Fax:* 864 455-7848
E-mail: kdasilva@ghs.org
Length: 4 Yrs   *ACGME Approved/Offered Positions:* 16
Program ID: 700-45-14-135

Tennessee

Memphis

University of Tennessee Program

Sponsor: University of Tennessee College of Medicine
LeBonheur Children's Medical Center
Methodist Healthcare - Memphis Hospitals
Regional Medical Center at Memphis
Veterans Affairs Medical Center (Memphis)
Prgm Director: Natascha Thompson, MD
956 Court Avenue, Room H316
Memphis, TN 38163
Tel: 901 448-3714   *Fax:* 901 448-7836
E-mail: nthomps6@utmem.edu
Length: 4 Yrs   *ACGME Approved/Offered Positions:* 40
Program ID: 700-47-32-071

Nashville

Vanderbilt University Program

Sponsor: Vanderbilt University Medical Center
Prgm Director: Sandra A Moutsios, MD
1215 21st Avenue South
Suite 6000 Medical Center East, North Tower
Nashville, TN 37232
Tel: 615 936-8590   *Fax:* 615 936-1269
E-mail: brooke.austin@vanderbilt.edu
Length: 4 Yrs   *ACGME Approved/Offered Positions:* 16
Program ID: 700-47-14-070

Texas

Galveston

University of Texas Medical Branch Hospitals Program

Sponsor: University of Texas Medical Branch Hospitals
Prgm Director: Maria N Luna, MD*
Dept of Pediatrics
301 University Blvd
Galveston, TX 77555
Tel: 409 772-4182   *Fax:* 409 772-2653
Length: 4 Yrs   *ACGME Approved/Offered Positions:* 16
Program ID: 700-48-14-113

Houston

Baylor College of Medicine Program

Sponsor: Baylor College of Medicine
Harris County Hospital District-Ben Taub General Hospital
Michael E DeBakey VA Medical Center - Houston
St Luke's Episcopal Hospital
Texas Children's Hospital
Prgm Director: Cynthia Peacock, MD
1709 Dryden Road
Suite 5.86B
Houston, TX 77030
Tel: 713 798-0104   *Fax:* 713 798-0198
Length: 4 Yrs   *ACGME Approved/Offered Positions:* 32
Program ID: 700-48-14-074

University of Texas at Houston Program

Sponsor: University of Texas Health Science Center at Houston
Lyndon B Johnson General Hospital
Memorial Hermann Hospital
Prgm Director: Mark A Farnie, MD
Dept of Internal Medicine
6431 Fannin St MSB 1.134
Houston, TX 77030
Tel: 713 500-6525   *Fax:* 713 500-6530
Length: 4 Yrs   *ACGME Approved/Offered Positions:* 24
Program ID: 700-48-14-075

Utah

Salt Lake City

University of Utah Program

Sponsor: University of Utah Medical Center
Primary Children's Medical Center
Veterans Affairs Medical Center (Salt Lake City)
Prgm Director: James F Bale Jr, MD
Medicine-Pediatrics Residency Program
30 North 1900 East, Room 4C104 SOM
Salt Lake City, UT 84132
Tel: 801 662-5700   *Fax:* 801 662-5755
Length: 4 Yrs   *ACGME Approved/Offered Positions:* 8
Program ID: 700-49-14-091

Virginia

Richmond

Virginia Commonwealth University Health System Program

Sponsor: Virginia Commonwealth University Health System
Medical College of Virginia Hospitals
Prgm Director: Greg Childress, MD
1101 E Marshall St
Box 980049
Richmond, VA 23298
Tel: 804 828-9713   *Fax:* 804 828-3068
E-mail: lklinger@mcvh-vcu.edu
Length: 4 Yrs   *ACGME Approved/Offered Positions:* 24
Program ID: 700-51-32-077

West Virginia

Charleston

Charleston Area Medical Center/West Virginia University (Charleston Division) Program

Sponsor: Charleston Area Medical Center/West Virginia University
Prgm Director: Gregory D Clarke, MD
Dept of Internal Medicine
3110 MacCorkle Ave SE
Charleston, WV 25304
Tel: 304 347-1341   *Fax:* 304 347-1344
Length: 4 Yrs   *ACGME Approved/Offered Positions:* 8
Program ID: 700-55-14-078

Huntington

Marshall University School of Medicine Program

Sponsor: Marshall University School of Medicine
Cabell Huntington Hospital
St Mary's Hospital
Prgm Director: Aaron M McGuffin, MD
1249 15th Street
Suite 1015
Huntington, WV 25701
Tel: 304 691-1743   *Fax:* 304 691-8640
Length: 4 Yrs   *ACGME Approved/Offered Positions:* 8
Program ID: 700-55-32-079

Morgantown

West Virginia University Program

Sponsor: West Virginia University School of Medicine
West Virginia University Hospitals
Prgm Director: Matthew D Brunner, MD
Department of Pediatrics Office of Education
PO Box 9214
Morgantown, WV 26506
Tel: 304 293-1202   *Fax:* 304 293-1216
E-mail: smatics@hsc.wvu.edu
Length: 4 Yrs   *ACGME Approved/Offered Positions:* 16
Program ID: 700-55-32-080

Note: * indicates a newly appointed program director

Wisconsin

Marshfield

Marshfield Clinic-St Joseph's Hospital Program

Sponsor: Marshfield Clinic-St Joseph's Hospital
Prgm Director: Jonathon A Forncrook, DO
1000 North Oak Avenue
Marshfield, WI 54449
Tel: 800 541-2895   *Fax:* 715 389-3142
E-mail: nanstad.nancy@marshfieldclinic.org
Length: 4 Yrs   *ACGME Approved/Offered Positions:* 8
Program ID: 700-56-14-109

Milwaukee

Medical College of Wisconsin Affiliated Hospitals Program

Sponsor: Medical College of Wisconsin Affiliated
   Hospitals, Inc
Prgm Director: LuAnn Moraski, DO
Office of Medical Education
8701 Watertown Plank Road
Milwaukee, WI 53226
Tel: 414 266-6809   *Fax:* 414 337-7068
Length: 4 Yrs   *ACGME Approved/Offered Positions:* 16
Program ID: 700-56-32-096

Interventional Cardiology (Internal Medicine)

Alabama

Birmingham

University of Alabama Medical Center Program

Sponsor: University of Alabama Hospital
Prgm Director: William B Hillegass, MD, MPH
1808 7th Avenue South, BDB 383
Birmingham, AL 35294
Tel: 205 934-7898   *Fax:* 205 934-0973
Length: 1 Yr   *ACGME Approved/Offered Positions:* 3
Program ID: 152-01-21-135

Arizona

Phoenix

Banner Good Samaritan Medical Center Program

Sponsor: Banner Good Samaritan Medical Center
Prgm Director: Nathan Laufer, MD
1111 East McDowell Road, WT-4
Phoenix, AZ 85006
Tel: 602 239-6743   *Fax:* 602 239-5094
Length: 1 Yr   *ACGME Approved/Offered Positions:* 3
Program ID: 152-03-21-095

College of Medicine, Mayo Clinic (Arizona) Program

Sponsor: College of Medicine, Mayo Clinic
Mayo Clinic Hospital
Prgm Director: F David Fortuin, MD
5777 East Mayo Boulevard
Phoenix, AZ 85054
Tel: 480 342-1398   *Fax:* 480 342-1606
Length: 1 Yr   *ACGME Approved/Offered Positions:* 1
Program ID: 152-03-31-153

Tucson

University of Arizona Program

Sponsor: University of Arizona College of Medicine
Southern Arizona VA Health Care Center (Tucson)
St Joseph's Hospital and Medical Center
St Luke's Medical Center
University Medical Center
University of Arizona/UPHK Graduate Medical Ed
   Consortium
Prgm Director: Karl B Kern, MD
1501 N Campbell Avenue, Room 5149
PO Box 245037
Tucson, AZ 85724
Tel: 520 626-6221   *Fax:* 520 626-0967
E-mail: pabrams@email.arizona.edu
Length: 1 Yr   *ACGME Approved/Offered Positions:* 2
Program ID: 152-03-12-131

Arkansas

Little Rock

University of Arkansas for Medical Sciences Program

Sponsor: University of Arkansas College of Medicine
Central Arkansas Veterans Healthcare System
UAMS Medical Center
Prgm Director: Joe K Bissett, MD*
4301 W Markham, #532
Little Rock, AR 72205
Tel: 501 686-7882   *Fax:* 501 686-8319
E-mail: mjmorrisbisbee@uams.edu
Length: 1 Yr   *ACGME Approved/Offered Positions:* 2
Program ID: 152-04-22-124

California

La Jolla

Scripps Clinic/Scripps Green Hospital Program

Sponsor: Scripps Clinic/Scripps Green Hospital
Prgm Director: Paul S Teirstein, MD
10666 N Torrey Pines Rd, S 1056
La Jolla, CA 92037
Tel: 858 554-9905   *Fax:* 858 554-6883
E-mail: gme@scripps.edu
Length: 1 Yr   *ACGME Approved/Offered Positions:* 2
Program ID: 152-05-21-109

Los Angeles

Cedars-Sinai Medical Center Program

Sponsor: Cedars-Sinai Medical Center
Prgm Director: Raj Makkar, MD
8631 W 3rd Street, #415E
Los Angeles, CA 90048
Tel: 310 423-3977   *Fax:* 310 423-0106
E-mail: MakkarR@cshs.org
Length: 1 Yr   *ACGME Approved/Offered Positions:* 2
Program ID: 152-05-21-137

Kaiser Permanente Southern California (Los Angeles) Program

Sponsor: Kaiser Permanente Southern California
Kaiser Foundation Hospital (Los Angeles)
Prgm Director: Vicken J Aharonian, MD
1526 N Edgemont Annex, Building 4th Floor
Los Angeles, CA 90027
Tel: 323 783-4079   *Fax:* 323 783-7819
Length: 1 Yr   *ACGME Approved/Offered Positions:* 3
Program ID: 152-05-31-002

UCLA Medical Center Program

Sponsor: UCLA David Geffen School of Medicine/UCLA
   Medical Center
Bakersfield Memorial Hospital
Santa Monica-UCLA Medical Center
UCLA Medical Center
Prgm Director: Jesse W Currier, MD
BH-307 Center for the Health Sciences
650 Charles E Young Drive, South
Los Angeles, CA 90095
Tel: 310 825-5280   *Fax:* 310 206-9133
E-mail: AJGuzman@mednet.ucla.edu
Length: 1 Yr   *ACGME Approved/Offered Positions:* 1
Program ID: 152-05-21-004

Programs

University of Southern California/LAC+USC Medical Center Program

Sponsor: University of Southern California/LAC+USC Medical Center
LAC+USC Medical Center
Prgm Director: Ray V Matthews, MD*
1510 San Pablo St
HCC 322
Los Angeles, CA 90033
Tel: 323 442-6130   *Fax:* 323 442-6133
E-mail: sarahlun@usc.edu
Length: 1 Yr   *ACGME Approved/Offered Positions:* 2
Program ID: 152-05-12-003

Orange

University of California (Irvine) Program

Sponsor: University of California (Irvine) Medical Center
Long Beach Memorial Medical Center
Prgm Director: Rex J Winters, MD
101 The City Drive South
Bldg 53, Rte 81, Room 100
Orange, CA 92868
Tel: 714 456-7945   *Fax:* 714 456-8895
E-mail: epwestbe@uci.edu
Length: 1 Yr   *ACGME Approved/Offered Positions:* 1
Program ID: 152-05-13-136

Sacramento

University of California (Davis) Health System Program

Sponsor: University of California (Davis) Health System
University of California (Davis) Medical Center
Prgm Director: Jason H Rogers, MD*
4860 Y Street, Suite 2820
Sacramento, CA 95817
Tel: 916 734-3764   *Fax:* 916 734-3764
E-mail: cardiofellow@ucdavis.edu
Length: 1 Yr   *ACGME Approved/Offered Positions:* 2
Program ID: 152-05-21-140

San Diego

University of California (San Diego) Program

Sponsor: University of California (San Diego) Medical Center
Veterans Affairs Medical Center (San Diego)
Prgm Director: Ehtisham Mahmud, MD
200 West Arbor Drive
San Diego, CA 92103
Tel: 619 543-5990   *Fax:* 619 543-5445
Length: 1 Yr   *ACGME Approved/Offered Positions:* 2
Program ID: 152-05-13-121

San Francisco

University of California (San Francisco) Program

Sponsor: University of California (San Francisco) School of Medicine
UCSF and Mount Zion Medical Centers
Veterans Affairs Medical Center (San Francisco)
Prgm Director: Thomas A Ports, MD
Moffitt Hospital, Room L-523
505 Parnassus Avenue
San Francisco, CA 94143
Tel: 415 353-8969   *Fax:* 415 476-1020
E-mail: ports@medicine.ucsf.edu
Length: 1 Yr   *ACGME Approved/Offered Positions:* 2
Program ID: 152-05-31-086

Stanford

Stanford University Program

Sponsor: Stanford Hospital and Clinics
Prgm Director: David P Lee, MD
300 Pasteur Drive, Room H2103
Stanford, CA 94305
Tel: 650 723-0180   *Fax:* 650 725-6766
Length: 1 Yr   *ACGME Approved/Offered Positions:* 2
Program ID: 152-05-13-005

Torrance

Los Angeles County-Harbor-UCLA Medical Center Program

Sponsor: Los Angeles County-Harbor-UCLA Medical Center
Hospital of the Good Samaritan
Prgm Director: David M Shavelle, MD
1225 Wilshire Blvd
Los Angeles, CA 90017
Tel: 213 977-2239   *Fax:* 213 977-2209
E-mail: dshavell@lacard.com
Length: 1 Yr   *ACGME Approved/Offered Positions:* 3
Program ID: 152-05-21-105

Colorado

Aurora

University of Colorado Denver Program

Sponsor: University of Colorado Denver School of Medicine
University of Colorado Hospital
Veterans Affairs Medical Center (Denver)
Prgm Director: John C Messenger, MD
12401 E 17th Avenue
Leprino Office Building, Box B132
Aurora, CO 80045
Tel: 720 848-6559   *Fax:* 720 848-7314
E-mail: john.messenger@ucdenver.edu
Length: 1 Yr   *ACGME Approved/Offered Positions:* 2
Program ID: 152-07-21-101

Connecticut

Bridgeport

Bridgeport Hospital/Yale University Program

Sponsor: Bridgeport Hospital
Prgm Director: Robert F Fishman, MD
267 Grant Street
Bridgeport, CT 06610
Tel: 203 384-3844   *Fax:* 203 384-3664
E-mail: rf@cardiacspecialists.com
Length: 1 Yr   *ACGME Approved/Offered Positions:* 1
Program ID: 152-08-21-099

Farmington

University of Connecticut Program

Sponsor: University of Connecticut School of Medicine
Hartford Hospital
Prgm Director: Francis J Kiernan, MD
Cardiac Laboratory
80 Seymour Street, Suite 285
Hartford, CT 06102
Tel: 860 545-2977   *Fax:* 860 545-3557
E-mail: lpoulin@harthosp.org
Length: 1 Yr   *ACGME Approved/Offered Positions:* 4
Program ID: 152-08-21-081

New Haven

Yale-New Haven Medical Center Program

Sponsor: Yale-New Haven Hospital
Veterans Affairs Medical Center (West Haven)
Prgm Director: Joseph J Brennan Jr, MD
PO Box 208017
New Haven, CT 06520
Tel: 203 785-4129   *Fax:* 203 737-2437
Length: 1 Yr   *ACGME Approved/Offered Positions:* 3
Program ID: 152-08-13-117

Delaware

Wilmington

Jefferson Medical College/Christiana Care Health Services Program

Sponsor: Jefferson Medical College
Christiana Care Health Services Inc
Prgm Director: James Hopkins, MD
4755 Ogletown-Stanton Road
Section of Cardiology, Room 2E99
Newark, DE 19718
Tel: 302 733-1212   *Fax:* 302 733-4998
E-mail: jhopkins@christianacare.org
Length: 1 Yr   *ACGME Approved/Offered Positions:* 2
Program ID: 152-09-21-155

District of Columbia

Washington

George Washington University Program

Sponsor: George Washington University School of Medicine
George Washington University Hospital (UHS)
Washington Adventist Hospital
Prgm Director: Jonathan S Reiner, MD
2150 Pennsylvania Avenue, NW
Suite 4-417
Washington, DC 20037
Tel: 202 741-2323   *Fax:* 202 741-2324
Length: 1 Yr   *ACGME Approved/Offered Positions:* 3
Program ID: 152-10-21-006

Georgetown University Hospital/Washington Hospital Center Program

Sponsor: Washington Hospital Center
Prgm Director: William O Suddath, MD
110 Irving Street, NW #4B-1
Washington, DC 20010
Tel: 202 877-2812   *Fax:* 202 877-3339
Length: 1 Yr   *ACGME Approved/Offered Positions:* 3
Program ID: 152-10-11-127

Florida

Gainesville

University of Florida Program

Sponsor: University of Florida College of Medicine
Florida Heart and Vascular Center
North Florida/South Georgia Veterans Health System
Shands Hospital at the University of Florida
Prgm Director: Karen M Smith, MD
1600 SW Archer Road, PO Box 100277
Gainesville, FL 32610
Tel: 352 392-0092   *Fax:* 352 846-0314
E-mail: hutchem@medicine.ufl.edu
Length: 1 Yr   *ACGME Approved/Offered Positions:* 3
Program ID: 152-11-13-108

Note: * indicates a newly appointed program director

Jacksonville

University of Florida College of Medicine Jacksonville Program

Sponsor: University of Florida College of Medicine Jacksonville
Shands Jacksonville Medical Center
Prgm Director: Theodore A Bass, MD
Department of Cardiology, Box C35
655 West 8th St, ACC 5th Fl
Jacksonville, FL 32209
Tel: 904 244-2655 *Fax:* 904 244-5913
E-mail: Interventcard.gme@jax.ufl.edu
Length: 1 Yr *ACGME Approved/Offered Positions:* 2
Program ID: 152-11-31-098

Miami

Jackson Memorial Hospital/Jackson Health System Program

Sponsor: Jackson Memorial Hospital/Jackson Health System
Veterans Affairs Medical Center (Miami)
Prgm Director: Alexandre Ferreira, MD
PO Box 016960 (Locator D-39)
Miami, FL 33101
Tel: 305 585-5527 *Fax:* 305 585-7089
E-mail: aferreir@med.miami.edu
Length: 1 Yr *ACGME Approved/Offered Positions:* 2
Program ID: 152-11-21-008

Miami Beach

Mount Sinai Medical Center of Florida Program

Sponsor: Mount Sinai Medical Center of Florida, Inc
Prgm Director: Ralph G Nader, MD*
Cardiac Cath Office
4300 Alton Road
Miami Beach, FL 33140
Tel: 305 532-6006 *Fax:* 305 532-5991
Length: 1 Yr *ACGME Approved/Offered Positions:* 2
Program ID: 152-11-12-133

Tampa

University of South Florida Program

Sponsor: University of South Florida College of Medicine
James A Haley Veterans Hospital
Tampa General Hospital
Prgm Director: Louis Carnendran, MD
South Tampa Center for Advanced Healthcare
2 Tampa General Circle, 5th Floor Cardiology
Tampa, FL 33606
Tel: 813 396-9156 *Fax:* 813 259-0669
E-mail: gszaltel@health.usf.edu
Length: 1 Yr *ACGME Approved/Offered Positions:* 2
Program ID: 152-11-31-148

Georgia

Atlanta

Emory University Program

Sponsor: Emory University School of Medicine
Crawford Long Hospital of Emory University
Emory University Hospital
Veterans Affairs Medical Center (Atlanta)
Prgm Director: John S Douglas Jr, MD*
1364 Clifton Road, NE
Suite F606
Atlanta, GA 30322
Tel: 404 727-7040 *Fax:* 404 712-1385
E-mail: jdoug01@emory.edu
Length: 1 Yr *ACGME Approved/Offered Positions:* 6
Program ID: 152-12-31-009

Illinois

Chicago

McGaw Medical Center of Northwestern University Program

Sponsor: McGaw Medical Center of Northwestern University
Northwestern Memorial Hospital
Prgm Director: Charles J Davidson, MD
251 E Huron #8-526
Chicago, IL 60611
Tel: 312 926-5421 *Fax:* 312 926-6137
Length: 1 Yr *ACGME Approved/Offered Positions:* 2
Program ID: 152-16-21-011

Rush University Medical Center Program

Sponsor: Rush University Medical Center
John H Stroger Hospital of Cook County
Prgm Director: R Jeffrey Snell, MD
1653 W Congress Parkway
Chicago, IL 60612
Tel: 312 942-6569 *Fax:* 312 563-3213
Length: 1 Yr *ACGME Approved/Offered Positions:* 2
Program ID: 152-16-31-012

University of Chicago Program

Sponsor: University of Chicago Medical Center
Prgm Director: John J Lopez, MD
5841 South Maryland Avenue
MC5076
Chicago, IL 60637
Tel: 773 702-1372 *Fax:* 773 702-0241
Length: 1 Yr *ACGME Approved/Offered Positions:* 2
Program ID: 152-16-21-014

University of Illinois College of Medicine at Chicago Program

Sponsor: University of Illinois College of Medicine at Chicago
Advocate Christ Medical Center
Jesse Brown Veterans Affairs Medical Center
University of Illinois Hospital and Clinics
Prgm Director: Bruce Abramowitz, MD
840 S Wood Street
M/C 715, Suite 929 CSB
Chicago, IL 60612
Tel: 708 684-5560 *Fax:* 708 684-3434
E-mail: Bruce.Abramowitz-MD@advocatehealth.com
Length: 1 Yr *ACGME Approved/Offered Positions:* 2
Program ID: 152-16-31-115

Maywood

Loyola University Program

Sponsor: Loyola University Medical Center
Prgm Director: Ferdinand S Leya, MD
2160 S First Avenue
Building 107, Room 1858
Maywood, IL 60153
Tel: 708 216-4225 *Fax:* 708 216-8795
Length: 1 Yr *ACGME Approved/Offered Positions:* 4
Program ID: 152-16-23-013

Indiana

Indianapolis

Indiana University School of Medicine Program

Sponsor: Indiana University School of Medicine
Clarian Methodist Hospital of Indiana
Richard L Roudebush Veterans Affairs Medical Center
Prgm Director: Jeffrey A Breall, MD, PhD
1800 N Capitol Ave, Suite E400
Indianapolis, IN 46202
Tel: 317 962-0561 *Fax:* 317 962-0113
Length: 1 Yr *ACGME Approved/Offered Positions:* 2
Program ID: 152-17-23-015

St Vincent Hospital and Health Care Center Program

Sponsor: St Vincent Hospitals and Health Care Center
Prgm Director: James B Hermiller, MD
8333 Naab Road
Indianapolis, IN 46260
Tel: 317 338-6666 *Fax:* 317 583-6046
E-mail: jhermill@thecaregroup.com
Length: 1 Yr *ACGME Approved/Offered Positions:* 2
Program ID: 152-17-31-112

Iowa

Iowa City

University of Iowa Hospitals and Clinics Program

Sponsor: University of Iowa Hospitals and Clinics
Veterans Affairs Medical Center (Iowa City)
Prgm Director: James D Rossen, MD
Department of Internal Medicine
200 Hawkins Drive
Iowa City, IA 52242
Tel: 319 356-3413 *Fax:* 319 356-4552
Length: 1 Yr *ACGME Approved/Offered Positions:* 2
Program ID: 152-18-31-089

Kansas

Kansas City

University of Kansas School of Medicine Program

Sponsor: University of Kansas School of Medicine
University of Kansas Hospital
Prgm Director: Robert Candipan, MD
3901 Rainbow Boulevard
1001 Eaton, MS 3006
Kansas City, KS 66160
Tel: 913 588-6015 *Fax:* 913 588-6010
E-mail: rshadduck@kumc.edu
Length: 1 Yr *ACGME Approved/Offered Positions:* 1
Program ID: 152-19-21-146

Kentucky

Lexington

University of Kentucky College of Medicine Program

Sponsor: University of Kentucky College of Medicine
University of Kentucky Hospital
Veterans Affairs Medical Center (Lexington)
Prgm Director: David J Moliterno, MD*
Room 326 CTW Building
900 South Limestone
Lexington, KY 40536
Tel: 859 323-5843 *Fax:* 859 323-6475
E-mail: moliterno@uky.edu
Length: 1 Yr *ACGME Approved/Offered Positions:* 2
Program ID: 152-20-21-016

Louisville

University of Louisville Program

Sponsor: University of Louisville School of Medicine
Jewish Hospital
University of Louisville Hospital
Veterans Affairs Medical Center (Louisville)
Prgm Director: Sohail Ikram, MBBS
550 South Jackson Street
ACB, Third Floor
Louisville, KY 40202
Tel: 502 852-4379 *Fax:* 502 852-7147
Length: 1 Yr *ACGME Approved/Offered Positions:* 3
Program ID: 152-20-31-017

Programs

Louisiana

New Orleans

Ochsner Clinic Foundation Program
Sponsor: Ochsner Clinic Foundation
Prgm Director: Tyrone J Collins, MD
1514 Jefferson Highway
New Orleans, LA 70121
Tel: 504 842-3786   *Fax:* 504 838-8853
E-mail: knoble@ochsner.org
Length: 1 Yr   *ACGME Approved/Offered Positions:* 4
Program ID: 152-21-31-020

Maryland

Baltimore

Johns Hopkins University Program
Sponsor: Johns Hopkins University School of Medicine
Johns Hopkins Hospital
Prgm Director: Jon R Resar, MD
Blalock 524
600 N Wolfe Street
Baltimore, MD 21287
Tel: 410 614-1132   *Fax:* 410 955-0223
Length: 1 Yr   *ACGME Approved/Offered Positions:* 3
Program ID: 152-23-21-022

University of Maryland Program
Sponsor: University of Maryland Medical System
Veterans Affairs Medical Center (Baltimore)
Prgm Director: David Zimrin, MD
22 S Greene Street
Room G3K18
Baltimore, MD 21201
Tel: 410 328-8706   *Fax:* 410 328-3530
E-mail: mbileck@medicine.umaryland.edu
Length: 1 Yr   *ACGME Approved/Offered Positions:* 3
Program ID: 152-23-12-023

Massachusetts

Boston

Beth Israel Deaconess Medical Center Program
Sponsor: Beth Israel Deaconess Medical Center
Prgm Director: Lawrence A Garcia, MD
Interventional Cardiology
One Deaconess Road - Baker 4
Boston, MA 02215
Tel: 617 632-7455   *Fax:* 617 632-7460
E-mail: ecabral1@bidmc.harvard.edu
Length: 1 Yr   *ACGME Approved/Offered Positions:* 5
Program ID: 152-24-21-024

Boston University Medical Center Program
Sponsor: Boston Medical Center
Prgm Director: Alice K Jacobs, MD
88 East Newton Street
Boston, MA 02118
Tel: 617 638-8707   *Fax:* 617 638-8719
Length: 1 Yr   *ACGME Approved/Offered Positions:* 2
Program ID: 152-24-12-026

Brigham and Women's Hospital Program
Sponsor: Brigham and Women's Hospital
Boston VA Healthcare System (Brockton-West Roxbury)
Prgm Director: Pinak B Shah, MD
75 Francis Street
Cath Lab Adminstration Office-BP100
Boston, MA 02115
Tel: 617 525-8581   *Fax:* 617 732-7122
Length: 1 Yr   *ACGME Approved/Offered Positions:* 5
Program ID: 152-24-12-028

Caritas St Elizabeth's Medical Center Program
Sponsor: Caritas St Elizabeth's Medical Center of Boston
Prgm Director: Jeffrey J Popma, MD
736 Cambridge Street
Boston, MA 02135
Tel: 617 789-2238
E-mail: jeffrey.popma@caritaschristi.org
Length: 1 Yr   *ACGME Approved/Offered Positions:* 2
Program ID: 152-24-12-150

Massachusetts General Hospital Program
Sponsor: Massachusetts General Hospital
Prgm Director: Igor Palacios, MD
GRB800
55 Fruit Street
Boston, MA 02114
Tel: 617 726-8424   *Fax:* 617 726-6800
E-mail: ipalacios@partners.org
Length: 1 Yr   *ACGME Approved/Offered Positions:* 5
Program ID: 152-24-21-029

Tufts Medical Center Program
Sponsor: Tufts Medical Center
Prgm Director: Carey D Kimmelstiel, MD, PhD
750 Washington Street
Box 315
Boston, MA 02111
Tel: 617 636-5914   *Fax:* 617 636-4769
Length: 1 Yr   *ACGME Approved/Offered Positions:* 2
Program ID: 152-24-23-025

Burlington

Lahey Clinic Program
Sponsor: Lahey Clinic
Prgm Director: Thomas C Piemonte, MD
41 Mall Road
Burlington, MA 01805
Tel: 781 744-8254   *Fax:* 781 744-3510
Length: 1 Yr   *ACGME Approved/Offered Positions:* 3
Program ID: 152-24-31-030

Springfield

Baystate Medical Center/Tufts University School of Medicine Program
Sponsor: Baystate Medical Center
Prgm Director: Marc J Schweiger, MD
759 Chestnut Street, S4652
Springfield, MA 01199
Tel: 413 794-4490   *Fax:* 413 794-0198
E-mail: nancy.lois@bhs.org
Length: 1 Yr   *ACGME Approved/Offered Positions:* 3
Program ID: 152-24-23-031

Worcester

St Vincent Hospital Program
Sponsor: St Vincent Hospital
Prgm Director: Eddison Ramsaran, MD
Worcester Medical Center
123 Summer Street, Suite 290
Worcester, MA 01608
Tel: 508 363-6162   *Fax:* 508 363-6225
E-mail: eddison.ramsaran@stvincenthospital.com
Length: 1 Yr   *ACGME Approved/Offered Positions:* 2
Program ID: 152-24-13-104

University of Massachusetts Program
Sponsor: University of Massachusetts Medical School
UMass Memorial Health Care (University Campus)
Prgm Director: Daniel Fisher, MD, PhD
Division of Cardiology
55 Lake Avenue North
Worcester, MA 01655
Tel: 508 856-5211   *Fax:* 508 856-4571
E-mail: Jacqueline.Jolie@umassmed.edu
Length: 1 Yr   *ACGME Approved/Offered Positions:* 2
Program ID: 152-24-21-032

Michigan

Ann Arbor

University of Michigan Program
Sponsor: University of Michigan Hospitals and Health Centers
Veterans Affairs Medical Center (Ann Arbor)
Prgm Director: Stanley Chetcuti, MD
Cardiovascular Center
1500 E Medical Center Drive, 2A 381
Ann Arbor, MI 48109
Tel: 734 615-3878   *Fax:* 734 764-4142
E-mail: eldert@umich.edu
Length: 1 Yr   *ACGME Approved/Offered Positions:* 3
Program ID: 152-25-21-033

Detroit

Henry Ford Hospital Program
Sponsor: Henry Ford Hospital
Prgm Director: Adam Greenbaum, MD*
2799 West Grand Boulevard
K-14
Detroit, MI 48202
Tel: 313 916-3975
E-mail: cvfellow@hfhs.org
Length: 1 Yr   *ACGME Approved/Offered Positions:* 3
Program ID: 152-25-12-034

St John Hospital and Medical Center Program
Sponsor: St John Hospital and Medical Center
Prgm Director: Thomas A LaLonde, MD
22101 Moross Road
2nd Floor VEP, Cath Lab
Detroit, MI 48236
Tel: 313 343-4612   *Fax:* 313 343-3730
Length: 1 Yr   *ACGME Approved/Offered Positions:* 4
Program ID: 152-25-13-088

Wayne State University/Detroit Medical Center Program
Sponsor: Wayne State University/Detroit Medical Center
Harper-Hutzel Hospital
Prgm Director: Theodore Schreiber, MD
Division of Cardiology
3980 John R Street
Detroit, MI 48201
Tel: 313 745-7025   *Fax:* 313 745-9222
E-mail: tschreib@dmc.org
Length: 1 Yr   *ACGME Approved/Offered Positions:* 3
Program ID: 152-25-31-035

Note: * indicates a newly appointed program director

Lansing

Michigan State University Program
Sponsor: Michigan State University College of Human Medicine
Borgess Medical Center
Michigan State University Clinical Center
Prgm Director: Tim A Fischell, MD
Borgess Medical Center
1521 Gull Road
Kalamazoo, MI 49048
Tel: 269 226-6943   *Fax:* 269 226-8349
E-mail: taf1@net-link.net
Length: 1 Yr   *ACGME Approved/Offered Positions:* 3
Program ID: 152-25-33-130

Royal Oak

William Beaumont Hospital Program
Sponsor: William Beaumont Hospital
Prgm Director: Cindy L Grines, MD
Division of Cardiology
3601 West Thirteen Mile Road
Royal Oak, MI 48073
Tel: 248 898-4176   *Fax:* 248 898-7239
E-mail: THaggerty@beaumont.edu
Length: 1 Yr   *ACGME Approved/Offered Positions:* 6
Program ID: 152-25-12-037

Southfield

Providence Hospital and Medical Centers Program
Sponsor: Providence Hospital and Medical Centers
Prgm Director: Marcel E Zughaib, MD
16001 West Nine Mile Road
Box 2043
Southfield, MI 48037
Tel: 248 849-7129   *Fax:* 248 849-5324
Length: 1 Yr   *ACGME Approved/Offered Positions:* 2
Program ID: 152-25-21-125

Minnesota

Minneapolis

University of Minnesota Program
Sponsor: University of Minnesota Medical School
Abbott-Northwestern Hospital/Allina Health System
University of Minnesota Medical Center, Division of Fairview
Veterans Affairs Medical Center (Minneapolis)
Prgm Director: Robert F Wilson, MD
Dept of Med/Cardiovascular Div
420 Delaware Street, SE, MMC 508
Minneapolis, MN 55455
Tel: 612 626-2451   *Fax:* 612 626-4411
E-mail: cvfellow@umn.edu
Length: 1 Yr   *ACGME Approved/Offered Positions:* 3
Program ID: 152-26-21-038

Rochester

College of Medicine, Mayo Clinic (Rochester) Program
Sponsor: College of Medicine, Mayo Clinic
Saint Marys Hospital of Rochester
Prgm Director: Gregory Barsness, MD
200 First Street SW
Rochester, MN 55905
Tel: 507 284-3304   *Fax:* 507 266-3594
Length: 1 Yr   *ACGME Approved/Offered Positions:* 5
Program ID: 152-26-12-039

Mississippi

Jackson

University of Mississippi Medical Center Program
Sponsor: University of Mississippi School of Medicine
St Dominic-Jackson Memorial Hospital
University Hospitals and Clinics
Veterans Affairs Medical Center (Jackson)
Prgm Director: Michael Winniford, MD
Division of Cardiovascular Diseases
2500 North State Street
Jackson, MS 39216
Tel: 601 984-5678   *Fax:* 601 984-5638
E-mail: mwinniford@medicine.umsmed.edu
Length: 1 Yr   *ACGME Approved/Offered Positions:* 2
Program ID: 152-27-13-145

Missouri

Kansas City

University of Missouri at Kansas City Program
Sponsor: University of Missouri-Kansas City School of Medicine
St Luke's Hospital-Kansas City
Prgm Director: Steven B Laster, MD
4401 Wornall Road
MAHI-5, Cardiovascular Education Coordinator
Kansas City, MO 64111
Tel: 816 932-5475   *Fax:* 816 932-5613
E-mail: jwheeler@saint-lukes.org
Length: 1 Yr   *ACGME Approved/Offered Positions:* 3
Program ID: 152-28-21-040

St Louis

St Louis University School of Medicine Program
Sponsor: St Louis University School of Medicine
St Louis University Hospital
Veterans Affairs Medical Center (St Louis)
Prgm Director: Michael J Lim, MD
3635 Vista Avenue at Grand Blvd
St Louis, MO 63110
Tel: 314 577-8860   *Fax:* 314 577-8861
Length: 1 Yr   *ACGME Approved/Offered Positions:* 1
Program ID: 152-28-23-042

Washington University/B-JH/SLCH Consortium Program
Sponsor: Washington University/B-JH/SLCH Consortium
Barnes-Jewish Hospital
Prgm Director: John M Lasala, MD, PhD
Campus Box 8086
660 South Euclid Avenue
St Louis, MO 63110
Tel: 314 362-3729   *Fax:* 314 747-1417
Length: 1 Yr   *ACGME Approved/Offered Positions:* 3
Program ID: 152-28-12-041

Nebraska

Omaha

Creighton University Program
Sponsor: Creighton University School of Medicine
Creighton University Medical Center (Tenet - SJH)
Prgm Director: Michael G Del Core, MD
The Cardiac Center
3006 Webster Street
Omaha, NE 68131
Tel: 402 282-4626   *Fax:* 402 280-5967
E-mail: michael.delcore@cardiac.creighton.edu
Length: 1 Yr   *ACGME Approved/Offered Positions:* 1
Program ID: 152-30-31-141

University of Nebraska Medical Center College of Medicine Program
Sponsor: University of Nebraska Medical Center College of Medicine
Nebraska Medical Center
Veterans Affairs Medical Center (Omaha)
Prgm Director: Edward L O'Leary, MD
982265 Nebraska Medical Center
Omaha, NE 68198
Tel: 402 559-5151   *Fax:* 402 559-8355
Length: 1 Yr   *ACGME Approved/Offered Positions:* 2
Program ID: 152-30-13-106

New Hampshire

Lebanon

Dartmouth-Hitchcock Medical Center Program
Sponsor: Mary Hitchcock Memorial Hospital
Prgm Director: John E Jayne, MD, BA
One Medical Center Drive
Lebanon, NH 03756
Tel: 603 650-5077   *Fax:* 603 650-0523
E-mail: John.E.Jayne@hitchcock.org
Length: 1 Yr   *ACGME Approved/Offered Positions:* 2
Program ID: 152-32-31-118

New Jersey

Camden

UMDNJ-Robert Wood Johnson Medical School (Camden) Program
Sponsor: Cooper Hospital-University Medical Center
Prgm Director: Janah I Aji, MD
1 Cooper Plaza
Camden, NJ 08103
Tel: 856 342-2057   *Fax:* 856 541-7416
E-mail: jones-jerry@cooperhealth.edu
Length: 1 Yr   *ACGME Approved/Offered Positions:* 2
Program ID: 152-33-13-100

New Brunswick

UMDNJ-Robert Wood Johnson Medical School Program
Sponsor: UMDNJ-Robert Wood Johnson Medical School
Robert Wood Johnson University Hospital
Prgm Director: Abel E Moreyra, MD
PO Box 19 - MEB Room 578
New Brunswick, NJ 08901
Tel: 732 235-7851   *Fax:* 732 235-8722
Length: 1 Yr   *ACGME Approved/Offered Positions:* 1
Program ID: 152-33-12-139

Newark

Newark Beth Israel Medical Center Program
Sponsor: Newark Beth Israel Medical Center
Prgm Director: Najam Wasty, MD
201 Lyons Avenue
Cardiac Cath Lab
Newark, NJ 07112
Tel: 973 926-7000   *Fax:* 973 923-8859
E-mail: lcrapps@sbhcs.com
Length: 1 Yr   *ACGME Approved/Offered Positions:* 2
Program ID: 152-33-12-142

Programs

South Orange

Seton Hall University School of Health and Medical Sciences Program

Sponsor: Seton Hall University School of Health and Medical Sciences
St Joseph's Regional Medical Center
St Michael's Medical Center (A Member of Catholic Hlth East)
Prgm Director: Fayez Shamoon, MD
111 Central Avenue
Newark, NJ 07102
Tel: 973 877-5163   *Fax:* 973 877-5124
Length: 1 Yr   *ACGME Approved/Offered Positions:* 2
Program ID: 152-33-12-080

New York

Albany

Albany Medical Center Program

Sponsor: Albany Medical Center
Prgm Director: Augustin Delago, MD
Mail Code 17
47 New Scotland Avenue
Albany, NY 12208
Tel: 518 262-5076   *Fax:* 518 262-5082
E-mail: brozowml@mail.amc.edu
Length: 1 Yr   *ACGME Approved/Offered Positions:* 1
Program ID: 152-35-12-113

Bronx

Albert Einstein College of Medicine (Montefiore) Program

Sponsor: Albert Einstein College of Medicine of Yeshiva University
Montefiore Medical Center-Henry and Lucy Moses Division
Montefiore Medical Center-Weiler Division
Prgm Director: V S Srinivas, MD
1825 Eastchester Road
Suite W1-120
Bronx, NY 10461
Tel: 718 904-2583   *Fax:* 718 918-1984
Length: 1 Yr   *ACGME Approved/Offered Positions:* 2
Program ID: 152-35-12-103

Brooklyn

Maimonides Medical Center Program

Sponsor: Maimonides Medical Center
Prgm Director: Jacob Shani, MD
4802 Tenth Avenue
Brooklyn, NY 11219
Tel: 718 283-6892   *Fax:* 718 635-7436
Length: 1 Yr   *ACGME Approved/Offered Positions:* 3
Program ID: 152-35-12-119

New York Methodist Hospital Program

Sponsor: New York Methodist Hospital
Prgm Director: Terrence Sacchi, MD
506 6th Street
Brooklyn, NY 11215
Tel: 718 780-5612   *Fax:* 718 780-3930
E-mail: mil9074@nyp.org
Length: 1 Yr   *ACGME Approved/Offered Positions:* 2
Program ID: 152-35-12-154

SUNY Health Science Center at Brooklyn Program

Sponsor: SUNY Health Science Center at Brooklyn
Staten Island University Hospital
University Hospital-SUNY Health Science Center at Brooklyn
Prgm Director: Jonathan Marmur, MD
450 Clarkson Avenue, Box 1257
Brooklyn, NY 11203
Tel: 718 270-3273   *Fax:* 718 270-4503
Length: 1 Yr   *ACGME Approved/Offered Positions:* 4
Program ID: 152-35-21-043

Great Neck

NSLIJHS-North Shore University Hospital/NYU School of Medicine Program

Sponsor: North Shore-Long Island Jewish Health System
Long Island Jewish Medical Center
North Shore University Hospital
Prgm Director: Lawrence Ong, MD
300 Community Drive
Manhasset, NY 11030
Tel: 516 562-4102   *Fax:* 516 562-2087
Length: 1 Yr   *ACGME Approved/Offered Positions:* 3
Program ID: 152-35-12-082

Mineola

Winthrop-University Hospital Program

Sponsor: Winthrop-University Hospital
Prgm Director: Kevin Marzo, MD
120 Mineola Boulevard
Suite 500
Mineola, NY 11501
Tel: 516 663-6951   *Fax:* 516 663-2926
E-mail: amaloney@winthrop.org
Length: 1 Yr   *ACGME Approved/Offered Positions:* 2
Program ID: 152-35-31-138

New York

Albert Einstein College of Medicine at Beth Israel Medical Center Program

Sponsor: Beth Israel Medical Center
Prgm Director: John Fox, MD
11 Dazian
16th Street First Avenue
New York, NY 10003
Tel: 212 420-3581   *Fax:* 212 420-2408
Length: 1 Yr   *ACGME Approved/Offered Positions:* 2
Program ID: 152-35-13-122

Lenox Hill Hospital Program

Sponsor: Lenox Hill Hospital
Prgm Director: Kirk N Garratt, MD, MSc
100 East 77th Street
New York, NY 10075
Tel: 212 434-2606   *Fax:* 212 434-2205
E-mail: kgarratt@lenoxhill.net
Length: 1 Yr   *ACGME Approved/Offered Positions:* 4
Program ID: 152-35-21-090

Mount Sinai School of Medicine Program

Sponsor: Mount Sinai School of Medicine
Mount Sinai Medical Center
Prgm Director: Annapoorna K Kini, MD
One Gustave L Levy Place, Box 1030
New York, NY 10029
Tel: 212 241-4021   *Fax:* 212 534-3845
Length: 1 Yr   *ACGME Approved/Offered Positions:* 6
Program ID: 152-35-21-107

New York Medical College at St Vincent's Hospital and Medical Center of New York Program

Sponsor: New York Medical College
St Vincent Catholic Medical Centers (Manhattan)
Prgm Director: John T Coppola, MD
153 West 11th Street
New York, NY 10011
Tel: 212 604-2231   *Fax:* 212 604-3225
Length: 1 Yr   *ACGME Approved/Offered Positions:* 3
Program ID: 152-35-32-046

New York Presbyterian Hospital (Columbia Campus) Program

Sponsor: New York Presbyterian Hospital
New York Presbyterian Hospital (Columbia Campus)
Prgm Director: George Dangas, MD, PhD
630 West 168th Street
New York, NY 10032
Tel: 212 851-9151   *Fax:* 212 851-9397
E-mail: trs2108@columbia.edu
Length: 1 Yr   *ACGME Approved/Offered Positions:* 3
Program ID: 152-35-12-045

New York Presbyterian Hospital (Cornell Campus) Program

Sponsor: New York Presbyterian Hospital
New York Presbyterian Hospital (Cornell Campus)
Prgm Director: Robert M Minutello, MD*
525 East 68th Street
Cardiac Cath Lab, F-439
New York, NY 10065
Tel: 212 746-4644   *Fax:* 212 746-8295
Length: 1 Yr   *ACGME Approved/Offered Positions:* 3
Program ID: 152-35-12-110

New York University School of Medicine Program

Sponsor: New York University School of Medicine
Manhattan VA Harbor Health Care System
Prgm Director: Frederick Feit, MD
560 First Avenue
TH 576
New York, NY 10016
Tel: 212 263-5656   *Fax:* 212 263-8534
Length: 1 Yr   *ACGME Approved/Offered Positions:* 3
Program ID: 152-35-11-123

St Luke's-Roosevelt Hospital Center Program

Sponsor: St Luke's-Roosevelt Hospital Center
Prgm Director: Jacqueline Tamis, MD
1111 Amsterdam Avenue
New York, NY 10025
Tel: 212 523-4008   *Fax:* 212 523-3915
E-mail: jtamis@chpnet.org
Length: 1 Yr   *ACGME Approved/Offered Positions:* 1
Program ID: 152-35-31-120

Rochester

University of Rochester Program

Sponsor: Strong Memorial Hospital of the University of Rochester
Prgm Director: Frederick S Ling, MD
Strong Memorial Hospital
601 Elmwood Avenue, Box 679
Rochester, NY 14642
Tel: 585 273-3229   *Fax:* 585 271-7667
Length: 1 Yr   *ACGME Approved/Offered Positions:* 3
Program ID: 152-35-21-048

Note: * indicates a newly appointed program director

Stony Brook

SUNY at Stony Brook Program
Sponsor: University Hospital - SUNY at Stony Brook
Prgm Director: William E Lawson, MD
Division of Cardiovascular Medicine
HSC 16-080
Stony Brook, NY 11794
Tel: 631 444-1066   *Fax:* 631 444-1054
E-mail: William.Lawson@Stonybrook.edu
Length: 1 Yr   *ACGME Approved/Offered Positions:* 2
Program ID: 152-35-23-049

Valhalla

New York Medical College at Westchester Medical Center Program
Sponsor: New York Medical College
Westchester Medical Center
Prgm Director: Melvin B Weiss, MD
Division of Cardiology
Macy 1 W
Valhalla, NY 10595
Tel: 914 493-7199   *Fax:* 914 493-1854
Length: 1 Yr   *ACGME Approved/Offered Positions:* 2
Program ID: 152-35-13-084

North Carolina

Chapel Hill

University of North Carolina Hospitals Program
Sponsor: University of North Carolina Hospitals
Prgm Director: George A Stouffer, MD
Division of Cardiology
CB 7075
Chapel Hill, NC 27599
Tel: 919 966-5141   *Fax:* 919 966-6955
Length: 1 Yr   *ACGME Approved/Offered Positions:* 2
Program ID: 152-36-21-050

Durham

Duke University Hospital Program
Sponsor: Duke University Hospital
Prgm Director: Michael H Sketch Jr, MD
Box 3157
Durham, NC 27710
Tel: 919 681-2704   *Fax:* 919 681-7223
E-mail: sketc002@mc.duke.edu
Length: 1 Yr   *ACGME Approved/Offered Positions:* 5
Program ID: 152-36-12-051

Greenville

Pitt County Memorial Hospital/East Carolina University Program
Sponsor: Pitt County Memorial Hospital
Prgm Director: Joseph D Babb, MD
600 Moye Blvd
ECHI Room 2245
Greenville, NC 27834
Tel: 252 744-5964   *Fax:* 252 744-7724
E-mail: davisk@ecu.edu
Length: 1 Yr   *ACGME Approved/Offered Positions:* 2
Program ID: 152-36-31-128

Winston-Salem

Wake Forest University School of Medicine Program
Sponsor: Wake Forest University Baptist Medical Center
Prgm Director: Michael A Kutcher, MD
Medical Center Boulevard
Winston-Salem, NC 27157
Tel: 336 716-2960   *Fax:* 336 716-9188
Length: 1 Yr   *ACGME Approved/Offered Positions:* 3
Program ID: 152-36-23-052

Ohio

Cincinnati

University Hospital/University of Cincinnati College of Medicine Program
Sponsor: University Hospital Inc
Prgm Director: Tarek Helmy, MD
Division of Cardiology
231 Albert Sabin Way
Cincinnati, OH 45267
Tel: 513 558-3070   *Fax:* 513 558-3116
E-mail: janet.rosing@uc.edu
Length: 1 Yr   *ACGME Approved/Offered Positions:* 2
Program ID: 152-38-21-053

Cleveland

Cleveland Clinic Foundation Program
Sponsor: Cleveland Clinic Foundation
Prgm Director: Samir R Kapadia, MD
9500 Euclid Avenue, Desk F-25
Cleveland, OH 44195
Tel: 216 444-6735   *Fax:* 216 445-4363
E-mail: meded@ccf.org
Length: 1 Yr   *ACGME Approved/Offered Positions:* 4
Program ID: 152-38-21-085

University Hospitals Case Medical Center Program
Sponsor: University Hospitals Case Medical Center
Veterans Affairs Medical Center (Cleveland)
Prgm Director: Michael J Cunningham, MD, MS*
11100 Euclid Avenue, Mailstop LKS5038
Cleveland, OH 44106
Tel: 216 844-7603   *Fax:* 216 844-3145
Length: 1 Yr   *ACGME Approved/Offered Positions:* 2
Program ID: 152-38-31-134

Columbus

Ohio State University Hospital Program
Sponsor: Ohio State University Hospital
Prgm Director: Raymond D Magorien, MD
473 W 12th Avenue, 200 HLRI
Columbus, OH 43210
Tel: 614 293-4146   *Fax:* 614 293-5614
Length: 1 Yr   *ACGME Approved/Offered Positions:* 3
Program ID: 152-38-12-054

Toledo

University of Toledo Program
Sponsor: University of Toledo
University Medical Center (Toledo)
Prgm Director: William R Colyer Jr, MD*
Health Sciences Campus
3000 Arlington Avenue, MS 1118
Toledo, OH 43614
Tel: 419 383-3697   *Fax:* 419 383-3041
E-mail: teri.diehl@utoledo.edu
Length: 1 Yr   *ACGME Approved/Offered Positions:* 1
Program ID: 152-38-22-129

Oklahoma

Oklahoma City

University of Oklahoma Health Sciences Center Program
Sponsor: University of Oklahoma College of Medicine
OU Medical Center - Presbyterian Tower
Veterans Affairs Medical Center (Oklahoma City)
Prgm Director: Eliot Schechter, MD
VA Medical Center
921 NE 13th Street
Oklahoma City, OK 73104
Tel: 405 456-5378   *Fax:* 405 456-1576
E-mail: eliot-schechter@ouhsc.edu
Length: 1 Yr   *ACGME Approved/Offered Positions:* 2
Program ID: 152-39-21-055

Pennsylvania

Danville

Geisinger Health System Program
Sponsor: Geisinger Health System
Geisinger Medical Center
Prgm Director: James C Blankenship, MD
Department of Cardiology, 21-60
100 North Academy Drive
Danville, PA 17822
Tel: 570 271-6423   *Fax:* 570 271-8056
E-mail: tkalejta@geisinger.edu
Length: 1 Yr   *ACGME Approved/Offered Positions:* 1
Program ID: 152-41-21-056

Hershey

Penn State University/Milton S Hershey Medical Center Program
Sponsor: Milton S Hershey Medical Center
Prgm Director: Mark Kozak, MD
500 University Drive
H047
Hershey, PA 17033
Tel: 717 531-6746   *Fax:* 717 531-0099
Length: 1 Yr   *ACGME Approved/Offered Positions:* 2
Program ID: 152-41-23-058

Philadelphia

Albert Einstein Healthcare Network Program
Sponsor: Albert Einstein Medical Center
Frankford Hospitals (Torresdale Campus)
Prgm Director: Shahriar Yazdanfar, MD
5401 Old York Road
Klein Building, Suite 363
Philadelphia, PA 19141
Tel: 215 456-7022   *Fax:* 215 456-2482
Length: 1 Yr   *ACGME Approved/Offered Positions:* 2
Program ID: 152-41-21-059

Drexel University College of Medicine/Hahnemann University Hospital Program
Sponsor: Drexel University College of
  Medicine/Hahnemann University
Hahnemann University Hospital (Tenet Health System)
Prgm Director: Gary S Ledley, MD*
245 N 15th Street, MS 470
Philadelphia, PA 19102
Tel: 215 762-7591   *Fax:* 215 246-5322
E-mail: gledley@drexelmed.edu
Length: 1 Yr   *ACGME Approved/Offered Positions:* 2
Program ID: 152-41-23-060

Programs

Temple University Hospital Program
Sponsor: Temple University Hospital
Prgm Director: Nelson M Wolf, MD
3401 N Broad Street
Philadelphia, PA 19140
Tel: 215 707-9587   *Fax:* 215 707-3946
Length: 1 Yr   *ACGME Approved/Offered Positions:* 2
Program ID: 152-41-12-144

Thomas Jefferson University Program
Sponsor: Thomas Jefferson University Hospital
Prgm Director: David L Fischman, MD
JHI, 925 Chestnut Street, Mezzanine
Philadelphia, PA 19107
Tel: 215 955-4332   *Fax:* 215 503-5650
E-mail: kim.berger@jefferson.edu
Length: 1 Yr   *ACGME Approved/Offered Positions:* 2
Program ID: 152-41-13-091

University of Pennsylvania Program
Sponsor: University of Pennsylvania Health System
Presbyterian Medical Center (UPHS)
Prgm Director: John W Hirshfeld Jr, MD
9th Floor Gates Pavilion
3400 Spruce Street
Philadelphia, PA 19104
Tel: 215 662-2181   *Fax:* 215 349-5894
E-mail: hirshfel@mail.med.upenn.edu
Length: 1 Yr   *ACGME Approved/Offered Positions:* 3
Program ID: 152-41-12-057

Pittsburgh

Allegheny General Hospital Program
Sponsor: Allegheny General Hospital
Washington Hospital
Prgm Director: David M Lasorda, DO
Division of Interventional Cardiology
320 East North Avenue
Pittsburgh, PA 15212
Tel: 412 359-4998   *Fax:* 412 359-6544
E-mail: cbowers3@wpahs.org
Length: 1 Yr   *ACGME Approved/Offered Positions:* 3
Program ID: 152-41-12-061

University of Pittsburgh Medical Center Medical Education Program
Sponsor: Univ of Pittsburgh Medical Center Medical
Education
UPMC Presbyterian Shadyside
Prgm Director: William D Anderson, MD
A333 PUH
200 Lothrop Street
Pittsburgh, PA 15213
Tel: 412 647-0211   *Fax:* 412 647-8117
Length: 1 Yr   *ACGME Approved/Offered Positions:* 3
Program ID: 152-41-21-116

Western Pennsylvania Hospital/Temple University Program
Sponsor: Western Pennsylvania Hospital
Western Pennsylvania Hospital/Forbes Regional Campus
Prgm Director: Venkatraman Srinivasan, MD
4800 Friendship Avenue
Department of Medicine
Pittsburgh, PA 15224
Tel: 412 578-6902   *Fax:* 412 578-7212
E-mail: rsantona@wpahs.org
Length: 1 Yr   *ACGME Approved/Offered Positions:* 2
Program ID: 152-41-21-062

Wynnewood

Lankenau Hospital Program
Sponsor: Lankenau Hospital
Prgm Director: Timothy Shapiro, MD
558 Lankenau MOB East
100 Lancaster Avenue
Wynnewood, PA 19096
Tel: 610 645-2682   *Fax:* 610 896-0643
Length: 1 Yr   *ACGME Approved/Offered Positions:* 2
Program ID: 152-41-31-096

Rhode Island

Providence

Brown University Program
Sponsor: Rhode Island Hospital-Lifespan
Prgm Director: David O Williams, MD*
Division of Cardiology, APC 814
593 Eddy Street
Providence, RI 02903
Tel: 401 444-4581   *Fax:* 401 444-8158
E-mail: dowilliams@lifespan.org
Length: 1 Yr   *ACGME Approved/Offered Positions:* 2
Program ID: 152-43-12-064

Brown University Program A
Sponsor: Rhode Island Hospital-Lifespan
Miriam Hospital-Lifespan
Prgm Director: Paul C Gordon, MD
164 Summit Avenue
Providence, RI 02906
Tel: 401 793-4102   *Fax:* 401 793-4049
Length: 1 Yr   *ACGME Approved/Offered Positions:* 2
Program ID: 152-43-21-063

South Carolina

Charleston

Medical University of South Carolina Program
Sponsor: Medical University of South Carolina College of
Medicine
MUSC Medical Center
Ralph H Johnson VA Medical Center (Charleston)
Prgm Director: Christopher D Nielsen, MD
25 Courtenay Drive, 7ART, Rm 7063
MSC 592
Charleston, SC 29425
Tel: 843 876-4807   *Fax:* 843 876-4809
Length: 1 Yr   *ACGME Approved/Offered Positions:* 3
Program ID: 152-45-21-087

Tennessee

Nashville

Vanderbilt University Program
Sponsor: Vanderbilt University Medical Center
Veterans Affairs Medical Center (Nashville)
Prgm Director: David X Zhao, MD
2220 Pierce Avenue
MRB11, Rm 358
Nashville, TN 37232
Tel: 615 936-0213
Length: 1 Yr   *ACGME Approved/Offered Positions:* 3
Program ID: 152-47-21-065

Texas

Dallas

Baylor University Medical Center Program
Sponsor: Baylor University Medical Center
Prgm Director: Kenneth B Johnson, MD
3500 Gaston Avenue
1st Floor Roberts, Medical Education
Dallas, TX 75226
Tel: 214 820-2234   *Fax:* 214 820-7272
E-mail: christina.hernandez@baylorhealth.edu
Length: 1 Yr   *ACGME Approved/Offered Positions:* 1
Program ID: 152-48-31-132

University of Texas Southwestern Medical School Program
Sponsor: University of Texas Southwestern Medical
School
Dallas County Hospital District-Parkland Memorial
Hospital
Dallas VA Medical Center
Prgm Director: Elizabeth M Holper, MD, MPH
5323 Harry Hines Boulevard
Dallas, TX 75390
Tel: 214 590-8617   *Fax:* 214 590-5032
E-mail: elizabeth.holper@utsouthwestern.edu
Length: 1 Yr   *ACGME Approved/Offered Positions:* 2
Program ID: 152-48-13-152

Galveston

University of Texas Medical Branch Hospitals Program
Sponsor: University of Texas Medical Branch Hospitals
Methodist Hospital (Houston)
Prgm Director: Charles Y Lui, MD, MSc
5-106 John Sealy Annex
301 University Blvd
Galveston, TX 77555
Tel: 409 772-1533   *Fax:* 409 772-4982
Length: 1 Yr   *ACGME Approved/Offered Positions:* 4
Program ID: 152-48-21-097

Houston

Baylor College of Medicine Program
Sponsor: Baylor College of Medicine
Harris County Hospital District-Ben Taub General
Hospital
Memorial Hermann Hospital
Methodist Hospital (Houston)
Michael E DeBakey VA Medical Center - Houston
Prgm Director: Nasser Lakkis, MD
Section of Cardiology
1709 Dryden, MS-BCM620, Ste 9.91
Houston, TX 77030
Tel: 713 798-0284   *Fax:* 713 798-0270
Length: 1 Yr   *ACGME Approved/Offered Positions:* 4
Program ID: 152-48-21-068

Baylor College of Medicine/St Luke's Episcopal Hospital Program
Sponsor: Baylor College of Medicine
St Luke's Episcopal Hospital
Prgm Director: Richard D Fish, MD
St. Luke's Episcopal Hospital
6720 Bertner (MC 1-133)
Houston, TX 77030
Tel: 832 355-6676   *Fax:* 832 355-8374
E-mail: mjones@sleh.com
Length: 1 Yr   *ACGME Approved/Offered Positions:* 6
Program ID: 152-48-23-067

Note: * indicates a newly appointed program director

University of Texas at Houston Program

Sponsor: University of Texas Health Science Center at Houston
Memorial Hermann Hospital
Prgm Director: Richard W Smalling, MD, PhD
Division of Cardiovascular Medicine
6431 Fannin St, MSB 1.246
Houston, TX 77030
Tel: 713 500-6577
E-mail: carol.mateo@uth.tmc.edu
Length: 1 Yr   *ACGME Approved/Offered Positions:* 3
Program ID: 152-48-12-069

San Antonio

University of Texas Health Science Center at San Antonio Program

Sponsor: University of Texas School of Medicine at San Antonio
Audie L Murphy Memorial Veterans Hospital (San Antonio)
University Health System
Prgm Director: Steven R Bailey, MD*
Department of Medicine, MC 7872
7703 Floyd Curl Drive
San Antonio, TX 78229
Tel: 210 567-3885   *Fax:* 210 567-6960
Length: 1 Yr   *ACGME Approved/Offered Positions:* 2
Program ID: 152-48-21-070

Temple

Texas A&M College of Medicine-Scott and White Program

Sponsor: Scott and White Memorial Hospital
Prgm Director: Scott Gantt, DO
2401 S 31st Street
Temple, TX 76508
Tel: 254 724-0108   *Fax:* 254 724-8067
E-mail: mwheeler@swmail.sw.org
Length: 1 Yr   *ACGME Approved/Offered Positions:* 2
Program ID: 152-48-12-071

Utah

Salt Lake City

University of Utah Program

Sponsor: University of Utah Medical Center
Intermountain Medical Center
Prgm Director: Andrew D Michaels, MD
30 North 1900 East
Rm 4A100 SOM
Salt Lake City, UT 84132
Tel: 801 585-1686   *Fax:* 801 581-7735
E-mail: katie.goodyear@hsc.utah.edu
Length: 1 Yr   *ACGME Approved/Offered Positions:* 2
Program ID: 152-49-12-094

Vermont

Burlington

University of Vermont Program

Sponsor: Fletcher Allen Health Care
Prgm Director: Matthew W Watkins, MD
McClure 1, Cardiology Unit
111 Colchester Avenue
Burlington, VT 05401
Tel: 802 847-2005   *Fax:* 802 847-4016
E-mail: roberta.frohock@vtmednet.org
Length: 1 Yr   *ACGME Approved/Offered Positions:* 2
Program ID: 152-50-21-073

Virginia

Charlottesville

University of Virginia Program

Sponsor: University of Virginia Medical Center
Prgm Director: Michael Ragosta III, MD
Box 800662
Charlottesville, VA 22908
Tel: 434 924-2420   *Fax:* 434 982-0901
E-mail: cee2j@virginia.edu
Length: 1 Yr   *ACGME Approved/Offered Positions:* 3
Program ID: 152-51-13-093

Richmond

Virginia Commonwealth University Health System Program

Sponsor: Virginia Commonwealth University Health System
Hunter Holmes McGuire VA Medical Center (Richmond)
Medical College of Virginia Hospitals
Prgm Director: George W Vetrovec, MD
PO Box 980036
1200 E Broad Street
Richmond, VA 23298
Tel: 804 628-1215   *Fax:* 804 828-8321
Length: 1 Yr   *ACGME Approved/Offered Positions:* 3
Program ID: 152-51-21-074

Washington

Seattle

University of Washington Program

Sponsor: University of Washington School of Medicine
University of Washington Medical Center
Prgm Director: Douglas K Stewart, MD
Division of Cardiology, Box 356422
1959 NE Pacific Street
Seattle, WA 98195
Tel: 206 685-1397   *Fax:* 206 685-9394
Length: 1 Yr   *ACGME Approved/Offered Positions:* 2
Program ID: 152-54-22-126

West Virginia

Huntington

Marshall University School of Medicine Program

Sponsor: Marshall University School of Medicine
St Mary's Hospital
Prgm Director: Mark Studeny, MD
1249 15th Street, Suite 4000
Huntington, WV 25701
Tel: 304 691-8500   *Fax:* 304 691-8530
E-mail: daileyc@marshall.edu
Length: 1 Yr   *ACGME Approved/Offered Positions:* 2
Program ID: 152-55-13-149

Morgantown

West Virginia University Program

Sponsor: West Virginia University School of Medicine
West Virginia University Hospitals
Prgm Director: Bradford E Warden, MD
4073 Robert C Byrd Health Sciences Center
PO Box 9168
Morgantown, WV 26506
Tel: 304 293-2801   *Fax:* 304 293-3651
E-mail: dhamilton@hsc.wvu.edu
Length: 1 Yr   *ACGME Approved/Offered Positions:* 2
Program ID: 152-55-21-092

Wisconsin

Madison

University of Wisconsin Program

Sponsor: University of Wisconsin Hospital and Clinics
Prgm Director: Matthew R Wolff, MD
600 Highland Avenue
Room G7/339 CSC
Madison, WI 53792
Tel: 608 263-4856   *Fax:* 608 263-0405
E-mail: fellowship@medicine.wisc.edu
Length: 1 Yr   *ACGME Approved/Offered Positions:* 2
Program ID: 152-56-21-077

Milwaukee

Aurora Health Care Program

Sponsor: Aurora Health Care
Aurora Sinai Medical Center
St Luke's Medical Center
Prgm Director: Tanvir Bajwa, MD
945 N 12th St, PO Box 342
Milwaukee, WI 53201
Tel: 414 219-7190   *Fax:* 414 219-7676
E-mail: jruffin@hrtcare.com
Length: 1 Yr   *ACGME Approved/Offered Positions:* 2
Program ID: 152-56-13-114

Programs

Medical Biochemical Genetics (Medical Genetics)

Maryland

Bethesda

National Institutes of Health Clinical Center Program
Sponsor: Clinical Center at the National Institutes of Health
Children's National Medical Center
Prgm Director: William A Gahl, MD, PhD
Building 10, Room 10C-103
MSC 1851
Bethesda, MD 20892
Tel: 301 402-1833   *Fax:* 301 480-7825
E-mail: gahlw@mail.nih.gov
Length: 1 Yr   *ACGME Approved/Offered Positions:* 4
Program ID: 131-23-12-001

Michigan

Detroit

Wayne State University Program
Sponsor: Wayne State University/Detroit Medical Center
Children's Hospital of Michigan
Detroit Receiving Hospital and University Health Center
Prgm Director: Gerald L Feldman, MD, PhD
540 East Canfield Avenue
3127 Scott Hall
Detroit, MI 48201
Tel: 313 577-6298   *Fax:* 313 577-9137
Length: 1 Yr   *ACGME Approved/Offered Positions:* 2
Program ID: 131-25-21-002

Ohio

Cincinnati

Cincinnati Children's Hospital Medical Center/University of Cincinnati College of Medicine Program
Sponsor: Cincinnati Children's Hospital Medical Center
Prgm Director: Nancy D Leslie, MD
3333 Burnet Avenue
ML 4006
Cincinnati, OH 45229
Tel: 513 636-2438   *Fax:* 513 636-7297
E-mail: geneticstraining@cchmc.org
Length: 1 Yr   *ACGME Approved/Offered Positions:* 1
Program ID: 131-38-13-003

Texas

Houston

Baylor College of Medicine Program
Sponsor: Baylor College of Medicine
Texas Children's Hospital
Prgm Director: V Reid Sutton, MD
6701 Fannin Street, Suite 1560 (CC1560)
Houston, TX 77030
Tel: 832 822-4292   *Fax:* 832 825-4294
E-mail: vsutton@bcm.edu
Length: 1 Yr   *ACGME Approved/Offered Positions:* 2
Program ID: 131-48-31-004

Medical Genetics

Alabama

Birmingham

University of Alabama Medical Center Program
Sponsor: University of Alabama Hospital
Children's Hospital of Alabama
Prgm Director: Nathaniel H Robin, MD
Department of Genetics
Kaul Building, Room 230
Birmingham, AL 35294
Tel: 205 996-2916   *Fax:* 205 934-9488
Length: 2 Yrs   *ACGME Approved/Offered Positions:* 4
Program ID: 130-01-13-056

California

Los Angeles

Cedars-Sinai Medical Center Program
Sponsor: Cedars-Sinai Medical Center
Los Angeles County-Harbor-UCLA Medical Center
UCLA Medical Center
Prgm Director: David L Rimoin, MD, PhD
8700 Beverly Boulevard
Suite 665-W
Los Angeles, CA 90048
Tel: 310 423-4461   *Fax:* 310 423-1869
E-mail: patricia.kearney@cshs.org
Length: 2 Yrs   *ACGME Approved/Offered Positions:* 12
Program ID: 130-05-21-010

Orange

University of California (Irvine) Program
Sponsor: University of California (Irvine) Medical Center
Prgm Director: Maureen Bocian, MD, MS
101 The City Drive South
ZC 4482
Orange, CA 92868
Tel: 714 456-5631   *Fax:* 714 456-6660
E-mail: mebocian@uci.edu
Length: 2 Yrs   *ACGME Approved/Offered Positions:* 2
Program ID: 130-05-21-042

San Diego

University of California (San Diego) Program
Sponsor: University of California (San Diego) Medical Center
Rady Children's Hospital
Prgm Director: Marilyn C Jones, MD
3020 Children's Way, MC: 5031
San Diego, CA 92123
Tel: 858 966-5840   *Fax:* 858 966-8550
Length: 2 Yrs   *ACGME Approved/Offered Positions:* 4
Program ID: 130-05-31-019

Stanford

Stanford University Program
Sponsor: Stanford Hospital and Clinics
UCSF and Mount Zion Medical Centers
Prgm Director: Gregory M Enns, MB, ChB
Department of Pediatrics, H-315
Stanford University School of Medicine
Stanford, CA 94305
Tel: 650 723-6858   *Fax:* 650 498-4555
E-mail: greg.enns@stanford.edu
Length: 2 Yrs   *ACGME Approved/Offered Positions:* 8
Program ID: 130-05-31-039

Note: * indicates a newly appointed program director

Colorado

Aurora

University of Colorado Denver Program
Sponsor: University of Colorado Denver School of
  Medicine
Children's Hospital (The)
University of Colorado Hospital
Prgm Director: Janet A Thomas, MD
The Children's Hospital, Mail Stop 8400
13121 E 17th Ave, PO Box 6508
Aurora, CO 80045
Tel: 303 724-2370   *Fax:* 720 777-7322
E-mail: thomas.janet@tchden.org
Length: 2 Yrs   *ACGME Approved/Offered Positions:* 4
Program ID: 130-07-21-027

Connecticut

Farmington

University of Connecticut Program
Sponsor: University of Connecticut School of Medicine
Connecticut Children's Medical Center
Univ of Connecticut Health Center/John Dempsey
  Hospital
Prgm Director: Robert M Greenstein, MD
Division of Human Genetics
65 Kane Street
West Hartford, CT 06119
Tel: 860 523-6499   *Fax:* 860 523-6465
E-mail: vtomlin@ccmckids.org
Length: 2 Yrs   *ACGME Approved/Offered Positions:* 2
Program ID: 130-08-21-041

New Haven

Yale-New Haven Medical Center Program
Sponsor: Yale-New Haven Hospital
Bridgeport Hospital
Prgm Director: James M McGrath, MD, PhD
Department of Genetics
PO Box 208005
New Haven, CT 06520
Tel: 203 785-2686   *Fax:* 203 785-3404
E-mail: james.mcgrath@yale.edu
Length: 2 Yrs   *ACGME Approved/Offered Positions:* 6
Program ID: 130-08-21-021

Florida

Gainesville

University of Florida Program
Sponsor: University of Florida College of Medicine
Shands Hospital at the University of Florida
Prgm Director: Roberto T Zori, MD*
PO Box 100296
Gainesville, FL 32610
Tel: 352 392-4104
Length: 2 Yrs   *ACGME Approved/Offered Positions:* 1
Program ID: 130-11-31-071

Miami

Jackson Memorial Hospital/Jackson Health System Program
Sponsor: Jackson Memorial Hospital/Jackson Health
  System
Miami Children's Hospital
Prgm Director: Parul Jayakar, MD, MS
Dr John T Macdonald Found Dept of Human Genetics
1601 NW 12th Avenue, Room 5041
Miami, FL 33136
Tel: 305 243-2559   *Fax:* 305 243-3919
E-mail: Parul.Jayakar@mch.com
Length: 2 Yrs   *ACGME Approved/Offered Positions:* 3
Program ID: 130-11-21-049

Georgia

Atlanta

Emory University Program
Sponsor: Emory University School of Medicine
Children's Healthcare of Atlanta at Egleston
Prgm Director: Margaret P Adam, MD, MS
2165 North Decatur Road
Decatur, GA 30033
Tel: 404 778-8530   *Fax:* 404 778-8562
E-mail: madam@genetics.emory.edu
Length: 2 Yrs   *ACGME Approved/Offered Positions:* 2
Program ID: 130-12-21-048

Illinois

Chicago

University of Chicago/Northwestern University Program
Sponsor: University of Chicago Medical Center
Children's Memorial Hospital
Prgm Director: Darrel J Waggoner, MD
5841 S Maryland Ave
MC 0077, Rm L-161
Chicago, IL 60637
Tel: 773 834-0555   *Fax:* 773 834-0556
E-mail: dwaggone@genetics.uchicago.edu
Length: 2 Yrs   *ACGME Approved/Offered Positions:* 2
Program ID: 130-16-21-057

Indiana

Indianapolis

Indiana University School of Medicine Program
Sponsor: Indiana University School of Medicine
Clarian Indiana University Hospital
Clarian Riley Hospital for Children
Prgm Director: Gail H Vance, MD
975 West Walnut Street, IB 264
Indianapolis, IN 46202
Tel: 317 278-0172   *Fax:* 317 278-1616
E-mail: ghvance@iupui.edu
Length: 2 Yrs   *ACGME Approved/Offered Positions:* 4
Program ID: 130-17-21-015

Iowa

Iowa City

University of Iowa Hospitals and Clinics Program
Sponsor: University of Iowa Hospitals and Clinics
Prgm Director: Kim M Keppler-Noreuil, MD
200 Hawkins Drive
Pediatrics/Genetics, W126 GH
Iowa City, IA 52242
Tel: 319 356-4890   *Fax:* 319 356-3347
E-mail: kim-keppler@uiowa.edu
Length: 2 Yrs   *ACGME Approved/Offered Positions:* 2
Program ID: 130-18-21-004

Louisiana

New Orleans

Tulane University Program
Sponsor: Tulane University School of Medicine
Medical Center of Louisiana at New Orleans
Tulane University Hospital and Clinics
Prgm Director: Hans C Andersson, MD
Hayward Genetics Center
1430 Tulane Avenue, SL 31
New Orleans, LA 70112
Tel: 504 988-5229   *Fax:* 504 988-1763
Length: 2 Yrs   *ACGME Approved/Offered Positions:* 2
Program ID: 130-21-21-025

Maryland

Baltimore

Johns Hopkins University Program
Sponsor: Johns Hopkins University School of Medicine
Johns Hopkins Hospital
Prgm Director: Ronald D Cohn, MD
Institute of Genetic Medicine
733 N Broadway, BRB, Suite 551
Baltimore, MD 21287
Tel: 410 955-3071
Length: 2 Yrs   *ACGME Approved/Offered Positions:* 6
Program ID: 130-23-21-043

Bethesda

National Institutes of Health Clinical Center Program
Sponsor: Clinical Center at the National Institutes of
  Health
Prgm Director: Maximilian Muenke, MD
National Institutes of Health
NIH Bldg 35, Room 1B-203
Bethesda, MD 20892
Tel: 301 402-8167   *Fax:* 301 480-7876
Length: 2 Yrs   *ACGME Approved/Offered Positions:* 17
Program ID: 130-23-21-022

Massachusetts

Boston

Boston University Medical Center Program
Sponsor: Boston Medical Center
Children's Hospital
Prgm Director: Aubrey Milunsky, MD
Center for Human Genetics
715 Albany Street, W-408
Boston, MA 02118
Tel: 617 638-7083   *Fax:* 617 638-7092
Length: 2 Yrs   *ACGME Approved/Offered Positions:* 2
Program ID: 130-24-31-074

Children's Hospital/Harvard Medical School Program

Sponsor: Children's Hospital
Beth Israel Deaconess Medical Center
Prgm Director: Mira Irons, MD
Genetics-Fegan 10
300 Longwood Avenue
Boston, MA 02115
Tel: 617 355-4697   *Fax:* 617 730-0466
Length: 2 Yrs   *ACGME Approved/Offered Positions:* 8
Program ID: 130-24-21-024

Tufts Medical Center Program

Sponsor: Tufts Medical Center
Prgm Director: Laurie A Demmer, MD, MA
800 Washington Street, #340
Boston, MA 02111
Tel: 617 636-4742   *Fax:* 617 636-0745
Length: 2 Yrs   *ACGME Approved/Offered Positions:* 4
Program ID: 130-24-21-052

Michigan

Ann Arbor

University of Michigan Program

Sponsor: University of Michigan Hospitals and Health
    Centers
Prgm Director: Donna M Martin, MD, PhD
D5240 Medical Professional Building
1500 E Medical Center Drive
Ann Arbor, MI 48109
Tel: 734 763-6767   *Fax:* 734 763-9512
E-mail: donnamm@umich.edu
Length: 2 Yrs   *ACGME Approved/Offered Positions:* 6
Program ID: 130-25-21-030

Detroit

Henry Ford Hospital Program

Sponsor: Henry Ford Hospital
Prgm Director: Jacquelyn R Roberson, MD
3031 W Grand Boulevard
New Center One, Suite 700
Detroit, MI 48202
Tel: 313 916-3115   *Fax:* 313 916-1730
E-mail: jrobers1@hfhs.org
Length: 2 Yrs   *ACGME Approved/Offered Positions:* 4
Program ID: 130-25-21-001

Wayne State University/Detroit Medical Center Program

Sponsor: Wayne State University/Detroit Medical Center
Children's Hospital of Michigan
Detroit Receiving Hospital and University Health Center
Harper-Hutzel Hospital
Prgm Director: Gerald L Feldman, MD, PhD
Center for Molecular Medicine and Genetics
540 E Canfield, 3127 Scott Hall
Detroit, MI 48201
Tel: 313 577-6298   *Fax:* 313 577-9137
E-mail: gfeldman@med.wayne.edu
Length: 2 Yrs   *ACGME Approved/Offered Positions:* 3
Program ID: 130-25-21-047

Minnesota

Rochester

College of Medicine, Mayo Clinic (Rochester) Program

Sponsor: College of Medicine, Mayo Clinic
Mayo Clinic (Rochester)
Prgm Director: Jay W Ellison, MD
200 1st St SW
Rochester, MN 55905
Tel: 507 266-2967   *Fax:* 507 284-1067
E-mail: ellison.jay@mayo.edu
Length: 2 Yrs   *ACGME Approved/Offered Positions:* 2
Program ID: 130-26-21-011

Missouri

Columbia

University of Missouri-Columbia Program

Sponsor: University of Missouri-Columbia School of
    Medicine
University Hospitals and Clinics
Prgm Director: Jerome L Gorski, MD
One Hospital Drive
Columbia, MO 65212
Tel: 573 882-6991   *Fax:* 573 884-3543
E-mail: gorskijl@missouri.edu
Length: 2 Yrs   *ACGME Approved/Offered Positions:* 2
Program ID: 130-28-31-053

St Louis

Washington University/B-JH/SLCH Consortium Program

Sponsor: Washington University/B-JH/SLCH Consortium
Barnes-Jewish Hospital
St Louis Children's Hospital
Prgm Director: Dorothy K Grange, MD*
WU Medical Center, Campus Box 8116
One Children's Place
St Louis, MO 63110
Tel: 314 454-6093   *Fax:* 314 454-2075
E-mail: grange_d@kids.wustl.edu
Length: 2 Yrs   *ACGME Approved/Offered Positions:* 2
Program ID: 130-28-22-070

New Jersey

Newark

UMDNJ-New Jersey Medical School Program

Sponsor: UMDNJ-New Jersey Medical School
UMDNJ-University Hospital
Prgm Director: Franklin Desposito, MD
Department of Pediatrics, MSB F-Level
185 South Orange Avenue
Newark, NJ 07103
Tel: 973 972-0673   *Fax:* 973 972-0795
Length: 2 Yrs   *ACGME Approved/Offered Positions:* 2
Program ID: 130-33-21-037

New York

Bronx

Albert Einstein College of Medicine Program

Sponsor: Albert Einstein College of Medicine of Yeshiva
    University
Montefiore Medical Center-Henry and Lucy Moses
    Division
Montefiore Medical Center-Weiler Division
Prgm Director: Susan J Gross, MD
1400 Pelham Parkway South
Department of Obstetrics & Gynecology, Room BS26
Bronx, NY 10461
Tel: 718 405-8150   *Fax:* 718 405-8154
Length: 2 Yrs   *ACGME Approved/Offered Positions:* 4
Program ID: 130-35-31-008

New York

Memorial Sloan-Kettering Cancer Center Program

Sponsor: Memorial Sloan-Kettering Cancer Center
New York Presbyterian Hospital (Cornell Campus)
Prgm Director: Jessica G Davis, MD
428 East 72 Street
Suite 100, Box 128
New York, NY 10021
Tel: 212 746-1496   *Fax:* 212 746-8893
Length: 2 Yrs   *ACGME Approved/Offered Positions:* 2
Program ID: 130-35-13-051

Mount Sinai School of Medicine Program

Sponsor: Mount Sinai School of Medicine
Mount Sinai Medical Center
Prgm Director: Ethylin Jabs, MD
One Gustave L Levy Place
Box 1497
New York, NY 10029
Tel: 212 241-7056   *Fax:* 212 241-7112
E-mail: Genetics.Residency@mssm.edu
Length: 4 Yrs   *ACGME Approved/Offered Positions:* 7
Program ID: 130-35-21-006

New York Presbyterian Hospital (Columbia Campus) Program

Sponsor: New York Presbyterian Hospital
New York Presbyterian Hospital (Columbia Campus)
Prgm Director: Kwame Anyane-Yeboa, MD
CHN6-601A
622 W 168th Street
New York, NY 10032
Tel: 212 305-6731   *Fax:* 212 305-9058
E-mail: ka8@columbia.edu
Length: 2 Yrs   *ACGME Approved/Offered Positions:* 2
Program ID: 130-35-21-050

North Carolina

Chapel Hill

University of North Carolina Hospitals Program

Sponsor: University of North Carolina Hospitals
Prgm Director: Cynthia M Powell, MD
CB 7487 - UNC Campus
Chapel Hill, NC 27599
Tel: 919 966-4202   *Fax:* 919 966-3025
Length: 2 Yrs   *ACGME Approved/Offered Positions:* 4
Program ID: 130-36-21-031

Note: * indicates a newly appointed program director

Durham

Duke University Hospital Program

Sponsor: Duke University Hospital
Prgm Director: Marie T McDonald, MD
Division of Medical Genetics
Box 3528
Durham, NC 27710
Tel: 919 684-2036
E-mail: mcdon035@mc.duke.edu
Length: 2 Yrs   *ACGME Approved/Offered Positions:* 4
Program ID: 130-36-21-018

Ohio

Cincinnati

Cincinnati Children's Hospital Medical Center/University of Cincinnati College of Medicine Program

Sponsor: Cincinnati Children's Hospital Medical Center
Prgm Director: Robert J Hopkin, MD
3333 Burnet Ave, ML4006
ML 4006
Cincinnati, OH 45229
Tel: 513 636-4760   *Fax:* 513 636-7297
E-mail: GeneticsTraining@cchmc.org
Length: 2 Yrs   *ACGME Approved/Offered Positions:* 4
Program ID: 130-38-21-013

Cleveland

University Hospitals Case Medical Center Program

Sponsor: University Hospitals Case Medical Center
Prgm Director: Shawn E McCandless, MD
Center for Human Genetics
11100 Euclid Ave, Lakeside 1500
Cleveland, OH 44106
Tel: 216 844-1612   *Fax:* 216 844-7497
E-mail: shawn.mccandless@case.edu
Length: 2 Yrs   *ACGME Approved/Offered Positions:* 4
Program ID: 130-38-21-007

Columbus

Nationwide Children's Hospital/Ohio State University Program

Sponsor: Nationwide Children's Hospital
Ohio State University Hospital
Prgm Director: Dennis W Bartholomew, MD
700 Children's Drive - Genetics Timken H235
Columbus, OH 43205
Tel: 614 722-3535   *Fax:* 614 722-3546
Length: 2 Yrs   *ACGME Approved/Offered Positions:* 2
Program ID: 130-38-12-072

Oklahoma

Oklahoma City

University of Oklahoma Health Sciences Center Program

Sponsor: University of Oklahoma College of Medicine
OU Medical Center
OU Medical Center - Children's Hospital
Prgm Director: John J Mulvihill, MD
940 NE 13th Street
Section of Genetics, Room B2418
Oklahoma City, OK 73104
Tel: 405 271-8685   *Fax:* 405 271-8697
E-mail: John-Mulvihill@ouhsc.edu
Length: 2 Yrs   *ACGME Approved/Offered Positions:* 4
Program ID: 130-39-13-073

Oregon

Portland

Oregon Health & Science University Program

Sponsor: Oregon Health & Science University Hospital
Shriners Hospitals for Children (Portland)
Prgm Director: Jone E Sampson, MD, RN
3181 SW Sam Jackson Park Road
Mail Code L103
Portland, OR 97239
Tel: 503 494-7210   *Fax:* 503 494-6886
E-mail: sampsojo@ohsu.edu
Length: 2 Yrs   *ACGME Approved/Offered Positions:* 4
Program ID: 130-40-21-009

Pennsylvania

Philadelphia

Children's Hospital of Philadelphia Program

Sponsor: Children's Hospital of Philadelphia
Prgm Director: Ian Krantz, MD
Div Human Genetics, Rm 1002ARC
3615 Civic Center Boulevard
Philadelphia, PA 19104
Tel: 215 590-3856   *Fax:* 215 590-3764
E-mail: ian2@mail.med.upenn.edu
Length: 2 Yrs   *ACGME Approved/Offered Positions:* 6
Program ID: 130-41-21-002

Pittsburgh

University of Pittsburgh Medical Center Medical Education Program

Sponsor: Univ of Pittsburgh Medical Center Medical Education
Children's Hospital of Pittsburgh of UPMC
Magee-Womens Hospital of UPMC
Prgm Director: William A Hogge, MD
Dept of Genetics, Magee-Womens Hospital
300 Halket St
Pittsburgh, PA 15213
Tel: 412 641-4212   *Fax:* 412 641-1133
Length: 2 Yrs   *ACGME Approved/Offered Positions:* 4
Program ID: 130-41-21-045

South Carolina

Greenwood

Greenwood Genetic Center Program

Sponsor: Greenwood Genetic Center
Self Regional Healthcare
Prgm Director: Robert A Saul, MD
101 Gregor Mendel Circle
Greenwood, SC 29646
Tel: 864 941-8100   *Fax:* 864 941-8114
E-mail: rsaul@ggc.org
Length: 2 Yrs   *ACGME Approved/Offered Positions:* 4
Program ID: 130-45-21-005

Tennessee

Nashville

Vanderbilt University Program

Sponsor: Vanderbilt University Medical Center
Prgm Director: Debra L Freedenberg, MD, PhD
DD-2205 Medical Center North
Nashville, TN 37232
Tel: 615 322-7601   *Fax:* 615 343-9951
Length: 2 Yrs   *ACGME Approved/Offered Positions:* 2
Program ID: 130-47-21-033

Texas

Dallas

University of Texas Southwestern Medical School Program

Sponsor: University of Texas Southwestern Medical School
Children's Medical Center of Dallas
Dallas County Hospital District-Parkland Memorial Hospital
Prgm Director: Joseph F Maher, MD
5323 Harry Hines Boulevard, NB10204
Dallas, TX 75390
Tel: 214 648-5866   *Fax:* 214 648-1666
E-mail: joseph.maher@utsouthwestern.edu
Length: 2 Yrs   *ACGME Approved/Offered Positions:* 2
Program ID: 130-48-13-058

Houston

Baylor College of Medicine Program

Sponsor: Baylor College of Medicine
Harris County Hospital District-Ben Taub General Hospital
Methodist Hospital (Houston)
St Joseph Medical Center
St Luke's Episcopal Hospital
Texas Children's Hospital
Prgm Director: V Reid Sutton, MD
Dept of Molecular and Human Genetics
One Baylor Plaza, MS-BCM225
Houston, TX 77030
Tel: 832 822-4292   *Fax:* 832 825-4294
E-mail: vsutton@bcm.tmc.edu
Length: 4 Yrs   *ACGME Approved/Offered Positions:* 12
Program ID: 130-48-21-012

University of Texas at Houston Program

Sponsor: University of Texas Health Science Center at Houston
Lyndon B Johnson General Hospital
Memorial Hermann Hospital
Shriners Hospitals for Children (Houston)
University of Texas School of Public Health
Prgm Director: Hope Northrup, MD
6431 Fannin Street, MSB 3.142
Houston, TX 77030
Tel: 713 500-5760   *Fax:* 713 500-5689
Length: 2 Yrs   *ACGME Approved/Offered Positions:* 6
Program ID: 130-48-21-034

Utah

Salt Lake City

University of Utah Program

Sponsor: University of Utah Medical Center
Primary Children's Medical Center
Prgm Director: John C Carey, MD, MPH
Room 2C412
50 North Medical Drive
Salt Lake City, UT 84132
Tel: 801 581-8943   *Fax:* 801 585-7252
E-mail: john.carey@hsc.utah.edu
Length: 2 Yrs   *ACGME Approved/Offered Positions:* 2
Program ID: 130-49-12-054

Programs

Virginia

Richmond

Virginia Commonwealth University Health System Program

Sponsor: Virginia Commonwealth University Health System
Medical College of Virginia Hospitals
Prgm Director: Joann N Bodurtha, MD, MPH
Box 980033
Richmond, VA 23298
Tel: 804 828-9632   *Fax:* 804 828-3760
Length: 2 Yrs   *ACGME Approved/Offered Positions:* 2
Program ID: 130-51-21-003

Washington

Seattle

University of Washington Program

Sponsor: University of Washington School of Medicine
Seattle Children's Hospital
University of Washington Medical Center
Prgm Director: Peter H Byers, MD
Box 357470
1959 NE Pacific Street
Seattle, WA 98195
Tel: 206 543-4206   *Fax:* 206 616-1899
Length: 2 Yrs   *ACGME Approved/Offered Positions:* 8
Program ID: 130-54-21-040

Wisconsin

Madison

University of Wisconsin Program

Sponsor: University of Wisconsin Hospital and Clinics
Prgm Director: David S Wargowski, MD
1500 Highland Avenue, #353
Madison, WI 53705
Tel: 608 263-8687   *Fax:* 608 263-3496
E-mail: wargowski@waisman.wisc.edu
Length: 2 Yrs   *ACGME Approved/Offered Positions:* 4
Program ID: 130-56-21-036

Note: * indicates a newly appointed program director

Medical Microbiology (Pathology)

Connecticut

New Haven

Yale-New Haven Medical Center Program

Sponsor: Yale-New Haven Hospital
Prgm Director: Sheldon M Campbell, MD, PhD*
333 Cedar Street CB 612
PO Box 208035
New Haven, CT 06520
Tel: 203 932-5711   *Fax:* 203 688-4111
E-mail: sheldon.campbell@yale.edu
Length: 1 Yr   *ACGME Approved/Offered Positions:* 1
Program ID: 314-08-21-011

Georgia

Atlanta

Emory University Program

Sponsor: Emory University School of Medicine
Emory University Hospital
Grady Health System
Prgm Director: Angela M Caliendo, MD, PhD
Department of Pathology, Room H-180
1364 Clifton Road, NE
Atlanta, GA 30322
Tel: 404 712-5721   *Fax:* 404 727-2519
E-mail: acalien@emory.edu
Length: 1 Yr   *ACGME Approved/Offered Positions:* 1
Program ID: 314-12-31-013

Indiana

Indianapolis

Indiana University School of Medicine Program

Sponsor: Indiana University School of Medicine
Clarian Pathology Laboratory
William N Wishard Memorial Hospital
Prgm Director: Stephen D Allen, MD
Department of Pathology and Laboratory Medicine
635 Barnhill Drive, MS 128
Indianapolis, IN 46202
Tel: 317 491-6643   *Fax:* 317 491-6649
Length: 1 Yr   *ACGME Approved/Offered Positions:* 2
Program ID: 314-17-21-001

Iowa

Iowa City

University of Iowa Hospitals and Clinics Program

Sponsor: University of Iowa Hospitals and Clinics
Prgm Director: Sandra S Richter, MD
Department of Pathology
200 Hawkins Drive, C606 GH
Iowa City, IA 52242
Tel: 319 356-2990
E-mail: sandra-richter@uiowa.edu
Length: 1 Yr   *ACGME Approved/Offered Positions:* 1
Program ID: 314-18-21-017

Maryland

Baltimore

Johns Hopkins University Program

Sponsor: Johns Hopkins University School of Medicine
Johns Hopkins Hospital
Prgm Director: Karen Carroll, MD
Johns Hopkins Hospital, Meyer Bldg, Room B1-193
600 North Wolfe Street
Baltimore, MD 21287
Tel: 410 955-5077   *Fax:* 410 614-8087
Length: 1 Yr   *ACGME Approved/Offered Positions:* 1
Program ID: 314-23-21-012

Massachusetts

Boston

Beth Israel Deaconess Medical Center/Harvard Medical School Program

Sponsor: Beth Israel Deaconess Medical Center
Prgm Director: James E Kirby, MD
Department of Pathology
330 Brookline Avenue, YA 309
Boston, MA 02215
Tel: 617 667-3648   *Fax:* 617 667-4533
E-mail: jallin@bidmc.harvard.edu
Length: 1 Yr   *ACGME Approved/Offered Positions:* 1
Program ID: 314-24-13-018

Minnesota

Rochester

College of Medicine, Mayo Clinic (Rochester) Program

Sponsor: College of Medicine, Mayo Clinic
Mayo Clinic (Rochester)
Prgm Director: Robin Patel, MD
200 First Street SW
Rochester, MN 55905
Tel: 507 538-6453   *Fax:* 507 538-3267
E-mail: pathologyeducation@mayo.edu
Length: 1 Yr   *ACGME Approved/Offered Positions:* 1
Program ID: 314-26-21-006

North Carolina

Durham

Duke University Hospital Program

Sponsor: Duke University Hospital
Prgm Director: L Barth Reller, MD
Department of Pathology
Box 3938
Durham, NC 27710
Tel: 919 684-6474   *Fax:* 919 684-8519
Length: 1 Yr   *ACGME Approved/Offered Positions:* 3
Program ID: 314-36-21-004

Ohio

Cleveland

Cleveland Clinic Foundation Program

Sponsor: Cleveland Clinic Foundation
Prgm Director: Nabin Shrestha, MD, MPH
Clinical Microbiology L40
9500 Euclid Avenue
Cleveland, OH 44195
Tel: 216 444-1687   *Fax:* 216 445-9446
E-mail: shrestn@ccf.org
Length: 1 Yr   *ACGME Approved/Offered Positions:* 1
Program ID: 314-38-21-008

Pennsylvania

Philadelphia

University of Pennsylvania Program
Sponsor: University of Pennsylvania Health System
Children's Hospital of Philadelphia
Prgm Director: Paul Edelstein, MD
Department of Pathology and Laboratory Medicine
3400 Spruce Street
Philadelphia, PA 19104
Tel: 215 662-6651   *Fax:* 215 662-6655
E-mail: phe@mail.med.upenn.edu
Length: 1 Yr   *ACGME Approved/Offered Positions:* 1
Program ID: 314-41-31-019

Texas

Dallas

University of Texas Southwestern Medical School Program
Sponsor: University of Texas Southwestern Medical School
Dallas County Hospital District-Parkland Memorial Hospital
Prgm Director: Paul M Southern Jr, MD
5323 Harry Hines Boulevard
Dallas, TX 75390
Tel: 214 648-3587
E-mail: paul.southern@utsouthwestern.edu
Length: 1 Yr   *ACGME Approved/Offered Positions:* 1
Program ID: 314-48-12-014

Galveston

University of Texas Medical Branch Hospitals Program
Sponsor: University of Texas Medical Branch Hospitals
Prgm Director: Juan P Olano, MD
301 University Boulevard
Department of Pathology
Galveston, TX 77555
Tel: 409 772-2870   *Fax:* 409 747-2400
E-mail: jolano@utmb.edu
Length: 1 Yr   *ACGME Approved/Offered Positions:* 1
Program ID: 314-48-21-010

Utah

Salt Lake City

University of Utah Program
Sponsor: University of Utah Medical Center
Prgm Director: Cathy A Petti, MD
500 Chipeta Way
Salt Lake City, UT 84108
Tel: 801 583-2787   *Fax:* 801 584-5207
Length: 1 Yr   *ACGME Approved/Offered Positions:* 1
Program ID: 314-49-12-016

Medical Toxicology (Emergency Medicine)

Arizona

Phoenix

Banner Good Samaritan Medical Center Program
Sponsor: Banner Good Samaritan Medical Center
Phoenix Children's Hospital
Prgm Director: Anne-Michelle Ruha, MD
925 E McDowell Road, 2nd Floor
Phoenix, AZ 85006
Tel: 602 239-2342   *Fax:* 602 239-4138
E-mail: michelle.ruha@bannerhealth.com
Length: 2 Yrs   *ACGME Approved/Offered Positions:* 4
Program ID: 118-03-21-001

Tucson

University of Arizona Program
Sponsor: University of Arizona College of Medicine
Arizona Poison and Drug Information Center
University Medical Center
Prgm Director: Frank Walter, MD*
1501 N Campbell Avenue
Box 245057
Tucson, AZ 85724
Tel: 520 626-1187   *Fax:* 520 626-1633
Length: 2 Yrs   *ACGME Approved/Offered Positions:* 2
Program ID: 118-03-31-024

California

Sacramento

University of California (Davis) Health System Program
Sponsor: University of California (Davis) Health System
University of California (Davis) Medical Center
VA Northern California Health Care System
Prgm Director: Timothy E Albertson, MD, PhD
4150 V Street
PSSB 3400
Sacramento, CA 95817
Tel: 916 734-3564   *Fax:* 916 734-7924
Length: 2 Yrs   *ACGME Approved/Offered Positions:* 2
Program ID: 118-05-21-008

Colorado

Denver

Denver Health Medical Center Program
Sponsor: Denver Health Medical Center
Prgm Director: Kennon Heard, MD
777 Bannock Street
Mail Code 0180
Denver, CO 80204
Tel: 303 739-1264   *Fax:* 303 739-1119
E-mail: kennon.heard@rmpdc.org
Length: 2 Yrs   *ACGME Approved/Offered Positions:* 4
Program ID: 118-07-31-013

Connecticut

Farmington

University of Connecticut/Hartford Hospital Program
Sponsor: University of Connecticut School of Medicine
Hartford Hospital
Univ of Connecticut Health Center/John Dempsey Hospital
Prgm Director: Charles A McKay Jr, MD
Division of Medical Toxicology/Poison Control Ctr
263 Farmington Ave
Farmington, CT 06030
Tel: 860 545-5411   *Fax:* 860 545-2137
E-mail: cmckay@harthosp.org
Length: 2 Yrs   *ACGME Approved/Offered Positions:* 4
Program ID: 118-08-12-006

District of Columbia

Washington

George Washington University Program
Sponsor: George Washington University School of Medicine
National Capital Poison Center
Prgm Director: Cathleen Clancy, MD
3201 New Mexico Avenue
Suite 310
Washington, DC 20016
Tel: 202 362-3867   *Fax:* 202 362-8377
E-mail: cat@poison.org
Length: 2 Yrs   *ACGME Approved/Offered Positions:* 4
Program ID: 118-10-12-027

Georgia

Atlanta

Emory University Program
Sponsor: Emory University School of Medicine
Centers for Disease Control and Prevention
Georgia Poison Control Center-Grady Health System
Prgm Director: Brent W Morgan, MD
80 Jesse Hill Jr Drive SE
Atlanta, GA 30303
Tel: 404 616-4403   *Fax:* 404 616-6657
E-mail: bmorgan@georgiapoisoncenter.org
Length: 2 Yrs   *ACGME Approved/Offered Positions:* 6
Program ID: 118-12-12-021

Illinois

Chicago

John H Stroger Hospital of Cook County Program
Sponsor: John H Stroger Hospital of Cook County
Illinois Poison Center
University of Illinois Hospital and Clinics
Prgm Director: Steven E Aks, DO
Department of Emergency Medicine, 10th Floor
1900 West Polk Street
Chicago, IL 60612
Tel: 312 864-0196   *Fax:* 312 864-9468
E-mail: saks@ccbh.org
Length: 2 Yrs   *ACGME Approved/Offered Positions:* 4
Program ID: 118-16-21-028

Programs

Indiana

Indianapolis

Indiana University School of Medicine Program
Sponsor: Indiana University School of Medicine
Clarian Methodist Hospital of Indiana
William N Wishard Memorial Hospital
Prgm Director: Louise W Kao, MD
1701 N Senate Blvd
Indianapolis, IN 46202
Tel: 317 962-8688   *Fax:* 317 962-2337
E-mail: Lkao@clarian.org
Length: 2 Yrs   *ACGME Approved/Offered Positions:* 4
Program ID: 118-17-12-017

Massachusetts

Boston

Children's Hospital/Boston Medical Center Program
Sponsor: Children's Hospital
Beth Israel Deaconess Medical Center
Cambridge Health Alliance
Prgm Director: Michele Burns Ewald, MD
IC Smith Building
300 Longwood Avenue
Boston, MA 02115
Tel: 617 355-6609   *Fax:* 617 730-0521
E-mail: michael.iocco@childrens.harvard.edu
Length: 2 Yrs   *ACGME Approved/Offered Positions:* 2
Program ID: 118-24-31-007

Worcester

University of Massachusetts Program
Sponsor: University of Massachusetts Medical School
Children's Hospital
UMass Memorial Health Care (University Campus)
Prgm Director: Edward W Boyer, MD, PhD
55 Lake Avenue North
Worcester, MA 01655
Tel: 508 334-7988   *Fax:* 508 334-7411
Length: 2 Yrs   *ACGME Approved/Offered Positions:* 6
Program ID: 118-24-21-015

Michigan

Detroit

Wayne State University/Detroit Medical Center Program
Sponsor: Wayne State University/Detroit Medical Center
Children's Hospital of Michigan
Prgm Director: Cynthia K Aaron, MD
4160 John R, Suite 616
Detroit, MI 48201
Tel: 313 745-5335   *Fax:* 313 745-5493
E-mail: caaron@dmc.org
Length: 2 Yrs   *ACGME Approved/Offered Positions:* 4
Program ID: 118-25-12-014

Minnesota

St. Paul

HealthPartners Institute for Medical Education Program
Sponsor: HealthPartners Institute for Medical Education
Regions Hospital
Hennepin County Medical Center
Prgm Director: Andrew Topliff, MD
Graduate Medical Education, Regions Hospital 11501G
640 Jackson Street
Saint Paul, MN 55101
Tel: 651 254-1504   *Fax:* 651 254-5044
E-mail: deb.k.collier@healthpartners.com
Length: 2 Yrs   *ACGME Approved/Offered Positions:* 2
Program ID: 118-26-13-029

New York

Great Neck

NSLIJHS-North Shore University Hospital/NYU School of Medicine Program
Sponsor: North Shore-Long Island Jewish Health System
Long Island Regional Poison and Drug Information Center
New York City Poison Control Center
North Shore University Hospital
Schneider Children's Hospital at Long Island Jewish Med Ctr
Prgm Director: Mark Su, MD
Department of Emergency Medicine
300 Community Drive
Manhasset, NY 11030
Tel: 516 562-2925   *Fax:* 516 562-3569
E-mail: msu@nshs.edu
Length: 2 Yrs   *ACGME Approved/Offered Positions:* 2
Program ID: 118-35-13-026

New York

New York University School of Medicine Program
Sponsor: New York University School of Medicine
Bellevue Hospital Center
New York City Poison Control Center
NYU Hospitals Center
Prgm Director: Lewis Nelson, MD
455 First Avenue, Room 123
New York, NY 10016
Tel: 212 447-8150   *Fax:* 212 447-8223
E-mail: lewis.nelson@nyumc.org
Length: 2 Yrs   *ACGME Approved/Offered Positions:* 6
Program ID: 118-35-31-002

North Carolina

Charlotte

Carolinas Medical Center Program
Sponsor: Carolinas Medical Center
Prgm Director: William P Kerns II, MD
Department of Emergency Medicine, MEB
1000 Blythe Boulevard
Charlotte, NC 28203
Tel: 704 355-5297   *Fax:* 704 355-8356
E-mail: rkerns@carolinashealthcare.org
Length: 2 Yrs   *ACGME Approved/Offered Positions:* 4
Program ID: 118-36-21-020

Ohio

Cincinnati

University Hospital/University of Cincinnati College of Medicine Program
Sponsor: University Hospital Inc
Prgm Director: Edward J Otten, MD
231 Albert Sabin Way
Cincinnati, OH 45267
Tel: 513 558-8094   *Fax:* 513 558-5791
Length: 2 Yrs   *ACGME Approved/Offered Positions:* 4
Program ID: 118-38-21-012

Oregon

Portland

Oregon Health & Science University Program
Sponsor: Oregon Health & Science University Hospital
Prgm Director: B Zane Horowitz, MD
3181 SW Sam Jackson Park Road
MC CSB-550
Portland, OR 97239
Tel: 503 494-4833   *Fax:* 503 494-4980
E-mail: horowiza@ohsu.edu
Length: 2 Yrs   *ACGME Approved/Offered Positions:* 4
Program ID: 118-40-21-003

Pennsylvania

Hershey

Penn State University/Milton S Hershey Medical Center Program
Sponsor: Milton S Hershey Medical Center
PinnacleHealth System-Harrisburg Hospital
Prgm Director: J Ward Donovan, MD
Harrisburg Hospital
111 S Front St
Harrisburg, PA 17101
Tel: 717 782-5187   *Fax:* 717 782-5188
E-mail: wdonovan@pinnaclehealth.org
Length: 2 Yrs   *ACGME Approved/Offered Positions:* 4
Program ID: 118-41-12-004

Philadelphia

Albert Einstein Healthcare Network Program
Sponsor: Albert Einstein Medical Center
Children's Hospital of Philadelphia
Prgm Director: Adam Rowden, DO
Department of Emergency Medicine, Korman B-9
5501 Old York Road
Philadelphia, PA 19141
Tel: 212 456-6679   *Fax:* 215 456-8502
E-mail: rowdena@einstein.edu
Length: 2 Yrs   *ACGME Approved/Offered Positions:* 2
Program ID: 118-41-31-030

Children's Hospital of Philadelphia Program
Sponsor: Children's Hospital of Philadelphia
University of Pennsylvania Health System
Prgm Director: Kevin C Osterhoudt, MD, MS
The Children's Hospital of Philadelphia
34th Street and Civic Center Boulevard
Philadelphia, PA 19104
Tel: 215 590-3335   *Fax:* 215 590-4454
E-mail: poisoncontroladmin@email.chop.edu
Length: 2 Yrs   *ACGME Approved/Offered Positions:* 2
Program ID: 118-41-22-023

Note: * indicates a newly appointed program director

Drexel University College of Medicine/Hahnemann University Hospital Program
Sponsor: Drexel University College of Medicine/Hahnemann University
Hahnemann University Hospital (Tenet Health System)
Mercy Fitzgerald Hospital
Mercy Philadelphia Hospital
St Christopher's Hospital for Children (Tenet Health System)
Prgm Director: Michael I Greenberg, MD, MPH
245 N 15th Street, Suite 2108
2nd Floor NCB, Mail Stop 1011
Philadelphia, PA 19102
Tel: 215 762-2368   *Fax:* 215 762-1307
E-mail: MGreenbe@drexelmed.edu
Length: 2 Yrs   *ACGME Approved/Offered Positions:* 4
Program ID: 118-41-31-019

Pittsburgh

University of Pittsburgh Medical Center Medical Education Program
Sponsor: Univ of Pittsburgh Medical Center Medical Education
Pittsburgh Poison Center
Prgm Director: Kenneth D Katz, MD*
UPMC Presbyterian, D-L45
200 Lothrop Street
Pittsburgh, PA 15213
Tel: 412 647-9922   *Fax:* 412 647-5053
Length: 2 Yrs   *ACGME Approved/Offered Positions:* 2
Program ID: 118-41-21-025

Texas

Dallas

University of Texas Southwestern Medical School Program
Sponsor: University of Texas Southwestern Medical School
Children's Medical Center of Dallas
Dallas County Hospital District-Parkland Memorial Hospital
Prgm Director: Kurt C Kleinschmidt, MD
Emergency Medicine / Section of Toxicology
5323 Harry Hines Boulevard
Dallas, TX 75390
Tel: 214 590-1354   *Fax:* 214 590-5008
Length: 2 Yrs   *ACGME Approved/Offered Positions:* 4
Program ID: 118-48-31-009

Virginia

Charlottesville

University of Virginia Program
Sponsor: University of Virginia Medical Center
Prgm Director: Mark A Kirk, MD
Department of Emergency Medicine
PO Box 800774
Charlottesville, VA 22908
Tel: 434 924-0348   *Fax:* 434 971-8657
Length: 2 Yrs   *ACGME Approved/Offered Positions:* 2
Program ID: 118-51-13-022

Medical Toxicology (Preventive Medicine)

California

San Diego

University of California (San Diego) Program
Sponsor: University of California (San Diego) Medical Center
California Poison Control System (CPSC)-San Diego
Naval Medical Center (San Diego)
Rady Children's Hospital
Scripps Mercy Hospital
Veterans Affairs Medical Center (San Diego)
Prgm Director: Binh T Ly, MD
Division of Medical Toxicology
200 W Arbor Drive, #8819
San Diego, CA 92103
Tel: 619 543-6213   *Fax:* 619 543-7598
E-mail: bly@ucsd.edu
Length: 2 Yrs   *ACGME Approved/Offered Positions:* 4
Program ID: 399-05-21-002

San Francisco

University of California (San Francisco) Program
Sponsor: University of California (San Francisco) School of Medicine
San Francisco General Hospital Medical Center
Prgm Director: Neal Benowitz, MD
Box 0843
1001 Potrero Avenue, Bldg 30, Ste 3500
San Francisco, CA 94143
Tel: 415 206-8324   *Fax:* 415 206-4956
E-mail: NBenowitz@medsfgh.ucsf.edu
Length: 2 Yrs   *ACGME Approved/Offered Positions:* 4
Program ID: 399-05-31-003

Molecular Genetic Pathology (Medical Genetics and Pathology)

Alabama

Birmingham

University of Alabama Medical Center Program
Sponsor: University of Alabama Hospital
Prgm Director: Bruce R Korf, MD, PhD
Kaul 230 720 20th Street South
Birmingham, AL 35294
Tel: 205 934-9411   *Fax:* 205 934-9488
Length: 1 Yr   *ACGME Approved/Offered Positions:* 2
Program ID: 190-01-31-012

Arizona

Tucson

University of Arizona Program
Sponsor: University of Arizona College of Medicine
Southern Arizona VA Health Care Center (Tucson)
University Medical Center
Prgm Director: Lisa Rimsza, MD
1501 N Campbell Avenue
PO Box 245043
Tucson, AZ 85724
Tel: 520 626-8396   *Fax:* 520 626-2521
E-mail: umstott@email.arizona.edu
Length: 1 Yr   *ACGME Approved/Offered Positions:* 1
Program ID: 190-03-21-013

California

Los Angeles

Cedars-Sinai Medical Center Program
Sponsor: Cedars-Sinai Medical Center
Prgm Director: Jean R Lopategui, MD
8700 Beverly Boulevard
Los Angeles, CA 90048
Tel: 310 423-5471   *Fax:* 310 423-0436
Length: 1 Yr   *ACGME Approved/Offered Positions:* 1
Program ID: 190-05-21-025

UCLA Medical Center Program
Sponsor: UCLA David Geffen School of Medicine/UCLA Medical Center
UCLA Medical Center
Prgm Director: Wayne W Grody, MD, PhD
10833 Le Conte Avenue
Los Angeles, CA 90095-1732
Tel: 310 825-5648   *Fax:* 310 794-4840
Length: 1 Yr   *ACGME Approved/Offered Positions:* 1
Program ID: 190-05-21-029

Programs

San Francisco

University of California (San Francisco) Program

Sponsor: University of California (San Francisco) School of Medicine
Stanford Hospital and Clinics
Prgm Director: Anna Berry, MD
185 Berry Street, Suite 290
San Francisco, CA 94107
Tel: 415 353-4812
Length: 1 Yr   *ACGME Approved/Offered Positions:* 1
Program ID: 190-05-21-021

Stanford

Stanford University Program

Sponsor: Stanford Hospital and Clinics
Prgm Director: Iris Schrijver, MD
Department of Pathology, Room L235
Stanford, CA 94305
Tel: 650 724-2403
E-mail: iris.schrijver@medcenter.stanford.edu
Length: 1 Yr   *ACGME Approved/Offered Positions:* 2
Program ID: 190-05-13-003

Georgia

Atlanta

Emory University Program

Sponsor: Emory University School of Medicine
Emory University Hospital
Prgm Director: Karen P Mann, MD, PhD
1364 Clifton Road, NE
Atlanta, GA 30322
Tel: 404 712-1264   *Fax:* 404 727-2519
E-mail: kmann@emory.edu
Length: 1 Yr   *ACGME Approved/Offered Positions:* 1
Program ID: 190-12-13-008

Illinois

Chicago

University of Chicago Program

Sponsor: University of Chicago Medical Center
Prgm Director: Darrel Waggoner, MD
5841 South Maryland Avenue
MC0077
Chicago, IL 60637
Tel: 773 834-0555   *Fax:* 773 834-0556
Length: 1 Yr   *ACGME Approved/Offered Positions:* 1
Program ID: 190-16-31-027

Iowa

Iowa City

University of Iowa Hospitals and Clinics Program

Sponsor: University of Iowa Hospitals and Clinics
Prgm Director: Peter L Nagy, MD, PhD
200 Hawkins Drive
C606 GH
Iowa City, IA 52242
Tel: 319 353-4594   *Fax:* 319 356-4916
E-mail: peter-nagy@uiowa.edu
Length: 1 Yr   *ACGME Approved/Offered Positions:* 1
Program ID: 190-18-31-018

Maryland

Baltimore

Johns Hopkins University Program

Sponsor: Johns Hopkins University School of Medicine
Johns Hopkins Hospital
Prgm Director: Christopher D Gocke, MD
600 N Wolfe Street, Park SB-202
Baltimore, MD 21287
Tel: 410 955-8363   *Fax:* 410 614-7440
Length: 1 Yr   *ACGME Approved/Offered Positions:* 1
Program ID: 190-23-13-022

Massachusetts

Boston

Brigham and Women's Hospital/Harvard Medical School Program

Sponsor: Brigham and Women's Hospital
Beth Israel Deaconess Medical Center
Children's Hospital
Dana-Farber Cancer Institute
Massachusetts General Hospital
Prgm Director: Janina A Longtine, MD
Shapiro 5, 016
75 Francis Street
Boston, MA 02115
Tel: 857 307-1539   *Fax:* 857 307-1544
E-mail: jlongtine@partners.org
Length: 1 Yr   *ACGME Approved/Offered Positions:* 4
Program ID: 190-24-13-010

Michigan

Ann Arbor

University of Michigan Program

Sponsor: University of Michigan Hospitals and Health Centers
Prgm Director: Kojo Elenitoba-Johnson, MD
Department of Pathology
109 Zina Pitcher Place, 4061 BSRB
Ann Arbor, MI 48109
Tel: 734 764-6374
E-mail: kojoelen@umich.edu
Length: 1 Yr   *ACGME Approved/Offered Positions:* 1
Program ID: 190-25-31-023

Minnesota

Minneapolis

University of Minnesota Program

Sponsor: University of Minnesota Medical School
University of Minnesota Medical Center, Division of Fairview
Prgm Director: Michelle M Dolan, MD*
MMC 609
420 Delaware Street SE
Minneapolis, MN 55455
Tel: 612 624-8136
Length: 1 Yr   *ACGME Approved/Offered Positions:* 1
Program ID: 190-26-13-019

Rochester

College of Medicine, Mayo Clinic (Rochester) Program

Sponsor: College of Medicine, Mayo Clinic
Mayo Clinic (Rochester)
Prgm Director: Kevin C Halling, MD, PhD
200 First Street, SW
Rochester, MN 55905
Tel: 507 284-9452
E-mail: pathologyeducation@mayo.edu
Length: 1 Yr   *ACGME Approved/Offered Positions:* 2
Program ID: 190-26-12-011

Missouri

St Louis

Washington University/B-JH/SLCH Consortium Program

Sponsor: Washington University/B-JH/SLCH Consortium
Barnes-Jewish Hospital
Prgm Director: John D Pfeifer, MD, PhD
Department of Pathology
660 South Euclid Avenue, Box 8118
St Louis, MO 63110
Tel: 314 747-0276   *Fax:* 314 362-4096
Length: 1 Yr   *ACGME Approved/Offered Positions:* 2
Program ID: 190-28-13-026

New Mexico

Albuquerque

University of New Mexico Program

Sponsor: University of New Mexico School of Medicine
University of New Mexico Hospital
Prgm Director: Mohammad A Vasef, MD
1001 Woodward Place NE
Albuquerque, NM 87102
Tel: 505 938-8468   *Fax:* 505 938-8414
E-mail: mvasef@salud.unm.edu
Length: 1 Yr   *ACGME Approved/Offered Positions:* 1
Program ID: 190-34-12-024

New York

New York

Mount Sinai School of Medicine Program

Sponsor: Mount Sinai School of Medicine
Mount Sinai Medical Center
Prgm Director: David Y Zhang, MD, PhD
Department of Pathology
One Gustave L Levy Place
New York, NY 10029
Tel: 212 659-8173   *Fax:* 212 427-2082
E-mail: allene.carter@mountsinai.org
Length: 1 Yr   *ACGME Approved/Offered Positions:* 1
Program ID: 190-35-12-020

Note: * indicates a newly appointed program director

North Carolina

Chapel Hill

University of North Carolina Hospitals Program
Sponsor: University of North Carolina Hospitals
Prgm Director: Margaret L Gulley, MD
Department of Pathology, CB7525
101 Manning Dr
Chapel Hill, NC 27599
Tel: 919 843-4595   *Fax:* 919 966-6718
E-mail: jBadstei@unch.unc.edu
Length: 1 Yr   *ACGME Approved/Offered Positions:* 1
Program ID: 190-36-12-002

Oklahoma

Oklahoma City

University of Oklahoma Health Sciences Center Program
Sponsor: University of Oklahoma College of Medicine
OU Medical Center
Prgm Director: Michael L Talbert, MD
940 Stanton L Young Boulevard, BMSB 451
Oklahoma City, OK 73104
Tel: 405 271-2422   *Fax:* 405 271-2328
E-mail: Dianne-Wright@ouhsc.edu
Length: 1 Yr   *ACGME Approved/Offered Positions:* 1
Program ID: 190-39-13-014

Oregon

Portland

Oregon Health & Science University Program
Sponsor: Oregon Health & Science University Hospital
Prgm Director: Richard D Press, MD, PhD
Department of Pathology, MC L113
3181 SW Sam Jackson Park Road
Portland, OR 97201
Tel: 503 494-2317   *Fax:* 503 494-2025
Length: 1 Yr   *ACGME Approved/Offered Positions:* 1
Program ID: 190-40-22-004

Pennsylvania

Philadelphia

University of Pennsylvania Program
Sponsor: University of Pennsylvania Health System
Prgm Director: Vivianna M Van Deerlin, MD, PhD
3400 Spruce Street, 7103 Founders
Philadelphia, PA 19104
Tel: 215 662-6550   *Fax:* 215 662-7529
E-mail: vivianna@mail.med.upenn.edu
Length: 1 Yr   *ACGME Approved/Offered Positions:* 2
Program ID: 190-41-21-001

Pittsburgh

University of Pittsburgh Medical Center Medical Education Program
Sponsor: Univ of Pittsburgh Medical Center Medical Education
UPMC Presbyterian Shadyside
Prgm Director: Jeffrey A Kant, MD, PhD
Scaife Hall, Suite 701
3550 Terrace Street
Pittsburgh, PA 15213
Tel: 412 648-8519   *Fax:* 412 383-9594
E-mail: kantja@upmc.edu
Length: 1 Yr   *ACGME Approved/Offered Positions:* 2
Program ID: 190-41-21-009

Tennessee

Nashville

Vanderbilt University Program
Sponsor: Vanderbilt University Medical Center
Prgm Director: Mary M Zutter, MD
1161 21st Avenue - Department of Pathology
C2102-C MCN
Nashville, TN 37232
Tel: 615 322-0146   *Fax:* 615 343-7961
Length: 1 Yr   *ACGME Approved/Offered Positions:* 1
Program ID: 190-47-31-016

Texas

Houston

Baylor College of Medicine Program
Sponsor: Baylor College of Medicine
Texas Children's Hospital
University of Texas M D Anderson Cancer Center
Prgm Director: Dolores Lopez-Terrada, MD, PhD
One Baylor Plaza
Houston, TX 77030
Tel: 713 798-5490
E-mail: dhterrad@texaschildrenshospital.org
Length: 1 Yr   *ACGME Approved/Offered Positions:* 2
Program ID: 190-48-22-007

University of Texas M D Anderson Cancer Center Program
Sponsor: University of Texas M D Anderson Cancer Center
Prgm Director: Rajyalakshmi (Raja) Luthra, PhD*
Department of Hematopathology, Box 72
1515 Holcombe Boulevard
Houston, TX 77030
Tel: 713 794-4780   *Fax:* 713 794-4773
Length: 1 Yr   *ACGME Approved/Offered Positions:* 1
Program ID: 190-48-12-015

Utah

Salt Lake City

University of Utah Program
Sponsor: University of Utah Medical Center
Primary Children's Medical Center
Prgm Director: Karl V Voelkerding, MD
30 North 1900 East
Salt Lake City, UT 84132
Tel: 801 583-2787   *Fax:* 801 584-5207
Length: 1 Yr   *ACGME Approved/Offered Positions:* 1
Program ID: 190-49-12-017

Virginia

Richmond

Virginia Commonwealth University Health System Program
Sponsor: Virginia Commonwealth University Health System
Virginia Commonwealth University School of Medicine
Prgm Director: David S Wilkinson, MD, PhD*
PO Box 980662
Richmond, VA 23298
Tel: 804 828-0183   *Fax:* 804 828-2869
Length: 1 Yr   *ACGME Approved/Offered Positions:* 1
Program ID: 190-51-11-005

Musculoskeletal Oncology (Orthopaedic Surgery)

District of Columbia

Washington

Washington Hospital Center/Georgetown University Program
Sponsor: Washington Hospital Center
Prgm Director: Robert M Henshaw, MD
110 Irving Street, NW, Suite C2173
Washington, DC 20010
Tel: 202 877-3970   *Fax:* 202 877-8959
E-mail: robert.m.henshaw@medstar.net
Length: 1 Yr   *ACGME Approved/Offered Positions:* 1
Program ID: 270-10-21-013

Florida

Gainesville

University of Florida Program
Sponsor: University of Florida College of Medicine
Shands Hospital at the University of Florida
Prgm Director: Mark T Scarborough, MD
Department of Orthopaedic Surgery
PO Box 112727
Gainesville, FL 32611
Tel: 352 273-7390   *Fax:* 352 273-7388
Length: 1 Yr   *ACGME Approved/Offered Positions:* 2
Program ID: 270-11-21-009

Miami

Jackson Memorial Hospital/Jackson Health System Program
Sponsor: Jackson Memorial Hospital/Jackson Health System
Miami Children's Hospital
University of Miami Hospital
Prgm Director: H Thomas Temple, MD
1611 NW 12th Avenue
Dept of Orthopaedic Surgery
Miami, FL 33136
Tel: 305 325-4475   *Fax:* 305 325-3928
E-mail: zmoore@med.miami.edu
Length: 1 Yr   *ACGME Approved/Offered Positions:* 2
Program ID: 270-11-22-016

Illinois

Chicago

University of Chicago Program
Sponsor: University of Chicago Medical Center
Prgm Director: Terrance Peabody, MD
5841 S Maryland Avenue, MC 3079
Chicago, IL 60637
Tel: 773 702-3442   *Fax:* 773 702-4384
Length: 1 Yr   *ACGME Approved/Offered Positions:* 1
Program ID: 270-16-21-001

Programs

Massachusetts

Boston

Massachusetts General Hospital/Harvard Medical School Program

Sponsor: Massachusetts General Hospital
Beth Israel Deaconess Medical Center
Children's Hospital
Prgm Director: Francis J Hornicek, MD, PhD
55 Fruit Street
Yawkey 3700
Boston, MA 02114
Tel: 617 724-6802   *Fax:* 617 726-6823
Length: 1 Yr   *ACGME Approved/Offered Positions:* 3
Program ID: 270-24-21-003

Minnesota

Rochester

College of Medicine, Mayo Clinic (Rochester) Program

Sponsor: College of Medicine, Mayo Clinic
Mayo Clinic (Rochester)
Rochester Methodist Hospital
Saint Marys Hospital of Rochester
Prgm Director: Michael G Rock, MD
200 First Street, SW
Rochester, MN 55905
Tel: 507 284-3316   *Fax:* 507 266-4323
E-mail: mgsm.roch.mn.orthopedics@mayo.edu
Length: 1 Yr   *ACGME Approved/Offered Positions:* 1
Program ID: 270-26-21-004

New Jersey

Newark

UMDNJ-New Jersey Medical School Program

Sponsor: UMDNJ-New Jersey Medical School
UMDNJ-University Hospital
Prgm Director: Joseph Benevenia, MD
90 Bergen Street
Dept of Orthopaedics, DOC Suite 7300
Newark, NJ 07101
Tel: 973 972-2153   *Fax:* 973 972-1080
E-mail: birthwma@umdnj.edu
Length: 1 Yr   *ACGME Approved/Offered Positions:* 1
Program ID: 270-33-31-017

New York

New York

Memorial Sloan-Kettering Cancer Center Program

Sponsor: Memorial Sloan-Kettering Cancer Center
Hospital for Special Surgery
Prgm Director: Carol D Morris, MD, MS*
1275 York Avenue
New York, NY 10021
Tel: 212 639-2893   *Fax:* 212 717-3573
Length: 1 Yr   *ACGME Approved/Offered Positions:* 2
Program ID: 270-35-21-005

Tennessee

Nashville

Vanderbilt University Program

Sponsor: Vanderbilt University Medical Center
Prgm Director: Herbert S Schwartz, MD
1215 21st Avenue South
Medical Center East, South Tower, Suite 4200
Nashville, TN 37232
Tel: 615 322-8890   *Fax:* 615 343-1028
E-mail: marla.johnson@vanderbilt.edu
Length: 1 Yr   *ACGME Approved/Offered Positions:* 1
Program ID: 270-47-13-018

Texas

Houston

University of Texas M D Anderson Cancer Center Program

Sponsor: University of Texas M D Anderson Cancer
Center
Prgm Director: Valerae O Lewis, BS, MD
1400 Holcome Boulevard, Unit 408
PO Box 301402
Houston, TX 77030
Tel: 713 792-5073   *Fax:* 713 792-8448
Length: 1 Yr   *ACGME Approved/Offered Positions:* 2
Program ID: 270-48-13-014

Musculoskeletal Radiology (Radiology-Diagnostic)

California

Los Angeles

Cedars-Sinai Medical Center Program

Sponsor: Cedars-Sinai Medical Center
Prgm Director: Thomas J Learch, MD
8700 Beverly Boulevard
Taper Building, Suite M335
Los Angeles, CA 90048
Tel: 310 423-3095   *Fax:* 310 423-8335
Length: 1 Yr   *ACGME Approved/Offered Positions:* 1
Program ID: 426-05-21-015

Michigan

Detroit

Henry Ford Hospital Program

Sponsor: Henry Ford Hospital
Prgm Director: Marnix T van Holsbeeck, MD
Department of Diagnostic Radiology
2799 West Grand Boulevard, E-328
Detroit, MI 48202
Tel: 313 916-7952   *Fax:* 313 916-8857
Length: 1 Yr   *ACGME Approved/Offered Positions:* 4
Program ID: 426-25-21-001

Royal Oak

William Beaumont Hospital Program

Sponsor: William Beaumont Hospital
Prgm Director: David R Marcantonio, MD
3601 West 13 Mile Road
Royal Oak, MI 48073
Tel: 248 898-6026
E-mail: David.Marcantonio@beaumont.edu
Length: 1 Yr   *ACGME Approved/Offered Positions:* 2
Program ID: 426-25-13-012
Uniformed Services Program

New York

Bronx

Albert Einstein College of Medicine Program

Sponsor: Albert Einstein College of Medicine of Yeshiva
University
Montefiore Medical Center-Weiler Division
Prgm Director: Beverly Thornhill, MD
Dept of Radiology
111 East 210th Street
Bronx, NY 10467
Tel: 718 920-5506   *Fax:* 718 798-7983
E-mail: eofrias@montefiore.org
Length: 1 Yr   *ACGME Approved/Offered Positions:* 1
Program ID: 426-35-21-002

Note: * indicates a newly appointed program director

New York

New York University School of Medicine Program

Sponsor: New York University School of Medicine
Bellevue Hospital Center
NYU Hospital for Joint Diseases
NYU Hospitals Center
Prgm Director: Leon D Rybak, MD
560 First Avenue
New York, NY 10016
Tel: 212 598-6643   *Fax:* 212 598-6125
Length: 1 Yr   *ACGME Approved/Offered Positions:* 5
Program ID: 426-35-11-006

Rochester

University of Rochester Program

Sponsor: Strong Memorial Hospital of the University of Rochester
Prgm Director: Johnny U V Monu, MD
Box 648
601 Elmwood Avenue
Rochester, NY 14642
Tel: 585 275-6359   *Fax:* 585 273-1033
E-mail: holly_stiner@urmc.rochester.edu
Length: 1 Yr   *ACGME Approved/Offered Positions:* 3
Program ID: 426-35-31-003

Stony Brook

SUNY at Stony Brook Program

Sponsor: University Hospital - SUNY at Stony Brook
Prgm Director: Elaine S Gould, MD
Department of Radiology
HSC Level 4 Room 120
Stony Brook, NY 11794
Tel: 631 444-2906   *Fax:* 631 444-7538
E-mail: egould@notes.cc.sunysb.edu
Length: 1 Yr   *ACGME Approved/Offered Positions:* 1
Program ID: 426-35-21-011

North Carolina

Winston-Salem

Wake Forest University School of Medicine Program

Sponsor: Wake Forest University Baptist Medical Center
Prgm Director: Leon Lenchik, MD
Medical Center Boulevard
Winston-Salem, NC 27157
Tel: 336 716-2478   *Fax:* 336 716-1278
E-mail: llenchik@wfubmc.edu
Length: 1 Yr   *ACGME Approved/Offered Positions:* 4
Program ID: 426-36-21-004

Ohio

Cleveland

Cleveland Clinic Foundation Program

Sponsor: Cleveland Clinic Foundation
Prgm Director: Bradford J Richmond, MD
9500 Euclid Avenue, A21
Desk A-21
Cleveland, OH 44195
Tel: 216 444-3931   *Fax:* 216 445-9445
E-mail: richmob@ccf.org
Length: 1 Yr   *ACGME Approved/Offered Positions:* 1
Program ID: 426-38-21-007

Pennsylvania

Philadelphia

Temple University Hospital Program

Sponsor: Temple University Hospital
Prgm Director: Sayed M Ali, MD*
3400 North Broad Street
Philadelphia, PA 19140
Tel: 215 707-6847   *Fax:* 215 707-5851
Length: 1 Yr   *ACGME Approved/Offered Positions:* 1
Program ID: 426-41-21-005

Thomas Jefferson University Program

Sponsor: Thomas Jefferson University Hospital
Prgm Director: Adam C Zoga, MD
Department of Radiology
132 South 10th Street, 10th Floor Main Building
Philadelphia, PA 19107
Tel: 215 955-8890   *Fax:* 215 923-1562
Length: 1 Yr   *ACGME Approved/Offered Positions:* 3
Program ID: 426-41-31-013

University of Pennsylvania Program

Sponsor: University of Pennsylvania Health System
Prgm Director: Judy S Blebea, MD
1 Silverstein
3400 Spruce Street
Philadelphia, PA 19104
Tel: 215 662-3019   *Fax:* 215 662-3037
Length: 1 Yr   *ACGME Approved/Offered Positions:* 3
Program ID: 426-41-13-009

Texas

Houston

University of Texas at Houston Program

Sponsor: University of Texas Health Science Center at Houston
Memorial Hermann Hospital
St Luke's Episcopal Hospital
University of Texas M D Anderson Cancer Center
Prgm Director: John E Madewell, MD
1515 Holcombe Boulevard
Unit 1273
Houston, TX 77030
Tel: 713 792-4973   *Fax:* 713 563-6626
Length: 1 Yr   *ACGME Approved/Offered Positions:* 2
Program ID: 426-48-12-014

Neonatal-Perinatal Medicine (Pediatrics)

Alabama

Birmingham

University of Alabama Medical Center Program

Sponsor: University of Alabama Hospital
Children's Hospital of Alabama
Cooper Green Hospital
Prgm Director: Waldemar A Carlo, MD
Division of Neonatalogy
525 New Hillman Building
Birmingham, AL 35233
Tel: 205 934-4680   *Fax:* 205 934-3100
Length: 3 Yrs   *ACGME Approved/Offered Positions:* 6
Program ID: 329-01-21-001

Arkansas

Little Rock

University of Arkansas for Medical Sciences Program

Sponsor: University of Arkansas College of Medicine
Arkansas Children's Hospital
UAMS Medical Center
Prgm Director: Ashley S Ross III, MD*
Neonatology, Slot 512 B
4301 W Markham St
Little Rock, AR 72205
Tel: 501 603-1255   *Fax:* 501 686-8937
E-mail: rossashleys@uams.edu
Length: 3 Yrs   *ACGME Approved/Offered Positions:* 4
Program ID: 329-04-21-105

California

Loma Linda

Loma Linda University Program

Sponsor: Loma Linda University Medical Center
Prgm Director: Andrew O Hopper, MD
11175 Campus Street
Division of Neonatology
Loma Linda, CA 92354
Tel: 909 558-7448   *Fax:* 909 558-0298
E-mail: ahopper@llu.edu
Length: 3 Yrs   *ACGME Approved/Offered Positions:* 7
Program ID: 329-05-21-062

Los Angeles

UCLA Medical Center Program

Sponsor: UCLA David Geffen School of Medicine/UCLA Medical Center
UCLA Medical Center
Prgm Director: Sherin U Devaskar, MD
10833 Le Conte Avenue, B2-375 MDCC
Los Angeles, CA 90095
Tel: 310 825-9436   *Fax:* 310 267-0154
E-mail: emanczuk@mednet.ucla.edu
Length: 3 Yrs   *ACGME Approved/Offered Positions:* 9
Program ID: 329-05-21-005

University of Southern California/ LAC+USC Medical Center Program

Sponsor: University of Southern California/LAC+USC Medical Center
Childrens Hospital Los Angeles
LAC+USC Medical Center
Prgm Director: Rangasamy Ramanathan, MD
Women's and Children's Hospital, Room L-919
1240 North Mission Road
Los Angeles, CA 90033
Tel: 323 226-3409   *Fax:* 323 226-3440
E-mail: ramanath@usc.edu
Length: 3 Yrs   *ACGME Approved/Offered Positions:* 15
Program ID: 329-05-21-004

Orange

University of California (Irvine) Program

Sponsor: University of California (Irvine) Medical Center
Prgm Director: Houchang D Modanlou, MD
Building 56, Suite 600, ZOT 4490
101 The City Drive South
Orange, CA 92868
Tel: 714 456-6933   *Fax:* 714 456-7658
Length: 3 Yrs   *ACGME Approved/Offered Positions:* 6
Program ID: 329-05-31-114

Sacramento

University of California (Davis) Health System Program

Sponsor: University of California (Davis) Health System
University of California (Davis) Medical Center
Prgm Director: Francis R Poulain, MD
Division of Neonatology
Surge I, Rm 1121
Davis, CA 95616
Tel: 916 752-3441   *Fax:* 916 752-6215
E-mail: matthew.castles@ucdmc.ucdavis.edu
Length: 3 Yrs   *ACGME Approved/Offered Positions:* 6
Program ID: 329-05-21-007

San Diego

University of California (San Diego) Program

Sponsor: University of California (San Diego) Medical Center
Rady Children's Hospital
Prgm Director: Neil N Finer, MD
Department of Pediatrics, Division of Neonatology
402 Dickinson St, MPF 1-140
San Diego, CA 92103
Tel: 619 543-3759   *Fax:* 619 543-3812
Length: 3 Yrs   *ACGME Approved/Offered Positions:* 9
Program ID: 329-05-31-096

San Francisco

University of California (San Francisco) Program

Sponsor: University of California (San Francisco) School of Medicine
UCSF and Mount Zion Medical Centers
Prgm Director: David H Rowitch, MD, PhD
Room U503, Box 0734
533 Parnassus Ave
San Francisco, CA 94143
Tel: 415 467-1888   *Fax:* 415 476-9976
E-mail: thompsonsh@peds.ucsf.edu
Length: 3 Yrs   *ACGME Approved/Offered Positions:* 9
Program ID: 329-05-21-009

Stanford

Stanford University Program

Sponsor: Stanford Hospital and Clinics
Lucile Salter Packard Children's Hospital at Stanford
Prgm Director: Louis P Halamek, MD
Division of Neonatal and Developmental Medicine
750 Welch Road, Suite 315
Palo Alto, CA 94304
Tel: 650 723-5711   *Fax:* 650 725-8351
E-mail: alaborde@stanford.edu
Length: 3 Yrs   *ACGME Approved/Offered Positions:* 7
Program ID: 329-05-21-010

Torrance

Los Angeles County-Harbor-UCLA Medical Center Program

Sponsor: Los Angeles County-Harbor-UCLA Medical Center
Children's Hospital of Orange County
Prgm Director: Virender Rehan, MD*
1000 W Carson Street
Torrance, CA 90509
Tel: 310 222-1975   *Fax:* 310 222-3887
E-mail: vrehan@labiomed.org
Length: 3 Yrs   *ACGME Approved/Offered Positions:* 6
Program ID: 329-05-11-116

Colorado

Aurora

University of Colorado Denver Program

Sponsor: University of Colorado Denver School of Medicine
Children's Hospital (The)
Prgm Director: Thomas A Parker, MD
13123 E 16th Ave
Box B070
Aurora, CO 80045
Tel: 303 724-2867   *Fax:* 720 777-7323
E-mail: parker.thomas@tchden.org
Length: 3 Yrs   *ACGME Approved/Offered Positions:* 9
Program ID: 329-07-21-012

Connecticut

Farmington

University of Connecticut Program

Sponsor: University of Connecticut School of Medicine
Connecticut Children's Medical Center
Univ of Connecticut Health Center/John Dempsey Hospital
Prgm Director: Aniruddha Vidwans, MD
Division of Neonatology
263 Farmington Avenue
Farmington, CT 06030
Tel: 860 679-2254   *Fax:* 860 679-1403
E-mail: vidwans@nso1.uchc.edu
Length: 3 Yrs   *ACGME Approved/Offered Positions:* 5
Program ID: 329-08-21-013

New Haven

Yale-New Haven Medical Center Program

Sponsor: Yale-New Haven Hospital
Prgm Director: Ian Gross, MD
Department of Pediatrics
PO Box 208064
New Haven, CT 06520
Tel: 203 688-2320   *Fax:* 203 688-5426
E-mail: ian.gross@yale.edu
Length: 3 Yrs   *ACGME Approved/Offered Positions:* 8
Program ID: 329-08-21-014

Delaware

Wilmington

Jefferson Medical College/duPont Hospital for Children Program

Sponsor: Jefferson Medical College
Christiana Care Health Services Inc
Prgm Director: Stephen Pearlman, MD
1025 Walnut Street, Suite 700
Philadelphia, PA 19107
Tel: 302 733-2410   *Fax:* 302 733-2602
Length: 3 Yrs   *ACGME Approved/Offered Positions:* 12
Program ID: 329-41-21-104

District of Columbia

Washington

Children's National Medical Center/ George Washington University Program

Sponsor: Children's National Medical Center
George Washington University Hospital (UHS)
Prgm Director: Khodayar Rais-Bahrami, MD
Department of Neonatology
111 Michigan Avenue, NW
Washington, DC 20010
Tel: 202 476-4764   *Fax:* 202 476-3459
E-mail: kraisbah@cnmc.org
Length: 3 Yrs   *ACGME Approved/Offered Positions:* 8
Program ID: 329-10-21-015

Georgetown University Hospital Program

Sponsor: Georgetown University Hospital
Prgm Director: Jayashree Ramasethu, MBBS, MD*
3800 Reservoir Rd NW
Suite M-3400
Washington, DC 20007
Tel: 202 444-8569   *Fax:* 202 444-4747
E-mail: jr65@gunet.georgetown.edu
Length: 3 Yrs   *ACGME Approved/Offered Positions:* 6
Program ID: 329-10-21-066

Florida

Gainesville

University of Florida Program

Sponsor: University of Florida College of Medicine
Shands Hospital at the University of Florida
Prgm Director: Josef Neu, MD
Division of Neonatology
1600 SW Archer Road, Room HD513
Gainesville, FL 32610
Tel: 352 392-4193   *Fax:* 352 846-3937
Length: 3 Yrs   *ACGME Approved/Offered Positions:* 6
Program ID: 329-11-21-016

Miami

Jackson Memorial Hospital/Jackson Health System Program

Sponsor: Jackson Memorial Hospital/Jackson Health System
Prgm Director: Eduardo Bancalari, MD
PO Box 016960 (R-131)
Miami, FL 33101
Tel: 305 585-2328   *Fax:* 305 545-6581
Length: 3 Yrs   *ACGME Approved/Offered Positions:* 9
Program ID: 329-11-21-017

Note: * indicates a newly appointed program director

Tampa

University of South Florida Program
Sponsor: University of South Florida College of Medicine
All Children's Hospital
Tampa General Hospital
Prgm Director: Terri L Ashmeade, MD
2 Tampa General Circle
STC 5th Floor
Tampa, FL 33606
Tel: 813 259-8812   *Fax:* 813 259-8810
E-mail: tashmead@health.usf.edu
Length: 3 Yrs   *ACGME Approved/Offered Positions:* 6
Program ID: 329-11-21-018

Georgia

Atlanta

Emory University Program
Sponsor: Emory University School of Medicine
Children's Healthcare of Atlanta at Egleston
Grady Health System
Prgm Director: James Moore, MD, PhD
Department of Pediatrics
Atlanta, GA 30322
Tel: 404 727-5765   *Fax:* 404 727-3236
E-mail: james_moore@oz.ped.emory.edu
Length: 3 Yrs   *ACGME Approved/Offered Positions:* 7
Program ID: 329-12-21-085

Augusta

Medical College of Georgia Program
Sponsor: Medical College of Georgia
Prgm Director: Jatinder Bhatia, MD
Section of Neonatology
1120 15th St, BIW 6033
Augusta, GA 30912
Tel: 706 721-2331   *Fax:* 706 721-7531
E-mail: jatindeb@mail.mcg.edu
Length: 3 Yrs   *ACGME Approved/Offered Positions:* 4
Program ID: 329-12-21-067

Hawaii

Honolulu

University of Hawaii Program
Sponsor: University of Hawaii John A Burns School of
Medicine
Kapiolani Medical Center for Women and Children
Tripler Army Medical Center
Prgm Director: Mark W Thompson, MD
1 Jarrett White Road
Honolulu, HI 96859
Tel: 808 433-6407   *Fax:* 808 433-6237
Length: 3 Yrs   *ACGME Approved/Offered Positions:* 6
Program ID: 329-14-21-019

Illinois

Chicago

John H Stroger Hospital of Cook County Program
Sponsor: John H Stroger Hospital of Cook County
Prgm Director: Suma P Pyati, MD
1901 West Harrison
Division of Neonatology, Room 4402
Chicago, IL 60612
Tel: 312 864-4043   *Fax:* 312 864-9943
E-mail: sumapyati@hotmail.com
Length: 3 Yrs   *ACGME Approved/Offered Positions:* 6
Program ID: 329-16-21-020

McGaw Medical Center of Northwestern University Program
Sponsor: McGaw Medical Center of Northwestern
University
Children's Memorial Hospital
Evanston Hospital
Northwestern Memorial Hospital
Prgm Director: Raye-Ann O deRegnier, MD
Div of Neonatology, #45
2300 Children's Plaza
Chicago, IL 60614
Tel: 773 880-4142   *Fax:* 773 880-3061
E-mail: r-deregnier@northwestern.edu
Length: 3 Yrs   *ACGME Approved/Offered Positions:* 9
Program ID: 329-16-21-021

University of Chicago Program
Sponsor: University of Chicago Medical Center
Prgm Director: William L Meadow, MD, PhD
5841 S Maryland Avenue, MC6060
Chicago, IL 60637
Tel: 773 702-6210   *Fax:* 773 702-0764
E-mail: wlm1@uchicago.edu
Length: 3 Yrs   *ACGME Approved/Offered Positions:* 9
Program ID: 329-16-11-098

University of Illinois College of Medicine at Chicago Program
Sponsor: University of Illinois College of Medicine at
Chicago
University of Illinois Hospital and Clinics
Prgm Director: Usha Raj, MD*
Division of Neonatology
840 S Wood Street
Chicago, IL 60612
Tel: 312 413-2867   *Fax:* 312 996-8352
E-mail: usharaj@uic.edu
Length: 3 Yrs   *ACGME Approved/Offered Positions:* 5
Program ID: 329-16-21-022

Maywood

Loyola University Program
Sponsor: Loyola University Medical Center
Prgm Director: Jonathan K Muraskas, MD
2160 South First Avenue
107-5811
Maywood, IL 60153
Tel: 708 216-1067   *Fax:* 708 216-5602
E-mail: bkanzia@lumc.edu
Length: 3 Yrs   *ACGME Approved/Offered Positions:* 6
Program ID: 329-16-21-069

Park Ridge

Advocate Lutheran General Hospital Program
Sponsor: Advocate Lutheran General Hospital
Prgm Director: Bhagya Puppala, MD
1775 Dempster Street
Park Ridge, IL 60068
Tel: 847 723-5313   *Fax:* 847 723-2338
E-mail: bhagya.puppala-md@advocatehealth.com
Length: 3 Yrs   *ACGME Approved/Offered Positions:* 6
Program ID: 329-16-21-070

Indiana

Indianapolis

Indiana University School of Medicine Program
Sponsor: Indiana University School of Medicine
Clarian Riley Hospital for Children
Prgm Director: David W Boyle, MD
Section of Neonatal-Perinatal Medicine
699 West Drive, RR208
Indianapolis, IN 46202
Tel: 317 274-4715   *Fax:* 317 274-2065
E-mail: neonatal@iupui.edu
Length: 3 Yrs   *ACGME Approved/Offered Positions:* 9
Program ID: 329-17-21-023

Iowa

Iowa City

University of Iowa Hospitals and Clinics Program
Sponsor: University of Iowa Hospitals and Clinics
Prgm Director: John A Widness, MD
Department of Pediatrics, Division of Neonatology
200 Hawkins Drive
Iowa City, IA 52242
Tel: 319 356-8102   *Fax:* 319 356-4685
E-mail: john-widness@uiowa.edu
Length: 3 Yrs   *ACGME Approved/Offered Positions:* 8
Program ID: 329-18-11-087

Kentucky

Lexington

University of Kentucky College of Medicine Program
Sponsor: University of Kentucky College of Medicine
University of Kentucky Hospital
Prgm Director: Henrietta S Bada, MD, MPH
Department of Pediatrics, Division of Neonatology
800 Rose Street, Room MS 477
Lexington, KY 40536
Tel: 859 323-1850   *Fax:* 859 257-6106
E-mail: hbada2@uky.edu
Length: 3 Yrs   *ACGME Approved/Offered Positions:* 6
Program ID: 329-20-21-024

Louisville

University of Louisville Program
Sponsor: University of Louisville School of Medicine
Kosair Children's Hospital (Norton Healthcare, Inc)
University of Louisville Hospital
Prgm Director: David H Adamkin, MD
Division of Neonatal Medicine
571 South Floyd Street, Suite 342
Louisville, KY 40202
Tel: 502 852-8470   *Fax:* 502 852-8473
E-mail: ulneomed@louisville.edu
Length: 3 Yrs   *ACGME Approved/Offered Positions:* 6
Program ID: 329-20-21-025

Programs

Louisiana

New Orleans

Louisiana State University/Tulane University Program

Sponsor: Louisiana State University School of Medicine
Children's Hospital (New Orleans)
East Jefferson General Hospital
Prgm Director: Duna Penn, MD, MS
200 Henry Clay Avenue
Attn: Duna Penn, MD, NICU
New Orleans, LA 70118
Tel: 504 894-6974   *Fax:* 504 896-2720
E-mail: dpenn@lsuhsc.edu
Length: 3 Yrs   *ACGME Approved/Offered Positions:* 6
Program ID: 329-21-21-106

Shreveport

Louisiana State University (Shreveport) Program

Sponsor: LSU Health Sciences Center-University
    Hospital
Prgm Director: Arun K Pramanik, MD
PO Box 33932
1501 Kings Highway Rm K5-03
Shreveport, LA 71130
Tel: 318 675-7276   *Fax:* 318 675-4660
E-mail: aprama@lsuhsc.edu
Length: 3 Yrs   *ACGME Approved/Offered Positions:* 6
Program ID: 329-21-11-088

Maryland

Baltimore

Johns Hopkins University Program

Sponsor: Johns Hopkins University School of Medicine
Johns Hopkins Hospital
Prgm Director: Susan W Aucott, MD
600 N Wolfe Street, Nelson 2-133
Baltimore, MD 21287
Tel: 410 955-5259   *Fax:* 410 955-0298
Length: 3 Yrs   *ACGME Approved/Offered Positions:* 6
Program ID: 329-23-21-026

University of Maryland Program

Sponsor: University of Maryland Medical System
Prgm Director: Rose Marie Viscardi, MD
Dept of Pediatrics - Neonatology-UMMS N5W68
22 South Greene Street
Baltimore, MD 21201
Tel: 410 328-6003   *Fax:* 410 328-1076
E-mail: rviscard@umaryland.edu
Length: 3 Yrs   *ACGME Approved/Offered Positions:* 6
Program ID: 329-23-21-027

Bethesda

National Capital Consortium Program

Sponsor: National Capital Consortium
National Naval Medical Center (Bethesda)
Prgm Director: Russell R Moores Jr, MD
Department of Pediatrics
4301 Jones Bridge Road
Bethesda, MD 20814
Tel: 301 295-9728   *Fax:* 301 319-8214
Length: 3 Yrs   *ACGME Approved/Offered Positions:* 6
Program ID: 329-10-11-090
Uniformed Services Program

Massachusetts

Boston

Children's Hospital/Boston Medical Center Program

Sponsor: Children's Hospital
Prgm Director: John A Zupancic, MD, ScD
Children's Hospital, Enders 961
300 Longwood Avenue
Boston, MA 02115
Tel: 617 919-2341   *Fax:* 617 730-0260
E-mail: rebecca.innis@childrens.harvard.edu
Length: 3 Yrs   *ACGME Approved/Offered Positions:* 18
Program ID: 329-24-21-028

Tufts Medical Center Program

Sponsor: Tufts Medical Center
Prgm Director: Christiane E Dammann, MD
Floating Hospital for Children
750 Washington Street, NEMC 44
Boston, MA 02111
Tel: 617 636-8738   *Fax:* 617 636-1456
Length: 3 Yrs   *ACGME Approved/Offered Positions:* 9
Program ID: 329-24-21-071

Worcester

University of Massachusetts Program

Sponsor: University of Massachusetts Medical School
UMass Memorial Health Care (Memorial Campus)
Prgm Director: Francis J Bednarek, MD
119 Belmont Street
Worcester, MA 01605
Tel: 508 334-6206   *Fax:* 508 334-6083
E-mail: franktia@aol.com
Length: 3 Yrs   *ACGME Approved/Offered Positions:* 3
Program ID: 329-24-21-029

Michigan

Ann Arbor

University of Michigan Program

Sponsor: University of Michigan Hospitals and Health
    Centers
Prgm Director: Robert E Schumacher, MD
F5790 Mott Hospital/5254
1500 E Medical Center Dr
Ann Arbor, MI 48109
Tel: 734 763-4109   *Fax:* 734 763-7728
E-mail: ped-npm-general@med.umich.edu
Length: 3 Yrs   *ACGME Approved/Offered Positions:* 6
Program ID: 329-25-21-030

Detroit

Children's Hospital of Michigan Program

Sponsor: Children's Hospital of Michigan
Harper-Hutzel Hospital
Prgm Director: Jorge L Lua, MD
3901 Beaubien Blvd
Detroit, MI 48201
Tel: 313 745-5638   *Fax:* 313 745-5867
E-mail: dnorman@dmc.org
Length: 3 Yrs   *ACGME Approved/Offered Positions:* 9
Program ID: 329-25-21-031

Lansing

Michigan State University Program

Sponsor: Michigan State University College of Human
    Medicine
Sparrow Hospital
Prgm Director: Ira H Gewolb, MD
Division of Neonatology
1215 E Michigan Ave
Lansing, MI 48912
Tel: 517 364-2670   *Fax:* 517 364-3994
E-mail: gewolb@msu.edu
Length: 3 Yrs   *ACGME Approved/Offered Positions:* 4
Program ID: 329-25-21-032

Minnesota

Minneapolis

University of Minnesota Program

Sponsor: University of Minnesota Medical School
Children's Hospitals and Clinics of Minnesota - St Paul
University of Minnesota Medical Center, Division of
    Fairview
Prgm Director: Catherine M Bendel, MD
MMC 39
420 Delaware St SE
Minneapolis, MN 55455
Tel: 612 626-3250   *Fax:* 612 624-8176
E-mail: bende001@umn.edu
Length: 3 Yrs   *ACGME Approved/Offered Positions:* 6
Program ID: 329-26-21-033

Rochester

College of Medicine, Mayo Clinic (Rochester) Program

Sponsor: College of Medicine, Mayo Clinic
Rochester Methodist Hospital
Saint Marys Hospital of Rochester
Prgm Director: Christopher Eugene Colby, MD
200 First Street SW
Rochester, MN 55905
Tel: 507 538-0154   *Fax:* 507 284-0160
E-mail: bartelsmith.susan@mayo.edu
Length: 3 Yrs   *ACGME Approved/Offered Positions:* 3
Program ID: 329-26-21-125

Missouri

Columbia

University of Missouri-Columbia Program

Sponsor: University of Missouri-Columbia School of
    Medicine
University Hospitals and Clinics
Prgm Director: John A Pardalos, MD
Dept of Child Health, N710
1 Hospital Drive
Columbia, MO 65212
Tel: 573 882-2272   *Fax:* 573 884-1795
E-mail: pardalosj@health.missouri.edu
Length: 3 Yrs   *ACGME Approved/Offered Positions:* 3
Program ID: 329-28-21-035

Note: * indicates a newly appointed program director

Kansas City

University of Missouri at Kansas City Program

Sponsor: University of Missouri-Kansas City School of Medicine
Children's Mercy Hospital
Truman Medical Center
Prgm Director: Felix A Okah, MD*
2401 Gillham Road
Kansas City, MO 64108
Tel: 816 234-3595   *Fax:* 816 234-3590
Length: 3 Yrs   *ACGME Approved/Offered Positions:* 6
Program ID: 329-28-11-091

St Louis

St Louis University School of Medicine Program

Sponsor: St Louis University School of Medicine
Cardinal Glennon Children's Hospital
Prgm Director: Farouk H Sadiq, MBBS
1465 S Grand Blvd
St Louis, MO 63104
Tel: 314 577-5642   *Fax:* 314 268-6410
Length: 3 Yrs   *ACGME Approved/Offered Positions:* 6
Program ID: 329-28-21-036

Washington University/B-JH/SLCH Consortium Program

Sponsor: Washington University/B-JH/SLCH Consortium
St Louis Children's Hospital
Prgm Director: Brian P Hackett, MD, PhD
Box 8116, Department of Pediatrics
660 South Euclid Avenue
St Louis, MO 63110
Tel: 314 286-2833   *Fax:* 314 454-4633
Length: 3 Yrs   *ACGME Approved/Offered Positions:* 15
Program ID: 329-28-21-037

New Hampshire

Lebanon

Dartmouth-Hitchcock Medical Center Program

Sponsor: Mary Hitchcock Memorial Hospital
Prgm Director: Gautham K Suresh, MD, MS*
Department of Pediatrics
One Medical Center Drive
Lebanon, NH 03756
Tel: 603 653-6063
Length: 3 Yrs   *ACGME Approved/Offered Positions:* 3
Program ID: 329-32-21-111

New Jersey

New Brunswick

UMDNJ-Robert Wood Johnson Medical School Program

Sponsor: UMDNJ-Robert Wood Johnson Medical School
Robert Wood Johnson University Hospital
Prgm Director: Thomas Hegyi, MD
MEB 312C
New Brunswick, NJ 08903
Tel: 732 235-8958   *Fax:* 732 235-6609
E-mail: hegyith@umdnj.edu
Length: 3 Yrs   *ACGME Approved/Offered Positions:* 9
Program ID: 329-33-21-092

New Mexico

Albuquerque

University of New Mexico Program

Sponsor: University of New Mexico School of Medicine
University of New Mexico Hospital
Prgm Director: Renate Savich, MD
Department of Pediatrics, Division of Neonatology
MSC10 5590, 1 University of New Mexico
Albuquerque, NM 87131
Tel: 505 272-3967   *Fax:* 505 272-1539
E-mail: rsavich@salud.unm.edu
Length: 3 Yrs   *ACGME Approved/Offered Positions:* 6
Program ID: 329-34-21-072

New York

Albany

Albany Medical Center Program

Sponsor: Albany Medical Center
Prgm Director: Joaquim M Pinheiro, MD, MPH
Department of Pediatrics, MC-101
47 New Scotland Avenue
Albany, NY 12208
Tel: 518 262-5421   *Fax:* 518 262-5881
E-mail: pinheij@mail.amc.edu
Length: 3 Yrs   *ACGME Approved/Offered Positions:* 3
Program ID: 329-35-21-038

Bronx

Albert Einstein College of Medicine Program

Sponsor: Albert Einstein College of Medicine of Yeshiva University
Montefiore Medical Center-Weiler Division
Prgm Director: Deborah E Campbell, MD
Jack D Weiler Hospital, Room 725
1825 Eastchester Road
Bronx, NY 10461
Tel: 718 904-4105   *Fax:* 718 904-2659
E-mail: dcampbel@montefiore.org
Length: 3 Yrs   *ACGME Approved/Offered Positions:* 3
Program ID: 329-35-21-039

Buffalo

University at Buffalo Program

Sponsor: University at Buffalo School of Medicine
Kaleida Health System (Women and Children's Hosp of Buffalo)
Prgm Director: Rita M Ryan, MD
Women's and Children's Hospital of Buffalo
219 Bryant Street
Buffalo, NY 14222
Tel: 716 878-7673   *Fax:* 716 878-7945
E-mail: rryan@upa.chob.edu
Length: 3 Yrs   *ACGME Approved/Offered Positions:* 6
Program ID: 329-35-21-041

Great Neck

NSLIJHS-Schneider Children's Hospital Program

Sponsor: North Shore-Long Island Jewish Health System
Schneider Children's Hospital at Long Island Jewish Med Ctr
Schneider Children's Hospital at North Shore University Hosp
Prgm Director: Dennis Davidson, MD
269-01 76th Avenue
New Hyde Park, NY 11040
Tel: 718 470-3440   *Fax:* 718 347-3850
E-mail: davidson@lij.edu
Length: 3 Yrs   *ACGME Approved/Offered Positions:* 12
Program ID: 329-35-21-074

New York

Mount Sinai School of Medicine Program

Sponsor: Mount Sinai School of Medicine
Mount Sinai Medical Center
Prgm Director: Ian R Holzman, MD
Department of Pediatrics
One Gustave L Levy Place, Box 1508
New York, NY 10029
Tel: 212 241-5446   *Fax:* 212 534-5207
Length: 3 Yrs   *ACGME Approved/Offered Positions:* 4
Program ID: 329-35-21-075

New York Presbyterian Hospital (Columbia Campus) Program

Sponsor: New York Presbyterian Hospital
New York Presbyterian Hospital (Columbia Campus)
Prgm Director: S David Rubenstein, MD
Children's Hospital of NY Presbyterian, Room 1201N
3959 Broadway
New York, NY 10032
Tel: 212 305-8500   *Fax:* 212 305-8796
Length: 3 Yrs   *ACGME Approved/Offered Positions:* 9
Program ID: 329-35-21-076

New York Presbyterian Hospital (Cornell Campus) Program

Sponsor: New York Presbyterian Hospital
New York Presbyterian Hospital (Cornell Campus)
Prgm Director: Jeffrey M Perlman, MBChB
525 East 68th Street, Suite N-506
New York, NY 10065
Tel: 212 746-3530   *Fax:* 212 746-8608
Length: 3 Yrs   *ACGME Approved/Offered Positions:* 8
Program ID: 329-35-21-042

New York University School of Medicine Program

Sponsor: New York University School of Medicine
Bellevue Hospital Center
Prgm Director: Karen D Hendricks-Munoz, MD, MPH
Tisch Hospital - HCC-7A
560 First Avenue
New York, NY 10016
Tel: 212 263-7477   *Fax:* 212 263-0134
E-mail: Karen.Hendricks-Munoz@med.nyu.edu
Length: 3 Yrs   *ACGME Approved/Offered Positions:* 5
Program ID: 329-35-21-108

Rochester

University of Rochester Program

Sponsor: Strong Memorial Hospital of the University of Rochester
Prgm Director: Ronnie Guillet, MD, PhD
Department of Pediatrics
601 Elmwood Avenue, Box 651
Rochester, NY 14642
Tel: 585 275-6209   *Fax:* 585 461-3614
Length: 3 Yrs   *ACGME Approved/Offered Positions:* 7
Program ID: 329-35-21-043

Stony Brook

SUNY at Stony Brook Program

Sponsor: University Hospital - SUNY at Stony Brook
Prgm Director: Sherry E Courtney, MD, MS*
Department of Pediatrics
HSC T 11- 060
Stony Brook, NY 11794
Tel: 631 444-7653   *Fax:* 631 444-9142
E-mail: sherry.courtney@notes.cc.sunysb.edu
Length: 3 Yrs   *ACGME Approved/Offered Positions:* 6
Program ID: 329-35-21-093

Programs

Valhalla

New York Medical College at Westchester Medical Center Program

Sponsor: New York Medical College
Westchester Medical Center
Prgm Director: Edmund F LaGamma, MD
Regional Neonatal Intensive Care Unit
Westchester Med Ctr - Maria Fareri Children's Hsp
Valhalla, NY 10595
Tel: 914 493-8558 *Fax:* 914 493-1488
E-mail: edmund_lagamma@nymc.edu
Length: 3 Yrs *ACGME Approved/Offered Positions:* 14
Program ID: 329-35-21-077

North Carolina

Chapel Hill

University of North Carolina Hospitals Program

Sponsor: University of North Carolina Hospitals
Prgm Director: Wayne A Price, MD
Department of Pediatrics, CB#7596
Fourth Floor UNC Hospital
Chapel Hill, NC 27599
Tel: 919 966-5063 *Fax:* 919 966-3034
E-mail: waprice@unc.edu
Length: 3 Yrs *ACGME Approved/Offered Positions:* 6
Program ID: 329-36-21-045

Durham

Duke University Hospital Program

Sponsor: Duke University Hospital
Prgm Director: Ronald N Goldberg, MD
Division of Neonatology
Box 3179
Durham, NC 27710
Tel: 919 681-6037 *Fax:* 919 681-6065
Length: 3 Yrs *ACGME Approved/Offered Positions:* 8
Program ID: 329-36-21-046

Greenville

Pitt County Memorial Hospital/East Carolina University Program

Sponsor: Pitt County Memorial Hospital
Prgm Director: James J Cummings, MD
Pediatrics-Neonatology
600 Moye Blvd Neonatal Rm 2002
Greenville, NC 27834
Tel: 252 744-4787 *Fax:* 252 744-3806
Length: 3 Yrs *ACGME Approved/Offered Positions:* 4
Program ID: 329-36-21-078

Winston-Salem

Wake Forest University School of Medicine Program

Sponsor: Wake Forest University Baptist Medical Center
Forsyth Memorial Hospital
Prgm Director: T Michael D O'Shea, MD, MPH
Medical Center Boulevard
Dept of Pediatrics
Winston-Salem, NC 27157
Tel: 336 716-4663 *Fax:* 336 716-2525
E-mail: moshea@wfubmc.edu
Length: 3 Yrs *ACGME Approved/Offered Positions:* 6
Program ID: 329-36-11-103

Ohio

Cincinnati

Cincinnati Children's Hospital Medical Center/University of Cincinnati College of Medicine Program

Sponsor: Cincinnati Children's Hospital Medical Center
Prgm Director: Ward R Rice, MD, PhD
Neonatology, MLC 7009
3333 Burnet Avenue
Cincinnati, OH 45229
Tel: 513 636-7368 *Fax:* 513 636-7868
Length: 3 Yrs *ACGME Approved/Offered Positions:* 12
Program ID: 329-38-21-047

Cleveland

Case Western Reserve University (MetroHealth) Program

Sponsor: MetroHealth Medical Center
Prgm Director: John J Moore, MD
2500 MetroHealth Drive
Cleveland, OH 44109
Tel: 216 778-5909 *Fax:* 216 778-3252
Length: 3 Yrs *ACGME Approved/Offered Positions:* 9
Program ID: 329-38-21-089

University Hospitals Case Medical Center Program

Sponsor: University Hospitals Case Medical Center
Prgm Director: Mary L Nock, MD*
Division of Neonatology
11100 Euclid Avenue
Cleveland, OH 44106
Tel: 216 844-3387
Length: 3 Yrs *ACGME Approved/Offered Positions:* 10
Program ID: 329-38-21-048

Columbus

Nationwide Children's Hospital/Ohio State University Program

Sponsor: Nationwide Children's Hospital
Ohio State University Hospital
Prgm Director: Kristina M Reber, MD
700 Children's Drive
Columbus, OH 43205
Tel: 614 722-4559 *Fax:* 614 722-4541
E-mail: diana.crenshaw@nationwidechildrens.org
Length: 3 Yrs *ACGME Approved/Offered Positions:* 9
Program ID: 329-38-21-049

Oklahoma

Oklahoma City

University of Oklahoma Health Sciences Center Program

Sponsor: University of Oklahoma College of Medicine
OU Medical Center - Children's Hospital
Prgm Director: Marilyn Escobedo, MD
Dept of Pediatrics
1200 Everett Drive, 7th Fl N Pavilion
Oklahoma City, OK 73104
Tel: 405 271-5215 *Fax:* 405 271-1236
E-mail: denise-harper@ouhsc.edu
Length: 3 Yrs *ACGME Approved/Offered Positions:* 3
Program ID: 329-39-21-079

Oregon

Portland

Oregon Health & Science University Program

Sponsor: Oregon Health & Science University Hospital
Prgm Director: JoDee M Anderson, MD
(CDRC-P)
707 SW Gaines Street
Portland, OR 97239
Tel: 503 494-6034 *Fax:* 503 494-1542
Length: 3 Yrs *ACGME Approved/Offered Positions:* 6
Program ID: 329-40-21-081

Pennsylvania

Hershey

Penn State University/Milton S Hershey Medical Center Program

Sponsor: Milton S Hershey Medical Center
Prgm Director: Charles Palmer, MB, ChB
PO Box 850, 500 University Drive
Hershey, PA 17033
Tel: 717 531-5685 *Fax:* 717 531-0856
E-mail: shollowell@psu.edu
Length: 3 Yrs *ACGME Approved/Offered Positions:* 6
Program ID: 329-41-21-050

Philadelphia

Children's Hospital of Philadelphia Program

Sponsor: Children's Hospital of Philadelphia
University of Pennsylvania Health System
Prgm Director: Susan Guttentag, MD
Division of Neonatology
34th St and Civic Center Blvd
Philadelphia, PA 19104
Tel: 215 590-2806 *Fax:* 215 590-4267
E-mail: guttentag@email.chop.edu
Length: 3 Yrs *ACGME Approved/Offered Positions:* 15
Program ID: 329-41-21-051

St Christopher's Hospital for Children Program

Sponsor: St Christopher's Hospital for Children (Tenet
Health System)
Hahnemann University Hospital (Tenet Health System)
Prgm Director: Alan B Zubrow, MD
Erie Avenue at Front Street
Philadelphia, PA 19134
Tel: 215 427-5202 *Fax:* 215 427-8192
Length: 3 Yrs *ACGME Approved/Offered Positions:* 9
Program ID: 329-41-21-082

Pittsburgh

University of Pittsburgh Medical Center Medical Education Program

Sponsor: Univ of Pittsburgh Medical Center Medical
Education
Children's Hospital of Pittsburgh of UPMC
Magee-Womens Hospital of UPMC
Prgm Director: Gary A Silverman, MD, PhD
Department of Pediatrics
300 Halket Street
Pittsburgh, PA 15213
Tel: 412 641-4111 *Fax:* 412 641-1844
Length: 3 Yrs *ACGME Approved/Offered Positions:* 12
Program ID: 329-41-21-052

Note: * indicates a newly appointed program director

Puerto Rico

San Juan

University of Puerto Rico Program

Sponsor: University of Puerto Rico School of Medicine
University Pediatric Hospital
Prgm Director: Marta Valcarcel, MD
PO Box 365067
San Juan, PR 00936
Tel: 787 777-3225   *Fax:* 787 758-5307
E-mail: mivalcar@prtc.net
Length: 3 Yrs   *ACGME Approved/Offered Positions:* 5
Program ID: 329-42-21-112

Rhode Island

Providence

Brown University Program

Sponsor: Women and Infants Hospital of Rhode Island
Prgm Director: Barbara S Stonestreet, MD
101 Dudley Street
Providence, RI 02905
Tel: 401 274-1122   *Fax:* 401 453-7571
E-mail: bstonestreet@wihri.org
Length: 3 Yrs   *ACGME Approved/Offered Positions:* 9
Program ID: 329-43-21-053

South Carolina

Charleston

Medical University of South Carolina Program

Sponsor: Medical University of South Carolina College of
  Medicine
MUSC Medical Center
Prgm Director: David J Annibale, MD
165 Ashley Avenue
Children's Hospital PO Box 250917
Charleston, SC 29425
Tel: 843 792-2112   *Fax:* 843 792-8801
E-mail: annibald@musc.edu
Length: 3 Yrs   *ACGME Approved/Offered Positions:* 6
Program ID: 329-45-21-100

Tennessee

Memphis

University of Tennessee Program

Sponsor: University of Tennessee College of Medicine
Regional Medical Center at Memphis
Prgm Director: Ajay J Talati, MD
Newborn Center
853 Jefferson Avenue- 2nd Fl
Memphis, TN 38163
Tel: 901 448-5950   *Fax:* 901 448-1691
Length: 3 Yrs   *ACGME Approved/Offered Positions:* 6
Program ID: 329-47-21-083

Nashville

Vanderbilt University Program

Sponsor: Vanderbilt University Medical Center
Prgm Director: Margaret G Rush, MD
11111 Doctor's Office Tower
2200 Children's Way
Nashville, TN 37232
Tel: 615 322-3476   *Fax:* 615 343-1763
E-mail: margaret.rush@vanderbilt.edu
Length: 3 Yrs   *ACGME Approved/Offered Positions:* 9
Program ID: 329-47-21-054

Texas

Dallas

University of Texas Southwestern Medical School Program

Sponsor: University of Texas Southwestern Medical
  School
Dallas County Hospital District-Parkland Memorial
  Hospital
Prgm Director: Luc P Brion, MD
5323 Harry Hines Boulevard
Dallas, TX 75390
Tel: 214 648-2835   *Fax:* 214 648-2481
E-mail: brenda.burrell@utsouthwestern.edu
Length: 3 Yrs   *ACGME Approved/Offered Positions:* 12
Program ID: 329-48-21-055

Galveston

University of Texas Medical Branch Hospitals Program

Sponsor: University of Texas Medical Branch Hospitals
Prgm Director: C Joan Richardson, MD
Department of Pediatrics
301 University Blvd
Galveston, TX 77555
Tel: 409 772-2815   *Fax:* 409 772-0747
Length: 3 Yrs   *ACGME Approved/Offered Positions:* 3
Program ID: 329-48-21-056

Houston

Baylor College of Medicine Program

Sponsor: Baylor College of Medicine
Texas Children's Hospital
Prgm Director: Ann R Stark, MD
Department of Pediatrics
One Baylor Plaza
Houston, TX 77030
Tel: 832 826-1380   *Fax:* 832 825-1386
E-mail: fellowship-program@neo.bcm.tmc.edu
Length: 3 Yrs   *ACGME Approved/Offered Positions:* 18
Program ID: 329-48-21-057

University of Texas at Houston Program

Sponsor: University of Texas Health Science Center at
  Houston
Memorial Hermann Hospital
Prgm Director: Suzanne M Lopez, MD
Department of Pediatrics
6431 Fannin St, Suite 3.242
Houston, TX 77030
Tel: 713 500-5284   *Fax:* 713 500-5794
E-mail: suzanne.m.lopez@uth.tmc.edu
Length: 3 Yrs   *ACGME Approved/Offered Positions:* 9
Program ID: 329-48-21-058

Lackland AFB

San Antonio Uniformed Services Health Education Consortium Program

Sponsor: San Antonio Uniformed Services Health
  Education Consortium
Wilford Hall Medical Center (AETC)
Prgm Director: Robert J DiGeronimo, MD
Department of Pediatrics/SGOBP
2200 Bergquist Drive, Suite 1
Lackland AFB, TX 78236
Tel: 210 292-2911   *Fax:* 210 292-6519
Length: 3 Yrs   *ACGME Approved/Offered Positions:* 9
Program ID: 329-48-21-059
Uniformed Services Program

San Antonio

University of Texas Health Science Center at San Antonio Program

Sponsor: University of Texas School of Medicine at San
  Antonio
University Health System
Prgm Director: Robert Castro, MD
7703 Floyd Curl Drive
MSC 7812
San Antonio, TX 78229
Tel: 210 567-5225   *Fax:* 210 567-5169
E-mail: petru@uthscsa.edu
Length: 3 Yrs   *ACGME Approved/Offered Positions:* 4
Program ID: 329-48-21-115

Utah

Salt Lake City

University of Utah Program

Sponsor: University of Utah Medical Center
Primary Children's Medical Center
Prgm Director: Robert H Lane, MD
Department of Pediatrics
PO Box 581289
Salt Lake City, UT 84158
Tel: 801 581-4178   *Fax:* 801 585-7395
Length: 3 Yrs   *ACGME Approved/Offered Positions:* 9
Program ID: 329-49-21-094

Vermont

Burlington

University of Vermont Program

Sponsor: Fletcher Allen Health Care
Prgm Director: Roger F Soll, MD
Neonatal-Perinatal Medicine
111 Colchester Avenue
Burlington, VT 05401
Tel: 802 847-2392   *Fax:* 802 847-5225
E-mail: roger.soll@vtmednet.org
Length: 3 Yrs   *ACGME Approved/Offered Positions:* 2
Program ID: 329-50-21-060

Virginia

Charlottesville

University of Virginia Program

Sponsor: University of Virginia Medical Center
Prgm Director: Karen D Fairchild, MD*
PO Box 800386
Charlottesville, VA 22908
Tel: 434 924-5496
E-mail: kdf2n@virginia.edu
Length: 3 Yrs   *ACGME Approved/Offered Positions:* 6
Program ID: 329-51-21-084

Richmond

Virginia Commonwealth University Health System Program

Sponsor: Virginia Commonwealth University Health
  System
Medical College of Virginia Hospitals
Prgm Director: Henry J Rozycki, MD
PO Box 980276
Richmond, VA 23298
Tel: 804 828-9964   *Fax:* 804 828-6662
E-mail: hrozycki@hsc.vcu.edu
Length: 3 Yrs   *ACGME Approved/Offered Positions:* 3
Program ID: 329-51-21-061

Programs

Washington

Seattle

University of Washington Program
Sponsor: University of Washington School of Medicine
Seattle Children's Hospital
University of Washington Medical Center
Prgm Director: Sandra E Juul, MD, PhD
Department of Pediatrics
1959 NE Pacific Street, Box 356320
Seattle, WA 98195
Tel: 206 543-3200   *Fax:* 206 543-8926
Length: 3 Yrs   *ACGME Approved/Offered Positions:* 6
Program ID: 329-54-21-095

West Virginia

Morgantown

West Virginia University Program
Sponsor: West Virginia University School of Medicine
West Virginia University Hospitals
Prgm Director: Mark J Polak, MD
1 Medical Center Drive
PO Box 9214
Morgantown, WV 26506
Tel: 304 293-1202   *Fax:* 304 293-4341
E-mail: mpolak@hsc.wvu.edu
Length: 3 Yrs   *ACGME Approved/Offered Positions:* 3
Program ID: 329-55-11-086

Wisconsin

Madison

University of Wisconsin Program
Sponsor: University of Wisconsin Hospital and Clinics
Meriter Hospital
Prgm Director: De-Ann M Pillers, MD, PhD*
Meriter Hospital
202 South Park Street, 6 Center
Madison, WI 53715
Tel: 608 417-6236   *Fax:* 608 417-6377
E-mail: pillersd@pediatrics.wisc.edu
Length: 3 Yrs   *ACGME Approved/Offered Positions:* 3
Program ID: 329-56-21-099

Milwaukee

Medical College of Wisconsin Affiliated Hospitals Program
Sponsor: Medical College of Wisconsin Affiliated
   Hospitals, Inc
Children's Hospital of Wisconsin
Froedtert Memorial Lutheran Hospital
Prgm Director: Girija G Konduri, MD
Children's Corporate Center
999 N 92nd Street
Wauwatosa, WI 53226
Tel: 414 266-6452   *Fax:* 414 266-6979
Length: 3 Yrs   *ACGME Approved/Offered Positions:* 9
Program ID: 329-56-21-110

Nephrology (Internal Medicine)

Alabama

Birmingham

University of Alabama Medical Center Program
Sponsor: University of Alabama Hospital
Cooper Green Hospital
Veterans Affairs Medical Center (Birmingham)
Prgm Director: Ashita J Tolwani, MD, MS
ZRB 624
1530 3rd Ave South
Birmingham, AL 35294
Tel: 205 996-2186   *Fax:* 205 996-6465
E-mail: atolwani@uab.edu
Length: 2 Yrs   *ACGME Approved/Offered Positions:* 14
Program ID: 148-01-21-107

Arizona

Tucson

University of Arizona Program
Sponsor: University of Arizona College of Medicine
Desert Dialysis Center
Southern Arizona VA Health Care Center (Tucson)
University Medical Center
University of Arizona/UPHK Graduate Medical Ed
   Consortium
Prgm Director: Joy L Logan, MD
Department of Internal Medicine
1501 North Campbell Avenue
Tucson, AZ 85724
Tel: 520 626-6371   *Fax:* 520 626-2024
Length: 2 Yrs   *ACGME Approved/Offered Positions:* 5
Program ID: 148-03-21-091

Arkansas

Little Rock

University of Arkansas for Medical Sciences Program
Sponsor: University of Arkansas College of Medicine
Central Arkansas Veterans Healthcare System
UAMS Medical Center
Prgm Director: Godela M Brosnahan, MD*
4301 West Markham, # 501
Little Rock, AR 72205
Tel: 501 257-5829   *Fax:* 501 686-7878
E-mail: bowmanjolyndar@uams.edu
Length: 2 Yrs   *ACGME Approved/Offered Positions:* 8
Program ID: 148-04-21-092

California

Loma Linda

Loma Linda University Program
Sponsor: Loma Linda University Medical Center
Jerry L Pettis Memorial Veterans Hospital
Prgm Director: Robert E Soderblom, MD
11234 Anderson Street
Room 1568
Loma Linda, CA 92354
Tel: 909 558-4911   *Fax:* 909 558-0490
Length: 2 Yrs   *ACGME Approved/Offered Positions:* 4
Program ID: 148-05-31-195

Los Angeles

Cedars-Sinai Medical Center Program
Sponsor: Cedars-Sinai Medical Center
VA Greater Los Angeles Healthcare System
Prgm Director: Alice Peng, MD
Nephrology Fellowship Program
8635 W 3rd Street, Suite 490W
Los Angeles, CA 90048
Tel: 310 423-2420   *Fax:* 310 423-8208
E-mail: renalfellowship@csmc.edu
Length: 2 Yrs   *ACGME Approved/Offered Positions:* 8
Program ID: 148-05-11-093

Kaiser Permanente Southern California (Los Angeles) Program
Sponsor: Kaiser Permanente Southern California
Kaiser Foundation Hospital (Los Angeles)
Prgm Director: Dean A Kujubu, MD
4700 Sunset Blvd, 2nd Floor
Los Angeles, CA 90027
Tel: 323 783-6195   *Fax:* 323 783-8288
Length: 2 Yrs   *ACGME Approved/Offered Positions:* 6
Program ID: 148-05-12-029

UCLA Medical Center Program
Sponsor: UCLA David Geffen School of Medicine/UCLA
   Medical Center
UCLA Medical Center
Prgm Director: Ira Kurtz, MD
Center for the Health Sciences
10833 Le Conte Avenue
Los Angeles, CA 90095
Tel: 310 206-6741   *Fax:* 310 825-6309
Length: 2 Yrs   *ACGME Approved/Offered Positions:* 4
Program ID: 148-05-11-110

University of Southern California/ LAC+USC Medical Center Program
Sponsor: University of Southern California/LAC+USC
   Medical Center
LAC+USC Medical Center
USC University Hospital
Prgm Director: Vito M Campese, MD
1200 North State Street, GNH 4250
Los Angeles, CA 90033
Tel: 323 226-7337   *Fax:* 323 226-5390
E-mail: eisert@usc.edu
Length: 2 Yrs   *ACGME Approved/Offered Positions:* 9
Program ID: 148-05-21-042

Orange

University of California (Irvine) Program
Sponsor: University of California (Irvine) Medical
   Center
VA Long Beach Healthcare System
Prgm Director: Madeleine V Pahl, MD*
Department of Internal Medicine
101 The City Drive South
Orange, CA 92668
Tel: 714 456-5142   *Fax:* 714 456-6034
Length: 2 Yrs   *ACGME Approved/Offered Positions:* 5
Program ID: 148-05-21-125

Sacramento

University of California (Davis) Health System Program
Sponsor: University of California (Davis) Health System
University of California (Davis) Medical Center
VA Northern California Health Care System
Prgm Director: Jane Y Yeun, MD
Division of Nephrology
4150 V Street, Suite 3500, PSSB
Sacramento, CA 95817
Tel: 916 734-3774   *Fax:* 916 734-7920
Length: 2 Yrs   *ACGME Approved/Offered Positions:* 6
Program ID: 148-05-21-082

Note: * indicates a newly appointed program director

San Diego

University of California (San Diego) Program
Sponsor: University of California (San Diego) Medical Center
Naval Medical Center (San Diego)
Veterans Affairs Medical Center (San Diego)
Prgm Director: Scott R Mullaney, MD*
Nephrology 111H
3350 La Jolla Village Drive
La Jolla, CA 92161
Tel: 858 522-7528   *Fax:* 858 552-7549
Length: 2 Yrs   *ACGME Approved/Offered Positions:* 10
Program ID: 148-05-21-149

San Francisco

University of California (San Francisco) Program
Sponsor: University of California (San Francisco) School of Medicine
San Francisco General Hospital Medical Center
UCSF and Mount Zion Medical Centers
Veterans Affairs Medical Center (San Francisco)
Prgm Director: Kerry C Cho, MD
Department of Medicine
521 Parnassus Avenue, C443, Box 0532
San Francisco, CA 94143
Tel: 415 476-1812   *Fax:* 415 476-3381
E-mail: kerry.cho@ucsf.edu
Length: 2 Yrs   *ACGME Approved/Offered Positions:* 11
Program ID: 148-05-21-127

Stanford

Stanford University Program
Sponsor: Stanford Hospital and Clinics
Santa Clara Valley Medical Center
Prgm Director: John D Scandling Jr, MD
Department of Medicine
780 Welch Road, Suite 106
Palo Alto, CA 94304
Tel: 650 723-6247   *Fax:* 650 721-1443
E-mail: ljlucente@stanford.edu
Length: 2 Yrs   *ACGME Approved/Offered Positions:* 10
Program ID: 148-05-21-019

Sylmar

UCLA-Olive View Program
Sponsor: Olive View/UCLA Medical Center
UCLA Medical Center
Prgm Director: Dalila B Corry, MD
14445 Olive View Dr
Department of Medicine, Rm 2B-182
Sylmar, CA 91342
Tel: 818 364-3205   *Fax:* 818 364-4573
E-mail: fellowships@uclasfvp.org
Length: 2 Yrs   *ACGME Approved/Offered Positions:* 5
Program ID: 148-05-21-111

Torrance

Los Angeles County-Harbor-UCLA Medical Center Program
Sponsor: Los Angeles County-Harbor-UCLA Medical Center
Prgm Director: Sharon G Adler, MD
1000 W Carson Street, Bin 400
Torrance, CA 90509
Tel: 310 222-3891   *Fax:* 310 782-1837
E-mail: sadler@LABiomed.org
Length: 2 Yrs   *ACGME Approved/Offered Positions:* 8
Program ID: 148-05-11-150

Colorado

Aurora

University of Colorado Denver Program
Sponsor: University of Colorado Denver School of Medicine
Denver Health Medical Center
University of Colorado Hospital
Veterans Affairs Medical Center (Denver)
Prgm Director: Stuart L Linas, MD
Box C-281, 4200 E Ninth Ave
Denver, CO 80262
Tel: 303 315-6734   *Fax:* 303 315-4852
Length: 2 Yrs   *ACGME Approved/Offered Positions:* 8
Program ID: 148-07-21-051

Connecticut

Farmington

University of Connecticut Program
Sponsor: University of Connecticut School of Medicine
Univ of Connecticut Health Center/John Dempsey Hospital
Prgm Director: Nancy D Adams, MD
Dept of Internal Medicine, Division of Nephrology
263 Farmington Avenue, MC-1119
Farmington, CT 06030
Tel: 860 679-2799   *Fax:* 860 679-3968
E-mail: jmenze@uchc.edu
Length: 2 Yrs   *ACGME Approved/Offered Positions:* 2
Program ID: 148-08-31-001

New Haven

Hospital of St Raphael Program
Sponsor: Hospital of St Raphael
Prgm Director: Joni H Hansson, MD
1450 Chapel Street
New Haven, CT 06511
Tel: 203 789-3989   *Fax:* 203 789-3222
E-mail: spane@srhs.org
Length: 2 Yrs   *ACGME Approved/Offered Positions:* 3
Program ID: 148-08-31-112

Yale-New Haven Medical Center Program
Sponsor: Yale-New Haven Hospital
Veterans Affairs Medical Center (West Haven)
Prgm Director: Mark A Perazella, MD
Dept of Medicine/Nephrology
PO Box 208029
New Haven, CT 06520
Tel: 203 785-4184   *Fax:* 203 785-7068
Length: 2 Yrs   *ACGME Approved/Offered Positions:* 8
Program ID: 148-08-21-020

Delaware

Wilmington

Jefferson Medical College/Christiana Care Health Services Program
Sponsor: Jefferson Medical College
Christiana Care Health Services Inc
Prgm Director: Robert Dressler, MD
Department of Medicine, Room 4A47
4755 Ogletown-Stanton Road, PO Box 6001
Newark, DE 19718
Tel: 302 733-6343   *Fax:* 302 733-6378
E-mail: nephrology.fellowship@christianacare.org
Length: 2 Yrs   *ACGME Approved/Offered Positions:* 2
Program ID: 148-09-12-196

District of Columbia

Washington

George Washington University Program
Sponsor: George Washington University School of Medicine
George Washington University Hospital (UHS)
Inova Fairfax Hospital
Veterans Affairs Medical Center (Washington, DC)
Prgm Director: Samir S Patel, MD
Department of Medicine, Suite 1-202
2150 Pennsylvania Avenue, NW
Washington, DC 20037
Tel: 202 741-2283   *Fax:* 202 741-2285
E-mail: spatel@mfa.gwu.edu
Length: 2 Yrs   *ACGME Approved/Offered Positions:* 5
Program ID: 148-10-21-095

Georgetown University Hospital Program
Sponsor: Georgetown University Hospital
Veterans Affairs Medical Center (Washington, DC)
Prgm Director: Shakil Aslam, MD
Department of Medicine, PHC F6003
3800 Reservoir Road, NW
Washington, DC 20007
Tel: 202 687-8543   *Fax:* 202 444-7893
E-mail: steelewe@gunet.georgetown.edu
Length: 2 Yrs   *ACGME Approved/Offered Positions:* 6
Program ID: 148-10-21-073

Georgetown University Hospital/Washington Hospital Center Program
Sponsor: Washington Hospital Center
Prgm Director: Jack Moore Jr, MD
110 Irving Street, NW
Suite 2A70
Washington, DC 20010
Tel: 202 877-6034   *Fax:* 202 877-8329
Length: 2 Yrs   *ACGME Approved/Offered Positions:* 4
Program ID: 148-10-11-114

Florida

Gainesville

University of Florida Program
Sponsor: University of Florida College of Medicine
North Florida/South Georgia Veterans Health System
Shands Hospital at the University of Florida
Prgm Director: Edward A Ross, MD
Department of Medicine, PO Box 100224
1600 SW Archer Road, Rm #CG-98
Gainesville, FL 32610
Tel: 352 392-4007   *Fax:* 352 392-5465
E-mail: rossea@medicine.ufl.edu
Length: 2 Yrs   *ACGME Approved/Offered Positions:* 10
Program ID: 148-11-21-031

Jacksonville

University of Florida College of Medicine Jacksonville Program
Sponsor: University of Florida College of Medicine Jacksonville
Shands Jacksonville Medical Center
Prgm Director: Charles W Heilig, MD, BS*
655 West 8th Street
B-0138, Clinical Center UF & Shands Jacksonville
Jacksonville, FL 32209
Tel: 904 244-4509   *Fax:* 904 244-4771
E-mail: charles.heilig@jax.ufl.edu
Length: 2 Yrs   *ACGME Approved/Offered Positions:* 4
Program ID: 148-11-13-194

Miami

Jackson Memorial Hospital/Jackson Health System Program

Sponsor: Jackson Memorial Hospital/Jackson Health System
DaVita Dialysis Center (Florida)
Prgm Director: Oliver Lenz, MD
1600 NW 10th Avenue
Suite 7168 (R-126)
Miami, FL 33136
Tel: 305 243-3583   *Fax:* 305 243-3506
E-mail: Olenz@med.miami.edu
Length: 2 Yrs   *ACGME Approved/Offered Positions:* 10
Program ID: 148-11-21-151

Tampa

University of South Florida Program

Sponsor: University of South Florida College of Medicine
H Lee Moffitt Cancer Center
James A Haley Veterans Hospital
Tampa General Hospital
Prgm Director: Jacques A Durr, MD
12901 Bruce B Downs Boulevard
Box 19
Tampa, FL 33612
Tel: 813 974-1469   *Fax:* 813 974-0023
E-mail: dpowell@health.usf.edu
Length: 2 Yrs   *ACGME Approved/Offered Positions:* 8
Program ID: 148-11-21-032

Weston

Cleveland Clinic (Florida) Program

Sponsor: Cleveland Clinic Florida
DaVita Dialysis Center (Florida)
Prgm Director: Mauro Braun, MD
2950 Cleveland Clinic Boulevard
Weston, FL 33331
Tel: 954 659-5148   *Fax:* 954 659-6192
E-mail: hernang1@ccf.org
Length: 2 Yrs   *ACGME Approved/Offered Positions:* 2
Program ID: 148-11-31-181

Georgia

Atlanta

Emory University Program

Sponsor: Emory University School of Medicine
Crawford Long Hospital of Emory University
Emory University Hospital
Grady Health System
Prgm Director: James L Bailey, MD
1639 Pierce Dr, NE
Renal Div, WMB, Room 338
Atlanta, GA 30322
Tel: 404 727-2525   *Fax:* 404 727-3425
Length: 2 Yrs   *ACGME Approved/Offered Positions:* 13
Program ID: 148-12-21-115

Augusta

Medical College of Georgia Program

Sponsor: Medical College of Georgia
Veterans Affairs Medical Center (Augusta)
Prgm Director: Pamela J Fall, MD
Department of Medicine
1120 15th Street, BA-9413
Augusta, GA 30912
Tel: 706 721-2861   *Fax:* 706 721-7136
Length: 2 Yrs   *ACGME Approved/Offered Positions:* 5
Program ID: 148-12-21-002

Illinois

Chicago

McGaw Medical Center of Northwestern University Program

Sponsor: McGaw Medical Center of Northwestern University
Evanston Hospital
Prgm Director: Shubhada Ahya, MD
Tarry 4-701
303 E Chicago Ave
Chicago, IL 60611
Tel: 312 926-4880   *Fax:* 312 926-4885
E-mail: dgannett@nmff.org
Length: 2 Yrs   *ACGME Approved/Offered Positions:* 6
Program ID: 148-16-21-058

Rush University Medical Center Program

Sponsor: Rush University Medical Center
Prgm Director: Roger A Rodby, MD
1653 West Congress Parkway
Chicago, IL 60612
Tel: 312 850-8434   *Fax:* 312 850-8431
Length: 2 Yrs   *ACGME Approved/Offered Positions:* 6
Program ID: 148-16-11-116

University of Chicago Program

Sponsor: University of Chicago Medical Center
Prgm Director: Richard J Quigg, MD*
5841 S Maryland Ave
Room S-511 - MC 5100
Chicago, IL 60637
Tel: 773 702-3630   *Fax:* 773 702-5818
Length: 2 Yrs   *ACGME Approved/Offered Positions:* 6
Program ID: 148-16-11-052

University of Illinois College of Medicine at Chicago Program

Sponsor: University of Illinois College of Medicine at Chicago
Jesse Brown Veterans Affairs Medical Center
John H Stroger Hospital of Cook County
University of Illinois Hospital and Clinics
Prgm Director: James P Lash, MD
840 South Wood Street, MC 793
Chicago, IL 60612
Tel: 312 996-6736   *Fax:* 312 996-7378
Length: 2 Yrs   *ACGME Approved/Offered Positions:* 8
Program ID: 148-16-21-117

Maywood

Loyola University Program

Sponsor: Loyola University Medical Center
Edward Hines, Jr Veterans Affairs Hospital
Prgm Director: Karen A Griffin, MD
Dept of Medicine, Room 7604
2160 S First Ave
Maywood, IL 60153
Tel: 708 216-3306   *Fax:* 708 216-4060
Length: 2 Yrs   *ACGME Approved/Offered Positions:* 8
Program ID: 148-16-21-003

Indiana

Indianapolis

Indiana University School of Medicine Program

Sponsor: Indiana University School of Medicine
Clarian Indiana University Hospital
Prgm Director: Pierre Dagher, MD
950 West Walnut Street
R2 202E
Indianapolis, IN 46202
Tel: 317 274-6374   *Fax:* 317 274-8575
E-mail: nfellow@iupui.edu
Length: 2 Yrs   *ACGME Approved/Offered Positions:* 10
Program ID: 148-17-21-129

Iowa

Iowa City

University of Iowa Hospitals and Clinics Program

Sponsor: University of Iowa Hospitals and Clinics
Prgm Director: Lawrence P Karniski, MD
Department of Medicine
200 Hawkins Drive
Iowa City, IA 52242
Tel: 319 356-3971   *Fax:* 319 356-2999
E-mail: lawrence-karniski@uiowa.edu
Length: 2 Yrs   *ACGME Approved/Offered Positions:* 6
Program ID: 148-18-21-083

Kansas

Kansas City

University of Kansas School of Medicine Program

Sponsor: University of Kansas School of Medicine
University of Kansas Hospital
Veterans Affairs Medical Center (Kansas City)
Prgm Director: Leigh D Quarles, MD
Department of Medicine-Nephrology
3901 Rainbow Boulevard
Kansas City, KS 66160
Tel: 913 588-6074   *Fax:* 913 588-3867
Length: 2 Yrs   *ACGME Approved/Offered Positions:* 7
Program ID: 148-19-21-096

Kentucky

Lexington

University of Kentucky College of Medicine Program

Sponsor: University of Kentucky College of Medicine
University of Kentucky Hospital
Veterans Affairs Medical Center (Lexington)
Prgm Director: B Peter Sawaya, MD
800 Rose Street
Room MN 564
Lexington, KY 40536
Tel: 859 323-5048   *Fax:* 859 323-0232
Length: 2 Yrs   *ACGME Approved/Offered Positions:* 4
Program ID: 148-20-21-152

Louisville

University of Louisville Program

Sponsor: University of Louisville School of Medicine
Norton Hospital
University of Louisville Hospital
Veterans Affairs Medical Center (Louisville)
Prgm Director: Eleanor D Lederer, MD
615 S Preston Street
Louisville, KY 40202
Tel: 502 852-5757   *Fax:* 502 852-4184
E-mail: edlede01@gwise.louisville.edu
Length: 2 Yrs   *ACGME Approved/Offered Positions:* 7
Program ID: 148-20-31-075

Note: * indicates a newly appointed program director

Louisiana

New Orleans

Louisiana State University Program

Sponsor: Louisiana State University School of Medicine
Medical Center of Louisiana at New Orleans
Ochsner Clinic Foundation
Ochsner Medical Center-Kenner
Prgm Director: Avanelle V Jack, MD*
2020 Gravier Street, 7th Floor Suite D, Box E7-20
New Orleans, LA 70112
Tel: 504 568-8655   *Fax:* 504 568-2127
E-mail: kadams2@lsuhsc.edu
Length: 2 Yrs   *ACGME Approved/Offered Positions:* 6
Program ID: 148-21-21-164

Tulane University Program

Sponsor: Tulane University School of Medicine
Medical Center of Louisiana at New Orleans
Tulane University Hospital and Clinics
Prgm Director: Eric Simon, MD
1430 Tulane Avenue, SL 45
New Orleans, LA 70112
Tel: 504 988-5346   *Fax:* 504 988-1909
Length: 2 Yrs   *ACGME Approved/Offered Positions:* 6
Program ID: 148-21-21-090

Shreveport

Louisiana State University (Shreveport) Program

Sponsor: LSU Health Sciences Center-University
   Hospital
Willis-Knighton Medical Center
Prgm Director: Kenneth Abreo, MD
1501 Kings Highway
PO Box 33932
Shreveport, LA 71130
Tel: 318 675-7402   *Fax:* 318 675-5913
E-mail: ctaylo1@lsuhsc.edu
Length: 2 Yrs   *ACGME Approved/Offered Positions:* 6
Program ID: 148-21-21-053

Maine

Portland

Maine Medical Center Program

Sponsor: Maine Medical Center
Southern Maine Dialysis Facility
Prgm Director: Mark G Parker, MD
22 Bramhall Street
Portland, ME 04102
Tel: 207 662-2417   *Fax:* 207 662-6306
Length: 2 Yrs   *ACGME Approved/Offered Positions:* 4
Program ID: 148-22-21-168

Maryland

Baltimore

Johns Hopkins University Program

Sponsor: Johns Hopkins University School of Medicine
Johns Hopkins Hospital
Prgm Director: Michael Choi, MD
1830 E Monument St, Suite 416
Baltimore, MD 21205
Tel: 410 955-5268   *Fax:* 410 955-0485
Length: 2 Yrs   *ACGME Approved/Offered Positions:* 8
Program ID: 148-23-11-059

Johns Hopkins University/Bayview Medical Center Program

Sponsor: Johns Hopkins University School of Medicine
Johns Hopkins Bayview Medical Center
Johns Hopkins Hospital
Prgm Director: David A Spector (KCF), MD
4940 Eastern Avenue
Division of Renal Medicine, B2 North
Baltimore, MD 21224
Tel: 410 550-0614   *Fax:* 410 550-7950
E-mail: dspector@jhmi.edu
Length: 2 Yrs   *ACGME Approved/Offered Positions:* 4
Program ID: 148-23-11-153

University of Maryland Program

Sponsor: University of Maryland Medical System
Prgm Director: Daniel J Salzberg, MD
Nephrology Division, Room N3W143
22 South Greene Street
Baltimore, MD 21201
Tel: 410 328-5720   *Fax:* 410 328-5685
Length: 2 Yrs   *ACGME Approved/Offered Positions:* 6
Program ID: 148-23-21-033

Bethesda

National Capital Consortium (Walter Reed) Program

Sponsor: National Capital Consortium
National Naval Medical Center (Bethesda)
Walter Reed Army Medical Center
Prgm Director: Erin M Bohen, MD
Department of Medicine, Nephrology Service
6825 16th Street, NW
Washington, DC 20307
Tel: 202 782-6462   *Fax:* 202 782-0185
Length: 2 Yrs   *ACGME Approved/Offered Positions:* 6
Program ID: 148-10-11-113
Uniformed Services Program

Massachusetts

Boston

Beth Israel Deaconess Medical Center Program

Sponsor: Beth Israel Deaconess Medical Center
Prgm Director: Robert S Brown, MD
Department of Medicine
330 Brookline Ave - DA517
Boston, MA 02215
Tel: 617 667-2147   *Fax:* 617 667-5276
E-mail: rbrown@bidmc.harvard.edu
Length: 2 Yrs   *ACGME Approved/Offered Positions:* 8
Program ID: 148-24-21-004

Boston University Medical Center Program

Sponsor: Boston Medical Center
Prgm Director: David J Salant, MD
Department of Medicine
88 East Newton Street
Boston, MA 02118
Tel: 617 638-7330   *Fax:* 617 638-7326
E-mail: djsalant@bu.edu
Length: 2 Yrs   *ACGME Approved/Offered Positions:* 8
Program ID: 148-24-21-130

Brigham and Women's Hospital Program

Sponsor: Brigham and Women's Hospital
Massachusetts General Hospital
Prgm Director: John K Tucker, MD
Department of Medicine
75 Francis Street
Boston, MA 02115
Tel: 617 525-6496   *Fax:* 617 732-6392
E-mail: jktucker@partners.org
Length: 2 Yrs   *ACGME Approved/Offered Positions:* 20
Program ID: 148-24-21-005

Tufts Medical Center Program

Sponsor: Tufts Medical Center
Prgm Director: Scott J Gilbert, MD
Division of Nephrology
800 Washington Street, Box 391
Boston, MA 02111
Tel: 617 636-2240   *Fax:* 617 636-8329
E-mail: sgilbert@tuftsmedicalcenter.org
Length: 2 Yrs   *ACGME Approved/Offered Positions:* 8
Program ID: 148-24-21-006

Springfield

Baystate Medical Center/Tufts University School of Medicine Program

Sponsor: Baystate Medical Center
Prgm Director: Gregory L Braden, MD
759 Chestnut Street, S2570
Springfield, MA 01199
Tel: 413 794-1155   *Fax:* 413 794-8075
E-mail: gail.wall@bhs.org
Length: 2 Yrs   *ACGME Approved/Offered Positions:* 4
Program ID: 148-24-13-185

Worcester

University of Massachusetts Program

Sponsor: University of Massachusetts Medical School
UMass Memorial Health Care (Memorial Campus)
UMass Memorial Health Care (University Campus)
Prgm Director: Pang-Yen Fan, MD
Department of Medicine
55 Lake Avenue North
Worcester, MA 01655
Tel: 508 334-2052   *Fax:* 508 856-3111
Length: 2 Yrs   *ACGME Approved/Offered Positions:* 6
Program ID: 148-24-21-007

Michigan

Ann Arbor

University of Michigan Program

Sponsor: University of Michigan Hospitals and Health
   Centers
Veterans Affairs Medical Center (Ann Arbor)
Prgm Director: Frank C Brosius, MD
1150 West Medical Center Drive
1560 MSRBII / SPC 5676
Ann Arbor, MI 48109
Tel: 734 936-5645   *Fax:* 734 763-0982
E-mail: bturgyan@med.umich.edu
Length: 2 Yrs   *ACGME Approved/Offered Positions:* 8
Program ID: 148-25-21-061

Detroit

Henry Ford Hospital Program

Sponsor: Henry Ford Hospital
Prgm Director: Mark D Faber, MD
2799 West Grand Boulevard
CFP-5
Detroit, MI 48202
Tel: 313 916-3664   *Fax:* 313 916-2554
E-mail: mfaber1@hfhs.org
Length: 2 Yrs   *ACGME Approved/Offered Positions:* 10
Program ID: 148-25-11-118

St John Hospital and Medical Center Program

Sponsor: St John Hospital and Medical Center
Prgm Director: Keith A Bellovich, DO
22201 Moross Road
Suite 150
Detroit, MI 48236
Tel: 313 886-8787   *Fax:* 313 343-0431
E-mail: Laura.Peppler-Maloney@stjohn.org
Length: 2 Yrs   *ACGME Approved/Offered Positions:* 5
Program ID: 148-25-21-174

Programs

Wayne State University/Detroit Medical Center Program

Sponsor: Wayne State University/Detroit Medical Center
Detroit Receiving Hospital and University Health Center
Harper-Hutzel Hospital
Karmanos Cancer Hospital
Prgm Director: Noreen F Rossi, MD
Division of Nephrology
4160 John R Street, Suite 908
Detroit, MI 48201
Tel: 313 745-7145   *Fax:* 313 745-8041
Length: 2 Yrs   *ACGME Approved/Offered Positions:* 6
Program ID: 148-25-21-040

Minnesota

Minneapolis

University of Minnesota Program

Sponsor: University of Minnesota Medical School
Hennepin County Medical Center
University of Minnesota Medical Center, Division of
   Fairview
Prgm Director: Hassan N Ibrahim, MD, MS
Department of Medicine, Renal Division
717 Delaware Street SE, Suite 353, Campus Mail Code
1932
Minneapolis, MN 55414
Tel: 612 624-9444   *Fax:* 612 626-3840
E-mail: ibrah007@umn.edu
Length: 2 Yrs   *ACGME Approved/Offered Positions:* 11
Program ID: 148-26-21-098

Rochester

College of Medicine, Mayo Clinic (Rochester) Program

Sponsor: College of Medicine, Mayo Clinic
Mayo Clinic (Rochester)
Rochester Methodist Hospital
Saint Marys Hospital of Rochester
Prgm Director: Suzanne M Norby, MD
200 First St SW
Eisenberg Subway 24
Rochester, MN 55905
Tel: 507 266-1044   *Fax:* 507 266-7891
E-mail: haake.wendy@mayo.edu
Length: 2 Yrs   *ACGME Approved/Offered Positions:* 10
Program ID: 148-26-21-046

Mississippi

Jackson

University of Mississippi Medical Center Program

Sponsor: University of Mississippi School of Medicine
University Hospitals and Clinics
Veterans Affairs Medical Center (Jackson)
Prgm Director: Michael F Flessner, MD, PhD
Division of Nephrology
2500 N State St
Jackson, MS 39216
Tel: 601 984-5670   *Fax:* 601 984-5765
Length: 2 Yrs   *ACGME Approved/Offered Positions:* 8
Program ID: 148-27-21-062

Missouri

Columbia

University of Missouri-Columbia Program

Sponsor: University of Missouri-Columbia School of
   Medicine
Dialysis Clinics, Inc
Harry S Truman Memorial Veterans Hospital
University Hospitals and Clinics
Prgm Director: Madhukar Misra, MD, MRCP*
Room CE 422, Clinical Support & Education Building
5 Hospital Drive
Columbia, MO 65212
Tel: 573 882-8557   *Fax:* 573 884-5690
E-mail: misraM@health.missouri.edu
Length: 2 Yrs   *ACGME Approved/Offered Positions:* 8
Program ID: 148-28-21-063

St Louis

St Louis University School of Medicine Program

Sponsor: St Louis University School of Medicine
SLU Care (the Ambulatory Practices of the UMG)
St Louis University Hospital
Veterans Affairs Medical Center (St Louis)
Prgm Director: Kevin Martin, MD
Division of Nephrology
1402 South Grand
St Louis, MO 63104
Tel: 314 577-8765   *Fax:* 314 771-0784
E-mail: martinkj@slu.edu
Length: 2 Yrs   *ACGME Approved/Offered Positions:* 8
Program ID: 148-28-21-076

Washington University/B-JH/SLCH Consortium Program

Sponsor: Washington University/B-JH/SLCH Consortium
Barnes-Jewish Hospital
Prgm Director: Aubrey Morrison, MBBS*
660 South Euclid Avenue
Box 8129
St Louis, MO 63110
Tel: 314 454-8495   *Fax:* 314 454-8430
E-mail: morrison@wustl.edu
Length: 2 Yrs   *ACGME Approved/Offered Positions:* 10
Program ID: 148-28-21-131

Nebraska

Omaha

University of Nebraska Medical Center College of Medicine Program

Sponsor: University of Nebraska Medical Center College
   of Medicine
Nebraska Medical Center
Renal Advantage Inc (Ames)
Renal Advantage, Inc (Center Street)
Veterans Affairs Medical Center (Omaha)
Prgm Director: Gerald C Groggel, MD
983040 Nebraska Medical Center
Omaha, NE 68198
Tel: 402 559-9227   *Fax:* 402 559-9504
Length: 2 Yrs   *ACGME Approved/Offered Positions:* 4
Program ID: 148-30-21-193

New Hampshire

Lebanon

Dartmouth-Hitchcock Medical Center Program

Sponsor: Mary Hitchcock Memorial Hospital
Prgm Director: Clay A Block, MD
One Medical Center Drive
Lebanon, NH 03756
Tel: 603 653-3830   *Fax:* 603 650-0924
E-mail: clay.a.block@hitchcock.org
Length: 2 Yrs   *ACGME Approved/Offered Positions:* 4
Program ID: 148-32-12-182

New Jersey

Camden

UMDNJ-Robert Wood Johnson Medical School (Camden) Program

Sponsor: Cooper Hospital-University Medical Center
DaVita Dialysis Center
Prgm Director: Lawrence S Weisberg, MD
One Cooper Plaza
Camden, NJ 08103
Tel: 856 757-7844   *Fax:* 856 757-7778
E-mail: weisberg-larry@cooperhealth.edu
Length: 2 Yrs   *ACGME Approved/Offered Positions:* 3
Program ID: 148-33-21-160

New Brunswick

UMDNJ-Robert Wood Johnson Medical School Program

Sponsor: UMDNJ-Robert Wood Johnson Medical School
Robert Wood Johnson University Hospital
Prgm Director: John A Walker, MD
Dept of Medicine/Division of Nephrology
One Robert Wood Johnson Place, MEB 412
New Brunswick, NJ 08903
Tel: 732 235-4453   *Fax:* 732 235-6124
Length: 2 Yrs   *ACGME Approved/Offered Positions:* 4
Program ID: 148-33-21-021

Newark

Newark Beth Israel Medical Center Program

Sponsor: Newark Beth Israel Medical Center
St Barnabas Medical Center
Prgm Director: Melvin Goldblat, MD
201 Lyons Avenue at Osborne Terrace
Newark, NJ 07112
Tel: 973 926-7600   *Fax:* 973 923-0646
Length: 2 Yrs   *ACGME Approved/Offered Positions:* 4
Program ID: 148-33-21-179

UMDNJ-New Jersey Medical School Program

Sponsor: UMDNJ-New Jersey Medical School
Hackensack University Medical Center
St Joseph's Regional Medical Center
UMDNJ-University Hospital
Veterans Affairs New Jersey Health Care System
Prgm Director: Leonard Meggs, BS, MD
185 South Orange Avenue, MSB-I524
Newark, NJ 07103
Tel: 973 972-4100   *Fax:* 973 972-3578
Length: 2 Yrs   *ACGME Approved/Offered Positions:* 6
Program ID: 148-33-21-159

Note: * indicates a newly appointed program director

New Mexico

Albuquerque

University of New Mexico Program

Sponsor: University of New Mexico School of Medicine
University of New Mexico Hospital
Veterans Affairs Medical Center (Albuquerque)
Prgm Director: Karen Servilla, MD
School of Medicine
1 University of New Mexico, MSC 10-5550
Albuquerque, NM 87131
Tel: 505 272-4750   *Fax:* 505 272-2349
E-mail: kservilla@salud.unm.edu
Length: 2 Yrs   *ACGME Approved/Offered Positions:* 7
Program ID: 148-34-21-119

New York

Bronx

Albert Einstein College of Medicine (Jacobi) Program

Sponsor: Albert Einstein College of Medicine of Yeshiva
    University
North Bronx Healthcare Network-Jacobi Medical Center
North Bronx Healthcare Network-North Central Bronx
    Hospital
Prgm Director: Anjali Acharya, MD
1400 Pelham Parkway South
Room 6E-23B
Bronx, NY 10461
Tel: 718 918-7901   *Fax:* 718 918-8364
E-mail: anjali.acharya@nbhn.net
Length: 2 Yrs   *ACGME Approved/Offered Positions:* 4
Program ID: 148-35-13-183

Albert Einstein College of Medicine Program

Sponsor: Albert Einstein College of Medicine of Yeshiva
    University
Montefiore Medical Center-Henry and Lucy Moses
    Division
Montefiore Medical Center-Weiler Division
Prgm Director: Vaughn W Folkert, MD
Division of Nephrology
1300 Morris Park Ave, Ullmann 617
Bronx, NY 10461
Tel: 718 430-3158   *Fax:* 718 430-8963
E-mail: vaughnwf@earthlink.net
Length: 2 Yrs   *ACGME Approved/Offered Positions:* 8
Program ID: 148-35-21-086

Brooklyn

Brookdale University Hospital and Medical Center Program

Sponsor: Brookdale University Hospital and Medical
    Center
Prgm Director: Shyan-Yih Chou, MD
One Brookdale Plaza
Brooklyn, NY 11212
Tel: 718 240-5615   *Fax:* 718 485-4064
Length: 2 Yrs   *ACGME Approved/Offered Positions:* 6
Program ID: 148-35-11-134

Long Island College Hospital Program

Sponsor: Long Island College Hospital
Prgm Director: Neal Mittman, MD
339 Hicks Street
Othmer 409
Brooklyn, NY 11201
Tel: 718 780-1247   *Fax:* 718 780-1415
E-mail: nmittman@chpnet.org
Length: 2 Yrs   *ACGME Approved/Offered Positions:* 6
Program ID: 148-35-11-023

Maimonides Medical Center Program

Sponsor: Maimonides Medical Center
Millennium Dialysis Center
Prgm Director: Sheldon Greenberg, MD
4802 10th Avenue
Brooklyn, NY 11219
Tel: 718 283-7908   *Fax:* 718 283-6621
Length: 2 Yrs   *ACGME Approved/Offered Positions:* 2
Program ID: 148-35-12-189

SUNY Health Science Center at Brooklyn Program

Sponsor: SUNY Health Science Center at Brooklyn
University Hospital-SUNY Health Science Center at
    Brooklyn
Veterans Affairs Medical Center (Brooklyn)
Prgm Director: Moro O Salifu, MD, MPH
450 Clarkson Ave
Box 52
Brooklyn, NY 11203
Tel: 718 270-1584   *Fax:* 718 270-3327
E-mail: renal.fellowship@downstate.edu
Length: 2 Yrs   *ACGME Approved/Offered Positions:* 10
Program ID: 148-35-21-008

Buffalo

University at Buffalo Program

Sponsor: University at Buffalo School of Medicine
Erie County Medical Center
Veterans Affairs Western New York Hospital
Prgm Director: James W Lohr, MD
3495 Bailey Avenue, Room 719D
Buffalo, NY 14215
Tel: 716 862-3204   *Fax:* 716 862-6784
Length: 2 Yrs   *ACGME Approved/Offered Positions:* 6
Program ID: 148-35-31-034

East Meadow

Nassau University Medical Center Program

Sponsor: Nassau University Medical Center
Prgm Director: Leah Balsam, MD
Department of Medicine
2201 Hempstead Turnpike
East Meadow, NY 11554
Tel: 516 572-8879   *Fax:* 516 572-0082
Length: 2 Yrs   *ACGME Approved/Offered Positions:* 3
Program ID: 148-35-21-077

Elmhurst

Mount Sinai School of Medicine (Elmhurst) Program

Sponsor: Mount Sinai School of Medicine
Elmhurst Hospital Center-Mount Sinai Services
Queens Hospital Center
Prgm Director: George N Coritsidis, MD
79-01 Broadway
Elmhurst, NY 11373
Tel: 718 334-2918   *Fax:* 718 334-6019
Length: 2 Yrs   *ACGME Approved/Offered Positions:* 4
Program ID: 148-35-12-192

Flushing

New York Hospital Medical Center of Queens/Cornell University Medical College Program

Sponsor: New York Hospital Medical Center of Queens
Prgm Director: Marilyn Galler, MD
56-45 Main Street
Flushing, NY 11355
Tel: 718 670-1151   *Fax:* 718 353-9819
E-mail: mag9026@nyp.org
Length: 2 Yrs   *ACGME Approved/Offered Positions:* 5
Program ID: 148-35-11-078

Great Neck

NSLIJHS-Albert Einstein College of Medicine at Long Island Jewish Medical Center Program

Sponsor: North Shore-Long Island Jewish Health System
Long Island Jewish Medical Center
Prgm Director: Hitesh H Shah, MD
100 Community Drive, 2nd Floor
Great Neck, NY 11021
Tel: 516 465-3010   *Fax:* 516 465-3011
E-mail: hshah@lij.edu
Length: 2 Yrs   *ACGME Approved/Offered Positions:* 4
Program ID: 148-35-21-120

NSLIJHS-North Shore University Hospital/NYU School of Medicine Program

Sponsor: North Shore-Long Island Jewish Health System
North Shore University Hospital
Prgm Director: Michael D Gitman, MD
Department of Medicine
300 Community Drive
Manhasset, NY 11030
Tel: 516 465-8210
Length: 2 Yrs   *ACGME Approved/Offered Positions:* 4
Program ID: 148-35-21-143

Mineola

Winthrop-University Hospital Program

Sponsor: Winthrop-University Hospital
Prgm Director: Nobuyuki Bill Miyawaki, MD
259 First Street
Mineola, NY 11501
Tel: 516 663-2171   *Fax:* 516 663-4619
E-mail: nmiyawaki@winthrop.org
Length: 2 Yrs   *ACGME Approved/Offered Positions:* 4
Program ID: 148-35-11-064

New York

Albert Einstein College of Medicine at Beth Israel Medical Center Program

Sponsor: Beth Israel Medical Center
Prgm Director: Donald A Feinfeld, MD
Department of Medicine
First Avenue at 16th Street
New York, NY 10003
Tel: 212 420-4070   *Fax:* 212 420-4117
E-mail: dfeinfel@chpnet.org
Length: 2 Yrs   *ACGME Approved/Offered Positions:* 4
Program ID: 148-35-11-055

Harlem Hospital Center Program

Sponsor: Harlem Hospital Center
New York Presbyterian Hospital (Columbia Campus)
Prgm Director: Velvie A Pogue, MD
135th Street & Lenox Avnue
Room 12-101 MLK
New York, NY 10037
Tel: 212 939-1449   *Fax:* 212 939-1452
E-mail: vap1@columbia.edu
Length: 2 Yrs   *ACGME Approved/Offered Positions:* 2
Program ID: 148-35-11-147

Lenox Hill Hospital Program

Sponsor: Lenox Hill Hospital
Prgm Director: Maria V DeVita, MD
100 East 77th Street
New York, NY 10075
Tel: 212 439-9251   *Fax:* 212 434-4528
Length: 2 Yrs   *ACGME Approved/Offered Positions:* 4
Program ID: 148-35-11-155

Programs

Mount Sinai School of Medicine Program

Sponsor: Mount Sinai School of Medicine
Mount Sinai Medical Center
Prgm Director: Michael J Ross, MD
Box 1243
One Gustave L Levy Place
New York, NY 10029
Tel: 212 241-0131   *Fax:* 212 987-0389
E-mail: michael.ross@mssm.edu
Length: 2 Yrs   *ACGME Approved/Offered Positions:* 12
Program ID: 148-35-31-136

New York Medical College (Metropolitan) Program

Sponsor: New York Medical College
Metropolitan Hospital Center
Montefiore Medical Center - North Division
Richmond University Medical Center
Prgm Director: Alf M Tannenberg, MD
1901 First Avenue
Room 1309
New York, NY 10029
Tel: 212 423-6401   *Fax:* 212 423-7923
E-mail: alf_tannenberg@nymc.edu
Length: 2 Yrs   *ACGME Approved/Offered Positions:* 6
Program ID: 148-35-31-047

New York Medical College at St Vincent's Hospital and Medical Center of New York Program

Sponsor: New York Medical College
St Vincent Catholic Medical Centers (Manhattan)
Prgm Director: Godfrey C Burns, MD
130 W 12th St Suite 3B
New York, NY 10011
Tel: 212 604-8322   *Fax:* 212 604-3322
E-mail: gburns@svcmcny.org
Length: 2 Yrs   *ACGME Approved/Offered Positions:* 4
Program ID: 148-35-11-024

New York Presbyterian Hospital (Columbia Campus) Program

Sponsor: New York Presbyterian Hospital
New York Presbyterian Hospital (Columbia Campus)
Prgm Director: Jai Radhakrishnan, MD, MS
622 West 168th Street
Room PH4-124
New York, NY 10032
Tel: 212 305-3273   *Fax:* 212 305-6692
E-mail: gsl40@columbia.edu
Length: 2 Yrs   *ACGME Approved/Offered Positions:* 6
Program ID: 148-35-11-079

New York Presbyterian Hospital (Cornell Campus) Program

Sponsor: New York Presbyterian Hospital
New York Presbyterian Hospital (Cornell Campus)
Prgm Director: Phyllis August, MD, MPH
525 East 68th Street
New York, NY 10065
Tel: 212 746-0822   *Fax:* 212 746-8091
Length: 2 Yrs   *ACGME Approved/Offered Positions:* 10
Program ID: 148-35-21-144

New York University School of Medicine Program

Sponsor: New York University School of Medicine
Bellevue Hospital Center
Manhattan VA Harbor Health Care System
NYU Hospitals Center
Prgm Director: Judith A Benstein, MD
550 First Avenue, OBV-A612
New York, NY 10016
Tel: 212 263-5654   *Fax:* 212 263-6385
E-mail: judith.benstein@nyumc.org
Length: 2 Yrs   *ACGME Approved/Offered Positions:* 6
Program ID: 148-35-21-101

St Luke's-Roosevelt Hospital Center Program

Sponsor: St Luke's-Roosevelt Hospital Center
Prgm Director: Germaine Chan, MD
Division of Nephrology
1111 Amsterdam Avenue
New York, NY 10025
Tel: 212 523-3530   *Fax:* 212 523-3945
E-mail: gchan@chpnet.org
Length: 2 Yrs   *ACGME Approved/Offered Positions:* 3
Program ID: 148-35-21-088

Rochester

University of Rochester Program

Sponsor: Strong Memorial Hospital of the University of Rochester
Prgm Director: Rebeca Monk, MD
601 Elmwood Avenue
PO Box 675
Rochester, NY 14642
Tel: 585 275-1554   *Fax:* 585 442-9201
E-mail: Marilyn_Miran@urmc.rochester.edu
Length: 2 Yrs   *ACGME Approved/Offered Positions:* 4
Program ID: 148-35-11-157

Stony Brook

SUNY at Stony Brook Program

Sponsor: University Hospital - SUNY at Stony Brook
Veterans Affairs Medical Center (Northport)
Prgm Director: Edward Nord, MD
T-16, Room 080
Stony Brook, NY 11794
Tel: 631 444-1617   *Fax:* 631 444-6174
Length: 2 Yrs   *ACGME Approved/Offered Positions:* 6
Program ID: 148-35-21-009

Syracuse

SUNY Upstate Medical University Program

Sponsor: SUNY Upstate Medical University
Veterans Affairs Medical Center (Syracuse)
Prgm Director: Margaret MacDougall, MD, PhD
750 East Adams Street
Syracuse, NY 13210
Tel: 315 464-5290   *Fax:* 315 464-5464
Length: 2 Yrs   *ACGME Approved/Offered Positions:* 4
Program ID: 148-35-21-089

Valhalla

New York Medical College at Westchester Medical Center Program

Sponsor: New York Medical College
Westchester Medical Center
Prgm Director: Maureen Brogan, MD
Dept of Medicine
Valhalla, NY 10595
Tel: 914 493-7701   *Fax:* 914 493-8502
E-mail: sharmila_bhagan@nymc.edu
Length: 2 Yrs   *ACGME Approved/Offered Positions:* 5
Program ID: 148-35-11-010

North Carolina

Chapel Hill

University of North Carolina Hospitals Program

Sponsor: University of North Carolina Hospitals
Prgm Director: Romulo E Colindres Sr, MD, MSPH
7024 Burnett-Womack Building
CB 7155
Chapel Hill, NC 27599
Tel: 919 966-2561   *Fax:* 919 966-4251
E-mail: renalfellowship@med.unc.edu
Length: 2 Yrs   *ACGME Approved/Offered Positions:* 6
Program ID: 148-36-21-121

Durham

Duke University Hospital Program

Sponsor: Duke University Hospital
Prgm Director: Stephen R Smith, MD
Box 3014
Durham, NC 27710
Tel: 919 660-6858   *Fax:* 919 684-4476
Length: 2 Yrs   *ACGME Approved/Offered Positions:* 8
Program ID: 148-36-21-122

Greenville

Pitt County Memorial Hospital/East Carolina University Program

Sponsor: Pitt County Memorial Hospital
Brody School of Medicine at East Carolina University
Prgm Director: Melanie I Hames, DO
2355 West Arlington Boulevard
Greenville, NC 27834
Tel: 252 744-1380   *Fax:* 252 744-1817
E-mail: calhounj@ecu.edu
Length: 2 Yrs   *ACGME Approved/Offered Positions:* 4
Program ID: 148-36-31-178

Winston-Salem

Wake Forest University School of Medicine Program

Sponsor: Wake Forest University Baptist Medical Center
Prgm Director: Scott G Satko, MD
1 Medical Center Boulevard
Winston-Salem, NC 27157
Tel: 336 716-4650   *Fax:* 336 716-4318
E-mail: ssatko@wfubmc.edu
Length: 2 Yrs   *ACGME Approved/Offered Positions:* 5
Program ID: 148-36-21-011

Ohio

Cincinnati

University Hospital/University of Cincinnati College of Medicine Program

Sponsor: University Hospital Inc
Veterans Affairs Medical Center (Cincinnati)
Prgm Director: Satwant Singh, MBBS, MD
Division of Nephrology and Hypertension
231 Albert Sabin Way, PO Box 670585
Cincinnati, OH 45267
Tel: 513 558-5471   *Fax:* 513 558-4309
E-mail: satwant.singh@uc.edu
Length: 2 Yrs   *ACGME Approved/Offered Positions:* 6
Program ID: 148-38-21-066

Note: * indicates a newly appointed program director

Cleveland

Cleveland Clinic Foundation Program

Sponsor: Cleveland Clinic Foundation
Prgm Director: Richard A Fatica, MD
9500 Euclid Avenue - Desk A51
Dept of Nephrology & Hypertension
Cleveland, OH 44195
Tel: 216 444-6780   *Fax:* 216 444-9378
E-mail: meded@ccf.org
Length: 2 Yrs   *ACGME Approved/Offered Positions:* 7
Program ID: 148-38-12-139

University Hospitals Case Medical Center Program

Sponsor: University Hospitals Case Medical Center
MetroHealth Medical Center
Veterans Affairs Medical Center (Cleveland)
Prgm Director: Lavinia A Negrea, MD
Division of Nephrology
11100 Euclid Avenue
Cleveland, OH 44106
Tel: 216 844-8272   *Fax:* 216 844-5204
E-mail: lavinia.negrea@case.edu
Length: 2 Yrs   *ACGME Approved/Offered Positions:* 6
Program ID: 148-38-21-137

Columbus

Ohio State University Hospital Program

Sponsor: Ohio State University Hospital
Ohio State University Hospitals, East
Prgm Director: Brad H Rovin, MD
Department of Internal Medicine
395 West 12th Avenue, Ground Floor
Columbus, OH 43210
Tel: 614 293-4997   *Fax:* 614 293-3073
E-mail: andrea.wissman@osumc.edu
Length: 2 Yrs   *ACGME Approved/Offered Positions:* 8
Program ID: 148-38-11-080

Toledo

University of Toledo Program

Sponsor: University of Toledo
St Vincent Mercy Medical Center
University Medical Center (Toledo)
Prgm Director: Deepak Malhotra, MD, PhD
Department of Medicine
3000 Arlington Avenue, Mail Stop 1186
Toledo, OH 43614
Tel: 419 383-3705   *Fax:* 419 383-3102
Length: 2 Yrs   *ACGME Approved/Offered Positions:* 4
Program ID: 148-38-21-012

Oklahoma

Oklahoma City

University of Oklahoma Health Sciences Center Program

Sponsor: University of Oklahoma College of Medicine
OU Medical Center
Veterans Affairs Medical Center (Oklahoma City)
Prgm Director: Lukas Haragsim, MD*
Nephrology / WP2250
OUHSC / 920 S L Young Blvd
Oklahoma City, OK 73104
Tel: 405 271-6842   *Fax:* 405 271-6496
Length: 2 Yrs   *ACGME Approved/Offered Positions:* 4
Program ID: 148-39-21-067

Oregon

Portland

Oregon Health & Science University Program

Sponsor: Oregon Health & Science University Hospital
Veterans Affairs Medical Center (Portland)
Prgm Director: Suzanne G Watnick, MD*
Division of Nephrology and Hypertension
3314 SW US Veterans Hospital Road PP262
Portland, OR 97239
Tel: 503 494-8490   *Fax:* 503 494-5330
E-mail: watnicks@ohsu.edu
Length: 2 Yrs   *ACGME Approved/Offered Positions:* 6
Program ID: 148-40-31-140

Pennsylvania

Danville

Geisinger Health System Program

Sponsor: Geisinger Health System
Geisinger Medical Center
Prgm Director: Michael F Schultz, MD
Nephrology Department 13-48
100 Academy Avenue
Danville, PA 17822
Tel: 570 271-6393   *Fax:* 570 271-5623
E-mail: nephfellow@gesinger.edu
Length: 2 Yrs   *ACGME Approved/Offered Positions:* 4
Program ID: 148-41-13-191

Hershey

Penn State University/Milton S Hershey Medical Center Program

Sponsor: Milton S Hershey Medical Center
Prgm Director: Ronald P Miller, MD
Division of Nephrology
H040, PO Box 850
Hershey, PA 17033
Tel: 717 531-8156   *Fax:* 717 531-6776
Length: 2 Yrs   *ACGME Approved/Offered Positions:* 4
Program ID: 148-41-11-013

Philadelphia

Albert Einstein Healthcare Network Program

Sponsor: Albert Einstein Medical Center
Prgm Director: Eric J Bloom, MD
5501 Old York Road
Philadelphia, PA 19141
Tel: 215 456-6970   *Fax:* 215 456-7154
E-mail: walshp@einstein.edu
Length: 2 Yrs   *ACGME Approved/Offered Positions:* 6
Program ID: 148-41-11-056

Drexel University College of Medicine/Hahnemann University Hospital Program

Sponsor: Drexel University College of
  Medicine/Hahnemann University
Hahnemann University Hospital (Tenet Health System)
Prgm Director: Sandra P Levison, MD
245 N 15th Street
Mail Stop 437
Philadelphia, PA 19102
Tel: 215 762-1172   *Fax:* 215 762-8366
E-mail: bsmith@drexelmed.edu
Length: 2 Yrs   *ACGME Approved/Offered Positions:* 8
Program ID: 148-41-21-102

Temple University Hospital Program

Sponsor: Temple University Hospital
Prgm Director: Joseph Benjamin, MBBS*
Department of Medicine
3322 N Broad Street, Suite 201
Philadelphia, PA 19140
Tel: 215 707-7937   *Fax:* 215 707-9697
E-mail: benjam@temple.edu
Length: 2 Yrs   *ACGME Approved/Offered Positions:* 6
Program ID: 148-41-21-026

Thomas Jefferson University Program

Sponsor: Thomas Jefferson University Hospital
Prgm Director: Rakesh Gulati, MD, MRCP
Division of Nephrology/Dialysis Unit
111 South 11th Street, Suite 4290
Philadelphia, PA 19107
Tel: 215 503-3000   *Fax:* 215 503-4099
E-mail: rakesh.gulati@jefferson.edu
Length: 2 Yrs   *ACGME Approved/Offered Positions:* 6
Program ID: 148-41-21-027

University of Pennsylvania Program

Sponsor: University of Pennsylvania Health System
Prgm Director: Jeffrey S Berns, MD
3400 Spruce Street
Philadelphia, PA 19104
Tel: 215 615-1677   *Fax:* 215 615-1688
E-mail: Jeffrey.Berns@uphs.upenn.edu
Length: 2 Yrs   *ACGME Approved/Offered Positions:* 14
Program ID: 148-41-21-018

Pittsburgh

Allegheny General Hospital Program

Sponsor: Allegheny General Hospital
Prgm Director: Richard J Marcus, MD
320 E North Avenue
Pittsburgh, PA 15212
Tel: 412 359-4008   *Fax:* 412 359-4136
E-mail: tbender@wpahs.org
Length: 2 Yrs   *ACGME Approved/Offered Positions:* 8
Program ID: 148-41-11-036

University of Pittsburgh Medical Center Medical Education Program

Sponsor: Univ of Pittsburgh Medical Center Medical
  Education
UPMC Presbyterian Shadyside
Prgm Director: James R Johnston, MD
A915 Scaife Hall
3550 Terrace Street
Pittsburgh, PA 15261
Tel: 412 647-8394   *Fax:* 412 647-6222
E-mail: jamiej@pitt.edu
Length: 2 Yrs   *ACGME Approved/Offered Positions:* 13
Program ID: 148-41-21-037

Wynnewood

Lankenau Hospital Program

Sponsor: Lankenau Hospital
Prgm Director: Robert L Benz, MD
100 Lancaster Avenue
Suite 130
Wynnewood, PA 19096
Tel: 610 649-1175   *Fax:* 610 649-3627
E-mail: roniaroller@aol.com
Length: 2 Yrs   *ACGME Approved/Offered Positions:* 3
Program ID: 148-41-11-028

Programs

Puerto Rico

San Juan

University of Puerto Rico Program
Sponsor: University of Puerto Rico School of Medicine
University Hospital
Prgm Director: Enrique Ortiz-Kidd, MD
University of Puerto Rico School of Medicine
PO Box 365067
San Juan, PR 00936
Tel: 787 758-2525   *Fax:* 787 754-1739
E-mail: rtzkdd@yahoo.com
Length: 2 Yrs   *ACGME Approved/Offered Positions:* 3
Program ID: 148-42-21-104

VA Caribbean Healthcare System Program
Sponsor: VA Caribbean Healthcare System
Prgm Director: Hector R Cordova, MD
Medical Service (111d)
10 Casia St
San Juan, PR 00921
Tel: 787 641-7582   *Fax:* 787 641-4561
Length: 2 Yrs   *ACGME Approved/Offered Positions:* 3
Program ID: 148-42-31-103

Rhode Island

Providence

Brown University Program
Sponsor: Rhode Island Hospital-Lifespan
Miriam Hospital-Lifespan
Veterans Affairs Medical Center (Providence)
Prgm Director: J Gary Abuelo, MD
593 Eddy Street
APC 9, Rm 952
Providence, RI 02903
Tel: 401 444-5033   *Fax:* 401 444-3944
Length: 2 Yrs   *ACGME Approved/Offered Positions:* 7
Program ID: 148-43-11-105

South Carolina

Charleston

Medical University of South Carolina Program
Sponsor: Medical University of South Carolina College of
   Medicine
MUSC Medical Center
Ralph H Johnson VA Medical Center (Charleston)
Prgm Director: David W Ploth, MD
96 Jonathan Lucas Street
MSC 629, CSB 829
Charleston, SC 29425
Tel: 843 792-4123   *Fax:* 843 792-8399
E-mail: plothdw@musc.edu
Length: 2 Yrs   *ACGME Approved/Offered Positions:* 10
Program ID: 148-45-21-156

Tennessee

Memphis

University of Tennessee Program
Sponsor: University of Tennessee College of Medicine
Methodist Healthcare - Memphis Hospitals
Regional Medical Center at Memphis
Veterans Affairs Medical Center (Memphis)
Prgm Director: Barry M Wall, MD
Department of Nephrology
1030 Jefferson Ave, 111B
Memphis, TN 38104
Tel: 901 523-8990   *Fax:* 901 577-7487
E-mail: barry.wall@va.gov
Length: 2 Yrs   *ACGME Approved/Offered Positions:* 6
Program ID: 148-47-21-123

Nashville

Vanderbilt University Program
Sponsor: Vanderbilt University Medical Center
Prgm Director: Julia Lewis, MD
Division of Nephrology, S-3223 MCN
21st and Garland
Nashville, TN 37232
Tel: 615 343-6105   *Fax:* 615 343-7156
Length: 2 Yrs   *ACGME Approved/Offered Positions:* 15
Program ID: 148-47-31-014

Texas

Dallas

Baylor University Medical Center Program
Sponsor: Baylor University Medical Center
Dallas Nephrology Associates
Prgm Director: Yousri Barri, MD
3500 Gaston Avenue
Nephrology Division
Dallas, TX 75246
Tel: 214 820-2350   *Fax:* 214 820-7367
Length: 2 Yrs   *ACGME Approved/Offered Positions:* 3
Program ID: 148-48-21-188

University of Texas Southwestern Medical School Program
Sponsor: University of Texas Southwestern Medical
   School
Dallas County Hospital District-Parkland Memorial
   Hospital
Dallas VA Medical Center
Prgm Director: Biff F Palmer, MD
5323 Harry Hines Blvd
Dallas, TX 75390
Tel: 214 648-3442   *Fax:* 214 648-2071
E-mail: nephrologyfellowship@utsouthwestern.edu
Length: 2 Yrs   *ACGME Approved/Offered Positions:* 14
Program ID: 148-48-21-084

Galveston

University of Texas Medical Branch Hospitals Program
Sponsor: University of Texas Medical Branch Hospitals
Prgm Director: Robert Beach, MD
301 University Blvd
4.200 John Sealy Annex
Galveston, TX 77555
Tel: 409 772-1811   *Fax:* 409 772-5451
E-mail: dcampbel@utmb.edu
Length: 2 Yrs   *ACGME Approved/Offered Positions:* 6
Program ID: 148-48-21-049

Houston

Baylor College of Medicine Program
Sponsor: Baylor College of Medicine
Harris County Hospital District-Ben Taub General
   Hospital
Methodist Hospital (Houston)
Michael E DeBakey VA Medical Center - Houston
St Luke's Episcopal Hospital
Prgm Director: William E Mitch, MD
Section of Nephrology
1709 Dryden Road, Suite 900
Houston, TX 77030
Tel: 713 798-8350   *Fax:* 713 798-3510
E-mail: lindaj@bcm.tmc.edu
Length: 2 Yrs   *ACGME Approved/Offered Positions:* 11
Program ID: 148-48-21-070

University of Texas at Houston Program
Sponsor: University of Texas Health Science Center at
   Houston
Lyndon B Johnson General Hospital
Memorial Hermann Hospital
University of Texas M D Anderson Cancer Center
Prgm Director: John R Foringer, MD*
Department of Medicine
6431 Fannin St, Suite 4.130
Houston, TX 77030
Tel: 713 500-6868   *Fax:* 713 500-6882
E-mail: John.R.Foringer@uth.tmc.edu
Length: 2 Yrs   *ACGME Approved/Offered Positions:* 12
Program ID: 148-48-31-015

Lubbock

Texas Tech University (Lubbock) Program
Sponsor: Texas Tech University Health Sciences Center
   at Lubbock
Dialysis Center of Lubbock
University Medical Center
Prgm Director: Melvin E Laski, MD
Department of Medicine
3601 4th Street
Lubbock, TX 79430
Tel: 806 743-3155   *Fax:* 806 743-3148
Length: 2 Yrs   *ACGME Approved/Offered Positions:* 4
Program ID: 148-48-21-081

San Antonio

University of Texas Health Science Center at San Antonio Program
Sponsor: University of Texas School of Medicine at San
   Antonio
Audie L Murphy Memorial Veterans Hospital (San
   Antonio)
University Health System
Wilford Hall Medical Center (AETC)
Prgm Director: Robert T Kunau Jr, MD
Medicine/Nephrology MSC 7882
7703 Floyd Curl Drive
San Antonio, TX 78229
Tel: 210 567-4700   *Fax:* 210 567-4712
Length: 2 Yrs   *ACGME Approved/Offered Positions:* 13
Program ID: 148-48-21-057

Temple

Texas A&M College of Medicine-Scott and White Program
Sponsor: Scott and White Memorial Hospital
Prgm Director: Allan E Nickel, MD*
2401 S 31st Street
Temple, TX 76508
Tel: 254 724-2111   *Fax:* 254 724-9280
Length: 2 Yrs   *ACGME Approved/Offered Positions:* 4
Program ID: 148-48-12-180

Note: * indicates a newly appointed program director

Utah

Salt Lake City

University of Utah Program
Sponsor: University of Utah Medical Center
Veterans Affairs Medical Center (Salt Lake City)
Prgm Director: Donald E Kohan, MD, PhD
Division of Nephrology, 4R312 SOM
30 North 1900 East
Salt Lake City, UT 84132
Tel: 801 581-6709   *Fax:* 801 581-4343
Length: 2 Yrs   *ACGME Approved/Offered Positions:* 3
Program ID: 148-49-21-141

Vermont

Burlington

University of Vermont Program
Sponsor: Fletcher Allen Health Care
Prgm Director: Alan Segal, MD, MS
Mailstop 443RE2, Rm 2309
1 South Prospect St
Burlington, VT 05401
Tel: 802 847-3104   *Fax:* 802 847-8736
E-mail: alan.segal@uvm.edu
Length: 2 Yrs   *ACGME Approved/Offered Positions:* 4
Program ID: 148-50-21-142

Virginia

Charlottesville

University of Virginia Program
Sponsor: University of Virginia Medical Center
Prgm Director: Mitchell H Rosner, MD
Department of Internal Medicine
PO Box 800133
Charlottesville, VA 22908
Tel: 434 924-5125   *Fax:* 434 924-5848
E-mail: mhr9r@virginia.edu
Length: 2 Yrs   *ACGME Approved/Offered Positions:* 8
Program ID: 148-51-21-016

Richmond

Virginia Commonwealth University Health System Program
Sponsor: Virginia Commonwealth University Health
System
Hunter Holmes McGuire VA Medical Center (Richmond)
Medical College of Virginia Hospitals
Prgm Director: Susan R DiGiovanni, MD
PO Box 980160
Richmond, VA 23298
Tel: 804 828-9682   *Fax:* 804 828-7567
E-mail: sdigiovanni@mcvh-vcu.edu
Length: 2 Yrs   *ACGME Approved/Offered Positions:* 8
Program ID: 148-51-21-017

Washington

Seattle

University of Washington Program
Sponsor: University of Washington School of Medicine
University of Washington Medical Center
Prgm Director: Rudolph Rodriguez, MD
Div of Nephrology, Box 356521
1959 NE Pacific St
Seattle, WA 98195
Tel: 206 277-3282   *Fax:* 206 764-2022
Length: 2 Yrs   *ACGME Approved/Offered Positions:* 10
Program ID: 148-54-21-072

West Virginia

Morgantown

West Virginia University Program
Sponsor: West Virginia University School of Medicine
West Virginia University Hospitals
Prgm Director: Karen MacKay, MD
Robert C Byrd Health Science Center
PO Box 9165
Morgantown, WV 26506
Tel: 304 293-2551   *Fax:* 304 293-7373
E-mail: jboord@hsc.wvu.edu
Length: 2 Yrs   *ACGME Approved/Offered Positions:* 4
Program ID: 148-55-11-165

Wisconsin

Madison

University of Wisconsin Program
Sponsor: University of Wisconsin Hospital and Clinics
Meriter Hospital
William S Middleton Veterans Hospital
Prgm Director: Bryan N Becker, MD
3034 Fish Hatchery Road
Suite B
Madison, WI 53713
Tel: 608 270-5671   *Fax:* 608 270-5677
Length: 2 Yrs   *ACGME Approved/Offered Positions:* 5
Program ID: 148-56-21-106

Milwaukee

Medical College of Wisconsin Affiliated Hospitals Program
Sponsor: Medical College of Wisconsin Affiliated
Hospitals, Inc
Clement J Zablocki Veterans Affairs Medical Center
Froedtert Memorial Lutheran Hospital
Prgm Director: Eric P Cohen, MD
9200 W Wisconsin Ave
CCC - 5th Floor
Milwaukee, WI 53226
Tel: 414 805-9050   *Fax:* 414 805-9059
Length: 2 Yrs   *ACGME Approved/Offered Positions:* 6
Program ID: 148-56-31-039

Neurodevelopmental Disabilities (Neurology)

District of Columbia

Washington

Children's National Medical Center/ George Washington University Program
Sponsor: Children's National Medical Center
George Washington University Hospital (UHS)
Prgm Director: Elliot S Gersh, MD*
Division of Neurodevelopmental Pediatrics
111 Michigan Avenue, NW
Washington, DC 20010
Tel: 240 568-7031
Length: 4 Yrs   *ACGME Approved/Offered Positions:* 2
Program ID: 186-10-12-008

Maryland

Baltimore

Johns Hopkins University Program
Sponsor: Johns Hopkins University School of Medicine
Johns Hopkins Hospital
Kennedy Krieger Institute
Prgm Director: Bruce K Shapiro, MD
707 North Broadway
Baltimore, MD 21205
Tel: 443 923-9136   *Fax:* 443 923-9165
Length: 4 Yrs   *ACGME Approved/Offered Positions:* 8
Program ID: 186-23-21-001

Massachusetts

Boston

Children's Hospital/Beth Israel Deaconess Medical Center/Harvard Medical School Program
Sponsor: Children's Hospital
Beth Israel Deaconess Medical Center
Seven Hills at Groton
Prgm Director: Sandra L Friedman, MD, MPH
300 Longwood Avenue
Boston, MA 02115
Tel: 617 355-6513   *Fax:* 617 267-9397
Length: 4 Yrs   *ACGME Approved/Offered Positions:* 4
Program ID: 186-24-22-002

Ohio

Cincinnati

Cincinnati Children's Hospital Medical Center/University of Cincinnati College of Medicine Program
Sponsor: Cincinnati Children's Hospital Medical Center
University of Cincinnati College of Medicine
Prgm Director: Mark B Schapiro, BA, MD
3333 Burnet Avenue
Cincinnati, OH 45229
Tel: 513 636-7558   *Fax:* 513 636-1888
Length: 4 Yrs   *ACGME Approved/Offered Positions:* 8
Program ID: 186-38-21-004

Programs

Oregon

Portland

Oregon Health & Science University Program
Sponsor: Oregon Health & Science University Hospital
Veterans Affairs Medical Center (Portland)
Prgm Director: Peter A Blasco, MD
707 SW Gaines Street
Portland, OR 97239
Tel: 503 494-2756   *Fax:* 503 494-6868
Length: 4 Yrs   *ACGME Approved/Offered Positions:* 4
Program ID: 186-40-11-006

Pennsylvania

Pittsburgh

University of Pittsburgh Medical Center Medical Education Program
Sponsor: Univ of Pittsburgh Medical Center Medical
  Education
Children's Hospital of Pittsburgh of UPMC
UPMC Presbyterian Shadyside
Prgm Director: Miya R Asato, MD*
3705 Fifth Avenue
Pittsburgh, PA 15213
Tel: 412 692-7490   *Fax:* 412 692-7303
Length: 4 Yrs   *ACGME Approved/Offered Positions:* 4
Program ID: 186-41-23-007

Texas

Houston

Baylor College of Medicine Program
Sponsor: Baylor College of Medicine
Texas Children's Hospital
Prgm Director: Sherry Seller Vinson, MD, MEd
Meyer Center for Developmental Pediatrics
6621 Fannin Street, MC:CC-1530
Houston, TX 77030
Tel: 832 822-3423   *Fax:* 832 825-3399
E-mail: sandrap@bcm.tmc.edu
Length: 4 Yrs   *ACGME Approved/Offered Positions:* 8
Program ID: 186-48-33-003

Neurological Surgery

Alabama

Birmingham

University of Alabama Medical Center Program
Sponsor: University of Alabama Hospital
Children's Hospital of Alabama
Veterans Affairs Medical Center (Birmingham)
Prgm Director: Mark N Hadley, MD
Faculty Office Tower 1030
510 Twentieth Street South
Birmingham, AL 35294
Tel: 205 934-1439   *Fax:* 205 975-6081
Length: 5 Yrs   *ACGME Approved/Offered Positions:* 15
Program ID: 160-01-21-003

Arizona

Phoenix

St Joseph's Hospital and Medical Center Program
Sponsor: St Joseph's Hospital and Medical Center
Prgm Director: Volker K H Sonntag, MD
Barrow Neurological Institute
350 West Thomas Road
Phoenix, AZ 85013
Tel: 602 406-3196   *Fax:* 602 406-4104
E-mail: Leah.Plush@chw.edu
Length: 5 Yrs   *ACGME Approved/Offered Positions:* 20
Program ID: 160-03-12-004

Tucson

University of Arizona Program
Sponsor: University of Arizona College of Medicine
Phoenix Children's Hospital
Southern Arizona VA Health Care Center (Tucson)
St Joseph's Hospital and Medical Center
Tucson Medical Center
University Medical Center
Prgm Director: Martin E Weinand, MD, BS
Division of Neurosurgery, AHSC
PO Box 245070
Tucson, AZ 85724
Tel: 520 626-0704   *Fax:* 520 626-8313
E-mail: mweinand@u.arizona.edu
Length: 5 Yrs   *ACGME Approved/Offered Positions:* 5
Program ID: 160-03-21-112

Arkansas

Little Rock

University of Arkansas for Medical Sciences Program
Sponsor: University of Arkansas College of Medicine
Arkansas Children's Hospital
Central Arkansas Veterans Healthcare System
UAMS Medical Center
Prgm Director: Ossama Al-Mefty, MD
4301 West Markham, Slot 507
Little Rock, AR 72205
Tel: 501 686-8757   *Fax:* 501 686-8767
Length: 5 Yrs   *ACGME Approved/Offered Positions:* 8
Program ID: 160-04-21-005

California

Loma Linda

Loma Linda University Program
Sponsor: Loma Linda University Medical Center
Prgm Director: Austin Colohan, MD
Room 2562 B
11234 Anderson Street
Loma Linda, CA 92354
Tel: 909 558-4417   *Fax:* 909 588-4825
E-mail: kzaugg@llu.edu
Length: 5 Yrs   *ACGME Approved/Offered Positions:* 8
Program ID: 160-05-11-008

Los Angeles

Cedars-Sinai Medical Center Program
Sponsor: Cedars-Sinai Medical Center
Prgm Director: Moise Danielpour, MD
8631 W 3rd Street, Suite 800E
Los Angeles, CA 90048
Tel: 310 423-7900   *Fax:* 310 423-0819
E-mail: nsrprogramcoordinator@cshs.org
Length: 5 Yrs   *ACGME Approved/Offered Positions:* 5
Program ID: 160-05-13-124

UCLA Medical Center Program
Sponsor: UCLA David Geffen School of Medicine/UCLA
  Medical Center
Los Angeles County-Harbor-UCLA Medical Center
UCLA Medical Center
VA Greater Los Angeles Healthcare System
Prgm Director: Neil A Martin, MD
17-384 Semel, Box 957039
10833 Le Conte Avenue
Los Angeles, CA 90095
Tel: 310 794-7362   *Fax:* 310 267-2707
E-mail: cbruton@mednet.ucla.edu
Length: 5 Yrs   *ACGME Approved/Offered Positions:* 15
Program ID: 160-05-21-010

University of Southern California/ LAC+USC Medical Center Program
Sponsor: University of Southern California/LAC+USC
  Medical Center
Childrens Hospital Los Angeles
LAC+USC Medical Center
USC University Hospital
Prgm Director: Steven L Giannotta, MD
1200 North State Street
Suite 5046
Los Angeles, CA 90033
Tel: 323 226-7421   *Fax:* 323 226-7833
E-mail: kguzman@usc.edu
Length: 5 Yrs   *ACGME Approved/Offered Positions:* 10
Program ID: 160-05-21-009

Orange

University of California (Irvine) Program
Sponsor: University of California (Irvine) Medical
  Center
Children's Hospital of Orange County
Kaiser Foundation Hospitals (Anaheim)
Prgm Director: Mark E Linskey, MD
101 The City Drive South
Building 56, Suite 400
Orange, CA 92868
Tel: 714 456-6966   *Fax:* 714 456-8212
Length: 5 Yrs   *ACGME Approved/Offered Positions:* 5
Program ID: 160-05-12-127

Note: * indicates a newly appointed program director

Sacramento

University of California (Davis) Health System Program

Sponsor: University of California (Davis) Health System
University of California (Davis) Medical Center
Prgm Director: Jan Paul Muizelaar, MD, PhD
4860 Y Street, Suite 3740
Sacramento, CA 95817
Tel: 916 734-3685   *Fax:* 916 703-5368
Length: 5 Yrs   *ACGME Approved/Offered Positions:* 5
Program ID: 160-05-11-006

San Diego

University of California (San Diego) Program

Sponsor: University of California (San Diego) Medical Center
Kaiser Foundation Hospital (San Diego)
Rady Children's Hospital
Veterans Affairs Medical Center (San Diego)
Prgm Director: Lawrence F Marshall, MD
200 West Arbor Drive #8893
San Diego, CA 92103
Tel: 619 543-5540   *Fax:* 619 543-2769
Length: 5 Yrs   *ACGME Approved/Offered Positions:* 8
Program ID: 160-05-21-100

San Francisco

University of California (San Francisco) Program

Sponsor: University of California (San Francisco) School of Medicine
UCSF and Mount Zion Medical Centers
Prgm Director: Nicholas M Barbaro, MD
505 Parnassus Avenue, Box-0112
San Francisco, CA 94143
Tel: 415 353-3904   *Fax:* 415 353-3907
Length: 5 Yrs   *ACGME Approved/Offered Positions:* 15
Program ID: 160-05-21-011

Stanford

Stanford University Program

Sponsor: Stanford Hospital and Clinics
Lucile Salter Packard Children's Hospital at Stanford
Veterans Affairs Palo Alto Health Care System
Prgm Director: Griffith R Harsh IV, MD, MBA
300 Pasteur Drive
Edward Building, R281
Stanford, CA 94305
Tel: 650 725-0701   *Fax:* 650 498-4686
E-mail: gharsh@stanford.edu
Length: 5 Yrs   *ACGME Approved/Offered Positions:* 13
Program ID: 160-05-21-012

Colorado

Aurora

University of Colorado Denver Program

Sponsor: University of Colorado Denver School of Medicine
Children's Hospital (The)
Denver Health Medical Center
University of Colorado Hospital
Veterans Affairs Medical Center (Denver)
Prgm Director: Robert E Breeze, MD
PO Box 6511
12631 East 17th Avenue, Box C307
Aurora, CO 80045
Tel: 303 724-2305   *Fax:* 303 724-2300
E-mail: robert.breeze@uchsc.edu
Length: 5 Yrs   *ACGME Approved/Offered Positions:* 10
Program ID: 160-07-21-102

Connecticut

New Haven

Yale-New Haven Medical Center Program

Sponsor: Yale-New Haven Hospital
Veterans Affairs Medical Center (West Haven)
Prgm Director: Charles C Duncan, MD
333 Cedar Street
PO Box 208082
New Haven, CT 06520
Tel: 203 785-2809   *Fax:* 203 785-6916
E-mail: peggy.mclaughlin@yale.edu
Length: 5 Yrs   *ACGME Approved/Offered Positions:* 10
Program ID: 160-08-21-015

District of Columbia

Washington

George Washington University Program

Sponsor: George Washington University School of Medicine
Children's National Medical Center
Clinical Center at the National Institutes of Health
George Washington University Hospital (UHS)
Inova Fairfax Hospital
Prgm Director: Anthony Caputy, MD
2150 Pennsylvania Avenue, NW Suite 7-420
Washington, DC 20037
Tel: 202 741-2735   *Fax:* 202 741-2742
Length: 5 Yrs   *ACGME Approved/Offered Positions:* 5
Program ID: 160-10-21-017

Georgetown University Hospital Program

Sponsor: Georgetown University Hospital
Children's National Medical Center
Washington Hospital Center
Prgm Director: Kevin M McGrail, MD
3800 Reservoir Road NW
7PHC
Washington, DC 20007
Tel: 202 444-7371   *Fax:* 202 444-7573
Length: 5 Yrs   *ACGME Approved/Offered Positions:* 10
Program ID: 160-10-21-016

Florida

Gainesville

University of Florida Program

Sponsor: University of Florida College of Medicine
North Florida/South Georgia Veterans Health System
Shands Hospital at the University of Florida
Prgm Director: James R Lister, MD, MBA
Department of Neurological Surgery
PO Box 100265
Gainesville, FL 32610
Tel: 352 273-9000   *Fax:* 352 392-8413
E-mail: jamie.dow@neurosurgery.ufl.edu
Length: 5 Yrs   *ACGME Approved/Offered Positions:* 15
Program ID: 160-11-21-018

Miami

Jackson Memorial Hospital/Jackson Health System Program

Sponsor: Jackson Memorial Hospital/Jackson Health System
Miami Children's Hospital
Veterans Affairs Medical Center (Miami)
Prgm Director: Roberto C Heros, MD
1095 NW 14th Terrace
Lois Pope LIFE Center (D4-6)
Miami, FL 33136
Tel: 305 243-6672   *Fax:* 305 243-3180
E-mail: imenendez@med.miami.edu
Length: 5 Yrs   *ACGME Approved/Offered Positions:* 13
Program ID: 160-11-21-019

Tampa

University of South Florida Program

Sponsor: University of South Florida College of Medicine
All Children's Hospital
H Lee Moffitt Cancer Center
James A Haley Veterans Hospital
Tampa General Hospital
Prgm Director: Fernando L Vale, MD
2 Tampa General Circle
7th Floor, Department of Neurosurgery
Tampa, FL 33606
Tel: 813 259-0901   *Fax:* 813 259-0944
E-mail: rdubault@health.usf.edu
Length: 5 Yrs   *ACGME Approved/Offered Positions:* 10
Program ID: 160-11-21-109

Georgia

Atlanta

Emory University Program

Sponsor: Emory University School of Medicine
Crawford Long Hospital of Emory University
Emory University Hospital
Grady Health System
Prgm Director: Nelson M Oyesiku, MD, PhD
1365 B Clifton Road
Suite 6200
Atlanta, GA 30322
Tel: 404 778-5969   *Fax:* 404 778-4472
Length: 5 Yrs   *ACGME Approved/Offered Positions:* 15
Program ID: 160-12-21-020

Augusta

Medical College of Georgia Program

Sponsor: Medical College of Georgia
Veterans Affairs Medical Center (Augusta)
Prgm Director: Cargill H Alleyne Jr, MD
Department of Neurosurgery
1120 15th Street, BI-3088
Augusta, GA 30912
Tel: 706 721-3071   *Fax:* 706 721-8084
E-mail: jmotley@mail.mcg.edu
Length: 5 Yrs   *ACGME Approved/Offered Positions:* 8
Program ID: 160-12-21-021

Programs

Illinois

Chicago

McGaw Medical Center of Northwestern University Program

Sponsor: McGaw Medical Center of Northwestern University
Children's Memorial Hospital
Evanston Hospital
Northwestern Memorial Hospital
Prgm Director: Stephen Ondra, MD
676 N St Clair St, Suite 2210
Chicago, IL 60611
Tel: 312 695-6282   *Fax:* 312 695-0225
Length: 5 Yrs   *ACGME Approved/Offered Positions:* 13
Program ID: 160-16-21-022

Rush University Medical Center Program

Sponsor: Rush University Medical Center
Advocate Lutheran General Hospital
Alexian Brothers Medical Center
Prgm Director: Richard W Byrne, MD
Department of Neurosurgery
1725 W Harrison Street, Ste 1115
Chicago, IL 60612
Tel: 312 942-6628   *Fax:* 312 563-3358
E-mail: rbyrne37@aol.com
Length: 5 Yrs   *ACGME Approved/Offered Positions:* 8
Program ID: 160-16-11-023

University of Chicago Program

Sponsor: University of Chicago Medical Center
Prgm Director: David M Frim, MD, PhD
5841 South Maryland Avenue MC 3026
Chicago, IL 60637
Tel: 773 702-8544   *Fax:* 773 702-3518
E-mail: hrice@surgery.bsd.uchicago.edu
Length: 5 Yrs   *ACGME Approved/Offered Positions:* 8
Program ID: 160-16-11-024

University of Illinois College of Medicine at Chicago Program

Sponsor: University of Illinois College of Medicine at Chicago
Advocate Christ Medical Center
Alexian Brothers Medical Center
University of Illinois Hospital and Clinics
Prgm Director: Sepideh Amin-Hanjani, MD
912 South Wood Street, M/C 799
Chicago, IL 60612
Tel: 312 996-4842   *Fax:* 312 996-9018
E-mail: hanjani@uic.edu
Length: 5 Yrs   *ACGME Approved/Offered Positions:* 8
Program ID: 160-16-21-025

Maywood

Loyola University Program

Sponsor: Loyola University Medical Center
Edward Hines, Jr Veterans Affairs Hospital
Prgm Director: Russ P Nockels, MD*
Building 105 Room 1900
2160 South First Avenue
Maywood, IL 60153
Tel: 708 216-0005   *Fax:* 708 216-4948
E-mail: lnagle@lumc.edu
Length: 5 Yrs   *ACGME Approved/Offered Positions:* 8
Program ID: 160-16-21-026

Peoria

University of Illinois College of Medicine at Peoria Program

Sponsor: University of Illinois College of Medicine at Peoria
Methodist Medical Center of Illinois
OSF St Francis Medical Center
Prgm Director: Julian J Lin, MD
530 NE Glen Oak Avenue, Room 3641
Peoria, IL 61637
Tel: 309 655-2642   *Fax:* 309 655-7696
E-mail: clb@uic.edu
Length: 5 Yrs   *ACGME Approved/Offered Positions:* 5
Program ID: 160-16-21-099

Indiana

Indianapolis

Indiana University School of Medicine Program

Sponsor: Indiana University School of Medicine
Clarian Indiana University Hospital
Clarian Methodist Hospital of Indiana
Clarian Riley Hospital for Children
Richard L Roudebush Veterans Affairs Medical Center
William N Wishard Memorial Hospital
Prgm Director: Paul B Nelson, MD
545 Barnhill Drive
Emerson Hall 139
Indianapolis, IN 46202
Tel: 317 274-5725   *Fax:* 317 274-7351
E-mail: mjgallag@iupui.edu
Length: 5 Yrs   *ACGME Approved/Offered Positions:* 10
Program ID: 160-17-11-027

Iowa

Iowa City

University of Iowa Hospitals and Clinics Program

Sponsor: University of Iowa Hospitals and Clinics
Veterans Affairs Medical Center (Iowa City)
Prgm Director: Matthew A Howard III, MD
200 Hawkins Drive
Iowa City, IA 52242
Tel: 319 356-8468   *Fax:* 319 353-6605
Length: 5 Yrs   *ACGME Approved/Offered Positions:* 10
Program ID: 160-18-11-028

Kansas

Kansas City

University of Kansas School of Medicine Program

Sponsor: University of Kansas School of Medicine
University of Kansas Hospital
Veterans Affairs Medical Center (Kansas City)
Prgm Director: John Grant, MBChB
3901 Rainbow Boulevard
Mail Stop 3021
Kansas City, KS 66160
Tel: 913 588-6122   *Fax:* 913 588-7570
E-mail: sciolek@kumc.edu
Length: 5 Yrs   *ACGME Approved/Offered Positions:* 5
Program ID: 160-19-21-029

Kentucky

Lexington

University of Kentucky College of Medicine Program

Sponsor: University of Kentucky College of Medicine
University of Kentucky Hospital
Prgm Director: Phillip Tibbs, MD*
Department of Neurosurgery
800 Rose Street, Room MS-107
Lexington, KY 40536
Tel: 859 323-6263   *Fax:* 859 257-8902
E-mail: sthomps@email.uky.edu
Length: 5 Yrs   *ACGME Approved/Offered Positions:* 10
Program ID: 160-20-21-030

Louisville

University of Louisville Program

Sponsor: University of Louisville School of Medicine
Kosair Children's Hospital (Norton Healthcare, Inc)
Norton Hospital
University of Louisville Hospital
Prgm Director: Christopher B Shields, MD
210 East Gray Street, Suite 1102
Louisville, KY 40202
Tel: 502 629-5510   *Fax:* 502 629-5512
E-mail: cbshields1@gmail.com
Length: 5 Yrs   *ACGME Approved/Offered Positions:* 5
Program ID: 160-20-31-031

Louisiana

New Orleans

Louisiana State University Program

Sponsor: Louisiana State University School of Medicine
Children's Hospital (New Orleans)
Medical Center of Louisiana at New Orleans
Ochsner Clinic Foundation
West Jefferson Medical Center
Prgm Director: Frank Culicchia, MD
2020 Gravier Street Suite 3G
New Orleans, LA 70112
Tel: 504 568-2641   *Fax:* 504 568-6127
E-mail: fculic@lsuhsc.edu
Length: 5 Yrs   *ACGME Approved/Offered Positions:* 5
Program ID: 160-21-21-032

Tulane University Program

Sponsor: Tulane University School of Medicine
Medical Center of Louisiana at New Orleans
Ochsner Clinic Foundation
Tulane University Hospital and Clinics
Veterans Affairs Medical Center (New Orleans)
Prgm Director: John W Walsh, MD, PhD*
Department of Neurological Surgery SL47
1430 Tulane Avenue
New Orleans, LA 70112
Tel: 504 988-5565   *Fax:* 504 988-5793
E-mail: jwalshmd@tulane.edu
Length: 5 Yrs   *ACGME Approved/Offered Positions:* 5
Program ID: 160-21-21-033

Note: * indicates a newly appointed program director

Shreveport

Louisiana State University (Shreveport) Program
Sponsor: LSU Health Sciences Center-University Hospital
Overton Brooks Veterans Affairs Medical Center
Willis-Knighton Medical Center
Prgm Director: Anil Nanda, MD
1501 Kings Highway
PO Box 33932
Shreveport, LA 71130
Tel: 318 675-6404   *Fax:* 318 675-4615
E-mail: rwood1@lsuhsc.edu
Length: 5 Yrs   *ACGME Approved/Offered Positions:* 10
Program ID: 160-21-13-119

Maryland

Baltimore

Johns Hopkins University Program
Sponsor: Johns Hopkins University School of Medicine
Johns Hopkins Hospital
Prgm Director: George I Jallo, MD
Harvey 811
600 North Wolfe Street
Baltimore, MD 21287
Tel: 410 955-7851   *Fax:* 410 955-7862
E-mail: gjallo1@jhmi.edu
Length: 5 Yrs   *ACGME Approved/Offered Positions:* 15
Program ID: 160-23-21-034

University of Maryland Program
Sponsor: University of Maryland Medical System
Greater Baltimore Medical Center
R Adams Cowley Shock Trauma Center/University of Maryland
Veterans Affairs Medical Center (Baltimore)
Prgm Director: William W Maggio, MD
Department of Neurosurgery
22 South Greene Street, Suite S12D
Baltimore, MD 21201
Tel: 410 328-3113   *Fax:* 410 328-0756
Length: 5 Yrs   *ACGME Approved/Offered Positions:* 10
Program ID: 160-23-21-035

Bethesda

National Capital Consortium Program
Sponsor: National Capital Consortium
Children's National Medical Center
National Naval Medical Center (Bethesda)
Walter Reed Army Medical Center
Prgm Director: Michael K Rosner, MD
Walter Reed Army Medical Center
6900 Geogia Avenue NW
Washington, DC 20307
Tel: 202 782-9800
E-mail: michael.rosner@us.army.mil
Length: 5 Yrs   *ACGME Approved/Offered Positions:* 6
Program ID: 160-10-21-118
Uniformed Services Program

Massachusetts

Boston

Children's Hospital/Brigham and Women's Hospital Program
Sponsor: Children's Hospital
Brigham and Women's Hospital
Prgm Director: Arthur L Day, MD
75 Francis Street
Boston, MA 02115
Tel: 617 525-6939   *Fax:* 617 734-8342
E-mail: aday1@partners.org
Length: 5 Yrs   *ACGME Approved/Offered Positions:* 10
Program ID: 160-24-21-036

Massachusetts General Hospital Program
Sponsor: Massachusetts General Hospital
Prgm Director: Emad Eskandar, MD*
15 Parkman Street, WAC 331
Boston, MA 02114
Tel: 617 724-6590   *Fax:* 617 726-7546
Length: 5 Yrs   *ACGME Approved/Offered Positions:* 13
Program ID: 160-24-31-037

Tufts Medical Center Program
Sponsor: Tufts Medical Center
Children's Hospital
Lahey Clinic
Prgm Director: Julian K Wu, MD
800 Washington Street, Box 178
Boston, MA 02111
Tel: 617 636-4500   *Fax:* 617 636-7587
Length: 5 Yrs   *ACGME Approved/Offered Positions:* 5
Program ID: 160-24-31-038

Michigan

Ann Arbor

University of Michigan Program
Sponsor: University of Michigan Hospitals and Health Centers
Prgm Director: Oren Sagher, MD
1500 E Medical Center Drive
3552 Taubman Center
Ann Arbor, MI 48109
Tel: 734 936-9593   *Fax:* 734 647-0964
Length: 5 Yrs   *ACGME Approved/Offered Positions:* 13
Program ID: 160-25-21-039

Detroit

Henry Ford Hospital Program
Sponsor: Henry Ford Hospital
Prgm Director: Jack P Rock, MD
2799 West Grand Boulevard
Detroit, MI 48202
Tel: 313 916-1093   *Fax:* 313 916-7139
Length: 5 Yrs   *ACGME Approved/Offered Positions:* 10
Program ID: 160-25-11-040

Wayne State University/Detroit Medical Center Program
Sponsor: Wayne State University/Detroit Medical Center
Children's Hospital of Michigan
Detroit Receiving Hospital and University Health Center
Harper-Hutzel Hospital
Prgm Director: Murali Guthikonda, MD
University Health Center, 6E
4201 St Antoine
Detroit, MI 48201
Tel: 313 745-4523   *Fax:* 313 745-4099
Length: 5 Yrs   *ACGME Approved/Offered Positions:* 5
Program ID: 160-25-21-041

Minnesota

Minneapolis

University of Minnesota Program
Sponsor: University of Minnesota Medical School
Hennepin County Medical Center
University of Minnesota Medical Center, Division of Fairview
Veterans Affairs Medical Center (Minneapolis)
Prgm Director: Stephen J Haines, MD
D429 Mayo Memorial Bldg, MMC 96
420 Delaware Street, SE
Minneapolis, MN 55455
Tel: 612 624-6666   *Fax:* 612 624-0644
E-mail: gigl0009@umn.edu
Length: 5 Yrs   *ACGME Approved/Offered Positions:* 10
Program ID: 160-26-21-042

Rochester

College of Medicine, Mayo Clinic (Rochester) Program
Sponsor: College of Medicine, Mayo Clinic
Mayo Clinic (Rochester)
Saint Marys Hospital of Rochester
Prgm Director: Fredric B Meyer, MD
200 First Street, SW
Rochester, MN 55905
Tel: 507 284-2254   *Fax:* 507 284-5206
Length: 5 Yrs   *ACGME Approved/Offered Positions:* 15
Program ID: 160-26-21-043

Mississippi

Jackson

University of Mississippi Medical Center Program
Sponsor: University of Mississippi School of Medicine
University Hospitals and Clinics
Veterans Affairs Medical Center (Jackson)
Prgm Director: Haynes L Harkey, MD
2500 North State Street
Jackson, MS 39216
Tel: 601 984-5705   *Fax:* 601 984-6986
Length: 5 Yrs   *ACGME Approved/Offered Positions:* 8
Program ID: 160-27-21-044

Missouri

Columbia

University of Missouri-Columbia Program
Sponsor: University of Missouri-Columbia School of Medicine
Boone Hospital Center
Surgery Center of Columbia
University Hospitals and Clinics
Prgm Director: N S Litofsky, MD
One Hospital Drive, N521
Columbia, MO 65212
Tel: 573 882-4909   *Fax:* 573 884-5184
E-mail: litofskyn@health.missouri.edu
Length: 5 Yrs   *ACGME Approved/Offered Positions:* 5
Program ID: 160-28-21-045

St Louis

St Louis University School of Medicine Program

Sponsor: St Louis University School of Medicine
Cardinal Glennon Children's Hospital
St Louis University Hospital
Prgm Director: Richard D Bucholz, MD
3635 Vista Avenue at Grand Boulevard
PO Box 15250
St Louis, MO 63110
Tel: 314 577-8795   *Fax:* 314 268-5061
E-mail: richard@bucholz.org
Length: 5 Yrs   *ACGME Approved/Offered Positions:* 5
Program ID: 160-28-21-047

Washington University/B-JH/SLCH Consortium Program

Sponsor: Washington University/B-JH/SLCH Consortium
Barnes-Jewish Hospital
St Louis Children's Hospital
Washington University School of Medicine
Prgm Director: Ralph G Dacey Jr, MD
Campus Box 8057
660 South Euclid Avenue
St Louis, MO 63110
Tel: 314 362-3636   *Fax:* 314 362-2107
E-mail: seamanm@nsurg.wustl.edu
Length: 5 Yrs   *ACGME Approved/Offered Positions:* 12
Program ID: 160-28-11-046

Nebraska

Omaha

University of Nebraska Medical Center College of Medicine Program

Sponsor: University of Nebraska Medical Center College of Medicine
Children's Hospital
Nebraska Medical Center
Nebraska Methodist Hospital
Prgm Director: Kenneth A Follett, MD, PhD
600 South 42nd Street
982035 Nebraska Medical Center
Omaha, NE 68198
Tel: 402 559-9605   *Fax:* 402 559-7779
E-mail: kdevney@unmc.edu
Length: 5 Yrs   *ACGME Approved/Offered Positions:* 8
Program ID: 160-30-21-111

New Hampshire

Lebanon

Dartmouth-Hitchcock Medical Center Program

Sponsor: Mary Hitchcock Memorial Hospital
Prgm Director: David W Roberts, MD
One Medical Center Drive
Lebanon, NH 03756
Tel: 603 650-8734   *Fax:* 603 650-7911
Length: 5 Yrs   *ACGME Approved/Offered Positions:* 5
Program ID: 160-32-21-048

New Jersey

Newark

UMDNJ-New Jersey Medical School Program

Sponsor: UMDNJ-New Jersey Medical School
Hackensack University Medical Center
UMDNJ-University Hospital
Prgm Director: Charles J Prestigiacomo, MD*
90 Bergen Street, Suite 8100
Newark, NJ 07103
Tel: 973 972-1163   *Fax:* 973 972-8553
E-mail: presticj@umdnj.edu
Length: 5 Yrs   *ACGME Approved/Offered Positions:* 10
Program ID: 160-33-21-106

New Mexico

Albuquerque

University of New Mexico Program

Sponsor: University of New Mexico School of Medicine
University of New Mexico Hospital
Veterans Affairs Medical Center (Albuquerque)
Prgm Director: Howard Yonas, MD
MSC 10 5615
1 University of New Mexico
Albuquerque, NM 87131
Tel: 505 272-3401   *Fax:* 505 272-6091
Length: 5 Yrs   *ACGME Approved/Offered Positions:* 5
Program ID: 160-34-21-115

New York

Albany

Albany Medical Center Program

Sponsor: Albany Medical Center
Prgm Director: A John Popp, MD
47 New Scotland Avenue
Albany, NY 12208
Tel: 518 262-5314   *Fax:* 518 262-2284
Length: 5 Yrs   *ACGME Approved/Offered Positions:* 8
Program ID: 160-35-21-049

Bronx

Albert Einstein College of Medicine Program

Sponsor: Albert Einstein College of Medicine of Yeshiva University
Montefiore Medical Center-Henry and Lucy Moses Division
St Luke's-Roosevelt Hospital Center
Prgm Director: Eugene S Flamm, MD
Montefiore Medical Center
111 E 210th Street
Bronx, NY 10467
Tel: 718 920-7400   *Fax:* 718 547-4591
E-mail: eflamm@montefiore.org
Length: 5 Yrs   *ACGME Approved/Offered Positions:* 8
Program ID: 160-35-21-051

Buffalo

University at Buffalo Program

Sponsor: University at Buffalo School of Medicine
Kaleida Health System (Buffalo General Hospital)
Kaleida Health System (Millard Fillmore Hospital)
Kaleida Health System (Women and Children's Hosp of Buffalo)
Roswell Park Cancer Institute
Prgm Director: Kevin J Gibbons, MD
Millard Fillmore Hospital
3 Gates Circle
Buffalo, NY 14209
Tel: 716 887-5200   *Fax:* 716 887-5045
E-mail: residency@buffns.org
Length: 5 Yrs   *ACGME Approved/Offered Positions:* 10
Program ID: 160-35-21-050

New York

Mount Sinai School of Medicine Program

Sponsor: Mount Sinai School of Medicine
Elmhurst Hospital Center-Mount Sinai Services
Mount Sinai Medical Center
Prgm Director: Joshua B Bederson, MD
One Gustave L Levy Place
Box 1136
New York, NY 10029
Tel: 212 241-2377   *Fax:* 212 241-7388
Length: 5 Yrs   *ACGME Approved/Offered Positions:* 10
Program ID: 160-35-21-053

New York Presbyterian Hospital (Columbia Campus) Program

Sponsor: New York Presbyterian Hospital
New York Presbyterian Hospital (Columbia Campus)
Prgm Director: Jeffrey N Bruce, MD
710 West 168th Street, Room 433
New York, NY 10032
Tel: 212 305-7346   *Fax:* 212 305-2026
E-mail: jt2374@columbia.edu
Length: 5 Yrs   *ACGME Approved/Offered Positions:* 12
Program ID: 160-35-11-055

New York Presbyterian Hospital (Cornell Campus) Program

Sponsor: New York Presbyterian Hospital
Memorial Sloan-Kettering Cancer Center
New York Presbyterian Hospital (Cornell Campus)
Prgm Director: Howard A Riina, MD
525 East 68th Street
Box 99
New York, NY 10065
Tel: 212 746-5149   *Fax:* 212 746-8416
Length: 5 Yrs   *ACGME Approved/Offered Positions:* 10
Program ID: 160-35-21-052

New York University School of Medicine Program

Sponsor: New York University School of Medicine
Bellevue Hospital Center
Manhattan VA Harbor Health Care System
NYU Hospitals Center
Prgm Director: Anthony K Frempong-Boadu, MD
550 First Avenue
New York, NY 10016
Tel: 212 263-6514   *Fax:* 212 263-8225
E-mail: Anthony.Frempong@med.nyu.edu
Length: 5 Yrs   *ACGME Approved/Offered Positions:* 10
Program ID: 160-35-21-054

Note: * indicates a newly appointed program director

Rochester

University of Rochester Program
Sponsor: Strong Memorial Hospital of the University of
   Rochester
Rochester General Hospital
Prgm Director: Howard J Silberstein, MD*
601 Elmwood Avenue, Box 670
Rochester, NY 14642
Tel: 585 273-1606   *Fax:* 585 756-5183
E-mail: hsilbers@gmail.com
Length: 5 Yrs   *ACGME Approved/Offered Positions:* 10
Program ID: 160-35-11-057

Syracuse

SUNY Upstate Medical University Program
Sponsor: SUNY Upstate Medical University
Crouse Hospital
St Joseph's Hospital Health Center
Veterans Affairs Medical Center (Syracuse)
Prgm Director: Walter A Hall, MD, MBA
750 East Adams Street
Syracuse, NY 13210
Tel: 315 464-5510   *Fax:* 315 464-6384
Length: 5 Yrs   *ACGME Approved/Offered Positions:* 8
Program ID: 160-35-21-058

Valhalla

New York Medical College at Westchester Medical Center Program
Sponsor: New York Medical College
St Vincent Catholic Medical Centers (Manhattan)
Westchester Medical Center
Prgm Director: Raj Murali, MD
Westchester Medical Center
Munger Pavilion
Valhalla, NY 10595
Tel: 914 493-8510   *Fax:* 914 594-3641
Length: 5 Yrs   *ACGME Approved/Offered Positions:* 5
Program ID: 160-35-21-108

North Carolina

Chapel Hill

University of North Carolina Hospitals Program
Sponsor: University of North Carolina Hospitals
Prgm Director: Eldad J Hadar, MD*
170 Manning Drive, CB 7060
Chapel Hill, NC 27599
Tel: 919 966-1374   *Fax:* 919 966-6627
Length: 5 Yrs   *ACGME Approved/Offered Positions:* 5
Program ID: 160-36-11-059

Durham

Duke University Hospital Program
Sponsor: Duke University Hospital
Durham Regional Hospital
Veterans Affairs Medical Center (Durham)
Prgm Director: Michael M Haglund, MD, PhD*
PO Box 3807
Durham, NC 27710
Tel: 919 684-3053   *Fax:* 919 681-6566
E-mail: haglu001@mc.duke.edu
Length: 5 Yrs   *ACGME Approved/Offered Positions:* 12
Program ID: 160-36-21-060

Winston-Salem

Wake Forest University School of Medicine Program
Sponsor: Wake Forest University Baptist Medical Center
Prgm Director: John A Wilson, MD
Medical Center Boulevard
Winston-Salem, NC 27157
Tel: 336 716-4024   *Fax:* 336 716-3065
E-mail: mherring@wfubmc.edu
Length: 5 Yrs   *ACGME Approved/Offered Positions:* 10
Program ID: 160-36-11-061

Ohio

Cincinnati

University Hospital/University of Cincinnati College of Medicine Program
Sponsor: University Hospital Inc
Christ Hospital
Cincinnati Children's Hospital Medical Center
TriHealth - Good Samaritan Hospital
Prgm Director: Philip V Theodosopoulos, MD*
231 Albert Sabin Way
PO Box 670515
Cincinnati, OH 45267
Tel: 513 558-3903   *Fax:* 513 558-7702
E-mail: philip.theodosopoulos@uc.edu
Length: 5 Yrs   *ACGME Approved/Offered Positions:* 15
Program ID: 160-38-21-064

Cleveland

Cleveland Clinic Foundation Program
Sponsor: Cleveland Clinic Foundation
Prgm Director: Edward C Benzel, MD
9500 Euclid Avenue
S80
Cleveland, OH 44195
Tel: 216 445-5515   *Fax:* 216 636-0454
E-mail: benzele@ccf.org
Length: 5 Yrs   *ACGME Approved/Offered Positions:* 15
Program ID: 160-38-22-066

University Hospitals Case Medical Center Program
Sponsor: University Hospitals Case Medical Center
MetroHealth Medical Center
Prgm Director: Alan R Cohen, MD
11100 Euclid Avenue
HAN 5042
Cleveland, OH 44106
Tel: 216 844-3472   *Fax:* 216 844-3014
E-mail: lois.hengenius@uhhospitals.org
Length: 5 Yrs   *ACGME Approved/Offered Positions:* 10
Program ID: 160-38-21-065

Columbus

Ohio State University Hospital Program
Sponsor: Ohio State University Hospital
Nationwide Children's Hospital
Prgm Director: Carole A Miller, MD
N-1014 Doan Hall
410 West 10th Avenue
Columbus, OH 43210
Tel: 614 293-6259   *Fax:* 614 293-4281
Length: 5 Yrs   *ACGME Approved/Offered Positions:* 10
Program ID: 160-38-21-067

Oklahoma

Oklahoma City

University of Oklahoma Health Sciences Center Program
Sponsor: University of Oklahoma College of Medicine
OU Medical Center
Veterans Affairs Medical Center (Oklahoma City)
Prgm Director: Timothy B Mapstone, MD
1000 N Lincoln, Suite 400
Oklahoma City, OK 73104
Tel: 405 271-4912   *Fax:* 405 271-3091
E-mail: rita-ullsmith@ouhsc.edu
Length: 5 Yrs   *ACGME Approved/Offered Positions:* 5
Program ID: 160-39-21-068

Oregon

Portland

Oregon Health & Science University Program
Sponsor: Oregon Health & Science University Hospital
Veterans Affairs Medical Center (Portland)
Prgm Director: Nathan R Selden, MD, PhD
3303 SW Bond Ave
CH 8N
Portland, OR 97239
Tel: 503 494-6207   *Fax:* 503 494-7161
E-mail: mastrand@ohsu.edu
Length: 5 Yrs   *ACGME Approved/Offered Positions:* 10
Program ID: 160-40-21-070

Pennsylvania

Hershey

Penn State University/Milton S Hershey Medical Center Program
Sponsor: Milton S Hershey Medical Center
Prgm Director: Jonas Sheehan, MD*
30 Hope Drive, PO Box 859
EC110, Suite 2750
Hershey, PA 17033
Tel: 717 531-1279
E-mail: lhamann1@hmc.psu.edu
Length: 5 Yrs   *ACGME Approved/Offered Positions:* 10
Program ID: 160-41-21-110

Philadelphia

Temple University Hospital Program
Sponsor: Temple University Hospital
Children's Memorial Hospital
Prgm Director: Jack Jallo, MD, PhD
3401 North Broad Street
Philadelphia, PA 19140
Tel: 215 707-1793   *Fax:* 215 707-3831
Length: 5 Yrs   *ACGME Approved/Offered Positions:* 5
Program ID: 160-41-21-073

Thomas Jefferson University Program
Sponsor: Thomas Jefferson University Hospital
Prgm Director: Robert H Rosenwasser, MD
111 S 11th Street
Philadelphia, PA 19107
Tel: 215 503-7008   *Fax:* 215 503-2452
E-mail: robert.rosenwasser@jefferson.edu
Length: 5 Yrs   *ACGME Approved/Offered Positions:* 15
Program ID: 160-41-21-074

Programs

University of Pennsylvania Program

Sponsor: University of Pennsylvania Health System
Children's Hospital of Philadelphia
Pennsylvania Hospital (UPHS)
Prgm Director: M Sean Grady, MD
3400 Spruce Street, 3rd Floor Silverstein Pav
Philadelphia, PA 19104
Tel: 215 349-8325   *Fax:* 215 349-5108
Length: 5 Yrs   *ACGME Approved/Offered Positions:* 15
Program ID: 160-41-21-075

Pittsburgh

Allegheny General Hospital Program

Sponsor: Allegheny General Hospital
Prgm Director: Matthew R Quigley, MD
420 East North Avenue, Suite 302
Pittsburgh, PA 15212
Tel: 412 359-6200
Length: 5 Yrs   *ACGME Approved/Offered Positions:* 5
Program ID: 160-41-31-116

University of Pittsburgh Medical Center Medical Education Program

Sponsor: Univ of Pittsburgh Medical Center Medical
   Education
Children's Hospital of Pittsburgh of UPMC
UPMC Presbyterian Shadyside
Prgm Director: L Dade Lunsford, MD
200 Lothrop Street, Suite B-400
Pittsburgh, PA 15213
Tel: 412 647-6781   *Fax:* 412 647-6483
E-mail: lukehartml@upmc.edu
Length: 5 Yrs   *ACGME Approved/Offered Positions:* 15
Program ID: 160-41-31-076

Puerto Rico

San Juan

University of Puerto Rico Program

Sponsor: University of Puerto Rico School of Medicine
University Hospital
University Pediatric Hospital
Prgm Director: Ricardo H Brau, MD
Medical Sciences Campus / Section of Neurosurgery
PO Box 365067
San Juan, PR 00936
Tel: 787 765-8276
E-mail: rbrau@hotmail.com
Length: 5 Yrs   *ACGME Approved/Offered Positions:* 8
Program ID: 160-42-21-078

Rhode Island

Providence

Brown University Program

Sponsor: Rhode Island Hospital-Lifespan
Prgm Director: Curtis Doberstein, MD*
55 Claverick Street
Suite 100
Providence, RI 02903
Tel: 401 621-8700   *Fax:* 401 621-8705
Length: 5 Yrs   *ACGME Approved/Offered Positions:* 5
Program ID: 160-43-21-103

South Carolina

Charleston

Medical University of South Carolina Program

Sponsor: Medical University of South Carolina College of
   Medicine
Prgm Director: Sunil J Patel, MD
96 Jonathan Lucas Street, Suite 428
PO Box 250616
Charleston, SC 29425
Tel: 843 792-3222   *Fax:* 843 792-8626
Length: 5 Yrs   *ACGME Approved/Offered Positions:* 5
Program ID: 160-45-11-079

Tennessee

Memphis

University of Tennessee Program

Sponsor: University of Tennessee College of Medicine
LeBonheur Children's Medical Center
Methodist Healthcare - Memphis Hospitals
Regional Medical Center at Memphis
Veterans Affairs Medical Center (Memphis)
Prgm Director: Frederick A Boop, MD
Department of Neurosurgery
847 Monroe Avenue, Suite 427
Memphis, TN 38163
Tel: 901 259-5321   *Fax:* 901 259-5300
E-mail: RBeene@UTmem.edu
Length: 5 Yrs   *ACGME Approved/Offered Positions:* 10
Program ID: 160-47-21-080

Nashville

Vanderbilt University Program

Sponsor: Vanderbilt University Medical Center
Veterans Affairs Medical Center (Nashville)
Prgm Director: Robert A Mericle, MD
T-4224 Medical Center North
1161 21st Avenue South
Nashville, TN 37232
Tel: 615 343-2452   *Fax:* 615 343-8104
E-mail: carol.j.jackson@vanderbilt.edu
Length: 5 Yrs   *ACGME Approved/Offered Positions:* 10
Program ID: 160-47-21-081

Texas

Dallas

University of Texas Southwestern Medical School Program

Sponsor: University of Texas Southwestern Medical
   School
Children's Medical Center of Dallas
Dallas County Hospital District-Parkland Memorial
   Hospital
Dallas VA Medical Center
University Hospitals Zale Lipshy
Prgm Director: Jonathan White, MD
5323 Harry Hines Blvd
Dallas, TX 75390
Tel: 214 648-4579   *Fax:* 214 648-2265
Length: 5 Yrs   *ACGME Approved/Offered Positions:* 10
Program ID: 160-48-21-082

Galveston

University of Texas Medical Branch Hospitals Program

Sponsor: University of Texas Medical Branch Hospitals
Memorial Hermann Hospital
Methodist Hospital (Houston)
University of Texas M D Anderson Cancer Center
Prgm Director: Joel T Patterson, MD*
301 University Boulevard
Galveston, TX 77555
Tel: 409 772-1500   *Fax:* 409 772-3166
Length: 5 Yrs   *ACGME Approved/Offered Positions:* 5
Program ID: 160-48-21-083

Houston

Baylor College of Medicine Program

Sponsor: Baylor College of Medicine
Harris County Hospital District-Ben Taub General
   Hospital
Michael E DeBakey VA Medical Center - Houston
St Luke's Episcopal Hospital
Texas Children's Hospital
University of Texas M D Anderson Cancer Center
Prgm Director: Daniel Yoshor, MD*
One Baylor Plaza
Houston, TX 77030
Tel: 713 798-4696   *Fax:* 713 798-3739
Length: 5 Yrs   *ACGME Approved/Offered Positions:* 15
Program ID: 160-48-21-084

Methodist Hospital (Houston) Program

Sponsor: Methodist Hospital (Houston)
Prgm Director: David S Baskin, MD
6560 Fannin St, Suite 944
Scurlock Tower
Houston, TX 77030
Tel: 713 441-3800   *Fax:* 713 793-1001
E-mail: ampatrick@tmhs.org
Length: 5 Yrs   *ACGME Approved/Offered Positions:* 5
Program ID: 160-48-12-123

University of Texas at Houston Program

Sponsor: University of Texas Health Science Center at
   Houston
Memorial Hermann Hospital
Prgm Director: Dong H Kim, MD*
6410 Fannin Street
Suite 1020
Houston, TX 77030
Tel: 713 500-6170   *Fax:* 713 500-0601
Length: 5 Yrs   *ACGME Approved/Offered Positions:* 5
Program ID: 160-48-31-126

San Antonio

University of Texas Health Science Center at San Antonio Program

Sponsor: University of Texas School of Medicine at San
   Antonio
Audie L Murphy Memorial Veterans Hospital (San
   Antonio)
Christus Santa Rosa Health Care Çorporation
Methodist Healthcare
University Health System
Prgm Director: David F Jimenez, MD
Department of Neurosurgery
7703 Floyd Curl Drive (MC 7843)
San Antonio, TX 78229
Tel: 210 567-5625   *Fax:* 210 567-6066
E-mail: jmenezd3@uthscsa.edu
Length: 5 Yrs   *ACGME Approved/Offered Positions:* 5
Program ID: 160-48-21-085

Note: * indicates a newly appointed program director

Utah

Salt Lake City

University of Utah Program
Sponsor: University of Utah Medical Center
Primary Children's Medical Center
Prgm Director: John Kestle, MD, MSc
Dept of Neurosurgery
175 N Medical Dr East, 5th Floor
Salt Lake City, UT 84132
Tel: 801 662-5340   *Fax:* 801 662-5345
E-mail: julie.service@hsc.utah.edu
Length: 5 Yrs   *ACGME Approved/Offered Positions:* 10
Program ID: 160-49-31-086

Vermont

Burlington

University of Vermont Program
Sponsor: Fletcher Allen Health Care
Maine Medical Center
Prgm Director: Bruce I Tranmer, MD
Fletcher 5
111 Colchester Ave
Burlington, VT 05401
Tel: 802 847-3072   *Fax:* 802 847-0680
Length: 5 Yrs   *ACGME Approved/Offered Positions:* 5
Program ID: 160-50-21-101

Virginia

Charlottesville

University of Virginia Program
Sponsor: University of Virginia Medical Center
Prgm Director: John A Jane Sr, MD, PhD
PO Box 800212
Charlottesville, VA 22908
Tel: 434 982-3244   *Fax:* 434 243-2954
Length: 5 Yrs   *ACGME Approved/Offered Positions:* 13
Program ID: 160-51-21-088

Richmond

Virginia Commonwealth University Health System Program
Sponsor: Virginia Commonwealth University Health System
Hunter Holmes McGuire VA Medical Center (Richmond)
Prgm Director: Robert S Graham, MD
Department of Neurosurgery
PO Box 980631
Richmond, VA 23298
Tel: 804 828-4480   *Fax:* 804 828-1953
E-mail: padams@mcvh-vcu.edu
Length: 5 Yrs   *ACGME Approved/Offered Positions:* 10
Program ID: 160-51-21-089

Washington

Seattle

University of Washington Program
Sponsor: University of Washington School of Medicine
Harborview Medical Center
Seattle Children's Hospital
University of Washington Medical Center
VA Puget Sound Health Care System
Prgm Director: Anthony M Avellino, MD, MBA
325 Ninth Avenue
Box 359924
Seattle, WA 98104
Tel: 206 987-4525   *Fax:* 206 987-3925
E-mail: anthony.avellino@seattlechildrens.org
Length: 5 Yrs   *ACGME Approved/Offered Positions:* 13
Program ID: 160-54-21-090

West Virginia

Morgantown

West Virginia University Program
Sponsor: West Virginia University School of Medicine
West Virginia University Hospitals
Prgm Director: Charles L Rosen, MD, PhD*
PO Box 9183
4300 Health Science Center
Morgantown, WV 26506
Tel: 304 293-5041   *Fax:* 304 293-4819
Length: 5 Yrs   *ACGME Approved/Offered Positions:* 5
Program ID: 160-55-11-091

Wisconsin

Madison

University of Wisconsin Program
Sponsor: University of Wisconsin Hospital and Clinics
Meriter Hospital
William S Middleton Veterans Hospital
Prgm Director: Robert J Dempsey, MD
Clinical Science Center, K4/822
600 Highland Avenue
Madison, WI 53792
Tel: 608 263-9585   *Fax:* 608 263-1728
Length: 5 Yrs   *ACGME Approved/Offered Positions:* 10
Program ID: 160-56-21-092

Milwaukee

Medical College of Wisconsin Affiliated Hospitals Program
Sponsor: Medical College of Wisconsin Affiliated Hospitals, Inc
Children's Hospital of Wisconsin
Clement J Zablocki Veterans Affairs Medical Center
Froedtert Memorial Lutheran Hospital
Prgm Director: Grant P Sinson, MD
Department of Neurosurgery
9200 West Wisconsin Avenue
Milwaukee, WI 53226
Tel: 414 805-5400   *Fax:* 414 955-0115
E-mail: kquinn@mcw.edu
Length: 5 Yrs   *ACGME Approved/Offered Positions:* 8
Program ID: 160-56-21-093

Neurology

Alabama

Birmingham

University of Alabama Medical Center Program
Sponsor: University of Alabama Hospital
Veterans Affairs Medical Center (Birmingham)
Prgm Director: Khurram Bashir, MD, MPH
619 19th Street South
Birmingham, AL 35294
Tel: 205 975-0447   *Fax:* 205 996-4150
E-mail: kbashir@uab.edu
Length: 4 Yrs   *ACGME Approved/Offered Positions:* 24
Program ID: 180-01-31-004

Mobile

University of South Alabama Program
Sponsor: University of South Alabama Hospitals
Infirmary West
University of South Alabama Medical Center
Prgm Director: Jorge Ivan Lopez, MD
Department of Neurology
3401 Medical Park Dr, Bldg 3, Suite 205
Mobile, AL 36693
Tel: 251 660-5108   *Fax:* 251 660-5924
E-mail: ilopez@usouthal.edu
Length: 3 Yrs   *ACGME Approved/Offered Positions:* 7
Program ID: 180-01-21-123

Arizona

Phoenix

St Joseph's Hospital and Medical Center Program
Sponsor: St Joseph's Hospital and Medical Center
Prgm Director: Steve S Chung, MD
Barrow Neurological Institute
350 W Thomas Road
Phoenix, AZ 85013
Tel: 602 406-6271   *Fax:* 602 798-0467
E-mail: ann.chowdhury@chw.edu
Length: 3 Yrs   *ACGME Approved/Offered Positions:* 18
Program ID: 180-03-12-005

Scottsdale

College of Medicine, Mayo Clinic (Arizona) Program
Sponsor: College of Medicine, Mayo Clinic
Mayo Clinic (Arizona)
Mayo Clinic Hospital
Prgm Director: David W Dodick, MD
13400 East Shea Boulevard
Scottsdale, AZ 85259
Tel: 480 301-8000   *Fax:* 480 301-9776
E-mail: glickler.peggy@mayo.edu
Length: 4 Yrs   *ACGME Approved/Offered Positions:* 12
Program ID: 180-03-11-150

Tucson

University of Arizona Program
Sponsor: University of Arizona College of Medicine
Southern Arizona VA Health Care Center (Tucson)
University Medical Center
Prgm Director: David M Labiner, MD
Department of Neurology
1501 N Campbell Ave, Box 245023
Tucson, AZ 85724
Tel: 520 626-2006   *Fax:* 520 626-2111
Length: 3 Yrs   *ACGME Approved/Offered Positions:* 13
Program ID: 180-03-21-006

University of Arizona/UPHK Graduate Medical Education Consortium Program
Sponsor: University of Arizona/UPHK Graduate Medical
  Ed Consortium
Tucson Medical Center
Prgm Director: John LaWall, MD
2800 East Ajo Way
Tucson, AZ 85713
Tel: 520 874-2747   *Fax:* 520 874-2745
Length: 3 Yrs   *ACGME Approved/Offered Positions:* 6
Program ID: 180-03-31-159

Arkansas

Little Rock

University of Arkansas for Medical Sciences Program
Sponsor: University of Arkansas College of Medicine
Central Arkansas Veterans Healthcare System
UAMS Medical Center
Prgm Director: Walter S Metzer, MD
Department of Neurology
4301 West Markham St, Slot 500
Little Rock, AR 72205
Tel: 501 296-1165   *Fax:* 501 686-8689
E-mail: wmetzer@uams.edu
Length: 4 Yrs   *ACGME Approved/Offered Positions:* 16
Program ID: 180-04-21-007

California

Loma Linda

Loma Linda University Program
Sponsor: Loma Linda University Medical Center
Jerry L Pettis Memorial Veterans Hospital
Prgm Director: Laura Nist, MD
Department of Neurology, Rm 11108 CP
PO Box 2000
Loma Linda, CA 92354
Tel: 909 558-4907   *Fax:* 909 558-0207
E-mail: msjohnson@llu.edu
Length: 3 Yrs   *ACGME Approved/Offered Positions:* 9
Program ID: 180-05-21-124

Los Angeles

Kaiser Permanente Southern California (Los Angeles) Program
Sponsor: Kaiser Permanente Southern California
Kaiser Foundation Hospital (Los Angeles)
Prgm Director: Sonja Potrebic, MD, PhD
Kaiser Foundation Hospital (Los Angeles)
1505 North Edgemont Street
Los Angeles, CA 90027
Tel: 323 783-8883   *Fax:* 323 783-4274
E-mail: Sonja.X.Potrebic@kp.org
Length: 4 Yrs   *ACGME Approved/Offered Positions:* 8
Program ID: 180-05-12-010

UCLA Medical Center Program
Sponsor: UCLA David Geffen School of Medicine/UCLA
  Medical Center
UCLA Medical Center
VA Greater Los Angeles Healthcare System
Prgm Director: Alon Y Avidan, MD, MPH*
David Geffen School of Medicine at UCLA
710 Westwood Plaza
Los Angeles, CA 90095
Tel: 310 825-0703   *Fax:* 310 825-6956
Length: 3 Yrs   *ACGME Approved/Offered Positions:* 27
Program ID: 180-05-21-012

University of Southern California/ LAC+USC Medical Center Program
Sponsor: University of Southern California/LAC+USC
  Medical Center
LAC+USC Medical Center
Prgm Director: Laura A Kalayjian, MD
1100 N State Street
Clinic Tower 4th Floor Rm A4E
Los Angeles, CA 90033
Tel: 323 409-4535   *Fax:* 323 441-8093
Length: 3 Yrs   *ACGME Approved/Offered Positions:* 15
Program ID: 180-05-21-011

Orange

University of California (Irvine) Program
Sponsor: University of California (Irvine) Medical
  Center
VA Long Beach Healthcare System
Prgm Director: William Cable, MBChB
101 The City Drive South
Bld 53-Room 203
Orange, CA 92868
Tel: 714 456-8276
E-mail: jlgottbr@uci.edu
Length: 3 Yrs   *ACGME Approved/Offered Positions:* 12
Program ID: 180-05-21-009

Sacramento

University of California (Davis) Health System Program
Sponsor: University of California (Davis) Health System
University of California (Davis) Medical Center
VA Northern California Health Care System
Prgm Director: David P Richman, MD
Department of Neurology
4860 Y Street, Suite 3700
Sacramento, CA 95817
Tel: 916 734-3514   *Fax:* 916 734-6525
Length: 4 Yrs   *ACGME Approved/Offered Positions:* 15
Program ID: 180-05-12-008

San Diego

University of California (San Diego) Program
Sponsor: University of California (San Diego) Medical
  Center
Veterans Affairs Medical Center (San Diego)
Prgm Director: Patrick A Delaney, MD*
Department of Neurology
200 West Arbor Drive (8465)
San Diego, CA 92103
Tel: 619 543-6266   *Fax:* 619 543-5793
E-mail: jhays@ucsd.edu
Length: 3 Yrs   *ACGME Approved/Offered Positions:* 12
Program ID: 180-05-21-014

San Francisco

University of California (San Francisco) Program
Sponsor: University of California (San Francisco) School
  of Medicine
UCSF and Mount Zion Medical Centers
Prgm Director: John W Engstrom, MD
505 Parnassus Ave, Room 798-M
San Francisco, CA 94143
Tel: 415 476-1489   *Fax:* 415 476-3428
E-mail: engstromj@neurology.ucsf.edu
Length: 4 Yrs   *ACGME Approved/Offered Positions:* 30
Program ID: 180-05-21-016

Stanford

Stanford University Program
Sponsor: Stanford Hospital and Clinics
Santa Clara Valley Medical Center
Prgm Director: Yuen T So, MD, PhD
Department of Neurology, Rm A343
300 Pasteur Dr
Stanford, CA 94305
Tel: 650 723-5184   *Fax:* 650 725-7459
Length: 3 Yrs   *ACGME Approved/Offered Positions:* 15
Program ID: 180-05-21-017

Torrance

Los Angeles County-Harbor-UCLA Medical Center Program
Sponsor: Los Angeles County-Harbor-UCLA Medical
  Center
Prgm Director: Hugh B McIntyre, MD, PhD
Department of Neurology, Box 492
1000 West Carson Street
Torrance, CA 90509
Tel: 310 222-3897   *Fax:* 310 533-8905
E-mail: oalvarez@labiomed.org
Length: 3 Yrs   *ACGME Approved/Offered Positions:* 9
Program ID: 180-05-11-018

Colorado

Aurora

University of Colorado Denver Program
Sponsor: University of Colorado Denver School of
  Medicine
Denver Health Medical Center
University of Colorado Hospital
Veterans Affairs Medical Center (Denver)
Prgm Director: Victoria S Pelak, MD
Department of Neurology B183
4200 East 9th Avenue
Denver, CO 80262
Tel: 303 315-0139
Length: 3 Yrs   *ACGME Approved/Offered Positions:* 14
Program ID: 180-07-21-019

Connecticut

Farmington

University of Connecticut Program
Sponsor: University of Connecticut School of Medicine
Hartford Hospital
Univ of Connecticut Health Center/John Dempsey
  Hospital
Prgm Director: Avinash Prasad, MD
Department of Neurology
80 Seymour Street
Hartford, CT 06102
Tel: 860 545-5047   *Fax:* 860 545-5003
Length: 3 Yrs   *ACGME Approved/Offered Positions:* 12
Program ID: 180-08-21-139

New Haven

Yale-New Haven Medical Center Program
Sponsor: Yale-New Haven Hospital
Veterans Affairs Medical Center (West Haven)
Prgm Director: George B Richerson, MD, PhD
15 York Street, LCI 712
PO Box 208018
New Haven, CT 06520
Tel: 203 785-6054   *Fax:* 203 785-6246
Length: 3 Yrs   *ACGME Approved/Offered Positions:* 18
Program ID: 180-08-21-021

Note: * indicates a newly appointed program director

District of Columbia

Washington

George Washington University Program
Sponsor: George Washington University School of Medicine
George Washington University Hospital (UHS)
Prgm Director: Perry K Richardson, MD
2150 Pennsylvania Ave, NW
Suite 7-404
Washington, DC 20037
Tel: 202 741-2719   *Fax:* 202 741-2721
E-mail: prichardson@mfa.gwu.edu
Length: 3 Yrs   *ACGME Approved/Offered Positions:* 6
Program ID: 180-10-21-023

Georgetown University Hospital Program
Sponsor: Georgetown University Hospital
Veterans Affairs Medical Center (Washington, DC)
Prgm Director: Carlo Tornatore, MD
Department of Neurology
3800 Reservoir Road, NW (7 PHC)
Washington, DC 20007
Tel: 202 444-2410   *Fax:* 202 444-2661
Length: 3 Yrs   *ACGME Approved/Offered Positions:* 18
Program ID: 180-10-21-022

Howard University Program
Sponsor: Howard University Hospital
Prgm Director: Annapurni Jayam-Trouth, MD
2041 Georgia Avenue, NW
Washington, DC 20060
Tel: 202 865-1546   *Fax:* 202 865-4395
Length: 3 Yrs   *ACGME Approved/Offered Positions:* 6
Program ID: 180-10-21-024

Florida

Gainesville

University of Florida Program
Sponsor: University of Florida College of Medicine
North Florida/South Georgia Veterans Health System
Shands Hospital at the University of Florida
Prgm Director: Hubert Fernandez, MD
Dept of Neurology, Suite L3-100
100 Newell Dr, POB 100236
Gainesville, FL 32610
Tel: 352 273-5550   *Fax:* 352 273-5575
Length: 3 Yrs   *ACGME Approved/Offered Positions:* 12
Program ID: 180-11-21-025

Jacksonville

College of Medicine, Mayo Clinic (Jacksonville) Program
Sponsor: College of Medicine, Mayo Clinic
Mayo Clinic (Jacksonville)
Mayo Clinic Florida Hospital
Prgm Director: David J Capobianco, MD
4500 San Pablo Road
Jacksonville, FL 32224
Tel: 904 953-0110   *Fax:* 904 953-0430
E-mail: mcj.neurology.residency@mayo.edu
Length: 3 Yrs   *ACGME Approved/Offered Positions:* 9
Program ID: 180-11-13-148

University of Florida College of Medicine Jacksonville Program
Sponsor: University of Florida College of Medicine Jacksonville
Shands Jacksonville Medical Center
Prgm Director: Scott Silliman, MD
580 West 8th Street, Box T17
Tower 1, 9th Floor
Jacksonville, FL 32209
Tel: 904 244-9696   *Fax:* 904 244-9481
E-mail: neurology.gme@jax.ufl.edu
Length: 3 Yrs   *ACGME Approved/Offered Positions:* 12
Program ID: 180-11-12-154

Miami

Jackson Memorial Hospital/Jackson Health System Program
Sponsor: Jackson Memorial Hospital/Jackson Health System
Veterans Affairs Medical Center (Miami)
Prgm Director: Richard S Isaacson, MD, BA
Clinical Research Building
1120 NW 14th Street, 13th Floor
Miami, FL 33136
Tel: 305 243-2120   *Fax:* 305 243-6546
Length: 4 Yrs   *ACGME Approved/Offered Positions:* 40
Program ID: 180-11-21-026

Tampa

University of South Florida Program
Sponsor: University of South Florida College of Medicine
James A Haley Veterans Hospital
Tampa General Hospital
Prgm Director: Charles W Brock, MD
12901 Bruce B Downs Blvd, MDC 55
Tampa, FL 33612
Tel: 813 972-7633   *Fax:* 813 978-5995
E-mail: charles.brock@va.gov
Length: 3 Yrs   *ACGME Approved/Offered Positions:* 20
Program ID: 180-11-21-027

Weston

Cleveland Clinic (Florida) Program
Sponsor: Cleveland Clinic Florida
Prgm Director: Efrain D Salgado, MD
2950 Cleveland Clinic Blvd
Neurology Residency Program
Weston, FL 33331
Tel: 954 659-5673   *Fax:* 954 659-5358
E-mail: neuroprg@ccf.org
Length: 3 Yrs   *ACGME Approved/Offered Positions:* 6
Program ID: 180-11-22-152

Georgia

Atlanta

Emory University Program
Sponsor: Emory University School of Medicine
Emory University Hospital
Grady Health System
Prgm Director: Jaffar Khan, MD
WMRB 6009 c/o Charlotte Whitehead
101 Woodruff Memorial Circle
Atlanta, GA 30322
Tel: 404 727-5004   *Fax:* 404 727-3157
E-mail: jkhan@emory.edu
Length: 3 Yrs   *ACGME Approved/Offered Positions:* 24
Program ID: 180-12-21-028

Augusta

Medical College of Georgia Program
Sponsor: Medical College of Georgia
Prgm Director: Jerry N Pruitt II, MD
Department of Neurology
1120 15th Street
Augusta, GA 30912
Tel: 706 721-1886   *Fax:* 706 721-1962
Length: 3 Yrs   *ACGME Approved/Offered Positions:* 12
Program ID: 180-12-21-029

Illinois

Chicago

McGaw Medical Center of Northwestern University Program
Sponsor: McGaw Medical Center of Northwestern University
Northwestern Memorial Hospital
Prgm Director: Tanya Simuni, MD
Department of Neurology
710 North Lake Shore Drive, Abbott Hall, 11th Fl
Chicago, IL 60611
Tel: 312 503-2970   *Fax:* 312 908-5073
Length: 3 Yrs   *ACGME Approved/Offered Positions:* 21
Program ID: 180-16-21-032

Rush University Medical Center Program
Sponsor: Rush University Medical Center
Prgm Director: Steven L Lewis, MD
Department of Neurological Sciences
1725 W Harrison St, Ste 1106
Chicago, IL 60612
Tel: 312 942-4500   *Fax:* 312 942-2380
E-mail: slewis@rush.edu
Length: 3 Yrs   *ACGME Approved/Offered Positions:* 18
Program ID: 180-16-11-033

University of Chicago Program
Sponsor: University of Chicago Medical Center
Prgm Director: Helene Rubeiz, MD
Department of Neurology
5841 South Maryland Avenue, MC 2030
Chicago, IL 60637
Tel: 773 702-0151   *Fax:* 773 834-3662
E-mail: mscofiel@neurology.bsd.uchicago.edu
Length: 3 Yrs   *ACGME Approved/Offered Positions:* 15
Program ID: 180-16-21-034

University of Illinois College of Medicine at Chicago Program
Sponsor: University of Illinois College of Medicine at Chicago
Advocate Christ Medical Center
Jesse Brown Veterans Affairs Medical Center
University of Illinois Hospital and Clinics
Prgm Director: Octavia B Kincaid, MD*
Department of Neurology (M/C 796)
912 South Wood Street, #855N
Chicago, IL 60612
Tel: 312 996-6496   *Fax:* 312 996-4169
Length: 3 Yrs   *ACGME Approved/Offered Positions:* 15
Program ID: 180-16-21-035

Maywood

Loyola University Program
Sponsor: Loyola University Medical Center
Edward Hines, Jr Veterans Affairs Hospital
Prgm Director: Jasvinder Chawla, MD, MBA
Department of Neurology
2160 South First Avenue
Maywood, IL 60153
Tel: 708 216-5332   *Fax:* 708 216-5617
E-mail: jchawla@lumc.edu
Length: 4 Yrs   *ACGME Approved/Offered Positions:* 20
Program ID: 180-16-21-036

Peoria

University of Illinois College of Medicine at Peoria Program

Sponsor: University of Illinois College of Medicine at Peoria
OSF St Francis Medical Center
Prgm Director: Gregory M Blume, MD
One Illini Drive, Box 1649
Peoria, IL 61656
Tel: 309 655-2702   *Fax:* 309 655-3069
E-mail: linnet@uic.edu
Length: 4 Yrs   *ACGME Approved/Offered Positions:* 8
Program ID: 180-16-21-147

Springfield

Southern Illinois University Program

Sponsor: Southern Illinois University School of Medicine
Memorial Medical Center
St John's Hospital
Prgm Director: Rodger J Elble, MD, PhD
Department of Neurology
PO Box 19643
Springfield, IL 62794
Tel: 217 545-0168   *Fax:* 217 545-1903
E-mail: relble@siumed.edu
Length: 4 Yrs   *ACGME Approved/Offered Positions:* 8
Program ID: 180-16-21-134

Indiana

Indianapolis

Indiana University School of Medicine Program

Sponsor: Indiana University School of Medicine
Clarian Indiana University Hospital
Clarian Riley Hospital for Children
William N Wishard Memorial Hospital
Prgm Director: James D Fleck, MD
Department of Neurology
545 Barnhill Drive, EH 125
Indianapolis, IN 46202
Tel: 317 274-4455   *Fax:* 317 278-4918
E-mail: prcowher@iupui.edu
Length: 3 Yrs   *ACGME Approved/Offered Positions:* 15
Program ID: 180-17-21-038

Iowa

Iowa City

University of Iowa Hospitals and Clinics Program

Sponsor: University of Iowa Hospitals and Clinics
Veterans Affairs Medical Center (Iowa City)
Prgm Director: Mark A Granner, MD
200 Hawkins Drive
Iowa City, IA 52242
Tel: 319 356-8754   *Fax:* 319 384-7199
Length: 4 Yrs   *ACGME Approved/Offered Positions:* 20
Program ID: 180-18-21-039

Kansas

Kansas City

University of Kansas School of Medicine Program

Sponsor: University of Kansas School of Medicine
Colmery-O'Neil Veterans Affairs Medical Center
University of Kansas Hospital
Veterans Affairs Medical Center (Kansas City)
Prgm Director: Richard Dubinsky, MD, MPH
Department of Neurology
3901 Rainbow Boulevard
Kansas City, KS 66160
Tel: 913 588-6970   *Fax:* 913 588-0673
Length: 4 Yrs   *ACGME Approved/Offered Positions:* 16
Program ID: 180-19-22-040

Kentucky

Lexington

University of Kentucky College of Medicine Program

Sponsor: University of Kentucky College of Medicine
University of Kentucky Hospital
Veterans Affairs Medical Center (Lexington)
Prgm Director: Michael R Dobbs, MD
Department of Neurology
740 South Limestone, Rm L445
Lexington, KY 40536
Tel: 859 218-5038   *Fax:* 859 323-5943
E-mail: kelli.herrera@uky.edu
Length: 4 Yrs   *ACGME Approved/Offered Positions:* 16
Program ID: 180-20-21-041

Louisville

University of Louisville Program

Sponsor: University of Louisville School of Medicine
Norton Hospital
University Neurologists, PSC
University of Louisville Hospital
Prgm Director: Kerri S Remmel, MD, PhD
500 S Preston Street
HSC-A, Rm 113
Louisville, KY 40292
Tel: 502 852-6328   *Fax:* 502 852-6344
Length: 3 Yrs   *ACGME Approved/Offered Positions:* 6
Program ID: 180-20-21-042

Louisiana

New Orleans

Louisiana State University Program

Sponsor: Louisiana State University School of Medicine
Medical Center of Louisiana at New Orleans
Touro Infirmary
West Jefferson Medical Center
Prgm Director: Amparo Gutierrez, MD
Department of Neurology
1542 Tulane Avenue - 7th floor
New Orleans, LA 70112
Tel: 504 568-4080   *Fax:* 504 568-7130
Length: 4 Yrs   *ACGME Approved/Offered Positions:* 12
Program ID: 180-21-21-043

Tulane University Program

Sponsor: Tulane University School of Medicine
Medical Center of Louisiana at New Orleans
Tulane University Hospital and Clinics
Veterans Affairs Medical Center (New Orleans)
Prgm Director: Jeffrey Nicholl, MD*
Department of Neurology
1440 Canal Street, Box TB-52
New Orleans, LA 70112
Tel: 504 988-2241   *Fax:* 504 988-3695
E-mail: jsnichollmd@yahoo.com
Length: 3 Yrs   *ACGME Approved/Offered Positions:* 9
Program ID: 180-21-21-044

Shreveport

Louisiana State University (Shreveport) Program

Sponsor: LSU Health Sciences Center-University Hospital
E A Conway Medical Center
Prgm Director: Roger E Kelley, MD
1501 Kings Highway
Department of Neurology
Shreveport, LA 71103
Tel: 318 813-1480
E-mail: rkelly@lsuhsc.edu
Length: 4 Yrs   *ACGME Approved/Offered Positions:* 12
Program ID: 180-21-31-153

Maryland

Baltimore

Johns Hopkins University Program

Sponsor: Johns Hopkins University School of Medicine
Johns Hopkins Bayview Medical Center
Johns Hopkins Hospital
Prgm Director: Argye B Hillis, MD, MA
600 N Wolfe Street
Meyer Building Suite 6-113
Baltimore, MD 21287
Tel: 410 614-2381   *Fax:* 410 614-9807
Length: 3 Yrs   *ACGME Approved/Offered Positions:* 21
Program ID: 180-23-21-045

University of Maryland Program

Sponsor: University of Maryland Medical System
Veterans Affairs Medical Center (Baltimore)
Prgm Director: Barney J Stern, MD
Department of Neurology
22 S Greene Street, N4W46
Baltimore, MD 21201
Tel: 410 328-3372   *Fax:* 410 328-5899
Length: 3 Yrs   *ACGME Approved/Offered Positions:* 18
Program ID: 180-23-31-046

Bethesda

National Capital Consortium Program

Sponsor: National Capital Consortium
Walter Reed Army Medical Center
Prgm Director: Mark E Landau, MD
Department of Neurology
6900 Georgia Avenue NW
Washington, DC 20307
Tel: 202 782-1661   *Fax:* 202 782-2295
Length: 4 Yrs   *ACGME Approved/Offered Positions:* 18
Program ID: 180-10-21-144
Uniformed Services Program

Note: * indicates a newly appointed program director

Massachusetts

Boston

Beth Israel Deaconess Medical Center/Harvard Medical School Program

Sponsor: Beth Israel Deaconess Medical Center
Prgm Director: Frank W Drislane, MD
Department of Neurology
330 Brookline Avenue
Boston, MA 02215
Tel: 617 667-2268   *Fax:* 617 667-2987
Length: 3 Yrs   *ACGME Approved/Offered Positions:* 21
Program ID: 180-24-21-049

Boston University Medical Center Program

Sponsor: Boston Medical Center
Veterans Affairs Medical Center (Boston)
Prgm Director: James A D Otis, MD
72 East Concord Street, Suite C-329
Boston, MA 02118
Tel: 617 638-5309   *Fax:* 617 638-5354
E-mail: jotis@bu.edu
Length: 3 Yrs   *ACGME Approved/Offered Positions:* 18
Program ID: 180-24-21-145

Massachusetts General Hospital/Brigham and Women's Hospital/Harvard Medical School Program

Sponsor: Massachusetts General Hospital
Brigham and Women's Hospital
Prgm Director: David M Greer, MD, MA*
WACC 720
55 Fruit Street
Boston, MA 02114
Tel: 617 726-1606   *Fax:* 617 643-5692
E-mail: vsagar1@partners.org
Length: 3 Yrs   *ACGME Approved/Offered Positions:* 45
Program ID: 180-24-31-050

Tufts Medical Center Program

Sponsor: Tufts Medical Center
Caritas St Elizabeth's Medical Center of Boston
Lahey Clinic
Prgm Director: Thomas D Sabin, MD
800 Washington St
Box 314
Boston, MA 02111
Tel: 617 636-7487   *Fax:* 617 636-8199
E-mail: rleblanc1@tuftsmedicalcenter.org
Length: 3 Yrs   *ACGME Approved/Offered Positions:* 18
Program ID: 180-24-21-051

Worcester

University of Massachusetts Program

Sponsor: University of Massachusetts Medical School
UMass Memorial Health Care (University Campus)
Prgm Director: Ann Mitchell, MD
55 Lake Avenue, North
Worcester, MA 01655
Tel: 508 856-2527   *Fax:* 508 856-3180
Length: 3 Yrs   *ACGME Approved/Offered Positions:* 15
Program ID: 180-24-21-121

Michigan

Ann Arbor

University of Michigan Program

Sponsor: University of Michigan Hospitals and Health Centers
Veterans Affairs Medical Center (Ann Arbor)
Prgm Director: Zachary N London, MD
1914 Taubman SPC 5316
1500 E Medical Ctr Dr
Ann Arbor, MI 48109
Tel: 734 936-9030   *Fax:* 734 936-8763
Length: 3 Yrs   *ACGME Approved/Offered Positions:* 18
Program ID: 180-25-31-052

Detroit

Henry Ford Hospital Program

Sponsor: Henry Ford Hospital
Prgm Director: Lori Schuh, MD
2799 W Grand Blvd
Department of Neurology K-11
Detroit, MI 48202
Tel: 313 916-7205   *Fax:* 313 916-5117
Length: 3 Yrs   *ACGME Approved/Offered Positions:* 18
Program ID: 180-25-21-129

Wayne State University/Detroit Medical Center Program

Sponsor: Wayne State University/Detroit Medical Center
Detroit Receiving Hospital and University Health Center
Harper-Hutzel Hospital
Prgm Director: Renee B Van Stavern, MD
8D University Health Center
4201 St Antoine
Detroit, MI 48201
Tel: 313 577-1245   *Fax:* 313 745-4216
Length: 3 Yrs   *ACGME Approved/Offered Positions:* 21
Program ID: 180-25-31-054

Lansing

Sparrow Hospital/Michigan State University Program

Sponsor: Sparrow Hospital
Michigan State University Clinical Center
Prgm Director: David I Kaufman, DO
MSU-Clinical Center A-217
138 Service Road
East Lansing, MI 48824
Tel: 517 432-9277   *Fax:* 517 432-9414
E-mail: david.kaufman@ht.msu.edu
Length: 3 Yrs   *ACGME Approved/Offered Positions:* 12
Program ID: 180-25-21-149

Minnesota

Minneapolis

University of Minnesota Program

Sponsor: University of Minnesota Medical School
Hennepin County Medical Center
University of Minnesota Medical Center, Division of Fairview
Veterans Affairs Medical Center (Minneapolis)
Prgm Director: Frederick G Langendorf, MD
Department of Neurology
420 Delaware St SE, MMC 295
Minneapolis, MN 55455
Tel: 612 626-6519   *Fax:* 612 625-7950
E-mail: lange002@umn.edu
Length: 4 Yrs   *ACGME Approved/Offered Positions:* 24
Program ID: 180-26-21-055

Rochester

College of Medicine, Mayo Clinic (Rochester) Program

Sponsor: College of Medicine, Mayo Clinic
Mayo Clinic (Rochester)
Saint Marys Hospital of Rochester
Prgm Director: Christopher J Boes, MD
Department of Neurology
200 First Street, SW
Rochester, MN 55905
Tel: 507 284-4205   *Fax:* 507 266-0178
E-mail: n-ed-cmte@mayo.edu
Length: 3 Yrs   *ACGME Approved/Offered Positions:* 27
Program ID: 180-26-21-057

Mississippi

Jackson

University of Mississippi Medical Center Program

Sponsor: University of Mississippi School of Medicine
University Hospitals and Clinics
Veterans Affairs Medical Center (Jackson)
Prgm Director: James J Corbett, MD
Department of Neurology
2500 North State Street
Jackson, MS 39216
Tel: 601 984-5500   *Fax:* 601 984-5503
E-mail: JCorbettMD@aol.com
Length: 4 Yrs   *ACGME Approved/Offered Positions:* 12
Program ID: 180-27-21-058

Missouri

Columbia

University of Missouri-Columbia Program

Sponsor: University of Missouri-Columbia School of Medicine
Harry S Truman Memorial Veterans Hospital
University Hospitals and Clinics
Prgm Director: Terry Rolan, MD
Department of Neurology
5 Hospital Drive, CE 507
Columbia, MO 65212
Tel: 573 882-3133   *Fax:* 573 884-4249
Length: 4 Yrs   *ACGME Approved/Offered Positions:* 12
Program ID: 180-28-21-059

St Louis

St Louis University School of Medicine Program

Sponsor: St Louis University School of Medicine
St Louis University Hospital
St Mary's Health Center
Veterans Affairs Medical Center (St Louis)
Prgm Director: Amy C Rauchway, DO*
3635 Vista Avenue at Grand Boulevard
Department of Neurology
St Louis, MO 63110
Tel: 314 977-4800   *Fax:* 314 977-4877
Length: 4 Yrs   *ACGME Approved/Offered Positions:* 20
Program ID: 180-28-21-060

Programs

Washington University/B-JH/SLCH Consortium Program

Sponsor: Washington University/B-JH/SLCH Consortium
Barnes-Jewish Hospital
St Louis ConnectCare
Prgm Director: Abdullah Nassief, MD
Department of Neurology
One Barnes-Jewish Hospital Plaza
St Louis, MO 63110
Tel: 314 362-3296   *Fax:* 314 362-2826
Length: 4 Yrs   *ACGME Approved/Offered Positions:* 32
Program ID: 180-28-21-061

Nebraska

Omaha

University of Nebraska Medical Center College of Medicine/Creighton University Program

Sponsor: University of Nebraska Medical Center College
of Medicine
Creighton University Medical Center (Tenet - SJH)
Nebraska Medical Center
Veterans Affairs Medical Center (Omaha)
Prgm Director: Sanjay P Singh, MD*
982045 Nebraska Medical Center
Omaha, NE 68198
Tel: 402 559-5804   *Fax:* 402 559-3341
Length: 3 Yrs   *ACGME Approved/Offered Positions:* 9
Program ID: 180-30-21-062

New Hampshire

Lebanon

Dartmouth-Hitchcock Medical Center Program

Sponsor: Mary Hitchcock Memorial Hospital
Veterans Affairs Medical Center (White River Junction)
Prgm Director: Morris Levin, MD
Section of Neurology
One Medical Center
Lebanon, NH 03756
Tel: 603 650-1880   *Fax:* 603 650-7617
Length: 3 Yrs   *ACGME Approved/Offered Positions:* 9
Program ID: 180-32-21-063

New Jersey

Camden

UMDNJ-Robert Wood Johnson Medical School (Camden) Program

Sponsor: Cooper Hospital-University Medical Center
Prgm Director: Joseph Campellone Jr, MD*
Division of Neurology
3 Cooper Plaza, Suite 320
Camden, NJ 08103
Tel: 856 342-2445   *Fax:* 856 964-0504
E-mail: campellone-joseph@cooperhealth.edu
Length: 3 Yrs   *ACGME Approved/Offered Positions:* 9
Program ID: 180-33-13-158

Edison

Seton Hall University School of Health and Medical Sciences Program

Sponsor: Seton Hall University School of Health and
Medical Sciences
JFK Medical Center
Prgm Director: Philip A Hanna, MD
NJ Neuroscience Institute, JFK Medical Center
65 James Street, PO Box 3059
Edison, NJ 08818
Tel: 732 321-7879   *Fax:* 732 632-1584
E-mail: phanna@solarishs.org
Length: 3 Yrs   *ACGME Approved/Offered Positions:* 12
Program ID: 180-33-21-142

New Brunswick

UMDNJ-Robert Wood Johnson Medical School Program

Sponsor: UMDNJ-Robert Wood Johnson Medical School
Robert Wood Johnson University Hospital
Prgm Director: Lawrence I Golbe, MD
97 Paterson Street
New Brunswick, NJ 08901
Tel: 732 235-7731   *Fax:* 732 235-7041
Length: 3 Yrs   *ACGME Approved/Offered Positions:* 9
Program ID: 180-33-21-157

Newark

UMDNJ-New Jersey Medical School Program

Sponsor: UMDNJ-New Jersey Medical School
Robert Wood Johnson University Hospital
UMDNJ-University Hospital
Veterans Affairs New Jersey Health Care System
Prgm Director: Machteld E Hillen, MD*
Department of Neurology
185 South Orange Ave, MSB H-506
Newark, NJ 07103
Tel: 973 972-9276   *Fax:* 973 972-9960
Length: 4 Yrs   *ACGME Approved/Offered Positions:* 22
Program ID: 180-33-21-064

New Mexico

Albuquerque

University of New Mexico Program

Sponsor: University of New Mexico School of Medicine
University of New Mexico Hospital
Veterans Affairs Medical Center (Albuquerque)
Prgm Director: John C Adair, MD*
MSC10 5620
1 University of New Mexico
Albuquerque, NM 87131
Tel: 505 272-8960   *Fax:* 505 272-6692
Length: 3 Yrs   *ACGME Approved/Offered Positions:* 12
Program ID: 180-34-21-065

New York

Albany

Albany Medical Center Program

Sponsor: Albany Medical Center
Prgm Director: Donald S Higgins Jr, MD
Department of Neurology
47 New Scotland Ave
Albany, NY 12208
Tel: 518 262-6488   *Fax:* 518 262-6261
Length: 3 Yrs   *ACGME Approved/Offered Positions:* 12
Program ID: 180-35-21-066

Bronx

Albert Einstein College of Medicine Program

Sponsor: Albert Einstein College of Medicine of Yeshiva
University
Montefiore Medical Center-Henry and Lucy Moses
Division
Montefiore Medical Center-Weiler Division
North Bronx Healthcare Network-Jacobi Medical Center
Prgm Director: Sheryl Haut, MD
Department of Neurology
1300 Morris Park Avenue
Bronx, NY 10461
Tel: 718 920-4898   *Fax:* 718 882-0216
E-mail: sarchill@aecom.yu.edu
Length: 3 Yrs   *ACGME Approved/Offered Positions:* 27
Program ID: 180-35-21-070

Brooklyn

SUNY Health Science Center at Brooklyn Program

Sponsor: SUNY Health Science Center at Brooklyn
Kings County Hospital Center
Long Island College Hospital
University Hospital-SUNY Health Science Center at
Brooklyn
Prgm Director: Helen A Valsamis, MD
450 Clarkson Avenue, Box 1213
Department of Neurology
Brooklyn, NY 11203
Tel: 718 270-4232   *Fax:* 718 270-3840
E-mail: marjorie.maxwell@downstate.edu
Length: 3 Yrs   *ACGME Approved/Offered Positions:* 28
Program ID: 180-35-21-079

Buffalo

University at Buffalo Program

Sponsor: University at Buffalo School of Medicine
Kaleida Health System (Buffalo General Hospital)
Kaleida Health System (Millard Fillmore Hospital)
Prgm Director: Alan H Lockwood, MD
Dept of Neurology, Jacobs Neurological Inst, BGH
100 High Street
Buffalo, NY 14203
Tel: 716 859-3496   *Fax:* 716 859-7573
E-mail: ejtamoga@buffalo.edu
Length: 4 Yrs   *ACGME Approved/Offered Positions:* 20
Program ID: 180-35-21-067

Great Neck

NSLIJHS-Albert Einstein College of Medicine at Long Island Jewish Medical Center Program

Sponsor: North Shore-Long Island Jewish Health System
Long Island Jewish Medical Center
North Shore University Hospital
Prgm Director: Ronald M Kanner, MD
Department of Neurology
270-05 76th Avenue
New Hyde Park, NY 11040
Tel: 718 470-7311   *Fax:* 718 347-3016
Length: 3 Yrs   *ACGME Approved/Offered Positions:* 21
Program ID: 180-35-21-074

New York

Albert Einstein College of Medicine at Beth Israel Medical Center Program

Sponsor: Beth Israel Medical Center
Prgm Director: Daniel MacGowan, MD
Beth Israel Medical Center
10 Union Square East, Suite 2Q
New York, NY 10003
Tel: 212 844-8497   *Fax:* 212 844-6185
E-mail: neurores@chpnet.org
Length: 3 Yrs   *ACGME Approved/Offered Positions:* 9
Program ID: 180-35-13-155

Note: * indicates a newly appointed program director

Mount Sinai School of Medicine Program

Sponsor: Mount Sinai School of Medicine
Mount Sinai Medical Center
Prgm Director: Seymour Gendelman, MD
Department of Neurology
One Gustave L Levy Place
New York, NY 10029
Tel: 212 241-8172   *Fax:* 212 241-9395
Length: 4 Yrs   *ACGME Approved/Offered Positions:* 20
Program ID: 180-35-21-075

New York Medical College at St Vincent's Hospital and Medical Center of New York Program

Sponsor: New York Medical College
St Vincent Catholic Medical Centers (Manhattan)
Maimonides Medical Center
Metropolitan Hospital Center
Prgm Director: Paul Mullin, MD
170 West 12th Street
Cronin 4th Floor
New York, NY 10011
Tel: 212 604-2415   *Fax:* 212 604-3101
Length: 3 Yrs   *ACGME Approved/Offered Positions:* 12
Program ID: 180-35-11-078

New York Presbyterian Hospital (Columbia Campus) Program

Sponsor: New York Presbyterian Hospital
New York Presbyterian Hospital (Columbia Campus)
Prgm Director: Blair Ford, MD
710 W 168th St
Neurological Institute
New York, NY 10032
Tel: 212 305-1338   *Fax:* 212 305-3648
E-mail: Neuroresidency@neuro.columbia.edu
Length: 3 Yrs   *ACGME Approved/Offered Positions:* 30
Program ID: 180-35-31-071

New York Presbyterian Hospital (Cornell Campus) Program

Sponsor: New York Presbyterian Hospital
Memorial Sloan-Kettering Cancer Center
New York Presbyterian Hospital (Cornell Campus)
Prgm Director: Alan Z Segal, MD
525 E 68th Street, Room F610
New York, NY 10021
Tel: 212 746-0225   *Fax:* 212 746-8532
E-mail: alukaj@med.cornell.edu
Length: 4 Yrs   *ACGME Approved/Offered Positions:* 24
Program ID: 180-35-21-072

New York University School of Medicine Program

Sponsor: New York University School of Medicine
Bellevue Hospital Center
Manhattan VA Harbor Health Care System
NYU Hospitals Center
Prgm Director: Anuradha Singh, MD*
Department of Neurology
550 First Avenue
New York, NY 10016
Tel: 212 263-6347   *Fax:* 212 263-8228
E-mail: singha03@nyumc.org
Length: 3 Yrs   *ACGME Approved/Offered Positions:* 24
Program ID: 180-35-21-077

Rochester

University of Rochester Program

Sponsor: Strong Memorial Hospital of the University of Rochester
Prgm Director: Ralph F Jozefowicz, MD
Department of Neurology
601 Elmwood Avenue, PO Box 673
Rochester, NY 14642
Tel: 585 275-2545   *Fax:* 585 244-2529
E-mail: ralph_jozefowicz@urmc.rochester.edu
Length: 4 Yrs   *ACGME Approved/Offered Positions:* 20
Program ID: 180-35-31-082

Stony Brook

SUNY at Stony Brook Program

Sponsor: University Hospital - SUNY at Stony Brook
Veterans Affairs Medical Center (Northport)
Prgm Director: Cara Harth, MD*
Dept of Neurology, T12/020
Stony Brook, NY 11794
Tel: 631 444-7878
Length: 3 Yrs   *ACGME Approved/Offered Positions:* 12
Program ID: 180-35-21-081

Syracuse

SUNY Upstate Medical University Program

Sponsor: SUNY Upstate Medical University
Crouse Hospital
Veterans Affairs Medical Center (Syracuse)
Prgm Director: Deborah Y Bradshaw, MD
Department of Neurology
750 East Adams Street
Syracuse, NY 13210
Tel: 315 464-5011   *Fax:* 315 464-5355
Length: 3 Yrs   *ACGME Approved/Offered Positions:* 18
Program ID: 180-35-21-083

Valhalla

New York Medical College at Westchester Medical Center Program

Sponsor: New York Medical College
Westchester Medical Center
Prgm Director: Venkat Ramani, MD
Department of Neurology
Munger Pavilion
Valhalla, NY 10595
Tel: 914 594-4293   *Fax:* 914 594-4295
Length: 3 Yrs   *ACGME Approved/Offered Positions:* 9
Program ID: 180-35-21-076

North Carolina

Chapel Hill

University of North Carolina Hospitals Program

Sponsor: University of North Carolina Hospitals
Prgm Director: Kevin A Kahn, MD
CB 7025 UNC Hospitals
Chapel Hill, NC 27599
Tel: 919 843-3133   *Fax:* 919 966-2922
E-mail: barbourc@neurology.unc.edu
Length: 3 Yrs   *ACGME Approved/Offered Positions:* 12
Program ID: 180-36-11-084

Durham

Duke University Hospital Program

Sponsor: Duke University Hospital
Veterans Affairs Medical Center (Durham)
Prgm Director: Joel C Morgenlander, MD
Department of Neurology
Box 2905
Durham, NC 27710
Tel: 919 684-5870   *Fax:* 919 684-0131
Length: 3 Yrs   *ACGME Approved/Offered Positions:* 12
Program ID: 180-36-21-085

Winston-Salem

Wake Forest University School of Medicine Program

Sponsor: Wake Forest University Baptist Medical Center
Prgm Director: Patrick S Reynolds, MD
Department of Neurology
Medical Center Boulevard
Winston-Salem, NC 27157
Tel: 336 716-2317   *Fax:* 336 716-9810
E-mail: preynold@wfubmc.edu
Length: 4 Yrs   *ACGME Approved/Offered Positions:* 16
Program ID: 180-36-21-086

Ohio

Cincinnati

University Hospital/University of Cincinnati College of Medicine Program

Sponsor: University Hospital Inc
Veterans Affairs Medical Center (Cincinnati)
Prgm Director: Brett Kissela, MD
Department of Neurology (ML 525)
260 Stetson Street, Suite 2300
Cincinnati, OH 45267
Tel: 513 558-2968   *Fax:* 513 558-4305
Length: 3 Yrs   *ACGME Approved/Offered Positions:* 12
Program ID: 180-38-21-088

Cleveland

Cleveland Clinic Foundation Program

Sponsor: Cleveland Clinic Foundation
Prgm Director: MaryAnn Mays, MD
Department of Neurology
9500 Euclid Avenue
Cleveland, OH 44195
Tel: 216 444-2945   *Fax:* 216 444-0230
E-mail: dillj@ccf.org
Length: 4 Yrs   *ACGME Approved/Offered Positions:* 32
Program ID: 180-38-11-090

University Hospitals Case Medical Center Program

Sponsor: University Hospitals Case Medical Center
Veterans Affairs Medical Center (Cleveland)
Prgm Director: David C Preston, MD
Department of Neurology - HH5040
11100 Euclid Avenue
Cleveland, OH 44106
Tel: 216 844-7776   *Fax:* 216 844-7624
E-mail: kristen.stacy@uhhospitals.org
Length: 3 Yrs   *ACGME Approved/Offered Positions:* 30
Program ID: 180-38-21-089

Columbus

Ohio State University Hospital Program

Sponsor: Ohio State University Hospital
Ohio State University Hospitals, East
Prgm Director: Sheri L Hart, MD, PhD*
1654 Upham Drive
Room 428 Means Hall
Columbus, OH 43210
Tel: 614 293-6195   *Fax:* 614 293-4688
E-mail: sheri.hart@osumc.edu
Length: 3 Yrs   *ACGME Approved/Offered Positions:* 12
Program ID: 180-38-21-092

Toledo

University of Toledo Program

Sponsor: University of Toledo
University Medical Center (Toledo)
Prgm Director: Noor A Pirzada, MD
MS 1195
3000 Arlington Avenue
Toledo, OH 43614
Tel: 419 383-3544   *Fax:* 419 383-3093
Length: 4 Yrs   *ACGME Approved/Offered Positions:* 12
Program ID: 180-38-21-143

Oklahoma

Oklahoma City

University of Oklahoma Health Sciences Center Program

Sponsor: University of Oklahoma College of Medicine
OU Medical Center - Presbyterian Tower
Veterans Affairs Medical Center (Oklahoma City)
Prgm Director: David L Gordon, MD*
711 Stanton L Young Blvd, Suite 215
Oklahoma City, OK 73104
Tel: 405 271-4113   *Fax:* 405 271-5723
E-mail: carole-clark@ouhsc.edu
Length: 4 Yrs   *ACGME Approved/Offered Positions:* 16
Program ID: 180-39-21-141

Oregon

Portland

Oregon Health & Science University Program

Sponsor: Oregon Health & Science University Hospital
Veterans Affairs Medical Center (Portland)
Prgm Director: David C Spencer, MD
Dept of Neurology, CR120
3181 SW Sam Jackson Park Road
Portland, OR 97239
Tel: 503 494-5753   *Fax:* 503 418-8373
E-mail: neuro@ohsu.edu
Length: 4 Yrs   *ACGME Approved/Offered Positions:* 14
Program ID: 180-40-31-095

Pennsylvania

Hershey

Penn State University/Milton S Hershey Medical Center Program

Sponsor: Milton S Hershey Medical Center
Prgm Director: Milind J Kothari, DO
30 Hope Drive
EC037
Hershey, PA 17033
Tel: 717 531-8692   *Fax:* 717 531-0384
Length: 3 Yrs   *ACGME Approved/Offered Positions:* 12
Program ID: 180-41-11-096

Philadelphia

Albert Einstein Healthcare Network Program

Sponsor: Albert Einstein Medical Center
St Christopher's Hospital for Children (Tenet Health System)
Prgm Director: George C Newman, MD, PhD
Department of Neurosensory Sciences
5501 Old York Road
Philadelphia, PA 19141
Tel: 215 456-7198   *Fax:* 215 456-7048
Length: 3 Yrs   *ACGME Approved/Offered Positions:* 9
Program ID: 180-41-33-162

Drexel University College of Medicine/Hahnemann University Hospital Program

Sponsor: Drexel University College of Medicine/Hahnemann University
Hahnemann University Hospital (Tenet Health System)
Prgm Director: Jyoti Pillai, MD
Broad and Vine Streets, MS 423
Philadelphia, PA 19102
Tel: 215 762-4592   *Fax:* 215 762-3161
E-mail: mcanales@drexelmed.edu
Length: 3 Yrs   *ACGME Approved/Offered Positions:* 20
Program ID: 180-41-21-097

Temple University Hospital Program

Sponsor: Temple University Hospital
Albert Einstein Medical Center
Prgm Director: David S Roby, MD
Suite C525 Parkinson Pavilion
3401 North Broad Street
Philadelphia, PA 19140
Tel: 215 707-3193   *Fax:* 215 707-8235
Length: 3 Yrs   *ACGME Approved/Offered Positions:* 12
Program ID: 180-41-21-100

Thomas Jefferson University Program

Sponsor: Thomas Jefferson University Hospital
Prgm Director: Christopher T Skidmore, MD*
900 Walnut Street Suite 200
Philadelphia, PA 19107
Tel: 215 955-1222   *Fax:* 215 955-0606
E-mail: Christopher.Skidmore@jefferson.edu
Length: 3 Yrs   *ACGME Approved/Offered Positions:* 27
Program ID: 180-41-21-101

University of Pennsylvania Program

Sponsor: University of Pennsylvania Health System
Prgm Director: Steven L Galetta, MD
3 West Gates Building
3400 Spruce Street
Philadelphia, PA 19104
Tel: 215 662-3381   *Fax:* 215 662-3362
Length: 3 Yrs   *ACGME Approved/Offered Positions:* 27
Program ID: 180-41-21-102

Pittsburgh

Allegheny General Hospital Program

Sponsor: Allegheny General Hospital
Prgm Director: Sandeep S Rana, MD
320 East North Avenue
7th Floor, South Tower
Pittsburgh, PA 15212
Tel: 412 359-8644   *Fax:* 412 359-8477
E-mail: mcardamo@wpahs.org
Length: 3 Yrs   *ACGME Approved/Offered Positions:* 9
Program ID: 180-41-21-140

University of Pittsburgh Medical Center Medical Education Program

Sponsor: Univ of Pittsburgh Medical Center Medical Education
UPMC Presbyterian Shadyside
Prgm Director: John J Doyle, MD
3471 Fifth Avenue, Suite 811
Pittsburgh, PA 15213
Tel: 412 692-4623   *Fax:* 412 692-4636
Length: 4 Yrs   *ACGME Approved/Offered Positions:* 20
Program ID: 180-41-21-103

Puerto Rico

San Juan

University of Puerto Rico Program

Sponsor: University of Puerto Rico School of Medicine
San Juan City Hospital
University Hospital
VA Caribbean Healthcare System
Prgm Director: Jesus R Velez-Borras, MD, BS
Section of Neurology
GPO Box 365067
San Juan, PR 00936
Tel: 787 754-0101   *Fax:* 787 751-3911
E-mail: jrvelez@msn.com
Length: 4 Yrs   *ACGME Approved/Offered Positions:* 12
Program ID: 180-42-21-104

Rhode Island

Providence

Brown University Program

Sponsor: Rhode Island Hospital-Lifespan
Prgm Director: Andrew S Blum, MD, PhD*
Physicians Office Building, Ste 324
110 Lockwood Street
Providence, RI 02903
Tel: 401 444-4364   *Fax:* 401 444-3236
E-mail: borourke1@lifespan.org
Length: 3 Yrs   *ACGME Approved/Offered Positions:* 15
Program ID: 180-43-21-131

South Carolina

Charleston

Medical University of South Carolina Program

Sponsor: Medical University of South Carolina College of Medicine
MUSC Medical Center
Ralph H Johnson VA Medical Center (Charleston)
Prgm Director: Paul B Pritchard III, MD
96 Jonathan Lucas St, Suite 309
PO Box 250606
Charleston, SC 29425
Tel: 843 792-3221   *Fax:* 843 792-8626
Length: 4 Yrs   *ACGME Approved/Offered Positions:* 14
Program ID: 180-45-21-105

Note: * indicates a newly appointed program director

Tennessee

Memphis

University of Tennessee Program

Sponsor: University of Tennessee College of Medicine
Methodist Healthcare - Memphis Hospitals
Regional Medical Center at Memphis
Veterans Affairs Medical Center (Memphis)
Prgm Director: Michael Jacewicz, MD
Department of Neurology
855 Monroe Avenue, Room 415
Memphis, TN 38163
Tel: 901 448-6661   *Fax:* 901 448-7440
Length: 3 Yrs   *ACGME Approved/Offered Positions:* 12
Program ID: 180-47-21-106

Nashville

Vanderbilt University Program

Sponsor: Vanderbilt University Medical Center
Veterans Affairs Medical Center (Nashville)
Prgm Director: David Charles, MD
1161 21st Avenue South
Suite A-1106, Medical Center North
Nashville, TN 37232
Tel: 615 936-1567   *Fax:* 615 936-2675
E-mail: Linda.Hurt@vanderbilt.edu
Length: 3 Yrs   *ACGME Approved/Offered Positions:* 15
Program ID: 180-47-21-107

Texas

Austin

University of Texas Medical Branch Hospitals (Austin) Program

Sponsor: University of Texas Medical Branch Hospitals
Seton Medical Center
Central Texas Veterans Hlth Care System Facilities (Austin)
University Medical Center at Brackenridge
Prgm Director: Darryl Camp, MD
601 E 15th Street
Brackenridge Annex
Austin, TX 78701
Tel: 512 324-7890
E-mail: flhart@seton.org
Length: 3 Yrs   *ACGME Approved/Offered Positions:* 9
Program ID: 180-48-12-156

Dallas

University of Texas Southwestern Medical School Program

Sponsor: University of Texas Southwestern Medical School
Dallas County Hospital District-Parkland Memorial Hospital
Prgm Director: Steven Vernino, MD, PhD
5323 Harry Hines Blvd
Dallas, TX 75390
Tel: 214 648-8816   *Fax:* 214 648-5080
E-mail: neurologyresidency@utsouthwestern.edu
Length: 4 Yrs   *ACGME Approved/Offered Positions:* 28
Program ID: 180-48-21-108

Galveston

University of Texas Medical Branch Hospitals Program

Sponsor: University of Texas Medical Branch Hospitals
Prgm Director: Joseph Oommen, MD
Department of Neurology
301 University Boulevard, John Sealy Annex, Room 9
Galveston, TX 77555
Tel: 409 772-8031   *Fax:* 409 772-6940
E-mail: dktabor@utmb.edu
Length: 3 Yrs   *ACGME Approved/Offered Positions:* 9
Program ID: 180-48-11-109

Houston

Baylor College of Medicine Program

Sponsor: Baylor College of Medicine
Methodist Hospital (Houston)
Michael E DeBakey VA Medical Center - Houston
St Luke's Episcopal Hospital
Prgm Director: Paul E Schulz, MD
Department of Neurology
6501 Fannin Street, Suite NB302
Houston, TX 77030
Tel: 713 798-6151   *Fax:* 713 798-8530
E-mail: nrp@bcm.tmc.edu
Length: 4 Yrs   *ACGME Approved/Offered Positions:* 40
Program ID: 180-48-21-110

Methodist Hospital (Houston) Program

Sponsor: Methodist Hospital (Houston)
Prgm Director: Ericka P Simpson, MD
6560 Fannin St, Suite 802
Houston, TX 77030
Tel: 713 441-3336   *Fax:* 713 793-7271
E-mail: esimpson@tmhs.org
Length: 3 Yrs   *ACGME Approved/Offered Positions:* 6
Program ID: 180-48-12-160

University of Texas at Houston Program

Sponsor: University of Texas Health Science Center at Houston
Lyndon B Johnson General Hospital
Memorial Hermann Hospital
University of Texas M D Anderson Cancer Center
Prgm Director: Mya C Schiess, MD
Department of Neurology 7.044/MSB
6431 Fannin Street
Houston, TX 77030
Tel: 713 500-7024
E-mail: ms.neur.coordinator@uth.tmc.edu
Length: 3 Yrs   *ACGME Approved/Offered Positions:* 17
Program ID: 180-48-31-111

Lackland AFB

San Antonio Uniformed Services Health Education Consortium Program

Sponsor: San Antonio Uniformed Services Health Education Consortium
Wilford Hall Medical Center (AETC)
Prgm Director: Patrick M Grogan, MD
59th Medical Operations Squadron/SGO5N
2200 Bergquist Drive, Ste 1
Lackland AFB, TX 78236
Tel: 210 292-3947   *Fax:* 210 292-3951
Length: 3 Yrs   *ACGME Approved/Offered Positions:* 6
Program ID: 180-48-21-127
Uniformed Services Program

San Antonio

University of Texas Health Science Center at San Antonio Program

Sponsor: University of Texas School of Medicine at San Antonio
Audie L Murphy Memorial Veterans Hospital (San Antonio)
University of Texas Health Science Center
Prgm Director: Merrill K Carolin, MD
Department of Neurology - MSC 7883
7703 Floyd Curl Drive
San Antonio, TX 78229
Tel: 210 617-5161   *Fax:* 210 567-4659
E-mail: carolin@uthscsa.edu
Length: 3 Yrs   *ACGME Approved/Offered Positions:* 8
Program ID: 180-48-21-112

Utah

Salt Lake City

University of Utah Program

Sponsor: University of Utah Medical Center
Veterans Affairs Medical Center (Salt Lake City)
Prgm Director: David R Renner, MD
Department of Neurology
CNC, 175 North Medical Drive East, 5th Floor
Salt Lake City, UT 84132
Tel: 801 585-5405   *Fax:* 801 581-4192
E-mail: david.renner@hsc.utah.edu
Length: 3 Yrs   *ACGME Approved/Offered Positions:* 12
Program ID: 180-49-21-113

Vermont

Burlington

University of Vermont Program

Sponsor: Fletcher Allen Health Care
Prgm Director: Christopher Commichau, MD
Department of Neurology
89 Beaumont Drive, Given C225
Burlington, VT 05405
Tel: 802 656-4590   *Fax:* 802 656-5678
E-mail: Penny.Potvin@med.uvm.edu
Length: 3 Yrs   *ACGME Approved/Offered Positions:* 9
Program ID: 180-50-11-114

Virginia

Charlottesville

University of Virginia Program

Sponsor: University of Virginia Medical Center
Prgm Director: Ted Burns, MD
PO Box 800394
Charlottesville, VA 22908
Tel: 434 924-5818   *Fax:* 434 982-1726
Length: 4 Yrs   *ACGME Approved/Offered Positions:* 24
Program ID: 180-51-11-115

Richmond

Virginia Commonwealth University Health System Program

Sponsor: Virginia Commonwealth University Health System
Hunter Holmes McGuire VA Medical Center (Richmond)
Medical College of Virginia Hospitals
Prgm Director: Scott A Vota, DO
PO Box 980599
1101 East Marshall Street, Room 6-005
Richmond, VA 23298
Tel: 804 828-9940   *Fax:* 804 828-6373
E-mail: neurores@vcu.edu
Length: 3 Yrs   *ACGME Approved/Offered Positions:* 18
Program ID: 180-51-21-116

Washington

Seattle

University of Washington Program

Sponsor: University of Washington School of Medicine
Harborview Medical Center
University of Washington Medical Center
VA Puget Sound Health Care System
Prgm Director: Phillip D Swanson, MD, PhD
Department of Neurology
Box 356465, 1959 NE Pacific St
Seattle, WA 98195
Tel: 206 543-2340   *Fax:* 206 685-8100
Length: 3 Yrs   *ACGME Approved/Offered Positions:* 15
Program ID: 180-54-21-117

Tacoma

Madigan Army Medical Center Program

Sponsor: Madigan Army Medical Center
Prgm Director: Jay C Erickson, MD, PhD
Neurology Service
9040A Fitzsimmons Drive
Tacoma, WA 98431
Tel: 253 968-1399   *Fax:* 253 968-0443
Length: 4 Yrs   *ACGME Approved/Offered Positions:* 8
Program ID: 180-54-21-138
Uniformed Services Program

West Virginia

Morgantown

West Virginia University Program

Sponsor: West Virginia University School of Medicine
West Virginia University Hospitals
Prgm Director: Gauri V Pawar, MD
Department of Neurology
PO Box 9180
Morgantown, WV 26506
Tel: 304 293-2342   *Fax:* 304 293-3352
Length: 3 Yrs   *ACGME Approved/Offered Positions:* 15
Program ID: 180-55-11-118

Wisconsin

Madison

University of Wisconsin Program

Sponsor: University of Wisconsin Hospital and Clinics
William S Middleton Veterans Hospital
Prgm Director: Nicholas Stanek, MD
Department of Neurology
600 Highland Ave, Room H6/574-5132 CSC
Madison, WI 53792
Tel: 608 263-5443   *Fax:* 608 263-0412
E-mail: lueck@neurology.wisc.edu
Length: 4 Yrs   *ACGME Approved/Offered Positions:* 12
Program ID: 180-56-21-119

Milwaukee

Medical College of Wisconsin Affiliated Hospitals Program

Sponsor: Medical College of Wisconsin Affiliated Hospitals, Inc
Clement J Zablocki Veterans Affairs Medical Center
Froedtert Memorial Lutheran Hospital
Prgm Director: Doug Woo, MD
9200 W Wisconsin Avenue
Department of Neurology
Milwaukee, WI 53226
Tel: 414 805-5254   *Fax:* 414 259-0469
E-mail: jdavies@mcw.edu
Length: 4 Yrs   *ACGME Approved/Offered Positions:* 20
Program ID: 180-56-21-120

Neuromuscular Medicine (Neurology)

California

Orange

University of California (Irvine) Program

Sponsor: University of California (Irvine) Medical Center
Long Beach Memorial Medical Center
Prgm Director: Annabel K Wang, MD
200 South Manchester Avenue
Suite 110
Orange, CA 92868
Tel: 714 456-2332   *Fax:* 714 456-5997
E-mail: akwang@uci.edu
Length: 1 Yr   *ACGME Approved/Offered Positions:* 1
Program ID: 183-05-31-020

Colorado

Aurora

University of Colorado Denver Program

Sponsor: University of Colorado Denver School of Medicine
University of Colorado Hospital
Prgm Director: Dianna Quan, MD
Department of Neurology
12631 E 17th Ave
Aurora, CO 80045
Tel: 303 724-2188   *Fax:* 303 724-2202
Length: 1 Yr   *ACGME Approved/Offered Positions:* 1
Program ID: 183-07-21-002

Connecticut

New Haven

Yale-New Haven Medical Center Program

Sponsor: Yale-New Haven Hospital
Veterans Affairs Medical Center (West Haven)
Prgm Director: Jonathan M Goldstein, MD
Department of Neurology
15 York Street, LCI7
New Haven, CT 06510
Tel: 203 688-2495   *Fax:* 203 688-3109
Length: 1 Yr   *ACGME Approved/Offered Positions:* 2
Program ID: 183-08-31-016

Florida

Miami

Jackson Memorial Hospital/Jackson Health System Program

Sponsor: Jackson Memorial Hospital/Jackson Health System
Prgm Director: D Ram Ayyar, MD
1120 NW 14th Street
CRB 1320
Miami, FL 33136
Tel: 305 243-2422   *Fax:* 305 243-8108
Length: 1 Yr   *ACGME Approved/Offered Positions:* 2
Program ID: 183-11-12-021

Note: * indicates a newly appointed program director

Illinois

Chicago

McGaw Medical Center of Northwestern University Program
Sponsor: McGaw Medical Center of Northwestern University
Northwestern Memorial Hospital
Prgm Director: Teepu Siddique, MD
Department of Neurology
303 East Chicago Avenue, Tarry 13-715
Chicago, IL 60611
Tel: 312 503-4737   *Fax:* 312 908-0865
E-mail: t-siddique@northwestern.edu
Length: 1 Yr   *ACGME Approved/Offered Positions:* 1
Program ID: 183-16-21-014

University of Illinois College of Medicine at Chicago Program
Sponsor: University of Illinois College of Medicine at Chicago
University of Illinois Hospital and Clinics
Prgm Director: Matthew N Meriggioli, MD
912 South Wood Street
Room 855N
Chicago, IL 60612
Tel: 312 996-6496   *Fax:* 312 996-4169
Length: 1 Yr   *ACGME Approved/Offered Positions:* 1
Program ID: 183-16-31-004

Kansas

Kansas City

University of Kansas School of Medicine Program
Sponsor: University of Kansas School of Medicine
University of Kansas Medical Center
Prgm Director: Mazen Dimachkie, MD
3901 Rainbow Boulevard
Mailstop 2012
Kansas City, KS 66160
Tel: 913 588-6970   *Fax:* 913 588-6965
Length: 1 Yr   *ACGME Approved/Offered Positions:* 1
Program ID: 183-19-12-017

Maryland

Baltimore

Johns Hopkins University Program
Sponsor: Johns Hopkins University School of Medicine
Johns Hopkins Hospital
Prgm Director: Ahmet Hoke, MD, PhD
600 North Wolfe Street
Pathology, Room 509
Baltimore, MD 21287
Tel: 410 955-2227   *Fax:* 410 502-5459
E-mail: ahoke@jhmi.edu
Length: 1 Yr   *ACGME Approved/Offered Positions:* 4
Program ID: 183-23-31-012

Massachusetts

Boston

Beth Israel Deaconess Medical Center/Harvard Medical School Program
Sponsor: Beth Israel Deaconess Medical Center
Children's Hospital
Prgm Director: Rachel Nardin, MD
330 Brookline Avenue
E/CC 810
Boston, MA 02215
Tel: 617 667-4382   *Fax:* 617 667-3175
E-mail: rnardin@bidmc.harvard.edu
Length: 1 Yr   *ACGME Approved/Offered Positions:* 3
Program ID: 183-24-13-019

Brigham and Women's Hospital/Massachusetts General Hospital/Harvard Medical School Program
Sponsor: Brigham and Women's Hospital
Massachusetts General Hospital
Prgm Director: Anthony A Amato, MD
Department of Neurology, Neuromuscular Division
75 Francis Street
Boston, MA 02115
Tel: 617 732-8046   *Fax:* 617 730-2885
Length: 1 Yr   *ACGME Approved/Offered Positions:* 6
Program ID: 183-24-12-005

Missouri

St Louis

Washington University/B-JH/SLCH Consortium Program
Sponsor: Washington University/B-JH/SLCH Consortium
St Louis Children's Hospital
Prgm Director: Muhammad Al-Lozi, MD
660 S Euclid Avenue, Box 8111
St Louis, MO 63110
Tel: 314 362-6981   *Fax:* 314 362-3752
E-mail: allozim@neuro.wustl.edu
Length: 1 Yr   *ACGME Approved/Offered Positions:* 5
Program ID: 183-28-21-018

New Jersey

Newark

UMDNJ-New Jersey Medical School Program
Sponsor: UMDNJ-New Jersey Medical School
Prgm Director: Nizar Souayah, MD
DOC 90 Bergen Street
Newark, NJ 07103
Tel: 973 972-8577   *Fax:* 973 972-8738
E-mail: formance@umdnj.edu
Length: 1 Yr   *ACGME Approved/Offered Positions:* 1
Program ID: 183-33-21-006

New York

Rochester

University of Rochester Program
Sponsor: Strong Memorial Hospital of the University of Rochester
Prgm Director: Emma Ciafaloni, MD
601 Elmwood Avenue, Box 673
Rochester, NY 14642
Tel: 585 275-4568   *Fax:* 585 273-1254
Length: 1 Yr   *ACGME Approved/Offered Positions:* 1
Program ID: 183-35-13-007

North Carolina

Durham

Duke University Hospital Program
Sponsor: Duke University Hospital
Prgm Director: Vern C Juel, MD
DUMC 3403
Trent Drive, Clinic 1L, Room 1255
Durham, NC 27710
Tel: 919 684-4044   *Fax:* 919 660-3853
E-mail: vern.juel@duke.edu
Length: 1 Yr   *ACGME Approved/Offered Positions:* 4
Program ID: 183-36-31-008

Ohio

Cleveland

Cleveland Clinic Foundation Program
Sponsor: Cleveland Clinic Foundation
Prgm Director: Kerry H Levin, MD
Neurology, Neuromuscular Center/S90
9500 Euclid Avenue
Cleveland, OH 44195
Tel: 216 444-8370   *Fax:* 216 445-4653
E-mail: levink@ccf.org
Length: 1 Yr   *ACGME Approved/Offered Positions:* 3
Program ID: 183-38-13-003

University Hospitals Case Medical Center Program
Sponsor: University Hospitals Case Medical Center
Prgm Director: Bashar Katirji, MD
11100 Euclid Avenue
Bolwell 2700
Cleveland, OH 44106
Tel: 216 844-4854   *Fax:* 216 844-7624
E-mail: bashar.Katirji@uhhospitals.org
Length: 1 Yr   *ACGME Approved/Offered Positions:* 2
Program ID: 183-38-21-010

Columbus

Ohio State University Hospital Program
Sponsor: Ohio State University Hospital
Nationwide Children's Hospital
Prgm Director: John T Kissel, MD
Department of Neurology, Room 461
Means Hall, 1654 Upham Drive
Columbus, OH 43210
Tel: 614 293-4981   *Fax:* 614 293-6111
Length: 1 Yr   *ACGME Approved/Offered Positions:* 1
Program ID: 183-38-13-015

Pennsylvania

Hershey

Penn State University/Milton S Hershey Medical Center Program
Sponsor: Milton S Hershey Medical Center
Prgm Director: Kevin Scott, MD*
30 Hope Drive, MC EC037
Hershey, PA 17033
Tel: 717 531-1377   *Fax:* 717 531-0384
Length: 1 Yr   *ACGME Approved/Offered Positions:* 1
Program ID: 183-41-12-009

Puerto Rico

San Juan

University of Puerto Rico Program
Sponsor: University of Puerto Rico School of Medicine
University Hospital
Prgm Director: Carlos A Luciano, MD
Medical Sciences Campus, Neurology Section
PO Box 365067
San Juan, PR 00936
Tel: 787 754-0101   *Fax:* 787 751-3911
E-mail: cluciano@rcm.upr.edu
Length: 1 Yr   *ACGME Approved/Offered Positions:* 1
Program ID: 183-42-12-013

Texas

Dallas

University of Texas Southwestern Medical School Program
Sponsor: University of Texas Southwestern Medical School
Children's Medical Center of Dallas
Prgm Director: Gil I Wolfe, MD
5323 Harry Hines Boulevard
Dallas, TX 75390
Tel: 214 648-9518   *Fax:* 214 648-9311
Length: 1 Yr   *ACGME Approved/Offered Positions:* 2
Program ID: 183-48-12-001

Vermont

Burlington

University of Vermont Program
Sponsor: Fletcher Allen Health Care
Prgm Director: Rup Tandan, MBBS
Neurology Department
89 Beaumont Avenue, Given C225
Burlington, VT 05405
Tel: 802 656-4588   *Fax:* 802 656-5678
E-mail: Rup.Tandan@uvm.edu
Length: 1 Yr   *ACGME Approved/Offered Positions:* 1
Program ID: 183-50-13-011

Neuropathology (Pathology)

Alabama

Birmingham

University of Alabama Medical Center Program
Sponsor: University of Alabama Hospital
Prgm Director: Cheryl A Palmer, MD
619 19th Street South
PD6A Suite 175
Birmingham, AL 35294
Tel: 205 934-2164   *Fax:* 205 975-7548
E-mail: capalmer@uab.edu
Length: 2 Yrs   *ACGME Approved/Offered Positions:* 2
Program ID: 315-01-21-061

Arizona

Phoenix

St Joseph's Hospital and Medical Center Program
Sponsor: St Joseph's Hospital and Medical Center
Maricopa County Forensic Science Center
Prgm Director: Stephen W Coons, MD
350 West Thomas Road
Phoenix, AZ 85013
Tel: 602 406-7088
E-mail: stephen.coons@chw.edu
Length: 2 Yrs   *ACGME Approved/Offered Positions:* 1
Program ID: 315-03-12-096

California

Los Angeles

UCLA Medical Center Program
Sponsor: UCLA David Geffen School of Medicine/UCLA Medical Center
UCLA Medical Center
Prgm Director: Harry V Vinters, MD
10833 Le Conte Avenue, Rm 18-170 CHS
Los Angeles, CA 90095
Tel: 310 825-6191   *Fax:* 310 206-8290
E-mail: hvinters@mednet.ucla.edu
Length: 2 Yrs   *ACGME Approved/Offered Positions:* 2
Program ID: 315-05-21-068

University of Southern California/LAC+USC Medical Center Program
Sponsor: University of Southern California/LAC+USC Medical Center
LAC+USC Medical Center
Prgm Director: Carol A Miller, MD
1200 North State Street
Los Angeles, CA 90033
Tel: 323 226-7123   *Fax:* 323 226-7487
Length: 2 Yrs   *ACGME Approved/Offered Positions:* 2
Program ID: 315-05-11-003

San Diego

University of California (San Diego) Program
Sponsor: University of California (San Diego) Medical Center
Veterans Affairs Medical Center (San Diego)
Prgm Director: Henry C Powell, MD, ScD
200 W Arbor Drive, Mail Code 8320
San Diego, CA 92103
Tel: 619 543-5966   *Fax:* 619 543-3730
E-mail: mmwahl@ucsd.edu
Length: 2 Yrs   *ACGME Approved/Offered Positions:* 2
Program ID: 315-05-21-005

San Francisco

University of California (San Francisco) Program
Sponsor: University of California (San Francisco) School of Medicine
UCSF and Mount Zion Medical Centers
Prgm Director: Andrew W Bollen, MD, DVM
505 Parnassus Avenue, Rm M-551
San Francisco, CA 94143
Tel: 415 476-5236   *Fax:* 415 476-7963
E-mail: joseph.coloff@ucsfmedctr.org
Length: 2 Yrs   *ACGME Approved/Offered Positions:* 2
Program ID: 315-05-21-006

Stanford

Stanford University Program
Sponsor: Stanford Hospital and Clinics
Prgm Director: Hannes Vogel, MD
Department of Pathology, Room R-241
300 Pasteur Drive
Stanford, CA 94305
Tel: 650 723-6041   *Fax:* 650 498-5394
E-mail: hvogel@stanford.edu
Length: 2 Yrs   *ACGME Approved/Offered Positions:* 2
Program ID: 315-05-21-007

District of Columbia

Washington

Armed Forces Institute of Pathology Program
Sponsor: Armed Forces Institute of Pathology
Prgm Director: Elizabeth J Rushing, MD
6825 16th Street NW
Washington, DC 20306
Tel: 202 782-1620   *Fax:* 202 782-4099
Length: 2 Yrs   *ACGME Approved/Offered Positions:* 4
Program ID: 315-10-12-001
Uniformed Services Program

Florida

Gainesville

University of Florida Program
Sponsor: University of Florida College of Medicine
North Florida/South Georgia Veterans Health System
Shands Hospital at the University of Florida
Prgm Director: Anthony T Yachnis, MD, MS*
1600 SW Archer Road
Box 100275
Gainesville, FL 32610
Tel: 352 265-0238   *Fax:* 352 265-0437
Length: 2 Yrs   *ACGME Approved/Offered Positions:* 1
Program ID: 315-11-21-010

Note: * indicates a newly appointed program director

Georgia

Atlanta

Emory University Program

Sponsor: Emory University School of Medicine
Emory University Hospital
Prgm Director: Daniel J Brat, MD, PhD
Department of Pathology
1364 Clifton Road, NE
Atlanta, GA 30322
Tel: 404 712-4278   *Fax:* 404 727-2519
E-mail: dbrat@emory.edu
Length: 2 Yrs   *ACGME Approved/Offered Positions:* 2
Program ID: 315-12-21-012

Illinois

Chicago

McGaw Medical Center of Northwestern University Program

Sponsor: McGaw Medical Center of Northwestern
    University
Cook County Medical Examiner's Office
Northwestern Memorial Hospital
Prgm Director: Eileen H Bigio, MD
Department of Pathology
303 East Chicago Avenue
Chicago, IL 60611
Tel: 312 926-9543   *Fax:* 312 926-9830
Length: 2 Yrs   *ACGME Approved/Offered Positions:* 1
Program ID: 315-16-21-097

Indiana

Indianapolis

Indiana University School of Medicine Program

Sponsor: Indiana University School of Medicine
Clarian Pathology Laboratory
Prgm Director: Jose Bonnin, MD
350 W 11th Street
Indianapolis, IN 46202
Tel: 317 491-6362   *Fax:* 317 491-6419
E-mail: jbonnin@clarian.org
Length: 2 Yrs   *ACGME Approved/Offered Positions:* 2
Program ID: 315-17-31-092

Maryland

Baltimore

Johns Hopkins University Program

Sponsor: Johns Hopkins University School of Medicine
Johns Hopkins Hospital
Prgm Director: Juan C Troncoso, MD
720 Rutland Avenue
558 Ross Research Building
Baltimore, MD 21205
Tel: 410 955-5632   *Fax:* 410 955-9777
E-mail: kwall2@jhmi.edu
Length: 2 Yrs   *ACGME Approved/Offered Positions:* 4
Program ID: 315-23-11-020

Massachusetts

Boston

Brigham and Women's Hospital Program

Sponsor: Brigham and Women's Hospital
Children's Hospital
Prgm Director: Umberto De Girolami, MD
75 Francis Street
Boston, MA 02115
Tel: 617 732-7532   *Fax:* 617 975-0944
E-mail: udegirolami@partners.org
Length: 2 Yrs   *ACGME Approved/Offered Positions:* 4
Program ID: 315-24-12-024

Massachusetts General Hospital Program

Sponsor: Massachusetts General Hospital
Prgm Director: Matthew P Frosch, MD
55 Fruit Street
Boston, MA 02114
Tel: 617 726-5156   *Fax:* 617 724-1813
Length: 2 Yrs   *ACGME Approved/Offered Positions:* 3
Program ID: 315-24-21-062

Minnesota

Rochester

College of Medicine, Mayo Clinic (Rochester) Program

Sponsor: College of Medicine, Mayo Clinic
Mayo Clinic (Rochester)
Prgm Director: Joseph E Parisi, MD
Neuropathology Fellowship Program
200 First Street, SW
Rochester, MN 55905
Tel: 507 538-6453   *Fax:* 507 538-3267
E-mail: pathologyeducation@mayo.edu
Length: 2 Yrs   *ACGME Approved/Offered Positions:* 2
Program ID: 315-26-21-081

Missouri

St Louis

Washington University/B-JH/SLCH Consortium Program

Sponsor: Washington University/B-JH/SLCH Consortium
Barnes-Jewish Hospital
Prgm Director: Robert E Schmidt, MD, PhD
660 South Euclid Ave, Box 8118
St Louis, MO 63110
Tel: 314 362-7429   *Fax:* 314 362-7765
E-mail: reschmidt@wustl.edu
Length: 2 Yrs   *ACGME Approved/Offered Positions:* 2
Program ID: 315-28-11-026

New York

Bronx

Albert Einstein College of Medicine Program

Sponsor: Albert Einstein College of Medicine of Yeshiva
    University
Montefiore Medical Center-Henry and Lucy Moses
    Division
Prgm Director: Karen Weidenheim, MD
111 East 210th Street
Bronx, NY 10467
Tel: 718 920-4446
Length: 2 Yrs   *ACGME Approved/Offered Positions:* 2
Program ID: 315-35-21-028

Brooklyn

SUNY Health Science Center at Brooklyn Program

Sponsor: SUNY Health Science Center at Brooklyn
Kings County Hospital Center
University Hospital-SUNY Health Science Center at
    Brooklyn
Prgm Director: Chandrakant Rao, MD
450 Clarkson Ave, Box 25
Brooklyn, NY 11203
Tel: 718 245-5320   *Fax:* 718 771-1632
E-mail: Chandrakant.Rao@downstate.edu
Length: 2 Yrs   *ACGME Approved/Offered Positions:* 1
Program ID: 315-35-21-032

New York

Mount Sinai School of Medicine Program

Sponsor: Mount Sinai School of Medicine
Mount Sinai Medical Center
Prgm Director: Daniel P Perl, MD
One Gustave L Levy Place
Box 1134
New York, NY 10029
Tel: 212 241-7371   *Fax:* 212 996-1343
Length: 2 Yrs   *ACGME Approved/Offered Positions:* 2
Program ID: 315-35-31-086

New York Presbyterian Hospital (Columbia Campus) Program

Sponsor: New York Presbyterian Hospital
New York Presbyterian Hospital (Columbia Campus)
Prgm Director: James E Goldman, MD, PhD
630 West 168th Street
PH 15, STEM Rm 124
New York, NY 10032
Tel: 212 305-4531   *Fax:* 212 305-4548
Length: 2 Yrs   *ACGME Approved/Offered Positions:* 2
Program ID: 315-35-21-029

New York University School of Medicine Program

Sponsor: New York University School of Medicine
Bellevue Hospital Center
Prgm Director: Thomas Wisniewski, MD
550 First Avenue (NB 4N30)
New York, NY 10016
Tel: 212 263-2152   *Fax:* 212 263-7528
E-mail: thomas.wisniewski@med.nyu.edu
Length: 2 Yrs   *ACGME Approved/Offered Positions:* 2
Program ID: 315-35-21-031

North Carolina

Chapel Hill

University of North Carolina Hospitals Program

Sponsor: University of North Carolina Hospitals
Prgm Director: Thomas W Bouldin, MD
Department of Pathology
CB 7525, Brinkhous-Bullitt Bldg
Chapel Hill, NC 27514
Tel: 919 843-1074   *Fax:* 919 966-6718
E-mail: tbouldin@med.unc.edu
Length: 2 Yrs   *ACGME Approved/Offered Positions:* 1
Program ID: 315-36-21-060

Durham

Duke University Hospital Program

Sponsor: Duke University Hospital
Prgm Director: Roger E McLendon, MD
Box 3712, M216 Davison Bldg
Durham, NC 27710
Tel: 919 684-6940   *Fax:* 919 681-7634
Length: 2 Yrs   *ACGME Approved/Offered Positions:* 2
Program ID: 315-36-11-035

Programs

Oregon

Portland

Oregon Health & Science University Program

Sponsor: Oregon Health & Science University Hospital
Prgm Director: Marjorie R Grafe, MD, PhD
Department of Pathology, L113
3181 SW Sam Jackson Park Road
Portland, OR 97239
Tel: 503 494-2321   *Fax:* 503 494-2025
E-mail: pathrap@ohsu.edu
Length: 2 Yrs   *ACGME Approved/Offered Positions:* 2
Program ID: 315-40-13-094

Pennsylvania

Philadelphia

University of Pennsylvania Program

Sponsor: University of Pennsylvania Health System
Prgm Director: Zissimos Mourelatos, MD
613 Stellar-Chance Laboratories
422 Curie Blvd
Philadelphia, PA 19104
Tel: 215 746-0014   *Fax:* 215 898-9969
Length: 2 Yrs   *ACGME Approved/Offered Positions:* 3
Program ID: 315-41-21-041

Pittsburgh

University of Pittsburgh Medical Center Medical Education Program

Sponsor: Univ of Pittsburgh Medical Center Medical
  Education
Children's Hospital of Pittsburgh of UPMC
UPMC Presbyterian Shadyside
Prgm Director: Clayton A Wiley, MD, PhD
200 Lothrop Street, Room A506
Pittsburgh, PA 15213
Tel: 412 647-0765   *Fax:* 412 647-5602
E-mail: wileyca@upmc.edu
Length: 2 Yrs   *ACGME Approved/Offered Positions:* 4
Program ID: 315-41-21-042

Rhode Island

Providence

Brown University Program

Sponsor: Rhode Island Hospital-Lifespan
Prgm Director: Edward G Stopa, MD
593 Eddy Street
Providence, RI 02903
Tel: 401 444-5155   *Fax:* 401 444-8514
E-mail: estopa@lifespan.org
Length: 2 Yrs   *ACGME Approved/Offered Positions:* 2
Program ID: 315-43-21-043

Tennessee

Nashville

Vanderbilt University Program

Sponsor: Vanderbilt University Medical Center
Prgm Director: Mark Becher, MD
Dept of Pathology, C-2318 MCN
21st Avenue, South
Nashville, TN 37232
Tel: 615 322-3998   *Fax:* 615 343-7089
Length: 2 Yrs   *ACGME Approved/Offered Positions:* 2
Program ID: 315-47-21-073

Texas

Dallas

University of Texas Southwestern Medical School Program

Sponsor: University of Texas Southwestern Medical
  School
Dallas County Hospital District-Parkland Memorial
  Hospital
University Hospitals Zale Lipshy
Prgm Director: Charles L White III, MD
5323 Harry Hines Boulevard
Dallas, TX 75390
Tel: 214 648-2148   *Fax:* 214 648-6325
E-mail: charles.white@utsouthwestern.edu
Length: 2 Yrs   *ACGME Approved/Offered Positions:* 3
Program ID: 315-48-21-083

Houston

Baylor College of Medicine Program

Sponsor: Baylor College of Medicine
Harris County Hospital District-Ben Taub General
  Hospital
Methodist Hospital (Houston)
Texas Children's Hospital
University of Texas M D Anderson Cancer Center
Prgm Director: Jerry C Goodman, MD*
One Baylor Plaza
Houston, TX 77030
Tel: 713 798-7234   *Fax:* 713 798-5838
Length: 2 Yrs   *ACGME Approved/Offered Positions:* 3
Program ID: 315-48-21-047

Methodist Hospital (Houston) Program

Sponsor: Methodist Hospital (Houston)
Memorial Hermann Hospital
Texas Children's Hospital
University of Texas M D Anderson Cancer Center
Prgm Director: Suzanne Z Powell, MD
6565 Fannin St, M227
Houston, TX 77030
Tel: 713 441-6486   *Fax:* 713 793-1603
E-mail: ljozwiak@tmhs.org
Length: 2 Yrs   *ACGME Approved/Offered Positions:* 2
Program ID: 315-48-22-095

Virginia

Charlottesville

University of Virginia Program

Sponsor: University of Virginia Medical Center
Prgm Director: M Beatriz S Lopes, MD
1215 Lee Street, Hosp Expansion
3rd Floor, Room 3025
Charlottesville, VA 22908
Tel: 434 924-9175   *Fax:* 434 924-9177
E-mail: bun4n@virginia.edu
Length: 2 Yrs   *ACGME Approved/Offered Positions:* 2
Program ID: 315-51-21-063

Richmond

Virginia Commonwealth University Health System Program

Sponsor: Virginia Commonwealth University Health
  System
Medical College of Virginia Hospitals
Prgm Director: Christine E Fuller, MD*
PO Box 980017
Richmond, VA 23298
Tel: 804 628-1293   *Fax:* 804 828-2869
Length: 2 Yrs   *ACGME Approved/Offered Positions:* 1
Program ID: 315-51-11-051

Washington

Seattle

University of Washington Program

Sponsor: University of Washington School of Medicine
Harborview Medical Center
University of Washington Medical Center
Prgm Director: Thomas J Montine, MD, PhD
Neuropathology, Box 359791
325 Ninth Avenue
Seattle, WA 98195
Tel: 206 744-3145   *Fax:* 206 744-8240
E-mail: residency@pathology.washington.edu
Length: 2 Yrs   *ACGME Approved/Offered Positions:* 2
Program ID: 315-54-11-052

Note: * indicates a newly appointed program director

Neuroradiology (Radiology-Diagnostic)

Alabama

Birmingham

University of Alabama Medical Center Program
Sponsor: University of Alabama Hospital
Prgm Director: Glenn H Roberson, MD
UAB Department of Radiology
619 South 19th Street
Birmingham, AL 35249
Tel: 205 934-3920   *Fax:* 205 975-9262
E-mail: groberson@uabmc.edu
Length: 1 Yr   *ACGME Approved/Offered Positions:* 4
Program ID: 423-01-21-001

Arizona

Phoenix

St Joseph's Hospital and Medical Center Program
Sponsor: St Joseph's Hospital and Medical Center
Prgm Director: Roger Bird, MD
St Joseph's Hospital & Medical Center
350 West Thomas Road
Phoenix, AZ 85013
Tel: 602 406-7783   *Fax:* 602 406-4550
E-mail: rbird@sniweb.net
Length: 1 Yr   *ACGME Approved/Offered Positions:* 8
Program ID: 423-03-21-002

Tucson

University of Arizona Program
Sponsor: University of Arizona College of Medicine
University Medical Center
Prgm Director: Joachim F Seeger, MD
PO Box 24-5067
1501 N Campbell Avenue
Tucson, AZ 85724
Tel: 520 626-7368   *Fax:* 520 626-1945
Length: 1 Yr   *ACGME Approved/Offered Positions:* 2
Program ID: 423-03-21-023

Arkansas

Little Rock

University of Arkansas for Medical Sciences Program
Sponsor: University of Arkansas College of Medicine
Central Arkansas Veterans Healthcare System
UAMS Medical Center
Prgm Director: Edgardo J Angtuaco, MD
4301 W Markham, Slot 556
Little Rock, AR 72205
Tel: 501 686-6932   *Fax:* 501 686-8932
E-mail: angtuacoedgardoj@uams.edu
Length: 1 Yr   *ACGME Approved/Offered Positions:* 2
Program ID: 423-04-21-043

California

Loma Linda

Loma Linda University Program
Sponsor: Loma Linda University Medical Center
Prgm Director: George Y Luh, MD
Neuroradiology B-623
11234 Anderson Street
Loma Linda, CA 92354
Tel: 909 558-7814   *Fax:* 909 558-0202
E-mail: pthomas@llu.edu
Length: 1 Yr   *ACGME Approved/Offered Positions:* 1
Program ID: 423-05-21-085

Los Angeles

Cedars-Sinai Medical Center Program
Sponsor: Cedars-Sinai Medical Center
Prgm Director: Franklin G Moser, MD
Imaging Housestaff Office
8700 Beverly Blvd, Taper Bldg, M335
Los Angeles, CA 90048
Tel: 310 423-4454   *Fax:* 310 423-8335
E-mail: imaging.housestaff@cshs.org
Length: 1 Yr   *ACGME Approved/Offered Positions:* 1
Program ID: 423-05-21-098

UCLA Medical Center Program
Sponsor: UCLA David Geffen School of Medicine/UCLA
  Medical Center
UCLA Medical Center
VA Greater Los Angeles Healthcare System
Prgm Director: J Pablo Villablanca, MD
10833 Le Conte Ave BL-428 CHS
Los Angeles, CA 90095
Tel: 310 206-1004   *Fax:* 310 206-5958
Length: 1 Yr   *ACGME Approved/Offered Positions:* 4
Program ID: 423-05-21-081

**University of Southern California/
LAC+USC Medical Center Program**
Sponsor: University of Southern California/LAC+USC
  Medical Center
LAC+USC Medical Center
USC University Hospital
Prgm Director: Chi-Shing Zee, MD
1200 N State Street
Room 3740A
Los Angeles, CA 90033
Tel: 323 226-7425   *Fax:* 323 226-4059
Length: 1 Yr   *ACGME Approved/Offered Positions:* 5
Program ID: 423-05-21-024

Sacramento

University of California (Davis) Health System Program
Sponsor: University of California (Davis) Health System
University of California (Davis) Medical Center
Prgm Director: Matthew Bobinski, MD, PhD*
Department of Radiology
4860 Y Street, Suite 3100
Sacramento, CA 95817
Tel: 916 734-6533   *Fax:* 916 734-6548
E-mail: matthew.bobinski@ucdmc.ucdavis.edu
Length: 1 Yr   *ACGME Approved/Offered Positions:* 3
Program ID: 423-05-13-104

San Diego

University of California (San Diego) Program
Sponsor: University of California (San Diego) Medical
  Center
Veterans Affairs Medical Center (San Diego)
Prgm Director: John R Hesselink, MD
200 West Arbor Drive
San Diego, CA 92103
Tel: 619 543-6766   *Fax:* 619 471-0544
Length: 1 Yr   *ACGME Approved/Offered Positions:* 2
Program ID: 423-05-21-074

San Francisco

University of California (San Francisco) Program
Sponsor: University of California (San Francisco) School
  of Medicine
UCSF and Mount Zion Medical Centers
Veterans Affairs Medical Center (San Francisco)
Prgm Director: William P Dillon Jr, MD
505 Parnassus Avenue, Ste L-358
San Francisco, CA 94143
Tel: 415 353-1668   *Fax:* 415 353-8593
Length: 1 Yr   *ACGME Approved/Offered Positions:* 7
Program ID: 423-05-21-044

Stanford

Stanford University Program
Sponsor: Stanford Hospital and Clinics
Prgm Director: Huy Do, MD
300 Pasteur Dr
Room S-047
Stanford, CA 94305
Tel: 650 723-7426   *Fax:* 650 498-5374
E-mail: kari.guy@stanford.edu
Length: 1 Yr   *ACGME Approved/Offered Positions:* 5
Program ID: 423-05-21-075

Torrance

Los Angeles County-Harbor-UCLA Medical Center Program
Sponsor: Los Angeles County-Harbor-UCLA Medical
  Center
Prgm Director: C Mark Mehringer, MD
1000 W Carson Street
Torrance, CA 90509
Tel: 310 222-2808   *Fax:* 310 618-9500
E-mail: phamm@labiomed.org
Length: 1 Yr   *ACGME Approved/Offered Positions:* 1
Program ID: 423-05-21-003

Colorado

Aurora

University of Colorado Denver Program
Sponsor: University of Colorado Denver School of
  Medicine
Children's Hospital (The)
University of Colorado Hospital
Prgm Director: Robert J Bert, MD, PhD
12401 E 17th Avenue, 5th floor, Room 516
Mail Stop F726, PO Box 6511
Aurora, CO 80045
Tel: 720 848-6617   *Fax:* 720 848-7315
Length: 1 Yr   *ACGME Approved/Offered Positions:* 2
Program ID: 423-07-21-084

Connecticut

New Haven

Yale-New Haven Medical Center Program

Sponsor: Yale-New Haven Hospital
Veterans Affairs Medical Center (West Haven)
Prgm Director: James J Abrahams, MD
333 Cedar Street
PO Box 208042
New Haven, CT 06520
Tel: 203 785-5102   *Fax:* 203 737-1241
Length: 1 Yr   *ACGME Approved/Offered Positions:* 8
Program ID: 423-08-21-025

District of Columbia

Washington

George Washington University Program

Sponsor: George Washington University School of
  Medicine
Clinical Center at the National Institutes of Health
George Washington University Hospital (UHS)
Prgm Director: Lucien M Levy, MD, PhD
Department of Radiology
900 23rd Street, NW
Washington, DC 20037
Tel: 202 715-5193   *Fax:* 202 715-5161
Length: 1 Yr   *ACGME Approved/Offered Positions:* 3
Program ID: 423-10-21-045

Georgetown University Hospital Program

Sponsor: Georgetown University Hospital
Prgm Director: Frank Berkowitz, MD
3800 Reservoir Road NW
Washington, DC 20007
Tel: 202 444-1679   *Fax:* 202 444-1804
E-mail: villaros@gunet.georgetown.edu
Length: 1 Yr   *ACGME Approved/Offered Positions:* 2
Program ID: 423-10-21-026

Florida

Gainesville

University of Florida Program

Sponsor: University of Florida College of Medicine
Shands Hospital at the University of Florida
Prgm Director: Jeffrey A Bennett, MD
Department of Radiology - Neuroradiology
PO Box 100374
Gainesville, FL 32610
Tel: 352 265-0291   *Fax:* 352 265-0279
E-mail: bennja@radiology.ufl.edu
Length: 1 Yr   *ACGME Approved/Offered Positions:* 3
Program ID: 423-11-21-046

Miami

Jackson Memorial Hospital/Jackson Health System Program

Sponsor: Jackson Memorial Hospital/Jackson Health
  System
University of Miami Hospital and Clinics
Prgm Director: Evelyn M Sklar, MD*
1611 NW 12th Avenue, WW279
Department of Radiology
Miami, FL 33136
Tel: 305 585-7500   *Fax:* 305 325-8591
E-mail: esklar@med.miami.edu
Length: 1 Yr   *ACGME Approved/Offered Positions:* 5
Program ID: 423-11-21-076

Georgia

Atlanta

Emory University Program

Sponsor: Emory University School of Medicine
Children's Healthcare of Atlanta at Egleston
Emory University Hospital
Grady Health System
Prgm Director: Patricia A Hudgins, MD
Department of Radiology/B-115
1364 Clifton Road, NE
Atlanta, GA 30322
Tel: 404 712-4583   *Fax:* 404 712-7957
E-mail: pataricia.hudgins@emoryhealthcare.org
Length: 1 Yr   *ACGME Approved/Offered Positions:* 7
Program ID: 423-12-21-005

Augusta

Medical College of Georgia Program

Sponsor: Medical College of Georgia
Prgm Director: Ramon E Figueroa, MD
1120 15th Street, BA 1411
Augusta, GA 30912
Tel: 706 721-3214   *Fax:* 706 721-5213
Length: 1 Yr   *ACGME Approved/Offered Positions:* 2
Program ID: 423-12-21-006

Illinois

Chicago

McGaw Medical Center of Northwestern University Program

Sponsor: McGaw Medical Center of Northwestern
  University
Children's Memorial Hospital
Northwestern Memorial Hospital
Prgm Director: Eric J Russell, MD, FACR
Department of Radiology
676 N Saint Clair St, Suite 800
Chicago, IL 60611
Tel: 312 695-1292   *Fax:* 312 695-4108
Length: 1 Yr   *ACGME Approved/Offered Positions:* 6
Program ID: 423-16-21-072

Rush University Medical Center Program

Sponsor: Rush University Medical Center
Prgm Director: Sharon E Byrd, MD
1653 W Congress Parkway
Chicago, IL 60612
Tel: 312 942-5781   *Fax:* 312 942-7244
Length: 1 Yr   *ACGME Approved/Offered Positions:* 3
Program ID: 423-16-21-008

University of Chicago Program

Sponsor: University of Chicago Medical Center
Prgm Director: Delilah Burrowes, MD*
Department of Radiology
5841 S Maryland Avenue
Chicago, IL 60637
Tel: 773 702-3550
E-mail: dburrowes@radiology.bsd.uchicago.edu
Length: 1 Yr   *ACGME Approved/Offered Positions:* 2
Program ID: 423-16-21-009

Peoria

University of Illinois College of Medicine at Peoria Program

Sponsor: University of Illinois College of Medicine at
  Peoria
OSF St Francis Medical Center
Prgm Director: Michael T Zagardo, MD
530 NE Glen Oak Avenue
Peoria, IL 61637
Tel: 309 624-3355   *Fax:* 309 655-7365
E-mail: marciao@uic.edu
Length: 1 Yr   *ACGME Approved/Offered Positions:* 1
Program ID: 423-16-21-095

Indiana

Indianapolis

Indiana University School of Medicine Program

Sponsor: Indiana University School of Medicine
Clarian Indiana University Hospital
Clarian Riley Hospital for Children
Richard L Roudebush Veterans Affairs Medical Center
William N Wishard Memorial Hospital
Prgm Director: Chang Y Ho, MD*
Department of Radiology, Room 0615
550 North University Boulevard
Indianapolis, IN 46202
Tel: 317 278-5855   *Fax:* 317 274-4135
Length: 1 Yr   *ACGME Approved/Offered Positions:* 4
Program ID: 423-17-21-028

Iowa

Iowa City

University of Iowa Hospitals and Clinics Program

Sponsor: University of Iowa Hospitals and Clinics
Prgm Director: Wendy R Smoker, MD
3893 JPP
200 Hawkins Drive
Iowa City, IA 52242
Tel: 319 356-1798   *Fax:* 319 353-6275
E-mail: wendy-smoker@uiowa.edu
Length: 1 Yr   *ACGME Approved/Offered Positions:* 4
Program ID: 423-18-21-011

Maryland

Baltimore

Johns Hopkins University Program

Sponsor: Johns Hopkins University School of Medicine
Johns Hopkins Hospital
Prgm Director: Nafi Aygun, MD
Phipps Basement B-112
600 N Wolfe Street
Baltimore, MD 21287
Tel: 410 614-3146   *Fax:* 410 955-0962
E-mail: naygun1@jhmi.edu
Length: 1 Yr   *ACGME Approved/Offered Positions:* 7
Program ID: 423-23-21-078

University of Maryland Program

Sponsor: University of Maryland Medical System
Prgm Director: Gregg H Zoarski, MD
Diagnostic Radiology Department
22 S Greene Street
Baltimore, MD 21201
Tel: 410 328-5112   *Fax:* 410 328-3168
E-mail: gzoarski@umm.edu
Length: 1 Yr   *ACGME Approved/Offered Positions:* 4
Program ID: 423-23-21-029

Note: * indicates a newly appointed program director

Massachusetts

Boston

Beth Israel Deaconess Medical Center Program A
Sponsor: Beth Israel Deaconess Medical Center
Tufts Medical Center
Prgm Director: Rafeeque Bhadelia, MD
330 Brookline Ave
WCCB-90
Boston, MA 02215
Tel: 617 754-2038   *Fax:* 617 754-2004
E-mail: rbhadeli@bidmc.harvard.edu
Length: 1 Yr   *ACGME Approved/Offered Positions:* 4
Program ID: 423-24-21-073

Boston University Medical Center Program
Sponsor: Boston Medical Center
Prgm Director: Glenn Barest, MD
Department of Radiology
88 East Newton Street
Boston, MA 02118
Tel: 617 638-6610   *Fax:* 617 638-6616
Length: 1 Yr   *ACGME Approved/Offered Positions:* 1
Program ID: 423-24-21-091

Brigham and Women's Hospital/Harvard Medical School Program
Sponsor: Brigham and Women's Hospital
Children's Hospital
Prgm Director: Liangge Hsu, MD
75 Francis Street
ASB1, L1, room 015
Boston, MA 02115
Tel: 617 732-7260   *Fax:* 617 264-5151
Length: 1 Yr   *ACGME Approved/Offered Positions:* 4
Program ID: 423-24-21-065

Massachusetts General Hospital/Harvard Medical School Program
Sponsor: Massachusetts General Hospital
Prgm Director: Pamela W Schaefer, MD
Gray 2 - B 273A
55 Fruit Street
Boston, MA 02114
Tel: 617 726-8320   *Fax:* 617 724-3338
E-mail: chynes@partners.org
Length: 1 Yr   *ACGME Approved/Offered Positions:* 10
Program ID: 423-24-21-047

Worcester

University of Massachusetts Program
Sponsor: University of Massachusetts Medical School
Central Massachusetts Magnetic Imaging Center, Inc
UMass Memorial Health Care (Memorial Campus)
UMass Memorial Health Care (University Campus)
Prgm Director: Deepak Takhtani, MD
55 Lake Avenue North
Worcester, MA 01655
Tel: 508 856-5740   *Fax:* 508 856-1860
E-mail: boisvern@ummhc.org
Length: 1 Yr   *ACGME Approved/Offered Positions:* 2
Program ID: 423-24-21-048

Michigan

Ann Arbor

University of Michigan Program
Sponsor: University of Michigan Hospitals and Health
  Centers
Prgm Director: Ellen Hoeffner, MD
Dept of Radiology, Room UH-B2 A209
1500 E Medical Center Drive
Ann Arbor, MI 48109
Tel: 734 615-8314   *Fax:* 734 764-2412
Length: 1 Yr   *ACGME Approved/Offered Positions:* 4
Program ID: 423-25-21-012

Detroit

Henry Ford Hospital Program
Sponsor: Henry Ford Hospital
Prgm Director: Suresh C Patel, MD
Department of Diagnostic Radiology
2799 West Grand Boulevard, E-328
Detroit, MI 48202
Tel: 313 916-7952   *Fax:* 313 916-8857
Length: 1 Yr   *ACGME Approved/Offered Positions:* 2
Program ID: 423-25-21-067

Wayne State University/Detroit Medical Center Program
Sponsor: Wayne State University/Detroit Medical Center
Children's Hospital of Michigan
Harper-Hutzel Hospital
Prgm Director: Imad Zak, MD
Detroit Medical Center - Wayne State University
3990 John R Street
Detroit, MI 48201
Tel: 313 745-3433   *Fax:* 313 577-8600
E-mail: izak@med.wayne.edu
Length: 1 Yr   *ACGME Approved/Offered Positions:* 2
Program ID: 423-25-21-066

Royal Oak

William Beaumont Hospital Program
Sponsor: William Beaumont Hospital
Prgm Director: Richard Silbergleit, MD, MBA
Department of Radiology
3601 W 13 Mile Road
Royal Oak, MI 48073
Tel: 248 898-0648   *Fax:* 248 898-4063
E-mail: josephine.kulick@beaumont.edu
Length: 1 Yr   *ACGME Approved/Offered Positions:* 3
Program ID: 423-25-21-050

Minnesota

Minneapolis

University of Minnesota Program
Sponsor: University of Minnesota Medical School
Hennepin County Medical Center
University of Minnesota Medical Center, Division of
  Fairview
Prgm Director: Stephen A Kieffer, MD
Dept of Radiology
420 Delaware St SE, MMC 292
Minneapolis, MN 55455
Tel: 612 626-4471   *Fax:* 612 626-8844
E-mail: kieff012@umn.edu
Length: 1 Yr   *ACGME Approved/Offered Positions:* 4
Program ID: 423-26-21-090

Rochester

College of Medicine, Mayo Clinic (Rochester) Program
Sponsor: College of Medicine, Mayo Clinic
Mayo Clinic (Rochester)
Rochester Methodist Hospital
Saint Marys Hospital of Rochester
Prgm Director: E Paul Lindell, MD*
200 First Street, SW
Rochester, MN 55905
Tel: 507 284-0440   *Fax:* 507 293-3980
E-mail: sorensonl.tammy@mayo.edu
Length: 1 Yr   *ACGME Approved/Offered Positions:* 5
Program ID: 423-26-21-013

Missouri

Columbia

University of Missouri-Columbia Program
Sponsor: University of Missouri-Columbia School of
  Medicine
University Hospitals and Clinics
Prgm Director: Dale F Vaslow, MD, PhD
Department of Radiology DC 069.10
One Hospital Drive
Columbia, MO 65212
Tel: 573 882-1026   *Fax:* 573 884-9976
E-mail: CrookJ@health.missouri.edu
Length: 1 Yr   *ACGME Approved/Offered Positions:* 1
Program ID: 423-28-21-108

St Louis

Washington University/B-JH/SLCH Consortium Program
Sponsor: Washington University/B-JH/SLCH Consortium
Barnes-Jewish Hospital
Prgm Director: Katie Vo, MD
510 S Kingshighway Blvd
Campus Box 8131
St Louis, MO 63110
Tel: 314 362-5950   *Fax:* 314 362-4886
E-mail: vok@wustl.edu
Length: 1 Yr   *ACGME Approved/Offered Positions:* 9
Program ID: 423-28-21-079

New Hampshire

Lebanon

Dartmouth-Hitchcock Medical Center Program
Sponsor: Mary Hitchcock Memorial Hospital
Prgm Director: Clifford J Eskey, MD, PhD
Department of Radiology
Lebanon, NH 03756
Tel: 603 650-7480   *Fax:* 603 650-5455
E-mail: Clifford.J.Eskey@hitchcock.org
Length: 1 Yr   *ACGME Approved/Offered Positions:* 1
Program ID: 423-32-12-102

Programs

New Mexico

Albuquerque

University of New Mexico Program

Sponsor: University of New Mexico School of Medicine
University of New Mexico Hospital
Veterans Affairs Medical Center (Albuquerque)
Prgm Director: Blaine L Hart, MD
Department of Radiology
MSC10 5530
Albuquerque, NM 87131
Tel: 505 272-0932   *Fax:* 505 272-5821
Length: 1 Yr   *ACGME Approved/Offered Positions:* 2
Program ID: 423-34-21-049

New York

Bronx

Albert Einstein College of Medicine Program

Sponsor: Albert Einstein College of Medicine of Yeshiva
    University
Montefiore Medical Center-Henry and Lucy Moses
    Division
Prgm Director: Jacqueline A Bello, MD
Department of Radiology
111 E 210th Street
Bronx, NY 10467
Tel: 718 920-4030   *Fax:* 718 920-4854
Length: 1 Yr   *ACGME Approved/Offered Positions:* 2
Program ID: 423-35-21-051

Brooklyn

SUNY Health Science Center at Brooklyn Program

Sponsor: SUNY Health Science Center at Brooklyn
Kings County Hospital Center
University Hospital-SUNY Health Science Center at
    Brooklyn
Prgm Director: Jaya Nath, MD
Department of Radiology
450 Clarkson Avenue
Brooklyn, NY 11203
Tel: 718 270-1603   *Fax:* 718 270-2667
E-mail: jnath@downstate.edu
Length: 1 Yr   *ACGME Approved/Offered Positions:* 2
Program ID: 423-35-31-103

Great Neck

NSLIJHS-Albert Einstein College of Medicine at Long Island Jewish Medical Center Program

Sponsor: North Shore-Long Island Jewish Health System
Long Island Jewish Medical Center
Prgm Director: Craig E Warshall, MD
270-05 76th Avenue
New Hyde Park, NY 11042
Tel: 718 470-7178   *Fax:* 718 343-7463
E-mail: cwarshal@lij.edu
Length: 1 Yr   *ACGME Approved/Offered Positions:* 1
Program ID: 423-35-21-033

NSLIJHS-North Shore University Hospital/NYU School of Medicine Program

Sponsor: North Shore-Long Island Jewish Health System
North Shore University Hospital
Prgm Director: Karen S Black, MD
300 Community Drive
Manhasset, NY 11030
Tel: 516 562-4800   *Fax:* 516 562-4794
E-mail: carolmg@nshs.edu
Length: 1 Yr   *ACGME Approved/Offered Positions:* 1
Program ID: 423-35-21-015

New York

Albert Einstein College of Medicine at Beth Israel Medical Center Program

Sponsor: Beth Israel Medical Center
Prgm Director: Daniel Lefton, MD*
Roosevelt Hospital
1000 Tenth Avenue
New York, NY 10019
Tel: 212 636-3360   *Fax:* 212 523-7050
E-mail: dlefton@chpnet.org
Length: 1 Yr   *ACGME Approved/Offered Positions:* 2
Program ID: 423-35-21-030

Mount Sinai School of Medicine Program

Sponsor: Mount Sinai School of Medicine
Mount Sinai Medical Center
Prgm Director: Thomas P Naidich, MD
1 Gustave L Levy Place Box 1234
New York, NY 10029
Tel: 212 241-3423   *Fax:* 212 241-4234
Length: 1 Yr   *ACGME Approved/Offered Positions:* 6
Program ID: 423-35-21-034

New York Presbyterian Hospital (Columbia Campus) Program

Sponsor: New York Presbyterian Hospital
New York Presbyterian Hospital (Columbia Campus)
Prgm Director: Robert L DeLaPaz, MD
MHB 3-111 Neuro
177 Ft Washington Avenue
New York, NY 10032
Tel: 212 305-9820   *Fax:* 212 305-9785
Length: 1 Yr   *ACGME Approved/Offered Positions:* 3
Program ID: 423-35-21-068

New York Presbyterian Hospital (Cornell Campus) Program

Sponsor: New York Presbyterian Hospital
Memorial Sloan-Kettering Cancer Center
New York Presbyterian Hospital (Cornell Campus)
Prgm Director: Pina C Sanelli, MD
Box 141
525 E 68th Street
New York, NY 10021
Tel: 212 746-2577   *Fax:* 212 746-8597
Length: 1 Yr   *ACGME Approved/Offered Positions:* 5
Program ID: 423-35-21-052

New York University School of Medicine Program

Sponsor: New York University School of Medicine
Bellevue Hospital Center
Manhattan VA Harbor Health Care System
Prgm Director: Bidyut K Pramanik, MD
MRI Department
530 First Avenue
New York, NY 10016
Tel: 212 263-3567   *Fax:* 212 263-8186
E-mail: bidyut.pramanik@nyumc.org
Length: 1 Yr   *ACGME Approved/Offered Positions:* 5
Program ID: 423-35-21-016

Rochester

University of Rochester Program

Sponsor: Strong Memorial Hospital of the University of
    Rochester
Prgm Director: P L Westesson, MD, PhD
University of Rochester Medical Ctr
601 Elwood Avenue, Box 648
Rochester, NY 14642
Tel: 585 275-1839   *Fax:* 585 473-4861
E-mail: holly_stiner@urmc.rochester.edu
Length: 1 Yr   *ACGME Approved/Offered Positions:* 5
Program ID: 423-35-21-031

Syracuse

SUNY Upstate Medical University Program

Sponsor: SUNY Upstate Medical University
Prgm Director: Amar S Swarnkar, MD
750 E Adams Street
Syracuse, NY 13210
Tel: 315 464-7434   *Fax:* 315 464-2570
Length: 1 Yr   *ACGME Approved/Offered Positions:* 2
Program ID: 423-35-21-032

Valhalla

New York Medical College at Westchester Medical Center Program

Sponsor: New York Medical College
Westchester Medical Center
Prgm Director: Michael S Tenner, MD
Department of Radiology
Valhalla, NY 10595
Tel: 914 493-8158   *Fax:* 914 493-1820
Length: 1 Yr   *ACGME Approved/Offered Positions:* 1
Program ID: 423-35-13-109

North Carolina

Chapel Hill

University of North Carolina Hospitals Program

Sponsor: University of North Carolina Hospitals
Prgm Director: Mauricio Castillo, MD
Department of Radiology
3326 Old Infirmary Bldg, CB # 7510
Chapel Hill, NC 27599
Tel: 919 966-3087   *Fax:* 919 966-1994
Length: 1 Yr   *ACGME Approved/Offered Positions:* 3
Program ID: 423-36-31-088

Durham

Duke University Hospital Program

Sponsor: Duke University Hospital
Prgm Director: James D Eastwood, MD
Box 3808
Durham, NC 27710
Tel: 919 684-7466   *Fax:* 919 684-7157
E-mail: eastw004@mc.duke.edu
Length: 1 Yr   *ACGME Approved/Offered Positions:* 8
Program ID: 423-36-21-070

Winston-Salem

Wake Forest University School of Medicine Program

Sponsor: Wake Forest University Baptist Medical Center
Prgm Director: Pearse Morris, MBChB*
Department of Radiology
Medical Center Boulevard
Winston-Salem, NC 27157
Tel: 336 716-2487   *Fax:* 336 716-2136
Length: 1 Yr   *ACGME Approved/Offered Positions:* 4
Program ID: 423-36-21-080

Note: * indicates a newly appointed program director

Ohio

Cincinnati

University Hospital/University of Cincinnati College of Medicine Program

Sponsor: University Hospital Inc
Prgm Director: Thomas A Tomsick, MD
PO Box 670762
234 Goodman - ML 762
Cincinnati, OH 45267
Tel: 513 584-7544   *Fax:* 513 584-9100
Length: 1 Yr   *ACGME Approved/Offered Positions:* 3
Program ID: 423-38-21-082

Cleveland

Cleveland Clinic Foundation Program

Sponsor: Cleveland Clinic Foundation
Prgm Director: Paul M Ruggieri, MD*
Department of Radiology
9500 Euclid Avenue, L-10
Cleveland, OH 44195
Tel: 216 445-7035   *Fax:* 216 444-3466
E-mail: meded@ccf.org
Length: 1 Yr   *ACGME Approved/Offered Positions:* 3
Program ID: 423-38-21-054

University Hospitals Case Medical Center Program

Sponsor: University Hospitals Case Medical Center
Prgm Director: Jeffrey L Sunshine, MD, PhD
11100 Euclid Avenue
Cleveland, OH 44106
Tel: 216 844-3116
E-mail: Marianne.Chaloupek@uhhospitals.org
Length: 1 Yr   *ACGME Approved/Offered Positions:* 2
Program ID: 423-38-21-017

Columbus

Ohio State University Hospital Program

Sponsor: Ohio State University Hospital
Prgm Director: Eric C Bourekas, MD
Department of Radiology
623 Means Hall, 1654 Upham Dr
Columbus, OH 43210
Tel: 614 293-8315   *Fax:* 614 293-6935
Length: 1 Yr   *ACGME Approved/Offered Positions:* 2
Program ID: 423-38-21-018

Oregon

Portland

Oregon Health & Science University Program

Sponsor: Oregon Health & Science University Hospital
Veterans Affairs Medical Center (Portland)
Prgm Director: James C Anderson, MD
Division of Neuroradiology, CR135
3181 SW Sam Jackson Park Rd
Portland, OR 97239
Tel: 503 494-7576   *Fax:* 503 494-7129
Length: 1 Yr   *ACGME Approved/Offered Positions:* 3
Program ID: 423-40-21-096

Pennsylvania

Hershey

Penn State University/Milton S Hershey Medical Center Program

Sponsor: Milton S Hershey Medical Center
Prgm Director: Dan T Nguyen, MD
PO Box 850
500 University Drive, H066
Hershey, PA 17033
Tel: 717 531-4682   *Fax:* 717 531-0006
E-mail: dnguyen1@psu.edu
Length: 1 Yr   *ACGME Approved/Offered Positions:* 1
Program ID: 423-41-21-097

Philadelphia

Drexel University College of Medicine/Hahnemann University Hospital Program

Sponsor: Drexel University College of Medicine/Hahnemann University
Hahnemann University Hospital (Tenet Health System)
Prgm Director: Robert Koenigsberg, DO
Broad and Vine Streets, MS 206
Philadelphia, PA 19102
Tel: 215 762-8804   *Fax:* 215 762-2350
E-mail: robert.koenigsberg@drexelmed.edu
Length: 1 Yr   *ACGME Approved/Offered Positions:* 2
Program ID: 423-41-31-106

Temple University Hospital Program

Sponsor: Temple University Hospital
Prgm Director: Jeffrey P Kochan, MD
3401 N Broad Street
Suite A
Philadelphia, PA 19140
Tel: 215 707-2640   *Fax:* 215 707-5851
E-mail: jkochan@temple.edu
Length: 1 Yr   *ACGME Approved/Offered Positions:* 2
Program ID: 423-41-21-056

Thomas Jefferson University Program

Sponsor: Thomas Jefferson University Hospital
Prgm Director: David P Friedman, MD
132 South 10th Street
Suite 1068 - Main Building
Philadelphia, PA 19107
Tel: 215 955-2714   *Fax:* 215 955-8741
E-mail: David.Friedman@jefferson.edu
Length: 1 Yr   *ACGME Approved/Offered Positions:* 4
Program ID: 423-41-21-083

University of Pennsylvania Program

Sponsor: University of Pennsylvania Health System
Children's Hospital of Philadelphia
Prgm Director: Linda J Bagley, MD
3400 Spruce Street
2 Dulles Building Rm 219
Philadelphia, PA 19104
Tel: 215 662-6865   *Fax:* 215 662-3283
Length: 1 Yr   *ACGME Approved/Offered Positions:* 7
Program ID: 423-41-21-037

Pittsburgh

Allegheny General Hospital Program

Sponsor: Allegheny General Hospital
Prgm Director: Melanie B Fukui, MD
320 East North Avenue
Pittsburgh, PA 15212
Tel: 412 359-4113   *Fax:* 412 359-6912
Length: 1 Yr   *ACGME Approved/Offered Positions:* 1
Program ID: 423-41-21-019

University of Pittsburgh Medical Center Medical Education Program

Sponsor: Univ of Pittsburgh Medical Center Medical Education
Children's Hospital of Pittsburgh of UPMC
UPMC Presbyterian Shadyside
Prgm Director: Barton F Branstetter IV, MD
Department of Radiology, D-132
200 Lothrop Street
Pittsburgh, PA 15213
Tel: 412 647-3530   *Fax:* 412 647-5359
E-mail: branstetterbf@upmc.edu
Length: 1 Yr   *ACGME Approved/Offered Positions:* 4
Program ID: 423-41-21-057

South Carolina

Charleston

Medical University of South Carolina Program

Sponsor: Medical University of South Carolina College of Medicine
MUSC Medical Center
Prgm Director: Zoran Rumboldt, MD, MSc
96 Jonathan Lucas Street, Ste 210
MSC 323
Charleston, SC 29425
Tel: 843 792-7179   *Fax:* 843 792-9319
Length: 1 Yr   *ACGME Approved/Offered Positions:* 2
Program ID: 423-45-12-107

Tennessee

Nashville

Vanderbilt University Program

Sponsor: Vanderbilt University Medical Center
Prgm Director: Jeff L Creasy, MD
1161 21st Avenue South
CCC-1121 Medical Center North
Nashville, TN 37232
Tel: 615 322-3780   *Fax:* 615 322-3764
E-mail: radprogram@vanderbilt.edu
Length: 1 Yr   *ACGME Approved/Offered Positions:* 3
Program ID: 423-47-21-058

Texas

Dallas

University of Texas Southwestern Medical School Program

Sponsor: University of Texas Southwestern Medical School
Dallas County Hospital District-Parkland Memorial Hospital
University Hospitals St Paul
Prgm Director: Glenn L Pride Jr, MD*
5323 Harry Hines Blvd
Dallas, TX 75390
Tel: 214 648-3928   *Fax:* 214 648-3904
E-mail: lee.pride@utsouthwestern.edu
Length: 1 Yr   *ACGME Approved/Offered Positions:* 6
Program ID: 423-48-21-059

Programs

Galveston

University of Texas Medical Branch Hospitals Program

Sponsor: University of Texas Medical Branch Hospitals
Prgm Director: Gregory Chaljub, MD
Dept of Radiology G-09
301 University Blvd, Route 0709
Galveston, TX 77555
Tel: 409 777-2230   *Fax:* 409 772-2303
E-mail: dlgillia@utmb.edu
Length: 1 Yr   *ACGME Approved/Offered Positions:* 2
Program ID: 423-48-21-020

Houston

Baylor College of Medicine Program

Sponsor: Baylor College of Medicine
Methodist Hospital (Houston)
St Luke's Episcopal Hospital
Texas Children's Hospital
University of Texas M D Anderson Cancer Center
Prgm Director: Pedro J Diaz-Marchan, MD
Department of Radiology
One Baylor Plaza, BCM 360
Houston, TX 77030
Tel: 713 798-6362   *Fax:* 713 798-8359
E-mail: lburlin@bcm.edu
Length: 1 Yr   *ACGME Approved/Offered Positions:* 5
Program ID: 423-48-21-060

University of Texas at Houston Program

Sponsor: University of Texas Health Science Center at
   Houston
Memorial Hermann Hospital
Michael E DeBakey VA Medical Center - Houston
Prgm Director: Clark M Sitton, MD, BS
6431 Fannin Street
MSB 2.130B
Houston, TX 77030
Tel: 713 704-1704   *Fax:* 713 704-1715
E-mail: csiton1@comcast.net
Length: 1 Yr   *ACGME Approved/Offered Positions:* 2
Program ID: 423-48-21-041

Utah

Salt Lake City

University of Utah Program

Sponsor: University of Utah Medical Center
Veterans Affairs Medical Center (Salt Lake City)
Prgm Director: Karen L Salzman, MD
30 North 1900 East #1A071
Salt Lake City, UT 84132
Tel: 801 581-4624   *Fax:* 801 585-7330
E-mail: alan.smith@hsc.utah.edu
Length: 1 Yr   *ACGME Approved/Offered Positions:* 5
Program ID: 423-49-21-062

Vermont

Burlington

University of Vermont Program

Sponsor: Fletcher Allen Health Care
Prgm Director: Grant J Linnell, DO*
Department of Radiology
111 Colchester Avenue
Burlington, VT 05401
Tel: 802 847-3592   *Fax:* 802 847-4822
Length: 1 Yr   *ACGME Approved/Offered Positions:* 1
Program ID: 423-50-31-101

Virginia

Charlottesville

University of Virginia Program

Sponsor: University of Virginia Medical Center
Prgm Director: C Douglas Phillips, MD
PO Box 800170
Charlottesville, VA 22908
Tel: 434 243-9312   *Fax:* 434 982-5753
Length: 1 Yr   *ACGME Approved/Offered Positions:* 4
Program ID: 423-51-21-063

Richmond

Virginia Commonwealth University Health System Program

Sponsor: Virginia Commonwealth University Health
   System
Medical College of Virginia Hospitals
Prgm Director: Warren A Stringer, MD
Dept of Radiology
Box 615, MCV Station
Richmond, VA 23298
Tel: 804 828-5099   *Fax:* 804 628-1132
E-mail: klrobb@vcu.edu
Length: 1 Yr   *ACGME Approved/Offered Positions:* 2
Program ID: 423-51-21-021

Washington

Seattle

University of Washington Program

Sponsor: University of Washington School of Medicine
Harborview Medical Center
University of Washington Medical Center
Prgm Director: Dean Shibata, MD*
Department of Radiology
Box 357115
Seattle, WA 98195
Tel: 206 598-3291   *Fax:* 206 598-8475
E-mail: shibatad@u.washington.edu
Length: 1 Yr   *ACGME Approved/Offered Positions:* 6
Program ID: 423-54-21-038

West Virginia

Morgantown

West Virginia University Program

Sponsor: West Virginia University School of Medicine
West Virginia University Hospitals
Prgm Director: Ansaar T Rai, MD
PO Box 9235
Morgantown, WV 26506
Tel: 304 293-3092   *Fax:* 304 293-3899
E-mail: jfast@hsc.wvu.edu
Length: 1 Yr   *ACGME Approved/Offered Positions:* 1
Program ID: 423-55-21-094

Wisconsin

Madison

University of Wisconsin Program

Sponsor: University of Wisconsin Hospital and Clinics
Prgm Director: Aaron S Field, MD, PhD*
E3/311 Clinical Science Center
600 Highland Avenue
Madison, WI 53792
Tel: 608 263-7952   *Fax:* 608 265-4152
Length: 1 Yr   *ACGME Approved/Offered Positions:* 3
Program ID: 423-56-21-022

Milwaukee

Medical College of Wisconsin Affiliated Hospitals Program

Sponsor: Medical College of Wisconsin Affiliated
   Hospitals, Inc
Froedtert Memorial Lutheran Hospital
Prgm Director: John L Ulmer, MD
Froedtert Memorial Lutheran Hospital
9200 West Wisconsin Ave
Milwaukee, WI 53226
Tel: 414 805-3122   *Fax:* 414 259-9290
E-mail: julmer@mcw.edu
Length: 1 Yr   *ACGME Approved/Offered Positions:* 4
Program ID: 423-56-21-039

Note: * indicates a newly appointed program director

Neurotology (Otolaryngology)

California

Los Angeles

University of Southern California Program
Sponsor: House Ear Clinic, Inc
LAC+USC Medical Center
St Vincent Medical Center
Prgm Director: William H Slattery III, MD
2100 West Third Street, Suite 111
Los Angeles, CA 90057
Tel: 213 483-9930   *Fax:* 213 484-5900
E-mail: pjavier@hei.org
Length: 2 Yrs   *ACGME Approved/Offered Positions:* 4
Program ID: 286-05-21-008

San Diego

University of California (San Diego) Program
Sponsor: University of California (San Diego) Medical
  Center
Kaiser Foundation Hospital (San Diego)
Scripps Clinic
Veterans Affairs Medical Center (San Diego)
Prgm Director: Jeffrey P Harris, MD, PhD
200 W Arbor Drive # 8895
San Diego, CA 92103
Tel: 619 543-7896   *Fax:* 619 543-5521
Length: 2 Yrs   *ACGME Approved/Offered Positions:* 2
Program ID: 286-05-21-014

Stanford

Stanford University Program
Sponsor: Stanford Hospital and Clinics
Prgm Director: Robert K Jackler, MD
801 Welch Road
Stanford, CA 94305
Tel: 650 725-6500   *Fax:* 650 725-8502
Length: 2 Yrs   *ACGME Approved/Offered Positions:* 2
Program ID: 286-05-12-016

Florida

Miami

Jackson Memorial Hospital/Jackson Health System Program
Sponsor: Jackson Memorial Hospital/Jackson Health
  System
Bascom Palmer Eye Institute-Anne Bates Leach Eye
  Hospital
Prgm Director: Thomas J Balkany, MD
PO Box 016960 (D48)
Miami, FL 33101
Tel: 305 585-8776   *Fax:* 305 326-7610
E-mail: epye@med.miami.edu
Length: 2 Yrs   *ACGME Approved/Offered Positions:* 1
Program ID: 286-11-13-009

Iowa

Iowa City

University of Iowa Hospitals and Clinics Program
Sponsor: University of Iowa Hospitals and Clinics
Prgm Director: Bruce J Gantz, MD
Dept of Otolaryngology-Head & Neck Surgery
200 Hawkins Drive 21201 PFP
Iowa City, IA 52242
Tel: 319 356-2173   *Fax:* 319 356-3967
E-mail: bruce-gantz@uiowa.edu
Length: 2 Yrs   *ACGME Approved/Offered Positions:* 2
Program ID: 286-18-21-003

Maryland

Baltimore

Johns Hopkins University Program
Sponsor: Johns Hopkins University School of Medicine
Johns Hopkins Hospital
Prgm Director: John P Carey, MD*
Department of Otolaryngology-Head and Neck Surgery
601 N Caroline Street, Room 6221
Baltimore, MD 21287
Tel: 410 955-7381   *Fax:* 410 955-0035
E-mail: cstansb3@jhmi.edu
Length: 2 Yrs   *ACGME Approved/Offered Positions:* 2
Program ID: 286-23-21-012

Massachusetts

Boston

Massachusetts Eye and Ear Infirmary/Harvard Medical School Program
Sponsor: Massachusetts Eye and Ear Infirmary
Prgm Director: Michael J McKenna, MD
243 Charles Street
Boston, MA 02114
Tel: 617 573-3654   *Fax:* 617 573-3939
Length: 2 Yrs   *ACGME Approved/Offered Positions:* 1
Program ID: 286-24-11-007

Michigan

Ann Arbor

University of Michigan Program
Sponsor: University of Michigan Hospitals and Health
  Centers
Prgm Director: H Alexander Arts, MD
1500 East Medical Center Drive
Ann Arbor, MI 48109
Tel: 734 936-8006   *Fax:* 734 936-9625
Length: 2 Yrs   *ACGME Approved/Offered Positions:* 2
Program ID: 286-25-21-001

Southfield

Providence Hospital/Michigan Ear Institute/Wayne State Program
Sponsor: Providence Hospital and Medical Centers
Prgm Director: Michael J LaRouere, MD
30055 Northwestern Highway, #101
Farmington Hills, MI 48334
Tel: 248 865-4444   *Fax:* 248 865-6161
Length: 2 Yrs   *ACGME Approved/Offered Positions:* 3
Program ID: 286-25-31-006

New York

New York

New York University School of Medicine Program
Sponsor: New York University School of Medicine
Bellevue Hospital Center
Manhattan VA Harbor Health Care System
NYU Hospitals Center
Prgm Director: J Thomas Roland Jr, MD
Department of Otolaryngology
550 First Avenue
New York, NY 10016
Tel: 212 263-6344   *Fax:* 212 263-8257
Length: 2 Yrs   *ACGME Approved/Offered Positions:* 2
Program ID: 286-35-21-004

Ohio

Columbus

Ohio State University Hospital Program
Sponsor: Ohio State University Hospital
Prgm Director: D Bradley Welling, MD, PhD
4100 University Hospitals Clinic
456 West 10th Avenue
Columbus, OH 43210
Tel: 614 293-8706   *Fax:* 614 293-7292
Length: 2 Yrs   *ACGME Approved/Offered Positions:* 2
Program ID: 286-38-21-002

Pennsylvania

Pittsburgh

University of Pittsburgh Medical Center Medical Education Program
Sponsor: Univ of Pittsburgh Medical Center Medical
  Education
UPMC Presbyterian Shadyside
Prgm Director: Barry E Hirsch, MD
Eye & Ear Institute, Suite 500
200 Lothrop Street
Pittsburgh, PA 15213
Tel: 412 647-2115   *Fax:* 412 647-2080
Length: 2 Yrs   *ACGME Approved/Offered Positions:* 1
Program ID: 286-41-21-017

Tennessee

Nashville

Vanderbilt University Program
Sponsor: Vanderbilt University Medical Center
St Thomas Hospital
Prgm Director: David S Haynes, MD
1215 21st Avenue South
Nashville, TN 37232
Tel: 615 343-6972   *Fax:* 615 343-9725
E-mail: Elizabeth.L.Warner@vanderbilt.edu
Length: 2 Yrs   *ACGME Approved/Offered Positions:* 4
Program ID: 286-47-13-013

Programs

Texas

Houston

Baylor College of Medicine Program
Sponsor: Baylor College of Medicine
Methodist Hospital (Houston)
Prgm Director: Jeffrey T Vrabec, MD
One Baylor Plaza
NA-102
Houston, TX 77030
Tel: 713 798-5118
E-mail: francesc@bcm.edu
Length: 2 Yrs   *ACGME Approved/Offered Positions:* 1
Program ID: 286-48-31-015

Virginia

Charlottesville

University of Virginia Program
Sponsor: University of Virginia Medical Center
Prgm Director: George Hashisaki, MD
PO Box 800713
Charlottesville, VA 22908
Tel: 434 924-2040   *Fax:* 434 982-3965
Length: 2 Yrs   *ACGME Approved/Offered Positions:* 1
Program ID: 286-51-21-005

Nuclear Medicine

Alabama

Birmingham

University of Alabama Medical Center Program
Sponsor: University of Alabama Hospital
Veterans Affairs Medical Center (Birmingham)
Prgm Director: Jon A Baldwin, DO
619 19th Street South
Jefferson Towers, Room J260
Birmingham, AL 35249
Tel: 205 934-1388   *Fax:* 205 934-5589
E-mail: jbaldwin@uabmc.edu
Length: 3 Yrs   *ACGME Approved/Offered Positions:* 3
Program ID: 200-01-21-007

Arkansas

Little Rock

University of Arkansas for Medical Sciences Program
Sponsor: University of Arkansas College of Medicine
Central Arkansas Veterans Healthcare System
UAMS Medical Center
Prgm Director: Twyla B Bartel, DO, MBA
4301 West Markham St
Slot 556
Little Rock, AR 72205
Tel: 501 350-0305   *Fax:* 501 686-6900
E-mail: TBBartel@uams.edu
Length: 3 Yrs   *ACGME Approved/Offered Positions:* 3
Program ID: 200-04-21-009

California

Los Angeles

UCLA Medical Center Program
Sponsor: UCLA David Geffen School of Medicine/UCLA
   Medical Center
UCLA Medical Center
Prgm Director: Johannes G Czernin, MD
200 Medical Plaza, Suite B114
Los Angeles, CA 90095
Tel: 310 206-3226   *Fax:* 310 206-4899
Length: 3 Yrs   *ACGME Approved/Offered Positions:* 5
Program ID: 200-05-11-013

University of Southern California/ LAC+USC Medical Center Program
Sponsor: University of Southern California/LAC+USC
   Medical Center
Kenneth Norris Jr Cancer Hospital and Research
   Institute
LAC+USC Medical Center
USC University Hospital
Prgm Director: Patrick M Colletti, MD, MS
1200 North State Street, Suite 5250
Los Angeles, CA 90033
Tel: 323 226-4218   *Fax:* 323 224-7830
E-mail: alloyd@usc.edu
Length: 3 Yrs   *ACGME Approved/Offered Positions:* 3
Program ID: 200-05-21-105

VA Greater Los Angeles Healthcare System Program
Sponsor: VA Greater Los Angeles Healthcare System
Childrens Hospital Los Angeles
Prgm Director: William H Blahd, MD
11301 Wilshire Blvd
Los Angeles, CA 90073
Tel: 310 268-3587   *Fax:* 310 268-4916
E-mail: william.blahd@va.gov
Length: 3 Yrs   *ACGME Approved/Offered Positions:* 4
Program ID: 200-05-31-014

Sacramento

University of California (Davis) Health System Program
Sponsor: University of California (Davis) Health System
University of California (Davis) Medical Center
Prgm Director: David K Shelton Jr, MD
Div of Nuclear Medicine
4860 Y Street, Suite 3100
Sacramento, CA 95817
Tel: 916 703-2273   *Fax:* 916 703-2274
E-mail: david.shelton@ucdmc.ucdavis.edu
Length: 3 Yrs   *ACGME Approved/Offered Positions:* 3
Program ID: 200-05-21-010

San Diego

University of California (San Diego) Program
Sponsor: University of California (San Diego) Medical
   Center
Veterans Affairs Medical Center (San Diego)
Prgm Director: Carl K Hoh, MD
200 West Arbor Drive
Mail Code: 8758
San Diego, CA 92103
Tel: 619 543-1986   *Fax:* 619 543-1975
Length: 3 Yrs   *ACGME Approved/Offered Positions:* 1
Program ID: 200-05-31-015

San Francisco

University of California (San Francisco) Program
Sponsor: University of California (San Francisco) School
   of Medicine
UCSF and Mount Zion Medical Centers
Prgm Director: Randall A Hawkins, MD, PhD
505 Parnassus Ave
Department of Radiology
San Francisco, CA 94143
Tel: 415 353-1886   *Fax:* 415 353-8571
E-mail: randy.hawkins@radiology.ucsf.edu
Length: 3 Yrs   *ACGME Approved/Offered Positions:* 2
Program ID: 200-05-21-016

Stanford

Stanford University Program
Sponsor: Stanford Hospital and Clinics
Veterans Affairs Palo Alto Health Care System
Prgm Director: Sanjiv S Gambhir, MD, PhD*
Room H0101
300 Pasteur Drive
Stanford, CA 94305
Tel: 650 725-2309   *Fax:* 650 724-4948
Length: 3 Yrs   *ACGME Approved/Offered Positions:* 4
Program ID: 200-05-21-018

Note: * indicates a newly appointed program director

Colorado

Aurora

University of Colorado Denver Program

Sponsor: University of Colorado Denver School of
Medicine
University of Colorado Hospital
Prgm Director: Jacqueline D Howard-Sachs, MD
12631 E 17th Avenue
MS 8200
Aurora, CO 80045
Tel: 303 372-6134   *Fax:* 303 848-1139
Length: 3 Yrs   *ACGME Approved/Offered Positions:* 1
Program ID: 200-07-21-108

Connecticut

New Haven

Yale-New Haven Medical Center Program

Sponsor: Yale-New Haven Hospital
Veterans Affairs Medical Center (West Haven)
Prgm Director: David W Cheng, MD, PhD
PO Box 208042
333 Cedar Street
New Haven, CT 06520
Tel: 203 785-7377   *Fax:* 203 785-5002
E-mail: keyonna.artis@yale.edu
Length: 3 Yrs   *ACGME Approved/Offered Positions:* 3
Program ID: 200-08-11-021

District of Columbia

Washington

Washington Hospital Center Program

Sponsor: Washington Hospital Center
Prgm Director: Douglas Van Nostrand, MD
Division of Nuclear Medicine
110 Irving Street, NW, Suite BB43
Washington, DC 20010
Tel: 202 877-0348   *Fax:* 202 877-6601
E-mail: trevor.w.forde@medstar.net
Length: 3 Yrs   *ACGME Approved/Offered Positions:* 4
Program ID: 200-10-13-116

Florida

Miami

Jackson Memorial Hospital/Jackson Health System Program

Sponsor: Jackson Memorial Hospital/Jackson Health
System
Prgm Director: Shabbir H Ezuddin, MD*
PO Box 016960
1611 NW 12th Ave, D-57
Miami, FL 33136
Tel: 305 585-7955   *Fax:* 305 547-2323
E-mail: sezuddin@med.miami.edu
Length: 3 Yrs   *ACGME Approved/Offered Positions:* 4
Program ID: 200-11-21-087

Georgia

Atlanta

Emory University Program

Sponsor: Emory University School of Medicine
Emory University Hospital
Grady Health System
Veterans Affairs Medical Center (Atlanta)
Prgm Director: Daniel J Lee, MD*
1364 Clifton Road, NE
D125
Atlanta, GA 30322
Tel: 404 712-4686   *Fax:* 404 712-7908
Length: 3 Yrs   *ACGME Approved/Offered Positions:* 6
Program ID: 200-12-21-083

Illinois

Chicago

Rush University Medical Center Program

Sponsor: Rush University Medical Center
Prgm Director: Amjad Ali, MD
1653 West Congress Parkway
Chicago, IL 60612
Tel: 312 942-5757   *Fax:* 312 942-5320
E-mail: amjad_ali@rush.edu
Length: 3 Yrs   *ACGME Approved/Offered Positions:* 2
Program ID: 200-16-11-027

Maywood

Loyola University Program

Sponsor: Loyola University Medical Center
Edward Hines, Jr Veterans Affairs Hospital
Prgm Director: Robert H Wagner, MD
Foster G McGaw Hospital
2160 S First Avenue
Maywood, IL 60153
Tel: 708 216-3777   *Fax:* 708 216-4206
Length: 3 Yrs   *ACGME Approved/Offered Positions:* 5
Program ID: 200-16-21-101

Indiana

Indianapolis

Indiana University School of Medicine Program

Sponsor: Indiana University School of Medicine
Clarian Indiana University Hospital
Prgm Director: Aslam R Siddiqui, MD
Room 1053
702 Barnhill Drive
Indianapolis, IN 46202
Tel: 317 278-6302   *Fax:* 317 274-2920
E-mail: rfpatter@iupui.edu
Length: 3 Yrs   *ACGME Approved/Offered Positions:* 1
Program ID: 200-17-21-093

Iowa

Iowa City

University of Iowa Hospitals and Clinics Program

Sponsor: University of Iowa Hospitals and Clinics
Veterans Affairs Medical Center (Iowa City)
Prgm Director: Michael M Graham, MD, PhD
Dept of Radiology
200 Hawkins Dr 3863 JPP
Iowa City, IA 52242
Tel: 319 356-4302   *Fax:* 319 356-2220
E-mail: michael-graham@uiowa.edu
Length: 3 Yrs   *ACGME Approved/Offered Positions:* 4
Program ID: 200-18-21-030

Maryland

Baltimore

Johns Hopkins University Program

Sponsor: Johns Hopkins University School of Medicine
Johns Hopkins Hospital
Prgm Director: Harvey Ziessman, MD
Room 3223
601 N Caroline Street
Baltimore, MD 21287
Tel: 410 955-6989   *Fax:* 410 287-2933
E-mail: tgthompson@jhmi.edu
Length: 3 Yrs   *ACGME Approved/Offered Positions:* 9
Program ID: 200-23-11-035

University of Maryland Program

Sponsor: University of Maryland Medical System
Veterans Affairs Medical Center (Baltimore)
Prgm Director: Chun Kim, MD
22 S Greene Street
Baltimore, MD 21201
Tel: 410 328-6890
Length: 3 Yrs   *ACGME Approved/Offered Positions:* 5
Program ID: 200-23-21-115

Bethesda

National Capital Consortium Program

Sponsor: National Capital Consortium
Walter Reed Army Medical Center
Prgm Director: Jennifer S Jurgens, MD
Nuclear Medicine Service, Bldg 2, Room 7A02
6900 Geogia Avenue NW
Washington, DC 20307
Tel: 202 782-0168   *Fax:* 202 728-9061
Length: 3 Yrs   *ACGME Approved/Offered Positions:* 4
Program ID: 200-10-12-002
Uniformed Services Program

Massachusetts

Boston

Brigham and Women's Hospital/Harvard Medical School Program

Sponsor: Brigham and Women's Hospital
Beth Israel Deaconess Medical Center
Boston VA Healthcare System (Brockton-West Roxbury)
Children's Hospital
Dana-Farber Cancer Institute
Prgm Director: S Ted Treves, MD
Division of Nuclear Medicine
300 Longwood Avenue
Boston, MA 02115
Tel: 617 355-7935   *Fax:* 617 730-0620
Length: 3 Yrs   *ACGME Approved/Offered Positions:* 8
Program ID: 200-24-21-038

Programs

Michigan

Ann Arbor

University of Michigan Program
Sponsor: University of Michigan Hospitals and Health
  Centers
Veterans Affairs Medical Center (Ann Arbor)
Prgm Director: Kirk A Frey, MD, PhD
1500 E Medical Center Drive
UH B1 G505/0028
Ann Arbor, MI 48109
Tel: 734 936-5388   *Fax:* 734 936-8182
E-mail: lfig@med.umich.edu
Length: 3 Yrs   *ACGME Approved/Offered Positions:* 3
Program ID: 200-25-11-039

Royal Oak

William Beaumont Hospital Program
Sponsor: William Beaumont Hospital
Prgm Director: Helena R Balon, MD
3601 West 13 Mile Road
Royal Oak, MI 48073
Tel: 248 898-4126   *Fax:* 248 898-0487
Length: 3 Yrs   *ACGME Approved/Offered Positions:* 4
Program ID: 200-25-11-040

Missouri

Columbia

University of Missouri-Columbia Program
Sponsor: University of Missouri-Columbia School of
  Medicine
University Hospitals and Clinics
Prgm Director: Amolak Singh, MD
Radiology Department, DC069.10
One Hospital Drive
Columbia, MO 65212
Tel: 573 882-7955   *Fax:* 573 884-8876
E-mail: SinghA@health.missouri.edu
Length: 3 Yrs   *ACGME Approved/Offered Positions:* 1
Program ID: 200-28-21-094

St Louis

St Louis University School of Medicine Program
Sponsor: St Louis University School of Medicine
St Louis University Hospital
Veterans Affairs Medical Center (St Louis)
Prgm Director: Medhat M Osman, MD, PhD
1402 S Grand Blvd
St Louis, MO 63104
Tel: 314 268-5781   *Fax:* 314 268-5116
Length: 3 Yrs   *ACGME Approved/Offered Positions:* 2
Program ID: 200-28-21-042

Washington University/B-JH/SLCH Consortium Program
Sponsor: Washington University/B-JH/SLCH Consortium
Barnes-Jewish Hospital
Prgm Director: Henry D Royal, MD
510 South Kingshighway Blvd
University Box 8223
St Louis, MO 63110
Tel: 314 362-2809   *Fax:* 314 362-2806
E-mail: henry.royal@rad.wustl.edu
Length: 3 Yrs   *ACGME Approved/Offered Positions:* 5
Program ID: 200-28-11-043

Nebraska

Omaha

University of Nebraska Medical Center College of Medicine Program
Sponsor: University of Nebraska Medical Center College
  of Medicine
Creighton University Medical Center (Tenet - SJH)
Nebraska Medical Center
Prgm Director: Jordan Hankins, MD
Department of Radiology
981045 Nebraska Medical Center
Omaha, NE 68198
Tel: 402 559-1018   *Fax:* 402 559-1011
Length: 3 Yrs   *ACGME Approved/Offered Positions:* 2
Program ID: 200-30-11-044

New York

Bronx

Albert Einstein College of Medicine Program
Sponsor: Albert Einstein College of Medicine of Yeshiva
  University
Montefiore Medical Center-Henry and Lucy Moses
  Division
Montefiore Medical Center-Weiler Division
Prgm Director: David M Milstein, MD
1825 Eastchester Road
Bronx, NY 10461
Tel: 718 904-4058   *Fax:* 718 904-2354
Length: 3 Yrs   *ACGME Approved/Offered Positions:* 6
Program ID: 200-35-21-047

Buffalo

University at Buffalo Program
Sponsor: University at Buffalo School of Medicine
Kaleida Health System (Buffalo General Hospital)
Mercy Hospital of Buffalo
Roswell Park Cancer Institute
Veterans Affairs Western New York Hospital
Prgm Director: Hani H Abdel Nabi, MD, PhD
105 Parker Hall
3435 Main Street
Buffalo, NY 14214
Tel: 716 838-5889   *Fax:* 716 838-4918
Length: 3 Yrs   *ACGME Approved/Offered Positions:* 4
Program ID: 200-35-21-046

Great Neck

NSLIJHS Program
Sponsor: North Shore-Long Island Jewish Health System
Long Island Jewish Medical Center
North Shore University Hospital
Prgm Director: Christopher J Palestro, MD
270-05 76th Avenue
New Hyde Park, NY 11040
Tel: 718 470-7080   *Fax:* 718 831-1147
Length: 3 Yrs   *ACGME Approved/Offered Positions:* 5
Program ID: 200-35-11-049

New York

Memorial Sloan-Kettering Cancer Center Program
Sponsor: Memorial Sloan-Kettering Cancer Center
Prgm Director: Neeta Pandit-Taskar, MD
1275 York Avenue
Room S-212
New York, NY 10021
Tel: 212 639-7372   *Fax:* 212 717-3263
Length: 3 Yrs   *ACGME Approved/Offered Positions:* 6
Program ID: 200-35-11-050

Mount Sinai School of Medicine Program
Sponsor: Mount Sinai School of Medicine
Mount Sinai Medical Center
Prgm Director: Sherif I Heiba, MD
Box 1141
One Gustave L Levy Pl
New York, NY 10029
Tel: 212 241-9373   *Fax:* 212 831-2851
Length: 3 Yrs   *ACGME Approved/Offered Positions:* 3
Program ID: 200-35-21-051

New York Medical College at St Vincent's Hospital and Medical Center of New York Program
Sponsor: New York Medical College
St Vincent Catholic Medical Centers (Manhattan)
Prgm Director: Hussein M Abdel-Dayem, MD
Department of Nuclear Medicine
153 W 11th Street
New York, NY 10011
Tel: 212 604-8783   *Fax:* 212 604-3119
E-mail: habdel@svcmcny.org
Length: 3 Yrs   *ACGME Approved/Offered Positions:* 3
Program ID: 200-35-12-054

New York Presbyterian Hospital (Columbia Campus) Program
Sponsor: New York Presbyterian Hospital
New York Presbyterian Hospital (Columbia Campus)
Prgm Director: Rashid A Fawwaz, MD, PhD
180 Fort Washington Avenue
HP 3 321 Dept of Radiology
New York, NY 10032
Tel: 212 305-7138   *Fax:* 212 305-4244
E-mail: rf5@columbia.edu
Length: 3 Yrs   *ACGME Approved/Offered Positions:* 2
Program ID: 200-35-21-099

New York Presbyterian Hospital (Cornell Campus) Program
Sponsor: New York Presbyterian Hospital
New York Presbyterian Hospital (Cornell Campus)
Prgm Director: Sofia Kung, MD, MS*
525 E 68th St, Starr 221
New York, NY 10021
Tel: 212 746-4586   *Fax:* 212 746-9010
Length: 3 Yrs   *ACGME Approved/Offered Positions:* 3
Program ID: 200-35-11-052

St Luke's-Roosevelt Hospital Center Program
Sponsor: St Luke's-Roosevelt Hospital Center
St Luke's-Roosevelt Hospital Center-Roosevelt Division
St Luke's-Roosevelt Hospital Center-St Luke's Division
Prgm Director: E Gordon DePuey, MD
1111 Amsterdam Ave at 114th St
New York, NY 10025
Tel: 212 523-3398   *Fax:* 212 523-3949
Length: 3 Yrs   *ACGME Approved/Offered Positions:* 2
Program ID: 200-35-11-084

North Carolina

Chapel Hill

University of North Carolina Hospitals Program
Sponsor: University of North Carolina Hospitals
Prgm Director: Amir H Khandani, MD*
CB 7510
Chapel Hill, NC 27599
Tel: 919 966-9897   *Fax:* 919 843-7147
Length: 3 Yrs   *ACGME Approved/Offered Positions:* 3
Program ID: 200-36-21-114

Note: * indicates a newly appointed program director

Durham

Duke University Hospital Program
Sponsor: Duke University Hospital
Prgm Director: R Edward Coleman, MD, BA
Department of Radiology
Box 3949-Erwin Road
Durham, NC 27710
Tel: 919 684-7245   *Fax:* 919 684-7135
Length: 3 Yrs   *ACGME Approved/Offered Positions:* 4
Program ID: 200-36-21-060

Winston-Salem

Wake Forest University School of Medicine Program
Sponsor: Wake Forest University Baptist Medical Center
Prgm Director: Paige B Clark, MD
Medical Center Blvd
Winston-Salem, NC 27157
Tel: 336 716-3590   *Fax:* 336 716-6108
Length: 3 Yrs   *ACGME Approved/Offered Positions:* 1
Program ID: 200-36-11-061

Ohio

Columbus

Ohio State University Hospital Program
Sponsor: Ohio State University Hospital
Arthur G James Cancer Hospital and Research Institute
Nationwide Children's Hospital
Prgm Director: Nathan C Hall, MD, PhD
Department of Radiology
410 West 10th Avenue
Columbus, OH 43210
Tel: 614 293-5774   *Fax:* 614 293-7806
Length: 3 Yrs   *ACGME Approved/Offered Positions:* 3
Program ID: 200-38-31-117

Oklahoma

Oklahoma City

University of Oklahoma Health Sciences Center Program
Sponsor: University of Oklahoma College of Medicine
OU Medical Center - Children's Hospital
OU Medical Center - Presbyterian Tower
Veterans Affairs Medical Center (Oklahoma City)
Prgm Director: Charles D Arnold, MD
PO Box 26307
Oklahoma City, OK 73126
Tel: 405 271-8001   *Fax:* 405 271-3462
Length: 3 Yrs   *ACGME Approved/Offered Positions:* 2
Program ID: 200-39-21-064

Oregon

Portland

Oregon Health & Science University Program
Sponsor: Oregon Health & Science University Hospital
Prgm Director: Jeffrey S Stevens, MD
Nuclear Medicine (OP23)
3181 SW Sam Jackson Park Rd
Portland, OR 97239
Tel: 503 494-2200   *Fax:* 503 494-4982
E-mail: stevensj@ohsu.edu
Length: 3 Yrs   *ACGME Approved/Offered Positions:* 1
Program ID: 200-40-21-065

Pennsylvania

Philadelphia

Thomas Jefferson University Program
Sponsor: Thomas Jefferson University Hospital
Prgm Director: Charles M Intenzo, MD
132 S 10th Street
Philadelphia, PA 19107
Tel: 215 955-7871   *Fax:* 215 923-0268
Length: 3 Yrs   *ACGME Approved/Offered Positions:* 2
Program ID: 200-41-21-100

University of Pennsylvania Program
Sponsor: University of Pennsylvania Health System
Prgm Director: Chaitanya Divgi, MD
3400 Spruce St
110 Donner
Philadelphia, PA 19104
Tel: 215 615-3687
Length: 3 Yrs   *ACGME Approved/Offered Positions:* 9
Program ID: 200-41-21-067

Puerto Rico

San Juan

University of Puerto Rico Program
Sponsor: University of Puerto Rico School of Medicine
University Hospital
VA Caribbean Healthcare System
Prgm Director: Frieda Silva de Roldan, MD
GPO Box 5067
San Juan, PR 00936
Tel: 787 625-9958   *Fax:* 787 758-2242
Length: 3 Yrs   *ACGME Approved/Offered Positions:* 4
Program ID: 200-42-21-069

South Carolina

Charleston

Medical University of South Carolina Program
Sponsor: Medical University of South Carolina College of Medicine
MUSC Medical Center
Prgm Director: Kenneth M Spicer, MD, PhD
Department of Radiology/Nuclear Medicine
96 Jonathan Lucas Street, MSC323
Charleston, SC 29425
Tel: 843 792-1957   *Fax:* 843 792-9503
Length: 3 Yrs   *ACGME Approved/Offered Positions:* 2
Program ID: 200-45-21-070

Tennessee

Knoxville

University of Tennessee Medical Center at Knoxville Program
Sponsor: University of Tennessee Graduate School of Medicine
University of Tennessee Memorial Hospital
Prgm Director: George Chacko, MD*
1924 Alcoa Highway
Knoxville, TN 37920
Tel: 865 305-9638
Length: 3 Yrs   *ACGME Approved/Offered Positions:* 4
Program ID: 200-47-21-109

Nashville

Vanderbilt University Program
Sponsor: Vanderbilt University Medical Center
Veterans Affairs Medical Center (Nashville)
Prgm Director: William H Martin, MD
1161 21st Avenue South
CCC-1121 Medical Center North
Nashville, TN 37232
Tel: 615 322-3780   *Fax:* 615 322-3764
E-mail: radprogram@vanderbilt.edu
Length: 3 Yrs   *ACGME Approved/Offered Positions:* 3
Program ID: 200-47-21-072

Texas

Dallas

University of Texas Southwestern Medical School Program
Sponsor: University of Texas Southwestern Medical School
Dallas County Hospital District-Parkland Memorial Hospital
Prgm Director: William A Erdman, MD
5323 Harry Hines Blvd
Dallas, TX 75390
Tel: 214 590-5120   *Fax:* 214 590-2720
E-mail: Dianna.Otterstad@UTSouthwestern.edu
Length: 3 Yrs   *ACGME Approved/Offered Positions:* 2
Program ID: 200-48-21-073

Houston

Baylor College of Medicine Program
Sponsor: Baylor College of Medicine
Harris County Hospital District-Ben Taub General Hospital
Methodist Hospital (Houston)
Michael E DeBakey VA Medical Center - Houston
St Luke's Episcopal Hospital
Prgm Director: Juliet Wendt, MD
Department of Radiology
One Baylor Plaza, BCM 360
Houston, TX 77030
Tel: 713 798-6362   *Fax:* 713 798-8359
E-mail: jwendt@bcm.tmc.edu
Length: 3 Yrs   *ACGME Approved/Offered Positions:* 4
Program ID: 200-48-21-075

San Antonio

University of Texas Health Science Center at San Antonio Program
Sponsor: University of Texas School of Medicine at San Antonio
Brooke Army Medical Center
University Health System
Wilford Hall Medical Center (AETC)
Prgm Director: Darlene Metter, MD
7703 Floyd Curl Drive, Mail Stop 7800
San Antonio, TX 78229
Tel: 210 567-5600   *Fax:* 210 567-6418
Length: 3 Yrs   *ACGME Approved/Offered Positions:* 4
Program ID: 200-48-31-085

Virginia

Richmond

Virginia Commonwealth University Health System Program
Sponsor: Virginia Commonwealth University Health System
Medical College of Virginia Hospitals
Prgm Director: Paul R Jolles, MD
1300 East Marshall Street - North 7
PO Box 980001
Richmond, VA 23298
Tel: 804 828-7975   *Fax:* 804 828-4181
E-mail: klrobb@vcu.edu
Length: 3 Yrs   *ACGME Approved/Offered Positions:* 2
Program ID: 200-51-21-077

Washington

Seattle

University of Washington Program
Sponsor: University of Washington School of Medicine
University of Washington Medical Center
Prgm Director: David H Lewis, MD
Box 356113
Seattle, WA 98195
Tel: 206 616-5781   *Fax:* 206 598-3687
Length: 3 Yrs   *ACGME Approved/Offered Positions:* 3
Program ID: 200-54-21-078

Wisconsin

Madison

University of Wisconsin Program
Sponsor: University of Wisconsin Hospital and Clinics
Prgm Director: Michael A Wilson, MD
600 Highland Avenue, E3/311 CSC
Madison, WI 53972
Tel: 608 263-5585   *Fax:* 608 265-7390
Length: 3 Yrs   *ACGME Approved/Offered Positions:* 2
Program ID: 200-56-21-079

Milwaukee

Medical College of Wisconsin Affiliated Hospitals Program
Sponsor: Medical College of Wisconsin Affiliated Hospitals, Inc
Clement J Zablocki Veterans Affairs Medical Center
Froedtert Memorial Lutheran Hospital
Prgm Director: Arthur Z Krasnow, MD
9200 West Wisconsin Avenue
Department of Radiology
Milwaukee, WI 53226
Tel: 414 805-3774   *Fax:* 414 771-3460
Length: 3 Yrs   *ACGME Approved/Offered Positions:* 2
Program ID: 200-56-21-080

Nuclear Radiology (Radiology-Diagnostic)

California

Los Angeles

Cedars-Sinai Medical Center Program
Sponsor: Cedars-Sinai Medical Center
Prgm Director: Alan D Waxman, MD
8700 Beverly Boulevard
Taper Building, M335
Los Angeles, CA 90048
Tel: 310 423-3095   *Fax:* 310 423-8335
E-mail: imaging.housestaff@cshs.org
Length: 1 Yr   *ACGME Approved/Offered Positions:* 1
Program ID: 425-05-21-073

Orange

University of California (Irvine) Program
Sponsor: University of California (Irvine) Medical Center
Prgm Director: Paul Lizotte, DO
Department of Radiology
101 City Drive, Rte 140
Orange, CA 92868
Tel: 714 456-6579   *Fax:* 714 456-6832
E-mail: mmcintos@uci.edu
Length: 1 Yr   *ACGME Approved/Offered Positions:* 1
Program ID: 425-05-21-069

Torrance

Los Angeles County-Harbor-UCLA Medical Center Program
Sponsor: Los Angeles County-Harbor-UCLA Medical Center
Prgm Director: Panukorn Vasinrapee, MD
1000 W Carson Street, Box 23
Torrance, CA 90509
Tel: 310 222-2842   *Fax:* 310 328-7288
E-mail: phamm@labiomed.org
Length: 1 Yr   *ACGME Approved/Offered Positions:* 1
Program ID: 425-05-31-065

Connecticut

New Haven

Yale-New Haven Medical Center Program
Sponsor: Yale-New Haven Hospital
Veterans Affairs Medical Center (West Haven)
Prgm Director: David W Cheng, MD, PhD
333 Cedar St
PO Box 208042
New Haven, CT 06520
Tel: 203 785-7377   *Fax:* 203 785-5002
E-mail: keyonna.artis@yale.edu
Length: 1 Yr   *ACGME Approved/Offered Positions:* 3
Program ID: 425-08-11-002

Georgia

Atlanta

Emory University Program
Sponsor: Emory University School of Medicine
Emory University Hospital
Grady Health System
Prgm Director: Daniel J Lee, MD*
Room D125
1364 Clifton Road, NE
Atlanta, GA 30322
Tel: 404 712-4686   *Fax:* 404 712-7908
Length: 1 Yr   *ACGME Approved/Offered Positions:* 2
Program ID: 425-12-21-056

Maryland

Baltimore

University of Maryland Program
Sponsor: University of Maryland Medical System
Prgm Director: Chun Kim MD, MD
22 S Greene Street
Baltimore, MD 21201
Tel: 410 328-6890
Length: 1 Yr   *ACGME Approved/Offered Positions:* 1
Program ID: 425-23-21-061

Massachusetts

Boston

Beth Israel Deaconess Medical Center Program
Sponsor: Beth Israel Deaconess Medical Center
Children's Hospital
Prgm Director: Thomas C Hill, MD
One Deaconess Road
Boston, MA 02215
Tel: 617 754-2615   *Fax:* 617 754-2545
Length: 1 Yr   *ACGME Approved/Offered Positions:* 1
Program ID: 425-24-21-045

Minnesota

Minneapolis

University of Minnesota Program
Sponsor: University of Minnesota Medical School
University of Minnesota Medical Center, Division of Fairview
Prgm Director: Jerry W Froelich, MD
420 Delaware Street, SE, MMC 292
Minneapolis, MN 55455
Tel: 612 626-2371   *Fax:* 612 626-5505
Length: 1 Yr   *ACGME Approved/Offered Positions:* 1
Program ID: 425-26-12-072

Rochester

College of Medicine, Mayo Clinic (Rochester) Program
Sponsor: College of Medicine, Mayo Clinic
Mayo Clinic (Rochester)
Prgm Director: Patrick J Peller, MD
200 First St SW
Rochester, MN 55905
Tel: 507 284-0440   *Fax:* 507 293-3680
E-mail: sorenson.tammy@mayo.edu
Length: 1 Yr   *ACGME Approved/Offered Positions:* 1
Program ID: 425-26-21-019

Note: * indicates a newly appointed program director

New York

New York

New York Presbyterian Hospital (Columbia Campus) Program
Sponsor: New York Presbyterian Hospital
New York Presbyterian Hospital (Columbia Campus)
Prgm Director: Rashid A Fawwaz, MD, PhD
Department of Radiology HP 3 321
180 Fort Washington Avenue
New York, NY 10032
Tel: 212 305-7138   *Fax:* 212 305-4244
E-mail: rf5@columbia.edu
Length: 1 Yr   *ACGME Approved/Offered Positions:* 1
Program ID: 425-35-21-042

New York University School of Medicine Program
Sponsor: New York University School of Medicine
NYU Hospitals Center
Prgm Director: Karen Mourtzikos, MD
560 First Avenue
HW-232
New York, NY 10016
Tel: 212 263-7410   *Fax:* 212 263-2039
Length: 1 Yr   *ACGME Approved/Offered Positions:* 1
Program ID: 425-35-21-007

Syracuse

SUNY Upstate Medical University Program
Sponsor: SUNY Upstate Medical University
Prgm Director: Michele Lisi, MD
750 East Adams Street
Syracuse, NY 13210
Tel: 315 464-7434   *Fax:* 315 464-2570
E-mail: jonesae@upstate.edu
Length: 1 Yr   *ACGME Approved/Offered Positions:* 1
Program ID: 425-35-21-008

North Carolina

Durham

Duke University Hospital Program
Sponsor: Duke University Hospital
Prgm Director: R Edward Coleman, MD
Box 3949, Department of Radiology
Erwin Road
Durham, NC 27710
Tel: 919 684-7245   *Fax:* 919 684-7135
Length: 1 Yr   *ACGME Approved/Offered Positions:* 4
Program ID: 425-36-21-024

Winston-Salem

Wake Forest University School of Medicine Program
Sponsor: Wake Forest University Baptist Medical Center
Prgm Director: Paige B Clark, MD
Medical Center Blvd
Department of Radiology
Winston-Salem, NC 27157
Tel: 336 716-3590   *Fax:* 336 716-6108
Length: 1 Yr   *ACGME Approved/Offered Positions:* 1
Program ID: 425-36-21-025

Ohio

Cincinnati

University Hospital/University of Cincinnati College of Medicine Program
Sponsor: University Hospital Inc
Prgm Director: Mariano Fernandez-Ulloa, MD
234 Goodman Street
Cincinnati, OH 45219
Tel: 513 584-9024   *Fax:* 513 584-7690
E-mail: fernanmo@healthall.com
Length: 1 Yr   *ACGME Approved/Offered Positions:* 1
Program ID: 425-38-13-064

Cleveland

Cleveland Clinic Foundation Program
Sponsor: Cleveland Clinic Foundation
Cleveland Clinic Hospital
Prgm Director: Donald R Neumann, MD, PhD
9500 Euclid Avenue
Cleveland, OH 44195
Tel: 216 444-2193   *Fax:* 216 444-3943
Length: 1 Yr   *ACGME Approved/Offered Positions:* 2
Program ID: 425-38-21-062

University Hospitals Case Medical Center Program
Sponsor: University Hospitals Case Medical Center
Prgm Director: James K O'Donnell, MD
Diagnostic Radiology Department
11100 Euclid Avenue
Cleveland, OH 44106
Tel: 216 844-1000   *Fax:* 216 844-3106
E-mail: Marianne.Chaloupek@uhhospitals.org
Length: 1 Yr   *ACGME Approved/Offered Positions:* 2
Program ID: 425-38-12-068

Columbus

Ohio State University Hospital Program
Sponsor: Ohio State University Hospital
Prgm Director: Nathan C Hall, MD, PhD
1654 Upham Drive
630 Means Hall
Columbus, OH 43210
Tel: 614 293-5774   *Fax:* 614 293-7806
Length: 1 Yr   *ACGME Approved/Offered Positions:* 1
Program ID: 425-38-13-070

Pennsylvania

Philadelphia

University of Pennsylvania Program
Sponsor: University of Pennsylvania Health System
Prgm Director: Chaitanya Divgi, MD
3400 Spruce Street, 110 Donner
Division of Nuclear Medicine
Philadelphia, PA 19104
Tel: 215 615-3687
Length: 1 Yr   *ACGME Approved/Offered Positions:* 6
Program ID: 425-41-21-043

Texas

Dallas

Baylor University Medical Center Program
Sponsor: Baylor University Medical Center
Prgm Director: Hamid R Latifi, MD, MA
3500 Gaston Avenue
Department of Radiology
Dallas, TX 75246
Tel: 214 820-6065   *Fax:* 214 820-2380
E-mail: HamidL@baylorhealth.edu
Length: 1 Yr   *ACGME Approved/Offered Positions:* 1
Program ID: 425-48-22-066

University of Texas Southwestern Medical School Program
Sponsor: University of Texas Southwestern Medical School
Dallas County Hospital District-Parkland Memorial Hospital
Dallas VA Medical Center
Prgm Director: William A Erdman, MD
5323 Harry Hines Boulevard
Dallas, TX 75390
Tel: 214 590-5120   *Fax:* 214 590-2720
E-mail: dianna.otterstad@utsouthwestern.edu
Length: 1 Yr   *ACGME Approved/Offered Positions:* 1
Program ID: 425-48-21-027

Utah

Salt Lake City

University of Utah Program
Sponsor: University of Utah Medical Center
Prgm Director: Kathryn A Morton, MD
Department of Radiology
30 North 1900 East, #1A71
Salt Lake City, UT 84132
Tel: 801 581-7553   *Fax:* 801 581-2414
Length: 1 Yr   *ACGME Approved/Offered Positions:* 1
Program ID: 425-49-31-071

Virginia

Charlottesville

University of Virginia Program
Sponsor: University of Virginia Medical Center
Prgm Director: Patrice K Rehm, MD
PO Box 800170
Charlottesville, VA 22908
Tel: 434 924-9391   *Fax:* 434 982-1618
Length: 1 Yr   *ACGME Approved/Offered Positions:* 1
Program ID: 425-51-11-028

West Virginia

Morgantown

West Virginia University Program
Sponsor: West Virginia University School of Medicine
West Virginia University Hospitals
Prgm Director: Gary D Marano, MD
2278 Health Sciences South, WVU PET Center
PO Box 9235
Morgantown, WV 26506
Tel: 304 293-1876   *Fax:* 304 293-3899
E-mail: jfast@hsc.wvu.edu
Length: 1 Yr   *ACGME Approved/Offered Positions:* 1
Program ID: 425-55-21-063

Programs

Obstetrics and Gynecology

Alabama

Birmingham

University of Alabama Medical Center Program
Sponsor: University of Alabama Hospital
Prgm Director: Larry C Kilgore, MD
619 19th Street South, OHB 549
Birmingham, AL 35249
Tel: 205 934-5631 *Fax:* 205 975-6411
Length: 4 Yrs *ACGME Approved/Offered Positions:* 28
Program ID: 220-01-11-018

Mobile

University of South Alabama Program
Sponsor: University of South Alabama Hospitals
USA Children's and Women's Hospital
Prgm Director: Craig D Sherman, MD
Department of Obstetrics-Gynecology
251 Cox Street, Suite 100
Mobile, AL 36604
Tel: 251 415-1557 *Fax:* 251 415-1552
E-mail: usaobgyn@jaguar1.usouthal.edu
Length: 4 Yrs *ACGME Approved/Offered Positions:* 16
Program ID: 220-01-21-020

Arizona

Phoenix

Banner Good Samaritan Medical Center Program
Sponsor: Banner Good Samaritan Medical Center
Prgm Director: John H Mattox, MD
Department of Obstetrics-Gynecology
1111 East McDowell Road, WT 4
Phoenix, AZ 85006
Tel: 602 239-4344 *Fax:* 602 239-2359
E-mail: janet.r.anderson@bannerhealth.com
Length: 4 Yrs *ACGME Approved/Offered Positions:* 32
Program ID: 220-03-21-024

Phoenix Integrated Residency Program
Sponsor: Maricopa Medical Center
St Joseph's Hospital and Medical Center
Prgm Director: R Michael Brady, MD
Department of Obstetrics-Gynecology
2601 East Roosevelt St
Phoenix, AZ 85008
Tel: 602 344-5444 *Fax:* 602 344-5894
E-mail: rbrady2@chw.edu
Length: 4 Yrs *ACGME Approved/Offered Positions:* 30
Program ID: 220-03-21-328

Tucson

University of Arizona Program
Sponsor: University of Arizona College of Medicine
University Medical Center
Prgm Director: James Maciulla, MD
Department of Obstetrics & Gynecology
1501 North Campbell Avenue, Box 245078
Tucson, AZ 85724
Tel: 520 626-6636 *Fax:* 520 626-2514
E-mail: soniag@email.arizona.edu
Length: 4 Yrs *ACGME Approved/Offered Positions:* 17
Program ID: 220-03-21-025

Arkansas

Little Rock

University of Arkansas for Medical Sciences Program
Sponsor: University of Arkansas College of Medicine
UAMS Medical Center
Prgm Director: Paul J Wendel, MD
Department of Obstetrics-Gynecology
4301 West Markham St, Slot 518
Little Rock, AR 72205
Tel: 501 526-7569 *Fax:* 501 686-8945
Length: 4 Yrs *ACGME Approved/Offered Positions:* 16
Program ID: 220-04-11-026

California

Bakersfield

Kern Medical Center Program
Sponsor: Kern Medical Center
Prgm Director: Antonio L Garcia, MD
Department of Obstetrics-Gynecology
1830 Flower Street
Bakersfield, CA 93305
Tel: 661 326-2236 *Fax:* 661 326-2235
E-mail: morenoa@kernmedctr.com
Length: 4 Yrs *ACGME Approved/Offered Positions:* 12
Program ID: 220-05-31-027

Fresno

University of California (San Francisco)/Fresno Program
Sponsor: UCSF Fresno Medical Education Program
Community Medical Centers (Fresno)
Prgm Director: Conrad R Chao, MD
Medical Education and Research Center
155 N Fresno Street
Fresno, CA 93701
Tel: 559 499-6545 *Fax:* 559 499-6541
Length: 4 Yrs *ACGME Approved/Offered Positions:* 12
Program ID: 220-05-31-029

Loma Linda

Loma Linda University Program
Sponsor: Loma Linda University Medical Center
Kaiser Foundation Hospital (Fontana)
Prgm Director: Melissa Y Kidder, MD
Dept of Obstetrics/Gynecology
11234 Anderson Street, LLHC/Concord Bldg, Ste E
Loma Linda, CA 92350
Tel: 909 558-6538 *Fax:* 909 558-0438
Length: 4 Yrs *ACGME Approved/Offered Positions:* 24
Program ID: 220-05-21-329

Los Angeles

Cedars-Sinai Medical Center Program
Sponsor: Cedars-Sinai Medical Center
California Hospital Medical Center
Prgm Director: Dotun Ogunyemi, MD
8700 Beverly Boulevard
Los Angeles, CA 90048
Tel: 310 423-3394 *Fax:* 310 423-0313
E-mail: OgunyemiD@cshs.org
Length: 4 Yrs *ACGME Approved/Offered Positions:* 24
Program ID: 220-05-31-034

Kaiser Permanente Southern California (Los Angeles) Program
Sponsor: Kaiser Permanente Southern California
Kaiser Foundation Hospital (Los Angeles)
Prgm Director: Michael W Weinberger, MD
Department of Obstetrics-Gynecology
4900 Sunset Boulevard, 5th Fl
Los Angeles, CA 90027
Tel: 323 783-4321 *Fax:* 323 783-0731
Length: 4 Yrs *ACGME Approved/Offered Positions:* 20
Program ID: 220-05-12-035

UCLA Medical Center Program
Sponsor: UCLA David Geffen School of Medicine/UCLA Medical Center
Olive View/UCLA Medical Center
UCLA Medical Center
Prgm Director: Lauren Nathan, MD*
10833 Le Conte Avenue, Room 27-139 CHS
Los Angeles, CA 90095
Tel: 310 206-6675 *Fax:* 310 206-3670
E-mail: lnathan@mednet.ucla.edu
Length: 4 Yrs *ACGME Approved/Offered Positions:* 31
Program ID: 220-05-31-038

University of Southern California/ LAC+USC Medical Center Program
Sponsor: University of Southern California/LAC+USC Medical Center
LAC+USC Medical Center
Prgm Director: Laila I Muderspach, MD
1240 North Mission Road, Rm 5K-13
Los Angeles, CA 90033
Tel: 323 226-3309 *Fax:* 323 226-2989
Length: 4 Yrs *ACGME Approved/Offered Positions:* 32
Program ID: 220-05-11-036

White Memorial Medical Center Program
Sponsor: White Memorial Medical Center
Prgm Director: Cinna T Wohlmuth, MD
1720 Cesar E Chavez Aveue
Los Angeles, CA 90033
Tel: 323 260-5810 *Fax:* 323 881-8601
E-mail: WohlmuCT@ah.org
Length: 4 Yrs *ACGME Approved/Offered Positions:* 12
Program ID: 220-05-21-039

Oakland

Kaiser Permanente Medical Group (Northern California/Oakland) Program
Sponsor: Kaiser Permanente Medical Group (Northern California)
Kaiser Permanente Medical Center (Oakland)
Prgm Director: Laura Minikel, MD
Department of Obstetrics & Gynecology
280 West MacArthur Blvd
Oakland, CA 94611
Tel: 510 752-7672 *Fax:* 510 752-1571
Length: 4 Yrs *ACGME Approved/Offered Positions:* 16
Program ID: 220-05-12-040

Orange

University of California (Irvine) Program
Sponsor: University of California (Irvine) Medical Center
Long Beach Memorial Medical Center
Prgm Director: Carol A Major, MD
Department of Obstetrics-Gynecology
101 City Drive, Building 56, Suite 800, Rte 81
Orange, CA 92868
Tel: 714 456-6707 *Fax:* 714 456-8360
E-mail: dogarcia@uci.edu
Length: 4 Yrs *ACGME Approved/Offered Positions:* 24
Program ID: 220-05-21-031

Note: * indicates a newly appointed program director

Sacramento

University of California (Davis) Health System Program

Sponsor: University of California (Davis) Health System
Kaiser Foundation Hospital (Sacramento)
University of California (Davis) Medical Center
Prgm Director: Mary C Ciotti, MD
Lawrence J Ellison Ambulatory Care
4860 Y Street, Suite 2500
Sacramento, CA 95817
Tel: 916 734-6019 *Fax:* 916 734-6031
Length: 4 Yrs *ACGME Approved/Offered Positions:* 24
Program ID: 220-05-21-028

San Diego

Naval Medical Center (San Diego) Program

Sponsor: Naval Medical Center (San Diego)
Prgm Director: William M Leininger, MD
Department of Obstetrics-Gynecology
34730 Bob Wilson Drive, Suite 100
San Diego, CA 92134
Tel: 619 532-9596 *Fax:* 619 532-6578
Length: 4 Yrs *ACGME Approved/Offered Positions:* 20
Program ID: 220-05-11-012
Uniformed Services Program

University of California (San Diego) Program

Sponsor: University of California (San Diego) Medical
    Center
Kaiser Foundation Hospital (San Diego)
Prgm Director: Christine B Miller, MD
200 West Arbor Drive, #8433
San Diego, CA 92103
Tel: 619 543-6922 *Fax:* 619 543-5767
E-mail: obresidents@ucsd.edu
Length: 4 Yrs *ACGME Approved/Offered Positions:* 24
Program ID: 220-05-21-044

San Francisco

Kaiser Permanente Medical Group (Northern California)/San Francisco Program

Sponsor: Kaiser Permanente Medical Group (Northern
    California)
Kaiser Permanente Medical Center (San Francisco)
Prgm Director: Gavin F Jacobson, MD*
2425 Geary Blvd Mezzanine 160
San Francisco, CA 94115
Tel: 415 833-8362 *Fax:* 415 833-4983
E-mail: gavin.jacobson@kp.org
Length: 4 Yrs *ACGME Approved/Offered Positions:* 16
Program ID: 220-05-12-045

University of California (San Francisco) Program

Sponsor: University of California (San Francisco) School
    of Medicine
San Francisco General Hospital Medical Center
UCSF and Mount Zion Medical Centers
Prgm Director: Amy M Autry, MD
Dept of Obstetrics-Gynecology
505 Parnassus Ave, Box 0132, M-1483
San Francisco, CA 94143
Tel: 415 476-5192 *Fax:* 415 476-1811
E-mail: schulerv@obgyn.ucsf.edu
Length: 4 Yrs *ACGME Approved/Offered Positions:* 36
Program ID: 220-05-21-047

San Jose

Santa Clara Valley Medical Center Program

Sponsor: Santa Clara Valley Medical Center
Prgm Director: Roger A Spencer, MD
Department of Obstetrics-Gynecology
751 South Bascom Avenue
San Jose, CA 95128
Tel: 408 885-5550 *Fax:* 408 885-5577
Length: 4 Yrs *ACGME Approved/Offered Positions:* 16
Program ID: 220-05-21-333

Santa Clara

Kaiser Permanente Medical Group (Northern California)/Santa Clara Program

Sponsor: Kaiser Permanente Medical Group (Northern
    California)
Kaiser Permanente Medical Center (Santa Clara)
Prgm Director: David K Levin, MD
Graduate Medical Education Office
710 Lawrence Expressway, Dept 384
Santa Clara, CA 95051
Tel: 408 851-3018 *Fax:* 408 851-3839
Length: 4 Yrs *ACGME Approved/Offered Positions:* 16
Program ID: 220-05-12-311

Stanford

Stanford University Program

Sponsor: Stanford Hospital and Clinics
Lucile Salter Packard Children's Hospital at Stanford
Prgm Director: Maurice L Druzin, MD
Department of Obstetrics/Gynecology
300 Pasteur Drive, Rm HH333
Stanford, CA 94305
Tel: 650 498-7570 *Fax:* 650 723-7737
E-mail: jsignor@stanford.edu
Length: 4 Yrs *ACGME Approved/Offered Positions:* 16
Program ID: 220-05-21-048

Torrance

Los Angeles County-Harbor-UCLA Medical Center Program

Sponsor: Los Angeles County-Harbor-UCLA Medical
    Center
Kaiser Foundation Hospital (Bellflower)
Prgm Director: Siri L Kjos, MD, MPA
Department of Obstetrics and Gynecology
1000 West Carson Street, Box 3
Torrance, CA 90509
Tel: 310 222-3565 *Fax:* 310 782-8148
E-mail: ObgynResidency@obgyn.humc.edu
Length: 4 Yrs *ACGME Approved/Offered Positions:* 20
Program ID: 220-05-21-050

Colorado

Aurora

University of Colorado Denver Program

Sponsor: University of Colorado Denver School of
    Medicine
Denver Health Medical Center
HealthONE Rose Medical Center
University of Colorado Hospital
Prgm Director: Ruben Alvero, MD*
Dept of Ob/Gyn
12631 E 17th Avenue, B198-6
Aurora, CO 80045
Tel: 303 724-2037
E-mail: ruben.alvero@uchsc.edu
Length: 4 Yrs *ACGME Approved/Offered Positions:* 36
Program ID: 220-07-31-052

Denver

Exempla St Joseph Hospital Program

Sponsor: Exempla St Joseph Hospital
Prgm Director: Nicholas A Peros, MD
Ob/Gyn Residency Program
1835 Franklin Street
Denver, CO 80218
Tel: 303 837-7595 *Fax:* 303 837-6677
E-mail: waltonl@exempla.org
Length: 4 Yrs *ACGME Approved/Offered Positions:* 20
Program ID: 220-07-21-051

Connecticut

Bridgeport

Bridgeport Hospital/Yale University Program

Sponsor: Bridgeport Hospital
Prgm Director: Stephen D Rosenman, MD, BS
Department of Obstetrics-Gynecology
PO Box 5000
Bridgeport, CT 06610
Tel: 203 384-3011 *Fax:* 203 384-3715
E-mail: psrose@bpthosp.org
Length: 4 Yrs *ACGME Approved/Offered Positions:* 12
Program ID: 220-08-11-054

Danbury

Danbury Hospital Program

Sponsor: Danbury Hospital
Prgm Director: Richard Ruben, MD
24 Hospital Ave
Danbury, CT 06810
Tel: 203 739-7872 *Fax:* 203 739-8750
E-mail: Richard.Ruben@danhosp.org
Length: 4 Yrs *ACGME Approved/Offered Positions:* 12
Program ID: 220-08-21-055

Farmington

University of Connecticut Program

Sponsor: University of Connecticut School of Medicine
Hartford Hospital
Hospital for Central Connecticut
Univ of Connecticut Health Center/John Dempsey
    Hospital
Prgm Director: John F Greene Jr, MD
263 Farmington Avenue
Farmington, CT 06030
Tel: 860 679-2853 *Fax:* 860 679-1228
Length: 4 Yrs *ACGME Approved/Offered Positions:* 36
Program ID: 220-08-21-355

Hartford

St Francis Hospital and Medical Center Program

Sponsor: St Francis Hospital and Medical Center
Prgm Director: Howard A Shaw, MD
Department of Obstetrics-Gynecology
114 Woodland Street
Hartford, CT 06105
Tel: 860 714-5170 *Fax:* 860 714-8008
Length: 4 Yrs *ACGME Approved/Offered Positions:* 16
Program ID: 220-08-11-059

Programs

New Haven

Yale-New Haven Medical Center Program
Sponsor: Yale-New Haven Hospital
Prgm Director: Errol R Norwitz, MD, PhD
333 Cedar Street, LCI 800
PO Box 208063
New Haven, CT 06520
Tel: 203 785-5855   *Fax:* 203 785-6885
E-mail: errol.norwitz@yale.edu
Length: 4 Yrs   *ACGME Approved/Offered Positions:* 25
Program ID: 220-08-21-060

Stamford

Stamford Hospital/Columbia University College of Physicians and Surgeons Program
Sponsor: Stamford Hospital
Prgm Director: Frances W Ginsburg, MD
Department of Obstetrics-Gynecology
30 Shelburne Road
Stamford, CT 06904
Tel: 203 276-7853   *Fax:* 203 276-7259
E-mail: fginsburg@stamhealth.org
Length: 4 Yrs   *ACGME Approved/Offered Positions:* 12
Program ID: 220-08-11-061

Delaware

Wilmington

Christiana Care Health Services Program
Sponsor: Christiana Care Health Services Inc
Prgm Director: Anthony C Sciscione, DO
4755 Ogletown Stanton Road
PO Box 6001
Newark, DE 19718
Tel: 302 733-6565   *Fax:* 302 733-2330
Length: 4 Yrs   *ACGME Approved/Offered Positions:* 16
Program ID: 220-09-11-062

District of Columbia

Washington

George Washington University Program
Sponsor: George Washington University School of Medicine
George Washington University Hospital (UHS)
Holy Cross Hospital of Silver Spring
Inova Fairfax Hospital
Prgm Director: Nancy D Gaba, MD
Department of Obstetrics-Gynecology
2150 Pennsylvania Avenue, NW 6A-429
Washington, DC 20037
Tel: 202 741-2532   *Fax:* 202 741-2550
Length: 4 Yrs   *ACGME Approved/Offered Positions:* 40
Program ID: 220-10-21-064

Georgetown University Hospital Program
Sponsor: Georgetown University Hospital
Virginia Hospital Center-Arlington
Washington Hospital Center
Prgm Director: Christine Colie, MD*
Department of Obstetrics-Gynecology
3800 Reservoir Road, NW (3 PHC)
Washington, DC 20007
Tel: 202 444-8531   *Fax:* 202 444-4018
E-mail: perryal@gunet.georgetown.edu
Length: 4 Yrs   *ACGME Approved/Offered Positions:* 24
Program ID: 220-10-21-063

Howard University Program
Sponsor: Howard University Hospital
Prince George's Hospital Center
Providence Hospital
Prgm Director: Diana P Broomfield, MD, MBA*
Department of Obstetrics-Gynecology
2041 Georgia Avenue, NW
Washington, DC 20060
Tel: 202 865-3168   *Fax:* 202 865-4174
E-mail: dbroomfield@huhosp.org
Length: 4 Yrs   *ACGME Approved/Offered Positions:* 16
Program ID: 220-10-21-065

Washington Hospital Center Program
Sponsor: Washington Hospital Center
Prgm Director: John D Buek, MD*
Department of Obstetrics-Gynecology
110 Irving Street, NW, Suite 5 B 63
Washington, DC 20010
Tel: 202 877-8957   *Fax:* 202 877-5435
E-mail: john.d.buek@medstar.net
Length: 4 Yrs   *ACGME Approved/Offered Positions:* 20
Program ID: 220-10-31-067

Florida

Gainesville

University of Florida Program
Sponsor: University of Florida College of Medicine
North Florida Regional Medical Center
Shands Hospital at the University of Florida
Prgm Director: W Patrick Duff, MD
Department of Obstetrics-Gynecology
PO Box 100294
Gainesville, FL 32610
Tel: 352 273-7673   *Fax:* 352 392-2808
E-mail: duffp@ufl.edu
Length: 4 Yrs   *ACGME Approved/Offered Positions:* 16
Program ID: 220-11-11-068

Jacksonville

University of Florida College of Medicine Jacksonville Program
Sponsor: University of Florida College of Medicine Jacksonville
Shands Jacksonville Medical Center
Prgm Director: Deborah S Lyon, MD*
Department of Obstetrics-Gynecology
653-1 West 8th St, LRC 3rd Fl, Box L17
Jacksonville, FL 32209
Tel: 904 244-3112   *Fax:* 904 244-3658
Length: 4 Yrs   *ACGME Approved/Offered Positions:* 24
Program ID: 220-11-21-069

Miami

Jackson Memorial Hospital/Jackson Health System Program
Sponsor: Jackson Memorial Hospital/Jackson Health System
University of Miami Sylvester Comprehensive Cancer Center
Prgm Director: Victor H Gonzalez-Quintero, MD, MPH
Holtz Center Room 4070
1611 NW 12th Avenue
Miami, FL 33136
Tel: 305 585-5640   *Fax:* 305 325-1282
Length: 4 Yrs   *ACGME Approved/Offered Positions:* 36
Program ID: 220-11-21-070

Orlando

Orlando Health Program
Sponsor: Orlando Health
Orlando Regional Medical Center
Winnie Palmer Hospital for Women and Babies
Prgm Director: Stephen J Carlan, MD
Department of Obstetrics-Gynecology
105 West Miller Street
Orlando, FL 32806
Tel: 407 841-5297   *Fax:* 407 481-0182
E-mail: cathy.horowitz@orlandohealth.com
Length: 4 Yrs   *ACGME Approved/Offered Positions:* 28
Program ID: 220-11-12-072

Pensacola

Florida State University College of Medicine (Pensacola) Program
Sponsor: Florida State University College of Medicine
Sacred Heart Hospital of Pensacola
Prgm Director: Clyde H Dorr II, MD
Division of Obstetrics-Gynecology
5045 Carpenter Creek Drive
Pensacola, FL 32503
Tel: 850 416-2450   *Fax:* 850 416-2467
Length: 4 Yrs   *ACGME Approved/Offered Positions:* 12
Program ID: 220-11-21-073

St. Petersburg

Bayfront Medical Center Program
Sponsor: Bayfront Medical Center
Prgm Director: Karen A Raimer, MD
Obstetrics/Gynecology Residency Program
700 6th Street South
St Petersburg, FL 33701
Tel: 727 893-6917   *Fax:* 727 893-6978
E-mail: obresidency@bayfront.org
Length: 4 Yrs   *ACGME Approved/Offered Positions:* 16
Program ID: 220-11-11-074

Tampa

University of South Florida Program
Sponsor: University of South Florida College of Medicine
H Lee Moffitt Cancer Center
Tampa General Hospital
Prgm Director: William N Spellacy, MD
2A Columbia Drive
STC, 6th Floor
Tampa, FL 33606
Tel: 813 259-8542   *Fax:* 813 259-8593
E-mail: kpaulina@hsc.usf.edu
Length: 4 Yrs   *ACGME Approved/Offered Positions:* 20
Program ID: 220-11-21-075

Georgia

Atlanta

Emory University Program
Sponsor: Emory University School of Medicine
Crawford Long Hospital of Emory University
Grady Health System
Prgm Director: Carla Roberts, MD, PhD*
Department of Gynecology-Obstetrics
69 Jesse Hill Jr Drive, SE
Atlanta, GA 30303
Tel: 404 616-3540   *Fax:* 404 521-3589
Length: 4 Yrs   *ACGME Approved/Offered Positions:* 37
Program ID: 220-12-21-076

Note: * indicates a newly appointed program director

Morehouse School of Medicine Program

Sponsor: Morehouse School of Medicine
Grady Health System
Tenet-South Fulton Medical Center
Prgm Director: Franklyn H Geary Jr, MD
Department of Obstetrics-Gynecology
720 Westview Drive, SW
Atlanta, GA 30310
Tel: 404 616-1692   *Fax:* 404 616-4131
E-mail: obgynres@msm.edu
Length: 4 Yrs   *ACGME Approved/Offered Positions:* 12
Program ID: 220-12-21-348

Augusta

Medical College of Georgia Program

Sponsor: Medical College of Georgia
University Hospital
Prgm Director: Michael Macfee, MD
1120 Fifteenth Street, BA 7310
Augusta, GA 30912
Tel: 706 721-2541   *Fax:* 706 721-2122
Length: 4 Yrs   *ACGME Approved/Offered Positions:* 16
Program ID: 220-12-21-078

Macon

Mercer University School of Medicine Program

Sponsor: Medical Center of Central Georgia
Prgm Director: Michael M Makii, MD
Department of Obstetrics-Gynecology
729 Pine Street
Macon, GA 31201
Tel: 478 633-1056   *Fax:* 478 749-9171
E-mail: makii.michael@mccg.org
Length: 4 Yrs   *ACGME Approved/Offered Positions:* 12
Program ID: 220-12-11-079

Savannah

Mercer University School of Medicine (Savannah) Program

Sponsor: Memorial Health-University Medical Center
Prgm Director: Donald G Gallup, MD
PO Box 23089
Savannah, GA 31403
Tel: 912 350-1368   *Fax:* 912 350-7969
Length: 4 Yrs   *ACGME Approved/Offered Positions:* 16
Program ID: 220-12-11-080

Hawaii

Honolulu

University of Hawaii Program

Sponsor: University of Hawaii John A Burns School of
   Medicine
Kapiolani Medical Center for Women and Children
Queen's Medical Center
Prgm Director: Janet M Burlingame, MD
Department of Obstetrics-Gynecology
1319 Punahou Street, Room 824
Honolulu, HI 96826
Tel: 808 203-6514   *Fax:* 808 955-2174
E-mail: gkamikaw@hawaii.edu
Length: 4 Yrs   *ACGME Approved/Offered Positions:* 25
Program ID: 220-14-31-081

Tripler AMC

Tripler Army Medical Center Program

Sponsor: Tripler Army Medical Center
Prgm Director: Christina C Hill, MD
Attn: MCHK-OB (OB/GYN Residency Director)
1 Jarrett White Road
Tripler AMC, HI 96859
Tel: 808 433-5184   *Fax:* 808 433-1552
Length: 4 Yrs   *ACGME Approved/Offered Positions:* 20
Program ID: 220-14-12-007
Uniformed Services Program

Illinois

Chicago

Advocate Illinois Masonic Medical Center Program

Sponsor: Advocate Illinois Masonic Medical Center
Prgm Director: Brenda Darrell, MD
Department of OB/GYN, 4th Floor
836 West Wellington Avenue
Chicago, IL 60657
Tel: 773 296-5591   *Fax:* 773 296-7207
E-mail: brenda.mcclain@advocatehealth.com
Length: 4 Yrs   *ACGME Approved/Offered Positions:* 12
Program ID: 220-16-21-085

John H Stroger Hospital of Cook County Program

Sponsor: John H Stroger Hospital of Cook County
Prgm Director: Fidel Abrego, MD, MBA
Department of Obstetrics-Gynecology
1901 West Harrison Street
Chicago, IL 60612
Tel: 312 864-5947   *Fax:* 312 864-9579
E-mail: ablake2@ccbhs.org
Length: 4 Yrs   *ACGME Approved/Offered Positions:* 16
Program ID: 220-16-31-084

McGaw Medical Center of Northwestern University Program

Sponsor: McGaw Medical Center of Northwestern
   University
Evanston Hospital
Northwestern Memorial Hospital
Prentice Women's Hospital
Prgm Director: Magdy Milad, MD, MS
250 East Superior, Suite 05-2177
Chicago, IL 60611
Tel: 312 472-4673   *Fax:* 312 472-4687
E-mail: rpoland@nmh.org
Length: 4 Yrs   *ACGME Approved/Offered Positions:* 40
Program ID: 220-16-21-089

Mercy Hospital and Medical Center Program

Sponsor: Mercy Hospital and Medical Center
Prgm Director: Susan H Porto, MD
Department of Obstetrics-Gynecology
2525 South Michigan Avenue
Chicago, IL 60616
Tel: 312 567-2490   *Fax:* 312 567-2628
E-mail: apagerivers@mercy-chicago.org
Length: 4 Yrs   *ACGME Approved/Offered Positions:* 12
Program ID: 220-16-11-086

Mount Sinai Hospital Medical Center of Chicago Program

Sponsor: Mount Sinai Hospital Medical Center of
   Chicago
Prgm Director: Josef Blankstein, MD
Department of Obstetrics-Gynecology
California Ave at 15th St, Rm F208
Chicago, IL 60608
Tel: 773 257-6459   *Fax:* 773 257-6359
E-mail: walsh@sinai.org
Length: 4 Yrs   *ACGME Approved/Offered Positions:* 12
Program ID: 220-16-11-088

Rush University Medical Center Program

Sponsor: Rush University Medical Center
Prgm Director: Xavier F Pombar, DO
Department of Obstetrics-Gynecology
1653 West Congress Parkway, 720 Pavilion
Chicago, IL 60612
Tel: 312 942-6610   *Fax:* 312 942-6606
E-mail: obgyn_residency@rush.edu
Length: 4 Yrs   *ACGME Approved/Offered Positions:* 24
Program ID: 220-16-21-090

St Joseph Hospital Program

Sponsor: St Joseph Hospital
Prgm Director: Abdol H Hosseinian, MD
Department of Obstetrics-Gynecology
2900 North Lake Shore Dirve
Chicago, IL 60657
Tel: 773 665-3132   *Fax:* 773 665-3718
E-mail: msamoy@reshealthcare.org
Length: 4 Yrs   *ACGME Approved/Offered Positions:* 12
Program ID: 220-16-11-091

University of Chicago Program

Sponsor: University of Chicago Medical Center
MacNeal Hospital
Prgm Director: Anita K Blanchard, MD
Pritzker School of Medicine
5841 S Maryland Ave
Chicago, IL 60637
Tel: 773 834-0598   *Fax:* 773 702-0840
E-mail: egilmore@babies.bsd.uchicago.edu
Length: 4 Yrs   *ACGME Approved/Offered Positions:* 24
Program ID: 220-16-11-092

University of Illinois College of Medicine at Chicago Program

Sponsor: University of Illinois College of Medicine at
   Chicago
Advocate Christ Medical Center
University of Illinois Hospital and Clinics
Prgm Director: Gary Loy, MD, MPH
Department of Ob-Gyn (M/C 808)
820 South Wood Street
Chicago, IL 60612
Tel: 312 996-0532   *Fax:* 312 996-4238
E-mail: sdowty@uic.edu
Length: 4 Yrs   *ACGME Approved/Offered Positions:* 28
Program ID: 220-16-11-093

Evanston

St Francis Hospital of Evanston Program

Sponsor: St Francis Hospital
Evanston Hospital
Resurrection Medical Center
Prgm Director: John V Knaus, DO
Department of Obstetrics-Gynecology
355 North Ridge Avenue
Evanston, IL 60202
Tel: 847 316-6229   *Fax:* 847 316-3307
E-mail: cclarke@reshealthcare.org
Length: 4 Yrs   *ACGME Approved/Offered Positions:* 8
Program ID: 220-16-21-094

Maywood

Loyola University Program

Sponsor: Loyola University Medical Center
Gottlieb Memorial Hospital
Prgm Director: John G Gianopoulos, MD*
Department of Obstetrics-Gynecology
2160 South First Avenue
Maywood, IL 60153
Tel: 708 216-5423   *Fax:* 708 216-9435
Length: 4 Yrs   *ACGME Approved/Offered Positions:* 16
Program ID: 220-16-21-095

Programs

Park Ridge

Advocate Lutheran General Hospital Program

Sponsor: Advocate Lutheran General Hospital
Prgm Director: Daniel E Pesch, MD*
Department of Obstetrics-Gynecology
1775 Dempster Street
Park Ridge, IL 60068
Tel: 847 723-6994   *Fax:* 847 723-1658
Length: 4 Yrs   *ACGME Approved/Offered Positions:* 12
Program ID: 220-16-21-325

Peoria

University of Illinois College of Medicine at Peoria Program

Sponsor: University of Illinois College of Medicine at Peoria
OSF St Francis Medical Center
Prgm Director: Rida W Boulos, MD, MPH
OSF Saint Francis Medical Center
530 NE Glen Oak Avenue
Peoria, IL 61637
Tel: 309 655-4163   *Fax:* 309 655-3739
E-mail: shearhod@uic.edu
Length: 4 Yrs   *ACGME Approved/Offered Positions:* 12
Program ID: 220-16-11-096

Springfield

Southern Illinois University Program

Sponsor: Southern Illinois University School of Medicine
Memorial Medical Center
St John's Hospital
Prgm Director: Erica Nelson, MD
Department of Obstetrics-Gynecology
PO Box 19640
Springfield, IL 62794
Tel: 217 545-6498   *Fax:* 217 545-7958
Length: 4 Yrs   *ACGME Approved/Offered Positions:* 12
Program ID: 220-16-21-097

Indiana

Indianapolis

Indiana University School of Medicine Program

Sponsor: Indiana University School of Medicine
Clarian Indiana University Hospital
Clarian Methodist Hospital of Indiana
William N Wishard Memorial Hospital
Prgm Director: Mary P Abernathy, MD, ScD
Department of Obstetrics-Gynecology
550 N University Blvd, RM 2440
Indianapolis, IN 46202
Tel: 317 274-8182   *Fax:* 317 630-2631
E-mail: obrespgm@iupui.edu
Length: 4 Yrs   *ACGME Approved/Offered Positions:* 40
Program ID: 220-17-21-099

St Vincent Hospital and Health Care Center Program

Sponsor: St Vincent Hospitals and Health Care Center
Prgm Director: Eric A Strand, MD
Department of Obstetrics-Gynecology
8111 Township Line Road
Indianapolis, IN 46260
Tel: 317 415-7503   *Fax:* 317 415-7529
E-mail: eastrand@stvincent.org
Length: 4 Yrs   *ACGME Approved/Offered Positions:* 20
Program ID: 220-17-11-101

Iowa

Iowa City

University of Iowa Hospitals and Clinics Program

Sponsor: University of Iowa Hospitals and Clinics
Prgm Director: Jennifer R Niebyl, MD
Dept of Obstetrics and Gynecology
200 Hawkins Drive
Iowa City, IA 52242
Tel: 319 356-1976   *Fax:* 319 384-8620
E-mail: jennifer-niebyl@uiowa.edu
Length: 4 Yrs   *ACGME Approved/Offered Positions:* 16
Program ID: 220-18-21-102

Kansas

Kansas City

University of Kansas School of Medicine Program

Sponsor: University of Kansas School of Medicine
University of Kansas Hospital
Prgm Director: John Wiley, MD*
Department of Obstetrics-Gynecology
3901 Rainbow Boulevard Wescoe 3rd
Kansas City, KS 66160
Tel: 913 588-2861   *Fax:* 913 588-6271
E-mail: jwiley@kumc.edu
Length: 4 Yrs   *ACGME Approved/Offered Positions:* 12
Program ID: 220-19-11-103

Wichita

University of Kansas (Wichita) Program

Sponsor: University of Kansas School of Medicine (Wichita)
Wesley Medical Center
Prgm Director: Travis W Stembridge, MD
550 N Hillside
Wichita, KS 67214
Tel: 316 962-3182   *Fax:* 316 962-3152
Length: 4 Yrs   *ACGME Approved/Offered Positions:* 20
Program ID: 220-19-11-104

Kentucky

Lexington

University of Kentucky College of Medicine Program

Sponsor: University of Kentucky College of Medicine
Central Baptist Hospital
University of Kentucky Hospital
Prgm Director: James E Ferguson II, MD
Department of Obstetrics-Gynecology
800 Rose Street, Room C373
Lexington, KY 40536
Tel: 859 323-6434   *Fax:* 859 257-3181
E-mail: tjnewb2@uky.edu
Length: 4 Yrs   *ACGME Approved/Offered Positions:* 20
Program ID: 220-20-11-105

Louisville

University of Louisville Program

Sponsor: University of Louisville School of Medicine
University of Louisville Hospital
Prgm Director: Christine L Cook, MD
Dept of Obstetrics, Gynecology & Women's Health
Louisville, KY 40292
Tel: 502 561-7441   *Fax:* 502 561-7577
E-mail: christine-cook@louisville.edu
Length: 4 Yrs   *ACGME Approved/Offered Positions:* 24
Program ID: 220-20-21-106

Louisiana

Baton Rouge

Louisiana State University (Baton Rouge) Program

Sponsor: Earl K Long Medical Center
Woman's Hospital
Prgm Director: Duane E Neumann, MD
5825 Airline Highway
Baton Rouge, LA 70805
Tel: 225 358-1179   *Fax:* 225 358-1076
Length: 4 Yrs   *ACGME Approved/Offered Positions:* 16
Program ID: 220-21-13-364

New Orleans

Louisiana State University Program

Sponsor: Louisiana State University School of Medicine
Medical Center of Louisiana at New Orleans
Touro Infirmary
University Medical Center (Lafayette)
Prgm Director: Rodney J Hoxsey, MD
Department of Obstetrics-Gynecology
533 Boliver St, Room 535
New Orleans, LA 70112
Tel: 504 568-4890   *Fax:* 504 568-6496
E-mail: cyeage@lsuhsc.edu
Length: 4 Yrs   *ACGME Approved/Offered Positions:* 28
Program ID: 220-21-21-107

Ochsner Clinic Foundation Program

Sponsor: Ochsner Clinic Foundation
Leonard J Chabert Medical Center
Prgm Director: Elizabeth R Lapeyre, MD*
Graduate Medical Education
1514 Jefferson Highway
New Orleans, LA 70121
Tel: 504 842-4155   *Fax:* 504 842-4152
E-mail: elapeyre@ochsner.org
Length: 4 Yrs   *ACGME Approved/Offered Positions:* 16
Program ID: 220-21-22-109

Tulane University Program

Sponsor: Tulane University School of Medicine
Huey P Long Regional Medical Center
Medical Center of Louisiana at New Orleans
Tulane University Hospital and Clinics
Prgm Director: Gabriella Pridjian, MD
Department of Obstetrics-Gynecology
1430 Tulane Avenue, SL 11
New Orleans, LA 70112
Tel: 504 988-2145   *Fax:* 504 988-2943
E-mail: kmorse@tulane.edu
Length: 4 Yrs   *ACGME Approved/Offered Positions:* 28
Program ID: 220-21-21-108

Shreveport

Louisiana State University (Shreveport) Program

Sponsor: LSU Health Sciences Center-University Hospital
E A Conway Medical Center
Prgm Director: James B Unger, MD, MBA
1501 Kings Highway
PO Box 33932
Shreveport, LA 71130
Tel: 318 675-8295   *Fax:* 318 675-4671
E-mail: junger@lsuhsc.edu
Length: 4 Yrs   *ACGME Approved/Offered Positions:* 24
Program ID: 220-21-11-110

Note: * indicates a newly appointed program director

Maine

Portland

Maine Medical Center Program
Sponsor: Maine Medical Center
Prgm Director: Donald W Wiper III, MD
Dept of Obstetrics/Gynecology
22 Bramhall Street
Portland, ME 04102
Tel: 207 662-2749   *Fax:* 207 662-6252
E-mail: wiperd@mmc.org
Length: 4 Yrs   *ACGME Approved/Offered Positions:* 16
Program ID: 220-22-11-111

Maryland

Baltimore

Franklin Square Hospital Center Program
Sponsor: Franklin Square Hospital Center
Prgm Director: Donovan Dietrick, MD
Dept of Ob/Gyn
9000 Franklin Square Drive
Baltimore, MD 21237
Tel: 443 777-6123   *Fax:* 443 777-8180
Length: 4 Yrs   *ACGME Approved/Offered Positions:* 12
Program ID: 220-23-21-112

Johns Hopkins University Program
Sponsor: Johns Hopkins University School of Medicine
Greater Baltimore Medical Center
Johns Hopkins Bayview Medical Center
Johns Hopkins Hospital
Prgm Director: Jessica L Bienstock, MD, MPH
Phipps 279
600 N Wolfe Street
Baltimore, MD 21287
Tel: 410 955-8487   *Fax:* 410 502-6683
Length: 4 Yrs   *ACGME Approved/Offered Positions:* 36
Program ID: 220-23-21-114

Sinai Hospital of Baltimore Program
Sponsor: Sinai Hospital of Baltimore
Prgm Director: Marc Lowen, MD
Department of Obstetrics-Gynecology
2401 W Belvedere Avenue, Blaustein Bldg 1st Fl
Baltimore, MD 21215
Tel: 410 601-9197   *Fax:* 410 601-8862
E-mail: mlowen6701@comcast.net
Length: 4 Yrs   *ACGME Approved/Offered Positions:* 16
Program ID: 220-23-12-118

University of Maryland Program
Sponsor: University of Maryland Medical System
Mercy Medical Center
Prgm Director: May H Blanchard, MD
Department of Obstetrics-Gynecology
22 S Greene Street
Baltimore, MD 21201
Tel: 410 328-5959   *Fax:* 410 328-0279
E-mail: mblanchard@upi.umaryland.edu
Length: 4 Yrs   *ACGME Approved/Offered Positions:* 24
Program ID: 220-23-21-121

Bethesda

National Capital Consortium Program
Sponsor: National Capital Consortium
National Naval Medical Center (Bethesda)
Walter Reed Army Medical Center
Prgm Director: Christopher M Zahn, MD
Uniformed Services University
4301 Jones Bridge Road
Bethesda, MD 20814
Tel: 301 295-2048   *Fax:* 301 295-1988
Length: 4 Yrs   *ACGME Approved/Offered Positions:* 24
Program ID: 220-10-21-354
Uniformed Services Program

Massachusetts

Boston

Beth Israel Deaconess Medical Center Program
Sponsor: Beth Israel Deaconess Medical Center
Prgm Director: Hope Ricciotti, MD
330 Brookline Ave
Kirstein 317
Boston, MA 02215
Tel: 617 667-2285   *Fax:* 617 667-4173
E-mail: sherlihy@bidmc.harvard.edu
Length: 4 Yrs   *ACGME Approved/Offered Positions:* 20
Program ID: 220-24-11-123

Boston University Medical Center Program
Sponsor: Boston Medical Center
Lahey Clinic
Prgm Director: Aviva Lee-Parritz, MD
Department of Obstetrics-Gynecology
85 East Concord Street
Boston, MA 02118
Tel: 617 414-5166   *Fax:* 617 414-5161
E-mail: Valerie.worrell@bmc.org
Length: 4 Yrs   *ACGME Approved/Offered Positions:* 17
Program ID: 220-24-21-124

Brigham and Women's Hospital Program
Sponsor: Brigham and Women's Hospital
Massachusetts General Hospital
Prgm Director: Lori R Berkowitz, MD
75 Francis Street, ASB1-3-078
Dept of Ob/Gyn
Boston, MA 02115
Tel: 617 732-7801   *Fax:* 617 730-2833
Length: 4 Yrs   *ACGME Approved/Offered Positions:* 44
Program ID: 220-24-11-125

Tufts Medical Center Program
Sponsor: Tufts Medical Center
Caritas St Elizabeth's Medical Center of Boston
Prgm Director: David Chelmow, MD
800 Washington Street
Box 022
Boston, MA 02111
Tel: 617 636-0265   *Fax:* 617 636-8315
Length: 4 Yrs   *ACGME Approved/Offered Positions:* 21
Program ID: 220-24-21-128

Springfield

Baystate Medical Center/Tufts University School of Medicine Program
Sponsor: Baystate Medical Center
Prgm Director: Heather Z Sankey, MD
Department of Obstetrics-Gynecology
759 Chestnut Street
Springfield, MA 01199
Tel: 413 794-5811   *Fax:* 413 794-8166
E-mail: Heather.Sankey@bhs.org
Length: 4 Yrs   *ACGME Approved/Offered Positions:* 21
Program ID: 220-24-12-129

Worcester

University of Massachusetts Program
Sponsor: University of Massachusetts Medical School
UMass Memorial Health Care (Memorial Campus)
Prgm Director: Robert E Berry Jr, MD
Department of OB-GYN - J4
119 Belmont Street
Worcester, MA 01605
Tel: 508 334-8459   *Fax:* 508 334-5371
E-mail: fragad@ummhc.org
Length: 4 Yrs   *ACGME Approved/Offered Positions:* 20
Program ID: 220-24-21-130

Michigan

Ann Arbor

St Joseph Mercy Hospital Program
Sponsor: St Joseph Mercy Hospital
Prgm Director: Robert D Stager, MD
5333 McAuley Drive
RHB-2108
Ypsilanti, MI 48197
Tel: 734 712-5171   *Fax:* 734 712-4151
E-mail: herrerbr@trinity-health.org
Length: 4 Yrs   *ACGME Approved/Offered Positions:* 16
Program ID: 220-25-31-131

University of Michigan Program
Sponsor: University of Michigan Hospitals and Health Centers
Prgm Director: Clark E Nugent, MD
1500 East Medical Center Drive
F4808 Mott
Ann Arbor, MI 48109
Tel: 734 936-7569   *Fax:* 734 647-1006
E-mail: mhardy@med.umich.edu
Length: 4 Yrs   *ACGME Approved/Offered Positions:* 24
Program ID: 220-25-31-132

Dearborn

Oakwood Hospital Program
Sponsor: Oakwood Hospital
Prgm Director: Todd L Allen, MD, MS
18101 Oakwood Blvd
Suite 126
Dearborn, MI 48123
Tel: 313 436-2582   *Fax:* 313 436-2783
E-mail: woodardm@oakwood.org
Length: 4 Yrs   *ACGME Approved/Offered Positions:* 16
Program ID: 220-25-31-133

Detroit

Henry Ford Hospital Program
Sponsor: Henry Ford Hospital
Prgm Director: David A Richardson, MD
Dept of Obstetrics & Gynecology
2799 West Grand Boulevard
Detroit, MI 48202
Tel: 313 916-1023   *Fax:* 313 916-5008
E-mail: jheymes1@hfhs.org
Length: 4 Yrs   *ACGME Approved/Offered Positions:* 12
Program ID: 220-25-11-136

St John Hospital and Medical Center Program
Sponsor: St John Hospital and Medical Center
Prgm Director: Michael Prysak, PhD, MD
22101 Moross Road
Detroit, MI 48236
Tel: 313 343-7798   *Fax:* 313 343-4932
Length: 4 Yrs   *ACGME Approved/Offered Positions:* 16
Program ID: 220-25-11-137

Wayne State University/Detroit Medical Center Program
Sponsor: Wayne State University/Detroit Medical Center
Harper-Hutzel Hospital
Sinai-Grace Hospital
Prgm Director: Theodore B Jones, MD*
7 Brush N, Mailbox #165
3980 John R Street
Detroit, MI 48201
Tel: 313 993-1388   *Fax:* 313 993-4100
Length: 4 Yrs   *ACGME Approved/Offered Positions:* 40
Program ID: 220-25-31-358

Programs

Flint

Hurley Medical Center/Michigan State University Program

Sponsor: Hurley Medical Center
Synergy Medical Education Alliance
Prgm Director: John Hebert, MD
Department of Obstetrics-Gynecology
One Hurley Plaza, Suite 101
Flint, MI 48503
Tel: 810 762-6426   *Fax:* 810 257-9076
E-mail: johnhebert@hurleymc.com
Length: 4 Yrs   *ACGME Approved/Offered Positions:* 12
Program ID: 220-25-31-140

Grand Rapids

Grand Rapids Medical Education and Research Center/Michigan State University Program

Sponsor: Grand Rapids Medical Education and Research Center
Saint Mary's Health Care (Grand Rapids)
Spectrum Health-Butterworth Hospital
Prgm Director: Stephen F Rechner, MD
330 Barclay NE
Suite 102
Grand Rapids, MI 49503
Tel: 616 391-1929   *Fax:* 616 391-3174
E-mail: Cathie.Hansen@Spectrum-Health.org
Length: 4 Yrs   *ACGME Approved/Offered Positions:* 32
Program ID: 220-25-21-141

Lansing

Sparrow Hospital/Michigan State University Program

Sponsor: Sparrow Hospital
Prgm Director: Matthew Allswede, MD
1215 East Michigan Avenue
PO Box 30480
Lansing, MI 48909
Tel: 517 364-2577   *Fax:* 517 485-3558
Length: 4 Yrs   *ACGME Approved/Offered Positions:* 16
Program ID: 220-25-31-143

Pontiac

Oakland Physicians Medical Center Program

Sponsor: Oakland Physicians Medical Center
St Joseph Mercy-Oakland
Prgm Director: Leonard G Dorey, MD
461 West Huron
Med Ed, 207
Pontiac, MI 48341
Tel: 248 857-7159   *Fax:* 248 857-6895
E-mail: obgyn@nomc.org
Length: 4 Yrs   *ACGME Approved/Offered Positions:* 8
Program ID: 220-25-11-144

Royal Oak

William Beaumont Hospital Program

Sponsor: William Beaumont Hospital
Prgm Director: Robert A Starr, MD
3601 West 13 Mile Road
Royal Oak, MI 48073
Tel: 248 551-0417   *Fax:* 248 551-8880
E-mail: rstarr@beaumont.edu
Length: 4 Yrs   *ACGME Approved/Offered Positions:* 24
Program ID: 220-25-11-146

Saginaw

Synergy Medical Education Alliance Program

Sponsor: Synergy Medical Education Alliance
Covenant HealthCare System-Harrison Campus
Prgm Director: Henry W Moon, MD*
1000 Houghton Avenue
Saginaw, MI 48602
Tel: 989 583-6828   *Fax:* 989 583-6941
E-mail: hmoon@synergymedical.org
Length: 4 Yrs   *ACGME Approved/Offered Positions:* 12
Program ID: 220-25-21-147

Southfield

Providence Hospital and Medical Centers Program

Sponsor: Providence Hospital and Medical Centers
Prgm Director: Robert A Welch, MD, MSA
Department of Obstetrics-Gynecology
16001 W Nine Mile Road, Box 2043
Southfield, MI 48075
Tel: 248 849-3048   *Fax:* 248 849-2844
Length: 4 Yrs   *ACGME Approved/Offered Positions:* 16
Program ID: 220-25-21-148

Minnesota

Minneapolis

University of Minnesota Program

Sponsor: University of Minnesota Medical School
Hennepin County Medical Center
Regions Hospital
University of Minnesota Medical Center, Division of Fairview
Prgm Director: Phillip N Rauk, MD
Department of Obstetrics-Gynecology
MMC 395, 420 Delaware Street SE
Minneapolis, MN 55455
Tel: 612 626-6513   *Fax:* 612 626-0665
E-mail: peder004@umn.edu
Length: 4 Yrs   *ACGME Approved/Offered Positions:* 36
Program ID: 220-26-21-149

Rochester

College of Medicine, Mayo Clinic (Rochester) Program

Sponsor: College of Medicine, Mayo Clinic
Mayo Clinic (Rochester)
Rochester Methodist Hospital
Prgm Director: Bruce W Johnston, MD
Department of Obstetrics-Gynecology
200 First Street, SW
Rochester, MN 55905
Tel: 507 266-3262   *Fax:* 507 266-9300
E-mail: fields.sherry@mayo.edu
Length: 4 Yrs   *ACGME Approved/Offered Positions:* 16
Program ID: 220-26-21-150

Mississippi

Jackson

University of Mississippi Medical Center Program

Sponsor: University of Mississippi School of Medicine
University Hospitals and Clinics
Prgm Director: Sheila D Bouldin, MD
Department of OB-Gyn
2500 North State Street
Jackson, MS 39216
Tel: 601 984-5325   *Fax:* 601 984-5477
E-mail: sbouldin@ob-gyn.umsmed.edu
Length: 4 Yrs   *ACGME Approved/Offered Positions:* 24
Program ID: 220-27-11-151

Missouri

Columbia

University of Missouri-Columbia Program

Sponsor: University of Missouri-Columbia School of Medicine
University Hospitals and Clinics
Prgm Director: Hung N Winn, MD, JD
500 North Keene Street, Suite 400
DC612.00
Columbia, MO 65201
Tel: 573 817-3096   *Fax:* 573 817-6645
E-mail: cranmerc@health.missouri.edu
Length: 4 Yrs   *ACGME Approved/Offered Positions:* 12
Program ID: 220-28-11-152

Kansas City

University of Missouri at Kansas City Program

Sponsor: University of Missouri-Kansas City School of Medicine
St Luke's Hospital-Kansas City
Truman Medical Center
Prgm Director: R Ryan Reynolds, MD*
2301 Holmes Street
Department of Obstetrics and Gynecology
Kansas City, MO 64108
Tel: 816 404-5150   *Fax:* 816 404-5152
Length: 4 Yrs   *ACGME Approved/Offered Positions:* 32
Program ID: 220-28-21-154

St Louis

St John's Mercy Medical Center Program

Sponsor: St John's Mercy Medical Center
Prgm Director: Dionysios K Veronikis, MD
615 S New Ballas Rd
St Louis, MO 63141
Tel: 314 251-6826   *Fax:* 314 251-4376
E-mail: kay.edwards@mercy.net
Length: 4 Yrs   *ACGME Approved/Offered Positions:* 20
Program ID: 220-28-22-157

St Louis University School of Medicine Program

Sponsor: St Louis University School of Medicine
St Mary's Health Center
Prgm Director: Mary T McLennan, MD
Department of Obstetrics, Gynecology and Women's Health
6420 Clayton Road, Suite 291
St Louis, MO 63117
Tel: 314 768-1031   *Fax:* 314 645-8771
E-mail: gallinil@slu.edu
Length: 4 Yrs   *ACGME Approved/Offered Positions:* 24
Program ID: 220-28-22-158

Washington University/B-JH/SLCH Consortium Program

Sponsor: Washington University/B-JH/SLCH Consortium
Barnes-Jewish Hospital
Prgm Director: Rebecca P McAlister, MD
Department of Obstetrics-Gynecology
4911 Barnes-Jewish Hospital Plaza
St Louis, MO 63110
Tel: 314 362-1016   *Fax:* 314 362-3328
E-mail: mcalisterr@wustl.edu
Length: 4 Yrs   *ACGME Approved/Offered Positions:* 36
Program ID: 220-28-21-155

Note: * indicates a newly appointed program director

Nebraska

Omaha

Creighton University Program

Sponsor: Creighton University School of Medicine
Alegent Health Bergan Mercy Health System
Creighton University Medical Center (Tenet - SJH)
Prgm Director: Caron J Gray, MD
601 N 30th St, Ste 4700
Omaha, NE 68131
Tel: 402 280-4438   *Fax:* 402 280-4496
E-mail: shellyerwin@creighton.edu
Length: 4 Yrs   *ACGME Approved/Offered Positions:* 16
Program ID: 220-30-21-160

University of Nebraska Medical Center College of Medicine Program

Sponsor: University of Nebraska Medical Center College of Medicine
Nebraska Medical Center
Nebraska Methodist Hospital
Prgm Director: Teresa G Berg, MD
Department of Obstetrics-Gynecology
983255 Nebraska Medical Center
Omaha, NE 68198
Tel: 402 559-6160   *Fax:* 402 559-9080
Length: 4 Yrs   *ACGME Approved/Offered Positions:* 16
Program ID: 220-30-21-161

Nevada

Las Vegas

University of Nevada School of Medicine (Las Vegas) Program

Sponsor: University of Nevada School of Medicine
University Medical Center of Southern Nevada
Prgm Director: Jon M Hazen, MD
Department of Obstetrics-Gynecology
2040 West Charleston Blvd, #200
Las Vegas, NV 89102
Tel: 702 671-2310   *Fax:* 702 671-2333
E-mail: caallen@medicine.nevada.edu
Length: 4 Yrs   *ACGME Approved/Offered Positions:* 12
Program ID: 220-31-21-318

New Hampshire

Lebanon

Dartmouth-Hitchcock Medical Center Program

Sponsor: Mary Hitchcock Memorial Hospital
Southern New Hampshire Medical Center
Prgm Director: Karen E George, MD
1 Medical Center Drive
Department of Obstetrics and Gynecology
Lebanon, NH 03756
Tel: 603 653-9289   *Fax:* 603 650-0906
E-mail: michelle.l.roy@hitchcock.org
Length: 4 Yrs   *ACGME Approved/Offered Positions:* 16
Program ID: 220-32-12-352

New Jersey

Camden

UMDNJ-Robert Wood Johnson Medical School (Camden) Program

Sponsor: Cooper Hospital-University Medical Center
Prgm Director: Robin L Perry, MD
Dept of Obstetrics and Gynecology
Three Cooper Plaza, Suite 221
Camden, NJ 08103
Tel: 856 342-2965   *Fax:* 856 365-1967
E-mail: robinson-rosalind@cooperhealth.edu
Length: 4 Yrs   *ACGME Approved/Offered Positions:* 16
Program ID: 220-33-11-162

Jersey City

Mount Sinai School of Medicine (Jersey City) Program

Sponsor: Mount Sinai School of Medicine
Jersey City Medical Center
Prgm Director: Carol Gagliardi, MD
Jersey City Medical Ctr/Wilzig Hospital
4 East, 355 Grand Street
Jersey City, NJ 07302
Tel: 201 915-2466   *Fax:* 201 915-2481
E-mail: obgyn@libertyhcs.org
Length: 4 Yrs   *ACGME Approved/Offered Positions:* 12
Program ID: 220-33-21-324

Livingston

St Barnabas Medical Center Program

Sponsor: St Barnabas Medical Center
Prgm Director: John Kindzierski, MD
94 Old Short Hills Road
Livingston, NJ 07039
Tel: 973 322-5669   *Fax:* 973 533-4492
E-mail: jtoolan@sbhcs.com
Length: 4 Yrs   *ACGME Approved/Offered Positions:* 20
Program ID: 220-33-12-163

Long Branch

Monmouth Medical Center Program

Sponsor: Monmouth Medical Center
Prgm Director: Robert A Graebe, MD
Department of Obstetrics-Gynecology
300 Second Avenue
Long Branch, NJ 07740
Tel: 732 923-6795   *Fax:* 732 923-2923
E-mail: pdavis@sbhcs.com
Length: 4 Yrs   *ACGME Approved/Offered Positions:* 8
Program ID: 220-33-11-164

Morristown

Atlantic Health (Morristown) Program

Sponsor: Atlantic Health
Morristown Memorial Hospital
Overlook Hospital
Prgm Director: Joseph Ramieri, MD
100 Madison Avenue
Morristown, NJ 07962
Tel: 973 971-5148   *Fax:* 973 290-7322
E-mail: obgyn.residency@atlantichealth.org
Length: 4 Yrs   *ACGME Approved/Offered Positions:* 16
Program ID: 220-33-31-365

Neptune

Jersey Shore University Medical Center Program

Sponsor: Jersey Shore University Medical Center
Prgm Director: Andrew N Blechman, MD
Department of Obstetrics-Gynecology
1945 State Route 33
Neptune, NJ 07753
Tel: 732 776-3790
E-mail: ablechman@meridianhealth.com
Length: 4 Yrs   *ACGME Approved/Offered Positions:* 12
Program ID: 220-33-12-165

New Brunswick

Drexel University College of Medicine/St Peter's University Hospital Program

Sponsor: St Peter's University Hospital
Prgm Director: John A Carlson, Jr, MD
254 Easton Avenue, MOB 4th Floor
New Brunswick, NJ 08901
Tel: 732 745-6654   *Fax:* 732 249-3475
Length: 4 Yrs   *ACGME Approved/Offered Positions:* 16
Program ID: 220-33-12-362

UMDNJ-Robert Wood Johnson Medical School Program

Sponsor: UMDNJ-Robert Wood Johnson Medical School
Raritan Bay Medical Center-Perth Amboy Division
Robert Wood Johnson University Hospital
Prgm Director: Gary A Ebert, MD
Department of Obstetrics-Gynecology
125 Paterson Street
New Brunswick, NJ 08901
Tel: 732 235-6375   *Fax:* 732 235-9855
Length: 4 Yrs   *ACGME Approved/Offered Positions:* 24
Program ID: 220-33-21-167

Newark

Newark Beth Israel Medical Center Program

Sponsor: Newark Beth Israel Medical Center
Prgm Director: Martin L Gimovsky, MD, BS
201 Lyons Avenue
Newark, NJ 07112
Tel: 973 926-4787   *Fax:* 973 923-7497
Length: 4 Yrs   *ACGME Approved/Offered Positions:* 13
Program ID: 220-33-21-321

UMDNJ-New Jersey Medical School Program

Sponsor: UMDNJ-New Jersey Medical School
Hackensack University Medical Center
Morristown Memorial Hospital
UMDNJ-University Hospital
Prgm Director: Jacquelyn S Loughlin, MD
Department of Obstetrics and Gynecology
185 South Orange Avenue, Room E506
Newark, NJ 07103
Tel: 973 972-5266   *Fax:* 973 972-4574
E-mail: loughljs@umdnj.edu
Length: 4 Yrs   *ACGME Approved/Offered Positions:* 24
Program ID: 220-33-31-166

Paterson

Mount Sinai School of Medicine (St Joseph's Regional Medical Center) Program

Sponsor: Mount Sinai School of Medicine
St Joseph's Regional Medical Center
Prgm Director: Sam H Hessami, MD
Department of Obstetrics-Gynecology
703 Main Street
Paterson, NJ 07503
Tel: 973 754-2702   *Fax:* 973 754-2725
E-mail: davidd@sjhmc.org
Length: 4 Yrs   *ACGME Approved/Offered Positions:* 8
Program ID: 220-33-21-323

Programs

New Mexico

Albuquerque

University of New Mexico Program

Sponsor: University of New Mexico School of Medicine
University of New Mexico Hospital
Prgm Director: Joseph (Tony) A Ogburn, MD
Dept of Ob/Gyn, MSC 10-5580
1 University of New Mexico
Albuquerque, NM 87131
Tel: 505 272-6383   *Fax:* 505 272-6385
E-mail: obresidentcoord@salud.unm.edu
Length: 4 Yrs   *ACGME Approved/Offered Positions:* 24
Program ID: 220-34-21-169

New York

Albany

Albany Medical Center Program

Sponsor: Albany Medical Center
St Peter's Hospital
Prgm Director: Norman F Angell, MD, PhD
Department of Obstetrics-Gynecology
47 New Scotland Avenue, Mail Code 42
Albany, NY 12208
Tel: 518 262-5026   *Fax:* 518 262-0750
E-mail: angelln@mail.amc.edu
Length: 4 Yrs   *ACGME Approved/Offered Positions:* 24
Program ID: 220-35-21-170

Bronx

Albert Einstein College of Medicine Program

Sponsor: Albert Einstein College of Medicine of Yeshiva
   University
Montefiore Medical Center-Henry and Lucy Moses
   Division
Montefiore Medical Center-Weiler Division
North Bronx Healthcare Network-Jacobi Medical Center
Prgm Director: Brian L Cohen, MD
Belfer Educational Center, Rm 510
1300 Morris Park Avenue
Bronx, NY 10461
Tel: 718 430-4031   *Fax:* 718 430-8774
E-mail: regan@aecom.yu.edu
Length: 4 Yrs   *ACGME Approved/Offered Positions:* 37
Program ID: 220-35-21-178

Bronx-Lebanon Hospital Center Program

Sponsor: Bronx-Lebanon Hospital Center
Prgm Director: Magdy Mikhail, MD
Department of Obstetrics-Gynecology
1650 Grand Concourse
Bronx, NY 10457
Tel: 718 239-8388   *Fax:* 718 239-8360
E-mail: mikhailgyn@aol.com
Length: 4 Yrs   *ACGME Approved/Offered Positions:* 17
Program ID: 220-35-11-180

Lincoln Medical and Mental Health Center Program

Sponsor: Lincoln Medical and Mental Health Center
Prgm Director: Ray A Mercado, DO
Dept of Obstetrics,Gynecology & Women's Health
234 East 149th Street, Room 5-18
Bronx, NY 10451
Tel: 718 579-5830   *Fax:* 718 579-4699
E-mail: ray.mercado@nychhc.org
Length: 4 Yrs   *ACGME Approved/Offered Positions:* 12
Program ID: 220-35-21-326

New York Medical College (Bronx) Program

Sponsor: New York Medical College
Montefiore Medical Center - North Division
Prgm Director: Kevin D Reilly, MD
Montefiore North Division
600 East 233rd Street
Bronx, NY 10466
Tel: 718 920-9649   *Fax:* 718 920-6812
Length: 4 Yrs   *ACGME Approved/Offered Positions:* 9
Program ID: 220-35-21-330

Brooklyn

Brooklyn Hospital Center Program

Sponsor: Brooklyn Hospital Center
Prgm Director: Angela D Kerr, MD*
Department of Obstetrics-Gynecology
121 DeKalb Avenue
Brooklyn, NY 11201
Tel: 718 250-6930   *Fax:* 718 250-8881
Length: 4 Yrs   *ACGME Approved/Offered Positions:* 16
Program ID: 220-35-12-182

Long Island College Hospital Program

Sponsor: Long Island College Hospital
Prgm Director: Thomasena L Ellison, MD*
339 Hicks Street
Brooklyn, NY 11201
Tel: 718 780-4847   *Fax:* 718 780-1484
Length: 4 Yrs   *ACGME Approved/Offered Positions:* 12
Program ID: 220-35-12-189

Lutheran Medical Center Program

Sponsor: Lutheran Medical Center
Prgm Director: Iffath Hoskins, MD
Department of Obstetrics-Gynecology
150 55th Street
Brooklyn, NY 11220
Tel: 718 630-6375   *Fax:* 718 630-6322
Length: 4 Yrs   *ACGME Approved/Offered Positions:* 12
Program ID: 220-35-11-191

Maimonides Medical Center Program

Sponsor: Maimonides Medical Center
Coney Island Hospital
Prgm Director: Carmen R Llopiz-Valle, MD
Department of Obstetrics-Gynecology
4802 Tenth Avenue
Brooklyn, NY 11219
Tel: 718 283-6432   *Fax:* 718 283-8468
E-mail: cllopiz-valle@maimonidesmed.org
Length: 4 Yrs   *ACGME Approved/Offered Positions:* 20
Program ID: 220-35-31-192

New York Methodist Hospital Program

Sponsor: New York Methodist Hospital
Prgm Director: Vincent T Pillari, MD
Department of Obstetrics-Gynecology
506 Sixth Street
Brooklyn, NY 11215
Tel: 718 780-3272   *Fax:* 718 780-3079
E-mail: vtp9002@nyp.org
Length: 4 Yrs   *ACGME Approved/Offered Positions:* 13
Program ID: 220-35-31-339

SUNY Health Science Center at Brooklyn Program

Sponsor: SUNY Health Science Center at Brooklyn
Kings County Hospital Center
University Hospital-SUNY Health Science Center at
   Brooklyn
Prgm Director: Ovadia Abulafia, MD
Department of Obstetrics-Gynecology
450 Clarkson Avenue, Box 24
Brooklyn, NY 11203
Tel: 718 270-2081   *Fax:* 718 270-4122
Length: 4 Yrs   *ACGME Approved/Offered Positions:* 24
Program ID: 220-35-21-208

Buffalo

University at Buffalo (Sisters of Charity) Program

Sponsor: University at Buffalo School of Medicine
Sisters of Charity Hospital
Prgm Director: Anthony R Pivarunas, DO
Department of Obstetrics-Gynecology
2157 Main Street
Buffalo, NY 14214
Tel: 716 862-1500   *Fax:* 716 862-1881
Length: 4 Yrs   *ACGME Approved/Offered Positions:* 12
Program ID: 220-35-21-171

University at Buffalo Program

Sponsor: University at Buffalo School of Medicine
Kaleida Health System (Millard Fillmore Hospital)
Kaleida Health System (Women and Children's Hosp of
   Buffalo)
Prgm Director: John Yeh, MD
Department of Gynecology-Obstetrics
219 Bryant Street
Buffalo, NY 14222
Tel: 716 878-7138   *Fax:* 716 888-3833
E-mail: acaster@buffalo.edu
Length: 4 Yrs   *ACGME Approved/Offered Positions:* 36
Program ID: 220-35-21-172

East Meadow

Nassau University Medical Center Program

Sponsor: Nassau University Medical Center
South Nassau Communities Hospital
Prgm Director: Desmond A White, MD
Department of Obstetrics-Gynecology
2201 Hempstead Turnpike
East Meadow, NY 11554
Tel: 516 572-6254   *Fax:* 516 572-3124
E-mail: dwhite1@numc.edu
Length: 4 Yrs   *ACGME Approved/Offered Positions:* 17
Program ID: 220-35-31-174

Flushing

Flushing Hospital Medical Center Program

Sponsor: Flushing Hospital Medical Center
Prgm Director: Allan J Jacobs, MD
4500 Parsons Boulvard
Flushing, NY 11355
Tel: 718 670-5440   *Fax:* 718 670-5780
Length: 4 Yrs   *ACGME Approved/Offered Positions:* 13
Program ID: 220-35-11-184

Great Neck

NSLIJHS-Albert Einstein College of Medicine at Long Island Jewish Medical Center Program

Sponsor: North Shore-Long Island Jewish Health System
Long Island Jewish Medical Center
Prgm Director: Leah A Kaufman, MD*
Long Island Jewish Medical Center
270-05 76th Avenue, Suite 1100
New Hyde Park, NY 11040
Tel: 718 470-7660   *Fax:* 718 962-6739
E-mail: lkaufman@nshs.edu
Length: 4 Yrs   *ACGME Approved/Offered Positions:* 21
Program ID: 220-35-21-190

Note: * indicates a newly appointed program director

NSLIJHS-North Shore University Hospital/NYU School of Medicine Program

Sponsor: North Shore-Long Island Jewish Health System
North Shore University Hospital
Prgm Director: Andrew W Menzin, MD
Department of Obstetrics-Gynecology
300 Community Drive
Manhasset, NY 11030
Tel: 516 562-4435   *Fax:* 516 562-1299
E-mail: amenzin@nshs.edu
Length: 4 Yrs   *ACGME Approved/Offered Positions:* 21
Program ID: 220-35-31-175

Jamaica

Jamaica Hospital Medical Center Program

Sponsor: Jamaica Hospital Medical Center
Prgm Director: Steven R Inglis, MD
89-06 135th Streeet, Suite 6A
Jamaica, NY 11418
Tel: 718 206-6808   *Fax:* 718 206-6829
Length: 4 Yrs   *ACGME Approved/Offered Positions:* 9
Program ID: 220-35-21-186

Mount Sinai School of Medicine (Jamaica) Program

Sponsor: Mount Sinai School of Medicine
Queens Hospital Center
Prgm Director: Molham Solomon, MD, MBA*
Department of Obstetrics & Gynecology
82-68 164th Street, Room B265
Jamaica, NY 11432
Tel: 718 883-4035   *Fax:* 718 883-6129
E-mail: solomomm@nychhc.org
Length: 4 Yrs   *ACGME Approved/Offered Positions:* 12
Program ID: 220-35-21-342

New York Medical College (Brooklyn-Queens) Program

Sponsor: New York Medical College
Caritas Health Care (Brooklyn-Queens)
Wyckoff Heights Medical Center
Prgm Director: Jahangir Ayromlooi, MD
St John Queens Hospital 4th Floor
90-02 Queens Blvd
Elmhurst, NY 11373
Tel: 718 558-1245   *Fax:* 718 558-1597
E-mail: jayromlooi@bqhcny.org
Length: 4 Yrs   *ACGME Approved/Offered Positions:* 12
Program ID: 220-35-21-183

Mineola

Winthrop-University Hospital Program

Sponsor: Winthrop-University Hospital
Prgm Director: Anthony M Vintzileos, MD
Department of Obstetrics-Gynecology
259 First Street
Mineola, NY 11501
Tel: 516 663-2264   *Fax:* 516 742-7821
E-mail: avintzileos@winthrop.org
Length: 4 Yrs   *ACGME Approved/Offered Positions:* 16
Program ID: 220-35-12-176

New York

Albert Einstein College of Medicine at Beth Israel Medical Center Program

Sponsor: Beth Israel Medical Center
Prgm Director: Laura MacIsaac, MD, MPH*
Medical Center
1st Avenue at 16th Street - 8 Baird
New York, NY 10003
Tel: 212 420-2956   *Fax:* 212 420-2980
Length: 4 Yrs   *ACGME Approved/Offered Positions:* 20
Program ID: 220-35-11-179

Lenox Hill Hospital Program

Sponsor: Lenox Hill Hospital
Prgm Director: Yoni Barnhard, MD*
130 E 77th Street
New York, NY 10075
Tel: 212 434-2160   *Fax:* 212 434-2180
E-mail: ybarnhard@lenoxhill.net
Length: 4 Yrs   *ACGME Approved/Offered Positions:* 12
Program ID: 220-35-11-188

Mount Sinai School of Medicine Program

Sponsor: Mount Sinai School of Medicine
Elmhurst Hospital Center-Mount Sinai Services
Mount Sinai Medical Center
Prgm Director: Janine M Popot, MD
One Gustave L Levy Place
Box 1170
New York, NY 10029
Tel: 212 241-5995
E-mail: janine.popot@mssm.edu
Length: 4 Yrs   *ACGME Approved/Offered Positions:* 29
Program ID: 220-35-21-196

New York Downtown Hospital Program

Sponsor: New York Downtown Hospital
Prgm Director: Allan Klapper, MD
Department of Obstetrics-Gynecology
170 William Street, 8th Floor
New York, NY 10038
Tel: 212 312-5880
E-mail: allan.klapper@downtownhospital.org
Length: 4 Yrs   *ACGME Approved/Offered Positions:* 12
Program ID: 220-35-21-198

New York Medical College at St Vincent's Hospital and Medical Center of New York Program

Sponsor: New York Medical College
St Vincent Catholic Medical Centers (Manhattan)
Prgm Director: George M Mussalli, MD
Department of Obstetrics-Gynecology
153 West 11th Street
New York, NY 10011
Tel: 212 604-2512   *Fax:* 212 604-2777
E-mail: gmussalli@svcmcny.org
Length: 4 Yrs   *ACGME Approved/Offered Positions:* 9
Program ID: 220-35-21-205

New York Presbyterian Hospital (Columbia Campus) Program

Sponsor: New York Presbyterian Hospital
New York Presbyterian Hospital (Columbia Campus)
Prgm Director: Richard L Berkowitz, MD, MPH
Department of Obstetrics and Gynecology
622 West 168th Street, PH 16
New York, NY 10032
Tel: 212 305-2376   *Fax:* 212 305-4672
E-mail: jka2113@columbia.edu
Length: 4 Yrs   *ACGME Approved/Offered Positions:* 24
Program ID: 220-35-21-201

New York Presbyterian Hospital (Cornell Campus) Program

Sponsor: New York Presbyterian Hospital
New York Hospital Medical Center of Queens
New York Presbyterian Hospital (Cornell Campus)
Prgm Director: Barry D Shaktman, MD
Department of Obstetrics-Gynecology
525 East 68th Street
New York, NY 10065
Tel: 212 746-3058   *Fax:* 212 746-8490
E-mail: cumc-obgyn@med.cornell.edu
Length: 4 Yrs   *ACGME Approved/Offered Positions:* 25
Program ID: 220-35-21-197

New York University School of Medicine Program

Sponsor: New York University School of Medicine
Bellevue Hospital Center
NYU Hospitals Center
Prgm Director: Scott W Smilen, MD
Suite 9E2
550 First Avenue
New York, NY 10016
Tel: 212 263-8886   *Fax:* 212 263-8251
E-mail: latoya.bishop@nyumc.org
Length: 4 Yrs   *ACGME Approved/Offered Positions:* 29
Program ID: 220-35-21-200

St Luke's-Roosevelt Hospital Center Program

Sponsor: St Luke's-Roosevelt Hospital Center
St Luke's-Roosevelt Hospital Center-Roosevelt Division
St Luke's-Roosevelt Hospital Center-St Luke's Division
Prgm Director: Lois E Brustman, MD
Department of Obstetrics-Gynecology
1000 Tenth Avenue, Suite 10C01
New York, NY 10019
Tel: 212 523-8366   *Fax:* 212 523-8012
E-mail: fwilliams@chpnet.org
Length: 4 Yrs   *ACGME Approved/Offered Positions:* 24
Program ID: 220-35-11-204

Rochester

Rochester General Hospital Program

Sponsor: Rochester General Hospital
Prgm Director: Maggie D Vill, MD
Dept of Ob/Gyn, Box 249
1425 Portland Avenue
Rochester, NY 14621
Tel: 585 922-4684   *Fax:* 585 922-5899
E-mail: bernadette.thomas@viahealth.org
Length: 4 Yrs   *ACGME Approved/Offered Positions:* 12
Program ID: 220-35-31-343

University of Rochester Program

Sponsor: Strong Memorial Hospital of the University of Rochester
Highland Hospital of Rochester
Prgm Director: Ruth Anne Queenan, MD, MBA
Dept of Obstetrics/Gynecology
601 Elmwood Avenue, Box 668
Rochester, NY 14642
Tel: 585 275-3733   *Fax:* 585 756-4967
E-mail: melanie_page@urmc.rochester.edu
Length: 4 Yrs   *ACGME Approved/Offered Positions:* 32
Program ID: 220-35-21-213

Staten Island

New York Medical College (Richmond) Program

Sponsor: New York Medical College
Richmond University Medical Center
Prgm Director: Jane M Ponterio, MD*
355 Bard Avenue
Staten Island, NY 10310
Tel: 718 983-0204   *Fax:* 718 494-7420
E-mail: jponterio@rumcsi.org
Length: 4 Yrs   *ACGME Approved/Offered Positions:* 12
Program ID: 220-35-12-206

Staten Island University Hospital Program

Sponsor: Staten Island University Hospital
Prgm Director: Mitchell Maiman, MD
Department of Obstetrics-Gynecology
475 Seaview Avenue
Staten Island, NY 10305
Tel: 718 226-9269   *Fax:* 718 226-6873
E-mail: obprogram@siuh.edu
Length: 4 Yrs   *ACGME Approved/Offered Positions:* 12
Program ID: 220-35-11-207

Stony Brook

SUNY at Stony Brook Program
Sponsor: University Hospital - SUNY at Stony Brook
Prgm Director: Todd R Griffin, MD
Department of Obstetrics-Gynecology
SUNY at Stony Brook
Stony Brook, NY 11794
Tel: 631 444-2757 *Fax:* 631 444-8954
Length: 4 Yrs *ACGME Approved/Offered Positions:* 20
Program ID: 220-35-21-316

Syracuse

SUNY Upstate Medical University Program
Sponsor: SUNY Upstate Medical University
Crouse Hospital
St Joseph's Hospital Health Center
Prgm Director: Shawky Badawy, MD
Dept of Ob/Gyn, 3rd Fl West Tower, Crouse Hospital
736 Irving Avenue
Syracuse, NY 13210
Tel: 315 470-7907 *Fax:* 315 470-2838
Length: 4 Yrs *ACGME Approved/Offered Positions:* 20
Program ID: 220-35-21-215

Valhalla

New York Medical College at Westchester Medical Center Program
Sponsor: New York Medical College
Metropolitan Hospital Center
Westchester Medical Center
Prgm Director: Sari Kaminsky, MD
Department of Obstetrics-Gynecology
1901 First Avenue
New York, NY 10029
Tel: 212 423-6796 *Fax:* 212 423-8121
E-mail: kaminsks@nychhc.org
Length: 4 Yrs *ACGME Approved/Offered Positions:* 17
Program ID: 220-35-21-199

North Carolina

Asheville

Mountain Area Health Education Center Program
Sponsor: Mountain Area Health Education Center
Mission Hospitals - Memorial Campus
Prgm Director: Elizabeth Buys, MD*
Department of Obstetrics & Gynecology
93 Victoria Road
Asheville, NC 28801
Tel: 828 771-5512 *Fax:* 828 251-0024
E-mail: beth.buys@mahec.net
Length: 4 Yrs *ACGME Approved/Offered Positions:* 16
Program ID: 220-36-21-340

Chapel Hill

University of North Carolina Hospitals Program
Sponsor: University of North Carolina Hospitals
Wake Medical Center
Prgm Director: AnnaMarie Connolly, MD
30134 NC Women's Hospital, CB 7600
UNC School of Medicine
Chapel Hill, NC 27514
Tel: 919 966-5096 *Fax:* 919 843-1480
Length: 4 Yrs *ACGME Approved/Offered Positions:* 28
Program ID: 220-36-21-216

Charlotte

Carolinas Medical Center Program
Sponsor: Carolinas Medical Center
Prgm Director: Robert V Higgins, MD
1000 Blythe Boulevard
PO Box 32861
Charlotte, NC 28232
Tel: 704 355-3153 *Fax:* 704 355-1941
E-mail: robert.higgins@carolinashealthcare.org
Length: 4 Yrs *ACGME Approved/Offered Positions:* 24
Program ID: 220-36-31-217

Durham

Duke University Hospital Program
Sponsor: Duke University Hospital
Cape Fear Valley Medical Center
Prgm Director: Fidel A Valea, MD
Department of Obstetrics/Gynecology
DUMC Box 3084, Baker House 203
Durham, NC 27710
Tel: 919 668-2591 *Fax:* 919 668-5547
Length: 4 Yrs *ACGME Approved/Offered Positions:* 32
Program ID: 220-36-21-219

Greenville

Pitt County Memorial Hospital/East Carolina University Program
Sponsor: Pitt County Memorial Hospital
Brody School of Medicine at East Carolina University
Prgm Director: Clifford C Hayslip Jr, MD*
Department of Obstetrics-Gynecology
600 Moye Boulevard
Greenville, NC 27834
Tel: 252 744-4669 *Fax:* 252 744-5329
Length: 4 Yrs *ACGME Approved/Offered Positions:* 20
Program ID: 220-36-21-220

Wilmington

New Hanover Regional Medical Center Program
Sponsor: New Hanover Regional Medical Center
Prgm Director: Brent D Wright, MD
2131 S 17th Street
PO Box 9025
Wilmington, NC 28402
Tel: 910 343-0161 *Fax:* 910 762-2896
Length: 4 Yrs *ACGME Approved/Offered Positions:* 16
Program ID: 220-36-11-218

Winston-Salem

Wake Forest University School of Medicine Program
Sponsor: Wake Forest University Baptist Medical Center
Forsyth Memorial Hospital
Prgm Director: Karen R Gerancher, MD*
Department of Obstetrics-Gynecology
Medical Center Boulevard
Winston-Salem, NC 27157
Tel: 336 716-4615 *Fax:* 336 716-6937
E-mail: kgeranch@wfubmc.edu
Length: 4 Yrs *ACGME Approved/Offered Positions:* 20
Program ID: 220-36-21-221

Ohio

Akron

Akron General Medical Center/NEOUCOM Program
Sponsor: Akron General Medical Center
Prgm Director: Eric L Jenison, MD
Department of Obstetrics-Gynecology
224 West Exchange Street, Suite 120
Akron, OH 44307
Tel: 330 344-6332 *Fax:* 330 996-2912
Length: 4 Yrs *ACGME Approved/Offered Positions:* 16
Program ID: 220-38-11-224

Summa Health System/NEOUCOM Program
Sponsor: Summa Health System
Akron City Hospital (Summa Health System)
Prgm Director: Edward M Ferris, MD*
Department of Obstetrics-Gynecology
525 East Market Street, Med II, PO Box 2090
Akron, OH 44304
Tel: 330 375-6119 *Fax:* 330 375-7813
E-mail: eferris1@aol.com
Length: 4 Yrs *ACGME Approved/Offered Positions:* 20
Program ID: 220-38-21-223

Canton

Aultman Hospital/NEOUCOM Program
Sponsor: Aultman Hospital
Prgm Director: Michael P Hopkins, MD, MEd
Department of Obstetrics and Gynecology
2600 Sixth Street, SW
Canton, OH 44710
Tel: 330 363-6214 *Fax:* 330 363-5228
E-mail: mhopkins@aultman.com
Length: 4 Yrs *ACGME Approved/Offered Positions:* 13
Program ID: 220-38-21-226

Cincinnati

TriHealth (Bethesda North and Good Samaritan Hospitals) Program
Sponsor: TriHealth
TriHealth - Bethesda North Hospital
TriHealth - Good Samaritan Hospital
Prgm Director: Michael S Baggish, MD
Department of Obstetrics-Gynecology
375 Dixmyth Avenue
Cincinnati, OH 45220
Tel: 513 872-3434 *Fax:* 513 872-9701
Length: 4 Yrs *ACGME Approved/Offered Positions:* 32
Program ID: 220-38-11-228

University Hospital/University of Cincinnati College of Medicine Program
Sponsor: University Hospital Inc
Christ Hospital
Prgm Director: Arthur T Ollendorff, MD
231 Albert Sabin Way, ML 0526
Cincinnati, OH 45267
Tel: 513 558-2860 *Fax:* 513 558-6138
Length: 4 Yrs *ACGME Approved/Offered Positions:* 28
Program ID: 220-38-21-229

Cleveland

Case Western Reserve University (MetroHealth)/Cleveland Clinic Foundation Program
Sponsor: MetroHealth Medical Center
Cleveland Clinic Foundation
Prgm Director: Thomas M Frank, MD
2500 MetroHealth Drive
Cleveland, OH 44109
Tel: 216 778-7856 *Fax:* 216 778-8642
E-mail: clotenero@metrohealth.org
Length: 4 Yrs *ACGME Approved/Offered Positions:* 28
Program ID: 220-38-21-327

Note: * indicates a newly appointed program director

University Hospitals Case Medical Center Program

Sponsor: University Hospitals Case Medical Center
Prgm Director: Nancy J Cossler, MD
Department of Obstetrics-Gynecology
11100 Euclid Ave
Cleveland, OH 44106
Tel: 216 844-8551   *Fax:* 216 844-3348
Length: 4 Yrs   *ACGME Approved/Offered Positions:* 20
Program ID: 220-38-21-230

Columbus

Ohio State University Hospital Program

Sponsor: Ohio State University Hospital
Mount Carmel
Mount Carmel St Ann's Hospital
Prgm Director: Philip Samuels, MD
Department of Obstetrics-Gynecology
1654 Upham Drive, 505 Means Hall
Columbus, OH 43210
Tel: 614 293-3773   *Fax:* 614 293-5877
Length: 4 Yrs   *ACGME Approved/Offered Positions:* 44
Program ID: 220-38-11-234

Riverside Methodist Hospitals (OhioHealth) Program

Sponsor: Riverside Methodist Hospitals (OhioHealth)
Prgm Director: Carl A Krantz, MD
Department of Medical Education (OB/GYN Program)
3535 Olentangy River Road
Columbus, OH 43214
Tel: 614 566-5762   *Fax:* 614 566-6852
E-mail: jstubbs2@ohiohealth.com
Length: 4 Yrs   *ACGME Approved/Offered Positions:* 20
Program ID: 220-38-32-235

Dayton

Wright State University Program

Sponsor: Wright State University Boonshoft School of Medicine
Miami Valley Hospital
Wright - Patterson Medical Center
Prgm Director: Mark S Campbell, MD
128 E Apple Street, Suite 3800 CHE
Dayton, OH 45409
Tel: 937 208-6272   *Fax:* 937 222-7255
E-mail: mscampbell@mvh.org
Length: 4 Yrs   *ACGME Approved/Offered Positions:* 24
Program ID: 220-38-21-236

Toledo

University of Toledo Program

Sponsor: University of Toledo
St Vincent Mercy Medical Center
Toledo Hospital
University Medical Center (Toledo)
Prgm Director: Terrence J Horrigan, MD
3120 Glendale Avenue
Room 1520 Ruppert Health Center
Toledo, OH 43614
Tel: 419 383-4591   *Fax:* 419 383-3090
E-mail: Amy.Flack@utoledo.edu
Length: 4 Yrs   *ACGME Approved/Offered Positions:* 16
Program ID: 220-38-22-237

Oklahoma

Oklahoma City

University of Oklahoma Health Sciences Center Program

Sponsor: University of Oklahoma College of Medicine
OU Medical Center
Prgm Director: Elisa A Crouse, MD, MS
Department of Obstetrics-Gynecology
PO Box 26901
Oklahoma City, OK 73190
Tel: 405 271-7449   *Fax:* 405 271-8547
E-mail: susan-glomset@ouhsc.edu
Length: 4 Yrs   *ACGME Approved/Offered Positions:* 24
Program ID: 220-39-11-239

Tulsa

University of Oklahoma College of Medicine-Tulsa Program

Sponsor: University of Oklahoma College of Medicine-Tulsa
Hillcrest Medical Center
Saint Francis Health System
St John Medical Center
Women's Health Care Specialists
Prgm Director: Nirupama K De Silva, MD*
Department of Obstetrics and Gynecology
1145 S Utica Ave, Suite 600
Tulsa, OK 74104
Tel: 918 582-0955   *Fax:* 918 582-0884
E-mail: Tulsaobgynres@ouhsc.edu
Length: 4 Yrs   *ACGME Approved/Offered Positions:* 16
Program ID: 220-39-21-240

Oregon

Portland

Oregon Health & Science University Program

Sponsor: Oregon Health & Science University Hospital
St Vincent Hospital and Medical Center
Prgm Director: Karen Adams, MD
Department of Obstetrics-Gynecology
3181 SW Sam Jackson Park Road, L466
Portland, OR 97239
Tel: 503 494-4495   *Fax:* 503 418-0658
E-mail: forsterv@ohsu.edu
Length: 4 Yrs   *ACGME Approved/Offered Positions:* 28
Program ID: 220-40-21-241

Pennsylvania

Abington

Abington Memorial Hospital Program

Sponsor: Abington Memorial Hospital
Prgm Director: Joel I Polin, MD
Department of Obstetrics and Gynecology
1200 Old York Road
Abington, PA 19001
Tel: 215 572-6222   *Fax:* 215 481-2048
E-mail: jpolin@amh.org
Length: 4 Yrs   *ACGME Approved/Offered Positions:* 20
Program ID: 220-41-12-242

Allentown

Lehigh Valley Hospital Network/Pennsylvania State University Program

Sponsor: Lehigh Valley Hospital Network
Prgm Director: Joseph E Patruno, MD*
PO Box 7017
17th & Chew Streets
Allentown, PA 18105
Tel: 610 969-2412   *Fax:* 610 969-3088
E-mail: teresa.benner@lvh.com
Length: 4 Yrs   *ACGME Approved/Offered Positions:* 20
Program ID: 220-41-11-243

Bethlehem

St Luke's Hospital Program

Sponsor: St Luke's Hospital
St Luke's Hospital (Allentown)
Prgm Director: James N Anasti, MD
801 Ostrum Street
Bethlehem, PA 18015
Tel: 610 954-4670   *Fax:* 610 954-2381
Length: 4 Yrs   *ACGME Approved/Offered Positions:* 20
Program ID: 220-41-31-244

Danville

Geisinger Health System Program

Sponsor: Geisinger Health System
Geisinger Medical Center
Prgm Director: Edie L Derian, MD
Department of Obstetrics/Gynecology
100 North Academy Avenue
Danville, PA 17822
Tel: 570 271-6296   *Fax:* 570 271-5819
E-mail: kgloss@geisinger.edu
Length: 4 Yrs   *ACGME Approved/Offered Positions:* 12
Program ID: 220-41-12-245

Hershey

Penn State University/Milton S Hershey Medical Center Program

Sponsor: Milton S Hershey Medical Center
PinnacleHealth System-Harrisburg Hospital
Prgm Director: Matthew F Davies, MD
Department of Obstetrics-Gynecology
500 University Drive, MCH103
Hershey, PA 17033
Tel: 717 531-5394   *Fax:* 717 531-0920
Length: 4 Yrs   *ACGME Approved/Offered Positions:* 20
Program ID: 220-41-21-246

Philadelphia

Albert Einstein Healthcare Network Program

Sponsor: Albert Einstein Medical Center
Prgm Director: Arnold W Cohen, MD
OB/GYN Lifter Bldg - Rm 1616
5501 Old York Road
Philadelphia, PA 19141
Tel: 215 456-6993   *Fax:* 215 456-2386
E-mail: cohenar@einstein.edu
Length: 4 Yrs   *ACGME Approved/Offered Positions:* 16
Program ID: 220-41-21-247

Programs

Drexel University College of Medicine/Hahnemann University Hospital Program

Sponsor: Drexel University College of Medicine/Hahnemann University Hahnemann University Hospital (Tenet Health System)
Prgm Director: Mark B Woodland, MD, MS
245 N 15th St MS 495
Room 16121, 16th Floor - NCB
Philadelphia, PA 19102
Tel: 215 762-8220   *Fax:* 215 762-1470
E-mail: Mark.Woodland@drexelmed.edu
Length: 4 Yrs   *ACGME Approved/Offered Positions:* 24
Program ID: 220-41-21-250

Pennsylvania Hospital of the University of Pennsylvania Health System Program

Sponsor: Pennsylvania Hospital (UPHS)
Prgm Director: Stephanie H Ewing, MD
2 Pine East
8th and Spruce Streets
Philadelphia, PA 19107
Tel: 215 829-3470   *Fax:* 215 829-3973
E-mail: reichara@pahosp.com
Length: 4 Yrs   *ACGME Approved/Offered Positions:* 24
Program ID: 220-41-11-252

Temple University Hospital Program

Sponsor: Temple University Hospital
Prgm Director: Vani Dandolu, MD, MPH*
7th Floor Zone B
3401 North Broad Street
Philadelphia, PA 19140
Tel: 215 707-3016   *Fax:* 215 707-1387
E-mail: vani.dandolu@temple.edu
Length: 4 Yrs   *ACGME Approved/Offered Positions:* 21
Program ID: 220-41-21-254

Thomas Jefferson University Program

Sponsor: Thomas Jefferson University Hospital
West Jersey Health System (Camden)
Prgm Director: Carmen J Sultana, MD
834 Chestnut Street, Suite 400
The Benjamin Franklin House
Philadelphia, PA 19107
Tel: 215 955-9217   *Fax:* 215 955-5041
Length: 4 Yrs   *ACGME Approved/Offered Positions:* 32
Program ID: 220-41-21-255

University of Pennsylvania Program

Sponsor: University of Pennsylvania Health System
Prgm Director: Thomas Bader, MD, MSc
585 Dulles Building
3400 Spruce Street
Philadelphia, PA 19104
Tel: 215 662-2459   *Fax:* 215 349-5893
Length: 4 Yrs   *ACGME Approved/Offered Positions:* 24
Program ID: 220-41-11-256

Pittsburgh

Allegheny General Hospital Program

Sponsor: Allegheny General Hospital
Prgm Director: Eugene A Scioscia Jr, MD
Department of Obstetrics and Gynecology
320 East North Avenue, 7th Floor, South Tower
Pittsburgh, PA 15212
Tel: 412 359-6890   *Fax:* 412 359-5133
Length: 4 Yrs   *ACGME Approved/Offered Positions:* 8
Program ID: 220-41-12-257

University of Pittsburgh Medical Center Medical Education Program

Sponsor: Univ of Pittsburgh Medical Center Medical Education
Magee-Womens Hospital of UPMC
Prgm Director: Gabriella G Gosman, MD
Department of Ob/Gyn/RS, Rm 2314
300 Halket Street
Pittsburgh, PA 15213
Tel: 412 641-1092   *Fax:* 412 641-2649
E-mail: dbrucha@mail.magee.edu
Length: 4 Yrs   *ACGME Approved/Offered Positions:* 36
Program ID: 220-41-11-258

Western Pennsylvania Hospital/Temple University Program

Sponsor: Western Pennsylvania Hospital
Prgm Director: Michael J Bonidie, MD
Department of Obstetrics-Gynecology
4800 Friendship Avenue
Pittsburgh, PA 15224
Tel: 412 578-5587   *Fax:* 412 578-4477
Length: 4 Yrs   *ACGME Approved/Offered Positions:* 12
Program ID: 220-41-11-261

Upland

Crozer-Chester Medical Center Program

Sponsor: Crozer-Chester Medical Center
Prgm Director: Guy Hewlett, MD
One Medical Center Boulevard
ACP 332
Upland, PA 19013
Tel: 610 447-7610   *Fax:* 610 447-7615
Length: 4 Yrs   *ACGME Approved/Offered Positions:* 12
Program ID: 220-41-21-367

West Reading

Reading Hospital and Medical Center Program

Sponsor: Reading Hospital and Medical Center
Prgm Director: A George Neubert, MD
Dept of Obstetrics/Gynecology
PO Box 16052
Reading, PA 19611
Tel: 610 988-8827   *Fax:* 610 988-9292
Length: 4 Yrs   *ACGME Approved/Offered Positions:* 16
Program ID: 220-41-12-262

Wynnewood

Lankenau Hospital Program

Sponsor: Lankenau Hospital
Prgm Director: Nancy S Roberts, MD
Suite 301 Lankenau Medical Bldg South
100 Lancaster Avenue
Wynnewood, PA 19096
Tel: 610 645-4650   *Fax:* 610 645-2422
E-mail: weisenbachr@mlhs.org
Length: 4 Yrs   *ACGME Approved/Offered Positions:* 16
Program ID: 220-41-11-249

York

York Hospital Program

Sponsor: York Hospital
Prgm Director: Marian D Damewood, MD
1001 South George Street
York, PA 17405
Tel: 717 851-2349   *Fax:* 717 851-2426
E-mail: mdamewood@wellspan.org
Length: 4 Yrs   *ACGME Approved/Offered Positions:* 12
Program ID: 220-41-11-263

Puerto Rico

Ponce

Hospital Episcopal San Lucas/Ponce School of Medicine Program

Sponsor: Hospital Episcopal San Lucas
Prgm Director: Joaquin Laboy, MD
Tito Castro Avenue, #917
PO Box 336810
Ponce, PR 00733
Tel: 787 844-2080   *Fax:* 787 844-1533
E-mail: laboyk@gmail.com
Length: 4 Yrs   *ACGME Approved/Offered Positions:* 12
Program ID: 220-42-21-346

San Juan

San Juan City Hospital Program

Sponsor: San Juan City Hospital
Prgm Director: Edgardo J Rivera, MD*
Department of Obstetrics-Gynecology
PMB 370, PO BOX 70344 Centro Medico de PR
San Juan, PR 00936
Tel: 787 724-8441   *Fax:* 787 722-0648
E-mail: dredgardorivera@gmail.com
Length: 4 Yrs   *ACGME Approved/Offered Positions:* 12
Program ID: 220-42-12-267

University of Puerto Rico Program

Sponsor: University of Puerto Rico School of Medicine University Hospital
Prgm Director: Juana I Rivera-Vīnas, MD
Medical Sciences Campus, Suite 887
PO Box 365067
San Juan, PR 00936
Tel: 787 756-0049   *Fax:* 787 764-7881
E-mail: jirivera@rcm.upr.edu
Length: 4 Yrs   *ACGME Approved/Offered Positions:* 20
Program ID: 220-42-11-268

Rhode Island

Providence

Brown University (Women and Infants Hospital of Rhode Island) Program

Sponsor: Women and Infants Hospital of Rhode Island
Prgm Director: Gary Frishman, MD*
Department of Obstetrics-Gynecology
101 Dudley Street
Providence, RI 02905
Tel: 401 274-1122   *Fax:* 401 276-7845
E-mail: Gary_Frishman@brown.edu
Length: 4 Yrs   *ACGME Approved/Offered Positions:* 32
Program ID: 220-43-21-269

South Carolina

Charleston

Medical University of South Carolina Program

Sponsor: Medical University of South Carolina College of Medicine
MUSC Medical Center
Prgm Director: Scott Sullivan, MD, MSc
96 Jonathan Lucas St
Suite 634, PO Box 250619
Charleston, SC 29425
Tel: 843 792-6486   *Fax:* 843 792-0533
E-mail: sullivas@musc.edu
Length: 4 Yrs   *ACGME Approved/Offered Positions:* 20
Program ID: 220-45-21-270

Note: * indicates a newly appointed program director

Columbia

Palmetto Health/University of South Carolina School of Medicine Program
Sponsor: Palmetto Health
Palmetto Health Richland
Prgm Director: Sarah E Smith, MD
Two Medical Park, Suite 208
Columbia, SC 29203
Tel: 803 779-4928   *Fax:* 803 434-4699
Length: 4 Yrs   *ACGME Approved/Offered Positions:* 16
Program ID: 220-45-11-271

Greenville

Greenville Hospital System/University of South Carolina School of Medicine Program
Sponsor: Greenville Hospital System/University of South Carolina
Prgm Director: David A Forstein, DO*
Department of Obstetrics-Gynecology
890 West Faris Road, MMOB Suite 470
Greenville, SC 29605
Tel: 864 455-7887   *Fax:* 864 455-6875
E-mail: dforstein@ghs.org
Length: 4 Yrs   *ACGME Approved/Offered Positions:* 24
Program ID: 220-45-11-272

Tennessee

Chattanooga

University of Tennessee College of Medicine at Chattanooga Program
Sponsor: University of Tennessee College of Medicine-Chattanooga
Erlanger Medical Center
Prgm Director: Joseph H Kipikasa, MD
Erlanger Medical Center
979 East Third St, Ste C-720
Chattanooga, TN 37403
Tel: 423 778-7515   *Fax:* 423 267-6244
E-mail: shanon.sims@erlanger.org
Length: 4 Yrs   *ACGME Approved/Offered Positions:* 16
Program ID: 220-47-21-274

Johnson City

East Tennessee State University Program
Sponsor: James H Quillen College of Medicine
Johnson City Medical Center/Mountain States Health Alliance
Prgm Director: Martin E Olsen, MD
Department of Obstetrics-Gynecology
PO Box 70569
Johnson City, TN 37614
Tel: 423 439-8097   *Fax:* 423 439-6766
Length: 4 Yrs   *ACGME Approved/Offered Positions:* 12
Program ID: 220-47-21-341

Knoxville

University of Tennessee Medical Center at Knoxville Program
Sponsor: University of Tennessee Graduate School of Medicine
University of Tennessee Memorial Hospital
Prgm Director: Robert F Elder, MD
Department of Obstetrics & Gynecology
1924 Alcoa Highway
Knoxville, TN 37920
Tel: 865 305-9584   *Fax:* 865 305-6639
E-mail: utobgyn@utmck.edu
Length: 4 Yrs   *ACGME Approved/Offered Positions:* 12
Program ID: 220-47-11-275

Memphis

University of Tennessee Program
Sponsor: University of Tennessee College of Medicine
Baptist Memorial Hospital
Regional Medical Center at Memphis
Prgm Director: Claudette J Shephard, MD
Department of Obstetrics-Gynecology
853 Jefferson Avenue Room E102
Memphis, TN 38163
Tel: 901 448-5393   *Fax:* 901 448-7075
E-mail: cshephard@utmem.edu
Length: 4 Yrs   *ACGME Approved/Offered Positions:* 44
Program ID: 220-47-21-276

Nashville

Meharry Medical College Program
Sponsor: Meharry Medical College School of Medicine
Metropolitan Nashville General Hospital
Middle Tennessee Medical Center
Prgm Director: Gwinnett Ladson, MD
1005 Dr D B Todd Jr Blvd
Nashville, TN 37208
Tel: 615 327-6284   *Fax:* 615 327-6296
E-mail: obgynresidency@mmc.edu
Length: 4 Yrs   *ACGME Approved/Offered Positions:* 12
Program ID: 220-47-23-361

Vanderbilt University Program
Sponsor: Vanderbilt University Medical Center
Prgm Director: Melinda S New, MD
R-1214 MCN
21st and Garland Avenues
Nashville, TN 37232
Tel: 615 343-8801   *Fax:* 615 343-8806
E-mail: debby.scraggins@vanderbilt.edu
Length: 4 Yrs   *ACGME Approved/Offered Positions:* 24
Program ID: 220-47-21-278

Texas

Amarillo

Texas Tech University (Amarillo) Program
Sponsor: Texas Tech University Health Sciences Center at Amarillo
Don and Cybil Harrington Cancer Center
Northwest Texas Health Care System
Prgm Director: Robert P Kauffman, MD
Department of Obstetrics/Gynecology
1400 Coulter Road
Amarillo, TX 79106
Tel: 806 356-4609   *Fax:* 806 354-5516
E-mail: robert.kauffman@ttuhsc.edu
Length: 4 Yrs   *ACGME Approved/Offered Positions:* 12
Program ID: 220-48-21-320

Austin

University of Texas Medical Branch (Austin) Program
Sponsor: University of Texas Medical Branch Hospitals
University Medical Center at Brackenridge
Prgm Director: Charles E L Brown, MD, MBA
1313 Red River St, Suite 303B
Austin, TX 78701
Tel: 512 324-7036   *Fax:* 512 324-7971
Length: 4 Yrs   *ACGME Approved/Offered Positions:* 20
Program ID: 220-48-12-360

Dallas

Baylor University Medical Center Program
Sponsor: Baylor University Medical Center
Prgm Director: R Wayne Inzer, MD
Department of Obstetrics-Gynecology
3500 Gaston Avenue
Dallas, TX 75246
Tel: 214 820-6226   *Fax:* 214 820-6080
E-mail: merijanb@baylorhealth.edu
Length: 4 Yrs   *ACGME Approved/Offered Positions:* 20
Program ID: 220-48-31-280

Methodist Health System Dallas Program
Sponsor: Methodist Health System Dallas
Prgm Director: Stephen K Patrick, MD
1441 N Beckley Avenue
PO Box 659999
Dallas, TX 75265
Tel: 214 947-2331   *Fax:* 214 947-2361
E-mail: stephenpatrick@mhd.com
Length: 4 Yrs   *ACGME Approved/Offered Positions:* 12
Program ID: 220-48-31-281

University of Texas Southwestern Medical School Program
Sponsor: University of Texas Southwestern Medical School
Dallas County Hospital District-Parkland Memorial Hospital
Prgm Director: George D Wendel Jr, MD
Department of Obstetrics-Gynecology
5323 Harry Hines Boulevard
Dallas, TX 75390
Tel: 214 648-4866   *Fax:* 214 648-4566
Length: 4 Yrs   *ACGME Approved/Offered Positions:* 80
Program ID: 220-48-31-282

El Paso

Texas Tech University Health Sciences Center Paul L Foster School of Medicine Program
Sponsor: Texas Tech University Hlth Sci Ctr Paul L Foster Sch of Med
R E Thomason General Hospital / Texas Tech University HSC
Prgm Director: Scott Poehlmann, MD*
Department of Obstetrics-Gynecology
4800 Alberta Avenue
El Paso, TX 79905
Tel: 915 545-6714   *Fax:* 915 545-0901
E-mail: scott.poehlmann@ttuhsc.edu
Length: 4 Yrs   *ACGME Approved/Offered Positions:* 16
Program ID: 220-48-11-315

Fort Worth

John Peter Smith Hospital (Tarrant County Hospital District) Program
Sponsor: John Peter Smith Hospital (Tarrant County Hospital District)
Prgm Director: David Moreland, MD
1500 South Main Street
Dept Ob/Gyn
Fort Worth, TX 76104
Tel: 817 927-1065   *Fax:* 817 927-1162
E-mail: sbramlett@jpshealth.org
Length: 4 Yrs   *ACGME Approved/Offered Positions:* 16
Program ID: 220-48-22-284

Galveston

University of Texas Medical Branch Hospitals Program

Sponsor: University of Texas Medical Branch Hospitals
University of Texas Medical School at Galveston
Prgm Director: Daniel M Breitkopf, MD
312 Clinical Sciences Building
301 University Boulevard
Galveston, TX 77555
Tel: 409 747-6624   *Fax:* 409 772-5803
E-mail: smbastie@utmb.edu
Length: 4 Yrs   *ACGME Approved/Offered Positions:* 32
Program ID: 220-48-21-285

Houston

Baylor College of Medicine Program

Sponsor: Baylor College of Medicine
Harris County Hospital District-Ben Taub General
  Hospital
St Luke's Episcopal Hospital
Prgm Director: Amy E Young, MD
Department of Obstetrics/Gynecology
1709 Dryden Street, Suite 1100
Houston, TX 77030
Tel: 713 798-5505   *Fax:* 713 798-6044
E-mail: vinas@bcm.tmc.edu
Length: 4 Yrs   *ACGME Approved/Offered Positions:* 48
Program ID: 220-48-31-286

Methodist Hospital (Houston) Program

Sponsor: Methodist Hospital (Houston)
St Joseph Medical Center
Prgm Director: Eugene C Toy, MD
6565 Fannin St, MGJ9-002
Houston, TX 77030
Tel: 713 756-5616   *Fax:* 713 657-7191
Length: 4 Yrs   *ACGME Approved/Offered Positions:* 20
Program ID: 220-48-31-288

University of Texas at Houston (Lyndon B Johnson General Hospital) Program

Sponsor: University of Texas Health Science Center at
  Houston
Lyndon B Johnson General Hospital
Prgm Director: Lisa M Hollier, MD
Dept of Ob/Gyn, Rm 2LD80001
5656 Kelley Street
Houston, TX 77026
Tel: 713 566-5983   *Fax:* 713 566-4521
Length: 4 Yrs   *ACGME Approved/Offered Positions:* 24
Program ID: 220-48-21-334

University of Texas at Houston (Memorial Hermann Hospital) Program

Sponsor: University of Texas Health Science Center at
  Houston
Memorial Hermann Hospital
Prgm Director: Pamela Promecene, MD
UT-Houston Medical School
6431 Fannin St, Suite 3.268
Houston, TX 77030
Tel: 713 500-6427   *Fax:* 713 500-0798
Length: 4 Yrs   *ACGME Approved/Offered Positions:* 24
Program ID: 220-48-21-289

Lackland AFB

San Antonio Uniformed Services Health Education Consortium Program

Sponsor: San Antonio Uniformed Services Health
  Education Consortium
Brooke Army Medical Center
Carl R Darnall Army Medical Center
Wilford Hall Medical Center (AETC)
Prgm Director: Randal D Robinson, MD
Wilford Hall Medical Center
2200 Bergquist Drive, Suite 1/59th MCCS-SGOBG
Lackland AFB, TX 78236
Tel: 210 292-6137   *Fax:* 210 292-7821
E-mail: randal.robinson@lackland.af.mil
Length: 4 Yrs   *ACGME Approved/Offered Positions:* 24
Program ID: 220-48-21-356
Uniformed Services Program

Lubbock

Texas Tech University (Lubbock) Program

Sponsor: Texas Tech University Health Sciences Center
  at Lubbock
University Medical Center
Prgm Director: Edward R Yeomans, MD*
Department of Obstetrics-Gynecology
3601 4th Street
Lubbock, TX 79430
Tel: 806 743-2295   *Fax:* 806 743-1025
Length: 4 Yrs   *ACGME Approved/Offered Positions:* 12
Program ID: 220-48-21-290

Odessa

Texas Tech University (Permian Basin) Program

Sponsor: Texas Tech University Health Sciences Center
  (Permian Basin)
Medical Center Hospital
Prgm Director: Moss Hampton, MD, BA*
701 West 5th Street
Odessa, TX 79763
Tel: 432 335-5221   *Fax:* 432 335-5240
Length: 4 Yrs   *ACGME Approved/Offered Positions:* 8
Program ID: 220-48-21-331

San Antonio

University of Texas Health Science Center at San Antonio Program

Sponsor: University of Texas School of Medicine at San
  Antonio
University Health System
Prgm Director: Elly Xenakis, MD
Mail Stop 7836 Obstetrics-Gynecology
7703 Floyd Curl Drive
San Antonio, TX 78229
Tel: 210 567-5009   *Fax:* 210 567-3013
E-mail: brewerk@uthscsa.edu
Length: 4 Yrs   *ACGME Approved/Offered Positions:* 24
Program ID: 220-48-21-292

Temple

Texas A&M College of Medicine-Scott and White Program

Sponsor: Scott and White Memorial Hospital
Prgm Director: Steven R Allen, MD
Scott & White Hospital
2401 South 31st Street
Temple, TX 76508
Tel: 254 724-7588   *Fax:* 254 724-7976
Length: 4 Yrs   *ACGME Approved/Offered Positions:* 16
Program ID: 220-48-21-293

Utah

Salt Lake City

University of Utah Program

Sponsor: University of Utah Medical Center
Intermountain Medical Center
Prgm Director: Michael L Draper, MD
Department of Obstetrics/Gynecology
30 North 1900 East, Room 2B200
Salt Lake City, UT 84132
Tel: 801 581-5501   *Fax:* 801 585-5146
E-mail: mike.draper@hsc.utah.edu
Length: 4 Yrs   *ACGME Approved/Offered Positions:* 24
Program ID: 220-49-21-294

Vermont

Burlington

University of Vermont Program

Sponsor: Fletcher Allen Health Care
Prgm Director: Christine A Murray, MD
251SM4
111 Colchester Avenue
Burlington, VT 05401
Tel: 802 847-4736   *Fax:* 802 847-5626
Length: 4 Yrs   *ACGME Approved/Offered Positions:* 12
Program ID: 220-50-21-295

Virginia

Charlottesville

University of Virginia Program

Sponsor: University of Virginia Medical Center
Prgm Director: Christian A Chisholm, MD
PO Box 800712
Charlottesville, VA 22908
Tel: 434 924-9930   *Fax:* 434 982-0058
E-mail: cchisholm@virginia.edu
Length: 4 Yrs   *ACGME Approved/Offered Positions:* 16
Program ID: 220-51-11-296

Newport News

Riverside Regional Medical Center Program

Sponsor: Riverside Regional Medical Center
Prgm Director: Jewell M Barnett, MD
Dept of Obstetrics/Gynecology
500 J Clyde Morris Boulevard, 3rd Floor
Newport News, VA 23601
Tel: 757 594-4737   *Fax:* 757 594-3184
E-mail: Betty.Hamrick@rivhs.com
Length: 4 Yrs   *ACGME Approved/Offered Positions:* 12
Program ID: 220-51-11-297

Norfolk

Eastern Virginia Medical School Program

Sponsor: Eastern Virginia Medical School
Chesapeake General Hospital
DePaul Medical Center
Sentara CarePlex Hospital
Sentara Norfolk General Hospital
Prgm Director: Gayatri Kapur, MD
601 Colley Avenue, Suite 243
Norfolk, VA 23507
Tel: 757 446-7470   *Fax:* 757 446-8998
E-mail: kapurg@evms.edu
Length: 4 Yrs   *ACGME Approved/Offered Positions:* 16
Program ID: 220-51-21-298

Note: * indicates a newly appointed program director

Portsmouth

Naval Medical Center (Portsmouth) Program
Sponsor: Naval Medical Center (Portsmouth)
Prgm Director: John D O'Boyle, MD
Department of Obstetrics-Gynecology
620 John Paul Jones Circle
Portsmouth, VA 23708
Tel: 757 953-4351   *Fax:* 757 953-5116
E-mail: john.oboyle@med.navy.mil
Length: 4 Yrs   *ACGME Approved/Offered Positions:* 24
Program ID: 220-51-11-014
Uniformed Services Program

Richmond

Virginia Commonwealth University Health System Program
Sponsor: Virginia Commonwealth University Health
    System
Medical College of Virginia Hospitals
Prgm Director: Stephen Cohen, MD, MBA
1250 E Marshall Street, Room 8-454
PO Box 980034
Richmond, VA 23298
Tel: 804 828-8614   *Fax:* 804 827-1229
E-mail: obgynres@vcu.edu
Length: 4 Yrs   *ACGME Approved/Offered Positions:* 24
Program ID: 220-51-11-299

Roanoke

Carilion Clinic Program
Sponsor: Carilion Clinic
Carilion Roanoke Memorial Hospital
Prgm Director: Patrice M Weiss, MD*
1906 Belleview Ave, SW
Medical Education Bldg, 2nd Floor
Roanoke, VA 24014
Tel: 540 853-0417   *Fax:* 540 344-5280
Length: 4 Yrs   *ACGME Approved/Offered Positions:* 12
Program ID: 220-51-31-300

Washington

Seattle

University of Washington Program
Sponsor: University of Washington School of Medicine
Harborview Medical Center
Swedish Medical Center
University of Washington Medical Center
Prgm Director: Seine Chiang, MD
BB667, Health Sciences Building
Box 356460
Seattle, WA 98195
Tel: 206 543-9626   *Fax:* 206 543-3915
E-mail: ejarrett@u.washington.edu
Length: 4 Yrs   *ACGME Approved/Offered Positions:* 24
Program ID: 220-54-21-301

Tacoma

Madigan Army Medical Center Program
Sponsor: Madigan Army Medical Center
Prgm Director: Michael K Chinn, MD
Department of Obstetrics-Gynecology
9040A Fitzsimmons Drive
Tacoma, WA 98431
Tel: 253 968-5161   *Fax:* 253 968-5508
E-mail: debbie.troop@amedd.army.mil
Length: 4 Yrs   *ACGME Approved/Offered Positions:* 16
Program ID: 220-54-12-010
Uniformed Services Program

West Virginia

Charleston

Charleston Area Medical Center/West Virginia University (Charleston Division) Program
Sponsor: Charleston Area Medical Center/West Virginia
    University
Prgm Director: Greg Heywood, MD
Suite 304
830 Pennsylvania Avenue
Charleston, WV 25302
Tel: 304 388-1515   *Fax:* 304 388-1586
E-mail: jennifer.cooperrider@camc.org
Length: 4 Yrs   *ACGME Approved/Offered Positions:* 12
Program ID: 220-55-11-303

Huntington

Marshall University School of Medicine Program
Sponsor: Marshall University School of Medicine
Cabell Huntington Hospital
Prgm Director: David C Jude, MD
Department of Obstetrics-Gynecology
1600 Medical Center Dr, Suite 4500
Huntington, WV 25701
Tel: 304 691-1454   *Fax:* 304 691-1453
E-mail: maxwellpoe@marshall.edu
Length: 4 Yrs   *ACGME Approved/Offered Positions:* 12
Program ID: 220-55-21-344

Morgantown

West Virginia University Program
Sponsor: West Virginia University School of Medicine
West Virginia University Hospitals
Prgm Director: Mahreen Hashmi, MD
4601 Health Sciences North
PO Box 9186
Morgantown, WV 26506
Tel: 304 293-7542   *Fax:* 304 293-5709
E-mail: klanham@hsc.wvu.edu
Length: 4 Yrs   *ACGME Approved/Offered Positions:* 12
Program ID: 220-55-11-304

Wisconsin

Madison

University of Wisconsin Program
Sponsor: University of Wisconsin Hospital and Clinics
Meriter Hospital
St Mary's Hospital
Prgm Director: Sabine Droste, MD
Meriter Hospital, 5-East
202 S Park Street
Madison, WI 53715
Tel: 608 263-1228   *Fax:* 608 263-0650
E-mail: rlwildes@wisc.edu
Length: 4 Yrs   *ACGME Approved/Offered Positions:* 24
Program ID: 220-56-21-306

Milwaukee

Aurora Health Care Program
Sponsor: Aurora Health Care
Aurora Sinai Medical Center
West Allis Memorial Hospital
Prgm Director: Tina C Mason, MD, MPH
945 North 12th Street
Milwaukee, WI 53233
Tel: 414 219-5725   *Fax:* 414 219-5611
E-mail: phyllis.groff@aurora.org
Length: 4 Yrs   *ACGME Approved/Offered Positions:* 12
Program ID: 220-56-12-308

Medical College of Wisconsin Affiliated Hospitals Program
Sponsor: Medical College of Wisconsin Affiliated
    Hospitals, Inc
Columbia St Mary's Hospitals
Froedtert Memorial Lutheran Hospital
Wheaton Franciscan Healthcare-St Joseph
Prgm Director: Paul M Lemen, MD
Department of Obstetrics-Gynecology
9200 West Wisconsin Avenue
Milwaukee, WI 53226
Tel: 414 805-6613   *Fax:* 414 805-6622
E-mail: ckuhlman@mcw.edu
Length: 4 Yrs   *ACGME Approved/Offered Positions:* 28
Program ID: 220-56-31-307

Oncology (Internal Medicine)

California

Los Angeles

University of Southern California/ LAC+USC Medical Center Program

Sponsor: University of Southern California/LAC+USC Medical Center
Kenneth Norris Jr Cancer Hospital and Research Institute
LAC+USC Medical Center
Prgm Director: Syma Iqbal, MD*
1441 Eastlake Avenue
Room 3444
Los Angeles, CA 90033
Tel: 323 865-3920   *Fax:* 323 865-0116
E-mail: dmoody@usc.edu
Length: 2 Yrs   *ACGME Approved/Offered Positions:* 7
Program ID: 147-05-21-045

Stanford

Stanford University Program

Sponsor: Stanford Hospital and Clinics
Prgm Director: James M Ford, MD
Division of Oncology
269 Campus Drive, Rm 1145
Stanford, CA 94305
Tel: 650 724-6467   *Fax:* 650 736-2282
E-mail: cmacklin@stanford.edu
Length: 2 Yrs   *ACGME Approved/Offered Positions:* 12
Program ID: 147-05-21-020

Connecticut

New Haven

Yale-New Haven Medical Center Program

Sponsor: Yale-New Haven Hospital
Veterans Affairs Medical Center (West Haven)
Prgm Director: Jill Lacy, MD
333 Cedar Street
PO Box 208032
New Haven, CT 06520
Tel: 203 737-1600   *Fax:* 203 785-7531
E-mail: jill.lacy@yale.edu
Length: 2 Yrs   *ACGME Approved/Offered Positions:* 11
Program ID: 147-08-21-021

District of Columbia

Washington

Howard University Program

Sponsor: Howard University Hospital
Prgm Director: Anita Aggarwal, DO, PhD*
2041 Georgia Avenue, NW
Washington, DC 20060
Tel: 202 865-1921
E-mail: aaggarwal@howard.edu
Length: 2 Yrs   *ACGME Approved/Offered Positions:* 2
Program ID: 147-10-21-116

Florida

Jacksonville

University of Florida College of Medicine Jacksonville Program

Sponsor: University of Florida College of Medicine Jacksonville
Baptist Medical Center
Shands Jacksonville Medical Center
Prgm Director: Janet R Hosenpud, MD, BA
655 West Eighth Street
Pavilion 4 North, Box P18
Jacksonville, FL 32209
Tel: 904 244-1658   *Fax:* 904 244-1681
E-mail: janet.hosenpud@jax.ufl.edu
Length: 2 Yrs   *ACGME Approved/Offered Positions:* 3
Program ID: 147-11-21-022

Louisiana

New Orleans

Ochsner Clinic Foundation Program

Sponsor: Ochsner Clinic Foundation
Prgm Director: John Cole, MD
Graduate Medical Education
1514 Jefferson Highway
New Orleans, LA 70121
Tel: 504 842-3261   *Fax:* 504 842-4533
E-mail: sclay@ochsner.org
Length: 2 Yrs   *ACGME Approved/Offered Positions:* 4
Program ID: 147-21-22-131

Maryland

Bethesda

National Institutes of Health Clinical Center Program

Sponsor: Clinical Center at the National Institutes of Health
National Naval Medical Center (Bethesda)
Prgm Director: Antonio T Fojo, MD, PhD
Building 10, Room 12N-226
10 Center Drive
Bethesda, MD 20892
Tel: 301 496-4916   *Fax:* 301 402-0172
E-mail: eddsja@mail.nih.gov
Length: 2 Yrs   *ACGME Approved/Offered Positions:* 24
Program ID: 147-23-21-183

Michigan

Royal Oak

William Beaumont Hospital Program

Sponsor: William Beaumont Hospital
Prgm Director: Ishmael Jaiyesimi, DO
3577 West 13 Mile Road, Suite 202
Royal Oak, MI 48073
Tel: 248 551-7117   *Fax:* 248 551-3154
E-mail: tmarcus@beaumonthospitals.com
Length: 2 Yrs   *ACGME Approved/Offered Positions:* 4
Program ID: 147-25-12-161

Nevada

Las Vegas

University of Nevada School of Medicine (Las Vegas) Program

Sponsor: University of Nevada School of Medicine
University Medical Center of Southern Nevada
Prgm Director: Nam Hoang Dang, MD, PhD
2040 West Charleston Boulevard
Suite 300
Las Vegas, NV 89102
Tel: 702 822-5468   *Fax:* 702 671-6442
Length: 2 Yrs   *ACGME Approved/Offered Positions:* 12
Program ID: 147-31-13-199

New York

Buffalo

University at Buffalo Program

Sponsor: University at Buffalo School of Medicine
Roswell Park Cancer Institute
Prgm Director: Ellis G Levine, MD
Elm and Carlton Streets
Buffalo, NY 14263
Tel: 716 845-8547   *Fax:* 716 845-8008
Length: 2 Yrs   *ACGME Approved/Offered Positions:* 12
Program ID: 147-35-31-008

East Meadow

Nassau University Medical Center Program

Sponsor: Nassau University Medical Center
Prgm Director: Linda Carmosino, MD
2201 Hempstead Turnpike
East Meadow, NY 11554
Tel: 516 542-4713   *Fax:* 516 572-5609
Length: 2 Yrs   *ACGME Approved/Offered Positions:* 3
Program ID: 147-35-21-085

Puerto Rico

San Juan

San Juan City Hospital Program

Sponsor: San Juan City Hospital
VA Caribbean Healthcare System
Prgm Director: Luis Baez, MD
Department of Medicine
Rio Piedras Station
San Juan, PR 00928
Tel: 787 758-7348   *Fax:* 787 641-4568
Length: 2 Yrs   *ACGME Approved/Offered Positions:* 4
Program ID: 147-42-11-088

Tennessee

Johnson City

East Tennessee State University Program

Sponsor: James H Quillen College of Medicine
Johnson City Medical Center/Mountain States Health Alliance
Veterans Affairs Medical Center (Mountain Home)
Prgm Director: Koyamangalath Krishnan, MD
Divsion of Medical Oncology
Box 70622 James H Quillen College
Johnson City, TN 37614
Tel: 423 439-6362   *Fax:* 423 439-6361
E-mail: streetd@etsu.edu
Length: 2 Yrs   *ACGME Approved/Offered Positions:* 7
Program ID: 147-47-21-195

Note: * indicates a newly appointed program director

Texas

Dallas

Baylor University Medical Center Program

Sponsor: Baylor University Medical Center
Prgm Director: Marvin J Stone, MD
3500 Gaston Avenue
Dallas, TX 75246
Tel: 214 820-3445   *Fax:* 214 820-2780
Length: 2 Yrs   *ACGME Approved/Offered Positions:* 5
Program ID: 147-48-31-076

Galveston

University of Texas Medical Branch Hospitals Program

Sponsor: University of Texas Medical Branch Hospitals
Prgm Director: Avi B Markowitz, MD
Department of Internal Medicine
301 University Boulevard
Galveston, TX 77555
Tel: 409 747-2270   *Fax:* 409 747-2369
Length: 2 Yrs   *ACGME Approved/Offered Positions:* 6
Program ID: 147-48-21-053

Temple

Texas A&M College of Medicine-Scott and White Program

Sponsor: Scott and White Memorial Hospital
Central Texas Veterans Affairs Healthcare System
Prgm Director: Frank Mott, MD
2401 South 31st Street
Temple, TX 76508
Tel: 254 724-0108   *Fax:* 254 724-8067
E-mail: mwheeler@swmail.sw.org
Length: 2 Yrs   *ACGME Approved/Offered Positions:* 6
Program ID: 147-48-21-186

Wisconsin

Madison

University of Wisconsin Program

Sponsor: University of Wisconsin Hospital and Clinics
William S Middleton Veterans Hospital
Prgm Director: Kyle D Holen, MD*
600 Highland Avenue, Room K4/610
UW Comprehensive Cancer Center
Madison, WI 53792
Tel: 608 265-0051   *Fax:* 608 265-8133
Length: 2 Yrs   *ACGME Approved/Offered Positions:* 8
Program ID: 147-56-21-111

Ophthalmology

Alabama

Birmingham

University of Alabama Medical Center Program

Sponsor: University of Alabama Hospital
Cooper Green Hospital
Eye Foundation Hospital
Veterans Affairs Medical Center (Birmingham)
Prgm Director: Russell W Read, MD, PhD*
Callahan Eye Foundation Hospital
700 South 18th Street, Suite 601
Birmingham, AL 35233
Tel: 205 325-8507   *Fax:* 205 325-8200
Length: 3 Yrs   *ACGME Approved/Offered Positions:* 15
Program ID: 240-01-21-015

Arizona

Tucson

University of Arizona Program

Sponsor: University of Arizona College of Medicine
Southern Arizona VA Health Care Center (Tucson)
University Medical Center
Prgm Director: Richard R Ober, MD
PO Box 245085
1501 N Campbell Avenue
Tucson, AZ 85724
Tel: 520 792-1450   *Fax:* 520 321-3665
E-mail: richard.ober@va.gov
Length: 3 Yrs   *ACGME Approved/Offered Positions:* 6
Program ID: 240-03-21-171

University of Arizona/UPHK Graduate Medical Education Consortium Program

Sponsor: University of Arizona/UPHK Graduate Medical Ed Consortium
Southern Arizona VA Health Care Center (Tucson)
Prgm Director: Joseph M Miller, MD, MPH
2800 East Ajo Way
Tucson, AZ 85713
Tel: 520 321-3677   *Fax:* 520 321-3665
Length: 3 Yrs   *ACGME Approved/Offered Positions:* 6
Program ID: 240-03-13-181

Arkansas

Little Rock

University of Arkansas for Medical Sciences Program

Sponsor: University of Arkansas College of Medicine
Arkansas Children's Hospital
Central Arkansas Veterans Healthcare System
UAMS Medical Center
Prgm Director: Richard A Harper, MD
4301 W Markham Street, Slot 523
Little Rock, AR 72205
Tel: 501 686-5150   *Fax:* 501 603-1289
E-mail: dozieramandal@uams.edu
Length: 3 Yrs   *ACGME Approved/Offered Positions:* 9
Program ID: 240-04-21-018

California

Loma Linda

Loma Linda University Program

Sponsor: Loma Linda University Medical Center
Jerry L Pettis Memorial Veterans Hospital
Riverside County Regional Medical Center
Prgm Director: Michael E Rauser, MD
11234 Anderson Street
FMO Ste 1800
Loma Linda, CA 92354
Tel: 909 558-2182   *Fax:* 909 558-2506
E-mail: mrauser@llu.edu
Length: 3 Yrs   *ACGME Approved/Offered Positions:* 12
Program ID: 240-05-21-023

Los Angeles

UCLA Medical Center Program

Sponsor: UCLA David Geffen School of Medicine/UCLA Medical Center
Los Angeles County-Harbor-UCLA Medical Center
Olive View/UCLA Medical Center
VA Greater Los Angeles Healthcare System
Prgm Director: Anthony C Arnold, MD
Suite 2-247
100 Stein Plaza-CHS
Los Angeles, CA 90095
Tel: 310 825-4344   *Fax:* 310 267-1918
E-mail: arnolda@ucla.edu
Length: 3 Yrs   *ACGME Approved/Offered Positions:* 24
Program ID: 240-05-21-027

University of Southern California/LAC+USC Medical Center Program

Sponsor: University of Southern California/LAC+USC Medical Center
LAC+USC Medical Center
USC University Hospital
Prgm Director: Alfredo A Sadun, MD, PhD
Doheny Eye Institute
1450 San Pablo Street
Los Angeles, CA 90033
Tel: 323 442-6417   *Fax:* 323 442-6407
Length: 3 Yrs   *ACGME Approved/Offered Positions:* 18
Program ID: 240-05-21-025

Orange

University of California (Irvine) Program

Sponsor: University of California (Irvine) Medical Center
VA Long Beach Healthcare System
Prgm Director: Jeremiah P Tao, MD*
118 Med Surge I
Bldg 810 Rm 118L
Irvine, CA 92697
Tel: 949 824-0327   *Fax:* 949 824-4015
E-mail: karen.tighe@uci.edu
Length: 3 Yrs   *ACGME Approved/Offered Positions:* 9
Program ID: 240-05-21-022

Sacramento

University of California (Davis) Health System Program

Sponsor: University of California (Davis) Health System
University of California (Davis) Medical Center
Prgm Director: Jeffrey J Caspar, MD
4860 Y Street
Suite 2400
Sacramento, CA 95817
Tel: 916 734-6957   *Fax:* 916 773-6197
E-mail: becky.glasgow@ucdmc.ucdavis.edu
Length: 3 Yrs   *ACGME Approved/Offered Positions:* 12
Program ID: 240-05-21-020

Programs

San Diego

Naval Medical Center (San Diego) Program

Sponsor: Naval Medical Center (San Diego)
Prgm Director: Elizabeth Hofmeister, MD, BS*
Department of Ophthalmology
34800 Bob Wilson Drive
San Diego, CA 92134
Tel: 619 532-6702   *Fax:* 619 532-7272
E-mail: elizabeth.hofmeister@med.navy.mil
Length: 3 Yrs   *ACGME Approved/Offered Positions:* 12
Program ID: 240-05-32-008
Uniformed Services Program

University of California (San Diego) Program

Sponsor: University of California (San Diego) Medical Center
Veterans Affairs Medical Center (San Diego)
Prgm Director: Leah Levi, MBBS
UCSD Shiley Eye Center (MC 0946)
9415 Campus Point Drive
La Jolla, CA 92093
Tel: 858 534-8858   *Fax:* 858 822-0040
E-mail: residency@eyecenter.ucsd.edu
Length: 3 Yrs   *ACGME Approved/Offered Positions:* 9
Program ID: 240-05-21-030

San Francisco

California Pacific Medical Center Program

Sponsor: California Pacific Medical Center
Alameda County Medical Center
Prgm Director: Susan Day, MD
Department of Ophthalmology
2340 Clay Street, 5th Floor
San Francisco, CA 94115
Tel: 415 600-6523   *Fax:* 415 600-3949
E-mail: meded@sutterhealth.org
Length: 3 Yrs   *ACGME Approved/Offered Positions:* 9
Program ID: 240-05-22-031

University of California (San Francisco) Program

Sponsor: University of California (San Francisco) School of Medicine
San Francisco General Hospital Medical Center
UCSF and Mount Zion Medical Centers
Veterans Affairs Medical Center (San Francisco)
Prgm Director: Shan C Lin, MD
Dept of Ophthalmology, K-301
10 Koret Way
San Francisco, CA 94143
Tel: 415 514-0952   *Fax:* 415 476-0336
E-mail: lins@vision.ucsf.edu
Length: 3 Yrs   *ACGME Approved/Offered Positions:* 15
Program ID: 240-05-21-032

Stanford

Stanford University Program

Sponsor: Stanford Hospital and Clinics
Santa Clara Valley Medical Center
Veterans Affairs Palo Alto Health Care System
Prgm Director: Christopher N Ta, MD
Department of Ophthalmology
Rm A157, 300 Pasteur Drive, MC 5308
Stanford, CA 94305
Tel: 650 498-4791   *Fax:* 650 498-4222
Length: 3 Yrs   *ACGME Approved/Offered Positions:* 12
Program ID: 240-05-21-033

Note: * indicates a newly appointed program director

Colorado

Aurora

University of Colorado Denver Program

Sponsor: University of Colorado Denver School of Medicine
Denver Health Medical Center
University of Colorado Hospital
Veterans Affairs Medical Center (Denver)
Prgm Director: Vikram D Durairaj, MD
1675 Ursula Street, Mailstop F731
PO Box 6510
Aurora, CO 80045
Tel: 720 848-5029   *Fax:* 720 848-5014
E-mail: ophthalmology.residency@uchsc.edu
Length: 3 Yrs   *ACGME Approved/Offered Positions:* 12
Program ID: 240-07-21-035

Connecticut

New Haven

Yale-New Haven Medical Center Program

Sponsor: Yale-New Haven Hospital
Veterans Affairs Medical Center (West Haven)
Prgm Director: Carlo R Bernardino, MD
Department of Ophthalmology and Visual Science
40 Temple Street, Suite 1B
New Haven, CT 06510
Tel: 203 785-6345   *Fax:* 203 785-5909
E-mail: robert.bernardino@yale.edu
Length: 3 Yrs   *ACGME Approved/Offered Positions:* 12
Program ID: 240-08-21-036

District of Columbia

Washington

George Washington University Program

Sponsor: George Washington University School of Medicine
George Washington University Hospital (UHS)
Veterans Affairs Medical Center (Martinsburg)
Prgm Director: Sanjeev Grewal, MD
2150 Pennsylvania Ave, NW
Floor 2A
Washington, DC 20037
Tel: 202 741-2825   *Fax:* 202 741-2821
E-mail: sgrewal@mfa.gwu.edu
Length: 3 Yrs   *ACGME Approved/Offered Positions:* 12
Program ID: 240-10-21-039

Georgetown University Hospital/Washington Hospital Center Program

Sponsor: Washington Hospital Center
Veterans Affairs Medical Center (Washington, DC)
Prgm Director: Jay M Lustbader, MD
110 Irving Street, NW
Suite 1A-1
Washington, DC 20010
Tel: 202 444-4968   *Fax:* 202 444-4978
E-mail: lustbadj@gunet.georgetown.edu
Length: 3 Yrs   *ACGME Approved/Offered Positions:* 18
Program ID: 240-10-32-041

Howard University Program

Sponsor: Howard University Hospital
National Naval Medical Center (Bethesda)
Prgm Director: Leslie S Jones, MD
2041 Georgia Avenue, NW, Suite 2100
Washington, DC 20060
Tel: 202 865-6425   *Fax:* 202 865-4259
Length: 3 Yrs   *ACGME Approved/Offered Positions:* 9
Program ID: 240-10-21-040

Florida

Gainesville

University of Florida Program

Sponsor: University of Florida College of Medicine
North Florida/South Georgia Veterans Health System
Shands Hospital at the University of Florida
Prgm Director: Sonal Tuli, MD
Dept of Ophthalmology
Box 100284, JHMHC
Gainesville, FL 32610
Tel: 352 392-3451   *Fax:* 352 392-7839
E-mail: stuli@eye.ufl.edu
Length: 3 Yrs   *ACGME Approved/Offered Positions:* 15
Program ID: 240-11-21-042

Jacksonville

University of Florida College of Medicine Jacksonville Program

Sponsor: University of Florida College of Medicine Jacksonville
Shands Jacksonville Medical Center
Prgm Director: K V Chalam, MD, PhD
580 West 8th Street
Jacksonville, FL 32209
Tel: 904 244-9361   *Fax:* 904 244-9391
Length: 3 Yrs   *ACGME Approved/Offered Positions:* 6
Program ID: 240-11-31-182

Miami

Jackson Memorial Hospital/Jackson Health System Program

Sponsor: Jackson Memorial Hospital/Jackson Health System
Bascom Palmer Eye Institute-Anne Bates Leach Eye Hospital
Prgm Director: Steven J Gedde, MD
Bascom Palmer Eye Institute
900 NW 17th Street
Miami, FL 33136
Tel: 800 329-7000   *Fax:* 305 326-6580
Length: 3 Yrs   *ACGME Approved/Offered Positions:* 21
Program ID: 240-11-11-043

Tampa

University of South Florida Program

Sponsor: University of South Florida College of Medicine
James A Haley Veterans Hospital
Tampa General Hospital
Prgm Director: Mitchell D Drucker, MD
MDC - Box 21
12901 Bruce B Downs Blvd
Tampa, FL 33612
Tel: 813 974-3820   *Fax:* 813 974-5621
E-mail: lswitzer@hsc.usf.edu
Length: 3 Yrs   *ACGME Approved/Offered Positions:* 12
Program ID: 240-11-21-044

Georgia

Atlanta

Emory University Program

Sponsor: Emory University School of Medicine
Emory University Hospital
Grady Health System
Veterans Affairs Medical Center (Atlanta)
Prgm Director: Maria M Aaron, MD
Emory Eye Center, Suite B2400
1365B Clifton Road, NE
Atlanta, GA 30322
Tel: 404 778-4530   *Fax:* 404 778-4002
Length: 3 Yrs   *ACGME Approved/Offered Positions:* 18
Program ID: 240-12-21-045

Augusta

Medical College of Georgia Program
Sponsor: Medical College of Georgia
Veterans Affairs Medical Center (Augusta)
Prgm Director: Lane D Ulrich, MD
1120 15th Street BA 2701
School of Medicine
Augusta, GA 30912
Tel: 706 721-1150   *Fax:* 706 721-1158
Length: 3 Yrs   *ACGME Approved/Offered Positions:* 9
Program ID: 240-12-21-046

Illinois

Chicago

John H Stroger Hospital of Cook County Program
Sponsor: John H Stroger Hospital of Cook County
Prgm Director: Richard Ahuja, MD
Division of Ophthalmology
1900 West Polk Street, Room 617
Chicago, IL 60612
Tel: 312 864-5171   *Fax:* 312 864-9753
Length: 3 Yrs   *ACGME Approved/Offered Positions:* 9
Program ID: 240-16-22-047

McGaw Medical Center of Northwestern University Program
Sponsor: McGaw Medical Center of Northwestern University
Evanston Hospital
Jesse Brown Veterans Affairs Medical Center
Northwestern Memorial Hospital
Prgm Director: Ann Bidwell, MD
645 N Michigan Avenue
Suite 440
Chicago, IL 60611
Tel: 312 908-8152   *Fax:* 312 503-8152
Length: 3 Yrs   *ACGME Approved/Offered Positions:* 12
Program ID: 240-16-21-049

Rush University Medical Center Program
Sponsor: Rush University Medical Center
Prgm Director: Jack A Cohen, MD
1653 W Congress Parkway
Chicago, IL 60612
Tel: 312 942-3903   *Fax:* 312 942-2140
Length: 3 Yrs   *ACGME Approved/Offered Positions:* 6
Program ID: 240-16-11-050

University of Chicago Program
Sponsor: University of Chicago Medical Center
Louis A Weiss Memorial Hospital
Prgm Director: Susan Ksiazek, MD*
Dept of Ophthalmology and Visual Science
5841 S Maryland Avenue, MC 2114
Chicago, IL 60637
Tel: 773 834-8429   *Fax:* 773 834-9711
Length: 3 Yrs   *ACGME Approved/Offered Positions:* 9
Program ID: 240-16-21-174

University of Illinois College of Medicine at Chicago Program
Sponsor: University of Illinois College of Medicine at Chicago
University of Illinois Hosp-Illinois Eye and Ear Infirmary
Prgm Director: Dimitri T Azar, MD*
Ophthalmology Edu Offc, Rm 159
1855 West Taylor Street
Chicago, IL 60612
Tel: 312 413-8467   *Fax:* 312 996-7770
Length: 3 Yrs   *ACGME Approved/Offered Positions:* 18
Program ID: 240-16-21-052

Maywood

Loyola University Program
Sponsor: Loyola University Medical Center
Edward Hines, Jr Veterans Affairs Hospital
Prgm Director: David Yoo, MD*
Foster G McGaw Hospital
2160 South First Avenue
Maywood, IL 60153
Tel: 708 216-4161   *Fax:* 708 216-3557
E-mail: ddement@lumc.edu
Length: 3 Yrs   *ACGME Approved/Offered Positions:* 12
Program ID: 240-16-21-054

Indiana

Indianapolis

Indiana University School of Medicine Program
Sponsor: Indiana University School of Medicine
Clarian Indiana University Hospital
Richard L Roudebush Veterans Affairs Medical Center
William N Wishard Memorial Hospital
Prgm Director: Darrell WuDunn, MD, PhD
702 Rotary Circle
Indianapolis, IN 46202
Tel: 317 274-2128   *Fax:* 317 274-2277
E-mail: phannah@iupui.edu
Length: 3 Yrs   *ACGME Approved/Offered Positions:* 18
Program ID: 240-17-21-055

Iowa

Iowa City

University of Iowa Hospitals and Clinics Program
Sponsor: University of Iowa Hospitals and Clinics
Veterans Affairs Medical Center (Iowa City)
Prgm Director: Thomas A Oetting, MD, MS
Dept of Ophthalmology & Visual Sciences
200 Hawkins Drive
Iowa City, IA 52242
Tel: 319 384-9958   *Fax:* 319 353-7699
E-mail: thomas-oetting@uiowa.edu
Length: 3 Yrs   *ACGME Approved/Offered Positions:* 15
Program ID: 240-18-11-056

Kansas

Kansas City

University of Kansas School of Medicine Program
Sponsor: University of Kansas School of Medicine
University of Kansas Hospital
Veterans Affairs Medical Center (Kansas City)
Prgm Director: Thomas J Whittaker, MD, JD
KU Eye
7400 State Line
Prairie Village, KS 66208
Tel: 913 588-6660   *Fax:* 913 588-0888
Length: 3 Yrs   *ACGME Approved/Offered Positions:* 9
Program ID: 240-19-21-057

Kentucky

Lexington

University of Kentucky College of Medicine Program
Sponsor: University of Kentucky College of Medicine
University of Kentucky Hospital
Veterans Affairs Medical Center (Lexington)
Prgm Director: Seema Capoor, MD, MBBS
Department of Ophthalmology and Visual Sciences
Kentucky Clinic E 302
Lexington, KY 40536
Tel: 859 218-2631   *Fax:* 859 323-1122
E-mail: scapoor@email.uky.edu
Length: 3 Yrs   *ACGME Approved/Offered Positions:* 9
Program ID: 240-20-21-058

Louisville

University of Louisville Program
Sponsor: University of Louisville School of Medicine
University of Louisville Hospital
Veterans Affairs Medical Center (Louisville)
Prgm Director: Joern B Soltau, MD
301 E Muhammad Ali Blvd
Kentucky Lions Eye Center
Louisville, KY 40202
Tel: 502 852-0710   *Fax:* 502 852-7349
Length: 3 Yrs   *ACGME Approved/Offered Positions:* 12
Program ID: 240-20-21-059

Louisiana

New Orleans

Louisiana State University/Ochsner Clinic Foundation Program
Sponsor: Louisiana State University School of Medicine
Earl K Long Medical Center
Leonard J Chabert Medical Center
LSU Health Science Center-Bogalusa Medical Center
Ochsner Clinic Foundation
Prgm Director: Marie D Acierno, MD
LSU Eye Center
2020 Gravier St Suite B
New Orleans, LA 70112
Tel: 504 568-2242   *Fax:* 504 568-2385
E-mail: gabbas@lsuhsc.edu
Length: 3 Yrs   *ACGME Approved/Offered Positions:* 24
Program ID: 240-21-21-177

Tulane University Program
Sponsor: Tulane University School of Medicine
Tulane University Hospital and Clinics
Veterans Affairs Medical Center (Alexandria)
Veterans Affairs Medical Center (Biloxi)
Veterans Affairs Medical Center (New Orleans)
Prgm Director: Ramesh S Ayyala, MD
Dept of Ophthalmology, Box SL-69
1430 Tulane Ave
New Orleans, LA 70112
Tel: 504 988-2261   *Fax:* 504 988-2684
Length: 3 Yrs   *ACGME Approved/Offered Positions:* 18
Program ID: 240-21-21-062

Programs

Shreveport

Louisiana State University (Shreveport) Program

Sponsor: LSU Health Sciences Center-University Hospital
Overton Brooks Veterans Affairs Medical Center
Prgm Director: Thomas B Redens, MD
1501 Kings Highway
PO Box 33932
Shreveport, LA 71130
Tel: 318 675-5012   *Fax:* 318 675-6000
Length: 3 Yrs   *ACGME Approved/Offered Positions:* 9
Program ID: 240-21-21-063

Maryland

Baltimore

Johns Hopkins University/Sinai Hospital of Baltimore Program

Sponsor: Johns Hopkins University School of Medicine
Greater Baltimore Medical Center
Johns Hopkins Hospital
Prgm Director: James P Dunn Jr, MD
600 N Wolfe Street
Wilmer B20
Baltimore, MD 21287
Tel: 410 955-8265   *Fax:* 410 614-9632
Length: 3 Yrs   *ACGME Approved/Offered Positions:* 21
Program ID: 240-23-21-065

Maryland General Hospital Program

Sponsor: Maryland General Hospital
Prgm Director: Samuel D Friedel, MD
827 Linden Ave
Baltimore, MD 21201
Tel: 410 225-8077   *Fax:* 410 225-8785
Length: 3 Yrs   *ACGME Approved/Offered Positions:* 6
Program ID: 240-23-12-066

Sinai Hospital of Baltimore Program

Sponsor: Sinai Hospital of Baltimore
Prgm Director: Colleen P Halfpenny, MD*
The Krieger Eye Institute
2411 West Belvedere Avenue
Baltimore, MD 21215
Tel: 410 601-5991   *Fax:* 410 601-8273
E-mail: chalfpen@lifebridgehealth.org
Length: 3 Yrs   *ACGME Approved/Offered Positions:* 6
Program ID: 240-23-12-179

University of Maryland Program

Sponsor: University of Maryland Medical System
Veterans Affairs Medical Center (Wilmington)
Prgm Director: Sajeev S Kathuria, MD
419 W Redwood Street
Suite 580
Baltimore, MD 21201
Tel: 410 328-8659   *Fax:* 410 328-6346
Length: 3 Yrs   *ACGME Approved/Offered Positions:* 12
Program ID: 240-23-21-068

Bethesda

National Capital Consortium (Walter Reed) Program

Sponsor: National Capital Consortium
Walter Reed Army Medical Center
Prgm Director: Andrew S Eiseman, MD
Ophthalmology Service, Department of Surgery
6900 Georgia Avenue NW
Washington, DC 20307
Tel: 202 782-8087   *Fax:* 202 782-6156
E-mail: andrew.eiseman@us.army.mil
Length: 3 Yrs   *ACGME Approved/Offered Positions:* 9
Program ID: 240-10-12-004
Uniformed Services Program

Note: * indicates a newly appointed program director

Massachusetts

Boston

Boston University Medical Center Program

Sponsor: Boston Medical Center
Veterans Affairs Medical Center (Boston)
Prgm Director: John W Gittinger Jr, MD
85 East Concord Street, 8th Floor
Department of Ophthalmology
Boston, MA 02118
Tel: 617 638-4552   *Fax:* 617 414-2299
E-mail: ophthalm@bu.edu
Length: 3 Yrs   *ACGME Approved/Offered Positions:* 12
Program ID: 240-24-21-069

Massachusetts Eye and Ear Infirmary Program

Sponsor: Massachusetts Eye and Ear Infirmary
Veterans Affairs Medical Center (Boston)
Prgm Director: John I Loewenstein, MD
243 Charles Street
Department of Ophthalmology
Boston, MA 02114
Tel: 617 573-3529   *Fax:* 617 573-3152
Length: 3 Yrs   *ACGME Approved/Offered Positions:* 24
Program ID: 240-24-21-070

Tufts Medical Center Program

Sponsor: Tufts Medical Center
Lahey Clinic
Prgm Director: Chandrasekharan Krishnan, MD
Tufts University School of Medicine
800 Washington Street, Box 450
Boston, MA 02111
Tel: 617 636-4648   *Fax:* 617 636-8315
Length: 3 Yrs   *ACGME Approved/Offered Positions:* 12
Program ID: 240-24-21-071

Michigan

Ann Arbor

University of Michigan Program

Sponsor: University of Michigan Hospitals and Health Centers
Veterans Affairs Medical Center (Ann Arbor)
Prgm Director: Shahzad I Mian, MD
W K Kellogg Eye Center, Box 0714
1000 Wall Street
Ann Arbor, MI 48105
Tel: 734 615-5476   *Fax:* 734 936-4784
E-mail: kwhitney@med.umich.edu
Length: 3 Yrs   *ACGME Approved/Offered Positions:* 21
Program ID: 240-25-11-072

Detroit

Henry Ford Hospital Program

Sponsor: Henry Ford Hospital
Prgm Director: Brian N Bachynski, MD
Department of Ophthalmology, K-10
2799 W Grand Blvd
Detroit, MI 48202
Tel: 313 916-3270   *Fax:* 313 916-2496
E-mail: landers1@hfhs.org
Length: 3 Yrs   *ACGME Approved/Offered Positions:* 15
Program ID: 240-25-12-073

Wayne State University/Detroit Medical Center Program

Sponsor: Wayne State University/Detroit Medical Center
Harper-Hutzel Hospital
Prgm Director: Mark S Juzych, MD, MHA
Kresge Eye Institute
4717 St Antoine
Detroit, MI 48201
Tel: 313 577-7614   *Fax:* 313 577-9675
E-mail: Juzych@aol.com
Length: 3 Yrs   *ACGME Approved/Offered Positions:* 21
Program ID: 240-25-21-075

Royal Oak

William Beaumont Hospital Program

Sponsor: William Beaumont Hospital
Prgm Director: Robert J Granadier, MD
3601 West 13 Mile Road
Royal Oak, MI 48073
Tel: 248 551-3643   *Fax:* 248 551-4362
Length: 3 Yrs   *ACGME Approved/Offered Positions:* 9
Program ID: 240-25-21-165

Minnesota

Minneapolis

University of Minnesota Program

Sponsor: University of Minnesota Medical School
Hennepin County Medical Center
Regions Hospital
University of Minnesota Medical Center, Division of Fairview
Veterans Affairs Medical Center (Minneapolis)
Prgm Director: Martha M Wright, MD
MMC 493 420 Delaware St SE
Minneapolis, MN 55455
Tel: 612 625-4400   *Fax:* 612 626-3119
Length: 3 Yrs   *ACGME Approved/Offered Positions:* 12
Program ID: 240-26-21-077

Rochester

College of Medicine, Mayo Clinic (Rochester) Program

Sponsor: College of Medicine, Mayo Clinic
Mayo Clinic (Rochester)
Rochester Methodist Hospital
Saint Marys Hospital of Rochester
Prgm Director: Michael A Mahr, MD
200 First St SW
Department of Ophthalmology
Rochester, MN 55905
Tel: 507 284-1709   *Fax:* 507 284-4612
E-mail: mahr.michael@mayo.edu
Length: 3 Yrs   *ACGME Approved/Offered Positions:* 12
Program ID: 240-26-21-078

Mississippi

Jackson

University of Mississippi Medical Center Program

Sponsor: University of Mississippi School of Medicine
University Hospitals and Clinics
Veterans Affairs Medical Center (Jackson)
Prgm Director: Kimberly W Crowder, MD
2500 N State St, McBryde Bldg
Third Floor, McBryde Building
Jackson, MS 39216
Tel: 601 815-4789   *Fax:* 601 815-3773
E-mail: kcrowder@ophth.umsmed.edu
Length: 3 Yrs   *ACGME Approved/Offered Positions:* 9
Program ID: 240-27-21-079

Missouri

Columbia

University of Missouri-Columbia Program

Sponsor: University of Missouri-Columbia School of Medicine
Harry S Truman Memorial Veterans Hospital
University Hospitals and Clinics
Prgm Director: Lenworth N Johnson, MD
Mason Eye Institute
One Hospital Drive
Columbia, MO 65212
Tel: 573 882-8470   *Fax:* 573 882-8474
E-mail: greene@health.missouri.edu
Length: 3 Yrs   *ACGME Approved/Offered Positions:* 9
Program ID: 240-28-22-080

Kansas City

University of Missouri at Kansas City Program

Sponsor: University of Missouri-Kansas City School of Medicine
Truman Medical Center
Prgm Director: Jean R Hausheer, MD
2300 Holmes Street
Kansas City, MO 64108
Tel: 816 404-1780
E-mail: hauseye@kc.rr.com
Length: 3 Yrs   *ACGME Approved/Offered Positions:* 9
Program ID: 240-28-21-081

St Louis

St Louis University School of Medicine Program

Sponsor: St Louis University School of Medicine
Anheuser-Busch Institute
Cardinal Glennon Children's Hospital
Prgm Director: Steven R Shields, MD
Saint Louis University Eye Institute
1755 S Grand Blvd
St Louis, MO 63104
Tel: 314 256-3231   *Fax:* 314 771-0596
E-mail: rennerj@slu.edu
Length: 3 Yrs   *ACGME Approved/Offered Positions:* 12
Program ID: 240-28-21-083

Washington University/B-JH/SLCH Consortium Program

Sponsor: Washington University/B-JH/SLCH Consortium
Barnes-Jewish Hospital
Veterans Affairs Medical Center (St Louis)
Prgm Director: Susan M Culican, MD, PhD
660 S Euclid Avenue
Campus Box 8096
St Louis, MO 63110
Tel: 314 362-5722   *Fax:* 314 362-2420
E-mail: hitt@vision.wustl.edu
Length: 3 Yrs   *ACGME Approved/Offered Positions:* 15
Program ID: 240-28-21-084

Nebraska

Omaha

University of Nebraska Medical Center College of Medicine Program

Sponsor: University of Nebraska Medical Center College of Medicine
Nebraska Medical Center
Veterans Affairs Medical Center (Omaha)
Prgm Director: Thomas W Hejkal, MD, PhD
985540 Nebraska Medical Center
Box 985540
Omaha, NE 68198
Tel: 402 559-4276   *Fax:* 402 559-5514
Length: 3 Yrs   *ACGME Approved/Offered Positions:* 6
Program ID: 240-30-21-085

New Jersey

Newark

UMDNJ-New Jersey Medical School Program

Sponsor: UMDNJ-New Jersey Medical School
Jersey City Medical Center
UMDNJ-University Hospital
Veterans Affairs New Jersey Health Care System
Prgm Director: Paul D Langer, MD
Department of Ophthalmology
Doctors Office Center, 90 Bergen Street, 6th Floor
Newark, NJ 07101
Tel: 973 972-2035   *Fax:* 973 972-2068
Length: 3 Yrs   *ACGME Approved/Offered Positions:* 15
Program ID: 240-33-21-086

New York

Albany

Albany Medical Center Program

Sponsor: Albany Medical Center
Veterans Affairs Medical Center (Albany)
Prgm Director: Sai B Gandham, MD
Lions Eye Institute
1220 New Scotland Road
Slingerlands, NY 12159
Tel: 518 533-6565   *Fax:* 518 533-6567
Length: 3 Yrs   *ACGME Approved/Offered Positions:* 9
Program ID: 240-35-21-087

Bronx

Albert Einstein College of Medicine Program

Sponsor: Albert Einstein College of Medicine of Yeshiva University
Montefiore Medical Center-Henry and Lucy Moses Division
Montefiore Medical Center-Weiler Division
North Bronx Healthcare Network-Jacobi Medical Center
North Bronx Healthcare Network-North Central Bronx Hospital
Prgm Director: Assumpta Madu A, MD, MBA*
Department of Ophthalmology
111 East 210th Street
Bronx, NY 10467
Tel: 718 920-8424   *Fax:* 718 881-5439
E-mail: amadu@montefiore.org
Length: 3 Yrs   *ACGME Approved/Offered Positions:* 12
Program ID: 240-35-21-093

Bronx-Lebanon Hospital Center Program

Sponsor: Bronx-Lebanon Hospital Center
Prgm Director: Martin Mayers, MD*
1650 Selwyn Avenue #1C
Bronx, NY 10457
Tel: 718 960-2044   *Fax:* 718 960-2045
Length: 3 Yrs   *ACGME Approved/Offered Positions:* 6
Program ID: 240-35-21-095

Brooklyn

SUNY Health Science Center at Brooklyn Program

Sponsor: SUNY Health Science Center at Brooklyn
Brookdale University Hospital and Medical Center
Coney Island Hospital
Kings County Hospital Center
Long Island College Hospital
Veterans Affairs Medical Center (Brooklyn)
Prgm Director: Monica Dweck, MD
450 Clarkson Ave Box 58
Department of Ophthalmology
Brooklyn, NY 11203
Tel: 718 270-1962   *Fax:* 718 270-2972
Length: 3 Yrs   *ACGME Approved/Offered Positions:* 21
Program ID: 240-35-21-113

Buffalo

University at Buffalo Program

Sponsor: University at Buffalo School of Medicine
Kaleida Health System (Women and Children's Hosp of Buffalo)
University at Buffalo Affiliated Physician Practices (UBAPP)
Veterans Affairs Western New York Hospital
Prgm Director: James D Reynolds, MD
1176 Main Street
Buffalo, NY 14209
Tel: 716 881-7916   *Fax:* 716 887-2991
Length: 3 Yrs   *ACGME Approved/Offered Positions:* 9
Program ID: 240-35-11-170

East Meadow

Nassau University Medical Center Program

Sponsor: Nassau University Medical Center
University Hospital - SUNY at Stony Brook
Veterans Affairs Medical Center (Northport)
Prgm Director: Marcelle M Morcos, MD
2201 Hempstead Turnpike
East Meadow, NY 11554
Tel: 516 572-6706   *Fax:* 516 572-9477
E-mail: mmorcosmd@yahoo.com
Length: 3 Yrs   *ACGME Approved/Offered Positions:* 12
Program ID: 240-35-31-091

Great Neck

NSLIJHS Program

Sponsor: North Shore-Long Island Jewish Health System
Long Island Jewish Medical Center
North Shore University Hospital
Queens Hospital Center
Prgm Director: Steven E Rubin, MD
Department of Ophthalmology, Suite 107
600 Northern Boulevard
Great Neck, NY 11021
Tel: 516 465-8444   *Fax:* 516 465-8407
E-mail: JMillspa@nshs.edu
Length: 3 Yrs   *ACGME Approved/Offered Positions:* 12
Program ID: 240-35-21-102

Programs

Jamaica

New York Medical College (Brooklyn-Queens) Program
Sponsor: New York Medical College
Caritas Health Care (Brooklyn-Queens)
Eye Care Center
Wyckoff Heights Medical Center
Prgm Director: Cono M Grasso, MD
161-10 Union Turnpike
Flushing, NY 11363
Tel: 718 380-8050 *Fax:* 718 380-5348
E-mail: cgrasso@bqhcny.org
Length: 3 Yrs *ACGME Approved/Offered Positions:* 6
Program ID: 240-35-21-098

New York

Mount Sinai School of Medicine Program
Sponsor: Mount Sinai School of Medicine
Elmhurst Hospital Center-Mount Sinai Services
Mount Sinai Medical Center
Veterans Affairs Medical Center (Bronx)
Prgm Director: Donna J Gagliuso, MD
Department of Ophthalmology, Box 1183
One Gustave L Levy Place
New York, NY 10029
Tel: 212 241-7659 *Fax:* 212 241-9994
Length: 3 Yrs *ACGME Approved/Offered Positions:* 12
Program ID: 240-35-21-104

New York Eye and Ear Infirmary Program
Sponsor: New York Eye and Ear Infirmary
Prgm Director: Paul A Sidoti, MD
310 East 14th Street
New York, NY 10003
Tel: 212 979-4590 *Fax:* 212 979-4268
E-mail: psidoti@nyee.edu
Length: 3 Yrs *ACGME Approved/Offered Positions:* 21
Program ID: 240-35-22-105

New York Medical College at St Vincent's Hospital and Medical Center of New York Program
Sponsor: New York Medical College
St Vincent Catholic Medical Centers (Manhattan)
Richmond University Medical Center
Prgm Director: Daniel F Rosberger, MD, PhD
Department of Ophthalmology
36 Seventh Avenue, Unit 7
New York, NY 10011
Tel: 212 604-8041 *Fax:* 212 604-8711
E-mail: maculacare@nyc.rr.com
Length: 3 Yrs *ACGME Approved/Offered Positions:* 9
Program ID: 240-35-22-112

New York Presbyterian Hospital (Columbia Campus) Program
Sponsor: New York Presbyterian Hospital
New York Presbyterian Hospital (Columbia Campus)
Prgm Director: Richard E Braunstein, MD
635 West 165th Street
EI - Box 44 (Suite 316B)
New York, NY 10032
Tel: 212 305-3339 *Fax:* 212 342-2714
E-mail: da229@columbia.edu
Length: 3 Yrs *ACGME Approved/Offered Positions:* 9
Program ID: 240-35-11-109

New York Presbyterian Hospital (Cornell Campus) Program
Sponsor: New York Presbyterian Hospital
New York Presbyterian Hospital (Cornell Campus)
Prgm Director: Christopher E Starr, MD
1305 York Avenue
11th Floor
New York, NY 10021
Tel: 646 962-2020 *Fax:* 646 962-0605
Length: 3 Yrs *ACGME Approved/Offered Positions:* 9
Program ID: 240-35-21-169

New York University School of Medicine Program
Sponsor: New York University School of Medicine
Bellevue Hospital Center
Manhattan Eye, Ear & Throat Hospital
Manhattan VA Harbor Health Care System
Prgm Director: Laurence T D Sperber, MD
550 First Avenue
NBV 5N 18
New York, NY 10016
Tel: 212 263-6434 *Fax:* 212 263-8749
Length: 3 Yrs *ACGME Approved/Offered Positions:* 21
Program ID: 240-35-21-108

St Luke's-Roosevelt Hospital Center Program
Sponsor: St Luke's-Roosevelt Hospital Center
Prgm Director: Kenneth E Merhige, MD
1111 Amsterdam Avenue
Ophthalmology Department
New York, NY 10025
Tel: 212 523-2562 *Fax:* 212 523-2478
Length: 3 Yrs *ACGME Approved/Offered Positions:* 6
Program ID: 240-35-31-111

Rochester

University of Rochester Program
Sponsor: Strong Memorial Hospital of the University of Rochester
Rochester General Hospital
Prgm Director: Matthew Gearinger, MD
601 Elmwood Avenue
Box 659
Rochester, NY 14642
Tel: 585 273-3954 *Fax:* 585 276-0292
E-mail: matthew_gearinger@urmc.rochester.edu
Length: 3 Yrs *ACGME Approved/Offered Positions:* 9
Program ID: 240-35-21-115

Stony Brook

SUNY at Stony Brook Program
Sponsor: University Hospital - SUNY at Stony Brook
Veterans Affairs Medical Center (Northport)
Prgm Director: Patrick Sibony, MD
Department of Ophthalmology
Health Sciences Center, L2, Rm 152
Stony Brook, NY 11794
Tel: 631 444-1111 *Fax:* 631 444-1543
E-mail: mtanderup@notes.cc.sunysb.edu
Length: 3 Yrs *ACGME Approved/Offered Positions:* 6
Program ID: 240-35-21-180

Syracuse

SUNY Upstate Medical University Program
Sponsor: SUNY Upstate Medical University
Crouse Hospital
Veterans Affairs Medical Center (Syracuse)
Prgm Director: Leon-Paul Noel, MD
550 Harrison Street
Suite 340
Syracuse, NY 13202
Tel: 315 464-5253 *Fax:* 315 464-6663
E-mail: vision@upstate.edu
Length: 3 Yrs *ACGME Approved/Offered Positions:* 7
Program ID: 240-35-21-116

Valhalla

New York Medical College at Westchester Medical Center Program
Sponsor: New York Medical College
Metropolitan Hospital Center
Montefiore Medical Center - North Division
Westchester Medical Center
Prgm Director: Steven B Zabin, MD
Westchester Medical Center
Macy Pavilion, Room 1044
Valhalla, NY 10595
Tel: 914 493-7671 *Fax:* 914 493-7445
Length: 3 Yrs *ACGME Approved/Offered Positions:* 10
Program ID: 240-35-21-107

North Carolina

Chapel Hill

University of North Carolina Hospitals Program
Sponsor: University of North Carolina Hospitals
Prgm Director: Travis A Meredith, MD*
Department of Ophthalmology
CB 7040, 5110 Bioinformatics Building
Chapel Hill, NC 27599
Tel: 919 843-0297 *Fax:* 919 966-1908
Length: 3 Yrs *ACGME Approved/Offered Positions:* 9
Program ID: 240-36-31-119

Durham

Duke University Hospital Program
Sponsor: Duke University Hospital
Veterans Affairs Medical Center (Durham)
Prgm Director: Pratap Challa, MD
Duke Eye Center, DUMC 3802
Erwin Road
Durham, NC 27710
Tel: 919 684-2975 *Fax:* 919 681-8267
E-mail: chall001@mc.duke.edu
Length: 3 Yrs *ACGME Approved/Offered Positions:* 15
Program ID: 240-36-31-118

Winston-Salem

Wake Forest University School of Medicine Program
Sponsor: Wake Forest University Baptist Medical Center
WG (Bill) Hefner VA Medical Center
Prgm Director: Timothy J Martin, MD
Department of Ophthalmology
Medical Center Blvd
Winston-Salem, NC 27157
Tel: 336 716-4091 *Fax:* 336 716-7994
Length: 3 Yrs *ACGME Approved/Offered Positions:* 9
Program ID: 240-36-11-120

Ohio

Akron

Summa Health System/NEOUCOM Program
Sponsor: Summa Health System
Akron City Hospital (Summa Health System)
Prgm Director: Deepak P Edward, MD
Department of Ophthalmology
75 Arch Street, Suite #512
Akron, OH 44304
Tel: 330 375-3867 *Fax:* 330 375-7985
E-mail: edwardd@summa-health.org
Length: 3 Yrs *ACGME Approved/Offered Positions:* 6
Program ID: 240-38-21-121

Note: * indicates a newly appointed program director

Cincinnati

University Hospital/University of Cincinnati College of Medicine Program

Sponsor: University Hospital Inc
Veterans Affairs Medical Center (Cincinnati)
Prgm Director: Karl C Golnik, MD, MEd
Department of Ophthalmology
260 Stetson Avenue, Suite 5300
Cincinnati, OH 45267
Tel: 513 558-5151   *Fax:* 513 558-3108
Length: 3 Yrs   *ACGME Approved/Offered Positions:* 12
Program ID: 240-38-21-122

Cleveland

Cleveland Clinic Foundation Program

Sponsor: Cleveland Clinic Foundation
MetroHealth Medical Center
Prgm Director: Elias I Traboulsi, MD
Cole Eye Institute, Desk i-32
9500 Euclid Avenue
Cleveland, OH 44195
Tel: 216 444-4363   *Fax:* 216 445-2226
Length: 3 Yrs   *ACGME Approved/Offered Positions:* 12
Program ID: 240-38-22-124

University Hospitals Case Medical Center Program

Sponsor: University Hospitals Case Medical Center
MetroHealth Medical Center
Veterans Affairs Medical Center (Cleveland)
Prgm Director: Robert L Tomsak, MD, PhD
11100 Euclid Avenue
Cleveland, OH 44106
Tel: 216 844-4883   *Fax:* 216 844-3160
E-mail: rtomsak@mac.com
Length: 3 Yrs   *ACGME Approved/Offered Positions:* 18
Program ID: 240-38-21-123

Columbus

Ohio State University Hospital Program

Sponsor: Ohio State University Hospital
Nationwide Children's Hospital
Veterans Affairs Medical Center (Columbus)
Veterans Affairs Medical Center (Dayton)
Prgm Director: Alan D Letson, MD
5825 Cramblett Hall
456 W Tenth Avenue
Columbus, OH 43210
Tel: 614 293-8041
Length: 3 Yrs   *ACGME Approved/Offered Positions:* 15
Program ID: 240-38-21-127

Oklahoma

Oklahoma City

University of Oklahoma Health Sciences Center Program

Sponsor: University of Oklahoma College of Medicine
McGee Eye Institute
OU Medical Center - Children's Hospital
Veterans Affairs Medical Center (Oklahoma City)
Prgm Director: Charles P Bogie III, MD, PhD*
Dean A McGee Eye Institute
608 Stanton L Young Blvd
Oklahoma City, OK 73104
Tel: 405 271-7816   *Fax:* 405 271-3013
E-mail: charles-bogie@dmei.org
Length: 3 Yrs   *ACGME Approved/Offered Positions:* 12
Program ID: 240-39-21-129

Oregon

Portland

Oregon Health & Science University Program

Sponsor: Oregon Health & Science University Hospital
Legacy Good Samaritan Hospital and Medical Center
Veterans Affairs Medical Center (Portland)
Prgm Director: Andreas K Lauer, MD
Casey Eye Institute
3375 SW Terwilliger Blvd
Portland, OR 97239
Tel: 503 494-3394   *Fax:* 503 494-9259
E-mail: bonys@ohsu.edu
Length: 3 Yrs   *ACGME Approved/Offered Positions:* 15
Program ID: 240-40-21-131

Pennsylvania

Danville

Geisinger Health System Program

Sponsor: Geisinger Health System
Geisinger Medical Center
Prgm Director: Vincent F Baldassano Jr, MD*
Department of Ophthalmology
100 North Academy Avenue
Danville, PA 17822
Tel: 570 271-6531   *Fax:* 570 271-7146
E-mail: vfbaldassano@geisinger.edu
Length: 3 Yrs   *ACGME Approved/Offered Positions:* 6
Program ID: 240-41-21-132

Hershey

Penn State University/Milton S Hershey Medical Center Program

Sponsor: Milton S Hershey Medical Center
Veterans Affairs Medical Center (Lebanon)
Prgm Director: Ingrid U Scott, MD, MPH
UPC1 - Suite 800, MC HU19
500 University Drive
Hershey, PA 17033
Tel: 717 531-4662   *Fax:* 717 531-5475
Length: 3 Yrs   *ACGME Approved/Offered Positions:* 9
Program ID: 240-41-11-133

Philadelphia

Drexel University College of Medicine/Hahnemann University Hospital Program

Sponsor: Drexel University College of Medicine/Hahnemann University
Hahnemann University Hospital (Tenet Health System)
Veterans Affairs Medical Center (Wilkes-Barre)
Prgm Director: Yelena Doych, MD, BA*
219 N Broad Street, 3rd Floor
Mail Stop 209
Philadelphia, PA 19107
Tel: 215 762-5605   *Fax:* 215 762-5600
E-mail: ydoych@drexelmed.edu
Length: 3 Yrs   *ACGME Approved/Offered Positions:* 9
Program ID: 240-41-21-134

Temple University Hospital Program

Sponsor: Temple University Hospital
Christiana Care Health Services Inc
Lankenau Hospital
Prgm Director: Gary F Domeracki, MD*
3401 North Broad Street
Philadelphia, PA 19140
Tel: 215 707-2727   *Fax:* 215 707-1684
E-mail: gary.domeracki@tuhs.temple.edu
Length: 3 Yrs   *ACGME Approved/Offered Positions:* 9
Program ID: 240-41-21-164

Thomas Jefferson University/Wills Eye Institute Program

Sponsor: Thomas Jefferson University Hospital
Wills Eye Institute
Prgm Director: Tara A Uhler, MD
840 Walnut Street
Philadelphia, PA 19107
Tel: 215 440-3170   *Fax:* 215 825-4732
E-mail: meded@willseye.org
Length: 3 Yrs   *ACGME Approved/Offered Positions:* 24
Program ID: 240-41-11-137

University of Pennsylvania Program

Sponsor: University of Pennsylvania Health System
Presbyterian Medical Center (UPHS)
Veterans Affairs Medical Center (Philadelphia)
Prgm Director: Nicholas J Volpe, MD
51 N 39th Street
Suite 515
Philadelphia, PA 19104
Tel: 215 662-8042   *Fax:* 215 243-4694
Length: 3 Yrs   *ACGME Approved/Offered Positions:* 15
Program ID: 240-41-21-136

Pittsburgh

University of Pittsburgh Medical Center Medical Education Program

Sponsor: Univ of Pittsburgh Medical Center Medical Education
UPMC Presbyterian Shadyside
Veterans Affairs Medical Center (Pittsburgh)
Prgm Director: Evan L Waxman, MD, PhD
Eye and Ear Institute of Pittsburgh
203 Lothrop Street
Pittsburgh, PA 15213
Tel: 412 647-9428   *Fax:* 412 647-5119
E-mail: waxmane@upmc.edu
Length: 3 Yrs   *ACGME Approved/Offered Positions:* 18
Program ID: 240-41-21-138

Puerto Rico

San Juan

University of Puerto Rico Program

Sponsor: University of Puerto Rico School of Medicine
University Hospital
VA Caribbean Healthcare System
Prgm Director: Luis A Serrano, MD*
Medical Sciences Campus
PO Box 365067
San Juan, PR 00936
Tel: 787 758-2525   *Fax:* 787 758-3488
E-mail: lserrano@rcm.upr.edu
Length: 3 Yrs   *ACGME Approved/Offered Positions:* 12
Program ID: 240-42-21-141

Rhode Island

Providence

Brown University Program

Sponsor: Rhode Island Hospital-Lifespan
Veterans Affairs Medical Center (Providence)
Prgm Director: William Tsiaras, MD*
Department of Ophthalmology
593 Eddy Street, APC-712
Providence, RI 02903
Tel: 401 444-4669   *Fax:* 401 444-6187
Length: 3 Yrs   *ACGME Approved/Offered Positions:* 6
Program ID: 240-43-11-142

Programs

South Carolina

Charleston

Medical University of South Carolina Program
Sponsor: Medical University of South Carolina College of Medicine
MUSC Medical Center
Ralph H Johnson VA Medical Center (Charleston)
Prgm Director: Matthew Nutaitis, MD
Storm Eye Institute
167 Ashley Avenue, PO Box 250676
Charleston, SC 29425
Tel: 843 792-8864   *Fax:* 843 792-3903
E-mail: maroneys@musc.edu
Length: 3 Yrs   *ACGME Approved/Offered Positions:* 12
Program ID: 240-45-21-143

Columbia

Palmetto Health/University of South Carolina School of Medicine Program
Sponsor: Palmetto Health
Palmetto Health Richland
William Jennings Bryan Dorn Veterans Hospital
Prgm Director: Richard M Davis, MD
Four Medical Park Road
Suite 301
Columbia, SC 29203
Tel: 803 434-7056   *Fax:* 803 434-2387
E-mail: rdavis@uscmed.sc.edu
Length: 3 Yrs   *ACGME Approved/Offered Positions:* 9
Program ID: 240-45-21-163

Tennessee

Memphis

University of Tennessee Program
Sponsor: University of Tennessee College of Medicine
Methodist Healthcare - Memphis Hospitals
Regional Medical Center at Memphis
Veterans Affairs Medical Center (Memphis)
Prgm Director: Natalie C Kerr, MD
Department of Ophthalmology
930 Madison Avenue, Suite 470
Memphis, TN 38163
Tel: 901 448-5883   *Fax:* 901 448-4564
Length: 3 Yrs   *ACGME Approved/Offered Positions:* 12
Program ID: 240-47-21-145

Nashville

Vanderbilt University Program
Sponsor: Vanderbilt University Medical Center
Veterans Affairs Medical Center (Nashville)
Prgm Director: Laura L Wayman, MD
2311 Pierce Avenue
Nashville, TN 37232
Tel: 615 936-4931   *Fax:* 615 936-4979
E-mail: laura.l.wayman@vanderbilt.edu
Length: 3 Yrs   *ACGME Approved/Offered Positions:* 15
Program ID: 240-47-31-147

Texas

Dallas

University of Texas Southwestern Medical School Program
Sponsor: University of Texas Southwestern Medical School
Dallas County Hospital District-Parkland Memorial Hospital
Dallas VA Medical Center
Prgm Director: Preston H Blomquist, MD
Department of Ophthalmology
5323 Harry Hines Blvd
Dallas, TX 75390
Tel: 214 648-3182   *Fax:* 214 645-9482
Length: 3 Yrs   *ACGME Approved/Offered Positions:* 27
Program ID: 240-48-21-148

Galveston

University of Texas Medical Branch Hospitals Program
Sponsor: University of Texas Medical Branch Hospitals
Prgm Director: Brian R Wong, MD
Department of Ophthalmology and Visual Sciences
301 University Boulevard
Galveston, TX 77555
Tel: 409 747-5801   *Fax:* 409 747-5433
E-mail: bwong@utmb.edu
Length: 3 Yrs   *ACGME Approved/Offered Positions:* 12
Program ID: 240-48-21-149

Houston

Baylor College of Medicine Program
Sponsor: Baylor College of Medicine
Harris County Hospital District-Ben Taub General Hospital
Methodist Hospital (Houston)
Michael E DeBakey VA Medical Center - Houston
Prgm Director: Elizabeth F Baze, MD
6565 Fannin St, NC205
Department of Ophthalmology
Houston, TX 77030
Tel: 713 798-5945   *Fax:* 713 798-8763
Length: 3 Yrs   *ACGME Approved/Offered Positions:* 18
Program ID: 240-48-21-150

University of Texas at Houston Program
Sponsor: University of Texas Health Science Center at Houston
Lyndon B Johnson General Hospital
Memorial Hermann Hospital
Prgm Director: Judianne Kellaway, MD, MEd
Dept of Ophthalmology and Visual Science
6431 Fannin St, MSB 7.024
Houston, TX 77030
Tel: 713 500-6003   *Fax:* 713 500-0682
E-mail: Phyllis.L.Rhodes@uth.tmc.edu
Length: 3 Yrs   *ACGME Approved/Offered Positions:* 12
Program ID: 240-48-21-151

Lackland AFB

San Antonio Uniformed Services Health Education Consortium Program
Sponsor: San Antonio Uniformed Services Health Education Consortium
Brooke Army Medical Center
Wilford Hall Medical Center (AETC)
Prgm Director: Richard G Lane II, MD*
WHMC/SGOSVA
2200 Bergquist Drive, Ste 1
Lackland AFB, TX 78236
Tel: 210 292-6573   *Fax:* 210 292-4796
Length: 3 Yrs   *ACGME Approved/Offered Positions:* 18
Program ID: 240-48-11-001
Uniformed Services Program

Lubbock

Texas Tech University (Lubbock) Program
Sponsor: Texas Tech University Health Sciences Center at Lubbock
University Medical Center
Veterans Affairs Medical Center (Big Spring)
Prgm Director: Kelly T Mitchell, MD
3601 4th Street
Dept of Ophthalmology/Visual Sciences
Lubbock, TX 79430
Tel: 806 743-9500   *Fax:* 806 743-2471
E-mail: diane.ramos@ttuhsc.edu
Length: 3 Yrs   *ACGME Approved/Offered Positions:* 9
Program ID: 240-48-21-152

San Antonio

University of Texas Health Science Center at San Antonio Program
Sponsor: University of Texas School of Medicine at San Antonio
Audie L Murphy Memorial Veterans Hospital (San Antonio)
University Health System
University of Texas Health Science Center
Prgm Director: Constance L Fry, MD
Health Science Center at San Antonio
7703 Floyd Curl Drive, Mail Code 6230
San Antonio, TX 78229
Tel: 210 567-8421   *Fax:* 210 567-8413
E-mail: fryc@uthscsa.edu
Length: 3 Yrs   *ACGME Approved/Offered Positions:* 12
Program ID: 240-48-21-153

Temple

Texas A&M College of Medicine-Scott and White Program
Sponsor: Scott and White Memorial Hospital
Central Texas Veterans Affairs Healthcare System
Prgm Director: Kyle H Smith, MD
2401 South 31st Street
Temple, TX 76508
Tel: 254 724-1058   *Fax:* 254 724-9050
E-mail: ksmith@swmail.sw.org
Length: 3 Yrs   *ACGME Approved/Offered Positions:* 9
Program ID: 240-48-21-154

Utah

Salt Lake City

University of Utah Program
Sponsor: University of Utah Medical Center
Veterans Affairs Medical Center (Salt Lake City)
Prgm Director: Mark D Mifflin, MD
John A Moran Eye Center
65 Mario Capecchi Drive
Salt Lake City, UT 84132
Tel: 801 585-7689   *Fax:* 801 581-3357
E-mail: elaine.schwanebeck@hsc.utah.edu
Length: 3 Yrs   *ACGME Approved/Offered Positions:* 9
Program ID: 240-49-21-155

Virginia

Charlottesville

University of Virginia Program
Sponsor: University of Virginia Medical Center
Prgm Director: Brian P Conway, MD
PO Box 800715
Charlottesville, VA 22908
Tel: 434 982-1086   *Fax:* 434 924-5180
E-mail: bpc@virginia.edu
Length: 3 Yrs   *ACGME Approved/Offered Positions:* 9
Program ID: 240-51-21-156

Note: * indicates a newly appointed program director

Norfolk

Eastern Virginia Medical School Program
Sponsor: Eastern Virginia Medical School
Sentara Norfolk General Hospital
Veterans Affairs Medical Center (Hampton)
Prgm Director: John D Sheppard Jr, MD, MSc
Department of Ophthalmology
880 Kempsville Road, Suite 2500
Norfolk, VA 23502
Tel: 757 461-0050   *Fax:* 757 461-4538
E-mail: croucher@evms.edu
Length: 3 Yrs   *ACGME Approved/Offered Positions:* 6
Program ID: 240-51-21-157

Richmond

Virginia Commonwealth University Health System Program
Sponsor: Virginia Commonwealth University Health System
Hunter Holmes McGuire VA Medical Center (Richmond)
Medical College of Virginia Hospitals
Prgm Director: Joseph D Iuorno, MD
401 N 11th Street, 4th Floor
MCVH Box 980438
Richmond, VA 23298
Tel: 804 828-5208   *Fax:* 804 828-8009
E-mail: bayala@mcvh-vcu.edu
Length: 3 Yrs   *ACGME Approved/Offered Positions:* 9
Program ID: 240-51-21-158

Washington

Seattle

University of Washington Program
Sponsor: University of Washington School of Medicine
Harborview Medical Center
University of Washington Medical Center
VA Puget Sound Health Care System
Prgm Director: Raghu C Mudumbai, MD
Dept of Ophthalmology Box 356485
1959 NE Pacific Street
Seattle, WA 98195
Tel: 206 221-5131   *Fax:* 206 543-4414
Length: 3 Yrs   *ACGME Approved/Offered Positions:* 12
Program ID: 240-54-21-159

Tacoma

Madigan Army Medical Center Program
Sponsor: Madigan Army Medical Center
Prgm Director: Mark L Nelson, MD
Attn: MCHJ-SOU
Ophthalmology Service
Tacoma, WA 98431
Tel: 253 968-1760   *Fax:* 253 968-1451
E-mail: nelsonml@us.army.mil
Length: 3 Yrs   *ACGME Approved/Offered Positions:* 6
Program ID: 240-54-21-175
Uniformed Services Program

West Virginia

Morgantown

West Virginia University Program
Sponsor: West Virginia University School of Medicine
Louis A Johnson Veterans Affairs Medical Center
West Virginia University Hospitals
Prgm Director: Geoffrey Bradford, MD
WVU Eye Institute, Dept of Ophthalmology
PO Box 9193, Stadium Drive
Morgantown, WV 26506
Tel: 304 598-6925   *Fax:* 304 598-6928
Length: 3 Yrs   *ACGME Approved/Offered Positions:* 9
Program ID: 240-55-21-160

Wisconsin

Madison

University of Wisconsin Program
Sponsor: University of Wisconsin Hospital and Clinics
William S Middleton Veterans Hospital
Prgm Director: Yasmin S Bradfield, MD
2870 University Ave, Ste 102
Madison, WI 53705
Tel: 608 263-5339   *Fax:* 608 263-7694
E-mail: ysbradfield@ophth.wisc.edu
Length: 3 Yrs   *ACGME Approved/Offered Positions:* 9
Program ID: 240-56-21-161

Milwaukee

Medical College of Wisconsin Affiliated Hospitals Program
Sponsor: Medical College of Wisconsin Affiliated Hospitals, Inc
Clement J Zablocki Veterans Affairs Medical Center
Froedtert Memorial Lutheran Hospital
Prgm Director: Bhavna P Sheth, MD
The Eye Institute
925 N 87th Street
Milwaukee, WI 53226
Tel: 414 456-7876   *Fax:* 414 456-6300
E-mail: bsheth@mcw.edu
Length: 3 Yrs   *ACGME Approved/Offered Positions:* 9
Program ID: 240-56-21-162

Orthopaedic Sports Medicine (Orthopaedic Surgery)

Alabama

Birmingham

American Sports Medicine Institute Program
Sponsor: American Sports Medicine Institute
Brookwood Medical Center
St Vincent's Hospital
Prgm Director: James R Andrews, MD
2660 10th Avenue South
Suite 505
Birmingham, AL 35205
Tel: 205 918-2134   *Fax:* 205 918-0800
E-mail: janf@asmi.org
Length: 1 Yr   *ACGME Approved/Offered Positions:* 9
Program ID: 268-01-31-026

Mobile

University of South Alabama Program
Sponsor: University of South Alabama Hospitals
Infirmary West
USA Children's and Women's Hospital
Prgm Director: Albert W Pearsall IV, MD
3421 Medical Park Drive
2 Medical Park
Mobile, AL 36693
Tel: 251 665-8250   *Fax:* 251 665-8565
E-mail: gdriver@usouthal.edu
Length: 1 Yr   *ACGME Approved/Offered Positions:* 1
Program ID: 268-01-21-112

Arizona

Tucson

University of Arizona Program
Sponsor: University of Arizona College of Medicine
Orthopaedic Clinic Association
Prgm Director: Robert E Hunter, MD
University of Arizona Health Sciences Center
PO Box 245064
Tucson, AZ 85724
Tel: 520 626-9245   *Fax:* 520 626-2668
Length: 1 Yr   *ACGME Approved/Offered Positions:* 2
Program ID: 268-03-31-081

California

Laguna Hills

Sports Clinic (Laguna Hills) Program
Sponsor: The Sports Clinic Orthopedic Medical Associates, Inc
Prgm Director: Wesley M Nottage, MD
23961 Calle de la Magdalena
Laguna Hills, CA 92653
Tel: 949 581-7001
E-mail: bigdog492653@yahoo.com
Length: 1 Yr   *ACGME Approved/Offered Positions:* 1
Program ID: 268-05-31-106

Long Beach

Long Beach Memorial Medical Center Program

Sponsor: Long Beach Memorial Medical Center
Southern California Center for Sports Medicine
Surgery Center of Long Beach
Prgm Director: Peter R Kurzweil, MD
2801 Atlantic Avenue
Long Beach, CA 90806
Tel: 562 424-6666   *Fax:* 562 989-0027
Length: 1 Yr   *ACGME Approved/Offered Positions:* 2
Program ID: 268-05-21-013

Los Angeles

Kerlan-Jobe Orthopaedic Clinic Program

Sponsor: Kerlan-Jobe Orthopaedic Clinic
SCA Surgery Center
Prgm Director: Neal S ElAttrache, MD
6801 Park Terrace
Suite 500
Los Angeles, CA 90045
Tel: 310 665-7257   *Fax:* 310 665-7145
Length: 1 Yr   *ACGME Approved/Offered Positions:* 8
Program ID: 268-05-21-030

UCLA Medical Center Program

Sponsor: UCLA David Geffen School of Medicine/UCLA
   Medical Center
Prgm Director: David McAllister, MD
10833 Le Conte Avenue
Room 76-143CHS
Los Angeles, CA 90095
Tel: 310 794-7930   *Fax:* 310 825-1311
Length: 1 Yr   *ACGME Approved/Offered Positions:* 2
Program ID: 268-05-31-114

USC Orthopaedic Surgery Associates Program

Sponsor: USC Orthopaedic Surgery Associates
USC University Hospital
Prgm Director: James E Tibone, MD
1520 San Pablo Street #2000
Los Angeles, CA 90033
Tel: 323 442-5860   *Fax:* 323 442-6990
Length: 1 Yr   *ACGME Approved/Offered Positions:* 2
Program ID: 268-05-13-113

Pasadena

Congress Medical Associates Program

Sponsor: Congress Medical Associates
Prgm Director: Gregory J Adamson, MD
800 South Raymond Ave
Second Floor
Pasadena, CA 91105
Tel: 626 795-8051   *Fax:* 626 795-0356
Length: 1 Yr   *ACGME Approved/Offered Positions:* 1
Program ID: 268-05-12-100

Kaiser Permanente Southern California (Orange County) Program

Sponsor: Kaiser Permanente Southern California
Prgm Director: Brent R Davis, MD
6670 Alton Parkway
Irvine, CA 92618
Tel: 949 932-5002
E-mail: brent.r.davis@kp.org
Length: 1 Yr   *ACGME Approved/Offered Positions:* 2
Program ID: 268-05-13-105

Kaiser Permanente Southern California (San Diego) Program

Sponsor: Kaiser Permanente Southern California
Kaiser Foundation Hospital (San Diego)
Prgm Director: Donald C Fithian, MD
250 Travelodge Drive
El Cajon, CA 92020
Tel: 619 441-3142   *Fax:* 619 441-3030
Length: 1 Yr   *ACGME Approved/Offered Positions:* 2
Program ID: 268-05-31-093

San Diego

San Diego Arthroscopy and Sports Medicine Program

Sponsor: Docere Foundation
Alvarado Hospital Medical Center
Grossmont Hospital
San Diego Sports Medicine and Orthopaedic Center
Scripps Clinic
University of California (San Diego) Medical Center
Veterans Affairs Medical Center (San Diego)
Prgm Director: James P Tasto, MD
6719 Alvarado Road, Suite 200
San Diego, CA 92120
Tel: 619 229-5018   *Fax:* 619 229-2968
Length: 1 Yr   *ACGME Approved/Offered Positions:* 4
Program ID: 268-05-21-101

San Francisco

University of California (San Francisco) Program

Sponsor: University of California (San Francisco) School
   of Medicine
UCSF and Mount Zion Medical Centers
Prgm Director: Christina R Allen, MD
Department of Sports Medicine
500 Parnassus Avenue, MU 320W
San Francisco, CA 94143
Tel: 415 353-7586   *Fax:* 415 353-9675
Length: 1 Yr   *ACGME Approved/Offered Positions:* 1
Program ID: 268-05-13-121

Santa Monica

Santa Monica Orthopaedic and Sports Medicine Group Program

Sponsor: Santa Monica Orthopaedic and Sports
   Medicine Group
Prgm Director: Bert Mandelbaum, MD
2020 Santa Monica Blvd, Suite 400
Santa Monica, CA 90404
Tel: 310 829-2663   *Fax:* 310 315-0326
Length: 1 Yr   *ACGME Approved/Offered Positions:* 2
Program ID: 268-05-31-098

Stanford

Stanford University Program

Sponsor: Stanford Hospital and Clinics
Prgm Director: Marc R Safran, MD
300 Pasteur Drive
R-105 Edwards Building
Stanford, CA 94305
Tel: 650 736-7600   *Fax:* 650 498-7186
E-mail: jackieg@stanford.edu
Length: 1 Yr   *ACGME Approved/Offered Positions:* 4
Program ID: 268-05-21-120

Van Nuys

Southern California Orthopaedic Institute Program

Sponsor: Southern California Orthopedic Institute
Prgm Director: Richard D Ferkel, MD
6815 Noble Street
Van Nuys, CA 91405
Tel: 818 901-6600   *Fax:* 818 901-6660
Length: 1 Yr   *ACGME Approved/Offered Positions:* 5
Program ID: 268-05-21-043

Colorado

Aspen

Aspen Sports Medicine Foundation Program

Sponsor: Aspen Sports Medicine Foundation
Prgm Director: Norman L Harris Jr, MD
100 E Main Street, Suite 101
Aspen, CO 81611
Tel: 970 920-4151   *Fax:* 970 544-1777
E-mail: afsmer@orthop.com
Length: 1 Yr   *ACGME Approved/Offered Positions:* 2
Program ID: 268-07-21-035

Golden

Panorama Orthopedics & Spine Center Program

Sponsor: Panorama Orthopedics & Spine Center
St Anthony Hospital Central
St Anthony Hospital North
Prgm Director: James Johnson, MD, MPH
660 Golden Ridge Road, Suite 250
Golden, CO 80401
Tel: 303 233-1223   *Fax:* 303 233-8755
E-mail: jjohnson@panoramaortho.com
Length: 1 Yr   *ACGME Approved/Offered Positions:* 1
Program ID: 268-07-21-124

Greenwood Village

Steadman Hawkins Clinic (Denver) Program

Sponsor: Steadman Hawkins Clinic (Denver)
Prgm Director: Theodore F Schlegel, MD
8200 E Belleview Avenue
Suite 615
Greenwood Village, CO 80111
Tel: 303 694-3333   *Fax:* 303 694-9666
E-mail: therbert@shcdenver.com
Length: 1 Yr   *ACGME Approved/Offered Positions:* 2
Program ID: 268-07-12-094

Vail

Steadman Hawkins Clinic Program

Sponsor: Steadman Hawkins Clinic
Vail Valley Medical Center
Prgm Director: J Richard Steadman, MD
181 W Meadow Drive, Suite 400
Vail, CO 81657
Tel: 970 479-5782   *Fax:* 970 479-9753
Length: 1 Yr   *ACGME Approved/Offered Positions:* 6
Program ID: 268-07-21-063

Connecticut

Farmington

University of Connecticut Program

Sponsor: University of Connecticut School of Medicine
Univ of Connecticut Health Center/John Dempsey
   Hospital
Prgm Director: John P Fulkerson, MD
Department of Orthopaedics
263 Farmington Ave
Farmington, CT 06032
Tel: 860 679-6645   *Fax:* 860 679-6649
Length: 1 Yr   *ACGME Approved/Offered Positions:* 1
Program ID: 268-08-21-006

Note: * indicates a newly appointed program director

Florida

Coral Gables

Doctors' Hospital Program
Sponsor: Doctors' Hospital (Baptist Health of South Florida)
Prgm Director: Harlan Selesnick, MD
1150 Campo Sano Avenue, Suite 301
Coral Gables, FL 33146
Tel: 786 308-3384   *Fax:* 786 308-3379
Length: 1 Yr   *ACGME Approved/Offered Positions:* 1
Program ID: 268-11-21-074

Doctor's Hospital Program A
Sponsor: Doctors' Hospital (Baptist Health of South Florida)
UHZ Sports Medicine Institute
Prgm Director: John W Uribe, MD
1150 Campo Sano Avenue
Suite 200
Coral Gables, FL 33146
Tel: 305 669-3320   *Fax:* 305 669-3352
Length: 1 Yr   *ACGME Approved/Offered Positions:* 2
Program ID: 268-11-21-015

Tampa

University of South Florida Program
Sponsor: University of South Florida College of Medicine
Prgm Director: Robert Pedowitz, MD, PhD
3500 East Fletcher Avenue
Suite 511, MDC 106
Tampa, FL 33613
Tel: 813 974-2351   *Fax:* 813 396-9195
E-mail: pedowitz@health.usf.edu
Length: 1 Yr   *ACGME Approved/Offered Positions:* 2
Program ID: 268-11-21-128

Georgia

Atlanta

Atlanta Sports Medicine Foundation Program
Sponsor: Atlanta Sports Medicine Foundation, Inc
Prgm Director: Scott D Gillogly, MD
3200 Downwood Circle, NW
Suite 500
Atlanta, GA 30327
Tel: 404 352-4500   *Fax:* 404 693-9003
E-mail: drheault@atlantasportsmedicine.com
Length: 1 Yr   *ACGME Approved/Offered Positions:* 2
Program ID: 268-12-31-126

Emory University Program
Sponsor: Emory University School of Medicine
Emory University Hospital
Prgm Director: Spero G Karas, MD
Department of Orthopaedics
59 Executive Park Drive South, Suite 1000
Atlanta, GA 30329
Tel: 404 778-7204
E-mail: kstrozi@emory.edu
Length: 1 Yr   *ACGME Approved/Offered Positions:* 2
Program ID: 268-12-12-107

Columbus

Hughston Foundation Program
Sponsor: Hughston Foundation
Hughston Orthopedic Hospital
Jack Hughston Memorial Hospital
The Hughston Clinic
Prgm Director: Champ L Baker Jr, MD
6262 Veteran's Parkway
PO Box 9517
Columbus, GA 31908
Tel: 706 494-3365   *Fax:* 706 494-3379
E-mail: rbunn@hughston.com
Length: 1 Yr   *ACGME Approved/Offered Positions:* 5
Program ID: 268-12-21-046

Illinois

Chicago

Rush University Medical Center Program
Sponsor: Rush University Medical Center
Prgm Director: Bernard R Bach Jr, MD
1725 West Harrison Street, Suite 1063
Chicago, IL 60612
Tel: 312 432-2321   *Fax:* 312 942-1517
E-mail: Phyllis_J_Velez@rush.edu
Length: 1 Yr   *ACGME Approved/Offered Positions:* 4
Program ID: 268-16-31-064

University of Chicago Program
Sponsor: University of Chicago Medical Center
Prgm Director: Sherwin S Ho, MD
5841 S Maryland Ave
MC 3079
Chicago, IL 60637
Tel: 773 702-5978   *Fax:* 773 702-0554
Length: 1 Yr   *ACGME Approved/Offered Positions:* 1
Program ID: 268-16-21-034

University of Illinois College of Medicine at Chicago Program
Sponsor: University of Illinois College of Medicine at Chicago
Prgm Director: Preston M Wolin, MD
Center for Athletic Medicine
830 W Diversey, Suite 300
Chicago, IL 60614
Tel: 773 248-4150   *Fax:* 773 248-4291
E-mail: pwolin@athleticmed.com
Length: 1 Yr   *ACGME Approved/Offered Positions:* 1
Program ID: 268-16-31-075

Indiana

Indianapolis

Indiana University School of Medicine Program
Sponsor: Indiana University School of Medicine
Clarian Methodist Hospital of Indiana
Prgm Director: Arthur C Rettig, MD
201 N Pennsylvania Parkway
Suite 325
Indianapolis, IN 46280
Tel: 317 817-1227   *Fax:* 317 817-1220
E-mail: phunker@methodistsports.com
Length: 1 Yr   *ACGME Approved/Offered Positions:* 3
Program ID: 268-17-21-003

Iowa

Iowa City

University of Iowa Hospitals and Clinics Program
Sponsor: University of Iowa Hospitals and Clinics
Prgm Director: Brian Wolf, MD, MS*
John Pappajohn Pavilion
200 Hawkins Drive
Iowa City, IA 52242
Tel: 319 353-7954   *Fax:* 319 384-9306
E-mail: brian-wolf@uiowa.edu
Length: 1 Yr   *ACGME Approved/Offered Positions:* 1
Program ID: 268-18-21-067

Kentucky

Lexington

University of Kentucky College of Medicine Program
Sponsor: University of Kentucky College of Medicine
University of Kentucky Hospital
Prgm Director: Darren L Johnson, MD, BS
Kentucky Clinic K401
740 S Limestone
Lexington, KY 40536
Tel: 859 323-5533   *Fax:* 859 323-2412
E-mail: csaitki@uky.edu
Length: 1 Yr   *ACGME Approved/Offered Positions:* 2
Program ID: 268-20-21-016

Louisiana

New Orleans

Ochsner Clinic Foundation Program
Sponsor: Ochsner Clinic Foundation
Prgm Director: Deryk G Jones, MD
1514 Jefferson Highway
New Orleans, LA 70121
Tel: 504 842-6793   *Fax:* 504 736-4810
E-mail: gchaisson@ochsner.org
Length: 1 Yr   *ACGME Approved/Offered Positions:* 2
Program ID: 268-21-21-116

Maryland

Baltimore

Union Memorial Hospital Program
Sponsor: Union Memorial Hospital
Prgm Director: Richard Y Hinton, MD, MPH
3333 N Calvert Street, Suite 400
Baltimore, MD 21218
Tel: 410 554-2865   *Fax:* 410 261-8105
E-mail: patricia.koehler@medstar.net
Length: 1 Yr   *ACGME Approved/Offered Positions:* 3
Program ID: 268-23-21-058

Massachusetts

Boston

Boston University Medical Center Program
Sponsor: Boston Medical Center
Prgm Director: Anthony A Schepsis, MD
720 Harrison Avenue
Doctors Building, Suite 808
Boston, MA 02118
Tel: 617 638-8933   *Fax:* 617 638-8493
Length: 1 Yr   *ACGME Approved/Offered Positions:* 1
Program ID: 268-24-21-080

Children's Hospital (Boston) Program
Sponsor: Children's Hospital
Beth Israel Deaconess Medical Center
New England Baptist Hospital
Prgm Director: Lyle J Micheli, MD
319 Longwood Avenue
Boston, MA 02115
Tel: 617 355-6247 *Fax:* 617 730-0694
E-mail: michelilyle@aol.com
Length: 1 Yr *ACGME Approved/Offered Positions:* 3
Program ID: 268-24-13-099

Massachusetts General Hospital/Harvard Medical School Program
Sponsor: Massachusetts General Hospital
Prgm Director: Thomas Gill, IV, MD
175 Cambridge Street
Suite 400, Sports Medicine
Boston, MA 02114
Tel: 617 726-7797 *Fax:* 617 726-6950
E-mail: tgill@partners.org
Length: 1 Yr *ACGME Approved/Offered Positions:* 3
Program ID: 268-24-31-049

New England Baptist Hospital Program
Sponsor: New England Baptist Hospital
Boston Outpatient Surgical Suites
Prgm Director: Mark E Steiner, MD
Department of Orthopedics
125 Parker Hill Avenue
Boston, MA 02120
Tel: 617 754-5413 *Fax:* 617 754-6443
E-mail: msteiner@caregroup.harvard.edu
Length: 1 Yr *ACGME Approved/Offered Positions:* 4
Program ID: 268-24-21-044

Worcester

University of Massachusetts Program
Sponsor: University of Massachusetts Medical School
UMass Memorial Health Care (Hahnemann Campus)
UMass Memorial Health Care (University Campus)
Prgm Director: Brian D Busconi, MD
Hahnemann Campus
281 Lincoln Street
Worcester, MA 01605
Tel: 508 856-4262 *Fax:* 508 334-7273
E-mail: michelle.auger@umassmed.edu
Length: 1 Yr *ACGME Approved/Offered Positions:* 2
Program ID: 268-24-31-047

Michigan

Ann Arbor

University of Michigan Program
Sponsor: University of Michigan Hospitals and Health Centers
Prgm Director: Bruce S Miller, MD, MS
24 Frank Lloyd Wright Drive
Ann Arbor, MI 48106
Tel: 734 930-7393 *Fax:* 734 930-7402
Length: 1 Yr *ACGME Approved/Offered Positions:* 2
Program ID: 268-25-12-089

Detroit

Detroit Medical Center Program
Sponsor: Detroit Medical Center Corporation
Michigan Orthopaedic Specialty Hospital, The
Oakwood Hospital
Providence Hospital and Medical Centers
Prgm Director: Stephen Lemos, MD, PhD
28800 Ryan Road
Suite 220
Warren, MI 48092
Tel: 586 558-2867 *Fax:* 586 558-4651
E-mail: selemos@comcast.net
Length: 1 Yr *ACGME Approved/Offered Positions:* 4
Program ID: 268-25-12-123

Henry Ford Hospital Program
Sponsor: Henry Ford Hospital
Prgm Director: Henry Goitz, MD
Center for Athletic Medicine
3525 Second Avenue
Detroit, MI 48202
Tel: 313 972-4076 *Fax:* 313 942-4202
E-mail: hgoitz1@hfhs.org
Length: 1 Yr *ACGME Approved/Offered Positions:* 2
Program ID: 268-25-21-108

Royal Oak

William Beaumont Hospital Program
Sponsor: William Beaumont Hospital
Prgm Director: Kyle Anderson, MD
3535 West 13 Mile Road
Suite 744
Royal Oak, MI 48073
Tel: 248 551-0426 *Fax:* 248 551-5404
E-mail: cmusich@beaumont.edu
Length: 1 Yr *ACGME Approved/Offered Positions:* 1
Program ID: 268-25-13-096

Minnesota

Minneaplis

The Orthopaedic Center Program
Sponsor: The Orthopaedic Center
Methodist Hospital
TRIA Orthopaedic Center
Prgm Director: David A Fischer, MD
8100 Northland Drive
Bloomington, MN 55431
Tel: 952 831-8742 *Fax:* 952 831-1626
Length: 1 Yr *ACGME Approved/Offered Positions:* 3
Program ID: 268-26-11-090

Minneapolis

Minnesota Sports Medicine Program
Sponsor: Minnesota Sports Medicine
University of Minnesota Medical Center, Division of Fairview
Prgm Director: J P Smith, MD
701 25th Avenue South
Suite 150
Minneapolis, MN 55454
Tel: 612 273-9196 *Fax:* 612 273-4560
E-mail: anitasteckling@ocpamn.com
Length: 1 Yr *ACGME Approved/Offered Positions:* 3
Program ID: 268-26-21-048

Mississippi

Jackson

Mississippi Sports Medicine and Orthopaedic Center Program
Sponsor: Mississippi Sports Medicine & Orthopaedic Center
Prgm Director: Larry D Field, MD
1325 E Fortification Street
Jackson, MS 39202
Tel: 601 354-4488 *Fax:* 601 914-1835
E-mail: lrhodes@msmoc.com
Length: 1 Yr *ACGME Approved/Offered Positions:* 4
Program ID: 268-27-21-071

Missouri

Kansas City

University of Missouri at Kansas City Program
Sponsor: University of Missouri-Kansas City School of Medicine
Kansas City Orthopaedic Institute
Menorah Medical Center
Truman Medical Center
Prgm Director: Jon E Browne, MD
3651 College Blvd, #100A
Leawood, KS 66211
Tel: 913 319-7500 *Fax:* 913 319-7691
E-mail: maryz@osmckc.com
Length: 1 Yr *ACGME Approved/Offered Positions:* 1
Program ID: 268-28-21-051

St Louis

Washington University/B-JH/SLCH Consortium Program
Sponsor: Washington University/B-JH/SLCH Consortium
Barnes-Jewish Hospital
Barnes-Jewish West County Hospital
Veterans Affairs Medical Center (St Louis)
Prgm Director: Matthew J Matava, MD
Campus Box 8233
660 S Euclid Ave
St Louis, MO 63110
Tel: 314 514-3569 *Fax:* 314 514-3689
E-mail: haegeleb@wudosis.wustl.edu
Length: 1 Yr *ACGME Approved/Offered Positions:* 1
Program ID: 268-28-21-076

New Mexico

Albuquerque

New Mexico Orthopaedics Program
Sponsor: New Mexico Orthopaedics Fellowship Foundation
Prgm Director: Anthony F Pachelli, MD
201 Cedar SE
Suite 6600
Albuquerque, NM 87106
Tel: 505 724-4353 *Fax:* 505 742-4384
E-mail: nmfellowship@nmortho.net
Length: 1 Yr *ACGME Approved/Offered Positions:* 1
Program ID: 268-34-21-104

University of New Mexico Program
Sponsor: University of New Mexico School of Medicine
University of New Mexico Hospital
Prgm Director: Daniel Wascher, MD*
Dept of Orthopaedics, MSC10 5600
1 University of New Mexico
Albuquerque, NM 87131
Tel: 505 272-4107 *Fax:* 505 272-8098
Length: 1 Yr *ACGME Approved/Offered Positions:* 1
Program ID: 268-34-22-092

Note: * indicates a newly appointed program director

Taos

Taos Orthopaedic Institute and Research Foundation Program

Sponsor: Taos Orthopaedic Institute and Research Foundation
Prgm Director: James H Lubowitz, MD
1219-A Gusdorf Road
Taos, NM 87571
Tel: 575 758-0009   *Fax:* 575 758-8736
E-mail: info@taosortho.com
Length: 1 Yr   *ACGME Approved/Offered Positions:* 3
Program ID: 268-34-21-095

New York

Buffalo

University at Buffalo Program

Sponsor: University at Buffalo School of Medicine
Erie County Medical Center
Kaleida Health System (Millard Fillmore Hospital)
Niagara Falls Memorial Medical Center
Prgm Director: Leslie J Bisson, MD
Sports Medicine Fellowship Program
4949 Harlem Road
Amherst, NY 14226
Tel: 716 898-5053   *Fax:* 716 898-3323
Length: 1 Yr   *ACGME Approved/Offered Positions:* 2
Program ID: 268-35-12-079

New York

Hospital for Special Surgery/Cornell Medical Center Program

Sponsor: Hospital for Special Surgery
Prgm Director: Scott Rodeo, MD
535 East 70th Street
New York, NY 10021
Tel: 212 606-1466   *Fax:* 212 606-1477
E-mail: academictraining@hss.edu
Length: 1 Yr   *ACGME Approved/Offered Positions:* 7
Program ID: 268-35-21-025

Lenox Hill Hospital Program

Sponsor: Lenox Hill Hospital
Prgm Director: Barton Nisonson, MD
130 East 77th Street
11th Floor
New York, NY 10075
Tel: 212 570-9120
Length: 1 Yr   *ACGME Approved/Offered Positions:* 3
Program ID: 268-35-11-004

New York Presbyterian Hospital (Columbia Campus) Program

Sponsor: New York Presbyterian Hospital
New York Presbyterian Hospital (Columbia Campus)
Prgm Director: Louis U Bigliani, MD
Department of Orthopaedic Surgery
622 West 168th Street PH 11
New York, NY 10032
Tel: 212 305-8188   *Fax:* 212 305-6193
E-mail: orthosrg@columbia.edu
Length: 1 Yr   *ACGME Approved/Offered Positions:* 2
Program ID: 268-35-31-130

New York University School of Medicine/Hospital for Joint Diseases Program

Sponsor: New York University School of Medicine
NYU Hospital for Joint Diseases
NYU Hospitals Center
Prgm Director: Orrin Sherman, MD
530 First Avenue
New York, NY 10016
Tel: 212 263-8961   *Fax:* 212 263-8750
Length: 1 Yr   *ACGME Approved/Offered Positions:* 2
Program ID: 268-35-31-078

Rochester

University of Rochester Program

Sponsor: Strong Memorial Hospital of the University of Rochester
Prgm Director: Michael D Maloney, MD
Department of Orthopaedics
601 Elmwood Avenue, Box 665
Rochester, NY 14642
Tel: 585 275-2988   *Fax:* 585 276-1934
E-mail: Mike_Maloney@urmc.rochester.edu
Length: 1 Yr   *ACGME Approved/Offered Positions:* 1
Program ID: 268-35-21-060

West Point

Keller Army Community Hospital Program

Sponsor: Keller Army Community Hospital
Hospital for Special Surgery
Prgm Director: Thomas M DeBerardino, MD
Orthopaedic Service
900 Washington Road
West Point, NY 10996
Tel: 845 938-4821   *Fax:* 845 938-6806
E-mail: thomas.deberardino@amedd.army.mil
Length: 1 Yr   *ACGME Approved/Offered Positions:* 2
Program ID: 268-35-21-055
Uniformed Services Program

North Carolina

Durham

Duke University Hospital Program

Sponsor: Duke University Hospital
Prgm Director: Dean C Taylor, MD
Division of Orthopaedic Surgery
Box 3615
Durham, NC 27710
Tel: 919 668-1894   *Fax:* 919 681-6357
E-mail: long0030@mc.duke.edu
Length: 1 Yr   *ACGME Approved/Offered Positions:* 3
Program ID: 268-36-31-091

Winston-Salem

Wake Forest University School of Medicine Program

Sponsor: Wake Forest University Baptist Medical Center
Prgm Director: David F Martin, MD
Department of Orthopaedic Surgery
Medical Center Boulevard, #1070
Winston-Salem, NC 27157
Tel: 336 716-4207   *Fax:* 336 716-3861
E-mail: hermance@wfubmc.edu
Length: 1 Yr   *ACGME Approved/Offered Positions:* 2
Program ID: 268-36-12-119

Ohio

Cincinnati

Cincinnati Sports Medicine and Orthopaedic Center Program

Sponsor: Cincinnati Sports Medicine & Orthopaedic Center
Prgm Director: Frank R Noyes, MD
10663 Montgomery Road
Cincinnati, OH 45242
Tel: 513 346-7292   *Fax:* 513 792-3230
E-mail: lraterman@csmoc.com
Length: 1 Yr   *ACGME Approved/Offered Positions:* 4
Program ID: 268-38-21-041

Mercy Hospital Anderson/University of Cincinnati College of Medicine Program

Sponsor: Mercy Hospital Anderson
University of Cincinnati College of Medicine
Wellington Orthopaedic and Sports Medicine (Blue Ash Office)
Prgm Director: Robert S Heidt Jr, MD
4701 Creek Rd, #110
Cincinnati, OH 45242
Tel: 513 554-8091   *Fax:* 513 588-2484
E-mail: rgwin@wellingtonortho.com
Length: 1 Yr   *ACGME Approved/Offered Positions:* 3
Program ID: 268-38-21-031

Cleveland

Cleveland Clinic Foundation Program

Sponsor: Cleveland Clinic Foundation
Prgm Director: Mark S Schickendantz, MD
5555 Transportation Blvd
Garfield Hts, OH 44125
Tel: 216 518-3472   *Fax:* 216 518-3490
E-mail: schickm@ccf.org
Length: 1 Yr   *ACGME Approved/Offered Positions:* 3
Program ID: 268-38-21-028

Columbus

Ohio State University Hospital Program

Sponsor: Ohio State University Hospital
Ohio State University Hospitals, East
Prgm Director: Christopher C Kaeding, MD
2050 Kenny Road
Pavilion Suite 3100
Columbus, OH 43221
Tel: 614 293-8813   *Fax:* 614 293-4399
Length: 1 Yr   *ACGME Approved/Offered Positions:* 2
Program ID: 268-38-21-008

Pennsylvania

Hershey

Penn State University/Milton S Hershey Medical Center Program

Sponsor: Milton S Hershey Medical Center
Prgm Director: Wayne J Sebastianelli, MD
1850 East Park Avenue
University Park, PA 16803
Tel: 814 235-4727
E-mail: wsebastianelli@psu.edu
Length: 1 Yr   *ACGME Approved/Offered Positions:* 1
Program ID: 268-41-13-109

Philadelphia

Pennsylvania Hospital of the University of Pennsylvania Health System Program

Sponsor: Pennsylvania Hospital (UPHS)
Christiana Care Health Services Inc
Cooper Hospital-University Medical Center
Prgm Director: Arthur R Bartolozzi, MD
800 Spruce Street
Philadelphia, PA 19107
Tel: 215 829-2205   *Fax:* 215 829-2478
E-mail: valarie.dallas@uphs.upenn.edu
Length: 1 Yr   *ACGME Approved/Offered Positions:* 2
Program ID: 268-41-31-110

Thomas Jefferson University Program

Sponsor: Thomas Jefferson University Hospital
Lankenau Hospital
Prgm Director: Michael G Ciccotti, MD
111 S 11th Street
Philadelphia, PA 19107
Tel: 215 955-1500
Length: 1 Yr   *ACGME Approved/Offered Positions:* 3
Program ID: 268-41-21-054

Programs

Pittsburgh

University of Pittsburgh Medical Center Medical Education Program

Sponsor: Univ of Pittsburgh Medical Center Medical Education
UPMC Presbyterian Shadyside
UPMC South Side
UPMC St Margaret
Prgm Director: Christopher D Harner, MD
3200 South Water Street
Pittsburgh, PA 15203
Tel: 412 432-3662   *Fax:* 412 432-3690
E-mail: dettyj@upmc.edu
Length: 1 Yr   *ACGME Approved/Offered Positions:* 5
Program ID: 268-41-21-018

Rhode Island

Providence

Brown University Program

Sponsor: Rhode Island Hospital-Lifespan
Miriam Hospital-Lifespan
Prgm Director: Paul D Fadale, MD
2 Dudley Street
Ste 200
Providence, RI 02905
Tel: 401 457-1538   *Fax:* 401 831-5926
E-mail: scastle@universityorthopedics.com
Length: 1 Yr   *ACGME Approved/Offered Positions:* 1
Program ID: 268-43-13-125

South Carolina

Greenville

Steadman Hawkins Clinic of the Carolinas Program

Sponsor: Steadman Hawkins Clinic of the Carolinas
Greenville Hospital System/University of South Carolina
Prgm Director: Richard J Hawkins, MD
1650 Skylyn Drive, Suite 200
Spartanburg, SC 29307
Tel: 864 454-7422   *Fax:* 864 454-8265
E-mail: rhawkins@ghs.org
Length: 1 Yr   *ACGME Approved/Offered Positions:* 6
Program ID: 268-45-13-117

Tennessee

Jackson

Sports, Orthopedics, and Spine Educational Foundation Program

Sponsor: Sports, Orthopedics, and Spine Educational Foundation
Prgm Director: Keith D Nord, MD
569 Skyline Drive, Suite 100
Jackson, TN 38301
Tel: 731 427-7888   *Fax:* 731 421-6597
Length: 1 Yr   *ACGME Approved/Offered Positions:* 1
Program ID: 268-47-31-118

Memphis

University of Tennessee Program

Sponsor: University of Tennessee College of Medicine
Baptist Hospital
Campbell Clinics & Surgery Center
Regional Medical Center at Memphis
Prgm Director: Frederick M Azar, MD
Department of Orthopaedics
1211 Union Avenue, Suite 510
Memphis, TN 38104
Tel: 901 759-3274   *Fax:* 901 759-3278
Length: 1 Yr   *ACGME Approved/Offered Positions:* 1
Program ID: 268-47-12-111

Nashville

Vanderbilt University Program

Sponsor: Vanderbilt University Medical Center
Prgm Director: John E Kuhn, MD, MS
Vanderbilt Sports Medicine Fellowship Program
Suite 3200, MCE South Tower, 1215 21st Ave South
Nashville, TN 37323
Tel: 615 322-7878   *Fax:* 615 343-9893
E-mail: colette.c.barrett@vanderbilt.edu
Length: 1 Yr   *ACGME Approved/Offered Positions:* 1
Program ID: 268-47-13-086

Texas

Houston

Baylor College of Medicine Program

Sponsor: Baylor College of Medicine
Kirby Surgical Center
Memorial Hermann Hospital
Methodist Hospital (Houston)
Michael E DeBakey VA Medical Center - Houston
St Luke's Episcopal Hospital
Prgm Director: Walter R Lowe, MD
Department of Orthopaedic Surgery
1709 Dryden Road, 12th floor
Houston, TX 77030
Tel: 713 986-5590   *Fax:* 713 986-5591
Length: 1 Yr   *ACGME Approved/Offered Positions:* 4
Program ID: 268-48-31-027

Methodist Hospital (Houston) Program

Sponsor: Methodist Hospital (Houston)
Prgm Director: David Lintner, MD
6560 Fannin St, #400
Houston, TX 77030
Tel: 713 441-3560   *Fax:* 713 790-2054
E-mail: jmasterson@tmhs.org
Length: 1 Yr   *ACGME Approved/Offered Positions:* 3
Program ID: 268-48-13-102

Lubbock

Texas Tech University (Lubbock) Program

Sponsor: Texas Tech University Health Sciences Center at Lubbock
Prgm Director: Richard Jon Pfeiffer, MD
3601 4th Street, MS 9436
Lubbock, TX 79430
Tel: 806 743-1703   *Fax:* 806 743-1020
E-mail: christy.morrison@ttuhsc.edu
Length: 1 Yr   *ACGME Approved/Offered Positions:* 1
Program ID: 268-48-31-122

Plano

Plano Orthopedic and Sports Medicine Center Program

Sponsor: Plano Orthopedic and Sports Medicine Center
Associated Orthopedic Sports Medicine (Plano)
Prgm Director: F Alan Barber, MD
5228 W Plano Parkway
Plano, TX 75093
Tel: 972 250-5690
Length: 1 Yr   *ACGME Approved/Offered Positions:* 2
Program ID: 268-48-31-103

San Antonio

University of Texas Health Science Center at San Antonio/Nix Medical Center Program

Sponsor: University of Texas School of Medicine at San Antonio
Baptist Memorial Healthcare System
Christus Santa Rosa Health Care Corporation
Methodist Healthcare
Nix Medical Center
Orthopaedic Surgery Center of San Antonio
South Texas Spinal Clinic (San Antonio)
Prgm Director: Jesse C DeLee, MD
2829 Babcock Rd, Suite 700
San Antonio, TX 78229
Tel: 210 804-6857   *Fax:* 210 804-5471
E-mail: gruelas@tsaog.com
Length: 1 Yr   *ACGME Approved/Offered Positions:* 2
Program ID: 268-48-21-042

Utah

Salt Lake City

University of Utah Program

Sponsor: University of Utah Medical Center
Prgm Director: Robert T Burks, MD
590 Wakara Way
Salt Lake City, UT 84108
Tel: 801 587-5455
E-mail: robert.burks@hsc.utah.edu
Length: 1 Yr   *ACGME Approved/Offered Positions:* 2
Program ID: 268-49-21-022

Virginia

Arlington

Virginia Hospital Center/Georgetown University Program

Sponsor: Virginia Hospital Center-Arlington
Nirschl Orthopedic Clinic
Reston Hospital Center
Prgm Director: Robert P Nirschl, MD, MS
1715 N George Mason Drive, Ste 504
Arlington, VA 22205
Tel: 703 525-2200   *Fax:* 703 522-2603
E-mail: nirschlorthopaedics@comcast.net
Length: 1 Yr   *ACGME Approved/Offered Positions:* 2
Program ID: 268-51-21-062

Charlottesville

University of Virginia Program

Sponsor: University of Virginia Medical Center
Prgm Director: David Diduch R, MD, MS
PO Box 800159
Charlottesville, VA 22908
Tel: 434 243-0274   *Fax:* 434 243-0290
Length: 1 Yr   *ACGME Approved/Offered Positions:* 2
Program ID: 268-51-21-057

Note: * indicates a newly appointed program director

Richmond

Orthopaedic Research of Virginia Program

Sponsor: Orthopaedic Research of Virginia
Town Center Orthopaedic Associates
Tuckahoe Orthopaedic Associates
Prgm Director: John F Meyers, MD
7660 E Parham Road, Suite 207
Richmond, VA 23294
Tel: 804 527-5960   *Fax:* 804 527-5961
Length: 1 Yr   *ACGME Approved/Offered Positions:* 4
Program ID: 268-51-21-039

Wisconsin

Madison

University of Wisconsin Program

Sponsor: University of Wisconsin Hospital and Clinics
Prgm Director: John F Orwin, MD
600 Highland Avenue, K4/751
Madison, WI 53792
Tel: 608 263-5636   *Fax:* 608 263-5631
E-mail: larsonl@orthorehab.wisc.edu
Length: 1 Yr   *ACGME Approved/Offered Positions:* 1
Program ID: 268-56-21-017

Orthopaedic Surgery

Alabama

Birmingham

University of Alabama Medical Center Program

Sponsor: University of Alabama Hospital
Children's Hospital of Alabama
University of Alabama at Birmingham/Highlands
Prgm Director: Steven M Theiss, MD*
510 20th Street South
Faculty Office Tower #940
Birmingham, AL 35294
Tel: 205 930-8494
E-mail: vicki.allen@ortho.uab.edu
Length: 5 Yrs   *ACGME Approved/Offered Positions:* 30
Program ID: 260-01-21-044

Mobile

University of South Alabama Program

Sponsor: University of South Alabama Hospitals
Infirmary West
Mobile Infirmary Medical Center
University of South Alabama Medical Center
USA Children's and Women's Hospital
Prgm Director: Frederick N Meyer, MD
3421 Medical Park Drive, Dept of Orthopaedic Surgery
2 Medical Park
Mobile, AL 36693
Tel: 251 665-8250   *Fax:* 251 665-8255
E-mail: gdriver@usouthal.edu
Length: 5 Yrs   *ACGME Approved/Offered Positions:* 15
Program ID: 260-01-11-182

Arizona

Phoenix

Banner Good Samaritan Medical Center Program

Sponsor: Banner Good Samaritan Medical Center
Arizona State University (Tempe)
Mayo Clinic Hospital
Phoenix Children's Hospital
Scottsdale Healthcare-Osborn
Prgm Director: Alex C McLaren, MD
Orthopaedic Residency
1300 N 12th Street, Suite 620
Phoenix, AZ 85006
Tel: 602 239-3671   *Fax:* 602 239-3788
E-mail: orthopaedic.residency@bannerhealth.com
Length: 5 Yrs   *ACGME Approved/Offered Positions:* 20
Program ID: 260-03-31-206

Tucson

University of Arizona Program

Sponsor: University of Arizona College of Medicine
University Medical Center
University Orthopaedic Specialists
Prgm Director: John T Ruth, MD
PO Box 245064
Tucson, AZ 85724
Tel: 520 626-9245   *Fax:* 520 626-2668
E-mail: brandess@email.arizona.edu
Length: 5 Yrs   *ACGME Approved/Offered Positions:* 15
Program ID: 260-03-31-054

Arkansas

Little Rock

University of Arkansas for Medical Sciences Program

Sponsor: University of Arkansas College of Medicine
Arkansas Children's Hospital
Central Arkansas Veterans Healthcare System
UAMS Medical Center
Prgm Director: R Dale Blasier, MD, MBA
4301 West Markham
Mail Slot 531
Little Rock, AR 72205
Tel: 501 686-5259   *Fax:* 501 603-1984
E-mail: ClintonDarleneM@uams.edu
Length: 5 Yrs   *ACGME Approved/Offered Positions:* 20
Program ID: 260-04-21-094

California

Loma Linda

Loma Linda University Program

Sponsor: Loma Linda University Medical Center
Arrowhead Regional Medical Center
Jerry L Pettis Memorial Veterans Hospital
Prgm Director: Montri D Wongworawat, MD
11406 Loma Linda Drive
Suite 218
Loma Linda, CA 92354
Tel: 909 558-6444   *Fax:* 909 558-6118
E-mail: orthoresidency@llu.edu
Length: 5 Yrs   *ACGME Approved/Offered Positions:* 20
Program ID: 260-05-21-063

Los Angeles

UCLA Medical Center Program

Sponsor: UCLA David Geffen School of Medicine/UCLA
   Medical Center
Shriners Hospitals for Children (Los Angeles)
UCLA Medical Center
VA Greater Los Angeles Healthcare System
Prgm Director: James V Luck Jr, MD, BA
10833 Le Conte Avenue
Room 72-225 CHS
Los Angeles, CA 90095
Tel: 213 742-1369   *Fax:* 213 742-1435
E-mail: koka@mednet.ucla.edu
Length: 5 Yrs   *ACGME Approved/Offered Positions:* 30
Program ID: 260-05-21-078

University of Southern California/ LAC+USC Medical Center Program

Sponsor: University of Southern California/LAC+USC
   Medical Center
Childrens Hospital Los Angeles
LAC+USC Medical Center
USC University Hospital
Prgm Director: David B Thordarson, MD
2025 Zonal Avenue, GNH 3900
Los Angeles, CA 90033
Tel: 323 226-7210   *Fax:* 323 226-2487
E-mail: orthopod@usc.edu
Length: 5 Yrs   *ACGME Approved/Offered Positions:* 50
Program ID: 260-05-21-193

Programs

Orange

University of California (Irvine) Program

Sponsor: University of California (Irvine) Medical
Center
Children's Hospital of Orange County
Kaiser Foundation Hospitals (Anaheim)
St Joseph Hospital (Orange)
VA Long Beach Healthcare System
Prgm Director: Nitin N Bhatia, MD*
101 City Drive South
Dept of Ortho Surgery, Pav III, 2nd Fl, Rte 81
Orange, CA 92868
Tel: 714 456-1699   *Fax:* 714 456-7547
Length: 5 Yrs   *ACGME Approved/Offered Positions:* 20
Program ID: 260-05-21-064

Sacramento

University of California (Davis) Health System Program

Sponsor: University of California (Davis) Health System
Shriners Hospitals for Children (Sacramento)
University of California (Davis) Medical Center
Prgm Director: Rolando F Roberto, MD, BS
Department of Orthopaedic Surgery
4860 Y Street, Suite 3800
Sacramento, CA 95817
Tel: 916 734-2937   *Fax:* 916 734-7904
Length: 5 Yrs   *ACGME Approved/Offered Positions:* 20
Program ID: 260-05-21-133

San Diego

Naval Medical Center (San Diego) Program

Sponsor: Naval Medical Center (San Diego)
Sharp HealthCare
Prgm Director: Michael A Thompson, MD
Department of Orthopaedics
34800 Bob Wilson Dr, Suite 112
San Diego, CA 92134
Tel: 619 532-8468   *Fax:* 619 532-8467
E-mail: Michael.Thompson2@med.navy.mil
Length: 5 Yrs   *ACGME Approved/Offered Positions:* 25
Program ID: 260-05-31-079
Uniformed Services Program

University of California (San Diego) Program

Sponsor: University of California (San Diego) Medical
Center
Rady Children's Hospital
Veterans Affairs Medical Center (San Diego)
Prgm Director: Alexandra K Schwartz, MD
350 Dickinson Street, Mail Code 8894
San Diego, CA 92103
Tel: 619 534-2539   *Fax:* 619 543-7510
E-mail: orthores@ucsd.edu
Length: 5 Yrs   *ACGME Approved/Offered Positions:* 20
Program ID: 260-05-21-109

San Francisco

St Mary's Hospital and Medical Center Program

Sponsor: St Mary's Hospital and Medical Center
Alameda County Medical Center
Kaiser Permanente Medical Center (Oakland)
Prgm Director: William A McGann, MD
450 Stanyan Street
Orthpaedic Education Offices
San Francisco, CA 94117
Tel: 415 750-5782   *Fax:* 415 750-5938
E-mail: William.Mcgann@chw.edu
Length: 5 Yrs   *ACGME Approved/Offered Positions:* 15
Program ID: 260-05-22-108

Note: * indicates a newly appointed program director

University of California (San Francisco) Program

Sponsor: University of California (San Francisco) School
of Medicine
San Francisco General Hospital Medical Center
UCSF and Mount Zion Medical Centers
Veterans Affairs Medical Center (San Francisco)
Prgm Director: Thomas Vail, MD
Dept of Orthopaedic Surgery
500 Parnassus Avenue MU320W
San Francisco, CA 94143
Tel: 415 502-5183
Length: 5 Yrs   *ACGME Approved/Offered Positions:* 30
Program ID: 260-05-21-002

Stanford

Stanford University Program

Sponsor: Stanford Hospital and Clinics
Santa Clara Valley Medical Center
Veterans Affairs Palo Alto Health Care System
Prgm Director: Timothy R McAdams, MD
Department of Orthopaedic Surgery
300 Pasteur Drive, Room R144
Stanford, CA 94305
Tel: 650 725-5903   *Fax:* 650 724-3044
E-mail: kdenny@stanford.edu
Length: 5 Yrs   *ACGME Approved/Offered Positions:* 20
Program ID: 260-05-21-098

Torrance

Los Angeles County-Harbor-UCLA Medical Center Program

Sponsor: Los Angeles County-Harbor-UCLA Medical
Center
Prgm Director: Louis M Kwong, MD
1000 West Carson Street, Box 422
Torrance, CA 90509
Tel: 310 222-2716   *Fax:* 310 533-8791
E-mail: lkwong@ladhs.org
Length: 5 Yrs   *ACGME Approved/Offered Positions:* 20
Program ID: 260-05-31-122

Colorado

Aurora

University of Colorado Denver Program

Sponsor: University of Colorado Denver School of
Medicine
Children's Hospital (The)
Denver Health Medical Center
University of Colorado Hospital
Veterans Affairs Medical Center (Denver)
Prgm Director: Steven J Morgan, MD
12631 E 17th Avenue
PO Box 6511, Mail Stop B-202
Aurora, CO 80045
Tel: 303 724-2961   *Fax:* 303 724-2978
Length: 5 Yrs   *ACGME Approved/Offered Positions:* 20
Program ID: 260-07-21-004

Connecticut

Farmington

University of Connecticut Program

Sponsor: University of Connecticut School of Medicine
Connecticut Children's Medical Center
Hartford Hospital
St Francis Hospital and Medical Center
Univ of Connecticut Health Center/John Dempsey
Hospital
Prgm Director: Bruce D Browner, MD, MS
MARB 4th Floor
263 Farmington Avenue
Farmington, CT 06034
Tel: 860 679-6640   *Fax:* 860 679-6649
E-mail: gcooper@nso.uchc.edu
Length: 5 Yrs   *ACGME Approved/Offered Positions:* 20
Program ID: 260-08-21-172

New Haven

Yale-New Haven Medical Center Program

Sponsor: Yale-New Haven Hospital
Veterans Affairs Medical Center (West Haven)
Prgm Director: Peter Jokl, MD
PO Box 208071
New Haven, CT 06520
Tel: 203 785-2579   *Fax:* 203 785-7132
Length: 5 Yrs   *ACGME Approved/Offered Positions:* 25
Program ID: 260-08-21-005

District of Columbia

Washington

George Washington University Program

Sponsor: George Washington University School of
Medicine
Children's National Medical Center
Clinical Center at the National Institutes of Health
George Washington University Hospital (UHS)
Sibley Memorial Hospital
Washington Hospital Center
Prgm Director: Robert J Neviaser, MD
2150 Pennsylvania Avenue, NW
Room 7-416
Washington, DC 20037
Tel: 202 741-3301   *Fax:* 202 741-3313
Length: 5 Yrs   *ACGME Approved/Offered Positions:* 20
Program ID: 260-10-21-083

Georgetown University Hospital Program

Sponsor: Georgetown University Hospital
Inova Fairfax Hospital
Virginia Hospital Center-Arlington
Washington Hospital Center
Prgm Director: Sam W Wiesel, MD
3800 Reservoir Road NW
G-PHC
Washington, DC 20007
Tel: 202 444-7095   *Fax:* 202 444-7573
Length: 5 Yrs   *ACGME Approved/Offered Positions:* 20
Program ID: 260-10-21-014

Howard University Program

Sponsor: Howard University Hospital
Children's National Medical Center
Providence Hospital
Sinai Hospital of Baltimore
Veterans Affairs Medical Center (Washington, DC)
Prgm Director: Terry L Thompson, MD
Department of Orthopaedic Surgery
2041 Georgia Ave, NW
Washington, DC 20060
Tel: 202 865-1182   *Fax:* 202 865-4904
E-mail: tthompson@howard.edu
Length: 5 Yrs   *ACGME Approved/Offered Positions:* 20
Program ID: 260-10-21-115

Florida

Gainesville

University of Florida Program

Sponsor: University of Florida College of Medicine
North Florida/South Georgia Veterans Health System
Shands at AGH
Shands Hospital at the University of Florida
Prgm Director: Mark Scarborough, MD
PO Box 112727
Gainesville, FL 32611
Tel: 352 273-7365   *Fax:* 352 273-7388
Length: 5 Yrs   *ACGME Approved/Offered Positions:* 20
Program ID: 260-11-21-123

Jacksonville

University of Florida College of Medicine Jacksonville Program

Sponsor: University of Florida College of Medicine
Jacksonville
Shands Jacksonville Medical Center
Prgm Director: John S Kirkpatrick, MD, MS
Department of Orthopaedic Surgery
655 West 8th Street, ACC 2nd Floor, Box C126
Jacksonville, FL 32209
Tel: 904 244-7757   *Fax:* 904 244-7744
E-mail: ortho.gme@jax.ufl.edu
Length: 5 Yrs   *ACGME Approved/Offered Positions:* 20
Program ID: 260-11-21-062

Miami

Jackson Memorial Hospital/Jackson Health System Program

Sponsor: Jackson Memorial Hospital/Jackson Health
System
University of Miami Hospital
Veterans Affairs Medical Center (Miami)
Prgm Director: Frank J Eismont, MD
Rehabilitation Center, 3rd Floor, Room 303
1611 NW 12th Avenue
Miami, FL 33136
Tel: 305 585-7138   *Fax:* 305 324-7658
E-mail: orthoapp@med.miami.edu
Length: 5 Yrs   *ACGME Approved/Offered Positions:* 35
Program ID: 260-11-21-076

Orlando

Orlando Health Program

Sponsor: Orlando Health
Arnold Palmer Hospital for Children
Florida Hospital Medical Center
Orlando Regional Medical Center
Prgm Director: Thomas A Csencsitz, MD, PhD
Medical Education - Orthopaedics
22 West Underwood, 4th Floor
Orlando, FL 32806
Tel: 321 841-1745   *Fax:* 321 843-7381
Length: 5 Yrs   *ACGME Approved/Offered Positions:* 15
Program ID: 260-11-22-184

Tampa

University of South Florida Program

Sponsor: University of South Florida College of Medicine
James A Haley Veterans Hospital
Lakeland Regional Medical Center
Shriners Hospitals for Children (Tampa)
St Joseph's Hospital
Tampa General Hospital
University Community Hospital
Prgm Director: G Douglas Letson, MD
3500 E Fletcher Avenue
Ste 511, MDC 106
Tampa, FL 33612
Tel: 813 745-2297   *Fax:* 813 745-8337
E-mail: douglas.letson@moffitt.org
Length: 5 Yrs   *ACGME Approved/Offered Positions:* 20
Program ID: 260-11-12-207

Georgia

Atlanta

Atlanta Medical Center Program

Sponsor: Atlanta Medical Center
Children's Healthcare of Atlanta
Prgm Director: Steven M Kane, MD*
303 Parkway Drive, NE
Box 423
Atlanta, GA 30312
Tel: 404 265-4609   *Fax:* 404 265-4989
Length: 5 Yrs   *ACGME Approved/Offered Positions:* 15
Program ID: 260-12-22-113

Emory University Program

Sponsor: Emory University School of Medicine
Emory University Hospital
Grady Health System
Prgm Director: Shervin V Oskouei, MD
Residency Coordinator's Office - 315 ESOM Building
49 Jesse Hill Jr Drive SE
Atlanta, GA 30303
Tel: 404 778-6363   *Fax:* 404 778-1551
E-mail: kstrozi@emory.edu
Length: 5 Yrs   *ACGME Approved/Offered Positions:* 25
Program ID: 260-12-21-039

Augusta

Medical College of Georgia Program

Sponsor: Medical College of Georgia
Veterans Affairs Medical Center (Augusta)
Prgm Director: S Marcus Fulcher, MD
1120 Fifteenth Street
Augusta, GA 30912
Tel: 706 721-4263   *Fax:* 706 721-6001
E-mail: mfulcher@mcg.edu
Length: 5 Yrs   *ACGME Approved/Offered Positions:* 15
Program ID: 260-12-21-114

Fort Gordon

Dwight David Eisenhower Army Medical Center Program

Sponsor: Dwight David Eisenhower Army Medical
Center
Children's Healthcare of Atlanta at Scottish Rite
Prgm Director: Russell A Davidson, MD
Orthopaedic Surgery Service
Fort Gordon, GA 30905
Tel: 706 787-1388
Length: 5 Yrs   *ACGME Approved/Offered Positions:* 10
Program ID: 260-12-21-192
Uniformed Services Program

Hawaii

Honolulu

University of Hawaii Program

Sponsor: University of Hawaii John A Burns School of
Medicine
Queen's Medical Center
Prgm Director: Robert E Atkinson, MD
School of Medicine
651 Ilalo St
Honolulu, HI 96813
Tel: 808 586-2920   *Fax:* 808 586-3022
E-mail: ortho@hawaii.edu
Length: 5 Yrs   *ACGME Approved/Offered Positions:* 10
Program ID: 260-14-21-068

Tripler AMC

Tripler Army Medical Center Program

Sponsor: Tripler Army Medical Center
Prgm Director: Joseph R Orchowski, MD
Orthopaedic Surgery Services, MCHK-DSO
1 Jarrett White Road
Tripler AMC, HI 96859
Tel: 808 433-3557   *Fax:* 808 433-1554
E-mail: joseph.orchowski@amedd.army.mil
Length: 5 Yrs   *ACGME Approved/Offered Positions:* 15
Program ID: 260-14-31-086
Uniformed Services Program

Illinois

Chicago

McGaw Medical Center of Northwestern University Program

Sponsor: McGaw Medical Center of Northwestern
University
Children's Memorial Hospital
Evanston Hospital
Jesse Brown Veterans Affairs Medical Center
Northwestern Memorial Hospital
Prgm Director: Michael F Schafer, MD
676 N St Clair Street
Suite 1350
Chicago, IL 60611
Tel: 312 926-4444   *Fax:* 312 926-4643
E-mail: j-broholm@northwestern.edu
Length: 5 Yrs   *ACGME Approved/Offered Positions:* 45
Program ID: 260-16-21-007

Rush University Medical Center Program

Sponsor: Rush University Medical Center
John H Stroger Hospital of Cook County
Shriners Hospitals for Children (Chicago)
Prgm Director: Joshua J Jacobs, MD
1653 West Congress Parkway
Room 1471, Jelke Building
Chicago, IL 60612
Tel: 312 942-5850   *Fax:* 312 942-2101
E-mail: Beverly_Kendall-Morgan@rush.edu
Length: 5 Yrs   *ACGME Approved/Offered Positions:* 25
Program ID: 260-16-31-174

University of Chicago Program

Sponsor: University of Chicago Medical Center
Louis A Weiss Memorial Hospital
Prgm Director: Brian C Toolan, MD
5841 S Maryland Ave, MC 3079
Chicago, IL 60637
Tel: 773 702-6984   *Fax:* 773 702-0076
E-mail: btoolan@surgery.bsd.uchicago.edu
Length: 5 Yrs   *ACGME Approved/Offered Positions:* 20
Program ID: 260-16-21-136

Programs

University of Illinois College of Medicine at Chicago Program

Sponsor: University of Illinois College of Medicine at Chicago
John H Stroger Hospital of Cook County
University of Illinois Hospital and Clinics
Prgm Director: Alfonso Mejia, MD, MPH
835 S Wolcott Avenue
Room E-270, M/C 844
Chicago, IL 60612
Tel: 312 996-7161   *Fax:* 312 996-9025
E-mail: mejia.alfonso@gmail.com
Length: 5 Yrs   *ACGME Approved/Offered Positions:* 35
Program ID: 260-16-21-047

Maywood

Loyola University Program

Sponsor: Loyola University Medical Center
Edward Hines, Jr Veterans Affairs Hospital
Shriners Hospitals for Children (Chicago)
Prgm Director: William J Hopkinson, MD
2160 S First Avenue
Maguire Building 105, Room 1700
Maywood, IL 60153
Tel: 708 216-4992   *Fax:* 708 216-5858
E-mail: ortho@lumc.edu
Length: 5 Yrs   *ACGME Approved/Offered Positions:* 25
Program ID: 260-16-21-050

Springfield

Southern Illinois University Program

Sponsor: Southern Illinois University School of Medicine
Memorial Medical Center
St John's Hospital
Prgm Director: Keith R Gabriel, MD*
PO Box 19679
Division of Orthopaedics
Springfield, IL 62794
Tel: 217 545-6155   *Fax:* 217 545-7901
E-mail: aweinhoeft@siumed.edu
Length: 5 Yrs   *ACGME Approved/Offered Positions:* 15
Program ID: 260-16-21-110

Indiana

Fort Wayne

Fort Wayne Medical Education Program

Sponsor: Fort Wayne Medical Education Program
Lutheran Hospital of Indiana
Parkview Memorial Hospital
St Joseph Hospital
Prgm Director: B Matthew Hicks, MD
750 Broadway, Suite 250
Fort Wayne, IN 46802
Tel: 260 436-8686   *Fax:* 260 459-0036
Length: 5 Yrs   *ACGME Approved/Offered Positions:* 10
Program ID: 260-17-22-138

Indianapolis

Indiana University School of Medicine Program

Sponsor: Indiana University School of Medicine
Clarian Indiana University Hospital
Clarian Methodist Hospital of Indiana
Clarian Riley Hospital for Children
Richard L Roudebush Veterans Affairs Medical Center
William N Wishard Memorial Hospital
Prgm Director: Randall T Loder, MD
541 Clinical Drive, Room 600
Indianapolis, IN 46202
Tel: 317 278-0961   *Fax:* 317 274-7197
E-mail: danders@iupui.edu
Length: 5 Yrs   *ACGME Approved/Offered Positions:* 25
Program ID: 260-17-21-008

Iowa

Iowa City

University of Iowa Hospitals and Clinics Program

Sponsor: University of Iowa Hospitals and Clinics
Veterans Affairs Medical Center (Iowa City)
Prgm Director: J Lawrence Marsh, MD
Orthopaedic Surgery, 01008 JPP
200 Hawkins Drive
Iowa City, IA 52242
Tel: 319 356-0430   *Fax:* 319 356-8999
E-mail: jeanette-marsh@uiowa.edu
Length: 5 Yrs   *ACGME Approved/Offered Positions:* 30
Program ID: 260-18-21-139

Kansas

Kansas City

University of Kansas School of Medicine Program

Sponsor: University of Kansas School of Medicine
Children's Mercy Hospital
University of Kansas Hospital
Veterans Affairs Medical Center (Kansas City)
Prgm Director: Kimberly J Templeton, MD*
Mail Stop 3017, 3901 Rainbow Boulevard
Kansas City, KS 66160
Tel: 913 588-7590   *Fax:* 913 588-6178
E-mail: ktemplet@kumc.edu
Length: 5 Yrs   *ACGME Approved/Offered Positions:* 20
Program ID: 260-19-21-140

Wichita

University of Kansas (Wichita) Program

Sponsor: University of Kansas School of Medicine (Wichita)
Shriners Hospitals for Children (St Louis)
Veterans Affairs Medical Center (Wichita)
Via Christi Regional Medical Center-St Francis
Wesley Medical Center
Prgm Director: David McQueen, MD
929 North St Francis
Orthopaedic Residency Program, Rm 4076
Wichita, KS 67214
Tel: 316 268-5988   *Fax:* 316 291-7799
E-mail: jridgewa@kumc.edu
Length: 5 Yrs   *ACGME Approved/Offered Positions:* 20
Program ID: 260-19-31-106

Kentucky

Lexington

University of Kentucky College of Medicine Program

Sponsor: University of Kentucky College of Medicine
Shriners Hospitals for Children (Lexington)
University of Kentucky Hospital
Veterans Affairs Medical Center (Lexington)
Prgm Director: William O Shaffer, MD, BS
740 S Limestone, K401
Lexington, KY 40536
Tel: 859 218-3091   *Fax:* 859 323-2412
E-mail: brian.judge@uky.edu
Length: 5 Yrs   *ACGME Approved/Offered Positions:* 20
Program ID: 260-20-21-059

Louisville

University of Louisville Program

Sponsor: University of Louisville School of Medicine
Jewish Hospital
Kosair Children's Hospital (Norton Healthcare, Inc)
Norton Medical Pavilion-Norton Healthcare, Inc
University of Louisville Hospital
Prgm Director: Craig S Roberts, MD
Department of Orthopaedic Surgery
210 E Gray Street, Suite 1003
Louisville, KY 40202
Tel: 502 852-5319   *Fax:* 502 852-7227
Length: 5 Yrs   *ACGME Approved/Offered Positions:* 20
Program ID: 260-20-21-009

Louisiana

New Orleans

Louisiana State University Program

Sponsor: Louisiana State University School of Medicine
Children's Hospital (New Orleans)
Earl K Long Medical Center
Medical Center of Louisiana at New Orleans
Ochsner Medical Center-Kenner
Prgm Director: Peter C Krause, MD
Department of Orthopaedic Surgery
2020 Gravier Street, Room 330 - Corridor J
New Orleans, LA 70112
Tel: 504 568-4680   *Fax:* 504 568-4466
Length: 5 Yrs   *ACGME Approved/Offered Positions:* 20
Program ID: 260-21-21-141

Ochsner Clinic Foundation Program

Sponsor: Ochsner Clinic Foundation
Leonard J Chabert Medical Center
Prgm Director: Mark S Meyer, MD
1514 Jefferson Highway
5th Floor - AT
New Orleans, LA 70121
Tel: 504 842-5932
E-mail: segilbert@ochsner.org
Length: 5 Yrs   *ACGME Approved/Offered Positions:* 12
Program ID: 260-21-22-056

Tulane University Program

Sponsor: Tulane University School of Medicine
Medical Center of Louisiana at New Orleans
Tulane University Hospital and Clinics
Prgm Director: John A Davis Jr, MD, DDS*
1430 Tulane Avenue, SL 32
New Orleans, LA 70112
Tel: 504 988-5192   *Fax:* 504 988-3517
E-mail: jdavis7@tulane.edu
Length: 5 Yrs   *ACGME Approved/Offered Positions:* 12
Program ID: 260-21-31-010

Note: * indicates a newly appointed program director

Shreveport

Louisiana State University (Shreveport) Program

Sponsor: LSU Health Sciences Center-University Hospital
Overton Brooks Veterans Affairs Medical Center
Shriners Hospitals for Children (Shreveport)
Prgm Director: Margaret L Olmedo, MD
PO Box 33932
1501 Kings Highway
Shreveport, LA 71103
Tel: 318 675-6180   *Fax:* 318 675-6186
E-mail: molmed@lsuhsc.edu
Length: 5 Yrs   *ACGME Approved/Offered Positions:* 15
Program ID: 260-21-21-043

Maryland

Baltimore

Johns Hopkins University Program

Sponsor: Johns Hopkins University School of Medicine
Good Samaritan Hospital of Maryland
Johns Hopkins Bayview Medical Center
Johns Hopkins Hospital
Prgm Director: Dawn LaPorte, MD
601 N Caroline Street, Suite 5223
Baltimore, MD 21287
Tel: 410 955-9663   *Fax:* 410 502-6816
Length: 5 Yrs   *ACGME Approved/Offered Positions:* 25
Program ID: 260-23-21-057

Union Memorial Hospital Program

Sponsor: Union Memorial Hospital
Johns Hopkins Hospital
Prgm Director: Leslie S Matthews, MD, MBA
201 East University Parkway
Baltimore, MD 21218
Tel: 410 554-2865
E-mail: kathy.lind@medstar.net
Length: 5 Yrs   *ACGME Approved/Offered Positions:* 10
Program ID: 260-23-31-087

University of Maryland Program

Sponsor: University of Maryland Medical System
Johns Hopkins Hospital
Veterans Affairs Medical Center (Baltimore)
Prgm Director: Robert S Sterling, MD
22 South Greene Street
Suite S11B
Baltimore, MD 21201
Tel: 410 328-6040   *Fax:* 410 328-0534
Length: 5 Yrs   *ACGME Approved/Offered Positions:* 25
Program ID: 260-23-31-088

Bethesda

National Capital Consortium Program

Sponsor: National Capital Consortium
National Naval Medical Center (Bethesda)
Walter Reed Army Medical Center
Prgm Director: Patricia L McKay, MD
Orthopaedic Surgery Service
8901 Wisconsin Avenue
Bethesda, MD 20889
Tel: 301 295-4293   *Fax:* 301 295-4141
Length: 5 Yrs   *ACGME Approved/Offered Positions:* 30
Program ID: 260-23-21-183
Uniformed Services Program

Massachusetts

Boston

Boston University Medical Center Program

Sponsor: Boston Medical Center
Lahey Clinic
Shriners Hospitals for Children (Springfield)
Veterans Affairs Medical Center (Boston)
Prgm Director: Paul Tornetta III, MD
850 Harrison Avenue
Dowling 2 North
Boston, MA 02118
Tel: 617 414-6295
Length: 5 Yrs   *ACGME Approved/Offered Positions:* 25
Program ID: 260-24-31-066

Massachusetts General Hospital/Brigham and Women's Hospital/Harvard Medical School Program

Sponsor: Massachusetts General Hospital
Beth Israel Deaconess Medical Center
Brigham and Women's Hospital
Children's Hospital
Prgm Director: Dempsey Springfield, MD*
55 Fruit Street, WHT 535
Boston, MA 02114
Tel: 617 726-5117   *Fax:* 617 726-3124
E-mail: dsheehan@partners.org
Length: 5 Yrs   *ACGME Approved/Offered Positions:* 60
Program ID: 260-24-21-011

Tufts Medical Center Program

Sponsor: Tufts Medical Center
New England Baptist Hospital
Newton-Wellesley Hospital
Prgm Director: Charles Cassidy, MD
Department of Orthopaedics, Box 306
800 Washington Street
Boston, MA 02111
Tel: 617 636-5172   *Fax:* 617 636-5178
E-mail: jdolph@tuftsmedicalcenter.org
Length: 5 Yrs   *ACGME Approved/Offered Positions:* 20
Program ID: 260-24-21-013

Worcester

University of Massachusetts Program

Sponsor: University of Massachusetts Medical School
UMass Memorial Health Care (Hahnemann Campus)
UMass Memorial Health Care (Memorial Campus)
UMass Memorial Health Care (University Campus)
Prgm Director: Thomas F Breen, MD
55 Lake Avenue North
Worcester, MA 01655
Tel: 508 856-4262   *Fax:* 508 334-7273
E-mail: michelle.auger@umassmed.edu
Length: 5 Yrs   *ACGME Approved/Offered Positions:* 20
Program ID: 260-24-21-170

Michigan

Ann Arbor

University of Michigan Program

Sponsor: University of Michigan Hospitals and Health Centers
Prgm Director: Paul Dougherty, MD*
1500 E Medical Center Drive
2912D Taubman Center
Ann Arbor, MI 48109
Tel: 734 615-3100   *Fax:* 734 647-3277
Length: 5 Yrs   *ACGME Approved/Offered Positions:* 30
Program ID: 260-25-21-074

Detroit

Detroit Medical Center Program

Sponsor: Detroit Medical Center Corporation
Children's Hospital of Michigan
Detroit Receiving Hospital and University Health Center
Providence Hospital and Medical Centers
Prgm Director: Ralph B Blasier, MD, JD
Department of Orthopaedic Surgery
6071 West Outer Drive
Detroit, MI 48235
Tel: 313 966-4750   *Fax:* 313 966-4760
E-mail: rblasier@dmc.org
Length: 5 Yrs   *ACGME Approved/Offered Positions:* 20
Program ID: 260-25-31-210

Henry Ford Hospital Program

Sponsor: Henry Ford Hospital
Prgm Director: Theodore W Parsons III, MD
2799 West Grand Blvd
Detroit, MI 48202
Tel: 313 916-3879   *Fax:* 313 916-0475
E-mail: tparson3@hfhs.org
Length: 5 Yrs   *ACGME Approved/Offered Positions:* 30
Program ID: 260-25-11-142

Flint

McLaren Regional Medical Center Program

Sponsor: McLaren Regional Medical Center
Hurley Medical Center
Prgm Director: Norman E Walter, MD
401 South Ballenger Highway
Attn: Orthopaedic Education Office
Flint, MI 48532
Tel: 810 342-2111   *Fax:* 810 342-3659
E-mail: ritak@mclaren.org
Length: 5 Yrs   *ACGME Approved/Offered Positions:* 10
Program ID: 260-25-12-089

Grand Rapids

Grand Rapids Medical Education and Research Center/Michigan State University Program

Sponsor: Grand Rapids Medical Education and Research Center
Saint Mary's Health Care (Grand Rapids)
Spectrum Health-Blodgett Hospital
Spectrum Health-Butterworth Hospital
Prgm Director: David Rispler, MD
Michigan State University - Orthopaedic Res Prog
300 Lafayette SE #3400
Grand Rapids, MI 49503
Tel: 616 685-6615
E-mail: tutschc@trinity-health.org
Length: 5 Yrs   *ACGME Approved/Offered Positions:* 25
Program ID: 260-25-21-195

Kalamazoo

Kalamazoo Center for Medical Studies/Michigan State University Program

Sponsor: Michigan State Univ/Kalamazoo Center for Medical Studies
Borgess Medical Center
Bronson Methodist Hospital
Midwest Orthopaedic Surgery
Prgm Director: Dale E Rowe, MD
Michigan State University
1000 Oakland Drive
Kalamazoo, MI 49008
Tel: 269 337-6250   *Fax:* 269 337-6441
Length: 5 Yrs   *ACGME Approved/Offered Positions:* 15
Program ID: 260-25-21-126

Royal Oak

William Beaumont Hospital Program
Sponsor: William Beaumont Hospital
Prgm Director: Harry N Herkowitz, MD
3601 West 13 Mile Road
3535 W 13 Mile Road, Suite 744
Royal Oak, MI 48073
Tel: 248 551-3140 *Fax:* 248 551-9520
E-mail: lthompson@beaumonthospitals.com
Length: 5 Yrs *ACGME Approved/Offered Positions:* 20
Program ID: 260-25-12-173

Minnesota

Minneapolis

University of Minnesota Program
Sponsor: University of Minnesota Medical School
Gillette Children's Hospital
Hennepin County Medical Center
Regions Hospital
University of Minnesota Medical Center, Division of
  Fairview
Veterans Affairs Medical Center (Minneapolis)
Prgm Director: Ann Van Heest, MD
2450 Riverside Avenue S, R200
Minneapolis, MN 55454
Tel: 612 273-1177 *Fax:* 612 273-7959
Length: 5 Yrs *ACGME Approved/Offered Positions:* 40
Program ID: 260-26-21-080

Rochester

College of Medicine, Mayo Clinic (Rochester) Program
Sponsor: College of Medicine, Mayo Clinic
Mayo Clinic (Jacksonville)
Mayo Clinic (Rochester)
Nemours Children's Clinic
Rochester Methodist Hospital
Saint Marys Hospital of Rochester
Prgm Director: Arlen D Hanssen, MD
200 First Street SW
Rochester, MN 55905
Tel: 507 284-3316 *Fax:* 507 266-4234
E-mail: price.natalie@mayo.edu
Length: 5 Yrs *ACGME Approved/Offered Positions:* 60
Program ID: 260-26-21-121

Mississippi

Jackson

University of Mississippi Medical Center Program
Sponsor: University of Mississippi School of Medicine
University Hospitals and Clinics
Veterans Affairs Medical Center (Jackson)
Prgm Director: Robert A McGuire, MD
2500 N State Street
Jackson, MS 39216
Tel: 601 984-5142 *Fax:* 601 984-5151
E-mail: salexander@orthopedics.umsmed.edu
Length: 5 Yrs *ACGME Approved/Offered Positions:* 20
Program ID: 260-27-21-006

Missouri

Columbia

University of Missouri-Columbia Program
Sponsor: University of Missouri-Columbia School of
  Medicine
Harry S Truman Memorial Veterans Hospital
University Hospitals and Clinics
Prgm Director: Barry J Gainor, MD
One Hospital Drive, MC213
Columbia, MO 65212
Tel: 573 882-5731 *Fax:* 573 882-1760
E-mail: bolands@health.missouri.edu
Length: 5 Yrs *ACGME Approved/Offered Positions:* 25
Program ID: 260-28-21-148

Kansas City

University of Missouri at Kansas City Program
Sponsor: University of Missouri-Kansas City School of
  Medicine
Children's Mercy Hospital
St Luke's Hospital-Kansas City
Truman Medical Center
Prgm Director: James J Hamilton, MD, MS
2301 Holmes Street
Kansas City, MO 64108
Tel: 816 404-5404 *Fax:* 816 404-5381
Length: 5 Yrs *ACGME Approved/Offered Positions:* 20
Program ID: 260-28-21-018

St Louis

St Louis University School of Medicine Program
Sponsor: St Louis University School of Medicine
Cardinal Glennon Children's Hospital
St John's Mercy Medical Center
St Louis University Hospital
Prgm Director: Berton R Moed, MD
3635 Vista Avenue at Grand Blvd
Department of Orthopaedic Surgery
St Louis, MO 63110
Tel: 314 577-8850 *Fax:* 314 268-5121
Length: 5 Yrs *ACGME Approved/Offered Positions:* 20
Program ID: 260-28-21-046

Washington University/B-JH/SLCH Consortium Program
Sponsor: Washington University/B-JH/SLCH Consortium
Barnes-Jewish Hospital
Prgm Director: Rick W Wright, MD
Orthopaedic Surgery, Campus Box 8233
660 South Euclid Avenue
St Louis, MO 63110
Tel: 314 747-2543 *Fax:* 314 362-4816
E-mail: orthsurg@wudosis.wustl.edu
Length: 5 Yrs *ACGME Approved/Offered Positions:* 30
Program ID: 260-28-21-060

Nebraska

Omaha

University of Nebraska Medical Center College of Medicine/Creighton University Program
Sponsor: University of Nebraska Medical Center College
  of Medicine
Alegent Health Bergan Mercy Health System
Children's Hospital
Nebraska Medical Center
Veterans Affairs Medical Center (Omaha)
Prgm Director: Matthew A Mormino, MD
Department of Orthopaedic Surgery
981080 Nebraska Medical Center
Omaha, NE 68198
Tel: 402 559-2258 *Fax:* 402 559-5511
E-mail: mamormin@unmc.edu
Length: 5 Yrs *ACGME Approved/Offered Positions:* 20
Program ID: 260-30-21-001

New Hampshire

Lebanon

Dartmouth-Hitchcock Medical Center Program
Sponsor: Mary Hitchcock Memorial Hospital
Prgm Director: Charles F Carr, MD
One Medical Center Drive
Lebanon, NH 03756
Tel: 603 653-6014 *Fax:* 603 653-3581
E-mail: Orthosurg.Residency.Program@Hitchcock.org
Length: 5 Yrs *ACGME Approved/Offered Positions:* 20
Program ID: 260-32-21-082

New Jersey

Long Branch

Monmouth Medical Center Program
Sponsor: Monmouth Medical Center
Children's Hospital of Philadelphia
Morristown Memorial Hospital
Prgm Director: Steve J Paragioudakis, MD, MBA*
300 Second Avenue, Room 251SW
Long Branch, NJ 07740
Tel: 732 923-6784 *Fax:* 732 923-7247
E-mail: doctorp1@verizon.net
Length: 5 Yrs *ACGME Approved/Offered Positions:* 10
Program ID: 260-33-11-146

New Brunswick

UMDNJ-Robert Wood Johnson Medical School Program
Sponsor: UMDNJ-Robert Wood Johnson Medical School
Jersey Shore University Medical Center
Robert Wood Johnson University Hospital
St Peter's University Hospital
Prgm Director: Charles J Gatt, MD
PO Box 19, 51 French Street
New Brunswick, NJ 08903
Tel: 732 235-7869 *Fax:* 732 235-6002
Length: 5 Yrs *ACGME Approved/Offered Positions:* 20
Program ID: 260-33-21-149

Note: * indicates a newly appointed program director

Newark

UMDNJ-New Jersey Medical School Program

Sponsor: UMDNJ-New Jersey Medical School
UMDNJ-University Hospital
Prgm Director: Joseph Benevenia, MD
90 Bergen Street, Suite 7300
Newark, NJ 07101
Tel: 973 972-5350   *Fax:* 973 972-1080
E-mail: birthwma@umdnj.edu
Length: 5 Yrs   *ACGME Approved/Offered Positions:* 30
Program ID: 260-33-31-102

South Orange

Seton Hall University School of Health and Medical Sciences Program

Sponsor: Seton Hall University School of Health and Medical Sciences
St Joseph's Regional Medical Center
Prgm Director: Vincent K McInerney, MD
St Joseph's Regional Medical Center
703 Main Street
Paterson, NJ 07503
Tel: 973 754-2926   *Fax:* 973 754-4357
Length: 5 Yrs   *ACGME Approved/Offered Positions:* 10
Program ID: 260-33-12-147

New Mexico

Albuquerque

University of New Mexico Program

Sponsor: University of New Mexico School of Medicine
University of New Mexico Hospital
Veterans Affairs Medical Center (Albuquerque)
Prgm Director: Robert Quinn, MD
MSC10 5600
1 University of New Mexico
Albuquerque, NM 87131
Tel: 505 272-4107   *Fax:* 505 272-8098
E-mail: jroberts@salud.unm.edu
Length: 5 Yrs   *ACGME Approved/Offered Positions:* 25
Program ID: 260-34-31-093

New York

Albany

Albany Medical Center Program

Sponsor: Albany Medical Center
Ellis Hospital
St Peter's Hospital
Veterans Affairs Medical Center (Albany)
Prgm Director: Richard L Uhl, MD
1367 Washington Avenue
Suite 202
Albany, NY 12206
Tel: 518 453-3079   *Fax:* 518 453-1463
E-mail: pangbuk@mail.amc.edu
Length: 5 Yrs   *ACGME Approved/Offered Positions:* 20
Program ID: 260-35-21-055

Bronx

Albert Einstein College of Medicine Program

Sponsor: Albert Einstein College of Medicine of Yeshiva University
Montefiore Medical Center-Henry and Lucy Moses Division
Montefiore Medical Center-Weiler Division
North Bronx Healthcare Network-Jacobi Medical Center
Prgm Director: I Martin Levy, MD
1695 Eastchester Road
2nd Floor
Bronx, NY 10461
Tel: 718 405-8132   *Fax:* 718 405-8135
Length: 5 Yrs   *ACGME Approved/Offered Positions:* 30
Program ID: 260-35-21-187

Brooklyn

Kingsbrook Jewish Medical Center Program

Sponsor: Kingsbrook Jewish Medical Center
St Vincent Catholic Medical Centers (Manhattan)
Prgm Director: Eli Bryk, MD
585 Schenectady Avenue
Brooklyn, NY 11203
Tel: 718 604-5483   *Fax:* 718 604-5575
Length: 5 Yrs   *ACGME Approved/Offered Positions:* 5
Program ID: 260-35-31-185

Maimonides Medical Center Program

Sponsor: Maimonides Medical Center
Prgm Director: Jack Choueka, MD
4802 Tenth Avenue
Brooklyn, NY 11219
Tel: 718 283-7400   *Fax:* 718 283-6199
Length: 5 Yrs   *ACGME Approved/Offered Positions:* 10
Program ID: 260-35-21-107

SUNY Health Science Center at Brooklyn Program

Sponsor: SUNY Health Science Center at Brooklyn
Veterans Affairs Medical Center (Brooklyn)
Brookdale University Hospital and Medical Center
Kings County Hospital Center
Long Island College Hospital
Staten Island University Hospital
Prgm Director: William P Urban Jr, MD
450 Clarkson Avenue
Box 30
Brooklyn, NY 11203
Tel: 718 270-2179   *Fax:* 718 270-3983
E-mail: orthosurg@downstate.edu
Length: 5 Yrs   *ACGME Approved/Offered Positions:* 30
Program ID: 260-35-21-144

Buffalo

University at Buffalo Program

Sponsor: University at Buffalo School of Medicine
Erie County Medical Center
Kaleida Health System (Buffalo General Hospital)
Kaleida Health System (Millard Fillmore Hospital)
Kaleida Health System (Women and Children's Hosp of Buffalo)
University at Buffalo Affiliated Physician Practices (UBAPP)
Prgm Director: Lawrence B Bone, MD
Department of Orthopaedic Surgery
462 Grider Street
Buffalo, NY 14215
Tel: 716 898-4735   *Fax:* 716 898-3323
Length: 5 Yrs   *ACGME Approved/Offered Positions:* 20
Program ID: 260-35-21-024

Great Neck

NSLIJHS-Albert Einstein College of Medicine at Long Island Jewish Medical Center Program

Sponsor: North Shore-Long Island Jewish Health System
Long Island Jewish Medical Center
North Shore University Hospital
Prgm Director: Nicholas A Sgaglione, MD
270-05 76th Avenue
Room 250
New Hyde Park, NY 11040
Tel: 718 470-7020   *Fax:* 718 962-2809
E-mail: jvetrano@lij.edu
Length: 5 Yrs   *ACGME Approved/Offered Positions:* 15
Program ID: 260-35-21-152

Jamaica

New York Medical College (Brooklyn-Queens) Program

Sponsor: New York Medical College
Caritas Health Care (Brooklyn-Queens)
St Vincent Catholic Medical Centers (Manhattan)
Prgm Director: John R Denton, MD
152-11 89th Avenue
Jamaica, NY 11432
Tel: 718 558-7240   *Fax:* 718 558-6181
E-mail: johnrdenton@aol.com
Length: 5 Yrs   *ACGME Approved/Offered Positions:* 15
Program ID: 260-35-21-124

New York

Hospital for Special Surgery/Cornell Medical Center Program

Sponsor: Hospital for Special Surgery
New York Hospital Medical Center of Queens
New York Presbyterian Hospital (Cornell Campus)
Prgm Director: Mathias P Bostrom, MD*
535 East 70th Street
New York, NY 10021
Tel: 212 606-1466
Length: 5 Yrs   *ACGME Approved/Offered Positions:* 40
Program ID: 260-35-21-022

Lenox Hill Hospital Program

Sponsor: Lenox Hill Hospital
Children's Hospital
Prgm Director: Elliott Hershman, MD*
130 East 77th Street
11th Floor
New York, NY 10075
Tel: 212 744-8114
E-mail: pkennemur@lenoxhill.net
Length: 5 Yrs   *ACGME Approved/Offered Positions:* 10
Program ID: 260-35-11-175

Mount Sinai School of Medicine Program

Sponsor: Mount Sinai School of Medicine
Elmhurst Hospital Center-Mount Sinai Services
Mount Sinai Medical Center
Prgm Director: Evan L Flatow, MD*
One Gustave L Levy Place, Box 1188
New York, NY 10029
Tel: 212 241-1621   *Fax:* 212 241-9429
E-mail: Amanda.Mercado@mountsinai.org
Length: 5 Yrs   *ACGME Approved/Offered Positions:* 15
Program ID: 260-35-21-065

New York Presbyterian Hospital (Columbia Campus) Program

Sponsor: New York Presbyterian Hospital
New York Presbyterian Hospital (Columbia Campus)
Prgm Director: William N Levine, MD
Department of Orthopaedic Surgery
622 West 168th Street, Rm PH11
New York, NY 10032
Tel: 212 305-5974   *Fax:* 212 305-6193
Length: 5 Yrs   *ACGME Approved/Offered Positions:* 30
Program ID: 260-35-31-128

Programs

New York University School of Medicine/Hospital for Joint Diseases Program

Sponsor: New York University School of Medicine
Bellevue Hospital Center
Jamaica Hospital Medical Center
NYU Hospital for Joint Diseases
NYU Hospitals Center
Prgm Director: Kenneth A Egol, MD
301 East 17th Street
Room 1402
New York, NY 10003
Tel: 212 598-3889   *Fax:* 212 598-6581
E-mail: kenneth.egol@nyumc.org
Length: 5 Yrs   *ACGME Approved/Offered Positions:* 60
Program ID: 260-35-12-125

St Luke's-Roosevelt Hospital Center Program

Sponsor: St Luke's-Roosevelt Hospital Center
Prgm Director: George L Unis, MD
1111 Amsterdam Avenue
Clark 7 - Room 5-703
New York, NY 10025
Tel: 212 523-2650   *Fax:* 212 523-4676
Length: 5 Yrs   *ACGME Approved/Offered Positions:* 15
Program ID: 260-35-11-041

Rochester

University of Rochester Program

Sponsor: Strong Memorial Hospital of the University of Rochester
Highland Hospital of Rochester
Prgm Director: C McCollister Evarts, MD*
601 Elmwood Avenue, Box 665
Rochester, NY 14642
Tel: 585 275-5168   *Fax:* 585 756-4721
Length: 5 Yrs   *ACGME Approved/Offered Positions:* 30
Program ID: 260-35-21-031

Stony Brook

SUNY at Stony Brook Program

Sponsor: University Hospital - SUNY at Stony Brook
Winthrop-University Hospital
Prgm Director: James Penna, MD
HSC T-18, Room 089
Department of Orthopaedics
Stony Brook, NY 11794
Tel: 631 444-1487   *Fax:* 631 444-3502
Length: 5 Yrs   *ACGME Approved/Offered Positions:* 25
Program ID: 260-35-21-181

Syracuse

SUNY Upstate Medical University Program

Sponsor: SUNY Upstate Medical University
Crouse Hospital
Veterans Affairs Medical Center (Syracuse)
Prgm Director: Stephen A Albanese, MD
750 East Adams Street
Syracuse, NY 13210
Tel: 315 464-5226   *Fax:* 315 464-6470
Length: 5 Yrs   *ACGME Approved/Offered Positions:* 20
Program ID: 260-35-21-048

Valhalla

New York Medical College at Westchester Medical Center Program

Sponsor: New York Medical College
Westchester Medical Center
St Vincent Catholic Medical Centers (Manhattan)
Prgm Director: David E Asprinio, MD
95 Grasslands Road/Macy Pavilion Room 008
Orthopaedic Surgery
Valhalla, NY 10595
Tel: 914 493-8743   *Fax:* 914 493-1230
E-mail: orthsurg@nymc.edu
Length: 5 Yrs   *ACGME Approved/Offered Positions:* 15
Program ID: 260-35-21-067

North Carolina

Chapel Hill

University of North Carolina Hospitals Program

Sponsor: University of North Carolina Hospitals
Wake Medical Center
Prgm Director: Edmund R Campion, MD
3144 Bioinformatics, CB7055
Chapel Hill, NC 27599
Tel: 919 966-9066   *Fax:* 919 966-6730
Length: 5 Yrs   *ACGME Approved/Offered Positions:* 25
Program ID: 260-36-21-081

Charlotte

Carolinas Medical Center Program

Sponsor: Carolinas Medical Center
Prgm Director: Steven L Frick, MD
PO Box 32861
1616 Scott Ave
Charlotte, NC 28203
Tel: 704 355-3184   *Fax:* 704 355-6041
Length: 5 Yrs   *ACGME Approved/Offered Positions:* 15
Program ID: 260-36-22-104

Durham

Duke University Hospital Program

Sponsor: Duke University Hospital
Children's Healthcare of Atlanta
Durham Regional Hospital
Shriners Hospitals for Children (Greenville)
Veterans Affairs Medical Center (Asheville)
Veterans Affairs Medical Center (Durham)
Prgm Director: William T Hardaker Jr, MD
Division of Orthopaedic Surgery
Box 3956
Durham, NC 27710
Tel: 919 684-3170   *Fax:* 919 681-7672
E-mail: wendy.thompson@duke.edu
Length: 5 Yrs   *ACGME Approved/Offered Positions:* 40
Program ID: 260-36-31-019

Winston-Salem

Wake Forest University School of Medicine Program

Sponsor: Wake Forest University Baptist Medical Center
Prgm Director: Ethan R Wiesler, MD
Medical Center Boulevard, Box 1070
Winston-Salem, NC 27157
Tel: 336 716-3946   *Fax:* 336 716-3861
Length: 5 Yrs   *ACGME Approved/Offered Positions:* 20
Program ID: 260-36-21-077

Ohio

Akron

Akron General Medical Center/NEOUCOM Program

Sponsor: Akron General Medical Center
Children's Hospital Medical Center of Akron
Prgm Director: Mark C Leeson, MD
400 Wabash Avenue 224/430
Akron, OH 44307
Tel: 330 344-6055   *Fax:* 330 996-2973
E-mail: kwalsh@agmc.org
Length: 5 Yrs   *ACGME Approved/Offered Positions:* 15
Program ID: 260-38-21-058

Summa Health System/NEOUCOM Program

Sponsor: Summa Health System
Akron City Hospital (Summa Health System)
Children's Hospital Medical Center of Akron
Prgm Director: Jeffrey T Junko, MD*
444 North Main Street
PO Box 2090
Akron, OH 44309
Tel: 330 379-5681   *Fax:* 330 379-5053
E-mail: labatep@summa-health.org
Length: 5 Yrs   *ACGME Approved/Offered Positions:* 15
Program ID: 260-38-21-015

Cincinnati

University Hospital/University of Cincinnati College of Medicine Program

Sponsor: University Hospital Inc
Cincinnati Children's Hospital Medical Center
Veterans Affairs Medical Center (Cincinnati)
Prgm Director: Keith Kenter, MD, MS
231 Albert Sabin Way
PO Box 670212
Cincinnati, OH 45267
Tel: 513 558-4592   *Fax:* 513 558-2220
E-mail: Kenterk@ucmail.uc.edu
Length: 5 Yrs   *ACGME Approved/Offered Positions:* 25
Program ID: 260-38-21-017

Cleveland

Cleveland Clinic Foundation Program

Sponsor: Cleveland Clinic Foundation
Prgm Director: Thomas E Kuivila, MD
9500 Euclid Avenue, A41
Cleveland, OH 44195
Tel: 216 444-2741   *Fax:* 216 445-3585
Length: 5 Yrs   *ACGME Approved/Offered Positions:* 30
Program ID: 260-38-22-042

University Hospitals Case Medical Center Program

Sponsor: University Hospitals Case Medical Center
MetroHealth Medical Center
Veterans Affairs Medical Center (Cleveland)
Prgm Director: Randall E Marcus, MD
11100 Euclid Avenue
Cleveland, OH 44106
Tel: 216 844-3040   *Fax:* 216 844-5970
E-mail: egreenberger@msn.com
Length: 5 Yrs   *ACGME Approved/Offered Positions:* 30
Program ID: 260-38-21-027

Note: * indicates a newly appointed program director

Columbus

Mount Carmel Program
Sponsor: Mount Carmel
Grant Medical Center (OhioHealth)
Nationwide Children's Hospital
Prgm Director: Richard A Fankhauser, MD
793 West State Street
MSB 3rd Floor
Columbus, OH 43222
Tel: 614 234-5354   *Fax:* 614 234-2772
Length: 5 Yrs   *ACGME Approved/Offered Positions:* 10
Program ID: 260-38-32-025

Ohio State University Hospital Program
Sponsor: Ohio State University Hospital
Nationwide Children's Hospital
Riverside Methodist Hospitals (OhioHealth)
Prgm Director: Laura Phieffer, MD
Department of Orthopaedics
N1050 Doan Hall / 410 W 10th Ave
Columbus, OH 43210
Tel: 614 293-6194   *Fax:* 614 293-3596
E-mail: panzo.6@osu.edu
Length: 5 Yrs   *ACGME Approved/Offered Positions:* 30
Program ID: 260-38-21-099

Dayton

Wright State University Program
Sponsor: Wright State University Boonshoft School of
Medicine
Children's Medical Center
Miami Valley Hospital
Prgm Director: Richard T Laughlin, MD
30 E Apple Street, Suite 2200
Dayton, OH 45409
Tel: 937 208-2127   *Fax:* 937 208-2920
Length: 5 Yrs   *ACGME Approved/Offered Positions:* 20
Program ID: 260-38-21-105

Toledo

University of Toledo Program
Sponsor: University of Toledo
St Vincent Mercy Medical Center
University Medical Center (Toledo)
Prgm Director: Nabil A Ebraheim, MD
3065 Arlington Avenue
Suite 2435
Toledo, OH 43614
Tel: 419 383-4020   *Fax:* 419 383-3526
Length: 5 Yrs   *ACGME Approved/Offered Positions:* 20
Program ID: 260-38-31-176

Oklahoma

Oklahoma City

University of Oklahoma Health Sciences Center Program
Sponsor: University of Oklahoma College of Medicine
McBride Clinic Orthopedic Hospital
OU Medical Center
Veterans Affairs Medical Center (Oklahoma City)
Prgm Director: Charles B Pasque, MD
PO Box 26901
Suite WP-1380
Oklahoma City, OK 73126
Tel: 405 271-4426   *Fax:* 405 271-3461
Length: 5 Yrs   *ACGME Approved/Offered Positions:* 25
Program ID: 260-39-21-053

Oregon

Portland

Oregon Health & Science University Program
Sponsor: Oregon Health & Science University Hospital
Legacy Emanuel Hospital and Health Center
Veterans Affairs Medical Center (Portland)
Prgm Director: Robert A Hart, MD*
Mail Code Ortho - OP-31
3181 SW Sam Jackson Park Road
Portland, OR 97239
Tel: 503 494-5842   *Fax:* 503 494-5050
Length: 5 Yrs   *ACGME Approved/Offered Positions:* 20
Program ID: 260-40-21-028

Pennsylvania

Bethlehem

St Luke's Hospital Program
Sponsor: St Luke's Hospital
Prgm Director: William G DeLong Jr, MD
801 Ostrum Street
Bethlehem, PA 18015
Tel: 610 954-2369   *Fax:* 610 954-1593
E-mail: mccarte@slhn.org
Length: 5 Yrs   *ACGME Approved/Offered Positions:* 10
Program ID: 260-41-21-212

Danville

Geisinger Health System Program
Sponsor: Geisinger Health System
Geisinger Medical Center
Prgm Director: Gary D Harter, MD
Department of Orthopaedic Surgery
100 N Academy Avenue
Danville, PA 17822
Tel: 570 271-6541   *Fax:* 570 271-5872
Length: 5 Yrs   *ACGME Approved/Offered Positions:* 10
Program ID: 260-41-22-155

Erie

Hamot Medical Center Program
Sponsor: Hamot Medical Center
Shriners Hospitals for Children (Erie)
Prgm Director: John D Lubahn, MD
201 State Street
Erie, PA 16550
Tel: 814 877-6257   *Fax:* 814 877-4010
E-mail: pat.rogers@hamot.org
Length: 5 Yrs   *ACGME Approved/Offered Positions:* 15
Program ID: 260-41-22-156

Hershey

Penn State University/Milton S Hershey Medical Center Program
Sponsor: Milton S Hershey Medical Center
Prgm Director: Paul J Juliano, MD
Penn State Orthopaedics, MC H089
30 Hope Drive, Building A, EC089
Hershey, PA 17033
Tel: 717 531-4833   *Fax:* 717 531-0498
E-mail: orthoresidency@hmc.psu.edu
Length: 5 Yrs   *ACGME Approved/Offered Positions:* 20
Program ID: 260-41-21-151

Philadelphia

Albert Einstein Healthcare Network Program
Sponsor: Albert Einstein Medical Center
Prgm Director: Eric A Williams, MD
5501 Old York Road
WCB4
Philadelphia, PA 19141
Tel: 215 456-6051   *Fax:* 215 324-2426
E-mail: pietrzas@einstein.edu
Length: 5 Yrs   *ACGME Approved/Offered Positions:* 10
Program ID: 260-41-11-157

Drexel University College of Medicine/Hahnemann University Hospital Program
Sponsor: Drexel University College of
Medicine/Hahnemann University
Abington Memorial Hospital
Hahnemann University Hospital (Tenet Health System)
St Christopher's Hospital for Children (Tenet Health
System)
Prgm Director: Stephen J Bosacco, MD
Department of Orthopaedic Surgery
245 N 15th Street, MS 420
Philadelphia, PA 19102
Tel: 215 762-8168   *Fax:* 215 762-3442
Length: 5 Yrs   *ACGME Approved/Offered Positions:* 20
Program ID: 260-41-21-026

Temple University Hospital Program
Sponsor: Temple University Hospital
Abington Memorial Hospital
Prgm Director: Joseph J Thoder, MD
Broad & Ontario Streets
3401 N Broad Street
Philadelphia, PA 19140
Tel: 215 707-8331   *Fax:* 215 707-3520
E-mail: marianne.kilbride@tuhs.temple.edu
Length: 5 Yrs   *ACGME Approved/Offered Positions:* 20
Program ID: 260-41-21-029

Thomas Jefferson University Program
Sponsor: Thomas Jefferson University Hospital
Bryn Mawr Hospital
Prgm Director: James J Purtill, MD
1015 Walnut Street
Room 801 Curtis Building
Philadelphia, PA 19107
Tel: 215 955-1500   *Fax:* 215 503-0530
Length: 5 Yrs   *ACGME Approved/Offered Positions:* 30
Program ID: 260-41-21-021

University of Pennsylvania Program
Sponsor: University of Pennsylvania Health System
Children's Hospital of Philadelphia
Pennsylvania Hospital (UPHS)
Presbyterian Medical Center (UPHS)
Veterans Affairs Medical Center (Philadelphia)
Prgm Director: Richard D Lackman, MD
3400 Spruce Street
2 Silverstein
Philadelphia, PA 19104
Tel: 215 662-3350   *Fax:* 215 349-5890
E-mail: richard.lackman@uphs.upenn.edu
Length: 5 Yrs   *ACGME Approved/Offered Positions:* 40
Program ID: 260-41-21-023

Pittsburgh

Allegheny General Hospital Program
Sponsor: Allegheny General Hospital
Prgm Director: Mark E Baratz, MD
1307 Federal Street
Pittsburgh, PA 15212
Tel: 412 359-6501   *Fax:* 412 359-6285
Length: 5 Yrs   *ACGME Approved/Offered Positions:* 15
Program ID: 260-41-21-201

Programs

University of Pittsburgh Medical Center Medical Education Program
Sponsor: Univ of Pittsburgh Medical Center Medical Education
Children's Hospital of Pittsburgh of UPMC
UPMC Presbyterian Shadyside
UPMC South Side
Veterans Affairs Medical Center (Pittsburgh)
Prgm Director: Vincent F Deeney, MD
3471 Fifth Avenue, Suite 1000
Pittsburgh, PA 15213
Tel: 412 605-3262   *Fax:* 412 687-3724
E-mail: moenichrj@upmc.edu
Length: 5 Yrs   *ACGME Approved/Offered Positions:* 40
Program ID: 260-41-21-030

Puerto Rico
San Juan
University of Puerto Rico Program
Sponsor: University of Puerto Rico School of Medicine
I Gonzalez Martinez Oncologic Hospital
San Juan City Hospital
University Hospital
University Pediatric Hospital
VA Caribbean Healthcare System
Prgm Director: Manuel Garcia-Ariz, MD
PO Box 365067
San Juan, PR 00936
Tel: 787 764-5095   *Fax:* 787 620-0714
E-mail: clrivera@rcm.upr.edu
Length: 5 Yrs   *ACGME Approved/Offered Positions:* 20
Program ID: 260-42-21-161

Rhode Island
Providence
Brown University Program
Sponsor: Rhode Island Hospital-Lifespan
Miriam Hospital-Lifespan
Veterans Affairs Medical Center (Providence)
Prgm Director: Christopher DiGiovannni, MD*
593 Eddy Street
Coop 1st Floor
Providence, RI 02903
Tel: 401 444-6351   *Fax:* 401 444-6994
E-mail: Christopher_DiGiovanni@brown.edu
Length: 5 Yrs   *ACGME Approved/Offered Positions:* 30
Program ID: 260-43-11-162

South Carolina
Charleston
Medical University of South Carolina Program
Sponsor: Medical University of South Carolina College of Medicine
MUSC Medical Center
Ralph H Johnson VA Medical Center (Charleston)
Prgm Director: John A Glaser, MD
96 Jonathan Lucas St, CSB 708
PO Box 250622
Charleston, SC 29425
Tel: 843 792-0601   *Fax:* 843 792-3674
E-mail: tuckerc@musc.edu
Length: 5 Yrs   *ACGME Approved/Offered Positions:* 15
Program ID: 260-45-21-052

Columbia
Palmetto Health/University of South Carolina School of Medicine Program
Sponsor: Palmetto Health
Palmetto Health Richland
William Jennings Bryan Dorn Veterans Hospital
Prgm Director: David E Koon Jr, MD, BS
Two Medical Park, Suite 404
Columbia, SC 29203
Tel: 803 434-6879   *Fax:* 803 434-7306
E-mail: david.koon@uscmed.sc.edu
Length: 5 Yrs   *ACGME Approved/Offered Positions:* 10
Program ID: 260-45-31-163

Greenville
Greenville Hospital System/University of South Carolina School of Medicine Program
Sponsor: Greenville Hospital System/University of South Carolina
Prgm Director: Kyle J Jeray, MD
Department of Orthopaedic Surgery
701 Grove Road, 2nd Floor Support Tower
Greenville, SC 29605
Tel: 864 455-7878   *Fax:* 864 455-7082
E-mail: fnelson@ghs.org
Length: 5 Yrs   *ACGME Approved/Offered Positions:* 20
Program ID: 260-45-21-033

Tennessee
Chattanooga
University of Tennessee College of Medicine at Chattanooga Program
Sponsor: University of Tennessee College of Medicine-Chattanooga
Erlanger Medical Center
T C Thompson Children's Hospital Medical Center
Prgm Director: William M Tew, MD
Department of Orthopaedic Surgery
975 E 3rd Street, Hospital Box 260
Chattanooga, TN 37403
Tel: 423 778-9008   *Fax:* 423 778-9009
E-mail: william.tew@erlanger.org
Length: 5 Yrs   *ACGME Approved/Offered Positions:* 15
Program ID: 260-47-11-164

Memphis
University of Tennessee Program
Sponsor: University of Tennessee College of Medicine
Campbell Clinics & Surgery Center
LeBonheur Children's Medical Center
Methodist Healthcare - Memphis Hospitals
Regional Medical Center at Memphis
Veterans Affairs Medical Center (Memphis)
Prgm Director: Frederick M Azar, MD
1211 Union Avenue, Suite 510
Memphis, TN 38104
Tel: 901 759-3275   *Fax:* 901 759-3278
E-mail: scoffill@utmem.edu
Length: 5 Yrs   *ACGME Approved/Offered Positions:* 40
Program ID: 260-47-21-061

Nashville
Vanderbilt University Program
Sponsor: Vanderbilt University Medical Center
Veterans Affairs Medical Center (Nashville)
Prgm Director: Herbert S Schwartz, MD
1215 21st Avenue South
MCE South Tower, Suite 4200
Nashville, TN 37232
Tel: 615 322-8890   *Fax:* 615 343-1028
Length: 5 Yrs   *ACGME Approved/Offered Positions:* 25
Program ID: 260-47-11-116

Texas
Dallas
University of Texas Southwestern Medical School Program
Sponsor: University of Texas Southwestern Medical School
Dallas County Hospital District-Parkland Memorial Hospital
Dallas VA Medical Center
Texas Scottish Rite Hospital for Children
Prgm Director: Joseph Borrelli, Jr, MD*
5323 Harry Hines Boulevard
Dallas, TX 75390
Tel: 214 645-3337   *Fax:* 214 645-3350
E-mail: joseph.borrelli@utsouthwestern.edu
Length: 5 Yrs   *ACGME Approved/Offered Positions:* 30
Program ID: 260-48-21-032

El Paso
William Beaumont Army Medical Center/Texas Tech University (El Paso) Program
Sponsor: William Beaumont Army Medical Center
Shriners Hospitals for Children (Spokane)
St Joseph's Hospital and Medical Center
Texas Tech University Hlth Sci Ctr Paul L Foster Sch of Med
University of Utah Medical Center
Prgm Director: Philip J Belmont Jr, MD, BS
5005 North Piedras Street
El Paso, TX 79920
Tel: 915 569-2288   *Fax:* 915 569-3382
E-mail: philip.belmont@us.army.mil
Length: 5 Yrs   *ACGME Approved/Offered Positions:* 20
Program ID: 260-48-21-198
Uniformed Services Program

Fort Sam Houston
San Antonio Uniformed Services Health Education Consortium (BAMC) Program
Sponsor: San Antonio Uniformed Services Health Education Consortium
Brooke Army Medical Center
University of Texas Health Science Center
Prgm Director: Tad L Gerlinger, MD*
Orthopaedic Surgery Service
3851 Roger Brooke Drive
Fort Sam Houston, TX 78234
Tel: 210 916-3410
Length: 5 Yrs   *ACGME Approved/Offered Positions:* 20
Program ID: 260-48-32-117
Uniformed Services Program

Fort Worth
John Peter Smith Hospital (Tarrant County Hospital District) Program
Sponsor: John Peter Smith Hospital (Tarrant County Hospital District)
Cook Children's Medical Center
Prgm Director: Russell A Wagner, MD
1500 South Main Street
Fort Worth, TX 76104
Tel: 817 927-1370   *Fax:* 817 927-3955
E-mail: rwagner@jpshealthnetwork.org
Length: 5 Yrs   *ACGME Approved/Offered Positions:* 20
Program ID: 260-48-22-100

Note: * indicates a newly appointed program director

Galveston

University of Texas Medical Branch Hospitals Program

Sponsor: University of Texas Medical Branch Hospitals
Prgm Director: Kelly D Carmichael, MD
301 University Boulevard
Galveston, TX 77555
Tel: 409 747-5727   *Fax:* 409 747-5704
E-mail: kdcarmic@utmb.edu
Length: 5 Yrs   *ACGME Approved/Offered Positions:* 25
Program ID: 260-48-21-165

Houston

Baylor College of Medicine Program

Sponsor: Baylor College of Medicine
Harris County Hospital District-Ben Taub General
  Hospital
Michael E DeBakey VA Medical Center - Houston
St Luke's Episcopal Hospital
Texas Children's Hospital
Prgm Director: John V Marymont, MD, MBA
Dept of Orthopedic Surgery
1709 Dryden Road, 12th Floor
Houston, TX 77030
Tel: 713 986-7390   *Fax:* 713 986-7391
Length: 5 Yrs   *ACGME Approved/Offered Positions:* 25
Program ID: 260-48-31-049

University of Texas at Houston Program

Sponsor: University of Texas Health Science Center at
  Houston
Lyndon B Johnson General Hospital
Memorial Hermann Hospital
Methodist Hospital (Houston)
Prgm Director: William C McGarvey, MD
6431 Fannin St, MSB 6.142
Houston, TX 77030
Tel: 713 500-7012   *Fax:* 713 500-6999
E-mail: kristey.tedder@uth.tmc.edu
Length: 5 Yrs   *ACGME Approved/Offered Positions:* 15
Program ID: 260-48-21-166

Lackland AFB

San Antonio Uniformed Services Health Education Consortium (WHMC) Program

Sponsor: San Antonio Uniformed Services Health
  Education Consortium
Wilford Hall Medical Center (AETC)
University Health System
Prgm Director: Craig R Ruder, MD
2200 Bergquist Drive, Suite 1
Lackland AFB, TX 78236
Tel: 210 292-5875   *Fax:* 210 292-5844
Length: 5 Yrs   *ACGME Approved/Offered Positions:* 20
Program ID: 260-48-31-120
Uniformed Services Program

Lubbock

Texas Tech University (Lubbock) Program

Sponsor: Texas Tech University Health Sciences Center
  at Lubbock
University Medical Center
Prgm Director: George W Brindley, MD
3601 4th Street Stop 9436
Lubbock, TX 79430
Tel: 806 743-2465   *Fax:* 806 743-1020
E-mail: christy.morrison@ttuhsc.edu
Length: 5 Yrs   *ACGME Approved/Offered Positions:* 15
Program ID: 260-48-31-160

San Antonio

University of Texas Health Science Center at San Antonio Program

Sponsor: University of Texas School of Medicine at San
  Antonio
Audie L Murphy Memorial Veterans Hospital (San
  Antonio)
Christus Santa Rosa Health Care Corporation
Methodist Healthcare
University Health System
Prgm Director: Daniel W Carlisle, MD
7703 Floyd Curl Drive
MC-7774
San Antonio, TX 78229
Tel: 210 567-5125   *Fax:* 210 567-5167
Length: 5 Yrs   *ACGME Approved/Offered Positions:* 30
Program ID: 260-48-31-095

Temple

Texas A&M College of Medicine-Scott and White Program

Sponsor: Scott and White Memorial Hospital
Prgm Director: Mark D Rahm, MD
2401 South 31st Street
Temple, TX 76508
Tel: 254 724-5455   *Fax:* 254 724-0764
Length: 5 Yrs   *ACGME Approved/Offered Positions:* 20
Program ID: 260-48-21-171

Utah

Salt Lake City

University of Utah Program

Sponsor: University of Utah Medical Center
Prgm Director: Alan Stotts, MD
590 Wakara Way
Salt Lake City, UT 84108
Tel: 801 587-5448   *Fax:* 801 587-5411
E-mail: alan.stotts@hsc.utah.edu
Length: 5 Yrs   *ACGME Approved/Offered Positions:* 25
Program ID: 260-49-31-034

Vermont

Burlington

University of Vermont Program

Sponsor: Fletcher Allen Health Care
Prgm Director: Claude E Nichols III, MD
Dept of Orthopaedics and Rehab
440 Stafford Building
Burlington, VT 05405
Tel: 802 656-2250   *Fax:* 802 656-4247
Length: 5 Yrs   *ACGME Approved/Offered Positions:* 15
Program ID: 260-50-11-167

Virginia

Charlottesville

University of Virginia Program

Sponsor: University of Virginia Medical Center
Carilion Roanoke Memorial Hospital
Prgm Director: Bobby Chhabra, MD, BA
PO Box 800159
Charlottesville, VA 22908
Tel: 434 243-0218   *Fax:* 434 243-0290
Length: 5 Yrs   *ACGME Approved/Offered Positions:* 25
Program ID: 260-51-21-129

Portsmouth

Naval Medical Center (Portsmouth) Program

Sponsor: Naval Medical Center (Portsmouth)
Prgm Director: Robert T Ruland, MD
620 John Paul Jones Circle
Portsmouth, VA 23708
Tel: 757 953-1886   *Fax:* 757 952-1908
E-mail: robert.ruland@med.navy.mil
Length: 5 Yrs   *ACGME Approved/Offered Positions:* 20
Program ID: 260-51-12-130
Uniformed Services Program

Richmond

Virginia Commonwealth University Health System Program

Sponsor: Virginia Commonwealth University Health
  System
Bon Secours St Mary's Hospital
Hunter Holmes McGuire VA Medical Center (Richmond)
Medical College of Virginia Hospitals
Prgm Director: Wilhelm A Zuelzer, MD
1200 E Broad Street
PO Box 980153
Richmond, VA 23298
Tel: 804 827-1204   *Fax:* 804 827-1728
E-mail: orthoresprog@vcu.edu
Length: 5 Yrs   *ACGME Approved/Offered Positions:* 25
Program ID: 260-51-21-035

Washington

Seattle

University of Washington Program

Sponsor: University of Washington School of Medicine
Harborview Medical Center
Seattle Children's Hospital
University of Washington Medical Center
VA Puget Sound Health Care System
Prgm Director: Douglas P Hanel, MD
Department of Orthopaedics Campus Box 354743
4245 Roosevelt Way NE, Ste E110
Seattle, WA 98105
Tel: 206 598-9960   *Fax:* 206 598-9979
E-mail: dhanel@u.washington.edu
Length: 5 Yrs   *ACGME Approved/Offered Positions:* 40
Program ID: 260-54-21-036

Tacoma

Madigan Army Medical Center Program

Sponsor: Madigan Army Medical Center
Harborview Medical Center
Prgm Director: Paul L Benfanti, MD
Attn: MCHJ-SOP
Orthopaedic Surgery Service
Tacoma, WA 98431
Tel: 253 968-3180   *Fax:* 253 968-1586
Length: 5 Yrs   *ACGME Approved/Offered Positions:* 15
Program ID: 260-54-32-178
Uniformed Services Program

Programs

West Virginia

Huntington

Marshall University School of Medicine Program
Sponsor: Marshall University School of Medicine
Cabell Huntington Hospital
Prgm Director: Ali Oliashirazi, MD
1600 Medical Center Drive
Suite G-500
Huntington, WV 25701
Tel: 304 691-1274
Length: 5 Yrs   *ACGME Approved/Offered Positions:* 15
Program ID: 260-55-13-205

Morgantown

West Virginia University Program
Sponsor: West Virginia University School of Medicine
Cincinnati Children's Hospital Medical Center
West Virginia University Hospitals
Prgm Director: Sanford E Emery, MD, MBA
Department of Orthopaedics
PO Box 9196
Morgantown, WV 26506
Tel: 304 293-1168   *Fax:* 304 293-0231
E-mail: cthompson@hsc.wvu.edu
Length: 5 Yrs   *ACGME Approved/Offered Positions:* 15
Program ID: 260-55-21-169

Wisconsin

Madison

University of Wisconsin Program
Sponsor: University of Wisconsin Hospital and Clinics
Meriter Hospital
Prgm Director: Matthew W Squire, MD, MS*
K/7 Clinical Science Center
600 Highland Avenue
Madison, WI 53792
Tel: 608 263-0888   *Fax:* 608 263-9458
E-mail: larsonl@orthorehab.wisc.edu
Length: 5 Yrs   *ACGME Approved/Offered Positions:* 25
Program ID: 260-56-21-097

Milwaukee

Medical College of Wisconsin Affiliated Hospitals Program
Sponsor: Medical College of Wisconsin Affiliated
   Hospitals, Inc
Children's Hospital of Wisconsin
Clement J Zablocki Veterans Affairs Medical Center
Froedtert Memorial Lutheran Hospital
Prgm Director: Gregory J Schmeling, MD
MCW Orthopaedics
9200 W Wisconsin Ave
Milwaukee, WI 53226
Tel: 414 805-7436   *Fax:* 414 805-7499
Length: 5 Yrs   *ACGME Approved/Offered Positions:* 25
Program ID: 260-56-21-037

Orthopaedic Surgery of the Spine (Orthopaedic Surgery)

Florida

Miami

Jackson Memorial Hospital/Jackson Health System Program
Sponsor: Jackson Memorial Hospital/Jackson Health
   System
Prgm Director: Frank J Eismont, MD
PO Box 016960 (D-27)
Dept of Orthopaedics
Miami, FL 33101
Tel: 305 585-7138   *Fax:* 305 324-7658
Length: 1 Yr   *ACGME Approved/Offered Positions:* 1
Program ID: 267-11-21-004

Illinois

Chicago

Rush University Medical Center Program
Sponsor: Rush University Medical Center
Shriners Hospitals for Children (Chicago)
Prgm Director: Howard S An, MD
1653 West Congress Parkway
Room 1471, Jelke Building
Chicago, IL 60612
Tel: 312 942-5850   *Fax:* 312 942-2101
E-mail: Beverly_Kendall-Morgan@rush.edu
Length: 1 Yr   *ACGME Approved/Offered Positions:* 3
Program ID: 267-16-21-015

Maryland

Baltimore

University of Maryland Program
Sponsor: University of Maryland Medical System
Veterans Affairs Medical Center (Baltimore)
Prgm Director: Steven C Ludwig, MD
22 South Greene Street
S11B
Baltimore, MD 21201
Tel: 410 328-6040   *Fax:* 410 328-0534
Length: 1 Yr   *ACGME Approved/Offered Positions:* 1
Program ID: 267-23-13-029

Massachusetts

Boston

Beth Israel Deaconess Medical Center/Harvard Medical School Program
Sponsor: Beth Israel Deaconess Medical Center
Prgm Director: Kevin J McGuire, MD, MS
330 Brookline Avenue, Stoneman 10
Boston, MA 02215
Tel: 617 667-2140   *Fax:* 617 667-2155
Length: 1 Yr   *ACGME Approved/Offered Positions:* 1
Program ID: 267-24-21-028

Michigan

Royal Oak

William Beaumont Hospital Program
Sponsor: William Beaumont Hospital
Prgm Director: Jeffrey S Fischgrund, MD
3535 West 13 Mile Road, #744
Royal Oak, MI 48073
Tel: 248 551-0426   *Fax:* 248 551-5404
E-mail: cmusich@beaumonthospitals.com
Length: 1 Yr   *ACGME Approved/Offered Positions:* 2
Program ID: 267-25-21-007

Minnesota

Minneapolis

Twin Cities Spine Center Program
Sponsor: Twin Cities Spine Center
Prgm Director: Ensor E Transfeldt, MD
913 East 26th Street
Suite 600
Minneapolis, MN 55404
Tel: 612 775-6200   *Fax:* 612 775-6222
E-mail: education@tcspine.com
Length: 1 Yr   *ACGME Approved/Offered Positions:* 5
Program ID: 267-26-21-010

Missouri

St Louis

Washington University/B-JH/SLCH Consortium Program
Sponsor: Washington University/B-JH/SLCH Consortium
Barnes-Jewish Hospital
Prgm Director: Keith H Bridwell, MD
Barnes-Jewish Hospital Spine Fellowship
660 S Euclid Avenue, Campus Box 8233
St Louis, MO 63110
Tel: 314 747-2536   *Fax:* 314 747-2600
Length: 1 Yr   *ACGME Approved/Offered Positions:* 4
Program ID: 267-28-21-016

New York

New York

Hospital for Special Surgery/Cornell Medical Center Program
Sponsor: Hospital for Special Surgery
Prgm Director: James Farmer, MD*
535 East 70th Street
New York, NY 10021
Tel: 212 606-1466   *Fax:* 212 606-1477
E-mail: academictraining@hss.edu
Length: 1 Yr   *ACGME Approved/Offered Positions:* 5
Program ID: 267-35-21-022

New York University School of Medicine/Hospital for Joint Diseases Program
Sponsor: New York University School of Medicine
NYU Hospital for Joint Diseases
NYU Hospitals Center
Prgm Director: Thomas J Errico, MD
301 East 17th Street, Room 1402
New York, NY 10003
Tel: 212 263-7182   *Fax:* 212 263-7180
Length: 1 Yr   *ACGME Approved/Offered Positions:* 3
Program ID: 267-35-21-011

Note: * indicates a newly appointed program director

Syracuse

SUNY Upstate Medical University Program
Sponsor: SUNY Upstate Medical University
Prgm Director: Stephen A Albanese, MD
550 Harrison Street
Syracuse, NY 13202
Tel: 315 464-5226   *Fax:* 315 464-6470
E-mail: bordeauj@upstate.edu
Length: 1 Yr   *ACGME Approved/Offered Positions:* 1
Program ID: 267-35-11-019

Ohio

Cincinnati

Cincinnati Children's Hospital Medical Center Program
Sponsor: Cincinnati Children's Hospital Medical Center
Christ Hospital
University of Cincinnati College of Medicine
Prgm Director: A Atiq Durrani, MD
Division of Pediatric Orthopaedic Surgery
3333 Burnet Avenue, MLC 2017
Cincinnati, OH 45229
Tel: 513 636-1383   *Fax:* 513 636-3928
E-mail: janis.messer@cchmc.org
Length: 1 Yr   *ACGME Approved/Offered Positions:* 2
Program ID: 267-38-12-027

Texas

Plano

Texas Back Institute Program
Sponsor: Texas Back Institute Research Foundation
Baylor Medical Center of Frisco
Denton Regional Medical Center
Denton Surgicare (Baylor Surgical of Denton)
Medical Center of Plano
North Texas Hospital
Presbyterian Hospital of Plano
Presbyterian Hospital of Rockwall
Presbyterian Plano Center for Diagnostics and Surgery
Texas Back Institute (Clinical Site)
Prgm Director: Richard Guyer, MD
6020 West Park Road
Suite 200
Plano, TX 75093
Tel: 972 608-5038   *Fax:* 972 608-5137
E-mail: rguyer@texasback.com
Length: 1 Yr   *ACGME Approved/Offered Positions:* 5
Program ID: 267-48-31-030

Virginia

Charlottesville

University of Virginia Program
Sponsor: University of Virginia Medical Center
Prgm Director: Mark F Abel, MD*
Department of Orthopaedic Surgery
PO Box 800159
Charlottesville, VA 22908
Tel: 434 243-0250
E-mail: mcf3f@virginia.edu
Length: 1 Yr   *ACGME Approved/Offered Positions:* 1
Program ID: 267-51-21-024

Orthopaedic Trauma (Orthopaedic Surgery)

Maryland

Baltimore

University of Maryland Program
Sponsor: University of Maryland Medical System
Prgm Director: Andrew N Pollak, MD
22 South Greene Street
Room T3R57
Baltimore, MD 21201
Tel: 410 328-8915   *Fax:* 410 328-0534
E-mail: apollak@umoa.umm.edu
Length: 1 Yr   *ACGME Approved/Offered Positions:* 4
Program ID: 269-23-21-008

New Jersey

Camden

UMDNJ-Robert Wood Johnson Medical School (Camden) Program
Sponsor: Cooper Hospital-University Medical Center
Prgm Director: Robert F Ostrum, MD
1 Cooper Plaza
Camden, NJ 08103
Tel: 856 968-7845
E-mail: ostrum-robert@cooperhealth.edu
Length: 1 Yr   *ACGME Approved/Offered Positions:* 1
Program ID: 269-33-21-013

New Mexico

Albuquerque

University of New Mexico Program
Sponsor: University of New Mexico School of Medicine
University of New Mexico Hospital
Prgm Director: Thomas A DeCoster, MD
Dept of Orthopaedics, MSC10 5600
1 University of New Mexico
Albuquerque, NM 87131
Tel: 505 272-4107   *Fax:* 505 272-8098
E-mail: jroberts@salud.unm.edu
Length: 1 Yr   *ACGME Approved/Offered Positions:* 1
Program ID: 269-34-13-010

New York

New York

Hospital for Special Surgery/Cornell Medical Center Program
Sponsor: Hospital for Special Surgery
Westchester Medical Center
Prgm Director: David L Helfet, MD
Department of Orthopaedic Surgery
535 East 70th Street
New York, NY 10021
Tel: 212 606-1888
E-mail: academictraining@hss.edu
Length: 1 Yr   *ACGME Approved/Offered Positions:* 3
Program ID: 269-35-12-012

North Carolina

Charlotte

Carolinas Medical Center Program
Sponsor: Carolinas Medical Center
Prgm Director: James F Kellam, MD
PO Box 32861
Charlotte, NC 28232
Tel: 704 355-6046   *Fax:* 704 355-7902
Length: 1 Yr   *ACGME Approved/Offered Positions:* 2
Program ID: 269-36-21-001

Ohio

Toledo

University of Toledo Program
Sponsor: University of Toledo
St Vincent Mercy Medical Center
University Medical Center (Toledo)
Prgm Director: Nabil A Ebraheim, MD
3065 Arlington Avenue
Toledo, OH 43614
Tel: 419 383-4020   *Fax:* 419 383-3526
Length: 1 Yr   *ACGME Approved/Offered Positions:* 2
Program ID: 269-38-21-007

Virginia

Richmond

Virginia Commonwealth University Health System Program
Sponsor: Virginia Commonwealth University Health System
Virginia Commonwealth University School of Medicine
Prgm Director: Mark C Willis Jr, MD
1200 E Broad Street
PO Box 980153
Richmond, VA 23298
Tel: 804 827-1332   *Fax:* 804 827-1728
E-mail: orthoresprog@vcu.edu
Length: 1 Yr   *ACGME Approved/Offered Positions:* 1
Program ID: 269-51-21-009

Programs

Otolaryngology

Alabama

Birmingham

University of Alabama Medical Center Program

Sponsor: University of Alabama Hospital
Children's Hospital of Alabama
University of Alabama at Birmingham/Highlands
Veterans Affairs Medical Center (Birmingham)
Prgm Director: Jeffery S Magnuson, MD
Boshell Diabetes Building Suite 563
1530 3rd Avenue South
Birmingham, AL 35294
Tel: 205 934-9766 *Fax:* 205 934-3993
E-mail: michelle.dickerson@ccc.uab.edu
Length: 5 Yrs *ACGME Approved/Offered Positions:* 15
Program ID: 280-01-21-010

Arizona

Phoenix

College of Medicine, Mayo Clinic (Arizona) Program

Sponsor: College of Medicine, Mayo Clinic
Mayo Clinic Hospital
Prgm Director: Michael L Hinni, MD
5777 East Mayo Boulevard
Phoenix, AZ 85054
Tel: 480 342-2812 *Fax:* 480 342-2170
E-mail: cummings.annette@mayo.edu
Length: 5 Yrs *ACGME Approved/Offered Positions:* 10
Program ID: 280-03-31-134

Arkansas

Little Rock

University of Arkansas for Medical Sciences Program

Sponsor: University of Arkansas College of Medicine
Arkansas Children's Hospital
Central Arkansas Veterans Healthcare System
UAMS Medical Center
Prgm Director: Samuel B Welch, MD, PhD*
4301 West Markham, Slot 543
Little Rock, AR 72205
Tel: 501 603-1214 *Fax:* 501 686-8029
E-mail: welchsamuelb@uams.edu
Length: 5 Yrs *ACGME Approved/Offered Positions:* 15
Program ID: 280-04-21-012

California

Loma Linda

Loma Linda University Program

Sponsor: Loma Linda University Medical Center
Jerry L Pettis Memorial Veterans Hospital
Riverside County Regional Medical Center
Prgm Director: Mark R Rowe, MD
11234 Anderson Street
Room 2586-A
Loma Linda, CA 92354
Tel: 909 558-8558 *Fax:* 909 558-4819
E-mail: tfoster@llu.edu
Length: 5 Yrs *ACGME Approved/Offered Positions:* 10
Program ID: 280-05-21-117

Note: * indicates a newly appointed program director

Los Angeles

UCLA Medical Center Program

Sponsor: UCLA David Geffen School of Medicine/UCLA
   Medical Center
Los Angeles County-Harbor-UCLA Medical Center
Olive View/UCLA Medical Center
UCLA Medical Center
VA Greater Los Angeles Healthcare System
Prgm Director: Gerald S Berke, MD
10833 Le Conte Avenue
CHS 62-132
Los Angeles, CA 90095
Tel: 310 825-5179 *Fax:* 310 206-1393
E-mail: gberke@mednet.ucla.edu
Length: 5 Yrs *ACGME Approved/Offered Positions:* 25
Program ID: 280-05-21-017

University of Southern California/ LAC+USC Medical Center Program

Sponsor: University of Southern California/LAC+USC
   Medical Center
LAC+USC Medical Center
USC University Hospital
Prgm Director: Uttam Sinha, MD, MS
Otolaryngology - Head and Neck Surgery
1200 N State Street, Room 4136
Los Angeles, CA 90033
Tel: 323 226-7315 *Fax:* 323 226-2780
E-mail: sinha@usc.edu
Length: 5 Yrs *ACGME Approved/Offered Positions:* 20
Program ID: 280-05-21-015

Oakland

Kaiser Permanente Medical Group (Northern California) Program

Sponsor: Kaiser Permanente Medical Group (Northern
   California)
Kaiser Permanente Medical Center (Oakland)
Kaiser Permanente Medical Center (Redwood City)
Kaiser Permanente Medical Center (San Francisco)
Prgm Director: Raul M Cruz, MD
280 W MacArthur Blvd
11th Floor, Medical Education Dept
Oakland, CA 94611
Tel: 510 752-6401 *Fax:* 510 752-7032
E-mail: kristen.strange@kp.org
Length: 5 Yrs *ACGME Approved/Offered Positions:* 10
Program ID: 280-05-22-020

Orange

University of California (Irvine) Program

Sponsor: University of California (Irvine) Medical
   Center
Children's Hospital of Orange County
Kaiser Foundation Hospitals (Anaheim)
VA Long Beach Healthcare System
Prgm Director: William B Armstrong, MD
Building 56, Suite 500, Rt 81
101 City Drive South
Orange, CA 92868
Tel: 714 456-5753 *Fax:* 714 456-5747
Length: 5 Yrs *ACGME Approved/Offered Positions:* 12
Program ID: 280-05-21-014

Sacramento

University of California (Davis) Health System Program

Sponsor: University of California (Davis) Health System
University of California (Davis) Medical Center
VA Northern California Health Care System
Prgm Director: Craig W Senders, MD
Department of Otolaryngology - HNS
2521 Stockton Boulevard, Suite 7200
Sacramento, CA 95817
Tel: 916 734-5332 *Fax:* 916 703-5011
Length: 5 Yrs *ACGME Approved/Offered Positions:* 15
Program ID: 280-05-21-013

San Diego

Naval Medical Center (San Diego) Program

Sponsor: Naval Medical Center (San Diego)
Kaiser Foundation Hospital (San Diego)
Prgm Director: Craig L Cupp, MD, EdD
Department of Otolaryngology-Head & Neck Surgery
34800 Bob Wilson Drive
San Diego, CA 92134
Tel: 619 532-9604 *Fax:* 619 532-5400
Length: 5 Yrs *ACGME Approved/Offered Positions:* 10
Program ID: 280-05-11-007
Uniformed Services Program

University of California (San Diego) Program

Sponsor: University of California (San Diego) Medical
   Center
Kaiser Foundation Hospital (San Diego)
Veterans Affairs Medical Center (San Diego)
Prgm Director: Deborah Watson, MD
200 W Arbor Drive #8895
San Diego, CA 92103
Tel: 858 642-3405 *Fax:* 858 552-7466
Length: 5 Yrs *ACGME Approved/Offered Positions:* 10
Program ID: 280-05-21-021

San Francisco

University of California (San Francisco) Program

Sponsor: University of California (San Francisco) School
   of Medicine
San Francisco General Hospital Medical Center
UCSF and Mount Zion Medical Centers
Veterans Affairs Medical Center (San Francisco)
Prgm Director: Andrew H Murr, MD
Otolaryngology - Head & Neck Surgery
400 Parnassus Avenue, Room A-730
San Francisco, CA 94143
Tel: 415 476-4952 *Fax:* 415 502-6437
E-mail: cdunne@ohns.ucsf.edu
Length: 5 Yrs *ACGME Approved/Offered Positions:* 15
Program ID: 280-05-21-022

Stanford

Stanford University Program

Sponsor: Stanford Hospital and Clinics
Lucile Salter Packard Children's Hospital at Stanford
Santa Clara Valley Medical Center
Veterans Affairs Palo Alto Health Care System
Prgm Director: Anna H Messner, MD
Department of Otolaryngology/Head & Neck Surgery
801 Welch Road
Stanford, CA 94305
Tel: 650 736-1455 *Fax:* 650 725-8502
E-mail: amessner@ohns.stanford.edu
Length: 5 Yrs *ACGME Approved/Offered Positions:* 20
Program ID: 280-05-21-023

Colorado

Aurora

University of Colorado Denver Program
Sponsor: University of Colorado Denver School of
  Medicine
Children's Hospital (The)
Denver Health Medical Center
University of Colorado Hospital
Veterans Affairs Medical Center (Denver)
Prgm Director: Mona M Abaza, MD
12631 E 17th Ave, B-205
PO Box 6511
Aurora, CO 80045
Tel: 303 724-1957   *Fax:* 303 724-1961
E-mail: alicia.gore@ucdenver.edu
Length: 5 Yrs   *ACGME Approved/Offered Positions:* 15
Program ID: 280-07-21-024

Connecticut

Farmington

University of Connecticut Program
Sponsor: University of Connecticut School of Medicine
Connecticut Children's Medical Center
Hartford Hospital
Hospital for Central Connecticut
St Francis Hospital and Medical Center
Univ of Connecticut Health Center/John Dempsey
  Hospital
Prgm Director: Gerald Leonard, MD
263 Farmington Avenue
Farmington, CT 06030
Tel: 860 679-3372   *Fax:* 860 679-8892
E-mail: thorp@nso.uchc.edu
Length: 5 Yrs   *ACGME Approved/Offered Positions:* 10
Program ID: 280-08-21-025

New Haven

Yale-New Haven Medical Center Program
Sponsor: Yale-New Haven Hospital
Hospital of St Raphael
Veterans Affairs Medical Center (West Haven)
Prgm Director: Dianne C Duffey, MD*
Department of Surgery, Section of Otolaryngology
333 Cedar Street, PO Box 208041
New Haven, CT 06520
Tel: 203 737-5199   *Fax:* 203 785-3970
Length: 5 Yrs   *ACGME Approved/Offered Positions:* 10
Program ID: 280-08-21-026

District of Columbia

Washington

George Washington University Program
Sponsor: George Washington University School of
  Medicine
Children's National Medical Center
George Washington University Hospital (UHS)
Holy Cross Hospital of Silver Spring
Inova Fairfax Hospital
Prgm Director: Steven A Bielamowicz, MD
2150 Pennsylvania Avenue, 6-301
Washington, DC 20037
Tel: 202 741-3260   *Fax:* 202 741-3218
E-mail: surmbn@gwumc.edu
Length: 5 Yrs   *ACGME Approved/Offered Positions:* 8
Program ID: 280-10-21-130

Georgetown University Hospital Program
Sponsor: Georgetown University Hospital
Veterans Affairs Medical Center (Washington, DC)
Washington Hospital Center
Prgm Director: Kenneth A Newkirk, MD*
3800 Reservoir Road, NW
1st Floor Gorman Building
Washington, DC 20007
Tel: 202 444-7078   *Fax:* 202 444-1312
Length: 5 Yrs   *ACGME Approved/Offered Positions:* 15
Program ID: 280-10-32-027

Florida

Gainesville

University of Florida Program
Sponsor: University of Florida College of Medicine
North Florida/South Georgia Veterans Health System
Shands Hospital at the University of Florida
Prgm Director: Patrick J Antonelli, MD, MS*
Box 100264
1600 SW Archer Road, Rm M2-228
Gainesville, FL 32610
Tel: 352 273-5199   *Fax:* 352 392-6781
Length: 5 Yrs   *ACGME Approved/Offered Positions:* 12
Program ID: 280-11-21-028

Miami

Jackson Memorial Hospital/Jackson Health System Program
Sponsor: Jackson Memorial Hospital/Jackson Health
  System
Bascom Palmer Eye Institute-Anne Bates Leach Eye
  Hospital
University of Miami Hospital
University of Miami Hospital and Clinics
Prgm Director: Donald T Weed, MD
Department of Otolaryngology D-48
PO BOX 016960
Miami, FL 33101
Tel: 305 243-9095   *Fax:* 305 326-7610
E-mail: epye@med.miami.edu
Length: 5 Yrs   *ACGME Approved/Offered Positions:* 15
Program ID: 280-11-21-029

Tampa

University of South Florida Program
Sponsor: University of South Florida College of Medicine
All Children's Hospital
H Lee Moffitt Cancer Center
James A Haley Veterans Hospital
Tampa General Hospital
Prgm Director: Kestutis Paul Boyev, MD
12901 Bruce B Downs Blvd, MDC 73
Tampa, FL 33612
Tel: 813 974-7036   *Fax:* 813 974-7314
E-mail: casanova@hsc.usf.edu
Length: 5 Yrs   *ACGME Approved/Offered Positions:* 10
Program ID: 280-11-31-030

Georgia

Atlanta

Emory University Program
Sponsor: Emory University School of Medicine
Crawford Long Hospital of Emory University
Emory University Hospital
Grady Health System
Veterans Affairs Medical Center (Atlanta)
Prgm Director: John M DelGaudio, MD
1365-A Clifton Road, NE
Room A2328
Atlanta, GA 30322
Tel: 404 778-5712   *Fax:* 404 778-0073
E-mail: john.delgaudio@emoryhealthcare.org
Length: 5 Yrs   *ACGME Approved/Offered Positions:* 15
Program ID: 280-12-21-031

Augusta

Medical College of Georgia Program
Sponsor: Medical College of Georgia
Veterans Affairs Medical Center (Augusta)
Prgm Director: Stil Kountakis, MD, PhD
Department of OTO-HNS
1120 Fifteenth St BP-4109
Augusta, GA 30912
Tel: 706 721-6100   *Fax:* 706 721-0112
E-mail: hoandrews@mcg.edu
Length: 5 Yrs   *ACGME Approved/Offered Positions:* 10
Program ID: 280-12-21-032

Hawaii

Tripler AMC

Tripler Army Medical Center Program
Sponsor: Tripler Army Medical Center
Prgm Director: Joseph C Sniezek, MD, BS
Attn: MCHK-DSH
1 Jarrett White Road
Tripler AMC, HI 96859
Tel: 808 433-3170   *Fax:* 808 433-9033
E-mail: joseph.sniezek@amedd.army.mil
Length: 5 Yrs   *ACGME Approved/Offered Positions:* 8
Program ID: 280-14-11-116
Uniformed Services Program

Illinois

Chicago

McGaw Medical Center of Northwestern University Program
Sponsor: McGaw Medical Center of Northwestern
  University
Evanston Hospital
John H Stroger Hospital of Cook County
Northwestern Memorial Hospital
Prgm Director: Alan G Micco, MD
676 N St Clair Street
13th Floor, Suite 1325
Chicago, IL 60611
Tel: 312 695-8140
E-mail: oto-hns@northwestern.edu
Length: 5 Yrs   *ACGME Approved/Offered Positions:* 15
Program ID: 280-16-21-033

Rush University Medical Center Program
Sponsor: Rush University Medical Center
Prgm Director: David D Caldarelli, MD
1653 W Congress Parkway
Chicago, IL 60612
Tel: 312 942-6303   *Fax:* 312 942-7925
E-mail: dianne_noibi@rush.edu
Length: 5 Yrs   *ACGME Approved/Offered Positions:* 5
Program ID: 280-16-21-034

University of Chicago Program

Sponsor: University of Chicago Medical Center
Prgm Director: Robert M Naclerio, MD
Section of Otolaryngology (MC 1035)
5841 S Maryland Avenue, RM E102
Chicago, IL 60637
Tel: 773 702-0080   *Fax:* 773 702-9813
Length: 5 Yrs   *ACGME Approved/Offered Positions:* 10
Program ID: 280-16-21-035

University of Illinois College of Medicine at Chicago Program

Sponsor: University of Illinois College of Medicine at Chicago
Children's Memorial Hospital
Jesse Brown Veterans Affairs Medical Center
John H Stroger Hospital of Cook County
University of Illinois Hosp-Illinois Eye and Ear Infirmary
Prgm Director: Thomas J Haberkamp, MD*
1855 W Taylor Street
Suite 242, M/C 648
Chicago, IL 60612
Tel: 312 996-6582   *Fax:* 312 996-4910
E-mail: stapes@uic.edu
Length: 5 Yrs   *ACGME Approved/Offered Positions:* 20
Program ID: 280-16-21-036

Maywood

Loyola University Program

Sponsor: Loyola University Medical Center
Edward Hines, Jr Veterans Affairs Hospital
Prgm Director: Sam Marzo, MD
2160 S First Avenue
Room 1870/105
Maywood, IL 60153
Tel: 708 216-8526   *Fax:* 708 216-4834
E-mail: smarzo@lumc.edu
Length: 5 Yrs   *ACGME Approved/Offered Positions:* 15
Program ID: 280-16-31-037

Springfield

Southern Illinois University Program

Sponsor: Southern Illinois University School of Medicine
Memorial Medical Center
St John's Hospital
Prgm Director: James P Malone, MD*
301 N Eighth Street
PO Box 19662
Springfield, IL 62794
Tel: 217 545-5140   *Fax:* 217 545-7781
Length: 5 Yrs   *ACGME Approved/Offered Positions:* 10
Program ID: 280-16-21-118

Indiana

Indianapolis

Indiana University School of Medicine Program

Sponsor: Indiana University School of Medicine
Clarian Indiana University Hospital
Clarian Riley Hospital for Children
Richard L Roudebush Veterans Affairs Medical Center
William N Wishard Memorial Hospital
Prgm Director: Richard T Miyamoto, MD, MS
699 West Drive, RR 132
Indianapolis, IN 46202
Tel: 317 278-1259   *Fax:* 317 278-3743
Length: 5 Yrs   *ACGME Approved/Offered Positions:* 15
Program ID: 280-17-21-038

Iowa

Iowa City

University of Iowa Hospitals and Clinics Program

Sponsor: University of Iowa Hospitals and Clinics
Prgm Director: Richard J Smith, MD
200 Hawkins Drive, 21151 PFP
Iowa City, IA 52242
Tel: 319 356-2173   *Fax:* 319 356-3967
Length: 5 Yrs   *ACGME Approved/Offered Positions:* 25
Program ID: 280-18-21-039

Kansas

Kansas City

University of Kansas School of Medicine Program

Sponsor: University of Kansas School of Medicine
St Luke's Hospital-Kansas City
Truman Medical Center
University of Kansas Hospital
Veterans Affairs Medical Center (Kansas City)
Prgm Director: Robert A Weatherly, MD*
3901 Rainbow Blvd
Mailstop 3010
Kansas City, KS 66160
Tel: 913 588-6739   *Fax:* 913 588-4676
E-mail: pcranmore@kumc.edu
Length: 5 Yrs   *ACGME Approved/Offered Positions:* 15
Program ID: 280-19-31-040

Kentucky

Lexington

University of Kentucky College of Medicine Program

Sponsor: University of Kentucky College of Medicine
University of Kentucky Hospital
Prgm Director: Raleigh O Jones Jr, MD, MBA
Otolaryngology - Head & Neck Surgery
800 Rose Street, Room C236
Lexington, KY 40536
Tel: 859 257-5097   *Fax:* 859 257-5096
Length: 5 Yrs   *ACGME Approved/Offered Positions:* 7
Program ID: 280-20-21-127

Louisville

University of Louisville Program

Sponsor: University of Louisville School of Medicine
Kosair Children's Hospital (Norton Healthcare, Inc)
Norton Hospital
University of Louisville Hospital
Veterans Affairs Medical Center (Louisville)
Prgm Director: Jeffrey M Bumpous, MD, BS
University of Louisville Medical Center
529 South Jackson Street, Third Floor
Louisville, KY 40202
Tel: 502 561-7268   *Fax:* 502 561-7280
E-mail: ent@louisville.edu
Length: 5 Yrs   *ACGME Approved/Offered Positions:* 7
Program ID: 280-20-21-041

Louisiana

New Orleans

Louisiana State University Program

Sponsor: Louisiana State University School of Medicine
Earl K Long Medical Center
Our Lady of the Lake Regional Medical Center
University Medical Center (Lafayette)
Prgm Director: Anna Maria Pou, MD
Department of Otolaryngology
533 Bolivar Street, 5th Floor
New Orleans, LA 70112
Tel: 504 568-4785   *Fax:* 504 568-2198
Length: 5 Yrs   *ACGME Approved/Offered Positions:* 15
Program ID: 280-21-31-042

Tulane University Program

Sponsor: Tulane University School of Medicine
Ochsner Clinic Foundation
Tulane University Hospital and Clinics
Veterans Affairs Medical Center (Biloxi)
Prgm Director: Ronald G Amedee, MD
Department of Otolaryngology-Head and Neck Surgery
1430 Tulane Avenue, SL 59
New Orleans, LA 70112
Tel: 504 988-5454   *Fax:* 504 988-7846
E-mail: ramedee@ochsner.org
Length: 5 Yrs   *ACGME Approved/Offered Positions:* 15
Program ID: 280-21-21-043

Shreveport

Louisiana State University (Shreveport) Program

Sponsor: LSU Health Sciences Center-University Hospital
Overton Brooks Veterans Affairs Medical Center
Prgm Director: Timothy S Lian, MD
1501 Kings Highway
Shreveport, LA 71130
Tel: 318 675-6262   *Fax:* 318 675-6260
Length: 5 Yrs   *ACGME Approved/Offered Positions:* 15
Program ID: 280-21-21-121

Maryland

Baltimore

Johns Hopkins University Program

Sponsor: Johns Hopkins University School of Medicine
Greater Baltimore Medical Center
Johns Hopkins Bayview Medical Center
Johns Hopkins Hospital
Prgm Director: Paul W Flint, MD
601 North Caroline Street
Room 6210
Baltimore, MD 21287
Tel: 410 955-1654   *Fax:* 410 955-6526
Length: 5 Yrs   *ACGME Approved/Offered Positions:* 20
Program ID: 280-23-21-047

University of Maryland Program

Sponsor: University of Maryland Medical System
Veterans Affairs Medical Center (Baltimore)
Prgm Director: David J Eisenman, MD*
Department of Otorhinolaryngology-HNS
16 South Eutaw Street, Suite 500
Baltimore, MD 21201
Tel: 410 328-5828   *Fax:* 410 328-5827
E-mail: deisenman@smail.umaryland.edu
Length: 5 Yrs   *ACGME Approved/Offered Positions:* 10
Program ID: 280-23-21-048

Note: * indicates a newly appointed program director

Bethesda

National Capital Consortium Program

Sponsor: National Capital Consortium
National Naval Medical Center (Bethesda)
Walter Reed Army Medical Center
Prgm Director: Martin P Sorensen, MD
Otolaryngology Department
8901 Wisconsin Avenue
Bethesda, MD 20889
Tel: 301 295-4677   *Fax:* 301 295-6666
Length: 5 Yrs   *ACGME Approved/Offered Positions:* 15
Program ID: 280-10-31-132
Uniformed Services Program

Massachusetts

Boston

Boston University Medical Center Program

Sponsor: Boston Medical Center
Lahey Clinic
Veterans Affairs Medical Center (Boston)
Prgm Director: Gregory A Grillone, MD
FGH Building - 820 Harrison Avenue, 4th Floor
Boston, MA 02118
Tel: 617 638-7066   *Fax:* 617 638-7965
E-mail: gregory.grillone@bmc.org
Length: 5 Yrs   *ACGME Approved/Offered Positions:* 15
Program ID: 280-24-31-051

Massachusetts Eye and Ear Infirmary/Harvard Medical School Program

Sponsor: Massachusetts Eye and Ear Infirmary
Beth Israel Deaconess Medical Center
Brigham and Women's Hospital
Prgm Director: Michael J Cunningham, MD
243 Charles Street
Boston, MA 02114
Tel: 617 573-3654   *Fax:* 617 573-3939
Length: 5 Yrs   *ACGME Approved/Offered Positions:* 20
Program ID: 280-24-21-049

Tufts Medical Center Program

Sponsor: Tufts Medical Center
Caritas St Elizabeth's Medical Center of Boston
Rhode Island Hospital-Lifespan
Prgm Director: Richard O Wein, MD*
800 Washington Street
Box 850
Boston, MA 02111
Tel: 617 636-8711   *Fax:* 617 636-1479
Length: 5 Yrs   *ACGME Approved/Offered Positions:* 10
Program ID: 280-24-31-050

Michigan

Ann Arbor

University of Michigan Program

Sponsor: University of Michigan Hospitals and Health Centers
Veterans Affairs Medical Center (Ann Arbor)
Prgm Director: Gregory T Wolf, MD
1500 E Medical Center Drive
1904 Taubman Center
Ann Arbor, MI 48109
Tel: 734 936-8029   *Fax:* 734 647-9691
Length: 5 Yrs   *ACGME Approved/Offered Positions:* 20
Program ID: 280-25-21-052

Detroit

Henry Ford Hospital Program

Sponsor: Henry Ford Hospital
Prgm Director: Mark A Zacharek, MD
2799 West Grand Boulevard
Detroit, MI 48202
Tel: 313 916-3275   *Fax:* 313 916-7263
E-mail: mzachar1@hfhs.org
Length: 5 Yrs   *ACGME Approved/Offered Positions:* 10
Program ID: 280-25-12-053

Wayne State University Program

Sponsor: Wayne State University School of Medicine
Crittenton Hospital Medical Center
Karmanos Cancer Hospital
Oakwood Hospital
Veterans Affairs Medical Center (Detroit)
Prgm Director: Robert H Mathog, MD
4201 St Antoine, 5E-UHC
Detroit, MI 48201
Tel: 313 577-0804   *Fax:* 313 577-8555
Length: 5 Yrs   *ACGME Approved/Offered Positions:* 20
Program ID: 280-25-21-137

Minnesota

Minneapolis

University of Minnesota Program

Sponsor: University of Minnesota Medical School
Hennepin County Medical Center
Regions Hospital
University of Minnesota Medical Center, Division of Fairview
Veterans Affairs Medical Center (Minneapolis)
Prgm Director: Franklin L Rimell, MD, MS
Mayo Mail Code 396
420 Delaware St SE
Minneapolis, MN 55455
Tel: 612 626-0932   *Fax:* 612 625-2101
E-mail: courc002@umn.edu
Length: 5 Yrs   *ACGME Approved/Offered Positions:* 20
Program ID: 280-26-31-055

Rochester

College of Medicine, Mayo Clinic (Rochester) Program

Sponsor: College of Medicine, Mayo Clinic
Mayo Clinic (Rochester)
Rochester Methodist Hospital
Saint Marys Hospital of Rochester
Prgm Director: Eric J Moore, MD
200 First Street, SW
Rochester, MN 55905
Tel: 507 284-3521   *Fax:* 507 538-7926
E-mail: chapman.barbara@mayo.edu
Length: 5 Yrs   *ACGME Approved/Offered Positions:* 20
Program ID: 280-26-21-056

Mississippi

Jackson

University of Mississippi Medical Center Program

Sponsor: University of Mississippi School of Medicine
University Hospitals and Clinics
Veterans Affairs Medical Center (Jackson)
Prgm Director: Christine B Franzese, MD, BS
Dept of Otolaryngology & Communicative Sciences
2500 North State Street
Jackson, MS 39216
Tel: 601 984-6885   *Fax:* 601 984-5085
E-mail: cfranzese@ent.umsmed.edu
Length: 5 Yrs   *ACGME Approved/Offered Positions:* 15
Program ID: 280-27-21-122

Missouri

Columbia

University of Missouri-Columbia Program

Sponsor: University of Missouri-Columbia School of Medicine
Harry S Truman Memorial Veterans Hospital
University Hospitals and Clinics
Prgm Director: C W David Chang, MD*
One Hospital Drive MA314 DC027.00
Columbia, MO 65212
Tel: 573 882-6737   *Fax:* 573 884-4205
E-mail: andersonva@health.missouri.edu
Length: 5 Yrs   *ACGME Approved/Offered Positions:* 11
Program ID: 280-28-21-058

St Louis

St Louis University School of Medicine Program

Sponsor: St Louis University School of Medicine
Cardinal Glennon Children's Hospital
St John's Mercy Medical Center
St Louis University Hospital
Prgm Director: Mark A Varvares, MD*
3635 Vista Avenue, 6FDT
Dept of Otolaryngology - Head and Neck Surgery
St Louis, MO 63110
Tel: 314 577-8887   *Fax:* 314 268-5111
E-mail: varvares@slu.edu
Length: 5 Yrs   *ACGME Approved/Offered Positions:* 10
Program ID: 280-28-21-059

Washington University/B-JH/SLCH Consortium Program

Sponsor: Washington University/B-JH/SLCH Consortium
Barnes-Jewish Hospital
St Louis Children's Hospital
Veterans Affairs Medical Center (St Louis)
Prgm Director: Joel A Goebel, MD
Department of Otolaryngology
660 S Euclid Ave, Campus Box 8115
St Louis, MO 63110
Tel: 314 747-0553   *Fax:* 314 362-7522
Length: 5 Yrs   *ACGME Approved/Offered Positions:* 25
Program ID: 280-28-21-060

Nebraska

Omaha

University of Nebraska Medical Center College of Medicine Program

Sponsor: University of Nebraska Medical Center College of Medicine
Boys Town National Research Hospital
Nebraska Medical Center
Nebraska Methodist Hospital
Veterans Affairs Medical Center (Omaha)
Prgm Director: Barbara M Heywood, MD
981225 Nebraska Medical Center
Omaha, NE 68198
Tel: 402 559-7777   *Fax:* 402 559-8940
E-mail: bheywood@unmc.edu
Length: 5 Yrs   *ACGME Approved/Offered Positions:* 10
Program ID: 280-30-21-061

Programs

New Hampshire

Lebanon

Dartmouth-Hitchcock Medical Center Program

Sponsor: Mary Hitchcock Memorial Hospital
Prgm Director: Daniel H Morrison, Jr, MD
Division of Otolaryngology
One Medical Center Drive
Lebanon, NH 03756
Tel: 603 650-8124   *Fax:* 603 650-7898
Length: 5 Yrs   *ACGME Approved/Offered Positions:* 5
Program ID: 280-32-12-136

New Jersey

Newark

UMDNJ-New Jersey Medical School Program

Sponsor: UMDNJ-New Jersey Medical School
Hackensack University Medical Center
UMDNJ-University Hospital
Veterans Affairs New Jersey Health Care System
Prgm Director: Soly Baredes, MD
90 Bergen Street
Suite 8100
Newark, NJ 07103
Tel: 973 972-4588   *Fax:* 973 972-3767
Length: 5 Yrs   *ACGME Approved/Offered Positions:* 10
Program ID: 280-33-31-062

New Mexico

Albuquerque

University of New Mexico Program

Sponsor: University of New Mexico School of Medicine
Presbyterian Healthcare Services
University of New Mexico Hospital
Veterans Affairs Medical Center (Albuquerque)
Prgm Director: Garth T Olson, MD
Department of Surgery-Otolayngology ACC-2
2211 Lomas Blvd NE
Albuquerque, NM 87131
Tel: 505 272-6451   *Fax:* 505 925-4310
Length: 5 Yrs   *ACGME Approved/Offered Positions:* 5
Program ID: 280-34-21-126

New York

Albany

Albany Medical Center Program

Sponsor: Albany Medical Center
Albany Medical Center South Clinical Campus
St Peter's Hospital
Veterans Affairs Medical Center (Albany)
Prgm Director: Jason Mouzakes, MD*
University ENT
35 Hackett Boulevard, First Floor
Albany, NY 12208
Tel: 518 262-5578   *Fax:* 518 262-5184
Length: 5 Yrs   *ACGME Approved/Offered Positions:* 10
Program ID: 280-35-21-063

Bronx

Albert Einstein College of Medicine Program

Sponsor: Albert Einstein College of Medicine of Yeshiva University
Beth Israel Medical Center
Long Island Jewish Medical Center
Montefiore Medical Center-Henry and Lucy Moses Division
North Bronx Healthcare Network-Jacobi Medical Center
Prgm Director: Marvin P Fried, MD
Medical Arts Pavilion Bldg 3rd Fl
111 East 210th Street
Bronx, NY 10467
Tel: 718 920-2991   *Fax:* 718 405-9014
E-mail: mfried@montefiore.org
Length: 5 Yrs   *ACGME Approved/Offered Positions:* 20
Program ID: 280-35-21-133

Brooklyn

SUNY Health Science Center at Brooklyn Program

Sponsor: SUNY Health Science Center at Brooklyn
Kings County Hospital Center
Long Island College Hospital
University Hospital-SUNY Health Science Center at Brooklyn
Veterans Affairs Medical Center (Brooklyn)
Prgm Director: Frank E Lucente, MD
450 Clarkson Avenue, Box 126
Brooklyn, NY 11203
Tel: 718 270-1638   *Fax:* 718 270-3924
E-mail: frank.lucente@downstate.edu
Length: 5 Yrs   *ACGME Approved/Offered Positions:* 15
Program ID: 280-35-21-123

Buffalo

University at Buffalo Program

Sponsor: University at Buffalo School of Medicine
Erie County Medical Center
Kaleida Health System (Buffalo General Hospital)
Kaleida Health System (Millard Fillmore Hospital)
Kaleida Health System (Women and Children's Hosp of Buffalo)
Roswell Park Cancer Institute
Veterans Affairs Western New York Hospital
Prgm Director: Nestor R Rigual, MD*
Department of Otolaryngology
1237 Delaware Avenue
Buffalo, NY 14209
Tel: 716 845-3158   *Fax:* 716 845-8646
E-mail: nestor.rigual@roswellpark.org
Length: 5 Yrs   *ACGME Approved/Offered Positions:* 10
Program ID: 280-35-13-135

New York

Mount Sinai School of Medicine Program

Sponsor: Mount Sinai School of Medicine
Elmhurst Hospital Center-Mount Sinai Services
Mount Sinai Medical Center
Veterans Affairs Medical Center (Bronx)
Prgm Director: Marita S Teng, MD
Department of Otolaryngology
One Gustave L Levy Place
New York, NY 10029
Tel: 718 334-3391   *Fax:* 718 334-5886
E-mail: marita.teng@mssm.edu
Length: 5 Yrs   *ACGME Approved/Offered Positions:* 20
Program ID: 280-35-21-069

New York Medical College (New York Eye and Ear Infirmary) Program

Sponsor: New York Medical College
New York Eye and Ear Infirmary
Beth Israel Medical Center
St Vincent Catholic Medical Centers (Manhattan)
Westchester Medical Center
Prgm Director: Steven D Schaefer, MD
Department of Otolaryngology
310 East 14th Street
New York, NY 10003
Tel: 212 979-4071   *Fax:* 212 979-4315
E-mail: galexiades@nyee.edu
Length: 5 Yrs   *ACGME Approved/Offered Positions:* 20
Program ID: 280-35-21-072

New York Presbyterian Hospital (Columbia and Cornell Campus) Program

Sponsor: New York Presbyterian Hospital
New York Presbyterian Hospital (Columbia Campus)
New York Presbyterian Hospital (Cornell Campus)
Prgm Director: Lanny G Close, MD
Dept of Otolaryngology/Head & Neck Surgery
630 W 168th Street, Box 21
New York, NY 10032
Tel: 212 305-5820   *Fax:* 212 305-2249
Length: 5 Yrs   *ACGME Approved/Offered Positions:* 20
Program ID: 280-35-11-074

New York University School of Medicine Program

Sponsor: New York University School of Medicine
Bellevue Hospital Center
Lenox Hill Hospital
NYU Hospitals Center
Prgm Director: Richard A Lebowitz, MD
550 First Avenue
New York, NY 10016
Tel: 212 263-7022   *Fax:* 212 263-8257
Length: 5 Yrs   *ACGME Approved/Offered Positions:* 20
Program ID: 280-35-21-073

Rochester

University of Rochester Program

Sponsor: Strong Memorial Hospital of the University of Rochester
Prgm Director: Timothy D Doerr, MD
601 Elmwood Avenue, Box 629
Rochester, NY 14642
Tel: 585 758-5700   *Fax:* 585 758-1293
E-mail: ent@urmc.rochester.edu
Length: 5 Yrs   *ACGME Approved/Offered Positions:* 10
Program ID: 280-35-21-078

Syracuse

SUNY Upstate Medical University Program

Sponsor: SUNY Upstate Medical University
Crouse Hospital
Veterans Affairs Medical Center (Syracuse)
Prgm Director: Robert M Kellman, MD
750 E Adams Street
Syracuse, NY 13210
Tel: 315 464-7281   *Fax:* 315 464-7298
E-mail: guyerm@upstate.edu
Length: 5 Yrs   *ACGME Approved/Offered Positions:* 15
Program ID: 280-35-21-079

Note: * indicates a newly appointed program director

North Carolina

Chapel Hill

University of North Carolina Hospitals Program

Sponsor: University of North Carolina Hospitals
Wake Medical Center
Prgm Director: Amelia F Drake, MD
170 Manning Drive
Phys Office Bldg, Ground Floor, CB 7070
Chapel Hill, NC 27599
Tel: 919 966-3342   *Fax:* 919 966-7941
E-mail: drakeaf@med.unc.edu
Length: 5 Yrs   *ACGME Approved/Offered Positions:* 20
Program ID: 280-36-21-080

Durham

Duke University Hospital Program

Sponsor: Duke University Hospital
Veterans Affairs Medical Center (Durham)
Prgm Director: Liana Puscas, MD
Box 3805
Durham, NC 27710
Tel: 919 681-7367   *Fax:* 919 668-6036
E-mail: Liana.Puscas@duke.edu
Length: 5 Yrs   *ACGME Approved/Offered Positions:* 10
Program ID: 280-36-21-081

Winston-Salem

Wake Forest University School of Medicine Program

Sponsor: Wake Forest University Baptist Medical Center
Prgm Director: Daniel J Kirse, MD, BS
Medical Center Boulevard
Watlington Hall 4th Fl
Winston-Salem, NC 27157
Tel: 336 716-3648   *Fax:* 336 716-3857
E-mail: shorner@wfubmc.edu
Length: 5 Yrs   *ACGME Approved/Offered Positions:* 12
Program ID: 280-36-11-082

Ohio

Cincinnati

University Hospital/University of Cincinnati College of Medicine Program

Sponsor: University Hospital Inc
Cincinnati Children's Hospital Medical Center
Veterans Affairs Medical Center (Cincinnati)
Prgm Director: Charles M Myer III, MD
Mail Location 528
231 Albert Sabin Way
Cincinnati, OH 45267
Tel: 513 636-4356   *Fax:* 513 636-2886
E-mail: charles.myer@cchmc.org
Length: 5 Yrs   *ACGME Approved/Offered Positions:* 20
Program ID: 280-38-21-083

Cleveland

Cleveland Clinic Foundation Program

Sponsor: Cleveland Clinic Foundation
Prgm Director: Peter C Weber, MD
9500 Euclid Avenue, A71
Cleveland, OH 44195
Tel: 216 444-6696   *Fax:* 216 636-1548
Length: 5 Yrs   *ACGME Approved/Offered Positions:* 15
Program ID: 280-38-22-085

University Hospitals Case Medical Center Program

Sponsor: University Hospitals Case Medical Center
MetroHealth Medical Center
Veterans Affairs Medical Center (Cleveland)
Prgm Director: James E Arnold, MD
Otolaryngology- Head & Neck Surgery
11100 Euclid Avenue LKS 5045 RM 4500
Cleveland, OH 44106
Tel: 216 844-5307   *Fax:* 216 844-5727
Length: 5 Yrs   *ACGME Approved/Offered Positions:* 15
Program ID: 280-38-21-124

Columbus

Ohio State University Hospital Program

Sponsor: Ohio State University Hospital
Arthur G James Cancer Hospital and Research Institute
Nationwide Children's Hospital
Prgm Director: L Arick Forrest, MD
Department of Otolaryngology-Head and Neck Surgery
456 W 10th Avenue, Room 4024B Cramblett Hall
Columbus, OH 43210
Tel: 614 293-9215   *Fax:* 614 293-7292
E-mail: eric.dilver@osumc.edu
Length: 5 Yrs   *ACGME Approved/Offered Positions:* 20
Program ID: 280-38-31-087

Oklahoma

Oklahoma City

University of Oklahoma Health Sciences Center Program

Sponsor: University of Oklahoma College of Medicine
OU Medical Center
Veterans Affairs Medical Center (Oklahoma City)
Prgm Director: Greg A Krempl, MD
Department of Otorhinolaryngology
PO Box 26901, WP1290
Oklahoma City, OK 73126
Tel: 405 271-8001   *Fax:* 405 271-3248
Length: 5 Yrs   *ACGME Approved/Offered Positions:* 13
Program ID: 280-39-21-088

Oregon

Portland

Oregon Health & Science University Program

Sponsor: Oregon Health & Science University Hospital
Veterans Affairs Medical Center (Portland)
Prgm Director: Mark K Wax, MD
3181 SW Sam Jackson Park Road PV-01
Portland, OR 97239
Tel: 503 494-4574   *Fax:* 503 494-4631
Length: 5 Yrs   *ACGME Approved/Offered Positions:* 15
Program ID: 280-40-21-089

Pennsylvania

Danville

Geisinger Health System Program

Sponsor: Geisinger Health System
Geisinger Medical Center
Prgm Director: J Scott Greene, MD
100 North Academy Avenue
Danville, PA 17822
Tel: 570 271-6427   *Fax:* 570 271-6854
E-mail: entres@geisinger.edu
Length: 5 Yrs   *ACGME Approved/Offered Positions:* 8
Program ID: 280-41-12-090

Hershey

Penn State University/Milton S Hershey Medical Center Program

Sponsor: Milton S Hershey Medical Center
Prgm Director: Johnathan D McGinn, MD
PO Box 850, MC H091
500 University Drive
Hershey, PA 17033
Tel: 717 531-6718   *Fax:* 717 531-6160
E-mail: eshultz@psu.edu
Length: 5 Yrs   *ACGME Approved/Offered Positions:* 8
Program ID: 280-41-11-091

Philadelphia

Temple University Hospital Program

Sponsor: Temple University Hospital
Abington Memorial Hospital
Fox Chase Cancer Center
St Christopher's Hospital for Children (Tenet Health System)
Prgm Director: Wasyl Szeremeta, MD, MBA
First Floor, Kresge West
3440 North Board Street
Philadelphia, PA 19140
Tel: 215 707-3665   *Fax:* 215 707-7523
Length: 5 Yrs   *ACGME Approved/Offered Positions:* 10
Program ID: 280-41-21-092

Thomas Jefferson University Program

Sponsor: Thomas Jefferson University Hospital
Alfred I duPont Hospital for Children
Prgm Director: Edmund A Pribitkin, MD
925 Chestnut Street
6th Floor
Philadelphia, PA 19107
Tel: 215 955-6784   *Fax:* 215 923-4532
E-mail: Edmund.Pribitkin@jefferson.edu
Length: 5 Yrs   *ACGME Approved/Offered Positions:* 20
Program ID: 280-41-21-093

University of Pennsylvania Program

Sponsor: University of Pennsylvania Health System
Children's Hospital of Philadelphia
Pennsylvania Hospital (UPHS)
Veterans Affairs Medical Center (Philadelphia)
Prgm Director: Michael J Ruckenstein, MD
Dept of Otorhinolaryngology: HNS
3400 Spruce Street, Silverstein Bldg, 5th Floor
Philadelphia, PA 19104
Tel: 215 662-6017   *Fax:* 215 662-4182
E-mail: bonnie.rosen@uphs.upenn.edu
Length: 5 Yrs   *ACGME Approved/Offered Positions:* 20
Program ID: 280-41-21-095

Pittsburgh

University of Pittsburgh Medical Center Medical Education Program

Sponsor: Univ of Pittsburgh Medical Center Medical Education
UPMC Presbyterian Shadyside
Prgm Director: Barry M Schaitkin, MD
200 Lothrop Street
Suite 500
Pittsburgh, PA 15213
Tel: 412 647-4789   *Fax:* 412 648-6300
Length: 5 Yrs   *ACGME Approved/Offered Positions:* 25
Program ID: 280-41-21-096

Programs

Puerto Rico

San Juan

University of Puerto Rico Program
Sponsor: University of Puerto Rico School of Medicine
San Juan City Hospital
University Hospital
VA Caribbean Healthcare System
Prgm Director: Carlos Gonzalez-Aquino, MD
PO Box 365067
San Juan, PR 00936
Tel: 787 765-0240
E-mail: carlosgonzalez@rcm.upr.edu
Length: 5 Yrs   *ACGME Approved/Offered Positions:* 10
Program ID: 280-42-31-098

South Carolina

Charleston

Medical University of South Carolina Program
Sponsor: Medical University of South Carolina College of Medicine
MUSC Medical Center
Ralph H Johnson VA Medical Center (Charleston)
Prgm Director: Ted A Meyer, MD, PhD*
MSC 550
135 Rutledge Avenue, Suite 1117
Charleston, SC 29425
Tel: 843 792-9572   *Fax:* 843 792-0546
E-mail: meyerta@musc.edu
Length: 5 Yrs   *ACGME Approved/Offered Positions:* 15
Program ID: 280-45-21-100

Tennessee

Memphis

University of Tennessee Program
Sponsor: University of Tennessee College of Medicine
Baptist Memorial Hospital
Methodist Healthcare - Memphis Hospitals
Regional Medical Center at Memphis
Veterans Affairs Medical Center (Memphis)
Prgm Director: Jerome W Thompson, MD, MBA
910 Madison Avenue, Room 428
Memphis, TN 38163
Tel: 901 448-8301   *Fax:* 901 448-5120
Length: 5 Yrs   *ACGME Approved/Offered Positions:* 13
Program ID: 280-47-21-101

Nashville

Vanderbilt University Program
Sponsor: Vanderbilt University Medical Center
Veterans Affairs Medical Center (Nashville)
Prgm Director: Brian B Burkey, MD
7209 Medical Center East, South Tower
1215 21st Avenue South
Nashville, TN 37232
Tel: 615 343-6972   *Fax:* 615 343-9725
E-mail: elizabeth.L.warner@vanderbilt.edu
Length: 5 Yrs   *ACGME Approved/Offered Positions:* 20
Program ID: 280-47-21-125

Texas

Dallas

University of Texas Southwestern Medical School Program
Sponsor: University of Texas Southwestern Medical School
Children's Medical Center of Dallas
Dallas County Hospital District-Parkland Memorial Hospital
Dallas VA Medical Center
John Peter Smith Hospital (Tarrant County Hospital District)
University Hospitals Zale Lipshy
Prgm Director: John M Truelson, MD
Dept of Otolaryngology-Head and Neck Surgery
5323 Harry Hines Blvd
Dallas, TX 75390
Tel: 214 648-3706   *Fax:* 214 648-9122
Length: 5 Yrs   *ACGME Approved/Offered Positions:* 20
Program ID: 280-48-21-102

Galveston

University of Texas Medical Branch Hospitals Program
Sponsor: University of Texas Medical Branch Hospitals
Prgm Director: Susan D McCammon, MD
John Sealy Annex 7104
301 University Boulevard
Galveston, TX 77555
Tel: 409 772-9932   *Fax:* 409 772-1715
E-mail: sdmccamm@utmb.edu
Length: 5 Yrs   *ACGME Approved/Offered Positions:* 15
Program ID: 280-48-11-103

Houston

Baylor College of Medicine Program
Sponsor: Baylor College of Medicine
Harris County Hospital District-Ben Taub General Hospital
Methodist Hospital (Houston)
Michael E DeBakey VA Medical Center - Houston
Texas Children's Hospital
University of Texas M D Anderson Cancer Center
Prgm Director: Masayoshi Takashima, MD*
One Baylor Plaza
NA-102
Houston, TX 77030
Tel: 713 798-7217
Length: 5 Yrs   *ACGME Approved/Offered Positions:* 25
Program ID: 280-48-31-104

University of Texas at Houston Program
Sponsor: University of Texas Health Science Center at Houston
Lyndon B Johnson General Hospital
Memorial Hermann Hospital
University of Texas M D Anderson Cancer Center
Prgm Director: Samer Fakhri, MD
6431 Fannin St., MSB 5.036
Houston, TX 77030
Tel: 713 500-5412   *Fax:* 713 383-3727
E-mail: samer.fakhri@uth.tmc.edu
Length: 5 Yrs   *ACGME Approved/Offered Positions:* 15
Program ID: 280-48-21-105

Lackland AFB

San Antonio Uniformed Services Health Education Consortium Program
Sponsor: San Antonio Uniformed Services Health Education Consortium
Audie L Murphy Memorial Veterans Hospital (San Antonio)
Brooke Army Medical Center
Carl R Darnall Army Medical Center
Wilford Hall Medical Center (AETC)
Prgm Director: COL Joseph A Brennan, MD
59 MDW/SG02O, Dept of Otolaryngology
2200 Bergquist Drive, Ste 1
Lackland AFB, TX 78236
Tel: 210 292-7075   *Fax:* 210 292-5621
E-mail: Joseph.Brennan@lackland.af.mil
Length: 5 Yrs   *ACGME Approved/Offered Positions:* 15
Program ID: 280-48-21-131
Uniformed Services Program

San Antonio

University of Texas Health Science Center at San Antonio Program
Sponsor: University of Texas School of Medicine at San Antonio
Audie L Murphy Memorial Veterans Hospital (San Antonio)
Christus Santa Rosa Health Care Corporation
Methodist Healthcare
University Health System
Prgm Director: Kevin C McMains, MD*
7703 Floyd Curl Drive, MC-7777
San Antonio, TX 78229
Tel: 210 567-5655   *Fax:* 210 567-3617
E-mail: mcmains@uthscsa.edu
Length: 5 Yrs   *ACGME Approved/Offered Positions:* 10
Program ID: 280-48-21-106

Utah

Salt Lake City

University of Utah Program
Sponsor: University of Utah Medical Center
LDS Hospital
Primary Children's Medical Center
Veterans Affairs Medical Center (Salt Lake City)
Prgm Director: Steven R Mobley, MD*
50 N Medical Drive
Room 3C120
Salt Lake City, UT 84132
Tel: 801 585-5223   *Fax:* 801 585-5744
E-mail: carlene.brennan@hsc.utah.edu
Length: 5 Yrs   *ACGME Approved/Offered Positions:* 15
Program ID: 280-49-21-107

Vermont

Burlington

University of Vermont Program
Sponsor: Fletcher Allen Health Care
Mary Hitchcock Memorial Hospital
Prgm Director: William J Brundage, MD
Fletcher Allen Health Care, ACC, West Pavilion 4
111 Colchester Avenue
Burlington, VT 05401
Tel: 802 847-4041   *Fax:* 802 847-8198
E-mail: william.brundage@vtmednet.org
Length: 5 Yrs   *ACGME Approved/Offered Positions:* 5
Program ID: 280-50-11-108

Note: * indicates a newly appointed program director

Virginia

Charlottesville

University of Virginia Program
Sponsor: University of Virginia Medical Center
Prgm Director: Bradley W Kesser, MD*
PO Box 800713
Charlottesville, VA 22908
Tel: 434 924-2040 *Fax:* 434 982-3965
E-mail: bwk2n@virginia.edu
Length: 5 Yrs *ACGME Approved/Offered Positions:* 15
Program ID: 280-51-21-109

Norfolk

Eastern Virginia Medical School Program
Sponsor: Eastern Virginia Medical School
Children's Hospital of the King's Daughters
Sentara Norfolk General Hospital
Prgm Director: John T Sinacori, MD
Department of Otolaryngology
600 Gresham Drive, Suite 1100 - River Pavilion
Norfolk, VA 23507
Tel: 757 388-6200 *Fax:* 757 624-2264
E-mail: corbussm@evms.edu
Length: 5 Yrs *ACGME Approved/Offered Positions:* 13
Program ID: 280-51-21-110

Portsmouth

Naval Medical Center (Portsmouth) Program
Sponsor: Naval Medical Center (Portsmouth)
Sentara Norfolk General Hospital
Prgm Director: William P Magdycz Jr, MD
Otolaryngology/Head & Neck Surgery Dept
620 John Paul Jones Circle
Portsmouth, VA 23708
Tel: 757 953-2831 *Fax:* 757 953-0166
E-mail: william.magdycz@med.navy.mil
Length: 5 Yrs *ACGME Approved/Offered Positions:* 10
Program ID: 280-51-21-120
Uniformed Services Program

Richmond

Virginia Commonwealth University Health System Program
Sponsor: Virginia Commonwealth University Health
  System
Hunter Holmes McGuire VA Medical Center (Richmond)
Medical College of Virginia Hospitals
Prgm Director: Evan R Reiter, MD
PO Box 980146
1201 E Marshall St, Ste 401
Richmond, VA 23298
Tel: 804 828-2766 *Fax:* 804 828-5779
E-mail: ent@vcu.edu
Length: 5 Yrs *ACGME Approved/Offered Positions:* 10
Program ID: 280-51-21-111

Washington

Seattle

University of Washington Program
Sponsor: University of Washington School of Medicine
Harborview Medical Center
Seattle Children's Hospital
University of Washington Medical Center
VA Puget Sound Health Care System
Prgm Director: Mark Whipple, MD
1959 NE Pacific Street, Rm BB 1165
Box 356515
Seattle, WA 98195
Tel: 206 685-3961 *Fax:* 206 543-5152
Length: 5 Yrs *ACGME Approved/Offered Positions:* 15
Program ID: 280-54-21-112

Tacoma

Madigan Army Medical Center Program
Sponsor: Madigan Army Medical Center
Virginia Mason Medical Center
Prgm Director: Douglas M Sorensen, MD
Attn: MCHJ-SET
Otolaryngology Service
Tacoma, WA 98431
Tel: 253 968-1420 *Fax:* 253 968-3154
E-mail: sorensendm@amedd.army.mil
Length: 5 Yrs *ACGME Approved/Offered Positions:* 10
Program ID: 280-54-31-005
Uniformed Services Program

West Virginia

Morgantown

West Virginia University Program
Sponsor: West Virginia University School of Medicine
Louis A Johnson Veterans Affairs Medical Center
West Virginia University Hospitals
Prgm Director: Stephen J Wetmore, MD, MBA
Health Sciences Center S, Rm 2222
PO Box 9200
Morgantown, WV 26506
Tel: 304 293-3233 *Fax:* 304 293-2902
Length: 5 Yrs *ACGME Approved/Offered Positions:* 15
Program ID: 280-55-11-113

Wisconsin

Madison

University of Wisconsin Program
Sponsor: University of Wisconsin Hospital and Clinics
William S Middleton Veterans Hospital
Prgm Director: G Mark Pyle, MD
Otolaryngology - Head & Neck Surgery
600 Highland Avenue K4/719
Madison, WI 53792
Tel: 608 265-0494 *Fax:* 608 252-0926
E-mail: oto-hns@surgery.wisc.edu
Length: 5 Yrs *ACGME Approved/Offered Positions:* 13
Program ID: 280-56-21-114

Milwaukee

Medical College of Wisconsin Affiliated Hospitals Program
Sponsor: Medical College of Wisconsin Affiliated
  Hospitals, Inc
Children's Hospital of Wisconsin
Clement J Zablocki Veterans Affairs Medical Center
Froedtert Memorial Lutheran Hospital
Prgm Director: Thomas M Kidder, MD
Department of Otolaryngology and Communication
Sciences
9200 West Wisconsin Avenue
Milwaukee, WI 53226
Tel: 414 805-5584 *Fax:* 414 805-7890
E-mail: dschact@mcw.edu
Length: 5 Yrs *ACGME Approved/Offered Positions:* 15
Program ID: 280-56-21-115

Pain Medicine

Alabama

Birmingham

University of Alabama Medical Center Program
Sponsor: University of Alabama Hospital
University of Alabama at Birmingham/Highlands
Prgm Director: Peter A Nagi, MD
845 Jefferson Tower
619 19th Street South
Birmingham, AL 35249
Tel: 205 934-6501 *Fax:* 205 996-7272
E-mail: kamara@uab.edu
Length: 1 Yr *ACGME Approved/Offered Positions:* 3
Program ID: 530-01-04-094

Arizona

Phoenix

College of Medicine, Mayo Clinic (Arizona) Program
Sponsor: College of Medicine, Mayo Clinic
Mayo Clinic Hospital
Mayo Clinic (Arizona)
Prgm Director: David P Seamans, MD
5777 East Mayo Boulevard
Phoenix, AZ 85054
Tel: 480 342-1272 *Fax:* 480 342-2319
E-mail: rubin.cindy@mayo.edu
Length: 1 Yr *ACGME Approved/Offered Positions:* 1
Program ID: 530-03-04-106

California

Loma Linda

Loma Linda University Program
Sponsor: Loma Linda University Medical Center
Jerry L Pettis Memorial Veterans Hospital
Prgm Director: Lowell W Reynolds, MD
11406 Loma Linda Drive
Ste 516
Loma Linda, CA 92354
Tel: 909 558-6202 *Fax:* 909 558-6110
E-mail: lreynolds@llu.edu
Length: 1 Yr *ACGME Approved/Offered Positions:* 4
Program ID: 530-05-34-001

Los Angeles

UCLA Medical Center Program
Sponsor: UCLA David Geffen School of Medicine/UCLA
  Medical Center
Santa Monica-UCLA Medical Center
Prgm Director: Francis M Ferrante, MD
Center for the Health Sciences
10833 Le Conte Avenue
Los Angeles, CA 90095
Tel: 310 267-8655 *Fax:* 310 267-3766
E-mail: ccamargo@mednet.ucla.edu
Length: 1 Yr *ACGME Approved/Offered Positions:* 4
Program ID: 530-05-04-076

Programs

University of Southern California/ LAC+USC Medical Center Program

Sponsor: University of Southern California/LAC+USC Medical Center
Kenneth Norris Jr Cancer Hospital and Research Institute
LAC+USC Medical Center
USC University Hospital
Prgm Director: Steven Richeimer, MD
1520 San Pablo Street, Suite 3450
Los Angeles, CA 90033
Tel: 323 442-6202   *Fax:* 323 442-7411
E-mail: morod21@hotmail.com
Length: 1 Yr   *ACGME Approved/Offered Positions:* 2
Program ID: 530-05-04-111

VA Greater Los Angeles Healthcare System Program

Sponsor: VA Greater Los Angeles Healthcare System
UCLA Medical Center
Prgm Director: Quynh Pham, MD
Department of PM&R (W117)
11301 Wilshire Boulevard
Los Angeles, CA 90073
Tel: 310 268-3342
E-mail: sanjog.pangarkar@med.va.gov
Length: 1 Yr   *ACGME Approved/Offered Positions:* 4
Program ID: 530-05-34-003

Orange

University of California (Irvine) Program

Sponsor: University of California (Irvine) Medical Center
Prgm Director: Arthur Zepeda, MD
Dept of Anesthesiology & Perioperative Care
333 City Blvd West, Ste 2150
Orange, CA 92868
Tel: 714 456-6653   *Fax:* 714 456-7702
Length: 1 Yr   *ACGME Approved/Offered Positions:* 2
Program ID: 530-05-04-002

Sacramento

University of California (Davis) Health System Program

Sponsor: University of California (Davis) Health System
University of California (Davis) Medical Center
Prgm Director: Gagan Mahajan, MD
Pain Management Academic Office
4860 Y Street, Suite 3020
Sacramento, CA 95817
Tel: 916 734-6824   *Fax:* 916 734-6827
E-mail: gmahajan@ucdavis.edu
Length: 1 Yr   *ACGME Approved/Offered Positions:* 6
Program ID: 530-05-04-064

San Diego

University of California (San Diego) Program

Sponsor: University of California (San Diego) Medical Center
Veterans Affairs Medical Center (San Diego)
Prgm Director: Mark S Wallace, MD
Department of Anesthesiology
9300 Campus Point Drive, #7651
La Jolla, CA 92037
Tel: 858 657-7030   *Fax:* 858 657-7035
E-mail: painfellowship@ucsd.edu
Length: 1 Yr   *ACGME Approved/Offered Positions:* 3
Program ID: 530-05-04-047

San Francisco

University of California (San Francisco) Program

Sponsor: University of California (San Francisco) School of Medicine
UCSF and Mount Zion Medical Centers
Veterans Affairs Medical Center (San Francisco)
Prgm Director: David J Lee, MD
Pain Management Center
2255 Post Street
San Francisco, CA 94143
Tel: 415 885-7347   *Fax:* 415 885-3883
E-mail: gouldc@anesthesia.ucsf.edu
Length: 1 Yr   *ACGME Approved/Offered Positions:* 5
Program ID: 530-05-04-082

Stanford

Stanford University Program

Sponsor: Stanford Hospital and Clinics
Veterans Affairs Palo Alto Health Care System
Prgm Director: Sean Mackey, MD, PhD
780 Welch Road
Suite 208
Palo Alto, CA 94304
Tel: 650 725-9636   *Fax:* 650 725-9642
E-mail: smackey@stanford.edu
Length: 1 Yr   *ACGME Approved/Offered Positions:* 7
Program ID: 530-05-04-059

Colorado

Aurora

University of Colorado Denver Program

Sponsor: University of Colorado Denver School of Medicine
University of Colorado Hospital
Prgm Director: Venu Akuthota, MD
Mail Stop F493
12631 East 17th Ave
Aurora, CO 80045
Tel: 720 848-1980   *Fax:* 720 848-2019
E-mail: vy.malcik@uchsc.edu
Length: 1 Yr   *ACGME Approved/Offered Positions:* 2
Program ID: 530-07-34-011

District of Columbia

Washington

Washington Hospital Center/National Rehabilitation Hospital Program

Sponsor: Washington Hospital Center
National Rehabilitation Hospital
Prgm Director: Malady S Kodgi, MD
110 Irving Street, NW
Washington, DC 20010
Tel: 202 877-3442   *Fax:* 202 877-8194
E-mail: pain.program@medstar.net
Length: 1 Yr   *ACGME Approved/Offered Positions:* 1
Program ID: 530-10-34-009

Florida

Gainesville

University of Florida Program

Sponsor: University of Florida College of Medicine
North Florida/South Georgia Veterans Health System
Shands Hospital at the University of Florida
Prgm Director: Andrea Trescot, MD
Box 100254
1600 Archer Road
Gainesville, FL 32610
Tel: 352 376-1611   *Fax:* 352 265-6922
E-mail: amt57@aol.com
Length: 1 Yr   *ACGME Approved/Offered Positions:* 4
Program ID: 530-11-04-046

Jacksonville

College of Medicine, Mayo Clinic (Jacksonville) Program

Sponsor: College of Medicine, Mayo Clinic
Mayo Clinic (Jacksonville)
Mayo Clinic Florida Hospital
Prgm Director: Salim M Ghazi, MD
4500 San Pablo Road
Jacksonville, FL 32224
Tel: 904 296-5289   *Fax:* 904 953-0430
E-mail: paglia.melissa@mayo.edu
Length: 1 Yr   *ACGME Approved/Offered Positions:* 2
Program ID: 530-11-04-054

Miami

Jackson Memorial Hospital/Jackson Health System Program

Sponsor: Jackson Memorial Hospital/Jackson Health System
University of Miami Sylvester Comprehensive Cancer Center
Veterans Affairs Medical Center (Miami)
Prgm Director: Dennis J Patin, MD
Dept of Anesthesiology, R-370
PO Box 016370
Miami, FL 33101
Tel: 305 243-5201   *Fax:* 305 243-5207
E-mail: dpatin@med.miami.edu
Length: 1 Yr   *ACGME Approved/Offered Positions:* 4
Program ID: 530-11-04-003

Tampa

University of South Florida Program

Sponsor: University of South Florida College of Medicine
James A Haley Veterans Hospital
Tampa General Hospital
Prgm Director: Charles W Brock, MD
Department of Neurology
12901 Bruce B Downs Boulevard, MDC 55
Tampa, FL 33612
Tel: 813 972-7633   *Fax:* 813 978-5995
E-mail: cbrock@health.usf.edu
Length: 1 Yr   *ACGME Approved/Offered Positions:* 1
Program ID: 530-11-18-006

Note: * indicates a newly appointed program director

Georgia

Atlanta

Emory University Program

Sponsor: Emory University School of Medicine
Crawford Long Hospital of Emory University
Emory University Hospital
Grady Health System
Prgm Director: Anne M McKenzie-Brown, MD
Dept of Anesthesiology, 3 B South
1364 Clifton Road, NE
Atlanta, GA 30322
Tel: 404 778-5582   *Fax:* 404 778-5194
Length: 1 Yr   *ACGME Approved/Offered Positions:* 5
Program ID: 530-12-04-004

Augusta

Medical College of Georgia Program

Sponsor: Medical College of Georgia
Prgm Director: William D Hammonds, MD, MPH
1120 15th Street
Augusta, GA 30912
Tel: 706 721-7754   *Fax:* 706 721-7753
E-mail: sdawkins@mcg.edu
Length: 1 Yr   *ACGME Approved/Offered Positions:* 3
Program ID: 530-12-04-105

Illinois

Chicago

John H Stroger Hospital of Cook County Program

Sponsor: John H Stroger Hospital of Cook County
Prgm Director: Silvio Glusman, MD, PhD
Department of Anesthesiology
1901 West Harrison Street
Chicago, IL 60612
Tel: 312 864-3221   *Fax:* 312 864-9276
Length: 1 Yr   *ACGME Approved/Offered Positions:* 4
Program ID: 530-16-04-077

McGaw Medical Center of Northwestern University Program

Sponsor: McGaw Medical Center of Northwestern
   University
Northwestern Memorial Hospital
Prgm Director: David R Walega, MD
Department of Anesthesiology
251 E Huron Street, Suite 5-704
Chicago, IL 60611
Tel: 312 926-8105   *Fax:* 312 926-9206
Length: 1 Yr   *ACGME Approved/Offered Positions:* 5
Program ID: 530-16-04-005

Rush University Medical Center Program

Sponsor: Rush University Medical Center
Prgm Director: Timothy R Lubenow, MD
1653 West Congress Parkway
Chicago, IL 60612
Tel: 312 942-6504   *Fax:* 312 942-5773
E-mail: sherri_sachs@rush.edu
Length: 1 Yr   *ACGME Approved/Offered Positions:* 4
Program ID: 530-16-04-095

University of Chicago Program

Sponsor: University of Chicago Medical Center
Prgm Director: Friedl Pantle-Fisher, MD
5841 South Maryland Avenue
Chicago, IL 60637
Tel: 773 834-3643   *Fax:* 773 834-2218
Length: 1 Yr   *ACGME Approved/Offered Positions:* 2
Program ID: 530-16-04-098

University of Illinois College of Medicine at Chicago Program

Sponsor: University of Illinois College of Medicine at
   Chicago
University of Illinois Hospital and Clinics
Prgm Director: Charles E Laurito, MD
Center for Pain Management MC 515
1740 West Taylor, Suite 3200
Chicago, IL 60612
Tel: 312 996-4020   *Fax:* 312 996-4019
E-mail: sharps@uic.edu
Length: 1 Yr   *ACGME Approved/Offered Positions:* 3
Program ID: 530-16-04-006

Maywood

Loyola University Program

Sponsor: Loyola University Medical Center
Prgm Director: Meda Raghavendra, MD
Department of Anesthesiology
2160 South First Avenue
Maywood, IL 60153
Tel: 708 216-5119   *Fax:* 708 216-1249
Length: 1 Yr   *ACGME Approved/Offered Positions:* 3
Program ID: 530-16-04-078

Indiana

Indianapolis

Indiana University School of Medicine Program

Sponsor: Indiana University School of Medicine
Clarian Indiana University Hospital
Clarian Riley Hospital for Children
Richard L Roudebush Veterans Affairs Medical Center
William N Wishard Memorial Hospital
Prgm Director: Dennis L Wagner, MD
1120 South Drive
Fesler Hall 204
Indianapolis, IN 46202
Tel: 317 274-2866   *Fax:* 317 274-0256
E-mail: cdeprez@iupui.edu
Length: 1 Yr   *ACGME Approved/Offered Positions:* 3
Program ID: 530-17-04-039

Iowa

Iowa City

University of Iowa Hospitals and Clinics Program

Sponsor: University of Iowa Hospitals and Clinics
Veterans Affairs Medical Center (Iowa City)
Prgm Director: Richard W Rosenquist, MD
Department of Anesthesia
200 Hawkins Drive 6 JCP
Iowa City, IA 52242
Tel: 319 353-7783   *Fax:* 319 356-3431
Length: 1 Yr   *ACGME Approved/Offered Positions:* 3
Program ID: 530-18-04-007

Kentucky

Lexington

University of Kentucky College of Medicine Program

Sponsor: University of Kentucky College of Medicine
University of Kentucky Hospital
Prgm Director: Joseph R Holtman Jr, MD, PhD
Dept of Anesthesiology, Room N-202
800 Rose Street
Lexington, KY 40536
Tel: 859 323-5956   *Fax:* 859 323-1924
E-mail: jrhol2@email.uky.edu
Length: 1 Yr   *ACGME Approved/Offered Positions:* 2
Program ID: 530-20-04-035

Louisville

University of Louisville Program

Sponsor: University of Louisville School of Medicine
University of Louisville Hospital
Prgm Director: Anil Vinayakan, MD
Department of Anesthesiology and Perioperative Med
530 S Jackson Street
Louisville, KY 40202
Tel: 502 852-1734   *Fax:* 502 852-3762
E-mail: anvina01@louisville.edu
Length: 1 Yr   *ACGME Approved/Offered Positions:* 1
Program ID: 530-20-04-108

Louisiana

New Orleans

Louisiana State University Program

Sponsor: Louisiana State University School of Medicine
Medical Center of Louisiana at New Orleans
Ochsner Clinic Foundation
Veterans Affairs Medical Center (New Orleans)
Prgm Director: Harry J Gould III, MD, PhD
1401 Foucher Street
Suite 10012
New Orleans, LA 70115
Tel: 504 897-8948   *Fax:* 504 897-7145
E-mail: mniles@lsuhsc.edu
Length: 1 Yr   *ACGME Approved/Offered Positions:* 3
Program ID: 530-21-34-013

Shreveport

Louisiana State University (Shreveport) Program

Sponsor: LSU Health Sciences Center-University
   Hospital
Prgm Director: Thomas Schult, MD
1501 Kings Highway
PO Box 33932
Shreveport, LA 71130
Tel: 318 675-4810   *Fax:* 318 675-6249
E-mail: thdosc49@yahoo.com
Length: 1 Yr   *ACGME Approved/Offered Positions:* 2
Program ID: 530-21-04-099

Programs

Maryland

Baltimore

Johns Hopkins University Program
Sponsor: Johns Hopkins University School of Medicine
Johns Hopkins Hospital
Prgm Director: Paul J Christo, MD, MBA
550 N Broadway
Suite 301
Baltimore, MD 21205
Tel: 410 955-1818   *Fax:* 410 502-6730
E-mail: pchrist2@jhmi.edu
Length: 1 Yr   *ACGME Approved/Offered Positions:* 4
Program ID: 530-23-04-008

University of Maryland Program
Sponsor: University of Maryland Medical System
University of Maryland-Kernan Hospital
Prgm Director: Thelma Wright, MD
Suite S11C00
22 S Greene Street
Baltimore, MD 21201
Tel: 410 448-6625   *Fax:* 410 448-7101
E-mail: mpurcell@anes.umm.edu
Length: 1 Yr   *ACGME Approved/Offered Positions:* 3
Program ID: 530-23-04-009

Bethesda

National Capital Consortium Program
Sponsor: National Capital Consortium
National Naval Medical Center (Bethesda)
Walter Reed Army Medical Center
Prgm Director: Scott R Griffith, MD*
6900 Georgia Avenue NW
Bldg 2, Ward 44
Washington, DC 20307
Tel: 202 782-6616
Length: 1 Yr   *ACGME Approved/Offered Positions:* 3
Program ID: 530-10-04-101
Uniformed Services Program

Massachusetts

Boston

Beth Israel Deaconess Medical Center Program
Sponsor: Beth Israel Deaconess Medical Center
Brigham and Women's Hospital
Children's Hospital
Prgm Director: Christine G Peeters-Asdourian, MD
Dept of Anesthesia, Critical Care & Pain Medicine
One Brookline Place, Ste 105
Brookline, MA 02445
Tel: 617 278-8037   *Fax:* 617 278-8040
E-mail: cpeeters@bidmc.harvard.edu
Length: 1 Yr   *ACGME Approved/Offered Positions:* 8
Program ID: 530-24-04-010

Brigham and Women's Hospital Program
Sponsor: Brigham and Women's Hospital
Prgm Director: Srdjan S Nedeljkovic, MD
Department of Anesthesiology
75 Francis Street
Boston, MA 02115
Tel: 617 732-9057   *Fax:* 617 732-9050
E-mail: hponde@partners.org
Length: 1 Yr   *ACGME Approved/Offered Positions:* 8
Program ID: 530-24-04-043

Caritas St Elizabeth's Medical Center Program
Sponsor: Caritas St Elizabeth's Medical Center of Boston
Prgm Director: Gordon Novak, MD
736 Cambridge Street, MMR-1
Boston, MA 02135
Tel: 617 789-2777   *Fax:* 617 254-6384
Length: 1 Yr   *ACGME Approved/Offered Positions:* 3
Program ID: 530-24-04-112

Children's Hospital Program
Sponsor: Children's Hospital
Beth Israel Deaconess Medical Center
Brigham and Women's Hospital
Prgm Director: Charles Berde, MD, PhD
Division of Pain Medicine, Department of Anesthesiology
333 Longwood Avenue
Boston, MA 02115
Tel: 617 355-2303   *Fax:* 617 730-0199
E-mail: christine.greco@childrens.harvard.edu
Length: 1 Yr   *ACGME Approved/Offered Positions:* 2
Program ID: 530-24-04-003

Harvard Medical School/Spaulding Rehabilitation Hospital Program
Sponsor: Spaulding Rehabilitation Hospital
Newton-Wellesley Hospital
Prgm Director: Alec L Meleger, MD
125 Nashua Street
Boston, MA 02114
Tel: 617 573-2178   *Fax:* 617 573-2769
Length: 1 Yr   *ACGME Approved/Offered Positions:* 1
Program ID: 530-24-34-004

Massachusetts General Hospital Program
Sponsor: Massachusetts General Hospital
Prgm Director: Gary J Brenner, MD, PhD
MGH Pain Center, WAC-333
15 Parkman Street
Boston, MA 02114
Tel: 617 726-3332   *Fax:* 617 724-2719
E-mail: gjbrenner@partners.org
Length: 1 Yr   *ACGME Approved/Offered Positions:* 6
Program ID: 530-24-04-040

Springfield

Baystate Medical Center/Tufts University School of Medicine Program
Sponsor: Baystate Medical Center
Prgm Director: Ravi K Narasimhan, MD
Porter 2
759 Chestnut Street
Springfield, MA 01199
Tel: 413 794-4326   *Fax:* 413 794-5349
E-mail: maria.lopez@bhs.org
Length: 1 Yr   *ACGME Approved/Offered Positions:* 3
Program ID: 530-24-04-011

Michigan

Ann Arbor

University of Michigan Program
Sponsor: University of Michigan Hospitals and Health Centers
Veterans Affairs Medical Center (Ann Arbor)
Prgm Director: Srinivas Chiravuri, MBBS, MD
Department of Anesthesiology
325 East Eisenhower Parkway suite 100
Ann Arbor, MI 48108
Tel: 734 936-7922   *Fax:* 734 936-6585
E-mail: dosborn@umich.edu
Length: 1 Yr   *ACGME Approved/Offered Positions:* 8
Program ID: 530-25-04-065

Detroit

Henry Ford Hospital Program
Sponsor: Henry Ford Hospital
Prgm Director: Henry R Kroll, MD
Anesthesiology Pain Fellowship Program
2799 West Grand Blvd
Detroit, MI 48202
Tel: 313 916-8234   *Fax:* 313 916-9434
E-mail: jrobert1@hfhs.org
Length: 1 Yr   *ACGME Approved/Offered Positions:* 3
Program ID: 530-25-04-061

Wayne State University/Detroit Medical Center Program
Sponsor: Wayne State University/Detroit Medical Center
Karmanos Cancer Hospital
Prgm Director: Todd Lininger, MD
Anesthesia Education Offices
3990 John R St, Box 162, Room 2901
Detroit, MI 48201
Tel: 313 745-7233   *Fax:* 313 993-3889
E-mail: telininger@msn.com
Length: 1 Yr   *ACGME Approved/Offered Positions:* 4
Program ID: 530-25-04-109

Minnesota

Rochester

College of Medicine, Mayo Clinic (Rochester) Program
Sponsor: College of Medicine, Mayo Clinic
Rochester Methodist Hospital
Prgm Director: Tim J Lamer, MD*
200 First Street, SW
Rochester, MN 55905
Tel: 507 266-2077   *Fax:* 507 284-0120
E-mail: painfellowship@mayo.edu
Length: 1 Yr   *ACGME Approved/Offered Positions:* 4
Program ID: 530-26-04-012

Mississippi

Jackson

University of Mississippi Medical Center Program
Sponsor: University of Mississippi School of Medicine
University Hospitals and Clinics
Prgm Director: Ike Eriator, MD, MPH
2500 North State Street
Department of Anesthesiology
Jackson, MS 39216
Tel: 601 984-5950   *Fax:* 601 984-5939
E-mail: ieriator@anesthesia.umsmed.edu
Length: 1 Yr   *ACGME Approved/Offered Positions:* 2
Program ID: 530-27-04-104

Missouri

St Louis

Washington University/B-JH/SLCH Consortium Program
Sponsor: Washington University/B-JH/SLCH Consortium
Barnes-Jewish Hospital
Prgm Director: Robert A Swarm, MD
Department of Anesthesiology
660 S Euclid Avenue
St Louis, MO 63110
Tel: 314 747-0202   *Fax:* 314 286-2675
E-mail: swarmr@wustl.edu
Length: 1 Yr   *ACGME Approved/Offered Positions:* 2
Program ID: 530-28-04-013

Note: * indicates a newly appointed program director

Nebraska

Omaha

University of Nebraska Medical Center College of Medicine Program

Sponsor: University of Nebraska Medical Center College of Medicine
Nebraska Medical Center
Prgm Director: Tyrus Soares, MD*
984455 Nebraska Medical Center
Omaha, NE 68198
Tel: 402 559-7405   *Fax:* 402 559-7372
E-mail: tsoares@unmc.edu
Length: 1 Yr   *ACGME Approved/Offered Positions:* 1
Program ID: 530-30-04-100

New Hampshire

Lebanon

Dartmouth-Hitchcock Medical Center Program

Sponsor: Mary Hitchcock Memorial Hospital
Prgm Director: Ralph D Beasley, MD
One Medical Center Drive
Lebanon, NH 03766
Tel: 603 650-8391   *Fax:* 603 650-8161
Length: 1 Yr   *ACGME Approved/Offered Positions:* 5
Program ID: 530-32-04-044

New Jersey

New Brunswick

UMDNJ-Robert Wood Johnson Medical School Program

Sponsor: UMDNJ-Robert Wood Johnson Medical School
Robert Wood Johnson University Hospital
Prgm Director: William Grubb, MD, DDS
CAB, Suite 3100
125 Paterson Street
New Brunswick, NJ 08901
Tel: 732 235-6153   *Fax:* 732 235-5100
E-mail: douglael@umdnj.edu
Length: 1 Yr   *ACGME Approved/Offered Positions:* 3
Program ID: 530-33-04-063

New Mexico

Albuquerque

University of New Mexico Program

Sponsor: University of New Mexico School of Medicine
University of New Mexico Hospital
Prgm Director: Robert Zuniga, MD
2701 Frontier NE MSC 11-6120
Surge Building Room 110
Albuquerque, NM 87131
Tel: 505 272-2610   *Fax:* 505 272-1300
Length: 1 Yr   *ACGME Approved/Offered Positions:* 2
Program ID: 530-34-04-015

New York

Buffalo

University at Buffalo Program

Sponsor: University at Buffalo School of Medicine
Erie County Medical Center
Roswell Park Cancer Institute
Prgm Director: Oscar deLeon-Casasola, MD
Hayes Annex A, Bldg 4
3435 Main St
Buffalo, NY 14214
Tel: 716 829-6102   *Fax:* 716 829-3640
Length: 1 Yr   *ACGME Approved/Offered Positions:* 2
Program ID: 530-35-04-017

New York

Albert Einstein College of Medicine at Beth Israel Medical Center Program

Sponsor: Beth Israel Medical Center
Prgm Director: Ronald Kaplan, MD
Department of Pain Medicine and Palliative Care
First Avenue at 16th Street
New York, NY 10003
Tel: 212 844-1479   *Fax:* 212 844-1503
Length: 1 Yr   *ACGME Approved/Offered Positions:* 6
Program ID: 530-35-04-062

Memorial Sloan-Kettering Cancer Center Program

Sponsor: Memorial Sloan-Kettering Cancer Center
Prgm Director: Eugenie Obbens, MD, PhD
Pain & Palliative Care Service
1275 York Avenue, Box 52
New York, NY 10065
Tel: 646 888-2680   *Fax:* 646 888-2732
Length: 1 Yr   *ACGME Approved/Offered Positions:* 5
Program ID: 530-35-18-004

Mount Sinai School of Medicine Program

Sponsor: Mount Sinai School of Medicine
Mount Sinai Medical Center
Prgm Director: Paru Pandya, MD
Box 1192
One Gustave L Levy Place
New York, NY 10029
Tel: 212 241-6372   *Fax:* 212 348-8695
Length: 1 Yr   *ACGME Approved/Offered Positions:* 5
Program ID: 530-35-04-066

New York Medical College at St Vincent's Hospital and Medical Center of New York Program

Sponsor: New York Medical College
St Vincent Catholic Medical Centers (Manhattan)
University Pain Center (New York Med Coll at St Vincent's)
Prgm Director: Amr Hosny, MD, MBA
153 West 11th Street
New York, NY 10011
Tel: 212 604-7566   *Fax:* 212 604-2637
Length: 1 Yr   *ACGME Approved/Offered Positions:* 4
Program ID: 530-35-04-070

New York Presbyterian Hospital (Columbia Campus) Program

Sponsor: New York Presbyterian Hospital
New York Presbyterian Hospital (Columbia Campus)
Prgm Director: Michael Weinberger, MD
622 West 168th Street
PH 5 East, Room 500
New York, NY 10032
Tel: 212 305-7114   *Fax:* 212 305-8883
E-mail: mlw45@columbia.edu
Length: 1 Yr   *ACGME Approved/Offered Positions:* 2
Program ID: 530-35-04-085

New York Presbyterian Hospital (Cornell Campus) Program

Sponsor: New York Presbyterian Hospital
Hospital for Special Surgery
Memorial Sloan-Kettering Cancer Center
New York Presbyterian Hospital (Cornell Campus)
Prgm Director: Sudhir A Diwan, MD, MS
Anesthesiology Department
525 East 68th Street, Box 124
New York, NY 10065
Tel: 212 746-2775   *Fax:* 212 746-8563
E-mail: sad2003@med.cornell.edu
Length: 1 Yr   *ACGME Approved/Offered Positions:* 8
Program ID: 530-35-04-049

New York University School of Medicine Program

Sponsor: New York University School of Medicine
Bellevue Hospital Center
NYU Hospital for Joint Diseases
NYU Hospitals Center
Prgm Director: Shengping Zou, MD
Suite 902
317 East 34th Street
New York, NY 10016
Tel: 212 201-1004   *Fax:* 212 685-5365
E-mail: shengping.zou@nyumc.org
Length: 1 Yr   *ACGME Approved/Offered Positions:* 3
Program ID: 530-35-04-084

St Luke's-Roosevelt Hospital Center Program

Sponsor: St Luke's-Roosevelt Hospital Center
Prgm Director: Ronny Hertz, MD, DDS
Department of Anesthesiology
428 West 59th Street
New York, NY 10019
Tel: 212 523-6357   *Fax:* 212 523-6217
Length: 1 Yr   *ACGME Approved/Offered Positions:* 4
Program ID: 530-35-04-018

Rochester

University of Rochester Program

Sponsor: Strong Memorial Hospital of the University of Rochester
Prgm Director: Joel L Kent, MD
Department of Anesthesiology, Box 604
601 Elmwood Avenue
Rochester, NY 14642
Tel: 585 276-3770   *Fax:* 585 276-0144
Length: 1 Yr   *ACGME Approved/Offered Positions:* 3
Program ID: 530-35-04-051

Syracuse

SUNY Upstate Medical University Program

Sponsor: SUNY Upstate Medical University
Veterans Affairs Medical Center (Syracuse)
Prgm Director: P Sebastian Thomas, MD
750 East Adams Street
Syracuse, NY 13210
Tel: 315 464-4891   *Fax:* 315 464-4905
Length: 1 Yr   *ACGME Approved/Offered Positions:* 4
Program ID: 530-35-04-092

North Carolina

Chapel Hill

University of North Carolina Hospitals Program

Sponsor: University of North Carolina Hospitals
Prgm Director: William S Blau, MD, PhD*
The Dept of Anesthesiology, School of Medicine
CB 7010, N2201 UNC Hospitals
Chapel Hill, NC 27599
Tel: 919 966-5136   *Fax:* 919 966-4873
E-mail: UNCAnesthesiology-Residency@aims.unc.edu
Length: 1 Yr   *ACGME Approved/Offered Positions:* 2
Program ID: 530-36-04-088

Durham

Duke University Hospital Program

Sponsor: Duke University Hospital
Veterans Affairs Medical Center (Durham)
Prgm Director: Dianne L Scott, MD
932 Morreene Road
Room 232
Durham, NC 27705
Tel: 919 684-3239
E-mail: scott002@mc.duke.edu
Length: 1 Yr   *ACGME Approved/Offered Positions:* 2
Program ID: 530-36-04-020

Winston-Salem

Wake Forest University School of Medicine Program

Sponsor: Wake Forest University Baptist Medical Center
Carolinas Pain Institute
Forsyth Memorial Hospital
Prgm Director: Richard L Rauck, MD
Department of Anesthesiology - Pain Management
145 Kimel Park Drive, Suite 330
Winston-Salem, NC 27103
Tel: 336 714-6408   *Fax:* 336 765-8492
E-mail: rskinner@wfubmc.edu
Length: 1 Yr   *ACGME Approved/Offered Positions:* 4
Program ID: 530-36-04-036

Ohio

Cincinnati

University Hospital/University of Cincinnati College of Medicine Program

Sponsor: University Hospital Inc
Prgm Director: Harsh Sachdeva, MD*
234 Goodman Avenue ML 0764
PO Box 670764
Cincinnati, OH 45267
Tel: 513 584-0909
Length: 1 Yr   *ACGME Approved/Offered Positions:* 3
Program ID: 530-38-04-021

Cleveland

Cleveland Clinic Foundation Program

Sponsor: Cleveland Clinic Foundation
Prgm Director: Samer Narouze, MD, MSc
Department of Pain Management
9500 Euclid Avenue
Cleveland, OH 44195
Tel: 216 445-9421   *Fax:* 216 444-0797
E-mail: narouzs@ccf.org
Length: 1 Yr   *ACGME Approved/Offered Positions:* 10
Program ID: 530-38-04-022

University Hospitals Case Medical Center Program

Sponsor: University Hospitals Case Medical Center
Veterans Affairs Medical Center (Cleveland)
Prgm Director: Salim M Hayek, MD, PhD
11100 Euclid Avenue
Cleveland, OH 44106
Tel: 216 983-2085   *Fax:* 216 983-2088
E-mail: terrah.northern@uhhospitals.org
Length: 1 Yr   *ACGME Approved/Offered Positions:* 3
Program ID: 530-38-04-097

Columbus

Ohio State University Hospital Program

Sponsor: Ohio State University Hospital
Prgm Director: Steven A Severyn, MD, MBA
N416 Doan Hall
410 W 10th Avenue
Columbus, OH 43210
Tel: 614 293-1070   *Fax:* 614 293-8557
E-mail: denise.mcmaster@osumc.edu
Length: 1 Yr   *ACGME Approved/Offered Positions:* 1
Program ID: 530-38-04-048

Oklahoma

Oklahoma City

University of Oklahoma Health Sciences Center Program

Sponsor: University of Oklahoma College of Medicine
OU Medical Center
Prgm Director: Badie S Mansour, MD
750 NE 13th St, Ste 200, OAC Bldg
Oklahoma City, OK 73104
Tel: 405 271-4354   *Fax:* 405 271-1216
E-mail: linda-murphy@ouhsc.edu
Length: 1 Yr   *ACGME Approved/Offered Positions:* 1
Program ID: 530-39-04-087

Oregon

Portland

Oregon Health & Science University Program

Sponsor: Oregon Health & Science University Hospital
Veterans Affairs Medical Center (Portland)
Prgm Director: David M Sibell, MD
Comprehensive Pain Center
3303 SW Bond Avenue, CH4P
Portland, OR 97239
Tel: 503 494-7246   *Fax:* 503 494-7635
E-mail: karlinge@ohsu.edu
Length: 1 Yr   *ACGME Approved/Offered Positions:* 3
Program ID: 530-40-04-023

Pennsylvania

Hershey

Penn State University/Milton S Hershey Medical Center Program

Sponsor: Milton S Hershey Medical Center
Prgm Director: David Giampetro, MD*
Department of Anesthesiology, HU32
500 University Drive
Hershey, PA 17033
Tel: 717 531-5680   *Fax:* 717 531-4328
Length: 1 Yr   *ACGME Approved/Offered Positions:* 3
Program ID: 530-41-04-024

Philadelphia

Temple University Hospital Program

Sponsor: Temple University Hospital
Christiana Care Health Services Inc
Prgm Director: Frank J Falco, MD
139 East Chestnut Hill Road
Newark, DE 19713
Tel: 302 369-1700   *Fax:* 302 369-1717
E-mail: serhart@midatlanticspine.com
Length: 1 Yr   *ACGME Approved/Offered Positions:* 4
Program ID: 530-41-34-010

Thomas Jefferson University Program

Sponsor: Thomas Jefferson University Hospital
Prgm Director: Dajie Wang, MD
834 Chestnut Street, Suite T-150
Philadelphia, PA 19107
Tel: 215 955-2108   *Fax:* 215 923-5086
Length: 1 Yr   *ACGME Approved/Offered Positions:* 3
Program ID: 530-41-04-041

University of Pennsylvania Program

Sponsor: University of Pennsylvania Health System
Pennsylvania Hospital (UPHS)
Prgm Director: Michael A Ashburn, MD, MPH
Penn Pain Medicine Center, 2nd Floor Tuttleman Ctr
1840 South Street
Philadelphia, PA 19146
Tel: 215 893-7251   *Fax:* 215 893-7265
E-mail: kathrine.teszner@uphs.upenn.edu
Length: 1 Yr   *ACGME Approved/Offered Positions:* 3
Program ID: 530-41-04-026

Pittsburgh

University of Pittsburgh Medical Center Medical Education Program

Sponsor: Univ of Pittsburgh Medical Center Medical Education
UPMC St Margaret
Prgm Director: Doris K Cope, MD, MS
200 Medical Arts Building
200 Delafield Avenue, Suite 2070
Pittsburgh, PA 15215
Tel: 412 784-5343   *Fax:* 412 784-5350
Length: 1 Yr   *ACGME Approved/Offered Positions:* 9
Program ID: 530-41-04-027

Western Pennsylvania Hospital/Temple University Program

Sponsor: Western Pennsylvania Hospital
Allegheny General Hospital
Prgm Director: Abraham J Kabazie, MD
4800 Friendship Avenue
Suite 459 MP
Pittsburgh, PA 15224
Tel: 412 578-5635   *Fax:* 412 578-4981
E-mail: jrandal@wpahs.org
Length: 1 Yr   *ACGME Approved/Offered Positions:* 4
Program ID: 530-41-04-107

York

Sinai Hospital of Baltimore (Center for Pain Management and Rehabilitation - East York) Program

Sponsor: Sinai Hospital of Baltimore
Orthopaedic and Spine Specialists
Prgm Director: Michael B Furman, MD, MS
1855 Powder Mill Road
York, PA 17402
Tel: 717 848-4800   *Fax:* 717 741-9539
E-mail: mfurman@orthospinesp.com
Length: 1 Yr   *ACGME Approved/Offered Positions:* 2
Program ID: 530-23-34-007

Note: * indicates a newly appointed program director

Tennessee

Nashville

Vanderbilt University Program
Sponsor: Vanderbilt University Medical Center
Prgm Director: Sukdeb Datta, MD
2501 TVC, 1301 Medical Center Drive
Nashville, TN 37232
Tel: 615 322-4311   *Fax:* 615 322-9089
Length: 1 Yr   *ACGME Approved/Offered Positions:* 2
Program ID: 530-47-04-001

Texas

Dallas

University of Texas Southwestern Medical School Program
Sponsor: University of Texas Southwestern Medical School
Dallas County Hospital District-Parkland Memorial Hospital
Dallas VA Medical Center
Prgm Director: Chandramouli Iyer, MD, MS*
5323 Harry Hines Boulevard
Dallas, TX 75390
Tel: 214 857-0385   *Fax:* 214 857-1867
E-mail: gabriela.pinto@utsouthwestern.edu
Length: 1 Yr   *ACGME Approved/Offered Positions:* 3
Program ID: 530-48-04-052

University of Texas Southwestern Medical School/John Peter Smith Hospital Program
Sponsor: University of Texas Southwestern Medical School
John Peter Smith Hospital (Tarrant County Hospital District)
Prgm Director: Steven L Simmons, DO
1500 South Main Street
Fort Worth, TX 76104
Tel: 817 927-1200   *Fax:* 817 927-1691
Length: 1 Yr   *ACGME Approved/Offered Positions:* 4
Program ID: 530-48-34-015

Galveston

University of Texas Medical Branch Hospitals Program
Sponsor: University of Texas Medical Branch Hospitals
Prgm Director: Gulshan Doulatram, MD*
Pain Clinic, 6th Floor UHC Bldg
301 University Blvd
Galveston, TX 77555
Tel: 409 772-1221   *Fax:* 409 772-1224
E-mail: gdoulatr@utmb.edu
Length: 1 Yr   *ACGME Approved/Offered Positions:* 2
Program ID: 530-48-04-103

Houston

University of Texas at Houston/M D Anderson Cancer Center Program
Sponsor: University of Texas Health Science Center at Houston
Prgm Director: Basem Hamid, MD
1400 Holcombe Boulevard
Unit 409
Houston, TX 77030
Tel: 713 745-7246   *Fax:* 713 745-0177
Length: 1 Yr   *ACGME Approved/Offered Positions:* 6
Program ID: 530-48-04-093

Lubbock

Texas Tech University (Lubbock) Program
Sponsor: Texas Tech University Health Sciences Center at Lubbock
University Medical Center
Prgm Director: Miles Day, MD
Dept of Anesthesiology, 1C282
3601 4th Street MS 8182
Lubbock, TX 79430
Tel: 806 743-7246   *Fax:* 806 743-2984
E-mail: krystle.johnston@ttuhsc.edu
Length: 1 Yr   *ACGME Approved/Offered Positions:* 5
Program ID: 530-48-04-030

San Antonio

University of Texas Health Science Center at San Antonio Program
Sponsor: University of Texas School of Medicine at San Antonio
Audie L Murphy Memorial Veterans Hospital (San Antonio)
University Health System
Prgm Director: Somayaji Ramamurthy, MD
Department of Anesthesiology
7703 Floyd Curl Drive
San Antonio, TX 78229
Tel: 210 567-4543   *Fax:* 210 567-4471
Length: 1 Yr   *ACGME Approved/Offered Positions:* 6
Program ID: 530-48-04-031

Utah

Salt Lake City

University of Utah Program
Sponsor: University of Utah Medical Center
Prgm Director: Bradford Hare, PhD, MD
Department of Anesthesiology
30 North 1900 East, Suite 3C444
Salt Lake City, UT 84132
Tel: 801 581-3622   *Fax:* 801 581-4367
E-mail: katija.snow@hsc.utah.edu
Length: 1 Yr   *ACGME Approved/Offered Positions:* 2
Program ID: 530-49-04-086

Vermont

Burlington

University of Vermont Program
Sponsor: Fletcher Allen Health Care
Prgm Director: Carlos A Pino, MD
Department of Anesthesiology
111 Colchester Avenue
Burlington, VT 05401
Tel: 802 847-2415
Length: 1 Yr   *ACGME Approved/Offered Positions:* 3
Program ID: 530-50-04-069

Virginia

Charlottesville

University of Virginia Program
Sponsor: University of Virginia Medical Center
Prgm Director: John C Rowlingson, MD
Dept of Anesthesiology
PO Box 801008
Charlottesville, VA 22908
Tel: 434 924-2283   *Fax:* 434 982-0019
E-mail: mw6r@virginia.edu
Length: 1 Yr   *ACGME Approved/Offered Positions:* 5
Program ID: 530-51-04-075

Portsmouth

Naval Medical Center (Portsmouth) Program
Sponsor: Naval Medical Center (Portsmouth)
Prgm Director: Michael A Mazzilli, MD
Department of Anesthesiology
620 John Paul Jones Circle
Portsmouth, VA 23708
Tel: 757 953-3158   *Fax:* 757 953-0870
Length: 1 Yr   *ACGME Approved/Offered Positions:* 1
Program ID: 530-51-04-032
Uniformed Services Program

Richmond

Virginia Commonwealth University Health System Program
Sponsor: Virginia Commonwealth University Health System
Hunter Holmes McGuire VA Medical Center (Richmond)
Medical College of Virginia Hospitals
Sheltering Arms Hospital
Prgm Director: Maged Hamza, MD*
PO Box 980677
Richmond, VA 23298
Tel: 804 323-2990   *Fax:* 804 323-2999
Length: 1 Yr   *ACGME Approved/Offered Positions:* 6
Program ID: 530-51-34-001

Washington

Seattle

University of Washington Program
Sponsor: University of Washington School of Medicine
University of Washington Medical Center
VA Puget Sound Health Care System
Prgm Director: Aysel Atli, MD, MPH*
Center for Pain Relief
1959 NE Pacific Street, Box 356044
Seattle, WA 98195
Tel: 206 221-6453   *Fax:* 206 543-2958
E-mail: aatli@u.washington.edu
Length: 1 Yr   *ACGME Approved/Offered Positions:* 4
Program ID: 530-54-04-034

Virginia Mason Medical Center Program
Sponsor: Virginia Mason Medical Center
Prgm Director: Daniel T Warren, MD*
925 Seneca Street
Graduate Medical Education H8-GME
Seattle, WA 98111
Tel: 206 583-6079   *Fax:* 206 583-2307
Length: 1 Yr   *ACGME Approved/Offered Positions:* 2
Program ID: 530-54-04-053

Wisconsin

Milwaukee

Medical College of Wisconsin Affiliated Hospitals Program
Sponsor: Medical College of Wisconsin Affiliated Hospitals, Inc
Clement J Zablocki Veterans Affairs Medical Center
Froedtert Memorial Lutheran Hospital
Prgm Director: Stephen E Abram, MD
Department of Anesthesiology
9200 West Wisconsin Avenue
Milwaukee, WI 53226
Tel: 414 805-6124   *Fax:* 414 805-6147
E-mail: sabram@mcw.edu
Length: 1 Yr   *ACGME Approved/Offered Positions:* 4
Program ID: 530-56-04-042

Programs

Pathology-Anatomic and Clinical

Alabama

Birmingham

Baptist Health System Program
Sponsor: Baptist Health System Inc
Baptist Medical Center-Princeton
Trinity Medical Center
Prgm Director: Kim M Parker, MD, RN
800 Montclair Road
Department of Pathology
Birmingham, AL 35213
Tel: 205 592-5052   *Fax:* 205 599-3736
E-mail: deborah.wilhite@bhsala.com
Length: 4 Yrs   *ACGME Approved/Offered Positions:* 8
Program ID: 300-01-21-017

University of Alabama Medical Center Program
Sponsor: University of Alabama Hospital
Veterans Affairs Medical Center (Birmingham)
Prgm Director: C Bruce Alexander, MD
619 South 19th Street, WP P220
Birmingham, AL 35233
Tel: 205 934-4303   *Fax:* 205 934-5499
Length: 4 Yrs   *ACGME Approved/Offered Positions:* 32
Program ID: 300-01-31-018

Mobile

University of South Alabama Program
Sponsor: University of South Alabama Hospitals
Infirmary West
University of South Alabama Medical Center
Prgm Director: Carole Boudreaux, MD
University of South Alabama Medical Center
2451 Fillingim Street
Mobile, AL 36617
Tel: 251 471-7786   *Fax:* 251 471-7884
E-mail: pathres@usouthal.edu
Length: 4 Yrs   *ACGME Approved/Offered Positions:* 15
Program ID: 300-01-11-019

Arizona

Phoenix

St Joseph's Hospital and Medical Center Program
Sponsor: St Joseph's Hospital and Medical Center
Prgm Director: Mary F Hahn, MD*
Department of Pathology
350 West Thomas Road
Phoenix, AZ 85013
Tel: 602 406-3402   *Fax:* 602 406-7132
Length: 4 Yrs   *ACGME Approved/Offered Positions:* 10
Program ID: 300-03-12-022

Tucson

University of Arizona Program
Sponsor: University of Arizona College of Medicine
Southern Arizona VA Health Care Center (Tucson)
University Medical Center
Prgm Director: Richard E Sobonya, MD
1501 North Campbell Avenue
PO Box 245108
Tucson, AZ 85724
Tel: 520 626-6830   *Fax:* 520 626-2521
E-mail: rsobonya@umcaz.edu
Length: 4 Yrs   *ACGME Approved/Offered Positions:* 16
Program ID: 300-03-21-023

Arkansas

Little Rock

University of Arkansas for Medical Sciences Program
Sponsor: University of Arkansas College of Medicine
Central Arkansas Veterans Healthcare System
UAMS Medical Center
Prgm Director: Harry H Brown, MD
4301 West Markham St
Department of Pathology, #517
Little Rock, AR 72205
Tel: 501 526-7507   *Fax:* 501 526-7983
E-mail: gordonreneen@uams.edu
Length: 4 Yrs   *ACGME Approved/Offered Positions:* 18
Program ID: 300-04-21-024

California

Loma Linda

Loma Linda University Program
Sponsor: Loma Linda University Medical Center
Jerry L Pettis Memorial Veterans Hospital
Prgm Director: Brian S Bull, MD
11234 Anderson Street
Department of Pathology & Lab Medicine, Room 2516
Loma Linda, CA 92354
Tel: 909 558-4094   *Fax:* 909 558-4189
Length: 4 Yrs   *ACGME Approved/Offered Positions:* 16
Program ID: 300-05-21-028

Los Angeles

Cedars-Sinai Medical Center Program
Sponsor: Cedars-Sinai Medical Center
Prgm Director: Wesley S Nichols Jr, MD
8700 Beverly Boulevard
Los Angeles, CA 90048
Tel: 310 423-4782   *Fax:* 310 423-0338
Length: 4 Yrs   *ACGME Approved/Offered Positions:* 20
Program ID: 300-05-12-030

UCLA Medical Center Program
Sponsor: UCLA David Geffen School of Medicine/UCLA
   Medical Center
UCLA Medical Center
Prgm Director: Charles R Lassman, MD, PhD
13-145A Center for Health Sciences
10833 Le Conte Avenue
Los Angeles, CA 90095
Tel: 310 825-5719   *Fax:* 310 267-2058
E-mail: apierro@mednet.ucla.edu
Length: 4 Yrs   *ACGME Approved/Offered Positions:* 20
Program ID: 300-05-11-034

University of Southern California/ LAC+USC Medical Center Program
Sponsor: University of Southern California/LAC+USC
   Medical Center
LAC+USC Medical Center
VA Greater Los Angeles Healthcare System
Prgm Director: Wesley Y Naritoku, MD, PhD
1100 North State Street, CT Room A7A
Los Angeles, CA 90033
Tel: 323 409-7148   *Fax:* 323 441-8193
E-mail: norona@usc.edu
Length: 4 Yrs   *ACGME Approved/Offered Positions:* 28
Program ID: 300-05-21-033

Orange

University of California (Irvine) Program
Sponsor: University of California (Irvine) Medical
   Center
Long Beach Memorial Medical Center
VA Long Beach Healthcare System
Prgm Director: Irina Maramica, MD, PhD*
Department of Pathology
101 The City Drive South
Orange, CA 92868
Tel: 714 456-6839   *Fax:* 714 456-5783
E-mail: iknezevi@uci.edu
Length: 4 Yrs   *ACGME Approved/Offered Positions:* 20
Program ID: 300-05-21-407

Sacramento

University of California (Davis) Health System Program
Sponsor: University of California (Davis) Health System
University of California (Davis) Medical Center
VA Northern California Health Care System
Prgm Director: Rajen Ramsamooj, MD
2315 Stockton Boulevard
Sacramento, CA 95817
Tel: 916 734-5534   *Fax:* 916 734-6468
E-mail: penny.young@ucdmc.ucdavis.edu
Length: 4 Yrs   *ACGME Approved/Offered Positions:* 16
Program ID: 300-05-11-025

San Diego

Naval Medical Center (San Diego) Program
Sponsor: Naval Medical Center (San Diego)
Prgm Director: CDR Michael M Quigley, MD, PhD
34800 Bob Wilson Drive
Laboartory Department
San Diego, CA 92134
Tel: 619 532-9308   *Fax:* 619 532-9403
E-mail: michael.quigley@med.navy.mil
Length: 4 Yrs   *ACGME Approved/Offered Positions:* 12
Program ID: 300-05-12-011
Uniformed Services Program

University of California (San Diego) Program
Sponsor: University of California (San Diego) Medical
   Center
Veterans Affairs Medical Center (San Diego)
Prgm Director: Brian Datnow, MD
Dept of Pathology Mail Code 8320
200 West Arbor Drive
San Diego, CA 92103
Tel: 619 543-5966   *Fax:* 619 543-3730
E-mail: mmwahl@ucsd.edu
Length: 4 Yrs   *ACGME Approved/Offered Positions:* 19
Program ID: 300-05-21-040

Note: * indicates a newly appointed program director

San Francisco

University of California (San Francisco) Program

Sponsor: University of California (San Francisco) School of Medicine
San Francisco General Hospital Medical Center
UCSF and Mount Zion Medical Centers
Veterans Affairs Medical Center (San Francisco)
Prgm Director: Patrick Treseler, MD, PhD
Department of Pathology
505 Parnassus Avenue, Box 0506
San Francisco, CA 94143
Tel: 415 514-1641   *Fax:* 415 353-1200
Length: 4 Yrs   *ACGME Approved/Offered Positions:* 29
Program ID: 300-05-21-044

Stanford

Stanford University Program

Sponsor: Stanford Hospital and Clinics
Veterans Affairs Palo Alto Health Care System
Prgm Director: Stephen J Galli, MD
Department of Pathology, L 235
300 Pasteur Drive
Stanford, CA 94305
Tel: 650 723-7975   *Fax:* 650 725-6902
E-mail: spabst@stanford.edu
Length: 4 Yrs   *ACGME Approved/Offered Positions:* 38
Program ID: 300-05-21-046

Torrance

Los Angeles County-Harbor-UCLA Medical Center Program

Sponsor: Los Angeles County-Harbor-UCLA Medical Center
Prgm Director: Holli M Mason, MD
Department of Pathology
1000 W Carson St
Torrance, CA 90509
Tel: 310 222-2250   *Fax:* 310 222-5333
E-mail: adflores@dhs.lacounty.gov
Length: 4 Yrs   *ACGME Approved/Offered Positions:* 16
Program ID: 300-05-11-047

Colorado

Aurora

University of Colorado Denver Program

Sponsor: University of Colorado Denver School of Medicine
Denver Health Medical Center
University of Colorado Hospital
Veterans Affairs Medical Center (Denver)
Prgm Director: Robert L Low, MD, PhD
12631 E 17th Avenue
Box B216, Mail Stop 6511
Aurora, CO 80045
Tel: 303 724-4307   *Fax:* 303 724-1105
Length: 4 Yrs   *ACGME Approved/Offered Positions:* 26
Program ID: 300-07-21-055

Colorado Springs

Penrose-St Francis Health Services Program

Sponsor: Penrose-St Francis Health Services
Prgm Director: Daniel C Mayes, MD*
2222 North Nevada Avenue
Colorado Springs, CO 80907
Tel: 719 776-5816   *Fax:* 719 776-2108
E-mail: danielmayes@centura.org
Length: 4 Yrs   *ACGME Approved/Offered Positions:* 6
Program ID: 300-07-12-048

Connecticut

Danbury

Danbury Hospital Program

Sponsor: Danbury Hospital
Prgm Director: Ramon N Kranwinkel, MD
24 Hospital Avenue
Danbury, CT 06810
Tel: 203 739-7338   *Fax:* 203 731-5343
E-mail: ramon.kranwinkel@danhosp.org
Length: 4 Yrs   *ACGME Approved/Offered Positions:* 8
Program ID: 300-08-11-057

Hartford

Hartford Hospital Program

Sponsor: Hartford Hospital
Prgm Director: Rebecca Williams, MD
80 Seymour Street
PO Box 5037
Hartford, CT 06102
Tel: 860 545-1593   *Fax:* 860 545-2204
Length: 4 Yrs   *ACGME Approved/Offered Positions:* 12
Program ID: 300-08-11-059

New Haven

Yale-New Haven Medical Center Program

Sponsor: Yale-New Haven Hospital
Veterans Affairs Medical Center (West Haven)
Prgm Director: John H Sinard, MD, PhD
Department of Pathology
PO Box 208023
New Haven, CT 06520
Tel: 203 785-6424   *Fax:* 203 785-3644
E-mail: john.sinard@yale.edu
Length: 4 Yrs   *ACGME Approved/Offered Positions:* 29
Program ID: 300-08-21-062

District of Columbia

Washington

George Washington University Program

Sponsor: George Washington University School of Medicine
George Washington University Hospital (UHS)
Veterans Affairs Medical Center (Washington, DC)
Prgm Director: Donald S Karcher, MD
2300 Eye Street, NW
Ross Hall, Room 502
Washington, DC 20037
Tel: 202 994-3391   *Fax:* 202 994-2618
E-mail: dkarcher@mfa.gwu.edu
Length: 4 Yrs   *ACGME Approved/Offered Positions:* 15
Program ID: 300-10-31-069

Georgetown University Hospital Program

Sponsor: Georgetown University Hospital
Prgm Director: Mary A Furlong, MD
3900 Reservoir Road, NW
Med Dent Bldg
Washington, DC 20007
Tel: 202 784-3636   *Fax:* 202 687-8934
Length: 4 Yrs   *ACGME Approved/Offered Positions:* 16
Program ID: 300-10-11-068

Howard University Program

Sponsor: Howard University Hospital
Prgm Director: Edward L Lee, MD
2041 Georgia Avenue, NW
Washington, DC 20060
Tel: 202 806-6306   *Fax:* 202 806-7022
Length: 4 Yrs   *ACGME Approved/Offered Positions:* 8
Program ID: 300-10-21-070

Washington Hospital Center Program

Sponsor: Washington Hospital Center
Prgm Director: Kirsten Alcorn, MD
110 Irving Street, NW
Washington, DC 20010
Tel: 202 877-5213   *Fax:* 202 877-3820
E-mail: kirsten.w.alcorn@medstar.net
Length: 4 Yrs   *ACGME Approved/Offered Positions:* 10
Program ID: 300-10-12-071

Florida

Gainesville

University of Florida Program

Sponsor: University of Florida College of Medicine
North Florida/South Georgia Veterans Health System
Shands Hospital at the University of Florida
Prgm Director: John D Reith, MD
PO Box 100275 JHMHC
1600 SW Archer Road
Gainesville, FL 32610
Tel: 352 265-0238   *Fax:* 352 265-6987
Length: 4 Yrs   *ACGME Approved/Offered Positions:* 17
Program ID: 300-11-21-073

Jacksonville

University of Florida College of Medicine Jacksonville Program

Sponsor: University of Florida College of Medicine Jacksonville
Shands Jacksonville Medical Center
Prgm Director: Shahla Masood, MD
Department of Pathology
655 West Eighth Street, Box C505
Jacksonville, FL 32209
Tel: 904 244-4889   *Fax:* 904 244-4060
E-mail: rebel.jones@jax.ufl.edu
Length: 4 Yrs   *ACGME Approved/Offered Positions:* 8
Program ID: 300-11-31-074

Miami

Jackson Memorial Hospital/Jackson Health System Program

Sponsor: Jackson Memorial Hospital/Jackson Health System
Prgm Director: Carol K Petito, MD
1611 NW 12th Avenue
Holtz Center 2053
Miami, FL 33136
Tel: 305 243-3584   *Fax:* 305 243-4086
Length: 4 Yrs   *ACGME Approved/Offered Positions:* 22
Program ID: 300-11-21-075

Miami Beach

Mount Sinai Medical Center of Florida Program

Sponsor: Mount Sinai Medical Center of Florida, Inc
Prgm Director: Lydia H Howard, MD
4300 Alton Road
Miami Beach, FL 33140
Tel: 305 674-2277   *Fax:* 305 674-2999
E-mail: cruzl@msmc.com
Length: 4 Yrs   *ACGME Approved/Offered Positions:* 8
Program ID: 300-11-31-076

Orlando

Orlando Health Program

Sponsor: Orlando Health
Orlando Regional Medical Center
Prgm Director: Shuan Li, MD
1414 Kuhl Avenue, MP44
Orlando, FL 32806
Tel: 321 841-8933   *Fax:* 321 843-6219
Length: 4 Yrs   *ACGME Approved/Offered Positions:* 10
Program ID: 300-11-12-077

Tampa

University of South Florida Program
Sponsor: University of South Florida College of Medicine
H Lee Moffitt Cancer Center
James A Haley Veterans Hospital
Tampa General Hospital
Prgm Director: Santo Nicosia, MD, MSc*
12901 Bruce B Downs Blvd
MDC 11
Tampa, FL 33612
Tel: 813 974-2745   *Fax:* 813 974-5536
E-mail: snicosia@health.usf.edu
Length: 4 Yrs   *ACGME Approved/Offered Positions:* 18
Program ID: 300-11-31-078

Georgia

Atlanta

Emory University Program
Sponsor: Emory University School of Medicine
Emory University Hospital
Grady Health System
Prgm Director: Shobha Sharma, MD
1364 Clifton Road, NE
Department of Pathology and Laboratory Medicine
Atlanta, GA 30322
Tel: 404 727-4283   *Fax:* 404 727-2519
E-mail: mmojonn@emory.edu
Length: 4 Yrs   *ACGME Approved/Offered Positions:* 40
Program ID: 300-12-21-080

Augusta

Medical College of Georgia Program
Sponsor: Medical College of Georgia
Veterans Affairs Medical Center (Augusta)
Prgm Director: D Greer Falls III, MD
Department of Pathology BA-1572
1120 15th Street
Augusta, GA 30912
Tel: 706 721-7453   *Fax:* 706 721-7781
E-mail: swillifo@mcg.edu
Length: 4 Yrs   *ACGME Approved/Offered Positions:* 14
Program ID: 300-12-21-082

Hawaii

Honolulu

University of Hawaii Program
Sponsor: University of Hawaii John A Burns School of
  Medicine
Kaiser Foundation Hospital (Moanalua)
Queen's Medical Center
Prgm Director: David M Shimizu, MD
John A Burns School of Medicine, Univ of HI
651 Ilalo Street #401A
Honolulu, HI 96813
Tel: 808 692-1131   *Fax:* 808 692-1256
E-mail: pathres@hawaii.edu
Length: 4 Yrs   *ACGME Approved/Offered Positions:* 10
Program ID: 300-14-21-085

Illinois

Chicago

McGaw Medical Center of Northwestern University Program
Sponsor: McGaw Medical Center of Northwestern
  University
Northwestern Memorial Hospital
Prgm Director: Beverly Nelson, MD*
Department of Pathology, Feinberg Pavilion
251 E Huron Street
Chicago, IL 60611
Tel: 312 926-9045   *Fax:* 312 926-0560
Length: 4 Yrs   *ACGME Approved/Offered Positions:* 22
Program ID: 300-16-21-094

Rush University Medical Center Program
Sponsor: Rush University Medical Center
Prgm Director: Elizabeth Cochran, MD
1653 West Congress Parkway
Chicago, IL 60612
Tel: 312 942-9133   *Fax:* 312 942-4228
E-mail: rachel_a_martin@rush.edu
Length: 4 Yrs   *ACGME Approved/Offered Positions:* 16
Program ID: 300-16-11-095

University of Chicago Program
Sponsor: University of Chicago Medical Center
Prgm Director: John Anastasi, MD
5841 S Maryland Avenue, MC 3083
Chicago, IL 60637
Tel: 773 702-6196   *Fax:* 773 702-1200
E-mail: john.anastasi@uchospitals.edu
Length: 4 Yrs   *ACGME Approved/Offered Positions:* 23
Program ID: 300-16-21-097

University of Illinois College of Medicine at Chicago Program
Sponsor: University of Illinois College of Medicine at
  Chicago
Advocate Illinois Masonic Medical Center
Advocate Lutheran General Hospital
University of Illinois Hospital and Clinics
Prgm Director: Frederick Behm, MD*
840 South Wood Street, Room 130 CSN
Chicago, IL 60612
Tel: 312 996-3150   *Fax:* 312 413-0156
Length: 4 Yrs   *ACGME Approved/Offered Positions:* 28
Program ID: 300-16-21-098

Evanston

McGaw Medical Center of Northwestern University (Evanston) Program
Sponsor: McGaw Medical Center of Northwestern
  University
Evanston Hospital
Prgm Director: Karen L Kaul, MD, PhD
2650 Ridge Avenue
Evanston, IL 60201
Tel: 847 570-2052   *Fax:* 847 733-5012
E-mail: k-kaul@northwestern.edu
Length: 4 Yrs   *ACGME Approved/Offered Positions:* 12
Program ID: 300-16-21-412

Maywood

Loyola University Program
Sponsor: Loyola University Medical Center
Edward Hines, Jr Veterans Affairs Hospital
Prgm Director: Eva M Wojcik, MD
2160 S First Avenue
Bldg 103, Room 0177
Maywood, IL 60153
Tel: 708 216-5591   *Fax:* 708 216-8225
E-mail: vbaertschi@lumc.edu
Length: 4 Yrs   *ACGME Approved/Offered Positions:* 16
Program ID: 300-16-21-394

Indiana

Indianapolis

Indiana University School of Medicine Program
Sponsor: Indiana University School of Medicine
Clarian Pathology Laboratory
Prgm Director: Carrie L Phillips, MD
Clarian Pathology Laboratory
350 W 11th Street, Room 4070
Indianapolis, IN 46202
Tel: 317 491-6494
Length: 4 Yrs   *ACGME Approved/Offered Positions:* 20
Program ID: 300-17-21-111

Muncie

Ball Memorial Hospital Program
Sponsor: Ball Memorial Hospital
Prgm Director: Janet E Roepke, MD, PhD
Pathology Residency Program
2401 W University Avenue
Muncie, IN 47303
Tel: 765 751-2702   *Fax:* 765 747-4466
E-mail: jjmiller@chsmail.org
Length: 4 Yrs   *ACGME Approved/Offered Positions:* 12
Program ID: 300-17-21-114

Iowa

Iowa City

University of Iowa Hospitals and Clinics Program
Sponsor: University of Iowa Hospitals and Clinics
Veterans Affairs Medical Center (Iowa City)
Prgm Director: Leslie A Bruch, MD*
Department of Pathology
5232 Roy Carver Pavilion
Iowa City, IA 52242
Tel: 319 384-8871
Length: 4 Yrs   *ACGME Approved/Offered Positions:* 20
Program ID: 300-18-21-116

Kansas

Kansas City

University of Kansas School of Medicine Program
Sponsor: University of Kansas School of Medicine
University of Kansas Hospital
Veterans Affairs Medical Center (Kansas City)
Prgm Director: Diane L Persons, MD, MA
3901 Rainbow Boulevard
2017 Wahl Hall West
Kansas City, KS 66160
Tel: 913 588-1728   *Fax:* 913 588-1777
E-mail: dpersons@kumc.edu
Length: 4 Yrs   *ACGME Approved/Offered Positions:* 18
Program ID: 300-19-21-117

Note: * indicates a newly appointed program director

Kentucky

Lexington

University of Kentucky College of Medicine Program

Sponsor: University of Kentucky College of Medicine
University of Kentucky Hospital
Veterans Affairs Medical Center (Lexington)
Prgm Director: Gregory J Davis, MD
Department of Pathology & Laboratory Medicine
800 Rose Street, Suite MS-117
Lexington, KY 40536
Tel: 859 323-6183   *Fax:* 859 323-2094
E-mail: gjdavis@email.uky.edu
Length: 4 Yrs   *ACGME Approved/Offered Positions:* 16
Program ID: 300-20-21-120

Louisville

University of Louisville Program

Sponsor: University of Louisville School of Medicine
University of Louisville Hospital
Prgm Director: Joseph C Parker Jr, MD, MS
530 South Jackson Street, C1R06
Louisville, KY 40202
Tel: 502 852-6515   *Fax:* 502 852-1771
E-mail: jcpark01@gwise.louisville.edu
Length: 4 Yrs   *ACGME Approved/Offered Positions:* 12
Program ID: 300-20-21-121

Louisiana

New Orleans

Louisiana State University Program

Sponsor: Louisiana State University School of Medicine
Medical Center of Louisiana at New Orleans
Ochsner Clinic Foundation
West Jefferson Medical Center
Prgm Director: Gary E Lipscomb, MD
Pathology Dept
1901 Perdido Street
New Orleans, LA 70112
Tel: 504 568-7002   *Fax:* 504 568-2049
Length: 4 Yrs   *ACGME Approved/Offered Positions:* 8
Program ID: 300-21-21-123

Tulane University Program

Sponsor: Tulane University School of Medicine
Tulane University Hospital and Clinics
Prgm Director: John R Krause, MD
1430 Tulane Ave, SL79
New Orleans, LA 70112
Tel: 504 988-2436   *Fax:* 504 988-7389
Length: 4 Yrs   *ACGME Approved/Offered Positions:* 8
Program ID: 300-21-21-122

Shreveport

Louisiana State University (Shreveport) Program

Sponsor: LSU Health Sciences Center-University
Hospital
Prgm Director: Marjorie R Fowler, MD
1501 Kings Highway, PO Box 33932
Shreveport, LA 71130
Tel: 318 675-5868   *Fax:* 318 675-8589
E-mail: MFowle@lsuhsc.edu
Length: 4 Yrs   *ACGME Approved/Offered Positions:* 12
Program ID: 300-21-31-126

Maryland

Baltimore

Johns Hopkins University Program

Sponsor: Johns Hopkins University School of Medicine
Johns Hopkins Hospital
Prgm Director: Edward F McCarthy Jr, MD
600 North Wolfe Street
Pathology 401
Baltimore, MD 21287
Tel: 410 955-3439   *Fax:* 410 614-9011
Length: 4 Yrs   *ACGME Approved/Offered Positions:* 34
Program ID: 300-23-11-129

University of Maryland Program

Sponsor: University of Maryland Medical System
Veterans Affairs Medical Center (Baltimore)
Prgm Director: Olga Ioffe, MD
22 South Greene Street
Baltimore, MD 21201
Tel: 410 328-5525   *Fax:* 410 328-5508
Length: 4 Yrs   *ACGME Approved/Offered Positions:* 17
Program ID: 300-23-31-135

Bethesda

National Capital Consortium Program

Sponsor: National Capital Consortium
National Naval Medical Center (Bethesda)
Walter Reed Army Medical Center
Prgm Director: Ross Barner, MD
Walter Reed Army Medical Center
Department of Pathology, Ward 47
Washington, DC 20307
Tel: 202 782-7744   *Fax:* 202 782-3217
E-mail: ross.barner@na.amedd.army.mil
Length: 4 Yrs   *ACGME Approved/Offered Positions:* 24
Program ID: 300-10-21-416
Uniformed Services Program

National Institutes of Health Clinical Center Program

Sponsor: Clinical Center at the National Institutes of
Health
Prgm Director: Elaine S Jaffe, MD
Bldg 10, Rm 2A33 MSC 1500
10 Center Drive
Bethesda, MD 20892
Tel: 301 496-0183   *Fax:* 301 402-2415
E-mail: hostlers@mail.nih.gov
Length: 3 Yrs   *ACGME Approved/Offered Positions:* 9
Program ID: 300-23-12-015

Massachusetts

Boston

Beth Israel Deaconess Medical Center/Harvard Medical School Program

Sponsor: Beth Israel Deaconess Medical Center
Prgm Director: James L Connolly, MD
Department of Pathology
330 Brookline Avenue
Boston, MA 02215
Tel: 617 667-4344   *Fax:* 617 667-7120
Length: 4 Yrs   *ACGME Approved/Offered Positions:* 32
Program ID: 300-24-31-419

Boston University Medical Center Program

Sponsor: Boston Medical Center
Office of the Chief Medical Examiner
Prgm Director: Carl J O'Hara, MD
670 Albany Street, 3rd Floor
Boston, MA 02118
Tel: 617 414-5182   *Fax:* 617 414-5315
Length: 4 Yrs   *ACGME Approved/Offered Positions:* 13
Program ID: 300-24-21-139

Brigham and Women's Hospital Program

Sponsor: Brigham and Women's Hospital
Dana-Farber Cancer Institute
Prgm Director: Gayle L Winters, MD
Department of Pathology
75 Francis Street
Boston, MA 02115
Tel: 617 732-8613   *Fax:* 617 232-9820
E-mail: marosado@partners.org
Length: 4 Yrs   *ACGME Approved/Offered Positions:* 35
Program ID: 300-24-31-146

Massachusetts General Hospital Program

Sponsor: Massachusetts General Hospital
Prgm Director: W Stephen Black-Schaffer, MD, MA
Dept of Pathology, WRN Building, Room 219
55 Fruit Street
Boston, MA 02114
Tel: 617 724-1463   *Fax:* 617 726-3226
E-mail: mghpath@partners.org
Length: 4 Yrs   *ACGME Approved/Offered Positions:* 35
Program ID: 300-24-31-143

Tufts Medical Center Program

Sponsor: Tufts Medical Center
Prgm Director: Maria L Garcia-Moliner, MD
800 Washington Street, Box 802
Boston, MA 02111
Tel: 617 636-7039   *Fax:* 617 636-8302
E-mail: mmoliner@tuftsmedicalcenter.org
Length: 4 Yrs   *ACGME Approved/Offered Positions:* 14
Program ID: 300-24-21-145

Pittsfield

Berkshire Medical Center Program

Sponsor: Berkshire Medical Center
Prgm Director: Rebecca L Johnson, MD
725 North Street
Pittsfield, MA 01201
Tel: 413 447-2565   *Fax:* 413 447-2097
E-mail: drathbun@bhs1.org
Length: 4 Yrs   *ACGME Approved/Offered Positions:* 8
Program ID: 300-24-11-153

Springfield

Baystate Medical Center/Tufts University School of Medicine Program

Sponsor: Baystate Medical Center
Prgm Director: Jean Henneberry, MD
Department of Pathology
759 Chestnut Street
Springfield, MA 01199
Tel: 413 794-5085   *Fax:* 413 794-5893
E-mail: lora.fillion@bhs.org
Length: 4 Yrs   *ACGME Approved/Offered Positions:* 16
Program ID: 300-24-21-413

Worcester

University of Massachusetts Program

Sponsor: University of Massachusetts Medical School
UMass Memorial Health Care (Memorial Campus)
UMass Memorial Health Care (University Campus)
Prgm Director: Zhong Jiang, MD*
One Innovation Drive
Three Biotech, Second Floor
Worcester, MA 01605
Tel: 508 793-6166   *Fax:* 508 793-6110
Length: 4 Yrs   *ACGME Approved/Offered Positions:* 16
Program ID: 300-24-21-400

Programs

Michigan

Ann Arbor

University of Michigan Program
Sponsor: University of Michigan Hospitals and Health Centers
Prgm Director: Joseph C Fantone, MD
M4211 MSI
1301 Catherine
Ann Arbor, MI 48109
Tel: 734 764-3270   *Fax:* 734 763-6476
Length: 4 Yrs   *ACGME Approved/Offered Positions:* 28
Program ID: 300-25-21-158

Detroit

Henry Ford Hospital Program
Sponsor: Henry Ford Hospital
Prgm Director: Richard Zarbo, MD, DMD
Department of Pathology
2799 West Grand Blvd
Detroit, MI 48202
Tel: 313 916-3194   *Fax:* 313 916-2385
Length: 4 Yrs   *ACGME Approved/Offered Positions:* 16
Program ID: 300-25-12-160

St John Hospital and Medical Center Program
Sponsor: St John Hospital and Medical Center
Prgm Director: Basim M Al-Khafaji, MD
Department of Pathology
22101 Moross Road
Detroit, MI 48236
Tel: 313 343-3520   *Fax:* 313 881-4727
E-mail: dana.trysh@stjohn.org
Length: 4 Yrs   *ACGME Approved/Offered Positions:* 8
Program ID: 300-25-12-162

Wayne State University/Detroit Medical Center Program
Sponsor: Wayne State University/Detroit Medical Center
Detroit Receiving Hospital and University Health Center
Harper-Hutzel Hospital
Prgm Director: William J Kupsky, MD
540 East Canfield Avenue
9374 Scott Hall
Detroit, MI 48201
Tel: 313 577-1102   *Fax:* 313 577-0057
Length: 4 Yrs   *ACGME Approved/Offered Positions:* 12
Program ID: 300-25-21-165

Royal Oak

William Beaumont Hospital Program
Sponsor: William Beaumont Hospital
Prgm Director: Michele T Rooney, MD
3601 West 13 Mile Road
Royal Oak, MI 48073
Tel: 248 898-9060   *Fax:* 248 898-1257
Length: 4 Yrs   *ACGME Approved/Offered Positions:* 12
Program ID: 300-25-21-173

Minnesota

Minneapolis

University of Minnesota Program
Sponsor: University of Minnesota Medical School
Abbott-Northwestern Hospital/Allina Health System
Hennepin County Medical Center
University of Minnesota Medical Center, Division of Fairview
Veterans Affairs Medical Center (Minneapolis)
Prgm Director: Alan G Rose, MD, MBChB
420 Delaware Street SE
Mayo Mail Code 76
Minneapolis, MN 55455
Tel: 612 273-5758   *Fax:* 612 273-1142
E-mail: rosex031@umn.edu
Length: 4 Yrs   *ACGME Approved/Offered Positions:* 26
Program ID: 300-26-31-178

Rochester

College of Medicine, Mayo Clinic (Rochester) Program
Sponsor: College of Medicine, Mayo Clinic
Mayo Clinic (Rochester)
Rochester Methodist Hospital
Saint Marys Hospital of Rochester
Prgm Director: Mary E Fidler, MD
Dept of Pathology
200 First Street, SW
Rochester, MN 55905
Tel: 507 284-1196   *Fax:* 507 538-3267
E-mail: pathologyeducation@mayo.edu
Length: 4 Yrs   *ACGME Approved/Offered Positions:* 20
Program ID: 300-26-21-179

Mississippi

Jackson

University of Mississippi Medical Center Program
Sponsor: University of Mississippi School of Medicine
University Hospitals and Clinics
Prgm Director: Anwer Siddiqi, MD, MS*
2500 North State Street
Jackson, MS 39216
Tel: 601 984-1891   *Fax:* 601 984-4967
E-mail: ASiddiqi@pathology.umsmed.edu
Length: 4 Yrs   *ACGME Approved/Offered Positions:* 12
Program ID: 300-27-21-182

Missouri

Columbia

University of Missouri-Columbia Program
Sponsor: University of Missouri-Columbia School of Medicine
Harry S Truman Memorial Veterans Hospital
University Hospitals and Clinics
Prgm Director: Alan M Luger, MD
One Hospital Drive
Columbia, MO 65212
Tel: 573 882-7910   *Fax:* 573 884-4612
Length: 4 Yrs   *ACGME Approved/Offered Positions:* 12
Program ID: 300-28-21-185

Kansas City

University of Missouri at Kansas City Program
Sponsor: University of Missouri-Kansas City School of Medicine
Truman Medical Center
Prgm Director: Russell M Fiorella, MD, MBA
2301 Holmes Street
Kansas City, MO 64108
Tel: 816 404-0577   *Fax:* 816 404-0572
E-mail: catherine.buck@tmcmed.org
Length: 4 Yrs   *ACGME Approved/Offered Positions:* 8
Program ID: 300-28-21-408

St Louis

St Louis University School of Medicine Program
Sponsor: St Louis University School of Medicine
Cardinal Glennon Children's Hospital
St Louis University Hospital
St Mary's Health Center
Prgm Director: Carole A Vogler, MD
1402 South Grand Boulevard
St Louis, MO 63104
Tel: 314 577-5348   *Fax:* 314 268-5641
E-mail: paradoea@slu.edu
Length: 4 Yrs   *ACGME Approved/Offered Positions:* 16
Program ID: 300-28-21-192

Washington University/B-JH/SLCH Consortium Program
Sponsor: Washington University/B-JH/SLCH Consortium
Barnes-Jewish Hospital
Prgm Director: Phyllis C Huettner, MD
660 South Euclid Avenue
St Louis, MO 63110
Tel: 314 362-0118   *Fax:* 314 362-0369
E-mail: weber@pathology.wustl.edu
Length: 4 Yrs   *ACGME Approved/Offered Positions:* 42
Program ID: 300-28-11-193

Nebraska

Omaha

Creighton University Program
Sponsor: Creighton University School of Medicine
Creighton University Medical Center (Tenet - SJH)
Veterans Affairs Medical Center (Omaha)
Prgm Director: William J Hunter, MD*
601 North 30th Street
Department of Pathology
Omaha, NE 68131
Tel: 402 449-4961   *Fax:* 402 280-5247
E-mail: kmartin@creighton.edu
Length: 4 Yrs   *ACGME Approved/Offered Positions:* 11
Program ID: 300-30-21-195

University of Nebraska Medical Center College of Medicine Program
Sponsor: University of Nebraska Medical Center College of Medicine
Nebraska Medical Center
Prgm Director: Subodh M Lele, MD
983135 Nebraska Medical Center
Omaha, NE 68198
Tel: 402 559-5180   *Fax:* 402 559-6018
E-mail: pathres@unmc.edu
Length: 4 Yrs   *ACGME Approved/Offered Positions:* 12
Program ID: 300-30-21-197

Note: * indicates a newly appointed program director

New Hampshire

Lebanon

Dartmouth-Hitchcock Medical Center Program

Sponsor: Mary Hitchcock Memorial Hospital
Prgm Director: Candice C Black, DO*
One Medical Center Drive
Lebanon, NH 03756
Tel: 603 650-8217 *Fax:* 603 650-4845
Length: 4 Yrs *ACGME Approved/Offered Positions:* 14
Program ID: 300-32-21-198

New Jersey

Livingston

St Barnabas Medical Center Program

Sponsor: St Barnabas Medical Center
Monmouth Medical Center
Prgm Director: Jonathan F Lara, MD
94 Old Short Hills Road
Livingston, NJ 07039
Tel: 973 322-5762 *Fax:* 973 322-5564
E-mail: Jlara@sbhcs.com
Length: 4 Yrs *ACGME Approved/Offered Positions:* 19
Program ID: 300-33-21-418

New Brunswick

UMDNJ-Robert Wood Johnson Medical School Program

Sponsor: UMDNJ-Robert Wood Johnson Medical School
Cooper Hospital-University Medical Center
Robert Wood Johnson University Hospital
Prgm Director: Billie Fyfe-Kirschner, MD
One Robert Wood Johnson Place
Medical Education Building, Room 212
New Brunswick, NJ 08903
Tel: 732 235-8121 *Fax:* 732 235-8124
E-mail: martinm7@umdnj.edu
Length: 4 Yrs *ACGME Approved/Offered Positions:* 10
Program ID: 300-33-21-215

Newark

UMDNJ-New Jersey Medical School Program

Sponsor: UMDNJ-New Jersey Medical School
Hackensack University Medical Center
UMDNJ-University Hospital
Veterans Affairs New Jersey Health Care System
Prgm Director: Seena Aisner, MD
185 South Orange Avenue
Newark, NJ 07103
Tel: 973 972-5722 *Fax:* 973 972-5724
E-mail: carabamd@umdnj.edu
Length: 4 Yrs *ACGME Approved/Offered Positions:* 16
Program ID: 300-33-21-381

New Mexico

Albuquerque

University of New Mexico Program

Sponsor: University of New Mexico School of Medicine
University of New Mexico Hospital
Veterans Affairs Medical Center (Albuquerque)
Prgm Director: Ian D Paul, MD*
1 Univ of New Mexico, MSC08-4640
Attn: Jeanne Lay
Albuquerque, NM 87131
Tel: 505 272-6994 *Fax:* 505 925-7399
E-mail: IDPaul@salud.unm.edu
Length: 4 Yrs *ACGME Approved/Offered Positions:* 16
Program ID: 300-34-21-218

New York

Albany

Albany Medical Center Program

Sponsor: Albany Medical Center
Veterans Affairs Medical Center (Albany)
Prgm Director: Ann B Boguniewicz, MD
Department of Pathology MC-81
47 New Scotland Avenue
Albany, NY 12208
Tel: 518 262-5436 *Fax:* 518 262-5861
E-mail: pathresidency@mail.amc.edu
Length: 4 Yrs *ACGME Approved/Offered Positions:* 18
Program ID: 300-35-21-219

Bronx

Albert Einstein College of Medicine Program

Sponsor: Albert Einstein College of Medicine of Yeshiva
University
Montefiore Medical Center-Henry and Lucy Moses
Division
Montefiore Medical Center-Weiler Division
Prgm Director: Jacob J Steinberg, MD
111 East 210th Street, C410
Pathology Administration Central 410
Bronx, NY 10467
Tel: 718 920-6573 *Fax:* 718 547-8349
E-mail: steinber@aecom.yu.edu
Length: 4 Yrs *ACGME Approved/Offered Positions:* 20
Program ID: 300-35-21-230

Brooklyn

SUNY Health Science Center at Brooklyn Program

Sponsor: SUNY Health Science Center at Brooklyn
Kings County Hospital Center
University Hospital-SUNY Health Science Center at
Brooklyn
Veterans Affairs Medical Center (Brooklyn)
Prgm Director: Peter J Howanitz, MD
450 Clarkson Avenue
Box 25
Brooklyn, NY 11203
Tel: 718 270-4522 *Fax:* 718 270-4524
E-mail: pathologyresidency@downstate.edu
Length: 4 Yrs *ACGME Approved/Offered Positions:* 24
Program ID: 300-35-21-260

Buffalo

University at Buffalo Program

Sponsor: University at Buffalo School of Medicine
Kaleida Health System (Buffalo General Hospital)
Kaleida Health System (Millard Fillmore Hospital)
Prgm Director: Amy M Sands, MD
100 High Street
Suite B-451
Buffalo, NY 14203
Tel: 716 859-3760 *Fax:* 716 859-4015
E-mail: wrscales@buffalo.edu
Length: 4 Yrs *ACGME Approved/Offered Positions:* 20
Program ID: 300-35-21-224

East Meadow

Nassau University Medical Center Program

Sponsor: Nassau University Medical Center
South Nassau Communities Hospital
Prgm Director: Jen H Lin, MD
2201 Hempstead Turnpike Box 47
East Meadow, NY 11554
Tel: 516 572-3201 *Fax:* 516 572-8894
E-mail: jlin@numc.edu
Length: 4 Yrs *ACGME Approved/Offered Positions:* 9
Program ID: 300-35-21-225

Great Neck

NSLIJHS-Albert Einstein College of Medicine at Long Island Jewish Medical Center Program

Sponsor: North Shore-Long Island Jewish Health System
Long Island Jewish Medical Center
North Shore University Hospital
Prgm Director: Michael J Esposito, MD
270-05 76th Avenue
Room B-67
New Hyde Park, NY 11040
Tel: 718 470-3077 *Fax:* 718 347-9171
E-mail: sullivan@lij.edu
Length: 4 Yrs *ACGME Approved/Offered Positions:* 16
Program ID: 300-35-21-245

Mineola

Winthrop-University Hospital Program

Sponsor: Winthrop-University Hospital
Prgm Director: Virginia M Donovan, MD
259 First Street
222 Professional Bldg, Suite 618
Mineola, NY 11501
Tel: 516 663-2450 *Fax:* 516 663-4584
E-mail: vdonovan@winthrop.org
Length: 4 Yrs *ACGME Approved/Offered Positions:* 8
Program ID: 300-35-12-229

New York

Lenox Hill Hospital Program

Sponsor: Lenox Hill Hospital
Prgm Director: William H Rodgers, MD, PhD*
100 East 77th Street
New York, NY 10075
Tel: 212 434-2330
Length: 4 Yrs *ACGME Approved/Offered Positions:* 8
Program ID: 300-35-11-243

Mount Sinai School of Medicine Program

Sponsor: Mount Sinai School of Medicine
Mount Sinai Medical Center
Veterans Affairs Medical Center (Bronx)
Prgm Director: James A Strauchen, MD
Department of Pathology
One Gustave L Levy Place
New York, NY 10029
Tel: 212 241-8014 *Fax:* 212 426-5129
E-mail: james.strauchen@mssm.edu
Length: 4 Yrs *ACGME Approved/Offered Positions:* 24
Program ID: 300-35-21-251

New York Medical College at St Vincent's Hospital and Medical Center of New York Program

Sponsor: New York Medical College
St Vincent Catholic Medical Centers (Manhattan)
Prgm Director: Fred B Smith, MD
170 West 12th Street
New York, NY 10011
Tel: 212 604-1564 *Fax:* 212 604-8426
E-mail: fredbsmith@pol.net
Length: 4 Yrs *ACGME Approved/Offered Positions:* 8
Program ID: 300-35-21-259

New York Presbyterian Hospital (Columbia Campus) Program

Sponsor: New York Presbyterian Hospital
New York Presbyterian Hospital (Columbia Campus)
Prgm Director: Charles C Marboe, MD
630 West 168th Street
New York, NY 10032
Tel: 212 305-8063 *Fax:* 212 305-6595
Length: 4 Yrs *ACGME Approved/Offered Positions:* 21
Program ID: 300-35-11-237

Programs

New York Presbyterian Hospital (Cornell Campus) Program
Sponsor: New York Presbyterian Hospital
Prgm Director: Debra Leonard, MD, PhD
525 East 68th Street
Room C-302
New York, NY 10021
Tel: 212 746-2041   *Fax:* 212 746-8855
Length: 4 Yrs   *ACGME Approved/Offered Positions:* 22
Program ID: 300-35-11-253

New York University School of Medicine Program
Sponsor: New York University School of Medicine
Bellevue Hospital Center
NYU Hospitals Center
Prgm Director: Michael A Bannan, MD
550 First Avenue
Smilow 301
New York, NY 10016
Tel: 212 263-2132
E-mail: michael.bannan@med.nyu.edu
Length: 4 Yrs   *ACGME Approved/Offered Positions:* 30
Program ID: 300-35-21-255

St Luke's-Roosevelt Hospital Center Program
Sponsor: St Luke's-Roosevelt Hospital Center
Beth Israel Medical Center
Prgm Director: Mark T Friedman, DO
1111 Amsterdam Ave
New York, NY 10025
Tel: 212 523-7274   *Fax:* 212 523-6394
Length: 4 Yrs   *ACGME Approved/Offered Positions:* 20
Program ID: 300-35-21-398

Rochester

University of Rochester Program
Sponsor: Strong Memorial Hospital of the University of Rochester
Prgm Director: Scott A Kirkley, MD
601 Elmwood Avenue, Box 626
Rochester, NY 14642
Tel: 585 275-5297   *Fax:* 585 273-1027
E-mail: betsy_mcdonald@urmc.rochester.edu
Length: 4 Yrs   *ACGME Approved/Offered Positions:* 21
Program ID: 300-35-21-263

Stony Brook

SUNY at Stony Brook Program
Sponsor: University Hospital - SUNY at Stony Brook
Prgm Director: Bernard P Lane, MD, MA
Department of Pathology, HOS 2-766
Stony Brook, NY 11794
Tel: 631 444-2224   *Fax:* 631 444-3419
E-mail: kpitisi@notes.cc.sunysb.edu
Length: 4 Yrs   *ACGME Approved/Offered Positions:* 14
Program ID: 300-35-21-396

Syracuse

SUNY Upstate Medical University Program
Sponsor: SUNY Upstate Medical University
Prgm Director: Gustavo de la Roza, MD
750 East Adams Street
Suite 2306, Weiskotten Hall
Syracuse, NY 13210
Tel: 315 464-4670   *Fax:* 315 464-4675
E-mail: phillips@upstate.edu
Length: 4 Yrs   *ACGME Approved/Offered Positions:* 16
Program ID: 300-35-21-265

Valhalla

New York Medical College at Westchester Medical Center Program
Sponsor: New York Medical College
Westchester Medical Center
Prgm Director: Maria E Aguero-Rosenfeld, MD
Basic Science Building
Department of Pathology, Room 413
Valhalla, NY 10595
Tel: 914 594-4150   *Fax:* 914 594-4163
E-mail: elizabeth_iannucci@nymc.edu
Length: 4 Yrs   *ACGME Approved/Offered Positions:* 10
Program ID: 300-35-11-266

North Carolina

Chapel Hill

University of North Carolina Hospitals Program
Sponsor: University of North Carolina Hospitals
Prgm Director: Thomas W Bouldin, MD
CB 7525
Chapel Hill, NC 27599
Tel: 919 966-4677   *Fax:* 919 966-6718
Length: 4 Yrs   *ACGME Approved/Offered Positions:* 15
Program ID: 300-36-11-267

Durham

Duke University Hospital Program
Sponsor: Duke University Hospital
Veterans Affairs Medical Center (Durham)
Prgm Director: Patrick J Buckley, MD, PhD
Box 3712
Durham, NC 27710
Tel: 919 681-6578   *Fax:* 919 684-1856
Length: 4 Yrs   *ACGME Approved/Offered Positions:* 24
Program ID: 300-36-21-269

Greenville

Pitt County Memorial Hospital/East Carolina University Program
Sponsor: Pitt County Memorial Hospital
Prgm Director: Peter J Kragel, MD
2100 Stantonsburg Road
PO Box 6028
Greenville, NC 27834
Tel: 252 847-4951   *Fax:* 252 847-8368
Length: 4 Yrs   *ACGME Approved/Offered Positions:* 12
Program ID: 300-36-21-404

Winston-Salem

Wake Forest University School of Medicine Program
Sponsor: Wake Forest University Baptist Medical Center
Prgm Director: Constance A Stanton, MD*
Department of Pathology
Medical Center Boulevard
Winston-Salem, NC 27157
Tel: 336 716-2631   *Fax:* 336 716-7595
E-mail: pathology-residency@wfubmc.edu
Length: 4 Yrs   *ACGME Approved/Offered Positions:* 20
Program ID: 300-36-11-270

Ohio

Akron

Summa Health System/NEOUCOM Program
Sponsor: Summa Health System
Akron City Hospital (Summa Health System)
Prgm Director: Raymond E Clarke, MD
525 East Market Street
Akron, OH 44304
Tel: 330 375-3786   *Fax:* 330 375-4874
Length: 4 Yrs   *ACGME Approved/Offered Positions:* 8
Program ID: 300-38-11-272

Cincinnati

University Hospital/University of Cincinnati College of Medicine Program
Sponsor: University Hospital Inc
Prgm Director: Gregory S Retzinger, MD, PhD*
Department of Pathology and Laboratory Medicine
231 Albert Sabin Way
Cincinnati, OH 45267
Tel: 513 558-3447   *Fax:* 513 558-2289
Length: 4 Yrs   *ACGME Approved/Offered Positions:* 15
Program ID: 300-38-21-276

Cleveland

Case Western Reserve University (MetroHealth) Program
Sponsor: MetroHealth Medical Center
Prgm Director: Joseph F Tomashefski Jr, MD
2500 MetroHealth Drive
Cleveland, OH 44109
Tel: 216 778-5181   *Fax:* 216 778-7112
Length: 4 Yrs   *ACGME Approved/Offered Positions:* 8
Program ID: 300-38-11-279

Cleveland Clinic Foundation Program
Sponsor: Cleveland Clinic Foundation
Prgm Director: Karl S Theil, MD
Pathology and Laboratory Medicine Institute
9500 Euclid Avenue, L21
Cleveland, OH 44195
Tel: 216 444-1086   *Fax:* 216 445-9444
Length: 4 Yrs   *ACGME Approved/Offered Positions:* 36
Program ID: 300-38-12-278

University Hospitals Case Medical Center Program
Sponsor: University Hospitals Case Medical Center
Prgm Director: Robert D Hoffman, MD, PhD
Department of Pathology
11100 Euclid Avenue
Cleveland, OH 44106
Tel: 216 844-3478   *Fax:* 216 844-4668
Length: 4 Yrs   *ACGME Approved/Offered Positions:* 21
Program ID: 300-38-21-277

Columbus

Ohio State University Hospital Program
Sponsor: Ohio State University Hospital
Prgm Director: Arwa Shana'ah, MD*
N-308 Doan Hall
410 West 10th Avenue
Columbus, OH 43210
Tel: 614 293-8184   *Fax:* 614 293-2075
E-mail: arwa.shanaah@osumc.edu
Length: 4 Yrs   *ACGME Approved/Offered Positions:* 16
Program ID: 300-38-21-286

Note: * indicates a newly appointed program director

Toledo

University of Toledo Program

Sponsor: University of Toledo
University Medical Center (Toledo)
Prgm Director: Robert E Mrak, MD, PhD*
3000 Arlington Avenue
Mail Stop 1068
Toledo, OH 43614
Tel: 419 383-3474
E-mail: Kimberley.Mitchell@utoledo.edu
Length: 4 Yrs   *ACGME Approved/Offered Positions:* 9
Program ID: 300-38-11-290

Youngstown

Western Reserve Care System/NEOUCOM Program

Sponsor: Forum Health/Western Reserve Care System
  (Youngstown)
Northside Medical Center
Prgm Director: Geoffrey Mendelsohn, MD
Northside Medical Center
500 Gypsy Lane
Youngstown, OH 44501
Tel: 330 884-3767   *Fax:* 330 884-3790
E-mail: gmendelsohn@forumhealth.org
Length: 4 Yrs   *ACGME Approved/Offered Positions:* 8
Program ID: 300-38-11-292

Oklahoma

Oklahoma City

University of Oklahoma Health Sciences Center Program

Sponsor: University of Oklahoma College of Medicine
OU Medical Center
Prgm Director: Michael L Talbert, MD
Department of Pathology
940 Stanton L Young, BMSB 451
Oklahoma City, OK 73104
Tel: 405 271-2422   *Fax:* 405 271-2328
E-mail: Dianne-Wright@ouhsc.edu
Length: 4 Yrs   *ACGME Approved/Offered Positions:* 16
Program ID: 300-39-21-295

Oregon

Portland

Oregon Health & Science University Program

Sponsor: Oregon Health & Science University Hospital
Kaiser Foundation Hospitals-Northwest Region
Veterans Affairs Medical Center (Portland)
Prgm Director: Richard M Scanlan, MD
Dept of Pathology, L-113
3181 SW Sam Jackson Park Road
Portland, OR 97239
Tel: 503 494-6776   *Fax:* 503 494-8148
E-mail: pathrap@ohsu.edu
Length: 4 Yrs   *ACGME Approved/Offered Positions:* 12
Program ID: 300-40-11-302

Pennsylvania

Hershey

Penn State University/Milton S Hershey Medical Center Program

Sponsor: Milton S Hershey Medical Center
Prgm Director: Dani S Zander, MD*
500 University Drive
PO Box 850
Hershey, PA 17033
Tel: 717 531-8351   *Fax:* 717 531-5021
E-mail: dzander@hmc.psu.edu
Length: 4 Yrs   *ACGME Approved/Offered Positions:* 12
Program ID: 300-41-11-308

Johnstown

Conemaugh Valley Memorial Hospital Program

Sponsor: Conemaugh Valley Memorial Hospital
Prgm Director: Curtis S Goldblatt, MD
1086 Franklin Street
Johnstown, PA 15905
Tel: 814 534-1624   *Fax:* 814 534-1635
E-mail: rnelson@conemaugh.org
Length: 4 Yrs   *ACGME Approved/Offered Positions:* 8
Program ID: 300-41-21-397

Philadelphia

Drexel University College of Medicine/Hahnemann University Hospital Program

Sponsor: Drexel University College of
  Medicine/Hahnemann University
Hahnemann University Hospital (Tenet Health System)
Prgm Director: Cheryl A Hanau, MD
Broad and Vine Streets
Mail Stop 435
Philadelphia, PA 19102
Tel: 215 762-1179
Length: 4 Yrs   *ACGME Approved/Offered Positions:* 21
Program ID: 300-41-21-316

Pennsylvania Hospital of the University of Pennsylvania Health System Program

Sponsor: Pennsylvania Hospital (UPHS)
Prgm Director: Tunde A Farkas, MD*
8th and Spruce Streets
Philadelphia, PA 19107
Tel: 215 829-6992   *Fax:* 215 829-7564
E-mail: tunde_farkas@uphs.upenn.edu
Length: 4 Yrs   *ACGME Approved/Offered Positions:* 11
Program ID: 300-41-11-318

Temple University Hospital Program

Sponsor: Temple University Hospital
Prgm Director: Matthew T Hurford, MD
3400 North Broad Street
Philadelphia, PA 19140
Tel: 215 707-7740   *Fax:* 215 707-2053
Length: 4 Yrs   *ACGME Approved/Offered Positions:* 12
Program ID: 300-41-11-321

Thomas Jefferson University Program

Sponsor: Thomas Jefferson University Hospital
Prgm Director: Fred Gorstein, MD
125 S 11th Street
Room 204 Pavilion
Philadelphia, PA 19107
Tel: 215 503-7206   *Fax:* 215 955-2519
E-mail: Fred.Gorstein@jefferson.edu
Length: 4 Yrs   *ACGME Approved/Offered Positions:* 14
Program ID: 300-41-11-322

University of Pennsylvania Program

Sponsor: University of Pennsylvania Health System
Prgm Director: Gordon Yu, MD
3400 Spruce Street
6 Founders
Philadelphia, PA 19104
Tel: 215 662-3211   *Fax:* 215 614-1856
E-mail: mary.ann.broda@uphs.upenn.edu
Length: 4 Yrs   *ACGME Approved/Offered Positions:* 30
Program ID: 300-41-21-314

Pittsburgh

Allegheny General Hospital Program

Sponsor: Allegheny General Hospital
Prgm Director: Katherine M Jasnosz, MD
320 East North Avenue
Pittsburgh, PA 15212
Tel: 412 359-6037   *Fax:* 412 359-3860
E-mail: kjasnosz@wpahs.org
Length: 4 Yrs   *ACGME Approved/Offered Positions:* 10
Program ID: 300-41-12-323

University of Pittsburgh Medical Center Medical Education Program

Sponsor: Univ of Pittsburgh Medical Center Medical
  Education
Magee-Womens Hospital of UPMC
UPMC Presbyterian Shadyside
Prgm Director: Trevor A Macpherson, MBChB, MS
A711 Scaife Hall
3550 Terrace Street
Pittsburgh, PA 15261
Tel: 412 802-6013   *Fax:* 412 802-6079
E-mail: training_path@upmc.edu
Length: 4 Yrs   *ACGME Approved/Offered Positions:* 33
Program ID: 300-41-21-324

Puerto Rico

San Juan

University of Puerto Rico Program

Sponsor: University of Puerto Rico School of Medicine
University Hospital
Prgm Director: Roman Velez-Rosario, MD
Department of Pathology
PO Box 365067
San Juan, PR 00936
Tel: 787 758-2525   *Fax:* 787 754-0710
Length: 4 Yrs   *ACGME Approved/Offered Positions:* 11
Program ID: 300-42-21-385

Rhode Island

Providence

Brown University Program

Sponsor: Rhode Island Hospital-Lifespan
Miriam Hospital-Lifespan
Prgm Director: Li Juan Wang, MD, PhD
593 Eddy St
Providence, RI 02903
Tel: 401 444-5981   *Fax:* 401 444-8514
E-mail: ACrouse@lifespan.org
Length: 4 Yrs   *ACGME Approved/Offered Positions:* 16
Program ID: 300-43-21-414

Programs

South Carolina

Charleston

Medical University of South Carolina Program

Sponsor: Medical University of South Carolina College of Medicine
MUSC Medical Center
Prgm Director: David Lewin, MD
165 Ashley Avenue, Suite 309
PO Box 250908
Charleston, SC 29425
Tel: 843 792-3121   *Fax:* 843 792-0555
Length: 4 Yrs   *ACGME Approved/Offered Positions:* 22
Program ID: 300-45-21-332

South Dakota

Sioux Falls

University of South Dakota Program

Sponsor: University of South Dakota School of Medicine
Royal C Johnson Veterans Affairs Medical Center
Sioux Valley Hospital University of SD Medical Center
Prgm Director: Joel A Ziebarth, MD
LCM Pathologists, PC
1400 West 22nd Street
Sioux Falls, SD 57117
Tel: 605 333-1730   *Fax:* 605 333-1966
E-mail: ktuschen@lcmpath.com
Length: 4 Yrs   *ACGME Approved/Offered Positions:* 6
Program ID: 300-46-21-333

Tennessee

Johnson City

East Tennessee State University Program

Sponsor: James H Quillen College of Medicine
Johnson City Medical Center/Mountain States Health Alliance
Veterans Affairs Medical Center (Mountain Home)
Prgm Director: Jerald Mullersman, MD, PhD
PO Box 70568
Johnson City, TN 37614
Tel: 423 439-6210   *Fax:* 423 439-8060
Length: 4 Yrs   *ACGME Approved/Offered Positions:* 8
Program ID: 300-47-21-399

Knoxville

University of Tennessee Medical Center at Knoxville Program

Sponsor: University of Tennessee Graduate School of Medicine
University of Tennessee Memorial Hospital
Prgm Director: John C Neff, MD
1924 Alcoa Highway, Drawer 108
Knoxville, TN 37920
Tel: 865 305-8994   *Fax:* 865 305-6866
E-mail: jneff@utk.edu
Length: 4 Yrs   *ACGME Approved/Offered Positions:* 10
Program ID: 300-47-11-335

Memphis

University of Tennessee Program

Sponsor: University of Tennessee College of Medicine
Baptist Memorial Hospital
Methodist Healthcare - Memphis Hospitals
Regional Medical Center at Memphis
St Jude Children's Research Hospital
University of Tennessee Department of Pathology
University of Tennessee Medical Center
Veterans Affairs Medical Center (Memphis)
Prgm Director: John Duckworth, MD
930 Madison Avenue
5th Floor
Memphis, TN 38163
Tel: 901 448-7027   *Fax:* 901 448-6979
Length: 4 Yrs   *ACGME Approved/Offered Positions:* 20
Program ID: 300-47-12-336

Nashville

Vanderbilt University Program

Sponsor: Vanderbilt University Medical Center
Prgm Director: Mary M Zutter, MD
1161 21st Avenue South
Department of Pathology, CC3322 MCN
Nashville, TN 37232
Tel: 615 343-4882   *Fax:* 615 343-7023
E-mail: pathres.prog@vanderbilt.edu
Length: 4 Yrs   *ACGME Approved/Offered Positions:* 25
Program ID: 300-47-21-341

Texas

Dallas

Baylor University Medical Center Program

Sponsor: Baylor University Medical Center
Prgm Director: Peter A Dysert II, MD*
3500 Gaston Avenue
Dallas, TX 75246
Tel: 214 820-3021
E-mail: Kandice.French@BaylorHealth.edu
Length: 4 Yrs   *ACGME Approved/Offered Positions:* 18
Program ID: 300-48-12-343

University of Texas Southwestern Medical School Program

Sponsor: University of Texas Southwestern Medical School
Dallas County Hospital District-Parkland Memorial Hospital
Prgm Director: Charles F Timmons, MD, PhD
5323 Harry Hines Boulevard
Dallas, TX 75390
Tel: 214 648-2466   *Fax:* 214 648-6323
E-mail: pathresprogdir@utsouthwestern.edu
Length: 4 Yrs   *ACGME Approved/Offered Positions:* 38
Program ID: 300-48-11-345

Galveston

University of Texas Medical Branch Hospitals Program

Sponsor: University of Texas Medical Branch Hospitals
Prgm Director: Juan P Olano, MD
301 University Boulevard
Galveston, TX 77555
Tel: 409 772-2870   *Fax:* 409 747-2400
Length: 4 Yrs   *ACGME Approved/Offered Positions:* 25
Program ID: 300-48-11-349

Houston

Baylor College of Medicine Program

Sponsor: Baylor College of Medicine
Harris County Hospital District-Ben Taub General Hospital
Michael E DeBakey VA Medical Center - Houston
Texas Children's Hospital
Prgm Director: Francis H Gannon, MD
One Baylor Plaza
Department of Pathology
Houston, TX 77030
Tel: 713 798-4340   *Fax:* 713 798-3665
Length: 4 Yrs   *ACGME Approved/Offered Positions:* 28
Program ID: 300-48-31-350

Methodist Hospital (Houston) Program

Sponsor: Methodist Hospital (Houston)
Memorial Hermann Hospital
Prgm Director: Suzanne Z Powell, MD
6565 Fannin St, MS205
Houston, TX 77030
Tel: 713 441-6486   *Fax:* 713 793-1603
E-mail: ljozwiak@tmhs.org
Length: 4 Yrs   *ACGME Approved/Offered Positions:* 20
Program ID: 300-48-23-420

University of Texas at Houston Program

Sponsor: University of Texas Health Science Center at Houston
Lyndon B Johnson General Hospital
Memorial Hermann Hospital
Prgm Director: Rhonda P Ghorbani, MD
6431 Fannin Street, MSB 2.262
Houston, TX 77030
Tel: 713 500-5372   *Fax:* 713 500-0712
E-mail: Rhonda.P.Ghorbani@uth.tmc.edu
Length: 4 Yrs   *ACGME Approved/Offered Positions:* 28
Program ID: 300-48-11-352

Lackland AFB

San Antonio Uniformed Services Health Education Consortium Program

Sponsor: San Antonio Uniformed Services Health Education Consortium
Brooke Army Medical Center
Wilford Hall Medical Center (AETC)
Prgm Director: Brian S Kendall, MD
Department of Pathology
2200 Berquist Dr, Ste 1
Lackland Air Force Base, TX 78236
Tel: 210 292-3842   *Fax:* 210 292-2269
Length: 4 Yrs   *ACGME Approved/Offered Positions:* 23
Program ID: 300-48-11-417
Uniformed Services Program

Lubbock

Texas Tech University (Lubbock) Program

Sponsor: Texas Tech University Health Sciences Center at Lubbock
Covenant Medical Center
University Medical Center
Prgm Director: Dale M Dunn, MD
3601 4th Street
Lubbock, TX 79430
Tel: 806 743-2172   *Fax:* 806 743-2152
E-mail: John.Omalley@ttuhsc.edu
Length: 4 Yrs   *ACGME Approved/Offered Positions:* 8
Program ID: 300-48-31-415

Note: * indicates a newly appointed program director

San Antonio

University of Texas Health Science Center at San Antonio Program

Sponsor: University of Texas School of Medicine at San Antonio
Audie L Murphy Memorial Veterans Hospital (San Antonio)
University Health System
University of Texas Health Science Center
Prgm Director: Larry J Fowler, MD
7703 Floyd Curl Drive
San Antonio, TX 78229
Tel: 210 567-4025   *Fax:* 210 567-2478
E-mail: fowler@uthscsa.edu
Length: 4 Yrs   *ACGME Approved/Offered Positions:* 16
Program ID: 300-48-21-356

Temple

Texas A&M College of Medicine-Scott and White Program

Sponsor: Scott and White Memorial Hospital
Prgm Director: V O Speights Jr, DO
2401 South 31st Street
Temple, TX 76508
Tel: 254 724-3688   *Fax:* 254 724-6329
E-mail: cdixon@swmail.sw.org
Length: 4 Yrs   *ACGME Approved/Offered Positions:* 12
Program ID: 300-48-12-357

Utah

Salt Lake City

University of Utah Program

Sponsor: University of Utah Medical Center
Primary Children's Medical Center
Prgm Director: Evelyn V Gopez, MD
Department of Pathology
30 North 1900 East
Salt Lake City, UT 84132
Tel: 801 587-4330   *Fax:* 801 581-7035
E-mail: Evelyn.Gopez@hsc.utah.edu
Length: 4 Yrs   *ACGME Approved/Offered Positions:* 19
Program ID: 300-49-21-360

Vermont

Burlington

University of Vermont Program

Sponsor: Fletcher Allen Health Care
Prgm Director: Abdelmonem Elhosseiny, MD
Department of Pathology and Laboratory Medicine
111 Colchester Avenue
Burlington, VT 05401
Tel: 802 847-0392   *Fax:* 802 847-3509
Length: 4 Yrs   *ACGME Approved/Offered Positions:* 15
Program ID: 300-50-11-361

Virginia

Charlottesville

University of Virginia Program

Sponsor: University of Virginia Medical Center
Prgm Director: Mark R Wick, MD
PO Box 800214
1215 Lee Street
Charlottesville, VA 22908
Tel: 434 924-9038   *Fax:* 434 924-9617
E-mail: bun4n@virginia.edu
Length: 4 Yrs   *ACGME Approved/Offered Positions:* 20
Program ID: 300-51-11-362

Richmond

Virginia Commonwealth University Health System Program

Sponsor: Virginia Commonwealth University Health System
Medical College of Virginia Hospitals
Prgm Director: Susan D Roseff, MD*
PO Box 980662
1101 E Marshall Street, Room 4-005
Richmond, VA 23298
Tel: 804 828-0255   *Fax:* 804 828-0876
E-mail: vbrown3@mcvh-vcu.edu
Length: 4 Yrs   *ACGME Approved/Offered Positions:* 22
Program ID: 300-51-11-366

Washington

Seattle

University of Washington Program

Sponsor: University of Washington School of Medicine
Harborview Medical Center
Seattle Cancer Care Alliance
University of Washington Medical Center
VA Puget Sound Health Care System
Prgm Director: Rochelle L Garcia, MD
Box 356100
1959 NE Pacific Street, NE110
Seattle, WA 98195
Tel: 206 598-4933   *Fax:* 206 598-4933
E-mail: residency@pathology.washington.edu
Length: 4 Yrs   *ACGME Approved/Offered Positions:* 27
Program ID: 300-54-21-367

Tacoma

Madigan Army Medical Center Program

Sponsor: Madigan Army Medical Center
Prgm Director: Anne L Champeaux, MD
Department of Pathology
MCHJ-H
Tacoma, WA 98431
Tel: 253 968-1905   *Fax:* 253 968-1084
E-mail: Anne.Champeaux@amedd.army.mil
Length: 4 Yrs   *ACGME Approved/Offered Positions:* 12
Program ID: 300-54-12-009
Uniformed Services Program

West Virginia

Morgantown

West Virginia University Program

Sponsor: West Virginia University School of Medicine
Louis A Johnson Veterans Affairs Medical Center
West Virginia University Hospitals
Prgm Director: Kymberly A Gyure, MD
Robert C Byrd Health Sciences Center, North
PO Box 9203
Morgantown, WV 26506
Tel: 304 293-3212   *Fax:* 304 293-2717
Length: 4 Yrs   *ACGME Approved/Offered Positions:* 12
Program ID: 300-55-11-373

Wisconsin

Madison

University of Wisconsin Program

Sponsor: University of Wisconsin Hospital and Clinics
Prgm Director: Erik A Ranheim, MD, PhD
600 Highland Avenue, B4/243-2472 CSC
Madison, WI 53792
Tel: 608 263-0057   *Fax:* 608 265-6215
E-mail: pathresidency@uwhealth.org
Length: 4 Yrs   *ACGME Approved/Offered Positions:* 20
Program ID: 300-56-31-376

Milwaukee

Medical College of Wisconsin Affiliated Hospitals Program

Sponsor: Medical College of Wisconsin Affiliated Hospitals, Inc
Froedtert Memorial Lutheran Hospital
Prgm Director: Richard A Komorowski, MD
9200 West Wisconsin Avenue
Milwaukee, WI 53226
Tel: 414 805-8443   *Fax:* 414 805-8444
E-mail: kmcbride@mcw.edu
Length: 4 Yrs   *ACGME Approved/Offered Positions:* 16
Program ID: 300-56-21-377

Pediatric Anesthesiology (Anesthesiology)

Arkansas

Little Rock

University of Arkansas for Medical Sciences Program
Sponsor: University of Arkansas College of Medicine
Arkansas Children's Hospital
Prgm Director: James M Vollers, MD
Div of Pediatric Anesthesia and Pain Medicine
800 Marshall Street, Slot 203
Little Rock, AR 72202
Tel: 501 364-3933   *Fax:* 501 364-3134
E-mail: colemanphyllisj@uams.edu
Length: 1 Yr   *ACGME Approved/Offered Positions:* 4
Program ID: 042-04-21-023

California

Loma Linda

Loma Linda University Program
Sponsor: Loma Linda University Medical Center
Prgm Director: Linda J Mason, MD
11234 Anderson Street
Department of Anesthesiology
Loma Linda, CA 92354
Tel: 909 558-4015   *Fax:* 909 558-0214
Length: 1 Yr   *ACGME Approved/Offered Positions:* 1
Program ID: 042-05-31-042

Los Angeles

Children's Hospital of Los Angeles/University of Southern California Program
Sponsor: Childrens Hospital Los Angeles
Prgm Director: Randall C Wetzel, MD, MBA*
Mail Stop 3
4650 W Sunset Blvd
Los Angeles, CA 90027
Tel: 323 361-2557   *Fax:* 323 361-1022
Length: 1 Yr   *ACGME Approved/Offered Positions:* 6
Program ID: 042-05-11-051

Sacramento

University of California (Davis) Health System Program
Sponsor: University of California (Davis) Health System
Children's Hospital-Oakland
University of California (Davis) Medical Center
Prgm Director: Cathy R Lammers, MD
Patient Support Services Bldg #1200
2315 Stockton Boulevard
Sacramento, CA 95817
Tel: 916 734-5311   *Fax:* 916 734-7980
E-mail: blythe.myers@ucdmc.ucdavis.edu
Length: 1 Yr   *ACGME Approved/Offered Positions:* 2
Program ID: 042-05-21-024

San Francisco

University of California (San Francisco) Program
Sponsor: University of California (San Francisco) School of Medicine
Children's Hospital-Oakland
UCSF and Mount Zion Medical Centers
Prgm Director: Maurice S Zwass, MD
Dept of Anesthesiology (Rm M680)
505 Parnassus Avenue
San Francisco, CA 94143
Tel: 415 476-8716   *Fax:* 415 502-4186
Length: 1 Yr   *ACGME Approved/Offered Positions:* 1
Program ID: 042-05-21-018

Stanford

Stanford University Program
Sponsor: Stanford Hospital and Clinics
Lucile Salter Packard Children's Hospital at Stanford
Prgm Director: Alice A Edler, MD, MEd
Department of Anesthesia, Rm H3580
300 Pasteur Drive
Stanford, CA 94305
Tel: 650 498-7919   *Fax:* 650 725-8544
E-mail: edlera@aol.com
Length: 1 Yr   *ACGME Approved/Offered Positions:* 4
Program ID: 042-05-31-019

Colorado

Aurora

University of Colorado Denver Program
Sponsor: University of Colorado Denver School of Medicine
Children's Hospital (The)
Prgm Director: Rita Agarwal, MD
13123 East 16th Avenue B090
Aurora, CO 80045
Tel: 720 777-2027   *Fax:* 720 777-7266
E-mail: Agarwal.Rita@tchden.org
Length: 1 Yr   *ACGME Approved/Offered Positions:* 6
Program ID: 042-07-21-020

Connecticut

New Haven

Yale-New Haven Medical Center Program
Sponsor: Yale-New Haven Hospital
Prgm Director: Sarah Khan, MD
PO Box 208051
333 Cedar Street
New Haven, CT 06520
Tel: 203 785-2802   *Fax:* 203 785-6664
Length: 1 Yr   *ACGME Approved/Offered Positions:* 2
Program ID: 042-08-21-005

Delaware

Wilmington

Thomas Jefferson University/duPont Hospital for Children Program
Sponsor: Thomas Jefferson University Hospital
Alfred I duPont Hospital for Children
Prgm Director: Andrew T Costarino Jr, MD
1600 Rockland Road
PO Box 269
Wilmington, DE 19803
Tel: 302 651-5160   *Fax:* 302 651-6410
Length: 1 Yr   *ACGME Approved/Offered Positions:* 2
Program ID: 042-09-31-055

Note: * indicates a newly appointed program director

District of Columbia

Washington

George Washington University Program
Sponsor: George Washington University School of Medicine
Children's National Medical Center
Prgm Director: Richard F Kaplan, MD
111 Michigan Avenue NW
Washington, DC 20010
Tel: 202 476-2025   *Fax:* 202 476-5999
E-mail: rkaplan@cnmc.org
Length: 1 Yr   *ACGME Approved/Offered Positions:* 9
Program ID: 042-10-21-006

Florida

Jacksonville

College of Medicine, Mayo Clinic (Jacksonville) Program
Sponsor: College of Medicine, Mayo Clinic
Wolfson Children's Hospital
Prgm Director: Stefanie F Schrum, MD
807 Children's Way
Jacksonville, FL 32207
Tel: 904 202-8332   *Fax:* 904 202-8340
E-mail: sschrum@nemours.org
Length: 1 Yr   *ACGME Approved/Offered Positions:* 2
Program ID: 042-11-21-031

Miami

Jackson Memorial Hospital/Jackson Health System Program
Sponsor: Jackson Memorial Hospital/Jackson Health System
Miami Children's Hospital
Prgm Director: Norman J Halliday, MD
1611 NW 12th Avenue
Miami, FL 33136
Tel: 305 585-6973   *Fax:* 305 585-8359
E-mail: nhalliday@med.miami.edu
Length: 1 Yr   *ACGME Approved/Offered Positions:* 2
Program ID: 042-11-31-007

Georgia

Atlanta

Emory University Program
Sponsor: Emory University School of Medicine
Children's Healthcare of Atlanta at Egleston
Prgm Director: Carolyn F Bannister, MD
1405 Clifton Road NE
Atlanta, GA 30322
Tel: 404 785-6670   *Fax:* 404 785-1362
E-mail: carolyn.bannister@emoryhealthcare.org
Length: 1 Yr   *ACGME Approved/Offered Positions:* 4
Program ID: 042-12-21-041

Illinois

Chicago

McGaw Medical Center of Northwestern University Program

Sponsor: McGaw Medical Center of Northwestern University
Children's Memorial Hospital
Prgm Director: Steven C Hall, MD
2300 Children's Plaza
Box 19
Chicago, IL 60614
Tel: 773 880-4414   *Fax:* 773 880-3331
Length: 1 Yr   *ACGME Approved/Offered Positions:* 6
Program ID: 042-16-21-011

University of Chicago/Comer Children's Hospital Program

Sponsor: University of Chicago Medical Center
University of Chicago Comer Children's Hospital
Prgm Director: Catherine Bachman, MD
Department of Pediatric Anesthesiology
5841 South Maryland Avenue, MC 4028
Chicago, IL 60637
Tel: 773 834-0492   *Fax:* 773 834-0063
E-mail: tc28@airway.uchicago.edu
Length: 1 Yr   *ACGME Approved/Offered Positions:* 1
Program ID: 042-16-13-059

University of Illinois College of Medicine at Chicago Program

Sponsor: University of Illinois College of Medicine at Chicago
University of Illinois Hospital and Clinics
Prgm Director: Timothy B McDonald, MD, JD
Dept of Anesthesiology, M/C 515
1740 W Taylor Street
Chicago, IL 60612
Tel: 312 996-4020   *Fax:* 312 996-4019
E-mail: tmcd@uic.edu
Length: 1 Yr   *ACGME Approved/Offered Positions:* 1
Program ID: 042-16-21-025

Indiana

Indianapolis

Indiana University School of Medicine Program

Sponsor: Indiana University School of Medicine
Clarian Riley Hospital for Children
Prgm Director: Scott G Walker, MD
702 Barnhill Drive, #2001
Indianapolis, IN 46202
Tel: 317 274-2874   *Fax:* 317 274-0282
Length: 1 Yr   *ACGME Approved/Offered Positions:* 5
Program ID: 042-17-11-047

Maryland

Baltimore

Johns Hopkins University Program

Sponsor: Johns Hopkins University School of Medicine
Johns Hopkins Hospital
Prgm Director: Dolores Njoku, MD
Dept of Anesthesiology, Blalock 904
600 North Wolfe Street
Baltimore, MD 21287
Tel: 410 955-6412   *Fax:* 410 502-5312
E-mail: dnjoku@jhmi.edu
Length: 1 Yr   *ACGME Approved/Offered Positions:* 4
Program ID: 042-23-21-028

Massachusetts

Boston

Children's Hospital/Harvard Medical School Program

Sponsor: Children's Hospital
Prgm Director: David B Waisel, MD
Dept of Anesthesiology, Perioperative & Pain Med
300 Longwood Avenue
Boston, MA 02115
Tel: 617 355-6457   *Fax:* 617 730-0894
Length: 1 Yr   *ACGME Approved/Offered Positions:* 19
Program ID: 042-24-21-004

Tufts Medical Center Program

Sponsor: Tufts Medical Center
Children's Hospital
Prgm Director: Aykut Bilge, MD, PhD
Dept of Anesthesiology, Box 298
800 Washington Street
Boston, MA 02111
Tel: 617 636-6044   *Fax:* 617 636-8384
E-mail: abilge@tufts-nemc.org
Length: 1 Yr   *ACGME Approved/Offered Positions:* 2
Program ID: 042-24-21-026

Michigan

Ann Arbor

University of Michigan Program

Sponsor: University of Michigan Hospitals and Health Centers
Prgm Director: Paul I Reynolds, MD
Pediatric Anesthesiology, F3900 Mott - SPC 5211
1500 E Medical Center Drive
Ann Arbor, MI 48109
Tel: 734 936-6986   *Fax:* 734 763-6651
E-mail: polaris@med.umich.edu
Length: 1 Yr   *ACGME Approved/Offered Positions:* 9
Program ID: 042-25-21-029

Detroit

Wayne State University/Detroit Medical Center Program

Sponsor: Wayne State University/Detroit Medical Center
Children's Hospital of Michigan
Prgm Director: Maria M Zestos, MD
3901 Beaubien Boulevard
Room 3B17
Detroit, MI 48201
Tel: 313 745-5535   *Fax:* 313 745-5448
E-mail: mzestos@med.wayne.edu
Length: 1 Yr   *ACGME Approved/Offered Positions:* 2
Program ID: 042-25-21-008

Minnesota

Rochester

College of Medicine, Mayo Clinic (Rochester) Program

Sponsor: College of Medicine, Mayo Clinic
Saint Marys Hospital of Rochester
Prgm Director: Randall P Flick, MD, MPH
Department of Anesthesiology, Mary Brigh 2-505C
200 First Street SW
Rochester, MN 55905
Tel: 507 284-2511   *Fax:* 507 255-2939
E-mail: flick.randall@mayo.edu
Length: 1 Yr   *ACGME Approved/Offered Positions:* 2
Program ID: 042-26-12-054

Missouri

St Louis

Washington University/B-JH/SLCH Consortium Program

Sponsor: Washington University/B-JH/SLCH Consortium
St Louis Children's Hospital
Prgm Director: Anshuman Sharma, MD, MBA
One Children's Place
Room 5S31
St Louis, MO 63110
Tel: 314 454-6215   *Fax:* 314 454-2296
E-mail: sharmanu@anest.wustl.edu
Length: 1 Yr   *ACGME Approved/Offered Positions:* 3
Program ID: 042-28-21-033

New Mexico

Albuquerque

University of New Mexico Program

Sponsor: University of New Mexico School of Medicine
Children's Hospital (The)
University of New Mexico Hospital
Prgm Director: Joyce F Phillips, MD*
2701 Frontier NE MSC 11-6120
Surge Building Room 110
Albuquerque, NM 87131
Tel: 505 272-2610   *Fax:* 505 272-1300
E-mail: anesthesiology@salud.unm.edu
Length: 1 Yr   *ACGME Approved/Offered Positions:* 1
Program ID: 042-34-21-012

New York

Buffalo

University at Buffalo Program

Sponsor: University at Buffalo School of Medicine
Kaleida Health System (Women and Children's Hosp of Buffalo)
Prgm Director: Doron Feldman, MD*
Women & Children's Hospital of Buffalo
219 Bryant St
Buffalo, NY 14222
Tel: 716 878-7701   *Fax:* 716 878-7316
E-mail: doronfeldman@verizon.net
Length: 1 Yr   *ACGME Approved/Offered Positions:* 1
Program ID: 042-35-21-035

New York

New York Presbyterian Hospital (Columbia Campus) Program

Sponsor: New York Presbyterian Hospital
New York Presbyterian Hospital (Columbia Campus)
Prgm Director: Lena Sun, MD
BHN 4-440
622 West 168th Street
New York, NY 10032
Tel: 212 305-2413   *Fax:* 212 305-2395
Length: 1 Yr   *ACGME Approved/Offered Positions:* 6
Program ID: 042-35-31-014

Programs

North Carolina

Chapel Hill

University of North Carolina Hospitals Program

Sponsor: University of North Carolina Hospitals
Prgm Director: Robert D Valley, MD
Dept of Anesthesiology, UNC School of Medicine
CB 7010, N2201 UNC Hospitals
Chapel Hill, NC 27599
Tel: 919 966-5136   *Fax:* 919 966-4873
E-mail: rvalley@aims.unc.edu
Length: 1 Yr   *ACGME Approved/Offered Positions:* 2
Program ID: 042-36-31-040

Durham

Duke University Hospital Program

Sponsor: Duke University Hospital
Prgm Director: B Craig Weldon, MD
Box 3094
DUMC
Durham, NC 27710
Tel: 919 681-3551   *Fax:* 919 684-9894
E-mail: craig.weldon@duke.edu
Length: 1 Yr   *ACGME Approved/Offered Positions:* 1
Program ID: 042-36-31-058

Ohio

Cincinnati

Cincinnati Children's Hospital Medical Center/University of Cincinnati College of Medicine Program

Sponsor: Cincinnati Children's Hospital Medical Center
Prgm Director: Paul J Samuels, MD
3333 Burnet Avenue
MLC 2001
Cincinnati, OH 45229
Tel: 513 636-7339   *Fax:* 513 636-7337
E-mail: debbie.klug@chmcc.org
Length: 1 Yr   *ACGME Approved/Offered Positions:* 12
Program ID: 042-38-21-009

Cleveland

Cleveland Clinic Foundation Program

Sponsor: Cleveland Clinic Foundation
Children's Hospital Medical Center of Akron
Prgm Director: Julie Niezgoda, MD
Anesthesiology Institute - P2
9500 Euclid Avenue
Cleveland, OH 44195
Tel: 216 444-0278   *Fax:* 216 444-9247
E-mail: aned@ccf.org
Length: 1 Yr   *ACGME Approved/Offered Positions:* 4
Program ID: 042-38-21-043

University Hospitals Case Medical Center Program

Sponsor: University Hospitals Case Medical Center
Prgm Director: Paul A Tripi, MD*
Dept of Anesthesiology and Perioperative Medicine
11100 Euclid Avenue
Cleveland, OH 44106
Tel: 216 844-7340   *Fax:* 216 844-3781
E-mail: paul.tripi@uhhospitals.org
Length: 1 Yr   *ACGME Approved/Offered Positions:* 2
Program ID: 042-38-21-015

Columbus

Nationwide Children's Hospital/Ohio State University Program

Sponsor: Nationwide Children's Hospital
Prgm Director: D Alan Tingley, MD, MBA
Department of Anesthesiology
700 Children's Drive
Columbus, OH 43205
Tel: 614 722-4200   *Fax:* 614 722-4203
Length: 1 Yr   *ACGME Approved/Offered Positions:* 2
Program ID: 042-38-21-061

Oklahoma

Oklahoma City

University of Oklahoma Health Sciences Center Program

Sponsor: University of Oklahoma College of Medicine
OU Medical Center - Children's Hospital
Prgm Director: Abhaya R Seshachar, MD, MBBS
750 NE 13th Street, Suite 200, OAC
Oklahoma City, OK 73104
Tel: 405 271-4351   *Fax:* 405 271-4015
E-mail: linda-murphy@ouhsc.edu
Length: 1 Yr   *ACGME Approved/Offered Positions:* 1
Program ID: 042-39-12-060

Oregon

Portland

Oregon Health & Science University Program

Sponsor: Oregon Health & Science University Hospital
Prgm Director: Kirk Lalwani, MD
UHS-2
3181 SW Sam Jackson Park Road
Portland, OR 97239
Tel: 503 418-5681   *Fax:* 503 494-4518
Length: 1 Yr   *ACGME Approved/Offered Positions:* 2
Program ID: 042-40-22-052

Pennsylvania

Hershey

Penn State University/Milton S Hershey Medical Center Program

Sponsor: Milton S Hershey Medical Center
Prgm Director: Patrick McQuillan, MD
500 University Drive
Hershey, PA 17033
Tel: 717 531-4264   *Fax:* 717 531-4110
E-mail: jmzeager@psu.edu
Length: 1 Yr   *ACGME Approved/Offered Positions:* 1
Program ID: 042-41-21-048

Philadelphia

Children's Hospital of Philadelphia Program

Sponsor: Children's Hospital of Philadelphia
Prgm Director: Alan Jay Schwartz, MD, MS
34th Street & Civic Center Boulevard
Philadelphia, PA 19104
Tel: 215 590-1885   *Fax:* 215 590-1415
E-mail: schwartza@email.chop.edu
Length: 1 Yr   *ACGME Approved/Offered Positions:* 10
Program ID: 042-41-31-044

St Christopher's Hospital for Children Program

Sponsor: St Christopher's Hospital for Children (Tenet Health System)
Children's Hospital of Philadelphia
Prgm Director: Roy E Schwartz, MD
Erie Avenue at Front Street
Philadelphia, PA 19134
Tel: 215 427-5220   *Fax:* 215 427-4339
E-mail: roy.schwartz@tenethealth.com
Length: 1 Yr   *ACGME Approved/Offered Positions:* 2
Program ID: 042-41-21-032

Pittsburgh

University of Pittsburgh Medical Center Medical Education Program

Sponsor: Univ of Pittsburgh Medical Center Medical Education
Children's Hospital of Pittsburgh of UPMC
Prgm Director: Franklyn P Cladis, MD
3705 Fifth Avenue
Pittsburgh, PA 15213
Tel: 412 692-5262   *Fax:* 412 692-8658
E-mail: cladfp@upmc.edu
Length: 1 Yr   *ACGME Approved/Offered Positions:* 9
Program ID: 042-41-21-010

Tennessee

Nashville

Vanderbilt University Program

Sponsor: Vanderbilt University Medical Center
Prgm Director: Ira S Landsman, MD
2200 Children's Way
Suite 3115
Nashville, TN 37232
Tel: 615 936-0023   *Fax:* 615 936-4294
E-mail: ira.landsman@vanderbilt.edu
Length: 1 Yr   *ACGME Approved/Offered Positions:* 4
Program ID: 042-47-21-021

Texas

Corpus Christi

University of Texas Medical Branch Hospitals (Corpus Christi) Program

Sponsor: University of Texas Medical Branch Hospitals
Driscoll Children's Hospital
Prgm Director: Adolph J Koska III, MD, PhD
3533 S Alameda
Corpus Christi, TX 78411
Tel: 361 694-5445   *Fax:* 361 694-5449
E-mail: jay.koska@dchstx.org
Length: 1 Yr   *ACGME Approved/Offered Positions:* 2
Program ID: 042-48-21-030

Dallas

University of Texas Southwestern Medical School Program

Sponsor: University of Texas Southwestern Medical School
Children's Medical Center of Dallas
Cook Children's Medical Center
Prgm Director: Stephen Q Hoang, MD
5323 Harry Hines Blvd
Dallas, TX 75390
Tel: 214 456-6393   *Fax:* 214 456-7232
E-mail: stephen.hoang@childrens.com
Length: 1 Yr   *ACGME Approved/Offered Positions:* 4
Program ID: 042-48-31-037

Note: * indicates a newly appointed program director

Houston

Baylor College of Medicine Program

Sponsor: Baylor College of Medicine
Texas Children's Hospital
Prgm Director: Nancy L Glass, MD, MBA
Texas Children's Hospital
6621 Fannin Street, Suite A300, MC 2-1495
Houston, TX 77030
Tel: 832 824-5800   *Fax:* 832 825-5801
E-mail: angelj@bcm.tmc.edu
Length: 1 Yr   *ACGME Approved/Offered Positions:* 6
Program ID: 042-48-21-022

Washington

Seattle

University of Washington Program

Sponsor: University of Washington School of Medicine
Seattle Children's Hospital
Prgm Director: Michael J Richards, MB, MRCP
Mail Stop W9824
4800 Sand Point Way NE
Seattle, WA 98105
Tel: 206 987-3996   *Fax:* 206 987-3935
E-mail: casey.jones@seattlechildrens.org
Length: 1 Yr   *ACGME Approved/Offered Positions:* 6
Program ID: 042-54-21-038

Wisconsin

Milwaukee

Medical College of Wisconsin Affiliated Hospitals Program

Sponsor: Medical College of Wisconsin Affiliated
  Hospitals, Inc
Children's Hospital of Wisconsin
Prgm Director: Susan R Staudt, MD, MEd
9000 West Wisconsin Avenue
PO Box 1997, MS-735
Milwaukee, WI 53201
Tel: 414 266-3560   *Fax:* 414 266-6092
E-mail: sstaudt@mcw.edu
Length: 1 Yr   *ACGME Approved/Offered Positions:* 8
Program ID: 042-56-21-039

Pediatric Cardiology (Pediatrics)

Arkansas

Little Rock

University of Arkansas for Medical Sciences Program

Sponsor: University of Arkansas College of Medicine
Arkansas Children's Hospital
Prgm Director: W Robert Morrow, MD
800 Marshall Street, Slot 512-3
Little Rock, AR 72202
Tel: 501 364-1479   *Fax:* 501 364-3667
E-mail: lrpulliam@uams.edu
Length: 3 Yrs   *ACGME Approved/Offered Positions:* 6
Program ID: 325-04-12-079

California

Los Angeles

Childrens Hospital Los Angeles Program

Sponsor: Childrens Hospital Los Angeles
LAC+USC Medical Center
Prgm Director: Alan B Lewis, MD
Division of Cardiology, MS 34
4650 Sunset Boulevard
Los Angeles, CA 90027
Tel: 323 361-4637   *Fax:* 323 361-1513
E-mail: alewis@chla.usc.edu
Length: 3 Yrs   *ACGME Approved/Offered Positions:* 6
Program ID: 325-05-11-001

UCLA Medical Center Program

Sponsor: UCLA David Geffen School of Medicine/UCLA
  Medical Center
UCLA Medical Center
Prgm Director: Daniel S Levi, MD
Division of Pediatric Cardiology
B2-427 MDCC, 10833 Le Conte Avenue
Los Angeles, CA 90095
Tel: 310 206-3478   *Fax:* 310 825-9524
E-mail: dlevi@ucla.edu
Length: 3 Yrs   *ACGME Approved/Offered Positions:* 7
Program ID: 325-05-21-002

San Diego

University of California (San Diego) Program

Sponsor: University of California (San Diego) Medical
  Center
Rady Children's Hospital
Prgm Director: Paul D Grossfeld, MD*
3020 Childrens Way MC 5004
San Diego, CA 92123
Tel: 858 966-5855   *Fax:* 858 571-7903
E-mail: pgrossfeld@ucsd.edu
Length: 3 Yrs   *ACGME Approved/Offered Positions:* 4
Program ID: 325-05-11-003

San Francisco

University of California (San Francisco) Program

Sponsor: University of California (San Francisco) School
  of Medicine
UCSF and Mount Zion Medical Centers
Prgm Director: Michael M Brook, MD
505 Parnassus Ave, Room M1235
Campus box 0544
San Francisco, CA 94143
Tel: 415 476-2981   *Fax:* 415 476-9976
E-mail: thompsonsh@peds.ucsf.edu
Length: 3 Yrs   *ACGME Approved/Offered Positions:* 6
Program ID: 325-05-21-004

Stanford

Stanford University Program

Sponsor: Stanford Hospital and Clinics
Lucile Salter Packard Children's Hospital at Stanford
Prgm Director: Daniel Bernstein, MD*
750 Welch Road, Suite 305
Palo Alto, CA 94304
Tel: 650 723-7913   *Fax:* 650 725-8343
E-mail: danb@stanford.edu
Length: 3 Yrs   *ACGME Approved/Offered Positions:* 6
Program ID: 325-05-21-062

Colorado

Aurora

University of Colorado Denver Program

Sponsor: University of Colorado Denver School of
  Medicine
Children's Hospital (The)
Prgm Director: Jill Ibrahim, MD
13123 East 16th Ave B100
Aurora, CO 80045
Tel: 720 777-3365   *Fax:* 720 777-7290
E-mail: starkey.jeanette@tchden.org
Length: 3 Yrs   *ACGME Approved/Offered Positions:* 9
Program ID: 325-07-21-054

Connecticut

New Haven

Yale-New Haven Medical Center Program

Sponsor: Yale-New Haven Hospital
Prgm Director: John Fahey, MD
Department of Pediatrics
333 Cedar Street, PO Box 208064
New Haven, CT 06520
Tel: 203 785-2022   *Fax:* 203 737-2786
Length: 3 Yrs   *ACGME Approved/Offered Positions:* 6
Program ID: 325-08-11-006

District of Columbia

Washington

Children's National Medical Center/ George Washington University Program

Sponsor: Children's National Medical Center
Prgm Director: Craig A Sable, MD
111 Michigan Avenue NW
Washington, DC 20010
Tel: 202 476-2020   *Fax:* 202 476-5700
Length: 3 Yrs   *ACGME Approved/Offered Positions:* 9
Program ID: 325-10-21-007

Programs

Florida

Gainesville

University of Florida Program
Sponsor: University of Florida College of Medicine
Shands Hospital at the University of Florida
Prgm Director: Frederick J Fricker, MD
1600 SW Archer Rd, HD 303
PO Box 100296
Gainesville, FL 32610
Tel: 352 273-7770   *Fax:* 352 392-0547
E-mail: frickfj@peds.ufl.edu
Length: 3 Yrs   *ACGME Approved/Offered Positions:* 4
Program ID: 325-11-11-008

Miami

Jackson Memorial Hospital/Jackson Health System Program
Sponsor: Jackson Memorial Hospital/Jackson Health System
Prgm Director: Sethuraman Swaminathan, MD
PO Box 016960 (R-76)
JMH, North Wing, Room 109
Miami, FL 33101
Tel: 305 585-6683   *Fax:* 305 324-6012
Length: 3 Yrs   *ACGME Approved/Offered Positions:* 6
Program ID: 325-11-21-009

Georgia

Atlanta

Emory University Program
Sponsor: Emory University School of Medicine
Children's Healthcare of Atlanta at Egleston
Prgm Director: Peter S Fischbach, MD, MA
Department of Pediatrics
1405 Clifton Road NE
Atlanta, GA 30322
Tel: 404 256-2593   *Fax:* 404 785-9188
E-mail: fischbachp@kidsheart.com
Length: 3 Yrs   *ACGME Approved/Offered Positions:* 12
Program ID: 325-12-21-010

Augusta

Medical College of Georgia Program
Sponsor: Medical College of Georgia
Prgm Director: William A Lutin, MD, PhD
1120 15th Street, BAA800W
Augusta, GA 30912
Tel: 706 721-2336   *Fax:* 706 721-3838
E-mail: wlutin@mail.mcg.edu
Length: 3 Yrs   *ACGME Approved/Offered Positions:* 3
Program ID: 325-12-11-011

Illinois

Chicago

McGaw Medical Center of Northwestern University Program
Sponsor: McGaw Medical Center of Northwestern University
Children's Memorial Hospital
Prgm Director: Peter Koenig, MD*
2300 Children's Plaza
Mail Code 21
Chicago, IL 60614
Tel: 773 880-4553   *Fax:* 773 880-8111
Length: 3 Yrs   *ACGME Approved/Offered Positions:* 6
Program ID: 325-16-11-013

Rush University Medical Center Program
Sponsor: Rush University Medical Center
Prgm Director: Ra-id Abdulla, MD
1653 West Congress Parkway, 770 Jones
Chicago, IL 60612
Tel: 312 942-7372   *Fax:* 312 942-9325
Length: 3 Yrs   *ACGME Approved/Offered Positions:* 6
Program ID: 325-16-31-081

Oak Lawn

Advocate Christ Medical Center Program
Sponsor: Advocate Christ Medical Center
Prgm Director: Sunthorn Muangmingsuk, MD
Advocate Hope Children's Hospital
4440 W 95th St
Oak Lawn, IL 60453
Tel: 708 684-5580   *Fax:* 708 684-4068
E-mail: sunthorn@thic.com
Length: 3 Yrs   *ACGME Approved/Offered Positions:* 6
Program ID: 325-16-21-067

Indiana

Indianapolis

Indiana University School of Medicine Program
Sponsor: Indiana University School of Medicine
Clarian Riley Hospital for Children
Prgm Director: Ronald M Payne, MD
Riley Research, Room #127
702 Barnhill Drive
Indianapolis, IN 46202
Tel: 317 278-6239   *Fax:* 317 278-9298
E-mail: rdhawkin@iupui.edu
Length: 3 Yrs   *ACGME Approved/Offered Positions:* 6
Program ID: 325-17-11-017

Iowa

Iowa City

University of Iowa Hospitals and Clinics Program
Sponsor: University of Iowa Hospitals and Clinics
Prgm Director: Heather L Bartlett, MD
Department of Pediatrics
200 Hawkins Drive
Iowa City, IA 52242
Tel: 319 356-2845   *Fax:* 319 356-4693
E-mail: heather-bartlett@uiowa.edu
Length: 3 Yrs   *ACGME Approved/Offered Positions:* 5
Program ID: 325-18-11-018

Maryland

Baltimore

Johns Hopkins University Program
Sponsor: Johns Hopkins University School of Medicine
Johns Hopkins Hospital
Prgm Director: Anne M Murphy, MD
600 N Wolfe St, Brady 516
Baltimore, MD 21287
Tel: 410 955-5987   *Fax:* 410 955-0897
Length: 3 Yrs   *ACGME Approved/Offered Positions:* 4
Program ID: 325-23-11-021

Massachusetts

Boston

Children's Hospital/Boston Medical Center Program
Sponsor: Children's Hospital
Prgm Director: Peter Lang, MD
300 Longwood Avenue
Boston, MA 02115
Tel: 617 355-8539   *Fax:* 617 739-6282
Length: 3 Yrs   *ACGME Approved/Offered Positions:* 21
Program ID: 325-24-11-022

Michigan

Ann Arbor

University of Michigan Program
Sponsor: University of Michigan Hospitals and Health Centers
Prgm Director: Macdonald Dick II, MD
L1242 Womens, SPC 5204
1500 East Medical Center Drive
Ann Arbor, MI 48109
Tel: 734 936-4038   *Fax:* 734 936-9470
E-mail: mdick@umich.edu
Length: 3 Yrs   *ACGME Approved/Offered Positions:* 15
Program ID: 325-25-11-023

Detroit

Children's Hospital of Michigan Program
Sponsor: Children's Hospital of Michigan
Prgm Director: Robert D Ross, MD
3901 Beaubien Boulevard
Detroit, MI 48201
Tel: 313 745-5956   *Fax:* 313 993-0894
E-mail: rross@dmc.org
Length: 3 Yrs   *ACGME Approved/Offered Positions:* 9
Program ID: 325-25-21-061

Minnesota

Minneapolis

University of Minnesota Program
Sponsor: University of Minnesota Medical School
University of Minnesota Medical Center, Division of Fairview
Prgm Director: Elizabeth A Braunlin, MD, PhD
420 Delaware Street SE
MMC 94
Minneapolis, MN 55455
Tel: 612 626-2755   *Fax:* 612 626-2467
Length: 3 Yrs   *ACGME Approved/Offered Positions:* 6
Program ID: 325-26-21-024

Rochester

College of Medicine, Mayo Clinic (Rochester) Program
Sponsor: College of Medicine, Mayo Clinic
Mayo Clinic (Rochester)
Saint Marys Hospital of Rochester
Prgm Director: Benjamin W Eidem, MD
200 First Street SW
Rochester, MN 55905
Tel: 507 538-0154   *Fax:* 507 284-0160
E-mail: bartelsmith.susan@mayo.edu
Length: 3 Yrs   *ACGME Approved/Offered Positions:* 6
Program ID: 325-26-21-025

Note: * indicates a newly appointed program director

Missouri

St Louis

Washington University/B-JH/SLCH Consortium Program

Sponsor: Washington University/B-JH/SLCH Consortium
St Louis Children's Hospital
Prgm Director: Mark C Johnson, MD
Department of Pediatrics
Campus Box 8116-NWT
St Louis, MO 63110
Tel: 314 454-6095   *Fax:* 314 454-2561
E-mail: johnson_m@kids.wustl.edu
Length: 3 Yrs   *ACGME Approved/Offered Positions:* 9
Program ID: 325-28-11-027

New Jersey

Newark

Newark Beth Israel Medical Center Program

Sponsor: Newark Beth Israel Medical Center
Prgm Director: Duraisamy Balaguru, MD
201 Lyons Avenue, Suite L5
Newark, NJ 07112
Tel: 973 926-3500   *Fax:* 973 926-8206
Length: 3 Yrs   *ACGME Approved/Offered Positions:* 3
Program ID: 325-33-13-080

New York

Great Neck

NSLIJHS-Schneider Children's Hospital Program

Sponsor: North Shore-Long Island Jewish Health System
Schneider Children's Hospital at Long Island Jewish
  Med Ctr
Prgm Director: Howard S Seiden, MD
269-01 76th Avenue
New Hyde Park, NY 11040
Tel: 718 470-7350   *Fax:* 718 347-5864
Length: 3 Yrs   *ACGME Approved/Offered Positions:* 6
Program ID: 325-35-21-030

New York

Mount Sinai School of Medicine Program

Sponsor: Mount Sinai School of Medicine
Mount Sinai Medical Center
Prgm Director: Shubhika Srivastava, MBBS
One Gustave L Levy Place, Box 1201
New York, NY 10029
Tel: 212 241-8662   *Fax:* 212 534-2659
E-mail: shubhika.srivastava@mssm.edu
Length: 3 Yrs   *ACGME Approved/Offered Positions:* 6
Program ID: 325-35-11-060

New York Presbyterian Hospital (Columbia Campus) Program

Sponsor: New York Presbyterian Hospital
New York Presbyterian Hospital (Columbia Campus)
Prgm Director: Allan J Hordof, MD
3959 Broadway, BHN 2nd Floor
New York, NY 10032
Tel: 212 305-4432   *Fax:* 212 305-4429
Length: 3 Yrs   *ACGME Approved/Offered Positions:* 15
Program ID: 325-35-11-034

New York University School of Medicine Program

Sponsor: New York University School of Medicine
Bellevue Hospital Center
NYU Hospitals Center
Prgm Director: Gillian Henry, MD*
160 East 32nd Street
Pediatric Cardiology
New York, NY 10016
Tel: 212 263-3051
E-mail: gillian.henry@nyumc.org
Length: 3 Yrs   *ACGME Approved/Offered Positions:* 3
Program ID: 325-35-21-033

Rochester

University of Rochester Program

Sponsor: Strong Memorial Hospital of the University of
  Rochester
Prgm Director: Roger P Vermilion, MD
Pediatric Cardiology, Box 631
601 Elmwood Avenue
Rochester, NY 14642
Tel: 585 275-6090   *Fax:* 585 275-7436
E-mail: pearl_bloom@urmc.rochester.edu
Length: 3 Yrs   *ACGME Approved/Offered Positions:* 3
Program ID: 325-35-21-035

North Carolina

Durham

Duke University Hospital Program

Sponsor: Duke University Hospital
Prgm Director: Stephanie B Wechsler, MD*
PO Box 3090 DUMC
Division of Pediatric Cardiology
Durham, NC 27710
Tel: 919 681-8485
E-mail: stephanie.wechsler@duke.edu
Length: 3 Yrs   *ACGME Approved/Offered Positions:* 9
Program ID: 325-36-11-037

Ohio

Cincinnati

Cincinnati Children's Hospital Medical Center/University of Cincinnati College of Medicine Program

Sponsor: Cincinnati Children's Hospital Medical Center
Prgm Director: Robert L Spicer, MD
Division of Cardiology
3333 Burnet Avenue
Cincinnati, OH 45229
Tel: 513 636-4888   *Fax:* 513 636-3952
E-mail: robert.spicer@chmcc.org
Length: 3 Yrs   *ACGME Approved/Offered Positions:* 9
Program ID: 325-38-11-038

Cleveland

University Hospitals Case Medical Center Program

Sponsor: University Hospitals Case Medical Center
Prgm Director: Francine G Erenberg, MD
Div of Pediatric Cardiology
11100 Euclid Avenue
Cleveland, OH 44106
Tel: 216 844-3528   *Fax:* 216 844-5478
E-mail: francine.erenberg@uhhospitals.org
Length: 3 Yrs   *ACGME Approved/Offered Positions:* 6
Program ID: 325-38-11-039

Columbus

Nationwide Children's Hospital/Ohio State University Program

Sponsor: Nationwide Children's Hospital
Prgm Director: David P Chan, MD
700 Children's Drive
Columbus, OH 43205
Tel: 614 722-2530   *Fax:* 614 722-2549
Length: 3 Yrs   *ACGME Approved/Offered Positions:* 9
Program ID: 325-38-21-070

Oregon

Portland

Oregon Health & Science University Program

Sponsor: Oregon Health & Science University Hospital
Prgm Director: Laurie B Armsby, MD
707 SW Gaines Road, CDRC-P
Portland, OR 97239
Tel: 503 494-8937   *Fax:* 503 494-2824
E-mail: leonarjo@ohsu.edu
Length: 3 Yrs   *ACGME Approved/Offered Positions:* 4
Program ID: 325-40-11-040

Pennsylvania

Philadelphia

Children's Hospital of Philadelphia Program

Sponsor: Children's Hospital of Philadelphia
Prgm Director: Paul M Weinberg, MD
34th St and Civic Center Blvd
Philadelphia, PA 19104
Tel: 215 590-3274   *Fax:* 215 590-5825
E-mail: weinberg@email.chop.edu
Length: 3 Yrs   *ACGME Approved/Offered Positions:* 18
Program ID: 325-41-11-041

Pittsburgh

University of Pittsburgh Medical Center Medical Education Program

Sponsor: Univ of Pittsburgh Medical Center Medical
  Education
Children's Hospital of Pittsburgh of UPMC
Prgm Director: Steven A Webber, MBChB, MRCP
Heart Center
3705 Fifth Avenue at De Soto Street
Pittsburgh, PA 15213
Tel: 412 692-3216   *Fax:* 412 692-6870
Length: 3 Yrs   *ACGME Approved/Offered Positions:* 7
Program ID: 325-41-11-043

South Carolina

Charleston

Medical University of South Carolina Program

Sponsor: Medical University of South Carolina College of
  Medicine
MUSC Medical Center
Prgm Director: Girish S Shirali, MBBS
165 Ashley Avenue, MSC 915
Room 601 Children's Hospital
Charleston, SC 29425
Tel: 843 792-3286   *Fax:* 843 792-3284
E-mail: shiralig@musc.edu
Length: 3 Yrs   *ACGME Approved/Offered Positions:* 9
Program ID: 325-45-11-044

Tennessee

Memphis

University of Tennessee Program
Sponsor: University of Tennessee College of Medicine
LeBonheur Children's Medical Center
Regional Medical Center at Memphis
St Jude Children's Research Hospital
Prgm Director: Thomas K Chin, MD
Department of Pediatrics
777 Washington Avenue, Suite 215
Memphis, TN 38105
Tel: 901 287-6380   *Fax:* 901 287-5107
Length: 3 Yrs   *ACGME Approved/Offered Positions:* 6
Program ID: 325-47-21-078

Nashville

Vanderbilt University Program
Sponsor: Vanderbilt University Medical Center
Prgm Director: James A Johns, MD
Vanderbilt Children's Hospital, Suite 5230 DOT
2200 Children's Way
Nashville, TN 37232
Tel: 615 322-7447   *Fax:* 615 322-2210
E-mail: james.johns@vanderbilt.edu
Length: 3 Yrs   *ACGME Approved/Offered Positions:* 6
Program ID: 325-47-11-045

Texas

Dallas

University of Texas Southwestern Medical School Program
Sponsor: University of Texas Southwestern Medical School
Children's Medical Center of Dallas
Prgm Director: Lynn Mahony, MD
5323 Harry Hines Boulevard
Dallas, TX 75390
Tel: 214 456-2333   *Fax:* 214 456-6154
Length: 3 Yrs   *ACGME Approved/Offered Positions:* 6
Program ID: 325-48-21-058

Houston

Baylor College of Medicine Program
Sponsor: Baylor College of Medicine
Texas Children's Hospital
Prgm Director: Steven R Neish, MD, MS
Pediatric Cardiology
6621 Fannin Street, MC 19345-C
Houston, TX 77030
Tel: 832 826-5752   *Fax:* 832 826-1901
Length: 3 Yrs   *ACGME Approved/Offered Positions:* 15
Program ID: 325-48-11-047

University of Texas at Houston Program
Sponsor: University of Texas Health Science Center at Houston
Memorial Hermann Hospital
Prgm Director: Syamasundar Rao, MD
6431 Fannin Street, MSB 3.130
Houston, TX 77030
Tel: 713 500-5738   *Fax:* 713 500-5751
Length: 3 Yrs   *ACGME Approved/Offered Positions:* 6
Program ID: 325-48-21-083

Utah

Salt Lake City

University of Utah Program
Sponsor: University of Utah Medical Center
Primary Children's Medical Center
Prgm Director: Susan P Etheridge, MD
100 North Medical Drive, Suite 1500
Salt Lake City, UT 84113
Tel: 801 662-5441   *Fax:* 801 662-5404
E-mail: susan.etheridge@intermountainmail.org
Length: 3 Yrs   *ACGME Approved/Offered Positions:* 6
Program ID: 325-49-13-072

Virginia

Charlottesville

University of Virginia Program
Sponsor: University of Virginia Medical Center
Prgm Director: George M McDaniel, MD*
PO Box 800386
Charlottesville, VA 22908
Tel: 434 924-9119   *Fax:* 434 924-5656
E-mail: gmm4q@virginia.edu
Length: 3 Yrs   *ACGME Approved/Offered Positions:* 6
Program ID: 325-51-21-050

Richmond

Virginia Commonwealth University Health System Program
Sponsor: Virginia Commonwealth University Health System
Medical College of Virginia Hospitals
Prgm Director: Sam Lee, MD*
PO Box 980342
1200 E Broad St
Richmond, VA 23298
Tel: 804 628-9611   *Fax:* 804 828-8517
Length: 3 Yrs   *ACGME Approved/Offered Positions:* 3
Program ID: 325-51-11-051

Washington

Seattle

University of Washington Program
Sponsor: University of Washington School of Medicine
Seattle Children's Hospital
Prgm Director: Troy Alan Johnston, MD
4800 Sand Point Way, NE
Seattle, WA 98105
Tel: 206 987-2015   *Fax:* 206 987-3839
Length: 3 Yrs   *ACGME Approved/Offered Positions:* 3
Program ID: 325-54-12-077

Wisconsin

Milwaukee

Medical College of Wisconsin Affiliated Hospitals Program
Sponsor: Medical College of Wisconsin Affiliated Hospitals, Inc
Children's Hospital of Wisconsin
Prgm Director: Peter Bartz, MD
9000 West Wisconsin Avenue
MS 713
Milwaukee, WI 53226
Tel: 414 266-2448   *Fax:* 414 266-3261
E-mail: pbartz@chw.org
Length: 3 Yrs   *ACGME Approved/Offered Positions:* 9
Program ID: 325-56-13-076

Pediatric Critical Care Medicine (Pediatrics)

Alabama

Birmingham

University of Alabama Medical Center Program
Sponsor: University of Alabama Hospital
Children's Hospital of Alabama
Prgm Director: Margaret K Winkler, MD
1600 7th Avenue South
ACC 504
Birmingham, AL 35233
Tel: 205 939-9387   *Fax:* 205 975-6505
Length: 3 Yrs   *ACGME Approved/Offered Positions:* 6
Program ID: 323-01-21-040

Arkansas

Little Rock

University of Arkansas for Medical Sciences Program
Sponsor: University of Arkansas College of Medicine
Arkansas Children's Hospital
Prgm Director: Richard T Fiser, MD
Critical Care Medicine, Slot 512-12
800 Marshall St
Little Rock, AR 72202
Tel: 501 364-1008   *Fax:* 501 364-3188
Length: 3 Yrs   *ACGME Approved/Offered Positions:* 6
Program ID: 323-04-21-006

California

Loma Linda

Loma Linda University Program
Sponsor: Loma Linda University Medical Center
Prgm Director: Shamel A Abd-Allah, MD
11175 Campus St, A1117
Dept of Peds, Pediatric Critical Care Division
Loma Linda, CA 92354
Tel: 909 558-4250   *Fax:* 909 558-0303
E-mail: sabd-Allah@llu.edu
Length: 3 Yrs   *ACGME Approved/Offered Positions:* 6
Program ID: 323-05-31-057

Los Angeles

Childrens Hospital Los Angeles Program
Sponsor: Childrens Hospital Los Angeles
Prgm Director: Niurka Rivero, MD
4650 Sunset Boulevard MS 12
Los Angeles, CA 90027
Tel: 323 361-2557   *Fax:* 323 361-1001
E-mail: nrivero@chla.usc.edu
Length: 3 Yrs   *ACGME Approved/Offered Positions:* 9
Program ID: 323-05-31-047

Note: * indicates a newly appointed program director

UCLA Medical Center Program

Sponsor: UCLA David Geffen School of Medicine/UCLA Medical Center
UCLA Medical Center
Prgm Director: Irwin K Weiss, MD
Department of Pediatrics
Box 951752
Los Angeles, CA 90095
Tel: 310 825-6752 *Fax:* 310 794-6623
Length: 3 Yrs *ACGME Approved/Offered Positions:* 8
Program ID: 323-05-21-023

San Diego

University of California (San Diego) Program

Sponsor: University of California (San Diego) Medical Center
Rady Children's Hospital
Prgm Director: Bradley M Peterson, MD
3020 Children's Way
MC 5065
San Diego, CA 92123
Tel: 858 966-5863 *Fax:* 858 279-8415
E-mail: bpeterson@rchsd.org
Length: 3 Yrs *ACGME Approved/Offered Positions:* 9
Program ID: 323-05-12-084

San Francisco

University of California (San Francisco) Program

Sponsor: University of California (San Francisco) School of Medicine
Children's Hospital-Oakland
UCSF and Mount Zion Medical Centers
Prgm Director: Jeffrey R Fineman, MD
505 Parnassus Avenue, M-680
Campus Box 0106
San Francisco, CA 94143
Tel: 415 502-6390 *Fax:* 415 502-4186
Length: 3 Yrs *ACGME Approved/Offered Positions:* 11
Program ID: 323-05-21-021

Stanford

Stanford University Program

Sponsor: Stanford Hospital and Clinics
Lucile Salter Packard Children's Hospital at Stanford
Prgm Director: David Cornfield, MD
770 Welch Road, Suite 350
Palo Alto, CA 94304
Tel: 650 723-5227 *Fax:* 650 498-5560
Length: 3 Yrs *ACGME Approved/Offered Positions:* 6
Program ID: 323-05-21-056

Torrance

Los Angeles County-Harbor-UCLA Medical Center Program

Sponsor: Los Angeles County-Harbor-UCLA Medical Center
Children's Hospital of Orange County
Prgm Director: Richard B Mink, MD
1000 West Carson Street, Box 491
Torrance, CA 90509
Tel: 310 222-4002 *Fax:* 310 320-2271
Length: 3 Yrs *ACGME Approved/Offered Positions:* 6
Program ID: 323-05-21-033

Colorado

Aurora

University of Colorado Denver Program

Sponsor: University of Colorado Denver School of Medicine
Children's Hospital (The)
University of Colorado Denver
Prgm Director: Eva N Grayck, MD
The Children's Hospital
13123 E 16th Avenue
Aurora, CO 80045
Tel: 303 724-2393 *Fax:* 720 777-7324
E-mail: eva.grayck@ucdenver.edu
Length: 3 Yrs *ACGME Approved/Offered Positions:* 7
Program ID: 323-07-21-034

Connecticut

New Haven

Yale-New Haven Medical Center Program

Sponsor: Yale-New Haven Hospital
Prgm Director: Clifford W Bogue, MD*
PO Box 208064
New Haven, CT 06520
Tel: 203 785-4651 *Fax:* 203 785-5833
Length: 3 Yrs *ACGME Approved/Offered Positions:* 6
Program ID: 323-08-21-036

Delaware

Wilmington

Jefferson Medical College/duPont Hospital for Children Program

Sponsor: Jefferson Medical College
Alfred I duPont Hospital for Children
Prgm Director: Scott Penfil, MD
1600 Rockland Road
PO Box 269
Wilmington, DE 19899
Tel: 302 651-5390 *Fax:* 302 651-5365
E-mail: spenfil@nemours.org
Length: 3 Yrs *ACGME Approved/Offered Positions:* 3
Program ID: 323-41-13-076

District of Columbia

Washington

Children's National Medical Center/George Washington University Program

Sponsor: Children's National Medical Center
Prgm Director: Jennifer J Schuette, MD*
111 Michigan Avenue NW
Suite 3-100
Washington, DC 20010
Tel: 202 476-2130 *Fax:* 202 476-5724
E-mail: jschuett@cnmc.org
Length: 3 Yrs *ACGME Approved/Offered Positions:* 9
Program ID: 323-10-21-035

Florida

Gainesville

University of Florida Program

Sponsor: University of Florida College of Medicine
Shands Hospital at the University of Florida
Prgm Director: Ann M LeVine, MD
PO Box 100296
Pediatric Critical Care Medicine
Gainesville, FL 32610
Tel: 352 265-0462 *Fax:* 352 265-0443
E-mail: levineam@peds.ufl.edu
Length: 3 Yrs *ACGME Approved/Offered Positions:* 5
Program ID: 323-11-21-020

Miami

Jackson Memorial Hospital/Jackson Health System Program

Sponsor: Jackson Memorial Hospital/Jackson Health System
Prgm Director: Michael A Nares, MD
PO Box 016960 (R-131)
Miami, FL 33101
Tel: 305 585-6051 *Fax:* 305 325-0293
E-mail: mbarreto@med.miami.edu
Length: 3 Yrs *ACGME Approved/Offered Positions:* 8
Program ID: 323-11-21-012

Miami Children's Hospital Program

Sponsor: Miami Children's Hospital
Prgm Director: Balagangadhar R Totapally, MBBS, MD
3100 SW 62nd Avenue
Miami, FL 33155
Tel: 305 662-2639 *Fax:* 305 663-0530
E-mail: bala.totapally@mch.com
Length: 3 Yrs *ACGME Approved/Offered Positions:* 6
Program ID: 323-11-21-061

Georgia

Atlanta

Emory University Program

Sponsor: Emory University School of Medicine
Children's Healthcare of Atlanta at Egleston
Prgm Director: Toni M Petrillo, MD*
1405 Clifton Road NE
Atlanta, GA 30322
Tel: 404 785-1753 *Fax:* 404 785-6233
E-mail: Toni.Petrillo@choa.org
Length: 3 Yrs *ACGME Approved/Offered Positions:* 7
Program ID: 323-12-21-030

Illinois

Chicago

McGaw Medical Center of Northwestern University Program

Sponsor: McGaw Medical Center of Northwestern University
Children's Memorial Hospital
Prgm Director: Denise M Goodman, MD, MS
Div of Pediatric Critical Care
2300 Children's Plaza, #73
Chicago, IL 60614
Tel: 773 880-4780 *Fax:* 773 880-6300
Length: 3 Yrs *ACGME Approved/Offered Positions:* 12
Program ID: 323-16-21-032

Programs

University of Chicago Program
Sponsor: University of Chicago Medical Center
University of Chicago Comer Children's Hospital
Prgm Director: Rachel K Wolfson, MD*
5841 S Maryland Avenue
MC 1145
Chicago, IL 60637
Tel: 773 834-7099   *Fax:* 773 702-4041
E-mail: rwolfson@peds.bsd.uchicago.edu
Length: 3 Yrs   *ACGME Approved/Offered Positions:* 9
Program ID: 323-16-21-031

Park Ridge

Advocate Lutheran General Hospital Program
Sponsor: Advocate Lutheran General Hospital
Prgm Director: Suresh Havalad, MD
1775 Dempster Street
Park Ridge, IL 60068
Tel: 847 723-5313   *Fax:* 847 723-2338
E-mail: suresh.havalad-md@advocatehealth.com
Length: 3 Yrs   *ACGME Approved/Offered Positions:* 3
Program ID: 323-16-21-046

Indiana

Indianapolis

Indiana University School of Medicine Program
Sponsor: Indiana University School of Medicine
Clarian Riley Hospital for Children
Prgm Director: G Kris Bysani, MD
702 Barnhill Drive, ROC 4270
Indianapolis, IN 46202
Tel: 317 278-7128   *Fax:* 317 274-5791
E-mail: gbysani@iupui.edu
Length: 3 Yrs   *ACGME Approved/Offered Positions:* 3
Program ID: 323-17-21-081

Iowa

Iowa City

University of Iowa Hospitals and Clinics Program
Sponsor: University of Iowa Hospitals and Clinics
Prgm Director: Jessica G Moreland, MD
Department of Pediatrics, 2 JCP
200 Hawkins Drive
Iowa City, IA 52242
Tel: 319 356-1615   *Fax:* 319 353-8597
E-mail: jessica-moreland@uiowa.edu
Length: 3 Yrs   *ACGME Approved/Offered Positions:* 4
Program ID: 323-18-21-077

Kentucky

Louisville

University of Louisville Program
Sponsor: University of Louisville School of Medicine
Kosair Children's Hospital (Norton Healthcare, Inc)
Prgm Director: Amy O Hardin, MD
Department of Pediatrics
571 S Floyd St, #332
Louisville, KY 40202
Tel: 502 852-3720   *Fax:* 502 852-3998
E-mail: mcmori01@louisville.edu
Length: 3 Yrs   *ACGME Approved/Offered Positions:* 3
Program ID: 323-20-21-071

Maryland

Baltimore

Johns Hopkins University Program
Sponsor: Johns Hopkins University School of Medicine
Johns Hopkins Hospital
Prgm Director: Z Leah Harris, MD
600 N Wolfe Street, Blalock 904
Baltimore, MD 21287
Tel: 410 955-2393   *Fax:* 410 502-5312
E-mail: rcabell2@jhmi.edu
Length: 3 Yrs   *ACGME Approved/Offered Positions:* 10
Program ID: 323-23-21-009

University of Maryland Program
Sponsor: University of Maryland Medical System
Prgm Director: Courtney L Robertson, MD*
29 South Greene Street
Suite 104
Baltimore, MD 21201
Tel: 410 328-6957   *Fax:* 410 328-0680
Length: 3 Yrs   *ACGME Approved/Offered Positions:* 4
Program ID: 323-23-21-070

Massachusetts

Boston

Children's Hospital/Boston Medical Center Program
Sponsor: Children's Hospital
Prgm Director: Jeffrey P Burns, MD, MPH
Division of Critical Care Medicine - Bader 634
300 Longwood Avenue
Boston, MA 02115
Tel: 617 355-7327   *Fax:* 617 730-0453
Length: 3 Yrs   *ACGME Approved/Offered Positions:* 15
Program ID: 323-24-21-019

Massachusetts General Hospital Program
Sponsor: Massachusetts General Hospital
Prgm Director: Natan Noviski, MD*
Pediatric Critical Care Medicine
175 Cambridge St, CRPZ-524
Boston, MA 02114
Tel: 617 724-4380   *Fax:* 617 724-4391
Length: 3 Yrs   *ACGME Approved/Offered Positions:* 6
Program ID: 323-24-21-048

Michigan

Ann Arbor

University of Michigan Program
Sponsor: University of Michigan Hospitals and Health
    Centers
Prgm Director: Thomas P Shanley, MD
F-6894 Mott/5243
1500 East Medical Center Drive
Ann Arbor, MI 48109
Tel: 734 764-5302   *Fax:* 734 647-5624
E-mail: tshanley@med.umich.edu
Length: 3 Yrs   *ACGME Approved/Offered Positions:* 6
Program ID: 323-25-21-008

Detroit

Children's Hospital of Michigan Program
Sponsor: Children's Hospital of Michigan
Prgm Director: Mary W Lieh-Lai, MD
3901 Beaubien Blvd
Detroit, MI 48201
Tel: 313 745-5629   *Fax:* 313 966-0105
Length: 3 Yrs   *ACGME Approved/Offered Positions:* 7
Program ID: 323-25-21-039

Minnesota

Minneapolis

University of Minnesota Program
Sponsor: University of Minnesota Medical School
University of Minnesota Medical Center, Division of
    Fairview
Prgm Director: Marie E Steiner, MD, MS
MMC 742
420 Delaware Street, SE
Minneapolis, MN 55455
Tel: 612 626-2778   *Fax:* 612 626-0413
E-mail: stein083@umn.edu
Length: 3 Yrs   *ACGME Approved/Offered Positions:* 6
Program ID: 323-26-21-005

Missouri

Kansas City

University of Missouri at Kansas City Program
Sponsor: University of Missouri-Kansas City School of
    Medicine
Children's Mercy Hospital
Prgm Director: Kelly S Tieves, DO, MS
2401 Gillham Road
Kansas City, MO 64108
Tel: 816 234-3041   *Fax:* 816 346-1376
Length: 3 Yrs   *ACGME Approved/Offered Positions:* 3
Program ID: 323-28-21-085

St Louis

Washington University/B-JH/SLCH Consortium Program
Sponsor: Washington University/B-JH/SLCH Consortium
St Louis Children's Hospital
Prgm Director: Matthew I Goldsmith, MD
660 S Euclid Avenue
Campus Box 8208
St Louis, MO 63110
Tel: 314 454-2527   *Fax:* 314 361-0733
E-mail: Goldsmith_M@kids.wustl.edu
Length: 3 Yrs   *ACGME Approved/Offered Positions:* 12
Program ID: 323-28-21-060

New Jersey

Camden

UMDNJ-Robert Wood Johnson Medical School (Camden) Program
Sponsor: Cooper Hospital-University Medical Center
Prgm Director: Arsenia M Asuncion, MD
Pediatric Intensive Care Unit
E & R Building, 401 Haddon Avenue, Suite 384
Camden, NJ 08103
Tel: 856 757-7857   *Fax:* 856 968-9598
E-mail: asuncion-arsenia@cooperhealth.edu
Length: 3 Yrs   *ACGME Approved/Offered Positions:* 3
Program ID: 323-33-31-049

New Brunswick

UMDNJ-Robert Wood Johnson Medical School Program
Sponsor: UMDNJ-Robert Wood Johnson Medical School
Robert Wood Johnson University Hospital
Prgm Director: Thomas Bojko, MD, MS
One Robert Wood Johnson Place
New Brunswick, NJ 08903
Tel: 732 235-7887   *Fax:* 732 235-9340
Length: 3 Yrs   *ACGME Approved/Offered Positions:* 3
Program ID: 323-33-12-080

Note: * indicates a newly appointed program director

New York

Bronx

Albert Einstein College of Medicine Program

Sponsor: Albert Einstein College of Medicine of Yeshiva University
Montefiore Medical Center-Henry and Lucy Moses Division
Prgm Director: Lewis P Singer, MD
111 East 210th Street
Bronx, NY 10467
Tel: 718 741-2477   *Fax:* 718 654-6692
E-mail: lsinger@montefiore.org
Length: 3 Yrs   *ACGME Approved/Offered Positions:* 4
Program ID: 323-35-21-004

Buffalo

University at Buffalo Program

Sponsor: University at Buffalo School of Medicine
Kaleida Health System (Women and Children's Hosp of Buffalo)
Prgm Director: Prashant Joshi, MD*
219 Bryant Street
Buffalo, NY 14222
Tel: 716 878-7849   *Fax:* 716 878-7101
Length: 3 Yrs   *ACGME Approved/Offered Positions:* 6
Program ID: 323-35-31-055

Great Neck

NSLIJHS-Schneider Children's Hospital Program

Sponsor: North Shore-Long Island Jewish Health System
Schneider Children's Hospital at Long Island Jewish Med Ctr
Prgm Director: Mayer Sagy, MD
L I Jewish Medical Center
New Hyde Park, NY 11040
Tel: 718 470-3330   *Fax:* 718 470-0159
Length: 3 Yrs   *ACGME Approved/Offered Positions:* 6
Program ID: 323-35-32-059

New York

New York Presbyterian Hospital (Columbia Campus) Program

Sponsor: New York Presbyterian Hospital
New York Presbyterian Hospital (Columbia Campus)
Prgm Director: Katherine Biagas, MD
Department of Pediatrics
630 W 168th Street, CHN 10-24
New York, NY 10032
Tel: 212 305-8458   *Fax:* 212 342-2293
Length: 3 Yrs   *ACGME Approved/Offered Positions:* 9
Program ID: 323-35-31-075

New York Presbyterian Hospital (Cornell Campus) Program

Sponsor: New York Presbyterian Hospital
New York Presbyterian Hospital (Cornell Campus)
Prgm Director: Joy D Howell, MD
525 East 68th Street
Room M-508
New York, NY 10065
Tel: 212 746-3272   *Fax:* 212 746-8332
E-mail: jdh2002@med.cornell.edu
Length: 3 Yrs   *ACGME Approved/Offered Positions:* 6
Program ID: 323-35-21-037

Rochester

University of Rochester Program

Sponsor: Strong Memorial Hospital of the University of Rochester
Prgm Director: Jeffrey Rubenstein, MD, MPH*
Department of Pediatrics
601 Elmwood Avenue, Box 667
Rochester, NY 14642
Tel: 585 275-8138   *Fax:* 585 275-0707
E-mail: jeffery_rubenstein@urmc.rochester.edu
Length: 3 Yrs   *ACGME Approved/Offered Positions:* 3
Program ID: 323-35-21-053

North Carolina

Chapel Hill

University of North Carolina Hospitals Program

Sponsor: University of North Carolina Hospitals
Prgm Director: Keith C Kocis, MD, MS*
Division of Pediatric Critical Care Medicine
Suite 20160 NC Women's Hosp, CB 7221
Chapel Hill, NC 27599
Tel: 919 966-7495   *Fax:* 919 966-6164
E-mail: KKocis@med.unc.edu
Length: 3 Yrs   *ACGME Approved/Offered Positions:* 6
Program ID: 323-36-21-016

Durham

Duke University Hospital Program

Sponsor: Duke University Hospital
Prgm Director: Ira M Cheifetz, MD
Box 3046
Durham, NC 27710
Tel: 919 681-3550   *Fax:* 919 681-8357
E-mail: Cheif002@mc.duke.edu
Length: 3 Yrs   *ACGME Approved/Offered Positions:* 9
Program ID: 323-36-21-038

Ohio

Cincinnati

Cincinnati Children's Hospital Medical Center/University of Cincinnati College of Medicine Program

Sponsor: Cincinnati Children's Hospital Medical Center
Prgm Director: Lesley A Doughty, MD
Division of Critical Care Medicine
3333 Burnet Avenue
Cincinnati, OH 45229
Tel: 513 636-4259   *Fax:* 513 636-4267
E-mail: lesley.doughty@cchmc.org
Length: 3 Yrs   *ACGME Approved/Offered Positions:* 12
Program ID: 323-38-21-015

Cleveland

University Hospitals Case Medical Center Program

Sponsor: University Hospitals Case Medical Center
Prgm Director: Katherine Mason, MD*
11100 Euclid Avenue
Cleveland, OH 44106
Tel: 216 844-3310
Length: 3 Yrs   *ACGME Approved/Offered Positions:* 12
Program ID: 323-38-21-051

Columbus

Nationwide Children's Hospital/Ohio State University Program

Sponsor: Nationwide Children's Hospital
Prgm Director: Mark W Hall, MD*
700 Children's Drive
Columbus, OH 43205
Tel: 614 722-3438   *Fax:* 614 722-3443
E-mail: Mark.Hall@NationwideChildrens.org
Length: 3 Yrs   *ACGME Approved/Offered Positions:* 6
Program ID: 323-38-22-078

Pennsylvania

Hershey

Penn State University/Milton S Hershey Medical Center Program

Sponsor: Milton S Hershey Medical Center
Prgm Director: Gary D Ceneviva, MD
Department of Pediatric Critical Care Medicine
500 University Drive - MC H085
Hershey, PA 17033
Tel: 717 531-5337   *Fax:* 717 531-0809
E-mail: shollowell@hmc.psu.edu
Length: 3 Yrs
Program ID: 323-41-31-082

Philadelphia

Children's Hospital of Philadelphia Program

Sponsor: Children's Hospital of Philadelphia
Prgm Director: Wynne Morrison, MD
Dept of Anesthesiology & Critical Care Medicine
34th and Civic Center Blvd
Philadelphia, PA 19104
Tel: 215 590-7430   *Fax:* 215 590-4327
Length: 3 Yrs   *ACGME Approved/Offered Positions:* 15
Program ID: 323-41-21-014

Pittsburgh

University of Pittsburgh Medical Center Medical Education Program

Sponsor: Univ of Pittsburgh Medical Center Medical Education
Children's Hospital of Pittsburgh of UPMC
Prgm Director: Robert S Clark, MD
3705 Fifth Avenue, Room 6840
Pittsburgh, PA 15213
Tel: 412 692-5164   *Fax:* 412 692-6076
Length: 3 Yrs   *ACGME Approved/Offered Positions:* 12
Program ID: 323-41-21-028

Puerto Rico

San Juan

University of Puerto Rico Program

Sponsor: University of Puerto Rico School of Medicine
University Pediatric Hospital
Prgm Director: Ricardo L García-De Jesús, MD
PO Box 365067
San Juan, PR 00936
Tel: 787 777-3535   *Fax:* 787 751-5306
E-mail: rigarcia@rcm.upr.edu
Length: 3 Yrs   *ACGME Approved/Offered Positions:* 3
Program ID: 323-42-21-069

Programs

Tennessee

Memphis

University of Tennessee Program
Sponsor: University of Tennessee College of Medicine
LeBonheur Children's Medical Center
Prgm Director: Stephanie A Storgion, MD
50 N Dunlap Street, Suite 4624
Memphis, TN 38103
Tel: 901 287-6303 *Fax:* 901 287-5198
E-mail: lcallen@utmem.edu
Length: 3 Yrs *ACGME Approved/Offered Positions:* 6
Program ID: 323-47-21-027

Nashville

Vanderbilt University Program
Sponsor: Vanderbilt University Medical Center
Prgm Director: Frederick E Barr, MD, MSc
5121 Doctors' Office Tower
2200 Children's Way
Nashville, TN 37232
Tel: 615 936-1305 *Fax:* 615 936-3467
Length: 3 Yrs *ACGME Approved/Offered Positions:* 9
Program ID: 323-47-21-062

Texas

Dallas

University of Texas Southwestern Medical School Program
Sponsor: University of Texas Southwestern Medical
School
Children's Medical Center of Dallas
Prgm Director: Steven G Kernie, MD, BA
5323 Harry Hines Blvd
Dallas, TX 75235
Tel: 214 456-7593 *Fax:* 214 456-7594
E-mail: steven.kernie@utsouthwestern.edu
Length: 3 Yrs *ACGME Approved/Offered Positions:* 12
Program ID: 323-48-21-041

Houston

Baylor College of Medicine Program
Sponsor: Baylor College of Medicine
Texas Children's Hospital
Prgm Director: M Hossein Tcharmtchi, MD
Department of Pediatrics
6621 Fannin St, WT6-006
Houston, TX 77030
Tel: 832 826-6230 *Fax:* 832 825-6229
E-mail: hammadt@bcm.edu
Length: 3 Yrs *ACGME Approved/Offered Positions:* 15
Program ID: 323-48-31-044

University of Texas at Houston Program
Sponsor: University of Texas Health Science Center at
Houston
Memorial Hermann Hospital
University of Texas M D Anderson Cancer Center
Prgm Director: Rodrigo Mejia, MD*
6431 Fannin St, MSB 3.228
Houston, TX 77030
Tel: 713 792-6620
E-mail: rmejia@mdanderson.org
Length: 3 Yrs *ACGME Approved/Offered Positions:* 3
Program ID: 323-48-13-079

San Antonio

University of Texas Health Science Center at San Antonio Program
Sponsor: University of Texas School of Medicine at San
Antonio
Christus Santa Rosa Health Care Corporation
University Health System
Prgm Director: Richard P Taylor, MD, MS
Pediatric Critical Care, MC 7829 - Department of Peds
7703 Floyd Curl Drive
San Antonio, TX 78229
Tel: 210 562-5816 *Fax:* 210 562-5200
Length: 3 Yrs *ACGME Approved/Offered Positions:* 3
Program ID: 323-48-21-072

Utah

Salt Lake City

University of Utah Program
Sponsor: University of Utah Medical Center
Primary Children's Medical Center
Prgm Director: Susan L Bratton, MD, MPH
Department of Pediatrics
295 Chipeta Way PO Box 581289
Salt Lake City, UT 84158
Tel: 801 587-7560 *Fax:* 801 581-8686
E-mail: Susan.Bratton@hsc.utah.edu
Length: 3 Yrs *ACGME Approved/Offered Positions:* 6
Program ID: 323-49-21-003

Virginia

Charlottesville

University of Virginia Program
Sponsor: University of Virginia Medical Center
Prgm Director: Noreen Crain, MD
UVA Children's Hospital
HSC Box 800386
Charlottesville, VA 22908
Tel: 434 982-1707 *Fax:* 434 982-3843
E-mail: Nc4v@virginia.edu
Length: 3 Yrs *ACGME Approved/Offered Positions:* 3
Program ID: 323-51-21-026

Richmond

Virginia Commonwealth University Health System Program
Sponsor: Virginia Commonwealth University Health
System
Medical College of Virginia Hospitals
Prgm Director: Monica S Relvas, MD*
Department of Pediatrics
PO Box 980530
Richmond, VA 23298
Tel: 804 828-4080 *Fax:* 804 628-2138
Length: 3 Yrs *ACGME Approved/Offered Positions:* 3
Program ID: 323-51-21-025

Washington

Seattle

University of Washington Program
Sponsor: University of Washington School of Medicine
Seattle Children's Hospital
Prgm Director: Harris P Baden, MD
4800 Sand Point Way NE
M/S W-8866
Seattle, WA 98105
Tel: 206 987-2140 *Fax:* 206 987-3866
Length: 3 Yrs *ACGME Approved/Offered Positions:* 9
Program ID: 323-54-21-013

Wisconsin

Madison

University of Wisconsin Program
Sponsor: University of Wisconsin Hospital and Clinics
Prgm Director: Michael Wilhelm, MD*
H4/470
600 Highland Avenue
Madison, WI 53792
Tel: 608 263-1905 *Fax:* 608 265-9243
E-mail: mwilhelm@pediatrics.wisc.edu
Length: 3 Yrs *ACGME Approved/Offered Positions:* 3
Program ID: 323-56-21-001

Milwaukee

Medical College of Wisconsin Affiliated Hospitals Program
Sponsor: Medical College of Wisconsin Affiliated
Hospitals, Inc
Children's Hospital of Wisconsin
Prgm Director: Karen J Marcdante, MD
9000 West Wisconsin Avenue
PO Box 1997, MS B550B
Milwaukee, WI 53226
Tel: 414 266-3392 *Fax:* 414 337-4185
Length: 3 Yrs *ACGME Approved/Offered Positions:* 9
Program ID: 323-56-21-002

Note: * indicates a newly appointed program director

Pediatric Emergency Medicine (Emergency Medicine)

California

Loma Linda

Loma Linda University Program
Sponsor: Loma Linda University Medical Center
Prgm Director: Lance A Brown, MD, MPH
Dept of Emergency Medicine A-108
11234 Anderson Street
Loma Linda, CA 92534
Tel: 909 558-7698   *Fax:* 909 558-0121
E-mail: labrown@llu.edu
Length: 2 Yrs   *ACGME Approved/Offered Positions:* 6
Program ID: 114-05-21-002

San Diego

University of California (San Diego) Program
Sponsor: University of California (San Diego) Medical Center
Rady Children's Hospital
Prgm Director: Paul T Ishimine, MD*
3020 Children's Way, MC 5075
San Diego, CA 92123
Tel: 858 966-8036   *Fax:* 858 966-7433
E-mail: tnyang@rchsd.org
Length: 3 Yrs   *ACGME Approved/Offered Positions:* 6
Program ID: 114-05-13-007

Connecticut

Farmington

University of Connecticut Program
Sponsor: University of Connecticut School of Medicine
Connecticut Children's Medical Center
Prgm Director: John C Brancato, MD
282 Washington Street
Pediatric Emergency Medicine
Hartford, CT 06106
Tel: 860 545-9195   *Fax:* 860 545-9202
E-mail: vtomlin@ccmckids.org
Length: 2 Yrs   *ACGME Approved/Offered Positions:* 3
Program ID: 114-08-31-006

Florida

Jacksonville

University of Florida College of Medicine Jacksonville Program
Sponsor: University of Florida College of Medicine Jacksonville
Shands Jacksonville Medical Center
Wolfson Children's Hospital
Prgm Director: Todd Wylie, MD, MPH
655 West 8th Street, Box C506
Jacksonville, FL 32209
Tel: 904 244-4046   *Fax:* 904 244-4077
E-mail: everlena.owens@jax.ufl.edu
Length: 2 Yrs   *ACGME Approved/Offered Positions:* 6
Program ID: 114-11-21-004

Orlando

Orlando Health Program
Sponsor: Orlando Health
Arnold Palmer Hospital for Children
Prgm Director: Jose Ramirez, MD
Emergency Department
92 West Miller Street
Orlando, FL 32806
Tel: 321 841-7448   *Fax:* 321 841-4046
E-mail: jose.ramirez@orlandohealth.com
Length: 2 Yrs   *ACGME Approved/Offered Positions:* 4
Program ID: 114-11-12-022

Georgia

Augusta

Medical College of Georgia Program
Sponsor: Medical College of Georgia
Prgm Director: Natalie E Lane, MD
AF-2034 Department of Emergency Medicine
Augusta, GA 30912
Tel: 706 721-4467   *Fax:* 706 721-7718
E-mail: nlane@mcg.edu
Length: 2 Yrs   *ACGME Approved/Offered Positions:* 2
Program ID: 114-12-12-014

Massachusetts

Springfield

Baystate Medical Center/Tufts University School of Medicine Program
Sponsor: Baystate Medical Center
Prgm Director: Blake Spirko, MD
Department of Emergency Medicine
759 Chestnut Street
Springfield, MA 01199
Tel: 413 794-5999   *Fax:* 413 794-8070
Length: 2 Yrs   *ACGME Approved/Offered Positions:* 4
Program ID: 114-24-31-013

Michigan

Ann Arbor

University of Michigan Program
Sponsor: University of Michigan Hospitals and Health Centers
Hurley Medical Center
Prgm Director: Michele M Nypaver, MD
1500 E Medical Center Drive, SPC 5305
B1-380 TC
Ann Arbor, MI 48109
Tel: 734 232-6166   *Fax:* 734 763-9298
E-mail: babcockk@med.umich.edu
Length: 2 Yrs   *ACGME Approved/Offered Positions:* 4
Program ID: 114-25-13-011

New Jersey

Camden

UMDNJ-Robert Wood Johnson Medical School (Camden) Program
Sponsor: Cooper Hospital-University Medical Center
Prgm Director: Elliott M Harris, MD
Department of Emergency Medicine
One Cooper Plaza
Camden, NJ 08103
Tel: 856 342-2627   *Fax:* 856 968-8272
E-mail: hood-ramie@cooperhealth.edu
Length: 2 Yrs   *ACGME Approved/Offered Positions:* 2
Program ID: 114-33-31-009

Morristown

Atlantic Health (Morristown) Program
Sponsor: Atlantic Health
Morristown Memorial Hospital
Prgm Director: Christopher S Amato, MD
Department of Emergency Medicine
100 Madison Avenue
Morristown, NJ 07962
Tel: 973 971-7926   *Fax:* 973 290-7202
E-mail: colleen.mayer@yahoo.com
Length: 2 Yrs   *ACGME Approved/Offered Positions:* 4
Program ID: 114-33-31-017

New York

Brooklyn

Maimonides Medical Center Program
Sponsor: Maimonides Medical Center
Prgm Director: Estevan Adan Garcia, MD
4802 Tenth Avenue
Brooklyn, NY 11219
Tel: 718 283-6352   *Fax:* 718 283-6037
E-mail: phainke@maimonidesmed.org
Length: 2 Yrs   *ACGME Approved/Offered Positions:* 2
Program ID: 114-35-13-020

Rochester

University of Rochester Program
Sponsor: Strong Memorial Hospital of the University of Rochester
Prgm Director: Lynn Babcock Cimpello, MD
Department of Emergency Medicine
601 Elmwood Avenue, Box 655
Rochester, NY 14642
Tel: 585 463-2942   *Fax:* 585 473-3516
Length: 2 Yrs   *ACGME Approved/Offered Positions:* 4
Program ID: 114-35-21-001

Syracuse

SUNY Upstate Medical University Program
Sponsor: SUNY Upstate Medical University
Prgm Director: Richard Cantor, MD
Department of Emergency Medicine
750 East Adams Street
Syracuse, NY 13210
Tel: 315 464-6224   *Fax:* 315 464-6229
E-mail: cantorr@upstate.edu
Length: 2 Yrs   *ACGME Approved/Offered Positions:* 2
Program ID: 114-35-12-012

North Carolina

Chapel Hill

University of North Carolina Hospitals Program
Sponsor: University of North Carolina Hospitals
Wake Medical Center
Prgm Director: Donna Moro-Sutherland, MD
Department of Emergency Medicine
3000 New Bern Avenue
Raleigh, NC 27610
Tel: 919 350-8823   *Fax:* 919 350-8874
E-mail: moro-sutherland@weppa.org
Length: 2 Yrs   *ACGME Approved/Offered Positions:* 4
Program ID: 114-36-12-018

Programs

Charlotte

Carolinas Medical Center Program
Sponsor: Carolinas Medical Center
Prgm Director: Randolph J Cordle, MD
Division of Pediatric Emergency Medicine
PO Box 32851
Charlotte, NC 28232
Tel: 704 355-0420 *Fax:* 704 355-8358
E-mail: randolph.cordle@carolinashealthcare.org
Length: 2 Yrs *ACGME Approved/Offered Positions:* 4
Program ID: 114-36-13-016

Winston-Salem

Wake Forest University School of Medicine Program
Sponsor: Wake Forest University Baptist Medical Center
Prgm Director: David Magilner, MD, MS
Department of Emergency Medicine
1 Medical Center Boulevard
Winston Salem, NC 27157
Tel: 336 716-4625 *Fax:* 336 716-5438
E-mail: nhollida@wfubmc.edu
Length: 2 Yrs *ACGME Approved/Offered Positions:* 2
Program ID: 114-36-31-021

Oregon

Portland

Oregon Health & Science University Program
Sponsor: Oregon Health & Science University Hospital
Legacy Emanuel Hospital and Health Center
Prgm Director: Garth Meckler, MD, MSPH
OHSU Department of Emergency Medicine
3181 SW Sam Jackson Park Road
Portland, OR 97239
Tel: 503 494-1475 *Fax:* 503 494-4997
E-mail: mecklerg@ohsu.edu
Length: 2 Yrs *ACGME Approved/Offered Positions:* 2
Program ID: 114-40-21-019

Pennsylvania

Philadelphia

Drexel University College of Medicine/Hahnemann University Hospital Program
Sponsor: Drexel University College of
  Medicine/Hahnemann University
Hahnemann University Hospital (Tenet Health System)
St Christopher's Hospital for Children (Tenet Health
  System)
Prgm Director: Colette C Mull, MD
Front Street at Erie Avenue
Philadelphia, PA 19134
Tel: 215 427-5006 *Fax:* 215 427-4668
E-mail: cmull@drexelmed.edu
Length: 2 Yrs *ACGME Approved/Offered Positions:* 4
Program ID: 114-41-21-003

Tennessee

Nashville

Vanderbilt University Program
Sponsor: Vanderbilt University Medical Center
Prgm Director: Thomas J Abramo, MD*
703 Oxford House
1313 21st Avenue South
Nashville, TN 37232
Tel: 615 936-4452 *Fax:* 615 322-4374
E-mail: thomas.j.abramo@vanderbilt.edu
Length: 2 Yrs *ACGME Approved/Offered Positions:* 4
Program ID: 114-47-21-008

Pediatric Emergency Medicine (Pediatrics)

Alabama

Birmingham

University of Alabama Medical Center Program
Sponsor: University of Alabama Hospital
Children's Hospital of Alabama
Prgm Director: Ann E Klasner, MD, MPH*
1600 7th Avenue South
Midtown Suite 205
Birmingham, AL 35233
Tel: 205 939-9587 *Fax:* 205 975-4623
E-mail: aklasner@peds.uab.edu
Length: 3 Yrs *ACGME Approved/Offered Positions:* 9
Program ID: 324-01-21-041

Arizona

Phoenix

Phoenix Children's Hospital/Maricopa Medical Center Program
Sponsor: Phoenix Children's Hospital
Prgm Director: Robert B Bulloch, MD
1919 E Thomas Road
Phoenix, AZ 85016
Tel: 602 546-5048 *Fax:* 602 546-1414
Length: 3 Yrs *ACGME Approved/Offered Positions:* 6
Program ID: 324-03-21-050

Arkansas

Little Rock

University of Arkansas for Medical Sciences Program
Sponsor: University of Arkansas College of Medicine
Arkansas Children's Hospital
Prgm Director: C James Graham, MD
Department of Pediatrics, Emergency Medicine Div
800 Marshall Street, Slot 512-16
Little Rock, AR 72202
Tel: 501 364-1050 *Fax:* 501 364-3480
E-mail: grahamjames@uams.edu
Length: 3 Yrs *ACGME Approved/Offered Positions:* 6
Program ID: 324-04-13-052

California

Los Angeles

Childrens Hospital Los Angeles Program
Sponsor: Childrens Hospital Los Angeles
Prgm Director: Deborah R Liu, MD
4650 Sunset Boulevard
MS 113
Los Angeles, CA 90027
Tel: 323 361-2109 *Fax:* 323 361-3891
E-mail: deliu@chla.usc.edu
Length: 3 Yrs *ACGME Approved/Offered Positions:* 9
Program ID: 324-05-21-001

Note: * indicates a newly appointed program director

Oakland

Children's Hospital-Oakland Program

Sponsor: Children's Hospital-Oakland
Prgm Director: Alan M Johnson, MD
747 52nd Street
Oakland, CA 94609
Tel: 510 428-3259   *Fax:* 510 450-5836
E-mail: aljohnson@mail.cho.org
Length: 3 Yrs   *ACGME Approved/Offered Positions:* 2
Program ID: 324-05-31-002

Torrance

Los Angeles County-Harbor-UCLA Medical Center Program

Sponsor: Los Angeles County-Harbor-UCLA Medical
  Center
UCLA Medical Center
Prgm Director: Marianne Gausche-Hill, MD
1000 W Carson Street, Box 21
Torrance, CA 90509
Tel: 310 222-3501   *Fax:* 310 782-1763
E-mail: mgausche@emedharbor.edu
Length: 3 Yrs   *ACGME Approved/Offered Positions:* 3
Program ID: 324-05-11-003

Colorado

Aurora

University of Colorado Denver Program

Sponsor: University of Colorado Denver School of
  Medicine
Children's Hospital (The)
Prgm Director: Genie E Roosevelt, MD, MPH
13123 East 16th Avenue, B251
Aurora, CO 80045
Tel: 303 724-2577   *Fax:* 720 777-7317
E-mail: scott.maggie@tchden.org
Length: 3 Yrs   *ACGME Approved/Offered Positions:* 6
Program ID: 324-07-21-004

Connecticut

New Haven

Yale-New Haven Medical Center Program

Sponsor: Yale-New Haven Hospital
Prgm Director: Lei Chen, MD*
840 Howard Ave
New Haven, CT 06504
Tel: 203 688-7970   *Fax:* 203 688-4195
E-mail: lei.chen@yale.edu
Length: 3 Yrs   *ACGME Approved/Offered Positions:* 6
Program ID: 324-08-21-045

Delaware

Wilmington

Jefferson Medical College/duPont Hospital for Children Program

Sponsor: Jefferson Medical College
Alfred I duPont Hospital for Children
Prgm Director: Magdy W Attia, MD
1600 Rockland Road
PO Box 269
Wilmington, DE 19899
Tel: 302 651-5860   *Fax:* 302 651-4227
Length: 3 Yrs   *ACGME Approved/Offered Positions:* 4
Program ID: 324-41-11-032

District of Columbia

Washington

Children's National Medical Center/ George Washington University Program

Sponsor: Children's National Medical Center
Prgm Director: Jennifer I Chapman, MD*
Children's National Medical Center
111 Michigan Avenue, NW
Washington, DC 20010
Tel: 202 476-4177   *Fax:* 202 476-3573
E-mail: jchapman@cnmc.org
Length: 3 Yrs   *ACGME Approved/Offered Positions:* 9
Program ID: 324-10-21-005

Florida

Miami

Miami Children's Hospital Program

Sponsor: Miami Children's Hospital
Prgm Director: Marc Y Linares, MD
3100 SW 62nd Avenue
Miami, FL 33155
Tel: 305 666-6511   *Fax:* 305 662-8291
E-mail: Marc.Linares@mch.com
Length: 3 Yrs   *ACGME Approved/Offered Positions:* 6
Program ID: 324-11-31-006

Georgia

Atlanta

Emory University Program

Sponsor: Emory University School of Medicine
Children's Healthcare of Atlanta at Egleston
Grady Health System
Prgm Director: Steven L Lanski, MD
CHOA@Egleston Division Pediatric Emergency Med
1405 Clifton Road
Atlanta, GA 30322
Tel: 404 785-7142   *Fax:* 404 785-7898
Length: 3 Yrs   *ACGME Approved/Offered Positions:* 9
Program ID: 324-12-21-007

Illinois

Chicago

McGaw Medical Center of Northwestern University Program

Sponsor: McGaw Medical Center of Northwestern
  University
Children's Memorial Hospital
Prgm Director: Elizabeth C Powell, MD, MPH
Pediatric Emergency Medicine #62
2300 Children's Plaza
Chicago, IL 60614
Tel: 773 880-8245   *Fax:* 773 880-8267
Length: 3 Yrs   *ACGME Approved/Offered Positions:* 6
Program ID: 324-16-21-008

Kentucky

Louisville

University of Louisville Program

Sponsor: University of Louisville School of Medicine
Kosair Children's Hospital (Norton Healthcare, Inc)
Prgm Director: In Kim, MD, MBA
Department of Pediatrics
571 S Floyd Street, Suite 300
Louisville, KY 40202
Tel: 502 629-7212   *Fax:* 502 629-5991
E-mail: in.kim@louisville.edu
Length: 3 Yrs   *ACGME Approved/Offered Positions:* 6
Program ID: 324-20-31-009

Maryland

Baltimore

Johns Hopkins University Program

Sponsor: Johns Hopkins University School of Medicine
Johns Hopkins Hospital
Prgm Director: Jennifer F Anders, MD
CMSC 144
600 North Wolfe Street
Baltimore, MD 21287
Tel: 410 955-6143
Length: 3 Yrs   *ACGME Approved/Offered Positions:* 6
Program ID: 324-23-21-010

Massachusetts

Boston

Children's Hospital/Boston Medical Center Program

Sponsor: Children's Hospital
Prgm Director: Richard G Bachur, MD
300 Longwood Avenue
Boston, MA 02115
Tel: 617 355-6624   *Fax:* 617 730-0335
E-mail: richard.bachur@childrens.harvard.edu
Length: 3 Yrs   *ACGME Approved/Offered Positions:* 18
Program ID: 324-24-21-011

Children's Hospital/Boston Medical Center Program A

Sponsor: Children's Hospital
Boston Medical Center
Prgm Director: David Dorfman, MD
88 E Newton Street, Vose 5
Boston, MA 02118
Tel: 617 414-5514   *Fax:* 617 414-4393
Length: 3 Yrs   *ACGME Approved/Offered Positions:* 5
Program ID: 324-24-31-012

Michigan

Detroit

Children's Hospital of Michigan Program

Sponsor: Children's Hospital of Michigan
Prgm Director: Nirmala Bhaya, MD
3901 Beaubien Boulevard
Detroit, MI 48201
Tel: 313 745-5260
E-mail: cstankov@dmc.org
Length: 3 Yrs   *ACGME Approved/Offered Positions:* 12
Program ID: 324-25-21-013

Minnesota

Minneapolis

University of Minnesota Program
Sponsor: University of Minnesota Medical School
Children's Hospitals and Clinics of Minnesota - Minneapolis
Children's Hospitals and Clinics of Minnesota - St Paul
Prgm Director: Manu Madhok, MD, MPH
2525 Chicago Avenue South
Minneapolis, MN 55404
Tel: 612 813-6822   *Fax:* 612 813-7362
Length: 3 Yrs   *ACGME Approved/Offered Positions:* 6
Program ID: 324-26-11-015

Missouri

Kansas City

University of Missouri at Kansas City Program
Sponsor: University of Missouri-Kansas City School of Medicine
Children's Mercy Hospital
Prgm Director: Christopher S Kennedy, MD
2401 Gillham Rd
Kansas City, MO 64108
Tel: 816 234-3665   *Fax:* 816 234-3039
Length: 3 Yrs   *ACGME Approved/Offered Positions:* 9
Program ID: 324-28-31-017

St Louis

St Louis University School of Medicine Program
Sponsor: St Louis University School of Medicine
Cardinal Glennon Children's Hospital
Prgm Director: Trevor L Tredway, MD, PhD*
1465 S Grand Boulevard
Room G637
St Louis, MO 63104
Tel: 314 577-5360
E-mail: tredway@slu.edu
Length: 3 Yrs   *ACGME Approved/Offered Positions:* 3
Program ID: 324-28-11-018

Washington University/B-JH/SLCH Consortium Program
Sponsor: Washington University/B-JH/SLCH Consortium
St Louis Children's Hospital
Prgm Director: Kristine G Williams, MD*
One Children's Place - Northwest Tower 9th Floor
St Louis, MO 63110
Tel: 314 454-2341   *Fax:* 314 454-4345
Length: 3 Yrs   *ACGME Approved/Offered Positions:* 6
Program ID: 324-28-21-016

New Jersey

Newark

Newark Beth Israel Medical Center Program
Sponsor: Newark Beth Israel Medical Center
Prgm Director: Michael D Rosen, MD*
201 Lyons Avenue at Osborne Terrace
Newark, NJ 07112
Tel: 973 926-6671   *Fax:* 973 282-0562
Length: 3 Yrs   *ACGME Approved/Offered Positions:* 6
Program ID: 324-33-12-057

New York

Bronx

Albert Einstein College of Medicine (Jacobi) Program
Sponsor: Albert Einstein College of Medicine of Yeshiva University
North Bronx Healthcare Network-Jacobi Medical Center
Prgm Director: Ellen F Crain, MD, PhD
Room 1B25
1400 Pelham Parkway South
Bronx, NY 10461
Tel: 718 918-5817   *Fax:* 718 918-7459
E-mail: ellen.crain@nbhn.net
Length: 3 Yrs   *ACGME Approved/Offered Positions:* 7
Program ID: 324-35-31-020

Albert Einstein College of Medicine Program
Sponsor: Albert Einstein College of Medicine of Yeshiva University
Montefiore Medical Center-Henry and Lucy Moses Division
Prgm Director: Jeffrey R Avner, MD
Pediatric Emergency Medicine
111 East 210th Street
Bronx, NY 10467
Tel: 718 920-5312   *Fax:* 718 798-6485
Length: 3 Yrs   *ACGME Approved/Offered Positions:* 3
Program ID: 324-35-21-019

Buffalo

University at Buffalo Program
Sponsor: University at Buffalo School of Medicine
Kaleida Health System (Women and Children's Hosp of Buffalo)
Prgm Director: Paula M Mazur, MD
219 Bryant Street
Buffalo, NY 14222
Tel: 716 878-7109   *Fax:* 716 888-3874
E-mail: pmazur@upa.chob.edu
Length: 3 Yrs   *ACGME Approved/Offered Positions:* 6
Program ID: 324-35-12-022

Great Neck

NSLIJHS-Schneider Children's Hospital Program
Sponsor: North Shore-Long Island Jewish Health System
Schneider Children's Hospital at Long Island Jewish Med Ctr
Prgm Director: Robert F Gochman, MD
Schneider Children's Hospital
269-01 76th Avenue
New Hyde Park, NY 11040
Tel: 718 470-7640   *Fax:* 718 343-5864
E-mail: rgochman@optonline.net
Length: 3 Yrs   *ACGME Approved/Offered Positions:* 5
Program ID: 324-35-12-025

New York

Mount Sinai School of Medicine Program
Sponsor: Mount Sinai School of Medicine
Mount Sinai Medical Center
Prgm Director: Adam E Vella, MD
1 Gustave L Levy Place
Box 1620
New York, NY 10029
Tel: 212 659-1666   *Fax:* 212 427-2180
E-mail: claribel.velasquez@mssm.edu
Length: 3 Yrs   *ACGME Approved/Offered Positions:* 3
Program ID: 324-35-12-047

New York Presbyterian Hospital (Columbia Campus) Program
Sponsor: New York Presbyterian Hospital
New York Presbyterian Hospital (Columbia Campus)
Prgm Director: Peter S Dayan, MD, MSc
622 W 168th Street, PH-137
New York, NY 10032
Tel: 212 305-9825   *Fax:* 212 305-6792
E-mail: cg278@columbia.edu
Length: 3 Yrs   *ACGME Approved/Offered Positions:* 3
Program ID: 324-35-31-023

New York Presbyterian Hospital (Cornell Campus) Program
Sponsor: New York Presbyterian Hospital
New York Presbyterian Hospital (Cornell Campus)
Prgm Director: Shari L Platt, MD
525 East 68th Street
Emergency Medicine / Box 573
New York, NY 10021
Tel: 212 746-3431   *Fax:* 212 746-4883
E-mail: slp9001@med.cornell.edu
Length: 3 Yrs   *ACGME Approved/Offered Positions:* 1
Program ID: 324-35-21-024

New York University School of Medicine Program
Sponsor: New York University School of Medicine
Bellevue Hospital Center
Prgm Director: Michael A Mojica, MD
New Bellevue Room 9 - West - 17
462 First Avenue
New York, NY 10016
Tel: 212 562-8147   *Fax:* 212 562-7752
E-mail: michael.mojica@nyumc.org
Length: 3 Yrs   *ACGME Approved/Offered Positions:* 6
Program ID: 324-35-31-026

Ohio

Akron

Children's Hospital Medical Center of Akron/NEOUCOM Program
Sponsor: Children's Hospital Medical Center of Akron
Prgm Director: Maria L Ramundo, MD
One Perkins Square
Akron, OH 44308
Tel: 330 543-8452   *Fax:* 330 543-3761
Length: 3 Yrs   *ACGME Approved/Offered Positions:* 9
Program ID: 324-38-21-027

Cincinnati

Cincinnati Children's Hospital Medical Center/University of Cincinnati College of Medicine Program
Sponsor: Cincinnati Children's Hospital Medical Center
Prgm Director: Constance M McAneney, MD, MS
Division of Emergency Medicine
3333 Burnet Avenue, MLC 2008
Cincinnati, OH 45229
Tel: 513 636-7966   *Fax:* 513 636-7967
Length: 3 Yrs   *ACGME Approved/Offered Positions:* 12
Program ID: 324-38-31-028

Cleveland

University Hospitals Case Medical Center Program
Sponsor: University Hospitals Case Medical Center
Prgm Director: Deanna Dahl-Grove, MD
11100 Euclid Avenue
Cleveland, OH 44106
Tel: 216 844-8716   *Fax:* 216 844-8233
Length: 3 Yrs   *ACGME Approved/Offered Positions:* 3
Program ID: 324-38-31-049

Note: * indicates a newly appointed program director

Columbus

Nationwide Children's Hospital/Ohio State University Program
Sponsor: Nationwide Children's Hospital
Prgm Director: Mary Jo A Bowman, MD
700 Children's Drive
Columbus, OH 43205
Tel: 614 722-4386   *Fax:* 614 722-4380
Length: 3 Yrs   *ACGME Approved/Offered Positions:* 12
Program ID: 324-38-11-029

Pennsylvania

Philadelphia

Children's Hospital of Philadelphia Program
Sponsor: Children's Hospital of Philadelphia
Prgm Director: Joel Fein, MD, MPH
34th Street and Civic Center Blvd
Emergency Medicine, Room AS01
Philadelphia, PA 19104
Tel: 215 590-1944   *Fax:* 215 590-4454
E-mail: fein@email.chop.edu
Length: 3 Yrs   *ACGME Approved/Offered Positions:* 12
Program ID: 324-41-21-030

Pittsburgh

University of Pittsburgh Medical Center Medical Education Program
Sponsor: Univ of Pittsburgh Medical Center Medical Education
Children's Hospital of Pittsburgh of UPMC
Prgm Director: Raymond D Pitetti, MD, MPH
3705 Fifth Avenue
Pittsburgh, PA 15213
Tel: 412 692-7980   *Fax:* 412 692-6540
Length: 3 Yrs   *ACGME Approved/Offered Positions:* 9
Program ID: 324-41-31-046

Rhode Island

Providence

Brown University Program
Sponsor: Rhode Island Hospital-Lifespan
Prgm Director: Dale W Steele, MD
Pediatric Emergency Medicine
593 Eddy Street, Claverick 2
Providence, RI 02903
Tel: 401 444-6680   *Fax:* 401 444-2583
Length: 3 Yrs   *ACGME Approved/Offered Positions:* 6
Program ID: 324-43-21-033

Tennessee

Memphis

University of Tennessee Program
Sponsor: University of Tennessee College of Medicine
LeBonheur Children's Medical Center
Prgm Director: Jay K Pershad, MD
50 N Dunlap Street
Memphis, TN 38103
Tel: 901 287-5986   *Fax:* 901 287-5025
E-mail: pershadj@lebonheur.org
Length: 3 Yrs   *ACGME Approved/Offered Positions:* 6
Program ID: 324-47-21-042

Texas

Dallas

University of Texas Southwestern Medical School Program
Sponsor: University of Texas Southwestern Medical School
Children's Medical Center of Dallas
Prgm Director: Susan Scott, MD
5323 Harry Hines Boulevard
Dallas, TX 75390
Tel: 214 456-8312   *Fax:* 214 456-8132
Length: 3 Yrs   *ACGME Approved/Offered Positions:* 9
Program ID: 324-48-21-034

Houston

Baylor College of Medicine Program
Sponsor: Baylor College of Medicine
Texas Children's Hospital
Prgm Director: Deborah C Hsu, MD, MEd*
One Baylor Plaza, TXCH-A210
Houston, TX 77030
Tel: 832 824-5468   *Fax:* 832 825-5424
E-mail: dchsu@texaschildrenshospital.org
Length: 3 Yrs   *ACGME Approved/Offered Positions:* 15
Program ID: 324-48-31-035

Utah

Salt Lake City

University of Utah Program
Sponsor: University of Utah Medical Center
Primary Children's Medical Center
Prgm Director: Bruce E Herman, MD
PO Box 581289
Salt Lake City, UT 84158
Tel: 801 587-7454   *Fax:* 801 587-7455
E-mail: bruce.herman@hsc.utah.edu
Length: 3 Yrs   *ACGME Approved/Offered Positions:* 6
Program ID: 324-49-31-044

Virginia

Falls Church

Inova Fairfax Hospital/Inova Fairfax Hospital for Children Program
Sponsor: Inova Fairfax Hospital
Prgm Director: Maybelle Kou, MD
c/o Department of Emergency Medicine
3300 Gallows Road
Falls Church, VA 22042
Tel: 703 776-3195   *Fax:* 703 776-2893
Length: 3 Yrs   *ACGME Approved/Offered Positions:* 4
Program ID: 324-51-21-036

Norfolk

Eastern Virginia Medical School Program
Sponsor: Eastern Virginia Medical School
Children's Hospital of the King's Daughters
Prgm Director: Michael P Poirier, MD
Children's Hospital of the King's Daughters
601 Children's Lane
Norfolk, VA 23507
Tel: 757 668-9220   *Fax:* 757 688-7568
Length: 3 Yrs   *ACGME Approved/Offered Positions:* 3
Program ID: 324-51-11-037

Washington

Seattle

University of Washington Program
Sponsor: University of Washington School of Medicine
Seattle Children's Hospital
Prgm Director: Eileen J Klein, MD, MPH
4800 Sand Point Way NE
Mail Stop B5520
Seattle, WA 98105
Tel: 206 987-1149   *Fax:* 206 987-3863
E-mail: eileen.klein@seattlechildrens.org
Length: 3 Yrs   *ACGME Approved/Offered Positions:* 3
Program ID: 324-54-21-038

Wisconsin

Milwaukee

Medical College of Wisconsin Affiliated Hospitals Program
Sponsor: Medical College of Wisconsin Affiliated Hospitals, Inc
Children's Hospital of Wisconsin
Prgm Director: David C Brousseau, MD, MS
Children's Corporate Center
999 N 92nd Street, Suite C550
Milwaukee, WI 53226
Tel: 414 266-2625   *Fax:* 414 266-2635
Length: 3 Yrs   *ACGME Approved/Offered Positions:* 9
Program ID: 324-56-21-039

Programs

Pediatric Endocrinology (Pediatrics)

Alabama

Birmingham

University of Alabama Medical Center Program
Sponsor: University of Alabama Hospital
Children's Hospital of Alabama
Prgm Director: Kenneth L McCormick, MD
1601 4th Avenue, South, CPP 230
Birmingham, AL 35233
Tel: 205 939-9107   *Fax:* 205 939-9821
E-mail: ken.mccormick@peds.uab.edu
Length: 3 Yrs   *ACGME Approved/Offered Positions:* 3
Program ID: 326-01-31-073

Arizona

Phoenix

Phoenix Children's Hospital/Maricopa Medical Center Program
Sponsor: Phoenix Children's Hospital
GSRMC/VA Medical Center
National Institutes of Health (NIH), Phoenix Branch
Prgm Director: Khalid S Hasan, MD
1919 East Thomas Road
Phoenix, AZ 85016
Tel: 602 546-0935   *Fax:* 602 546-0610
E-mail: khasan@phoenixchildrens.com
Length: 3 Yrs   *ACGME Approved/Offered Positions:* 3
Program ID: 326-03-12-072

Tucson

University of Arizona Program
Sponsor: University of Arizona College of Medicine
University Medical Center
Prgm Director: Mark D Wheeler, MD
Section of Endocrinology
1501 N Campbell Avenue, Box 245073
Tucson, AZ 85724
Tel: 520 626-6077   *Fax:* 520 626-2881
Length: 3 Yrs   *ACGME Approved/Offered Positions:* 3
Program ID: 326-03-13-089

Arkansas

Little Rock

University of Arkansas for Medical Sciences Program
Sponsor: University of Arkansas College of Medicine
Arkansas Children's Hospital
Prgm Director: J Paul Frindik, MD
800 Marshall Street
Little Rock, AR 72202
Tel: 501 364-1430   *Fax:* 501 364-6299
Length: 3 Yrs   *ACGME Approved/Offered Positions:* 3
Program ID: 326-04-21-040

California

Los Angeles

Childrens Hospital Los Angeles Program
Sponsor: Childrens Hospital Los Angeles
Prgm Director: Mitchell E Geffner, MD
Division of Endocrinology
4650 Sunset Boulevard MS 61
Los Angeles, CA 90027
Tel: 323 361-7032   *Fax:* 323 361-1350
Length: 3 Yrs   *ACGME Approved/Offered Positions:* 6
Program ID: 326-05-11-001

UCLA Medical Center Program
Sponsor: UCLA David Geffen School of Medicine/UCLA
Medical Center
UCLA Medical Center
Prgm Director: Kuk-Wha Lee, MD, PhD
22-315 MDCC
10833 Le Conte Avenue
Los Angeles, CA 90095
Tel: 310 206-5843
Length: 3 Yrs   *ACGME Approved/Offered Positions:* 6
Program ID: 326-05-21-003

Sacramento

University of California (Davis) Health System Program
Sponsor: University of California (Davis) Health System
University of California (Davis) Medical Center
Prgm Director: Dennis Styne, MD
2516 Stockton Boulevard - 3rd Floor
Sacramento, CA 95817
Tel: 916 734-7098   *Fax:* 916 734-7070
Length: 3 Yrs   *ACGME Approved/Offered Positions:* 3
Program ID: 326-05-12-087

San Diego

University of California (San Diego) Program
Sponsor: University of California (San Diego) Medical
Center
Rady Children's Hospital
Prgm Director: Michael E Gottschalk, MD, PhD
Dept of Peds, Div of Endocrinology
9500 Gilman Drive, 0831
La Jolla, CA 92093
Tel: 858 966-4032   *Fax:* 858 966-6227
Length: 3 Yrs   *ACGME Approved/Offered Positions:* 3
Program ID: 326-05-31-004

San Francisco

University of California (San Francisco) Program
Sponsor: University of California (San Francisco) School
of Medicine
UCSF and Mount Zion Medical Centers
Prgm Director: Walter L Miller, MD
Department of Pediatrics
515 Parnassus Avenue, Suite S-672
San Francisco, CA 94143
Tel: 415 476-2598   *Fax:* 415 476-6286
E-mail: wlmlab@ucsf.edu
Length: 3 Yrs   *ACGME Approved/Offered Positions:* 6
Program ID: 326-05-21-005

Stanford

Stanford University Program
Sponsor: Stanford Hospital and Clinics
Lucile Salter Packard Children's Hospital at Stanford
Prgm Director: Darrell M Wilson, MD
Dept of Pediatrics, Room G 313
300 Pasteur Drive
Stanford, CA 94305
Tel: 650 723-5791
E-mail: dwilson@stanford.edu
Length: 3 Yrs   *ACGME Approved/Offered Positions:* 3
Program ID: 326-05-21-055

Torrance

Los Angeles County-Harbor-UCLA Medical Center Program
Sponsor: Los Angeles County-Harbor-UCLA Medical
Center
Prgm Director: Wai-Nang Paul Lee, MD, MBA
Box 446
1000 West Carson Street
Torrance, CA 90509
Tel: 310 222-6729   *Fax:* 310 222-3887
E-mail: lee@labiomed.org
Length: 3 Yrs   *ACGME Approved/Offered Positions:* 3
Program ID: 326-05-11-006

Colorado

Aurora

University of Colorado Denver Program
Sponsor: University of Colorado Denver School of
Medicine
Children's Hospital (The)
Prgm Director: Philip S Zeitler, MD, PhD
1056 East 19th Avenue
Box B-265
Denver, CO 80218
Tel: 720 777-6128   *Fax:* 303 864-5679
E-mail: zeitler.philip@tchden.org
Length: 3 Yrs   *ACGME Approved/Offered Positions:* 6
Program ID: 326-07-21-007

Connecticut

Farmington

University of Connecticut Program
Sponsor: University of Connecticut School of Medicine
Connecticut Children's Medical Center
Prgm Director: Elizabeth Estrada, MD
Div of Pediatric Endocrinology
282 Washington Street
Hartford, CT 06106
Tel: 860 545-9370   *Fax:* 860 545-9376
E-mail: vtomlin@ccmckids.org
Length: 3 Yrs   *ACGME Approved/Offered Positions:* 1
Program ID: 326-08-21-054

New Haven

Yale-New Haven Medical Center Program
Sponsor: Yale-New Haven Hospital
Prgm Director: Thomas O Carpenter, MD
Department of Pediatrics
PO Box 208064
New Haven, CT 06520
Tel: 203 785-4279   *Fax:* 203 737-2829
E-mail: kelly.byron@yale.edu
Length: 3 Yrs   *ACGME Approved/Offered Positions:* 6
Program ID: 326-08-21-053

Note: * indicates a newly appointed program director

Florida

Gainesville

University of Florida Program
Sponsor: University of Florida College of Medicine
Shands Hospital at the University of Florida
Prgm Director: Janet H Silverstein, MD
J Hillis Miller Health Center
Box 100296
Gainesville, FL 32610
Tel: 352 334-1390   *Fax:* 352 334-1325
E-mail: silvejh@peds.ufl.edu
Length: 3 Yrs   *ACGME Approved/Offered Positions:* 3
Program ID: 326-11-31-008

Jacksonville

University of Florida College of Medicine Jacksonville Program
Sponsor: University of Florida College of Medicine Jacksonville
Nemours Children's Clinic
Wolfson Children's Hospital
Prgm Director: Robert C Olney, MD
Division of Endocrinology
807 Children's Way
Jacksonville, FL 32207
Tel: 904 390-3674   *Fax:* 904 858-3948
E-mail: rolney@nemours.org
Length: 3 Yrs   *ACGME Approved/Offered Positions:* 3
Program ID: 326-11-21-085

Miami

Jackson Memorial Hospital/Jackson Health System Program
Sponsor: Jackson Memorial Hospital/Jackson Health System
Prgm Director: Gary D Berkovitz, MD
Pediatric Endocrinology
1601 W 12th Avenue, MCCD 3044A (D820)
Miami, FL 33136
Tel: 305 243-5707   *Fax:* 305 243-6309
E-mail: gberkovitz@med.miami.edu
Length: 3 Yrs   *ACGME Approved/Offered Positions:* 3
Program ID: 326-11-21-067

St. Petersburg

University of South Florida Program
Sponsor: University of South Florida College of Medicine
All Children's Hospital
Prgm Director: Dorothy I Shulman, MD*
All Children's Hospital
801 6th Street South, Box 6900
St Petersburg, FL 33701
Tel: 727 767-4233   *Fax:* 727 767-3275
Length: 3 Yrs   *ACGME Approved/Offered Positions:* 3
Program ID: 326-11-31-083

Georgia

Atlanta

Emory University Program
Sponsor: Emory University School of Medicine
Children's Healthcare of Atlanta at Egleston
Grady Health System
Prgm Director: Eric I Felner, MD, MS
Department of Pediatrics
2015 Uppergate Drive
Atlanta, GA 30322
Tel: 404 727-9811   *Fax:* 404 727-3423
E-mail: efelner@emory.edu
Length: 3 Yrs   *ACGME Approved/Offered Positions:* 6
Program ID: 326-12-21-042

Illinois

Chicago

McGaw Medical Center of Northwestern University Program
Sponsor: McGaw Medical Center of Northwestern University
Children's Memorial Hospital
Prgm Director: Donald Zimmerman, MD
2300 Children's Plaza
Box 54
Chicago, IL 60614
Tel: 773 327-7740   *Fax:* 773 327-7741
Length: 3 Yrs   *ACGME Approved/Offered Positions:* 3
Program ID: 326-16-21-060

University of Chicago Program
Sponsor: University of Chicago Medical Center
University of Chicago Comer Children's Hospital
Prgm Director: Dianne Deplewski, MD*
Comer Children's Hospital
5841 S Maryland Avenue MC 5053
Chicago, IL 60637
Tel: 773 702-6432   *Fax:* 773 702-0443
Length: 3 Yrs   *ACGME Approved/Offered Positions:* 6
Program ID: 326-16-11-010

Indiana

Indianapolis

Indiana University School of Medicine Program
Sponsor: Indiana University School of Medicine
Clarian Riley Hospital for Children
Prgm Director: John S Fuqua, MD
Riley Hospital for Children
702 Barnhill Drive, Room 5960
Indianapolis, IN 46202
Tel: 317 274-3889   *Fax:* 317 274-3882
E-mail: jsfuqua@iupui.edu
Length: 3 Yrs   *ACGME Approved/Offered Positions:* 6
Program ID: 326-17-21-052

Iowa

Iowa City

University of Iowa Hospitals and Clinics Program
Sponsor: University of Iowa Hospitals and Clinics
Prgm Director: Michael Tansey, MD*
Department of Pediatrics
200 Hawkins Drive
Iowa City, IA 52242
Tel: 319 356-4511
Length: 3 Yrs   *ACGME Approved/Offered Positions:* 3
Program ID: 326-18-11-011

Louisiana

New Orleans

Louisiana State University Program
Sponsor: Louisiana State University School of Medicine
Children's Hospital (New Orleans)
Prgm Director: Stuart A Chalew, MD
200 Henry Clay Avenue
New Orleans, LA 70118
Tel: 504 896-9441   *Fax:* 504 894-5139
Length: 3 Yrs   *ACGME Approved/Offered Positions:* 4
Program ID: 326-21-31-071

Maryland

Baltimore

Johns Hopkins University Program
Sponsor: Johns Hopkins University School of Medicine
Johns Hopkins Hospital
Prgm Director: David W Cooke, MD
200 N Wolfe Street, 3120
Baltimore, MD 21287
Tel: 410 955-6463   *Fax:* 410 955-9773
Length: 3 Yrs   *ACGME Approved/Offered Positions:* 6
Program ID: 326-23-21-012

Bethesda

National Capital Consortium Program
Sponsor: National Capital Consortium
National Naval Medical Center (Bethesda)
Walter Reed Army Medical Center
Prgm Director: Andrew J Bauer, MD
Department of Pediatrics
4301 Jones Bridge Road
Bethesda, MD 20814
Tel: 301 295-9716   *Fax:* 301 295-0190
E-mail: abauer@usuhs.mil
Length: 3 Yrs   *ACGME Approved/Offered Positions:* 6
Program ID: 326-10-11-041
Uniformed Services Program

National Institutes of Health Clinical Center/NICHD/Georgetown University Hospital Program
Sponsor: Clinical Center at the National Institutes of Health
Prgm Director: Constantine A Stratakis, MD, ScD
10 Center Drive, Building 10
Room 9D42 MSC 1830
Bethesda, MD 20892
Tel: 301 496-6683   *Fax:* 301 480-0378
Length: 3 Yrs   *ACGME Approved/Offered Positions:* 9
Program ID: 326-23-21-056

Massachusetts

Boston

Children's Hospital/Boston Medical Center Program
Sponsor: Children's Hospital
Prgm Director: Joseph A Majzoub, MD
300 Longwood Avenue
Karp 4-125
Boston, MA 02115
Tel: 617 919-2930   *Fax:* 617 730-0244
Length: 3 Yrs   *ACGME Approved/Offered Positions:* 9
Program ID: 326-24-11-014

Massachusetts General Hospital Program
Sponsor: Massachusetts General Hospital
Prgm Director: Madhusmita Misra, MD, MPH*
Yawkey 6800
55 Fruit Street
Boston, MA 02114
Tel: 617 726-3870   *Fax:* 617 726-5072
E-mail: mmisra@partners.org
Length: 3 Yrs   *ACGME Approved/Offered Positions:* 6
Program ID: 326-24-31-015

Springfield

Baystate Medical Center/Tufts University School of Medicine Program

Sponsor: Baystate Medical Center
Prgm Director: Holley F Allen, MD, MSPH
759 Chestnut Street
Springfield, MA 01199
Tel: 413 794-4441   *Fax:* 413 794-3623
Length: 3 Yrs   *ACGME Approved/Offered Positions:* 3
Program ID: 326-24-12-084

Michigan

Ann Arbor

University of Michigan Program

Sponsor: University of Michigan Hospitals and Health Centers
Prgm Director: Delia M Vazquez, MD
C S Mott Children's Hospital
Room D1205 Medical Professional Bldg
Ann Arbor, MI 48109
Tel: 734 764-5175   *Fax:* 734 615-3353
Length: 3 Yrs   *ACGME Approved/Offered Positions:* 6
Program ID: 326-25-21-016

Minnesota

Minneapolis

University of Minnesota Program

Sponsor: University of Minnesota Medical School
University of Minnesota Medical Center, Division of Fairview
Prgm Director: Antoinette Moran, MD
MMC 404 Mayo, 13-124 PWB
516 Delaware Street, SE
Minneapolis, MN 55455
Tel: 612 624-5409   *Fax:* 612 626-5262
Length: 3 Yrs   *ACGME Approved/Offered Positions:* 3
Program ID: 326-26-21-043

Rochester

College of Medicine, Mayo Clinic (Rochester) Program

Sponsor: College of Medicine, Mayo Clinic
Mayo Clinic (Rochester)
Saint Marys Hospital of Rochester
Prgm Director: W Frederick Schwenk II, MD
200 First St SW
Rochester, MN 55905
Tel: 507 538-0154   *Fax:* 507 284-0160
E-mail: bartelsmith.susan@mayo.edu
Length: 3 Yrs   *ACGME Approved/Offered Positions:* 3
Program ID: 326-26-21-017

Missouri

Kansas City

University of Missouri at Kansas City Program

Sponsor: University of Missouri-Kansas City School of Medicine
Children's Mercy Hospital
Prgm Director: Jill D Jacobson, MD
2401 Gillham Road
Kansas City, MO 64108
Tel: 816 234-1660   *Fax:* 816 855-1919
E-mail: jjacobson@cmh.edu
Length: 3 Yrs   *ACGME Approved/Offered Positions:* 6
Program ID: 326-28-11-018

St Louis

Washington University/B-JH/SLCH Consortium Program

Sponsor: Washington University/B-JH/SLCH Consortium
St Louis Children's Hospital
Washington University School of Medicine
Prgm Director: Paul W Hruz, MD, PhD*
Division of Pediatric Endocrinology and Diabetes
660 S Euclid Ave, Campus Box 8208
St Louis, MO 63110
Tel: 314 286-2797   *Fax:* 314 286-2893
E-mail: hruz_p@kids.wustl.edu
Length: 3 Yrs   *ACGME Approved/Offered Positions:* 6
Program ID: 326-28-11-019

New York

Bronx

Albert Einstein College of Medicine Program

Sponsor: Albert Einstein College of Medicine of Yeshiva University
Montefiore Medical Center-Henry and Lucy Moses Division
Montefiore Medical Center-Weiler Division
Prgm Director: Morri Markowitz, MD
Division of Pediatric Endocrinology
111 East 210th Street
Bronx, NY 10467
Tel: 718 920-4664   *Fax:* 718 405-5609
E-mail: markowit@aecom.yu.edu
Length: 3 Yrs   *ACGME Approved/Offered Positions:* 3
Program ID: 326-35-21-020

Brooklyn

SUNY Health Science Center at Brooklyn Program

Sponsor: SUNY Health Science Center at Brooklyn
Kings County Hospital Center
Maimonides Medical Center
University Hospital-SUNY Health Science Center at Brooklyn
Prgm Director: Svetlana Ten, MD
450 Clarkson Avenue, Box 51
Brooklyn, NY 11203
Tel: 718 283-8894   *Fax:* 718 635-7276
Length: 3 Yrs   *ACGME Approved/Offered Positions:* 6
Program ID: 326-35-21-022

Buffalo

University at Buffalo Program

Sponsor: University at Buffalo School of Medicine
Kaleida Health System (Women and Children's Hosp of Buffalo)
Prgm Director: Teresa Quattrin, MD
219 Bryant Street
Buffalo, NY 14222
Tel: 716 878-7588   *Fax:* 716 888-3827
Length: 3 Yrs   *ACGME Approved/Offered Positions:* 3
Program ID: 326-35-21-021

Great Neck

NSLIJHS-Schneider Children's Hospital Program

Sponsor: North Shore-Long Island Jewish Health System
Prgm Director: Phyllis W Speiser, MD
400 Lakeville Road
Suite 180
New Hyde Park, NY 11040
Tel: 718 470-3290   *Fax:* 718 470-4565
Length: 3 Yrs   *ACGME Approved/Offered Positions:* 3
Program ID: 326-35-21-044

Mineola

Winthrop-University Hospital Program

Sponsor: Winthrop-University Hospital
Prgm Director: Mariano Castro-Magana, MD
120 Mineola Blvd, Suite 210
Mineola, NY 11501
Tel: 516 663-9408   *Fax:* 516 663-2122
Length: 3 Yrs   *ACGME Approved/Offered Positions:* 3
Program ID: 326-35-31-057

New York

Mount Sinai School of Medicine Program

Sponsor: Mount Sinai School of Medicine
Mount Sinai Medical Center
Prgm Director: Robert Rapaport, MD
One Gustave L Levy Place, Box 1616
New York, NY 10029
Tel: 212 241-6936   *Fax:* 212 876-2503
Length: 3 Yrs   *ACGME Approved/Offered Positions:* 6
Program ID: 326-35-11-023

New York Presbyterian Hospital (Columbia Campus) Program

Sponsor: New York Presbyterian Hospital
New York Presbyterian Hospital (Columbia Campus)
Prgm Director: Sharon E Oberfield, MD
630 West 168th Street, PH-5E-522
New York, NY 10032
Tel: 212 305-6559   *Fax:* 212 305-4778
Length: 3 Yrs   *ACGME Approved/Offered Positions:* 4
Program ID: 326-35-21-070

New York Presbyterian Hospital (Cornell Campus) Program

Sponsor: New York Presbyterian Hospital
Memorial Sloan-Kettering Cancer Center
New York Presbyterian Hospital (Cornell Campus)
Prgm Director: Maria G Vogiatzi, MD
525 East 68th Street Box 103
New York, NY 10065
Tel: 212 746-3462   *Fax:* 212 746-3807
E-mail: mca2003@med.cornell.edu
Length: 3 Yrs   *ACGME Approved/Offered Positions:* 9
Program ID: 326-35-21-049

New York University School of Medicine Program

Sponsor: New York University School of Medicine
Bellevue Hospital Center
NYU Hospitals Center
Prgm Director: Raphael David, MD
550 First Avenue
New York, NY 10016
Tel: 212 263-6462   *Fax:* 212 562-3273
Length: 3 Yrs   *ACGME Approved/Offered Positions:* 3
Program ID: 326-35-21-045

Stony Brook

SUNY at Stony Brook Program

Sponsor: University Hospital - SUNY at Stony Brook
Prgm Director: Thomas A Wilson, MD
Department of Pediatrics
Stony Brook, NY 11794
Tel: 631 444-3429   *Fax:* 631 444-6045
E-mail: thomas.a.wilson@sunysb.edu
Length: 3 Yrs   *ACGME Approved/Offered Positions:* 3
Program ID: 326-35-21-061

Note: * indicates a newly appointed program director

North Carolina

Chapel Hill

University of North Carolina Hospitals Program

Sponsor: University of North Carolina Hospitals
Prgm Director: Anna Spagnoli, MD*
Division of Pediatric Endocrinology
3341 MBRB, CB 7039
Chapel Hill, NC 27599
Tel: 919 966-4435   *Fax:* 919 966-2423
Length: 3 Yrs   *ACGME Approved/Offered Positions:* 6
Program ID: 326-36-21-025

Durham

Duke University Hospital Program

Sponsor: Duke University Hospital
Prgm Director: Deanna W Adkins, MD
Department of Pediatric Endocrinology
3000 Erwin Road Box 3080
Durham, NC 27705
Tel: 919 684-8225   *Fax:* 919 684-8613
Length: 3 Yrs   *ACGME Approved/Offered Positions:* 3
Program ID: 326-36-21-026

Ohio

Cincinnati

Cincinnati Children's Hospital Medical Center/University of Cincinnati College of Medicine Program

Sponsor: Cincinnati Children's Hospital Medical Center
Prgm Director: Susan Rose, MD
Division of Endocrinology
3333 Burnet Avenue
Cincinnati, OH 45229
Tel: 513 636-0299   *Fax:* 513 636-7486
E-mail: susan.rose@cchmc.org
Length: 3 Yrs   *ACGME Approved/Offered Positions:* 9
Program ID: 326-38-21-027

Cleveland

University Hospitals Case Medical Center Program

Sponsor: University Hospitals Case Medical Center
Cleveland Clinic Foundation
Prgm Director: Naveen K Uli, MBBS
Division of Pediatric Endocrinology and Metabolism
11100 Euclid Avenue, RB&C Suite 737
Cleveland, OH 44106
Tel: 216 844-3661   *Fax:* 216 844-8900
E-mail: Naveen.Uli@UHhospitals.org
Length: 3 Yrs   *ACGME Approved/Offered Positions:* 6
Program ID: 326-38-21-028

Columbus

Nationwide Children's Hospital/Ohio State University Program

Sponsor: Nationwide Children's Hospital
Prgm Director: Robert P Hoffman, MD
700 Children's Drive, ED 544
Columbus, OH 43205
Tel: 614 722-4322   *Fax:* 614 722-4440
E-mail: marion.fazi@nationwidechildrens.org
Length: 3 Yrs   *ACGME Approved/Offered Positions:* 3
Program ID: 326-38-13-086

Oklahoma

Oklahoma City

University of Oklahoma Health Sciences Center Program

Sponsor: University of Oklahoma College of Medicine
OU Medical Center - Children's Hospital
Prgm Director: Steven Chernausek, MD*
940 NE 13th Street, CH 2B2426
Oklahoma City, OK 73104
Tel: 405 271-6764   *Fax:* 405 271-3093
Length: 3 Yrs   *ACGME Approved/Offered Positions:* 6
Program ID: 326-39-12-077

Oregon

Portland

Oregon Health & Science University Program

Sponsor: Oregon Health & Science University Hospital
Prgm Director: Bruce A Boston, MD
Department of Pediatrics
707 SW Gaines St
Portland, OR 97239
Tel: 503 494-1927   *Fax:* 503 494-1933
E-mail: bostonbr@ohsu.edu
Length: 3 Yrs   *ACGME Approved/Offered Positions:* 6
Program ID: 326-40-12-031

Pennsylvania

Philadelphia

Children's Hospital of Philadelphia Program

Sponsor: Children's Hospital of Philadelphia
Prgm Director: Andrea Kelly, MD
3615 Civic Center Blvd
Abramson Research Center, 8th Floor, Rm 802
Philadelphia, PA 19104
Tel: 215 590-3420   *Fax:* 215 590-1605
E-mail: upshaw@email.chop.edu
Length: 3 Yrs   *ACGME Approved/Offered Positions:* 9
Program ID: 326-41-21-032

St Christopher's Hospital for Children Program

Sponsor: St Christopher's Hospital for Children (Tenet Health System)
Prgm Director: Francesco De Luca, MD
Erie Avenue at Front Street
Philadelphia, PA 19134
Tel: 215 427-8100   *Fax:* 215 427-8105
E-mail: francesco.deluca@drexelmed.edu
Length: 3 Yrs   *ACGME Approved/Offered Positions:* 3
Program ID: 326-41-31-078

Pittsburgh

University of Pittsburgh Medical Center Medical Education Program

Sponsor: Univ of Pittsburgh Medical Center Medical Education
Children's Hospital of Pittsburgh of UPMC
Prgm Director: Selma F Witchel, MD
Children's Hospital of Pittsburgh
3705 Fifth Avenue
Pittsburgh, PA 15213
Tel: 412 692-5172   *Fax:* 412 692-5834
Length: 3 Yrs   *ACGME Approved/Offered Positions:* 7
Program ID: 326-41-21-033

Rhode Island

Providence

Brown University Program

Sponsor: Rhode Island Hospital-Lifespan
Women and Infants Hospital of Rhode Island
Prgm Director: Charlotte M Boney, MD, MS
Div of Pediatric Endocrinology
593 Eddy Street
Providence, RI 02903
Tel: 401 444-5504   *Fax:* 401 444-2534
E-mail: Charlotte_Boney@brown.edu
Length: 3 Yrs   *ACGME Approved/Offered Positions:* 3
Program ID: 326-43-21-034

South Carolina

Charleston

Medical University of South Carolina Program

Sponsor: Medical University of South Carolina College of Medicine
MUSC Medical Center
Prgm Director: Yaw Appiagyei-Dankah, MD
96 Jonathan Lucas Street, CSB 316
PO Box 250608
Charleston, SC 29425
Tel: 843 792-6807   *Fax:* 843 792-0548
E-mail: appiag@musc.edu
Length: 3 Yrs   *ACGME Approved/Offered Positions:* 3
Program ID: 326-45-21-076

Tennessee

Memphis

University of Tennessee Program

Sponsor: University of Tennessee College of Medicine
LeBonheur Children's Medical Center
Prgm Director: Robert Ferry Jr, MD*
50 N Dunlap Street
Memphis, TN 38103
Tel: 901 287-6292   *Fax:* 901 287-5198
Length: 3 Yrs   *ACGME Approved/Offered Positions:* 3
Program ID: 326-47-31-035

Nashville

Vanderbilt University Program

Sponsor: Vanderbilt University Medical Center
Prgm Director: William E Russell, MD
11136 Doctors' Office Tower
2200 Children's Way
Nashville, TN 37232
Tel: 615 936-1874   *Fax:* 615 343-5845
E-mail: bill.russell@vanderbilt.edu
Length: 3 Yrs   *ACGME Approved/Offered Positions:* 3
Program ID: 326-47-21-036

Texas

Dallas

University of Texas Southwestern Medical School Program

Sponsor: University of Texas Southwestern Medical School
Children's Medical Center of Dallas
Prgm Director: Perrin C White, MD
5323 Harry Hines Boulevard, G2236
Dallas, TX 75390
Tel: 214 648-3501   *Fax:* 214 648-9772
E-mail: Perrin.White@UTSouthwestern.edu
Length: 3 Yrs   *ACGME Approved/Offered Positions:* 6
Program ID: 326-48-31-069

Houston

Baylor College of Medicine Program

Sponsor: Baylor College of Medicine
Harris County Hospital District-Ben Taub General
  Hospital
Texas Children's Hospital
Prgm Director: Morey W Haymond, MD
6621 Fannin St, CCC1020.05
Pediatrics Endocrinology & Metabolism
Houston, TX 77030
Tel: 713 798-6776   *Fax:* 713 798-7119
Length: 3 Yrs   *ACGME Approved/Offered Positions:* 12
Program ID: 326-48-21-051

University of Texas at Houston Program

Sponsor: University of Texas Health Science Center at
  Houston
Memorial Hermann Hospital
Prgm Director: Patrick G Brosnan, MD
6431 Fannin St
Suite MSB 3.122
Houston, TX 77030
Tel: 713 500-5646   *Fax:* 713 500-0526
E-mail: patrick.g.brosnan@uth.tmc.edu
Length: 3 Yrs   *ACGME Approved/Offered Positions:* 3
Program ID: 326-48-21-066

San Antonio

University of Texas Health Science Center at San Antonio Program

Sponsor: University of Texas School of Medicine at San
  Antonio
Audie L Murphy Memorial Veterans Hospital (San
  Antonio)
Christus Santa Rosa Health Care Corporation
University Health System
Prgm Director: Jane L Lynch, MD, BS
540F Pediatrics, Mail Code 7806
7703 Floyd Curl Drive
San Antonio, TX 78229
Tel: 210 567-5283   *Fax:* 210 567-0492
E-mail: lynchj2@uthscsa.edu
Length: 3 Yrs   *ACGME Approved/Offered Positions:* 6
Program ID: 326-48-12-082

Virginia

Charlottesville

University of Virginia Program

Sponsor: University of Virginia Medical Center
Prgm Director: William L Clarke, MD
PO Box 800386
Charlottesville, VA 22908
Tel: 434 924-5897   *Fax:* 434 924-9181
Length: 3 Yrs   *ACGME Approved/Offered Positions:* 3
Program ID: 326-51-11-039

Note: * indicates a newly appointed program director

Washington

Seattle

University of Washington Program

Sponsor: University of Washington School of Medicine
Seattle Children's Hospital
Prgm Director: Patricia Y Fechner, MD
4800 Sand Point Way, NE
Mail Stop A5902
Seattle, WA 98105
Tel: 206 987-5037   *Fax:* 206 987-2720
E-mail: patricia.fechner@seattlechildrens.org
Length: 3 Yrs   *ACGME Approved/Offered Positions:* 3
Program ID: 326-54-31-081

Wisconsin

Madison

University of Wisconsin Program

Sponsor: University of Wisconsin Hospital and Clinics
Prgm Director: David B Allen, MD
600 Highland Ave H4/448
Madison, WI 53792
Tel: 608 263-5835   *Fax:* 608 265-7957
Length: 3 Yrs   *ACGME Approved/Offered Positions:* 1
Program ID: 326-56-21-059

Milwaukee

Medical College of Wisconsin Affiliated Hospitals Program

Sponsor: Medical College of Wisconsin Affiliated
  Hospitals, Inc
Children's Hospital of Wisconsin
Prgm Director: Patricia A Donohoue, MD*
Department of Pediatrics, MRFC
8701 Watertown Plank Road
Milwaukee, WI 53226
Tel: 414 266-6750   *Fax:* 414 266-6749
Length: 3 Yrs   *ACGME Approved/Offered Positions:* 6
Program ID: 326-56-12-080

Pediatric Gastroenterology (Pediatrics)

Alabama

Birmingham

University of Alabama Medical Center Program

Sponsor: University of Alabama Hospital
Children's Hospital of Alabama
Prgm Director: Shehzad A Saeed, MD
1600 7th Avenue South, ACC Suite 618
Birmingham, AL 35233
Tel: 205 939-9918   *Fax:* 205 939-9919
Length: 3 Yrs   *ACGME Approved/Offered Positions:* 3
Program ID: 332-01-21-001

California

Los Angeles

Childrens Hospital Los Angeles Program

Sponsor: Childrens Hospital Los Angeles
Prgm Director: Frank R Sinatra, MD
4650 Sunset Blvd
Mailstop 78
Los Angeles, CA 90027
Tel: 323 226-5603   *Fax:* 323 226-4380
Length: 3 Yrs   *ACGME Approved/Offered Positions:* 3
Program ID: 332-05-21-051

UCLA Medical Center Program

Sponsor: UCLA David Geffen School of Medicine/UCLA
  Medical Center
UCLA Medical Center
Prgm Director: Marvin E Ament, MD
10833 Le Conte Avenue, MDCC 12-383
Los Angeles, CA 90095
Tel: 310 206-6134   *Fax:* 310 206-0203
Length: 3 Yrs   *ACGME Approved/Offered Positions:* 6
Program ID: 332-05-31-004

San Diego

University of California (San Diego) Program

Sponsor: University of California (San Diego) Medical
  Center
Rady Children's Hospital
Prgm Director: Joel E Lavine, MD, PhD
200 West Arbor Drive
MC 8450
San Diego, CA 92103
Tel: 619 543-7544   *Fax:* 619 543-7537
Length: 3 Yrs   *ACGME Approved/Offered Positions:* 6
Program ID: 332-05-11-055

San Francisco

University of California (San Francisco) Program

Sponsor: University of California (San Francisco) School
  of Medicine
UCSF and Mount Zion Medical Centers
Prgm Director: Melvin B Heyman, MD, MPH
M U 4-East, Room 403 UCSF
500 Parnassus Avenue
San Francisco, CA 94143
Tel: 415 476-5892   *Fax:* 415 476-1343
Length: 3 Yrs   *ACGME Approved/Offered Positions:* 6
Program ID: 332-05-21-047

Stanford

Stanford University Program

Sponsor: Stanford Hospital and Clinics
Lucile Salter Packard Children's Hospital at Stanford
Prgm Director: John Alan Kerner Jr, MD
Lucile Packard Children's Hospital
750 Welch Road, Suite 116
Palo Alto, CA 94304
Tel: 650 723-5070   *Fax:* 650 498-5608
E-mail: john.kerner@stanford.edu
Length: 3 Yrs   *ACGME Approved/Offered Positions:* 6
Program ID: 332-05-11-005

Colorado

Aurora

University of Colorado Denver Program

Sponsor: University of Colorado Denver School of
    Medicine
Children's Hospital (The)
Prgm Director: Michael R Narkewicz, MD
13123 E 16th Ave, B290
Aurora, CO 80045
Tel: 720 777-6669   *Fax:* 720 777-7277
E-mail: Narkewicz.Michael@tchden.org
Length: 3 Yrs   *ACGME Approved/Offered Positions:* 6
Program ID: 332-07-21-006

Connecticut

New Haven

Yale-New Haven Medical Center Program

Sponsor: Yale-New Haven Hospital
Prgm Director: Dinesh S Pashankar, MBBS, MD
333 Cedar Street, FMP 408
PO Box 208064
New Haven, CT 06520
Tel: 203 785-4649   *Fax:* 203 737-1384
E-mail: Dinesh.Pashankar@yale.edu
Length: 3 Yrs   *ACGME Approved/Offered Positions:* 3
Program ID: 332-08-21-007

Delaware

Wilmington

Jefferson Medical College/duPont Hospital for Children Program

Sponsor: Jefferson Medical College
Alfred I duPont Hospital for Children
Prgm Director: Seema Khan, MBBS*
1600 Rockland Road
Wilmington, DE 19803
Tel: 302 651-5928   *Fax:* 301 651-5838
E-mail: sekhan@nemours.org
Length: 3 Yrs   *ACGME Approved/Offered Positions:* 6
Program ID: 332-41-12-058

Florida

Gainesville

University of Florida Program

Sponsor: University of Florida College of Medicine
Shands Hospital at the University of Florida
Prgm Director: Joel M Andres, MD
PO Box 100296
1600 SW Archer Road
Gainesville, FL 32610
Tel: 352 733-0094   *Fax:* 352 733-0392
Length: 3 Yrs   *ACGME Approved/Offered Positions:* 3
Program ID: 332-11-21-011

Miami

Jackson Memorial Hospital/Jackson Health System Program

Sponsor: Jackson Memorial Hospital/Jackson Health
    System
Prgm Director: Lesley Smith, MD, MBA
1601 NW 12th Avenue, Room 3005A
Miami, FL 33136
Tel: 305 243-6426   *Fax:* 305 243-2617
E-mail: lsmith10@med.miami.edu
Length: 3 Yrs   *ACGME Approved/Offered Positions:* 3
Program ID: 332-11-21-067

Georgia

Atlanta

Emory University Program

Sponsor: Emory University School of Medicine
Children's Healthcare of Atlanta at Egleston
Prgm Director: Rene Romero Jr, MD
2015 Uppergate Drive, NE
Atlanta, GA 30322
Tel: 404 727-4921   *Fax:* 404 727-4069
Length: 3 Yrs   *ACGME Approved/Offered Positions:* 5
Program ID: 332-12-31-057

Illinois

Chicago

McGaw Medical Center of Northwestern University Program

Sponsor: McGaw Medical Center of Northwestern
    University
Children's Memorial Hospital
Prgm Director: Jeffrey Brown, MD
2300 Children's Plaza
Box 57
Chicago, IL 60614
Tel: 773 880-4643   *Fax:* 773 880-4036
E-mail: jrbrown@childrensmemorial.org
Length: 3 Yrs   *ACGME Approved/Offered Positions:* 6
Program ID: 332-16-21-056

University of Chicago Program

Sponsor: University of Chicago Medical Center
Prgm Director: Ranjana Gokhale, MD
5841 S Maryland Avenue, MC 4065
MC 4065
Chicago, IL 60637
Tel: 773 702-6418   *Fax:* 773 702-0666
E-mail: rgokhale@peds.bsd.uchicago.edu
Length: 3 Yrs   *ACGME Approved/Offered Positions:* 3
Program ID: 332-16-21-012

Indiana

Indianapolis

Indiana University School of Medicine Program

Sponsor: Indiana University School of Medicine
Clarian Riley Hospital for Children
Prgm Director: Marian D Pfefferkorn, MD
Indiana University School of Medicine
702 Barnhill Drive, Room ROC 4210
Indianapolis, IN 46202
Tel: 317 274-3774   *Fax:* 317 274-8521
Length: 3 Yrs   *ACGME Approved/Offered Positions:* 4
Program ID: 332-17-21-013

Iowa

Iowa City

University of Iowa Hospitals and Clinics Program

Sponsor: University of Iowa Hospitals and Clinics
Prgm Director: Aliye Uc, MD
Department of Pediatrics
200 Hawkins Drive
Iowa City, IA 52242
Tel: 319 356-2950   *Fax:* 319 353-8967
Length: 3 Yrs   *ACGME Approved/Offered Positions:* 3
Program ID: 332-18-21-053

Kentucky

Louisville

University of Louisville Program

Sponsor: University of Louisville School of Medicine
Kosair Children's Hospital (Norton Healthcare, Inc)
Prgm Director: Thomas C Stephen, MD
Dept of Ped Gastroenterology
571 S Floyd Street, Room 325
Louisville, KY 40202
Tel: 502 852-3874   *Fax:* 502 852-4093
Length: 3 Yrs   *ACGME Approved/Offered Positions:* 2
Program ID: 332-20-21-014

Louisiana

New Orleans

Louisiana State University Program

Sponsor: Louisiana State University School of Medicine
Children's Hospital (New Orleans)
Prgm Director: Paul E Hyman, MD*
Children's Hospital
200 Henry Clay Ave
New Orleans, LA 70118
Tel: 504 896-9334   *Fax:* 504 896-2720
Length: 3 Yrs   *ACGME Approved/Offered Positions:* 2
Program ID: 332-21-21-015

Maryland

Baltimore

Johns Hopkins University Program

Sponsor: Johns Hopkins University School of Medicine
Johns Hopkins Hospital
Prgm Director: Carmen Cuffari, MD
Brady 320, 600 North Wolfe Street
Baltimore, MD 21287
Tel: 410 955-8769   *Fax:* 410 955-1464
Length: 3 Yrs   *ACGME Approved/Offered Positions:* 4
Program ID: 332-23-21-016

University of Maryland Program

Sponsor: University of Maryland Medical System
Prgm Director: Samra S Blanchard, MD
Department of Pediatric Gastroenterology
22 S Greene Street, N5W70
Baltimore, MD 21201
Tel: 410 328-0812   *Fax:* 410 328-1072
E-mail: sblanchard@peds.umaryland.edu
Length: 3 Yrs   *ACGME Approved/Offered Positions:* 3
Program ID: 332-23-21-061

Bethesda

National Capital Consortium Program

Sponsor: National Capital Consortium
Walter Reed Army Medical Center
Prgm Director: Carolyn A Sullivan, MD
Department of Pediatrics
4301 Jones Bridge Road
Bethesda, MD 20814
Tel: 202 782-9737   *Fax:* 202 782-8136
E-mail: carolyn.sullivan@us.army.mil
Length: 3 Yrs   *ACGME Approved/Offered Positions:* 3
Program ID: 332-10-21-010
Uniformed Services Program

Massachusetts

Boston

Children's Hospital/Boston Medical Center Program

Sponsor: Children's Hospital
Prgm Director: Paul Rufo, MD, MSc*
Children's Hospital, Boston
300 Longwood Avenue, Enders Bldg 720
Boston, MA 02115
Tel: 617 355-6058
E-mail: cacilda.teixeira@childrens.harvard.edu
Length: 3 Yrs   *ACGME Approved/Offered Positions:* 16
Program ID: 332-24-31-018

Massachusetts General Hospital Program

Sponsor: Massachusetts General Hospital
Prgm Director: Gary Russell, MD*
175 Cambridge St
5th Floor
Boston, MA 02114
Tel: 617 726-1450   *Fax:* 617 724-2710
E-mail: grussell@partners.org
Length: 3 Yrs   *ACGME Approved/Offered Positions:* 6
Program ID: 332-24-31-069

Michigan

Ann Arbor

University of Michigan Program

Sponsor: University of Michigan Hospitals and Health
  Centers
Prgm Director: M James Lopez, MD, PhD
1500 E Medical Center Drive
D5200 MPB, SPC 5718
Ann Arbor, MI 48109
Tel: 734 763-9650   *Fax:* 734 763-7359
E-mail: jamlopez@med.umich.edu
Length: 3 Yrs   *ACGME Approved/Offered Positions:* 6
Program ID: 332-25-21-019

Detroit

Children's Hospital of Michigan Program

Sponsor: Children's Hospital of Michigan
Prgm Director: Mohammad El-baba, MD*
3901 Beaubien Boulevard
Detroit, MI 48201
Tel: 313 745-5585   *Fax:* 313 745-5155
Length: 3 Yrs   *ACGME Approved/Offered Positions:* 2
Program ID: 332-25-21-020

Minnesota

Minneapolis

University of Minnesota Program

Sponsor: University of Minnesota Medical School
Hennepin County Medical Center
University of Minnesota Medical Center, Division of
  Fairview
Prgm Director: Glenn R Gourley, MD*
MMC 185
420 Delaware Street SE
Minneapolis, MN 55455
Tel: 612 624-8112   *Fax:* 612 626-0639
E-mail: pedsigi@umn.edu
Length: 3 Yrs   *ACGME Approved/Offered Positions:* 1
Program ID: 332-26-21-048

Rochester

College of Medicine, Mayo Clinic (Rochester) Program

Sponsor: College of Medicine, Mayo Clinic
Mayo Clinic (Rochester)
Saint Marys Hospital of Rochester
Prgm Director: Mounif El Youssef, MD
200 First Street, SW
Rochester, MN 55905
Tel: 507 538-0154   *Fax:* 507 284-0160
E-mail: el-youssef.mounif@mayo.edu
Length: 3 Yrs   *ACGME Approved/Offered Positions:* 2
Program ID: 332-26-21-021

Missouri

Kansas City

University of Missouri at Kansas City Program

Sponsor: University of Missouri-Kansas City School of
  Medicine
Children's Mercy Hospital
Prgm Director: James F Daniel, MD
Children's Mercy Hospital
2401 Gillham Road
Kansas City, MO 64108
Tel: 816 234-3016   *Fax:* 816 855-1721
E-mail: jdaniel@cmh.edu
Length: 3 Yrs   *ACGME Approved/Offered Positions:* 3
Program ID: 332-28-11-065

St Louis

Washington University/B-JH/SLCH Consortium Program

Sponsor: Washington University/B-JH/SLCH Consortium
St Louis Children's Hospital
Prgm Director: Phillip I Tarr, MD
Campus Box 8208, 660 South Euclid Avenue
St Louis, MO 63110
Tel: 314 286-2848   *Fax:* 314 286-2895
Length: 3 Yrs   *ACGME Approved/Offered Positions:* 6
Program ID: 332-28-31-023

Nebraska

Omaha

University of Nebraska Medical Center College of Medicine/Creighton University Program

Sponsor: University of Nebraska Medical Center College
  of Medicine
Children's Hospital
Nebraska Medical Center
Prgm Director: Thomas M Attard, MD
985161 Nebraska Medical Center
Omaha, NE 68198
Tel: 402 559-2412   *Fax:* 402 559-9525
E-mail: tattard@unmc.edu
Length: 3 Yrs   *ACGME Approved/Offered Positions:* 3
Program ID: 332-30-21-024

New York

Bronx

Albert Einstein College of Medicine Program

Sponsor: Albert Einstein College of Medicine of Yeshiva
  University
Montefiore Medical Center-Henry and Lucy Moses
  Division
Prgm Director: Yolanda Rivas, MD*
3415 Bainbridge Ave
Bronx, NY 10467
Tel: 718 741-2332   *Fax:* 718 515-5426
E-mail: yrivas@montefiore.org
Length: 3 Yrs   *ACGME Approved/Offered Positions:* 3
Program ID: 332-35-21-050

Brooklyn

SUNY Health Science Center at Brooklyn Program

Sponsor: SUNY Health Science Center at Brooklyn
Kings County Hospital Center
University Hospital-SUNY Health Science Center at
  Brooklyn
Prgm Director: William Treem, MD
450 Clarkson Avenue, Box 49
Brooklyn, NY 11203
Tel: 718 270-3090   *Fax:* 718 270-1985
E-mail: william.treem@downstate.edu
Length: 3 Yrs   *ACGME Approved/Offered Positions:* 3
Program ID: 332-35-21-026

Buffalo

University at Buffalo Program

Sponsor: University at Buffalo School of Medicine
Kaleida Health System (Women and Children's Hosp of
  Buffalo)
University at Buffalo Affiliated Physician Practices
  (UBAPP)
Prgm Director: Susan S Baker, MD, PhD
219 Bryant Street
Buffalo, NY 14222
Tel: 716 878-7198   *Fax:* 716 888-3842
Length: 3 Yrs   *ACGME Approved/Offered Positions:* 6
Program ID: 332-35-13-060

Note: * indicates a newly appointed program director

Great Neck

NSLIJHS-Schneider Children's Hospital Program

Sponsor: North Shore-Long Island Jewish Health System
Schneider Children's Hospital at Long Island Jewish
  Med Ctr
Prgm Director: Toba Weinstein, MD
269-01 76th Avenue
New Hyde Park, NY 11040
Tel: 718 470-3430   *Fax:* 718 962-2908
Length: 3 Yrs   *ACGME Approved/Offered Positions:* 2
Program ID: 332-35-31-027

New York

Mount Sinai School of Medicine Program

Sponsor: Mount Sinai School of Medicine
Mount Sinai Medical Center
Prgm Director: Keith J Benkov, MD
One Gustave L Levy Place
New York, NY 10029
Tel: 212 241-5415   *Fax:* 212 831-7974
Length: 3 Yrs   *ACGME Approved/Offered Positions:* 3
Program ID: 332-35-11-028

New York Presbyterian Hospital (Columbia Campus) Program

Sponsor: New York Presbyterian Hospital
New York Presbyterian Hospital (Columbia Campus)
Prgm Director: Steven J Lobritto, MD
3959 Broadway
CHN 726
New York, NY 10032
Tel: 212 305-7082   *Fax:* 212 305-8995
E-mail: sjl12@columbia.edu
Length: 3 Yrs   *ACGME Approved/Offered Positions:* 6
Program ID: 332-35-21-030

New York Presbyterian Hospital (Cornell Campus) Program

Sponsor: New York Presbyterian Hospital
New York Presbyterian Hospital (Cornell Campus)
Prgm Director: Robbyn E Sockolow, MD
525 E 68th Street, J-114
New York, NY 10065
Tel: 212 746-3520   *Fax:* 212 746-8577
Length: 3 Yrs   *ACGME Approved/Offered Positions:* 3
Program ID: 332-35-32-029

Rochester

University of Rochester Program

Sponsor: Strong Memorial Hospital of the University of
  Rochester
Prgm Director: Thomas M Rossi, MD
601 Elmwood Avenue
Box 667
Rochester, NY 14642
Tel: 585 275-2647   *Fax:* 585 275-0707
E-mail: Wendy_Saetta@urmc.rochester.edu
Length: 3 Yrs   *ACGME Approved/Offered Positions:* 3
Program ID: 332-35-21-064

Stony Brook

SUNY at Stony Brook Program

Sponsor: University Hospital - SUNY at Stony Brook
Prgm Director: Anupama Chawla, MD
HSC T11 Room 080
Department of Pediatrics
Stony Brook, NY 11794
Tel: 631 444-8115   *Fax:* 631 444-6045
E-mail: anupama.chawla@stonybrook.edu
Length: 3 Yrs   *ACGME Approved/Offered Positions:* 3
Program ID: 332-35-13-072

Valhalla

New York Medical College at Westchester Medical Center Program

Sponsor: New York Medical College
Westchester Medical Center
Prgm Director: Stuart H Berezin, MD
Division of Pediatric Gastroenterology
Munger Pavilion Rm 101
Valhalla, NY 10595
Tel: 914 594-4610   *Fax:* 914 594-4392
Length: 3 Yrs   *ACGME Approved/Offered Positions:* 3
Program ID: 332-35-31-031

Ohio

Cincinnati

Cincinnati Children's Hospital Medical Center/University of Cincinnati College of Medicine Program

Sponsor: Cincinnati Children's Hospital Medical Center
Prgm Director: Lee A Denson, MD
3333 Burnet Avenue
Bldg C, MLC 2010
Cincinnati, OH 45229
Tel: 513 636-7575   *Fax:* 513 636-5581
Length: 3 Yrs   *ACGME Approved/Offered Positions:* 12
Program ID: 332-38-21-033

Cleveland

Cleveland Clinic Foundation Program

Sponsor: Cleveland Clinic Foundation
Prgm Director: Lori Mahajan, MD
Pediatric Institute, Peds Gastro/Nutrition
9500 Euclid Avenue, Desk A111
Cleveland, OH 44195
Tel: 216 445-1572   *Fax:* 216 444-2974
Length: 3 Yrs   *ACGME Approved/Offered Positions:* 6
Program ID: 332-38-31-034

University Hospitals Case Medical Center Program

Sponsor: University Hospitals Case Medical Center
MetroHealth Medical Center
Prgm Director: Patrice J Tyson, MD*
Div of Pediatric Gastroenterology
11100 Euclid Ave, Suite 737, Mailstop 6004
Cleveland, OH 44106
Tel: 216 844-1765   *Fax:* 216 844-8397
E-mail: Patrice.Tyson@uhhospitals.org
Length: 3 Yrs   *ACGME Approved/Offered Positions:* 3
Program ID: 332-38-11-035

Columbus

Nationwide Children's Hospital/Ohio State University Program

Sponsor: Nationwide Children's Hospital
Prgm Director: Steven H Erdman, MD
700 Children's Drive
Columbus, OH 43205
Tel: 614 722-3474   *Fax:* 614 722-3454
E-mail: marykay.miller@nationwidechildrens.org
Length: 3 Yrs   *ACGME Approved/Offered Positions:* 6
Program ID: 332-38-12-062

Pennsylvania

Philadelphia

Children's Hospital of Philadelphia Program

Sponsor: Children's Hospital of Philadelphia
Prgm Director: Elizabeth B Rand, MD
34th Street & Civic Center Blvd
Philadelphia, PA 19104
Tel: 215 590-3247   *Fax:* 215 590-5326
E-mail: Dibruno@email.chop.edu
Length: 3 Yrs   *ACGME Approved/Offered Positions:* 12
Program ID: 332-41-21-038

St Christopher's Hospital for Children Program

Sponsor: St Christopher's Hospital for Children (Tenet
  Health System)
Prgm Director: Alan D Baldridge, MD
Section of Gastroenterology
Erie Avenue at Front Street
Philadelphia, PA 19134
Tel: 215 427-6673   *Fax:* 215 427-6782
E-mail: alan.baldridgemd@tenethealth.com
Length: 3 Yrs   *ACGME Approved/Offered Positions:* 3
Program ID: 332-41-13-068

Pittsburgh

University of Pittsburgh Medical Center Medical Education Program

Sponsor: Univ of Pittsburgh Medical Center Medical
  Education
Children's Hospital of Pittsburgh of UPMC
Magee-Womens Hospital of UPMC
Prgm Director: Mark E Lowe, MD, PhD
3705 Fifth Avenue
Pittsburgh, PA 15213
Tel: 412 692-5412   *Fax:* 412 692-8906
E-mail: mark.lowe@chp.edu
Length: 3 Yrs   *ACGME Approved/Offered Positions:* 6
Program ID: 332-41-21-040

Rhode Island

Providence

Brown University Program

Sponsor: Rhode Island Hospital-Lifespan
Prgm Director: David Kawatu, MD, MSc*
MPH-131
593 Eddy Street
Providence, RI 02903
Tel: 401 444-2827   *Fax:* 401 444-8748
E-mail: david_kawatu@brown.edu
Length: 3 Yrs   *ACGME Approved/Offered Positions:* 5
Program ID: 332-43-21-041

Tennessee

Nashville

Vanderbilt University Program

Sponsor: Vanderbilt University Medical Center
Prgm Director: Sari A Acra, MD, MPH
MRB IV Room 1025
2215 Garland Ave
Nashville, TN 37232
Tel: 615 322-7449   *Fax:* 615 343-8915
E-mail: sari.acra@vanderbilt.edu
Length: 3 Yrs   *ACGME Approved/Offered Positions:* 6
Program ID: 332-47-21-042

Programs

Texas

Dallas

University of Texas Southwestern Medical School Program

Sponsor: University of Texas Southwestern Medical School
Children's Medical Center of Dallas
Dallas County Hospital District-Parkland Memorial Hospital
Prgm Director: Norberto Rodriguez-Baez, MD
1935 Medical Distric Drive
Dallas, TX 75235
Tel: 214 456-8032   *Fax:* 214 456-8006
Length: 3 Yrs   *ACGME Approved/Offered Positions:* 9
Program ID: 332-48-11-045

Houston

Baylor College of Medicine Program

Sponsor: Baylor College of Medicine
Texas Children's Hospital
Prgm Director: Mark A Gilger, MD
6621 Fannin Street, MC CC1010.00
Houston, TX 77030
Tel: 832 822-3616   *Fax:* 832 825-3633
Length: 3 Yrs   *ACGME Approved/Offered Positions:* 9
Program ID: 332-48-21-043

University of Texas at Houston Program

Sponsor: University of Texas Health Science Center at Houston
Lyndon B Johnson General Hospital
Memorial Hermann Hospital
University of Texas M D Anderson Cancer Center
Prgm Director: Jon Marc Rhoads, MD
Department of Pediatrics, Division of Gastroenterology
6431 Fannin Street, MSB 3.137
Houston, TX 77030
Tel: 713 500-7642   *Fax:* 713 500-5750
Length: 3 Yrs   *ACGME Approved/Offered Positions:* 6
Program ID: 332-48-31-073

Washington

Seattle

University of Washington Program

Sponsor: University of Washington School of Medicine
Seattle Children's Hospital
Prgm Director: Karen F Murray, MD
4800 Sand Point Way NE
PO Box 5371, Mailstop W-7830
Seattle, WA 98105
Tel: 206 987-2587   *Fax:* 206 987-2721
E-mail: brianne.vanderlinden@seattlechildrens.org
Length: 3 Yrs   *ACGME Approved/Offered Positions:* 3
Program ID: 332-54-21-071

Wisconsin

Milwaukee

Medical College of Wisconsin Affiliated Hospitals Program

Sponsor: Medical College of Wisconsin Affiliated Hospitals, Inc
Children's Hospital of Wisconsin
Prgm Director: Praveen S Goday, MBBS*
8701 Watertown Plank Road
Division of Pediatric Gastroenterology
Milwaukee, WI 53226
Tel: 414 266-3690   *Fax:* 414 266-3676
Length: 3 Yrs   *ACGME Approved/Offered Positions:* 6
Program ID: 332-56-21-046

Pediatric Hematology/ Oncology (Pediatrics)

Alabama

Birmingham

University of Alabama Medical Center Program

Sponsor: University of Alabama Hospital
Children's Hospital of Alabama
Prgm Director: Roger L Berkow, MD*
Children's Hospital of Alabama
1600 7th Avenue South, ACC 512
Birmingham, AL 35233
Tel: 205 939-9285   *Fax:* 205 975-1941
E-mail: rberkow@peds.uab.edu
Length: 3 Yrs   *ACGME Approved/Offered Positions:* 6
Program ID: 327-01-21-043

Arizona

Phoenix

Phoenix Children's Hospital/Maricopa Medical Center Program

Sponsor: Phoenix Children's Hospital
Translational Genomics Research Institute
Prgm Director: Michael M Henry, MD
Center for Cancer and Blood Disorders
1919 East Thomas Road
Phoenix, AZ 85016
Tel: 602 546-0920   *Fax:* 602 546-0276
E-mail: mhenry@phoenixchildrens.com
Length: 3 Yrs   *ACGME Approved/Offered Positions:* 6
Program ID: 327-03-13-079

Arkansas

Little Rock

University of Arkansas for Medical Sciences Program

Sponsor: University of Arkansas College of Medicine
Arkansas Children's Hospital
Prgm Director: Kimo C Stine, MD
800 Marshall Street
Little Rock, AR 72202
Tel: 501 364-1494   *Fax:* 501 364-3634
Length: 3 Yrs   *ACGME Approved/Offered Positions:* 3
Program ID: 327-04-31-086

California

Los Angeles

Childrens Hospital Los Angeles Program

Sponsor: Childrens Hospital Los Angeles
Prgm Director: Rima F Jubran, MD, MPH
Division of Hematology-Oncology
4650 Sunset Boulevard
Los Angeles, CA 90027
Tel: 323 361-5639   *Fax:* 323 361-7128
E-mail: rjubran@chla.usc.edu
Length: 3 Yrs   *ACGME Approved/Offered Positions:* 10
Program ID: 327-05-11-001

Note: * indicates a newly appointed program director

UCLA Medical Center Program
Sponsor: UCLA David Geffen School of Medicine/UCLA
  Medical Center
UCLA Medical Center
Prgm Director: Kathleen M Sakamoto, MD, PhD*
Div of Pediatric Hematology-Oncology
10833 Le Conte Avenue
Los Angeles, CA 90095
Tel: 310 794-7007 *Fax:* 310 206-8089
E-mail: kms@ucla.edu
Length: 3 Yrs *ACGME Approved/Offered Positions:* 6
Program ID: 327-05-21-003

Oakland

Children's Hospital-Oakland Program
Sponsor: Children's Hospital-Oakland
Prgm Director: Caroline A Hastings, MD
747 52nd Street
Oakland, CA 94609
Tel: 510 428-3631 *Fax:* 510 601-3916
Length: 3 Yrs *ACGME Approved/Offered Positions:* 4
Program ID: 327-05-31-056

Orange

**Children's Hospital of Orange County
Program**
Sponsor: Children's Hospital of Orange County
Prgm Director: Diane J Nugent, MD
455 S Main Street
Orange, CA 92868
Tel: 714 532-8744 *Fax:* 714 532-8771
E-mail: djn0@choc.org
Length: 3 Yrs *ACGME Approved/Offered Positions:* 9
Program ID: 327-05-21-057

Sacramento

**University of California (Davis) Health
System Program**
Sponsor: University of California (Davis) Health System
University of California (Davis) Medical Center
Prgm Director: Theodore Zwerdling, MD
2516 Stockton Boulevard
Room 371
Sacramento, CA 95817
Tel: 916 734-2781 *Fax:* 916 451-3014
Length: 3 Yrs *ACGME Approved/Offered Positions:* 3
Program ID: 327-05-21-084

San Diego

**University of California (San Diego)
Program**
Sponsor: University of California (San Diego) Medical
  Center
Rady Children's Hospital
University of California San Diego Cancer Center
Prgm Director: William D Roberts, MD
3020 Children's Way
Mail Code 5035
San Diego, CA 92123
Tel: 858 966-5811 *Fax:* 858 966-8035
Length: 3 Yrs *ACGME Approved/Offered Positions:* 6
Program ID: 327-05-13-085

San Francisco

**University of California (San Francisco)
Program**
Sponsor: University of California (San Francisco) School
  of Medicine
UCSF and Mount Zion Medical Centers
Prgm Director: Michelle Hermiston, MD, PhD
505 Parnassus Ave
Box 0106
San Francisco, CA 94143
Tel: 415 476-2413 *Fax:* 415 502-4372
E-mail: HermistonM@peds.ucsf.edu
Length: 3 Yrs *ACGME Approved/Offered Positions:* 6
Program ID: 327-05-21-006

Stanford

Stanford University Program
Sponsor: Stanford Hospital and Clinics
Lucile Salter Packard Children's Hospital at Stanford
Prgm Director: Neyssa Marina, MD
Pediatric Hematology/Oncology - Mail Code 5798
1000 Welch Road, Suite 300
Palo Alto, CA 94304
Tel: 650 723-5535 *Fax:* 650 723-5231
Length: 3 Yrs *ACGME Approved/Offered Positions:* 9
Program ID: 327-05-21-004

Colorado

Aurora

University of Colorado Denver Program
Sponsor: University of Colorado Denver School of
  Medicine
Children's Hospital (The)
Prgm Director: Timothy P Garrington, MD*
Center for Cancer and Blood Disorders
13123 East 16th Avenue
Aurora, CO 80045
Tel: 720 777-8365 *Fax:* 720 777-7279
E-mail: garrington.timothy@tchden.org
Length: 3 Yrs *ACGME Approved/Offered Positions:* 9
Program ID: 327-07-21-007

Connecticut

New Haven

**Yale-New Haven Medical Center
Program**
Sponsor: Yale-New Haven Hospital
Prgm Director: Diana S Beardsley, MD, PhD
333 Cedar Street, LMP 2073
PO Box 208064
New Haven, CT 06520
Tel: 203 785-4640 *Fax:* 203 737-2228
Length: 3 Yrs *ACGME Approved/Offered Positions:* 3
Program ID: 327-08-21-008

District of Columbia

Washington

**Children's National Medical Center/
George Washington University Program**
Sponsor: Children's National Medical Center
Prgm Director: Michael F Guerrera, MD
111 Michigan Avenue NW
Suite 4W 600
Washington, DC 20010
Tel: 202 476-2800 *Fax:* 202 476-5685
E-mail: mfguerre@cnmc.org
Length: 3 Yrs *ACGME Approved/Offered Positions:* 12
Program ID: 327-10-21-009

Florida

Gainesville

University of Florida Program
Sponsor: University of Florida College of Medicine
Shands Hospital at the University of Florida
Prgm Director: William B Slayton, MD
Box 100296, UFHSC
Gainesville, FL 32610
Tel: 352 392-5633 *Fax:* 352 392-8725
E-mail: slaytwb@peds.ufl.edu
Length: 3 Yrs *ACGME Approved/Offered Positions:* 6
Program ID: 327-11-31-010

Georgia

Atlanta

Emory University Program
Sponsor: Emory University School of Medicine
Children's Healthcare of Atlanta at Egleston
Children's Healthcare of Atlanta at Scottish Rite
Prgm Director: Thomas C Abshire, MD
Department of Pediatric, Hematology/Oncology
2015 Uppergate Drive, Room 434
Atlanta, GA 30322
Tel: 404 785-0083 *Fax:* 404 727-4455
E-mail: thomas.abshire@emory.edu
Length: 3 Yrs *ACGME Approved/Offered Positions:* 9
Program ID: 327-12-21-041

Illinois

Chicago

**McGaw Medical Center of Northwestern
University Program**
Sponsor: McGaw Medical Center of Northwestern
  University
Children's Memorial Hospital
Prgm Director: Joanna L Weinstein, MD*
Division of Hematology/Oncology, Box 30
2300 Children's Plaza
Chicago, IL 60614
Tel: 773 880-4562 *Fax:* 773 880-3223
E-mail: jweinstein@childrensmemorial.org
Length: 3 Yrs *ACGME Approved/Offered Positions:* 9
Program ID: 327-16-21-011

University of Chicago Program
Sponsor: University of Chicago Medical Center
University of Chicago Comer Children's Hospital
Prgm Director: Eric C Beyer, MD, PhD
5841 South Maryland Avenue
Box MC 4060
Chicago, IL 60637
Tel: 773 834-1498 *Fax:* 773 702-9881
E-mail: ebeyer@peds.bsd.uchicago.edu
Length: 3 Yrs *ACGME Approved/Offered Positions:* 6
Program ID: 327-16-11-050

Programs

Indiana

Indianapolis

Indiana University School of Medicine Program
Sponsor: Indiana University School of Medicine
Clarian Riley Hospital for Children
Prgm Director: Terry A Vik, MD
Clarian Riley Hospital for Children
702 Barnhill Drive
Indianapolis, IN 46202
Tel: 317 274-8967   *Fax:* 317 278-0616
E-mail: tvik@iupui.edu
Length: 3 Yrs   *ACGME Approved/Offered Positions:* 6
Program ID: 327-17-21-012

Iowa

Iowa City

University of Iowa Hospitals and Clinics Program
Sponsor: University of Iowa Hospitals and Clinics
Prgm Director: Thomas W Loew, MD
Dept of Pediatrics, 2530 JCP
200 Hawkins Drive
Iowa City, IA 52242
Tel: 319 356-2437   *Fax:* 319 356-7659
E-mail: thomas-loew@uiowa.edu
Length: 3 Yrs   *ACGME Approved/Offered Positions:* 3
Program ID: 327-18-11-013

Louisiana

New Orleans

Louisiana State University Program
Sponsor: Louisiana State University School of Medicine
Children's Hospital (New Orleans)
Prgm Director: Maria C Velez, MD
Children's Hospital
200 Henry Clay Ave, Suite 4109
New Orleans, LA 70118
Tel: 504 896-9740   *Fax:* 504 896-9758
E-mail: mvelez@lsuhsc.edu
Length: 3 Yrs   *ACGME Approved/Offered Positions:* 6
Program ID: 327-21-21-048

Maryland

Baltimore

Johns Hopkins University Program
Sponsor: Johns Hopkins University School of Medicine
Johns Hopkins Hospital
Prgm Director: Kenneth J Cohen, MD, MBA
600 N Wolfe Street, CMSC 800
Baltimore, MD 21287
Tel: 410 614-5055   *Fax:* 410 955-0028
E-mail: kcohen@jhmi.edu
Length: 3 Yrs   *ACGME Approved/Offered Positions:* 21
Program ID: 327-23-21-014

Bethesda

National Capital Consortium Program
Sponsor: National Capital Consortium
Walter Reed Army Medical Center
Prgm Director: Col Gary Crouch, MD*
Department of Pediatrics
1600 Georgia Ave, NW
Washington, DC 20307
Tel: 202 782-9453   *Fax:* 202 782-7020
Length: 3 Yrs   *ACGME Approved/Offered Positions:* 6
Program ID: 327-10-21-044
Uniformed Services Program

Massachusetts

Boston

Children's Hospital/Boston Medical Center Program
Sponsor: Children's Hospital
Dana-Farber Cancer Institute
Prgm Director: David A Williams, MD*
300 Longwood Avenue
Boston, MA 02115
Tel: 617 919-2697   *Fax:* 617 730-0934
Length: 3 Yrs   *ACGME Approved/Offered Positions:* 19
Program ID: 327-24-11-015

Michigan

Ann Arbor

University of Michigan Program
Sponsor: University of Michigan Hospitals and Health Centers
Prgm Director: Steven W Pipe, MD
1500 East Medical Center Drive
D4202 MPB 5718
Ann Arbor, MI 48109
Tel: 734 647-2893   *Fax:* 734 615-0464
E-mail: ummdswp@med.umich.edu
Length: 3 Yrs   *ACGME Approved/Offered Positions:* 9
Program ID: 327-25-21-016

Detroit

Children's Hospital of Michigan Program
Sponsor: Children's Hospital of Michigan
Prgm Director: Jeffrey W Taub, MD
3901 Beaubien Blvd
Detroit, MI 48201
Tel: 313 745-5515   *Fax:* 313 745-5237
Length: 3 Yrs   *ACGME Approved/Offered Positions:* 6
Program ID: 327-25-21-017

Grand Rapids

Grand Rapids Medical Education and Research Center/Michigan State University Program
Sponsor: Grand Rapids Medical Education and Research Center
Spectrum Health-Butterworth Hospital
Van Andel Research Institute
Prgm Director: Albert S Cornelius, MD
100 Michigan Street NE MC 85
Grand Rapids, MI 49503
Tel: 616 391-2086   *Fax:* 616 391-8873
Length: 3 Yrs   *ACGME Approved/Offered Positions:* 3
Program ID: 327-25-13-076

Minnesota

Minneapolis

University of Minnesota Program
Sponsor: University of Minnesota Medical School
University of Minnesota Medical Center, Division of Fairview
Prgm Director: Michael J Burke, MD*
MMC 484
420 Delaware Street, SE
Minneapolis, MN 55455
Tel: 612 626-2778   *Fax:* 612 626-2815
Length: 3 Yrs   *ACGME Approved/Offered Positions:* 6
Program ID: 327-26-21-018

Rochester

College of Medicine, Mayo Clinic (Rochester) Program
Sponsor: College of Medicine, Mayo Clinic
Mayo Clinic (Rochester)
Saint Marys Hospital of Rochester
Prgm Director: Shakila P Khan, MD
Dept of Pediatric Hematology/Oncology
200 First Street SW
Rochester, MN 55905
Tel: 507 538-0154   *Fax:* 507 284-0160
E-mail: bartelsmith.susan@mayo.edu
Length: 3 Yrs   *ACGME Approved/Offered Positions:* 3
Program ID: 327-26-21-019

Mississippi

Jackson

University of Mississippi Medical Center Program
Sponsor: University of Mississippi School of Medicine
University Hospitals and Clinics
Prgm Director: Gail Megason, MD
2500 North State Street
Jackson, MS 39216
Tel: 601 984-5226   *Fax:* 601 984-5279
Length: 3 Yrs   *ACGME Approved/Offered Positions:* 2
Program ID: 327-27-12-055

Missouri

Kansas City

University of Missouri at Kansas City Program
Sponsor: University of Missouri-Kansas City School of Medicine
Children's Mercy Hospital
Prgm Director: Gerald M Woods, MD
2401 Gillham Road
Kansas City, MO 64108
Tel: 816 234-3265   *Fax:* 816 855-1700
Length: 3 Yrs   *ACGME Approved/Offered Positions:* 6
Program ID: 327-28-21-060

St Louis

Washington University/B-JH/SLCH Consortium Program
Sponsor: Washington University/B-JH/SLCH Consortium
St Louis Children's Hospital
Prgm Director: Robert J Hayashi, MD
Pediatric Hematology-Oncology
One Children's Place, Box 8116
St Louis, MO 63110
Tel: 314 454-4327   *Fax:* 314 454-2780
Length: 3 Yrs   *ACGME Approved/Offered Positions:* 9
Program ID: 327-28-11-020

Note: * indicates a newly appointed program director

New Jersey

New Brunswick

UMDNJ-Robert Wood Johnson Medical School Program

Sponsor: UMDNJ-Robert Wood Johnson Medical School
Robert Wood Johnson University Hospital
Prgm Director: Margaret Masterson, MD
CINJ
195 Little Albany Street
New Brunswick, NJ 08901
Tel: 732 235-8864 *Fax:* 732 235-8334
Length: 3 Yrs *ACGME Approved/Offered Positions:* 3
Program ID: 327-33-12-063

New York

Bronx

Albert Einstein College of Medicine Program

Sponsor: Albert Einstein College of Medicine of Yeshiva University
Montefiore Medical Center-Henry and Lucy Moses Division
Prgm Director: Adam Levy, MD
Division of Pediatric Hematology-Oncology
3415 Bainbridge Avenue
Bronx, NY 10467
Tel: 718 741-2342 *Fax:* 718 920-6506
E-mail: adlevy@montefiore.org
Length: 3 Yrs *ACGME Approved/Offered Positions:* 4
Program ID: 327-35-21-071

Buffalo

University at Buffalo Program

Sponsor: University at Buffalo School of Medicine
Kaleida Health System (Women and Children's Hosp of Buffalo)
Prgm Director: Martin L Brecher, MD
219 Bryant Street
Buffalo, NY 14222
Tel: 716 845-2333 *Fax:* 716 845-8003
E-mail: martin.brecher@roswellpark.org
Length: 3 Yrs *ACGME Approved/Offered Positions:* 2
Program ID: 327-35-21-021

Great Neck

NSLIJHS-Schneider Children's Hospital Program

Sponsor: North Shore-Long Island Jewish Health System
Schneider Children's Hospital at Long Island Jewish Med Ctr
Prgm Director: Mark Atlas, MD
Pediatric Hematology/Oncology
269-01 76th Ave
New Hyde Park, NY 11040
Tel: 718 470-3460 *Fax:* 718 343-4642
E-mail: matlas@lij.edu
Length: 3 Yrs *ACGME Approved/Offered Positions:* 7
Program ID: 327-35-21-023

New York

New York Presbyterian Hospital (Columbia Campus) Program

Sponsor: New York Presbyterian Hospital
New York Presbyterian Hospital (Columbia Campus)
Prgm Director: Mitchell S Cairo, MD
3959 Broadway, CHN 1003
New York, NY 10032
Tel: 212 305-8316 *Fax:* 212 305-8428
E-mail: mc1310@columbia.edu
Length: 3 Yrs *ACGME Approved/Offered Positions:* 6
Program ID: 327-35-11-027

New York Presbyterian Hospital (Cornell Campus) Program

Sponsor: New York Presbyterian Hospital
Memorial Sloan-Kettering Cancer Center
Prgm Director: Paul A Meyers, MD
Memorial Sloan Kettering Cancer Ctr
1275 York Avenue
New York, NY 10065
Tel: 212 639-5952 *Fax:* 212 717-3447
E-mail: wernerw@mskcc.org
Length: 3 Yrs *ACGME Approved/Offered Positions:* 21
Program ID: 327-35-21-024

New York University School of Medicine Program

Sponsor: New York University School of Medicine
NYU Hospitals Center
Prgm Director: Margaret Karpatkin, MD
Pediatric Hematology/Oncology
550 First Avenue
New York, NY 10016
Tel: 212 263-6428 *Fax:* 212 263-8099
Length: 3 Yrs *ACGME Approved/Offered Positions:* 6
Program ID: 327-35-21-026

Rochester

University of Rochester Program

Sponsor: Strong Memorial Hospital of the University of Rochester
Prgm Director: Craig Mullen, MD, PhD
Box 777
601 Elmwood Avenue
Rochester, NY 14642
Tel: 585 275-5372 *Fax:* 585 273-1039
E-mail: craig_mullen@urmc.rochester.edu
Length: 3 Yrs *ACGME Approved/Offered Positions:* 3
Program ID: 327-35-21-049

North Carolina

Chapel Hill

University of North Carolina Hospitals Program

Sponsor: University of North Carolina Hospitals
Prgm Director: Julie Blatt, MD
170 Manning Dr
CB 7236, Physicians Office Bldg 1185 A Rm 1106
Chapel Hill, NC 27599
Tel: 919 966-0590 *Fax:* 919 966-7629
Length: 3 Yrs *ACGME Approved/Offered Positions:* 9
Program ID: 327-36-21-058

Durham

Duke University Hospital Program

Sponsor: Duke University Hospital
Prgm Director: Susan G Kreissman, MD
Box 2916
Room 222, Bell Bldg, 100 Bell Service Road
Durham, NC 27710
Tel: 919 684-3401 *Fax:* 919 681-7950
Length: 3 Yrs *ACGME Approved/Offered Positions:* 9
Program ID: 327-36-21-029

Ohio

Akron

Children's Hospital Medical Center of Akron/NEOUCOM Program

Sponsor: Children's Hospital Medical Center of Akron
Prgm Director: Jeffrey D Hord, MD
Division of Pediatric Hematology/Oncology
One Perkins Square
Akron, OH 44308
Tel: 330 543-8580 *Fax:* 330 543-3220
Length: 3 Yrs *ACGME Approved/Offered Positions:* 3
Program ID: 327-38-13-082

Cincinnati

Cincinnati Children's Hospital Medical Center/University of Cincinnati College of Medicine Program

Sponsor: Cincinnati Children's Hospital Medical Center
Prgm Director: Franklin O Smith III, MD*
3333 Burnet Avenue
MLC7015
Cincinnati, OH 45229
Tel: 513 636-8811 *Fax:* 513 636-3549
E-mail: brenda.ingram@cchmc.org
Length: 3 Yrs *ACGME Approved/Offered Positions:* 15
Program ID: 327-38-21-030

Cleveland

Cleveland Clinic Foundation Program

Sponsor: Cleveland Clinic Foundation
Prgm Director: Kate Gowans, MD
9500 Euclid Avenue
Desk S20
Cleveland, OH 44195
Tel: 216 445-3588 *Fax:* 216 444-3577
E-mail: gowansk@ccf.org
Length: 3 Yrs *ACGME Approved/Offered Positions:* 3
Program ID: 327-38-31-078

University Hospitals Case Medical Center Program

Sponsor: University Hospitals Case Medical Center
Rainbow Babies and Children's Hospital
Prgm Director: Alex Y Huang, MD, PhD
11100 Euclid Avenue
Cleveland, OH 44106
Tel: 216 844-3345 *Fax:* 216 844-5431
E-mail: alex.huang@uhhospitals.org
Length: 3 Yrs *ACGME Approved/Offered Positions:* 6
Program ID: 327-38-21-031

Columbus

Nationwide Children's Hospital/Ohio State University Program

Sponsor: Nationwide Children's Hospital
Prgm Director: Nicholas D Yeager, MD
700 Children's Drive
Columbus, OH 43205
Tel: 614 722-3553 *Fax:* 614 722-3699
E-mail: Nicholas.Yeager@Nationwidechildrens.org
Length: 3 Yrs *ACGME Approved/Offered Positions:* 9
Program ID: 327-38-21-042

Oregon

Portland

Oregon Health & Science University Program

Sponsor: Oregon Health & Science University Hospital
Prgm Director: Linda C Stork, MD
3181 SW Sam Jackson Park Road
CDRCP
Portland, OR 97239
Tel: 503 494-0829   *Fax:* 503 494-0714
E-mail: storkl@ohsu.edu
Length: 3 Yrs   *ACGME Approved/Offered Positions:* 6
Program ID: 327-40-21-072

Pennsylvania

Hershey

Penn State University/Milton S Hershey Medical Center Program

Sponsor: Milton S Hershey Medical Center
Prgm Director: Melanie Comito, MD
Division of Pediatric Hematology-Oncology
500 University Drive, H085
Hershey, PA 17033
Tel: 717 531-6012   *Fax:* 717 531-4789
E-mail: mcomito@psu.edu
Length: 3 Yrs   *ACGME Approved/Offered Positions:* 3
Program ID: 327-41-31-081

Philadelphia

Children's Hospital of Philadelphia Program

Sponsor: Children's Hospital of Philadelphia
Prgm Director: Stephan A Grupp, MD, PhD*
34th Street and Civic Center Blvd
Philadelphia, PA 19104
Tel: 215 590-5475   *Fax:* 215 590-3770
E-mail: grupp@email.chop.edu
Length: 3 Yrs   *ACGME Approved/Offered Positions:* 18
Program ID: 327-41-21-032

St Christopher's Hospital for Children Program

Sponsor: St Christopher's Hospital for Children (Tenet Health System)
Prgm Director: Lewis L Hsu, MD, PhD*
Sections of Hematology and Oncology
Erie Avenue at Front Street
Philadelphia, PA 19134
Tel: 215 427-5096   *Fax:* 215 427-4281
E-mail: Lewis.Hsu@tenethealth.com
Length: 3 Yrs   *ACGME Approved/Offered Positions:* 3
Program ID: 327-41-12-051

Pittsburgh

University of Pittsburgh Medical Center Medical Education Program

Sponsor: Univ of Pittsburgh Medical Center Medical Education
Children's Hospital of Pittsburgh of UPMC
Prgm Director: Arthur K Ritchey, MD
3705 Fifth Avenue
Pittsburgh, PA 15213
Tel: 412 692-5055   *Fax:* 412 692-7693
Length: 3 Yrs   *ACGME Approved/Offered Positions:* 6
Program ID: 327-41-21-066

Puerto Rico

San Juan

University of Puerto Rico Program

Sponsor: University of Puerto Rico School of Medicine
University Pediatric Hospital
Prgm Director: Pedro J Santiago-Borrero, MD
GPO Box 365067
San Juan, PR 00936
Tel: 787 777-3535   *Fax:* 787 751-5812
E-mail: pjsantiago@centennialpr.net
Length: 3 Yrs   *ACGME Approved/Offered Positions:* 2
Program ID: 327-42-21-065

Rhode Island

Providence

Brown University Program

Sponsor: Rhode Island Hospital-Lifespan
Prgm Director: Anjulika Chawla, MD
Multiphasic Building, 1st Floor
593 Eddy Street
Providence, RI 02903
Tel: 401 444-5171   *Fax:* 401 444-8845
E-mail: achawla@lifespan.org
Length: 3 Yrs   *ACGME Approved/Offered Positions:* 3
Program ID: 327-43-21-033

South Carolina

Charleston

Medical University of South Carolina Program

Sponsor: Medical University of South Carolina College of Medicine
MUSC Medical Center
Prgm Director: Ram V Kalpatthi, MD*
MSC 558
135 Rutledge Avenue, Room 480
Charleston, SC 29425
Tel: 843 792-2957   *Fax:* 843 792-8912
E-mail: kalpattr@musc.edu
Length: 3 Yrs   *ACGME Approved/Offered Positions:* 3
Program ID: 327-45-21-068

Tennessee

Memphis

University of Tennessee Program

Sponsor: University of Tennessee College of Medicine
St Jude Children's Research Hospital
Prgm Director: Jeffrey E Rubnitz, MD, PhD
Department of Hematology-Oncology
262 Danny Thomas Place
Memphis, TN 38105
Tel: 901 595-2388   *Fax:* 901 521-9005
Length: 3 Yrs   *ACGME Approved/Offered Positions:* 18
Program ID: 327-47-31-034

Nashville

Vanderbilt University Program

Sponsor: Vanderbilt University Medical Center
Prgm Director: Haydar A Frangoul, MD, MS
Div of Ped Hematology-Oncology
397 Preston Research Bldg, 2220 Pierce Avenue
Nashville, TN 37232
Tel: 615 936-1762   *Fax:* 615 936-1767
Length: 3 Yrs   *ACGME Approved/Offered Positions:* 6
Program ID: 327-47-21-035

Texas

Dallas

University of Texas Southwestern Medical School Program

Sponsor: University of Texas Southwestern Medical School
Children's Medical Center of Dallas
Prgm Director: Patrick J Leavey, MB, MD
Department of Pediatrics
5323 Harry Hines Blvd
Dallas, TX 75390
Tel: 214 648-3074   *Fax:* 214 648-2764
E-mail: patrick.leavey@utsouthwestern.edu
Length: 3 Yrs   *ACGME Approved/Offered Positions:* 12
Program ID: 327-48-21-046

Houston

Baylor College of Medicine Program

Sponsor: Baylor College of Medicine
Texas Children's Hospital
Prgm Director: David G Poplack, MD
Texas Children's Hospital
6621 Fannin Street, CC1410.00
Houston, TX 77030
Tel: 832 822-4200   *Fax:* 832 825-4299
Length: 3 Yrs   *ACGME Approved/Offered Positions:* 18
Program ID: 327-48-21-037

University of Texas at Houston Program

Sponsor: University of Texas Health Science Center at Houston
University of Texas M D Anderson Cancer Center
Prgm Director: Laura L Worth, MD, PhD
Division of Pediatrics-Unit 87
1515 Holcombe Boulevard
Houston, TX 77030
Tel: 713 792-7751   *Fax:* 713 794-0608
Length: 3 Yrs   *ACGME Approved/Offered Positions:* 9
Program ID: 327-48-21-038

San Antonio

University of Texas Health Science Center at San Antonio Program

Sponsor: University of Texas School of Medicine at San Antonio
Prgm Director: Gail E Tomlinson, MD
7703 Floyd Curl Drive
San Antonio, TX 78229
Tel: 210 704-3111   *Fax:* 210 562-9014
Length: 3 Yrs   *ACGME Approved/Offered Positions:* 6
Program ID: 327-48-12-087

Utah

Salt Lake City

University of Utah Program

Sponsor: University of Utah Medical Center
Primary Children's Medical Center
Prgm Director: Zeinab Afify, ChB*
100 N Mario Capecchi Drive
Salt Lake City, UT 84113
Tel: 801 662-4700   *Fax:* 801 662-4705
Length: 3 Yrs   *ACGME Approved/Offered Positions:* 6
Program ID: 327-49-21-039

Note: * indicates a newly appointed program director

Virginia

Richmond

Virginia Commonwealth University Health System Program

Sponsor: Virginia Commonwealth University Health System
Medical College of Virginia Hospitals
Prgm Director: Kamar Godder, MD, MPH
1101 East Marshall Street
PO Box 980121
Richmond, VA 23298
Tel: 804 828-9605   *Fax:* 804 828-6455
Length: 3 Yrs   *ACGME Approved/Offered Positions:* 3
Program ID: 327-51-21-080

Washington

Seattle

University of Washington Program

Sponsor: University of Washington School of Medicine
Fred Hutchinson Cancer Research Center
Seattle Children's Hospital
Prgm Director: Julie R Park, MD
1100 Fairview Avenue N, D2-373
Seattle, WA 98109
Tel: 206 987-1947   *Fax:* 206 987-5182
Length: 3 Yrs   *ACGME Approved/Offered Positions:* 9
Program ID: 327-54-21-040

Wisconsin

Madison

University of Wisconsin Program

Sponsor: University of Wisconsin Hospital and Clinics
Prgm Director: Sinisa Dovat, MD
K4/438 CSC
600 Highland Avenue
Madison, WI 53792
Tel: 608 262-2415   *Fax:* 608 265-9721
Length: 3 Yrs   *ACGME Approved/Offered Positions:* 4
Program ID: 327-56-21-059

Milwaukee

Medical College of Wisconsin Affiliated Hospitals Program

Sponsor: Medical College of Wisconsin Affiliated Hospitals, Inc
Children's Hospital of Wisconsin
Prgm Director: Michael E Kelly, MD, PhD
MACC Fund Research Center
8701 Watertown Plank Road
Milwaukee, WI 53222
Tel: 414 456-4170   *Fax:* 414 456-6543
E-mail: dmenzel@mcw.edu
Length: 3 Yrs   *ACGME Approved/Offered Positions:* 3
Program ID: 327-56-21-063

Pediatric Infectious Diseases (Pediatrics)

Alabama

Birmingham

University of Alabama Medical Center Program

Sponsor: University of Alabama Hospital
Children's Hospital of Alabama
Prgm Director: Suresh B Boppana, MD
CHB 308
1600 6th Avenue South
Birmingham, AL 35233
Tel: 205 996-7765   *Fax:* 205 975-6549
Length: 3 Yrs   *ACGME Approved/Offered Positions:* 6
Program ID: 335-01-21-001

Arkansas

Little Rock

University of Arkansas for Medical Sciences Program

Sponsor: University of Arkansas College of Medicine
Arkansas Children's Hospital
UAMS Medical Center
Prgm Director: Gary Wheeler, MD, MA
800 Marshall Street
Little Rock, AR 72202
Tel: 501 364-1416   *Fax:* 501 364-3551
E-mail: wheelergary@uams.edu
Length: 3 Yrs   *ACGME Approved/Offered Positions:* 1
Program ID: 335-04-21-002

California

Los Angeles

Childrens Hospital Los Angeles Program

Sponsor: Childrens Hospital Los Angeles
Prgm Director: Jill A Hoffman, MD*
4650 Sunset Boulevard, MS 51
Los Angeles, CA 90027
Tel: 323 361-2509   *Fax:* 323 361-1183
E-mail: jhoffman@chla.usc.edu
Length: 3 Yrs   *ACGME Approved/Offered Positions:* 3
Program ID: 335-05-31-004

UCLA Medical Center Program

Sponsor: UCLA David Geffen School of Medicine/UCLA Medical Center
UCLA Medical Center
Prgm Director: Paul A Krogstad, MD, MS
10833 Le Conte Avenue
MDCC Room 22-442
Los Angeles, CA 90095
Tel: 310 825-5235   *Fax:* 310 206-4764
Length: 3 Yrs   *ACGME Approved/Offered Positions:* 4
Program ID: 335-05-11-005

University of Southern California/LAC+USC Medical Center Program

Sponsor: University of Southern California/LAC+USC Medical Center
LAC+USC Medical Center
Prgm Director: Andrea Kovacs, MD
1640 Marengo Street, HRA 300
Los Angeles, CA 90033
Tel: 323 266-6447   *Fax:* 323 226-2505
E-mail: mca@keck.usc.edu
Length: 3 Yrs   *ACGME Approved/Offered Positions:* 1
Program ID: 335-05-13-072

Oakland

Children's Hospital-Oakland Program

Sponsor: Children's Hospital-Oakland
Prgm Director: Ann M Petru, MD*
747 Fifty Second Street
Oakland, CA 94609
Tel: 510 428-3336   *Fax:* 510 601-3957
Length: 3 Yrs   *ACGME Approved/Offered Positions:* 6
Program ID: 335-05-12-006

San Diego

University of California (San Diego) Program

Sponsor: University of California (San Diego) Medical Center
Rady Children's Hospital
Prgm Director: Stephen A Spector, MD
Stein Clinical Research Building, Room 430
9500 Gilman Drive, MC 0672
La Jolla, CA 92093
Tel: 858 534-7170   *Fax:* 858 534-7411
Length: 3 Yrs   *ACGME Approved/Offered Positions:* 6
Program ID: 335-05-13-007

San Francisco

University of California (San Francisco) Program

Sponsor: University of California (San Francisco) School of Medicine
UCSF and Mount Zion Medical Centers
Prgm Director: Peggy S Weintrub, MD
500 Parnassus Avenue, MU4 East Room 410
Box 0136
San Francisco, CA 94143
Tel: 415 476-0301   *Fax:* 415 476-1343
E-mail: khouryr@peds.ucsf.edu
Length: 3 Yrs   *ACGME Approved/Offered Positions:* 3
Program ID: 335-05-22-008

Stanford

Stanford University Program

Sponsor: Stanford Hospital and Clinics
Lucile Salter Packard Children's Hospital at Stanford
Prgm Director: Hayley Gans, MD
Department of Pediatrics MC 5208
300 Pasteur Drive
Stanford, CA 94305
Tel: 650 725-8935   *Fax:* 650 725-8040
E-mail: hagans@stanford.edu
Length: 3 Yrs   *ACGME Approved/Offered Positions:* 3
Program ID: 335-05-23-009

Torrance

Los Angeles County-Harbor-UCLA Medical Center Program

Sponsor: Los Angeles County-Harbor-UCLA Medical Center
Prgm Director: Margaret A Keller, MD
1000 W Carson Street, Liu Building-RB3-Box 467
Torrance, CA 90509
Tel: 310 781-3636   *Fax:* 310 972-2962
Length: 3 Yrs   *ACGME Approved/Offered Positions:* 6
Program ID: 335-05-21-010

Programs

Colorado

Aurora

University of Colorado Denver Program
Sponsor: University of Colorado Denver School of
    Medicine
Children's Hospital (The)
Prgm Director: Ann-Christine Nyquist, MD, MSPH
13123 East 16th Avenue, B055
Aurora, CO 80045
Tel: 720 777-6025   *Fax:* 720 777-7295
E-mail: nyquist.ann-christine@tchden.org
Length: 3 Yrs   *ACGME Approved/Offered Positions:* 4
Program ID: 335-07-21-011

Connecticut

New Haven

**Yale-New Haven Medical Center
Program**
Sponsor: Yale-New Haven Hospital
Prgm Director: Michael Cappello, MD*
333 Cedar Street
Box 208064
New Haven, CT 06520
Tel: 203 737-4320   *Fax:* 203 737-5972
E-mail: michael.cappello@yale.edu
Length: 3 Yrs   *ACGME Approved/Offered Positions:* 6
Program ID: 335-08-21-012

District of Columbia

Washington

**Children's National Medical Center/
George Washington University Program**
Sponsor: Children's National Medical Center
Prgm Director: Barbara A Jantausch, MD, BS
111 Michigan Avenue NW
Washington, DC 20010
Tel: 202 476-6151   *Fax:* 202 476-3850
Length: 3 Yrs   *ACGME Approved/Offered Positions:* 6
Program ID: 335-10-21-013

Florida

Jacksonville

**University of Florida College of Medicine
Jacksonville Program**
Sponsor: University of Florida College of Medicine
    Jacksonville
Shands Jacksonville Medical Center
Wolfson Children's Hospital
Prgm Director: Ana M Alvarez, MD
Pediatrics Dept, Box L16
653-1 W 8th St, LRC 3rd Fl
Jacksonville, FL 32209
Tel: 904 244-3051   *Fax:* 904 244-5341
E-mail: renee.williams@jax.ufl.edu
Length: 3 Yrs   *ACGME Approved/Offered Positions:* 3
Program ID: 335-11-21-015

Miami

**Jackson Memorial Hospital/Jackson
Health System Program**
Sponsor: Jackson Memorial Hospital/Jackson Health
    System
Prgm Director: Charles D Mitchell, MD, MS
1580 NW 10th Avenue, Room 286
Batchelor Children's Research Institute
Miami, FL 33136
Tel: 305 243-2755   *Fax:* 305 243-5562
E-mail: cmitchel@med.miami.edu
Length: 3 Yrs   *ACGME Approved/Offered Positions:* 3
Program ID: 335-11-31-064

Georgia

Atlanta

Emory University Program
Sponsor: Emory University School of Medicine
Centers for Disease Control and Prevention
Children's Healthcare of Atlanta at Egleston
Veterans Affairs Medical Center (Atlanta)
Prgm Director: Paul W Spearman, MD
Department of Pediatrics
2015 Uppergate Drive
Atlanta, GA 30322
Tel: 404 727-5642   *Fax:* 404 727-9223
E-mail: paul.spearman@emory.edu
Length: 3 Yrs   *ACGME Approved/Offered Positions:* 6
Program ID: 335-12-21-017

Illinois

Chicago

**McGaw Medical Center of Northwestern
University Program**
Sponsor: McGaw Medical Center of Northwestern
    University
Children's Memorial Hospital
Prgm Director: Stanford T Shulman, MD
2300 Children's Plaza
Box 20
Chicago, IL 60614
Tel: 773 880-4187   *Fax:* 773 880-8226
E-mail: sshulman@northwestern.edu
Length: 3 Yrs   *ACGME Approved/Offered Positions:* 3
Program ID: 335-16-21-018

University of Chicago Program
Sponsor: University of Chicago Medical Center
University of Chicago Comer Children's Hospital
Prgm Director: Kenneth A Alexander, MD, PhD
5841 South Maryland Avenue
(MC 6054)
Chicago, IL 60637
Tel: 773 702-6176   *Fax:* 773 702-1196
E-mail: kalexander@peds.bsd.uchicago.edu
Length: 3 Yrs   *ACGME Approved/Offered Positions:* 3
Program ID: 335-16-31-019

Kentucky

Louisville

University of Louisville Program
Sponsor: University of Louisville School of Medicine
Kosair Children's Hospital (Norton Healthcare, Inc)
Prgm Director: Kristina A Bryant, MD
571 South Floyd Street, Suite 321
Louisville, KY 40202
Tel: 502 852-3774   *Fax:* 502 852-3939
E-mail: k0brya01@louisville.edu
Length: 3 Yrs   *ACGME Approved/Offered Positions:* 1
Program ID: 335-20-21-021

Louisiana

New Orleans

Tulane University Program
Sponsor: Tulane University School of Medicine
Children's Hospital (New Orleans)
Tulane Hospital for Children
Tulane University Hospital and Clinics
Prgm Director: James E Robinson, MD
1430 Tulane Avenue,SL 37
New Orleans, LA 70112
Tel: 504 988-5422   *Fax:* 504 988-2613
Length: 3 Yrs   *ACGME Approved/Offered Positions:* 3
Program ID: 335-21-21-022

Maryland

Baltimore

Johns Hopkins University Program
Sponsor: Johns Hopkins University School of Medicine
Johns Hopkins Hospital
Prgm Director: Deborah Persaud, MD
David M Rubenstein Child Health Building
200 North Wolfe Street #3095
Baltimore, MD 21287
Tel: 410 614-3917   *Fax:* 410 614-1315
Length: 3 Yrs   *ACGME Approved/Offered Positions:* 3
Program ID: 335-23-21-023

University of Maryland Program
Sponsor: University of Maryland Medical System
University of Maryland-Kernan Hospital
Prgm Director: Ina Stephens, MD*
685 West Baltimore Street, Room 480 HSF
Baltimore, MD 21201
Tel: 410 706-5328   *Fax:* 410 706-6205
E-mail: istephen@medicine.umaryland.edu
Length: 3 Yrs   *ACGME Approved/Offered Positions:* 3
Program ID: 335-23-31-024

Bethesda

National Capital Consortium Program
Sponsor: National Capital Consortium
Walter Reed Army Medical Center
Prgm Director: Michael Rajnik, MD
4301 Jones Bridge Road
Bethesda, MD 20814
Tel: 301 295-3391   *Fax:* 301 295-3898
E-mail: mrajnik@usuhs.mil
Length: 3 Yrs   *ACGME Approved/Offered Positions:* 6
Program ID: 335-10-31-014
Uniformed Services Program

Massachusetts

Boston

**Children's Hospital/Boston Medical
Center Program**
Sponsor: Children's Hospital
Prgm Director: Robert N Husson, MD
300 Longwood Avenue
Enders Building, Enders 761
Boston, MA 02115
Tel: 617 919-2900   *Fax:* 617 730-0254
E-mail: robert.husson@childrens.harvard.edu
Length: 3 Yrs   *ACGME Approved/Offered Positions:* 9
Program ID: 335-24-21-025

Children's Hospital/Boston Medical Center Program A
Sponsor: Children's Hospital
Boston Medical Center
Prgm Director: Elizabeth D Barnett, MD
670 Albany Street, 6th Floor, BioSquare III
Boston, MA 02118
Tel: 617 414-5591   *Fax:* 617 414-7230
Length: 3 Yrs   *ACGME Approved/Offered Positions:* 3
Program ID: 335-24-31-026

Michigan

Ann Arbor

University of Michigan Program
Sponsor: University of Michigan Hospitals and Health
   Centers
Prgm Director: Janet R Gilsdorf, MD
1500 E Medical Center Drive
L2225, Women's/5244
Ann Arbor, MI 48109
Tel: 734 763-2440   *Fax:* 734 936-7635
Length: 3 Yrs   *ACGME Approved/Offered Positions:* 6
Program ID: 335-25-21-027

Detroit

Children's Hospital of Michigan Program
Sponsor: Children's Hospital of Michigan
Prgm Director: Basim I Asmar, MD
3901 Beaubien Boulevard
Detroit, MI 48201
Tel: 313 745-5863   *Fax:* 313 993-8846
Length: 3 Yrs   *ACGME Approved/Offered Positions:* 2
Program ID: 335-25-31-028

Minnesota

Minneapolis

University of Minnesota Program
Sponsor: University of Minnesota Medical School
University of Minnesota Medical Center, Division of
   Fairview
Prgm Director: Mark R Schleiss, MD
420 Delaware Street SE
MMC-296
Minneapolis, MN 55455
Tel: 612 624-1966   *Fax:* 612 624-8927
E-mail: schleiss@umn.edu
Length: 3 Yrs   *ACGME Approved/Offered Positions:* 3
Program ID: 335-26-21-029

Rochester

College of Medicine, Mayo Clinic (Rochester) Program
Sponsor: College of Medicine, Mayo Clinic
Saint Marys Hospital of Rochester
Prgm Director: Thomas G Boyce, MD, MPH
200 First Street SW
Rochester, MN 55905
Tel: 507 538-0154   *Fax:* 507 284-0160
E-mail: bartelsmith.susan@mayo.edu
Length: 3 Yrs   *ACGME Approved/Offered Positions:* 3
Program ID: 335-26-12-069

Missouri

Kansas City

University of Missouri at Kansas City Program
Sponsor: University of Missouri-Kansas City School of
   Medicine
Children's Mercy Hospital
Prgm Director: Mary A Jackson, MD
2401 Gillham Road
Kansas City, MO 64108
Tel: 816 234-3061   *Fax:* 816 346-1328
E-mail: mjackson@cmh.edu
Length: 3 Yrs   *ACGME Approved/Offered Positions:* 3
Program ID: 335-28-31-068

St Louis

Washington University/B-JH/SLCH Consortium Program
Sponsor: Washington University/B-JH/SLCH Consortium
St Louis Children's Hospital
Prgm Director: Gregory A Storch, MD
One Children's Place
St Louis, MO 63110
Tel: 314 286-2887   *Fax:* 314 286-2895
Length: 3 Yrs   *ACGME Approved/Offered Positions:* 6
Program ID: 335-28-21-030

Nebraska

Omaha

University of Nebraska Medical Center College of Medicine/Creighton University Program
Sponsor: University of Nebraska Medical Center College
   of Medicine
Children's Hospital
Creighton University Medical Center (Tenet - SJH)
Prgm Director: José R Romero, MD*
Department of Pediatrics
982165 Nebraska Medical Center
Omaha, NE 68198
Tel: 402 559-8883   *Fax:* 402 559-9333
E-mail: jrromero@unmc.edu
Length: 3 Yrs   *ACGME Approved/Offered Positions:* 3
Program ID: 335-30-21-031

New Jersey

Newark

UMDNJ-New Jersey Medical School Program
Sponsor: UMDNJ-New Jersey Medical School
UMDNJ-University Hospital
Prgm Director: Peter N Wenger, MD*
PO Box 1709, 185 S Orange Avenue
Newark, NJ 07101
Tel: 973 972-4498   *Fax:* 973 972-7625
E-mail: wengerpn@umdnj.edu
Length: 3 Yrs   *ACGME Approved/Offered Positions:* 3
Program ID: 335-33-21-062

New York

Bronx

Albert Einstein College of Medicine Program
Sponsor: Albert Einstein College of Medicine of Yeshiva
   University
Montefiore Medical Center-Henry and Lucy Moses
   Division
Montefiore Medical Center-Weiler Division
Prgm Director: Nathan Litman, MD
111 E 210th Street
Department of Pediatrics
Bronx, NY 10467
Tel: 718 741-2470   *Fax:* 718 654-6692
Length: 3 Yrs   *ACGME Approved/Offered Positions:* 3
Program ID: 335-35-21-034

Brooklyn

SUNY Health Science Center at Brooklyn Program
Sponsor: SUNY Health Science Center at Brooklyn
Kings County Hospital Center
University Hospital-SUNY Health Science Center at
   Brooklyn
Prgm Director: Margaret R Hammerschlag, MD
450 Clarkson Avenue, Box 49
Brooklyn, NY 11203
Tel: 718 270-3097   *Fax:* 718 270-1985
E-mail: mhammerschlag@downstate.edu
Length: 3 Yrs   *ACGME Approved/Offered Positions:* 2
Program ID: 335-35-11-036

Great Neck

NSLIJHS-Schneider Children's Hospital Program
Sponsor: North Shore-Long Island Jewish Health System
North Shore University Hospital
Schneider Children's Hospital at Long Island Jewish
   Med Ctr
Schneider Children's Hospital at North Shore University
   Hosp
Prgm Director: Lorry G Rubin, MD
269-01 76th Avenue
New Hyde Park, NY 11040
Tel: 718 470-3415   *Fax:* 718 470-0887
Length: 3 Yrs   *ACGME Approved/Offered Positions:* 2
Program ID: 335-35-12-037

New York

Mount Sinai School of Medicine Program
Sponsor: Mount Sinai School of Medicine
Mount Sinai Medical Center
Prgm Director: Roberto Posada, MD
One Gustave L Levy Place, Box 1657
New York, NY 10029
Tel: 212 241-1468   *Fax:* 212 426-4813
Length: 3 Yrs   *ACGME Approved/Offered Positions:* 9
Program ID: 335-35-13-038

New York Presbyterian Hospital (Columbia Campus) Program
Sponsor: New York Presbyterian Hospital
New York Presbyterian Hospital (Columbia Campus)
Prgm Director: Natalie Neu, MD, MPH
630 W 168th Street, PH 4 West Room 468
New York, NY 10032
Tel: 212 305-9683   *Fax:* 212 342-5218
Length: 3 Yrs   *ACGME Approved/Offered Positions:* 3
Program ID: 335-35-21-040

Programs

New York University School of Medicine Program

Sponsor: New York University School of Medicine
Bellevue Hospital Center
NYU Hospitals Center
Prgm Director: Henry J Pollack, MD
550 First Avenue
New York, NY 10016
Tel: 212 263-8197   *Fax:* 212 263-7806
Length: 3 Yrs   *ACGME Approved/Offered Positions:* 3
Program ID: 335-35-21-065

Rochester

University of Rochester Program

Sponsor: Strong Memorial Hospital of the University of Rochester
Prgm Director: Mary T Caserta, MD
601 Elmwood Avenue, Box 690
Rochester, NY 14642
Tel: 585 275-5944   *Fax:* 585 273-1104
E-mail: mary_caserta@urmc.rochester.edu
Length: 3 Yrs   *ACGME Approved/Offered Positions:* 3
Program ID: 335-35-31-041

Stony Brook

SUNY at Stony Brook Program

Sponsor: University Hospital - SUNY at Stony Brook
Prgm Director: Sharon A Nachman, MD
Department of Pediatrics
HSC T11 030
Stony Brook, NY 11794
Tel: 631 444-7692   *Fax:* 631 444-7292
Length: 3 Yrs   *ACGME Approved/Offered Positions:* 1
Program ID: 335-35-31-063

Syracuse

SUNY Upstate Medical University Program

Sponsor: SUNY Upstate Medical University
Crouse Hospital
Prgm Director: Leonard B Weiner, MD
750 East Adams Street
Room 5400
Syracuse, NY 13210
Tel: 315 464-6331   *Fax:* 315 464-7564
Length: 3 Yrs   *ACGME Approved/Offered Positions:* 1
Program ID: 335-35-11-042

North Carolina

Durham

Duke University Hospital Program

Sponsor: Duke University Hospital
Prgm Director: William J Steinbach, MD*
Box 3499
Duke University Medical Center
Durham, NC 27710
Tel: 919 681-1504   *Fax:* 919 684-8902
E-mail: stein022@mc.duke.edu
Length: 3 Yrs   *ACGME Approved/Offered Positions:* 6
Program ID: 335-36-31-044

Ohio

Cincinnati

Cincinnati Children's Hospital Medical Center/University of Cincinnati College of Medicine Program

Sponsor: Cincinnati Children's Hospital Medical Center
Prgm Director: Beverly L Connelly, MD
3333 Burnet Avenue
Cincinnati, OH 45229
Tel: 513 636-8492   *Fax:* 513 636-7598
E-mail: Ann.Carstens@cchmc.org
Length: 3 Yrs   *ACGME Approved/Offered Positions:* 4
Program ID: 335-38-21-045

Cleveland

Cleveland Clinic Foundation Program

Sponsor: Cleveland Clinic Foundation
Prgm Director: Johanna Goldfarb, MD
Pediatric Institute, Infectious Diseases
9500 Euclid Avenue Desk S25
Cleveland, OH 44195
Tel: 216 445-6863   *Fax:* 216 636-3405
E-mail: goldfaj@ccf.org
Length: 3 Yrs   *ACGME Approved/Offered Positions:* 3
Program ID: 335-38-13-067

University Hospitals Case Medical Center Program

Sponsor: University Hospitals Case Medical Center
Prgm Director: Grace A McComsey, MD
11100 Euclid Avenue
Mail Stop 8A
Cleveland, OH 44106
Tel: 216 884-3645   *Fax:* 216 844-8362
E-mail: mccomsey.grace@clevelandactu.org
Length: 3 Yrs   *ACGME Approved/Offered Positions:* 3
Program ID: 335-38-31-046

Columbus

Nationwide Children's Hospital/Ohio State University Program

Sponsor: Nationwide Children's Hospital
Prgm Director: William J Barson, MD, MS
Section of Infectious Diseases
700 Children's Drive
Columbus, OH 43205
Tel: 614 722-4456   *Fax:* 614 722-4458
E-mail: william.barson@nationwidechildrens.org
Length: 3 Yrs   *ACGME Approved/Offered Positions:* 3
Program ID: 335-38-12-071

Pennsylvania

Philadelphia

Children's Hospital of Philadelphia Program

Sponsor: Children's Hospital of Philadelphia
Prgm Director: Theoklis E Zaoutis, MD
34th Street and Civic Center Blvd
Abramson Research Building, Room 1202
Philadelphia, PA 19104
Tel: 267 426-5570   *Fax:* 215 590-2025
Length: 3 Yrs   *ACGME Approved/Offered Positions:* 6
Program ID: 335-41-21-047

St Christopher's Hospital for Children Program

Sponsor: St Christopher's Hospital for Children (Tenet Health System)
Prgm Director: Sarah S Long, MD
Erie Avenue at Front Street, Suite 1112
Philadelphia, PA 19134
Tel: 215 427-5204   *Fax:* 215 427-8389
Length: 3 Yrs   *ACGME Approved/Offered Positions:* 2
Program ID: 335-41-31-048

Pittsburgh

University of Pittsburgh Medical Center Medical Education Program

Sponsor: Univ of Pittsburgh Medical Center Medical Education
Children's Hospital of Pittsburgh of UPMC
Magee-Womens Hospital of UPMC
Prgm Director: Lee Antoinette Darville, MD*
3705 Fifth Avenue
Pittsburgh, PA 15213
Tel: 412 692-5198   *Fax:* 412 692-8499
Length: 3 Yrs   *ACGME Approved/Offered Positions:* 3
Program ID: 335-41-11-049

Rhode Island

Providence

Brown University Program

Sponsor: Rhode Island Hospital-Lifespan
Women and Infants Hospital of Rhode Island
Prgm Director: Penelope H Dennehy, MD*
593 Eddy Street
Providence, RI 02903
Tel: 401 444-8360   *Fax:* 401 444-5650
E-mail: pdennehy@lifespan.org
Length: 3 Yrs   *ACGME Approved/Offered Positions:* 3
Program ID: 335-43-21-050

Tennessee

Memphis

University of Tennessee Program

Sponsor: University of Tennessee College of Medicine
LeBonheur Children's Medical Center
St Jude Children's Research Hospital
Prgm Director: Elisabeth Adderson, MD
262 Danny Thomas Place, MS 320
Memphis, TN 38105
Tel: 901 595-3459   *Fax:* 901 595-3099
E-mail: elisabeth.adderson@stjude.org
Length: 3 Yrs   *ACGME Approved/Offered Positions:* 7
Program ID: 335-47-21-051

Nashville

Vanderbilt University Program

Sponsor: Vanderbilt University Medical Center
Prgm Director: James E Crowe Jr, MD
Peds ID, D-7235 MCN
1161 21st Ave South
Nashville, TN 37232
Tel: 615 343-8064   *Fax:* 615 343-4456
E-mail: james.crowe@vanderbilt.edu
Length: 3 Yrs   *ACGME Approved/Offered Positions:* 6
Program ID: 335-47-31-052

Note: * indicates a newly appointed program director

Texas

Dallas

University of Texas Southwestern Medical School Program
Sponsor: University of Texas Southwestern Medical School
Children's Medical Center of Dallas
Dallas County Hospital District-Parkland Memorial Hospital
Prgm Director: George H McCracken Jr, MD
5323 Harry Hines Boulevard
F3.202
Dallas, TX 75390
Tel: 214 648-3439   *Fax:* 214 648-2961
Length: 3 Yrs   *ACGME Approved/Offered Positions:* 6
Program ID: 335-48-21-053

Galveston

University of Texas Medical Branch Hospitals Program
Sponsor: University of Texas Medical Branch Hospitals
Prgm Director: Tasnee Chonmaitree, MD
301 University Boulevard
Galveston, TX 77555
Tel: 409 772-2798   *Fax:* 409 747-1753
E-mail: tchonmai@utmb.edu
Length: 3 Yrs   *ACGME Approved/Offered Positions:* 3
Program ID: 335-48-31-054

Houston

Baylor College of Medicine Program
Sponsor: Baylor College of Medicine
Texas Children's Hospital
Prgm Director: Judith R Campbell, MD
One Baylor Plaza, Room 302A
Houston, TX 77030
Tel: 713 798-4790   *Fax:* 713 798-7249
Length: 3 Yrs   *ACGME Approved/Offered Positions:* 9
Program ID: 335-48-11-055

University of Texas at Houston Program
Sponsor: University of Texas Health Science Center at Houston
Memorial Hermann Hospital
Prgm Director: Gloria P Heresi, MD
Department of Pediatrics - Ped Infectious Diseases
6431 Fannin St, MSB 6.132a
Houston, TX 77030
Tel: 713 500-5714   *Fax:* 713 500-5688
Length: 3 Yrs   *ACGME Approved/Offered Positions:* 1
Program ID: 335-48-12-056

Utah

Salt Lake City

University of Utah Program
Sponsor: University of Utah Medical Center
Primary Children's Medical Center
Prgm Director: Andrew T Pavia, MD
30 North 1900 East Room 2A100
Salt Lake City, UT 84132
Tel: 801 581-4831   *Fax:* 801 585-3789
E-mail: andy.pavia@hsc.utah.edu
Length: 3 Yrs   *ACGME Approved/Offered Positions:* 3
Program ID: 335-49-31-070

Virginia

Norfolk

Eastern Virginia Medical School Program
Sponsor: Eastern Virginia Medical School
Children's Hospital of the King's Daughters
Prgm Director: Stephen Buescher, MD
855 W Brambleton Avenue
Norfolk, VA 23510
Tel: 757 668-6464   *Fax:* 757 668-6476
E-mail: BueschES@evms.edu
Length: 3 Yrs   *ACGME Approved/Offered Positions:* 3
Program ID: 335-51-21-058

Richmond

Virginia Commonwealth University Health System Program
Sponsor: Virginia Commonwealth University Health System
Medical College of Virginia Hospitals
Prgm Director: Beth C Marshall, MD
1101 East Marshall Street
PO Box 980163
Richmond, VA 23298
Tel: 804 828-1808   *Fax:* 804 827-0575
Length: 3 Yrs   *ACGME Approved/Offered Positions:* 3
Program ID: 335-51-31-059

Washington

Seattle

University of Washington Program
Sponsor: University of Washington School of Medicine
Seattle Children's Hospital
Prgm Director: Glen S Tamura, MD, PhD
4800 Sand Point Way NE
R-5441
Seattle, WA 98105
Tel: 206 987-1918   *Fax:* 206 987-3890
E-mail: glen.tamura@seattlechildrens.org
Length: 3 Yrs   *ACGME Approved/Offered Positions:* 9
Program ID: 335-54-21-060

Pediatric Nephrology (Pediatrics)

Alabama

Birmingham

University of Alabama Medical Center Program
Sponsor: University of Alabama Hospital
Children's Hospital of Alabama
Prgm Director: William Frank Tenney, MD
1600 7th Avenue South
ACC 516
Birmingham, AL 35233
Tel: 205 939-9781   *Fax:* 205 975-7051
Length: 3 Yrs
Program ID: 328-01-12-076

California

Los Angeles

UCLA Medical Center Program
Sponsor: UCLA David Geffen School of Medicine/UCLA Medical Center
UCLA Medical Center
Prgm Director: Robert B Ettenger, MD
Box 951752
Los Angeles, CA 90095
Tel: 310 206-6987   *Fax:* 310 825-0442
Length: 3 Yrs   *ACGME Approved/Offered Positions:* 6
Program ID: 328-05-21-002

San Diego

University of California (San Diego) Program
Sponsor: University of California (San Diego) Medical Center
Rady Children's Hospital
Prgm Director: Robert H Mak, MB, PhD
9500 Gilman Drive
MC 0634
La Jolla, CA 92093
Tel: 858 822-6717   *Fax:* 858 822-6776
Length: 3 Yrs   *ACGME Approved/Offered Positions:* 3
Program ID: 328-05-21-047

San Francisco

University of California (San Francisco) Program
Sponsor: University of California (San Francisco) School of Medicine
UCSF and Mount Zion Medical Centers
Prgm Director: Anthony A Portale, MD
533 Parnassus Avenue, Room U585
San Francisco, CA 94143
Tel: 415 476-2423   *Fax:* 415 476-9976
Length: 3 Yrs   *ACGME Approved/Offered Positions:* 3
Program ID: 328-05-11-022

Stanford

Stanford University Program
Sponsor: Stanford Hospital and Clinics
Lucile Salter Packard Children's Hospital at Stanford
Prgm Director: Paul C Grimm, MD
Department of Pediatrics, G306
300 Pasteur Drive
Stanford, CA 94305
Tel: 650 723-7903 *Fax:* 650 498-6714
E-mail: pgrimm@stanford.edu
Length: 3 Yrs *ACGME Approved/Offered Positions:* 6
Program ID: 328-05-21-029

Connecticut

New Haven

Yale-New Haven Medical Center Program
Sponsor: Yale-New Haven Hospital
Prgm Director: Alda Tufro, MD, PhD*
Department of Pediatrics
333 Cedar Street, PO Box 208064
New Haven, CT 06520
Tel: 203 785-4643 *Fax:* 203 785-3462
Length: 3 Yrs *ACGME Approved/Offered Positions:* 3
Program ID: 328-08-21-004

District of Columbia

Washington

Children's National Medical Center/ George Washington University Program
Sponsor: Children's National Medical Center
Prgm Director: John K Hurley, MD
111 Michigan Avenue NW
Washington, DC 20010
Tel: 202 476-5058 *Fax:* 202 476-3475
E-mail: jhurley@cnmc.org
Length: 3 Yrs *ACGME Approved/Offered Positions:* 3
Program ID: 328-10-12-073

Florida

Gainesville

University of Florida Program
Sponsor: University of Florida College of Medicine
Shands Hospital at the University of Florida
Prgm Director: Vikas R Dharnidharka, MD
Division of Pediatric Nephrology
PO Box 100296, JHMHC
Gainesville, FL 32610
Tel: 352 392-4434 *Fax:* 352 392-7107
Length: 3 Yrs *ACGME Approved/Offered Positions:* 3
Program ID: 328-11-31-006

Miami

Jackson Memorial Hospital/Jackson Health System Program
Sponsor: Jackson Memorial Hospital/Jackson Health System
Prgm Director: Gaston E Zilleruelo, MD
Department of Pediatrics (M-714)
PO Box 016960
Miami, FL 33101
Tel: 305 585-6726 *Fax:* 305 585-7025
E-mail: GZilleruelo@med.miami.edu
Length: 3 Yrs *ACGME Approved/Offered Positions:* 3
Program ID: 328-11-21-032

Note: * indicates a newly appointed program director

Georgia

Atlanta

Emory University Program
Sponsor: Emory University School of Medicine
Children's Healthcare of Atlanta at Egleston
Prgm Director: Barry L Warshaw, MD
2015 Uppergate Drive NE
Atlanta, GA 30322
Tel: 404 727-5750 *Fax:* 404 727-8213
Length: 3 Yrs *ACGME Approved/Offered Positions:* 3
Program ID: 328-12-31-074

Illinois

Chicago

McGaw Medical Center of Northwestern University Program
Sponsor: McGaw Medical Center of Northwestern University
Children's Memorial Hospital
Prgm Director: Craig B Langman, MD
2300 Children's Plaza, Box 37
Chicago, IL 60614
Tel: 773 327-3930 *Fax:* 773 327-5071
E-mail: c-langman@northwestern.edu
Length: 3 Yrs *ACGME Approved/Offered Positions:* 6
Program ID: 328-16-21-030

Louisiana

New Orleans

Tulane University Program
Sponsor: Tulane University School of Medicine
Medical Center of Louisiana at New Orleans
Tulane Hospital for Children
Prgm Director: Ihor B Yosypiv, MD
1430 Tulane Avenue
Department of Pediatrics
New Orleans, LA 70112
Tel: 504 988-5377 *Fax:* 504 988-1852
Length: 3 Yrs *ACGME Approved/Offered Positions:* 3
Program ID: 328-21-13-078

Maryland

Baltimore

Johns Hopkins University Program
Sponsor: Johns Hopkins University School of Medicine
Johns Hopkins Hospital
Prgm Director: Alicia Neu, MD*
200 North Wolfe Street, Room 3065
Baltimore, MD 21287
Tel: 410 955-2467 *Fax:* 410 614-3680
Length: 3 Yrs *ACGME Approved/Offered Positions:* 6
Program ID: 328-23-13-056

Massachusetts

Boston

Children's Hospital/Boston Medical Center Program
Sponsor: Children's Hospital
Prgm Director: David M Briscoe, MB, ChB*
300 Longwood Avenue
Boston, MA 02115
Tel: 617 355-6129 *Fax:* 617 730-0569
Length: 3 Yrs *ACGME Approved/Offered Positions:* 6
Program ID: 328-24-11-010

Michigan

Ann Arbor

University of Michigan Program
Sponsor: University of Michigan Hospitals and Health Centers
Prgm Director: David B Kershaw, MD
Mott F6865/5297
1500 East Medical Center Drive
Ann Arbor, MI 48109
Tel: 734 936-4210 *Fax:* 734 763-6997
E-mail: dkershaw@umich.edu
Length: 3 Yrs *ACGME Approved/Offered Positions:* 6
Program ID: 328-25-21-034

Detroit

Children's Hospital of Michigan Program
Sponsor: Children's Hospital of Michigan
Prgm Director: Tej K Mattoo, MD, MRCP
3901 Beaubien Boulevard
Detroit, MI 48201
Tel: 313 745-5604 *Fax:* 313 966-0039
Length: 3 Yrs *ACGME Approved/Offered Positions:* 3
Program ID: 328-25-31-068

Grand Rapids

Grand Rapids Medical Education and Research Center/Michigan State University Program
Sponsor: Grand Rapids Medical Education and Research Center
Spectrum Health-Butterworth Hospital
Prgm Director: Timothy E Bunchman, MD
100 Michigan Street NE
Grand Rapids, MI 49503
Tel: 616 391-3788 *Fax:* 616 391-7930
Length: 3 Yrs *ACGME Approved/Offered Positions:* 3
Program ID: 328-25-13-075

Minnesota

Minneapolis

University of Minnesota Program
Sponsor: University of Minnesota Medical School
University of Minnesota Medical Center, Division of Fairview
Prgm Director: S Michael Mauer, MD*
Department of Pediatrics
420 Delaware Street SE, Mayo Mail Code 491
Minneapolis, MN 55455
Tel: 612 626-2780
E-mail: mauer002@umn.edu
Length: 3 Yrs *ACGME Approved/Offered Positions:* 4
Program ID: 328-26-21-035

Missouri

Kansas City

University of Missouri at Kansas City Program
Sponsor: University of Missouri-Kansas City School of Medicine
Children's Mercy Hospital
Prgm Director: Douglas L Blowey, MD
2401 Gillham Road
Kansas City, MO 64108
Tel: 816 234-3010 *Fax:* 816 234-3494
E-mail: dblowey@cmh.edu
Length: 3 Yrs *ACGME Approved/Offered Positions:* 3
Program ID: 328-28-11-038

St Louis

Washington University/B-JH/SLCH Consortium Program
Sponsor: Washington University/B-JH/SLCH Consortium
St Louis Children's Hospital
Prgm Director: Stanley P Hmiel, MD, PhD
9th Fl, NW Tower, St Louis Children's Hospital
One Children's Place
St Louis, MO 63110
Tel: 314 454-6043   *Fax:* 314 454-4283
Length: 3 Yrs   *ACGME Approved/Offered Positions:* 6
Program ID: 328-28-21-031

New York

Bronx

Albert Einstein College of Medicine Program
Sponsor: Albert Einstein College of Medicine of Yeshiva University
Montefiore Medical Center-Henry and Lucy Moses Division
Prgm Director: Frederick J Kaskel, MD, PhD
Division of Pediatric Nephrology
111 E 210th Street
Bronx, NY 10467
Tel: 718 655-1120   *Fax:* 718 652-3136
E-mail: fkaskel@montefiore.org
Length: 3 Yrs   *ACGME Approved/Offered Positions:* 7
Program ID: 328-35-21-011

Brooklyn

SUNY Health Science Center at Brooklyn Program
Sponsor: SUNY Health Science Center at Brooklyn
University Hospital-SUNY Health Science Center at Brooklyn
Prgm Director: Morris J Schoeneman, MD
450 Clarkson Avenue, Box 49
Brooklyn, NY 11203
Tel: 718 270-1626   *Fax:* 718 270-1985
E-mail: morris.schoeneman@downstate.edu
Length: 3 Yrs   *ACGME Approved/Offered Positions:* 3
Program ID: 328-35-21-012

Buffalo

University at Buffalo Program
Sponsor: University at Buffalo School of Medicine
Kaleida Health System (Women and Children's Hospital of Buffalo)
Prgm Director: Wayne R Waz, MD
219 Bryant Street
Buffalo, NY 14222
Tel: 716 878-7355   *Fax:* 716 888-3801
E-mail: wwaz@upa.chob.edu
Length: 3 Yrs   *ACGME Approved/Offered Positions:* 3
Program ID: 328-35-21-024

New York

Mount Sinai School of Medicine Program
Sponsor: Mount Sinai School of Medicine
Mount Sinai Medical Center
Prgm Director: Lisa M Satlin, MD
One Gustave L Levy Place, Box 1664
New York, NY 10029
Tel: 212 241-6187   *Fax:* 212 426-1972
E-mail: lisa.satlin@mssm.edu
Length: 3 Yrs   *ACGME Approved/Offered Positions:* 3
Program ID: 328-35-31-051

Rochester

University of Rochester Program
Sponsor: Strong Memorial Hospital of the University of Rochester
Prgm Director: Marc E Lande, MD
601 Elmwood Avenue, Box 777
Rochester, NY 14642
Tel: 585 275-9784   *Fax:* 585 756-8054
E-mail: Marc_Lande@urmc.rochester.edu
Length: 3 Yrs   *ACGME Approved/Offered Positions:* 3
Program ID: 328-35-21-050

North Carolina

Chapel Hill

University of North Carolina Hospitals Program
Sponsor: University of North Carolina Hospitals
Prgm Director: Debbie S Gipson, MD, MSPH
Division of Nephrology and Hypertension
CB 7155, 7024 Burnett-Womack Building
Chapel Hill, NC 27599
Tel: 919 966-2561   *Fax:* 919 966-4251
E-mail: Debbie_Gipson@med.unc.edu
Length: 3 Yrs   *ACGME Approved/Offered Positions:* 3
Program ID: 328-36-22-070

Ohio

Cincinnati

Cincinnati Children's Hospital Medical Center/University of Cincinnati College of Medicine Program
Sponsor: Cincinnati Children's Hospital Medical Center
Prgm Director: John J Bissler, MD
3333 Burnet Avenue
MLC 7022 Nephrology
Cincinnati, OH 45229
Tel: 513 636-4531   *Fax:* 513 636-7407
E-mail: john.bissler@cchmc.org
Length: 3 Yrs   *ACGME Approved/Offered Positions:* 6
Program ID: 328-38-21-015

Columbus

Nationwide Children's Hospital/Ohio State University Program
Sponsor: Nationwide Children's Hospital
Prgm Director: John D Mahan, MD
700 Children's Drive
Columbus, OH 43205
Tel: 614 722-4360   *Fax:* 614 722-6482
Length: 3 Yrs   *ACGME Approved/Offered Positions:* 3
Program ID: 328-38-11-069

Pennsylvania

Philadelphia

Children's Hospital of Philadelphia Program
Sponsor: Children's Hospital of Philadelphia
Prgm Director: Kevin E Meyers, MD
Division of Nephrology
34th Street & Civic Center Blvd
Philadelphia, PA 19104
Tel: 215 590-2449   *Fax:* 215 590-3705
E-mail: meyersk@email.chop.edu
Length: 3 Yrs   *ACGME Approved/Offered Positions:* 6
Program ID: 328-41-21-025

Pittsburgh

University of Pittsburgh Medical Center Medical Education Program
Sponsor: Univ of Pittsburgh Medical Center Medical Education
Children's Hospital of Pittsburgh of UPMC
Prgm Director: Demetrius Ellis, MD
3705 Fifth Avenue
Pittsburgh, PA 15213
Tel: 412 692-5182   *Fax:* 412 692-7443
Length: 3 Yrs   *ACGME Approved/Offered Positions:* 6
Program ID: 328-41-21-077

Tennessee

Memphis

University of Tennessee Program
Sponsor: University of Tennessee College of Medicine
LeBonheur Children's Medical Center
Prgm Director: Robert J Wyatt, MD, MS
50 N Dunlap, Room 301
Memphis, TN 38103
Tel: 901 287-5376   *Fax:* 901 287-5036
Length: 3 Yrs   *ACGME Approved/Offered Positions:* 3
Program ID: 328-47-31-018

Nashville

Vanderbilt University Program
Sponsor: Vanderbilt University Medical Center
Prgm Director: Kathy Jabs, MD
1161 21st Avenue South, MCN C-4204
Nashville, TN 37232
Tel: 615 322-7416   *Fax:* 615 322-7929
E-mail: kathy.jabs@vanderbilt.edu
Length: 3 Yrs   *ACGME Approved/Offered Positions:* 3
Program ID: 328-47-21-046

Texas

Dallas

University of Texas Southwestern Medical School Program
Sponsor: University of Texas Southwestern Medical School
Children's Medical Center of Dallas
Prgm Director: Michel G Baum, MD
5323 Harry Hines Blvd
Dallas, TX 75390
Tel: 214 648-3438   *Fax:* 214 648-2034
E-mail: michel.baum@utsouthwestern.edu
Length: 3 Yrs   *ACGME Approved/Offered Positions:* 9
Program ID: 328-48-21-019

Houston

Baylor College of Medicine Program
Sponsor: Baylor College of Medicine
Texas Children's Hospital
Prgm Director: Eileen D Brewer, MD
One Baylor Plaza
Houston, TX 77030
Tel: 832 824-3800   *Fax:* 832 825-3889
E-mail: ebrewer@bcm.edu
Length: 3 Yrs   *ACGME Approved/Offered Positions:* 6
Program ID: 328-48-21-026

Programs

University of Texas at Houston Program
Sponsor: University of Texas Health Science Center at Houston
Memorial Hermann Hospital
Prgm Director: Rita D Swinford, MD
6431 Fannin Street, MSB 3.124
Houston, TX 77030
Tel: 713 500-5670
Length: 3 Yrs   *ACGME Approved/Offered Positions:* 4
Program ID: 328-48-21-041

San Antonio

University of Texas Health Science Center at San Antonio Program
Sponsor: University of Texas School of Medicine at San Antonio
Christus Santa Rosa Health Care Corporation
University Health System
University of Texas Health Science Center
Prgm Director: Mazen Arar, MBBS
7703 Floyd Curl Drive
MSC-7813
San Antonio, TX 78229
Tel: 210 562-5365   *Fax:* 210 704-3777
E-mail: arar@uthscsa.edu
Length: 3 Yrs   *ACGME Approved/Offered Positions:* 3
Program ID: 328-48-13-072

Virginia

Charlottesville

University of Virginia Program
Sponsor: University of Virginia Medical Center
Prgm Director: Victoria F Norwood, MD
Barringer 2331 - Hospital West
PO Box 800386
Charlottesville, VA 22908
Tel: 434 924-2096   *Fax:* 434 924-5505
E-mail: vfn6t@virginia.edu
Length: 3 Yrs   *ACGME Approved/Offered Positions:* 3
Program ID: 328-51-11-027

Washington

Seattle

University of Washington Program
Sponsor: University of Washington School of Medicine
Seattle Children's Hospital
Prgm Director: Sangeeta R Hingorani, MD, MPH
Division of Nephrology
4800 Sand Point Way NE, A-7931
Seattle, WA 98105
Tel: 206 987-2524   *Fax:* 206 987-2636
Length: 3 Yrs   *ACGME Approved/Offered Positions:* 6
Program ID: 328-54-21-042

Pediatric Orthopaedics (Orthopaedic Surgery)

California

Los Angeles

Orthopaedic Hospital Program
Sponsor: Orthopaedic Hospital
Santa Monica-UCLA Medical Center
Prgm Director: James V Luck Jr, MD*
Administration
2400 S Flower Street
Los Angeles, CA 90007
Tel: 213 742-1369   *Fax:* 213 742-1435
E-mail: nhamasak@laoh.ucla.edu
Length: 1 Yr   *ACGME Approved/Offered Positions:* 1
Program ID: 265-05-21-043

Delaware

Wilmington

Thomas Jefferson University/duPont Hospital for Children Program
Sponsor: Thomas Jefferson University Hospital
Alfred I duPont Hospital for Children
Prgm Director: William G Mackenzie, MD
1600 Rockland Road
Wilmington, DE 19803
Tel: 302 651-5890   *Fax:* 302 651-5951
Length: 1 Yr   *ACGME Approved/Offered Positions:* 3
Program ID: 265-41-31-004

Florida

Orlando

Orlando Health Program
Sponsor: Orlando Health
Arnold Palmer Hospital for Children
Orlando Regional Medical Center
Prgm Director: Charles T Price, MD
Medical Education
86 W Underwood St
Orlando, FL 32806
Tel: 407 650-7518   *Fax:* 407 650-7550
E-mail: Julie.Brown@orhs.org
Length: 1 Yr   *ACGME Approved/Offered Positions:* 1
Program ID: 265-11-11-037

Georgia

Atlanta

Children's Healthcare of Atlanta Scottish Rite Program
Sponsor: Children's Healthcare of Atlanta
Prgm Director: Michael T Busch, MD*
5445 Meridian Mark Road
Suite 250
Atlanta, GA 30342
Tel: 678 686-6818   *Fax:* 678 686-6865
Length: 1 Yr   *ACGME Approved/Offered Positions:* 2
Program ID: 265-12-21-022

Hawaii

Honolulu

Shriners Hospitals for Children (Honolulu) Program
Sponsor: Shriners Hospitals for Children (Honolulu)
Prgm Director: Ellen M Raney, MD
1310 Punahou Street
Honolulu, HI 96826
Tel: 808 951-3640   *Fax:* 808 942-8573
Length: 1 Yr   *ACGME Approved/Offered Positions:* 1
Program ID: 265-14-21-029

Louisiana

New Orleans

Louisiana State University Program
Sponsor: Louisiana State University School of Medicine
Children's Hospital (New Orleans)
Prgm Director: Stephen D Heinrich, MD, MS*
200 Henry Clay Avenue
New Orleans, LA 70118
Tel: 504 896-9569   *Fax:* 504 896-9849
E-mail: sheinric@chnola.org
Length: 1 Yr   *ACGME Approved/Offered Positions:* 1
Program ID: 265-21-21-016

Massachusetts

Boston

Children's Hospital Program
Sponsor: Children's Hospital
Prgm Director: James R Kasser, MD
Department of Orthopaedic Surgery
300 Longwood Avenue
Boston, MA 02115
Tel: 617 355-6617   *Fax:* 617 730-0465
E-mail: james.kasser@childrens.harvard.edu
Length: 1 Yr   *ACGME Approved/Offered Positions:* 3
Program ID: 265-24-21-008

Michigan

Ann Arbor

University of Michigan Program
Sponsor: University of Michigan Hospitals and Health Centers
Prgm Director: Frances A Farley, MD
1500 East Medical Center Drive
Ann Arbor, MI 48109
Tel: 734 936-5694
Length: 1 Yr   *ACGME Approved/Offered Positions:* 1
Program ID: 265-25-12-047

Minnesota

Minneapolis

University of Minnesota Program
Sponsor: University of Minnesota Medical School
Gillette Children's Hospital
Prgm Director: Kevin Walker, MD
200 University Avenue East
St Paul, MN 55101
Tel: 651 229-3948   *Fax:* 651 312-3188
E-mail: walke009@umn.edu
Length: 1 Yr   *ACGME Approved/Offered Positions:* 1
Program ID: 265-26-31-046

Note: * indicates a newly appointed program director

Missouri

St Louis

Washington University/B-JH/SLCH Consortium Program
Sponsor: Washington University/B-JH/SLCH Consortium
Shriners Hospitals for Children (St Louis)
St Louis Children's Hospital
Prgm Director: Perry L Schoenecker, MD
2001 South Lindbergh Blvd
St Louis, MO 63131
Tel: 314 872-7824   *Fax:* 314 872-7808
Length: 1 Yr   *ACGME Approved/Offered Positions:* 1
Program ID: 265-28-21-006

New York

New York

Hospital for Special Surgery/Cornell Medical Center Program
Sponsor: Hospital for Special Surgery
New York Presbyterian Hospital (Cornell Campus)
Prgm Director: Roger Widmann, MD
535 E 70th Street
New York, NY 10021
Tel: 212 606-1466   *Fax:* 212 606-1477
E-mail: academictraining@hss.edu
Length: 1 Yr   *ACGME Approved/Offered Positions:* 1
Program ID: 265-35-12-024

New York University School of Medicine/Hospital for Joint Diseases Program
Sponsor: New York University School of Medicine
NYU Hospital for Joint Diseases
Prgm Director: Wallace B Lehman, MD
301 East 17th Street
New York, NY 10003
Tel: 212 598-6403   *Fax:* 212 598-6084
Length: 1 Yr   *ACGME Approved/Offered Positions:* 1
Program ID: 265-35-12-007

Ohio

Cincinnati

Cincinnati Children's Hospital Medical Center/University of Cincinnati College of Medicine Program
Sponsor: Cincinnati Children's Hospital Medical Center
Prgm Director: Alvin H Crawford, MD
3333 Burnet Avenue
MLC 2017
Cincinnati, OH 45229
Tel: 513 636-4785   *Fax:* 513 636-3928
E-mail: alvin.crawford@cchmc.org
Length: 1 Yr   *ACGME Approved/Offered Positions:* 2
Program ID: 265-38-21-039

Columbus

Nationwide Children's Hospital/Ohio State University Program
Sponsor: Nationwide Children's Hospital
Prgm Director: Kevin E Klingele, MD*
700 Children's Drive
Columbus, OH 43205
Tel: 614 722-3393   *Fax:* 614 722-3373
E-mail: teaya.rough@nationwidechildrens.org
Length: 1 Yr   *ACGME Approved/Offered Positions:* 1
Program ID: 265-38-22-044

Oregon

Portland

Shriners Hospitals for Children (Portland) Program
Sponsor: Shriners Hospitals for Children (Portland)
Oregon Health & Science University Hospital
Prgm Director: Michael D Aiona, MD*
3101 SW Sam Jackson Park Road
Portland, OR 97239
Tel: 503 221-3486   *Fax:* 503 221-3490
Length: 1 Yr   *ACGME Approved/Offered Positions:* 1
Program ID: 265-40-21-005

Pennsylvania

Philadelphia

Children's Hospital of Philadelphia Program
Sponsor: Children's Hospital of Philadelphia
Prgm Director: John P Dormans, MD
34th Street and Civic Center Boulevard
2nd Floor Wood Building
Philadelphia, PA 19104
Tel: 215 590-1527   *Fax:* 215 590-1101
Length: 1 Yr   *ACGME Approved/Offered Positions:* 3
Program ID: 265-41-21-040

Rhode Island

Providence

Brown University Program
Sponsor: Rhode Island Hospital-Lifespan
Prgm Director: Michael G Ehrlich, MD
593 Eddy Street
Providence, RI 02903
Tel: 401 444-5895   *Fax:* 401 444-6518
E-mail: Michael_Ehrlich@brown.edu
Length: 1 Yr   *ACGME Approved/Offered Positions:* 1
Program ID: 265-43-13-045

Tennessee

Memphis

University of Tennessee Program
Sponsor: University of Tennessee College of Medicine
Campbell Clinics & Surgery Center
LeBonheur Children's Medical Center
Prgm Director: James H Beaty, MD
1211 Union Ave
Suite 510
Memphis, TN 38104
Tel: 901 759-3274   *Fax:* 901 759-3278
E-mail: rgraham5@utmem.edu
Length: 1 Yr   *ACGME Approved/Offered Positions:* 1
Program ID: 265-47-21-034

Texas

Dallas

University of Texas Southwestern Medical School Program
Sponsor: University of Texas Southwestern Medical School
Texas Scottish Rite Hospital for Children
Prgm Director: John A Herring, MD
2222 Welborn Street
Dallas, TX 75219
Tel: 214 559-7556   *Fax:* 214 559-7570
Length: 1 Yr   *ACGME Approved/Offered Positions:* 5
Program ID: 265-48-21-013

Houston

Baylor College of Medicine Program
Sponsor: Baylor College of Medicine
Shriners Hospitals for Children (Houston)
Texas Children's Hospital
Prgm Director: Douglas A Barnes, MD*
6977 Main Street
Houston, TX 77030
Tel: 713 793-3776   *Fax:* 713 793-3779
Length: 1 Yr   *ACGME Approved/Offered Positions:* 2
Program ID: 265-48-31-002

Utah

Salt Lake City

University of Utah Program
Sponsor: University of Utah Medical Center
Primary Children's Medical Center
Shriners Hospital for Children (Intermountain Unit)
Prgm Director: James W Roach, MD, MBA*
Fairfax Road and Virginia Street
Salt Lake City, UT 84103
Tel: 801 536-3600   *Fax:* 801 536-3868
E-mail: jroach@shrinenet.org
Length: 1 Yr   *ACGME Approved/Offered Positions:* 2
Program ID: 265-49-31-015

Programs

Pediatric Otolaryngology (Otolaryngology)

Colorado

Aurora

University of Colorado Denver Program
Sponsor: University of Colorado Denver School of Medicine
Children's Hospital (The)
Prgm Director: Kenny H Chan, MD
13123 East 16th Avenue
Aurora, CO 80045
Tel: 720 777-8675   *Fax:* 720 777-7269
E-mail: chan.kennyh@tchden.org
Length: 1 Yr   *ACGME Approved/Offered Positions:* 1
Program ID: 288-07-12-008

District of Columbia

Washington

George Washington University/Children's National Medical Center Program
Sponsor: Children's National Medical Center
Prgm Director: Sukgi Choi, MD
111 Michigan Avenue NW
Washington, DC 20010
Tel: 202 476-3852   *Fax:* 202 476-5038
Length: 1 Yr   *ACGME Approved/Offered Positions:* 2
Program ID: 288-10-31-007

Iowa

Iowa City

University of Iowa Hospitals and Clinics Program
Sponsor: University of Iowa Hospitals and Clinics
Prgm Director: Richard J H Smith, MD
Head and Neck Surgery 21151 PFP
Iowa City, IA 52242
Tel: 319 356-3612   *Fax:* 319 356-4547
Length: 1 Yr   *ACGME Approved/Offered Positions:* 1
Program ID: 288-18-21-003

Ohio

Cincinnati

Cincinnati Children's Hospital Medical Center/University of Cincinnati College of Medicine Program
Sponsor: Cincinnati Children's Hospital Medical Center
Prgm Director: Jay Paul Willging, MD
3333 Burnet Avenue ML 2018
Cincinnati, OH 45229
Tel: 513 636-2287   *Fax:* 513 636-8133
E-mail: tricia.davis@cchmc.org
Length: 1 Yr   *ACGME Approved/Offered Positions:* 3
Program ID: 288-38-21-004

Pennsylvania

Philadelphia

Children's Hospital of Philadelphia Program
Sponsor: Children's Hospital of Philadelphia
Prgm Director: Ralph F Wetmore, MD
34th Street & Civic Center Boulevard
ENT, 1 Wood Center
Philadelphia, PA 19104
Tel: 215 590-1582   *Fax:* 215 590-3986
Length: 1 Yr   *ACGME Approved/Offered Positions:* 2
Program ID: 288-41-13-006

Pittsburgh

University of Pittsburgh Medical Center Medical Education Program
Sponsor: Univ of Pittsburgh Medical Center Medical Education
Children's Hospital of Pittsburgh of UPMC
Prgm Director: Cuneyt M Alper, MD
Department of Pediatric Otolaryngology
3705 Fifth Avenue
Pittsburgh, PA 15213
Tel: 412 692-8577   *Fax:* 412 692-6074
E-mail: marsha.clark@chp.edu
Length: 1 Yr   *ACGME Approved/Offered Positions:* 2
Program ID: 288-41-21-001

Texas

Houston

Baylor College of Medicine Program
Sponsor: Baylor College of Medicine
Texas Children's Hospital
Prgm Director: Carla M Giannoni, MD
Texas Children's Hospital
6701 Fannin St, Suite 610.22
Houston, TX 77030
Tel: 832 822-3267   *Fax:* 832 825-3251
E-mail: pediotofellowship@bcm.tmc.edu
Length: 1 Yr   *ACGME Approved/Offered Positions:* 2
Program ID: 288-48-21-005

Pediatric Pathology (Pathology)

California

Los Angeles

Childrens Hospital Los Angeles Program
Sponsor: Childrens Hospital Los Angeles
Prgm Director: Paul Pattengale, MD
4650 Sunset Boulevard
Los Angeles, CA 90027
Tel: 323 669-5608   *Fax:* 323 668-1047
Length: 1 Yr   *ACGME Approved/Offered Positions:* 2
Program ID: 316-05-21-029

Colorado

Aurora

University of Colorado Denver Program
Sponsor: University of Colorado Denver School of Medicine
Children's Hospital (The)
Prgm Director: Mark A Lovell, MD*
1056 East 19th Avenue
Department of Pathology B-120
Denver, CO 80218
Tel: 303 861-6718   *Fax:* 303 831-4112
Length: 1 Yr   *ACGME Approved/Offered Positions:* 1
Program ID: 316-07-21-022

Florida

Miami

Jackson Memorial Hospital/Jackson Health System Program
Sponsor: Jackson Memorial Hospital/Jackson Health System
Prgm Director: Maria M Rodriguez, MD
1611 NW 12th Avenue
Department of Pathology
Miami, FL 33136
Tel: 305 585-6637   *Fax:* 305 585-5311
E-mail: mmrod@miami.edu
Length: 1 Yr   *ACGME Approved/Offered Positions:* 1
Program ID: 316-11-21-026

Tampa

University of South Florida Program
Sponsor: University of South Florida College of Medicine
All Children's Hospital
Tampa General Hospital
Prgm Director: Enid Gilbert-Barness, MD
PO Box 1289
1 Tampa General Circle
Tampa, FL 33606
Tel: 813 844-7565   *Fax:* 813 844-1427
Length: 1 Yr   *ACGME Approved/Offered Positions:* 1
Program ID: 316-11-21-015

Note: * indicates a newly appointed program director

Illinois

Chicago

McGaw Medical Center of Northwestern University Program

Sponsor: McGaw Medical Center of Northwestern University
Children's Memorial Hospital
Prgm Director: Pauline Chou, MD
Department of Pathology and Laboratory Medicine
2300 Children's Plaza, Box 17
Chicago, IL 60614
Tel: 773 880-4439   *Fax:* 773 880-8127
E-mail: pchou@childrensmemorial.org
Length: 1 Yr   *ACGME Approved/Offered Positions:* 1
Program ID: 316-16-21-024

Indiana

Indianapolis

Indiana University School of Medicine Program

Sponsor: Indiana University School of Medicine
Clarian Pathology Laboratory
Clarian Riley Hospital for Children
Prgm Director: Philip Faught, MD
702 Barnhill Drive, Room 2536
Indianapolis, IN 46202
Tel: 317 274-2616   *Fax:* 317 274-2810
E-mail: pfaught@iupui.edu
Length: 1 Yr   *ACGME Approved/Offered Positions:* 1
Program ID: 316-17-21-002

Massachusetts

Boston

Children's Hospital Program

Sponsor: Children's Hospital
Brigham and Women's Hospital
Office of the Chief Medical Examiner
Prgm Director: Theonia K Boyd, MD
300 Longwood Avenue
Bader 1
Boston, MA 02115
Tel: 617 355-7431   *Fax:* 617 730-0207
E-mail: Theonia.Boyd@childrens.harvard.edu
Length: 1 Yr   *ACGME Approved/Offered Positions:* 4
Program ID: 316-24-21-017

Michigan

Detroit

Wayne State University/Detroit Medical Center Program

Sponsor: Wayne State University/Detroit Medical Center
Children's Hospital of Michigan
Prgm Director: Raja Rabah, MD*
Department of Pathology
3901 Beaubien Boulevard
Detroit, MI 48201
Tel: 313 745-5765   *Fax:* 313 993-8754
E-mail: rrabah@dmc.org
Length: 1 Yr   *ACGME Approved/Offered Positions:* 1
Program ID: 316-25-21-004

Missouri

Kansas City

University of Missouri-Kansas City School of Medicine/Children's Mercy Hospital Program

Sponsor: University of Missouri-Kansas City School of Medicine
Children's Mercy Hospital
Prgm Director: Vivekanand Singh, MD*
2401 Gillham Road
Kansas City, MO 64108
Tel: 816 234-3234   *Fax:* 816 802-1492
E-mail: vsingh@cmh.edu
Length: 1 Yr   *ACGME Approved/Offered Positions:* 1
Program ID: 316-28-13-028

St Louis

St Louis University School of Medicine Program

Sponsor: St Louis University School of Medicine
Cardinal Glennon Children's Hospital
Prgm Director: Cirilo Sotelo-Avila, MD
1465 S Grand Blvd, Rm G320
St Louis, MO 63104
Tel: 314 268-6424   *Fax:* 314 268-6420
Length: 1 Yr   *ACGME Approved/Offered Positions:* 1
Program ID: 316-28-21-008

Washington University/B-JH/SLCH Consortium Program

Sponsor: Washington University/B-JH/SLCH Consortium
Barnes-Jewish Hospital
St Louis Children's Hospital
Prgm Director: Frances V White, MD*
660 S Euclid Avenue
Campus Box 8118
St Louis, MO 63110
Tel: 314 362-0111   *Fax:* 314 747-2663
Length: 1 Yr   *ACGME Approved/Offered Positions:* 1
Program ID: 316-28-21-019

New York

Brooklyn

SUNY Health Science Center at Brooklyn Program

Sponsor: SUNY Health Science Center at Brooklyn
Kings County Hospital Center
University Hospital-SUNY Health Science Center at Brooklyn
Prgm Director: Virginia M Anderson, MD
450 Clarkson, Box 25
Brooklyn, NY 11203
Tel: 718 270-1294   *Fax:* 718 270-3313
Length: 1 Yr   *ACGME Approved/Offered Positions:* 1
Program ID: 316-35-31-018

New York

New York University School of Medicine Program

Sponsor: New York University School of Medicine
Bellevue Hospital Center
Prgm Director: M Alba Greco, MD
TH 461
560 First Avenue
New York, NY 10016
Tel: 212 263-6443   *Fax:* 212 263-3204
E-mail: mag10@nyu.edu
Length: 1 Yr   *ACGME Approved/Offered Positions:* 1
Program ID: 316-35-21-007

Ohio

Akron

Children's Hospital Medical Center of Akron/NEOUCOM Program

Sponsor: Children's Hospital Medical Center of Akron
Prgm Director: Dimitris P Agamanolis, MD
Department of Pathology
One Perkins Square
Akron, OH 44308
Tel: 330 543-8219
E-mail: dagamanolis@chmca.org
Length: 1 Yr   *ACGME Approved/Offered Positions:* 2
Program ID: 316-38-31-012

Cincinnati

Cincinnati Children's Hospital Medical Center/University of Cincinnati College of Medicine Program

Sponsor: Cincinnati Children's Hospital Medical Center
University of Cincinnati College of Medicine
Prgm Director: Margaret H Collins, MD
3333 Burnet Avenue
MLC 1010
Cincinnati, OH 45229
Tel: 513 636-4261   *Fax:* 513 636-3924
Length: 1 Yr   *ACGME Approved/Offered Positions:* 2
Program ID: 316-38-21-021

Columbus

Nationwide Children's Hospital/Ohio State University Program

Sponsor: Nationwide Children's Hospital
Prgm Director: Samir Kahwash, MD
700 Children's Drive
Anatomic Pathology
Columbus, OH 43205
Tel: 614 722-5427   *Fax:* 614 722-5308
E-mail: samir.kahwash@nationwidechildrens.org
Length: 1 Yr   *ACGME Approved/Offered Positions:* 2
Program ID: 316-38-21-010

Pennsylvania

Philadelphia

Children's Hospital of Philadelphia Program

Sponsor: Children's Hospital of Philadelphia
Prgm Director: Eduardo D Ruchelli, MD
324 S 34th Street
Department of Pathology, Room 5NW12
Philadelphia, PA 19104
Tel: 215 590-1728   *Fax:* 215 590-1736
E-mail: ruchelli@email.chop.edu
Length: 1 Yr   *ACGME Approved/Offered Positions:* 2
Program ID: 316-41-31-014

St Christopher's Hospital for Children Program

Sponsor: St Christopher's Hospital for Children (Tenet Health System)
Prgm Director: Judy Mae Pascasio, MD
Erie Avenue at Front Street
Philadelphia, PA 19134
Tel: 215 427-5272   *Fax:* 215 427-4284
E-mail: judy.pascasio@drexelmed.edu
Length: 1 Yr   *ACGME Approved/Offered Positions:* 1
Program ID: 316-41-21-013

Programs

Pittsburgh

University of Pittsburgh Medical Center Medical Education Program

Sponsor: Univ of Pittsburgh Medical Center Medical Education
Children's Hospital of Pittsburgh of UPMC
Magee-Womens Hospital of UPMC
Prgm Director: Ronald Jaffe, MBChB
3705 Fifth Avenue
Pittsburgh, PA 15213
Tel: 412 692-5655   *Fax:* 412 692-6550
Length: 1 Yr   *ACGME Approved/Offered Positions:* 1
Program ID: 316-41-11-016

Rhode Island

Providence

Brown University (Women and Infants Hospital of Rhode Island) Program

Sponsor: Women and Infants Hospital of Rhode Island
Rhode Island Hospital-Lifespan
Prgm Director: Monique E De Paepe, MD, MS
101 Dudley Street
Providence, RI 02905
Tel: 401 274-1122   *Fax:* 401 453-7681
E-mail: mdepaepe@wihri.org
Length: 1 Yr   *ACGME Approved/Offered Positions:* 2
Program ID: 316-43-21-005

Tennessee

Memphis

University of Tennessee Program

Sponsor: University of Tennessee College of Medicine
LeBonheur Children's Medical Center
Regional Medical Center at Memphis
St Jude Children's Research Hospital
University of Tennessee Department of Pathology
Prgm Director: Douglas Shanklin, MD
930 Madison Avenue 5th Floor
Memphis, TN 38163
Tel: 901 448-6344   *Fax:* 901 448-6979
Length: 1 Yr   *ACGME Approved/Offered Positions:* 1
Program ID: 316-47-31-033

Texas

Dallas

University of Texas Southwestern Medical School Program

Sponsor: University of Texas Southwestern Medical School
Children's Medical Center of Dallas
Prgm Director: Ana M Gomez, MD, PhD
Department of Pathology
1935 Medical District Drive, B2280
Dallas, TX 75235
Tel: 214 456-8723   *Fax:* 214 456-6199
E-mail: ana.gomez@childrens.com
Length: 1 Yr   *ACGME Approved/Offered Positions:* 2
Program ID: 316-48-21-003

Houston

Baylor College of Medicine Program

Sponsor: Baylor College of Medicine
Texas Children's Hospital
Prgm Director: Edwina J Popek, DO
Department of Pathology, MC 1-2261
6621 Fannin Street
Houston, TX 77030
Tel: 832 824-1870   *Fax:* 832 825-1032
E-mail: ejpopek@texaschildrenshospital.org
Length: 1 Yr   *ACGME Approved/Offered Positions:* 2
Program ID: 316-48-31-009

Utah

Salt Lake City

University of Utah Program

Sponsor: University of Utah Medical Center
Primary Children's Medical Center
Prgm Director: Hong (Holly) Zhou, MD*
100 North Mario Capecchi Drive
Pediatric Pathology
Salt Lake City, UT 84113
Tel: 801 662-2155   *Fax:* 801 662-2165
Length: 1 Yr   *ACGME Approved/Offered Positions:* 1
Program ID: 316-49-22-032

Washington

Seattle

University of Washington Program

Sponsor: University of Washington School of Medicine
Seattle Children's Hospital
Prgm Director: Laura Finn, MD
4800 Sand Point Way, NE
Seattle, WA 98105
Tel: 206 987-2103   *Fax:* 206 987-3840
Length: 1 Yr   *ACGME Approved/Offered Positions:* 1
Program ID: 316-54-11-031

Pediatric Pulmonology (Pediatrics)

Alabama

Birmingham

University of Alabama Medical Center Program

Sponsor: University of Alabama Hospital
Children's Hospital of Alabama
Prgm Director: Hector H Gutierrez, MD
1600 7th Avenue South
Suite 620 ACC
Birmingham, AL 35233
Tel: 205 939-9583   *Fax:* 205 975-5983
E-mail: wmclaurin@peds.uab.edu
Length: 3 Yrs   *ACGME Approved/Offered Positions:* 3
Program ID: 330-01-21-001

Arizona

Tucson

University of Arizona Program

Sponsor: University of Arizona College of Medicine
Tucson Medical Center
University Medical Center
Prgm Director: Mark A Brown, MD
Box 245073
1501 N Campbell Avenue
Tucson, AZ 85724
Tel: 520 626-7780   *Fax:* 520 626-9465
E-mail: mabrown@arc.arizona.edu
Length: 3 Yrs   *ACGME Approved/Offered Positions:* 3
Program ID: 330-03-21-002

Arkansas

Little Rock

University of Arkansas for Medical Sciences Program

Sponsor: University of Arkansas College of Medicine
Arkansas Children's Hospital
UAMS Medical Center
Prgm Director: Martin L Bauer, MD
Section of Pulmonology, Departments of Pediatrics
800 Marshall Street, Slot 512-17
Little Rock, AR 72202
Tel: 501 364-1006   *Fax:* 501 364-3930
E-mail: BauerMartinL@uams.edu
Length: 3 Yrs   *ACGME Approved/Offered Positions:* 3
Program ID: 330-04-31-057

Note: * indicates a newly appointed program director

California

Long Beach

University of California (Irvine) Program
Sponsor: University of California (Irvine) Medical Center
Long Beach Memorial Medical Center
Miller Children's Hospital
Prgm Director: Eliezer Nussbaum, MD
2801 Atlantic Avenue
Long Beach, CA 90806
Tel: 562 933-8749   *Fax:* 562 933-8744
E-mail: enussbaum@memorialcare.org
Length: 3 Yrs   *ACGME Approved/Offered Positions:* 3
Program ID: 330-05-21-003

Los Angeles

Childrens Hospital Los Angeles Program
Sponsor: Childrens Hospital Los Angeles
Prgm Director: Thomas G Keens, MD
Division of Pediatric Pulmonology
4650 Sunset Blvd, Box 83
Los Angeles, CA 90027
Tel: 323 361-2101   *Fax:* 323 361-1355
E-mail: tkeens@chla.usc.edu
Length: 3 Yrs   *ACGME Approved/Offered Positions:* 6
Program ID: 330-05-21-004

Oakland

Children's Hospital-Oakland Program
Sponsor: Children's Hospital-Oakland
Prgm Director: Karen A Hardy, MD
747 52nd Street
Oakland, CA 94609
Tel: 510 428-3305   *Fax:* 510 597-7154
Length: 3 Yrs   *ACGME Approved/Offered Positions:* 3
Program ID: 330-05-13-055

San Diego

University of California (San Diego) Program
Sponsor: University of California (San Diego) Medical Center
Rady Children's Hospital
Prgm Director: Mark S Pian, MD
3020 Children's Way
Mail Code 5070
San Diego, CA 92123
Tel: 858 966-5846   *Fax:* 858 966-8533
Length: 3 Yrs   *ACGME Approved/Offered Positions:* 3
Program ID: 330-05-13-064

San Francisco

University of California (San Francisco) Program
Sponsor: University of California (San Francisco) School of Medicine
UCSF and Mount Zion Medical Centers
Prgm Director: Dennis W Nielson, MD, PhD
521 Parnassus Avenue, C344
Box 0632
San Francisco, CA 94143
Tel: 415 476-2072   *Fax:* 415 476-9278
Length: 3 Yrs   *ACGME Approved/Offered Positions:* 3
Program ID: 330-05-21-005

Stanford

Stanford University Program
Sponsor: Stanford Hospital and Clinics
Lucile Salter Packard Children's Hospital at Stanford
Prgm Director: John Mark, MD
770 Welch Road-Suite 350
Palo Alto, CA 94304
Tel: 650 723-5191   *Fax:* 650 723-5201
Length: 3 Yrs   *ACGME Approved/Offered Positions:* 1
Program ID: 330-05-13-061

Colorado

Aurora

University of Colorado Denver Program
Sponsor: University of Colorado Denver School of Medicine
Children's Hospital (The)
Prgm Director: Jeffrey S Wagener, MD*
13123 East 16th Avenue
Aurora, CO 80045
Tel: 720 777-2522
E-mail: Burghardt.Kendra@tchden.org
Length: 3 Yrs   *ACGME Approved/Offered Positions:* 6
Program ID: 330-07-21-008

Connecticut

Farmington

University of Connecticut Program
Sponsor: University of Connecticut School of Medicine
Connecticut Children's Medical Center
Prgm Director: Anita Bhandari, MD*
Pediatric Pulmonology
282 Washington Street
Hartford, CT 06106
Tel: 860 545-9440   *Fax:* 860 545-9445
E-mail: vtomlin@ccmckids.org
Length: 3 Yrs   *ACGME Approved/Offered Positions:* 1
Program ID: 330-08-21-007

New Haven

Yale-New Haven Medical Center Program
Sponsor: Yale-New Haven Hospital
Prgm Director: Alia Bazzy-Asaad, MD
Fitkin Bldg, Rm 520
333 Cedar Street
New Haven, CT 06520
Tel: 203 785-2480   *Fax:* 203 785-6337
E-mail:
Length: 3 Yrs   *ACGME Approved/Offered Positions:* 3
Program ID: 330-08-21-014

District of Columbia

Washington

Children's National Medical Center/ George Washington University Program
Sponsor: Children's National Medical Center
Prgm Director: Iman R Sami-Zakhari, MD
111 Michigan Avenue NW
Washington, DC 20010
Tel: 202 476-5718   *Fax:* 202 476-5864
E-mail: isami@cnmc.org
Length: 3 Yrs   *ACGME Approved/Offered Positions:* 5
Program ID: 330-10-21-049

Florida

Gainesville

University of Florida Program
Sponsor: University of Florida College of Medicine
Shands Hospital at the University of Florida
Prgm Director: Sarah E Chesrown, MD, PhD
Department of Pediatrics
PO Box 100296 HSC
Gainesville, FL 32610
Tel: 352 273-8380   *Fax:* 352 392-4450
E-mail: chesrse@peds.ufl.edu
Length: 3 Yrs   *ACGME Approved/Offered Positions:* 3
Program ID: 330-11-21-017

Miami

Jackson Memorial Hospital/Jackson Health System Program
Sponsor: Jackson Memorial Hospital/Jackson Health System
Prgm Director: Andrew Colin, MD
Batchelor Children's Research Institute
1st Floor (D-820)
Miami, FL 33136
Tel: 305 243-3185   *Fax:* 305 243-1262
Length: 3 Yrs   *ACGME Approved/Offered Positions:* 3
Program ID: 330-11-21-054

Georgia

Atlanta

Emory University Program
Sponsor: Emory University School of Medicine
Children's Healthcare of Atlanta at Egleston
Prgm Director: Dawn M Simon, MD*
2015 Uppergate Drive, NE
Atlanta, GA 30322
Tel: 404 712-8206   *Fax:* 404 712-9712
E-mail: dawn_simon@oz.ped.emory.edu
Length: 3 Yrs   *ACGME Approved/Offered Positions:* 3
Program ID: 330-12-12-062

Illinois

Chicago

McGaw Medical Center of Northwestern University Program
Sponsor: McGaw Medical Center of Northwestern University
Children's Memorial Hospital
Prgm Director: Susanna A McColley, MD
Div of Pulmonary Medicine
2300 Children's Plaza, #43
Chicago, IL 60614
Tel: 773 975-8631   *Fax:* 773 880-6300
Length: 3 Yrs   *ACGME Approved/Offered Positions:* 3
Program ID: 330-16-21-052

University of Chicago Program
Sponsor: University of Chicago Medical Center
University of Chicago Comer Children's Hospital
Prgm Director: Oren Lakser, MD
Department of Pediatrics
5841 South Maryland Avenue MC 4064
Chicago, IL 60637
Tel: 773 702-6178   *Fax:* 773 834-1444
Length: 3 Yrs   *ACGME Approved/Offered Positions:* 3
Program ID: 330-16-21-060

Indiana

Indianapolis

Indiana University School of Medicine Program

Sponsor: Indiana University School of Medicine
Clarian Riley Hospital for Children
Prgm Director: Michelle S Howenstine, MD
702 Barnhill Drive, Room ROC 4270
Indianapolis, IN 46202
Tel: 317 274-7208   *Fax:* 317 274-5791
E-mail: mhowenst@iupui.edu
Length: 3 Yrs   *ACGME Approved/Offered Positions:* 3
Program ID: 330-17-21-016

Iowa

Iowa City

University of Iowa Hospitals and Clinics Program

Sponsor: University of Iowa Hospitals and Clinics
Prgm Director: Miles M Weinberger, MD, BA
Pediatric Department-JCP
200 Hawkins Drive
Iowa City, IA 52242
Tel: 319 356-3485   *Fax:* 319 356-7171
E-mail: miles-weinberger@uiowa.edu
Length: 3 Yrs   *ACGME Approved/Offered Positions:* 6
Program ID: 330-18-21-013

Maryland

Baltimore

Johns Hopkins University Program

Sponsor: Johns Hopkins University School of Medicine
Johns Hopkins Hospital
Prgm Director: Sharon A McGrath-Morrow, MD*
200 N Wolfe Street
Baltimore, MD 21287
Tel: 410 955-2035   *Fax:* 410 955-1030
Length: 3 Yrs   *ACGME Approved/Offered Positions:* 9
Program ID: 330-23-21-015

Massachusetts

Boston

Children's Hospital/Boston Medical Center Program

Sponsor: Children's Hospital
Prgm Director: Debra M Boyer, MD
300 Longwood Avenue
Boston, MA 02115
Tel: 617 355-6105   *Fax:* 617 730-0084
E-mail: donna.giromini@childrens.harvard.edu
Length: 3 Yrs   *ACGME Approved/Offered Positions:* 9
Program ID: 330-24-21-009

Massachusetts General Hospital Program

Sponsor: Massachusetts General Hospital
Prgm Director: Kenan Haver, MD
175 Cambridge Street
Charles River Plaza, Suite 559A
Boston, MA 02114
Tel: 617 724-2872   *Fax:* 617 724-4306
E-mail: edonovan@partners.org
Length: 3 Yrs   *ACGME Approved/Offered Positions:* 3
Program ID: 330-24-21-036

Michigan

Ann Arbor

University of Michigan Program

Sponsor: University of Michigan Hospitals and Health Centers
Prgm Director: Marc B Hershenson, MD
1500 E Medical Center Drive
L2221 Women's/Box 5212
Ann Arbor, MI 48109
Tel: 734 764-9580   *Fax:* 734 764-3200
Length: 3 Yrs   *ACGME Approved/Offered Positions:* 3
Program ID: 330-25-21-010

Minnesota

Minneapolis

University of Minnesota Program

Sponsor: University of Minnesota Medical School
University of Minnesota Medical Center, Division of Fairview
Prgm Director: Warren E Regelmann, MD
MMC 742
420 Delaware Street, SE
Minneapolis, MN 55455
Tel: 612 626-2916   *Fax:* 612 626-0413
Length: 3 Yrs   *ACGME Approved/Offered Positions:* 3
Program ID: 330-26-21-018

Missouri

St Louis

Washington University/B-JH/SLCH Consortium Program

Sponsor: Washington University/B-JH/SLCH Consortium
St Louis Children's Hospital
Prgm Director: Thomas Ferkol Jr, MD
St Louis Children's Hospital
One Children's Place
St Louis, MO 63110
Tel: 314 454-2694   *Fax:* 314 454-2515
Length: 3 Yrs   *ACGME Approved/Offered Positions:* 6
Program ID: 330-28-21-020

New York

Bronx

Albert Einstein College of Medicine Program

Sponsor: Albert Einstein College of Medicine of Yeshiva University
Montefiore Medical Center-Henry and Lucy Moses Division
Prgm Director: Raanan Arens, MD
111 East 210th Street
Bronx, NY 10467
Tel: 718 515-2330   *Fax:* 718 515-2608
Length: 3 Yrs   *ACGME Approved/Offered Positions:* 1
Program ID: 330-35-21-063

Brooklyn

SUNY Health Science Center at Brooklyn Program

Sponsor: SUNY Health Science Center at Brooklyn
Kings County Hospital Center
University Hospital-SUNY Health Science Center at Brooklyn
Prgm Director: Haesoon Lee, MD
Pediatric Department Box 49
450 Clarkson Avenue
Brooklyn, NY 11203
Tel: 718 221-5316   *Fax:* 718 221-5343
E-mail: haesoon.lee@downstate.edu
Length: 3 Yrs   *ACGME Approved/Offered Positions:* 2
Program ID: 330-35-21-021

Mineola

Winthrop-University Hospital Program

Sponsor: Winthrop-University Hospital
University Hospital - SUNY at Stony Brook
Prgm Director: Melodi Pirzada, MD
120 Mineola Blvd Suite 210
Mineola, NY 11501
Tel: 516 663-4600   *Fax:* 516 663-3826
Length: 3 Yrs   *ACGME Approved/Offered Positions:* 3
Program ID: 330-35-21-050

New York

Mount Sinai School of Medicine Program

Sponsor: Mount Sinai School of Medicine
Mount Sinai Medical Center
Prgm Director: Andrew S Ting, MD
One Gustave L Levy Place
Box 1202B
New York, NY 10029
Tel: 212 241-7788   *Fax:* 212 876-3255
Length: 3 Yrs   *ACGME Approved/Offered Positions:* 2
Program ID: 330-35-32-042

New York Presbyterian Hospital (Columbia Campus) Program

Sponsor: New York Presbyterian Hospital
New York Presbyterian Hospital (Columbia Campus)
Prgm Director: Michael R Bye, MD
3959 Broadway,CH 7 C
Children's Lung Center
New York, NY 10032
Tel: 212 305-4519   *Fax:* 212 305-6103
Length: 3 Yrs   *ACGME Approved/Offered Positions:* 3
Program ID: 330-35-21-040

Rochester

University of Rochester Program

Sponsor: Strong Memorial Hospital of the University of Rochester
Prgm Director: Eulalia R Cheng, MD
601 Elmwood Avenue, Box 667
Rochester, NY 14642
Tel: 585 275-2464   *Fax:* 585 275-8706
Length: 3 Yrs   *ACGME Approved/Offered Positions:* 1
Program ID: 330-35-21-023

Valhalla

New York Medical College at Westchester Medical Center Program

Sponsor: New York Medical College
Westchester Medical Center
Prgm Director: Allen J Dozor, MD
Munger Pavilion, Room 106
Valhalla, NY 10595
Tel: 914 493-7585   *Fax:* 914 594-4336
Length: 3 Yrs   *ACGME Approved/Offered Positions:* 4
Program ID: 330-35-31-041

Note: * indicates a newly appointed program director

North Carolina

Chapel Hill

University of North Carolina Hospitals Program

Sponsor: University of North Carolina Hospitals
Prgm Director: Stephanie D Davis, MD
Department of Pediatrics
5th Floor Bioinformatics, CB 7220
Chapel Hill, NC 27599
Tel: 919 966-1055   *Fax:* 919 966-6179
Length: 3 Yrs   *ACGME Approved/Offered Positions:* 6
Program ID: 330-36-21-019

Durham

Duke University Hospital Program

Sponsor: Duke University Hospital
Prgm Director: Thomas M Murphy, MD*
Box 2994
302 Bell Building
Durham, NC 27710
Tel: 919 684-2214   *Fax:* 919 684-2292
E-mail: murph016@mc.duke.edu
Length: 3 Yrs   *ACGME Approved/Offered Positions:* 3
Program ID: 330-36-21-044

Ohio

Cincinnati

Cincinnati Children's Hospital Medical Center/University of Cincinnati College of Medicine Program

Sponsor: Cincinnati Children's Hospital Medical Center
Prgm Director: Barbara A Chini, MD
3333 Burnet Avenue, C 5, MLC 2021
Cincinnati, OH 45229
Tel: 513 636-6771   *Fax:* 513 636-4615
Length: 3 Yrs   *ACGME Approved/Offered Positions:* 9
Program ID: 330-38-21-026

Cleveland

University Hospitals Case Medical Center Program

Sponsor: University Hospitals Case Medical Center
Prgm Director: James F Chmiel, MD, MPH
Pediatric Pulmonology - MS 6006
11100 Euclid Avenue
Cleveland, OH 44106
Tel: 216 844-3267   *Fax:* 216 844-5916
E-mail: james.chmiel@UHhospitals.org
Length: 3 Yrs   *ACGME Approved/Offered Positions:* 6
Program ID: 330-38-21-027

Columbus

Nationwide Children's Hospital/Ohio State University Program

Sponsor: Nationwide Children's Hospital
Prgm Director: Elizabeth D Allen, MD
700 Children's Drive, ED-442
Columbus, OH 43205
Tel: 614 722-4766   *Fax:* 614 722-4755
E-mail: beth.allen@nationwidechildrens.org
Length: 3 Yrs   *ACGME Approved/Offered Positions:* 6
Program ID: 330-38-21-043

Pennsylvania

Philadelphia

Children's Hospital of Philadelphia Program

Sponsor: Children's Hospital of Philadelphia
Prgm Director: Howard B Panitch, MD
34th Street & Civic Center Blvd
Philadelphia, PA 19104
Tel: 215 590-3749   *Fax:* 215 590-3500
E-mail: panitch@email.chop.edu
Length: 3 Yrs   *ACGME Approved/Offered Positions:* 6
Program ID: 330-41-21-034

Pittsburgh

University of Pittsburgh Medical Center Medical Education Program

Sponsor: Univ of Pittsburgh Medical Center Medical Education
Children's Hospital of Pittsburgh of UPMC
Prgm Director: Geoffrey Kurland, MD
One Children's Place
3705 Fifth Avenue
Pittsburgh, PA 15213
Tel: 412 692-5630   *Fax:* 412 692-6645
Length: 3 Yrs   *ACGME Approved/Offered Positions:* 6
Program ID: 330-41-21-035

Tennessee

Nashville

Vanderbilt University Program

Sponsor: Vanderbilt University Medical Center
Prgm Director: Paul E Moore, MD
2200 Children's Way
DOT 11215
Nashville, TN 37232
Tel: 615 343-7617   *Fax:* 615 343-7727
Length: 3 Yrs   *ACGME Approved/Offered Positions:* 1
Program ID: 330-47-31-059

Texas

Houston

Baylor College of Medicine Program

Sponsor: Baylor College of Medicine
Texas Children's Hospital
Prgm Director: Christopher M Oermann, MD
Pediatric Pulmonolgy
6621 Fannin St, CCC Suite 1040.00
Houston, TX 77030
Tel: 832 822-3300   *Fax:* 832 825-3308
Length: 3 Yrs   *ACGME Approved/Offered Positions:* 6
Program ID: 330-48-21-029

University of Texas at Houston Program

Sponsor: University of Texas Health Science Center at Houston
Memorial Hermann Hospital
Prgm Director: Giuseppe N Colasurdo, MD
6431 Fannin St, MSB 3.228
Houston, TX 77030
Tel: 713 500-5650   *Fax:* 713 500-0588
E-mail: Cindy.Jon@uth.tmc.edu
Length: 3 Yrs   *ACGME Approved/Offered Positions:* 3
Program ID: 330-48-21-056

Virginia

Charlottesville

University of Virginia Program

Sponsor: University of Virginia Medical Center
Prgm Director: John F Hunt, MD
Pediatric Respiratory Medicine
PO Box 800386
Charlottesville, VA 22908
Tel: 434 243-9377   *Fax:* 434 982-4328
Length: 3 Yrs   *ACGME Approved/Offered Positions:* 1
Program ID: 330-51-21-053

Washington

Seattle

University of Washington Program

Sponsor: University of Washington School of Medicine
Seattle Children's Hospital
Prgm Director: Ronald L Gibson, MD, PhD
Department of Pediatrics
Box 359300, Mail Stop A-5937
Seattle, WA 98195
Tel: 206 987-2174   *Fax:* 206 987-2639
E-mail: holly.kaopuiki@seattlechildrens.org
Length: 3 Yrs   *ACGME Approved/Offered Positions:* 3
Program ID: 330-54-21-031

Wisconsin

Madison

University of Wisconsin Program

Sponsor: University of Wisconsin Hospital and Clinics
Prgm Director: Michael J Rock, MD
Room K4/946
600 Highland Avenue
Madison, WI 53792
Tel: 608 263-8555   *Fax:* 608 263-0510
Length: 3 Yrs   *ACGME Approved/Offered Positions:* 2
Program ID: 330-56-21-030

Milwaukee

Medical College of Wisconsin Affiliated Hospitals Program

Sponsor: Medical College of Wisconsin Affiliated Hospitals, Inc
Children's Hospital of Wisconsin
Prgm Director: William M Gershan, MD
9000 West Wisconsin Avenue
MS B620
Milwaukee, WI 53226
Tel: 414 266-6730   *Fax:* 414 266-6742
E-mail: wgershan@mcw.edu
Length: 3 Yrs   *ACGME Approved/Offered Positions:* 6
Program ID: 330-56-21-047

Programs

Pediatric Radiology (Radiology-Diagnostic)

Arkansas

Little Rock

University of Arkansas for Medical Sciences Program
Sponsor: University of Arkansas College of Medicine
Arkansas Children's Hospital
Prgm Director: Sadaf T Bhutta, MBBS
Department of Radiology
800 Marshall Street, Slot 105
Little Rock, AR 72202
Tel: 501 364-4911
Length: 1 Yr   *ACGME Approved/Offered Positions:* 1
Program ID: 424-04-21-005

California

Loma Linda

Loma Linda University Program
Sponsor: Loma Linda University Medical Center
Prgm Director: Liliane H Gibbs, MD*
11234 Anderson Street
Loma Linda, CA 92354
Tel: 909 558-4281   *Fax:* 909 558-0266
E-mail: lgibbs@ahs.llumc.edu
Length: 1 Yr   *ACGME Approved/Offered Positions:* 2
Program ID: 424-05-31-049

Los Angeles

Childrens Hospital Los Angeles Program
Sponsor: Childrens Hospital Los Angeles
Prgm Director: Marvin D Nelson Jr, MD, MBA
4650 Sunset Boulevard, MS-81
Los Angeles, CA 90027
Tel: 323 361-4572   *Fax:* 323 361-3018
Length: 1 Yr   *ACGME Approved/Offered Positions:* 3
Program ID: 424-05-21-003

UCLA Medical Center Program
Sponsor: UCLA David Geffen School of Medicine/UCLA Medical Center
UCLA Medical Center
Prgm Director: Maria I Boechat, MD
Department of Radiological Sciences
757 Westwood Plaza
Los Angeles, CA 90095
Tel: 310 825-6798   *Fax:* 310 267-2022
Length: 1 Yr   *ACGME Approved/Offered Positions:* 1
Program ID: 424-05-21-022

Sacramento

University of California (Davis) Health System Program
Sponsor: University of California (Davis) Health System
Shriners Hospitals for Children (Sacramento)
Prgm Director: Sandra W Gorges, MD
UCDMC
4860 Y Street, Suite 3100
Sacramento, CA 95817
Tel: 916 703-2265   *Fax:* 916 703-2258
Length: 1 Yr   *ACGME Approved/Offered Positions:* 1
Program ID: 424-05-12-063

San Francisco

University of California (San Francisco) Program
Sponsor: University of California (San Francisco) School of Medicine
Prgm Director: Heike E Daldrup-Link, MD, PhD*
Department of Radiology
505 Parnassus Avenue
San Francisco, CA 94143
Tel: 415 476-4328   *Fax:* 415 353-1796
E-mail: daldrup@radiology.ucsf.edu
Length: 1 Yr   *ACGME Approved/Offered Positions:* 1
Program ID: 424-05-21-042

Stanford

Stanford University Program
Sponsor: Stanford Hospital and Clinics
Lucile Salter Packard Children's Hospital at Stanford
Prgm Director: Richard A Barth, MD
Diagnostic Radiology MC 5654
LPCH 1690-B, 725 Welch Road
Palo Alto, CA 94305
Tel: 650 725-2548   *Fax:* 650 497-8745
Length: 1 Yr   *ACGME Approved/Offered Positions:* 3
Program ID: 424-05-21-023

Colorado

Aurora

University of Colorado Denver Program
Sponsor: University of Colorado Denver School of Medicine
Children's Hospital (The)
Prgm Director: John D Strain, MD
13123 E 16th Ave
Aurora, CO 80045
Tel: 303 764-8630   *Fax:* 303 764-8669
Length: 1 Yr   *ACGME Approved/Offered Positions:* 3
Program ID: 424-07-21-037

District of Columbia

Washington

Children's National Medical Center/ George Washington University Program
Sponsor: Children's National Medical Center
Prgm Director: Dorothy I Bulas, MD
111 Michigan Avenue NW
Washington, DC 20010
Tel: 202 476-5432   *Fax:* 202 476-3644
E-mail: yjones@cnmc.org
Length: 1 Yr   *ACGME Approved/Offered Positions:* 4
Program ID: 424-10-21-024

Florida

Miami

Miami Children's Hospital Program
Sponsor: Miami Children's Hospital
Prgm Director: Ricardo Restrepo, MD
Department of Radiology
3100 SW 62nd Ave
Miami, FL 33155
Tel: 305 666-6511   *Fax:* 305 669-6580
E-mail: nolan.altman@mch.com
Length: 1 Yr   *ACGME Approved/Offered Positions:* 2
Program ID: 424-11-21-025

Georgia

Atlanta

Emory University Program
Sponsor: Emory University School of Medicine
Children's Healthcare of Atlanta at Egleston
Prgm Director: Paula N Dickson, MD
1405 Clifton Road, NE
Atlanta, GA 30322
Tel: 404 785-6532   *Fax:* 404 785-1216
Length: 1 Yr   *ACGME Approved/Offered Positions:* 3
Program ID: 424-12-21-035

Illinois

Chicago

McGaw Medical Center of Northwestern University Program
Sponsor: McGaw Medical Center of Northwestern University
Children's Memorial Hospital
Prgm Director: Ellen C Benya, MD
2300 Children's Plaza, #9
Department of Medical Imaging
Chicago, IL 60614
Tel: 773 880-3521   *Fax:* 773 880-3517
E-mail: ebenya@childrensmemorial.org
Length: 1 Yr   *ACGME Approved/Offered Positions:* 3
Program ID: 424-16-21-017

Indiana

Indianapolis

Indiana University School of Medicine Program
Sponsor: Indiana University School of Medicine
Clarian Riley Hospital for Children
Prgm Director: Richard B Gunderman, MD, PhD
Department of Radiology
702 Barnhill Drive, Room 1053
Indianapolis, IN 46202
Tel: 317 278-6302   *Fax:* 317 274-2920
E-mail: rfpatter@iupui.edu
Length: 1 Yr   *ACGME Approved/Offered Positions:* 2
Program ID: 424-17-21-007

Iowa

Iowa City

University of Iowa Hospitals and Clinics Program
Sponsor: University of Iowa Hospitals and Clinics
Prgm Director: Simon C Kao, MD
200 Hawkins Drive
Iowa City, IA 52242
Tel: 319 356-4447   *Fax:* 319 356-2220
E-mail: simon-kao@uiowa.edu
Length: 1 Yr   *ACGME Approved/Offered Positions:* 1
Program ID: 424-18-21-008

Note: * indicates a newly appointed program director

Maryland

Baltimore

Johns Hopkins University Program

Sponsor: Johns Hopkins University School of Medicine
Johns Hopkins Hospital
Prgm Director: Jane E Benson, MD
600 N Wolfe Street
Nelson B173
Baltimore, MD 21287
Tel: 410 955-6141   *Fax:* 410 502-3633
E-mail: jbenson@jhmi.edu
Length: 1 Yr   *ACGME Approved/Offered Positions:* 1
Program ID: 424-23-21-038

Massachusetts

Boston

Children's Hospital Program

Sponsor: Children's Hospital
Prgm Director: Michael Callahan, MD
300 Longwood Avenue
Boston, MA 02115
Tel: 617 355-8382   *Fax:* 617 730-0549
Length: 1 Yr   *ACGME Approved/Offered Positions:* 10
Program ID: 424-24-21-027

Massachusetts General Hospital/Harvard Medical School Program

Sponsor: Massachusetts General Hospital
Prgm Director: Sjirk J Westra, MD
Division of Pediatric Radiology
55 Fruit Street, White 246
Boston, MA 02114
Tel: 617 724-4207   *Fax:* 617 726-8360
E-mail: swestra@partners.org
Length: 1 Yr   *ACGME Approved/Offered Positions:* 1
Program ID: 424-24-12-058

Michigan

Ann Arbor

University of Michigan Program

Sponsor: University of Michigan Hospitals and Health Centers
Prgm Director: Peter J Strouse, MD
CS Mott Children's Hospital
1500 E Medical Center Drive
Ann Arbor, MI 48109
Tel: 734 763-2570   *Fax:* 734 764-9351
Length: 1 Yr   *ACGME Approved/Offered Positions:* 2
Program ID: 424-25-21-018

Detroit

Wayne State University/Detroit Medical Center Program

Sponsor: Wayne State University/Detroit Medical Center
Children's Hospital of Michigan
Prgm Director: Jeffrey M Zerin, MD
Department of Pediatric Imaging
3901 Beaubien Blvd
Detroit, MI 48201
Tel: 313 745-7080   *Fax:* 313 993-0393
Length: 1 Yr   *ACGME Approved/Offered Positions:* 3
Program ID: 424-25-21-019

Minnesota

Minneapolis

University of Minnesota Program

Sponsor: University of Minnesota Medical School
University of Minnesota Medical Center, Division of Fairview
Prgm Director: F Glen Seidel, MD
420 Delaware Street, SE, MMC 292
Minneapolis, MN 55455
Tel: 612 626-5548   *Fax:* 612 626-5580
Length: 1 Yr   *ACGME Approved/Offered Positions:* 2
Program ID: 424-26-21-064

Missouri

Columbia

University of Missouri-Columbia Program

Sponsor: University of Missouri-Columbia School of Medicine
Children's Mercy Hospital
University Hospitals and Clinics
Prgm Director: Brian A Green, MD*
Department of Radiology DC 069.10
One Hospital Drive
Columbia, MO 65212
Tel: 573 882-1026   *Fax:* 573 884-8876
E-mail: CrookJ@health.missouri.edu
Length: 1 Yr   *ACGME Approved/Offered Positions:* 1
Program ID: 424-28-31-059

Kansas City

University of Missouri at Kansas City/Children's Mercy Hospitals and Clinics Program

Sponsor: University of Missouri-Kansas City School of Medicine
Children's Mercy Hospital
Prgm Director: James C Brown, MD*
Radiology Department
2401 Gillham Road
Kansas City, MO 64108
Tel: 816 234-3273   *Fax:* 816 983-6912
Length: 1 Yr   *ACGME Approved/Offered Positions:* 3
Program ID: 424-28-31-062

St Louis

Washington University/B-JH/SLCH Consortium Program

Sponsor: Washington University/B-JH/SLCH Consortium
St Louis Children's Hospital
Prgm Director: Rebecca Hulett, MD
510 South Kingshighway Blvd
St Louis, MO 63110
Tel: 314 454-6229   *Fax:* 314 454-2868
E-mail: hulettr@mir.wustl.edu
Length: 1 Yr   *ACGME Approved/Offered Positions:* 2
Program ID: 424-28-21-009

Nebraska

Omaha

University of Nebraska Medical Center College of Medicine Program

Sponsor: University of Nebraska Medical Center College of Medicine
Children's Hospital
Prgm Director: Sandra M Allbery, MD
8200 Dodge Street
Radiology Department
Omaha, NE 68114
Tel: 402 955-5630   *Fax:* 402 955-5601
Length: 1 Yr   *ACGME Approved/Offered Positions:* 1
Program ID: 424-30-13-061

New York

Bronx

Albert Einstein College of Medicine Program

Sponsor: Albert Einstein College of Medicine of Yeshiva University
Montefiore Medical Center-Henry and Lucy Moses Division
Prgm Director: Benjamin Taragin, MD
Department of Radiology
111 East 210th Street
Bronx, NY 10467
Tel: 718 920-4865   *Fax:* 718 920-4854
Length: 1 Yr   *ACGME Approved/Offered Positions:* 1
Program ID: 424-35-13-065

Buffalo

Women and Children's Hospital of Buffalo/University at Buffalo Program

Sponsor: Kaleida Health System (Women and Children's Hosp of Buffalo)
Prgm Director: Vaseem Iqbal, MD, MBA*
219 Bryant Street
Graduate Medical Education
Buffalo, NY 14222
Tel: 716 878-7502   *Fax:* 716 878-7001
Length: 1 Yr   *ACGME Approved/Offered Positions:* 1
Program ID: 424-35-21-029

Great Neck

NSLIJHS-Albert Einstein College of Medicine at Long Island Jewish Medical Center Program

Sponsor: North Shore-Long Island Jewish Health System
Long Island Jewish Medical Center
Prgm Director: Edward Wind, MD*
Department of Radiology
270-05 76th Avenue
New Hyde Park, NY 11042
Tel: 718 470-3403   *Fax:* 718 470-3893
E-mail: eacobacc@lij.edu
Length: 1 Yr   *ACGME Approved/Offered Positions:* 1
Program ID: 424-35-21-010

New York

New York Presbyterian Hospital (Columbia Campus) Program

Sponsor: New York Presbyterian Hospital
New York Presbyterian Hospital (Columbia Campus)
Prgm Director: Carrie R Shapiro, MD
622 West 168th Street
CHN-3-330
New York, NY 10032
Tel: 212 305-3320   *Fax:* 212 305-5777
Length: 1 Yr   *ACGME Approved/Offered Positions:* 2
Program ID: 424-35-21-011

Programs

New York University School of Medicine Program

Sponsor: New York University School of Medicine
Bellevue Hospital Center
Prgm Director: Nancy R Fefferman, MD
560 First Avenue
New York, NY 10016
Tel: 212 263-5362   *Fax:* 212 263-5838
Length: 1 Yr   *ACGME Approved/Offered Positions:* 1
Program ID: 424-35-21-030

Rochester

University of Rochester Program

Sponsor: Strong Memorial Hospital of the University of Rochester
Prgm Director: Nina B Klionsky, MD
601 Elmwood Avenue, Box 648
Rochester, NY 14642
Tel: 585 275-3000   *Fax:* 585 273-1033
E-mail: holly_stiner@urmc.rochester.edu
Length: 1 Yr   *ACGME Approved/Offered Positions:* 1
Program ID: 424-35-21-012

North Carolina

Durham

Duke University Hospital Program

Sponsor: Duke University Hospital
Prgm Director: Donald P Frush, MD
Box 3808
1905A McGovern-Davison Children's Health Center
Durham, NC 27710
Tel: 919 684-7293   *Fax:* 919 684-7151
Length: 1 Yr   *ACGME Approved/Offered Positions:* 2
Program ID: 424-36-21-031

Ohio

Akron

Children's Hospital Medical Center of Akron/NEOUCOM Program

Sponsor: Children's Hospital Medical Center of Akron
Prgm Director: Michael D Rubin, MD
Department of Radiology
One Perkins Square
Akron, OH 44308
Tel: 330 543-3279   *Fax:* 330 543-3760
E-mail: mrubin@chmca.org
Length: 1 Yr   *ACGME Approved/Offered Positions:* 1
Program ID: 424-38-21-020

Cincinnati

Cincinnati Children's Hospital Medical Center/University of Cincinnati College of Medicine Program

Sponsor: Cincinnati Children's Hospital Medical Center
Prgm Director: Eric J Crotty, MD
Department of Radiology
3333 Burnet Ave
Cincinnati, OH 45229
Tel: 513 636-2165   *Fax:* 513 636-8145
E-mail: eric.crotty@cchmc.org
Length: 1 Yr   *ACGME Approved/Offered Positions:* 9
Program ID: 424-38-21-001

Columbus

Nationwide Children's Hospital/Ohio State University Program

Sponsor: Nationwide Children's Hospital
Prgm Director: William E Shiels II, DO
700 Children's Drive
Columbus, OH 43205
Tel: 614 722-2363   *Fax:* 614 722-2332
E-mail: Paula.Collins@nationwidechildrens.org
Length: 1 Yr   *ACGME Approved/Offered Positions:* 4
Program ID: 424-38-12-053

Oklahoma

Oklahoma City

University of Oklahoma Health Sciences Center Program

Sponsor: University of Oklahoma College of Medicine
OU Medical Center - Children's Hospital
Prgm Director: Faridali G Ramji, MD
PO Box 26901
Oklahoma City, OK 73190
Tel: 405 271-5125   *Fax:* 405 271-3462
Length: 1 Yr   *ACGME Approved/Offered Positions:* 1
Program ID: 424-39-31-054

Oregon

Portland

Oregon Health & Science University Program

Sponsor: Oregon Health & Science University Hospital
Prgm Director: Katharine L Hopkins, MD
Division of Pediatric Radiology, DC7R
3181 SW Sam Jackson Park Road
Portland, OR 97239
Tel: 503 418-5267   *Fax:* 503 418-5269
Length: 1 Yr   *ACGME Approved/Offered Positions:* 1
Program ID: 424-40-21-060

Pennsylvania

Philadelphia

Children's Hospital of Philadelphia Program

Sponsor: Children's Hospital of Philadelphia
Prgm Director: Avrum N Pollock, MD
324 South 34th Street
Philadelphia, PA 19104
Tel: 215 590-0460   *Fax:* 215 590-1345
E-mail: pollocka@email.chop.edu
Length: 1 Yr   *ACGME Approved/Offered Positions:* 10
Program ID: 424-41-21-032

St Christopher's Hospital for Children Program

Sponsor: St Christopher's Hospital for Children (Tenet Health System)
Prgm Director: Eleanor M Smergel, MD
Erie Avenue at Front Street
Philadelphia, PA 19134
Tel: 215 427-5233   *Fax:* 215 427-4378
E-mail: eleanor.smergel@tenethealth.com
Length: 1 Yr   *ACGME Approved/Offered Positions:* 1
Program ID: 424-41-21-039

Pittsburgh

University of Pittsburgh Medical Center Medical Education Program

Sponsor: Univ of Pittsburgh Medical Center Medical Education
Children's Hospital of Pittsburgh of UPMC
Prgm Director: Stefano C Bartoletti, MD*
Department of Radiology
3705 Fifth Avenue
Pittsburgh, PA 15213
Tel: 412 692-5510
E-mail: stefano.bartoletti@chp.edu
Length: 1 Yr   *ACGME Approved/Offered Positions:* 3
Program ID: 424-41-21-002

Tennessee

Nashville

Vanderbilt University Program

Sponsor: Vanderbilt University Medical Center
Prgm Director: Richard M Heller, MD
Diagnostic Imaging, Ste 1415
2200 Children's Way
Nashville, TN 37232
Tel: 615 936-4943   *Fax:* 615 936-4944
E-mail: radprogram@vanderbilt.edu
Length: 1 Yr   *ACGME Approved/Offered Positions:* 1
Program ID: 424-47-21-021

Texas

Dallas

University of Texas Southwestern Medical School Program

Sponsor: University of Texas Southwestern Medical School
Children's Medical Center of Dallas
Dallas County Hospital District-Parkland Memorial Hospital
Prgm Director: Nancy K Rollins, MD
Department of Radiology
1935 Medical District Drive
Dallas, TX 75235
Tel: 214 456-2809   *Fax:* 214 456-6015
Length: 1 Yr   *ACGME Approved/Offered Positions:* 4
Program ID: 424-48-21-015

Galveston

University of Texas Medical Branch Hospitals Program

Sponsor: University of Texas Medical Branch Hospitals
Prgm Director: Leonard E Swischuck, MD
Department of Radiology, G-09
301 University Blvd, Route 0709
Galveston, TX 77555
Tel: 409 747-2849   *Fax:* 409 772-7120
E-mail: femcdani@utmb.edu
Length: 1 Yr   *ACGME Approved/Offered Positions:* 1
Program ID: 424-48-21-014

Houston

Baylor College of Medicine Program

Sponsor: Baylor College of Medicine
Texas Children's Hospital
Prgm Director: Scott R Dorfman, MD*
6621 Fannin Street
MC 2-2521
Houston, TX 77030
Tel: 832 824-5324   *Fax:* 832 825-5241
Length: 1 Yr   *ACGME Approved/Offered Positions:* 3
Program ID: 424-48-21-016

Note: * indicates a newly appointed program director

Washington

Seattle

University of Washington Program
Sponsor: University of Washington School of Medicine
Seattle Children's Hospital
Prgm Director: David K Brewer, MD
Department of Radiology, R5417
4800 Sand Point Way NE
Seattle, WA 98105
Tel: 206 987-5861   *Fax:* 206 987-2341
Length: 1 Yr   *ACGME Approved/Offered Positions:* 3
Program ID: 424-54-21-033

Wisconsin

Milwaukee

Medical College of Wisconsin Affiliated Hospitals Program
Sponsor: Medical College of Wisconsin Affiliated
    Hospitals, Inc
Children's Hospital of Wisconsin
Prgm Director: Smita S Bailey, MD*
PO Box 1997/MS 721
9000 West Wisconsin Avenue
Milwaukee, WI 53201
Tel: 414 266-3110   *Fax:* 414 266-1525
Length: 1 Yr   *ACGME Approved/Offered Positions:* 1
Program ID: 424-56-21-034

Pediatric Rehabilitation Medicine (Physical Medicine and Rehabilitation)

Alabama

Birmingham

University of Alabama Medical Center Program
Sponsor: University of Alabama Hospital
Children's Hospital of Alabama
Prgm Director: Charles R Law, MD
1600 7th Avenue South, ACC 406
Birmingham, AL 35233
Tel: 205 212-7277   *Fax:* 205 939-9793
E-mail: claw@peds.uab.edu
Length: 2 Yrs   *ACGME Approved/Offered Positions:* 1
Program ID: 346-01-13-012

Colorado

Aurora

University of Colorado Denver Program
Sponsor: University of Colorado Denver School of
    Medicine
Children's Hospital (The)
Prgm Director: Pamela E Wilson, MD
13123 E 16th Avenue
Aurora, CO 80045
Tel: 720 777-8354   *Fax:* 720 777-7297
E-mail: siegfried.maryjane@tchden.org
Length: 2 Yrs   *ACGME Approved/Offered Positions:* 2
Program ID: 346-07-21-001

Delaware

Wilmington

Thomas Jefferson University/duPont Hospital for Children Program
Sponsor: Alfred I duPont Hospital for Children
Prgm Director: Michael A Alexander, MD
1600 Rockland Road
Wilmington, DE 19899
Tel: 302 651-5601   *Fax:* 302 651-5612
E-mail: pwest@nemours.org
Length: 2 Yrs   *ACGME Approved/Offered Positions:* 1
Program ID: 346-09-31-005

Illinois

Chicago

McGaw Medical Center of Northwestern University Program
Sponsor: McGaw Medical Center of Northwestern
    University
Children's Memorial Hospital
Rehabilitation Institute of Chicago
Prgm Director: Shubhra Mukherjee, MD*
345 East Superior Street
Chicago, IL 60611
Tel: 312 238-2842   *Fax:* 312 238-1208
Length: 2 Yrs   *ACGME Approved/Offered Positions:* 1
Program ID: 346-16-21-003

Maryland

Baltimore

Johns Hopkins University Program
Sponsor: Johns Hopkins University School of Medicine
Kennedy Krieger Institute
Prgm Director: Frank S Pidcock, MD
707 North Broadway
Baltimore, MD 21205
Tel: 443 923-9440   *Fax:* 443 923-9445
E-mail: pidcock@kennedykrieger.org
Length: 2 Yrs   *ACGME Approved/Offered Positions:* 2
Program ID: 346-23-31-009

Minnesota

Rochester

College of Medicine, Mayo Clinic (Rochester) Program
Sponsor: College of Medicine, Mayo Clinic
Mayo Clinic (Rochester)
Saint Marys Hospital of Rochester
Prgm Director: Sherilyn W Driscoll, MD
Department of PM&R
200 First Street SW
Rochester, MN 55905
Tel: 507 284-2946   *Fax:* 507 284-3431
E-mail: pmreduc@mayo.edu
Length: 2 Yrs   *ACGME Approved/Offered Positions:* 1
Program ID: 346-26-31-013

St. Paul

University of Minnesota/Gillette Children's Specialty Healthcare Program
Sponsor: University of Minnesota Medical School
Gillette Children's Hospital
Prgm Director: Marcia E Ward, MD
200 East University Avenue
St Paul, MN 55101
Tel: 651 325-2317   *Fax:* 651 265-7443
E-mail: mward@gillettechildrens.com
Length: 2 Yrs   *ACGME Approved/Offered Positions:* 3
Program ID: 346-26-13-008

Programs

Missouri

Kansas City

University of Kansas Medical Center/Children's Mercy Hospital and Clinics Program
Sponsor: Children's Mercy Hospital
Prgm Director: Robert Rinaldi, MD
2401 Gillham Road
Kansas City, MO 64108
Tel: 816 234-3970   *Fax:* 816 983-6845
E-mail: rrinaldi@cmh.edu
Length: 2 Yrs   *ACGME Approved/Offered Positions:* 2
Program ID: 346-28-13-004

New York

Syracuse

SUNY Upstate Medical University Program
Sponsor: SUNY Upstate Medical University
Prgm Director: Margaret A Turk, MD
PM&R 3rd floor Jacobsen Hall
750 East Adams Street
Syracuse, NY 13210
Tel: 315 464-5820   *Fax:* 315 464-8699
Length: 2 Yrs   *ACGME Approved/Offered Positions:* 1
Program ID: 346-35-21-011

Ohio

Cincinnati

Cincinnati Children's Hospital Medical Center/University of Cincinnati College of Medicine Program
Sponsor: Cincinnati Children's Hospital Medical Center
Prgm Director: David W Pruitt, MD*
Pediatric Rehabilitation Medicine
3333 Burnet Avenue MLC 4009
Cincinnati, OH 45229
Tel: 513 636-7480   *Fax:* 513 636-7360
E-mail: david.pruitt@cchmc.org
Length: 2 Yrs   *ACGME Approved/Offered Positions:* 2
Program ID: 346-38-12-006

Columbus

Nationwide Children's Hospital/Ohio State University Program
Sponsor: Nationwide Children's Hospital
Prgm Director: Ellen S Kaitz, MD
700 Children's Drive ED 482
Columbus, OH 43205
Tel: 614 722-5051   *Fax:* 614 722-5058
E-mail: Ellen.Kaitz@nationwidechildrens.org
Length: 2 Yrs   *ACGME Approved/Offered Positions:* 2
Program ID: 346-38-12-010

Virginia

Richmond

Virginia Commonwealth University Health System Program
Sponsor: Virginia Commonwealth University Health System
Children's Hospital
Medical College of Virginia Hospitals
Prgm Director: Eugenio Monasterio, MD
PO Box 980661
Richmond, VA 23298
Tel: 804 228-5836   *Fax:* 804 228-5970
E-mail: emonasterio@chva.org
Length: 2 Yrs   *ACGME Approved/Offered Positions:* 2
Program ID: 346-51-31-002

Wisconsin

Milwaukee

Medical College of Wisconsin Affiliated Hospitals/Children's Hospital of Wisconsin Program
Sponsor: Medical College of Wisconsin Affiliated Hospitals, Inc
Children's Hospital of Wisconsin
Prgm Director: Elizabeth Moberg-Wolff, MD
Department of PM&R
Milwaukee, WI 53226
Tel: 414 266-3085   *Fax:* 414 266-3485
E-mail: emoberg@chw.org
Length: 2 Yrs   *ACGME Approved/Offered Positions:* 2
Program ID: 346-56-21-007

Pediatric Rheumatology (Pediatrics)

California

Los Angeles

Childrens Hospital Los Angeles Program
Sponsor: Childrens Hospital Los Angeles
Prgm Director: Katherine Marzan, MD
4650 Sunset Boulevard, MS 60
Los Angeles, CA 90027
Tel: 323 361-2119   *Fax:* 323 361-1130
E-mail: kmarzan@chla.usc.edu
Length: 3 Yrs   *ACGME Approved/Offered Positions:* 3
Program ID: 331-05-31-028

UCLA Medical Center Program
Sponsor: UCLA David Geffen School of Medicine/UCLA Medical Center
UCLA Medical Center
Prgm Director: Deborah McCurdy, MD
10833 Le Conte Avenue
MDCC Room 12-430
Los Angeles, CA 90095
Tel: 310 206-1826   *Fax:* 310 825-9832
Length: 3 Yrs   *ACGME Approved/Offered Positions:* 6
Program ID: 331-05-31-030

San Francisco

University of California (San Francisco) Program
Sponsor: University of California (San Francisco) School of Medicine
UCSF and Mount Zion Medical Centers
Prgm Director: Emily von Scheven, MD
Dept of Pediatric Rheumatology-U-127
505 Parnassus Avenue, Box 0107
San Francisco, CA 94143
Tel: 415 476-2491   *Fax:* 415 502-7540
Length: 3 Yrs   *ACGME Approved/Offered Positions:* 3
Program ID: 331-05-31-002

Stanford

Stanford University Program
Sponsor: Stanford Hospital and Clinics
Lucile Salter Packard Children's Hospital at Stanford
Prgm Director: Tzielan Lee, MD*
300 Pasteur Drive, Rm A-085
Stanford, CA 94305
Tel: 650 723-8295   *Fax:* 650 736-4344
E-mail: emig@stanford.edu
Length: 3 Yrs   *ACGME Approved/Offered Positions:* 6
Program ID: 331-05-31-024

Delaware

Wilmington

Jefferson Medical College/duPont Hospital for Children Program
Sponsor: Jefferson Medical College
Alfred I duPont Hospital for Children
Prgm Director: AnneMarie C Brescia, MD
1600 Rockland Road
Wilmington, DE 19803
Tel: 302 651-5970   *Fax:* 302 651-5942
E-mail: abrescia@nemours.org
Length: 3 Yrs   *ACGME Approved/Offered Positions:* 3
Program ID: 331-41-21-023

Note: * indicates a newly appointed program director

Illinois

Chicago

McGaw Medical Center of Northwestern University Program

Sponsor: McGaw Medical Center of Northwestern University
Children's Memorial Hospital
Prgm Director: Marisa S Klein-Gitelman, MD, MPH
Division of Rheumatology
2300 Children's Plaza, #50
Chicago, IL 60614
Tel: 773 880-4360   *Fax:* 773 880-4179
E-mail: klein-gitelman@northwestern.edu
Length: 3 Yrs   *ACGME Approved/Offered Positions:* 3
Program ID: 331-16-21-004

University of Chicago Program

Sponsor: University of Chicago Medical Center
LaRabida Children's Hospital and Research Center
University of Chicago Comer Children's Hospital
Prgm Director: Karen B Onel, MD
5841 South Maryland Avenue
MC5044
Chicago, IL 60637
Tel: 773 702-2232   *Fax:* 773 702-4766
E-mail: kbonel@peds.bsd.uchicago.edu
Length: 3 Yrs   *ACGME Approved/Offered Positions:* 1
Program ID: 331-16-31-005

Indiana

Indianapolis

Indiana University School of Medicine Program

Sponsor: Indiana University School of Medicine
Clarian Riley Hospital for Children
Prgm Director: Suzanne L Bowyer, MD*
Riley Hospital - RR307
699 West Dr
Indianapolis, IN 46202
Tel: 317 274-2172   *Fax:* 317 278-3031
Length: 3 Yrs   *ACGME Approved/Offered Positions:* 3
Program ID: 331-17-21-029

Massachusetts

Boston

Children's Hospital/Boston Medical Center Program

Sponsor: Children's Hospital
Brigham and Women's Hospital
Prgm Director: Robert Sundel, MD
300 Longwood Avenue
Boston, MA 02115
Tel: 617 355-6524   *Fax:* 617 730-0249
Length: 3 Yrs   *ACGME Approved/Offered Positions:* 4
Program ID: 331-24-21-007

Tufts Medical Center Program

Sponsor: Tufts Medical Center
Prgm Director: Jorge M Lopez, MD
Tufts Medical Center
800 Washington Street, Box 190
Boston, MA 02111
Tel: 617 636-4198   *Fax:* 617 636-8388
E-mail: jlopez@tuftsmedicalcenter.org
Length: 3 Yrs   *ACGME Approved/Offered Positions:* 3
Program ID: 331-24-31-008

Michigan

Ann Arbor

University of Michigan Program

Sponsor: University of Michigan Hospitals and Health Centers
Prgm Director: Barbara S Adams, MD
MPB D5249
1500 East Medical Center Drive
Ann Arbor, MI 48109
Tel: 734 764-2224   *Fax:* 734 936-9090
Length: 3 Yrs   *ACGME Approved/Offered Positions:* 6
Program ID: 331-25-21-022

Missouri

St Louis

St Louis University School of Medicine Program

Sponsor: St Louis University School of Medicine
Cardinal Glennon Children's Hospital
St Louis University Hospital
Prgm Director: Terry L Moore, MD
Room R211A Doisy Hall
1402 South Grand Boulevard
St Louis, MO 63104
Tel: 314 977-8838   *Fax:* 314 977-8818
Length: 3 Yrs   *ACGME Approved/Offered Positions:* 1
Program ID: 331-28-21-009

Washington University/B-JH/SLCH Consortium Program

Sponsor: Washington University/B-JH/SLCH Consortium
St Louis Children's Hospital
Prgm Director: Anthony R French, MD, PhD*
St Louis Children's Hospital
One Children's Place
St Louis, MO 63110
Tel: 314 286-2885   *Fax:* 314 286-2895
Length: 3 Yrs   *ACGME Approved/Offered Positions:* 6
Program ID: 331-28-31-010

New York

Bronx

Albert Einstein College of Medicine Program

Sponsor: Albert Einstein College of Medicine of Yeshiva University
Montefiore Medical Center-Henry and Lucy Moses Division
Prgm Director: Norman T Ilowite, MD
Montefiore Medical Center
3415 Bainbridge Avenue
Bronx, NY 10467
Tel: 718 741-2456   *Fax:* 718 944-0463
E-mail: nilowite@montefiore.org
Length: 3 Yrs   *ACGME Approved/Offered Positions:* 3
Program ID: 331-35-21-032

Great Neck

NSLIJHS-Schneider Children's Hospital Program

Sponsor: North Shore-Long Island Jewish Health System
Schneider Children's Hospital at Long Island Jewish Med Ctr
Prgm Director: Beth Gottlieb, MD, MS
Long Island Jewish Medical Center
269-01 76th Avenue
New Hyde Park, NY 11040
Tel: 718 470-3530   *Fax:* 718 831-0182
E-mail: gottlieb@lij.edu
Length: 3 Yrs   *ACGME Approved/Offered Positions:* 3
Program ID: 331-35-21-011

New York

New York Presbyterian Hospital (Columbia Campus) Program

Sponsor: New York Presbyterian Hospital
Prgm Director: Lisa Imundo, MD
3959 Broadway, CHN-106
New York, NY 10032
Tel: 212 305-9304   *Fax:* 212 305-4932
E-mail: cm2556@columbia.edu
Length: 3 Yrs   *ACGME Approved/Offered Positions:* 3
Program ID: 331-35-11-013

New York Presbyterian Hospital (Cornell Campus) Program

Sponsor: New York Presbyterian Hospital
Hospital for Special Surgery
Prgm Director: Thomas J A Lehman, MD
535 E 70th Street
New York, NY 10021
Tel: 212 606-1151   *Fax:* 212 606-1938
E-mail: academictraining@hss.edu
Length: 3 Yrs   *ACGME Approved/Offered Positions:* 4
Program ID: 331-35-31-012

North Carolina

Durham

Duke University Hospital Program

Sponsor: Duke University Hospital
Prgm Director: Laura E Schanberg, MD
Box 3212
Durham, NC 27710
Tel: 919 684-6627   *Fax:* 919 684-6616
Length: 3 Yrs   *ACGME Approved/Offered Positions:* 3
Program ID: 331-36-21-015

Ohio

Cincinnati

Cincinnati Children's Hospital Medical Center/University of Cincinnati College of Medicine Program

Sponsor: Cincinnati Children's Hospital Medical Center
Prgm Director: Jennifer L Huggins, MD*
University of Cincinnati College of Medicine
3333 Burnet Avenue MLC 4010
Cincinnati, OH 45229
Tel: 513 636-2143   *Fax:* 513 636-4116
Length: 3 Yrs   *ACGME Approved/Offered Positions:* 6
Program ID: 331-38-21-016

Cleveland

University Hospitals Case Medical Center Program

Sponsor: University Hospitals Case Medical Center
Prgm Director: Nora G Singer, MD
11100 Euclid Avenue
Mailstop 6008B
Cleveland, OH 44106
Tel: 216 844-3645   *Fax:* 216 844-7587
E-mail: nora.singer@uhhospitals.org
Length: 3 Yrs   *ACGME Approved/Offered Positions:* 3
Program ID: 331-38-12-031

Programs

Columbus

Nationwide Children's Hospital/Ohio State University Program

Sponsor: Nationwide Children's Hospital
Ohio State University Hospital
Prgm Director: Charles H Spencer, MD
Rheumatology Division
700 Children's Drive
Columbus, OH 43205
Tel: 614 722-5525   *Fax:* 614 722-3194
E-mail: Charles.Spencer@nationwidechildrens.org
Length: 3 Yrs   *ACGME Approved/Offered Positions:* 3
Program ID: 331-38-13-033

Pennsylvania

Philadelphia

Children's Hospital of Philadelphia Program

Sponsor: Children's Hospital of Philadelphia
Prgm Director: David D Sherry, MD
3615 Civic Center Boulevard
Suite 1102 Abramson Research Center
Philadelphia, PA 19104
Tel: 215 590-7180   *Fax:* 215 590-1258
E-mail: sherry@email.chop.edu
Length: 3 Yrs   *ACGME Approved/Offered Positions:* 6
Program ID: 331-41-21-025

Pittsburgh

University of Pittsburgh Medical Center Medical Education Program

Sponsor: Univ of Pittsburgh Medical Center Medical
Education
Children's Hospital of Pittsburgh of UPMC
Prgm Director: Raphael Hirsch, MD
3705 Fifth Avenue
Pittsburgh, PA 15213
Tel: 412 692-5970   *Fax:* 412 692-5054
Length: 3 Yrs   *ACGME Approved/Offered Positions:* 6
Program ID: 331-41-13-026

Tennessee

Memphis

University of Tennessee Program

Sponsor: University of Tennessee College of Medicine
LeBonheur Children's Medical Center
Regional Medical Center at Memphis
St Jude Children's Research Hospital
Prgm Director: Linda K Myers, MD
50 N Dunlap Street
Room 301 West Pt Tower
Memphis, TN 38103
Tel: 901 448-5774   *Fax:* 901 287-5036
Length: 3 Yrs   *ACGME Approved/Offered Positions:* 1
Program ID: 331-47-21-017

Texas

Dallas

University of Texas Southwestern Medical School Program

Sponsor: University of Texas Southwestern Medical
School
Children's Medical Center of Dallas
Texas Scottish Rite Hospital for Children
Prgm Director: Lynn G Punaro, MD
Department of Pediatrics
5323 Harry Hines Blvd MC 9063
Dallas, TX 75390
Tel: 214 648-3388   *Fax:* 214 648-3557
E-mail: Sharon.Moore@utsouthwestern.edu
Length: 3 Yrs   *ACGME Approved/Offered Positions:* 6
Program ID: 331-48-31-021

Houston

Baylor College of Medicine Program

Sponsor: Baylor College of Medicine
Texas Children's Hospital
Prgm Director: Maria D Perez, MD
6621 Fannin St, MC 3-2290
Houston, TX 77030
Tel: 832 824-3830   *Fax:* 832 825-3837
Length: 3 Yrs   *ACGME Approved/Offered Positions:* 3
Program ID: 331-48-21-020

Washington

Seattle

University of Washington Program

Sponsor: University of Washington School of Medicine
Seattle Children's Hospital
University of Washington Medical Center
Prgm Director: Helen M Emery, MD
Rheumatology - R-5420
4800 Sand Point Way NE
Seattle, WA 98105
Tel: 206 987-2057   *Fax:* 206 987-5060
E-mail: helen.emery@seattlechildrens.org
Length: 3 Yrs   *ACGME Approved/Offered Positions:* 3
Program ID: 331-54-21-019

Wisconsin

Milwaukee

Medical College of Wisconsin Affiliated Hospitals Program

Sponsor: Medical College of Wisconsin Affiliated
Hospitals, Inc
Children's Hospital of Wisconsin
Prgm Director: Calvin B Williams, MD, PhD
Children's Corporate Center, Suite C465
999 N 92nd Street
Wauwatosa, WI 53226
Tel: 414 266-6700   *Fax:* 414 266-6695
E-mail: cwilliam@mcw.edu
Length: 3 Yrs   *ACGME Approved/Offered Positions:* 3
Program ID: 331-56-22-027

Pediatric Sports Medicine (Pediatrics)

Massachusetts

Boston

Children's Hospital/Boston Medical Center Program

Sponsor: Children's Hospital
Prgm Director: Pierre d'Hemecourt, MD
319 Longwood Avenue
Boston, MA 02115
Tel: 617 355-8597   *Fax:* 617 730-0178
Length: 1 Yr   *ACGME Approved/Offered Positions:* 3
Program ID: 333-24-31-009

New Jersey

Neptune

Jersey Shore University Medical Center Program

Sponsor: Jersey Shore University Medical Center
Prgm Director: Stephen G Rice, MD, PhD
1945 State Route 33, Box 397
Neptune, NJ 07754
Tel: 732 776-2384   *Fax:* 732 776-4403
E-mail: srice@meridianhealth.com
Length: 1 Yr   *ACGME Approved/Offered Positions:* 2
Program ID: 333-33-21-001

Ohio

Akron

Children's Hospital Medical Center of Akron/NEOUCOM Program

Sponsor: Children's Hospital Medical Center of Akron
Prgm Director: Julie M Kerr, MD
One Perkins Square
Suite 7300
Akron, OH 44308
Tel: 330 543-8260   *Fax:* 330 543-3851
Length: 1 Yr   *ACGME Approved/Offered Positions:* 2
Program ID: 333-38-12-003

Cincinnati

Cincinnati Children's Hospital Medical Center/University of Cincinnati College of Medicine Program

Sponsor: Cincinnati Children's Hospital Medical Center
Prgm Director: Jon Divine, MD
3333 Burnet Avenue, MLC 10001
Cincinnati, OH 45229
Tel: 513 636-1246   *Fax:* 513 636-0516
E-mail: jon.divine@cchmc.org
Length: 1 Yr   *ACGME Approved/Offered Positions:* 2
Program ID: 333-38-12-010

Cleveland

University Hospitals Case Medical Center Program

Sponsor: University Hospitals Case Medical Center
Prgm Director: Amanda K Weiss Kelly, MD
11000 Euclid Avenue
Mailstop RBC 6019
Cleveland, OH 44106-5000
Tel: 216 844-3595   *Fax:* 216 844-8444
Length: 1 Yr   *ACGME Approved/Offered Positions:* 2
Program ID: 333-38-13-012

Note: * indicates a newly appointed program director

Columbus

Nationwide Children's Hospital/Ohio State University Program

Sponsor: Nationwide Children's Hospital
Prgm Director: Richard E Rodenberg Jr, MD
584 County Line Road West
Westerville, OH 43082
Tel: 614 355-6000   *Fax:* 614 355-6072
E-mail: richard.rodenberg@nationwidechildrens.org
Length: 1 Yr   *ACGME Approved/Offered Positions:* 3
Program ID: 333-38-31-013

Tennessee

Nashville

Vanderbilt University Program

Sponsor: Vanderbilt University Medical Center
Prgm Director: Andrew Gregory, MD
Medical Center East, South Tower
Suite 3200
Nashville, TN 37232
Tel: 615 322-9009   *Fax:* 615 343-9893
E-mail: andrew.gregory@vanderbilt.edu
Length: 1 Yr   *ACGME Approved/Offered Positions:* 2
Program ID: 333-47-12-008

Texas

Houston

Baylor College of Medicine Program

Sponsor: Baylor College of Medicine
Texas Children's Hospital
Prgm Director: Albert C Hergenroeder, MD
Texas Children's Hospital
6621 Fannin St, CC1710.00
Houston, TX 77030
Tel: 832 822-3658   *Fax:* 832 825-3689
Length: 1 Yr   *ACGME Approved/Offered Positions:* 2
Program ID: 333-48-21-004

Wisconsin

Madison

University of Wisconsin Program

Sponsor: University of Wisconsin Hospital and Clinics
Prgm Director: David T Bernhardt, MD
621 Science Drive
Madison, WI 53711
Tel: 608 263-6477   *Fax:* 608 263-0503
Length: 1 Yr   *ACGME Approved/Offered Positions:* 1
Program ID: 333-56-13-007

Pediatric Surgery (General Surgery)

Alabama

Birmingham

University of Alabama Medical Center Program

Sponsor: University of Alabama Hospital
Children's Hospital of Alabama
Prgm Director: Keith E Georgeson, MD
1600 7th Avenue South
ACC 300
Birmingham, AL 35233
Tel: 205 939-9688   *Fax:* 205 975-4972
E-mail: keith.georgeson@ccc.uab.edu
Length: 2 Yrs   *ACGME Approved/Offered Positions:* 2
Program ID: 445-01-21-032

Arkansas

Little Rock

University of Arkansas for Medical Sciences Program

Sponsor: University of Arkansas College of Medicine
Arkansas Children's Hospital
Prgm Director: Samuel D Smith, MD
800 Marshall Street
Little Rock, AR 72202
Tel: 501 364-2942   *Fax:* 501 364-1516
E-mail: smithsamueld@uams.edu
Length: 2 Yrs   *ACGME Approved/Offered Positions:* 2
Program ID: 445-04-21-028

California

Los Angeles

Childrens Hospital Los Angeles Program

Sponsor: Childrens Hospital Los Angeles
Prgm Director: Henri R Ford, MD
4650 Sunset Boulevard
MS 72
Los Angeles, CA 90027
Tel: 323 361-2104   *Fax:* 323 361-3534
E-mail: hford@chla.usc.edu
Length: 2 Yrs   *ACGME Approved/Offered Positions:* 2
Program ID: 445-05-21-001

Stanford

Stanford University Program

Sponsor: Stanford Hospital and Clinics
Lucile Salter Packard Children's Hospital at Stanford
Prgm Director: Craig T Albanese, MD
Department of Surgery
780 Welch Road, Suite 206
Stanford, CA 94305
Tel: 650 724-3664   *Fax:* 650 724-5344
Length: 2 Yrs   *ACGME Approved/Offered Positions:* 2
Program ID: 445-05-31-048

Colorado

Aurora

University of Colorado Denver Program

Sponsor: University of Colorado Denver School of Medicine
Children's Hospital (The)
Prgm Director: Moritz M Ziegler, MD
13123 E 16th Ave
Department of Pediatric Surgery, B-323
Denver, CO 80045
Tel: 720 777-6524   *Fax:* 720 777-7271
E-mail: ziegler.moritz@tchden.org
Length: 2 Yrs   *ACGME Approved/Offered Positions:* 2
Program ID: 445-07-21-027

Connecticut

New Haven

Yale-New Haven Medical Center Program

Sponsor: Yale-New Haven Hospital
Prgm Director: Larry Moss, MD
333 Cedar Street
PO Box 208062
New Haven, CT 06510
Tel: 203 785-2701   *Fax:* 203 785-3820
E-mail: larry.moss@yale.edu
Length: 2 Yrs   *ACGME Approved/Offered Positions:* 2
Program ID: 445-08-21-030

District of Columbia

Washington

Children's National Medical Center/ George Washington University Program

Sponsor: Children's National Medical Center
Prgm Director: Philip C Guzzetta Jr, MD
111 Michigan Ave, NW
Washington, DC 20010
Tel: 202 476-2151   *Fax:* 202 476-4174
Length: 2 Yrs   *ACGME Approved/Offered Positions:* 2
Program ID: 445-10-21-015

Florida

Gainesville

University of Florida Program

Sponsor: University of Florida College of Medicine
Shands Hospital at the University of Florida
Prgm Director: Mike K Chen, MD
Department of Surgery
1600 SW Archer Road, Room N6-10
Gainesville, FL 32610
Tel: 352 392-3718   *Fax:* 352 392-9081
E-mail: mike.chen@surgery.ufl.edu
Length: 2 Yrs   *ACGME Approved/Offered Positions:* 2
Program ID: 445-11-13-047

Programs

Georgia

Atlanta

Emory University Program

Sponsor: Emory University School of Medicine
Children's Healthcare of Atlanta at Egleston
Prgm Director: Mark L Wulkan, MD
Emory University
2015 Uppergate Dr NE
Atlanta, GA 30322
Tel: 404 727-3779   *Fax:* 404 727-2120
E-mail: mark.wulkan@oz.ped.emory.edu
Length: 2 Yrs   *ACGME Approved/Offered Positions:* 2
Program ID: 445-12-21-033

Illinois

Chicago

McGaw Medical Center of Northwestern University Program

Sponsor: McGaw Medical Center of Northwestern
University
Children's Memorial Hospital
Prgm Director: Marleta Reynolds, MD
2300 Children's Plaza, #63
Chicago, IL 60614
Tel: 773 880-4292   *Fax:* 773 880-4588
E-mail: vrodr@childrensmemorial.org
Length: 2 Yrs   *ACGME Approved/Offered Positions:* 2
Program ID: 445-16-21-002

University of Chicago Program

Sponsor: University of Chicago Medical Center
University of Chicago Comer Children's Hospital
Prgm Director: Donald C Liu, MD, PhD
5839 S Maryland Avenue, MC 4062
Chicago, IL 60637
Tel: 773 702-6175   *Fax:* 773 702-1192
Length: 2 Yrs   *ACGME Approved/Offered Positions:* 2
Program ID: 445-16-31-041

Indiana

Indianapolis

Indiana University School of Medicine Program

Sponsor: Indiana University School of Medicine
Clarian Riley Hospital for Children
Prgm Director: Frederick J Rescorla, MD
Indiana University School of Medicine
702 Barnhill Drive, Suite 2500
Indianapolis, IN 46202
Tel: 317 274-4604   *Fax:* 317 274-4613
E-mail: frescorl@iupui.edu
Length: 2 Yrs   *ACGME Approved/Offered Positions:* 2
Program ID: 445-17-21-019

Kentucky

Louisville

University of Louisville Program

Sponsor: University of Louisville School of Medicine
Kosair Children's Hospital (Norton Healthcare, Inc)
Prgm Director: Mary E Fallat, MD
315 East Broadway
Suite 565
Louisville, KY 40202
Tel: 502 629-8630   *Fax:* 502 583-9735
E-mail: mefall01@louisville.edu
Length: 2 Yrs   *ACGME Approved/Offered Positions:* 1
Program ID: 445-20-31-044

Maryland

Baltimore

Johns Hopkins University Program

Sponsor: Johns Hopkins University School of Medicine
Johns Hopkins Hospital
University of Maryland Medical System
Prgm Director: Paul M Colombani, MD, MBA
600 North Wolfe Street, Rm Harvey 320
Baltimore, MD 21287
Tel: 410 955-2717   *Fax:* 410 502-5314
Length: 2 Yrs   *ACGME Approved/Offered Positions:* 2
Program ID: 445-23-21-003

Massachusetts

Boston

Children's Hospital Program

Sponsor: Children's Hospital
Prgm Director: Craig W Lillehei, MD
300 Longwood Ave
Department of Surgery
Boston, MA 02115
Tel: 617 355-3039   *Fax:* 617 730-0475
E-mail: craig.lillehei@childrens.harvard.edu
Length: 2 Yrs   *ACGME Approved/Offered Positions:* 2
Program ID: 445-24-21-016

Michigan

Ann Arbor

University of Michigan Program

Sponsor: University of Michigan Hospitals and Health
Centers
Prgm Director: Ronald B Hirschl, MD
1405 E Ann Street
F3970 Mott Children's Hospital
Ann Arbor, MI 48109
Tel: 734 764-6846   *Fax:* 734 936-9784
Length: 2 Yrs   *ACGME Approved/Offered Positions:* 2
Program ID: 445-25-21-018

Detroit

Wayne State University/Detroit Medical Center Program

Sponsor: Wayne State University/Detroit Medical Center
Children's Hospital of Michigan
Prgm Director: Marc L Cullen, MD
3901 Beaubien Boulevard
Carls Building, 3rd Floor
Detroit, MI 48201
Tel: 313 745-5839   *Fax:* 313 966-7696
E-mail: dkovach@dmc.org
Length: 2 Yrs   *ACGME Approved/Offered Positions:* 2
Program ID: 445-25-11-004

Missouri

Kansas City

University of Missouri at Kansas City Program

Sponsor: University of Missouri-Kansas City School of
Medicine
Children's Mercy Hospital
Prgm Director: George W Holcomb III, MD, MBA
2401 Gillham Rd
Kansas City, MO 64108
Tel: 816 234-3578   *Fax:* 816 983-6885
E-mail: ksmith@cmh.edu
Length: 2 Yrs   *ACGME Approved/Offered Positions:* 2
Program ID: 445-28-11-005

St Louis

Washington University/B-JH/SLCH Consortium Program

Sponsor: Washington University/B-JH/SLCH Consortium
St Louis Children's Hospital
Prgm Director: Patrick A Dillon, MD
One Children's Place
Suite 5S40
St Louis, MO 63110
Tel: 314 454-6022   *Fax:* 314 454-2442
E-mail: dillonp@wudosis.wustl.edu
Length: 2 Yrs   *ACGME Approved/Offered Positions:* 2
Program ID: 445-28-21-034

New York

Buffalo

University at Buffalo Program

Sponsor: University at Buffalo School of Medicine
Kaleida Health System (Women and Children's Hosp of
Buffalo)
Prgm Director: Michael G Caty, MD
219 Bryant Street
Buffalo, NY 14222
Tel: 716 878-7785   *Fax:* 716 888-3850
E-mail: caty@acsu.buffalo.edu
Length: 2 Yrs   *ACGME Approved/Offered Positions:* 2
Program ID: 445-35-21-017

Great Neck

NSLIJHS-Schneider Children's Hospital Program

Sponsor: North Shore-Long Island Jewish Health System
Schneider Children's Hospital at Long Island Jewish
Med Ctr
Prgm Director: Andrew R Hong, MD
269-01 76th Avenue
New Hyde Park, NY 11040
Tel: 718 470-3636   *Fax:* 718 347-1233
E-mail: hong@lij.edu
Length: 2 Yrs   *ACGME Approved/Offered Positions:* 2
Program ID: 445-35-12-039

New York

New York Presbyterian Hospital (Columbia Campus) Program

Sponsor: New York Presbyterian Hospital
New York Presbyterian Hospital (Columbia Campus)
Prgm Director: Charles J Stolar, MD
3959 Broadway
CHN215
New York, NY 10032
Tel: 212 342-8586   *Fax:* 212 305-5971
E-mail: cjs3@Columbia.edu
Length: 2 Yrs   *ACGME Approved/Offered Positions:* 2
Program ID: 445-35-11-006

Note: * indicates a newly appointed program director

Ohio

Cincinnati

Cincinnati Children's Hospital Medical Center/University of Cincinnati College of Medicine Program

Sponsor: Cincinnati Children's Hospital Medical Center
Prgm Director: Frederick C Ryckman, MD
3333 Burnet Avenue
Cincinnati, OH 45229
Tel: 513 636-7365   *Fax:* 513 636-7657
Length: 2 Yrs   *ACGME Approved/Offered Positions:* 2
Program ID: 445-38-11-008

Columbus

Nationwide Children's Hospital/Ohio State University Program

Sponsor: Nationwide Children's Hospital
Prgm Director: Donna A Caniano, MD
700 Children's Drive
ED - 379
Columbus, OH 43205
Tel: 614 722-3912   *Fax:* 614 722-3903
E-mail: donna.caniano@nationwidechildrens.org
Length: 2 Yrs   *ACGME Approved/Offered Positions:* 2
Program ID: 445-38-21-012

Oklahoma

Oklahoma City

University of Oklahoma Health Sciences Center Program

Sponsor: University of Oklahoma College of Medicine
OU Medical Center - Children's Hospital
Prgm Director: David W Tuggle, MD
PO Box 26307
Oklahoma City, OK 73126
Tel: 405 271-5922   *Fax:* 405 271-3278
Length: 2 Yrs   *ACGME Approved/Offered Positions:* 2
Program ID: 445-39-11-009

Oregon

Portland

Oregon Health & Science University Program

Sponsor: Oregon Health & Science University Hospital
Legacy Emanuel Hospital and Health Center
Prgm Director: Mark Silen, MD, MBA
3181 SW Sam Jackson Park Road
Mail Code: CDW-7
Portland, OR 97239
Tel: 503 494-7764
E-mail: silenm@ohsu.edu
Length: 2 Yrs   *ACGME Approved/Offered Positions:* 2
Program ID: 445-40-13-043

Pennsylvania

Philadelphia

Children's Hospital of Philadelphia Program

Sponsor: Children's Hospital of Philadelphia
Prgm Director: Alan W Flake, MD
34th Street and Civic Center Blvd
5th Floor Wood Building
Philadelphia, PA 19104
Tel: 215 590-2727   *Fax:* 215 590-4875
E-mail: corcoranc@email.chop.edu
Length: 2 Yrs   *ACGME Approved/Offered Positions:* 3
Program ID: 445-41-11-014

St Christopher's Hospital for Children Program

Sponsor: St Christopher's Hospital for Children (Tenet Health System)
Prgm Director: Marshall Z Schwartz, MD
Erie Avenue at Front Street
Philadelphia, PA 19134
Tel: 215 427-5446   *Fax:* 215 427-4616
E-mail: irene.brown@tenethealth.com
Length: 2 Yrs   *ACGME Approved/Offered Positions:* 2
Program ID: 445-41-21-010

Pittsburgh

University of Pittsburgh Medical Center Medical Education Program

Sponsor: Univ of Pittsburgh Medical Center Medical Education
Children's Hospital of Pittsburgh of UPMC
Prgm Director: Barbara A Gaines, MD*
3705 Fifth Avenue at De Soto Street
Pittsburgh, PA 15213
Tel: 412 692-5053   *Fax:* 412 692-8299
Length: 2 Yrs   *ACGME Approved/Offered Positions:* 2
Program ID: 445-41-11-013

Rhode Island

Providence

Brown University Program

Sponsor: Rhode Island Hospital-Lifespan
Women and Infants Hospital of Rhode Island
Prgm Director: Thomas F Tracy Jr, MD, MS
Hasbro Children's Hospital, Rm 147
593 Eddy Street
Providence, RI 02903
Tel: 401 444-7605   *Fax:* 401 444-7629
E-mail: Thomas_Tracy@brown.edu
Length: 2 Yrs   *ACGME Approved/Offered Positions:* 2
Program ID: 445-43-21-031

Tennessee

Memphis

University of Tennessee Program

Sponsor: University of Tennessee College of Medicine
LeBonheur Children's Medical Center
Prgm Director: Max R Langham Jr, MD
777 Washington Avenue, Suite P-220
Memphis, TN 38105
Tel: 901 287-6300   *Fax:* 901 287-5191
E-mail: mlangham@utmem.edu
Length: 2 Yrs   *ACGME Approved/Offered Positions:* 2
Program ID: 445-47-21-025

Nashville

Vanderbilt University/Monroe Carell, Jr Children's Hospital Program

Sponsor: Vanderbilt University Medical Center
Monroe Carell, Jr Children's Hospital at Vanderbilt
Prgm Director: Wallace W Neblett, MD
2200 Children's Way
The Doctor's Office Tower, Suite 4150
Nashville, TN 37232
Tel: 615 936-1050
Length: 2 Yrs   *ACGME Approved/Offered Positions:* 2
Program ID: 445-47-21-046

Texas

Dallas

University of Texas Southwestern Medical School Program

Sponsor: University of Texas Southwestern Medical School
Children's Medical Center of Dallas
Dallas County Hospital District-Parkland Memorial Hospital
Prgm Director: Michael A Skinner, MD*
c/o CMC, 1935 Medical District Dr
B3250
Dallas, TX 75235
Tel: 214 456-6040   *Fax:* 214 456-6320
Length: 2 Yrs   *ACGME Approved/Offered Positions:* 2
Program ID: 445-48-21-022

Houston

Baylor College of Medicine Program

Sponsor: Baylor College of Medicine
Texas Children's Hospital
Prgm Director: Jed G Nuchtern, MD
Clinical Care Center, Suite 650
6621 Fannin St, CC650
Houston, TX 77030
Tel: 832 822-8135   *Fax:* 832 825-3141
E-mail: khicks@bcm.edu
Length: 2 Yrs   *ACGME Approved/Offered Positions:* 2
Program ID: 445-48-21-020

University of Texas at Houston Program

Sponsor: University of Texas Health Science Center at Houston
Memorial Hermann Hospital
Texas Children's Hospital
University of Texas M D Anderson Cancer Center
Prgm Director: Kevin P Lally, MD, MS
Health Science Center at Houston
6431 Fannin Street, Suite 5.258
Houston, TX 77030
Tel: 713 500-7300   *Fax:* 713 500-7295
E-mail: kevin.p.lally@uth.tmc.edu
Length: 2 Yrs   *ACGME Approved/Offered Positions:* 2
Program ID: 445-48-12-042

Washington

Seattle

University of Washington Program

Sponsor: University of Washington School of Medicine
Seattle Children's Hospital
Prgm Director: John H Waldhausen, MD
4800 Sand Point Way NE
Dept of Surgery, M/S W-7729
Seattle, WA 98105
Tel: 206 987-2039   *Fax:* 206 987-3925
E-mail: caity.gerhardt@seattlechildrens.org
Length: 2 Yrs   *ACGME Approved/Offered Positions:* 2
Program ID: 445-54-11-011

Programs

Wisconsin

Milwaukee

Medical College of Wisconsin Affiliated Hospitals/Children's Hospital of Wisconsin Program
Sponsor: Medical College of Wisconsin Affiliated Hospitals, Inc
Children's Hospital of Wisconsin
Prgm Director: Keith T Oldham, MD
Children's Corporate Center
999 North 92nd Street, C320
Milwaukee, WI 53226
Tel: 414 266-6557 *Fax:* 414 266-6579
E-mail: koldham@chw.org
Length: 2 Yrs *ACGME Approved/Offered Positions:* 2
Program ID: 445-56-31-038

Pediatric Transplant Hepatology (Pediatrics)

Georgia

Atlanta

Emory University Program
Sponsor: Emory University School of Medicine
Children's Healthcare of Atlanta at Egleston
Prgm Director: Rene Romero, MD
Division of Pediatric Gastroenterology
2015 Uppergate Dr NE
Atlanta, GA 30322
Tel: 404 785-1832
E-mail: rene.romero@choa.org
Length: 1 Yr *ACGME Approved/Offered Positions:* 1
Program ID: 338-12-32-004

Illinois

Chicago

McGaw Medical Center of Northwestern University Program
Sponsor: McGaw Medical Center of Northwestern University
Children's Memorial Hospital
Prgm Director: Estella M Alonso, MD
Ward 4-334
303 E Chicago Avenue
Chicago, IL 60611
Tel: 773 880-4643 *Fax:* 773 975-8671
E-mail: drjones@childrensmemorial.org
Length: 1 Yr *ACGME Approved/Offered Positions:* 1
Program ID: 338-16-32-003

Ohio

Cincinnati

Cincinnati Children's Hospital Medical Center Program
Sponsor: Cincinnati Children's Hospital Medical Center
Prgm Director: William F Balistreri, MD
3333 Burnet Avenue
Cincinnati, OH 45229
Tel: 513 636-4594 *Fax:* 513 636-7805
Length: 1 Yr *ACGME Approved/Offered Positions:* 1
Program ID: 338-38-32-002

Pennsylvania

Pittsburgh

University of Pittsburgh Medical Center Medical Education Program
Sponsor: Univ of Pittsburgh Medical Center Medical Education
Children's Hospital of Pittsburgh of UPMC
Prgm Director: Benjamin L Shneider, MD
Suite 503 Medical Arts Building
3705 Fifth Avenue
Pittsburgh, PA 15213
Tel: 412 692-5412
Length: 1 Yr *ACGME Approved/Offered Positions:* 1
Program ID: 338-41-32-001

Pediatric Urology (Urology)

California

San Diego

University of California (San Diego) Program
Sponsor: University of California (San Diego) Medical Center
Naval Medical Center (San Diego)
Rady Children's Hospital
Prgm Director: George W Kaplan, MD, MS
7930 Frost Street, Suite 300
San Diego, CA 92123
Tel: 858 279-8527 *Fax:* 858 279-8876
E-mail: gkaplan@chsd.org
Length: 1 Yr *ACGME Approved/Offered Positions:* 1
Program ID: 485-05-21-004
Uniformed Services Program

San Francisco

University of California (San Francisco) Program
Sponsor: University of California (San Francisco) School of Medicine
Natividad Medical Center
UCSF and Mount Zion Medical Centers
Prgm Director: Laurence S Baskin, MD
A633, Box 0738
400 Parnassus Avenue A633
San Francisco, CA 94143
Tel: 415 476-1611 *Fax:* 415 476-8849
E-mail: kkojimoto@urology.ucsf.edu
Length: 1 Yr *ACGME Approved/Offered Positions:* 1
Program ID: 485-05-21-011

Stanford

Stanford University Program
Sponsor: Stanford Hospital and Clinics
Santa Clara Valley Medical Center
Prgm Director: Linda D Shortliffe, MD
300 Pasteur Drive, S-287
Stanford, CA 94305
Tel: 650 498-5042 *Fax:* 650 723-4055
E-mail: ldshortliffe@stanford.edu
Length: 1 Yr *ACGME Approved/Offered Positions:* 1
Program ID: 485-05-12-024

District of Columbia

Washington

George Washington University/Children's National Medical Center Program
Sponsor: Children's National Medical Center
Prgm Director: Hans G Pohl, MD*
111 Michigan Avenue NW
Washington, DC 20010
Tel: 202 476-5042 *Fax:* 202 476-4739
Length: 1 Yr *ACGME Approved/Offered Positions:* 1
Program ID: 485-10-13-025

Note: * indicates a newly appointed program director

Georgia

Atlanta

Emory University Program
Sponsor: Emory University School of Medicine
Children's Healthcare of Atlanta at Egleston
Children's Healthcare of Atlanta at Scottish Rite
Prgm Director: Edwin A Smith, MD
5445 Meridian Mark Road, NE, Suite 420
Atlanta, GA 30342
Tel: 404 252-5206   *Fax:* 404 252-1268
Length: 1 Yr   *ACGME Approved/Offered Positions:* 1
Program ID: 485-12-21-017

Illinois

Chicago

McGaw Medical Center of Northwestern University Program
Sponsor: McGaw Medical Center of Northwestern
   University
Children's Memorial Hospital
Prgm Director: William E Kaplan, MD
2300 Children's Plaza
Division of Urology, Box 24
Chicago, IL 60614
Tel: 773 880-4428   *Fax:* 773 880-3339
E-mail: wkaplan@childrensmemorial.org
Length: 1 Yr   *ACGME Approved/Offered Positions:* 1
Program ID: 485-16-12-018

Indiana

Indianapolis

Indiana University School of Medicine Program
Sponsor: Indiana University School of Medicine
Clarian Riley Hospital for Children
St Vincent Hospitals and Health Care Center
Prgm Director: Richard C Rink, MD
702 N Barnhill Drive, Suite 4230
Indianapolis, IN 46202
Tel: 317 274-7472   *Fax:* 317 274-7481
Length: 1 Yr   *ACGME Approved/Offered Positions:* 1
Program ID: 485-17-21-015

Maryland

Baltimore

Johns Hopkins University Program
Sponsor: Johns Hopkins University School of Medicine
Johns Hopkins Hospital
Prgm Director: John P Gearhart, MD
Marburg 146
600 North Wolfe Street
Baltimore, MD 21287
Tel: 410 955-8710   *Fax:* 410 955-0833
E-mail: jgearha2@jhmi.edu
Length: 1 Yr   *ACGME Approved/Offered Positions:* 1
Program ID: 485-23-21-009

Massachusetts

Boston

Children's Hospital/Harvard Medical School Program
Sponsor: Children's Hospital
Prgm Director: Bartley G Cilento Jr, MD, MPH*
300 Longwood Avenue
Boston, MA 02115
Tel: 617 355-2080
Length: 1 Yr   *ACGME Approved/Offered Positions:* 2
Program ID: 485-24-21-006

New York

Great Neck

NSLIJHS-Schneider Children's Hospital Program
Sponsor: North Shore-Long Island Jewish Health System
Long Island Jewish Medical Center
Schneider Children's Hospital at North Shore University
   Hosp
Prgm Director: Lane S Palmer, MD
1999 Marcus Avenue, M-18
New Hyde Park, NY 11042
Tel: 516 466-6953   *Fax:* 516 466-5608
Length: 1 Yr   *ACGME Approved/Offered Positions:* 1
Program ID: 485-35-21-016

Ohio

Cincinnati

Cincinnati Children's Hospital Medical Center/University of Cincinnati College of Medicine Program
Sponsor: Cincinnati Children's Hospital Medical Center
Prgm Director: Pramod P Reddy, MD
Division of Pediatric Urology
3333 Burnet Avenue MLC 5037
Cincinnati, OH 45229
Tel: 513 803-0451   *Fax:* 513 636-6753
E-mail: pramod.reddy@cchmc.org
Length: 1 Yr   *ACGME Approved/Offered Positions:* 1
Program ID: 485-38-21-014

Columbus

Nationwide Children's Hospital/Ohio State University Program
Sponsor: Nationwide Children's Hospital
Prgm Director: Stephen A Koff, MD
Education Building, Room ED314
700 Children's Drive
Columbus, OH 43205
Tel: 614 722-6625   *Fax:* 614 722-6627
E-mail: stephen.koff@nationwidechildrens.org
Length: 1 Yr   *ACGME Approved/Offered Positions:* 1
Program ID: 485-38-12-022

Oklahoma

Oklahoma City

University of Oklahoma Health Sciences Center/Children's Hospital Program
Sponsor: University of Oklahoma College of Medicine
OU Medical Center - Children's Hospital
Prgm Director: Bradley P Kropp, MD
920 Stanton L Young Boulevard
WP 3150
Oklahoma City, OK 73104
Tel: 405 271-6900   *Fax:* 405 271-3118
E-mail: brad-kropp@ouhsc.edu
Length: 1 Yr   *ACGME Approved/Offered Positions:* 1
Program ID: 485-39-13-027

Pennsylvania

Philadelphia

Children's Hospital of Philadelphia Program
Sponsor: Children's Hospital of Philadelphia
Prgm Director: Thomas F Kolon, MD, MS
34th Street & Civic Center Blvd
Urology, 3 Wood Center
Philadelphia, PA 19104
Tel: 215 590-4690   *Fax:* 215 590-3985
E-mail: kolon@email.chop.edu
Length: 1 Yr   *ACGME Approved/Offered Positions:* 1
Program ID: 485-41-21-002

Thomas Jefferson University Program
Sponsor: Thomas Jefferson University Hospital
Alfred I duPont Hospital for Children
Prgm Director: Julia S Barthold, MD*
1600 Rockland Road
PO Box 269
Wilmington, DE 19899
Tel: 302 651-5258   *Fax:* 302 651-6410
E-mail: jbarthol@nemours.org
Length: 1 Yr   *ACGME Approved/Offered Positions:* 1
Program ID: 485-41-31-023

Pittsburgh

University of Pittsburgh Medical Center Medical Education Program
Sponsor: Univ of Pittsburgh Medical Center Medical
   Education
Children's Hospital of Pittsburgh of UPMC
Prgm Director: Francis X Schneck, MD*
3705 Fifth Avenue
G205 DeSoto Wing
Pittsburgh, PA 15213
Tel: 412 687-5437   *Fax:* 412 687-5545
Length: 1 Yr   *ACGME Approved/Offered Positions:* 1
Program ID: 485-41-21-020

Tennessee

Memphis

University of Tennessee/LeBonheur Children's Medical Center Program
Sponsor: University of Tennessee College of Medicine
LeBonheur Children's Medical Center
Prgm Director: Mark A Williams, MD*
956 Court Avenue
Suite H210
Memphis, TN 38163
Tel: 901 287-4030   *Fax:* 901 287-4094
E-mail: markwilliams.md@gmail.com
Length: 1 Yr   *ACGME Approved/Offered Positions:* 1
Program ID: 485-47-12-029

Programs

Nashville

Vanderbilt University Program
Sponsor: Vanderbilt University Medical Center
Prgm Director: John W Brock III, MD
A-1302 Medical Center North
Nashville, TN 37232
Tel: 615 343-5604   *Fax:* 615 322-8990
Length: 1 Yr   *ACGME Approved/Offered Positions:* 1
Program ID: 485-47-13-019

Texas

Dallas

Children's Medical Center of Dallas/University of Texas Southwestern Medical School Program
Sponsor: University of Texas Southwestern Medical School
Children's Medical Center of Dallas
Texas Scottish Rite Hospital for Children
Prgm Director: Warren Snodgrass, MD*
Department of Pediatric Urology
2350 Stemmons Frwy, Suite F4300
Dallas, TX 75207
Tel: 214 456-2481   *Fax:* 214 456-8803
E-mail: warren.snodgrass@childrens.com
Length: 1 Yr   *ACGME Approved/Offered Positions:* 2
Program ID: 485-48-31-021

Houston

Baylor College of Medicine Program
Sponsor: Baylor College of Medicine
Texas Children's Hospital
Prgm Director: Edmond T Gonzales Jr, MD
Clinical Care Center, Suite 660
6621 Fannin St
Houston, TX 77030
Tel: 832 822-3172   *Fax:* 832 825-3159
E-mail: colleenk@bcm.edu
Length: 1 Yr   *ACGME Approved/Offered Positions:* 1
Program ID: 485-48-21-008

Washington

Seattle

University of Washington Program
Sponsor: University of Washington School of Medicine
Seattle Children's Hospital
Prgm Director: Richard W Grady, MD
PO Box 5371
Seattle, WA 98105
Tel: 206 987-2130   *Fax:* 206 987-3925
Length: 1 Yr   *ACGME Approved/Offered Positions:* 2
Program ID: 485-54-21-012

Wisconsin

Milwaukee

Medical College of Wisconsin Affiliated Hospitals/Children's Hospital of Wisconsin Program
Sponsor: Medical College of Wisconsin Affiliated Hospitals, Inc
Children's Hospital of Wisconsin
Prgm Director: Michael E Mitchell, MD
999 N 92nd Street, #330
Milwaukee, WI 53226
Tel: 414 337-7757   *Fax:* 414 266-1752
E-mail: gradecki@chw.org
Length: 1 Yr   *ACGME Approved/Offered Positions:* 1
Program ID: 485-56-12-026

Pediatrics

Alabama

Birmingham

University of Alabama Medical Center Program
Sponsor: University of Alabama Hospital
Children's Hospital of Alabama
Prgm Director: Michele H Nichols, MD
1600 7th Avenue South
Suite 604-ACC
Birmingham, AL 35233
Tel: 205 939-9589   *Fax:* 205 939-9977
E-mail: uabkids@peds.uab.edu
Length: 3 Yrs   *ACGME Approved/Offered Positions:* 70
Program ID: 320-01-21-017

Mobile

University of South Alabama Program
Sponsor: University of South Alabama Hospitals
USA Children's and Women's Hospital
Prgm Director: Franklin Trimm, MD
1700 Center St
Mobile, AL 36604
Tel: 251 415-1087   *Fax:* 251 415-1387
E-mail: pedsresidency@southalabama.edu
Length: 3 Yrs   *ACGME Approved/Offered Positions:* 27
Program ID: 320-01-21-019

Arizona

Phoenix

Phoenix Children's Hospital/Maricopa Medical Center Program
Sponsor: Phoenix Children's Hospital
Maricopa Medical Center
Prgm Director: Grace L Caputo, MD, MPH
1919 E Thomas Rd
Phoenix, AZ 85016
Tel: 602 546-2923   *Fax:* 602 546-0806
E-mail: sbarker@phoenixchildrens.com
Length: 3 Yrs   *ACGME Approved/Offered Positions:* 72
Program ID: 320-03-32-020

St Joseph's Hospital and Medical Center Program
Sponsor: St Joseph's Hospital and Medical Center
Prgm Director: Lilia Parra-Roide, MD
350 West Thomas Road
Phoenix, AZ 85013
Tel: 602 406-3519   *Fax:* 602 406-4102
E-mail: lilia.parra-roide@chw.edu
Length: 3 Yrs   *ACGME Approved/Offered Positions:* 30
Program ID: 320-03-21-371

Tucson

University of Arizona Program
Sponsor: University of Arizona College of Medicine
Tucson Medical Center
University Medical Center
Prgm Director: Conrad J Clemens, MD, MPH
1501 North Campbell Avenue
PO Box 245073
Tucson, AZ 85724
Tel: 520 626-7944   *Fax:* 520 626-5652
Length: 3 Yrs   *ACGME Approved/Offered Positions:* 43
Program ID: 320-03-21-021

Note: * indicates a newly appointed program director

Arkansas

Little Rock

University of Arkansas for Medical Sciences Program

Sponsor: University of Arkansas College of Medicine
Arkansas Children's Hospital
Prgm Director: Henry C Farrar, MD
800 Marshall Street, Slot 512-19A
Little Rock, AR 72202
Tel: 501 364-1874   *Fax:* 501 364-3196
Length: 3 Yrs   *ACGME Approved/Offered Positions:* 66
Program ID: 320-04-21-022

California

Fresno

University of California (San Francisco)/Fresno Program

Sponsor: UCSF Fresno Medical Education Program
Children's Hospital Central California
Community Medical Centers (Fresno)
Prgm Director: Robert H Kezirian, MD
Mail Stop GE20
9300 Valley Children's Place
Madera, CA 93638
Tel: 559 353-5141   *Fax:* 559 353-5318
E-mail: rkezirian@childrenscentralcal.org
Length: 3 Yrs   *ACGME Approved/Offered Positions:* 30
Program ID: 320-05-11-024

Loma Linda

Loma Linda University Program

Sponsor: Loma Linda University Medical Center
Prgm Director: Sharon K Riesen, MD
11234 Anderson Street, Coleman Pavilion A1111
Loma Linda, CA 92354
Tel: 909 558-4174   *Fax:* 909 558-4184
E-mail: pedresoffice@llu.edu
Length: 3 Yrs   *ACGME Approved/Offered Positions:* 66
Program ID: 320-05-11-026

Los Angeles

Childrens Hospital Los Angeles Program

Sponsor: Childrens Hospital Los Angeles
Prgm Director: Eyal Ben-Isaac, MD
4650 Sunset Blvd, MS 68
Los Angeles, CA 90027
Tel: 323 361-2122   *Fax:* 323 361-7926
Length: 3 Yrs   *ACGME Approved/Offered Positions:* 83
Program ID: 320-05-11-028

Kaiser Permanente Southern California (Los Angeles) Program

Sponsor: Kaiser Permanente Southern California
Kaiser Foundation Hospital (Los Angeles)
Prgm Director: Steven D Woods, MD, MSPH
Center for Medical Education
4733 Sunset Blvd, 3rd Floor
Los Angeles, CA 90027
Tel: 323 783-5311   *Fax:* 323 783-8681
Length: 3 Yrs   *ACGME Approved/Offered Positions:* 21
Program ID: 320-05-12-029

UCLA Medical Center Program

Sponsor: UCLA David Geffen School of Medicine/UCLA Medical Center
UCLA Medical Center
Prgm Director: M Virginia Barrow, MD
Department of Pediatrics
757 Westwood Plaza, Room 3108
Los Angeles, CA 90095
Tel: 310 267-9128   *Fax:* 310 267-3842
E-mail: EOng@mednet.ucla.edu
Length: 3 Yrs   *ACGME Approved/Offered Positions:* 87
Program ID: 320-05-21-032

University of Southern California/ LAC+USC Medical Center Program

Sponsor: University of Southern California/LAC+USC Medical Center
LAC+USC Medical Center
Prgm Director: Rukmani Vasan, MD, MEd
Women's & Children's Hospital
1240 N Mission Road, Rm L-902
Los Angeles, CA 90033
Tel: 323 226-3691   *Fax:* 323 226-4380
E-mail: rvasan@usc.edu
Length: 3 Yrs   *ACGME Approved/Offered Positions:* 33
Program ID: 320-05-11-030

White Memorial Medical Center Program

Sponsor: White Memorial Medical Center
Prgm Director: Ernie Guzman, MD
Department of Pediatrics
1720 E Cesar E Chavez Avenue
Los Angeles, CA 90033
Tel: 323 268-5000   *Fax:* 323 881-8601
Length: 3 Yrs   *ACGME Approved/Offered Positions:* 13
Program ID: 320-05-11-033

Oakland

Children's Hospital-Oakland Program

Sponsor: Children's Hospital-Oakland
Prgm Director: James S Wright, MD
747 52nd Street
Oakland, CA 94609
Tel: 510 428-3830
Length: 3 Yrs   *ACGME Approved/Offered Positions:* 78
Program ID: 320-05-31-034

Kaiser Permanente Medical Group (Northern California) Program

Sponsor: Kaiser Permanente Medical Group (Northern California)
Kaiser Permanente Medical Center (Oakland)
Prgm Director: Elizabeth Culler, MD
Department of Pediatrics
280 West MacArthur Blvd
Oakland, CA 94611
Tel: 510 752-1490   *Fax:* 510 752-1571
Length: 3 Yrs   *ACGME Approved/Offered Positions:* 18
Program ID: 320-05-12-035

Orange

Children's Hospital of Orange County Program

Sponsor: Children's Hospital of Orange County
Prgm Director: James D Korb, MD
455 South Main Street
Orange, CA 92668
Tel: 714 532-8338   *Fax:* 714 289-4010
E-mail: dliebold@choc.org
Length: 3 Yrs   *ACGME Approved/Offered Positions:* 50
Program ID: 320-05-21-386

University of California (Irvine) Program

Sponsor: University of California (Irvine) Medical Center
Long Beach Memorial Medical Center
Prgm Director: Khanh-Van Le-Bucklin, MD
101 The City Drive ZOT 4482
City Tower, Suite 800
Orange, CA 92868
Tel: 714 456-5631   *Fax:* 714 456-6660
Length: 3 Yrs   *ACGME Approved/Offered Positions:* 48
Program ID: 320-05-21-025

Sacramento

University of California (Davis) Health System Program

Sponsor: University of California (Davis) Health System
University of California (Davis) Medical Center
Prgm Director: Richard J Pan, MD, MPH*
Department of Pediatrics
2315 Stockton Blvd
Sacramento, CA 95817
Tel: 916 734-2428   *Fax:* 916 456-2236
E-mail: PedResidency@ucdavis.edu
Length: 3 Yrs   *ACGME Approved/Offered Positions:* 36
Program ID: 320-05-11-023

San Diego

Naval Medical Center (San Diego) Program

Sponsor: Naval Medical Center (San Diego)
Prgm Director: Christine L Johnson, BA, MD
34520 Bob Wilson Drive
Pediatrics Suite 100
San Diego, CA 92134
Tel: 619 532-9868   *Fax:* 619 532-9902
Length: 3 Yrs   *ACGME Approved/Offered Positions:* 24
Program ID: 320-05-11-012
Uniformed Services Program

University of California (San Diego) Program

Sponsor: University of California (San Diego) Medical Center
Rady Children's Hospital
Prgm Director: Sherry C Huang, MD
3020 Children's Way
Mail Code 5124
San Diego, CA 92123
Tel: 858 966-8793   *Fax:* 858 966-7966
E-mail: shuang@ucsd.edu
Length: 3 Yrs   *ACGME Approved/Offered Positions:* 42
Program ID: 320-05-31-036

San Francisco

University of California (San Francisco) Program

Sponsor: University of California (San Francisco) School of Medicine
San Francisco General Hospital Medical Center
UCSF and Mount Zion Medical Centers
Prgm Director: Daniel C West, MD*
505 Parnassus Avenue, M-691
Box 0110
San Francisco, CA 94143
Tel: 415 476-5001   *Fax:* 415 476-4009
E-mail: pedsapp@ucsf.edu
Length: 3 Yrs   *ACGME Approved/Offered Positions:* 84
Program ID: 320-05-21-040

Stanford

Stanford University Program

Sponsor: Stanford Hospital and Clinics
Lucile Salter Packard Children's Hospital at Stanford
Santa Clara Valley Medical Center
Prgm Director: William D Rhine, MD
c/o Lucile S Packard Children's Hospital
725 Welch Road
Palo Alto, CA 94304
Tel: 650 497-8979   *Fax:* 650 497-8228
E-mail: wrhine@stanford.edu
Length: 3 Yrs   *ACGME Approved/Offered Positions:* 60
Program ID: 320-05-21-041

Programs

Torrance

Los Angeles County-Harbor-UCLA Medical Center Program
Sponsor: Los Angeles County-Harbor-UCLA Medical Center
Prgm Director: Monica Sifuentes, MD*
1000 W Carson Street, Box 17
Torrance, CA 90509
Tel: 310 222-3080   *Fax:* 310 533-8579
E-mail: lpayne@labiomed.org
Length: 3 Yrs   *ACGME Approved/Offered Positions:* 30
Program ID: 320-05-11-042

Colorado

Aurora

University of Colorado Denver Program
Sponsor: University of Colorado Denver School of Medicine
Children's Hospital (The)
Denver Health Medical Center
Prgm Director: Adam A Rosenberg, MD
13123 E 16th Avenue
Office of Medical Education - Box 158
Aurora, CO 80045
Tel: 720 777-6918   *Fax:* 720 777-7258
E-mail: pedrespro@tchden.org
Length: 3 Yrs   *ACGME Approved/Offered Positions:* 84
Program ID: 320-07-21-043

Connecticut

Farmington

University of Connecticut Program
Sponsor: University of Connecticut School of Medicine
Connecticut Children's Medical Center
Prgm Director: Edwin L Zalneraitis, MD
Department of Pediatrics
263 Farmington Avenue
Farmington, CT 06030
Tel: 860 545-9970   *Fax:* 860 545-9159
E-mail: avelez@ccmckids.org
Length: 3 Yrs   *ACGME Approved/Offered Positions:* 51
Program ID: 320-08-21-045

New Haven

Yale-New Haven Medical Center Program
Sponsor: Yale-New Haven Hospital
Prgm Director: Alan H Friedman, MD
Department of Pediatrics
333 Cedar Street, PO Box 208064
New Haven, CT 06520
Tel: 203 785-3898   *Fax:* 203 737-2461
E-mail: annmarie.healy@yale.edu
Length: 3 Yrs   *ACGME Approved/Offered Positions:* 54
Program ID: 320-08-21-046

Delaware

Wilmington

Jefferson Medical College/duPont Hospital for Children Program
Sponsor: Jefferson Medical College
Alfred I duPont Hospital for Children
Prgm Director: Steven M Selbst, MD
1600 Rockland Road
PO Box 269
Wilmington, DE 19803
Tel: 302 651-5874   *Fax:* 302 651-5954
Length: 3 Yrs   *ACGME Approved/Offered Positions:* 63
Program ID: 320-41-21-210

District of Columbia

Washington

Children's National Medical Center/George Washington University Program
Sponsor: Children's National Medical Center
Prgm Director: Dewesh Agrawal, MD
111 Michigan Avenue NW
Medical Education Suite W35-600
Washington, DC 20010
Tel: 202 476-3670   *Fax:* 202 476-4741
Length: 3 Yrs   *ACGME Approved/Offered Positions:* 90
Program ID: 320-10-21-051

Georgetown University Hospital Program
Sponsor: Georgetown University Hospital
Prgm Director: Wolfgang P Rennert, MD, ScD
Department of Pediatrics
3800 Reservoir Road, NW, 2 PHC
Washington, DC 20007
Tel: 202 444-8799   *Fax:* 202 444-1359
E-mail: gupedres@georgetown.edu
Length: 3 Yrs   *ACGME Approved/Offered Positions:* 31
Program ID: 320-10-21-050

Florida

Gainesville

University of Florida Program
Sponsor: University of Florida College of Medicine
Shands Hospital at the University of Florida
Prgm Director: Maureen A Novak, MD
1600 SW Archer Road Room HD110
PO Box 100296 Peds Medical Education
Gainesville, FL 32610
Tel: 352 273-8234   *Fax:* 352 273-8593
E-mail: novakma@peds.ufl.edu
Length: 3 Yrs   *ACGME Approved/Offered Positions:* 54
Program ID: 320-11-31-053

Jacksonville

University of Florida College of Medicine Jacksonville Program
Sponsor: University of Florida College of Medicine Jacksonville
Shands Jacksonville Medical Center
UF Pediatric Multispecialty Center
Wolfson Children's Hospital
Prgm Director: James Kirk, DO
Pediatrics Office of Medical Education
820 Prudential Drive, Howard Bldg Suite 614
Jacksonville, FL 32207
Tel: 904 202-4210   *Fax:* 904 202-4219
Length: 3 Yrs   *ACGME Approved/Offered Positions:* 33
Program ID: 320-11-21-055

Miami

Jackson Memorial Hospital/Jackson Health System Program
Sponsor: Jackson Memorial Hospital/Jackson Health System
Prgm Director: Barry Gelman, MD
Department of Pediatrics (R-131)
PO Box 016960
Miami, FL 33101
Tel: 305 585-6042   *Fax:* 305 545-6018
E-mail: b.gelman@miami.edu
Length: 3 Yrs   *ACGME Approved/Offered Positions:* 62
Program ID: 320-11-11-056

Miami Children's Hospital Program
Sponsor: Miami Children's Hospital
Prgm Director: Beatriz M Cunill-De Sautu, MD*
Medical Education Department
3100 SW 62nd Avenue
Miami, FL 33155
Tel: 305 663-8462   *Fax:* 305 669-6531
Length: 3 Yrs   *ACGME Approved/Offered Positions:* 69
Program ID: 320-11-12-057

Orlando

Orlando Health Program
Sponsor: Orlando Health
Arnold Palmer Hospital for Children
Prgm Director: Joan Y Meek, MD, MS
Medical Education Pediatrics
86 West Underwood Street, Suite 202
Orlando, FL 32806
Tel: 407 649-6876   *Fax:* 407 872-0544
E-mail: pedsres@orhs.org
Length: 3 Yrs   *ACGME Approved/Offered Positions:* 42
Program ID: 320-11-31-058

Pensacola

Florida State University College of Medicine (Pensacola) Program
Sponsor: Florida State University College of Medicine
Sacred Heart Hospital of Pensacola
Prgm Director: Peter J Jennings, MD*
5153 North Ninth Avenue
6th Floor Nemours
Pensacola, FL 32504
Tel: 850 416-7658   *Fax:* 850 416-7677
Length: 3 Yrs   *ACGME Approved/Offered Positions:* 20
Program ID: 320-11-21-059

St. Petersburg

University of South Florida Program
Sponsor: University of South Florida College of Medicine
All Children's Hospital
Tampa General Hospital
Prgm Director: Valarie Panzarino, MD
801 6th Street South
St Petersburg, FL 33701
Tel: 727 767-4106   *Fax:* 727 767-8804
Length: 3 Yrs   *ACGME Approved/Offered Positions:* 59
Program ID: 320-11-21-060

Note: * indicates a newly appointed program director

Georgia

Atlanta

Emory University Program
Sponsor: Emory University School of Medicine
Children's Healthcare of Atlanta at Egleston
Grady Health System
Prgm Director: Susie Buchter, MD
Department of Pediatrics
49 Jesse Hill Jr Drive SE
Atlanta, GA 30303
Tel: 404 778-1440   *Fax:* 404 778-1401
E-mail: residency@oz.ped.emory.edu
Length: 3 Yrs   *ACGME Approved/Offered Positions:* 57
Program ID: 320-12-21-061

Morehouse School of Medicine Program
Sponsor: Morehouse School of Medicine
Children's Healthcare of Atlanta at Scottish Rite
Grady Health System
Prgm Director: Yolanda H Wimberly, MD, MS
720 Westview Drive SW
Atlanta, GA 30310
Tel: 404 756-1376   *Fax:* 404 756-1357
E-mail: ywimberly@msm.edu
Length: 3 Yrs   *ACGME Approved/Offered Positions:* 18
Program ID: 320-12-21-414

Augusta

Medical College of Georgia Program
Sponsor: Medical College of Georgia
Prgm Director: Valera L Hudson, MD
1446 Harper Street
BG 2101A
Augusta, GA 30912
Tel: 706 721-9442   *Fax:* 706 721-9463
E-mail: pharrison@mail.mcg.edu
Length: 3 Yrs   *ACGME Approved/Offered Positions:* 36
Program ID: 320-12-21-062

Macon

Mercer University School of Medicine Program
Sponsor: Medical Center of Central Georgia
Prgm Director: Debbie West, MD*
777 Hemlock Street
Hospital Box 42
Macon, GA 31201
Tel: 478 633-7500   *Fax:* 478 633-5002
E-mail: beard.teresa@mccg.org
Length: 3 Yrs   *ACGME Approved/Offered Positions:* 18
Program ID: 320-12-21-398

Savannah

Mercer University School of Medicine (Savannah) Program
Sponsor: Memorial Health-University Medical Center
Prgm Director: Eric M Pearlman, MD, PhD
4700 Waters Avenue
PO Box 23089
Savannah, GA 31403
Tel: 912 350-8193   *Fax:* 912 350-3604
E-mail: pearler1@memorialhealth.com
Length: 3 Yrs   *ACGME Approved/Offered Positions:* 18
Program ID: 320-12-21-400

Hawaii

Honolulu

University of Hawaii Program
Sponsor: University of Hawaii John A Burns School of Medicine
Kapiolani Medical Center for Women and Children
Prgm Director: Daniel T Murai, MD
1319 Punahou Street 7th Floor
Pediatrics
Honolulu, HI 96826
Tel: 808 983-8387   *Fax:* 808 983-6994
E-mail: mkeawe@hawaii.edu
Length: 3 Yrs   *ACGME Approved/Offered Positions:* 30
Program ID: 320-14-21-063

Tripler AMC

Tripler Army Medical Center Program
Sponsor: Tripler Army Medical Center
Prgm Director: Richard K Kynion, MD*
Department of Pediatrics, Attn: MCHK-PE
1 Jarrett White Road
Tripler AMC, HI 96859
Tel: 808 433-6345
Length: 3 Yrs   *ACGME Approved/Offered Positions:* 18
Program ID: 320-14-21-007
Uniformed Services Program

Illinois

Chicago

John H Stroger Hospital of Cook County Program
Sponsor: John H Stroger Hospital of Cook County
Prgm Director: Norell Rosado, MD
Department of Pediatrics
1900 W Polk Street, Room 1135
Chicago, IL 60612
Tel: 312 864-4154   *Fax:* 312 864-9717
E-mail: nrosadoc@hotmail.com
Length: 3 Yrs   *ACGME Approved/Offered Positions:* 39
Program ID: 320-16-11-065

McGaw Medical Center of Northwestern University Program
Sponsor: McGaw Medical Center of Northwestern University
Children's Memorial Hospital
Prgm Director: Sharon M Unti, MD
2300 Children's Plaza #18
Chicago, IL 60614
Tel: 773 880-4302   *Fax:* 773 880-3067
Length: 3 Yrs   *ACGME Approved/Offered Positions:* 93
Program ID: 320-16-21-070

Mount Sinai Hospital Medical Center of Chicago Program
Sponsor: Mount Sinai Hospital Medical Center of Chicago
Advocate Christ Medical Center
University of Illinois Hospital and Clinics
Prgm Director: Michael S Lotke, MD
Department of Pediatrics, F-444
California Avenue at 15th Street
Chicago, IL 60608
Tel: 773 257-6183   *Fax:* 773 257-6193
E-mail: barmo@sinai.org
Length: 3 Yrs   *ACGME Approved/Offered Positions:* 18
Program ID: 320-16-21-408

Rush University Medical Center Program
Sponsor: Rush University Medical Center
Prgm Director: Jane E Kramer, MD
Jones Building, Room 770
1653 W Congress Parkway
Chicago, IL 60612
Tel: 312 942-4174   *Fax:* 312 942-2243
E-mail: Jane_E_Kramer@rush.edu
Length: 3 Yrs   *ACGME Approved/Offered Positions:* 33
Program ID: 320-16-31-069

University of Chicago Program
Sponsor: University of Chicago Medical Center
University of Chicago Comer Children's Hospital
Prgm Director: Madelyn Kahana, MD
Department of Pediatrics
5721 S Maryland Avenue, MC 8016
Chicago, IL 60637
Tel: 773 702-5444   *Fax:* 773 834-0748
E-mail: recruitment@peds.bsd.uchicago.edu
Length: 3 Yrs   *ACGME Approved/Offered Positions:* 51
Program ID: 320-16-11-073

University of Illinois College of Medicine at Chicago Program
Sponsor: University of Illinois College of Medicine at Chicago
University of Illinois Hospital and Clinics
Prgm Director: Margaret A Scotellaro, MD*
Department of Pediatrics (MC 856)
840 South Wood Street
Chicago, IL 60612
Tel: 312 355-1130   *Fax:* 312 413-0243
E-mail: darce@uic.edu
Length: 3 Yrs   *ACGME Approved/Offered Positions:* 48
Program ID: 320-16-11-074

Maywood

Loyola University Program
Sponsor: Loyola University Medical Center
Prgm Director: Karen R Judy, MD
2160 S First Avenue
Maywood, IL 60153
Tel: 708 327-9131   *Fax:* 708 327-9132
E-mail: pedscoord@lumc.edu
Length: 3 Yrs   *ACGME Approved/Offered Positions:* 30
Program ID: 320-16-21-075

Oak Lawn

Advocate Christ Medical Center Program
Sponsor: Advocate Christ Medical Center
Prgm Director: Mark M Butterly, MD*
4440 West 95th Street
Oak Lawn, IL 60453
Tel: 708 684-1215   *Fax:* 708 684-3142
Length: 3 Yrs   *ACGME Approved/Offered Positions:* 39
Program ID: 320-16-21-382

Park Ridge

Advocate Lutheran General Hospital Program
Sponsor: Advocate Lutheran General Hospital
Prgm Director: Julie K Stamos, MD
1775 Dempster Street, 2 South
Park Ridge, IL 60068
Tel: 847 723-8409   *Fax:* 847 723-2325
Length: 3 Yrs   *ACGME Approved/Offered Positions:* 36
Program ID: 320-16-12-077

Programs

Peoria

University of Illinois College of Medicine at Peoria Program

Sponsor: University of Illinois College of Medicine at Peoria
OSF St Francis Medical Center
Prgm Director: Elizabeth S Kramer, MD
OSF Saint Francis Medical Center
530 NE Glen Oak Avenue
Peoria, IL 61637
Tel: 309 655-2274   *Fax:* 309 655-2565
E-mail: chelle@uic.edu
Length: 3 Yrs   *ACGME Approved/Offered Positions:* 18
Program ID: 320-16-21-078

Springfield

Southern Illinois University Program

Sponsor: Southern Illinois University School of Medicine
St John's Hospital
Prgm Director: Michelle Miner, MD*
Dept of Pediatrics
PO Box 19658
Springfield, IL 62794
Tel: 217 545-7827   *Fax:* 217 545-2905
E-mail: pedsresidency@siumed.edu
Length: 3 Yrs   *ACGME Approved/Offered Positions:* 18
Program ID: 320-16-21-079

Indiana

Indianapolis

Indiana University School of Medicine Program

Sponsor: Indiana University School of Medicine
Clarian Riley Hospital for Children
Prgm Director: Jerry L Rushton, MD, MPH
5867 Riley Hospital
702 Barnhill Drive
Indianapolis, IN 46202
Tel: 317 274-4034   *Fax:* 317 274-1476
E-mail: prp@iupui.edu
Length: 3 Yrs   *ACGME Approved/Offered Positions:* 87
Program ID: 320-17-21-080

St Vincent Hospital and Health Care Center Program

Sponsor: St Vincent Hospitals and Health Care Center
Prgm Director: Niceta C Bradburn, MD
8414 Naab Rd
Suite 200
Indianapolis, IN 46260
Tel: 317 338-7650   *Fax:* 317 415-7922
Length: 3 Yrs   *ACGME Approved/Offered Positions:* 12
Program ID: 320-17-12-420

Iowa

Des Moines

Central Iowa Health System (Iowa Methodist Medical Center) Program

Sponsor: Central Iowa Health System (Iowa Methodist/Iowa Lutheran)
Prgm Director: Ken L Cheyne, MD
1200 Pleasant Street
Des Moines, IA 50309
Tel: 515 241-4497   *Fax:* 515 241-4405
E-mail: pedresid@ihs.org
Length: 3 Yrs   *ACGME Approved/Offered Positions:* 18
Program ID: 320-18-31-082

Iowa City

University of Iowa Hospitals and Clinics Program

Sponsor: University of Iowa Hospitals and Clinics
Prgm Director: Stacy McConkey, MD
Department of Pediatrics
200 Hawkins Drive, 2576 JCP
Iowa City, IA 52242
Tel: 319 353-6847
E-mail: stacy-mcconkey@uiowa.edu
Length: 3 Yrs   *ACGME Approved/Offered Positions:* 39
Program ID: 320-18-11-083

Kansas

Kansas City

University of Kansas School of Medicine Program

Sponsor: University of Kansas School of Medicine
University of Kansas Hospital
Prgm Director: Lisa Gilmer, MD
Department of Pediatrics, Mail Stop 4004
3901 Rainbow Blvd
Kansas City, KS 66160
Tel: 913 588-6917   *Fax:* 913 588-6280
E-mail: mzawicki@kumc.edu
Length: 3 Yrs   *ACGME Approved/Offered Positions:* 30
Program ID: 320-19-11-084

Wichita

University of Kansas (Wichita) Program

Sponsor: University of Kansas School of Medicine (Wichita)
Wesley Medical Center
Prgm Director: Katherine J Melhorn, MD
1010 North Kansas
Wichita, KS 67214
Tel: 316 293-2631   *Fax:* 316 293-2689
Length: 3 Yrs   *ACGME Approved/Offered Positions:* 15
Program ID: 320-19-21-086

Kentucky

Lexington

University of Kentucky College of Medicine Program

Sponsor: University of Kentucky College of Medicine
University of Kentucky Hospital
Prgm Director: Stefan G Kiessling, MD*
Kentucky Clinic Room J 430
740 South Limestone Street
Lexington, KY 40536
Tel: 859 257-1552   *Fax:* 859 257-7799
Length: 3 Yrs   *ACGME Approved/Offered Positions:* 26
Program ID: 320-20-21-087

Louisville

University of Louisville Program

Sponsor: University of Louisville School of Medicine
Kosair Children's Hospital (Norton Healthcare, Inc)
Prgm Director: Kimberly A Boland, MD*
571 S Floyd Street
Suite 300
Louisville, KY 40202
Tel: 502 629-8828   *Fax:* 502 629-6783
E-mail: k.boland@louisville.edu
Length: 3 Yrs   *ACGME Approved/Offered Positions:* 61
Program ID: 320-20-21-088

Louisiana

New Orleans

Louisiana State University Program

Sponsor: Louisiana State University School of Medicine
Children's Hospital (New Orleans)
Prgm Director: Bonnie Desselle, MD
200 Henry Clay Avenue
New Orleans, LA 70118
Tel: 504 896-9263
E-mail: bdesse@lsuhsc.edu
Length: 3 Yrs   *ACGME Approved/Offered Positions:* 56
Program ID: 320-21-21-090

Tulane University Program

Sponsor: Tulane University School of Medicine
Ochsner Clinic Foundation
Tulane Hospital for Children
Prgm Director: Hosea J Doucet III, MD, MPH
1430 Tulane Ave, SL-37
Department of Pediatrics
New Orleans, LA 70112
Tel: 504 988-5458   *Fax:* 504 988-6808
E-mail: cdempsey@tulane.edu
Length: 3 Yrs   *ACGME Approved/Offered Positions:* 36
Program ID: 320-21-21-092

Shreveport

Louisiana State University (Shreveport) Program

Sponsor: LSU Health Sciences Center-University Hospital
Prgm Director: Paul D Cooper, MD
Dept of Pediatrics, LSUHSC-S
1501 Kings Highway, PO Box 33932
Shreveport, LA 71130
Tel: 318 675-6076   *Fax:* 318 675-6059
E-mail: pcoope@lsuhsc.edu
Length: 3 Yrs   *ACGME Approved/Offered Positions:* 24
Program ID: 320-21-11-093

Maine

Portland

Maine Medical Center Program

Sponsor: Maine Medical Center
Prgm Director: Brian P Youth, MD
The Barbara Bush Children's Hospital
22 Bramhall Street
Portland, ME 04102
Tel: 207 662-2353   *Fax:* 207 662-6272
Length: 3 Yrs   *ACGME Approved/Offered Positions:* 18
Program ID: 320-22-11-094

Maryland

Baltimore

Johns Hopkins University Program

Sponsor: Johns Hopkins University School of Medicine
Johns Hopkins Hospital
Prgm Director: Julia A McMillan, MD
CMSC 2-124
600 North Wolfe Street
Baltimore, MD 21287
Tel: 410 955-2727   *Fax:* 410 955-9850
Length: 3 Yrs   *ACGME Approved/Offered Positions:* 83
Program ID: 320-23-21-096

Note: * indicates a newly appointed program director

Sinai Hospital of Baltimore Program
Sponsor: Sinai Hospital of Baltimore
Prgm Director: Tracey A Clark, MD*
2401 West Belvedere Avenue
Baltimore, MD 21215
Tel: 410 601-6899   *Fax:* 410 601-0606
E-mail: tclark@lifebridgehealth.org
Length: 3 Yrs   *ACGME Approved/Offered Positions:* 24
Program ID: 320-23-11-099

University of Maryland Program
Sponsor: University of Maryland Medical System
Prgm Director: Erin Giudice, MD
22 S Greene Street, Room N5W56
Baltimore, MD 21201
Tel: 410 328-6662   *Fax:* 410 328-0646
E-mail: pschmidt@peds.umaryland.edu
Length: 3 Yrs   *ACGME Approved/Offered Positions:* 44
Program ID: 320-23-21-100

Bethesda

National Capital Consortium Program
Sponsor: National Capital Consortium
National Naval Medical Center (Bethesda)
Walter Reed Army Medical Center
Prgm Director: Clifton E Yu, MD
Department of Pediatrics
6900 Georgia Avenue NW
Washington, DC 20307
Tel: 202 782-1899   *Fax:* 301 295-5657
E-mail: clifton.yu@amedd.army.mil
Length: 3 Yrs   *ACGME Approved/Offered Positions:* 32
Program ID: 320-10-21-401
Uniformed Services Program

Massachusetts

Boston

Children's Hospital/Boston Medical Center Program
Sponsor: Children's Hospital
Boston Medical Center
Prgm Director: Ted Sectish, MD
300 Longwood Avenue
Department of Medicine HU2
Boston, MA 02115
Tel: 617 355-7681   *Fax:* 617 730-0469
Length: 3 Yrs   *ACGME Approved/Offered Positions:* 116
Program ID: 320-24-21-403

Massachusetts General Hospital Program
Sponsor: Massachusetts General Hospital
Prgm Director: Emmett V Schmidt, MD, PhD
175 Cambridge Street, CPZS-501C
Boston, MA 02114
Tel: 617 724-7505   *Fax:* 617 726-5961
Length: 3 Yrs   *ACGME Approved/Offered Positions:* 49
Program ID: 320-24-31-103

Tufts Medical Center Program
Sponsor: Tufts Medical Center
Prgm Director: Lynne Karlson, MD
800 Washington Street, Box 391
Boston, MA 02111
Tel: 617 636-5078   *Fax:* 617 636-7719
Length: 3 Yrs   *ACGME Approved/Offered Positions:* 38
Program ID: 320-24-21-104

Springfield

Baystate Medical Center/Tufts University School of Medicine Program
Sponsor: Baystate Medical Center
Prgm Director: Barbara W Stechenberg, MD
759 Chestnut Street
Springfield, MA 01199
Tel: 413 794-5379   *Fax:* 413 794-3623
Length: 3 Yrs   *ACGME Approved/Offered Positions:* 27
Program ID: 320-24-12-106

Worcester

University of Massachusetts Program
Sponsor: University of Massachusetts Medical School
UMass Memorial Health Care (University Campus)
Prgm Director: William J Durbin, MD
University Campus
55 Lake Avenue North
Worcester, MA 01655
Tel: 508 856-3590   *Fax:* 508 856-3779
E-mail: gretchen.jones@umassmed.edu
Length: 3 Yrs   *ACGME Approved/Offered Positions:* 24
Program ID: 320-24-21-107

Michigan

Ann Arbor

University of Michigan Program
Sponsor: University of Michigan Hospitals and Health Centers
Prgm Director: Hilary M Haftel, MD, MEd
1500 E Medical Center Drive
D3232 MPB, SPC 5718
Ann Arbor, MI 48109
Tel: 734 764-1258   *Fax:* 734 763-4208
E-mail: hils@umich.edu
Length: 3 Yrs   *ACGME Approved/Offered Positions:* 56
Program ID: 320-25-21-109

Detroit

Children's Hospital of Michigan Program
Sponsor: Children's Hospital of Michigan
Prgm Director: Anne M Mortensen, MD
3901 Beaubien Boulevard
Office of Pediatric Education
Detroit, MI 48201
Tel: 313 966-0254   *Fax:* 313 993-7118
E-mail: chomped@wayne.edu
Length: 3 Yrs   *ACGME Approved/Offered Positions:* 86
Program ID: 320-25-21-110

St John Hospital and Medical Center Program
Sponsor: St John Hospital and Medical Center
Prgm Director: Douglas K Ziegler, MD
22151 Moross Road, Suite 222
Detroit, MI 48236
Tel: 313 343-7979   *Fax:* 313 343-3939
E-mail: douglas.ziegler@stjohn.org
Length: 3 Yrs   *ACGME Approved/Offered Positions:* 24
Program ID: 320-25-11-113

Flint

Hurley Medical Center/Michigan State University Program
Sponsor: Hurley Medical Center
Prgm Director: Melissa Hamp, MD, MPH
3W Pediatric Education
One Hurley Plaza
Flint, MI 48503
Tel: 810 257-9283   *Fax:* 810 257-9736
E-mail: mhamp1@hurleymc.com
Length: 3 Yrs   *ACGME Approved/Offered Positions:* 15
Program ID: 320-25-31-115

Grand Rapids

Grand Rapids Medical Education and Research Center/Michigan State University Program
Sponsor: Grand Rapids Medical Education and Research Center
Spectrum Health-Butterworth Hospital
Prgm Director: Jeri W Kessenich, MD
1000 Monroe Ave NW
Grand Rapids, MI 49503
Tel: 616 391-3670   *Fax:* 616 391-2255
E-mail: kimberly.longstreet@devoschildrens.org
Length: 3 Yrs   *ACGME Approved/Offered Positions:* 36
Program ID: 320-25-21-116

Kalamazoo

Kalamazoo Center for Medical Studies/Michigan State University Program
Sponsor: Michigan State Univ/Kalamazoo Center for Medical Studies
Bronson Methodist Hospital
Prgm Director: Donald E Greydanus, MD
1000 Oakland Drive
Kalamazoo, MI 49008
Tel: 269 337-6450   *Fax:* 269 337-6474
Length: 3 Yrs   *ACGME Approved/Offered Positions:* 24
Program ID: 320-25-21-391

Lansing

Michigan State University Program
Sponsor: Michigan State University College of Human Medicine
Sparrow Hospital
Prgm Director: Yakov Sigal, MD*
Suite 640 Sparrow Professional Building
1200 E Michigan Ave
Lansing, MI 48912
Tel: 517 485-1153   *Fax:* 517 485-1593
Length: 3 Yrs   *ACGME Approved/Offered Positions:* 24
Program ID: 320-25-21-114

Royal Oak

William Beaumont Hospital Program
Sponsor: William Beaumont Hospital
Prgm Director: Kalli J Doyle, MD
3601 West 13 Mile Road
Royal Oak, MI 48073
Tel: 248 898-0413   *Fax:* 248 898-9677
Length: 3 Yrs   *ACGME Approved/Offered Positions:* 18
Program ID: 320-25-12-119

Minnesota

Minneapolis

University of Minnesota Program
Sponsor: University of Minnesota Medical School
Children's Hospitals and Clinics of Minnesota - St Paul
Hennepin County Medical Center
University of Minnesota Medical Center, Division of Fairview
Prgm Director: John Andrews, MD
Mayo Mail Code 391
420 Delaware Street, SE
Minneapolis, MN 55455
Tel: 612 624-4477   *Fax:* 612 626-7042
E-mail: pedsres@umn.edu
Length: 3 Yrs   *ACGME Approved/Offered Positions:* 70
Program ID: 320-26-21-120

Rochester

College of Medicine, Mayo Clinic (Rochester) Program

Sponsor: College of Medicine, Mayo Clinic
Mayo Clinic (Rochester)
Saint Marys Hospital of Rochester
Prgm Director: Robert Voigt, MD
200 First Street, SW
Rochester, MN 55905
Tel: 507 538-0154   *Fax:* 507 284-0160
E-mail: jordan.carrie@mayo.edu
Length: 3 Yrs   *ACGME Approved/Offered Positions:* 34
Program ID: 320-26-21-121

Mississippi

Jackson

University of Mississippi Medical Center Program

Sponsor: University of Mississippi School of Medicine
University Hospitals and Clinics
Prgm Director: Jeffrey Crout, MD*
2500 North State Street
Jackson, MS 39216
Tel: 601 984-5200   *Fax:* 601 984-2086
Length: 3 Yrs   *ACGME Approved/Offered Positions:* 36
Program ID: 320-27-12-122

Missouri

Columbia

University of Missouri-Columbia Program

Sponsor: University of Missouri-Columbia School of Medicine
University Hospitals and Clinics
Prgm Director: Joy C Drass, MD*
Dept of Child Hlth, Room N-702
One Hospital Drive
Columbia, MO 65212
Tel: 573 882-4730   *Fax:* 573 882-5226
E-mail: adamskrausp@health.missouri.edu
Length: 3 Yrs   *ACGME Approved/Offered Positions:* 18
Program ID: 320-28-11-123

Kansas City

University of Missouri at Kansas City Program

Sponsor: University of Missouri-Kansas City School of Medicine
Children's Mercy Hospital
Prgm Director: Denise F Bratcher, DO
2401 Gillham Road
Kansas City, MO 64108
Tel: 816 234-3371   *Fax:* 816 983-6430
E-mail: dbratcher@cmh.edu
Length: 3 Yrs   *ACGME Approved/Offered Positions:* 72
Program ID: 320-28-11-124

St Louis

St Louis University School of Medicine Program

Sponsor: St Louis University School of Medicine
Cardinal Glennon Children's Hospital
Prgm Director: Heidi M Sallee, MD
1465 S Grand Blvd
St Louis, MO 63104
Tel: 314 577-5634   *Fax:* 314 577-5616
Length: 3 Yrs   *ACGME Approved/Offered Positions:* 39
Program ID: 320-28-21-127

Washington University/B-JH/SLCH Consortium Program

Sponsor: Washington University/B-JH/SLCH Consortium
St Louis Children's Hospital
Prgm Director: Andrew J White, MD
Department of Pediatrics
One Children's Place
St Louis, MO 63110
Tel: 314 454-6006   *Fax:* 314 454-4102
E-mail: white@kids.wustl.edu
Length: 3 Yrs   *ACGME Approved/Offered Positions:* 87
Program ID: 320-28-11-125

Nebraska

Omaha

University of Nebraska Medical Center College of Medicine/Creighton University Program

Sponsor: University of Nebraska Medical Center College of Medicine
Children's Hospital
Nebraska Medical Center
Prgm Director: John N Walburn, MD
982185 Nebraska Medical Center
Omaha, NE 68198
Tel: 402 559-5380   *Fax:* 402 559-5137
Length: 3 Yrs   *ACGME Approved/Offered Positions:* 41
Program ID: 320-30-21-383

Nevada

Las Vegas

University of Nevada School of Medicine (Las Vegas) Program

Sponsor: University of Nevada School of Medicine
University Medical Center of Southern Nevada
Sunrise Hospital and Medical Center
Prgm Director: Jack Lazerson, MD
Department of Pediatrics
2040 West Charleston Blvd, #402
Las Vegas, NV 89102
Tel: 702 671-2231   *Fax:* 702 671-2233
E-mail: cdapello@medicine.nevada.edu
Length: 3 Yrs   *ACGME Approved/Offered Positions:* 36
Program ID: 320-31-21-407

New Hampshire

Lebanon

Dartmouth-Hitchcock Medical Center Program

Sponsor: Mary Hitchcock Memorial Hospital
Prgm Director: Diane Kittredge, MD*
One Medical Center Drive
Lebanon, NH 03756
Tel: 603 653-6080
E-mail: pediatric.residency.program@hitchcock.org
Length: 3 Yrs   *ACGME Approved/Offered Positions:* 21
Program ID: 320-32-22-130

New Jersey

Camden

UMDNJ-Robert Wood Johnson Medical School (Camden) Program

Sponsor: Cooper Hospital-University Medical Center
Prgm Director: William R Graessle, MD
Department of Pediatrics
E&R Bldg, 401 Haddon Ave, 3rd Floor
Camden, NJ 08103
Tel: 856 757-7904   *Fax:* 856 968-9598
E-mail: ortiz-ramonita@cooperhealth.edu
Length: 3 Yrs   *ACGME Approved/Offered Positions:* 30
Program ID: 320-33-31-251

Long Branch

Monmouth Medical Center Program

Sponsor: Monmouth Medical Center
Prgm Director: Renuka Verma, MD
300 Second Avenue
Long Branch, NJ 07740
Tel: 732 923-7251   *Fax:* 732 923-7255
E-mail: reverma@sbhcs.com
Length: 3 Yrs   *ACGME Approved/Offered Positions:* 16
Program ID: 320-33-11-133

Morristown

Atlantic Health Program

Sponsor: Atlantic Health
Morristown Memorial Hospital
Prgm Director: Alan Meltzer, MD
Pediatric Medical Education - Box 10
100 Madison Avenue
Morristown, NJ 07962
Tel: 973 971-7802   *Fax:* 973 290-7693
E-mail: alan.meltzer@atlantichealth.org
Length: 3 Yrs   *ACGME Approved/Offered Positions:* 36
Program ID: 320-33-21-412

Neptune

Jersey Shore University Medical Center Program

Sponsor: Jersey Shore University Medical Center
Prgm Director: Paul M Schwartzberg, DO*
Department of Pediatrics
1945 State Route 33
Neptune, NJ 07754
Tel: 732 776-4865   *Fax:* 732 776-3161
E-mail: pschwartzberg@meridianhealth.com
Length: 3 Yrs   *ACGME Approved/Offered Positions:* 19
Program ID: 320-33-11-134

New Brunswick

St Peter's University Hospital Program

Sponsor: St Peter's University Hospital
Prgm Director: William Bernstein, MD
254 Easton Avenue
New Brunswick, NJ 08901
Tel: 732 745-8600   *Fax:* 732 828-6825
E-mail: gailmorris@saintpetersuh.com
Length: 3 Yrs   *ACGME Approved/Offered Positions:* 18
Program ID: 320-33-31-419

UMDNJ-Robert Wood Johnson Medical School Program

Sponsor: UMDNJ-Robert Wood Johnson Medical School
Robert Wood Johnson University Hospital
Prgm Director: Michael J Kelly, MD
125 Paterson Street
Dept of Pediatrics/MEB Room 308
New Brunswick, NJ 08903
Tel: 732 235-7883   *Fax:* 732 235-6609
E-mail: kellymj@umdnj.edu
Length: 3 Yrs   *ACGME Approved/Offered Positions:* 36
Program ID: 320-33-21-136

Note: * indicates a newly appointed program director

Newark

Newark Beth Israel Medical Center Program

Sponsor: Newark Beth Israel Medical Center
St Barnabas Medical Center
Prgm Director: Joshua S Rosenblatt, MD
201 Lyons Avenue
Newark, NJ 07112
Tel: 973 926-3233   *Fax:* 973 923-2441
Length: 3 Yrs   *ACGME Approved/Offered Positions:* 39
Program ID: 320-33-21-362

UMDNJ-New Jersey Medical School Program

Sponsor: UMDNJ-New Jersey Medical School
Hackensack University Medical Center
UMDNJ-University Hospital
Prgm Director: Susan G Mautone, MD
185 South Orange Avenue MSB F-603
Newark, NJ 07103
Tel: 973 972-7160   *Fax:* 973 972-1019
E-mail: cherbapa@umdnj.edu
Length: 3 Yrs   *ACGME Approved/Offered Positions:* 49
Program ID: 320-33-21-135

Paterson

Mount Sinai School of Medicine (St Joseph's Regional Medical Center) Program

Sponsor: Mount Sinai School of Medicine
St Joseph's Regional Medical Center
Prgm Director: Thomas J Daley, MD
703 Main Street
Paterson, NJ 07503
Tel: 973 754-2543   *Fax:* 973 754-2546
Length: 3 Yrs   *ACGME Approved/Offered Positions:* 36
Program ID: 320-33-21-364

New Mexico

Albuquerque

University of New Mexico Program

Sponsor: University of New Mexico School of Medicine
University of New Mexico Hospital
Prgm Director: Benjamin D Hoffman, MD
Department of Pediatrics
MSC10 5590, 1 Univ of New Mexico
Albuquerque, NM 87131
Tel: 505 272-3909   *Fax:* 505 272-6845
E-mail: bhoffman@salud.unm.edu
Length: 3 Yrs   *ACGME Approved/Offered Positions:* 39
Program ID: 320-34-11-138

New York

Albany

Albany Medical Center Program

Sponsor: Albany Medical Center
Prgm Director: Patricia Hopkins-Braddock, MD
47 New Scotland Avenue MC 88
Pediatric Housestaff Office
Albany, NY 12208
Tel: 518 262-5127   *Fax:* 518 262-6776
E-mail: hopkinp@mail.amc.edu
Length: 3 Yrs   *ACGME Approved/Offered Positions:* 30
Program ID: 320-35-21-139

Bronx

Albert Einstein College of Medicine (Jacobi) Program

Sponsor: Albert Einstein College of Medicine of Yeshiva University
North Bronx Healthcare Network-Jacobi Medical Center
Prgm Director: Auxford Burks, MD
1400 Pelham Parkway South
Jacobi Room 829
Bronx, NY 10461
Tel: 718 918-6315   *Fax:* 718 918-6960
E-mail: aburks@aecom.yu.edu
Length: 3 Yrs   *ACGME Approved/Offered Positions:* 45
Program ID: 320-35-21-410

Albert Einstein College of Medicine Program

Sponsor: Albert Einstein College of Medicine of Yeshiva University
Montefiore Medical Center-Henry and Lucy Moses Division
Prgm Director: Catherine C Skae, MD
111 East 210th Street
Bronx, NY 10467
Tel: 718 741-2460   *Fax:* 718 654-6692
E-mail: cskae@montefiore.org
Length: 3 Yrs   *ACGME Approved/Offered Positions:* 69
Program ID: 320-35-21-363

Bronx-Lebanon Hospital Center Program

Sponsor: Bronx-Lebanon Hospital Center
Prgm Director: Ayoade O Adeniyi, MD, MBA
1650 Selwyn Avenue
Department of Pediatrics
Bronx, NY 10457
Tel: 718 960-1417   *Fax:* 718 518-5124
E-mail: mgascot@bronxleb.org
Length: 3 Yrs   *ACGME Approved/Offered Positions:* 45
Program ID: 320-35-11-146

Lincoln Medical and Mental Health Center Program

Sponsor: Lincoln Medical and Mental Health Center
Prgm Director: Magda D Mendez, MD*
Department of Pediatrics
234 East 149th Street
Bronx, NY 10451
Tel: 718 579-5030   *Fax:* 718 579-4700
Length: 3 Yrs   *ACGME Approved/Offered Positions:* 51
Program ID: 320-35-31-394

St Barnabas Hospital Program

Sponsor: St Barnabas Hospital
Prgm Director: David H Rubin, MD
4422 Third Avenue
Bronx, NY 10457
Tel: 718 960-9331   *Fax:* 718 960-9418
E-mail: drubin@stbarnabas-ny.org
Length: 3 Yrs   *ACGME Approved/Offered Positions:* 18
Program ID: 320-35-21-416

Brooklyn

Brookdale University Hospital and Medical Center Program

Sponsor: Brookdale University Hospital and Medical Center
Prgm Director: Myron Sokal, MD
One Brookdale Plaza
Room 300 CHC Bldg
Brooklyn, NY 11212
Tel: 718 240-5629   *Fax:* 718 240-6515
Length: 3 Yrs   *ACGME Approved/Offered Positions:* 42
Program ID: 320-35-11-147

Brooklyn Hospital Center Program

Sponsor: Brooklyn Hospital Center
Wyckoff Heights Medical Center
Prgm Director: Sarah A Rawstron, MBBS
121 DeKalb Avenue
Brooklyn, NY 11201
Tel: 718 250-6955   *Fax:* 718 250-8735
Length: 3 Yrs   *ACGME Approved/Offered Positions:* 37
Program ID: 320-35-11-148

Maimonides Medical Center/Infants and Children's Hospital of Brooklyn Program

Sponsor: Maimonides Medical Center
Coney Island Hospital
Prgm Director: Henry A Schaeffer, MD
4802 Tenth Avenue
Brooklyn, NY 11219
Tel: 718 283-8918   *Fax:* 718 635-8855
Length: 3 Yrs   *ACGME Approved/Offered Positions:* 84
Program ID: 320-35-21-157

New York Methodist Hospital Program

Sponsor: New York Methodist Hospital
Prgm Director: Pramod Narula, MD
506 Sixth Street
Brooklyn, NY 11215
Tel: 718 780-5260   *Fax:* 718 780-3266
Length: 3 Yrs   *ACGME Approved/Offered Positions:* 27
Program ID: 320-35-11-158

SUNY Health Science Center at Brooklyn Program

Sponsor: SUNY Health Science Center at Brooklyn
Kings County Hospital Center
Long Island College Hospital
University Hospital-SUNY Health Science Center at Brooklyn
Prgm Director: Stephen Wadowski, MD
450 Clarkson Avenue, Box 49
Brooklyn, NY 11203
Tel: 718 270-2078   *Fax:* 718 270-1985
E-mail: pediatrics@downstate.edu
Length: 3 Yrs   *ACGME Approved/Offered Positions:* 111
Program ID: 320-35-21-173

Woodhull Medical and Mental Health Center Program

Sponsor: Woodhull Medical and Mental Health Center
Prgm Director: Raymol M Varghese, MD
Department of Pediatrics
760 Broadway
Brooklyn, NY 11206
Tel: 718 963-7956   *Fax:* 718 963-7957
E-mail: Raymol.Varghese@woodhullhc.nychhc.org
Length: 3 Yrs   *ACGME Approved/Offered Positions:* 32
Program ID: 320-35-32-387

Buffalo

University at Buffalo Program

Sponsor: University at Buffalo School of Medicine
Kaleida Health System (Women and Children's Hosp of Buffalo)
Prgm Director: Lorna K Fitzpatrick, MD
219 Bryant Street
Buffalo, NY 14222
Tel: 716 878-7355   *Fax:* 716 878-7185
Length: 3 Yrs   *ACGME Approved/Offered Positions:* 46
Program ID: 320-35-21-140

East Meadow

Nassau University Medical Center Program

Sponsor: Nassau University Medical Center
Prgm Director: Michael P Frogel, MD*
2201 Hempstead Turnpike
East Meadow, NY 11554
Tel: 516 572-6177   *Fax:* 516 572-5483
E-mail: mfrogel@numc.edu
Length: 3 Yrs   *ACGME Approved/Offered Positions:* 30
Program ID: 320-35-21-141

Programs

Elmhurst

Mount Sinai School of Medicine (Elmhurst) Program

Sponsor: Mount Sinai School of Medicine
Elmhurst Hospital Center-Mount Sinai Services
Mount Sinai Medical Center
Prgm Director: Melvin Gertner, MD
Room A7-34
79-01 Broadway
Elmhurst, NY 11373
Tel: 718 334-3380   *Fax:* 718 334-2862
E-mail: gertnerm@nychhc.org
Length: 3 Yrs   *ACGME Approved/Offered Positions:* 39
Program ID: 320-35-21-162

Flushing

Flushing Hospital Medical Center Program

Sponsor: Flushing Hospital Medical Center
Jamaica Hospital Medical Center
Prgm Director: Susana Rapaport, MD
4500 Parsons Boulevard
Flushing, NY 11355
Tel: 718 670-5535   *Fax:* 718 670-3031
E-mail: rdisanza.flushing@jhmc.org
Length: 3 Yrs   *ACGME Approved/Offered Positions:* 25
Program ID: 320-35-31-261

Great Neck

NSLIJHS-Schneider Children's Hospital Program

Sponsor: North Shore-Long Island Jewish Health System
Schneider Children's Hospital at Long Island Jewish
   Med Ctr
Schneider Children's Hospital at North Shore University
   Hosp
Prgm Director: Stephen R Barone, MD
269-01 76th Ave
New Hyde Park, NY 11040
Tel: 718 470-3157   *Fax:* 718 343-5864
E-mail: barone@nshs.edu
Length: 3 Yrs   *ACGME Approved/Offered Positions:* 126
Program ID: 320-35-21-155

Mineola

Winthrop-University Hospital Program

Sponsor: Winthrop-University Hospital
Prgm Director: Jill Leavens-Maurer, MD
259 First Street
Mineola, NY 11501
Tel: 516 663-2288   *Fax:* 516 663-8955
Length: 3 Yrs   *ACGME Approved/Offered Positions:* 48
Program ID: 320-35-11-143

New York

Harlem Hospital Center Program

Sponsor: Harlem Hospital Center
Prgm Director: Diane Ferran, MD, MPH
Department of Pediatrics, MLK 17-110
506 Lenox Avenue
New York, NY 10037
Tel: 212 939-4019   *Fax:* 212 939-4022
Length: 3 Yrs   *ACGME Approved/Offered Positions:* 24
Program ID: 320-35-11-151

Mount Sinai School of Medicine Program

Sponsor: Mount Sinai School of Medicine
Mount Sinai Medical Center
Prgm Director: Joel A Forman, MD
One Gustave L Levy Place, Box 1512
New York, NY 10029
Tel: 212 241-6934   *Fax:* 212 241-4309
E-mail: joel.forman@mssm.edu
Length: 3 Yrs   *ACGME Approved/Offered Positions:* 52
Program ID: 320-35-11-161

New York Medical College (Metropolitan) Program

Sponsor: New York Medical College
Metropolitan Hospital Center
Westchester Medical Center
Prgm Director: Jason Mack, MD
1901 First Avenue
New York, NY 10029
Tel: 212 423-7834   *Fax:* 212 534-7831
E-mail: mackj@nychhc.org
Length: 3 Yrs   *ACGME Approved/Offered Positions:* 21
Program ID: 320-35-21-393

New York Presbyterian Hospital (Columbia Campus) Program

Sponsor: New York Presbyterian Hospital
New York Presbyterian Hospital (Columbia Campus)
Prgm Director: Elizabeth A Wedemeyer, MD
630 West 168th Street
New York, NY 10032
Tel: 212 305-8504   *Fax:* 212 305-8881
Length: 3 Yrs   *ACGME Approved/Offered Positions:* 60
Program ID: 320-35-11-167

New York Presbyterian Hospital (Cornell Campus) Program

Sponsor: New York Presbyterian Hospital
New York Presbyterian Hospital (Cornell Campus)
Prgm Director: Susan B Bostwick, MD, MBA
525 East 68th Street, Box 139
New York, NY 10065
Tel: 212 746-3131   *Fax:* 212 746-3140
Length: 3 Yrs   *ACGME Approved/Offered Positions:* 60
Program ID: 320-35-21-149

New York University School of Medicine Program

Sponsor: New York University School of Medicine
Bellevue Hospital Center
NYU Hospitals Center
Prgm Director: Rhonda M Graves, MD
Department of Pediatrics
550 First Avenue, NBV-8S4-11
New York, NY 10016
Tel: 212 263-6425   *Fax:* 212 263-8172
E-mail: pedsprog@med.nyu.edu
Length: 3 Yrs   *ACGME Approved/Offered Positions:* 56
Program ID: 320-35-21-166

Rochester

University of Rochester Program

Sponsor: Strong Memorial Hospital of the University of
   Rochester
Rochester General Hospital
Prgm Director: William S Varade, MD*
Golisano Children's Hospital at Strong
601 Elmwood Ave, Box 777-R
Rochester, NY 14642
Tel: 585 275-6918   *Fax:* 585 442-6580
E-mail: chaspedres@urmc.rochester.edu
Length: 3 Yrs   *ACGME Approved/Offered Positions:* 48
Program ID: 320-35-21-174

Staten Island

New York Medical College (Richmond) Program

Sponsor: New York Medical College
Richmond University Medical Center
Prgm Director: Simon S Rabinowitz, PhD, MD
355 Bard Avenue
Room 314
Staten Island, NY 10310
Tel: 718 818-4636   *Fax:* 718 818-2739
E-mail: dharasek@rumcsi.org
Length: 3 Yrs   *ACGME Approved/Offered Positions:* 18
Program ID: 320-35-11-171

Stony Brook

SUNY at Stony Brook Program

Sponsor: University Hospital - SUNY at Stony Brook
Prgm Director: Susan Guralnick, MD
Department of Pediatrics
HSC, T11- 020
Stony Brook, NY 11794
Tel: 631 444-2020   *Fax:* 631 444-2894
Length: 3 Yrs   *ACGME Approved/Offered Positions:* 40
Program ID: 320-35-21-365

Syracuse

SUNY Upstate Medical University Program

Sponsor: SUNY Upstate Medical University
Crouse Hospital
Prgm Director: John S Andrake, MD
Department of Pediatrics
750 E Adams Street
Syracuse, NY 13210
Tel: 315 464-5800   *Fax:* 315 464-7564
Length: 3 Yrs   *ACGME Approved/Offered Positions:* 36
Program ID: 320-35-21-175

Valhalla

New York Medical College at Westchester Medical Center Program

Sponsor: New York Medical College
Westchester Medical Center
Prgm Director: Theresa Hetzler, MD
Education Office, Room 3419
Woods Road
Valhalla, NY 10595
Tel: 914 493-6668   *Fax:* 914 493-5056
Length: 3 Yrs   *ACGME Approved/Offered Positions:* 48
Program ID: 320-35-11-176

North Carolina

Chapel Hill

University of North Carolina Hospitals Program

Sponsor: University of North Carolina Hospitals
Moses H Cone Memorial Hospital
Wake Medical Center
Prgm Director: Harvey J Hamrick, MD
Pediatric Education Office
UNC School of Medicine CB 7593
Chapel Hill, NC 27599
Tel: 919 966-3172   *Fax:* 919 966-8419
E-mail: uncped@med.unc.edu
Length: 3 Yrs   *ACGME Approved/Offered Positions:* 52
Program ID: 320-36-21-178

Note: * indicates a newly appointed program director

Charlotte

Carolinas Medical Center Program

Sponsor: Carolinas Medical Center
Prgm Director: Suzette S Caudle, MD
Department of Pediatrics
PO Box 32861
Charlotte, NC 28232
Tel: 704 381-6800   *Fax:* 704 381-6841
E-mail: suzette.caudle@carolinashealthcare.org
Length: 3 Yrs   *ACGME Approved/Offered Positions:* 24
Program ID: 320-36-11-179

Durham

Duke University Hospital Program

Sponsor: Duke University Hospital
Prgm Director: Betty B Staples, MD*
Pediatric Residency Program
PO Box 3127
Durham, NC 27710
Tel: 919 684-2356   *Fax:* 919 681-5825
E-mail: duke.peds.res@mc.duke.edu
Length: 3 Yrs   *ACGME Approved/Offered Positions:* 48
Program ID: 320-36-21-180

Greenville

Pitt County Memorial Hospital/East Carolina University Program

Sponsor: Pitt County Memorial Hospital
Brody School of Medicine at East Carolina University
Prgm Director: Karin M Hillenbrand, MD
3E-139 Brody Medical Sciences Building
Department of Pediatrics
Greenville, NC 27834
Tel: 252 744-3041   *Fax:* 252 744-8377
E-mail: hillenbrandk@ecu.edu
Length: 3 Yrs   *ACGME Approved/Offered Positions:* 30
Program ID: 320-36-12-182

Winston-Salem

Wake Forest University School of Medicine Program

Sponsor: Wake Forest University Baptist Medical Center
Prgm Director: Marcia M Wofford, MD
Dept of Pediatrics
Medical Center Boulevard
Winston-Salem, NC 27157
Tel: 336 716-2523   *Fax:* 336 716-7100
Length: 3 Yrs   *ACGME Approved/Offered Positions:* 41
Program ID: 320-36-11-183

Ohio

Akron

Children's Hospital Medical Center of Akron/NEOUCOM Program

Sponsor: Children's Hospital Medical Center of Akron
Prgm Director: Jeffrey A Kempf, DO
Department of Medical Education
One Perkins Square
Akron, OH 44308
Tel: 330 543-8407   *Fax:* 330 543-8157
E-mail: jkempf1@chmca.org
Length: 3 Yrs   *ACGME Approved/Offered Positions:* 46
Program ID: 320-38-11-184

Cincinnati

Cincinnati Children's Hospital Medical Center/University of Cincinnati College of Medicine Program

Sponsor: Cincinnati Children's Hospital Medical Center
Prgm Director: Javier A Gonzalez del Rey, MD, MEd
3333 Burnet Avenue
ML-5018
Cincinnati, OH 45229
Tel: 513 636-4906   *Fax:* 513 636-7905
Length: 3 Yrs   *ACGME Approved/Offered Positions:* 123
Program ID: 320-38-21-185

Cleveland

Case Western Reserve University (MetroHealth) Program

Sponsor: MetroHealth Medical Center
Prgm Director: Abdulla K Gori, MD
2500 MetroHealth Drive
Cleveland, OH 44109
Tel: 216 778-5906   *Fax:* 216 778-4223
E-mail: agori@metrohealth.org
Length: 3 Yrs   *ACGME Approved/Offered Positions:* 24
Program ID: 320-38-21-369

Cleveland Clinic Foundation Program

Sponsor: Cleveland Clinic Foundation
Prgm Director: Gary D Williams, MD
9500 Euclid Avenue
Cleveland, OH 44195
Tel: 216 444-5510   *Fax:* 216 445-8241
Length: 3 Yrs   *ACGME Approved/Offered Positions:* 39
Program ID: 320-38-31-189

University Hospitals Case Medical Center Program

Sponsor: University Hospitals Case Medical Center
Prgm Director: Martha S Wright, MD
11100 Euclid Avenue
RBC 838
Cleveland, OH 44106
Tel: 216 844-3641   *Fax:* 216 844-7166
E-mail: martha.wright@uhhospitals.org
Length: 3 Yrs   *ACGME Approved/Offered Positions:* 86
Program ID: 320-38-21-367

Columbus

Nationwide Children's Hospital/Doctors Hospital Program

Sponsor: Nationwide Children's Hospital
Prgm Director: John D Mahan Jr, MD
700 Children's Drive, Room ED680
Columbus, OH 43205
Tel: 614 722-4409   *Fax:* 614 722-6132
E-mail: barnesm@chi.osu.edu
Length: 3 Yrs   *ACGME Approved/Offered Positions:* 15
Program ID: 320-38-21-418

Nationwide Children's Hospital/Ohio State University Program

Sponsor: Nationwide Children's Hospital
Prgm Director: John D Mahan Jr, MD
700 Children's Drive - Room ED680
Columbus, OH 43205
Tel: 614 722-4409   *Fax:* 614 722-6132
Length: 3 Yrs   *ACGME Approved/Offered Positions:* 78
Program ID: 320-38-21-192

Dayton

Wright State University Program

Sponsor: Wright State University Boonshoft School of Medicine
Children's Medical Center
Wright - Patterson Medical Center
Prgm Director: Ann E Burke, MD
One Children's Plaza
Dayton, OH 45404
Tel: 937 641-3433   *Fax:* 937 641-5931
Length: 3 Yrs   *ACGME Approved/Offered Positions:* 42
Program ID: 320-38-21-193

Toledo

University of Toledo Program

Sponsor: University of Toledo
St Vincent Mercy Medical Center
Toledo Children's Hospital
Prgm Director: Randall Schlievert, MD
MOB 2 Suite 1100
Toledo, OH 43608
Tel: 419 251-8095
E-mail: randall.schlievert@utoledo.edu
Length: 3 Yrs   *ACGME Approved/Offered Positions:* 24
Program ID: 320-38-21-194

Oklahoma

Oklahoma City

University of Oklahoma Health Sciences Center Program

Sponsor: University of Oklahoma College of Medicine
OU Medical Center - Children's Hospital
Prgm Director: Kristi L Ludwig, MD*
Department of Pediatrics
1200 Everett Drive, 10th Floor East
Oklahoma City, OK 73104
Tel: 405 271-4417   *Fax:* 405 271-2920
Length: 3 Yrs   *ACGME Approved/Offered Positions:* 39
Program ID: 320-39-11-196

Tulsa

University of Oklahoma College of Medicine-Tulsa Program

Sponsor: University of Oklahoma College of Medicine-Tulsa
Saint Francis Health System
Prgm Director: Deborah E Lowen, MD
4502 E 41st Street
Tulsa, OK 74135
Tel: 918 660-3416   *Fax:* 918 660-3426
E-mail: deborah-lowen@ouhsc.edu
Length: 3 Yrs   *ACGME Approved/Offered Positions:* 18
Program ID: 320-39-21-197

Oregon

Portland

Oregon Health & Science University Program

Sponsor: Oregon Health & Science University Hospital
Prgm Director: Cindy Ferrell, MD, MEd*
Department of Pediatrics
707 SW Gaines Street, Mail: CDRC-P
Portland, OR 97239
Tel: 503 418-5170   *Fax:* 503 418-5337
E-mail: pedsres@ohsu.edu
Length: 3 Yrs   *ACGME Approved/Offered Positions:* 39
Program ID: 320-40-12-199

Programs

Pennsylvania

Danville

Geisinger Health System Program

Sponsor: Geisinger Health System
Geisinger Medical Center
Prgm Director: Paul Bellino, MD
100 N Academy Ave
Danville, PA 17822
Tel: 570 271-5606   *Fax:* 570 271-5885
Length: 3 Yrs   *ACGME Approved/Offered Positions:* 31
Program ID: 320-41-11-200

Hershey

Penn State University/Milton S Hershey Medical Center Program

Sponsor: Milton S Hershey Medical Center
Prgm Director: Kelly R Leite, DO
PO Box 850, Mail Code H085
Hershey, PA 17033
Tel: 717 531-8603   *Fax:* 717 531-0856
E-mail: shollowell@hmc.psu.edu
Length: 3 Yrs   *ACGME Approved/Offered Positions:* 50
Program ID: 320-41-21-372

Philadelphia

Albert Einstein Healthcare Network Program

Sponsor: Albert Einstein Medical Center
St Christopher's Hospital for Children (Tenet Health System)
Prgm Director: Robert S Wimmer, MD
Department of Pediatrics
5501 Old York Road, Paley 1st Floor
Philadelphia, PA 19141
Tel: 215 456-6595   *Fax:* 215 456-3436
Length: 3 Yrs   *ACGME Approved/Offered Positions:* 30
Program ID: 320-41-11-204

Children's Hospital of Philadelphia Program

Sponsor: Children's Hospital of Philadelphia
Prgm Director: Stephen Ludwig, MD
Pediatric Residency Program
34th Street & Civic Center Boulevard, Room 9NW55
Philadelphia, PA 19104
Tel: 215 590-2162   *Fax:* 215 590-2768
E-mail: pedres@email.chop.edu
Length: 3 Yrs   *ACGME Approved/Offered Positions:* 121
Program ID: 320-41-21-205

St Christopher's Hospital for Children Program

Sponsor: St Christopher's Hospital for Children (Tenet Health System)
Prgm Director: Robert McGregor, MD
Erie Avenue at Front Street
Philadelphia, PA 19134
Tel: 215 427-5127   *Fax:* 215 427-4805
Length: 3 Yrs   *ACGME Approved/Offered Positions:* 76
Program ID: 320-41-12-209

Pittsburgh

University of Pittsburgh Medical Center Medical Education Program

Sponsor: Univ of Pittsburgh Medical Center Medical Education
Children's Hospital of Pittsburgh of UPMC
Prgm Director: Dena Hofkosh, MD
3705 Fifth Avenue
Pediatric Residency Program
Pittsburgh, PA 15213
Tel: 412 692-6541   *Fax:* 412 692-7231
Length: 3 Yrs   *ACGME Approved/Offered Positions:* 84
Program ID: 320-41-21-211

Upland

Crozer-Chester Medical Center Program

Sponsor: Crozer-Chester Medical Center
Children's Hospital of Philadelphia
Prgm Director: Beth Moughan, MD
30 Medical Center Boulevard
Professional Office Building I, Suite 402
Upland, PA 19013
Tel: 610 447-6680   *Fax:* 610 447-6677
Length: 3 Yrs   *ACGME Approved/Offered Positions:* 18
Program ID: 320-41-21-206

Puerto Rico

Ponce

Hospital Episcopal San Lucas/Ponce School of Medicine Program

Sponsor: Hospital Episcopal San Lucas
Prgm Director: Luisa I Alvarado, MD
917 Tito Castro Ave
PO Box 336810
Ponce, PR 00733
Tel: 787 844-2080   *Fax:* 787 844-1372
E-mail: lalvarado@psm.edu
Length: 3 Yrs   *ACGME Approved/Offered Positions:* 18
Program ID: 320-42-11-215

San Juan

San Juan City Hospital Program

Sponsor: San Juan City Hospital
San Jorge Children's Hospital
Prgm Director: Cherie Torres-Silva, MD, MPH
PMB 498
PO Box 70344
San Juan, PR 00936
Tel: 787 765-7618   *Fax:* 787 765-7618
E-mail: ctorressilva@aol.com
Length: 3 Yrs   *ACGME Approved/Offered Positions:* 27
Program ID: 320-42-11-216

University of Puerto Rico Program

Sponsor: University of Puerto Rico School of Medicine
University Pediatric Hospital
Prgm Director: Yasmin Pedrogo, MD*
GPO Box 365067
San Juan, PR 00936
Tel: 787 753-6390   *Fax:* 787 777-3227
E-mail: yasmin.pedrogo@gmail.com
Length: 3 Yrs   *ACGME Approved/Offered Positions:* 39
Program ID: 320-42-11-217

Rhode Island

Providence

Brown University Program

Sponsor: Rhode Island Hospital-Lifespan
Women and Infants Hospital of Rhode Island
Prgm Director: Adam D Pallant, MD, PhD
593 Eddy Street
Providence, RI 02903
Tel: 401 444-6072   *Fax:* 401 444-2988
E-mail: apallant@lifespan.org
Length: 3 Yrs   *ACGME Approved/Offered Positions:* 56
Program ID: 320-43-21-218

South Carolina

Charleston

Medical University of South Carolina Program

Sponsor: Medical University of South Carolina College of Medicine
MUSC Medical Center
Prgm Director: William M Southgate, MD*
Department of Pediatrics
165 Ashley Avenue Room 684CH
Charleston, SC 29425
Tel: 843 792-8285   *Fax:* 843 792-8801
E-mail: southgaw@musc.edu
Length: 3 Yrs   *ACGME Approved/Offered Positions:* 42
Program ID: 320-45-11-219

Columbia

Palmetto Health/University of South Carolina School of Medicine Program

Sponsor: Palmetto Health
Palmetto Health Richland
Prgm Director: Robert C Holleman Jr, MD
14 Medical Park, Suite 400
Columbia, SC 29203
Tel: 803 434-4569   *Fax:* 803 434-3855
E-mail: ashley.lynn@palmettohealth.org
Length: 3 Yrs   *ACGME Approved/Offered Positions:* 30
Program ID: 320-45-21-220

Greenville

Greenville Hospital System/University of South Carolina School of Medicine Program

Sponsor: Greenville Hospital System/University of South Carolina
Prgm Director: Kerry K Sease, MD, MPH
701 Grove Road, Balcony Suite 4
Greenville, SC 29605
Tel: 864 455-7879   *Fax:* 864 455-3884
E-mail: ksease@ghs.org
Length: 3 Yrs   *ACGME Approved/Offered Positions:* 27
Program ID: 320-45-12-221

Note: * indicates a newly appointed program director

Tennessee

Chattanooga

University of Tennessee College of Medicine at Chattanooga Program

Sponsor: University of Tennessee College of Medicine-Chattanooga
T C Thompson Children's Hospital Medical Center
Prgm Director: Janara J Huff, MD
Department of Pediatrics
910 Blackford Street
Chattanooga, TN 37403
Tel: 423 778-6217   *Fax:* 423 778-6020
E-mail: patty.wolfe@erlanger.org
Length: 3 Yrs   *ACGME Approved/Offered Positions:* 24
Program ID: 320-47-11-222

Johnson City

East Tennessee State University Program

Sponsor: James H Quillen College of Medicine
Johnson City Medical Center/Mountain States Health
  Alliance
Prgm Director: Rebecca R Powers, MD
East Tennessee State University
PO Box 70578
Johnson City, TN 37614
Tel: 423 439-6763   *Fax:* 423 439-8066
E-mail: powersr@etsu.edu
Length: 3 Yrs   *ACGME Approved/Offered Positions:* 15
Program ID: 320-47-21-381

Memphis

University of Tennessee Program

Sponsor: University of Tennessee College of Medicine
LeBonheur Children's Medical Center
Prgm Director: Mark C Bugnitz, MD
50 North Dunlap
Memphis, TN 38103
Tel: 901 287-6756   *Fax:* 901 287-4581
Length: 3 Yrs   *ACGME Approved/Offered Positions:* 54
Program ID: 320-47-31-225

Nashville

Vanderbilt University Program

Sponsor: Vanderbilt University Medical Center
Prgm Director: Rebecca R Swan, MD
2200 Children's Way
8161 Doctor's Office Tower
Nashville, TN 37232
Tel: 615 322-3023   *Fax:* 615 343-4655
Length: 3 Yrs   *ACGME Approved/Offered Positions:* 67
Program ID: 320-47-21-227

Texas

Amarillo

Texas Tech University (Amarillo) Program

Sponsor: Texas Tech University Health Sciences Center
  at Amarillo
Northwest Texas Health Care System
Prgm Director: Fred A McCurdy, MD, PhD
Department of Pediatrics
1400 S Coulter Road
Amarillo, TX 79106
Tel: 806 354-5570   *Fax:* 806 354-5536
E-mail: paige.tipton@ttuhsc.edu
Length: 3 Yrs   *ACGME Approved/Offered Positions:* 15
Program ID: 320-48-21-370

Austin

University of Texas Medical Branch (Austin) Program

Sponsor: University of Texas Medical Branch Hospitals
Dell Children's Medical Center of Central Texas
Prgm Director: George A Edwards, MD
4900 Mueller Boulevard
Austin, TX 78723
Tel: 512 324-0165   *Fax:* 512 324-0786
E-mail: jbehnke@seton.org
Length: 3 Yrs   *ACGME Approved/Offered Positions:* 45
Program ID: 320-48-21-421

Corpus Christi

Driscoll Children's Hospital Program

Sponsor: Driscoll Children's Hospital
Christus Spohn Memorial Hospital
Prgm Director: William H Dirksen, MD
3533 S Alameda
PO Drawer 6530
Corpus Christi, TX 78411
Tel: 361 694-5464   *Fax:* 361 694-5466
E-mail: resapps@dchstx.org
Length: 3 Yrs   *ACGME Approved/Offered Positions:* 42
Program ID: 320-48-11-229

Dallas

University of Texas Southwestern Medical School Program

Sponsor: University of Texas Southwestern Medical
  School
Children's Medical Center of Dallas
Prgm Director: Patty Hicks, MD
Department of Pediatrics
5323 Harry Hines Blvd
Dallas, TX 75390
Tel: 214 456-6358   *Fax:* 214 456-2625
E-mail: peds@email.swmed.edu
Length: 3 Yrs   *ACGME Approved/Offered Positions:* 90
Program ID: 320-48-21-230

El Paso

Texas Tech University Health Sciences Center Paul L Foster School of Medicine Program

Sponsor: Texas Tech University Hlth Sci Ctr Paul L
  Foster Sch of Med
R E Thomason General Hospital / Texas Tech University
  HSC
Prgm Director: Gilbert A Handal, MD
Department of Pediatrics
4800 Alberta Avenue
El Paso, TX 79905
Tel: 915 545-6787   *Fax:* 915 545-6976
Length: 3 Yrs   *ACGME Approved/Offered Positions:* 45
Program ID: 320-48-11-234

Galveston

University of Texas Medical Branch Hospitals Program

Sponsor: University of Texas Medical Branch Hospitals
Prgm Director: Cassandra M Pruitt, MD*
Department of Pediatrics
301 University Blvd
Galveston, TX 77555
Tel: 409 747-0534   *Fax:* 409 747-0721
E-mail: ccastro@utmb.edu
Length: 3 Yrs   *ACGME Approved/Offered Positions:* 36
Program ID: 320-48-11-231

Houston

Baylor College of Medicine Program

Sponsor: Baylor College of Medicine
Harris County Hospital District-Ben Taub General
  Hospital
Texas Children's Hospital
Prgm Director: Mark A Ward, MD
Texas Childrens Hospital
Houston, TX 77030
Tel: 832 824-1177   *Fax:* 832 825-1187
E-mail: parker@bcm.edu
Length: 3 Yrs   *ACGME Approved/Offered Positions:* 128
Program ID: 320-48-21-232

University of Texas at Houston Program

Sponsor: University of Texas Health Science Center at
  Houston
Lyndon B Johnson General Hospital
Memorial Hermann Hospital
Prgm Director: Sharon S Crandell, MD
Department of Pediatrics-MSB 3.244
6431 Fannin Street
Houston, TX 77030
Tel: 713 500-5800   *Fax:* 713 500-5805
E-mail: shirlene.edwards@uth.tmc.edu
Length: 3 Yrs   *ACGME Approved/Offered Positions:* 60
Program ID: 320-48-21-233

Lackland AFB

San Antonio Uniformed Services Health Education Consortium Program

Sponsor: San Antonio Uniformed Services Health
  Education Consortium
Wilford Hall Medical Center (AETC)
Prgm Director: Woodson S Jones, MD
Attn: Lt Col Woodson Scott Jones
2200 Bergquist Drive, Suite 1
Lackland AFB, TX 78236
Tel: 210 292-5097   *Fax:* 210 292-5238
Length: 3 Yrs   *ACGME Approved/Offered Positions:* 42
Program ID: 320-48-21-406
Uniformed Services Program

Lubbock

Texas Tech University (Lubbock) Program

Sponsor: Texas Tech University Health Sciences Center
  at Lubbock
University Medical Center
Prgm Director: Surendra K Varma, MD
Department of Pediatrics
Lubbock, TX 79430
Tel: 806 743-2244   *Fax:* 806 743-2314
E-mail: surendra.varma@ttuhsc.edu
Length: 3 Yrs   *ACGME Approved/Offered Positions:* 21
Program ID: 320-48-21-260

San Antonio

University of Texas Health Science Center at San Antonio Program

Sponsor: University of Texas School of Medicine at San
  Antonio
Christus Santa Rosa Health Care Corporation
University Health System
Prgm Director: Jon A Courand, MD
Department of Pediatrics
7703 Floyd Curl Drive MC 7816
San Antonio, TX 78229
Tel: 210 562-5325   *Fax:* 210 562-5835
Length: 3 Yrs   *ACGME Approved/Offered Positions:* 45
Program ID: 320-48-21-235

Programs

Temple

Texas A&M College of Medicine-Scott and White Program

Sponsor: Scott and White Memorial Hospital
Prgm Director: Lisa M Warren, DO*
2401 South 31st Street
Temple, TX 76508
Tel: 254 724-5092   *Fax:* 254 724-0274
E-mail: pediatricresidency@swmail.sw.org
Length: 3 Yrs   *ACGME Approved/Offered Positions:* 18
Program ID: 320-48-21-236

Utah

Salt Lake City

University of Utah Program

Sponsor: University of Utah Medical Center
Primary Children's Medical Center
Prgm Director: James F Bale Jr, MD
Pediatric Residency Office
100 N Mario Capecchi Drive
Salt Lake City, UT 84113
Tel: 801 662-5702   *Fax:* 801 662-5755
E-mail: peds.res@hsc.utah.edu
Length: 3 Yrs   *ACGME Approved/Offered Positions:* 62
Program ID: 320-49-21-237

Vermont

Burlington

University of Vermont Program

Sponsor: Fletcher Allen Health Care
Prgm Director: Ann P Guillot, MD
Vermont Children's Hospital at FAHC
111 Colchester Avenue, Smith 565
Burlington, VT 05401
Tel: 802 847-3544   *Fax:* 802 847-5557
Length: 3 Yrs   *ACGME Approved/Offered Positions:* 18
Program ID: 320-50-11-238

Virginia

Charlottesville

University of Virginia Program

Sponsor: University of Virginia Medical Center
Prgm Director: Linda A Waggoner-Fountain, MD
PO Box 800386
Charlottesville, VA 22908
Tel: 434 924-9148   *Fax:* 434 924-5244
E-mail: lwm@virginia.edu
Length: 3 Yrs   *ACGME Approved/Offered Positions:* 35
Program ID: 320-51-11-239

Falls Church

Inova Fairfax Hospital/Inova Fairfax Hospital for Children Program

Sponsor: Inova Fairfax Hospital
Prgm Director: Kathleen M Donnelly, MD
3300 Gallows Road
Falls Church, VA 22042
Tel: 703 776-6652   *Fax:* 703 776-4098
E-mail: Kathleen.Donnelly@inova.org
Length: 3 Yrs   *ACGME Approved/Offered Positions:* 33
Program ID: 320-51-21-399

Norfolk

Eastern Virginia Medical School Program

Sponsor: Eastern Virginia Medical School
Children's Hospital of the King's Daughters
Prgm Director: Clarence W Gowen Jr, MD
Eastern Virginia Medical School
601 Children's Lane
Norfolk, VA 23507
Tel: 757 668-7293   *Fax:* 757 668-9766
E-mail: PedRes@chkd.org
Length: 3 Yrs   *ACGME Approved/Offered Positions:* 48
Program ID: 320-51-21-240

Portsmouth

Naval Medical Center (Portsmouth) Program

Sponsor: Naval Medical Center (Portsmouth)
Prgm Director: Timothy J Porea, MD, MPH*
Department of Pediatrics
620 John Paul Jones Circle
Portsmouth, VA 23708
Tel: 757 953-2958   *Fax:* 757 953-5116
Length: 3 Yrs   *ACGME Approved/Offered Positions:* 30
Program ID: 320-51-21-014
Uniformed Services Program

Richmond

Virginia Commonwealth University Health System Program

Sponsor: Virginia Commonwealth University Health System
Medical College of Virginia Hospitals
Prgm Director: Suzanne R Lavoie, MD
Dept of Pediatrics, Pediatric Residency Program
1001 East Marshall Street, Room 1-031
Richmond, VA 23298
Tel: 804 827-0534   *Fax:* 804 828-2435
E-mail: dbarrett2@mcvh-vcu.edu
Length: 3 Yrs   *ACGME Approved/Offered Positions:* 45
Program ID: 320-51-21-241

Washington

Seattle

University of Washington Program

Sponsor: University of Washington School of Medicine
Seattle Children's Hospital
Prgm Director: Richard P Shugerman, MD
4800 Sand Point Way NE, G-0061
Seattle, WA 98105
Tel: 206 987-2688   *Fax:* 206 987-3843
Length: 3 Yrs   *ACGME Approved/Offered Positions:* 86
Program ID: 320-54-21-358

Tacoma

Madigan Army Medical Center Program

Sponsor: Madigan Army Medical Center
Prgm Director: Robert A Puntel, MD
Department of Pediatrics
MCHJ-P
Tacoma, WA 98431
Tel: 253 968-1852   *Fax:* 253 968-0384
E-mail: robert.puntel@us.army.mil
Length: 3 Yrs   *ACGME Approved/Offered Positions:* 21
Program ID: 320-54-11-010
Uniformed Services Program

West Virginia

Charleston

Charleston Area Medical Center/West Virginia University (Charleston Division) Program

Sponsor: Charleston Area Medical Center/West Virginia University
Prgm Director: Raheel R Khan, MD
830 Pennsylvania Avenue - Suite 104
Charleston, WV 25302
Tel: 304 388-1549   *Fax:* 304 388-2926
E-mail: Raheel.Khan@camc.org
Length: 3 Yrs   *ACGME Approved/Offered Positions:* 15
Program ID: 320-55-21-243

Huntington

Marshall University School of Medicine Program

Sponsor: Marshall University School of Medicine
Cabell Huntington Hospital
Prgm Director: Bob Miller, MD
Department of Pediatrics
1600 Medical Center Dr, Suite 3500
Huntington, WV 25701
Tel: 304 691-1313   *Fax:* 304 691-1375
E-mail: miller12@marshall.edu
Length: 3 Yrs   *ACGME Approved/Offered Positions:* 18
Program ID: 320-55-21-380

Morgantown

West Virginia University Program

Sponsor: West Virginia University School of Medicine
West Virginia University Hospitals
Prgm Director: John R Phillips, MD
Robert C Byrd Health Sciences Ctr
PO Box 9214
Morgantown, WV 26506
Tel: 304 293-1198   *Fax:* 304 293-1216
Length: 3 Yrs   *ACGME Approved/Offered Positions:* 18
Program ID: 320-55-11-245

Wisconsin

Madison

University of Wisconsin Program

Sponsor: University of Wisconsin Hospital and Clinics
Meriter Hospital
Prgm Director: John G Frohna, MD, MPH
Department of Pediatrics
600 Highland Avenue, H4/455
Madison, WI 53792
Tel: 608 263-8557   *Fax:* 608 263-0722
E-mail: residency@pediatrics.wisc.edu
Length: 3 Yrs   *ACGME Approved/Offered Positions:* 39
Program ID: 320-56-21-247

Marshfield

Marshfield Clinic-St Joseph's Hospital Program

Sponsor: Marshfield Clinic-St Joseph's Hospital
Prgm Director: Divya-Devi Joshi, MD
1000 North Oak Avenue
Marshfield, WI 54449
Tel: 715 387-5267   *Fax:* 715 387-5163
E-mail: disch.shirley@marshfieldclinic.org
Length: 3 Yrs   *ACGME Approved/Offered Positions:* 12
Program ID: 320-56-31-248

Note: * indicates a newly appointed program director

Milwaukee

Medical College of Wisconsin Affiliated Hospitals Program

Sponsor: Medical College of Wisconsin Affiliated
  Hospitals, Inc
Children's Hospital of Wisconsin
Prgm Director: James J Nocton, MD
8701 Watertown Plank Road
PO Box 26509
Milwaukee, WI 53226
Tel: 414 266-6810
Length: 3 Yrs   *ACGME Approved/Offered Positions:* 68
Program ID: 320-56-21-249

Physical Medicine and Rehabilitation

Alabama

Birmingham

University of Alabama Medical Center Program

Sponsor: University of Alabama Hospital
Prgm Director: Amie B Jackson, MD
619 South 19th Street, SRC/190
Birmingham, AL 35249
Tel: 205 934-3330   *Fax:* 205 975-9754
Length: 3 Yrs   *ACGME Approved/Offered Positions:* 12
Program ID: 340-01-21-002

Arkansas

Little Rock

University of Arkansas for Medical Sciences Program

Sponsor: University of Arkansas College of Medicine
Arkansas Children's Hospital
Baptist Health Rehabilitation Institute of Arkansas
Central Arkansas Veterans Healthcare System
UAMS Medical Center
Prgm Director: Kevin M Means, MD
Department of Physical Medicine and Rehabilitation
4301 West Markham St, #602
Little Rock, AR 72205
Tel: 501 221-1311   *Fax:* 501 225-0627
E-mail: KMMeans@uams.edu
Length: 4 Yrs   *ACGME Approved/Offered Positions:* 16
Program ID: 340-04-21-083

California

Loma Linda

Loma Linda University Program

Sponsor: Loma Linda University Medical Center
Jerry L Pettis Memorial Veterans Hospital
Prgm Director: Murray E Brandstater, MD, PhD
Dept of Physical Medicine & Rehabilitation
11406 Loma Linda Drive, Suite 516
Loma Linda, CA 92354
Tel: 909 558-6202   *Fax:* 909 558-6110
E-mail: mbrandstater@pol.net
Length: 4 Yrs   *ACGME Approved/Offered Positions:* 24
Program ID: 340-05-21-077

Los Angeles

VA Greater Los Angeles Healthcare System Program

Sponsor: VA Greater Los Angeles Healthcare System
Prgm Director: Quynh G Pham, MD
Department of PM&R, W-117
11301 Wilshire Boulevard
Los Angeles, CA 90073
Tel: 310 268-3342   *Fax:* 310 268-4224
Length: 3 Yrs   *ACGME Approved/Offered Positions:* 26
Program ID: 340-05-21-007

Orange

University of California (Irvine) Program

Sponsor: University of California (Irvine) Medical
  Center
Long Beach Memorial Medical Center
VA Long Beach Healthcare System
Prgm Director: Marc Evensen, MD
101 The City Drive South
Rte 81 Bldg 53 Rm B17
Orange, CA 92868
Tel: 714 456-6444   *Fax:* 714 456-5102
E-mail: wens@uci.edu
Length: 3 Yrs   *ACGME Approved/Offered Positions:* 15
Program ID: 340-05-21-005

Sacramento

University of California (Davis) Health System Program

Sponsor: University of California (Davis) Health System
University of California (Davis) Medical Center
Prgm Director: Carol Vandenakker Albanese, MD
2315 Stockton Boulevard
Sacramento, CA 95817
Tel: 916 734-5292   *Fax:* 916 734-7838
Length: 4 Yrs   *ACGME Approved/Offered Positions:* 11
Program ID: 340-05-21-004

Stanford

Stanford University Program

Sponsor: Stanford Hospital and Clinics
Santa Clara Valley Medical Center
Veterans Affairs Palo Alto Health Care System
Prgm Director: Jeffrey K Teraoka, MD
Physical Medicine and Rehabilitation
3801 Miranda Ave - MC 117
Palo Alto, CA 94304
Tel: 650 723-1410   *Fax:* 650 498-7546
Length: 3 Yrs   *ACGME Approved/Offered Positions:* 20
Program ID: 340-05-21-008

Colorado

Aurora

University of Colorado Denver Program

Sponsor: University of Colorado Denver School of
  Medicine
Children's Hospital (The)
Denver Health Medical Center
HealthONE Swedish Medical Center
University of Colorado Hospital
Veterans Affairs Medical Center (Denver)
Prgm Director: Susan D Apkon, MD
Physical Medicine and Rehabilitation
Mail Stop F-493
Aurora, CO 80045
Tel: 720 777-3934
E-mail: apkon.susan@tchden.org
Length: 3 Yrs   *ACGME Approved/Offered Positions:* 12
Program ID: 340-07-21-009

District of Columbia

Washington

Washington Hospital Center/Georgetown University Hospital/National Rehabilitation Hospital Program

Sponsor: National Rehabilitation Hospital
Prgm Director: Sandeep Simlote, MD
102 Irving Street, NW
Washington, DC 20010
Tel: 202 877-1627   *Fax:* 202 877-1166
E-mail: sandeep.simlote@medstar.net
Length: 3 Yrs   *ACGME Approved/Offered Positions:* 12
Program ID: 340-10-21-087

Florida

Miami

Jackson Memorial Hospital/Jackson Health System Program

Sponsor: Jackson Memorial Hospital/Jackson Health System
Veterans Affairs Medical Center (Miami)
Prgm Director: Andrew Sherman, MD, MS
PO Box 016960 (D-461)
Miami, FL 33101
Tel: 305 585-1431   *Fax:* 305 585-1340
E-mail: cdavis@med.miami.edu
Length: 3 Yrs   *ACGME Approved/Offered Positions:* 15
Program ID: 340-11-21-107

Tampa

University of South Florida/James A Haley Veterans Hospital Program

Sponsor: University of South Florida College of Medicine
James A Haley Veterans Hospital
Tampa General Hospital
Prgm Director: Steven G Scott, DO
Department of Neurology
12901 Bruce B Downs Blvd, Room 4106
Tampa, FL 33612
Tel: 813 972-7506   *Fax:* 813 978-5852
E-mail: laura.manore@va.gov
Length: 4 Yrs   *ACGME Approved/Offered Positions:* 8
Program ID: 340-11-13-106

Georgia

Atlanta

Emory University Program

Sponsor: Emory University School of Medicine
Emory University Hospital
The Shepherd Center
Veterans Affairs Medical Center (Atlanta)
Prgm Director: Michael K Schaufele, MD
Department of Rehabilitation Medicine
1441 Clifton Road, NE - Room 118
Atlanta, GA 30322
Tel: 404 712-5511   *Fax:* 404 712-5895
E-mail: miki_dejean@emory.org
Length: 3 Yrs   *ACGME Approved/Offered Positions:* 18
Program ID: 340-12-21-011

Illinois

Chicago

McGaw Medical Center of Northwestern University Program

Sponsor: McGaw Medical Center of Northwestern University
Northwestern Memorial Hospital
Rehabilitation Institute of Chicago
Prgm Director: James A Sliwa, DO
Rehabilitation Institute of Chicago
345 East Superior Street
Chicago, IL 60611
Tel: 312 238-4093   *Fax:* 312 238-5846
E-mail: rbailey@ric.org
Length: 4 Yrs   *ACGME Approved/Offered Positions:* 40
Program ID: 340-16-21-014

Rush University Medical Center Program

Sponsor: Rush University Medical Center
Oak Forest Hospital of Cook County
Prgm Director: Christopher Reger, MD
Department of PM&R
1653 West Congress Parkway
Chicago, IL 60612
Tel: 312 942-3675   *Fax:* 312 942-4234
Length: 4 Yrs   *ACGME Approved/Offered Positions:* 16
Program ID: 340-16-21-082

Schwab Rehabilitation Hospital and Care Network/University of Chicago Program

Sponsor: Schwab Rehabilitation Hospital and Care Network
Prgm Director: Michelle S Gittler, MD
1401 S California Boulevard
Chicago, IL 60608
Tel: 773 522-5853   *Fax:* 773 522-5855
Length: 3 Yrs   *ACGME Approved/Offered Positions:* 15
Program ID: 340-16-22-012

Maywood

Loyola University Program

Sponsor: Loyola University Medical Center
Edward Hines, Jr Veterans Affairs Hospital
Prgm Director: Monica L Steiner, MD
2160 S First Avenue
Maguire - 1700
Maywood, IL 60153
Tel: 708 216-4254   *Fax:* 708 216-9348
E-mail: mostein@lumc.edu
Length: 4 Yrs   *ACGME Approved/Offered Positions:* 12
Program ID: 340-16-31-016

Wheaton

Marianjoy Rehabilitation Hospital Program

Sponsor: Marianjoy Rehabilitation Hospital
Jesse Brown Veterans Affairs Medical Center
Prgm Director: Noel Rao, MD
26W171 Roosevelt Road
Wheaton, IL 60187
Tel: 630 909-7290   *Fax:* 630 909-7291
E-mail: yspedale@marianjoy.org
Length: 3 Yrs   *ACGME Approved/Offered Positions:* 18
Program ID: 340-16-21-097

Indiana

Indianapolis

Indiana University School of Medicine Program

Sponsor: Indiana University School of Medicine
Clarian Indiana University Hospital
Rehabilitation Hospital of Indiana (Indianapolis)
Prgm Director: Ralph M Buschbacher, MD
Clinical Building 626
541 N Clinical Drive
Indianapolis, IN 46202
Tel: 317 278-0200   *Fax:* 317 278-0206
E-mail: cherrera@iupui.edu
Length: 3 Yrs   *ACGME Approved/Offered Positions:* 9
Program ID: 340-17-21-098

Kansas

Kansas City

University of Kansas School of Medicine Program

Sponsor: University of Kansas School of Medicine
University of Kansas Hospital
Prgm Director: George Varghese, MD
Department of PM&R
39th and Rainbow Boulevard
Kansas City, KS 66160
Tel: 913 588-6777   *Fax:* 913 588-6765
Length: 3 Yrs   *ACGME Approved/Offered Positions:* 9
Program ID: 340-19-21-018

Kentucky

Lexington

University of Kentucky College of Medicine Program

Sponsor: University of Kentucky College of Medicine
Cardinal Hill Hospital
University of Kentucky Hospital
Veterans Affairs Medical Center (Lexington)
Prgm Director: Robert B Nickerson, MD
Dept of Physical Medicine & Rehab
B280 Wing C Kentucky Clinic
Lexington, KY 40536
Tel: 859 257-4890   *Fax:* 859 323-1123
E-mail: rnick1@email.uky.edu
Length: 4 Yrs   *ACGME Approved/Offered Positions:* 16
Program ID: 340-20-21-079

Louisville

University of Louisville Program

Sponsor: University of Louisville School of Medicine
Frazier Rehabilitation Institute
Veterans Affairs Medical Center (Louisville)
Prgm Director: Kenneth A Mook, MD, PhD
Frazier Rehab Institute, 15th Floor
220 Abraham Flexner Way
Louisville, KY 40202
Tel: 502 582-7465   *Fax:* 502 582-7601
E-mail: k.mook@insightbb.com
Length: 3 Yrs   *ACGME Approved/Offered Positions:* 6
Program ID: 340-20-11-019

Note: * indicates a newly appointed program director

Louisiana

New Orleans

Louisiana State University Program

Sponsor: Louisiana State University School of Medicine
Medical Center of Louisiana at New Orleans
Ochsner Clinic Foundation
Touro Infirmary
Veterans Affairs Medical Center (New Orleans)
Prgm Director: Stephen Kishner, MD, MHA
Section of PM&R, c/o Touro Rehabilitation Center
Touro Infirmary, 1401 Foucher Street, Suite 10012
New Orleans, LA 70115
Tel: 504 897-8978   *Fax:* 504 897-7145
E-mail: skishn@lsuhsc.edu
Length: 4 Yrs   *ACGME Approved/Offered Positions:* 20
Program ID: 340-21-21-020

Maryland

Baltimore

Johns Hopkins University Program

Sponsor: Johns Hopkins University School of Medicine
Good Samaritan Hospital of Maryland
Johns Hopkins Hospital
Prgm Director: Samuel Mayer, MD, BS
600 North Wolfe Street
Phipps Building 160
Baltimore, MD 21287
Tel: 410 502-2447   *Fax:* 410 614-4033
E-mail: rmayer2@jhmi.edu
Length: 3 Yrs   *ACGME Approved/Offered Positions:* 15
Program ID: 340-23-21-105

Sinai Hospital of Baltimore Program

Sponsor: Sinai Hospital of Baltimore
Veterans Affairs Medical Center (Baltimore)
Prgm Director: Melanie C Brown, MD
Dept of Rehabilitation Medicine
2401 W Belvedere Ave
Baltimore, MD 21215
Tel: 410 601-0670   *Fax:* 410 601-9692
Length: 3 Yrs   *ACGME Approved/Offered Positions:* 12
Program ID: 340-23-22-021

Bethesda

National Capital Consortium Program

Sponsor: National Capital Consortium
Walter Reed Army Medical Center
Prgm Director: Jeffrey M Gambel, MD, MPH
National Capital Consortium
Physical Medicine & Rehab Svc, Bldg 2, Rm 3J
Washington, DC 20307
Tel: 202 782-6369   *Fax:* 202 782-0970
Length: 3 Yrs   *ACGME Approved/Offered Positions:* 12
Program ID: 340-10-21-074
Uniformed Services Program

Massachusetts

Boston

Boston University Medical Center Program

Sponsor: Boston Medical Center
Prgm Director: Steve R Williams, MD
732 Harrison Avenue
Preston 511
Boston, MA 02118
Tel: 617 414-0044   *Fax:* 617 638-7313
Length: 3 Yrs   *ACGME Approved/Offered Positions:* 14
Program ID: 340-24-11-024

Harvard Medical School/Spaulding Rehabilitation Hospital Program

Sponsor: Spaulding Rehabilitation Hospital
Massachusetts General Hospital
Prgm Director: Kevin C O'Connor, MD*
125 Nashua Street
Boston, MA 02114
Tel: 617 573-2770   *Fax:* 617 573-2769
Length: 3 Yrs   *ACGME Approved/Offered Positions:* 21
Program ID: 340-24-21-094

Tufts Medical Center Program

Sponsor: Tufts Medical Center
New England Rehabilitation Hospital
New England Sinai Hospital and Rehabilitation Center
Veterans Affairs Medical Center (Boston)
Prgm Director: Joseph A Hanak, MD
Department of PM&R
800 Washington Street, Box 400
Boston, MA 02111
Tel: 617 636-5625   *Fax:* 617 636-4240
E-mail: jhanak@tuftsmedicalcenter.org
Length: 3 Yrs   *ACGME Approved/Offered Positions:* 18
Program ID: 340-24-21-023

Michigan

Ann Arbor

University of Michigan Program

Sponsor: University of Michigan Hospitals and Health
    Centers
Prgm Director: M Catherine Spires, MD, MA
Department of PM&R, Box 0744
325 E Eisenhower Blvd, Suite 100
Ann Arbor, MI 48108
Tel: 734 936-7201   *Fax:* 734 763-4224
E-mail: twileyr@med.umich.edu
Length: 3 Yrs   *ACGME Approved/Offered Positions:* 18
Program ID: 340-25-21-025

Detroit

Wayne State University/Detroit Medical Center Program

Sponsor: Wayne State University/Detroit Medical Center
Rehabilitation Institute
Prgm Director: Lawrence Horn, MD
Rehabilitation Institute of Michigan
261 Mack Ave, Suite 839-B
Detroit, MI 48201
Tel: 313 745-9880   *Fax:* 313 745-1063
E-mail: csturr@med.wayne.edu
Length: 3 Yrs   *ACGME Approved/Offered Positions:* 15
Program ID: 340-25-21-027

Lansing

Michigan State University Program

Sponsor: Michigan State University College of Human
    Medicine
Ingham Regional Medical Center
McLaren Regional Medical Center
Sparrow Hospital
Prgm Director: Michael T Andary, MD, MS
Suite 520 Sparrow Professional Building
1200 E Michigan Avenue
Lansing, MI 48912
Tel: 517 353-0713   *Fax:* 517 432-1339
E-mail: andary@msu.edu
Length: 3 Yrs   *ACGME Approved/Offered Positions:* 9
Program ID: 340-25-21-100

Royal Oak

William Beaumont Hospital Program

Sponsor: William Beaumont Hospital
Prgm Director: Martin S Tamler, MD
3601 West 13 Mile Road
Royal Oak, MI 48073
Tel: 248 898-0161   *Fax:* 248 898-3631
Length: 4 Yrs   *ACGME Approved/Offered Positions:* 16
Program ID: 340-25-21-076

Minnesota

Minneapolis

University of Minnesota Program

Sponsor: University of Minnesota Medical School
Hennepin County Medical Center
Regions Hospital
University of Minnesota Medical Center, Division of
    Fairview
Veterans Affairs Medical Center (Minneapolis)
Prgm Director: Charlotte L Roehr, MD*
MMC 297 UMHC, 500 Boyton HSB
410 Church Street
Minneapolis, MN 55455
Tel: 612 626-4913   *Fax:* 612 624-6686
Length: 3 Yrs   *ACGME Approved/Offered Positions:* 12
Program ID: 340-26-21-028

Rochester

College of Medicine, Mayo Clinic (Rochester) Program

Sponsor: College of Medicine, Mayo Clinic
Mayo Clinic (Rochester)
Saint Marys Hospital of Rochester
Prgm Director: Brian E Grogg, MD
Department of PM&R
200 First Street SW
Rochester, MN 55905
Tel: 507 284-2946
Length: 3 Yrs   *ACGME Approved/Offered Positions:* 27
Program ID: 340-26-21-030

Missouri

Columbia

University of Missouri-Columbia Program

Sponsor: University of Missouri-Columbia School of
    Medicine
Harry S Truman Memorial Veterans Hospital
Howard A Rusk (HealthSouth) Rehabilitation Center
University Hospitals and Clinics
Prgm Director: Joseph E Burris, MD
Department of PM&R, DC046.00
1 Hospital Drive
Columbia, MO 65212
Tel: 573 882-3101   *Fax:* 573 884-4540
Length: 3 Yrs   *ACGME Approved/Offered Positions:* 12
Program ID: 340-28-21-031

St Louis

Washington University/B-JH/SLCH Consortium Program

Sponsor: Washington University/B-JH/SLCH Consortium
Barnes-Jewish Hospital
The Rehabilitation Institute of St Louis
Prgm Director: Oksana Volshteyn, MD
4444 Forest Park Ave
Campus Box 8518
St Louis, MO 63108
Tel: 314 454-7757   *Fax:* 314 454-5300
E-mail: volshteyno@neuro.wustl.edu
Length: 4 Yrs   *ACGME Approved/Offered Positions:* 15
Program ID: 340-28-11-032

New Jersey

Edison

JFK Medical Center Program

Sponsor: JFK Medical Center
St Peter's University Hospital
Prgm Director: Sara J Cuccurullo, MD
65 James Street
PO Box 3059
Edison, NJ 08818
Tel: 732 321-7000   *Fax:* 732 321-7330
Length: 3 Yrs   *ACGME Approved/Offered Positions:* 12
Program ID: 340-33-21-033

Newark

UMDNJ-New Jersey Medical School Program

Sponsor: UMDNJ-New Jersey Medical School
Kessler Institute for Rehabilitation
Veterans Affairs New Jersey Health Care System
Prgm Director: Susan V Garstang, MD
30 Bergen Street, ADMC 101
Box 1709
Newark, NJ 07101
Tel: 973 972-3606   *Fax:* 973 972-5148
E-mail: garstasv@umdnj.edu
Length: 3 Yrs   *ACGME Approved/Offered Positions:* 27
Program ID: 340-33-32-034

New York

Albany

Albany Medical Center Program

Sponsor: Albany Medical Center
Veterans Affairs Medical Center (Albany)
Prgm Director: Andrew H Dubin, MD
Department of PM&R
43 New Scotland Avenue, MC 79
Albany, NY 12208
Tel: 518 262-5633
Length: 4 Yrs   *ACGME Approved/Offered Positions:* 8
Program ID: 340-35-21-035

Bronx

Albert Einstein College of Medicine Program

Sponsor: Albert Einstein College of Medicine of Yeshiva
   University
Jamaica Hospital Medical Center
Montefiore Medical Center-Henry and Lucy Moses
   Division
Montefiore Medical Center-Weiler Division
North Bronx Healthcare Network-Jacobi Medical Center
Prgm Director: Mark A Thomas, MD
Montefiore Medical Center
111 East 210th Street
Bronx, NY 10467
Tel: 718 920-2753   *Fax:* 718 920-5048
Length: 3 Yrs   *ACGME Approved/Offered Positions:* 25
Program ID: 340-35-21-043

Brooklyn

Kingsbrook Jewish Medical Center Program

Sponsor: Kingsbrook Jewish Medical Center
Prgm Director: Meg A Krilov, MD, MA
Department of PM&R
585 Schenectady Avenue, DMRI 221
Brooklyn, NY 11203
Tel: 718 604-5341   *Fax:* 718 604-5272
Length: 3 Yrs   *ACGME Approved/Offered Positions:* 15
Program ID: 340-35-22-041

SUNY Health Science Center at Brooklyn Program

Sponsor: SUNY Health Science Center at Brooklyn
Kings County Hospital Center
St John's Episcopal Hospital-South Shore
Staten Island University Hospital
University Hospital-SUNY Health Science Center at
   Brooklyn
Prgm Director: Paul A Pipia, MD, MS
450 Clarkson Avenue Box 30
Brooklyn, NY 11203
Tel: 718 270-2951   *Fax:* 718 270-8199
Length: 3 Yrs   *ACGME Approved/Offered Positions:* 21
Program ID: 340-35-21-048

Buffalo

University at Buffalo Program

Sponsor: University at Buffalo School of Medicine
Erie County Medical Center
Kaleida Health System (Buffalo General Hospital)
Veterans Affairs Western New York Hospital
Prgm Director: Thomas D Polisoto, MD
Rehab Residency Office-Rm G221
462 Grider Street
Buffalo, NY 14215
Tel: 716 898-3218   *Fax:* 716 898-3652
E-mail: gthomson@buffalo.edu
Length: 4 Yrs   *ACGME Approved/Offered Positions:* 16
Program ID: 340-35-21-036

East Meadow

Nassau University Medical Center Program

Sponsor: Nassau University Medical Center
Prgm Director: Lyn Weiss, MD
Department of PM&R
2201 Hempstead Turnpike, 5th Floor
East Meadow, NY 11554
Tel: 516 572-6525   *Fax:* 516 572-3170
Length: 3 Yrs   *ACGME Approved/Offered Positions:* 13
Program ID: 340-35-11-037

Great Neck

NSLIJHS-Albert Einstein College of Medicine at Long Island Jewish Medical Center Program

Sponsor: North Shore-Long Island Jewish Health System
Long Island Jewish Medical Center
North Shore University Hospital at Glen Cove
Southside Hospital
Prgm Director: Matthew M Shatzer, DO*
270-05 76th Avenue
New Hyde Park, NY 11040
Tel: 516 465-8729   *Fax:* 516 465-8723
E-mail: vruiz@nshs.edu
Length: 3 Yrs   *ACGME Approved/Offered Positions:* 12
Program ID: 340-35-21-042

New York

Mount Sinai School of Medicine Program

Sponsor: Mount Sinai School of Medicine
Elmhurst Hospital Center-Mount Sinai Services
Mount Sinai Medical Center
Veterans Affairs Medical Center (Bronx)
Prgm Director: Joseph E Herrera, DO*
One Gustave L Levy Place
Box 1240
New York, NY 10029
Tel: 212 659-9351   *Fax:* 212 348-5901
Length: 3 Yrs   *ACGME Approved/Offered Positions:* 21
Program ID: 340-35-21-044

New York Medical College at St Vincent's Hospital and Medical Center of New York Program

Sponsor: New York Medical College
St Vincent Catholic Medical Centers (Manhattan)
Prgm Director: Julian Sosner, MD
Medical Center
170 West 12th Street, Suite 2G
New York, NY 10011
Tel: 212 604-8923   *Fax:* 212 604-2608
E-mail: jsosner@svcmcny.org
Length: 3 Yrs   *ACGME Approved/Offered Positions:* 11
Program ID: 340-35-11-047

New York Presbyterian Hospital (Columbia and Cornell Campus) Program

Sponsor: New York Presbyterian Hospital
New York Presbyterian Hospital (Columbia Campus)
New York Presbyterian Hospital (Cornell Campus)
Prgm Director: Nancy E Strauss, MD
180 Fort Washington Avenue
Harkness Pavilion
New York, NY 10032
Tel: 212 305-8592   *Fax:* 212 305-4258
Length: 3 Yrs   *ACGME Approved/Offered Positions:* 24
Program ID: 340-35-21-039

New York University School of Medicine Program

Sponsor: New York University School of Medicine
Bellevue Hospital Center
Manhattan VA Harbor Health Care System
Rusk Institute of Rehabilitation Medicine
Prgm Director: Alex Moroz, MD
400 East 34th Street
Suite 600
New York, NY 10016
Tel: 212 263-6110   *Fax:* 212 263-8815
Length: 3 Yrs   *ACGME Approved/Offered Positions:* 41
Program ID: 340-35-21-046

Rochester

University of Rochester Program

Sponsor: Strong Memorial Hospital of the University of
   Rochester
Prgm Director: K Rao Poduri, MD
PO Box 664
601 Elmwood Avenue
Rochester, NY 14642
Tel: 585 275-3274   *Fax:* 585 442-2949
E-mail: KR_Poduri@urmc.rochester.edu
Length: 4 Yrs   *ACGME Approved/Offered Positions:* 12
Program ID: 340-35-21-051

Note: * indicates a newly appointed program director

Stony Brook

SUNY at Stony Brook Program

Sponsor: University Hospital - SUNY at Stony Brook
St Charles Hospital and Rehabilitation Center
Veterans Affairs Medical Center (Northport)
Prgm Director: Susan M Stickevers, MD, BA
Northport VA Med Center & St Charles Hospital
79 Middleville Road
Northport, NY 11768
Tel: 631 261-4400   *Fax:* 631 266-6022
E-mail: Susan.Stickevers@va.gov
Length: 3 Yrs   *ACGME Approved/Offered Positions:* 9
Program ID: 340-35-21-103

Syracuse

SUNY Upstate Medical University Program

Sponsor: SUNY Upstate Medical University
Veterans Affairs Medical Center (Syracuse)
Prgm Director: Robert J Weber, MD
750 E Adams Street
Syracuse, NY 13210
Tel: 315 464-5820   *Fax:* 315 464-8699
Length: 3 Yrs   *ACGME Approved/Offered Positions:* 12
Program ID: 340-35-21-093

Valhalla

New York Medical College (Metropolitan) Program

Sponsor: New York Medical College
Metropolitan Hospital Center
Prgm Director: Maria P de Araujo, MD
Rm 557, Munger Pavilion
Valhalla, NY 10595
Tel: 914 594-4275   *Fax:* 914 594-4276
E-mail: pmr@nymc.edu
Length: 3 Yrs   *ACGME Approved/Offered Positions:* 9
Program ID: 340-35-21-045

North Carolina

Chapel Hill

University of North Carolina Hospitals Program

Sponsor: University of North Carolina Hospitals
Prgm Director: Michael Y Lee, MD, MHA
Main Hospital Room N1181, (CB7200)
Chapel Hill, NC 27599
Tel: 919 966-5165   *Fax:* 919 843-0164
Length: 4 Yrs   *ACGME Approved/Offered Positions:* 12
Program ID: 340-36-21-104

Charlotte

Carolinas Medical Center Program

Sponsor: Carolinas Medical Center
Carolinas Rehabilitation
Prgm Director: Vu Q Nguyen, MD
Department of PM&R
1100 Blythe Boulevard
Charlotte, NC 28203
Tel: 704 355-4406   *Fax:* 704 355-0709
Length: 3 Yrs   *ACGME Approved/Offered Positions:* 12
Program ID: 340-36-21-095

Greenville

Pitt County Memorial Hospital/East Carolina University Program

Sponsor: Pitt County Memorial Hospital
Prgm Director: Raymund V Millan, MD
Department of Physical Med & Rehab
600 Moye Boulevard
Greenville, NC 27834
Tel: 252 847-7907   *Fax:* 252 847-0840
E-mail: battleb@ecu.edu
Length: 4 Yrs   *ACGME Approved/Offered Positions:* 19
Program ID: 340-36-21-091

Ohio

Cincinnati

University Hospital/University of Cincinnati College of Medicine Program

Sponsor: University Hospital Inc
Drake Center Inc
Veterans Affairs Medical Center (Cincinnati)
Prgm Director: Mary McMahon, MD
PO Box 670530
231 Albert Sabin Way
Cincinnati, OH 45267
Tel: 513 558-7635   *Fax:* 513 558-4458
E-mail: dukemy@uc.edu
Length: 4 Yrs   *ACGME Approved/Offered Positions:* 12
Program ID: 340-38-21-086

Cleveland

Case Western Reserve University (MetroHealth) Program

Sponsor: MetroHealth Medical Center
Cleveland Clinic Foundation
Prgm Director: Gary S Clark, MD, MHA
2500 MetroHealth Drive
Department of Physical Medicine & Rehabilitation
Cleveland, OH 44109
Tel: 216 778-3205   *Fax:* 216 778-7393
E-mail: rkarim@metrohealth.org
Length: 4 Yrs   *ACGME Approved/Offered Positions:* 21
Program ID: 340-38-31-053

Columbus

Ohio State University Hospital Program

Sponsor: Ohio State University Hospital
Prgm Director: Daniel M Clinchot, MD
1018 Dodd Rehabilitation Hospital
480 Medical Center Drive
Columbus, OH 43210
Tel: 614 293-4295   *Fax:* 614 293-3809
E-mail: Clinchot.1@osu.edu
Length: 4 Yrs   *ACGME Approved/Offered Positions:* 21
Program ID: 340-38-21-054

Toledo

University of Toledo Program

Sponsor: University of Toledo
University Medical Center (Toledo)
Prgm Director: Steven J Farrell, MD
Physical Medicine & Rehabilitation
3065 Arlington Avenue
Toledo, OH 43614
Tel: 419 383-5090   *Fax:* 419 383-3596
E-mail: steven.farrell@utoledo.edu
Length: 3 Yrs   *ACGME Approved/Offered Positions:* 6
Program ID: 340-38-21-080

Pennsylvania

Philadelphia

Temple University Hospital Program

Sponsor: Temple University Hospital
Moss Rehabilitation Hospital
Prgm Director: Ian B Maitin, MD, MBA
3401 N Broad Street
Philadelphia, PA 19140
Tel: 215 707-7021   *Fax:* 215 707-9168
E-mail: maitin@temple.edu
Length: 3 Yrs   *ACGME Approved/Offered Positions:* 30
Program ID: 340-41-21-056

Thomas Jefferson University Program

Sponsor: Thomas Jefferson University Hospital
Magee Rehabilitation Hospital
Moss Rehabilitation Hospital
Prgm Director: Christopher S Formal, MD
25 South 9th Street
Philadelphia, PA 19107
Tel: 215 587-3057   *Fax:* 215 587-9405
E-mail: cformal@comcast.net
Length: 3 Yrs   *ACGME Approved/Offered Positions:* 21
Program ID: 340-41-21-057

University of Pennsylvania Program

Sponsor: University of Pennsylvania Health System
Veterans Affairs Medical Center (Philadelphia)
Prgm Director: Richard Salcido, MD
Dept of Physical Medicine and Rehabilitation
5 West Gates, 3400 Spruce Street
Philadelphia, PA 19104
Tel: 215 662-3620   *Fax:* 215 349-8680
E-mail: richard.salcido@uphs.upenn.edu
Length: 4 Yrs   *ACGME Approved/Offered Positions:* 16
Program ID: 340-41-21-058

Pittsburgh

University of Pittsburgh Medical Center Medical Education (Mercy) Program

Sponsor: Univ of Pittsburgh Medical Center Medical Education
Mercy Hospital of Pittsburgh
Prgm Director: Mary Ann Miknevich, MD
Physical Medicine and Rehabilitation
1400 Locust Street
Pittsburgh, PA 15219
Tel: 412 232-7608   *Fax:* 412 281-3536
E-mail: miknma@upmc.edu
Length: 3 Yrs   *ACGME Approved/Offered Positions:* 14
Program ID: 340-41-22-059

University of Pittsburgh Medical Center Medical Education Program

Sponsor: Univ of Pittsburgh Medical Center Medical Education
UPMC McKeesport
UPMC Presbyterian Shadyside
UPMC South Side
Prgm Director: Wendy M Helkowski, MD
3471 Fifth Avenue, Room 201 Kaufmann Bldg
Pittsburgh, PA 15213
Tel: 412 648-6138   *Fax:* 412 692-4410
Length: 4 Yrs   *ACGME Approved/Offered Positions:* 20
Program ID: 340-41-21-075

Puerto Rico

San Juan

University of Puerto Rico Program
Sponsor: University of Puerto Rico School of Medicine
HealthSouth Rehabilitation Hospital
University Hospital
University Pediatric Hospital
Prgm Director: William F Micheo, MD
Medical Sciences Campus
PO Box 365067
San Juan, PR 00936
Tel: 787 751-9625   *Fax:* 787 754-1478
E-mail: wmicheo@usa.net
Length: 4 Yrs   *ACGME Approved/Offered Positions:* 13
Program ID: 340-42-31-062

VA Caribbean Healthcare System Program
Sponsor: VA Caribbean Healthcare System
Prgm Director: Ana V Cintrón-Rodríguez, MD
PM&R Service (117)
10 Casia Street
San Juan, PR 00921
Tel: 787 641-7582   *Fax:* 787 641-5716
E-mail: Ana.Cintron@va.gov
Length: 4 Yrs   *ACGME Approved/Offered Positions:* 12
Program ID: 340-42-31-063

Texas

Dallas

Baylor University Medical Center Program
Sponsor: Baylor University Medical Center
Baylor Institute for Rehabilitation
Prgm Director: Rita G Hamilton, DO*
909 N Washington Avenue
Dallas, TX 75246
Tel: 214 820-7192   *Fax:* 214 820-8892
E-mail: pmrdallas@baylorhealth.edu
Length: 3 Yrs   *ACGME Approved/Offered Positions:* 9
Program ID: 340-48-31-064

University of Texas Southwestern Medical School Program
Sponsor: University of Texas Southwestern Medical School
Dallas County Hospital District-Parkland Memorial Hospital
Dallas VA Medical Center
University Hospitals Zale Lipshy
Prgm Director: Samuel Bierner, MD
Physical Medicine & Rehabilitation Department
5323 Harry Hines Boulevard
Dallas, TX 75390
Tel: 214 648-8826   *Fax:* 214 648-9207
E-mail: Terri.Isbell@UTSouthwestern.edu
Length: 3 Yrs   *ACGME Approved/Offered Positions:* 21
Program ID: 340-48-21-065

Houston

Baylor College of Medicine Program
Sponsor: Baylor College of Medicine
Memorial Hermann Hospital
Michael E DeBakey VA Medical Center - Houston
The Institute for Rehabilitation and Research
Prgm Director: Martin Grabois, MD
PM&R Alliance Education Office
1333 Moursund Street, Suite A-220
Houston, TX 77030
Tel: 713 799-5034   *Fax:* 713 797-5982
E-mail: PMandR@bcm.edu
Length: 3 Yrs   *ACGME Approved/Offered Positions:* 39
Program ID: 340-48-21-066

University of Texas at Houston Program
Sponsor: University of Texas Health Science Center at Houston
Memorial Hermann Hospital
Michael E DeBakey VA Medical Center - Houston
The Institute for Rehabilitation and Research
Prgm Director: Gerard E Francisco, MD
1333 Moursund, Suite A-220
Houston, TX 77030
Tel: 713 797-5246   *Fax:* 713 799-6997
Length: 3 Yrs   *ACGME Approved/Offered Positions:* 12
Program ID: 340-48-21-101

San Antonio

University of Texas Health Science Center at San Antonio Program
Sponsor: University of Texas School of Medicine at San Antonio
Audie L Murphy Memorial Veterans Hospital (San Antonio)
San Antonio Warm Springs Rehabilitation Hospital
University Health System
Prgm Director: Tracy R Johnson, MD
Department of PM&R
7703 Floyd Curl Drive
San Antonio, TX 78229
Tel: 210 617-5300   *Fax:* 210 617-5391
Length: 4 Yrs   *ACGME Approved/Offered Positions:* 32
Program ID: 340-48-21-067

Utah

Salt Lake City

University of Utah Program
Sponsor: University of Utah Medical Center
Veterans Affairs Medical Center (Salt Lake City)
Prgm Director: Joseph B Webster, MD
Div of Physical Medicine and Rehabilitation
30 North 1900 East
Salt Lake City, UT 84132
Tel: 801 585-2589   *Fax:* 801 587-7287
E-mail: joseph.webster@hsc.utah.edu
Length: 3 Yrs   *ACGME Approved/Offered Positions:* 12
Program ID: 340-49-21-068

Virginia

Charlottesville

University of Virginia Program
Sponsor: University of Virginia Medical Center
UVA HealthSouth Rehabilitation Hospital
Prgm Director: Mary G Bryant, MD
PO Box 801004
545 Ray C Hunt Drive, Suite 240
Charlottesville, VA 22908
Tel: 434 243-5628   *Fax:* 434 243-5639
E-mail: MGB9E@virginia.edu
Length: 4 Yrs   *ACGME Approved/Offered Positions:* 14
Program ID: 340-51-21-089

Norfolk

Eastern Virginia Medical School Program
Sponsor: Eastern Virginia Medical School
Sentara Norfolk General Hospital
Veterans Affairs Medical Center (Hampton)
Prgm Director: Jean E Shelton, MD
Dept of Physical Medicine & Rehab
721 Fairfax Avenue, 3rd Floor
Norfolk, VA 23507
Tel: 757 446-5915   *Fax:* 757 446-5969
E-mail: sheltoje@evms.edu
Length: 3 Yrs   *ACGME Approved/Offered Positions:* 11
Program ID: 340-51-21-081

Richmond

Virginia Commonwealth University Health System Program
Sponsor: Virginia Commonwealth University Health System
Hunter Holmes McGuire VA Medical Center (Richmond)
Medical College of Virginia Hospitals
Prgm Director: William O McKinley, MD
1223 East Marshall Street
Box 980677
Richmond, VA 23298
Tel: 804 828-4233   *Fax:* 804 828-5074
Length: 3 Yrs   *ACGME Approved/Offered Positions:* 18
Program ID: 340-51-21-069

Washington

Seattle

University of Washington Program
Sponsor: University of Washington School of Medicine
Harborview Medical Center
University of Washington Medical Center
VA Puget Sound Health Care System
Prgm Director: Teresa L Massagli, MD
Department of Rehabilitation Medicine
Box 356490, 1959 NE Pacific St
Seattle, WA 98195
Tel: 206 685-0936   *Fax:* 206 685-3244
E-mail: klr@u.washington.edu
Length: 4 Yrs   *ACGME Approved/Offered Positions:* 31
Program ID: 340-54-21-070

Wisconsin

Madison

University of Wisconsin Program
Sponsor: University of Wisconsin Hospital and Clinics
Prgm Director: Bonnie J Weigert, MD
6630 University Avenue
Middleton, WI 53562
Tel: 608 263-8640   *Fax:* 608 263-9271
E-mail: BWeigert@uwhealth.org
Length: 4 Yrs   *ACGME Approved/Offered Positions:* 12
Program ID: 340-56-21-072

Milwaukee

Medical College of Wisconsin Affiliated Hospitals Program
Sponsor: Medical College of Wisconsin Affiliated Hospitals, Inc
Clement J Zablocki Veterans Affairs Medical Center
Froedtert Memorial Lutheran Hospital
Prgm Director: Diane W Braza, MD*
Physical Medicine and Rehabilitation
9200 W Wisconsin Avenue
Milwaukee, WI 53226
Tel: 414 456-7197
Length: 3 Yrs   *ACGME Approved/Offered Positions:* 15
Program ID: 340-56-21-071

Note: * indicates a newly appointed program director

Plastic Surgery

Alabama

Birmingham

University of Alabama Medical Center Program

Sponsor: University of Alabama Hospital
Children's Hospital of Alabama
University of Alabama at Birmingham/Highlands
Veterans Affairs Medical Center (Birmingham)
Prgm Director: Jorge I de la Torre, MD
510 20th Street South
FOT-1164
Birmingham, AL 35294
Tel: 205 934-2307   *Fax:* 205 975-6155
E-mail: barbara.norman@ccc.uab.edu
Length: 3 Yrs   *ACGME Approved/Offered Positions:* 6
Program ID: 360-01-21-121

Arizona

Phoenix

College of Medicine, Mayo Clinic (Arizona) Program

Sponsor: College of Medicine, Mayo Clinic
Mayo Clinic Hospital
Phoenix Children's Hospital
St Joseph's Hospital and Medical Center
Prgm Director: Anthony A Smith, MD
5777 Mayo Boulevard
Phoenix, AZ 85054
Tel: 480 342-1379   *Fax:* 480 342-2027
Length: 2 Yrs   *ACGME Approved/Offered Positions:* 4
Program ID: 360-03-31-142

California

Los Angeles

UCLA Medical Center Program

Sponsor: UCLA David Geffen School of Medicine/UCLA
    Medical Center
UCLA Medical Center
Prgm Director: Timothy A Miller, MD
200 UCLA Medical Plaza, Suite 465
Los Angeles, CA 90095
Tel: 310 825-5898   *Fax:* 310 206-4190
Length: 3 Yrs   *ACGME Approved/Offered Positions:* 8
Program ID: 360-05-21-009

University of Southern California/ LAC+USC Medical Center Program

Sponsor: University of Southern California/LAC+USC
    Medical Center
Kaiser Permanente Southern California
LAC+USC Medical Center
Prgm Director: Randolph Sherman, MD*
1510 San Pablo Street, Suite 415
Los Angeles, CA 90033
Tel: 323 442-7903   *Fax:* 323 442-7901
Length: 3 Yrs   *ACGME Approved/Offered Positions:* 3
Program ID: 360-05-21-118

Orange

University of California (Irvine) Program

Sponsor: University of California (Irvine) Medical
    Center
Kaiser Foundation Hospital (Bellflower)
Kaiser Foundation Hospitals (Anaheim)
Long Beach Memorial Medical Center
Mission Hospital Regional Medical Center
Prgm Director: Gregory R Evans, MD
200 S Manchester Ave Ste 650
Orange, CA 92868
Tel: 714 456-5253   *Fax:* 714 456-7718
E-mail: gevans@uci.edu
Length: 3 Yrs   *ACGME Approved/Offered Positions:* 2
Program ID: 360-05-21-008

Sacramento

University of California (Davis) Health System Program

Sponsor: University of California (Davis) Health System
University of California (Davis) Medical Center
Prgm Director: Thomas R Stevenson, MD
2221 Stockton Blvd, 2nd Floor
Room 2125
Sacramento, CA 95817
Tel: 916 734-2568   *Fax:* 916 734-7104
Length: 3 Yrs   *ACGME Approved/Offered Positions:* 6
Program ID: 360-05-21-113

San Diego

University of California (San Diego) Program

Sponsor: University of California (San Diego) Medical
    Center
Rady Children's Hospital
Veterans Affairs Medical Center (San Diego)
Prgm Director: Marek K Dobke, MD, PhD
200 West Arbor Drive
San Diego, CA 92103
Tel: 619 543-6084   *Fax:* 619 543-3645
Length: 3 Yrs   *ACGME Approved/Offered Positions:* 2
Program ID: 360-05-21-010

San Francisco

University of California (San Francisco) Program

Sponsor: University of California (San Francisco) School
    of Medicine
San Francisco General Hospital Medical Center
UCSF and Mount Zion Medical Centers
Prgm Director: William Y Hoffman, MD
505 Parnassus Avenue, M593
Box 0932
San Francisco, CA 94143
Tel: 415 353-4285   *Fax:* 415 353-4320
E-mail: william.hoffman@ucsfmedctr.org
Length: 3 Yrs   *ACGME Approved/Offered Positions:* 9
Program ID: 360-05-22-012

Connecticut

New Haven

Yale-New Haven Medical Center Program

Sponsor: Yale-New Haven Hospital
Bridgeport Hospital
Hospital of St Raphael
Prgm Director: John A Persing, MD
330 Cedar Street, Room 330
PO Box 208041
New Haven, CT 06520
Tel: 203 785-2573   *Fax:* 203 785-5714
E-mail: john.persing@yale.edu
Length: 3 Yrs   *ACGME Approved/Offered Positions:* 6
Program ID: 360-08-21-015

Florida

Gainesville

University of Florida Program

Sponsor: University of Florida College of Medicine
North Florida/South Georgia Veterans Health System
Shands Hospital at the University of Florida
Prgm Director: Michael B Seagle, MD
Box 100286
Gainesville, FL 32610
Tel: 352 273-8670   *Fax:* 352 273-8639
E-mail: brent.seagle@surgery.ufl.edu
Length: 3 Yrs   *ACGME Approved/Offered Positions:* 3
Program ID: 360-11-21-019

Miami

Jackson Memorial Hospital/Jackson Health System Program

Sponsor: Jackson Memorial Hospital/Jackson Health
    System
University of Miami Hospital
Veterans Affairs Medical Center (Miami)
Prgm Director: Seth R Thaller, MD, DMD
PO Box 016960 (R88)
Jackson Memorial Hospital
Miami, FL 33101
Tel: 305 585-5285   *Fax:* 305 324-7384
Length: 3 Yrs   *ACGME Approved/Offered Positions:* 6
Program ID: 360-11-21-022

Tampa

University of South Florida Program

Sponsor: University of South Florida College of Medicine
H Lee Moffitt Cancer Center
Tampa General Hospital
Veterans Affairs Medical Center (Bay Pines)
Prgm Director: David J Smith Jr, MD
12901 Bruce B Downs Boulevard, MDC-16
Tampa, FL 33612
Tel: 813 974-6159   *Fax:* 813 974-8106
E-mail: wmccrore@health.usf.edu
Length: 3 Yrs   *ACGME Approved/Offered Positions:* 6
Program ID: 360-11-12-140

Weston

Cleveland Clinic (Florida) Program

Sponsor: Cleveland Clinic Florida
Joe Di Maggio Children's Hospital
Memorial Regional Hospital
Prgm Director: Michel C Samson, MD
2950 Cleveland Clinic Boulevard
Weston, FL 33331
Tel: 954 659-5000   *Fax:* 954 659-5210
E-mail: samsonm1@ccf.org
Length: 3 Yrs   *ACGME Approved/Offered Positions:* 4
Program ID: 360-11-31-139

Programs

Georgia

Atlanta

Emory University Program
Sponsor: Emory University School of Medicine
Emory University Hospital
Grady Health System
Prgm Director: Thomas R Hester Jr, MD
3200 Downwood Circle
Suite 640A
Atlanta, GA 30327
Tel: 678 420-7045   *Fax:* 678 420-7016
Length: 3 Yrs   *ACGME Approved/Offered Positions:* 9
Program ID: 360-12-21-024

Augusta

Medical College of Georgia Program
Sponsor: Medical College of Georgia
Veterans Affairs Medical Center (Augusta)
Prgm Director: Edmond F Ritter, MD*
1467 Harper Street, HB-5040
Augusta, GA 30912
Tel: 706 721-6945   *Fax:* 706 721-6931
Length: 3 Yrs   *ACGME Approved/Offered Positions:* 4
Program ID: 360-12-21-111

Illinois

Chicago

Rush University Medical Center Program
Sponsor: Rush University Medical Center
Prgm Director: John W Polley, MD
1725 W Harrison St, Suite 425
Professional Building 1
Chicago, IL 60612
Tel: 312 563-3000   *Fax:* 312 563-2514
E-mail: john_polley@rush.edu
Length: 3 Yrs   *ACGME Approved/Offered Positions:* 2
Program ID: 360-16-11-026

University of Chicago Program
Sponsor: University of Chicago Medical Center
Prgm Director: David H Song, MD
5841 S Maryland Avenue, MC6035
Chicago, IL 60637
Tel: 773 702-6302   *Fax:* 773 702-1634
E-mail: jtomczak@surgery.bsd.uchicago.edu
Length: 3 Yrs   *ACGME Approved/Offered Positions:* 6
Program ID: 360-16-11-027

University of Illinois College of Medicine at Chicago Program
Sponsor: University of Illinois College of Medicine at Chicago
Advocate Christ Medical Center
John H Stroger Hospital of Cook County
Mount Sinai Hospital Medical Center of Chicago
University of Illinois Hospital and Clinics
Prgm Director: Mimis Cohen, MD
M/C 958, Suite 515 CSN
820 South Wood Street
Chicago, IL 60612
Tel: 312 996-9313   *Fax:* 312 413-0495
E-mail: mncohen@uic.edu
Length: 3 Yrs   *ACGME Approved/Offered Positions:* 6
Program ID: 360-16-21-028

Maywood

Loyola University Program
Sponsor: Loyola University Medical Center
Edward Hines, Jr Veterans Affairs Hospital
Prgm Director: Victor Cimino, MD, DDS
EMS 110, Room 3262
Maywood, IL 60153
Tel: 708 327-2653   *Fax:* 708 327-3463
E-mail: kechert@lumc.edu
Length: 3 Yrs   *ACGME Approved/Offered Positions:* 3
Program ID: 360-16-21-029

Indiana

Indianapolis

Indiana University School of Medicine Program
Sponsor: Indiana University School of Medicine
Clarian Indiana University Hospital
Clarian Riley Hospital for Children
Richard L Roudebush Veterans Affairs Medical Center
St Vincent Hospitals and Health Care Center
William N Wishard Memorial Hospital
Prgm Director: John J Coleman III, MD
Emerson Hall 232
545 Barnhill Drive
Indianapolis, IN 46202
Tel: 317 274-8106   *Fax:* 317 278-8746
Length: 3 Yrs   *ACGME Approved/Offered Positions:* 6
Program ID: 360-17-11-031

Kentucky

Louisville

University of Louisville Program
Sponsor: University of Louisville School of Medicine
University of Louisville Hospital
Prgm Director: Bradon J Wilhelmi, MD, BS
Department of Surgery, Division of Plastic Surgery
550 South Jackson Street, ACB-2nd Floor
Louisville, KY 40202
Tel: 502 852-6880   *Fax:* 502 852-8915
E-mail: bjwilh01@louisville.edu
Length: 3 Yrs   *ACGME Approved/Offered Positions:* 4
Program ID: 360-20-21-034

Louisiana

New Orleans

Louisiana State University Program
Sponsor: Louisiana State University School of Medicine
Houma Outpatient Surgery Center
Medical Center of Louisiana at New Orleans
West Jefferson Medical Center
Prgm Director: Charles L Dupin, MD
533 Bolivar Street
Room 508
New Orleans, LA 70112
Tel: 504 349-6460   *Fax:* 504 349-6463
E-mail: cldupinmd@gmail.com
Length: 3 Yrs   *ACGME Approved/Offered Positions:* 4
Program ID: 360-21-11-035

Tulane University Program
Sponsor: Tulane University School of Medicine
Ochsner Clinic Foundation
Tulane University Hospital and Clinics
Tulane-Lakeside Hospital
Prgm Director: R Edward Newsome Jr, MD
c/o Edward Newsome, MD
1430 Tulane Avenue, SL-22
New Orleans, LA 70112
Tel: 504 988-5500   *Fax:* 504 988-3740
E-mail: newsome@tulane.edu
Length: 3 Yrs   *ACGME Approved/Offered Positions:* 4
Program ID: 360-21-31-137

Maryland

Baltimore

Johns Hopkins University/University of Maryland Program
Sponsor: Johns Hopkins University School of Medicine
Johns Hopkins Bayview Medical Center
Johns Hopkins Hospital
Union Memorial Hospital
University of Maryland Medical System
Prgm Director: Richard J Redett III, MD
601 N Caroline Street, Room 8152C
Baltimore, MD 21287
Tel: 410 955-9475   *Fax:* 410 955-7060
E-mail: rredett@jhmi.edu
Length: 3 Yrs   *ACGME Approved/Offered Positions:* 4
Program ID: 360-23-21-037

Massachusetts

Boston

Brigham and Women's Hospital/Harvard Medical School Program
Sponsor: Brigham and Women's Hospital
Beth Israel Deaconess Medical Center
Children's Hospital
Massachusetts General Hospital
Prgm Director: Julian J Pribaz, MD
75 Francis Street
Boston, MA 02115
Tel: 617 732-6390   *Fax:* 617 730-2855
E-mail: surgeryeducation@partners.org
Length: 3 Yrs   *ACGME Approved/Offered Positions:* 9
Program ID: 360-24-21-135

Burlington

Lahey Clinic Program
Sponsor: Lahey Clinic
Maine Medical Center
Prgm Director: Jeffrey Weinzweig, MD
Lahey Clinic
41 Mall Road
Burlington, MA 01805
Tel: 781 744-8583   *Fax:* 781 744-8080
Length: 3 Yrs   *ACGME Approved/Offered Positions:* 4
Program ID: 360-24-21-125

Worcester

University of Massachusetts Program
Sponsor: University of Massachusetts Medical School
UMass Memorial Health Care (Hahnemann Campus)
UMass Memorial Health Care (University Campus)
Prgm Director: Douglas M Rothkopf, MD
55 Lake Avenue North
Worcester, MA 01655
Tel: 508 334-5942   *Fax:* 508 856-7593
Length: 3 Yrs   *ACGME Approved/Offered Positions:* 6
Program ID: 360-24-21-117

Note: * indicates a newly appointed program director

Michigan

Detroit

Wayne State University/Detroit Medical Center Program

Sponsor: Wayne State University/Detroit Medical Center
Harper-Hutzel Hospital
Providence Hospital and Medical Centers
William Beaumont Hospital
Prgm Director: Eti Gursel, MD
Harper Professional Building, #1017
3990 John R Street
Detroit, MI 48201
Tel: 313 745-7514   *Fax:* 313 993-0595
E-mail: tmmaya@aol.com
Length: 3 Yrs   *ACGME Approved/Offered Positions:* 6
Program ID: 360-25-21-043

Grand Rapids

Grand Rapids Medical Education and Research Center/Michigan State University Program

Sponsor: Grand Rapids Medical Education and Research
   Center
Saint Mary's Health Care (Grand Rapids)
Spectrum Health-Blodgett Hospital
Spectrum Health-Butterworth Hospital
Prgm Director: Steven L Ringler, MD
221 Michigan Street, NE
Suite 200A
Grand Rapids, MI 49503
Tel: 616 391-1909   *Fax:* 616 391-8611
Length: 3 Yrs   *ACGME Approved/Offered Positions:* 4
Program ID: 360-25-22-044

Minnesota

Minneapolis

University of Minnesota Program

Sponsor: University of Minnesota Medical School
Regions Hospital
University of Minnesota Medical Center, Division of
   Fairview
Veterans Affairs Medical Center (Minneapolis)
Prgm Director: Bruce L Cunningham, MD, MS
420 Delaware Street SE
MMC 122
Minneapolis, MN 55455
Tel: 612 625-0697   *Fax:* 612 624-4441
E-mail: cunni001@umn.edu
Length: 3 Yrs   *ACGME Approved/Offered Positions:* 6
Program ID: 360-26-21-131

Rochester

College of Medicine, Mayo Clinic (Rochester) Program

Sponsor: College of Medicine, Mayo Clinic
Mayo Clinic (Rochester)
Rochester Methodist Hospital
Saint Marys Hospital of Rochester
Prgm Director: Uldis Bite, MD
200 First Street SW
Rochester, MN 55905
Tel: 507 284-4068   *Fax:* 507 284-5994
E-mail: hollermann.lori@mayo.edu
Length: 3 Yrs   *ACGME Approved/Offered Positions:* 4
Program ID: 360-26-21-047

Mississippi

Jackson

University of Mississippi Medical Center Program

Sponsor: University of Mississippi School of Medicine
University Hospitals and Clinics
Veterans Affairs Medical Center (Jackson)
Prgm Director: Michael F Angel, MD
2500 North State Street
Jackson, MS 39216
Tel: 601 984-5180   *Fax:* 601 984-5183
Length: 3 Yrs   *ACGME Approved/Offered Positions:* 6
Program ID: 360-27-21-126

Missouri

St Louis

St Louis University School of Medicine Program

Sponsor: St Louis University School of Medicine
Cardinal Glennon Children's Hospital
St Louis University Hospital
St Mary's Health Center
Prgm Director: Christian E Paletta, MD
3635 Vista Avenue at Grand Blvd
PO Box 15250
St Louis, MO 63110
Tel: 314 577-8793   *Fax:* 314 268-5062
Length: 3 Yrs   *ACGME Approved/Offered Positions:* 6
Program ID: 360-28-21-051

Washington University/B-JH/SLCH Consortium Program

Sponsor: Washington University/B-JH/SLCH Consortium
Barnes-Jewish Hospital
Prgm Director: Keith E Brandt, MD
660 South Euclid Avenue, 1150 NW Tower
Campus Box 8238
St Louis, MO 63110
Tel: 314 747-0541   *Fax:* 314 362-4536
Length: 3 Yrs   *ACGME Approved/Offered Positions:* 9
Program ID: 360-28-21-052

Nebraska

Omaha

University of Nebraska Medical Center College of Medicine Program

Sponsor: University of Nebraska Medical Center College
   of Medicine
Nebraska Medical Center
Prgm Director: Perry J Johnson, MD
983335 Nebraska Medical Center
Omaha, NE 68198
Tel: 402 559-8363   *Fax:* 402 559-9513
Length: 3 Yrs   *ACGME Approved/Offered Positions:* 2
Program ID: 360-30-13-136

New Hampshire

Lebanon

Dartmouth-Hitchcock Medical Center Program

Sponsor: Mary Hitchcock Memorial Hospital
Prgm Director: Carolyn L Kerrigan, MD
Section of Plastic Surgery
One Medical Center Drive
Lebanon, NH 03756
Tel: 603 650-8467   *Fax:* 603 650-8456
Length: 3 Yrs   *ACGME Approved/Offered Positions:* 3
Program ID: 360-32-21-129

New Jersey

Camden

UMDNJ-Robert Wood Johnson Medical School (Camden) Program

Sponsor: Cooper Hospital-University Medical Center
Prgm Director: Martha S Matthews, MD
Dept of Surgery, Office of Surgical Education
3 Cooper Plaza, Suite 411
Camden, NJ 08103
Tel: 856 342-3012   *Fax:* 856 365-7582
E-mail: cooneycl@umdnj.edu
Length: 3 Yrs   *ACGME Approved/Offered Positions:* 2
Program ID: 360-33-21-132

Newark

UMDNJ-New Jersey Medical School Program

Sponsor: UMDNJ-New Jersey Medical School
Hackensack University Medical Center
UMDNJ-University Hospital
Prgm Director: Mark S Granick, MD
140 Bergen Street, E1620
Newark, NJ 07103
Tel: 973 972-8092   *Fax:* 973 972-8268
Length: 3 Yrs   *ACGME Approved/Offered Positions:* 4
Program ID: 360-33-21-119

New York

Albany

Albany Medical Center Program

Sponsor: Albany Medical Center
Albany Medical Center South Clinical Campus
Prgm Director: Stephane A Braun, MD*
47 New Scotland Avenue
Mail Code 61PL
Albany, NY 12208
Tel: 518 262-4880   *Fax:* 518 262-5999
E-mail: brauns@mail.amc.edu
Length: 3 Yrs   *ACGME Approved/Offered Positions:* 4
Program ID: 360-35-21-055

Bronx

Albert Einstein College of Medicine Program

Sponsor: Albert Einstein College of Medicine of Yeshiva
   University
Montefiore Medical Center-Henry and Lucy Moses
   Division
North Bronx Healthcare Network-Jacobi Medical Center
Prgm Director: David A Staffenberg, MD, ScD
Department of Plastic Surgery
1625 Poplar St, Suite 200
Bronx, NY 10461
Tel: 718 405-8337   *Fax:* 718 405-8345
E-mail: dstaffen@montefiore.org
Length: 3 Yrs   *ACGME Approved/Offered Positions:* 8
Program ID: 360-35-21-064

East Meadow

Nassau University Medical Center Program

Sponsor: Nassau University Medical Center
North Shore University Hospital
Winthrop-University Hospital
Prgm Director: Roger L Simpson, MD, MBA
Long Island Plastic Surgical Group
999 Franklin Avenue
Garden City, NY 11530
Tel: 516 535-6744   *Fax:* 516 742-9543
E-mail: jwatson@lipsg.com
Length: 3 Yrs   *ACGME Approved/Offered Positions:* 6
Program ID: 360-35-21-058

New York

Mount Sinai School of Medicine Program

Sponsor: Mount Sinai School of Medicine
Elmhurst Hospital Center-Mount Sinai Services
Mount Sinai Medical Center
Veterans Affairs Medical Center (Bronx)
Westchester Medical Center
Prgm Director: Lester Silver, MD, MS
One Gustave L Levy Place
Box 1259
New York, NY 10029
Tel: 212 241-5873   *Fax:* 212 534-2654
Length: 3 Yrs   *ACGME Approved/Offered Positions:* 6
Program ID: 360-35-21-065

New York Presbyterian Hospital (Cornell Campus) Program

Sponsor: New York Presbyterian Hospital
New York Presbyterian Hospital (Columbia Campus)
New York Presbyterian Hospital (Cornell Campus)
Prgm Director: Robert T Grant, MD, MSc
161 Fort Washington Avenue
Suite 601
New York, NY 10032
Tel: 212 305-3103   *Fax:* 212 305-9848
E-mail: rg424@columbia.edu
Length: 3 Yrs   *ACGME Approved/Offered Positions:* 9
Program ID: 360-35-21-060

New York University School of Medicine Program

Sponsor: New York University School of Medicine
Bellevue Hospital Center
NYU Hospitals Center
Prgm Director: Pierre B Saadeh, MD*
Institute of Reconstructive Plastic Surgery
560 First Avenue
New York, NY 10016
Tel: 212 263-8452   *Fax:* 212 263-1063
Length: 3 Yrs   *ACGME Approved/Offered Positions:* 9
Program ID: 360-35-21-066

Rochester

University of Rochester Program

Sponsor: Strong Memorial Hospital of the University of
   Rochester
Rochester General Hospital
Prgm Director: Howard N Langstein, MD
601 Elmwood Avenue, Box 661
Rochester, NY 14642
Tel: 585 275-5818   *Fax:* 585 276-1985
E-mail: howard_langstein@urmc.rochester.edu
Length: 3 Yrs   *ACGME Approved/Offered Positions:* 4
Program ID: 360-35-12-070

North Carolina

Chapel Hill

University of North Carolina Hospitals Program

Sponsor: University of North Carolina Hospitals
Carolinas Medical Center
Prgm Director: Charles S Hultman, MD
7040 Burnett-Womack
CB 7195
Chapel Hill, NC 27599
Tel: 919 966-4446   *Fax:* 919 966-3814
E-mail: scott_hultman@med.unc.edu
Length: 3 Yrs   *ACGME Approved/Offered Positions:* 6
Program ID: 360-36-11-072

Durham

Duke University Hospital Program

Sponsor: Duke University Hospital
Durham Regional Hospital
Veterans Affairs Medical Center (Durham)
Prgm Director: Michael R Zenn, MD
PO Box 3945
Durham, NC 27710
Tel: 919 684-2666   *Fax:* 919 684-4954
Length: 3 Yrs   *ACGME Approved/Offered Positions:* 9
Program ID: 360-36-21-073

Ohio

Akron

Summa Health System/NEOUCOM Program

Sponsor: Summa Health System
Akron City Hospital (Summa Health System)
Akron General Medical Center
Children's Hospital Medical Center of Akron
Prgm Director: James A Lehman Jr, MD
525 East Market Street
Medical Education/Mary Yanik
Akron, OH 44304
Tel: 330 375-3783   *Fax:* 330 375-3751
E-mail: williamsja@summa-health.org
Length: 3 Yrs   *ACGME Approved/Offered Positions:* 4
Program ID: 360-38-21-075

Cincinnati

University Hospital/University of Cincinnati College of Medicine Program

Sponsor: University Hospital Inc
Cincinnati Children's Hospital Medical Center
Prgm Director: W John Kitzmiller, MD
231 Albert Sabin Way
PO Box 670558
Cincinnati, OH 45267
Tel: 513 558-4363   *Fax:* 513 558-0570
E-mail: hohk@uc.edu
Length: 3 Yrs   *ACGME Approved/Offered Positions:* 3
Program ID: 360-38-21-112

Cleveland

Cleveland Clinic Foundation Program

Sponsor: Cleveland Clinic Foundation
Prgm Director: Risal Djohan, MD*
Department of Plastic Surgery
9500 Euclid Avenue, Desk A-60
Cleveland, OH 44195
Tel: 216 445-2433   *Fax:* 216 444-9419
Length: 3 Yrs   *ACGME Approved/Offered Positions:* 4
Program ID: 360-38-21-079

Columbus

Ohio State University Hospital Program

Sponsor: Ohio State University Hospital
Grant Medical Center (OhioHealth)
Mount Carmel
Nationwide Children's Hospital
Riverside Methodist Hospitals (OhioHealth)
Prgm Director: Michael J Miller, MD, BS
N 809 Doan Hall
410 West 10th Ave
Columbus, OH 43210
Tel: 614 293-9885   *Fax:* 614 293-9024
E-mail: michael.miller@osumc.edu
Length: 3 Yrs   *ACGME Approved/Offered Positions:* 3
Program ID: 360-38-21-081

Dayton

Wright State University Program

Sponsor: Wright State University Boonshoft School of
   Medicine
Children's Medical Center
Good Samaritan Hospital and Health Center
Kettering Medical Center
Miami Valley Hospital
Prgm Director: R Michael Johnson, MD
One Wyoming Street
WCHE7819
Dayton, OH 45409
Tel: 937 208-4955   *Fax:* 937 341-8477
E-mail: michael.johnson@wright.edu
Length: 3 Yrs   *ACGME Approved/Offered Positions:* 3
Program ID: 360-38-13-141

Oklahoma

Oklahoma City

University of Oklahoma Health Sciences Center Program

Sponsor: University of Oklahoma College of Medicine
OU Medical Center
OU Medical Center - Children's Hospital
Veterans Affairs Medical Center (Oklahoma City)
Prgm Director: Kamal Sawan, MD
920 Stanton L Young Boulevard
Williams Pavillion Suite 2220
Oklahoma City, OK 73104
Tel: 405 271-4864   *Fax:* 405 271-2738
E-mail: kamal-sawan@ouhsc.edu
Length: 3 Yrs   *ACGME Approved/Offered Positions:* 2
Program ID: 360-39-21-085

Oregon

Portland

Oregon Health & Science University Program

Sponsor: Oregon Health & Science University Hospital
Prgm Director: Juliana E Hansen, MD
3181 SW Sam Jackson Park Road
Portland, OR 97239
Tel: 503 494-7824   *Fax:* 503 494-0441
E-mail: kotsovos@ohsu.edu
Length: 3 Yrs   *ACGME Approved/Offered Positions:* 6
Program ID: 360-40-21-116

Pennsylvania

Allentown

Lehigh Valley Hospital Network Program

Sponsor: Lehigh Valley Hospital Network
Prgm Director: Robert X Murphy Jr, MD, MS
Department of Surgery
Cedar Crest & I-78, PO Box 689
Allentown, PA 18105
Tel: 484 884-1021   *Fax:* 484 884-1028
E-mail: robert.murphy@lvh.com
Length: 3 Yrs   *ACGME Approved/Offered Positions:* 3
Program ID: 360-41-22-086

Note: * indicates a newly appointed program director

Hershey

Penn State University/Milton S Hershey Medical Center Program

Sponsor: Milton S Hershey Medical Center
PinnacleHealth Hospitals
Prgm Director: Donald R Mackay, MBChB, DDS
500 University Drive
PO Box 850
Hershey, PA 17033
Tel: 717 531-4340   *Fax:* 717 531-4339
E-mail: rhowe@psu.edu
Length: 3 Yrs   *ACGME Approved/Offered Positions:* 4
Program ID: 360-41-21-087

Philadelphia

Temple University Hospital Program

Sponsor: Temple University Hospital
Abington Memorial Hospital
St Christopher's Hospital for Children (Tenet Health System)
Prgm Director: Chris D Tzarnas, MD
3322 North Broad Street
3rd Floor
Philadelphia, PA 19140
Tel: 215 707-2776
E-mail: chris.tzarnas@tuhs.temple.edu
Length: 2 Yrs   *ACGME Approved/Offered Positions:* 4
Program ID: 360-41-12-143

University of Pennsylvania Program

Sponsor: University of Pennsylvania Health System
Bryn Mawr Hospital
Children's Hospital of Philadelphia
Pennsylvania Hospital (UPHS)
Prgm Director: Richard E Kirschner, MD
3400 Spruce Street
10 Penn Tower
Philadelphia, PA 19104
Tel: 215 662-7075   *Fax:* 215 662-2172
E-mail: kris.gallagher@uphs.upenn.edu
Length: 3 Yrs   *ACGME Approved/Offered Positions:* 9
Program ID: 360-41-21-089

Pittsburgh

University of Pittsburgh Medical Center Medical Education Program

Sponsor: Univ of Pittsburgh Medical Center Medical Education
Magee-Womens Hospital of UPMC
UPMC Presbyterian Shadyside
Prgm Director: Joseph E Losee, MD
3550 Terrace Street
683 Scaife Hall
Pittsburgh, PA 15261
Tel: 412 383-8082   *Fax:* 412 383-8986
E-mail: beedlend@upmc.edu
Length: 3 Yrs   *ACGME Approved/Offered Positions:* 21
Program ID: 360-41-21-090

Rhode Island

Providence

Brown University Program

Sponsor: Rhode Island Hospital-Lifespan
Veterans Affairs Medical Center (Providence)
Prgm Director: Lee E Edstrom, MD
2 Dudley Street
Medical Office Center, Suite 190
Providence, RI 02905
Tel: 401 444-4188   *Fax:* 401 444-4863
Length: 3 Yrs   *ACGME Approved/Offered Positions:* 4
Program ID: 360-43-21-092

South Carolina

Charleston

Medical University of South Carolina Program

Sponsor: Medical University of South Carolina College of Medicine
MUSC Medical Center
Trident Medical Center
Prgm Director: John H Robinson, MD
Division of Plastic Surgery
96 Jonathan Lucas St, PO Box 250613
Charleston, SC 29425
Tel: 843 792-3072   *Fax:* 843 792-3315
Length: 3 Yrs   *ACGME Approved/Offered Positions:* 4
Program ID: 360-45-22-093

Tennessee

Chattanooga

University of Tennessee College of Medicine at Chattanooga Program

Sponsor: University of Tennessee College of Medicine-Chattanooga
Erlanger Medical Center
Prgm Director: Larry A Sargent, MD
Department of Plastic Surgery
979 East Third Street, Suite C-920
Chattanooga, TN 37403
Tel: 423 778-9047   *Fax:* 423 778-9984
E-mail: UTPlastics@thepsg.org
Length: 3 Yrs   *ACGME Approved/Offered Positions:* 4
Program ID: 360-47-11-094

Memphis

University of Tennessee Program

Sponsor: University of Tennessee College of Medicine
Methodist Healthcare - Memphis Hospitals
Regional Medical Center at Memphis
Prgm Director: Robert D Wallace, MD
910 Madison Avenue, #315
Memphis, TN 38103
Tel: 901 448-1350   *Fax:* 901 347-8295
Length: 3 Yrs   *ACGME Approved/Offered Positions:* 6
Program ID: 360-47-31-095

Nashville

Vanderbilt University Program

Sponsor: Vanderbilt University Medical Center
Prgm Director: R Bruce Shack, MD
Department of Plastic Surgery
D-4207 Medical Center North
Nashville, TN 37232
Tel: 615 936-0198   *Fax:* 615 936-0167
E-mail: bruce.shack@vanderbilt.edu
Length: 3 Yrs   *ACGME Approved/Offered Positions:* 6
Program ID: 360-47-21-096

Texas

Dallas

University of Texas Southwestern Medical School Program

Sponsor: University of Texas Southwestern Medical School
Baylor University Medical Center
Dallas County Hospital District-Parkland Memorial Hospital
University Hospitals St Paul
Prgm Director: Jeffrey E Janis, MD
1801 Inwood Rd WA4212
Department of Plastic Surgery
Dallas, TX 75390
Tel: 214 645-3116   *Fax:* 214 645-7947
E-mail: Jeffrey.Janis@UTSouthwestern.edu
Length: 3 Yrs   *ACGME Approved/Offered Positions:* 6
Program ID: 360-48-21-097

Galveston

University of Texas Medical Branch Hospitals Program

Sponsor: University of Texas Medical Branch Hospitals
Prgm Director: Linda G Phillips, MD
301 University Boulevard
6.124 McCullough Bldg
Galveston, TX 77555
Tel: 409 772-1257   *Fax:* 409 772-1872
Length: 3 Yrs   *ACGME Approved/Offered Positions:* 4
Program ID: 360-48-11-098

Houston

Methodist Hospital (Houston) Program

Sponsor: Methodist Hospital (Houston)
St Joseph Medical Center
Prgm Director: Benjamin E Cohen, MD
GWS 3rd Floor
Houston, TX 77002
Tel: 713 951-0400   *Fax:* 713 951-0314
Length: 3 Yrs   *ACGME Approved/Offered Positions:* 4
Program ID: 360-48-12-100

University of Texas at Houston Program

Sponsor: University of Texas Health Science Center at Houston
Memorial Hermann Hospital
Prgm Director: Donald H Parks, BA, MD
6431 Fannin St, Suite 4.156
Houston, TX 77030
Tel: 713 500-7181   *Fax:* 713 500-0716
E-mail: maple10@comcast.net
Length: 3 Yrs   *ACGME Approved/Offered Positions:* 4
Program ID: 360-48-31-101

San Antonio

University of Texas Health Science Center at San Antonio Program

Sponsor: University of Texas School of Medicine at San Antonio
Audie L Murphy Memorial Veterans Hospital (San Antonio)
Christus Santa Rosa Health Care Corporation
University Health System
Prgm Director: Howard T Wang, MD
7703 Floyd Curl Drive, Room 230F
MSC 7844
San Antonio, TX 78229
Tel: 210 567-6989   *Fax:* 210 567-6390
E-mail: wanght@uthscsa.edu
Length: 3 Yrs   *ACGME Approved/Offered Positions:* 6
Program ID: 360-48-31-134

Temple

Texas A&M College of Medicine-Scott and White Program

Sponsor: Scott and White Memorial Hospital
Central Texas Veterans Affairs Healthcare System
Prgm Director: Robert A Weber, MD
2401 South 31st Street
Temple, TX 76508
Tel: 254 724-0630   *Fax:* 254 724-8627
E-mail: dgillam@swmail.sw.org
Length: 3 Yrs   *ACGME Approved/Offered Positions:* 4
Program ID: 360-48-21-130

Utah

Salt Lake City

University of Utah Program

Sponsor: University of Utah Medical Center
Primary Children's Medical Center
Veterans Affairs Medical Center (Salt Lake City)
Prgm Director: W Bradford Rockwell, MD
30 North 1900 East, #3B400
Salt Lake City, UT 84132
Tel: 801 585-3253   *Fax:* 801 581-5794
Length: 3 Yrs   *ACGME Approved/Offered Positions:* 4
Program ID: 360-49-21-103

Virginia

Charlottesville

University of Virginia Program

Sponsor: University of Virginia Medical Center
Prgm Director: Thomas Gampper, MD*
Box 800376
Charlottesville, VA 22908
Tel: 434 924-1234
E-mail: TJG6F@virginia.edu
Length: 3 Yrs   *ACGME Approved/Offered Positions:* 4
Program ID: 360-51-11-104

Richmond

Virginia Commonwealth University Health System Program

Sponsor: Virginia Commonwealth University Health
   System
Bon Secours St Mary's Hospital
Hunter Holmes McGuire VA Medical Center (Richmond)
Medical College of Virginia Hospitals
Prgm Director: Andrea L Pozez, MD
Box 980154, MCV Station
401 N 11th Street, Suite 520
Richmond, VA 23298
Tel: 804 828-3033   *Fax:* 804 828-0489
Length: 3 Yrs   *ACGME Approved/Offered Positions:* 4
Program ID: 360-51-21-108

Washington

Seattle

University of Washington Program

Sponsor: University of Washington School of Medicine
Harborview Medical Center
Seattle Children's Hospital
University of Washington Medical Center
Prgm Director: Matthew B Klein, MD, MS*
Box 359796
325 9th Avenue
Seattle, WA 98104
Tel: 206 744-3209   *Fax:* 206 744-3656
Length: 3 Yrs   *ACGME Approved/Offered Positions:* 9
Program ID: 360-54-21-123

Plastic Surgery-Integrated

California

Loma Linda

Loma Linda University Program

Sponsor: Loma Linda University Medical Center
Kaiser Foundation Hospital (Fontana)
Riverside County Regional Medical Center
Prgm Director: Subhas C Gupta, MD, PhD
11175 Campus Street
Coleman Pavilion, Suite 21126
Loma Linda, CA 92354
Tel: 909 558-8085   *Fax:* 909 558-4175
E-mail: sgupta@llu.edu
Length: 6 Yrs   *ACGME Approved/Offered Positions:* 12
Program ID: 362-05-21-133

Los Angeles

University of Southern California/LAC+USC Medical Center Program

Sponsor: University of Southern California/LAC+USC
   Medical Center
Cedars-Sinai Medical Center
Kaiser Permanente Southern California
LAC+USC Medical Center
USC University Hospital
Prgm Director: Randolph Sherman, MD
1510 San Pablo Street, Suite 415
Los Angeles, CA 90033
Tel: 323 442-7903   *Fax:* 323 442-7901
Length: 6 Yrs   *ACGME Approved/Offered Positions:* 18
Program ID: 362-05-21-118

Orange

University of California (Irvine) Program

Sponsor: University of California (Irvine) Medical
   Center
Children's Hospital of Orange County
Kaiser Foundation Hospital (Bellflower)
Kaiser Foundation Hospitals (Anaheim)
Long Beach Memorial Medical Center
VA Long Beach Healthcare System
Prgm Director: Gregory R Evans, MD
200 S Manchester Ave Ste 650
Orange, CA 92868
Tel: 714 456-5253   *Fax:* 714 456-7718
E-mail: gevans@uci.edu
Length: 6 Yrs   *ACGME Approved/Offered Positions:* 12
Program ID: 362-05-21-008

Stanford

Stanford University Program

Sponsor: Stanford Hospital and Clinics
Kaiser Permanente Medical Center (Santa Clara)
Santa Clara Valley Medical Center
Veterans Affairs Palo Alto Health Care System
Prgm Director: Gordon Lee, MD
Division of Plastic Surgery
770 Welch Road, Suite 400
Palo Alto, CA 94304
Tel: 650 723-5824   *Fax:* 650 725-6605
E-mail: glee@stanford.edu
Length: 6 Yrs   *ACGME Approved/Offered Positions:* 18
Program ID: 362-05-31-013

Note: * indicates a newly appointed program director

Connecticut

New Haven

Yale-New Haven Medical Center Program
Sponsor: Yale-New Haven Hospital
Prgm Director: John A Persing, MD
333 Cedar Street, Room 330
PO Box 208041
New Haven, CT 06520
Tel: 203 785-2573   *Fax:* 203 785-5714
E-mail: john.persing@yale.edu
Length: 6 Yrs   *ACGME Approved/Offered Positions:* 12
Program ID: 362-08-21-015

District of Columbia

Washington

Georgetown University Hospital Program
Sponsor: Georgetown University Hospital
Washington Hospital Center
Prgm Director: Stephen B Baker, MD, DDS
3800 Reservoir Road, NW (1 PHC)
Washington, DC 20007
Tel: 202 444-9302   *Fax:* 202 444-7204
E-mail: sbb6@gunet.georgetown.edu
Length: 6 Yrs   *ACGME Approved/Offered Positions:* 18
Program ID: 362-10-21-017

Florida

Tampa

University of South Florida Program
Sponsor: University of South Florida College of Medicine
H Lee Moffitt Cancer Center
Tampa General Hospital
Veterans Affairs Medical Center (Bay Pines)
Prgm Director: David J Smith Jr, MD
12901 Bruce B Downs Boulevard, MDC-16
Tampa, FL 33612
Tel: 813 974-6159   *Fax:* 813 974-8106
E-mail: wmccrore@health.usf.edu
Length: 6 Yrs   *ACGME Approved/Offered Positions:* 18
Program ID: 362-11-12-140

Illinois

Chicago

McGaw Medical Center of Northwestern University Program
Sponsor: McGaw Medical Center of Northwestern University
Children's Memorial Hospital
Northwestern Memorial Hospital
Shriners Hospitals for Children (Chicago)
Prgm Director: Gregory A Dumanian, MD
675 N St Clair Street, Suite 19-250
Chicago, IL 60611
Tel: 312 695-6022   *Fax:* 312 695-5672
E-mail: gdumania@nmh.org
Length: 6 Yrs   *ACGME Approved/Offered Positions:* 12
Program ID: 362-16-21-025

Springfield

Southern Illinois University Program
Sponsor: Southern Illinois University School of Medicine
Memorial Medical Center
St John's Hospital
Prgm Director: Reuben Bueno Jr, MD
PO Box 19653
Springfield, IL 62794
Tel: 217 545-7031
E-mail: rbueno@siumed.edu
Length: 6 Yrs   *ACGME Approved/Offered Positions:* 12
Program ID: 362-16-21-030

Kansas

Kansas City

University of Kansas School of Medicine Program
Sponsor: University of Kansas School of Medicine
St Luke's Hospital-Kansas City
University of Kansas Hospital
Veterans Affairs Medical Center (Kansas City)
Prgm Director: Richard A Korentager, MD*
Sutherland Institute
3901 Rainbow Boulevard
Kansas City, KS 66160
Tel: 913 588-2067   *Fax:* 913 588-2061
E-mail: rkorentager@kumc.edu
Length: 6 Yrs   *ACGME Approved/Offered Positions:* 12
Program ID: 362-19-11-032

Kentucky

Lexington

University of Kentucky College of Medicine Program
Sponsor: University of Kentucky College of Medicine
University of Kentucky Hospital
Veterans Affairs Medical Center (Lexington)
Prgm Director: Henry C Vasconez, MD
Kentucky Clinic - Suite K454
Lexington, KY 40536
Tel: 859 323-6435   *Fax:* 859 323-3823
E-mail: jcicle@uky.edu
Length: 6 Yrs   *ACGME Approved/Offered Positions:* 12
Program ID: 362-20-21-033

Maryland

Baltimore

Johns Hopkins University/University of Maryland Program
Sponsor: Johns Hopkins University School of Medicine
Johns Hopkins Bayview Medical Center
Johns Hopkins Hospital
University of Maryland Medical System
Prgm Director: Richard J Redett III, MD
601 N Caroline Street, Room 8152C
Baltimore, MD 21287
Tel: 410 955-9475   *Fax:* 410 955-7060
E-mail: rredett@jhmi.edu
Length: 6 Yrs   *ACGME Approved/Offered Positions:* 12
Program ID: 362-23-21-037

Massachusetts

Boston

Brigham and Women's Hospital/Harvard Medical School Program
Sponsor: Brigham and Women's Hospital
Beth Israel Deaconess Medical Center
Massachusetts General Hospital
Prgm Director: Julian J Pribaz, MD
75 Francis Street
Boston, MA 02115
Tel: 617 732-6390   *Fax:* 617 730-2855
E-mail: surgeryeducation@partners.org
Length: 6 Yrs   *ACGME Approved/Offered Positions:* 18
Program ID: 362-24-21-135

Worcester

University of Massachusetts Program
Sponsor: University of Massachusetts Medical School
UMass Memorial Health Care (Hahnemann Campus)
UMass Memorial Health Care (Memorial Campus)
UMass Memorial Health Care (University Campus)
Prgm Director: Douglas M Rothkopf, MD
55 Lake Avenue North
Worcester, MA 01655
Tel: 508 334-5942   *Fax:* 508 856-7593
Length: 6 Yrs   *ACGME Approved/Offered Positions:* 12
Program ID: 362-24-21-117

Michigan

Ann Arbor

University of Michigan Program
Sponsor: University of Michigan Hospitals and Health Centers
Prgm Director: William M Kuzon Jr, MD, PhD
2130 Taubman Center
1500 East Medical Center Drive
Ann Arbor, MI 48109
Tel: 734 936-5890   *Fax:* 734 763-5354
E-mail: wkuzon@med.umich.edu
Length: 6 Yrs   *ACGME Approved/Offered Positions:* 18
Program ID: 362-25-21-042

Missouri

Columbia

University of Missouri-Columbia Program
Sponsor: University of Missouri-Columbia School of Medicine
Harry S Truman Memorial Veterans Hospital
University Hospitals and Clinics
Prgm Director: Charles L Puckett, MD
Plastic Surgery M-349
One Hospital Drive
Columbia, MO 65212
Tel: 573 882-2275   *Fax:* 573 884-4788
E-mail: puckettc@health.missouri.edu
Length: 6 Yrs   *ACGME Approved/Offered Positions:* 12
Program ID: 362-28-21-049

Programs

Nevada

Las Vegas

University of Nevada School of Medicine (Las Vegas) Program

Sponsor: University of Nevada School of Medicine
VA Southern Nevada Healthcare System
Las Vegas Surgery Center
Sahara Surgery Center
Specialty Surgery Center
Sunrise Hospital and Medical Center
University Medical Center of Southern Nevada
Prgm Director: William A Zamboni, MD
2040 West Charleston, Suite 301
Las Vegas, NV 89102
Tel: 702 671-2278   *Fax:* 702 671-2245
E-mail: sthomas@medicine.nevada.edu
Length: 5 Yrs   *ACGME Approved/Offered Positions:* 5
Program ID: 362-31-21-138

New York

Albany

Albany Medical Center Program

Sponsor: Albany Medical Center
Albany Medical Center South Clinical Campus
St Peter's Hospital
Veterans Affairs Medical Center (Albany)
Prgm Director: Stephane A Braun, MD
47 New Scotland Avenue
Mail Code 61PL
Albany, NY 12208
Tel: 518 262-4880   *Fax:* 518 262-5999
E-mail: brauns@mail.amc.edu
Length: 6 Yrs   *ACGME Approved/Offered Positions:* 6
Program ID: 362-35-21-055

North Carolina

Winston-Salem

Wake Forest University School of Medicine Program

Sponsor: Wake Forest University Baptist Medical Center
Prgm Director: Lisa R David, MD
Medical Center Boulevard
Winston-Salem, NC 27157
Tel: 336 716-0803   *Fax:* 336 716-8759
E-mail: lcauble@wfubmc.edu
Length: 6 Yrs   *ACGME Approved/Offered Positions:* 12
Program ID: 362-36-11-074

Ohio

Cincinnati

University Hospital/University of Cincinnati College of Medicine Program

Sponsor: University Hospital Inc
Cincinnati Children's Hospital Medical Center
Prgm Director: W John Kitzmiller, MD
231 Albert Sabin Way
PO Box 670558
Cincinnati, OH 45267
Tel: 513 558-4363   *Fax:* 513 558-0570
E-mail: hohk@uc.edu
Length: 6 Yrs   *ACGME Approved/Offered Positions:* 6
Program ID: 362-38-21-112

Cleveland

University Hospitals Case Medical Center Program

Sponsor: University Hospitals Case Medical Center
MetroHealth Medical Center
Veterans Affairs Medical Center (Cleveland)
Prgm Director: Bahman Guyuron, MD
c/o Plastic Surgery
11100 Euclid Avenue
Cleveland, OH 44106
Tel: 440 461-7999   *Fax:* 440 461-4713
E-mail: bguyuron@aol.com
Length: 6 Yrs   *ACGME Approved/Offered Positions:* 12
Program ID: 362-38-21-078

Columbus

Ohio State University Hospital Program

Sponsor: Ohio State University Hospital
Grant Medical Center (OhioHealth)
Mount Carmel
Nationwide Children's Hospital
Riverside Methodist Hospitals (OhioHealth)
Prgm Director: Michael J Miller, MD, BS
N 809 Doan Hall
410 West 10th Ave
Columbus, OH 43210
Tel: 614 293-9885   *Fax:* 614 293-9024
E-mail: michael.miller@osumc.edu
Length: 6 Yrs   *ACGME Approved/Offered Positions:* 12
Program ID: 362-38-21-081

Pennsylvania

Pittsburgh

University of Pittsburgh Medical Center Medical Education Program

Sponsor: Univ of Pittsburgh Medical Center Medical Education
Magee-Womens Hospital of UPMC
UPMC Presbyterian Shadyside
Prgm Director: Joseph E Losee, MD
3550 Terrace Street
683 Scaife Hall
Pittsburgh, PA 15261
Tel: 412 383-8082   *Fax:* 412 383-8986
E-mail: beedlend@upmc.edu
Length: 6 Yrs   *ACGME Approved/Offered Positions:* 21
Program ID: 362-41-21-090

Texas

Dallas

University of Texas Southwestern Medical School Program

Sponsor: University of Texas Southwestern Medical School
Baylor University Medical Center
Dallas County Hospital District-Parkland Memorial Hospital
Dallas VA Medical Center
University Hospitals St Paul
Prgm Director: Jeffrey E Janis, MD
1801 Inwood Rd WA4212
Department of Plastic Surgery
Dallas, TX 75390
Tel: 214 645-3116   *Fax:* 214 645-7947
E-mail: Jeffrey.Janis@UTSouthwestern.edu
Length: 6 Yrs   *ACGME Approved/Offered Positions:* 18
Program ID: 362-48-21-097

Galveston

University of Texas Medical Branch Hospitals Program

Sponsor: University of Texas Medical Branch Hospitals
Shriners Hospitals for Children (Galveston Burns Institute)
Prgm Director: Linda G Phillips, MD
301 University Boulevard
6.124 McCullough Bldg
Galveston, TX 77555
Tel: 409 772-1257   *Fax:* 409 772-1872
Length: 6 Yrs   *ACGME Approved/Offered Positions:* 18
Program ID: 362-48-11-098

Houston

Baylor College of Medicine Program

Sponsor: Baylor College of Medicine
Harris County Hospital District-Ben Taub General Hospital
Methodist Hospital (Houston)
St Luke's Episcopal Hospital
Texas Children's Hospital
University of Texas M D Anderson Cancer Center
Prgm Director: Larry H Hollier Jr, MD
6701 Fannin St, CC 610.00
Houston, TX 77030
Tel: 832 822-3140   *Fax:* 832 825-0175
E-mail: plasticprograms@bcm.tmc.edu
Length: 6 Yrs   *ACGME Approved/Offered Positions:* 18
Program ID: 362-48-31-099

Virginia

Charlottesville

University of Virginia Program

Sponsor: University of Virginia Medical Center
Prgm Director: Thomas Gampper, MD
Box 800376
Charlottesville, VA 22908
Tel: 434 924-1234
E-mail: TJG6F@virginia.edu
Length: 6 Yrs   *ACGME Approved/Offered Positions:* 6
Program ID: 362-51-11-104

Wisconsin

Madison

University of Wisconsin Program

Sponsor: University of Wisconsin Hospital and Clinics
Meriter Hospital
St Mary's Hospital
Prgm Director: Michael L Bentz, MD
G5/361 Clinical Science Center
600 Highland Avenue
Madison, WI 53792
Tel: 608 263-1367   *Fax:* 608 265-9695
E-mail: draeger@surgery.wisc.edu
Length: 5 Yrs   *ACGME Approved/Offered Positions:* 15
Program ID: 362-56-21-109

Note: * indicates a newly appointed program director

Milwaukee

Medical College of Wisconsin Affiliated Hospitals Program

Sponsor: Medical College of Wisconsin Affiliated Hospitals, Inc
Children's Hospital of Wisconsin
Clement J Zablocki Veterans Affairs Medical Center
Froedtert Memorial Lutheran Hospital
Prgm Director: William W Dzwierzynski, MD
8700 Watertown Plank Road
Milwaukee, WI 53226
Tel: 414 805-5465   *Fax:* 414 259-0901
E-mail: bruening@mcw.edu
Length: 5 Yrs   *ACGME Approved/Offered Positions:* 10
Program ID: 362-56-21-110

Preventive Medicine: Aerospace Medicine

Florida

Pensacola

Naval Operational Medicine Institute Program

Sponsor: Naval Operational Medicine Institute
Naval Aerospace Medical Institute
Prgm Director: Nils S Erikson, MD
Aerospace Medicine Residency
220 Hovey Road
Pensacola, FL 32508
Tel: 850 452-8125   *Fax:* 850 452-5194
E-mail: RAMDir-nomi@med.navy.mil
Length: 1 Yr   *ACGME Approved/Offered Positions:* 17
Program ID: 380-11-66-051
Uniformed Services Program

Ohio

Dayton

Wright State University Program

Sponsor: Wright State University Boonshoft School of Medicine
Prgm Director: Robin E Dodge, MD, MS
Department of Community Health
3640 Colonel Glenn Highway
Dayton, OH 45435
Tel: 937 775-1400   *Fax:* 937 775-1403
E-mail: betty.somers@wright.edu
Length: 2 Yrs   *ACGME Approved/Offered Positions:* 6
Program ID: 380-38-66-052

Texas

Brooks City-Base

USAF School of Aerospace Medicine Program

Sponsor: USAF School of Aerospace Medicine
Prgm Director: Thomas D Luna, MD, MPH
2601 Louis Bauer Drive
Brooks City-Base, TX 78235
Tel: 210 536-3020   *Fax:* 210 536-1779
E-mail: thomas.luna@brooks.af.mil
Length: 1 Yr   *ACGME Approved/Offered Positions:* 21
Program ID: 380-48-66-053
Uniformed Services Program

Galveston

University of Texas Medical Branch Hospitals (NASA) Program

Sponsor: University of Texas Medical Branch Hospitals
NASA Johnson Space Center
University of Texas Medical School at Galveston
Prgm Director: Richard T Jennings, MD, MS
Preventive Medicine and Community Health
301 University Boulevard
Galveston, TX 77555
Tel: 409 772-1128   *Fax:* 409 747-6129
E-mail: ryschulz@utmb.edu
Length: 2 Yrs   *ACGME Approved/Offered Positions:* 8
Program ID: 380-48-66-118

Preventive Medicine: General Preventive Medicine

California

Loma Linda

Loma Linda University Program

Sponsor: Loma Linda University Medical Center
Prgm Director: Tunis A Darnell, MD, MPH
11234 Anderson Street
Nichol Hall, Room 1516
Loma Linda, CA 92350
Tel: 909 558-4918   *Fax:* 909 558-4087
E-mail: tdarnell@llu.edu
Length: 3 Yrs   *ACGME Approved/Offered Positions:* 15
Program ID: 380-05-21-033

San Diego

University of California (San Diego)/San Diego State University Program

Sponsor: University of California (San Diego) Medical Center
Graduate School of Public Health
Scripps Clinic
Prgm Director: Linda L Hill, MD, MPH
Department of Family and Preventive Medicine
9500 Gilman Drive MC 0811
La Jolla, CA 92093
Tel: 858 457-7297   *Fax:* 858 622-1463
E-mail: pmr@ucsd.edu
Length: 2 Yrs   *ACGME Approved/Offered Positions:* 10
Program ID: 380-05-21-038

San Francisco

University of California (San Francisco)/University of California School of Public Health Program

Sponsor: University of California (San Francisco) School of Medicine
Department of Public Health (San Francisco)
UCSF and Mount Zion Medical Centers
University of California School of Public Health
Prgm Director: George W Rutherford, MD, MA
50 Beale Street
Suite 1200
San Francisco, CA 94105
Tel: 415 597-9108   *Fax:* 415 597-9125
E-mail: crogers@psg.ucsf.edu
Length: 2 Yrs   *ACGME Approved/Offered Positions:* 8
Program ID: 380-05-32-008

Programs

Colorado

Denver

Colorado School of Public Health Program

Sponsor: Colorado School of Public Health
Centers for Disease Control and Prevention
Clinica Campesina
Colorado Department of Public Health and Environment
Colorado Foundation for Medical Care
Denver Health Medical Center
Health District of Northern Larimer County
Jefferson County Health and Environment
Kaiser Permanente Health Care Group (Denver)
Plan de Salud del Valle, Inc
Tri-County Health Dept
University of Colorado Denver
Veterans Affairs Medical Center (Denver)
Prgm Director: Carolyn G DiGuiseppi, MD, MPH
4200 E 9th Ave
B-119
Denver, CO 80262
Tel: 303 315-6850   *Fax:* 303 315-1010
E-mail: fayette.augillard@ucdenver.edu
Length: 2 Yrs   *ACGME Approved/Offered Positions:* 6
Program ID: 380-07-21-041

Illinois

Chicago

John H Stroger Hospital of Cook County Program

Sponsor: John H Stroger Hospital of Cook County
University of Illinois School of Public Health
Prgm Director: David N Goldberg, MD
1901 West Harrison
Chicago, IL 60612
Tel: 312 864-4429   *Fax:* 312 864-9500
E-mail: David_Goldberg@rush.edu
Length: 2 Yrs   *ACGME Approved/Offered Positions:* 4
Program ID: 380-16-21-050

Louisiana

New Orleans

Tulane University School of Public Health and Tropical Medicine Program

Sponsor: Tulane University School of Medicine
Louisiana Office of Public Health
Tulane Univ School of Public Health and Tropical Medicine
Veterans Affairs Medical Center (New Orleans)
Prgm Director: Amita Toprani, MD, MPH*
Preventive Medicine Residency Program
1430 Tulane Avenue, TB3
New Orleans, LA 70112
Tel: 504 988-4700   *Fax:* 504 988-4701
E-mail: amiester@tulane.edu
Length: 2 Yrs   *ACGME Approved/Offered Positions:* 2
Program ID: 380-21-21-014

Maryland

Baltimore

Johns Hopkins Bloomberg School of Public Health Program

Sponsor: Johns Hopkins Bloomberg School of Public Health
Prgm Director: Miriam H Alexander, MD, MPH
615 North Wolfe Street
Room WB602
Baltimore, MD 21205
Tel: 410 614-4567   *Fax:* 410 614-8126
Length: 2 Yrs   *ACGME Approved/Offered Positions:* 29
Program ID: 380-23-11-015

University of Maryland Program

Sponsor: University of Maryland Medical System
Prgm Director: Sania Amr, MD, MS
132C Howard Hall
660 W Redwood Street
Baltimore, MD 21201
Tel: 410 706-1466   *Fax:* 410 706-4425
E-mail: lhorne@som.umaryland.edu
Length: 2 Yrs   *ACGME Approved/Offered Positions:* 8
Program ID: 380-23-11-016

Bethesda

National Capital Consortium (USUHS) Program

Sponsor: National Capital Consortium
Uniformed Svcs Univ of Health Sci Hebert School of Medicine
Prgm Director: Daniel G Burnett, MD, MPH*
PMB Room A1040A
4301 Jones Bridge Road
Bethesda, MD 20814
Tel: 301 295-3719   *Fax:* 301 295-0335
E-mail: daniel.burnett@usuhs.mil
Length: 2 Yrs   *ACGME Approved/Offered Positions:* 12
Program ID: 380-23-21-044
Uniformed Services Program

National Capital Consortium (Walter Reed Army Institute of Research) Program

Sponsor: National Capital Consortium
Walter Reed Army Institute of Research
Prgm Director: Steven B Cersovsky, MD, MPH
Division of Preventive Medicine
503 Robert Grant Avenue, Room 2A32
Silver Spring, MD 20910
Tel: 301 319-9218   *Fax:* 301 319-9104
E-mail: steven.cersovsky@amedd.army.mil
Length: 2 Yrs   *ACGME Approved/Offered Positions:* 14
Program ID: 380-10-21-002
Uniformed Services Program

Massachusetts

Boston

Boston University Medical Center Program

Sponsor: Boston Medical Center
Boston University School of Public Health
Prgm Director: Jane M Liebschutz, MD, MPH
801 Massachusetts Avenue, 2nd Floor
Boston, MA 02118
Tel: 617 414-7399   *Fax:* 617 414-4676
Length: 2 Yrs   *ACGME Approved/Offered Positions:* 10
Program ID: 380-24-21-037

Worcester

University of Massachusetts Program

Sponsor: University of Massachusetts Medical School
UMass Memorial Health Care (University Campus)
Prgm Director: Jacalyn Coghlin-Strom, MD, MPH
Dept of Family Medicine and Community Health
55 Lake Avenue North
Worcester, MA 01655
Tel: 508 856-5615   *Fax:* 508 856-1212
Length: 2 Yrs   *ACGME Approved/Offered Positions:* 6
Program ID: 380-24-21-018

Michigan

Ann Arbor

University of Michigan School of Public Health Program A

Sponsor: University of Michigan School of Public Health
Henry Ford Hospital
Prgm Director: Matthew L Boulton, MD, MPH
Office of Public Health Practice
109 Observatory Street
Ann Arbor, MI 48109
Tel: 734 764-6478   *Fax:* 734 764-9293
E-mail: sphprevmed@umich.edu
Length: 2 Yrs   *ACGME Approved/Offered Positions:* 12
Program ID: 380-25-21-125

Minnesota

Rochester

College of Medicine, Mayo Clinic (Rochester) Program

Sponsor: College of Medicine, Mayo Clinic
Mayo Clinic (Rochester)
University of Minnesota School of Public Health
Prgm Director: Prathibha Varkey, MD, MPH
200 First Street, SW
Mayo Clinic, BA5A
Rochester, MN 55905
Tel: 507 284-9966   *Fax:* 507 284-4251
E-mail: domonoske.cynthia@mayo.edu
Length: 2 Yrs   *ACGME Approved/Offered Positions:* 3
Program ID: 380-26-21-020

New Hampshire

Lebanon

Dartmouth-Hitchcock Leadership in Preventive Medicine Program

Sponsor: Mary Hitchcock Memorial Hospital
Concord Hospital
Prgm Director: Paul B Batalden, MD
HB 7251
One Medical Center Drive
Lebanon, NH 03756
Tel: 603 653-3229   *Fax:* 603 653-3201
E-mail: dhlpmr@hitchcock.org
Length: 2 Yrs   *ACGME Approved/Offered Positions:* 40
Program ID: 380-32-13-126

Note: * indicates a newly appointed program director

New York

Buffalo

University at Buffalo Program
Sponsor: University at Buffalo School of Medicine
Kaleida Health System (Buffalo General Hospital)
Roswell Park Cancer Institute
Prgm Director: Michael F Noe, MD, MPH
School of Public Health and Health Professions
435 Kimball Tower 3435 Main Street
Buffalo, NY 14214
Tel: 716 829-6941   *Fax:* 716 829-2034
Length: 2 Yrs   *ACGME Approved/Offered Positions:* 8
Program ID: 380-35-21-045

New York

Mount Sinai School of Medicine Program
Sponsor: Mount Sinai School of Medicine
Mount Sinai Medical Center
Prgm Director: Elizabeth J Garland, MD, MS
One Gustave L Levy Place
Box 1043
New York, NY 10029
Tel: 212 824-7056   *Fax:* 212 360-6965
Length: 2 Yrs   *ACGME Approved/Offered Positions:* 6
Program ID: 380-35-21-024

New York Presbyterian Hospital (Cornell Campus) Program
Sponsor: New York Presbyterian Hospital
Columbia University School of Public Health
Prgm Director: Alvin I Mushlin, MD, MSc
New York Weill Cornell Center, Public Health Dept
411 East 69th Street, 3rd Floor
New York, NY 10021
Tel: 212 746-1269   *Fax:* 212 746-8544
E-mail: mmontalv@med.cornell.edu
Length: 2 Yrs   *ACGME Approved/Offered Positions:* 2
Program ID: 380-35-21-023

North Carolina

Chapel Hill

University of North Carolina Hospitals Program
Sponsor: University of North Carolina Hospitals
University of North Carolina School of Medicine
University of North Carolina School of Public Health
Prgm Director: Deborah S Porterfield, MD, MPH
121 MacNider
School of Medicine
Chapel Hill, NC 27599
Tel: 919 843-8267   *Fax:* 919 966-7499
E-mail: uncpm@med.unc.edu
Length: 2 Yrs   *ACGME Approved/Offered Positions:* 20
Program ID: 380-36-21-026

Tennessee

Nashville

Meharry Medical College Program
Sponsor: Meharry Medical College School of Medicine
Alvin C York Veterans Affairs Medical Center
Prgm Director: Cynthia J Moriarty, MD, MSPH
Department of Family and Community Medicine
1005 Dr D B Todd Jr, Blvd
Nashville, TN 37208
Tel: 615 327-6782   *Fax:* 615 327-6131
Length: 3 Yrs   *ACGME Approved/Offered Positions:* 6
Program ID: 380-47-21-028

Texas

Brooks City-Base

USAF School of Aerospace Medicine Program B
Sponsor: USAF School of Aerospace Medicine
Prgm Director: Paula Corrigan, MD, MPH*
2601 Louis Bauer Drive
Brooks City-Base, TX 78235
Tel: 210 536-4099   *Fax:* 210 536-1779
Length: 1 Yr   *ACGME Approved/Offered Positions:* 10
Program ID: 380-48-21-122
Uniformed Services Program

Galveston

University of Texas Medical Branch Hospitals Program
Sponsor: University of Texas Medical Branch Hospitals
Prgm Director: A Nelson Avery, MD*
301 University Boulevard
Galveston, TX 77555
Tel: 409 772-5845   *Fax:* 409 747-6129
E-mail: ryschulz@utmb.edu
Length: 2 Yrs   *ACGME Approved/Offered Positions:* 4
Program ID: 380-48-21-049

Preventive Medicine: Occupational Medicine

California

Loma Linda

Loma Linda University Program A
Sponsor: Loma Linda University Medical Center
Arrowhead Regional Medical Center
Jerry L Pettis Memorial Veterans Hospital
Patton State Hospital
Prgm Director: Wayne Dysinger, MD, MPH
Nichol Hall, Room 1516
Loma Linda, CA 92350
Tel: 909 558-4918   *Fax:* 909 558-4087
Length: 2 Yrs   *ACGME Approved/Offered Positions:* 4
Program ID: 380-05-77-123

Los Angeles

UCLA School of Public Health Program
Sponsor: UCLA David Geffen School of Medicine/UCLA
  Medical Center
Kaiser Permanente Southern California
UCLA School of Public Health
Prgm Director: Philip Harber, MD, MPH
10880 Wilshire Blvd
Suite 1800
Los Angeles, CA 90024
Tel: 310 794-8144   *Fax:* 310 794-8145
E-mail: pharber@mednet.ucla.edu
Length: 2 Yrs   *ACGME Approved/Offered Positions:* 4
Program ID: 380-05-77-057

Orange

University of California (Irvine) Program
Sponsor: University of California (Irvine) Medical
  Center
University of California (Irvine) College of Medicine
Prgm Director: Dean B Baker, MD, MPH
5201 California Avenue
Suite 100
Irvine, CA 92617
Tel: 949 824-8641   *Fax:* 949 824-2345
E-mail: lisrael@uci.edu
Length: 2 Yrs   *ACGME Approved/Offered Positions:* 6
Program ID: 380-05-77-058

San Francisco

University of California (San Francisco) Program
Sponsor: University of California (San Francisco) School
  of Medicine
UCSF and Mount Zion Medical Centers
University of California School of Public Health
Prgm Director: Gina M Solomon, MD, MPH*
Division of Occupational & Environmental Medicine
Box 0843
San Francisco, CA 94143
Tel: 415 206-4279   *Fax:* 415 206-8949
E-mail: gina.solomon@ucsf.edu
Length: 2 Yrs   *ACGME Approved/Offered Positions:* 8
Program ID: 380-05-77-059

Programs

Colorado

Denver

Colorado School of Public Health Program A
Sponsor: Colorado School of Public Health
Prgm Director: E B Gottschall, MD, MSPH
4200 East 9th Avenue, Box B - 119
Denver, CO 80262
Tel: 303 398-1520   *Fax:* 303 398-1452
Length: 2 Yrs   *ACGME Approved/Offered Positions:* 5
Program ID: 380-07-77-060

Connecticut

Farmington

University of Connecticut Program
Sponsor: University of Connecticut School of Medicine
Univ of Connecticut Health Center/John Dempsey
   Hospital
Prgm Director: John D Meyer, MD, MPH
270 Farmington Avenue
Exchange Suite 262
Farmington, CT 06030
Tel: 860 679-4947   *Fax:* 860 679-1349
E-mail: meyer@uchc.edu
Length: 2 Yrs   *ACGME Approved/Offered Positions:* 4
Program ID: 380-08-77-061

New Haven

Yale-New Haven Medical Center Program
Sponsor: Yale-New Haven Hospital
Veterans Affairs Medical Center (West Haven)
Prgm Director: Oyebode A Taiwo, MD, MPH
Yale University School of Medicine
135 College Street, 3rd Floor
New Haven, CT 06510
Tel: 203 785-7231   *Fax:* 203 785-7391
Length: 2 Yrs   *ACGME Approved/Offered Positions:* 4
Program ID: 380-08-77-062

Florida

Tampa

University of South Florida Program
Sponsor: University of South Florida College of Medicine
James A Haley Veterans Hospital
University of South Florida College of Public Health
Prgm Director: Stuart M Brooks, MD
Dept of Environmental & Occupational Health
13201 Bruce B Downs Boulevard MDC 56
Tampa, FL 33612
Tel: 813 974-6626   *Fax:* 813 974-7544
Length: 2 Yrs   *ACGME Approved/Offered Positions:* 8
Program ID: 380-11-77-064

Illinois

Chicago

University of Illinois College of Medicine at Chicago Program
Sponsor: University of Illinois College of Medicine at
   Chicago
University of Illinois Hospital and Clinics
University of Illinois School of Public Health
Prgm Director: Susan N Buchanan, MD, MPH
M/C 684
835 S Wolcott Avenue, Room E-144
Chicago, IL 60612
Tel: 312 996-0806   *Fax:* 312 413-8485
E-mail: sbucha3@uic.edu
Length: 2 Yrs   *ACGME Approved/Offered Positions:* 7
Program ID: 380-16-77-066

Iowa

Iowa City

University of Iowa Hospitals and Clinics Program
Sponsor: University of Iowa Hospitals and Clinics
Prgm Director: Fredric E Gerr, MD
Dept of Occupational & Environmental Health
100 Oakdale Campus #140 IREH
Iowa City, IA 52242
Tel: 319 335-4212
E-mail: marlene-thompson@uiowa.edu
Length: 2 Yrs   *ACGME Approved/Offered Positions:* 6
Program ID: 380-18-77-069

Kentucky

Lexington

University of Kentucky College of Medicine Program A
Sponsor: University of Kentucky College of Medicine
Prgm Director: Ray F Garman, MD, MPH
Dept of Preventive Med & Environmental Health
121 Washington Avenue, Suite 220
Lexington, KY 40536
Tel: 859 257-5166   *Fax:* 859 257-8982
E-mail: ray.garman@uky.edu
Length: 2 Yrs   *ACGME Approved/Offered Positions:* 4
Program ID: 380-20-77-070

Maryland

Baltimore

Johns Hopkins Bloomberg School of Public Health Program A
Sponsor: Johns Hopkins Bloomberg School of Public
   Health
Johns Hopkins Hospital
University of Maryland Medical System
Prgm Director: Virginia Weaver, MD, MPH
Occupational Medicine Residency Program
615 North Wolfe Street, Rm WB602
Baltimore, MD 21205
Tel: 410 955-4355   *Fax:* 410 955-1811
E-mail: occmed@jhsph.edu
Length: 2 Yrs   *ACGME Approved/Offered Positions:* 12
Program ID: 380-23-77-072

Bethesda

National Capital Consortium (USUHS) Program A
Sponsor: National Capital Consortium
Uniformed Svcs Univ of Health Sci Hebert School of
   Medicine
Prgm Director: Timothy M Mallon, MD, MPH
PMB, Room A-1040A
4301 Jones Bridge Road
Bethesda, MD 20814
Tel: 301 295-3718   *Fax:* 301 295-0335
Length: 2 Yrs   *ACGME Approved/Offered Positions:* 15
Program ID: 380-23-77-073
Uniformed Services Program

Massachusetts

Boston

Harvard School of Public Health Program
Sponsor: Harvard School of Public Health
Cambridge Health Alliance
Harvard Sch of Public Health Occ Med Physician
   Activities
Prgm Director: Stefanos N Kales, MD, MPH
Environmental & Occupational Med & Epidemiology
665 Huntington Avenue
Boston, MA 02115
Tel: 617 665-1580   *Fax:* 617 432-0219
E-mail: skales@hsph.harvard.edu
Length: 2 Yrs   *ACGME Approved/Offered Positions:* 12
Program ID: 380-24-77-074

Minnesota

St. Paul

HealthPartners Institute for Medical Education Program
Sponsor: HealthPartners Institute for Medical
   Education
Regions Hospital
HealthPartners St Paul Clinic
University of Minnesota School of Public Health
Prgm Director: Fozia A Abrar, MD, MPH*
HealthPartners St Paul Clinic, 205 S Wabasha
MS 31300A, Occupational Medicine Residency
St Paul, MN 55107
Tel: 651 293-8279
Length: 2 Yrs   *ACGME Approved/Offered Positions:* 7
Program ID: 380-26-77-079

New Jersey

New Brunswick

UMDNJ-Robert Wood Johnson Medical School Program
Sponsor: UMDNJ-Robert Wood Johnson Medical School
Prgm Director: Michael Gochfeld, MD, PhD
170 Frelinghuysen Road
Piscataway, NJ 08854
Tel: 732 445-0123   *Fax:* 732 445-0130
E-mail: gochfeld@eohsi.rutgers.edu
Length: 2 Yrs   *ACGME Approved/Offered Positions:* 4
Program ID: 380-33-77-081

Note: * indicates a newly appointed program director

New York

New York

Mount Sinai School of Medicine Program A

Sponsor: Mount Sinai School of Medicine
Mount Sinai Medical Center
Prgm Director: Debra J Milek, MD, MPH
Department of Community Medicine
One Gustave L Levy Place, Box 1057
New York, NY 10029
Tel: 212 824-7057   *Fax:* 212 360-6965
Length: 2 Yrs   *ACGME Approved/Offered Positions:* 4
Program ID: 380-35-77-082

North Carolina

Durham

Duke University Hospital Program

Sponsor: Duke University Hospital
University of North Carolina School of Public Health
Prgm Director: Dennis J Darcey, MD, MSPH
Division of Occupational Medicine
PO Box 3834
Durham, NC 27710
Tel: 919 684-3591   *Fax:* 919 286-1021
Length: 2 Yrs   *ACGME Approved/Offered Positions:* 4
Program ID: 380-36-77-084

Ohio

Cincinnati

University Hospital/University of Cincinnati College of Medicine Program

Sponsor: University Hospital Inc
Prgm Director: Clara S Ross, MD, JD
Occupational Medicine Residency Program
PO Box 670056
Cincinnati, OH 45267
Tel: 513 558-0687   *Fax:* 513 558-6272
E-mail: occmed@uc.edu
Length: 2 Yrs   *ACGME Approved/Offered Positions:* 8
Program ID: 380-38-77-085

Pennsylvania

Philadelphia

University of Pennsylvania Program

Sponsor: University of Pennsylvania Health System
Alliance Occupational Medicine
Brookhaven National Laboratory Occupational Medicine Clinic
Carle Foundation Hospital
Chrysler Corporation, LLC (Occupational Medicine Clinic)
Concentra Medical Centers (Maryland)
Concentra Medical Centers (Michigan)
Concentra Medical Centers (Wisconsin)
Dow Chemical Company
Kaiser Permanente - Martinez Medical Offices
Lawrence and Memorial Hospitals
National Medical Advisory Services
Progressive Rehabilitation Services
Sandia National Laboratories
St Vincent's Medical Center
Prgm Director: Edward Emmett, MD, MS
Occupational Medicine, Silverstein/Ground Floor
3400 Spruce Street
Philadelphia, PA 19104
Tel: 215 349-5708   *Fax:* 215 662-4430
Length: 1 Yr   *ACGME Approved/Offered Positions:* 12
Program ID: 380-41-77-124

Tennessee

Nashville

Meharry Medical College Program A

Sponsor: Meharry Medical College School of Medicine
Alvin C York Veterans Affairs Medical Center
Metropolitan Nashville General Hospital
Prgm Director: Sangita Chakrabarty, MD, MSPH
Division of Occupational
1005 Dr D B Todd Jr, Blvd
Nashville, TN 37208
Tel: 615 327-6782   *Fax:* 615 327-6131
E-mail: mcohen@mmc.edu
Length: 3 Yrs   *ACGME Approved/Offered Positions:* 6
Program ID: 380-47-77-088

Texas

Brooks City-Base

USAF School of Aerospace Medicine Program A

Sponsor: USAF School of Aerospace Medicine
Prgm Director: Steven M Hetrick, MD, MPH
2601 Louis Bauer Drive
Brooks City-Base, TX 78235
Tel: 210 536-3897   *Fax:* 210 536-1779
E-mail: steven.hetrick@brooks.af.mil
Length: 1 Yr   *ACGME Approved/Offered Positions:* 24
Program ID: 380-48-77-089
Uniformed Services Program

Galveston

University of Texas Medical Branch Hospitals Program

Sponsor: University of Texas Medical Branch Hospitals
Prgm Director: A Nelson Avery, MD
Preventive Medicine and Community Health
301 University Boulevard
Galveston, TX 77555
Tel: 409 747-0791   *Fax:* 409 747-6129
E-mail: ryschulz@utmb.edu
Length: 2 Yrs   *ACGME Approved/Offered Positions:* 4
Program ID: 380-48-77-121

Houston

University of Texas at Houston Program

Sponsor: University of Texas Health Science Center at Houston
University of Texas School of Public Health
Prgm Director: George Delclos, MD, MPH*
1200 Hermann Pressler, Room W1002
Houston, TX 77030
Tel: 713 500-9459   *Fax:* 713 500-9442
E-mail: George.Delclos@uth.tmc.edu
Length: 2 Yrs   *ACGME Approved/Offered Positions:* 6
Program ID: 380-48-77-090

Tyler

University of Texas Health Center at Tyler Program

Sponsor: University of Texas Health Center at Tyler
Stephen F Austin State University
Prgm Director: Jeffrey L Levin, MD, MSPH
11937 US Hwy 271
Tyler, TX 75708
Tel: 903 877-5636   *Fax:* 903 877-7982
E-mail: michelle.harris@uthct.edu
Length: 2 Yrs   *ACGME Approved/Offered Positions:* 3
Program ID: 380-48-77-091

Utah

Salt Lake City

University of Utah Program

Sponsor: University of Utah Medical Center
Prgm Director: Eric M Wood, MD, MPH
RMCOEH
391 Chipeta Suite C
Salt Lake City, UT 84108
Tel: 801 581-7780   *Fax:* 801 585-3759
Length: 2 Yrs   *ACGME Approved/Offered Positions:* 12
Program ID: 380-49-77-092

Washington

Seattle

University of Washington School of Public Health and Community Medicine Program

Sponsor: University of Washington School of Public Health
Harborview Medical Center
Prgm Director: Victor C Van Hee, MD, MPH*
Harborview Medical Center
325 - 9th Avenue, Box 359739
Seattle, WA 98104
Tel: 206 744-9398   *Fax:* 206 744-9935
Length: 2 Yrs   *ACGME Approved/Offered Positions:* 6
Program ID: 380-54-77-093

West Virginia

Morgantown

West Virginia University Program

Sponsor: West Virginia University School of Medicine
West Virginia University Hospitals
Prgm Director: Christopher J Martin, MD, MSc
PO Box 9190
3858 Health Science Center South
Morgantown, WV 26506
Tel: 304 293-3693   *Fax:* 304 293-2629
E-mail: cmartin@hsc.wvu.edu
Length: 2 Yrs   *ACGME Approved/Offered Positions:* 8
Program ID: 380-55-77-094

Programs

Preventive Medicine: Public Health and General Preventive Medicine

California

Sacramento

California Department of Public Health Program
Sponsor: California Department of Public Health
UCLA School of Public Health
University of California (Davis) Medical Center
University of California School of Public Health
Prgm Director: Kathleen H Acree, MD, MPH
1616 Capitol Avenue, MS 7213
PO Box 997377
Sacramento, CA 95899
Tel: 916 552-9900   *Fax:* 916 552-9729
E-mail: kathleen.acree@cdph.ca.gov
Length: 2 Yrs   *ACGME Approved/Offered Positions:* 8
Program ID: 380-05-88-097

Connecticut

Derby

Griffin Hospital Program
Sponsor: Griffin Hospital
Yale University School of Public Health
Prgm Director: Haq Nawaz, MD, MPH
130 Division Street
Derby, CT 06418
Tel: 203 732-7327   *Fax:* 203 732-7185
Length: 2 Yrs   *ACGME Approved/Offered Positions:* 6
Program ID: 380-08-88-119

Florida

West Palm Beach

Palm Beach County Public Health Department Program
Sponsor: Palm Beach County Public Health Department
West Palm Beach VA Medical Center
Prgm Director: Jean Marie Malecki, MD, MPH
PO Box 29
West Palm Beach, FL 33402
Tel: 561 355-3120   *Fax:* 561 355-3165
E-mail: Jean_Malecki@doh.state.fl.us
Length: 2 Yrs   *ACGME Approved/Offered Positions:* 6
Program ID: 380-11-88-098

Note: * indicates a newly appointed program director

Georgia

Atlanta

Centers for Disease Control and Prevention Program
Sponsor: Centers for Disease Control and Prevention
Prgm Director: Gail M Stennies, MD, MPH
Public Health Service - DHHS
1600 Clifton Road, NE MS E-92
Atlanta, GA 30333
Tel: 404 498-6140   *Fax:* 404 498-6105
E-mail: gstennies@cdc.gov
Length: 1 Yr   *ACGME Approved/Offered Positions:* 13
Program ID: 380-12-88-109

Emory University Program A
Sponsor: Emory University School of Medicine
Centers for Disease Control and Prevention
Georgia Dept of Human Resources-Division of Public Health
Grady Health System
Rollins School of Public Health of Emory University
Veterans Affairs Medical Center (Atlanta)
Prgm Director: Wayne Blount, MD, MPH
Department of Family and Preventive Medicine
49 Jesse Hill Jr Drive SE
Atlanta, GA 30303
Tel: 404 213-6537
E-mail: bwbloun@emory.edu
Length: 2 Yrs   *ACGME Approved/Offered Positions:* 4
Program ID: 380-12-88-110

Morehouse School of Medicine Program
Sponsor: Morehouse School of Medicine
Centers for Disease Control and Prevention
Georgia Dept of Human Resources-Division of Public Health
Veterans Affairs Medical Center (Atlanta)
Prgm Director: Beverly D Taylor, MD
720 Westview Drive SW
Atlanta, GA 30310
Tel: 404 752-1620   *Fax:* 404 752-1160
Length: 2 Yrs   *ACGME Approved/Offered Positions:* 8
Program ID: 380-12-88-108

New York

Albany

SUNY at Albany School of Public Health Program
Sponsor: New York State Department of Health
SUNY at Albany School of Public Health
Prgm Director: Mary S Applegate, MD, MPH
GEC 100
One University Place
Rensselaer, NY 12144
Tel: 518 402-0283   *Fax:* 518 402-0329
E-mail: mapplegate@uamail.albany.edu
Length: 2 Yrs   *ACGME Approved/Offered Positions:* 5
Program ID: 380-35-88-111

New York

New York City Department of Health and Mental Hygiene Program
Sponsor: New York City Department of Health and Mental Hygiene
Columbia University School of Public Health
Prgm Director: Andrea Lyman, MD, MS
Public Health/Preventive Medicine Residency Program
2 Lafayette Street CN65
New York, NY 10007
Tel: 212 341-3957   *Fax:* 212 676-2172
E-mail: healthrp@health.nyc.gov
Length: 2 Yrs   *ACGME Approved/Offered Positions:* 8
Program ID: 380-35-88-104

Rochester

University of Rochester Program
Sponsor: Strong Memorial Hospital of the University of Rochester
Prgm Director: James A Tacci, MD, MPH
601 Elmwood Avenue, Box 644
Rochester, NY 14642
Tel: 585 275-7882   *Fax:* 585 461-4532
Length: 2 Yrs   *ACGME Approved/Offered Positions:* 4
Program ID: 380-35-88-127

Stony Brook

SUNY at Stony Brook Program
Sponsor: University Hospital - SUNY at Stony Brook
Columbia University School of Public Health
Nassau County Department of Health
Suffolk County Department of Health Services
Prgm Director: Dorothy S Lane, MD, MPH
Department of Preventive Medicine
HSC L3-086
Stony Brook, NY 11794
Tel: 631 444-2094   *Fax:* 631 444-2202
E-mail: dlane@notes.cc.sunysb.edu
Length: 2 Yrs   *ACGME Approved/Offered Positions:* 8
Program ID: 380-35-88-112

Oregon

Portland

Oregon Health & Science University Program
Sponsor: Oregon Health & Science University Hospital
Prgm Director: John D Stull, MD, MPH
Public Health & Preventive Medicine, CB669
3181 SW Sam Jackson Park Road
Portland, OR 97239
Tel: 503 494-2012   *Fax:* 503 494-4981
E-mail: stullj@ohsu.edu
Length: 2 Yrs   *ACGME Approved/Offered Positions:* 8
Program ID: 380-40-88-115

South Carolina

Columbia

University of South Carolina School of Medicine Program
Sponsor: University of South Carolina School of Medicine
Prgm Director: Joshua R Mann, MD, MPH
Family & Preventive Medicine
3209 Colonial Drive
Columbia, SC 29203
Tel: 803 434-4575   *Fax:* 803 434-8374
E-mail: lisa.cole@uscmed.sc.edu
Length: 2 Yrs   *ACGME Approved/Offered Positions:* 8
Program ID: 380-45-88-116

Texas

Austin

Texas Department of State Health Services Program
Sponsor: Texas Department of State Health Services
University of Texas School of Public Health
Prgm Director: Sandra Guerra-Cantu, MD, MPH
Public Health Region 8
7430 Louis Pasteur Drive
San Antonio, TX 78229
Tel: 210 949-2003   *Fax:* 210 949-2015
E-mail: sandra.guerra-cantu@dshs.state.tx.us
Length: 1 Yr   *ACGME Approved/Offered Positions:* 4
Program ID: 380-48-88-105

Virginia

Richmond

Virginia Commonwealth University Health System Program

Sponsor: Virginia Commonwealth University Health System
Commonwealth of Virginia Department of Health
Prgm Director: Gonzalo M Bearman, MD, MPH
PO Box 980663
1001 E Broad Street
Richmond, VA 23298
Tel: 804 828-2121   *Fax:* 804 828-2125
E-mail: gbearman@mcvh-vcu.edu
Length: 2 Yrs   *ACGME Approved/Offered Positions:* 1
Program ID: 380-51-88-106

Washington

Tacoma

Madigan Army Medical Center Program

Sponsor: Madigan Army Medical Center
Uniformed Svcs Univ of Health Sci Hebert School of Medicine
University of Washington School of Public Health
Prgm Director: Andrew R Wiesen, MD
Department of Preventive Medicine
MCHJ-PV
Tacoma, WA 98431
Tel: 253 968-4479   *Fax:* 253 968-4483
Length: 2 Yrs   *ACGME Approved/Offered Positions:* 14
Program ID: 380-54-88-107
Uniformed Services Program

Procedural Dermatology (Dermatology)

Alabama

Birmingham

Dermatology Associates (Birmingham) Program

Sponsor: Dermatology Associates
Prgm Director: Gary D Monheit, MD
2100 16th Avenue South, Suite 202
Birmingham, AL 35205
Tel: 205 933-0987   *Fax:* 205 930-1756
E-mail: info@totalskinandbeauty.com
Length: 1 Yr   *ACGME Approved/Offered Positions:* 1
Program ID: 081-01-21-011

University of Alabama Medical Center Program

Sponsor: University of Alabama Hospital
Children's Hospital of Alabama
Cooper Green Hospital
Veterans Affairs Medical Center (Birmingham)
Prgm Director: Conway C Huang, MD
Department of Dermatology
1530 3rd Avenue South, EFH 414
Birmingham, AL 35294
Tel: 205 801-8406   *Fax:* 205 583-8070
E-mail: chuang@uabmc.edu
Length: 1 Yr   *ACGME Approved/Offered Positions:* 1
Program ID: 081-01-31-033

California

La Jolla

Scripps Clinic/Scripps Green Hospital Program

Sponsor: Scripps Clinic/Scripps Green Hospital
Scripps Clinic
Prgm Director: Hubert T Greenway, MD
10666 N Torrey Pines Road
La Jolla, CA 92037
Tel: 858 554-8646   *Fax:* 858 554-6271
E-mail: gme@scripps.edu
Length: 1 Yr   *ACGME Approved/Offered Positions:* 2
Program ID: 081-05-31-008

Loma Linda

Loma Linda University Program

Sponsor: Loma Linda University Medical Center
Prgm Director: Abel Torres, MD, JD
11370 Anderson Street, Suite 2600
Loma Linda, CA 92354
Tel: 909 558-2842   *Fax:* 909 558-2448
Length: 1 Yr   *ACGME Approved/Offered Positions:* 1
Program ID: 081-05-21-021

Los Angeles

Moy Dermatology Clinic (Los Angeles) Program

Sponsor: Ronald L Moy Dermatology Clinic
VA Greater Los Angeles Healthcare System
Prgm Director: Ronald L Moy, MD
100 UCLA Medical Plaza
Suite 590
Los Angeles, CA 90024
Tel: 310 794-7422   *Fax:* 310 208-2158
Length: 1 Yr   *ACGME Approved/Offered Positions:* 1
Program ID: 081-05-12-023

UCLA Medical Center Program

Sponsor: UCLA David Geffen School of Medicine/UCLA Medical Center
UCLA Medical Center
VA Greater Los Angeles Healthcare System
Prgm Director: Gary P Lask, MD
200 UCLA Medical Plaza
Suite 465
Los Angeles, CA 90095
Tel: 310 825-6911   *Fax:* 310 206-6371
E-mail: tdevany@mednet.ucla.edu
Length: 1 Yr   *ACGME Approved/Offered Positions:* 1
Program ID: 081-05-12-039

Sacramento

University of California (Davis) Health System Program

Sponsor: University of California (Davis) Health System
Laser & Skin Surgery Center of Northern California
University of California (Davis) Medical Center
VA Northern California Health Care System
Prgm Director: Daniel B Eisen, MD*
Department of Dermatology
3301 C Street, Suite 1400
Sacramento, CA 95816
Tel: 916 734-6118   *Fax:* 916 442-5702
E-mail: dbeisen@ucdavis.edu
Length: 1 Yr   *ACGME Approved/Offered Positions:* 1
Program ID: 081-05-13-034

San Francisco

University of California (San Francisco) Program

Sponsor: University of California (San Francisco) School of Medicine
UCSF and Mount Zion Medical Centers
Prgm Director: Roy C Grekin, MD
1701 Divisadero Street, Box 0316
San Francisco, CA 94143
Tel: 415 353-7839   *Fax:* 415 353-7838
Length: 1 Yr   *ACGME Approved/Offered Positions:* 3
Program ID: 081-05-21-007

Illinois

Chicago

McGaw Medical Center of Northwestern University Program

Sponsor: McGaw Medical Center of Northwestern University
Northwestern Memorial Hospital
Prgm Director: Murad Alam, MD
Department of Dermatology
676 N St Clair Street, Suite 1600
Chicago, IL 60611
Tel: 312 695-7932   *Fax:* 312 695-0664
E-mail: msferruz@nmff.org
Length: 1 Yr   *ACGME Approved/Offered Positions:* 1
Program ID: 081-16-12-035

Indiana

Indianapolis

St Vincent Hospital Program

Sponsor: St Vincent Hospitals and Health Care Center
Prgm Director: C William Hanke, MD, MPH
13450 North Meridian, Suite 355
Carmel, IN 46032
Tel: 317 582-8484   *Fax:* 317 582-8481
Length: 1 Yr   *ACGME Approved/Offered Positions:* 1
Program ID: 081-17-31-006

Massachusetts

Boston

Boston University Medical Center Program

Sponsor: Boston Medical Center
Prgm Director: Niels Krejci-Papa, MD*
609 Albany Street, Building J Bldg
Boston, MA 02118
Tel: 617 414-6973   *Fax:* 617 638-5511
Length: 1 Yr   *ACGME Approved/Offered Positions:* 1
Program ID: 081-24-12-009

Michigan

Ann Arbor

University of Michigan Program

Sponsor: University of Michigan Hospitals and Health
  Centers
Prgm Director: Timothy S Wang, MD, BS
Department of Dermatology
1910 Taubman Center
Ann Arbor, MI 48109
Tel: 734 936-4190   *Fax:* 734 936-6674
E-mail: timothyw@umich.edu
Length: 1 Yr   *ACGME Approved/Offered Positions:* 1
Program ID: 081-25-21-036

Minnesota

Minneapolis

University of Minnesota Program

Sponsor: University of Minnesota Medical School
Prgm Director: Peter K Lee, MD, PhD
420 Delaware Street, SE
MMC 98/PWB 4-240
Minneapolis, MN 55545
Tel: 612 625-5199   *Fax:* 612 626-3318
Length: 1 Yr   *ACGME Approved/Offered Positions:* 1
Program ID: 081-26-21-040

Rochester

College of Medicine, Mayo Clinic (Rochester) Program

Sponsor: College of Medicine, Mayo Clinic
Mayo Clinic (Rochester)
Prgm Director: Randall K Roenigk, MD
200 First Street SW
Rochester, MN 55905
Tel: 507 284-3736   *Fax:* 507 284-2072
E-mail: mayodermfellows@mayo.edu
Length: 1 Yr   *ACGME Approved/Offered Positions:* 2
Program ID: 081-26-21-003

New Jersey

Camden

UMDNJ-Robert Wood Johnson Medical School (Camden) Program

Sponsor: Cooper Hospital-University Medical Center
Prgm Director: Naomi Lawrence, MD
10000 Sagemore Drive
Suite 10103
Marlton, NJ 08053
Tel: 856 596-3040   *Fax:* 856 596-5651
Length: 1 Yr   *ACGME Approved/Offered Positions:* 1
Program ID: 081-33-12-020

Note: * indicates a newly appointed program director

Hackensack

Skin Laser and Surgery Specialist of NY/NJ (Hackensack) Program

Sponsor: Skin Laser and Surgery Specialists of New
  York/New Jersey
Prgm Director: David J Goldberg, MD
20 Prospect Avenue, Suite 702
Hackensack, NJ 07601
Tel: 201 441-9980   *Fax:* 201 441-9893
E-mail: Roseann@skinandlasers.com
Length: 1 Yr   *ACGME Approved/Offered Positions:* 1
Program ID: 081-33-13-024

Morristown

Affiliated Dermatologist and Dermatologic Surgeons (Morristown) Program

Sponsor: Affiliated Dermatologists and Dermatologic
  Surgeons
Prgm Director: Arlene S Rogachefsky, MD
182 South Street, Suite 1
Morristown, NJ 07960
Tel: 973 267-0577   *Fax:* 973 539-5401
E-mail: manageADDS@aol.com
Length: 1 Yr   *ACGME Approved/Offered Positions:* 1
Program ID: 081-33-21-013

New York

Brooklyn

SUNY Health Science Center at Brooklyn Program

Sponsor: SUNY Health Science Center at Brooklyn
Long Island Skin Cancer & Dermatologic Surgery
University Hospital-SUNY Health Science Center at
  Brooklyn
Veterans Affairs Medical Center (Brooklyn)
Prgm Director: Daniel Mark Siegel, MD, MS
450 Clarkson Avenue
Brooklyn, NY 11203
Tel: 718 270-1229   *Fax:* 718 270-2794
Length: 1 Yr   *ACGME Approved/Offered Positions:* 2
Program ID: 081-35-12-005

New York

Laser and Skin Surgery Center of New York Program

Sponsor: Laser and Skin Surgery Center of New York
Prgm Director: Roy G Geronemus, MD
317 East 34 Street
New York, NY 10016
Tel: 212 686-7306   *Fax:* 212 686-7305
E-mail: mail@laserskinsurgery.com
Length: 1 Yr   *ACGME Approved/Offered Positions:* 1
Program ID: 081-35-21-032

Mount Sinai School of Medicine Program

Sponsor: Mount Sinai School of Medicine
Mount Sinai Medical Center
Prgm Director: David Kriegel, MD
One Gustave L Levy Place, Box 1047
New York, NY 10029
Tel: 212 659-9530   *Fax:* 212 348-7434
E-mail: dkriegs@rcn.com
Length: 1 Yr   *ACGME Approved/Offered Positions:* 1
Program ID: 081-35-31-004

New York Presbyterian Hospital (Columbia Campus) Program

Sponsor: New York Presbyterian Hospital
Prgm Director: Desiree Ratner, MD
161 Fort Washington Avenue, 12th Floor
New York, NY 10032
Tel: 212 305-3625   *Fax:* 212 342-0280
Length: 1 Yr   *ACGME Approved/Offered Positions:* 1
Program ID: 081-35-13-030

New York University School of Medicine Program

Sponsor: New York University School of Medicine
Laser and Skin Surgery Center of New York
Memorial Sloan-Kettering Cancer Center
NYU Hospitals Center
Prgm Director: Vicki J Levine, MD
Department of Dermatology
550 First Avenue, H100
New York, NY 10016
Tel: 212 263-3722   *Fax:* 212 263-8752
Length: 1 Yr   *ACGME Approved/Offered Positions:* 1
Program ID: 081-35-13-037

Rochester

University of Rochester Program

Sponsor: Strong Memorial Hospital of the University of
  Rochester
Prgm Director: Marc D Brown, MD
601 Elmwood Avenue, Box 697
Rochester, NY 14642
Tel: 585 275-0193   *Fax:* 585 275-0022
E-mail: marc_brown@urmc.rochester.edu
Length: 1 Yr   *ACGME Approved/Offered Positions:* 1
Program ID: 081-35-21-029

North Carolina

Winston-Salem

Skin Surgery Center (Winston-Salem) Program

Sponsor: Skin Surgery Center (Winston-Salem)
Prgm Director: John Albertini, MD
125 Sunnynoll Court, Suite 100
Winston-Salem, NC 27106
Tel: 336 724-2434   *Fax:* 336 724-6123
E-mail: dcombs@skinsurgerycenter.net
Length: 1 Yr   *ACGME Approved/Offered Positions:* 1
Program ID: 081-36-31-014

Ohio

Kettering

Dayton Skin Surgery Center Program

Sponsor: Dayton Skin Surgery Center
Prgm Director: Heidi B Donnelly, MD
500 Lincoln Park Drive
Suite 200
Kettering, OH 45429
Tel: 937 293-5567   *Fax:* 937 293-5568
E-mail: hdonnelly@daytonskinsurgery.org
Length: 1 Yr   *ACGME Approved/Offered Positions:* 1
Program ID: 081-38-12-025

Pennsylvania

Danville

Geisinger Health System Program

Sponsor: Geisinger Health System
Geisinger Medical Center
Prgm Director: Victor J Marks, MD
Department of Dermatology
115 Woodbine Lane
Danville, PA 17822
Tel: 570 271-8074   *Fax:* 570 271-5940
Length: 1 Yr   *ACGME Approved/Offered Positions:* 2
Program ID: 081-41-31-002

Philadelphia

Dermatologic Surgicenter (Philadelphia) Program

Sponsor: Dermatologic Surgicenter (Philadelphia)
Prgm Director: Anthony Benedetto, DO
1200 Locust Street
Philadelphia, PA 19107
Tel: 215 546-3666   *Fax:* 215 545-6060
Length: 1 Yr   *ACGME Approved/Offered Positions:* 1
Program ID: 081-41-31-038

Pittsburgh

Zitelli Dermatology Clinic/UPMC Presbyterian Shadyside Program

Sponsor: Zitelli and Brodland PC
UPMC Presbyterian Shadyside
Prgm Director: David G Brodland, MD
5200 Center Avenue, Suite 303
Pittsburgh, PA 15232
Tel: 412 681-9400   *Fax:* 412 681-5240
E-mail: dgbrodland@aol.com
Length: 1 Yr   *ACGME Approved/Offered Positions:* 2
Program ID: 081-41-13-022

South Carolina

Charleston

Medical University of South Carolina Program

Sponsor: Medical University of South Carolina College of Medicine
MUSC Medical Center
Prgm Director: Pearon G Lang Jr, MD
135 Rutledge Avenue, 11th Floor
PO Box 250578
Charleston, SC 29425
Tel: 843 792-0463   *Fax:* 843 792-9804
E-mail: barrusc@musc.edu
Length: 1 Yr   *ACGME Approved/Offered Positions:* 1
Program ID: 081-45-12-001

Texas

Dallas

University of Texas Southwestern Medical School Program

Sponsor: University of Texas Southwestern Medical School
Prgm Director: R Stan Taylor III, MD
5323 Harry Hines Boulevard
Dallas, TX 75390
Tel: 214 645-8951   *Fax:* 214 645-8955
Length: 1 Yr   *ACGME Approved/Offered Positions:* 2
Program ID: 081-48-21-018

Houston

Baylor College of Medicine Program

Sponsor: Baylor College of Medicine
Baylor Clinic
Michael E DeBakey VA Medical Center - Houston
Prgm Director: Ida F Orengo, MD
Department of Dermatology
One Baylor Plaza, F800
Houston, TX 77030
Tel: 713 798-7620   *Fax:* 713 798-6923
Length: 1 Yr   *ACGME Approved/Offered Positions:* 1
Program ID: 081-48-13-019

University of Texas M D Anderson Cancer Center Program

Sponsor: University of Texas M D Anderson Cancer Center
Prgm Director: Tri H Nguyen, MD
1515 Holcombe Boulevard
Box 434
Houston, TX 77030
Tel: 713 563-1665   *Fax:* 713 745-3597
Length: 1 Yr   *ACGME Approved/Offered Positions:* 1
Program ID: 081-48-13-028

Vermont

Burlington

University of Vermont Program

Sponsor: Fletcher Allen Health Care
Prgm Director: Glenn D Goldman, MD
Division of Dermatology
89 Beaumont Avenue Given D-208
Burlington, VT 05405
Tel: 802 656-5605   *Fax:* 802 656-5606
Length: 1 Yr   *ACGME Approved/Offered Positions:* 1
Program ID: 081-50-31-016

Virginia

Richmond

Virginia Commonwealth University Health System Program

Sponsor: Virginia Commonwealth University Health System
Medical College of Virginia Hospitals
Prgm Director: Algin B Garrett, MD
401 N 11th Street
PO Box 980164
Richmond, VA 23298
Tel: 804 628-3139   *Fax:* 804 828-9596
E-mail: ssmith6@mcvh-vcu.edu
Length: 1 Yr   *ACGME Approved/Offered Positions:* 1
Program ID: 081-51-21-027

Washington

Seattle

University of Washington Program

Sponsor: University of Washington School of Medicine
University of Washington Medical Center
Prgm Director: Daniel Berg, MD
4225 Roosevelt Way NE
Box 354697
Seattle, WA 98105
Tel: 206 598-2112   *Fax:* 206 598-4200
E-mail: danberg@u.washington.edu
Length: 1 Yr   *ACGME Approved/Offered Positions:* 1
Program ID: 081-54-12-017

Wisconsin

Madison

University of Wisconsin Program

Sponsor: University of Wisconsin Hospital and Clinics
Prgm Director: Stephen N Snow, MD
451 Junction Road Mohs Surgery Clinic
Mohs Surgery Clinic
Madison, WI 53717
Tel: 608 263-6229   *Fax:* 608 262-8137
Length: 1 Yr   *ACGME Approved/Offered Positions:* 1
Program ID: 081-56-31-026

Psychiatry

Alabama

Birmingham

University of Alabama Medical Center Program

Sponsor: University of Alabama Hospital
Veterans Affairs Medical Center (Birmingham)
Prgm Director: Daniel C Dahl, MD
Callahan Eye Foundation Hospital
1720 University Blvd, Room 337
Birmingham, AL 35233
Tel: 205 934-3041   *Fax:* 205 934-4659
E-mail: ddcardin@uab.edu
Length: 4 Yrs   *ACGME Approved/Offered Positions:* 28
Program ID: 400-01-11-009

Mobile

University of South Alabama Program

Sponsor: University of South Alabama Hospitals
Alta Pointe Health Systems
University of South Alabama Medical Center
Veterans Affairs Medical Center (Biloxi)
Prgm Director: Deborah R Simkin, MD
2400 Gordon Smith Dr
Mobile, AL 36617
Tel: 251 450-4359   *Fax:* 251 450-4523
E-mail: mapplin@altapointe.org
Length: 4 Yrs   *ACGME Approved/Offered Positions:* 16
Program ID: 400-01-22-232

Arizona

Phoenix

Banner Good Samaritan Medical Center Program

Sponsor: Banner Good Samaritan Medical Center
Prgm Director: James B McLoone, MD
925 East McDowell Road
4th Floor
Phoenix, AZ 85006
Tel: 602 239-6880   *Fax:* 602 239-6988
E-mail: jo.russo@bannerhealth.com
Length: 4 Yrs   *ACGME Approved/Offered Positions:* 20
Program ID: 400-03-12-010

Maricopa Medical Center Program

Sponsor: Maricopa Medical Center
Prgm Director: William S James, MD
Desert Vista Campus #101
570 W Brown Rd
Mesa, AZ 85201
Tel: 480 344-2028   *Fax:* 480 344-2157
E-mail: leticia_rasillo@medprodoctors.com
Length: 4 Yrs   *ACGME Approved/Offered Positions:* 22
Program ID: 400-03-22-011

Tucson

University of Arizona Program

Sponsor: University of Arizona College of Medicine
Southern Arizona VA Health Care Center (Tucson)
University Medical Center
Prgm Director: Steven T Herron, MD
1501 North Campbell Avenue
PO Box 245002
Tucson, AZ 85724
Tel: 520 626-6795   *Fax:* 520 626-6050
Length: 4 Yrs   *ACGME Approved/Offered Positions:* 48
Program ID: 400-03-21-012

Programs

University of Arizona/UPHK Graduate Medical Education Consortium Program

Sponsor: University of Arizona/UPHK Graduate Medical Ed Consortium
University Medical Center
Prgm Director: Richard Van Rhoads, MD
2800 East Ajo Way
Tucson, AZ 85713
Tel: 520 874-4705   *Fax:* 520 874-2030
Length: 4 Yrs   *ACGME Approved/Offered Positions:* 12
Program ID: 400-03-21-301

Arkansas

Little Rock

University of Arkansas for Medical Sciences Program

Sponsor: University of Arkansas College of Medicine
Arkansas State Hospital (DBHS)
Central Arkansas Veterans Healthcare System
UAMS Medical Center
Prgm Director: Ben Guise, MD
UAMS 4301 West Markham
Mail Slot 589
Little Rock, AR 72205
Tel: 501 686-5803   *Fax:* 501 686-7424
Length: 4 Yrs   *ACGME Approved/Offered Positions:* 32
Program ID: 400-04-22-014

California

Bakersfield

UCLA-Kern Medical Center Program

Sponsor: Kern Medical Center
Kern County Mental Health Department
Prgm Director: Tai P Yoo, MD, MBA
1700 Mt Vernon Avenue
Bakersfield, CA 93306
Tel: 661 326-2248   *Fax:* 661 862-7682
E-mail: princel@kernmedctr.com
Length: 4 Yrs   *ACGME Approved/Offered Positions:* 20
Program ID: 400-05-22-298

Fresno

University of California (San Francisco)/Fresno Program

Sponsor: UCSF Fresno Medical Education Program
Community Medical Centers (Fresno)
Fresno County Health Services
University Psychiatry Associates
VA Central California Health Care System
Prgm Director: Craig C Campbell, MD, MS
155 N Fresno Street, Suite 338
Fresno, CA 93701
Tel: 559 499-6580   *Fax:* 559 499-6581
E-mail: craig.campbell@fresno.ucsf.edu
Length: 4 Yrs   *ACGME Approved/Offered Positions:* 16
Program ID: 400-05-21-018

Loma Linda

Loma Linda University Program

Sponsor: Loma Linda University Medical Center
Jerry L Pettis Memorial Veterans Hospital
Prgm Director: Mary Ann Schaepper, MD, MEd
11374 Mtn View Avenue
Loma Linda, CA 92354
Tel: 909 558-6094   *Fax:* 909 558-6093
Length: 4 Yrs   *ACGME Approved/Offered Positions:* 28
Program ID: 400-05-21-021

Los Angeles

Cedars-Sinai Medical Center Program

Sponsor: Cedars-Sinai Medical Center
Prgm Director: Waguih W IsHak, MD
8730 Alden Drive, Suite W-101
Los Angeles, CA 90048
Tel: 310 423-3481   *Fax:* 310 423-3947
E-mail: Yvonne.Neely@cshs.org
Length: 4 Yrs   *ACGME Approved/Offered Positions:* 24
Program ID: 400-05-11-022

UCLA Medical Center Program

Sponsor: UCLA David Geffen School of Medicine/UCLA Medical Center
UCLA Neuropsychiatric Hospital
Prgm Director: James E Spar, MD
760 Westwood Plaza
C8-225
Los Angeles, CA 90024
Tel: 310 825-0038   *Fax:* 310 825-6483
E-mail: kamaya@mednet.ucla.edu
Length: 4 Yrs   *ACGME Approved/Offered Positions:* 55
Program ID: 400-05-21-025

UCLA-San Fernando Valley/VA Greater Los Angeles Program

Sponsor: VA Greater Los Angeles Healthcare System
Olive View/UCLA Medical Center
Prgm Director: Murray A Brown, MD
UCLA/San Fernando Valley Psychiatry (116A3)
16111 Plummer Street
Sepulveda, CA 91343
Tel: 818 895-9349   *Fax:* 818 895-9437
Length: 4 Yrs   *ACGME Approved/Offered Positions:* 31
Program ID: 400-05-31-032

University of Southern California/LAC+USC Medical Center Program

Sponsor: University of Southern California/LAC+USC Medical Center
LAC+USC Medical Center
Prgm Director: Isabel T Lagomasino, MD, MS
2250 Alcazar Street, Suite 2200
Los Angeles, CA 90033
Tel: 323 442-4001   *Fax:* 323 442-5555
E-mail: psychres@usc.edu
Length: 4 Yrs   *ACGME Approved/Offered Positions:* 48
Program ID: 400-05-11-023

Orange

University of California (Irvine) Program

Sponsor: University of California (Irvine) Medical Center
VA Long Beach Healthcare System
Prgm Director: Barry F Chaitin, MD*
101 City Drive South
Route 88
Orange, CA 92868
Tel: 714 456-5951   *Fax:* 714 456-6190
E-mail: bchaitin@uci.edu
Length: 4 Yrs   *ACGME Approved/Offered Positions:* 34
Program ID: 400-05-21-020

Sacramento

University of California (Davis) Health System Program

Sponsor: University of California (Davis) Health System
Sacramento County Health and Human Services
University of California (Davis) Medical Center
Prgm Director: Mark E Servis, MD
2315 Stockton Boulevard
Sacramento, CA 95817
Tel: 916 734-2614   *Fax:* 916 734-3384
E-mail: david.williams@ucdmc.ucdavis.edu
Length: 4 Yrs   *ACGME Approved/Offered Positions:* 32
Program ID: 400-05-31-017

San Diego

Naval Medical Center (San Diego) Program

Sponsor: Naval Medical Center (San Diego)
University of California (San Diego) Medical Center
Prgm Director: James J Reeves, MD
34800 Bob Wilson Drive
Suite 108
San Diego, CA 92134
Tel: 619 532-8554   *Fax:* 619 532-8353
Length: 4 Yrs   *ACGME Approved/Offered Positions:* 20
Program ID: 400-05-21-253
Uniformed Services Program

University of California (San Diego) Program

Sponsor: University of California (San Diego) Medical Center
Veterans Affairs Medical Center (San Diego)
Prgm Director: Sidney Zisook, MD
Dept of Psychiatry
9500 Gilman Drive, 9116A
La Jolla, CA 92093
Tel: 858 534-4040   *Fax:* 858 822-0231
E-mail: restrain@ucsd.edu
Length: 4 Yrs   *ACGME Approved/Offered Positions:* 40
Program ID: 400-05-21-026

San Francisco

California Pacific Medical Center Program

Sponsor: California Pacific Medical Center
Prgm Director: David A Goldberg, MD
2340 Clay Street, 7th Floor
San Francisco, CA 94115
Tel: 415 600-3642   *Fax:* 415 600-3525
Length: 4 Yrs   *ACGME Approved/Offered Positions:* 16
Program ID: 400-05-22-028

University of California (San Francisco) Program

Sponsor: University of California (San Francisco) School of Medicine
San Francisco General Hospital Medical Center
UCSF Med Ctr/Langley Porter Psychiatric Hosp and Clinics
Veterans Affairs Medical Center (San Francisco)
Prgm Director: Ellen Haller, MD
Langley Porter Psychiatric Inst
401 Parnassus Avenue - RTP
San Francisco, CA 94143
Tel: 415 476-7799   *Fax:* 415 476-7722
E-mail: ellenh@lppi.ucsf.edu
Length: 4 Yrs   *ACGME Approved/Offered Positions:* 64
Program ID: 400-05-21-030

San Mateo

San Mateo County Behavioral Health and Recovery Services Program

Sponsor: San Mateo County Behavioral Health and Recovery Services
San Mateo Medical Center
Prgm Director: Alan K Louie, MD
Psychiatry Residency Training
222 West 39th Avenue
San Mateo, CA 94403
Tel: 650 573-2530   *Fax:* 650 573-2527
E-mail: alouie@co.sanmateo.ca.us
Length: 4 Yrs   *ACGME Approved/Offered Positions:* 16
Program ID: 400-05-22-031

Note: * indicates a newly appointed program director

Stanford

Stanford University Program

Sponsor: Stanford Hospital and Clinics
Kaiser Permanente Medical Center (Santa Clara)
Veterans Affairs Palo Alto Health Care System
Prgm Director: C Barr Taylor, MD
Office of Academic Affairs, Dept of Psychiatry
401 Quarry Road, Room 2204
Stanford, CA 94305
Tel: 650 725-5732   *Fax:* 650 725-3762
E-mail: faehouck@stanford.edu
Length: 4 Yrs   *ACGME Approved/Offered Positions:* 48
Program ID: 400-05-31-033

Torrance

Los Angeles County-Harbor-UCLA Medical Center Program

Sponsor: Los Angeles County-Harbor-UCLA Medical
   Center
Prgm Director: Karl S Burgoyne, MD
1000 West Carson Street
Box 8
Torrance, CA 90509
Tel: 310 222-3137   *Fax:* 310 320-6973
E-mail: kburgoyne@ladhs.org
Length: 4 Yrs   *ACGME Approved/Offered Positions:* 32
Program ID: 400-05-11-035

Colorado

Aurora

University of Colorado Denver Program

Sponsor: University of Colorado Denver School of
   Medicine
Denver Health Medical Center
University of Colorado Hospital
Veterans Affairs Medical Center (Denver)
Prgm Director: Alexis A Giese, MD
13001 E 17th Pl, Bldg 500, Rm E2328
PO Box 6508, Campus Box F546
Aurora, CO 80045
Tel: 303 724-6020   *Fax:* 303 724-4963
E-mail: tammy.samuels@uchsc.edu
Length: 4 Yrs   *ACGME Approved/Offered Positions:* 45
Program ID: 400-07-21-038

Connecticut

Farmington

University of Connecticut Program

Sponsor: University of Connecticut School of Medicine
Hartford Hospital
Univ of Connecticut Health Center/John Dempsey
   Hospital
Prgm Director: Leighton Y Huey, MD
c/o Terri Carrier
263 Farmington Avenue, MC1935
Farmington, CT 06030
Tel: 860 679-4733   *Fax:* 860 679-1246
E-mail: residency@psychiatry.uchc.edu
Length: 4 Yrs   *ACGME Approved/Offered Positions:* 28
Program ID: 400-08-21-266

Hartford

Institute of Living/Hartford Hospital Program

Sponsor: Hartford Hospital
Institute of Living
Prgm Director: Adrienne Bentman, MD
200 Retreat Avenue
Hartford, CT 06106
Tel: 860 545-7183   *Fax:* 860 545-7403
E-mail: sjdupre@harthosp.org
Length: 4 Yrs   *ACGME Approved/Offered Positions:* 24
Program ID: 400-08-21-295

New Haven

Yale-New Haven Medical Center Program

Sponsor: Yale-New Haven Hospital
Connecticut Mental Health Center
Hospital of St Raphael
Veterans Affairs Medical Center (West Haven)
Yale University Health Service
Prgm Director: Robert Rohrbaugh, MD*
300 George Street, Suite 901
New Haven, CT 06511
Tel: 203 737-2433   *Fax:* 203 785-4207
E-mail: robert.rohrbaugh@yale.edu
Length: 4 Yrs   *ACGME Approved/Offered Positions:* 86
Program ID: 400-08-21-042

Delaware

New Castle

Delaware Psychiatric Center Program

Sponsor: Delaware Psychiatric Center
Christiana Care Health Services Inc
Community Mental Health Clinic - Dover
Community Mental Health Clinic - Wilmington
Prgm Director: S Imran Tirmizi, MD
1901 North DuPont Highway
Springer Building
New Castle, DE 19720
Tel: 302 255-2995   *Fax:* 302 255-4452
E-mail: imran.tirmizi@state.de.us
Length: 4 Yrs   *ACGME Approved/Offered Positions:* 16
Program ID: 400-09-31-046

District of Columbia

Washington

George Washington University Program

Sponsor: George Washington University School of
   Medicine
George Washington University Hospital (UHS)
Inova Fairfax Hospital
Prgm Director: James L Griffith, MD, MS
Department of Psychiatry
2150 Pennsylvania Avenue, NW
Washington, DC 20037
Tel: 202 741-2879   *Fax:* 202 741-2891
E-mail: gwupsychresident@mfa.gwu.edu
Length: 4 Yrs   *ACGME Approved/Offered Positions:* 27
Program ID: 400-10-21-048

Georgetown University Hospital Program

Sponsor: Georgetown University Hospital
Veterans Affairs Medical Center (Washington, DC)
Prgm Director: Alan Newman, MD
3800 Reservoir Rd NW
6th Floor Kober-Kogan
Washington, DC 20007
Tel: 202 687-5494   *Fax:* 202 687-6658
Length: 4 Yrs   *ACGME Approved/Offered Positions:* 28
Program ID: 400-10-21-047

Howard University Program

Sponsor: Howard University Hospital
Veterans Affairs Medical Center (Washington, DC)
Prgm Director: Janice G Hutchinson, MD
2041 Georgia Avenue, NW
Washington, DC 20060
Tel: 202 865-6611   *Fax:* 202 865-6212
E-mail: jchutchinson@howard.edu
Length: 4 Yrs   *ACGME Approved/Offered Positions:* 16
Program ID: 400-10-21-049

St Elizabeths Hospital-DC Department of Mental Health Program

Sponsor: St Elizabeth's Hospital-DC Department of
   Mental Health
Andromeda Transcultural Health
Providence Hospital
University of the District of Columbia
Washington School of Psychiatry
Prgm Director: Farooq Mohyuddin, MD
Barton Hall/Building #117, 2nd Floor, Room 200
2700 Martin Luther King, Jr, Avenue SE
Washington, DC 20032
Tel: 202 645-8777   *Fax:* 202 645-5981
Length: 4 Yrs   *ACGME Approved/Offered Positions:* 40
Program ID: 400-10-21-239

Florida

Gainesville

University of Florida Program

Sponsor: University of Florida College of Medicine
North Florida/South Georgia Veterans Health System
Shands Hospital at the University of Florida
Prgm Director: Michael R Ware, MD*
PO Box 100256, JHMHC
Gainesville, FL 32610
Tel: 352 392-8013   *Fax:* 352 392-7447
Length: 4 Yrs   *ACGME Approved/Offered Positions:* 28
Program ID: 400-11-21-050

Miami

Jackson Memorial Hospital/Jackson Health System Program

Sponsor: Jackson Memorial Hospital/Jackson Health
   System
Mount Sinai Medical Center of Florida, Inc
Veterans Affairs Medical Center (Miami)
Prgm Director: Richard M Steinbook, MD
1695 NW 9th Ave #2101
Miami, FL 33136
Tel: 305 355-8264   *Fax:* 305 355-7266
Length: 4 Yrs   *ACGME Approved/Offered Positions:* 48
Program ID: 400-11-21-051

Tampa

University of South Florida Program

Sponsor: University of South Florida College of Medicine
James A Haley Veterans Hospital
Tampa General Hospital
University Psychiatry Center
Prgm Director: Brian Keefe, MD
3515 East Fletcher Avenue
Tampa, FL 33613
Tel: 813 974-2805   *Fax:* 813 974-2478
E-mail: kisaac@health.usf.edu
Length: 4 Yrs   *ACGME Approved/Offered Positions:* 32
Program ID: 400-11-21-052

Programs

Georgia

Atlanta

Emory University Program
Sponsor: Emory University School of Medicine
Emory University Hospital
Grady Health System
Veterans Affairs Medical Center (Atlanta)
Prgm Director: William M McDonald, MD
Department of Psychiatry & Behavioral Sciences
Tufts House 2004 Ridgewood Road, Suite 218
Atlanta, GA 30322
Tel: 404 727-5157 *Fax:* 404 727-4746
Length: 4 Yrs *ACGME Approved/Offered Positions:* 50
Program ID: 400-12-21-053

Morehouse School of Medicine Program
Sponsor: Morehouse School of Medicine
Georgia Regional Hospital at Atlanta
Grady Health System
Veterans Affairs Medical Center (Atlanta)
Prgm Director: John O Gaston, MD
720 Westview Drive SW
Atlanta, GA 30310
Tel: 404 756-1451 *Fax:* 404 756-1459
E-mail: tburns@msm.edu
Length: 4 Yrs *ACGME Approved/Offered Positions:* 16
Program ID: 400-12-21-262

Augusta

Medical College of Georgia Program
Sponsor: Medical College of Georgia
Veterans Affairs Medical Center (Augusta)
Prgm Director: Stewart Shevitz, MD
997 St Sebastian Way
Augusta, GA 30912
Tel: 706 721-6715 *Fax:* 706 721-1793
Length: 4 Yrs *ACGME Approved/Offered Positions:* 24
Program ID: 400-12-21-054

Hawaii

Honolulu

University of Hawaii Program
Sponsor: University of Hawaii John A Burns School of
  Medicine
DOH AMHD Community Mental Health Centers
Hawaii State Hospital
Queen's Medical Center
VA Pacific Islands Health Care System (Honolulu)
Prgm Director: Courtenay R Matsu, MD
1356 Lusitana Street, 4th Floor
Honolulu, HI 96813
Tel: 808 586-2900 *Fax:* 808 586-2940
E-mail: klevec@dop.hawaii.edu
Length: 4 Yrs *ACGME Approved/Offered Positions:* 28
Program ID: 400-14-31-055

Tripler AMC

Tripler Army Medical Center Program
Sponsor: Tripler Army Medical Center
Prgm Director: Millard D Brown, MD
Attn: MCHK-PSRT (Psychiatry GME-MAJ Brown)
1 Jarrett White Road
Tripler AMC, HI 96859
Tel: 808 433-5780 *Fax:* 808 433-3864
E-mail: millard.brown@us.army.mil
Length: 4 Yrs *ACGME Approved/Offered Positions:* 28
Program ID: 400-14-11-233
Uniformed Services Program

Illinois

Chicago

McGaw Medical Center of Northwestern University Program
Sponsor: McGaw Medical Center of Northwestern
  University
Children's Memorial Hospital
Evanston Hospital
Jesse Brown Veterans Affairs Medical Center
Northwestern Memorial Hospital
Prgm Director: Joan M Anzia, MD
446 East Ontario
7th Floor, Suite 200
Chicago, IL 60611
Tel: 312 926-8058 *Fax:* 312 926-7612
E-mail: janzia@nmh.org
Length: 4 Yrs *ACGME Approved/Offered Positions:* 32
Program ID: 400-16-21-060

Rush University Medical Center Program
Sponsor: Rush University Medical Center
Prgm Director: Daniel Levin, MD
2150 W Harrison St
Chicago, IL 60612
Tel: 312 942-2099 *Fax:* 312 924-3186
Length: 4 Yrs *ACGME Approved/Offered Positions:* 32
Program ID: 400-16-11-061

University of Chicago Program
Sponsor: University of Chicago Medical Center
MacNeal Hospital
Prgm Director: Deborah Spitz, MD
5841 S Maryland Avenue, MC 3077
Chicago, IL 60637
Tel: 773 702-0529 *Fax:* 773 702-4297
E-mail: btyrpin@bsd.uchicago.edu
Length: 4 Yrs *ACGME Approved/Offered Positions:* 26
Program ID: 400-16-31-062

University of Illinois College of Medicine at Chicago Program
Sponsor: University of Illinois College of Medicine at
  Chicago
Jesse Brown Veterans Affairs Medical Center
University of Illinois Hospital and Clinics
Prgm Director: Robert W Marvin, MD
Department of Psychiatry (M/C 913)
912 South Wood Street
Chicago, IL 60612
Tel: 312 996-7380 *Fax:* 312 996-3514
E-mail: recruit@psych.uic.edu
Length: 4 Yrs *ACGME Approved/Offered Positions:* 48
Program ID: 400-16-21-063

Maywood

Loyola University Program
Sponsor: Loyola University Medical Center
Edward Hines, Jr Veterans Affairs Hospital
Prgm Director: David C Schilling, MD
2160 South First Avenue
Maywood, IL 60153
Tel: 708 216-5059 *Fax:* 708 216-5885
E-mail: DSchil1@lumc.edu
Length: 4 Yrs *ACGME Approved/Offered Positions:* 16
Program ID: 400-16-21-064

North Chicago

The Chicago Medical School at Rosalind Franklin University of Medicine and Science Program
Sponsor: Chicago Medical School/Rosalind Franklin
  Univ of Med & Sci
Mount Sinai Hospital Medical Center of Chicago
Veterans Affairs Medical Center (North Chicago)
Prgm Director: David A Garfield, MD
RFUMS/The Chicago Medical School
3333 Green Bay Road
North Chicago, IL 60064
Tel: 847 578-8705 *Fax:* 847 578-3328
Length: 4 Yrs *ACGME Approved/Offered Positions:* 24
Program ID: 400-16-31-056

Park Ridge

Advocate Lutheran General Hospital Program
Sponsor: Advocate Lutheran General Hospital
Prgm Director: Michael Wagner, MD
Department of Psychiatry, 8 South
1775 West Dempster St
Park Ridge, IL 60068
Tel: 847 723-5887 *Fax:* 847 723-7312
E-mail: lgh-psychres@advocatehealth.com
Length: 4 Yrs *ACGME Approved/Offered Positions:* 12
Program ID: 400-16-21-257

Springfield

Southern Illinois University Program
Sponsor: Southern Illinois University School of Medicine
Memorial Medical Center
St John's Hospital
Prgm Director: Jeffrey I Bennett, MD
PO Box 19642
Springfield, IL 62794
Tel: 217 545-7627 *Fax:* 217 545-2275
E-mail: vsmith@siumed.edu
Length: 4 Yrs *ACGME Approved/Offered Positions:* 20
Program ID: 400-16-21-065

Indiana

Indianapolis

Indiana University School of Medicine Program
Sponsor: Indiana University School of Medicine
Clarian Indiana University Hospital
Clarian Methodist Hospital of Indiana
Clarian Riley Hospital for Children
Larue D Carter Memorial Hospital
Richard L Roudebush Veterans Affairs Medical Center
William N Wishard Memorial Hospital
Prgm Director: Alan D Schmetzer, MD
1111 West Tenth Street
Indianapolis, IN 46202
Tel: 317 274-7423 *Fax:* 317 247-1248
E-mail: jtsouder@iupui.edu
Length: 4 Yrs *ACGME Approved/Offered Positions:* 32
Program ID: 400-17-21-066

Note: * indicates a newly appointed program director

Iowa

Iowa City

University of Iowa Hospitals and Clinics Program

Sponsor: University of Iowa Hospitals and Clinics
Veterans Affairs Medical Center (Iowa City)
Prgm Director: Catherine Woodman, MD
200 Hawkins Drive 2880 JPP
Iowa City, IA 52242
Tel: 319 356-1373 *Fax:* 319 356-2587
Length: 4 Yrs *ACGME Approved/Offered Positions:* 28
Program ID: 400-18-21-069

Kansas

Kansas City

University of Kansas School of Medicine Program

Sponsor: University of Kansas School of Medicine
Dwight D Eisenhower Veterans Affairs Medical Center
Johnson County Mental Health Center
University of Kansas Hospital
Veterans Affairs Medical Center (Kansas City)
Wyandot Mental Health Center, Inc
Prgm Director: Barry I Liskow, MD
3901 Rainbow Boulevard
1009 Olathe Pavilion
Kansas City, KS 66160
Tel: 913 588-6412 *Fax:* 913 588-6414
Length: 4 Yrs *ACGME Approved/Offered Positions:* 34
Program ID: 400-19-21-070

Wichita

University of Kansas (Wichita) Program

Sponsor: University of Kansas School of Medicine (Wichita)
Via Christi Regional Medical Center-Good Shepherd
Via Christi Regional Medical Center-St Francis
Via Christi Regional Medical Center-St Joseph
Prgm Director: Russell E Scheffer, MD*
1010 North Kansas
Wichita, KS 67214
Tel: 316 293-2669
Length: 4 Yrs *ACGME Approved/Offered Positions:* 20
Program ID: 400-19-21-254

Kentucky

Lexington

University of Kentucky College of Medicine Program

Sponsor: University of Kentucky College of Medicine
University of Kentucky Hospital
Veterans Affairs Medical Center (Lexington)
Prgm Director: Cletus Carvalho, MD*
3470 Blazer Parkway
Lexington, KY 40509
Tel: 859 323-6861
E-mail: cscarv2@email.uky.edu
Length: 4 Yrs *ACGME Approved/Offered Positions:* 24
Program ID: 400-20-21-074

Louisville

University of Louisville Program

Sponsor: University of Louisville School of Medicine
Norton Hospital
University of Louisville Hospital
Veterans Affairs Medical Center (Louisville)
Prgm Director: Barbara Fitzgerald, MD
501 East Broadway
Suite 340
Louisville, KY 40202
Tel: 502 852-5395 *Fax:* 502 852-3751
E-mail: barbara.fitzgerald@louisville.edu
Length: 4 Yrs *ACGME Approved/Offered Positions:* 36
Program ID: 400-20-21-075

Louisiana

New Orleans

Louisiana State University/Ochsner Clinic Foundation Program

Sponsor: Louisiana State University School of Medicine
Medical Center of Louisiana at New Orleans
Metropolitan Human Services District
Ochsner Clinic Foundation
Odyssey House Louisiana
Prgm Director: Erich J Conrad, MD*
Department of Psychiatry
2020 Gravier Street
New Orleans, LA 70112
Tel: 504 568-7912 *Fax:* 504 568-6006
E-mail: econra@lsuhsc.edu
Length: 4 Yrs *ACGME Approved/Offered Positions:* 40
Program ID: 400-21-21-291

Tulane University Program

Sponsor: Tulane University School of Medicine
Jefferson Parish Human Services Authority
Medical Center of Louisiana at New Orleans
Tulane University Hospital and Clinics
Veterans Affairs Medical Center (New Orleans)
Prgm Director: Patrick T O'Neill, MD
1440 Canal Street
TB-53
New Orleans, LA 70112
Tel: 504 988-4272 *Fax:* 504 988-4270
E-mail: psychres@tulane.edu
Length: 4 Yrs *ACGME Approved/Offered Positions:* 39
Program ID: 400-21-21-078

Shreveport

Louisiana State University (Shreveport) Program

Sponsor: LSU Health Sciences Center-University Hospital
Overton Brooks Veterans Affairs Medical Center
Prgm Director: Anita S Kablinger, MD
1501 Kings Highway
PO Box 33932
Shreveport, LA 71130
Tel: 318 813-2070 *Fax:* 318 813-2080
E-mail: tthom6@lsuhsc.edu
Length: 4 Yrs *ACGME Approved/Offered Positions:* 24
Program ID: 400-21-21-274

Maine

Portland

Maine Medical Center Program

Sponsor: Maine Medical Center
The Acadia Hospital
Prgm Director: George N McNeil Jr, MD
22 Bramhall Street
Portland, ME 04102
Tel: 207 662-2370 *Fax:* 207 662-6957
E-mail: mcneig@mmc.org
Length: 4 Yrs *ACGME Approved/Offered Positions:* 20
Program ID: 400-22-11-080

Maryland

Baltimore

Johns Hopkins University Program

Sponsor: Johns Hopkins University School of Medicine
Johns Hopkins Bayview Medical Center
Johns Hopkins Hospital
Prgm Director: John R Lipsey, MD
600 North Wolfe Street/Meyer 3-181
Baltimore, MD 21287
Tel: 410 955-7162 *Fax:* 410 955-0152
Length: 4 Yrs *ACGME Approved/Offered Positions:* 47
Program ID: 400-23-21-081

University of Maryland/Sheppard Pratt Program

Sponsor: University of Maryland Medical System
Mercy Medical Center
Sheppard Pratt Health System
Veterans Affairs Medical Center (Baltimore)
Walter P Carter Mental Health Center
Prgm Director: M Philip Luber, MD
Department of Psychiatry
701 W Pratt St, Rm 474
Baltimore, MD 21201
Tel: 410 328-6325 *Fax:* 410 328-1212
Length: 4 Yrs *ACGME Approved/Offered Positions:* 70
Program ID: 400-23-21-289

Bethesda

National Capital Consortium Program

Sponsor: National Capital Consortium
Malcolm Grow Medical Center
National Naval Medical Center (Bethesda)
Walter Reed Army Medical Center
Prgm Director: Scott C Moran, MD
4301 Jones Bridge Road
Bethesda, MD 20814
Tel: 202 782-7104 *Fax:* 202 782-6480
E-mail: smoran@nccpsychiatry.info
Length: 4 Yrs *ACGME Approved/Offered Positions:* 56
Program ID: 400-10-21-287
Uniformed Services Program

National Institutes of Health Clinical Center Program

Sponsor: Clinical Center at the National Institutes of Health
Prgm Director: Maryland Pao, MD
NIH Clinical Center, 10/CRC/Room 6-5340
Bethesda, MD 20892
Tel: 301 435-5770 *Fax:* 301 402-2588
Length: 3 Yrs *ACGME Approved/Offered Positions:* 6
Program ID: 400-23-12-245

Massachusetts

Boston

Boston University Medical Center Program

Sponsor: Boston Medical Center
Edith Nourse Rogers Memorial Veterans Hospital (Bedford)
Veterans Affairs Medical Center (Boston)
Prgm Director: Janet E Osterman, MD
850 Harrison Avenue, Dowling 7S, Rm 7203
Boston, MA 02118
Tel: 617 638-8540 *Fax:* 617 638-8542
E-mail: maria@bu.edu
Length: 4 Yrs *ACGME Approved/Offered Positions:* 32
Program ID: 400-24-21-089

Brigham and Women's Hospital/Harvard Medical School Program

Sponsor: Brigham and Women's Hospital
Beth Israel Deaconess Medical Center
Caritas Carney Hospital
Faulkner Hospital
Massachusetts Mental Health Center
Mount Auburn Hospital
Prgm Director: William E Greenberg, MD
330 Brookline Avenue
Boston, MA 02215
Tel: 617 667-4766 *Fax:* 617 667-5575
Length: 4 Yrs *ACGME Approved/Offered Positions:* 64
Program ID: 400-24-31-277

Caritas St Elizabeth's Medical Center Program

Sponsor: Caritas St Elizabeth's Medical Center of Boston
Prgm Director: Zamir Nestelbaum, MD, MPH*
736 Cambridge Street
QN3P
Boston, MA 02135
Tel: 617 789-3307 *Fax:* 617 789-2168
Length: 4 Yrs *ACGME Approved/Offered Positions:* 20
Program ID: 400-24-21-092

Massachusetts General Hospital/McLean Hospital Program

Sponsor: Massachusetts General Hospital
Erich Lindemann Mental Health Center
McLean Hospital
Newton-Wellesley Hospital
Prgm Director: Kathy M Sanders, MD
15 Parkman St, Wang 812
Boston, MA 02114
Tel: 617 726-0895 *Fax:* 617 724-0308
E-mail: jlittlefield2@partners.org
Length: 4 Yrs *ACGME Approved/Offered Positions:* 64
Program ID: 400-24-21-288

Tufts Medical Center Program

Sponsor: Tufts Medical Center
Lemuel Shattuck Hospital
Prgm Director: Jonathan Schindelheim, MD
800 Washington Street #1007
Boston, MA 02111
Tel: 617 636-3303 *Fax:* 617 636-1277
E-mail: jschindelheim@tuftsmedicalcenter.org
Length: 4 Yrs *ACGME Approved/Offered Positions:* 24
Program ID: 400-24-21-093

Brockton

Boston VA Healthcare System (Brockton-West Roxbury)/Harvard Medical School Program

Sponsor: Boston VA Healthcare System (Brockton-West Roxbury)
Prgm Director: Mark S Bauer, MD
940 Belmont Street - 116A7
Brockton, MA 02301
Tel: 508 583-4500 *Fax:* 774 826-1859
E-mail: mark.bauer@va.gov
Length: 4 Yrs *ACGME Approved/Offered Positions:* 32
Program ID: 400-24-21-279

Cambridge

Cambridge Health Alliance Program

Sponsor: Cambridge Health Alliance
Massachusetts Institute of Technology Mental Health Services
Spaulding Rehabilitation Hospital
Prgm Director: Marshall Forstein, MD
Macht Building
1493 Cambridge Street
Cambridge, MA 02139
Tel: 617 665-1189 *Fax:* 617 665-3449
E-mail: mforstein@cha.harvard.edu
Length: 4 Yrs *ACGME Approved/Offered Positions:* 32
Program ID: 400-24-11-094

Pittsfield

Berkshire Medical Center Program

Sponsor: Berkshire Medical Center
Brien Center for Mental Health
Prgm Director: Alex N Sabo, MD
725 North Street
Pittsfield, MA 01201
Tel: 413 447-2162 *Fax:* 413 447-2041
E-mail: nhamilton@bhs1.org
Length: 4 Yrs *ACGME Approved/Offered Positions:* 16
Program ID: 400-24-13-302

Springfield

Baystate Medical Center/Tufts University School of Medicine Program

Sponsor: Baystate Medical Center
Behavioral Health Network, Inc
Prgm Director: Steven V Fischel, MD, PhD
759 Chestnut Street
Springfield, MA 01199
Tel: 413 794-3376 *Fax:* 413 794-9803
E-mail: steven.fischel@bhs.org
Length: 4 Yrs *ACGME Approved/Offered Positions:* 16
Program ID: 400-24-31-303

Stockbridge

Austen Riggs Center Program

Sponsor: Austen Riggs Center
Prgm Director: David Mintz, MD
PO Box 962
25 Main Street
Stockbridge, MA 01262
Tel: 413 931-5315 *Fax:* 413 298-4020
E-mail: david.mintz@austenriggs.net
Length: 1 Yr *ACGME Approved/Offered Positions:* 2
Program ID: 400-24-11-249

Worcester

University of Massachusetts Program

Sponsor: University of Massachusetts Medical School
Prgm Director: Sheldon Benjamin, MD
55 Lake Avenue, North
Worcester, MA 01655
Tel: 508 856-4087 *Fax:* 508 856-5000
Length: 4 Yrs *ACGME Approved/Offered Positions:* 28
Program ID: 400-24-21-234

Michigan

Ann Arbor

University of Michigan Program

Sponsor: University of Michigan Hospitals and Health Centers
Veterans Affairs Medical Center (Ann Arbor)
Prgm Director: Michael Jibson, MD, PhD
1500 E Medical Center Drive
MCHC, F6135 SPC 5295
Ann Arbor, MI 48109
Tel: 734 764-6875 *Fax:* 734 936-9116
E-mail: resedpsych@umich.edu
Length: 4 Yrs *ACGME Approved/Offered Positions:* 48
Program ID: 400-25-21-097

Detroit

Henry Ford Hospital Program

Sponsor: Henry Ford Hospital
Kingswood Hospital
Prgm Director: Lisa MacLean, MD
One Ford Place, 1C09
Detroit, MI 48202
Tel: 313 874-6611 *Fax:* 313 874-6655
E-mail: redward1@hfhs.org
Length: 4 Yrs *ACGME Approved/Offered Positions:* 24
Program ID: 400-25-21-235

Wayne State University/Detroit Medical Center Program

Sponsor: Wayne State University/Detroit Medical Center
Sinai-Grace Hospital
University Psychiatric Centers
Veterans Affairs Medical Center (Detroit)
Prgm Director: Beth Ann Brooks, MD
2751 E Jefferson
Suite 400
Detroit, MI 48207
Tel: 313 577-5267 *Fax:* 313 577-2233
Length: 4 Yrs *ACGME Approved/Offered Positions:* 46
Program ID: 400-25-21-283

Kalamazoo

Kalamazoo Center for Medical Studies/Michigan State University Program

Sponsor: Michigan State Univ/Kalamazoo Center for Medical Studies
Borgess Medical Center
Prgm Director: Robert D Strung, MD
1000 Oakland Drive
Kalamazoo, MI 49008
Tel: 269 337-6375 *Fax:* 269 337-6378
E-mail: psychiatry@kcms.msu.edu
Length: 4 Yrs *ACGME Approved/Offered Positions:* 16
Program ID: 400-25-31-284

Lansing

Michigan State University Program

Sponsor: Michigan State University College of Human Medicine
Clinton-Eaton-Ingham Community Mental Health Center
Marquette General Hospital
Sparrow Hospital
Prgm Director: Jed G Magen, DO, MS
Department of Psychiatry
A-233 East Fee Hall
East Lansing, MI 48824
Tel: 517 353-4362 *Fax:* 517 432-0927
Length: 4 Yrs *ACGME Approved/Offered Positions:* 35
Program ID: 400-25-21-101

Note: * indicates a newly appointed program director

Minnesota

Minneapolis

Hennepin County Medical Center/Regions Hospital Program

Sponsor: Hennepin County Medical Center
Regions Hospital
Prgm Director: Amitahb A Tipnis, MD, MBA*
701 Park Avenue South
Mail Code B5
Minneapolis, MN 55415
Tel: 612 873-7571   *Fax:* 612 904-4350
E-mail: amitabh.tipnis@hcmed.org
Length: 4 Yrs   *ACGME Approved/Offered Positions:* 28
Program ID: 400-26-21-285

University of Minnesota Program

Sponsor: University of Minnesota Medical School
University of Minnesota Medical Center, Division of
   Fairview
Veterans Affairs Medical Center (Minneapolis)
Prgm Director: Thomas Mackenzie, MD
F282/2A West
2450 Riverside Avenue
Minneapolis, MN 55454
Tel: 612 273-9822   *Fax:* 612 273-9779
E-mail: brenn036@umn.edu
Length: 4 Yrs   *ACGME Approved/Offered Positions:* 33
Program ID: 400-26-21-106

Rochester

College of Medicine, Mayo Clinic (Rochester) Program

Sponsor: College of Medicine, Mayo Clinic
Mayo Clinic (Rochester)
Rochester Methodist Hospital
Saint Marys Hospital of Rochester
Prgm Director: Barbara M Rohland, MD, MS
200 First Street SW
Rochester, MN 55905
Tel: 507 284-0325   *Fax:* 507 284-4345
E-mail: mgsm.roch.mn.psychiatry@mayo.edu
Length: 4 Yrs   *ACGME Approved/Offered Positions:* 35
Program ID: 400-26-21-107

Mississippi

Jackson

University of Mississippi Medical Center Program

Sponsor: University of Mississippi School of Medicine
University Hospitals and Clinics
Veterans Affairs Medical Center (Jackson)
Prgm Director: Allen Richert, MD
2500 North State Street
Attn: Carol Porter - BOX 139
Jackson, MS 39216
Tel: 601 815-1368   *Fax:* 601 815-7623
E-mail: lcporter@psychiatry.umsmed.edu
Length: 4 Yrs   *ACGME Approved/Offered Positions:* 24
Program ID: 400-27-11-108

Missouri

Columbia

University of Missouri-Columbia Program

Sponsor: University of Missouri-Columbia School of
   Medicine
Harry S Truman Memorial Veterans Hospital
Mid-Missouri Mental Health Center
University Hospitals and Clinics
Prgm Director: Andrew Resnik, MD
One Hospital Drive, DC067.00
Columbia, MO 65212
Tel: 573 882-8907   *Fax:* 573 884-5936
Length: 4 Yrs   *ACGME Approved/Offered Positions:* 24
Program ID: 400-28-21-109

Kansas City

University of Missouri at Kansas City Program

Sponsor: University of Missouri-Kansas City School of
   Medicine
Truman Medical Center
Western Missouri Mental Health Center
Prgm Director: Timothy Dellenbaugh, MD
1000 East 24th Street
Kansas City, MO 64108
Tel: 816 512-7439   *Fax:* 816 512-7440
Length: 4 Yrs   *ACGME Approved/Offered Positions:* 24
Program ID: 400-28-21-110

St Louis

St Louis University School of Medicine Program

Sponsor: St Louis University School of Medicine
St Louis University Hospital
Veterans Affairs Medical Center (St Louis)
Prgm Director: Miggie Greenberg, MD
1438 South Grand Boulevard
St Louis, MO 63104
Tel: 314 977-4828   *Fax:* 314 977-4877
Length: 4 Yrs   *ACGME Approved/Offered Positions:* 24
Program ID: 400-28-21-113

Washington University/B-JH/SLCH Consortium Program

Sponsor: Washington University/B-JH/SLCH Consortium
Barnes-Jewish Hospital
Metropolitan St Louis Psychiatric Center
Prgm Director: Nuri B Farber, MD
Dept of Psychiatry, Box 8134
660 South Euclid Avenue
St Louis, MO 63110
Tel: 314 362-2462   *Fax:* 314 362-0193
Length: 4 Yrs   *ACGME Approved/Offered Positions:* 40
Program ID: 400-28-21-114

Nebraska

Omaha

Creighton University/University of Nebraska Program

Sponsor: Creighton University School of Medicine
Alegent Health Immanuel Medical Center
Creighton University Medical Center (Tenet - SJH)
Nebraska Medical Center
Veterans Affairs Medical Center (Omaha)
Prgm Director: William H Roccaforte, MD
985582 Nebraska Medical Center
Omaha, NE 68198
Tel: 402 552-6244   *Fax:* 402 552-6247
E-mail: vthomsen@unmc.edu
Length: 4 Yrs   *ACGME Approved/Offered Positions:* 32
Program ID: 400-30-21-116

Nevada

Las Vegas

University of Nevada School of Medicine (Las Vegas) Program

Sponsor: University of Nevada School of Medicine
VA Southern Nevada Healthcare System
Harmony Healthcare
Southern Nevada Adult Mental Health Services
Prgm Director: Gregory P Brown, MD
2810 West Charleston Blvd
Suite 78
Las Vegas, NV 89102
Tel: 702 258-3415   *Fax:* 702 870-2572
E-mail: gbrown@medicine.nevada.edu
Length: 4 Yrs   *ACGME Approved/Offered Positions:* 16
Program ID: 400-31-21-297

Reno

University of Nevada School of Medicine Program

Sponsor: University of Nevada School of Medicine
Ioannis A Lougaris Veterans Affairs Medical Center
Northern Nevada Adult Mental Health Services
Renown Medical Center
University of Nevada, Reno - Student Health Center
West Hills Hospital
Prgm Director: Mark H Broadhead, MD
Department of Psychiatry and Behavioral Sciences
Nelson Building/354
Reno, NV 89557
Tel: 775 682-8458   *Fax:* 775 784-1428
E-mail: mbroadhead@medicine.nevada.edu
Length: 4 Yrs   *ACGME Approved/Offered Positions:* 16
Program ID: 400-31-21-263

New Hampshire

Lebanon

Dartmouth-Hitchcock Medical Center Program

Sponsor: Mary Hitchcock Memorial Hospital
Veterans Affairs Medical Center (White River Junction)
Prgm Director: Ronald L Green, MD
One Medical Center Drive
Lebanon, NH 03756
Tel: 603 650-5820   *Fax:* 603 650-5842
Length: 4 Yrs   *ACGME Approved/Offered Positions:* 36
Program ID: 400-32-21-117

New Jersey

Camden

UMDNJ-Robert Wood Johnson Medical School (Camden) Program

Sponsor: Cooper Hospital-University Medical Center
AtlantiCare Regional Medical Center
Prgm Director: Consuelo C Cagande, MD
401 Haddon Avenue
Camden, NJ 08103
Tel: 856 757-7719   *Fax:* 856 757-9651
E-mail: rile-viktoria@cooperhealth.edu
Length: 4 Yrs   *ACGME Approved/Offered Positions:* 20
Program ID: 400-33-21-255

Programs

Elizabeth

Seton Hall University School of Health and Medical Sciences Program

Sponsor: Seton Hall University School of Health and Medical Sciences
Trinitas Hospital
Prgm Director: Purabi Bharatiya, MD
655 East Jersey Street
Elizabeth, NJ 07206
Tel: 908 994-7207   *Fax:* 908 994-7503
E-mail: pbharatiya@trinitas.org
Length: 4 Yrs   *ACGME Approved/Offered Positions:* 15
Program ID: 400-33-12-300

Newark

UMDNJ-New Jersey Medical School Program

Sponsor: UMDNJ-New Jersey Medical School
Hackensack University Medical Center
UMDNJ-University Behavioral Health Care
UMDNJ-University Hospital
Veterans Affairs New Jersey Health Care System
Prgm Director: Giovanni Caracci, MD
183 South Orange Avenue, BHSB, Room E-1447
Newark, NJ 07103
Tel: 973 972-4670   *Fax:* 973 972-0870
Length: 4 Yrs   *ACGME Approved/Offered Positions:* 29
Program ID: 400-33-21-119

Paramus

Bergen Regional Medical Center Program

Sponsor: Bergen Regional Medical Center
Prgm Director: M Javed Iqbal, MD
230 East Ridgewood Avenue
Paramus, NJ 07652
Tel: 201 967-4132   *Fax:* 201 967-4290
Length: 4 Yrs   *ACGME Approved/Offered Positions:* 29
Program ID: 400-33-12-120

Piscataway

UMDNJ-Robert Wood Johnson Medical School Program

Sponsor: UMDNJ-Robert Wood Johnson Medical School
UMDNJ-University Behavioral HealthCare
Jersey Shore University Medical Center
Prgm Director: Barbara Palmeri, MD
Department of Psychiatry
671 Hoes Lane, UBHC C-205
Piscataway, NJ 08854
Tel: 732 235-4433   *Fax:* 732 235-4649
E-mail: fitzgeck@umdnj.edu
Length: 4 Yrs   *ACGME Approved/Offered Positions:* 24
Program ID: 400-33-21-121

Stratford

UMDNJ-School of Osteopathic Medicine Program

Sponsor: UMDNJ-School of Osteopathic Medicine
Kennedy Memorial Hospitals-University Med Ctr-Cherry Hill
Prgm Director: Douglas M Leonard, DO
2250 Chapel Avenue West, Suite 100
Cherry Hill, NJ 08002
Tel: 856 482-9000   *Fax:* 856 482-1159
E-mail: leonardm@umdnj.edu
Length: 4 Yrs   *ACGME Approved/Offered Positions:* 16
Program ID: 400-33-13-292

New Mexico

Albuquerque

University of New Mexico Program

Sponsor: University of New Mexico School of Medicine
University of New Mexico Hospital
Veterans Affairs Medical Center (Albuquerque)
Prgm Director: Stephen F Lewis, MD
MSC09 5030
1 University of New Mexico
Albuquerque, NM 87131
Tel: 505 272-5417   *Fax:* 505 272-4639
E-mail: SFLewis@salud.unm.edu
Length: 4 Yrs   *ACGME Approved/Offered Positions:* 39
Program ID: 400-34-21-123

New York

Albany

Albany Medical Center Program

Sponsor: Albany Medical Center
Capital District Psychiatric Center
Veterans Affairs Medical Center (Albany)
Prgm Director: Victoria I Balkoski, MD
Department of Psychiatry MC-164
47 New Scotland Avenue
Albany, NY 12208
Tel: 518 262-5511   *Fax:* 518 262-6111
Length: 4 Yrs   *ACGME Approved/Offered Positions:* 24
Program ID: 400-35-22-124

Bronx

Albert Einstein College of Medicine at Bronx-Lebanon Hospital Center Program

Sponsor: Bronx-Lebanon Hospital Center
Prgm Director: Lizica C Troneci, MD
1276 Fulton Avenue, 4 South
Bronx, NY 10456
Tel: 718 901-6488   *Fax:* 718 901-8656
Length: 4 Yrs   *ACGME Approved/Offered Positions:* 24
Program ID: 400-35-21-135

Albert Einstein College of Medicine Program

Sponsor: Albert Einstein College of Medicine of Yeshiva University
Bronx Psychiatric Center
Montefiore Medical Center-Henry and Lucy Moses Division
Prgm Director: Peter Buckley, MD
Department of Psychiatry & Behavioral Sciences
3331 Bainbridge Avenue
Bronx, NY 10467
Tel: 718 920-7967   *Fax:* 718 882-3185
Length: 4 Yrs   *ACGME Approved/Offered Positions:* 48
Program ID: 400-35-11-131

Lincoln Medical and Mental Health Center Program

Sponsor: Lincoln Medical and Mental Health Center
Prgm Director: Brian Ladds, MD
234 East 149th Street
Bronx, NY 10451
Tel: 718 579-4883   *Fax:* 718 579-4860
E-mail: brian.ladds@nychhc.org
Length: 4 Yrs   *ACGME Approved/Offered Positions:* 13
Program ID: 400-35-11-133

Brooklyn

Brookdale University Hospital and Medical Center Program

Sponsor: Brookdale University Hospital and Medical Center
Prgm Director: Pierre Jean-Noel, MD, MBA
One Brookdale Plaza
Brooklyn, NY 11212
Tel: 718 240-5469   *Fax:* 718 240-5451
E-mail: pjeannoe@brookdale.edu
Length: 4 Yrs   *ACGME Approved/Offered Positions:* 20
Program ID: 400-35-11-136

Maimonides Medical Center Program

Sponsor: Maimonides Medical Center
Prgm Director: Barry S Rand, MD
4802 Tenth Avenue
Brooklyn, NY 11219
Tel: 718 283-8181   *Fax:* 718 283-8567
E-mail: brand@maimonidesmed.org
Length: 4 Yrs   *ACGME Approved/Offered Positions:* 27
Program ID: 400-35-21-143

SUNY Health Science Center at Brooklyn Program

Sponsor: SUNY Health Science Center at Brooklyn
Kings County Hospital Center
Prgm Director: Michael F Myers, MD*
450 Clarkson Avenue, Box 1203
Brooklyn, NY 11203
Tel: 718 270-2902
E-mail: michael.myers@downstate.edu
Length: 4 Yrs   *ACGME Approved/Offered Positions:* 40
Program ID: 400-35-21-154

Buffalo

University at Buffalo Program

Sponsor: University at Buffalo School of Medicine
Buffalo Psychiatric Center
Erie County Medical Center
Kaleida Health System (Buffalo General Hospital)
Kaleida Health System (Millard Fillmore Hospital)
Kaleida Health System (Women and Children's Hosp of Buffalo)
Veterans Affairs Western New York Hospital
Prgm Director: Cynthia A Pristach, MD
462 Grider Street
Buffalo, NY 14215
Tel: 716 898-4221   *Fax:* 716 898-4538
E-mail: sunypsyres@aol.com
Length: 4 Yrs   *ACGME Approved/Offered Positions:* 28
Program ID: 400-35-21-126

East Meadow

Nassau University Medical Center Program

Sponsor: Nassau University Medical Center
Prgm Director: Jacob E Sperber, MD
2201 Hempstead Turnpike
East Meadow, NY 11554
Tel: 516 572-6511   *Fax:* 516 572-3210
E-mail: jsperber@numc.edu
Length: 4 Yrs   *ACGME Approved/Offered Positions:* 28
Program ID: 400-35-11-128

Elmhurst

Mount Sinai School of Medicine (Elmhurst) Program

Sponsor: Mount Sinai School of Medicine
Elmhurst Hospital Center-Mount Sinai Services
Prgm Director: David B Schnur, MD*
Elmhurst Hospital Center
79-01 Broadway, Room H3-135
Elmhurst, NY 11373
Tel: 718 334-3268   *Fax:* 718 334-3441
Length: 4 Yrs   *ACGME Approved/Offered Positions:* 29
Program ID: 400-35-11-242

Note: * indicates a newly appointed program director

Great Neck

NSLIJHS-Albert Einstein College of Medicine at Long Island Jewish Medical Center Program

Sponsor: North Shore-Long Island Jewish Health System
Hillside Hospital (Long Island Jewish Medical Center)
Prgm Director: Bruce R Levy, MD
75-59 263rd Street
Glen Oaks, NY 11004
Tel: 718 470-8005   *Fax:* 718 962-7717
E-mail: dwinheim@lij.edu
Length: 4 Yrs   *ACGME Approved/Offered Positions:* 68
Program ID: 400-35-21-142

Jamaica

Jamaica Hospital Medical Center Program

Sponsor: Jamaica Hospital Medical Center
Brookdale University Hospital and Medical Center
Flushing Hospital Medical Center
Prgm Director: Richard S Deucher, MD
8900 Van Wyck Expressway
Jamaica, NY 11418
Tel: 718 206-7708   *Fax:* 718 291-2066
Length: 4 Yrs   *ACGME Approved/Offered Positions:* 16
Program ID: 400-35-13-294

New York

Albert Einstein College of Medicine at Beth Israel Medical Center Program

Sponsor: Beth Israel Medical Center
Prgm Director: David M Roane, MD
First Avenue at 16th Street
Fierman Hall 9th Floor
New York, NY 10003
Tel: 212 420-2318   *Fax:* 212 420-3442
E-mail: psyresident@chpnet.org
Length: 4 Yrs   *ACGME Approved/Offered Positions:* 47
Program ID: 400-35-11-134

Harlem Hospital Center Program

Sponsor: Harlem Hospital Center
Prgm Director: James McKnight, MD*
506 Lenox Avenue
Womens Pavilion 540
New York, NY 10037
Tel: 212 939-3060
E-mail: jvc960@aol.com
Length: 4 Yrs   *ACGME Approved/Offered Positions:* 28
Program ID: 400-35-11-140

Mount Sinai School of Medicine (North General) Program

Sponsor: Mount Sinai School of Medicine
North General Hospital
Prgm Director: Sabina Singh, MD
1879 Madison Avenue
New York, NY 10035
Tel: 212 423-4414   *Fax:* 212 423-4095
E-mail: sabina.singh@ngsc.org
Length: 4 Yrs   *ACGME Approved/Offered Positions:* 20
Program ID: 400-35-31-278

Mount Sinai School of Medicine Program

Sponsor: Mount Sinai School of Medicine
Mount Sinai Medical Center
Veterans Affairs Medical Center (Bronx)
Prgm Director: Ronald O Rieder, MD
One Gustave L Levy Place
Box 1230
New York, NY 10029
Tel: 212 659-8792   *Fax:* 212 849-2509
Length: 4 Yrs   *ACGME Approved/Offered Positions:* 45
Program ID: 400-35-11-146

New York Medical College (Metropolitan) Program

Sponsor: New York Medical College
Metropolitan Hospital Center
Prgm Director: Charmaine Rapaport, MD*
Room 4M4
1901 First Avenue
New York, NY 10029
Tel: 212 423-7061   *Fax:* 212 423-6341
Length: 4 Yrs   *ACGME Approved/Offered Positions:* 26
Program ID: 400-35-11-148

New York Medical College at St Vincent's Hospital and Medical Center of New York Program

Sponsor: New York Medical College
St Vincent Catholic Medical Centers (Manhattan)
Prgm Director: Scot McAfee, MD
Reiss Pavilion, Room 175
144 West 12th Street
New York, NY 10011
Tel: 212 604-8795   *Fax:* 212 604-8197
Length: 4 Yrs   *ACGME Approved/Offered Positions:* 46
Program ID: 400-35-12-152

New York Presbyterian Hospital (Columbia Campus)/New York State Psychiatric Institute Program

Sponsor: New York Presbyterian Hospital
New York Presbyterian Hospital (Columbia Campus)
New York State Psychiatric Institute
Prgm Director: Maria A Oquendo, MD*
1051 Riverside Drive
Unit 103
New York, NY 10032
Tel: 212 543-5835   *Fax:* 212 543-6017
E-mail: perezal@pi.cpmc.columbia.edu
Length: 4 Yrs   *ACGME Approved/Offered Positions:* 50
Program ID: 400-35-21-138

New York Presbyterian Hospital (Cornell Campus) Program

Sponsor: New York Presbyterian Hospital
New York Presbyterian Hospital (Cornell Campus)
Prgm Director: Elizabeth L Auchincloss, MD
525 East 68th Street, Box 140
Room - Baker 1202
New York, NY 10065
Tel: 212 746-3722   *Fax:* 212 746-8886
E-mail: elauchin@med.cornell.edu
Length: 4 Yrs   *ACGME Approved/Offered Positions:* 48
Program ID: 400-35-11-147

New York University School of Medicine Program

Sponsor: New York University School of Medicine
Bellevue Hospital Center
Lenox Hill Hospital
Manhattan Psychiatric Center
Manhattan VA Harbor Health Care System
NYU Hospitals Center
Prgm Director: Ze'ev Levin, MD
Department of Psychiatry
550 First Avenue (NBV 20 N 11)
New York, NY 10016
Tel: 212 263-6238   *Fax:* 212 263-6497
Length: 4 Yrs   *ACGME Approved/Offered Positions:* 75
Program ID: 400-35-21-149

St Luke's-Roosevelt Hospital Center Program

Sponsor: St Luke's-Roosevelt Hospital Center
St Luke's-Roosevelt Hospital Center-Roosevelt Division
St Luke's-Roosevelt Hospital Center-St Luke's Division
Prgm Director: Prameet Singh, MBBS
1090 Amsterdam Avenue 16F
New York, NY 10025
Tel: 212 523-5089   *Fax:* 212 523-1685
Length: 4 Yrs   *ACGME Approved/Offered Positions:* 36
Program ID: 400-35-21-270

Queens Village

Creedmoor Psychiatric Center Program

Sponsor: Creedmoor Psychiatric Center
Caritas Health Care (Brooklyn-Queens)
New York Presbyterian Hospital (Columbia Campus)
Prgm Director: Mark F Sorensen, MD
79-25 Winchester Boulevard
Building 40, Ward 2A
Queens Village, NY 11427
Tel: 718 264-5030   *Fax:* 718 264-5027
E-mail: crmdmfs@omh.state.ny.us
Length: 4 Yrs   *ACGME Approved/Offered Positions:* 16
Program ID: 400-35-12-139

Rochester

University of Rochester Program

Sponsor: Strong Memorial Hospital of the University of Rochester
Prgm Director: Sue K DiGiovanni, MD
300 Crittenden Boulevard
Rochester, NY 14642
Tel: 585 275-7056   *Fax:* 585 276-2292
E-mail: marylee_gramlich@urmc.rochester.edu
Length: 4 Yrs   *ACGME Approved/Offered Positions:* 16
Program ID: 400-35-11-158

Staten Island

New York Medical College (Richmond) Program

Sponsor: New York Medical College
Richmond University Medical Center
Prgm Director: Pankaj R Patel, MD
355 Bard Avenue
Staten Island, NY 10310
Tel: 718 818-4112   *Fax:* 718 818-4671
E-mail: ppatel@rumcsi.org
Length: 4 Yrs   *ACGME Approved/Offered Positions:* 20
Program ID: 400-35-12-153

Stony Brook

SUNY at Stony Brook Program

Sponsor: University Hospital - SUNY at Stony Brook
Prgm Director: Michael Schwartz, MD
T-10, Room 020
Stony Brook, NY 11794
Tel: 631 444-3005   *Fax:* 631 444-7534
Length: 4 Yrs   *ACGME Approved/Offered Positions:* 24
Program ID: 400-35-21-159

Syracuse

SUNY Upstate Medical University Program

Sponsor: SUNY Upstate Medical University
Veterans Affairs Medical Center (Syracuse)
Prgm Director: John M Manring, MD
750 East Adams Street
Syracuse, NY 13210
Tel: 315 464-3106   *Fax:* 315 464-3163
E-mail: GallingL@upstate.edu
Length: 4 Yrs   *ACGME Approved/Offered Positions:* 26
Program ID: 400-35-21-160

Valhalla

New York Medical College at Westchester Medical Center Program

Sponsor: New York Medical College
Danbury Hospital
St Vincent Catholic Medical Centers (Westchester)
Westchester Medical Center
Prgm Director: Wendy L Thompson, MD
Westchester Medical Center
Beh Health Center 3rd Floor Residency Training
Valhalla, NY 10595
Tel: 914 493-1863   *Fax:* 914 493-1015
E-mail: thompsonw@wcmc.com
Length: 4 Yrs   *ACGME Approved/Offered Positions:* 40
Program ID: 400-35-21-162

North Carolina

Chapel Hill

University of North Carolina Hospitals Program

Sponsor: University of North Carolina Hospitals
Central Regional Hospital (Raleigh Campus)
Prgm Director: Karon Dawkins, MD
Department of Psychiatry
CB 7160, 10625 Neurosciences Hospital
Chapel Hill, NC 27599
Tel: 919 966-4764   *Fax:* 919 966-2220
Length: 4 Yrs   *ACGME Approved/Offered Positions:* 60
Program ID: 400-36-21-166

Durham

Duke University Hospital Program

Sponsor: Duke University Hospital
Veterans Affairs Medical Center (Durham)
Prgm Director: Grace Thrall, MD
Box 3837
Durham, NC 27710
Tel: 919 684-2258   *Fax:* 919 684-2290
Length: 4 Yrs   *ACGME Approved/Offered Positions:* 64
Program ID: 400-36-21-167

Greenville

Pitt County Memorial Hospital/East Carolina University Program

Sponsor: Pitt County Memorial Hospital
Brody School of Medicine at East Carolina University
Prgm Director: Diana J Antonacci, MD
ECU Outpatient Clinic
905 Johns Hopkins Drive
Greenville, NC 27834
Tel: 252 744-2663   *Fax:* 252 744-4237
E-mail: antonaccid@ecu.edu
Length: 4 Yrs   *ACGME Approved/Offered Positions:* 32
Program ID: 400-36-21-169

Winston-Salem

Wake Forest University School of Medicine Program

Sponsor: Wake Forest University Baptist Medical Center
WG (Bill) Hefner VA Medical Center
Prgm Director: Harold W Elliott, MD
Medical Center Boulevard
Winston-Salem, NC 27157
Tel: 336 716-4551   *Fax:* 336 716-6830
E-mail: helliott@wfubmc.edu
Length: 4 Yrs   *ACGME Approved/Offered Positions:* 24
Program ID: 400-36-21-171

North Dakota

Fargo

University of North Dakota Program

Sponsor: Univ of North Dakota School of Medicine and Health Sciences
Veterans Affairs Medical and Regional Office Center (Fargo)
MeritCare Health System
Prgm Director: David W Abbott, MD
1919 Elm Street North
Fargo, ND 58102
Tel: 701 293-4113   *Fax:* 701 293-4109
E-mail: psychres@medicine.nodak.edu
Length: 4 Yrs   *ACGME Approved/Offered Positions:* 16
Program ID: 400-37-21-251

Ohio

Cincinnati

University Hospital/University of Cincinnati College of Medicine Program

Sponsor: University Hospital Inc
Veterans Affairs Medical Center (Cincinnati)
Prgm Director: Aurora J Bennett, MD*
Psychiatry Residency Training Program
PO Box 670559
Cincinnati, OH 45267
Tel: 513 558-4004   *Fax:* 513 558-3477
Length: 4 Yrs   *ACGME Approved/Offered Positions:* 36
Program ID: 400-38-21-173

Cleveland

Case Western Reserve University (MetroHealth) Program

Sponsor: MetroHealth Medical Center
Prgm Director: Toni Love Johnson, MD
2500 MetroHealth Drive
Cleveland, OH 44109
Tel: 216 778-4973   *Fax:* 216 778-2397
E-mail: psychresident@metrohealth.org
Length: 4 Yrs   *ACGME Approved/Offered Positions:* 20
Program ID: 400-38-21-240

Cleveland Clinic Foundation Program

Sponsor: Cleveland Clinic Foundation
Prgm Director: David W Streem, MD
9500 Euclid Avenue, P57
Cleveland, OH 44195
Tel: 216 444-5851   *Fax:* 216 445-3879
E-mail: psyched@ccf.org
Length: 4 Yrs   *ACGME Approved/Offered Positions:* 24
Program ID: 400-38-22-175

University Hospitals Case Medical Center Program

Sponsor: University Hospitals Case Medical Center
Mental Health Services (Cleveland)
UHHS Richmond Hts Hospital
Veterans Affairs Medical Center (Cleveland)
Prgm Director: Susan J Stagno, MD*
10524 Euclid Avenue
8th Floor
Cleveland, OH 44106
Tel: 216 844-3450   *Fax:* 216 844-4741
E-mail: tamika.williams@uhhospitals.org
Length: 4 Yrs   *ACGME Approved/Offered Positions:* 32
Program ID: 400-38-21-174

Columbus

Ohio State University Hospital Program

Sponsor: Ohio State University Hospital
Prgm Director: Julie A Niedermier, MD
Neuroscience Facility, Suite 140
1670 Upham Drive
Columbus, OH 43210
Tel: 614 293-4540   *Fax:* 614 293-4200
E-mail: Julie.Niedermier@osumc.edu
Length: 4 Yrs   *ACGME Approved/Offered Positions:* 24
Program ID: 400-38-21-281

Dayton

Wright State University Program

Sponsor: Wright State University Boonshoft School of Medicine
Good Samaritan Hospital and Health Center
Kettering Medical Center
Miami Valley Hospital
Veterans Affairs Medical Center (Dayton)
Wright - Patterson Medical Center
Prgm Director: David G Bienenfeld, MD
PO Box 927
Dayton, OH 45401
Tel: 937 223-8840   *Fax:* 937 223-0758
E-mail: David.Bienenfeld@wright.edu
Length: 4 Yrs   *ACGME Approved/Offered Positions:* 40
Program ID: 400-38-21-178

Rootstown

Northeastern Ohio Universities College of Medicine Program

Sponsor: Northeastern Ohio Universities College of Medicine
Akron General Medical Center
Prgm Director: Joseph D Varley, MD
400 Wabash Avenue
Akron, OH 44307
Tel: 330 344-6511   *Fax:* 330 996-2943
E-mail: jonesw@summa-health.org
Length: 4 Yrs   *ACGME Approved/Offered Positions:* 17
Program ID: 400-38-21-180

Toledo

University of Toledo Program

Sponsor: University of Toledo
Northcoast Behavioral Healthcare (Toledo Campus)
University Medical Center (Toledo)
Prgm Director: Kristi S Williams, MD
Department of Psychiatry
3000 Arlington Avenue, MS 1193
Toledo, OH 43614
Tel: 419 383-5674   *Fax:* 419 383-3183
E-mail: Kristi.Williams@Utoledo.edu
Length: 4 Yrs   *ACGME Approved/Offered Positions:* 14
Program ID: 400-38-21-181

Oklahoma

Norman

Griffin Memorial Hospital Program

Sponsor: Griffin Memorial Hospital
Central Oklahoma Community Mental Health Center
St Anthony Hospital
Prgm Director: Lori L Hake, DO*
900 East Main
PO Box 151
Norman, OK 73070
Tel: 405 573-6602   *Fax:* 405 573-6684
E-mail: nsnodgra@odmhsas.org
Length: 4 Yrs   *ACGME Approved/Offered Positions:* 20
Program ID: 400-39-21-183

Note: * indicates a newly appointed program director

Oklahoma City

University of Oklahoma Health Sciences Center Program
Sponsor: University of Oklahoma College of Medicine
OU Medical Center
Veterans Affairs Medical Center (Oklahoma City)
Prgm Director: Theresa S Garton, MD*
Dept of Psychiatry & Behavioral Sciences
PO Box 26901, WP 3440
Oklahoma City, OK 73190
Tel: 405 271-5121   *Fax:* 405 271-8775
E-mail: theresa-garton@ouhsc.edu
Length: 4 Yrs   *ACGME Approved/Offered Positions:* 16
Program ID: 400-39-21-184

Tulsa

University of Oklahoma College of Medicine-Tulsa Program
Sponsor: University of Oklahoma College of Medicine-Tulsa
Laureate Psychiatric Clinic and Hospital
Prgm Director: Bryan K Touchet, MD*
Suite 2F09
4502 E 41st Street
Tulsa, OK 74135
Tel: 918 660-3518   *Fax:* 918 660-3517
Length: 4 Yrs   *ACGME Approved/Offered Positions:* 22
Program ID: 400-39-21-246

Oregon

Portland

Oregon Health & Science University Program
Sponsor: Oregon Health & Science University Hospital
Veterans Affairs Medical Center (Portland)
Prgm Director: Donald Rosen, MD
3181 SW Sam Jackson Park Road
UHN 80
Portland, OR 97239
Tel: 503 494-6149   *Fax:* 503 494-6152
E-mail: garbol@ohsu.edu
Length: 4 Yrs   *ACGME Approved/Offered Positions:* 33
Program ID: 400-40-21-185

Pennsylvania

Hershey

Penn State University/Milton S Hershey Medical Center Program
Sponsor: Milton S Hershey Medical Center
Pennsylvania Psychiatric Institute
Prgm Director: Ravi Singareddy, MBBS*
Department of Psychiatry MC H073, PO Box 850
Hershey, PA 17033
Tel: 717 531-8136   *Fax:* 717 531-6491
E-mail: rsingareddy@hmc.psu.edu
Length: 4 Yrs   *ACGME Approved/Offered Positions:* 22
Program ID: 400-41-11-187

Philadelphia

Albert Einstein Healthcare Network Program
Sponsor: Albert Einstein Medical Center
Belmont Center for Comprehensive Treatment
Prgm Director: Kimberly R Best, MD
5501 Old York Road
Philadelphia, PA 19141
Tel: 215 456-9015   *Fax:* 215 456-9105
E-mail: psychres@einstein.edu
Length: 4 Yrs   *ACGME Approved/Offered Positions:* 36
Program ID: 400-41-31-189

Drexel University College of Medicine/Hahnemann University Hospital Program
Sponsor: Drexel University College of Medicine/Hahnemann University
Friends Hospital
Hahnemann University Hospital (Tenet Health System)
Northwestern Human Services of Philadelphia
Prgm Director: R Bryan Chambliss, MD
4641 Roosevelt Boulevard
PO Box 45358
Philadelphia, PA 19124
Tel: 215 831-7841   *Fax:* 215 831-5042
E-mail: r.chambliss@drexelmed.edu
Length: 4 Yrs   *ACGME Approved/Offered Positions:* 32
Program ID: 400-41-21-192

Temple University Hospital Program
Sponsor: Temple University Hospital
Episcopal Hospital (TUHS)
Prgm Director: Ellen H Sholevar, MD
Suite 105, Medical Arts Building
100 East Lehigh Avenue
Philadelphia, PA 19125
Tel: 215 707-8495   *Fax:* 215 707-0726
E-mail: psychres@temple.edu
Length: 4 Yrs   *ACGME Approved/Offered Positions:* 32
Program ID: 400-41-21-195

Thomas Jefferson University Program
Sponsor: Thomas Jefferson University Hospital
Prgm Director: Kenneth M Certa, MD
833 Chestnut Street
Suite 210
Philadelphia, PA 19107
Tel: 215 955-6655   *Fax:* 215 503-2853
E-mail: kenneth.certa@jefferson.edu
Length: 4 Yrs   *ACGME Approved/Offered Positions:* 36
Program ID: 400-41-21-196

University of Pennsylvania Program
Sponsor: University of Pennsylvania Health System
Pennsylvania Hospital (UPHS)
Veterans Affairs Medical Center (Philadelphia)
Prgm Director: Anthony Rostain, MD, MA
3535 Market Street
2nd Floor
Philadelphia, PA 19104
Tel: 215 746-7210   *Fax:* 215 746-7204
E-mail: rostain@mail.med.upenn.edu
Length: 4 Yrs   *ACGME Approved/Offered Positions:* 42
Program ID: 400-41-21-197

Pittsburgh

Allegheny General Hospital Program
Sponsor: Allegheny General Hospital
Prgm Director: Gary Swanson, MD
320 East North Avenue
Pittsburgh, PA 15212
Tel: 412 330-4242   *Fax:* 412 330-4010
Length: 4 Yrs   *ACGME Approved/Offered Positions:* 16
Program ID: 400-41-21-272

University of Pittsburgh Medical Center Medical Education Program
Sponsor: Univ of Pittsburgh Medical Center Medical Education
UPMC McKeesport
UPMC Western Psychiatric Institute and Clinic
Prgm Director: Michael J Travis, MD
3811 O'Hara Street
Pittsburgh, PA 15213
Tel: 412 246-5320   *Fax:* 412 246-5335
E-mail: wpic_ort@upmc.edu
Length: 4 Yrs   *ACGME Approved/Offered Positions:* 60
Program ID: 400-41-31-198

Puerto Rico

Ponce

Ponce School of Medicine Program
Sponsor: Ponce School of Medicine
Ponce School Mental Health Clinics
VA Caribbean Healthcare System
Prgm Director: Ana I Torres, MD
VA CHCS Department of Psychiatry (116A)
10 Casia Street
San Juan, PR 00921
Tel: 787 641-7582   *Fax:* 787 641-4555
E-mail: antorres@psm.edu
Length: 4 Yrs   *ACGME Approved/Offered Positions:* 16
Program ID: 400-42-12-296

San Juan

University of Puerto Rico Program
Sponsor: University of Puerto Rico School of Medicine
First Hospital Panamericano
University of Puerto Rico Hospital at Carolina
University Pediatric Hospital
Prgm Director: Luz N Colon de Marti, MD
PO Box 365067
San Juan, PR 00936
Tel: 787 766-0940   *Fax:* 787 766-0940
Length: 4 Yrs   *ACGME Approved/Offered Positions:* 24
Program ID: 400-42-31-201

Rhode Island

Providence

Brown University (Butler Hospital) Program
Sponsor: Butler Hospital
Miriam Hospital-Lifespan
Rhode Island Hospital-Lifespan
Veterans Affairs Medical Center (Providence)
Prgm Director: Jane Eisen, MD
345 Blackstone Boulevard
Providence, RI 02906
Tel: 401 455-6375   *Fax:* 401 455-6497
E-mail: Psychiatry_Residency@brown.edu
Length: 4 Yrs   *ACGME Approved/Offered Positions:* 39
Program ID: 400-43-21-203

South Carolina

Charleston

Medical University of South Carolina Program
Sponsor: Medical University of South Carolina College of Medicine
MUSC Medical Center
Ralph H Johnson VA Medical Center (Charleston)
Prgm Director: Alberto B Santos, MA, MD
171 Ashley Avenue
PO Box 250861
Charleston, SC 29425
Tel: 843 792-0192   *Fax:* 843 792-6894
E-mail: pucalm@musc.edu
Length: 4 Yrs   *ACGME Approved/Offered Positions:* 52
Program ID: 400-45-21-204

Columbia

Palmetto Health/University of South Carolina School of Medicine Program
Sponsor: Palmetto Health
Palmetto Health Baptist
Palmetto Health Richland
University of South Carolina School of Medicine
William Jennings Bryan Dorn Veterans Hospital
Prgm Director: Nioaka N Campbell, MD
15 Medical Park, Suite 141
3555 Harden Street
Columbia, SC 29203
Tel: 803 434-1433   *Fax:* 803 434-4062
E-mail: donnak.smith@palmettohealth.org
Length: 4 Yrs   *ACGME Approved/Offered Positions:* 26
Program ID: 400-45-31-205

South Dakota

Sioux Falls

University of South Dakota Program
Sponsor: University of South Dakota School of Medicine
Avera McKennan Hospital and University Health Center
Royal C Johnson Veterans Affairs Medical Center
Prgm Director: Heather Chester-Adam, MD*
4400 West 69th Street
Suite 1500
Sioux Falls, SD 57108
Tel: 605 322-5707   *Fax:* 605 322-5736
Length: 4 Yrs   *ACGME Approved/Offered Positions:* 18
Program ID: 400-46-21-260

Tennessee

Johnson City

East Tennessee State University Program
Sponsor: James H Quillen College of Medicine
Johnson City Medical Center/Mountain States Health
 Alliance
Veterans Affairs Medical Center (Mountain Home)
Woodridge Hospital/Mountain States Health Alliance
Prgm Director: Hetal K Brahmbhatt, MD
Box 70567
Veterans Affairs Medical Center Campus
Johnson City, TN 37614
Tel: 423 439-2225   *Fax:* 423 439-2250
E-mail: brahmbha@etsu.edu
Length: 4 Yrs   *ACGME Approved/Offered Positions:* 25
Program ID: 400-47-21-258

Memphis

University of Tennessee Program
Sponsor: University of Tennessee College of Medicine
Regional Medical Center at Memphis
University of Tennessee Medical Center
Veterans Affairs Medical Center (Memphis)
Prgm Director: Allesa Jackson-English, MD*
135 North Pauline, 1st Floor
Memphis, TN 38105
Tel: 901 448-4567   *Fax:* 901 448-2968
Length: 4 Yrs   *ACGME Approved/Offered Positions:* 16
Program ID: 400-47-21-206

Nashville

Meharry Medical College Program
Sponsor: Meharry Medical College School of Medicine
Alvin C York Veterans Affairs Medical Center
Middle Tennessee Mental Health Institute
Prgm Director: Shagufta Jabeen, MD
1005 Dr D B Todd Jr Blvd
Nashville, TN 37208
Tel: 615 327-6491   *Fax:* 615 327-6260
E-mail: sjabeen@mmc.edu
Length: 4 Yrs   *ACGME Approved/Offered Positions:* 18
Program ID: 400-47-21-207

Vanderbilt University Program
Sponsor: Vanderbilt University Medical Center
Veterans Affairs Medical Center (Nashville)
Prgm Director: Jeffrey G Stovall, MD*
Vanderbilt Psychiatric Hospital
1601 23rd Ave South, Ste 3105
Nashville, TN 37212
Tel: 615 343-3840   *Fax:* 615 327-7136
Length: 4 Yrs   *ACGME Approved/Offered Positions:* 32
Program ID: 400-47-11-208

Texas

Austin

Austin Medical Education Programs of Seton Healthcare Network Program
Sponsor: Austin Medical Education Program of Seton
 Healthcare Network
Seton Shoal Creek Hospital
University Medical Center at Brackenridge
Prgm Director: Kari M Wolf, MD
Seton Shoal Creek Hospital
3501 Mills Avenue
Austin, TX 78731
Tel: 512 324-2036   *Fax:* 512 324-2084
E-mail: tpowell@seton.org
Length: 4 Yrs   *ACGME Approved/Offered Positions:* 24
Program ID: 400-48-13-299

Dallas

University of Texas Southwestern Medical School Program
Sponsor: University of Texas Southwestern Medical
 School
Dallas County Hospital District-Parkland Memorial
 Hospital
Dallas VA Medical Center
Texas Health Presbyterian Dallas
University Hospitals Zale Lipshy
Prgm Director: Paul C Mohl, MD
5323 Harry Hines Boulevard
Dallas, TX 75390
Tel: 214 648-7312
Length: 4 Yrs   *ACGME Approved/Offered Positions:* 68
Program ID: 400-48-21-211

El Paso

Texas Tech University Health Sciences Center Paul L Foster School of Medicine Program
Sponsor: Texas Tech University Hlth Sci Ctr Paul L
 Foster Sch of Med
El Paso Psychiatric Center
Prgm Director: Frank L Giordano, MD
Department of Neuropsychiatry
4800 Alberta Avenue
El Paso, TX 79905
Tel: 915 545-6834   *Fax:* 915 545-6442
E-mail: debi.grady@ttuhsc.edu
Length: 4 Yrs   *ACGME Approved/Offered Positions:* 12
Program ID: 400-48-11-217

Fort Worth

John Peter Smith Hospital (Tarrant County Hospital District) Program
Sponsor: John Peter Smith Hospital (Tarrant County
 Hospital District)
Prgm Director: A Scott Winter, MD
John Peter Smith Hospital
1500 South Main Street
Fort Worth, TX 76104
Tel: 817 927-3636   *Fax:* 817 923-8769
E-mail: swinter@jpshealth.org
Length: 4 Yrs   *ACGME Approved/Offered Positions:* 16
Program ID: 400-48-21-282

Galveston

University of Texas Medical Branch Hospitals Program
Sponsor: University of Texas Medical Branch Hospitals
Prgm Director: Cindy L Wigg, MD
Department of Psychiatry
301 University Blvd
Galveston, TX 77555
Tel: 409 747-9786   *Fax:* 409 747-9788
E-mail: cwigg@utmb.edu
Length: 4 Yrs   *ACGME Approved/Offered Positions:* 32
Program ID: 400-48-11-212

Houston

Baylor College of Medicine Program
Sponsor: Baylor College of Medicine
Harris County Hospital District-Ben Taub General
 Hospital
Michael E DeBakey VA Medical Center - Houston
Prgm Director: Kim-Lan Czelusta, MD
One Baylor Plaza BCM 350
Houston, TX 77030
Tel: 713 798-4872   *Fax:* 713 798-1479
E-mail: kfore@bcm.edu
Length: 4 Yrs   *ACGME Approved/Offered Positions:* 51
Program ID: 400-48-21-213

University of Texas at Houston Program
Sponsor: University of Texas Health Science Center at
 Houston
Harris County Psychiatric Center
Memorial Hermann Hospital
Prgm Director: Anu A Matorin, MD
1300 Moursund, Room 267A
Houston, TX 77030
Tel: 713 500-2570
E-mail: restrain@uth.tmc.edu
Length: 4 Yrs   *ACGME Approved/Offered Positions:* 48
Program ID: 400-48-31-215

Lubbock

Texas Tech University (Lubbock) Program
Sponsor: Texas Tech University Health Sciences Center
 at Lubbock
University Medical Center
Prgm Director: Terry C McMahon, MD
3601 4th Street
Psychiatry, MS 8103
Lubbock, TX 79430
Tel: 806 743-2800   *Fax:* 806 743-4250
Length: 4 Yrs   *ACGME Approved/Offered Positions:* 16
Program ID: 400-48-21-256

Note: * indicates a newly appointed program director

San Antonio

University of Texas Health Science Center at San Antonio Program

Sponsor: University of Texas School of Medicine at San Antonio
Audie L Murphy Memorial Veterans Hospital (San Antonio)
University Health System
Wilford Hall Medical Center (AETC)
Prgm Director: Kenneth L Matthews, MD
7703 Floyd Curl Drive
San Antonio, TX 78229
Tel: 210 567-5430   *Fax:* 210 567-0817
E-mail: cardenasy@uthscsa.edu
Length: 4 Yrs   *ACGME Approved/Offered Positions:* 78
Program ID: 400-48-31-218

Temple

Texas A&M College of Medicine-Scott and White Program

Sponsor: Scott and White Memorial Hospital
Central Texas Veterans Affairs Healthcare System
Prgm Director: Jane Ripperger-Suhler, MD
Department of Psychiatry
2401 South 31st Street
Temple, TX 76508
Tel: 254 724-1768   *Fax:* 254 724-2949
E-mail: dwinkler@swmail.sw.org
Length: 4 Yrs   *ACGME Approved/Offered Positions:* 20
Program ID: 400-48-21-276

Utah

Salt Lake City

University of Utah Program

Sponsor: University of Utah Medical Center
University of Utah Counseling Center
University of Utah Neuropsychiatric Institute
Valley Mental Health
Veterans Affairs Medical Center (Salt Lake City)
Prgm Director: Meredith Alden, MD, PhD
30 North 1900 East
Salt Lake City, UT 84132
Tel: 801 581-4096   *Fax:* 801 581-5604
Length: 4 Yrs   *ACGME Approved/Offered Positions:* 24
Program ID: 400-49-21-219

Vermont

Burlington

University of Vermont Program

Sponsor: Fletcher Allen Health Care
Prgm Director: Richard A Bernstein, MD
111 Colchester Ave, Patrick 428
Burlington, VT 05401
Tel: 802 847-2259   *Fax:* 802 847-2733
E-mail: psychiatryresidency@vtmednet.org
Length: 4 Yrs   *ACGME Approved/Offered Positions:* 16
Program ID: 400-50-11-241

Virginia

Charlottesville

University of Virginia Program

Sponsor: University of Virginia Medical Center
Prgm Director: Zachariah C Dameron III, MD*
PO Box 800623
Charlottesville, VA 22908
Tel: 434 924-5408   *Fax:* 434 924-5149
E-mail: dameron@virginia.edu
Length: 4 Yrs   *ACGME Approved/Offered Positions:* 48
Program ID: 400-51-21-220

Norfolk

Eastern Virginia Medical School Program

Sponsor: Eastern Virginia Medical School
Sentara Norfolk General Hospital
Veterans Affairs Medical Center (Hampton)
Virginia Beach Comprehensive Mental Health Services
Prgm Director: Edwin E Gatewood III, MD
358 Mowbray Arch, Ste 203
Norfolk, VA 23507
Tel: 757 446-5884   *Fax:* 757 446-5918
Length: 4 Yrs   *ACGME Approved/Offered Positions:* 16
Program ID: 400-51-21-221

Portsmouth

Naval Medical Center (Portsmouth) Program

Sponsor: Naval Medical Center (Portsmouth)
Prgm Director: Gail H Manos, MD
620 John Paul Jones Circle
Portsmouth, VA 23708
Tel: 757 953-5260   *Fax:* 757 953-5275
E-mail: ghmanos@cox.net
Length: 4 Yrs   *ACGME Approved/Offered Positions:* 18
Program ID: 400-51-12-007
Uniformed Services Program

Richmond

Virginia Commonwealth University Health System Program

Sponsor: Virginia Commonwealth University Health System
Hunter Holmes McGuire VA Medical Center (Richmond)
MCV-Virginia Treatment Center for Children
Medical College of Virginia Hospitals
Prgm Director: John R Urbach, MD
1200 East Broad Street
PO Box 980710
Richmond, VA 23298
Tel: 804 828-7912   *Fax:* 804 828-1474
E-mail: cdyeatts@vcu.edu
Length: 4 Yrs   *ACGME Approved/Offered Positions:* 38
Program ID: 400-51-21-223

Roanoke

Carilion Clinic Program

Sponsor: Carilion Clinic
Carilion Roanoke Memorial Hospital
Veterans Affairs Medical Center (Salem)
Prgm Director: Brian E Wood, DO
Dept of Psychiatry
1970 Roanoke Boulevard (116A7)
Salem, VA 24153
Tel: 540 982-2463   *Fax:* 540 983-1086
Length: 4 Yrs   *ACGME Approved/Offered Positions:* 32
Program ID: 400-51-21-267

Washington

Seattle

University of Washington Program

Sponsor: University of Washington School of Medicine
Harborview Medical Center
Sacred Heart Medical Center
University of Washington Medical Center
VA Puget Sound Health Care System
Veterans Affairs Medical Center (Boise)
Prgm Director: Deborah S Cowley, MD
Box 356560
Seattle, WA 98195
Tel: 206 543-6577   *Fax:* 206 685-8952
E-mail: dcowley@u.washington.edu
Length: 4 Yrs   *ACGME Approved/Offered Positions:* 73
Program ID: 400-54-21-225

West Virginia

Charleston

Charleston Area Medical Center/West Virginia University (Charleston Division) Program

Sponsor: Charleston Area Medical Center/West Virginia University
Prgm Director: T O Dickey III, MD
3200 MacCorkle Ave SE
Department of Behavioral Medicine/Psychiatry
Charleston, WV 25304
Tel: 304 388-1022   *Fax:* 304 388-1021
Length: 4 Yrs   *ACGME Approved/Offered Positions:* 16
Program ID: 400-55-21-264

Morgantown

West Virginia University Program

Sponsor: West Virginia University School of Medicine
West Virginia University Hospitals
Prgm Director: C Rolly Sullivan, MD*
Department of Behavioral Medicine and Psychiatry
930 Chestnut Ridge Road
Morgantown, WV 26505
Tel: 304 293-5323   *Fax:* 304 293-8724
E-mail: sbienekcate@hsc.wvu.edu
Length: 4 Yrs   *ACGME Approved/Offered Positions:* 24
Program ID: 400-55-21-226

Wisconsin

Madison

University of Wisconsin Program

Sponsor: University of Wisconsin Hospital and Clinics
William S Middleton Veterans Hospital
Prgm Director: Arthur C Walaszek, MD
6001 Research Park Blvd
Madison, WI 53719
Tel: 608 263-6106   *Fax:* 608 261-5653
E-mail: psych.residency@uwhealth.org
Length: 4 Yrs   *ACGME Approved/Offered Positions:* 32
Program ID: 400-56-21-228

Milwaukee

Medical College of Wisconsin Affiliated Hospitals Program

Sponsor: Medical College of Wisconsin Affiliated Hospitals, Inc
Clement J Zablocki Veterans Affairs Medical Center
Columbia St Mary's Hospitals
Froedtert Memorial Lutheran Hospital
Milwaukee County Behavioral Health Division
Prgm Director: Jon A Lehrmann, MD
8701 Watertown Plank Road
Milwaukee, WI 53226
Tel: 414 955-8998   *Fax:* 414 955-6299
E-mail: jlehrman@mcw.edu
Length: 4 Yrs   *ACGME Approved/Offered Positions:* 32
Program ID: 400-56-21-229

Psychosomatic Medicine (Psychiatry)

California

Los Angeles

Cedars-Sinai Medical Center/VA Greater Los Angeles Healthcare System Program
Sponsor: Cedars-Sinai Medical Center
VA Greater Los Angeles Healthcare System
Prgm Director: Thomas R Garrick, MD
11301 Wilshire Boulevard
Los Angeles, CA 90073
Tel: 310 268-3141   *Fax:* 310 268-4461
E-mail: thomas.garrick@va.gov
Length: 1 Yr   *ACGME Approved/Offered Positions:* 2
Program ID: 409-05-13-027

Sacramento

University of California (Davis) Health System Program
Sponsor: University of California (Davis) Health System
University of California (Davis) Medical Center
Prgm Director: James Bourgeois, OD, MD
2230 Stockton Boulevard
Sacramento, CA 95817
Tel: 916 734-4941   *Fax:* 916 734-3384
E-mail: james.bourgeois@ucdmc.ucdavis.edu
Length: 1 Yr   *ACGME Approved/Offered Positions:* 1
Program ID: 409-05-31-008

Colorado

Aurora

University of Colorado Denver Program
Sponsor: University of Colorado Denver School of Medicine
National Jewish Medical and Research Center
University of Colorado Hospital
Prgm Director: Alison M Heru, MD
13001 E 17th Place
Bld 500, Room E2338, Mail Stop F546
Aurora, CO 80045
Tel: 303 398-1114   *Fax:* 303 270-2115
E-mail: tammy.samuels@uchsc.edu
Length: 1 Yr   *ACGME Approved/Offered Positions:* 2
Program ID: 409-07-21-042

Connecticut

Hartford

Institute of Living/Hartford Hospital Program
Sponsor: Hartford Hospital
Prgm Director: Carl F Washburn Jr, MD
200 Retreat Avenue
Hartford, CT 06106
Tel: 860 545-7183   *Fax:* 860 545-7403
E-mail: cwashbu@harthosp.org
Length: 1 Yr   *ACGME Approved/Offered Positions:* 2
Program ID: 409-08-12-003

New Haven

Yale-New Haven Medical Center Program
Sponsor: Yale-New Haven Hospital
Veterans Affairs Medical Center (West Haven)
Prgm Director: Paul Desan, MD, PhD
20 York Street CB2039
New Haven, CT 06504
Tel: 203 785-2618   *Fax:* 203 737-2221
E-mail: paul.desan@yale.edu
Length: 1 Yr   *ACGME Approved/Offered Positions:* 5
Program ID: 409-08-13-031

District of Columbia

Washington

Georgetown University Hospital/Washington Hospital Center Program
Sponsor: Georgetown University Hospital
Clinical Center at the National Institutes of Health
Washington Hospital Center
Prgm Director: Steven Epstein, MD
Department of Psychiatry
3800 Reservoir Rd, NW
Washington, DC 20007
Tel: 202 784-0682   *Fax:* 202 687-6658
Length: 1 Yr   *ACGME Approved/Offered Positions:* 3
Program ID: 409-10-31-002

Florida

Miami

Jackson Memorial Hospital/Jackson Health System Program
Sponsor: Jackson Memorial Hospital/Jackson Health System
Prgm Director: Martha M Kato, MD
1695 NW 9th Avenue #2435
Miami, FL 33136
Tel: 305 355-8260   *Fax:* 305 355-7266
E-mail: mkato@med.miami.edu
Length: 1 Yr   *ACGME Approved/Offered Positions:* 2
Program ID: 409-11-13-039

Georgia

Atlanta

Emory University Program
Sponsor: Emory University School of Medicine
Emory University Hospital
Grady Health System
Veterans Affairs Medical Center (Atlanta)
Prgm Director: Raymond Young, MD*
Dept of Psychiatry, Tufts House Rm 214
2004 Ridgewood Dr
Atlanta, GA 30322
Tel: 404 728-6302   *Fax:* 404 728-6269
Length: 1 Yr   *ACGME Approved/Offered Positions:* 2
Program ID: 409-12-12-017

Louisiana

New Orleans

Louisiana State University Program
Sponsor: Louisiana State University School of Medicine
Medical Center of Louisiana at New Orleans
Prgm Director: Erich J Conrad, MD
2020 Gravier Street
7th Floor, Lions Building
New Orleans, LA 70112
Tel: 504 568-7912   *Fax:* 504 568-6006
Length: 1 Yr   *ACGME Approved/Offered Positions:* 1
Program ID: 409-21-13-043

Shreveport

Louisiana State University (Shreveport) Program
Sponsor: LSU Health Sciences Center-University Hospital
Prgm Director: Mary Jo Fitz-Gerald, MD
School of Medicine - Department of Psychiatry
1501 Kings Highway
Shreveport, LA 71130
Tel: 318 675-6040   *Fax:* 318 675-6054
Length: 1 Yr   *ACGME Approved/Offered Positions:* 1
Program ID: 409-21-31-024

Maryland

Baltimore

University of Maryland Program
Sponsor: University of Maryland Medical System
Veterans Affairs Medical Center (Baltimore)
Prgm Director: Mark J Ehrenreich, MD
Box 349, Department of Psychiatry
22 S Greene Street
Baltimore, MD 21201
Tel: 410 328-6090   *Fax:* 410 328-1757
Length: 1 Yr   *ACGME Approved/Offered Positions:* 3
Program ID: 409-23-31-010

Massachusetts

Boston

Boston University Medical Center Program
Sponsor: Boston Medical Center
Veterans Affairs Medical Center (Boston)
Prgm Director: Isidore Berenbaum, MD
88 East Newton Street, Suite B410
Boston, MA 02118
Tel: 617 638-8670   *Fax:* 617 638-8724
E-mail: bbq@bu.edu
Length: 1 Yr   *ACGME Approved/Offered Positions:* 2
Program ID: 409-24-21-007

Brigham and Women's Hospital Program
Sponsor: Brigham and Women's Hospital
Boston VA Healthcare System (Brockton-West Roxbury)
Dana-Farber Cancer Institute
Faulkner Hospital
Prgm Director: David F Gitlin, MD
75 Francis Street
Boston, MA 02115
Tel: 617 732-6701   *Fax:* 617 732-1275
E-mail: dgitlin@partners.org
Length: 1 Yr   *ACGME Approved/Offered Positions:* 6
Program ID: 409-24-13-016

Note: * indicates a newly appointed program director

Massachusetts General Hospital Program

Sponsor: Massachusetts General Hospital
Prgm Director: Gregory Fricchione, MD
Warren 605
55 Fruit Street
Boston, MA 02114
Tel: 617 726-5758   *Fax:* 617 726-5946
E-mail: lmcaviney@partners.org
Length: 1 Yr   *ACGME Approved/Offered Positions:* 3
Program ID: 409-24-21-026

Cambridge

Cambridge Health Alliance Program

Sponsor: Cambridge Health Alliance
Prgm Director: Robert C Joseph, MD, MS
Behavioral Health
1493 Cambridge Street
Cambridge, MA 02139
Tel: 617 665-1544   *Fax:* 617 665-1204
E-mail: rjoseph@challiance.org
Length: 1 Yr   *ACGME Approved/Offered Positions:* 2
Program ID: 409-24-31-012

Michigan

Ann Arbor

University of Michigan Program

Sponsor: University of Michigan Hospitals and Health Centers
Veterans Affairs Medical Center (Ann Arbor)
Prgm Director: Michelle B Riba, MD*
4250 Plymouth Road
Rachel Upjohn Building
Ann Arbor, MI 48109
Tel: 734 764-6879   *Fax:* 734 936-1130
E-mail: mriba@med.umich.edu
Length: 1 Yr   *ACGME Approved/Offered Positions:* 2
Program ID: 409-25-12-025

Minnesota

Minneapolis

University of Minnesota Program

Sponsor: University of Minnesota Medical School
University of Minnesota Medical Center, Division of Fairview
Veterans Affairs Medical Center (Minneapolis)
Prgm Director: Jan Apple, MD
One Veterans Drive (116A)
Minneapolis, MN 55417
Tel: 612 467-1722
E-mail: janellenapple@gmail.com
Length: 1 Yr   *ACGME Approved/Offered Positions:* 2
Program ID: 409-26-12-033

Rochester

College of Medicine, Mayo Clinic (Rochester) Program

Sponsor: College of Medicine, Mayo Clinic
Rochester Methodist Hospital
Saint Marys Hospital of Rochester
Prgm Director: James R Rundell, MD
200 First Street SW
Rochester, MN 55905
Tel: 507 284-0325   *Fax:* 507 284-4345
E-mail: mgsm.roch.mn.psychiatry@mayo.edu
Length: 1 Yr   *ACGME Approved/Offered Positions:* 1
Program ID: 409-26-21-013

New York

Bronx

Albert Einstein College of Medicine Program

Sponsor: Albert Einstein College of Medicine of Yeshiva University
Montefiore Medical Center-Henry and Lucy Moses Division
Montefiore Medical Center-Weiler Division
Prgm Director: Mary Alice O'Dowd, MD
111 East 210th Street
Bronx, NY 10467
Tel: 718 920-4796   *Fax:* 718 920-6538
E-mail: modowd@montefiore.org
Length: 1 Yr   *ACGME Approved/Offered Positions:* 4
Program ID: 409-35-12-015

Great Neck

NSLIJHS-Albert Einstein College of Medicine at Long Island Jewish Medical Center Program

Sponsor: North Shore-Long Island Jewish Health System
Long Island Jewish Medical Center
North Shore University Hospital
Prgm Director: David Straker, DO*
400 Lakeville Road
New Hyde Park, NY 11040
Tel: 718 470-4652
Length: 1 Yr   *ACGME Approved/Offered Positions:* 4
Program ID: 409-35-13-019

Jamaica

Jamaica Hospital Medical Center Program

Sponsor: Jamaica Hospital Medical Center
Flushing Hospital Medical Center
Prgm Director: Adam Richard Chester, DO
Department of Psychiatry
8900 Van Wyck Expressway
Jamaica, NY 11418
Tel: 718 670-4414   *Fax:* 718 670-4473
Length: 1 Yr   *ACGME Approved/Offered Positions:* 2
Program ID: 409-35-31-028

New York

Albert Einstein College of Medicine at Beth Israel Medical Center Program

Sponsor: Beth Israel Medical Center
Prgm Director: Nancy Maruyama, MD*
First Avenue and 16th Street, Fierman 509
New York, NY 10003
Tel: 212 420-4094   *Fax:* 212 420-4332
E-mail: nmaruyam@chpnet.org
Length: 1 Yr   *ACGME Approved/Offered Positions:* 2
Program ID: 409-35-31-005

Memorial Sloan-Kettering Cancer Center/New York Presbyterian Hospital (Cornell Campus) Program

Sponsor: Memorial Sloan-Kettering Cancer Center
New York Presbyterian Hospital (Cornell Campus)
Prgm Director: Andrew J Roth, MD
Memorial Sloan-Kettering Cancer Center
1275 York Avenue-Box 421
New York, NY 10021
Tel: 646 888-0020   *Fax:* 212 888-2356
E-mail: rotha@mskcc.org
Length: 1 Yr   *ACGME Approved/Offered Positions:* 8
Program ID: 409-35-31-020

Mount Sinai School of Medicine Program

Sponsor: Mount Sinai School of Medicine
Mount Sinai Medical Center
Veterans Affairs Medical Center (Bronx)
Prgm Director: Kim Klipstein, MD
One Gustave L Levy Place
Box 1230
New York, NY 10029
Tel: 212 659-8712   *Fax:* 212 369-6817
E-mail: kim.klipstein@mssm.edu
Length: 1 Yr   *ACGME Approved/Offered Positions:* 3
Program ID: 409-35-21-001

New York Presbyterian Hospital (Columbia Campus) Program

Sponsor: New York Presbyterian Hospital
Prgm Director: Peter A Shapiro, MD
Department of Psychiatry
622 West 168th Street, Box 427
New York, NY 10032
Tel: 212 305-9985   *Fax:* 212 305-1249
Length: 1 Yr   *ACGME Approved/Offered Positions:* 2
Program ID: 409-35-13-023

New York University School of Medicine Program

Sponsor: New York University School of Medicine
Bellevue Hospital Center
Manhattan VA Harbor Health Care System
NYU Hospitals Center
Prgm Director: Asher Aladjem, MD
550 First Avenue
New York, NY 10016
Tel: 212 562-2526   *Fax:* 212 562-8985
Length: 1 Yr   *ACGME Approved/Offered Positions:* 2
Program ID: 409-35-21-022

St Luke's-Roosevelt Hospital Center Program

Sponsor: St Luke's-Roosevelt Hospital Center
Prgm Director: Melvin R Gilbert, MD, MBA
Department of Psychiatry
1090 Amsterdam Avenue, 16th Floor
New York, NY 10025
Tel: 212 523-3763   *Fax:* 212 523-2056
E-mail: mgilbert@chpnet.org
Length: 1 Yr   *ACGME Approved/Offered Positions:* 2
Program ID: 409-35-21-030

Syracuse

SUNY Upstate Medical University Program

Sponsor: SUNY Upstate Medical University
Veterans Affairs Medical Center (Syracuse)
Prgm Director: Adekola O Alao, MD
750 East Adams Street, Room 1702
Syracuse, NY 13210
Tel: 315 464-5631   *Fax:* 315 464-5632
Length: 1 Yr   *ACGME Approved/Offered Positions:* 2
Program ID: 409-35-12-006

Valhalla

New York Medical College at Westchester Medical Center Program

Sponsor: New York Medical College
Westchester Medical Center
Prgm Director: Yvette Smolin, MD
Behavioral Health Center
Room N301
Valhalla, NY 10595
Tel: 914 493-1310   *Fax:* 914 493-1015
E-mail: y.smolin@worldnet.att.net
Length: 1 Yr   *ACGME Approved/Offered Positions:* 2
Program ID: 409-35-31-032

Programs

Ohio

Cleveland

Cleveland Clinic Foundation Program
Sponsor: Cleveland Clinic Foundation
Prgm Director: Kathy L Coffman, MD
9500 Euclid Avenue
Psychiatry & Psychology/P57
Cleveland, OH 44195
Tel: 216 444-8832   *Fax:* 216 445-7032
E-mail: coffmak@ccf.org
Length: 1 Yr   *ACGME Approved/Offered Positions:* 2
Program ID: 409-38-13-014

University Hospitals Case Medical Center Program
Sponsor: University Hospitals Case Medical Center
Prgm Director: Joseph Locala, MD
Department of Psychiatry - W O Walker Center
10524 Euclid Avenue
Cleveland, OH 44106
Tel: 216 844-3658   *Fax:* 216 983-5131
Length: 1 Yr   *ACGME Approved/Offered Positions:* 2
Program ID: 409-38-13-035

Oregon

Portland

Oregon Health & Science University Program
Sponsor: Oregon Health & Science University Hospital
Veterans Affairs Medical Center (Portland)
Prgm Director: Steven K Dobscha, MD
Portland VA Medical Center
3710 SW US Veterans Hospital Road (R&D 66)
Portland, OR 97207
Tel: 503 220-8262   *Fax:* 503 220-3499
E-mail: dobschas@ohsu.edu
Length: 1 Yr   *ACGME Approved/Offered Positions:* 2
Program ID: 409-40-12-029

Pennsylvania

Philadelphia

Thomas Jefferson University Program
Sponsor: Thomas Jefferson University Hospital
Prgm Director: Elisabeth Kunkel, MD
1020 Sansom Street
Thompson Building, Suite 1652
Philadelphia, PA 19107
Tel: 215 955-6685   *Fax:* 215 955-8473
E-mail: elisabeth.kunkel@jefferson.edu
Length: 1 Yr   *ACGME Approved/Offered Positions:* 2
Program ID: 409-41-21-038

University of Pennsylvania Program
Sponsor: University of Pennsylvania Health System
Veterans Affairs Medical Center (Philadelphia)
Prgm Director: Robert M Weinrieb, MD
3400 Spruce Street
Founders Blg 1
Philadelphia, PA 19104
Tel: 215 662-2858   *Fax:* 215 615-0584
E-mail: weinrieb_b@mail.trc.upenn.edu
Length: 1 Yr   *ACGME Approved/Offered Positions:* 2
Program ID: 409-41-31-036

Tennessee

Nashville

Vanderbilt University Program
Sponsor: Vanderbilt University Medical Center
Prgm Director: Amanda G Wilson, MD*
1601 23rd Avenue South
Suite 3105
Nashville, TN 37212
Tel: 615 343-2630   *Fax:* 615 327-7136
E-mail: amanda.wilson@vanderbilt.edu
Length: 1 Yr   *ACGME Approved/Offered Positions:* 2
Program ID: 409-47-31-040

Texas

Dallas

University of Texas Southwestern Medical School Program
Sponsor: University of Texas Southwestern Medical School
Dallas County Hospital District-Parkland Memorial Hospital
Dallas VA Medical Center
University Hospitals Zale Lipshy
Prgm Director: Celia Jenkins, MD
5323 Harry Hines Boulevard
Dallas, TX 75390
Tel: 214 648-3408   *Fax:* 214 648-8030
E-mail: shaniquwa.davis@utsouthwesten.edu
Length: 1 Yr   *ACGME Approved/Offered Positions:* 2
Program ID: 409-48-21-034

San Antonio

University of Texas Health Science Center at San Antonio Program
Sponsor: University of Texas School of Medicine at San Antonio
Audie L Murphy Memorial Veterans Hospital (San Antonio)
University Health System
University of Texas Health Science Center
Prgm Director: Brenda J Talley, MD
Mail Code 7792
7703 Floyd Curl Drive
San Antonio, TX 78229
Tel: 210 567-5430   *Fax:* 210 567-0817
E-mail: talley@uthscsa.edu
Length: 1 Yr   *ACGME Approved/Offered Positions:* 2
Program ID: 409-48-12-041

Virginia

Falls Church

George Washington University Program
Sponsor: George Washington University School of Medicine
Inova Fairfax Hospital
George Washington University Hospital (UHS)
Prgm Director: Catherine Chang Crone, MD
Department of Psychiatry
3300 Gallows Road
Falls Church, VA 22042
Tel: 703 776-3380   *Fax:* 703 776-3029
E-mail: cathy.crone@inova.org
Length: 1 Yr   *ACGME Approved/Offered Positions:* 3
Program ID: 409-10-21-018

Richmond

Virginia Commonwealth University Health System Program
Sponsor: Virginia Commonwealth University Health System
Virginia Commonwealth University School of Medicine
Prgm Director: James L Levenson, MD
PO Box 980268, West Hospital, 8th Floor
Richmond, VA 23298
Tel: 804 828-0762   *Fax:* 804 828-7675
E-mail: jlevenson@mcvh-vcu.edu
Length: 1 Yr   *ACGME Approved/Offered Positions:* 2
Program ID: 409-51-12-009

Washington

Seattle

University of Washington Program
Sponsor: University of Washington School of Medicine
Harborview Medical Center
University of Washington Medical Center
Prgm Director: Karina K Uldall, MD, MPH*
Department of Psychiatry & Behavioral Sciences
Box 356560
Seattle, WA 98125
Tel: 206 991-6224   *Fax:* 206 744-3427
Length: 1 Yr   *ACGME Approved/Offered Positions:* 2
Program ID: 409-54-21-011

Note: * indicates a newly appointed program director

Pulmonary Disease (Internal Medicine)

Arizona

Scottsdale

College of Medicine, Mayo Clinic (Arizona) Program
Sponsor: College of Medicine, Mayo Clinic
Mayo Clinic (Arizona)
Mayo Clinic Hospital
Prgm Director: Lewis J Wesselius, MD
13400 East Shea Boulevard
Scottsdale, AZ 85259
Tel: 480 301-7149   *Fax:* 480 301-4869
Length: 2 Yrs   *ACGME Approved/Offered Positions:* 2
Program ID: 149-03-13-206

California

Fresno

University of California (San Francisco)/Fresno Program
Sponsor: UCSF Fresno Medical Education Program
Community Medical Centers (Fresno)
VA Central California Health Care System
Prgm Director: Kathryn L Bilello, MD
155 N Fresno Street
Fresno, CA 93701
Tel: 559 459-4135   *Fax:* 559 459-6119
E-mail: KBilello@fresno.ucsf.edu
Length: 2 Yrs   *ACGME Approved/Offered Positions:* 6
Program ID: 149-05-21-209

Connecticut

Bridgeport

Bridgeport Hospital/Yale University Program
Sponsor: Bridgeport Hospital
Prgm Director: Armand J Wolff, MD*
267 Grant Street
Bridgeport, CT 06610
Tel: 203 384-5009   *Fax:* 203 330-7498
E-mail: pawolf@bpthosp.org
Length: 2 Yrs   *ACGME Approved/Offered Positions:* 4
Program ID: 149-08-21-199

Norwalk

Norwalk Hospital/Yale University Program
Sponsor: Norwalk Hospital
Prgm Director: Jonathan M Fine, MD
Department of Medicine
Maple Street
Norwalk, CT 06856
Tel: 203 855-3543   *Fax:* 203 852-2738
Length: 2 Yrs   *ACGME Approved/Offered Positions:* 4
Program ID: 149-08-31-003

District of Columbia

Washington

Howard University Program
Sponsor: Howard University Hospital
Prgm Director: Alvin V Thomas Jr, MD
Department of Internal Medicine
2041 Georgia Avenue NW
Washington, DC 20060
Tel: 202 865-6798   *Fax:* 202 865-4669
E-mail: alothompson@howard.edu
Length: 2 Yrs   *ACGME Approved/Offered Positions:* 3
Program ID: 149-10-21-086

Illinois

North Chicago

The Chicago Medical School at Rosalind Franklin University of Medicine and Science Program
Sponsor: Chicago Medical School/Rosalind Franklin University of Medicine & Science
Mount Sinai Hospital Medical Center of Chicago
Veterans Affairs Medical Center (North Chicago)
Prgm Director: Ashok M Fulambarker, MD
Division of Pulmonary Medicine-Dept of Medicine
3333 Green Bay Road
North Chicago, IL 60064
Tel: 224 610-4587   *Fax:* 224 610-3895
E-mail: anita.abron@rosalindfranklin.edu
Length: 2 Yrs   *ACGME Approved/Offered Positions:* 4
Program ID: 149-16-21-051

Springfield

Southern Illinois University Program
Sponsor: Southern Illinois University School of Medicine
Memorial Medical Center
St John's Hospital
Prgm Director: Joseph Q Henkle, MD
PO Box 19636
Springfield, IL 62794
Tel: 217 545-0187   *Fax:* 217 788-5543
Length: 2 Yrs   *ACGME Approved/Offered Positions:* 4
Program ID: 149-16-21-194

New Jersey

South Orange

Seton Hall University School of Health and Medical Sciences Program
Sponsor: Seton Hall University School of Health and Medical Sciences
St Joseph's Regional Medical Center
St Michael's Medical Center (A Member of Catholic Hlth East)
Prgm Director: M Anees Khan, MD
703 Main Street
Paterson, NJ 07503
Tel: 973 754-2450   *Fax:* 973 754-2469
Length: 2 Yrs   *ACGME Approved/Offered Positions:* 7
Program ID: 149-33-11-156

New York

Bronx

Bronx-Lebanon Hospital Center Program
Sponsor: Bronx-Lebanon Hospital Center
Prgm Director: Gilda Diaz-Fuentes, MD
1650 Selwyn Ave, Suite 10C
Bronx, NY 10457
Tel: 718 466-8160   *Fax:* 718 960-1333
E-mail: gfuentes@bronxleb.org
Length: 2 Yrs   *ACGME Approved/Offered Positions:* 5
Program ID: 149-35-11-102

Brooklyn

Brooklyn Hospital Center Program
Sponsor: Brooklyn Hospital Center
Wyckoff Heights Medical Center
Prgm Director: Farhad Arjomand, MD*
Department of Medicine
121 DeKalb Avenue, Suite 7E, Maynard Bldg
Brooklyn, NY 11201
Tel: 718 250-6950   *Fax:* 718 250-6110
Length: 2 Yrs   *ACGME Approved/Offered Positions:* 5
Program ID: 149-35-12-185

Interfaith Medical Center Program
Sponsor: Interfaith Medical Center
Prgm Director: M Frances J Schmidt, MD
1545 Atlantic Avenue
Brooklyn, NY 11213
Tel: 718 613-4063   *Fax:* 718 613-4893
Length: 2 Yrs   *ACGME Approved/Offered Positions:* 4
Program ID: 149-35-21-179

Maimonides Medical Center Program
Sponsor: Maimonides Medical Center
Prgm Director: Sidney Tessler, MD
4802 10th Avenue
Brooklyn, NY 11219
Tel: 718 283-8380   *Fax:* 718 283-7884
Length: 2 Yrs   *ACGME Approved/Offered Positions:* 4
Program ID: 149-35-11-158

Jamaica

New York Medical College (Brooklyn-Queens) Program
Sponsor: New York Medical College
Caritas Health Care (Brooklyn-Queens)
Prgm Director: Albert Miller, MD
152-11 89th Ave
Room 342
Jamaica, NY 11432
Tel: 718 558-7227   *Fax:* 718 558-7203
E-mail: almiller@bqhcny.org
Length: 2 Yrs   *ACGME Approved/Offered Positions:* 4
Program ID: 149-35-22-047

New York

Harlem Hospital Center Program
Sponsor: Harlem Hospital Center
Prgm Director: John S Schicchi, MD
Dept of Medicine, Rm 12-106
506 Lenox Avenue
New York, NY 10037
Tel: 212 939-1455   *Fax:* 212 939-1456
Length: 2 Yrs   *ACGME Approved/Offered Positions:* 4
Program ID: 149-35-11-168

Programs

Lenox Hill Hospital Program
Sponsor: Lenox Hill Hospital
Prgm Director: Larry DiFabrizio, MD
100 East 77th Street
3 Achelis
New York, NY 10021
Tel: 212 434-2158   *Fax:* 212 434-3396
E-mail: mhill@lenoxhill.net
Length: 2 Yrs   *ACGME Approved/Offered Positions:* 3
Program ID: 149-35-11-181

Memorial Sloan-Kettering Cancer Center/New York Presbyterian Hospital (Cornell Campus) Program
Sponsor: Memorial Sloan-Kettering Cancer Center
Prgm Director: Jean T Santamauro, MD
1275 York Avenue
New York, NY 10065
Tel: 212 639-8002   *Fax:* 212 717-3116
E-mail: pulmonary@mskcc.org
Length: 2 Yrs   *ACGME Approved/Offered Positions:* 4
Program ID: 149-35-21-173

Pennsylvania

Pittsburgh

Western Pennsylvania Hospital/Temple University Program
Sponsor: Western Pennsylvania Hospital
Prgm Director: Paul Fiehler, MD
4800 Friendship Ave
Pittsburgh, PA 15224
Tel: 412 687-5573   *Fax:* 412 687-8854
Length: 2 Yrs   *ACGME Approved/Offered Positions:* 3
Program ID: 149-41-11-042

Puerto Rico

San Juan

San Juan City Hospital Program
Sponsor: San Juan City Hospital
Prgm Director: Raul A Reyes, MD
PO Box 70344
PMB 330
San Juan, PR 00936
Tel: 787 765-5147   *Fax:* 787 765-3692
E-mail: matorther@yahoo.com
Length: 2 Yrs   *ACGME Approved/Offered Positions:* 4
Program ID: 149-42-13-210

University of Puerto Rico Program
Sponsor: University of Puerto Rico School of Medicine
University Hospital
VA Caribbean Healthcare System
Prgm Director: Angel F Laureano, MD*
Department of Medicine
PO Box 365067
San Juan, PR 00936
Tel: 787 758-2525
Length: 2 Yrs   *ACGME Approved/Offered Positions:* 2
Program ID: 149-42-21-121

Rhode Island

Providence

Roger Williams Medical Center Program
Sponsor: Roger Williams Medical Center
Prgm Director: Michael Passero, MD
825 Chalkstone Ave
Providence, RI 02908
Tel: 401 456-2302   *Fax:* 401 456-2016
Length: 2 Yrs   *ACGME Approved/Offered Positions:* 2
Program ID: 149-43-31-043

South Carolina

Columbia

Palmetto Health/University of South Carolina School of Medicine Program
Sponsor: Palmetto Health
Palmetto Health Richland
William Jennings Bryan Dorn Veterans Hospital
Prgm Director: James A Barker, MD
School of Medicine
8 Medical Park, Suite 410
Columbia, SC 29203
Tel: 803 799-5022   *Fax:* 803 454-2682
E-mail: lorie.collins@uscmed.sc.edu
Length: 2 Yrs   *ACGME Approved/Offered Positions:* 6
Program ID: 149-45-12-208

Tennessee

Knoxville

University of Tennessee Medical Center at Knoxville Program
Sponsor: University of Tennessee Graduate School of Medicine
University of Tennessee Memorial Hospital
Prgm Director: Tina M Dudney, MD
1940 Alcoa Highway
Suite E210
Knoxville, TN 37920
Tel: 865 524-7471   *Fax:* 865 305-9144
E-mail: ptrentha@utmck.edu
Length: 2 Yrs   *ACGME Approved/Offered Positions:* 4
Program ID: 149-47-31-207

West Virginia

Huntington

Marshall University School of Medicine Program
Sponsor: Marshall University School of Medicine
Cabell Huntington Hospital
St Mary's Hospital
Veterans Affairs Medical Center (Huntington)
Prgm Director: Nancy J Munn, MD
Department of Medicine
1249 15th Street, Suite 3000
Huntington, WV 25701
Tel: 304 691-1092   *Fax:* 304 691-1693
E-mail: cummings18@marshall.edu
Length: 2 Yrs   *ACGME Approved/Offered Positions:* 5
Program ID: 149-55-21-183

Pulmonary Disease and Critical Care Medicine (Internal Medicine)

Alabama

Birmingham

University of Alabama Medical Center Program
Sponsor: University of Alabama Hospital
Veterans Affairs Medical Center (Birmingham)
Prgm Director: J Allen D Cooper Jr, MD
422 Tinsley Harrison Towers
1900 University Boulevard
Birmingham, AL 35294
Tel: 205 934-4328   *Fax:* 205 934-7315
E-mail: allenc@uab.edu
Length: 3 Yrs   *ACGME Approved/Offered Positions:* 15
Program ID: 156-01-21-105

Mobile

University of South Alabama Program
Sponsor: University of South Alabama Hospitals
Infirmary West
University of South Alabama Medical Center
Prgm Director: Ronald C Allison, MD
2451 Fillingim Street, 10-G
Mobile, AL 36617
Tel: 251 471-7847   *Fax:* 251 471-7889
Length: 3 Yrs   *ACGME Approved/Offered Positions:* 6
Program ID: 156-01-12-145

Arizona

Phoenix

Banner Good Samaritan Medical Center Program
Sponsor: Banner Good Samaritan Medical Center
Carl T Hayden VA Medical Center
Prgm Director: Richard A Robbins, MD
650 East Indian School Road
Phoenix, AZ 85012
Tel: 602 277-5551   *Fax:* 602 222-2746
Length: 3 Yrs   *ACGME Approved/Offered Positions:* 6
Program ID: 156-03-13-129

Tucson

University of Arizona Program
Sponsor: University of Arizona College of Medicine
Southern Arizona VA Health Care Center (Tucson)
University Medical Center
University of Arizona/UPHK Graduate Medical Ed Consortium
Prgm Director: Linda S Snyder, MD
1501 N Campbell Avenue
PO Box 245030, Room 2342
Tucson, AZ 85724
Tel: 520 626-6114
E-mail: hhill@arc.arizona.edu
Length: 3 Yrs   *ACGME Approved/Offered Positions:* 6
Program ID: 156-03-21-001

Note: * indicates a newly appointed program director

Arkansas

Little Rock

University of Arkansas for Medical Sciences Program

Sponsor: University of Arkansas College of Medicine
Central Arkansas Veterans Healthcare System
UAMS Medical Center
Prgm Director: Marcia L Erbland, MD
4301 W Markham, Slot 555
Little Rock, AR 72205
Tel: 501 686-5526   *Fax:* 501 686-7893
Length: 3 Yrs   *ACGME Approved/Offered Positions:* 6
Program ID: 156-04-21-002

California

Loma Linda

Loma Linda University Program

Sponsor: Loma Linda University Medical Center
Jerry L Pettis Memorial Veterans Hospital
Prgm Director: Philip M Gold, MD
11234 Anderson Street
Room 6433
Loma Linda, CA 92354
Tel: 909 558-4489   *Fax:* 909 558-0581
Length: 3 Yrs   *ACGME Approved/Offered Positions:* 6
Program ID: 156-05-21-113

Los Angeles

Cedars-Sinai Medical Center Program

Sponsor: Cedars-Sinai Medical Center
VA Greater Los Angeles Healthcare System
Prgm Director: Michael Lewis, MD
8700 Beverly Blvd
Room 6732
Los Angeles, CA 90048
Tel: 310 423-1832   *Fax:* 310 423-0129
Length: 3 Yrs   *ACGME Approved/Offered Positions:* 21
Program ID: 156-05-21-003

UCLA Medical Center Program

Sponsor: UCLA David Geffen School of Medicine/UCLA Medical Center
UCLA Medical Center
Prgm Director: John A Belperio, MD
Center for the Health Sciences
10833 Le Conte Ave Rm 37-131
Los Angeles, CA 90095
Tel: 310 825-5615   *Fax:* 310 206-8622
E-mail: hdraper@mednet.ucla.edu
Length: 3 Yrs   *ACGME Approved/Offered Positions:* 6
Program ID: 156-05-31-114

University of Southern California/ LAC+USC Medical Center Program

Sponsor: University of Southern California/LAC+USC Medical Center
LAC+USC Medical Center
USC University Hospital
Prgm Director: Zea Borok, MD
2020 Zonal Avenue
IRD 620
Los Angeles, CA 90033
Tel: 323 226-7923   *Fax:* 323 226-2738
E-mail: pccm@usc.edu
Length: 3 Yrs   *ACGME Approved/Offered Positions:* 18
Program ID: 156-05-31-004

Orange

University of California (Irvine) Program

Sponsor: University of California (Irvine) Medical Center
Long Beach Memorial Medical Center
VA Long Beach Healthcare System
Prgm Director: Mathew Brenner, MD*
Department of Medicine, Room 119, Building 53, Route 81
101 The City Drive South
Orange, CA 92868
Tel: 714 456-5150   *Fax:* 714 456-8349
Length: 3 Yrs   *ACGME Approved/Offered Positions:* 9
Program ID: 156-05-11-005

Sacramento

University of California (Davis) Health System Program

Sponsor: University of California (Davis) Health System
University of California (Davis) Medical Center
VA Northern California Health Care System
Prgm Director: Brian M Morrissey, MD
Division of Pulmonary & Critical Care Medicine
4150 V Street, Suite 3400
Sacramento, CA 95817
Tel: 916 734-3565   *Fax:* 916 734-7924
E-mail: betty.boyd@ucdmc.ucdavis.edu
Length: 3 Yrs   *ACGME Approved/Offered Positions:* 11
Program ID: 156-05-12-006

San Diego

Naval Medical Center (San Diego) Program

Sponsor: Naval Medical Center (San Diego)
University of California (San Diego) Medical Center
Prgm Director: John F Perri, DO
34740 Bob Wilson Drive
Suite 300
San Diego, CA 92134
Tel: 619 532-5990   *Fax:* 619 532-7625
E-mail: john.perri@med.navy.mil
Length: 3 Yrs   *ACGME Approved/Offered Positions:* 7
Program ID: 156-05-13-007
Uniformed Services Program

University of California (San Diego) Program

Sponsor: University of California (San Diego) Medical Center
Veterans Affairs Medical Center (San Diego)
Prgm Director: Peter F Fedullo, MD
200 W Arbor Drive
San Diego, CA 92103
Tel: 619 543-7752   *Fax:* 619 543-7334
E-mail: pfedullo@ucsd.edu
Length: 3 Yrs   *ACGME Approved/Offered Positions:* 15
Program ID: 156-05-22-008

San Francisco

California Pacific Medical Center Program

Sponsor: California Pacific Medical Center
Alameda County Medical Center
Prgm Director: Christopher R Brown, MD*
2351 Clay Street #380
San Francisco, CA 94115
Tel: 415 923-3421   *Fax:* 415 600-1414
Length: 3 Yrs   *ACGME Approved/Offered Positions:* 3
Program ID: 156-05-32-130

University of California (San Francisco) Program

Sponsor: University of California (San Francisco) School of Medicine
San Francisco General Hospital Medical Center
UCSF and Mount Zion Medical Centers
Prgm Director: Stephen C Lazarus, MD
Department of Medicine
505 Parnassus Avenue, Room 1087-M
San Francisco, CA 94143
Tel: 415 476-6926   *Fax:* 415 476-5712
E-mail: patrick.manalastas@ucsf.edu
Length: 3 Yrs   *ACGME Approved/Offered Positions:* 21
Program ID: 156-05-23-009

Stanford

Stanford University Program

Sponsor: Stanford Hospital and Clinics
Veterans Affairs Palo Alto Health Care System
Prgm Director: Glenn D Rosen, MD
300 Pasteur Drive, Room H3143
Stanford, CA 94305
Tel: 650 723-6381   *Fax:* 650 725-5489
Length: 3 Yrs   *ACGME Approved/Offered Positions:* 18
Program ID: 156-05-21-010

Torrance

Los Angeles County-Harbor-UCLA Medical Center Program

Sponsor: Los Angeles County-Harbor-UCLA Medical Center
Prgm Director: Kathy E Sietsema, MD*
1000 W Carson Street
Box 405
Torrance, CA 90509
Tel: 310 222-3801
Length: 3 Yrs   *ACGME Approved/Offered Positions:* 6
Program ID: 156-05-11-115

Colorado

Aurora

University of Colorado Denver Program

Sponsor: University of Colorado Denver School of Medicine
National Jewish Medical and Research Center
University of Colorado Hospital
Prgm Director: Marvin I Schwarz, MD
12700 East 19th Ave
Box C272
Aurora, CO 80045
Tel: 303 724-4075   *Fax:* 303 724-6042
Length: 3 Yrs   *ACGME Approved/Offered Positions:* 18
Program ID: 156-07-21-097

Connecticut

Farmington

University of Connecticut Program

Sponsor: University of Connecticut School of Medicine
Hospital for Central Connecticut
St Francis Hospital and Medical Center
Univ of Connecticut Health Center/John Dempsey Hospital
Prgm Director: Mark Metersky, MD
263 Farmington Avenue
Farmington, CT 06030
Tel: 860 679-3585   *Fax:* 860 679-1103
E-mail: plocharsky@nso.uchc.edu
Length: 3 Yrs   *ACGME Approved/Offered Positions:* 6
Program ID: 156-08-21-011

New Haven

Yale-New Haven Medical Center Program

Sponsor: Yale-New Haven Hospital
Prgm Director: Margaret A Pisani, MD, MPH*
300 Cedar Street, TAC 441 S
PO Box 208057
New Haven, CT 06520
Tel: 203 785-3207 *Fax:* 203 785-3826
Length: 3 Yrs *ACGME Approved/Offered Positions:* 17
Program ID: 156-08-21-104

District of Columbia

Washington

George Washington University Program

Sponsor: George Washington University School of
  Medicine
George Washington University Hospital (UHS)
Inova Fairfax Hospital
Veterans Affairs Medical Center (Washington, DC)
Prgm Director: Guillermo Gutierrez, MD, PhD
Ross Hall Suite 707
2300 Eye Street, NW
Washington, DC 20037
Tel: 202 741-2180 *Fax:* 202 741-2238
E-mail: tlyons@mfa.gwu.edu
Length: 3 Yrs *ACGME Approved/Offered Positions:* 9
Program ID: 156-10-21-080

Georgetown University Hospital Program

Sponsor: Georgetown University Hospital
Prgm Director: Charles A Read, MD
Department of Medicine
3800 Reservoir Road, NW
Washington, DC 20007
Tel: 202 444-8830 *Fax:* 202 444-2336
E-mail: peraltar@gunet.georgetown.edu
Length: 3 Yrs *ACGME Approved/Offered Positions:* 6
Program ID: 156-10-21-013

Georgetown University Hospital/Washington Hospital Center Program

Sponsor: Washington Hospital Center
Prgm Director: Burton W Lee, MD
110 Irving Street, NW, 2A-68
Department of Pulmonary & Critical Care Medicine
Washington, DC 20010
Tel: 202 877-7856 *Fax:* 202 291-0386
E-mail: burton.w.lee@medstar.net
Length: 3 Yrs *ACGME Approved/Offered Positions:* 6
Program ID: 156-10-12-141

Florida

Gainesville

University of Florida Program

Sponsor: University of Florida College of Medicine
North Florida/South Georgia Veterans Health System
Shands Hospital at the University of Florida
Prgm Director: Michael A Jantz, MD
PO Box 100225
Department of Medicine
Gainesville, FL 32610
Tel: 352 392-2666 *Fax:* 352 392-0821
E-mail: tami.pomponi@medicine.ufl.edu
Length: 3 Yrs *ACGME Approved/Offered Positions:* 10
Program ID: 156-11-21-014

Jacksonville

College of Medicine, Mayo Clinic (Jacksonville) Program

Sponsor: College of Medicine, Mayo Clinic
Mayo Clinic (Jacksonville)
Mayo Clinic Florida Hospital
Prgm Director: Margaret M Johnson, MD
4500 San Pablo Road
Jacksonville, FL 32224
Tel: 904 953-0421 *Fax:* 904 953-0430
E-mail: paglia.melissa@mayo.edu
Length: 3 Yrs *ACGME Approved/Offered Positions:* 6
Program ID: 156-11-13-147

University of Florida College of Medicine Jacksonville Program

Sponsor: University of Florida College of Medicine
  Jacksonville
Shands Jacksonville Medical Center
Prgm Director: James D Cury, MD
655 West Eighth Street
Jacksonville, FL 32209
Tel: 904 244-3071 *Fax:* 904 244-5090
E-mail: PulmonaryCC.gme@jax.ufl.edu
Length: 3 Yrs *ACGME Approved/Offered Positions:* 6
Program ID: 156-11-31-148

Miami

Jackson Memorial Hospital/Jackson Health System Program

Sponsor: Jackson Memorial Hospital/Jackson Health
  System
Veterans Affairs Medical Center (Miami)
Prgm Director: Horst J Baier, MD, JD
Jackson Memorial Hospital North Wing Room 224
1611 NW 12th Avenue
Miami, FL 33136
Tel: 305 585-7340 *Fax:* 305 324-0869
E-mail: hbaier@miami.edu
Length: 3 Yrs *ACGME Approved/Offered Positions:* 13
Program ID: 156-11-31-015

Tampa

University of South Florida Program

Sponsor: University of South Florida College of Medicine
H Lee Moffitt Cancer Center
James A Haley Veterans Hospital
Tampa General Hospital
Prgm Director: David A Solomon, MD
13000 Bruce B Downs Blvd (111C)
Tampa, FL 33612
Tel: 813 972-7543 *Fax:* 813 979-3606
E-mail: poswald@hsc.usf.edu
Length: 3 Yrs *ACGME Approved/Offered Positions:* 10
Program ID: 156-11-21-102

Georgia

Atlanta

Emory University Program

Sponsor: Emory University School of Medicine
Emory University Hospital
Prgm Director: David A Schulman, MD, MPH
Pulmonary & Critical Care Medicine-Suite 205
615 Michael Street, Suite 205
Atlanta, GA 30322
Tel: 404 712-8286 *Fax:* 404 712-8227
E-mail: daschul@emory.edu
Length: 3 Yrs *ACGME Approved/Offered Positions:* 18
Program ID: 156-12-21-016

Augusta

Medical College of Georgia Program

Sponsor: Medical College of Georgia
Veterans Affairs Medical Center (Augusta)
Prgm Director: Thomas A Dillard, MD
1120 15th Street
Section of Pulmonary Diseases, Room BBR5513
Augusta, GA 30912
Tel: 706 721-2566 *Fax:* 706 721-3069
Length: 3 Yrs *ACGME Approved/Offered Positions:* 7
Program ID: 156-12-31-017

Illinois

Chicago

John H Stroger Hospital of Cook County Program

Sponsor: John H Stroger Hospital of Cook County
Prgm Director: Aiman Tulaimat, MD*
1900 W Polk St
Room 1401
Chicago, IL 60612
Tel: 312 864-7387 *Fax:* 312 864-7394
Length: 3 Yrs *ACGME Approved/Offered Positions:* 6
Program ID: 156-16-21-018

McGaw Medical Center of Northwestern University Program

Sponsor: McGaw Medical Center of Northwestern
  University
Northwestern Memorial Hospital
Prgm Director: Peter H Sporn, MD
Division of Pulmonary and Critical Care Medicine
240 E Huron St, McGaw M-300
Chicago, IL 60611
Tel: 312 908-7737 *Fax:* 312 908-4650
E-mail: o-garcia@northwestern.edu
Length: 3 Yrs *ACGME Approved/Offered Positions:* 9
Program ID: 156-16-21-081

Rush University Medical Center Program

Sponsor: Rush University Medical Center
Prgm Director: Robert A Balk, MD
1653 W Congress Parkway, 297 Jelke
Chicago, IL 60612
Tel: 312 942-5873 *Fax:* 312 942-8187
Length: 3 Yrs *ACGME Approved/Offered Positions:* 9
Program ID: 156-16-31-019

University of Chicago Program

Sponsor: University of Chicago Medical Center
Prgm Director: John McConville, MD
MC 6076
5841 South Maryland Avenue
Chicago, IL 60637
Tel: 773 834-3500 *Fax:* 773 702-4427
Length: 3 Yrs *ACGME Approved/Offered Positions:* 11
Program ID: 156-16-21-091

University of Illinois College of Medicine at Chicago Program

Sponsor: University of Illinois College of Medicine at
  Chicago
Jesse Brown Veterans Affairs Medical Center
Mercy Hospital and Medical Center
University of Illinois Hospital and Clinics
Prgm Director: Dean E Schraufnagel, MD
Department of Medicine, M/C 719
840 S Wood Street
Chicago, IL 60612
Tel: 312 996-8039 *Fax:* 312 996-4665
E-mail: rccm@uic.edu
Length: 3 Yrs *ACGME Approved/Offered Positions:* 12
Program ID: 156-16-21-020

Note: * indicates a newly appointed program director

Maywood

Loyola University Program
Sponsor: Loyola University Medical Center
Edward Hines, Jr Veterans Affairs Hospital
Prgm Director: Sean M Forsythe, MD
Pulmonary and Critical Care Medicine
Bldg 54, Room 131A
Maywood, IL 60153
Tel: 708 216-5402   *Fax:* 708 216-6839
E-mail: sforsy1@lumc.edu
Length: 3 Yrs   *ACGME Approved/Offered Positions:* 12
Program ID: 156-16-31-021

Indiana

Indianapolis

Indiana University School of Medicine Program
Sponsor: Indiana University School of Medicine
Clarian Indiana University Hospital
William N Wishard Memorial Hospital
Prgm Director: Mark O Farber, MD
Richard L Roudebush Veterans Affairs Medical cent
1481 West 10th Street, 111P-IU
Indianapolis, IN 46202
Tel: 317 988-3918   *Fax:* 317 988-3976
E-mail: mofarber@iupui.edu
Length: 3 Yrs   *ACGME Approved/Offered Positions:* 15
Program ID: 156-17-21-022

Iowa

Iowa City

University of Iowa Hospitals and Clinics Program
Sponsor: University of Iowa Hospitals and Clinics
Prgm Director: Jeffrey S Wilson, MD
200 Hawkins Drive
C33-GH
Iowa City, IA 52242
Tel: 319 356-2752   *Fax:* 319 353-6406
Length: 3 Yrs   *ACGME Approved/Offered Positions:* 12
Program ID: 156-18-21-023

Kansas

Kansas City

University of Kansas School of Medicine Program
Sponsor: University of Kansas School of Medicine
University of Kansas Hospital
Veterans Affairs Medical Center (Kansas City)
Prgm Director: Steven Q Simpson, MD
39th & Rainbow Blvd
4030 Sudler
Kansas City, KS 66160
Tel: 913 588-6045   *Fax:* 913 588-4098
Length: 3 Yrs   *ACGME Approved/Offered Positions:* 12
Program ID: 156-19-21-024

Kentucky

Lexington

University of Kentucky College of Medicine Program
Sponsor: University of Kentucky College of Medicine
Veterans Affairs Medical Center (Lexington)
Prgm Director: Rolando Berger, MD
740 S Limestone, L543
Lexington, KY 40536
Tel: 859 323-5045   *Fax:* 859 257-2418
E-mail: gjpark2@email.uky.edu
Length: 3 Yrs   *ACGME Approved/Offered Positions:* 9
Program ID: 156-20-21-101

Louisville

University of Louisville Program
Sponsor: University of Louisville School of Medicine
Floyd Memorial Hospital
Jewish Hospital
Norton Hospital
University of Louisville Hospital
Veterans Affairs Medical Center (Louisville)
Prgm Director: Mohamed Saad, MD
550 S Jackson Street
Ambulatory Care Building, A3L01
Louisville, KY 40202
Tel: 502 852-5841   *Fax:* 502 852-1359
E-mail: d0stot01@gwise.louisville.edu
Length: 3 Yrs   *ACGME Approved/Offered Positions:* 7
Program ID: 156-20-21-077

Louisiana

New Orleans

Louisiana State University Program
Sponsor: Louisiana State University School of Medicine
Medical Center of Louisiana at New Orleans
Ochsner Clinic Foundation
Prgm Director: David E Taylor, MD
Pulmonary/Critical Care Medicine
1901 Perdido Street, Suite 3205
New Orleans, LA 70112
Tel: 504 568-4634   *Fax:* 504 568-4295
E-mail: dtaylor@ochsner.org
Length: 3 Yrs   *ACGME Approved/Offered Positions:* 11
Program ID: 156-21-21-025

Tulane University Program
Sponsor: Tulane University School of Medicine
Kindred Hospital
Medical Center of Louisiana at New Orleans
Tulane University Hospital and Clinics
Prgm Director: Francesco Simeone, MD*
1430 Tulane Ave, SL 9
New Orleans, LA 70112
Tel: 504 988-3541   *Fax:* 504 988-2144
E-mail: fsimeone@tulane.edu
Length: 3 Yrs   *ACGME Approved/Offered Positions:* 10
Program ID: 156-21-21-120

Shreveport

Louisiana State University (Shreveport) Program
Sponsor: LSU Health Sciences Center-University Hospital
Overton Brooks Veterans Affairs Medical Center
Prgm Director: Donald K Payne, MD
Department of Medicine
1501 Kings Highway
Shreveport, LA 71130
Tel: 318 675-5920   *Fax:* 318 675-5988
E-mail: Vjohn1@lsuhsc.edu
Length: 3 Yrs   *ACGME Approved/Offered Positions:* 7
Program ID: 156-21-31-026

Maine

Portland

Maine Medical Center Program
Sponsor: Maine Medical Center
Prgm Director: Joel A Wirth, MD
Division of Pulmonary and Critical Care Medicine
22 Bramhall Street
Portland, ME 04102
Tel: 207 662-2770   *Fax:* 207 662-4691
Length: 3 Yrs   *ACGME Approved/Offered Positions:* 6
Program ID: 156-22-21-027

Maryland

Baltimore

Johns Hopkins University Program
Sponsor: Johns Hopkins University School of Medicine
Johns Hopkins Bayview Medical Center
Johns Hopkins Hospital
Prgm Director: Henry E Fessler, MD
Pulmonary and Critical Care Medicine
1830 Monument Street, 5th Floor
Baltimore, MD 21287
Tel: 410 955-3467   *Fax:* 410 955-0036
E-mail: hfessler@jhmi.edu
Length: 3 Yrs   *ACGME Approved/Offered Positions:* 24
Program ID: 156-23-21-028

University of Maryland Program
Sponsor: University of Maryland Medical System
Veterans Affairs Medical Center (Baltimore)
Prgm Director: Nevins W Todd, MD
22 S Greene St, Box 353
Baltimore, MD 21201
Tel: 410 605-7000   *Fax:* 410 605-7915
E-mail: ntodd@medicine.umaryland.edu
Length: 3 Yrs   *ACGME Approved/Offered Positions:* 14
Program ID: 156-23-21-107

Bethesda

National Capital Consortium (Walter Reed) Program
Sponsor: National Capital Consortium
National Naval Medical Center (Bethesda)
Walter Reed Army Medical Center
Prgm Director: Janet N Myers, MD*
Pulmonary & Critical Care Medicine Service Ward 77
6900 Georgia Avenue NW
Washington, DC 20307
Tel: 301 319-4301   *Fax:* 301 295-5792
Length: 3 Yrs   *ACGME Approved/Offered Positions:* 15
Program ID: 156-10-21-082
Uniformed Services Program

Massachusetts

Boston

Boston University Medical Center Program
Sponsor: Boston Medical Center
Veterans Affairs Medical Center (Boston)
Prgm Director: Christine L Campbell-Reardon, MD
Pulmonary Center, R304
715 Albany Street
Boston, MA 02118
Tel: 617 638-8636   *Fax:* 617 536-8093
Length: 3 Yrs   *ACGME Approved/Offered Positions:* 15
Program ID: 156-24-21-090

Caritas St Elizabeth's Medical Center Program

Sponsor: Caritas St Elizabeth's Medical Center of Boston
Prgm Director: Bartolome Celli, MD
736 Cambridge Street
Boston, MA 02135
Tel: 617 789-2554   *Fax:* 617 562-7756
E-mail: bcelli@copdnet.org
Length: 3 Yrs   *ACGME Approved/Offered Positions:* 6
Program ID: 156-24-31-031

Massachusetts General Hospital Program

Sponsor: Massachusetts General Hospital
Beth Israel Deaconess Medical Center
Brigham and Women's Hospital
Prgm Director: David M Systrom, MD
55 Fruit Street
Pulmonary and Care Unit, Bulfinch 148
Boston, MA 02114
Tel: 617 724-9970   *Fax:* 617 726-6878
E-mail: dsystrom@partners.org
Length: 3 Yrs   *ACGME Approved/Offered Positions:* 30
Program ID: 156-24-21-079

Tufts Medical Center Program

Sponsor: Tufts Medical Center
Prgm Director: Erik Garpestad, MD
800 Washington Street
Box 369
Boston, MA 02111
Tel: 617 636-5388   *Fax:* 617 636-6361
Length: 3 Yrs   *ACGME Approved/Offered Positions:* 9
Program ID: 156-24-21-030

Burlington

Lahey Clinic Program

Sponsor: Lahey Clinic
Prgm Director: Anthony C Campagna, MD
Department of Pulmonary and Critical Care Medicine
41 Mall Road
Burlington, MA 01805
Tel: 781 744-8481   *Fax:* 781 744-3443
E-mail: anthony.c.campagna@lahey.org
Length: 3 Yrs   *ACGME Approved/Offered Positions:* 6
Program ID: 156-24-21-029

Worcester

University of Massachusetts Program

Sponsor: University of Massachusetts Medical School
UMass Memorial Health Care (University Campus)
Prgm Director: Oren P Schaefer, MD*
55 Lake Avenue North
Worcester, MA 01655
Tel: 508 856-3122   *Fax:* 508 856-3999
E-mail: schaefeo@ummhc.org
Length: 3 Yrs   *ACGME Approved/Offered Positions:* 6
Program ID: 156-24-12-134

Michigan

Ann Arbor

University of Michigan Program

Sponsor: University of Michigan Hospitals and Health Centers
Prgm Director: Marc Peters-Golden, MD
6301 MSRB III
1150 W Medical Center Dr
Ann Arbor, MI 48109
Tel: 734 763-9077   *Fax:* 734 764-4556
Length: 3 Yrs   *ACGME Approved/Offered Positions:* 12
Program ID: 156-25-21-032

Detroit

Henry Ford Hospital Program

Sponsor: Henry Ford Hospital
Prgm Director: Michael Eichenhorn, MD*
2799 W Grand Boulevard #K-17
Detroit, MI 48202
Tel: 313 916-2436
Length: 3 Yrs   *ACGME Approved/Offered Positions:* 20
Program ID: 156-25-31-033

Wayne State University/Detroit Medical Center Program

Sponsor: Wayne State University/Detroit Medical Center
Detroit Receiving Hospital and University Health Center
Harper-Hutzel Hospital
Prgm Director: James A Rowley, MD
3 Hudson
3980 John R Street
Detroit, MI 48201
Tel: 313 966-0695   *Fax:* 313 745-2481
E-mail: raudritsh@med.wayne.edu
Length: 3 Yrs   *ACGME Approved/Offered Positions:* 18
Program ID: 156-25-21-116

Minnesota

Minneapolis

University of Minnesota Program

Sponsor: University of Minnesota Medical School
University of Minnesota Medical Center, Division of Fairview
Prgm Director: Melissa B King-Biggs, MD
Department of Medicine - MMC 276
420 Delaware Street, SE
Minneapolis, MN 55455
Tel: 612 624-0999   *Fax:* 612 625-2174
E-mail: paccsedu@umn.edu
Length: 3 Yrs   *ACGME Approved/Offered Positions:* 13
Program ID: 156-26-21-109

Rochester

College of Medicine, Mayo Clinic (Rochester) Program

Sponsor: College of Medicine, Mayo Clinic
Mayo Clinic (Rochester)
Saint Marys Hospital of Rochester
Prgm Director: Ulrich Specks, MD
Gonda 18S, Pulmonary and Critical Care
200 First Street SW
Rochester, MN 55905
Tel: 507 284-2964   *Fax:* 507 266-4372
Length: 3 Yrs   *ACGME Approved/Offered Positions:* 15
Program ID: 156-26-21-034

Mississippi

Jackson

University of Mississippi Medical Center Program

Sponsor: University of Mississippi School of Medicine
University Hospitals and Clinics
Veterans Affairs Medical Center (Jackson)
Prgm Director: Douglas Campbell, MD
Division of Pulmonary and Critical Care Medicine
2500 N State Street
Jackson, MS 39216
Tel: 601 984-5650   *Fax:* 601 984-5658
E-mail: dhaynes@medicine.umsmed.edu
Length: 3 Yrs   *ACGME Approved/Offered Positions:* 7
Program ID: 156-27-12-124

Missouri

Columbia

University of Missouri-Columbia Program

Sponsor: University of Missouri-Columbia School of Medicine
Harry S Truman Memorial Veterans Hospital
University Hospitals and Clinics
Prgm Director: Rajiv Dhand, MD
Five Hospital Drive
CEC 404, Clinical Support and Education Building
Columbia, MO 65212
Tel: 573 882-9072   *Fax:* 573 884-4892
Length: 3 Yrs   *ACGME Approved/Offered Positions:* 9
Program ID: 156-28-21-035

Kansas City

University of Missouri at Kansas City Program

Sponsor: University of Missouri-Kansas City School of Medicine
St Luke's Hospital-Kansas City
Truman Medical Center
Prgm Director: Gary Salzman, MD
2411 Holmes
Kansas City, MO 64108
Tel: 816 235-1974   *Fax:* 816 235-5514
E-mail: gleeses@umkc.edu
Length: 3 Yrs   *ACGME Approved/Offered Positions:* 6
Program ID: 156-28-31-036

St Louis

St Louis University School of Medicine Program

Sponsor: St Louis University School of Medicine
St John's Mercy Medical Center
St Louis University Hospital
Prgm Director: George M Matuschak, MD*
1402 South Grand Boulevard, 7th Fl Desloge Towers
Pulmonary Disease/Critical Care Medicine
St Louis, MO 63104
Tel: 314 577-8856   *Fax:* 314 577-8859
E-mail: kstot@att.net
Length: 3 Yrs   *ACGME Approved/Offered Positions:* 6
Program ID: 156-28-12-038

Washington University/B-JH/SLCH Consortium Program

Sponsor: Washington University/B-JH/SLCH Consortium
Barnes-Jewish Hospital
Washington University School of Medicine
Prgm Director: Daniel B Rosenbluth, MD
Box 8052
660 S Euclid Avenue
St Louis, MO 63110
Tel: 314 454-8762   *Fax:* 314 454-7524
E-mail: lwetzel@im.wustl.edu
Length: 3 Yrs   *ACGME Approved/Offered Positions:* 15
Program ID: 156-28-11-037

Nebraska

Omaha

Creighton University Program

Sponsor: Creighton University School of Medicine
Creighton University Medical Center (Tenet - SJH)
Veterans Affairs Medical Center (Omaha)
Prgm Director: Lee E Morrow, MD, MS
601 North 30th Street
Suite 3820
Omaha, NE 68131
Tel: 402 449-5680   *Fax:* 402 280-5256
E-mail: lmorrow@creighton.edu
Length: 3 Yrs   *ACGME Approved/Offered Positions:* 6
Program ID: 156-30-21-103

Note: * indicates a newly appointed program director

University of Nebraska Medical Center College of Medicine Program

Sponsor: University of Nebraska Medical Center College of Medicine
Nebraska Medical Center
Prgm Director: Craig A Piquette, MD
Pulmonary and Critical Care Medicine Section
Box 985300 Nebraska Medical Center
Omaha, NE 68198
Tel: 402 943-5515   *Fax:* 402 977-5697
E-mail: slatense@unmc.edu
Length: 3 Yrs   *ACGME Approved/Offered Positions:* 9
Program ID: 156-30-21-093

New Hampshire

Lebanon

Dartmouth-Hitchcock Medical Center Program

Sponsor: Mary Hitchcock Memorial Hospital
Veterans Affairs Medical Center (White River Junction)
Prgm Director: H Worth Parker, MD*
Department of Medicine
1 Medical Center Drive
Lebanon, NH 03756
Tel: 603 650-5533   *Fax:* 603 650-0580
Length: 3 Yrs   *ACGME Approved/Offered Positions:* 3
Program ID: 156-32-21-039

New Jersey

Camden

UMDNJ-Robert Wood Johnson Medical School (Camden) Program

Sponsor: Cooper Hospital-University Medical Center
Prgm Director: Ramya Lotano, MD
Three Cooper Plaza, Suite 312
Camden, NJ 08103
Tel: 856 342-2407   *Fax:* 856 541-3968
E-mail: lotano-ramya@cooperhealth.edu
Length: 3 Yrs   *ACGME Approved/Offered Positions:* 6
Program ID: 156-33-21-040

New Brunswick

UMDNJ-Robert Wood Johnson Medical School Program

Sponsor: UMDNJ-Robert Wood Johnson Medical School
Deborah Heart and Lung Center
Robert Wood Johnson University Hospital
University Medical Center at Princeton
Veterans Affairs New Jersey Health Care System
Prgm Director: Andrew A Martin, MD
Dept of Medicine, Div of Pulmonary/CCM-MEB 568
One Robert Wood Johnson Place
New Brunswick, NJ 08903
Tel: 732 235-7840   *Fax:* 732 235-7048
Length: 3 Yrs   *ACGME Approved/Offered Positions:* 6
Program ID: 156-33-11-042

Newark

Newark Beth Israel Medical Center Program

Sponsor: Newark Beth Israel Medical Center
Prgm Director: Jennifer A LaRosa, MD, BA*
400 Osborne Terrace
Suite L4
Newark, NJ 07112
Tel: 973 926-7929   *Fax:* 973 923-8063
E-mail: jlarosa@sbhcs.com
Length: 3 Yrs   *ACGME Approved/Offered Positions:* 6
Program ID: 156-33-21-132

UMDNJ-New Jersey Medical School Program

Sponsor: UMDNJ-New Jersey Medical School
Hackensack University Medical Center
UMDNJ-University Hospital
Veterans Affairs New Jersey Health Care System
Prgm Director: Zaza Cohen, MD
150 Bergen Street
University Hospital, I-354
Newark, NJ 07103
Tel: 973 972-6111   *Fax:* 973 972-6228
Length: 3 Yrs   *ACGME Approved/Offered Positions:* 12
Program ID: 156-33-31-041

New Mexico

Albuquerque

University of New Mexico Program

Sponsor: University of New Mexico School of Medicine
University of New Mexico Hospital
Veterans Affairs Medical Center (Albuquerque)
Prgm Director: Helen K Busby, MD
1 University of New Mexico
MSC 10-5550
Albuquerque, NM 87131
Tel: 505 272-4751   *Fax:* 505 272-8700
E-mail: afinkenhoefer@salud.unm.edu
Length: 3 Yrs   *ACGME Approved/Offered Positions:* 6
Program ID: 156-34-21-108

New York

Albany

Albany Medical Center Program

Sponsor: Albany Medical Center
Veterans Affairs Medical Center (Albany)
Prgm Director: Scott Beegle, MD
Department of Medicine MC 17
43 New Scotland Avenue
Albany, NY 12208
Tel: 518 262-5196   *Fax:* 518 262-6472
E-mail: brozowml@mail.amc.edu
Length: 3 Yrs   *ACGME Approved/Offered Positions:* 6
Program ID: 156-35-21-043

Bronx

Albert Einstein College of Medicine Program

Sponsor: Albert Einstein College of Medicine of Yeshiva University
Montefiore Medical Center-Henry and Lucy Moses Division
North Bronx Healthcare Network-Jacobi Medical Center
Prgm Director: Andrew R Berman, MD
111 East 210th Street
Bronx, NY 10467
Tel: 718 920-6054   *Fax:* 718 904-2163
Length: 3 Yrs   *ACGME Approved/Offered Positions:* 12
Program ID: 156-35-21-092

Brooklyn

New York Methodist Hospital Program

Sponsor: New York Methodist Hospital
Prgm Director: Suhail Raoof, MD
506 Sixth Street
Brooklyn, NY 11215
Tel: 718 780-5835   *Fax:* 718 780-5836
Length: 3 Yrs   *ACGME Approved/Offered Positions:* 6
Program ID: 156-35-31-135

SUNY Health Science Center at Brooklyn Program

Sponsor: SUNY Health Science Center at Brooklyn
Prgm Director: A Ross Hill, MD
450 Clarkson Avenue, Box 19
Brooklyn, NY 11203
Tel: 718 453-3690   *Fax:* 718 270-1733
Length: 3 Yrs   *ACGME Approved/Offered Positions:* 18
Program ID: 156-35-12-137

Buffalo

University at Buffalo Program

Sponsor: University at Buffalo School of Medicine
Kaleida Health System (Buffalo General Hospital)
Veterans Affairs Western New York Hospital
Prgm Director: M Jeffrey Mador, MD
3595 Bailey Ave
Buffalo, NY 14215
Tel: 716 862-8629   *Fax:* 716 862-8632
E-mail: mador@buffalo.edu
Length: 3 Yrs   *ACGME Approved/Offered Positions:* 7
Program ID: 156-35-31-044

Flushing

New York Hospital Medical Center of Queens/Cornell University Medical College Program

Sponsor: New York Hospital Medical Center of Queens
Prgm Director: Stephen R Karbowitz, MD
56-45 Main Street
Flushing, NY 11355
Tel: 718 670-1405   *Fax:* 718 461-2943
Length: 3 Yrs   *ACGME Approved/Offered Positions:* 4
Program ID: 156-35-13-143

Great Neck

NSLIJHS-Albert Einstein College of Medicine at Long Island Jewish Medical Center Program

Sponsor: North Shore-Long Island Jewish Health System
Long Island Jewish Medical Center
Prgm Director: Mark J Rosen, MD
270-05 76th Avenue
New Hyde Park, NY 11040
Tel: 516 465-5433   *Fax:* 516 465-5454
Length: 3 Yrs   *ACGME Approved/Offered Positions:* 6
Program ID: 156-35-13-047

NSLIJHS-North Shore University Hospital/NYU School of Medicine Program

Sponsor: North Shore-Long Island Jewish Health System
North Shore University Hospital
Prgm Director: Effie Singas, MD
300 Community Drive
Manhasset, NY 11030
Tel: 516 465-5402
E-mail: ydicanio@lij.edu
Length: 3 Yrs   *ACGME Approved/Offered Positions:* 6
Program ID: 156-35-11-045

Mineola

Winthrop-University Hospital Program

Sponsor: Winthrop-University Hospital
Prgm Director: Jonathan S Ilowite, MD
222 Station Plaza North, Suite 400
Mineola, NY 11501
Tel: 516 663-2004   *Fax:* 516 663-4888
Length: 3 Yrs   *ACGME Approved/Offered Positions:* 7
Program ID: 156-35-12-046

Programs

New York

Albert Einstein College of Medicine at Beth Israel Medical Center Program

Sponsor: Beth Israel Medical Center
Prgm Director: Patricia C Villamena, MD*
Department of Medicine
First Avenue at 16th Street
New York, NY 10003
Tel: 212 420-2377   *Fax:* 212 420-4684
E-mail: pvillame@chpnet.org
Length: 3 Yrs   *ACGME Approved/Offered Positions:* 9
Program ID: 156-35-22-048

Mount Sinai School of Medicine Program

Sponsor: Mount Sinai School of Medicine
Elmhurst Hospital Center-Mount Sinai Services
Mount Sinai Medical Center
Queens Hospital Center
Prgm Director: Scott Lorin, MD
Department of Medicine
One Gustave L Levy Place
New York, NY 10029
Tel: 212 241-7389   *Fax:* 212 876-5519
Length: 3 Yrs   *ACGME Approved/Offered Positions:* 19
Program ID: 156-35-23-049

New York Medical College at St Vincent's Hospital and Medical Center of New York Program

Sponsor: New York Medical College
St Vincent Catholic Medical Centers (Manhattan)
Prgm Director: Joseph C Cicenia III, MD*
153 West 11th Street
Cronin 554a
New York, NY 10011
Tel: 212 604-2892   *Fax:* 212 604-3667
Length: 3 Yrs   *ACGME Approved/Offered Positions:* 6
Program ID: 156-35-11-052

New York Presbyterian Hospital (Columbia Campus) Program

Sponsor: New York Presbyterian Hospital
New York Presbyterian Hospital (Columbia Campus)
Prgm Director: Charles A Powell, MD
630 W 168th Street
New York, NY 10032
Tel: 212 305-9817   *Fax:* 212 305-8464
E-mail: ac2409@columbia.edu
Length: 3 Yrs   *ACGME Approved/Offered Positions:* 12
Program ID: 156-35-13-125

New York Presbyterian Hospital (Cornell Campus) Program

Sponsor: New York Presbyterian Hospital
New York Presbyterian Hospital (Cornell Campus)
Prgm Director: Ronald G Crystal, MD
525 East 68th Street, Starr 505
Box 96
New York, NY 10021
Tel: 212 746-2258   *Fax:* 212 746-8808
Length: 3 Yrs   *ACGME Approved/Offered Positions:* 15
Program ID: 156-35-21-083

New York University School of Medicine Program

Sponsor: New York University School of Medicine
Bellevue Hospital Center
Prgm Director: Doreen J Addrizzo-Harris, MD
550 First Avenue
New York, NY 10016
Tel: 212 263-6479   *Fax:* 212 263-8442
Length: 3 Yrs   *ACGME Approved/Offered Positions:* 22
Program ID: 156-35-21-050

St Luke's-Roosevelt Hospital Center Program

Sponsor: St Luke's-Roosevelt Hospital Center
Prgm Director: Edward Eden, MD
1000 10th Avenue
New York, NY 10019
Tel: 212 523-7352   *Fax:* 212 523-8426
Length: 3 Yrs   *ACGME Approved/Offered Positions:* 6
Program ID: 156-35-31-051

Rochester

University of Rochester Program

Sponsor: Strong Memorial Hospital of the University of Rochester
Prgm Director: David Trawick, MD, PhD
Pulmonary and Critical Care Division
601 Elmwood Avenue, Box 692
Rochester, NY 14642
Tel: 585 275-4861   *Fax:* 585 273-1114
E-mail: david_trawick@urmc.rochester.edu
Length: 3 Yrs   *ACGME Approved/Offered Positions:* 9
Program ID: 156-35-31-099

Stony Brook

SUNY at Stony Brook Program

Sponsor: University Hospital - SUNY at Stony Brook
Veterans Affairs Medical Center (Northport)
Prgm Director: Hussein D Foda, MD
HSC 17-040
Stony Brook, NY 11794
Tel: 631 444-3869   *Fax:* 631 444-7502
Length: 3 Yrs   *ACGME Approved/Offered Positions:* 9
Program ID: 156-35-21-106

Syracuse

SUNY Upstate Medical University Program

Sponsor: SUNY Upstate Medical University
Veterans Affairs Medical Center (Syracuse)
Prgm Director: Robert J Lenox, MD
750 East Adams Street
Syracuse, NY 13210
Tel: 315 464-4184   *Fax:* 315 464-6228
Length: 3 Yrs   *ACGME Approved/Offered Positions:* 8
Program ID: 156-35-12-053

Valhalla

New York Medical College at Westchester Medical Center Program

Sponsor: New York Medical College
Metropolitan Hospital Center
St Vincent's Medical Center
Westchester Medical Center
Prgm Director: Dipak Chandy, MD
Pulmonary Laboratory
Macy Pavilion, 1st Floor
Valhalla, NY 10595
Tel: 914 493-7518   *Fax:* 914 493-8130
E-mail: chandyd@wcmc.com
Length: 3 Yrs   *ACGME Approved/Offered Positions:* 8
Program ID: 156-35-13-054

North Carolina

Chapel Hill

University of North Carolina Hospitals Program

Sponsor: University of North Carolina Hospitals
Prgm Director: Shannon S Carson, MD
Div of Pulm/Critical Care Medicine, CB#7020
4124 Bioinformatics Bldg, 130 Mason Farm Rd
Chapel Hill, NC 27599
Tel: 919 966-2531   *Fax:* 919 966-7013
E-mail: Shannon_Carson@med.unc.edu
Length: 3 Yrs   *ACGME Approved/Offered Positions:* 10
Program ID: 156-36-21-055

Durham

Duke University Hospital Program

Sponsor: Duke University Hospital
Veterans Affairs Medical Center (Durham)
Prgm Director: Loretta G Que, MD
Box 3315 Room 0570 Duke South
Durham, NC 27710
Tel: 919 668-4289   *Fax:* 919 668-0494
E-mail: que00001@mc.duke.edu
Length: 3 Yrs   *ACGME Approved/Offered Positions:* 18
Program ID: 156-36-21-117

Greenville

Pitt County Memorial hospital/East Carolina University Program

Sponsor: Pitt County Memorial Hospital
Brody School of Medicine at East Carolina University
Prgm Director: Thomson C Pancoast, MD
600 Moye Boulevard, Suite 3E 149
Greenville, NC 27858
Tel: 252 744-2543   *Fax:* 252 744-4887
Length: 3 Yrs   *ACGME Approved/Offered Positions:* 4
Program ID: 156-36-31-133

Winston-Salem

Wake Forest University School of Medicine Program

Sponsor: Wake Forest University Baptist Medical Center
Prgm Director: Wendy C Moore, MD
Medical Center Boulevard
Winston-Salem, NC 27157
Tel: 336 713-7520   *Fax:* 336 713-7544
E-mail: wmoore@wfubmc.edu
Length: 3 Yrs   *ACGME Approved/Offered Positions:* 12
Program ID: 156-36-21-094

Ohio

Cincinnati

University Hospital/University of Cincinnati College of Medicine Program

Sponsor: University Hospital Inc
Veterans Affairs Medical Center (Cincinnati)
Prgm Director: Mitchell C Rashkin, MD
PO Box 670564
Cincinnati, OH 45267
Tel: 513 558-4831   *Fax:* 513 558-4858
E-mail: mitchell.rashkin@uc.edu
Length: 3 Yrs   *ACGME Approved/Offered Positions:* 12
Program ID: 156-38-21-056

Note: * indicates a newly appointed program director

Cleveland

Case Western Reserve University (MetroHealth) Program
Sponsor: MetroHealth Medical Center
Prgm Director: Dennis H Auckley, MD
Department of Medicine
2500 MetroHealth Drive
Cleveland, OH 44109
Tel: 216 778-3925   *Fax:* 216 778-3240
Length: 3 Yrs   *ACGME Approved/Offered Positions:* 9
Program ID: 156-38-31-057

Cleveland Clinic Foundation Program
Sponsor: Cleveland Clinic Foundation
Prgm Director: Peter J Mazzone, MD, MPH
Respiratory Institute
9500 Euclid Avenue, A90
Cleveland, OH 44195
Tel: 216 445-4812   *Fax:* 216 445-8160
E-mail: mazzonp@ccf.org
Length: 3 Yrs   *ACGME Approved/Offered Positions:* 18
Program ID: 156-38-11-058

University Hospitals Case Medical Center Program
Sponsor: University Hospitals Case Medical Center
Veterans Affairs Medical Center (Cleveland)
Prgm Director: Rana B Hejal, MD
11100 Euclid Avenue
Department of Pulmonary Medicine
Cleveland, OH 44106
Tel: 216 983-0871   *Fax:* 216 844-8708
Length: 3 Yrs   *ACGME Approved/Offered Positions:* 9
Program ID: 156-38-21-110

Columbus

Ohio State University Hospital Program
Sponsor: Ohio State University Hospital
Arthur G James Cancer Hospital and Research Institute
Prgm Director: John G Mastronarde, MD
Department of Internal Medicine
473 W 12th Avenue, 201 HLRI
Columbus, OH 43210
Tel: 614 247-7707   *Fax:* 614 293-4799
E-mail: john.mastronarde@osumc.edu
Length: 3 Yrs   *ACGME Approved/Offered Positions:* 15
Program ID: 156-38-12-059

Toledo

University of Toledo Program
Sponsor: University of Toledo
University Medical Center (Toledo)
Prgm Director: Dan E Olson, MD, PhD
3000 Arlington Avenue
Mail Stop 1186
Toledo, OH 43614
Tel: 419 383-3543   *Fax:* 419 383-6243
Length: 3 Yrs   *ACGME Approved/Offered Positions:* 6
Program ID: 156-38-21-087

Oklahoma

Oklahoma City

University of Oklahoma Health Sciences Center Program
Sponsor: University of Oklahoma College of Medicine
OU Medical Center
Veterans Affairs Medical Center (Oklahoma City)
Prgm Director: Paul V Carlile, MD
920 Stanton L Young Boulevard, WP1310
Oklahoma City, OK 73104
Tel: 405 271-6173   *Fax:* 405 271-5892
E-mail: priscilla-peer@ouhsc.edu
Length: 3 Yrs   *ACGME Approved/Offered Positions:* 12
Program ID: 156-39-21-060

Oregon

Portland

Oregon Health & Science University Program
Sponsor: Oregon Health & Science University Hospital
Veterans Affairs Medical Center (Portland)
Prgm Director: Dane Nichols, MD
3181 SW Sam Jackson Park Road
Mailcode UHN 67
Portland, OR 97239
Tel: 503 494-6668   *Fax:* 503 494-6670
Length: 3 Yrs   *ACGME Approved/Offered Positions:* 10
Program ID: 156-40-21-061

Pennsylvania

Hershey

Penn State University/Milton S Hershey Medical Center Program
Sponsor: Milton S Hershey Medical Center
Prgm Director: Margaret M Wojnar, MD
University Hospital
500 University Drive
Hershey, PA 17033
Tel: 717 531-6525   *Fax:* 717 531-5785
Length: 3 Yrs   *ACGME Approved/Offered Positions:* 9
Program ID: 156-41-21-119

Philadelphia

Albert Einstein Healthcare Network Program
Sponsor: Albert Einstein Medical Center
Prgm Director: Michael Lippmann, MD
5401 Old York Road, Klein 363
Philadelphia, PA 19141
Tel: 215 456-6950   *Fax:* 215 455-1933
Length: 3 Yrs   *ACGME Approved/Offered Positions:* 6
Program ID: 156-41-13-127

Drexel University College of Medicine/Hahnemann University Hospital Program
Sponsor: Drexel University College of Medicine/Hahnemann University
Hahnemann University Hospital (Tenet Health System)
Prgm Director: Michael S Sherman, MD
245 North 15th street, MS 107
Philadelphia, PA 19102
Tel: 215 762-7013   *Fax:* 215 762-8728
E-mail: pulmonary.fellowship@drexel.edu
Length: 3 Yrs   *ACGME Approved/Offered Positions:* 10
Program ID: 156-41-21-062

Temple University Hospital Program
Sponsor: Temple University Hospital
Prgm Director: Kathleen J Brennan, MD*
3401 North Broad Street
7th Floor Parkinson Pavilion
Philadelphia, PA 19140
Tel: 215 707-2237   *Fax:* 215 707-6867
Length: 3 Yrs   *ACGME Approved/Offered Positions:* 12
Program ID: 156-41-11-064

Thomas Jefferson University Program
Sponsor: Thomas Jefferson University Hospital
Prgm Director: Michael Baram, MD*
834 Walnut Street
Suite 650
Philadelphia, PA 19107
Tel: 215 955-6591   *Fax:* 215 955-0830
E-mail: michael.baram@jefferson.edu
Length: 3 Yrs   *ACGME Approved/Offered Positions:* 12
Program ID: 156-41-12-065

University of Pennsylvania Program
Sponsor: University of Pennsylvania Health System
Prgm Director: Robert M Kotloff, MD
3400 Spruce Street
838 W Gates Bldg
Philadelphia, PA 19104
Tel: 215 349-5488   *Fax:* 215 614-0869
Length: 3 Yrs   *ACGME Approved/Offered Positions:* 18
Program ID: 156-41-21-088

Pittsburgh

Allegheny General Hospital Program
Sponsor: Allegheny General Hospital
Prgm Director: Brian W Carlin, MD
320 East North Avenue
Pittsburgh, PA 15212
Tel: 412 359-3038   *Fax:* 412 359-6609
E-mail: bcarlin@wpahs.org
Length: 3 Yrs   *ACGME Approved/Offered Positions:* 9
Program ID: 156-41-21-139

University of Pittsburgh Medical Center Medical Education Program
Sponsor: Univ of Pittsburgh Medical Center Medical Education
UPMC Presbyterian Shadyside
Prgm Director: John W Kreit, MD
628 NW Montefiore Hospital
3459 Fifth Avenue
Pittsburgh, PA 15213
Tel: 412 692-2118   *Fax:* 412 692-2260
Length: 3 Yrs   *ACGME Approved/Offered Positions:* 18
Program ID: 156-41-13-066

Puerto Rico

San Juan

VA Caribbean Healthcare System Program
Sponsor: VA Caribbean Healthcare System
Prgm Director: William Rodriguez-Cintron, MD
10 Casia Street
OPA Building, IF218
San Juan, PR 00921
Tel: 787 641-7582   *Fax:* 787 641-9541
Length: 3 Yrs   *ACGME Approved/Offered Positions:* 6
Program ID: 156-42-21-126

Rhode Island

Providence

Brown University Program
Sponsor: Rhode Island Hospital-Lifespan
Memorial Hospital of Rhode Island
Roger Williams Medical Center
Veterans Affairs Medical Center (Providence)
Prgm Director: Nicholas S Ward, MD
593 Eddy Street
Providence, RI 02903
Tel: 401 444-8760   *Fax:* 401 444-5914
Length: 3 Yrs   *ACGME Approved/Offered Positions:* 12
Program ID: 156-43-21-121

South Carolina

Charleston

Medical University of South Carolina Program

Sponsor: Medical University of South Carolina College of Medicine
MUSC Medical Center
Prgm Director: Marc A Judson, MD*
96 Jonathan Lucas Street
MSC 630, Room 812 CSB
Charleston, SC 29425
Tel: 843 792-3162   *Fax:* 843 792-0732
Length: 3 Yrs   *ACGME Approved/Offered Positions:* 12
Program ID: 156-45-21-067

Tennessee

Johnson City

East Tennessee State University Program

Sponsor: James H Quillen College of Medicine
Johnson City Medical Center/Mountain States Health Alliance
Veterans Affairs Medical Center (Mountain Home)
Wellmont Health System - Bristol Regional Medical Center
Prgm Director: Ryland P Byrd Jr, MD
Pulmonary Division
Mountain Home, TN 37684
Tel: 423 926-1171   *Fax:* 423 979-3471
E-mail: ryland.byrd@med.va.gov
Length: 3 Yrs   *ACGME Approved/Offered Positions:* 6
Program ID: 156-47-31-122

Memphis

University of Tennessee Program

Sponsor: University of Tennessee College of Medicine
Methodist Healthcare - Memphis Hospitals
Regional Medical Center at Memphis
Veterans Affairs Medical Center (Memphis)
Prgm Director: Muthiah P Muthiah, MD
Pulmonary, Critical Care, & Sleep Medicine
956 Court Avenue, Room H-314
Memphis, TN 38163
Tel: 901 448-5311   *Fax:* 901 448-7726
Length: 3 Yrs   *ACGME Approved/Offered Positions:* 9
Program ID: 156-47-21-118

Nashville

Vanderbilt University Program

Sponsor: Vanderbilt University Medical Center
Veterans Affairs Medical Center (Nashville)
Prgm Director: John H Newman, MD
Div of Allergy, Pulmonary & Critical Care Med
T-1217 Medical Center North
Nashville, TN 37232
Tel: 615 322-6943   *Fax:* 615 343-1809
E-mail: michael.t.beasley@vanderbilt.edu
Length: 3 Yrs   *ACGME Approved/Offered Positions:* 12
Program ID: 156-47-21-068

Texas

Dallas

University of Texas Southwestern Medical School Program

Sponsor: University of Texas Southwestern Medical School
Dallas County Hospital District-Parkland Memorial Hospital
Dallas VA Medical Center
University Hospitals St Paul
Prgm Director: W Douglas Pitcher, MD
Pulmonary Disease Department
5323 Harry Hines Blvd
Dallas, TX 75235
Tel: 214 688-3429   *Fax:* 214 857-0520
E-mail: Becky.Ward@va.gov
Length: 3 Yrs   *ACGME Approved/Offered Positions:* 14
Program ID: 156-48-21-069

Fort Sam Houston

San Antonio Uniformed Services Health Education Consortium Program

Sponsor: San Antonio Uniformed Services Health Education Consortium
Brooke Army Medical Center
Wilford Hall Medical Center (AETC)
Prgm Director: Kenneth R Kemp, MD
Wilford Hall Medical Center/MCCP
2200 Bergquist Drive, Suite 1
Lackland AFB, TX 78236
Tel: 210 916-0325   *Fax:* 210 292-6180
Length: 3 Yrs   *ACGME Approved/Offered Positions:* 12
Program ID: 156-48-21-070
Uniformed Services Program

Galveston

University of Texas Medical Branch Hospitals Program

Sponsor: University of Texas Medical Branch Hospitals
Prgm Director: Alexander G Duarte, MD
Division of Pulmonary and Critical Care Medicine
5.112 John Sealy Annex, Rte 0561
Galveston, TX 77555
Tel: 409 772-2436   *Fax:* 409 772-9532
Length: 3 Yrs   *ACGME Approved/Offered Positions:* 9
Program ID: 156-48-21-112

Houston

Baylor College of Medicine Program

Sponsor: Baylor College of Medicine
Harris County Hospital District-Ben Taub General Hospital
Methodist Hospital (Houston)
Michael E DeBakey VA Medical Center - Houston
Prgm Director: Kalpalatha K Guntupalli, MD
Pulmonary and Critical Care Section of Medicine
1709 Dryden, Ste 900
Houston, TX 77030
Tel: 713 798-2435   *Fax:* 713 873-2373
E-mail: kkg@bcm.tmc.edu
Length: 3 Yrs   *ACGME Approved/Offered Positions:* 21
Program ID: 156-48-21-084

University of Texas at Houston Program

Sponsor: University of Texas Health Science Center at Houston
Lyndon B Johnson General Hospital
Memorial Hermann Hospital
University of Texas M D Anderson Cancer Center
Prgm Director: Bela Patel, MD
Division of Pulmonary, Critical Care and Sleep Med
6431 Fannin St, Suite 1.274
Houston, TX 77030
Tel: 713 500-6833   *Fax:* 713 500-6829
Length: 3 Yrs   *ACGME Approved/Offered Positions:* 10
Program ID: 156-48-31-071

San Antonio

University of Texas Health Science Center at San Antonio Program

Sponsor: University of Texas School of Medicine at San Antonio
Audie L Murphy Memorial Veterans Hospital (San Antonio)
University Health System
Prgm Director: Stephanie M Levine, MD
7703 Floyd Curl Drive
MC 7885
San Antonio, TX 78229
Tel: 210 617-5256   *Fax:* 210 949-3006
E-mail: levines@uthscsa.edu
Length: 3 Yrs   *ACGME Approved/Offered Positions:* 9
Program ID: 156-48-11-072

Temple

Texas A&M College of Medicine-Scott and White Program

Sponsor: Scott and White Memorial Hospital
Central Texas Veterans Affairs Healthcare System
Prgm Director: Dennis L Myers, MD
2401 South 31st Street
Temple, TX 76508
Tel: 254 724-2111   *Fax:* 254 724-9280
E-mail: dmyers@swmail.sw.org
Length: 3 Yrs   *ACGME Approved/Offered Positions:* 12
Program ID: 156-48-21-128

Utah

Salt Lake City

University of Utah Program

Sponsor: University of Utah Medical Center
LDS Hospital
Prgm Director: Karl A Sanders, MD
30 North 1900 East
Salt Lake City, UT 84132
Tel: 801 581-7806
Length: 3 Yrs   *ACGME Approved/Offered Positions:* 12
Program ID: 156-49-21-089

Vermont

Burlington

University of Vermont Program

Sponsor: Fletcher Allen Health Care
Prgm Director: David A Kaminsky, MD
Pulmonary and Critical Care Medicine Unit
MCHV Campus Smith 140
Burlington, VT 05405
Tel: 802 847-6177   *Fax:* 802 847-8194
E-mail: pulmonary@vtmednet.org
Length: 3 Yrs   *ACGME Approved/Offered Positions:* 6
Program ID: 156-50-21-111

Virginia

Charlottesville

University of Virginia Program

Sponsor: University of Virginia Medical Center
Prgm Director: Charles E Rose, MD*
Pulmonary/Critical Care
PO Box 800546
Charlottesville, VA 22908
Tel: 434 243-4845   *Fax:* 434 924-9682
Length: 3 Yrs   *ACGME Approved/Offered Positions:* 6
Program ID: 156-51-21-085

Note: * indicates a newly appointed program director

Richmond

Virginia Commonwealth University Health System Program

Sponsor: Virginia Commonwealth University Health System
Hunter Holmes McGuire VA Medical Center (Richmond)
Medical College of Virginia Hospitals
Prgm Director: Lisa K Brath, MD
1200 E Broad Street
PO Box 980050
Richmond, VA 23298
Tel: 804 828-9071   *Fax:* 804 828-2578
E-mail: lbrath@mcvh-vcu.edu
Length: 3 Yrs   *ACGME Approved/Offered Positions:* 9
Program ID: 156-51-21-073

Washington

Seattle

University of Washington Program

Sponsor: University of Washington School of Medicine
Prgm Director: Mark R Tonelli, MD, MA
Division of Pulmonary & Critical Care Medicine
BB-1253 Health Sciences Center, Box 356522
Seattle, WA 98195
Tel: 206 543-3166   *Fax:* 206 685-8673
E-mail: pccmfelo@u.washington.edu
Length: 3 Yrs   *ACGME Approved/Offered Positions:* 21
Program ID: 156-54-21-074

West Virginia

Morgantown

West Virginia University Program

Sponsor: West Virginia University School of Medicine
HealthSouth Mountain Regional Rehabilitation Hospital
Louis A Johnson Veterans Affairs Medical Center
West Virginia University Hospitals
Prgm Director: Luis Teba, MD
PO Box 9166
1 Medical Center Drive
Morgantown, WV 26506
Tel: 304 293-4661   *Fax:* 304 293-3724
Length: 3 Yrs   *ACGME Approved/Offered Positions:* 6
Program ID: 156-55-21-075

Wisconsin

Madison

University of Wisconsin Program

Sponsor: University of Wisconsin Hospital and Clinics
Prgm Director: Mark S Regan, MD
K4/910 Clinical Science Center 9988
600 Highland Avenue
Madison, WI 53792
Tel: 608 263-3035   *Fax:* 608 263-3104
Length: 3 Yrs   *ACGME Approved/Offered Positions:* 9
Program ID: 156-56-21-076

Milwaukee

Medical College of Wisconsin Affiliated Hospitals Program

Sponsor: Medical College of Wisconsin Affiliated Hospitals, Inc
Clement J Zablocki Veterans Affairs Medical Center
Froedtert Memorial Lutheran Hospital
St Luke's Medical Center
Prgm Director: Kenneth W Presberg, MD
Department of Medicine
9200 W Wisconsin Avenue
Milwaukee, WI 53226
Tel: 414 456-7040   *Fax:* 414 456-6211
E-mail: presberg@mcw.edu
Length: 3 Yrs   *ACGME Approved/Offered Positions:* 12
Program ID: 156-56-21-100

Radiation Oncology

Alabama

Birmingham

University of Alabama Medical Center Program

Sponsor: University of Alabama Hospital
Prgm Director: John Fiveash, MD
619 South 19th Street
WTI 116
Birmingham, AL 35249
Tel: 205 975-0224   *Fax:* 205 975-0784
Length: 4 Yrs   *ACGME Approved/Offered Positions:* 8
Program ID: 430-01-21-002

Arizona

Tucson

University of Arizona Program

Sponsor: University of Arizona College of Medicine
University Medical Center
Prgm Director: Scott P Tannehill, MD, BS*
1501 North Campbell Avenue
PO Box 245081
Tucson, AZ 85724
Tel: 520 626-6724   *Fax:* 520 626-3141
Length: 4 Yrs   *ACGME Approved/Offered Positions:* 6
Program ID: 430-03-11-003

California

Duarte

City of Hope National Medical Center Program

Sponsor: City of Hope National Medical Center
Prgm Director: Richard D Pezner, MD
1500 East Duarte Road
Duarte, CA 91010
Tel: 626 301-8247   *Fax:* 626 301-8496
E-mail: radiationresident@coh.org
Length: 4 Yrs   *ACGME Approved/Offered Positions:* 4
Program ID: 430-05-13-139

Loma Linda

Loma Linda University Program

Sponsor: Loma Linda University Medical Center
Prgm Director: David A Bush, MD
Department of Radiation Medicine
11234 Anderson Street B121
Loma Linda, CA 92354
Tel: 909 558-4280   *Fax:* 909 558-4083
E-mail: uharris@llu.edu
Length: 4 Yrs   *ACGME Approved/Offered Positions:* 5
Program ID: 430-05-21-006

Los Angeles

Kaiser Permanente Southern California (Los Angeles) Program

Sponsor: Kaiser Permanente Southern California
Kaiser Foundation Hospital (Los Angeles)
Prgm Director: Kenneth Lodin, MD
Department of Radiation Oncology
4950 Sunset Boulevard, 2nd Floor
Los Angeles, CA 90027
Tel: 323 783-2841   *Fax:* 323 783-5927
Length: 4 Yrs   *ACGME Approved/Offered Positions:* 8
Program ID: 430-05-21-115

Programs

UCLA Medical Center Program

Sponsor: UCLA David Geffen School of Medicine/UCLA Medical Center
UCLA Medical Center
Prgm Director: Steve P Lee, MD, PhD
Department of Radiation Oncology
200 Medical Plaza, Ste B-265
Los Angeles, CA 90095
Tel: 310 267-5575   *Fax:* 310 794-9795
E-mail: SPLee@mednet.ucla.edu
Length: 4 Yrs   *ACGME Approved/Offered Positions:* 6
Program ID: 430-05-21-008

University of Southern California/ LAC+USC Medical Center Program

Sponsor: University of Southern California/LAC+USC Medical Center
Kenneth Norris Jr Cancer Hospital and Research Institute
LAC+USC Medical Center
Prgm Director: Paul G Pagnini, MD
OPD 1P2
2010 Zonal Avenue
Los Angeles, CA 90033
Tel: 323 226-5017   *Fax:* 323 226-5970
E-mail: pagnini@usc.edu
Length: 4 Yrs   *ACGME Approved/Offered Positions:* 6
Program ID: 430-05-11-007

Orange

University of California (Irvine) Program

Sponsor: University of California (Irvine) Medical Center
City of Hope National Medical Center
Long Beach Memorial Medical Center
University of California (Irvine) College of Medicine
VA Long Beach Healthcare System
Prgm Director: Jeffrey V Kuo, MD
Department of Radiation Oncology
101 The City Drive, South/ B-23, Rte 26/ Zot-2690
Orange, CA 92868
Tel: 714 456-8074   *Fax:* 714 456-7170
E-mail: thuymt@uci.edu
Length: 4 Yrs   *ACGME Approved/Offered Positions:* 5
Program ID: 430-05-21-005

Sacramento

University of California (Davis) Health System Program

Sponsor: University of California (Davis) Health System
University of California (Davis) Medical Center
Prgm Director: Allen M Chen, MD*
4501 X Street, Suite G140
Sacramento, CA 95817
Tel: 916 734-8051
E-mail: allen.chen@ucdmc.ucdavis.edu
Length: 4 Yrs   *ACGME Approved/Offered Positions:* 5
Program ID: 430-05-22-132

San Francisco

California Pacific Medical Center Program

Sponsor: California Pacific Medical Center
Seton Medical Center
St Francis Memorial Hospital
Prgm Director: John W Lee, MD
Department of Radiation Oncology
2333 Buchanan Street
San Francisco, CA 94115
Tel: 415 600-3600   *Fax:* 415 600-3634
E-mail: cpmcradonc@sutterhealth.org
Length: 4 Yrs   *ACGME Approved/Offered Positions:* 4
Program ID: 430-05-22-012

University of California (San Francisco) Program

Sponsor: University of California (San Francisco) School of Medicine
UCSF and Mount Zion Medical Centers
Prgm Director: Daphne A Haas-Kogan, MD*
Department of Radiation Oncology
505 Parnassus Avenue, Room L-08
San Francisco, CA 94143
Tel: 415 353-7187   *Fax:* 415 353-9883
Length: 4 Yrs   *ACGME Approved/Offered Positions:* 12
Program ID: 430-05-21-013

Stanford

Stanford University Program

Sponsor: Stanford Hospital and Clinics
Prgm Director: Sarah S Donaldson, MD
Department of Radiation Oncology
875 Blake Wilbur Drive, G224
Stanford, CA 94305
Tel: 650 723-3865   *Fax:* 650 725-3865
Length: 4 Yrs   *ACGME Approved/Offered Positions:* 13
Program ID: 430-05-11-014

Colorado

Aurora

University of Colorado Denver Program

Sponsor: University of Colorado Denver School of Medicine
University of Colorado Hospital
Prgm Director: Arthur K Liu, MD*
1665 N Ursula Street, Suite 1032
PO Box 1650, MSTOP F-706
Aurora, CO 80045
Tel: 720 848-0156   *Fax:* 720 848-0238
E-mail: arthur.liu@uchsc.edu
Length: 4 Yrs   *ACGME Approved/Offered Positions:* 6
Program ID: 430-07-13-130

Connecticut

New Haven

Yale-New Haven Medical Center Program

Sponsor: Yale-New Haven Hospital
Lawrence and Memorial Hospitals
William W Backus Hospital
Prgm Director: Lynn D Wilson, MD, MPH
20 York St
New Haven, CT 06510
Tel: 203 737-1202   *Fax:* 203 785-2673
Length: 4 Yrs   *ACGME Approved/Offered Positions:* 9
Program ID: 430-08-11-017

District of Columbia

Washington

Georgetown University Hospital Program

Sponsor: Georgetown University Hospital
Washington Hospital Center
Prgm Director: Anatoly Dritschilo, MD*
Department of Radiation Medicine, Bles Bldg LL
3800 Reservoir Road, NW
Washington, DC 20007
Tel: 202 444-3062   *Fax:* 202 444-3786
E-mail: dritscha@georgetown.edu
Length: 4 Yrs   *ACGME Approved/Offered Positions:* 6
Program ID: 430-10-21-112

Florida

Gainesville

University of Florida Program

Sponsor: University of Florida College of Medicine
Shands Hospital at the University of Florida
Prgm Director: Robert J Amdur, MD
Shands Medical Plaza
PO Box 100385
Gainesville, FL 32610
Tel: 352 265-0287   *Fax:* 352 265-0759
E-mail: boonev@shands.ufl.edu
Length: 4 Yrs   *ACGME Approved/Offered Positions:* 9
Program ID: 430-11-12-022

Jacksonville

College of Medicine, Mayo Clinic (Jacksonville) Program

Sponsor: College of Medicine, Mayo Clinic
Mayo Clinic (Jacksonville)
Prgm Director: Steven J Buskirk, MD
4500 San Pablo Road
Jacksonville, FL 32224
Tel: 904 953-0490   *Fax:* 904 953-0430
E-mail: townsend.katherine@mayo.edu
Length: 4 Yrs   *ACGME Approved/Offered Positions:* 4
Program ID: 430-11-31-133

Miami

Jackson Memorial Hospital/Jackson Health System Program

Sponsor: Jackson Memorial Hospital/Jackson Health System
University of Miami Sylvester Comprehensive Cancer Center
Prgm Director: May Abdel-Wahab, MD
Dept of Radiation Therapy (D-31)
1475 Northwest 12th Avenue
Miami, FL 33136
Tel: 305 243-4210   *Fax:* 305 243-4363
Length: 4 Yrs   *ACGME Approved/Offered Positions:* 6
Program ID: 430-11-21-023

Tampa

University of South Florida Program

Sponsor: University of South Florida College of Medicine
H Lee Moffitt Cancer Center
James A Haley Veterans Hospital
Prgm Director: Eleanor Harris, MD
12902 Magnolia Drive
MCC-GME
Tampa, FL 33612
Tel: 813 745-8535   *Fax:* 813 745-5996
E-mail: mary.ostien@moffitt.org
Length: 4 Yrs   *ACGME Approved/Offered Positions:* 6
Program ID: 430-11-31-136

Georgia

Atlanta

Emory University Program

Sponsor: Emory University School of Medicine
Crawford Long Hospital of Emory University
Grady Health System
Veterans Affairs Medical Center (Atlanta)
Prgm Director: Ashesh Jani, MD
1365 Clifton Road, NE, Suite A1300
Atlanta, GA 30322
Tel: 404 778-4763   *Fax:* 404 778-4492
E-mail: ashesh@radonc.emory.org
Length: 4 Yrs   *ACGME Approved/Offered Positions:* 12
Program ID: 430-12-21-125

Note: * indicates a newly appointed program director

Illinois

Chicago

McGaw Medical Center of Northwestern University Program

Sponsor: McGaw Medical Center of Northwestern University
Northwestern Memorial Hospital
Prgm Director: Julia Choo, MD
Department of Radiation Oncology
251 East Huron St, L-178
Chicago, IL 60611
Tel: 312 926-2520   *Fax:* 312 926-6374
Length: 4 Yrs   *ACGME Approved/Offered Positions:* 8
Program ID: 430-16-21-027

Rush University Medical Center Program

Sponsor: Rush University Medical Center
Prgm Director: Katherine L Griem, MD, FACR
500 South Paulina, 013 Atrium
Department of Radiation Oncology
Chicago, IL 60612
Tel: 312 942-5751   *Fax:* 312 563-2857
E-mail: Katherine_L_Griem@rush.edu
Length: 4 Yrs   *ACGME Approved/Offered Positions:* 6
Program ID: 430-16-11-028

University of Chicago/University of Illinois College of Medicine at Chicago Program

Sponsor: University of Chicago Medical Center
Adventist La Grange Memorial Hospital
University of Illinois Hospital and Clinics
Prgm Director: Philip P Connell, MD
5758 South Maryland Avenue
MC 9006
Chicago, IL 60637
Tel: 773 702-4056   *Fax:* 773 834-7340
E-mail: dhallman@radonc.uchicago.edu
Length: 4 Yrs   *ACGME Approved/Offered Positions:* 12
Program ID: 430-16-11-116

Maywood

Loyola University Program

Sponsor: Loyola University Medical Center
Edward Hines, Jr Veterans Affairs Hospital
Prgm Director: Suneel Nagda, MD*
2160 South First Avenue
Maguire Center, Ste 2944
Maywood, IL 60153
Tel: 708 216-2562   *Fax:* 708 216-6076
E-mail: snagda@lumc.edu
Length: 4 Yrs   *ACGME Approved/Offered Positions:* 6
Program ID: 430-16-22-031

Indiana

Indianapolis

Indiana University School of Medicine Program

Sponsor: Indiana University School of Medicine
Clarian Indiana University Hospital
Richard L Roudebush Veterans Affairs Medical Center
Prgm Director: Mark P Langer, MD
Department of Radiation Oncology
535 Barnhill Drive, RT 041
Indianapolis, IN 46202
Tel: 317 274-1343   *Fax:* 317 274-2486
Length: 4 Yrs   *ACGME Approved/Offered Positions:* 7
Program ID: 430-17-11-032

Iowa

Iowa City

University of Iowa Hospitals and Clinics Program

Sponsor: University of Iowa Hospitals and Clinics
Prgm Director: Mark C Smith, MD
200 Hawkins Drive
Iowa City, IA 52242
Tel: 319 353-8836   *Fax:* 319 356-1530
E-mail: diane-crossett@uiowa.edu
Length: 4 Yrs   *ACGME Approved/Offered Positions:* 7
Program ID: 430-18-11-033

Kansas

Kansas City

University of Kansas School of Medicine Program

Sponsor: University of Kansas School of Medicine
University of Kansas Hospital
Prgm Director: Fen Wang, MD, PhD
3901 Rainbow Blvd
Kansas City, KS 66160
Tel: 913 588-3600   *Fax:* 913 588-3663
E-mail: fwang1@kumc.edu
Length: 4 Yrs   *ACGME Approved/Offered Positions:* 4
Program ID: 430-19-21-034

Kentucky

Lexington

University of Kentucky College of Medicine Program

Sponsor: University of Kentucky College of Medicine
University of Kentucky Hospital
Prgm Director: Mahesh Kudrimoti, MD
Department of Radiation Medicine
800 Rose Street
Lexington, KY 40536
Tel: 859 323-0283   *Fax:* 859 257-4931
E-mail: mkudr0@email.uky.edu
Length: 4 Yrs   *ACGME Approved/Offered Positions:* 4
Program ID: 430-20-11-035

Louisville

University of Louisville Program

Sponsor: University of Louisville School of Medicine
Floyd Memorial Hospital
University of Louisville Hospital
Prgm Director: William J Spanos, MD
James Graham Brown Cancer Center
529 South Jackson St
Louisville, KY 40202
Tel: 502 561-2700   *Fax:* 502 561-2709
E-mail: wjspan01@gwise.louisville.edu
Length: 4 Yrs   *ACGME Approved/Offered Positions:* 6
Program ID: 430-20-11-036

Maryland

Baltimore

Johns Hopkins University Program

Sponsor: Johns Hopkins University School of Medicine
Johns Hopkins Hospital
Prgm Director: Deborah A Frassica, MD
The Sidney Kimmell Comprehensive Cancer Center
401 North Broadway, Weinberg 1440
Baltimore, MD 21231
Tel: 410 955-7390   *Fax:* 410 502-1419
E-mail: frassde@jhmi.edu
Length: 4 Yrs   *ACGME Approved/Offered Positions:* 12
Program ID: 430-23-11-039

University of Maryland Program

Sponsor: University of Maryland Medical System
Prgm Director: William F Regine, MD
Department of Radiation Oncology
22 South Greene Street
Baltimore, MD 21201
Tel: 410 328-2326   *Fax:* 410 328-6911
E-mail: mmohiuddin@umm.edu
Length: 4 Yrs   *ACGME Approved/Offered Positions:* 8
Program ID: 430-23-21-040

Bethesda

National Capital Consortium Program

Sponsor: National Capital Consortium
National Cancer Institute
National Naval Medical Center (Bethesda)
Walter Reed Army Medical Center
Prgm Director: John J O'Connell, MD*
CRC Building 10, Room B2-3561
9000 Rockville Pike
Bethesda, MD 20892
Tel: 202 782-1886
Length: 4 Yrs   *ACGME Approved/Offered Positions:* 6
Program ID: 430-10-21-113
Uniformed Services Program

Massachusetts

Boston

Brigham and Women's Hospital/Massachusetts General Hospital/Harvard Medical School Program

Sponsor: Brigham and Women's Hospital
Beth Israel Deaconess Medical Center
Boston Medical Center
Dana-Farber Cancer Institute
Massachusetts General Hospital
Prgm Director: Jay R Harris, MD
Dana Farber Cancer Institute
44 Binney Street
Boston, MA 02215
Tel: 617 632-2291   *Fax:* 617 632-2290
Length: 4 Yrs   *ACGME Approved/Offered Positions:* 30
Program ID: 430-24-11-131

Tufts Medical Center Program

Sponsor: Tufts Medical Center
Rhode Island Hospital-Lifespan
Prgm Director: David E Wazer, MD
Department of Radiation Oncology
800 Washington Street, NEMC-359
Boston, MA 02111
Tel: 617 636-7673   *Fax:* 617 636-4513
Length: 4 Yrs   *ACGME Approved/Offered Positions:* 7
Program ID: 430-24-21-044

Programs

Michigan

Ann Arbor

University of Michigan Program
Sponsor: University of Michigan Hospitals and Health
  Centers
Prgm Director: Edgar Ben-Josef, MD
1500 East Medical Center Drive
UH-B2C490, SPC 5010
Ann Arbor, MI 48109
Tel: 734 936-8207   *Fax:* 734 763-7370
Length: 4 Yrs   *ACGME Approved/Offered Positions:* 11
Program ID: 430-25-11-045

Detroit

Henry Ford Hospital Program
Sponsor: Henry Ford Hospital
Prgm Director: Mohamed Elshaikh, MD
2799 West Grand Boulevard
Detroit, MI 48202
Tel: 313 916-1015   *Fax:* 313 916-3235
E-mail: melshai1@hfhs.org
Length: 4 Yrs   *ACGME Approved/Offered Positions:* 6
Program ID: 430-25-12-046

Wayne State University/Detroit Medical Center Program
Sponsor: Wayne State University/Detroit Medical Center
Huron Valley-Sinai Hospital
Karmanos Cancer Hospital
Sinai-Grace Hospital
Weisberg Cancer Treatment Center
Prgm Director: Maria T Vlachaki, MD, PhD
Department of Radiation Oncology - 1212 Scott Hall
540 E Canfield
Detroit, MI 48201
Tel: 313 966-2274   *Fax:* 313 966-9400
E-mail: mvlachaki@med.wayne.edu
Length: 4 Yrs   *ACGME Approved/Offered Positions:* 8
Program ID: 430-25-21-048

Royal Oak

William Beaumont Hospital Program
Sponsor: William Beaumont Hospital
Prgm Director: Inga S Grills, MD*
3601 West 13 Mile Road
Royal Oak, MI 48073
Tel: 248 551-7032   *Fax:* 248 551-0089
Length: 4 Yrs   *ACGME Approved/Offered Positions:* 12
Program ID: 430-25-12-049

Minnesota

Minneapolis

University of Minnesota Program
Sponsor: University of Minnesota Medical School
United Hospital
University of Minnesota Medical Center, Division of
  Fairview
University of Minnesota Physicians Radiation Therapy
  Center
Veterans Affairs Medical Center (Minneapolis)
Prgm Director: James B Orner, MD
UMHC MMC 494
420 Delaware Street SE
Minneapolis, MN 55455
Tel: 612 626-2631   *Fax:* 612 626-7060
Length: 4 Yrs   *ACGME Approved/Offered Positions:* 6
Program ID: 430-26-21-050

Rochester

College of Medicine, Mayo Clinic (Rochester) Program
Sponsor: College of Medicine, Mayo Clinic
Mayo Clinic (Rochester)
Prgm Director: Paul D Brown, MD
200 First Street SW
Rochester, MN 55905
Tel: 507 266-1175   *Fax:* 507 284-0079
E-mail: quinones.pamela@mayo.edu
Length: 4 Yrs   *ACGME Approved/Offered Positions:* 10
Program ID: 430-26-21-051

Missouri

St Louis

Washington University/B-JH/SLCH Consortium Program
Sponsor: Washington University/B-JH/SLCH Consortium
Barnes-Jewish Hospital
Prgm Director: Imran Zoberi, MD
Washington University School of Medicine
4921 Parkview Place - LL, Campus Box 8224
St Louis, MO 63110
Tel: 314 362-8525   *Fax:* 314 362-8521
E-mail: chuycke@radonc.wustl.edu
Length: 4 Yrs   *ACGME Approved/Offered Positions:* 14
Program ID: 430-28-11-054

New Jersey

New Brunswick

UMDNJ-Robert Wood Johnson Medical School Program
Sponsor: UMDNJ-Robert Wood Johnson Medical School
Robert Wood Johnson University Hospital
UMDNJ-University Hospital
Veterans Affairs New Jersey Health Care System
Prgm Director: Bruce Haffty, MD
Department of Radiation Oncology
195 Little Albany Street
New Brunswick, NJ 08903
Tel: 732 235-6181   *Fax:* 732 235-7493
Length: 4 Yrs   *ACGME Approved/Offered Positions:* 8
Program ID: 430-33-13-135

New York

Bronx

Albert Einstein College of Medicine Program
Sponsor: Albert Einstein College of Medicine of Yeshiva
  University
Montefiore Medical Center-Henry and Lucy Moses
  Division
Montefiore Medical Center-Weiler Division
Prgm Director: Marnee Spierer, MD
111 E 210th Street
Bronx, NY 10467
Tel: 718 920-2838   *Fax:* 718 231-5064
E-mail: mspierer@montefiore.org
Length: 4 Yrs   *ACGME Approved/Offered Positions:* 7
Program ID: 430-35-21-061

Brooklyn

New York Methodist Hospital Program
Sponsor: New York Methodist Hospital
Leading Edge Radiation Oncology Services
Prgm Director: Hosny Selim, MD
506 Sixth Street
Box 159-008
Brooklyn, NY 11215
Tel: 718 780-3677   *Fax:* 718 780-3637
Length: 4 Yrs   *ACGME Approved/Offered Positions:* 4
Program ID: 430-35-22-064

SUNY Health Science Center at Brooklyn Program
Sponsor: SUNY Health Science Center at Brooklyn
Kings County Hospital Center
Long Island College Hospital
University Hospital-SUNY Health Science Center at
  Brooklyn
Prgm Director: Marvin Z Rotman, MD, BA
Box 1211
450 Clarkson Avenue
Brooklyn, NY 11203
Tel: 718 270-2181   *Fax:* 718 270-1535
Length: 4 Yrs   *ACGME Approved/Offered Positions:* 8
Program ID: 430-35-21-070

Buffalo

University at Buffalo Program
Sponsor: University at Buffalo School of Medicine
Roswell Park Cancer Institute
Prgm Director: Mohamed Khan, MD
Department of Radiation Medicine
Elm and Carlton Streets
Buffalo, NY 14263
Tel: 716 845-1180   *Fax:* 716 845-8254
Length: 4 Yrs   *ACGME Approved/Offered Positions:* 6
Program ID: 430-35-21-122

Flushing

New York Hospital Medical Center of Queens/Cornell University Medical College Program
Sponsor: New York Hospital Medical Center of Queens
New York Presbyterian Hospital (Cornell Campus)
Prgm Director: David L Sherr, MD
Stich Radiation Center
525 East 68th Street, Box 575
New York, NY 10065
Tel: 212 746-3614   *Fax:* 212 746-8749
E-mail: dls9003@med.cornell.edu
Length: 4 Yrs   *ACGME Approved/Offered Positions:* 6
Program ID: 430-35-22-126

New York

Memorial Sloan-Kettering Cancer Center Program
Sponsor: Memorial Sloan-Kettering Cancer Center
Prgm Director: Suzanne L Wolden, MD
Box 22
1275 York Avenue
New York, NY 10065
Tel: 212 639-5148   *Fax:* 212 639-2417
E-mail: ghanooi@mskcc.org
Length: 4 Yrs   *ACGME Approved/Offered Positions:* 16
Program ID: 430-35-21-063

Mount Sinai School of Medicine Program
Sponsor: Mount Sinai School of Medicine
Mount Sinai Medical Center
Prgm Director: Richard G Stock, MD
1184 5th Avenue
One Gustave L Levy Place
New York, NY 10029
Tel: 212 241-7502   *Fax:* 212 410-7194
Length: 4 Yrs   *ACGME Approved/Offered Positions:* 6
Program ID: 430-35-21-119

Note: * indicates a newly appointed program director

New York Presbyterian Hospital (Columbia Campus) Program
Sponsor: New York Presbyterian Hospital
New York Presbyterian Hospital (Columbia Campus)
Prgm Director: K S C Chao, MD*
Department of Radiation Oncology
622 West 168th Street
New York, NY 10032
Tel: 212 305-9880   *Fax:* 212 305-5935
Length: 4 Yrs   *ACGME Approved/Offered Positions:* 6
Program ID: 430-35-11-068

New York University School of Medicine Program
Sponsor: New York University School of Medicine
NYU Hospitals Center
Prgm Director: Ashwatha Narayana, MD
566 First Avenue
New York, NY 10016
Tel: 212 263-3279   *Fax:* 212 263-3716
Length: 4 Yrs   *ACGME Approved/Offered Positions:* 6
Program ID: 430-35-21-067

Rochester

University of Rochester Program
Sponsor: Strong Memorial Hospital of the University of Rochester
Highland Hospital of Rochester
Prgm Director: Ralph A Brasacchio, MD
601 Elmwood Avenue Box 647
Rochester, NY 14642
Tel: 585 275-5575   *Fax:* 585 275-1531
E-mail: RadOncResidency@rochester.edu
Length: 4 Yrs   *ACGME Approved/Offered Positions:* 6
Program ID: 430-35-11-071

Syracuse

SUNY Upstate Medical University Program
Sponsor: SUNY Upstate Medical University
Prgm Director: Jeffrey A Bogart, MD
750 East Adams Street
Syracuse, NY 13210
Tel: 315 464-5276   *Fax:* 315 464-5943
Length: 4 Yrs   *ACGME Approved/Offered Positions:* 6
Program ID: 430-35-11-072

North Carolina

Chapel Hill

University of North Carolina Hospitals Program
Sponsor: University of North Carolina Hospitals
Prgm Director: Mahesh A Varia, MD
Department of Radiation Oncology, RM 1056
101 Manning Drive
Chapel Hill, NC 27514
Tel: 919 966-7700   *Fax:* 919 966-7681
E-mail: werner@med.unc.edu
Length: 4 Yrs   *ACGME Approved/Offered Positions:* 4
Program ID: 430-36-11-073

Durham

Duke University Hospital Program
Sponsor: Duke University Hospital
Veterans Affairs Medical Center (Durham)
Prgm Director: William R Lee, MD, MEd*
Department of Radiation Oncology
Box 3085
Durham, NC 27710
Tel: 919 668-5640   *Fax:* 919 668-7345
Length: 4 Yrs   *ACGME Approved/Offered Positions:* 10
Program ID: 430-36-21-074

Winston-Salem

Wake Forest University School of Medicine Program
Sponsor: Wake Forest University Baptist Medical Center
Prgm Director: Kevin P McMullen, MD
Medical Center Boulevard
Winston-Salem, NC 27157
Tel: 336 713-6505   *Fax:* 336 713-6565
E-mail: kmcmulle@wfubmc.edu
Length: 4 Yrs   *ACGME Approved/Offered Positions:* 6
Program ID: 430-36-11-075

Ohio

Cincinnati

University Hospital/University of Cincinnati College of Medicine Program
Sponsor: University Hospital Inc
Veterans Affairs Medical Center (Cincinnati)
Prgm Director: Ruth F Lavigne, MD*
Mail Location 757
234 Goodman Street
Cincinnati, OH 45267
Tel: 513 584-4775   *Fax:* 513 584-4007
Length: 4 Yrs   *ACGME Approved/Offered Positions:* 6
Program ID: 430-38-21-076

Cleveland

Cleveland Clinic Foundation Program
Sponsor: Cleveland Clinic Foundation
Prgm Director: Gregory M Videtic, MD
Department of Radiation Oncology
9500 Euclid Avenue, T28
Cleveland, OH 44195
Tel: 216 444-9797   *Fax:* 216 445-1217
Length: 4 Yrs   *ACGME Approved/Offered Positions:* 8
Program ID: 430-38-12-078

University Hospitals Case Medical Center Program
Sponsor: University Hospitals Case Medical Center
Prgm Director: Janice Lyons, MD
Department of Radiation Oncology
11100 Euclid Avenue, B181
Cleveland, OH 44106
Tel: 216 844-2536   *Fax:* 216 844-2005
E-mail: janice.lyons@uhhospitals.org
Length: 4 Yrs   *ACGME Approved/Offered Positions:* 5
Program ID: 430-38-11-077

Columbus

Ohio State University Hospital Program
Sponsor: Ohio State University Hospital
Prgm Director: Simon S Lo, MB, ChB
A James Cancer Hospital
300 W 10th Avenue
Columbus, OH 43210
Tel: 614 293-8415   *Fax:* 614 293-4044
E-mail: Simon.Lo@osumc.edu
Length: 4 Yrs   *ACGME Approved/Offered Positions:* 4
Program ID: 430-38-11-079

Oklahoma

Oklahoma City

University of Oklahoma Health Sciences Center Program
Sponsor: University of Oklahoma College of Medicine
OU Medical Center
Veterans Affairs Medical Center (Oklahoma City)
Prgm Director: Elizabeth J Syzek, MD
Department of Radiation Oncology
825 NE 10th, #1430
Oklahoma City, OK 73104
Tel: 405 271-3016   *Fax:* 405 271-8297
Length: 4 Yrs   *ACGME Approved/Offered Positions:* 4
Program ID: 430-39-12-137

Oregon

Portland

Oregon Health & Science University Program
Sponsor: Oregon Health & Science University Hospital
Prgm Director: John M Holland, MD
3181 SW Sam Jackson Park Road
Mail Code: KPV4
Portland, OR 97239
Tel: 503 494-8756   *Fax:* 503 346-0237
Length: 4 Yrs   *ACGME Approved/Offered Positions:* 4
Program ID: 430-40-21-081

Pennsylvania

Philadelphia

Drexel University College of Medicine/Hahnemann University Hospital Program
Sponsor: Drexel University College of Medicine/Hahnemann University
Abington Memorial Hospital
Hahnemann University Hospital (Tenet Health System)
Prgm Director: Usha Babaria, MD
245 N 15th Street, MS 200
Philadelphia, PA 19102
Tel: 215 762-3419   *Fax:* 215 762-8523
Length: 4 Yrs   *ACGME Approved/Offered Positions:* 5
Program ID: 430-41-11-084

Fox Chase Cancer Center Program
Sponsor: Fox Chase Cancer Center
Prgm Director: Gary M Freedman, MD
333 Cottman Avenue
Philadelphia, PA 19111
Tel: 215 728-3016   *Fax:* 215 214-1629
E-mail: gary.freedman@fccc.edu
Length: 4 Yrs   *ACGME Approved/Offered Positions:* 8
Program ID: 430-41-21-123

Thomas Jefferson University Program
Sponsor: Thomas Jefferson University Hospital
Prgm Director: Maria Werner-Wasik, MD
Bodine Center for Cancer Treatment
111 South 11th Street
Philadelphia, PA 19107
Tel: 215 955-6700   *Fax:* 215 955-0412
Length: 4 Yrs   *ACGME Approved/Offered Positions:* 8
Program ID: 430-41-11-086

University of Pennsylvania Program

Sponsor: University of Pennsylvania Health System
Veterans Affairs Medical Center (Philadelphia)
Prgm Director: Neha Vapiwala, MD
Department of Radiation Oncology
3400 Spruce Street, 2 Donner Building
Philadelphia, PA 19104
Tel: 215 662-3694   *Fax:* 215 615-1658
E-mail: vapiwala@xrt.upenn.edu
Length: 4 Yrs   *ACGME Approved/Offered Positions:* 15
Program ID: 430-41-21-087

Pittsburgh

Allegheny General Hospital Program

Sponsor: Allegheny General Hospital
Prgm Director: David S Parda, MD
Department of Radiation Oncology
320 East North Avenue
Pittsburgh, PA 15212
Tel: 412 359-8084   *Fax:* 412 359-4265
Length: 4 Yrs   *ACGME Approved/Offered Positions:* 4
Program ID: 430-41-31-127

University of Pittsburgh Medical Center Medical Education Program

Sponsor: Univ of Pittsburgh Medical Center Medical
   Education
UPMC Presbyterian Shadyside
Prgm Director: Sushil Beriwal, MD
UPMC Shadyside
5230 Centre Avenue
Pittsburgh, PA 15232
Tel: 412 641-4600   *Fax:* 412 641-6601
Length: 4 Yrs   *ACGME Approved/Offered Positions:* 6
Program ID: 430-41-21-129

South Carolina

Charleston

Medical University of South Carolina Program

Sponsor: Medical University of South Carolina College of
   Medicine
Hollings Cancer Center-Mt Pleasant
MUSC Medical Center
Prgm Director: David T Marshall, MD, MS
169 Ashley Avenue
MSC 318
Charleston, SC 29425
Tel: 843 792-3273   *Fax:* 843 792-5498
E-mail: marshadt@musc.edu
Length: 4 Yrs   *ACGME Approved/Offered Positions:* 6
Program ID: 430-45-21-092

Tennessee

Nashville

Vanderbilt University Medical Center Program

Sponsor: Vanderbilt University Medical Center
Prgm Director: Bapsi Chak, MD
1301 22nd Avenue S
B-902 TVC
Nashville, TN 37232
Tel: 615 322-2555   *Fax:* 615 343-0161
E-mail: bapsi.chak@vanderbilt.edu
Length: 4 Yrs   *ACGME Approved/Offered Positions:* 8
Program ID: 430-47-12-128

Texas

Dallas

University of Texas Southwestern Medical School Program

Sponsor: University of Texas Southwestern Medical
   School
Prgm Director: Ann E Spangler, MD, MS
5801 Forest Park Road
Dallas, TX 75390
Tel: 214 645-7600   *Fax:* 214 645-7617
E-mail: Ann.Spangler@UTSouthwestern.edu
Length: 4 Yrs   *ACGME Approved/Offered Positions:* 8
Program ID: 430-48-12-134

Galveston

University of Texas Medical Branch Hospitals Program

Sponsor: University of Texas Medical Branch Hospitals
Prgm Director: Sandra S Hatch, MD
301 University Boulevard
Galveston, TX 77555
Tel: 409 772-6561   *Fax:* 409 747-0064
E-mail: shatch@utmb.edu
Length: 4 Yrs   *ACGME Approved/Offered Positions:* 5
Program ID: 430-48-11-097

Houston

Baylor College of Medicine Program

Sponsor: Baylor College of Medicine
Harris County Hospital District-Ben Taub General
   Hospital
Methodist Hospital (Houston)
Michael E DeBakey VA Medical Center - Houston
St Luke's Episcopal Hospital
Prgm Director: Manoj A Reddy, MD*
One Baylor Plaza, MS: BCM 360
Texas Medical Center
Houston, TX 77030
Tel: 713 794-7190
Length: 4 Yrs   *ACGME Approved/Offered Positions:* 8
Program ID: 430-48-21-098

University of Texas M D Anderson Cancer Center Program

Sponsor: University of Texas M D Anderson Cancer
   Center
Prgm Director: Christopher Crane, MD
Department of Radiation Oncology, Unit 97
1515 Holcombe Boulevard
Houston, TX 77030
Tel: 713 563-2340
E-mail: tdavenpo@mdanderson.org
Length: 4 Yrs   *ACGME Approved/Offered Positions:* 24
Program ID: 430-48-22-099

San Antonio

University of Texas Health Science Center at San Antonio Program

Sponsor: University of Texas School of Medicine at San
   Antonio
Audie L Murphy Memorial Veterans Hospital (San
   Antonio)
Cancer Therapy and Research Center at UTHSCSA
University Health System
Prgm Director: Gregory P Swanson, MD
Department of Radiation Oncology, MS Code 7889
7703 Floyd Curl Drive
San Antonio, TX 78229
Tel: 210 450-5647   *Fax:* 210 949-5085
E-mail: swansong@uthscsa.edu
Length: 4 Yrs   *ACGME Approved/Offered Positions:* 6
Program ID: 430-48-21-100

Utah

Salt Lake City

University of Utah Program

Sponsor: University of Utah Medical Center
LDS Hospital
Prgm Director: Ying J Hitchcock, MD
Huntsman Cancer Hospital
1950 Circle of Hope, Rm 1570
Salt Lake City, UT 84112
Tel: 801 581-8781   *Fax:* 801 585-3502
E-mail: jakob.rinderknecht@hci.utah.edu
Length: 4 Yrs   *ACGME Approved/Offered Positions:* 7
Program ID: 430-49-12-102

Virginia

Charlottesville

University of Virginia Program

Sponsor: University of Virginia Medical Center
Prgm Director: Pual W Read, MD, PhD
Dept of Radiation Oncology
PO Box 800383
Charlottesville, VA 22908
Tel: 434 924-5191   *Fax:* 434 243-9789
Length: 4 Yrs   *ACGME Approved/Offered Positions:* 6
Program ID: 430-51-11-104

Richmond

Virginia Commonwealth University Health System Program

Sponsor: Virginia Commonwealth University Health
   System
Hunter Holmes McGuire VA Medical Center (Richmond)
Medical College of Virginia Hospitals
Prgm Director: Michael G Chang, MD
401 College Street
Campus Box 980058
Richmond, VA 23298
Tel: 804 828-7232   *Fax:* 804 828-6042
E-mail: mgchang@vcu.edu
Length: 4 Yrs   *ACGME Approved/Offered Positions:* 8
Program ID: 430-51-11-106

Washington

Seattle

University of Washington Program

Sponsor: University of Washington School of Medicine
Seattle Cancer Care Alliance
University of Washington Medical Center
VA Puget Sound Health Care System
Prgm Director: James G Douglas, MD, MS
1959 NE Pacific Street
Box 356043
Seattle, WA 98195
Tel: 206 598-4121   *Fax:* 206 598-3786
Length: 4 Yrs   *ACGME Approved/Offered Positions:* 10
Program ID: 430-54-21-107

Wisconsin

Madison

University of Wisconsin Program

Sponsor: University of Wisconsin Hospital and Clinics
Prgm Director: Deepak Khuntia, MD
600 Highland Ave, K4/334-3684 CSC
Madison, WI 53792
Tel: 608 263-5009   *Fax:* 608 262-6256
Length: 4 Yrs   *ACGME Approved/Offered Positions:* 8
Program ID: 430-56-21-108

Note: * indicates a newly appointed program director

Milwaukee

Medical College of Wisconsin Affiliated Hospitals Program

Sponsor: Medical College of Wisconsin Affiliated Hospitals, Inc
Clement J Zablocki Veterans Affairs Medical Center
Community Memorial Hospital
Froedtert Memorial Lutheran Hospital
Prgm Director: Colleen A Lawton, MD
8701 Watertown Plank Road
Milwaukee, WI 53226
Tel: 414 805-4472   *Fax:* 414 805-4369
Length: 4 Yrs   *ACGME Approved/Offered Positions:* 8
Program ID: 430-56-21-109

Radiology-Diagnostic

Alabama

Birmingham

Baptist Health System Program

Sponsor: Baptist Health System Inc
Baptist Medical Center-Princeton
Trinity Medical Center
Prgm Director: Bibb Allen Jr, MD
800 Montclair Road
Department of Radiology
Birmingham, AL 35213
Tel: 205 592-1257   *Fax:* 205 592-5211
E-mail: patricia.logan@bhsala.com
Length: 4 Yrs   *ACGME Approved/Offered Positions:* 13
Program ID: 420-01-21-006

University of Alabama Medical Center Program

Sponsor: University of Alabama Hospital
Veterans Affairs Medical Center (Birmingham)
Prgm Director: Joseph C Sullivan III, MD*
Department of Radiology
619 South 19th Street
Birmingham, AL 35249
Tel: 205 934-3166   *Fax:* 205 975-4413
E-mail: jcsullivan@uabmc.edu
Length: 4 Yrs   *ACGME Approved/Offered Positions:* 36
Program ID: 420-01-11-007

Mobile

University of South Alabama Program

Sponsor: University of South Alabama Hospitals
Infirmary West
University of South Alabama Medical Center
Prgm Director: Jeffrey Campbell Brandon, MD
Department of Radiology
2451 Fillingim Street
Mobile, AL 36617
Tel: 251 471-7879   *Fax:* 251 471-7882
E-mail: jbrandon@usouthal.edu
Length: 4 Yrs   *ACGME Approved/Offered Positions:* 20
Program ID: 420-01-11-008

Arizona

Phoenix

Maricopa Medical Center Program

Sponsor: Maricopa Medical Center
St Joseph's Hospital and Medical Center
Prgm Director: Mary J Connell, MD
2601 East Roosevelt Street
Phoenix, AZ 85008
Tel: 602 344-1513   *Fax:* 602 344-1004
Length: 4 Yrs   *ACGME Approved/Offered Positions:* 12
Program ID: 420-03-31-255

St Joseph's Hospital and Medical Center Program

Sponsor: St Joseph's Hospital and Medical Center
Prgm Director: Randy Richardson, MD
Department of Diagnostic Imaging
350 West Thomas Road
Phoenix, AZ 85013
Tel: 602 406-6994   *Fax:* 602 406-7191
Length: 4 Yrs   *ACGME Approved/Offered Positions:* 17
Program ID: 420-03-12-010

Tucson

University of Arizona Program

Sponsor: University of Arizona College of Medicine
Southern Arizona VA Health Care Center (Tucson)
University Medical Center
Prgm Director: William K Erly, MD
PO Box 245067
1501 North Campbell Avenue
Tucson, AZ 85724
Tel: 520 626-7368   *Fax:* 520 626-3669
Length: 4 Yrs   *ACGME Approved/Offered Positions:* 24
Program ID: 420-03-21-011

University of Arizona/UPHK Graduate Medical Education Consortium Program

Sponsor: University of Arizona/UPHK Graduate Medical Ed Consortium
Arizona Telemedicine Network
Phoenix Children's Hospital
Southern Arizona VA Health Care Center (Tucson)
Prgm Director: Theron W Ovitt, MD*
2800 East Ajo Way
Graduate Medical Education
Tucson, AZ 85713
Tel: 520 626-6007   *Fax:* 520 626-3669
Length: 4 Yrs   *ACGME Approved/Offered Positions:* 20
Program ID: 420-03-13-258

Arkansas

Little Rock

University of Arkansas for Medical Sciences Program

Sponsor: University of Arkansas College of Medicine
Arkansas Children's Hospital
Central Arkansas Veterans Healthcare System
UAMS Medical Center
Prgm Director: Robert F Buchmann, DO
Arkansas Children's Hospital
800 Marshall Street
Little Rock, AR 72202
Tel: 501 364-4865   *Fax:* 501 364-4863
Length: 4 Yrs   *ACGME Approved/Offered Positions:* 32
Program ID: 420-04-21-012

California

Loma Linda

Loma Linda University Program

Sponsor: Loma Linda University Medical Center
Prgm Director: Douglas C Smith, MD
11234 Anderson Street
PO Box 2000
Loma Linda, CA 92354
Tel: 909 558-7814   *Fax:* 909 558-0202
E-mail: pthomas@llu.edu
Length: 4 Yrs   *ACGME Approved/Offered Positions:* 36
Program ID: 420-05-21-015

Los Angeles

Cedars-Sinai Medical Center Program

Sponsor: Cedars-Sinai Medical Center
Prgm Director: Marcel Maya, MD
Attn: Dora Thompson
S Mark Taper, 8700 Beverly Boulevard, M335
Los Angeles, CA 90048
Tel: 310 423-3419   *Fax:* 310 423-8335
E-mail: thompsonda@cshs.org
Length: 4 Yrs   *ACGME Approved/Offered Positions:* 16
Program ID: 420-05-21-018

Programs

Kaiser Permanente Southern California (Los Angeles) Program

Sponsor: Kaiser Permanente Southern California
Kaiser Foundation Hospital (Los Angeles)
Prgm Director: George G Vatakencherry, MD
Center for Medical Education
4733 Sunset Blvd, 3rd Floor
Los Angeles, CA 90027
Tel: 323 783-4631
E-mail: george.g.vatakencherry@kp.org
Length: 4 Yrs   *ACGME Approved/Offered Positions:* 12
Program ID: 420-05-12-020

UCLA Medical Center Program

Sponsor: UCLA David Geffen School of Medicine/UCLA
  Medical Center
Olive View/UCLA Medical Center
UCLA Medical Center
VA Greater Los Angeles Healthcare System
Prgm Director: Robert D Suh, MD
David Geffen School of Medicine at UCLA
10833 Le Conte Avenue, B2-170 CHS
Los Angeles, CA 90095
Tel: 310 825-7532   *Fax:* 310 794-5734
Length: 4 Yrs   *ACGME Approved/Offered Positions:* 48
Program ID: 420-05-11-023

University of Southern California/ LAC+USC Medical Center Program

Sponsor: University of Southern California/LAC+USC
  Medical Center
LAC+USC Medical Center
Prgm Director: M Victoria Marx, MD*
Department of Diagnostic Radiology
1200 North State Street, D&T 3D321
Los Angeles, CA 90033
Tel: 323 409-7270   *Fax:* 323 226-2280
Length: 4 Yrs   *ACGME Approved/Offered Positions:* 44
Program ID: 420-05-11-021

Orange

University of California (Irvine) Program

Sponsor: University of California (Irvine) Medical
  Center
VA Long Beach Healthcare System
Prgm Director: Arash Anavim, MD*
101 The City Drive South
Route 140, Radiology
Orange, CA 92868
Tel: 714 456-6579   *Fax:* 714 456-6832
E-mail: aanavim@uci.edu
Length: 4 Yrs   *ACGME Approved/Offered Positions:* 24
Program ID: 420-05-21-014

Sacramento

University of California (Davis) Health System Program

Sponsor: University of California (Davis) Health System
University of California (Davis) Medical Center
Prgm Director: Rebecca Stein-Wexler, MD
Department of Radiology
4860 Y Street, Suite 3100
Sacramento, CA 95817
Tel: 916 703-2271   *Fax:* 916 703-2258
E-mail: rebecca.steinwexler@ucdmc.ucdavis.edu
Length: 4 Yrs   *ACGME Approved/Offered Positions:* 30
Program ID: 420-05-11-013

San Diego

Naval Medical Center (San Diego) Program

Sponsor: Naval Medical Center (San Diego)
Prgm Director: Stephen L Ferrara, MD
Radiology, Suite 204
34800 Bob Wilson Drive
San Diego, CA 92134
Tel: 619 532-6755   *Fax:* 619 532-8714
E-mail: stephen.ferrara@med.navy.mil
Length: 4 Yrs   *ACGME Approved/Offered Positions:* 28
Program ID: 420-05-21-914
Uniformed Services Program

University of California (San Diego) Program

Sponsor: University of California (San Diego) Medical
  Center
Veterans Affairs Medical Center (San Diego)
Prgm Director: Mahmood F Mafee, MD
200 West Arbor Drive
San Diego, CA 92103
Tel: 619 543-6641   *Fax:* 619 543-3746
Length: 4 Yrs   *ACGME Approved/Offered Positions:* 40
Program ID: 420-05-21-027

San Francisco

University of California (San Francisco) Program

Sponsor: University of California (San Francisco) School
  of Medicine
San Francisco General Hospital Medical Center
UCSF and Mount Zion Medical Centers
Veterans Affairs Medical Center (San Francisco)
Prgm Director: Aliya Qayyum, MBBS*
Department of Radiology, Box 0628
505 Parnassus Avenue, Suite M391
San Francisco, CA 94143
Tel: 415 353-8753   *Fax:* 415 476-0616
Length: 4 Yrs   *ACGME Approved/Offered Positions:* 52
Program ID: 420-05-21-031

San Jose

Santa Clara Valley Medical Center Program

Sponsor: Santa Clara Valley Medical Center
Prgm Director: Rajul Pandit, MD
Department of Radiology
751 South Bascom Avenue
San Jose, CA 95128
Tel: 408 885-6370   *Fax:* 408 885-6360
Length: 4 Yrs   *ACGME Approved/Offered Positions:* 18
Program ID: 420-05-31-032

Santa Barbara

Santa Barbara Cottage Hospital Program

Sponsor: Santa Barbara Cottage Hospital
Prgm Director: Bernard Chow, MD*
PO Box 689
Pueblo at Bath Street
Santa Barbara, CA 93102
Tel: 805 569-7279   *Fax:* 805 569-8279
Length: 4 Yrs   *ACGME Approved/Offered Positions:* 10
Program ID: 420-05-22-033

Stanford

Stanford University Program

Sponsor: Stanford Hospital and Clinics
Veterans Affairs Palo Alto Health Care System
Prgm Director: Terry S Desser, MD
Department of Diagnostic Radiology
300 Pasteur Drive, Mail code 5621
Stanford, CA 94305
Tel: 650 723-7816   *Fax:* 650 723-1909
E-mail: iworthey@stanford.edu
Length: 4 Yrs   *ACGME Approved/Offered Positions:* 40
Program ID: 420-05-21-034

Torrance

Los Angeles County-Harbor-UCLA Medical Center Program

Sponsor: Los Angeles County-Harbor-UCLA Medical
  Center
Prgm Director: Richard Renslo, MD
Box 27
1000 W Carson Street
Torrance, CA 90509
Tel: 310 222-2847   *Fax:* 310 618-9500
E-mail: phamm@labiomed.org
Length: 4 Yrs   *ACGME Approved/Offered Positions:* 20
Program ID: 420-05-11-035

Travis AFB

David Grant Medical Center Program

Sponsor: David Grant Medical Center
Prgm Director: Robert A Jesinger, MD, MS*
Department of Radiology
101 Bodin Circle
Travis AFB, CA 94535
Tel: 707 423-7669   *Fax:* 707 423-7207
E-mail: robert.jesinger@travis.af.mil
Length: 4 Yrs   *ACGME Approved/Offered Positions:* 12
Program ID: 420-05-21-001
Uniformed Services Program

Colorado

Aurora

University of Colorado Denver Program

Sponsor: University of Colorado Denver School of
  Medicine
Denver Health Medical Center
University of Colorado Hospital
Veterans Affairs Medical Center (Denver)
Prgm Director: David Rubinstein, MD
Department of Radiology
12631 E 17th Avenue, MS 8200
Aurora, CO 80045
Tel: 303 724-1982   *Fax:* 303 724-1983
E-mail: david.rubinstein@ucdenver.edu
Length: 4 Yrs   *ACGME Approved/Offered Positions:* 32
Program ID: 420-07-21-038

Connecticut

Bridgeport

Bridgeport Hospital/Yale University Program

Sponsor: Bridgeport Hospital
Prgm Director: Noel Velasco, MD
Diagnostic Radiology
267 Grant Street
Bridgeport, CT 06610
Tel: 203 384-3834   *Fax:* 203 384-3833
E-mail: pnvela@bpthosp.org
Length: 4 Yrs   *ACGME Approved/Offered Positions:* 16
Program ID: 420-08-12-039

Note: * indicates a newly appointed program director

St Vincent's Medical Center Program
Sponsor: St Vincent's Medical Center
Prgm Director: Joseph A Gagliardi, MD
2800 Main Street
Bridgeport, CT 06606
Tel: 203 576-5533   *Fax:* 203 581-6537
E-mail: bhastava@stvincents.org
Length: 4 Yrs   *ACGME Approved/Offered Positions:* 12
Program ID: 420-08-11-040

Farmington

University of Connecticut Program
Sponsor: University of Connecticut School of Medicine
St Francis Hospital and Medical Center
Univ of Connecticut Health Center/John Dempsey
   Hospital
Prgm Director: Harold Moskowitz, MD
263 Farmington Avenue
Farmington, CT 06030
Tel: 860 679-2345   *Fax:* 860 679-1090
E-mail: moskowitz@uchc.edu
Length: 4 Yrs   *ACGME Approved/Offered Positions:* 8
Program ID: 420-08-21-225

Hartford

Hartford Hospital Program
Sponsor: Hartford Hospital
Prgm Director: Frederick U Conard III, MD
PO Box 5037
80 Seymour Street
Hartford, CT 06102
Tel: 860 545-5114   *Fax:* 860 545-4074
Length: 4 Yrs   *ACGME Approved/Offered Positions:* 20
Program ID: 420-08-22-041

New Haven

Hospital of St Raphael Program
Sponsor: Hospital of St Raphael
Prgm Director: Philip A Dinauer, MD
Department of Radiology
1450 Chapel Street
New Haven, CT 06511
Tel: 203 789-6289   *Fax:* 203 789-4118
Length: 4 Yrs   *ACGME Approved/Offered Positions:* 16
Program ID: 420-08-22-042

Yale-New Haven Medical Center Program
Sponsor: Yale-New Haven Hospital
Veterans Affairs Medical Center (West Haven)
Prgm Director: Syed Ahmad Jamal Bokhari, MD*
20 York Street
New Haven, CT 06520
Tel: 203 785-7377   *Fax:* 203 785-4328
E-mail: jamal.bokhari@yale.edu
Length: 4 Yrs   *ACGME Approved/Offered Positions:* 38
Program ID: 420-08-21-043

Norwalk

Norwalk Hospital Program
Sponsor: Norwalk Hospital
Yale-New Haven Hospital
Prgm Director: Edward B Strauss, MD
Department of Radiology
Maple Street
Norwalk, CT 06856
Tel: 203 852-2715   *Fax:* 203 855-3967
E-mail: susie.mccusker@norwalkhealth.org
Length: 4 Yrs   *ACGME Approved/Offered Positions:* 10
Program ID: 420-08-21-216

Delaware

Wilmington

Christiana Care Health Services Program
Sponsor: Christiana Care Health Services Inc
Prgm Director: Michael B Sneider, MD
4755 Ogletown-Stanton Road
Newark, DE 19718
Tel: 302 733-5582   *Fax:* 302 733-5589
E-mail: msneider@christianacare.org
Length: 4 Yrs   *ACGME Approved/Offered Positions:* 24
Program ID: 420-09-11-044

District of Columbia

Washington

George Washington University Program
Sponsor: George Washington University School of
   Medicine
George Washington University Hospital (UHS)
Prgm Director: Robert K Zeman, MD
900 23rd Street, NW
Room G-113
Washington, DC 20037
Tel: 202 715-5154   *Fax:* 202 715-4901
E-mail: gwuradrz@yahoo.com
Length: 4 Yrs   *ACGME Approved/Offered Positions:* 16
Program ID: 420-10-21-046

Georgetown University Hospital Program
Sponsor: Georgetown University Hospital
Prgm Director: Sandra J Allison, MD
Department of Radiology
3800 Reservoir Road, NW
Washington, DC 20007
Tel: 202 444-3380   *Fax:* 202 444-1804
E-mail: villaros@gunet.georgetown.edu
Length: 4 Yrs   *ACGME Approved/Offered Positions:* 24
Program ID: 420-10-11-045

Florida

Gainesville

University of Florida Program
Sponsor: University of Florida College of Medicine
North Florida/South Georgia Veterans Health System
Shands Hospital at the University of Florida
Prgm Director: Lori A Deitte, MD*
Department of Radiology
PO Box 100374
Gainesville, FL 32610
Tel: 352 265-0291   *Fax:* 352 265-0279
Length: 4 Yrs   *ACGME Approved/Offered Positions:* 44
Program ID: 420-11-21-048

Jacksonville

College of Medicine, Mayo Clinic (Jacksonville) Program
Sponsor: College of Medicine, Mayo Clinic
Mayo Clinic (Jacksonville)
St Luke's Hospital
Prgm Director: Thomas H Berquist, MD
4500 San Pablo Road
Jacksonville, FL 32224
Tel: 904 953-0490   *Fax:* 904 953-0430
Length: 4 Yrs   *ACGME Approved/Offered Positions:* 16
Program ID: 420-11-21-250

University of Florida College of Medicine Jacksonville Program
Sponsor: University of Florida College of Medicine
   Jacksonville
Shands Jacksonville Medical Center
Prgm Director: Barry M McCook, MD*
655 W 8th Street, Box C90
Department of Radiology
Jacksonville, FL 32209
Tel: 904 244-4225   *Fax:* 904 244-4296
E-mail: johneise.croxton@jax.ufl.edu
Length: 4 Yrs   *ACGME Approved/Offered Positions:* 20
Program ID: 420-11-21-223

Miami

Jackson Memorial Hospital/Jackson Health System Program
Sponsor: Jackson Memorial Hospital/Jackson Health
   System
Prgm Director: Robert P Henry Jr, MD, BA*
Department of Radiology (R-130)
1611 NW 12th Avenue, WW 279
Miami, FL 33136
Tel: 305 585-7500   *Fax:* 305 355-4051
E-mail: rphenry@med.miami.edu
Length: 4 Yrs   *ACGME Approved/Offered Positions:* 40
Program ID: 420-11-21-049

Miami Beach

Mount Sinai Medical Center of Florida Program
Sponsor: Mount Sinai Medical Center of Florida, Inc
Prgm Director: Tyler Neitlich, MD*
Department of Radiology
4300 Alton Road
Miami Beach, FL 33140
Tel: 305 674-2680   *Fax:* 305 674-3919
Length: 4 Yrs   *ACGME Approved/Offered Positions:* 20
Program ID: 420-11-21-050

Tampa

University of South Florida Program
Sponsor: University of South Florida College of Medicine
H Lee Moffitt Cancer Center
James A Haley Veterans Hospital
Tampa General Hospital
Prgm Director: Todd R Hazelton, MD
Box 17
12901 Bruce B Downs Blvd
Tampa, FL 33612
Tel: 813 974-6311   *Fax:* 813 974-3482
Length: 4 Yrs   *ACGME Approved/Offered Positions:* 26
Program ID: 420-11-21-051

Georgia

Atlanta

Emory University Program
Sponsor: Emory University School of Medicine
Emory University Hospital
Grady Health System
Prgm Director: Mark E Mullins, MD, PhD*
Dept of Radiology
1364 Clifton Road, NE, Rm D125A
Atlanta, GA 30322
Tel: 404 712-2916   *Fax:* 404 712-7908
Length: 4 Yrs   *ACGME Approved/Offered Positions:* 56
Program ID: 420-12-21-052

Programs

Augusta

Medical College of Georgia Program

Sponsor: Medical College of Georgia
Veterans Affairs Medical Center (Augusta)
Prgm Director: Gilberto Sostre, MD*
BA -1411
1120 15th Street
Augusta, GA 30912
Tel: 706 721-3214   *Fax:* 706 721-5213
E-mail: nucradgil@aol.com
Length: 4 Yrs   *ACGME Approved/Offered Positions:* 20
Program ID: 420-12-21-053

Savannah

Mercer University School of Medicine (Savannah) Program

Sponsor: Memorial Health-University Medical Center
Prgm Director: Deborah J Conway, MD*
Department of Radiology
4700 Waters Avenue
Savannah, GA 31403
Tel: 912 350-7394   *Fax:* 912 350-7363
E-mail: larismi1@memorialhealth.com
Length: 4 Yrs   *ACGME Approved/Offered Positions:* 16
Program ID: 420-12-12-054

Hawaii

Tripler AMC

Tripler Army Medical Center Program

Sponsor: Tripler Army Medical Center
Prgm Director: Kevin M Nakamura, MD*
Department of Radiology
1 Jarrett White Road
Tripler AMC, HI 96859
Tel: 808 433-6588   *Fax:* 808 433-4688
Length: 4 Yrs   *ACGME Approved/Offered Positions:* 22
Program ID: 420-14-21-933
Uniformed Services Program

Illinois

Chicago

Advocate Illinois Masonic Medical Center Program

Sponsor: Advocate Illinois Masonic Medical Center
Prgm Director: Kevin J Kirshenbaum, MD
836 West Wellington Avenue
Chicago, IL 60657
Tel: 773 296-7820   *Fax:* 773 296-7821
Length: 4 Yrs   *ACGME Approved/Offered Positions:* 12
Program ID: 420-16-21-217

John H Stroger Hospital of Cook County Program

Sponsor: John H Stroger Hospital of Cook County
Prgm Director: Patrick M Dunne, MD
Department of Radiology
1901 W Harrison St
Chicago, IL 60612
Tel: 312 864-3731   *Fax:* 312 864-9855
Length: 4 Yrs   *ACGME Approved/Offered Positions:* 16
Program ID: 420-16-21-055

McGaw Medical Center of Northwestern University Program

Sponsor: McGaw Medical Center of Northwestern
 University
Evanston Hospital
Northwestern Memorial Hospital
Prgm Director: Robert K Ryu, MD
676 N St Clair Street
Suite 800
Chicago, IL 60611
Tel: 312 695-3718   *Fax:* 312 695-5645
E-mail: jclark@nmff.org
Length: 4 Yrs   *ACGME Approved/Offered Positions:* 36
Program ID: 420-16-21-059

Rush University Medical Center Program

Sponsor: Rush University Medical Center
Prgm Director: Joy S Sclamberg, MD
Department of Diagnostic Radiology
1653 West Congress Parkway
Chicago, IL 60612
Tel: 312 942-5781   *Fax:* 312 942-8180
Length: 4 Yrs   *ACGME Approved/Offered Positions:* 20
Program ID: 420-16-11-060

University of Chicago Program

Sponsor: University of Chicago Medical Center
Prgm Director: Gregory S Stacy, MD*
Dept of Radiology, MC 2026
5841 South Maryland Avenue
Chicago, IL 60637
Tel: 773 834-3046   *Fax:* 773 702-1161
E-mail: sstacy@radiology.bsd.uchicago.edu
Length: 4 Yrs   *ACGME Approved/Offered Positions:* 34
Program ID: 420-16-11-061

University of Illinois College of Medicine at Chicago Program

Sponsor: University of Illinois College of Medicine at
 Chicago
Mercy Hospital and Medical Center
University of Illinois Hospital and Clinics
Prgm Director: Edward A Michals, MD*
1740 W Taylor Street, Suite 2483
Chicago, IL 60612
Tel: 312 996-0235   *Fax:* 312 355-2098
Length: 4 Yrs   *ACGME Approved/Offered Positions:* 34
Program ID: 420-16-21-062

Evanston

St Francis Hospital of Evanston Program

Sponsor: St Francis Hospital
Resurrection Medical Center
Prgm Director: Joseph D Calandra, MD
355 Ridge Avenue
Evanston, IL 60202
Tel: 847 316-6101   *Fax:* 847 316-2241
Length: 4 Yrs   *ACGME Approved/Offered Positions:* 8
Program ID: 420-16-12-063

Maywood

Loyola University Program

Sponsor: Loyola University Medical Center
Prgm Director: Laurie M Lomasney, MD
Department of Radiology
2160 South First Avenue
Maywood, IL 60153
Tel: 708 216-1084   *Fax:* 708 216-0899
Length: 4 Yrs   *ACGME Approved/Offered Positions:* 24
Program ID: 420-16-11-064

Peoria

University of Illinois College of Medicine at Peoria Program

Sponsor: University of Illinois College of Medicine at
 Peoria
OSF St Francis Medical Center
Prgm Director: Terry M Brady, MD
530 NE Glen Oak Avenue
Peoria, IL 61637
Tel: 309 655-7768   *Fax:* 309 655-7365
E-mail: lorid@uic.edu
Length: 4 Yrs   *ACGME Approved/Offered Positions:* 16
Program ID: 420-16-21-243

Springfield

Southern Illinois University Program

Sponsor: Southern Illinois University School of Medicine
Memorial Medical Center
St John's Hospital
Prgm Director: John B Becker Jr, MD
MMC Box 101
701 N 1st Street
Springfield, IL 62781
Tel: 217 757-2387   *Fax:* 217 788-5588
E-mail: skelton.stacie@mhsil.com
Length: 4 Yrs   *ACGME Approved/Offered Positions:* 20
Program ID: 420-16-21-065

Indiana

Indianapolis

Indiana University School of Medicine Program

Sponsor: Indiana University School of Medicine
Clarian Indiana University Hospital
Clarian Methodist Hospital of Indiana
Clarian Riley Hospital for Children
William N Wishard Memorial Hospital
Prgm Director: Darel E Heitkamp, MD
Department of Radiology
550 North University Avenue, Room 0641
Indianapolis, IN 46202
Tel: 317 274-3424
E-mail: deheitka@iupui.edu
Length: 4 Yrs   *ACGME Approved/Offered Positions:* 68
Program ID: 420-17-21-066

Iowa

Iowa City

University of Iowa Hospitals and Clinics Program

Sponsor: University of Iowa Hospitals and Clinics
Prgm Director: Joan E Maley, MD
200 Hawkins Drive
Department of Radiology
Iowa City, IA 52242
Tel: 319 356-3452   *Fax:* 319 356-2220
E-mail: joan-maley@uiowa.edu
Length: 4 Yrs   *ACGME Approved/Offered Positions:* 33
Program ID: 420-18-21-068

Note: * indicates a newly appointed program director

Kansas

Kansas City

University of Kansas School of Medicine Program

Sponsor: University of Kansas School of Medicine
University of Kansas Hospital
Veterans Affairs Medical Center (Kansas City)
Prgm Director: Philip L Johnson, MD
Department of Radiology, Mail Stop 4032
3901 Rainbow Blvd
Kansas City, KS 66160
Tel: 913 588-6805   *Fax:* 913 588-7899
E-mail: pjohnson@kumc.edu
Length: 4 Yrs   *ACGME Approved/Offered Positions:* 24
Program ID: 420-19-11-069

Wichita

University of Kansas (Wichita) Program

Sponsor: University of Kansas School of Medicine
(Wichita)
Wesley Medical Center
Prgm Director: Kamran Ali, MD*
Medical Education - Radiology
550 N Hillside
Wichita, KS 67214
Tel: 316 962-2211   *Fax:* 316 962-7231
E-mail: becky.mann@wesleymc.com
Length: 4 Yrs   *ACGME Approved/Offered Positions:* 12
Program ID: 420-19-12-070

Kentucky

Lexington

University of Kentucky College of Medicine Program

Sponsor: University of Kentucky College of Medicine
University of Kentucky Hospital
Prgm Director: Michael A Brooks, MD*
Department of Diagnostic Radiology
800 Rose Street, Room HX315E
Lexington, KY 40536
Tel: 859 323-7209   *Fax:* 859 323-2510
E-mail: sajone2@email.uky.edu
Length: 4 Yrs   *ACGME Approved/Offered Positions:* 24
Program ID: 420-20-21-071

Louisville

University of Louisville Program

Sponsor: University of Louisville School of Medicine
University of Louisville Hospital
Veterans Affairs Medical Center (Louisville)
Prgm Director: Peter C Hentzen, MD, PhD
Department of Radiology
530 S Jackson Street, Suite C07
Louisville, KY 40202
Tel: 502 852-5875   *Fax:* 502 852-1754
Length: 4 Yrs   *ACGME Approved/Offered Positions:* 20
Program ID: 420-20-21-230

Louisiana

New Orleans

Louisiana State University Program

Sponsor: Louisiana State University School of Medicine
Children's Hospital (New Orleans)
Medical Center of Louisiana at New Orleans
Prgm Director: Leonard Bok, MD, MBA
Department of Radiology
2020 Gravier Street, Room 755
New Orleans, LA 70112
Tel: 504 568-4647   *Fax:* 504 568-8955
E-mail: sjoh21@lsuhsc.edu
Length: 4 Yrs   *ACGME Approved/Offered Positions:* 12
Program ID: 420-21-31-259

Ochsner Clinic Foundation Program

Sponsor: Ochsner Clinic Foundation
Prgm Director: James M Milburn, MD
1514 Jefferson Highway
New Orleans, LA 70121
Tel: 504 842-4796   *Fax:* 504 842-7132
E-mail: kdixon@ochsner.org
Length: 4 Yrs   *ACGME Approved/Offered Positions:* 20
Program ID: 420-21-12-074

Tulane University Program

Sponsor: Tulane University School of Medicine
Tulane University Hospital and Clinics
Prgm Director: Cynthia W Hanemann, MD*
1430 Tulane Avenue SL54
New Orleans, LA 70112
Tel: 504 988-7627   *Fax:* 504 988-7616
E-mail: chaneman@tulane.edu
Length: 4 Yrs   *ACGME Approved/Offered Positions:* 16
Program ID: 420-21-21-235

Shreveport

Louisiana State University (Shreveport) Program

Sponsor: LSU Health Sciences Center-University
Hospital
Prgm Director: Mardjohan Hardjasudarma, MD, MS
PO Box 33932
1501 Kings Highway
Shreveport, LA 71130
Tel: 318 675-6232   *Fax:* 318 675-6351
Length: 4 Yrs   *ACGME Approved/Offered Positions:* 14
Program ID: 420-21-11-075

Maine

Portland

Maine Medical Center Program

Sponsor: Maine Medical Center
Prgm Director: Scott E Fredericks, MD*
Department of Diagnostic Radiology
22 Bramhall Street
Portland, ME 04102
Tel: 207 662-2571   *Fax:* 207 662-5255
Length: 4 Yrs   *ACGME Approved/Offered Positions:* 20
Program ID: 420-22-11-076

Maryland

Baltimore

Johns Hopkins University Program

Sponsor: Johns Hopkins University School of Medicine
Johns Hopkins Bayview Medical Center
Johns Hopkins Hospital
Prgm Director: Stanley S Siegelman, MD
601 North Caroline Street
Room 4210
Baltimore, MD 21287
Tel: 410 955-5677   *Fax:* 410 955-8597
Length: 4 Yrs   *ACGME Approved/Offered Positions:* 36
Program ID: 420-23-11-077

University of Maryland Program

Sponsor: University of Maryland Medical System
Prgm Director: Charles S Resnik, MD
Department of Radiology
22 South Greene Street
Baltimore, MD 21201
Tel: 410 328-3477   *Fax:* 410 328-0641
E-mail: bstewart@umm.edu
Length: 4 Yrs   *ACGME Approved/Offered Positions:* 32
Program ID: 420-23-11-079

Bethesda

National Capital Consortium Program

Sponsor: National Capital Consortium
National Naval Medical Center (Bethesda)
Walter Reed Army Medical Center
Prgm Director: Fletcher M Munter, MD
Department of Radiology
6900 Geogia Avenue NW
Washington, DC 20307
Tel: 202 782-1679   *Fax:* 202 782-3393
E-mail: fletcher.munter@amedd.army.mil
Length: 4 Yrs   *ACGME Approved/Offered Positions:* 40
Program ID: 420-10-21-247
Uniformed Services Program

Massachusetts

Boston

Beth Israel Deaconess Medical Center Program

Sponsor: Beth Israel Deaconess Medical Center
Prgm Director: Bettina Siewert, MD
330 Brookline Avenue
E CC-4 Radiology
Boston, MA 02215
Tel: 617 667-3532   *Fax:* 617 667-3537
Length: 4 Yrs   *ACGME Approved/Offered Positions:* 40
Program ID: 420-24-21-080

Boston University Medical Center Program

Sponsor: Boston Medical Center
Veterans Affairs Medical Center (Boston)
Prgm Director: Avneesh Gupta, MD
88 East Newton Street
Boston, MA 02118
Tel: 617 638-6610   *Fax:* 617 638-6616
Length: 4 Yrs   *ACGME Approved/Offered Positions:* 40
Program ID: 420-24-21-081

Brigham and Women's Hospital/Harvard Medical School Program

Sponsor: Brigham and Women's Hospital
Prgm Director: Barbara N Weissman, MD
Department of Radiology
75 Francis Street
Boston, MA 02115
Tel: 617 732-6295   *Fax:* 617 264-5250
E-mail: bwhradres@partners.org
Length: 4 Yrs   *ACGME Approved/Offered Positions:* 40
Program ID: 420-24-21-085

Programs

Massachusetts General Hospital/Harvard Medical School Program
Sponsor: Massachusetts General Hospital
Prgm Director: Theresa C McLoud, MD
Dept of Radiology, FND 216
Boston, MA 02114
Tel: 617 724-4255   *Fax:* 617 726-3077
Length: 4 Yrs   *ACGME Approved/Offered Positions:* 44
Program ID: 420-24-31-083

Tufts Medical Center Program
Sponsor: Tufts Medical Center
Prgm Director: Judith Katz, MD
Department of Radiology
800 Washington Street, #299
Boston, MA 02111
Tel: 617 636-4564   *Fax:* 617 636-0041
E-mail: jkatz@tuftsmedicalcenter.org
Length: 4 Yrs   *ACGME Approved/Offered Positions:* 22
Program ID: 420-24-21-086

Burlington

Lahey Clinic Program
Sponsor: Lahey Clinic
Prgm Director: Christopher D Scheirey, MD*
Department of Diagnostic Radiology
41 Mall Road
Burlington, MA 01805
Tel: 781 744-8170   *Fax:* 781 744-5232
E-mail: christopher.scheirey@lahey.org
Length: 4 Yrs   *ACGME Approved/Offered Positions:* 20
Program ID: 420-24-22-082

Cambridge

Mount Auburn Hospital Program
Sponsor: Mount Auburn Hospital
Prgm Director: Pierre Sasson, MD
Department of Radiology
330 Mount Auburn Street
Cambridge, MA 02138
Tel: 617 441-1610   *Fax:* 617 499-5193
Length: 4 Yrs   *ACGME Approved/Offered Positions:* 12
Program ID: 420-24-11-087

Springfield

Baystate Medical Center/Tufts University School of Medicine Program
Sponsor: Baystate Medical Center
Prgm Director: Stephen C O'Connor, MD
Department of Radiology
759 Chestnut Street
Springfield, MA 01199
Tel: 413 794-3333   *Fax:* 413 794-4382
E-mail: teresa.lalli@bhs.org
Length: 4 Yrs   *ACGME Approved/Offered Positions:* 16
Program ID: 420-24-12-088

Worcester

St Vincent Hospital Program
Sponsor: St Vincent Hospital
Prgm Director: David A Bader, MD
Department of Radiology
123 Summer Street
Worcester, MA 01608
Tel: 508 363-7034   *Fax:* 508 363-7224
E-mail: alice.persico@stvincenthospital.com
Length: 4 Yrs   *ACGME Approved/Offered Positions:* 8
Program ID: 420-24-12-089

University of Massachusetts Program
Sponsor: University of Massachusetts Medical School
UMass Memorial Health Care (Memorial Campus)
UMass Memorial Health Care (University Campus)
Prgm Director: Joseph Makris, MD
55 Lake Avenue North
Worcester, MA 01655
Tel: 508 856-2783
E-mail: rad.residency@umassmed.edu
Length: 4 Yrs   *ACGME Approved/Offered Positions:* 16
Program ID: 420-24-21-090

Michigan

Ann Arbor

University of Michigan Program
Sponsor: University of Michigan Hospitals and Health Centers
Prgm Director: Janet E Bailey, MD
Department of Radiology
1500 East Medical Center Drive
Ann Arbor, MI 48109
Tel: 734 936-8869   *Fax:* 734 763-9523
Length: 4 Yrs   *ACGME Approved/Offered Positions:* 45
Program ID: 420-25-21-091

Dearborn

Oakwood Hospital Program
Sponsor: Oakwood Hospital
Prgm Director: John H Finger, MD
18101 Oakwood Boulevard
Dearborn, MI 48124
Tel: 313 436-2583   *Fax:* 313 436-2809
E-mail: john.finger@oakwood.org
Length: 4 Yrs   *ACGME Approved/Offered Positions:* 24
Program ID: 420-25-12-092

Detroit

Henry Ford Hospital Program
Sponsor: Henry Ford Hospital
Prgm Director: Eric M Spickler, MD
Department of Radiology
2799 West Grand Boulevard
Detroit, MI 48202
Tel: 313 916-1384   *Fax:* 313 916-8857
Length: 4 Yrs   *ACGME Approved/Offered Positions:* 36
Program ID: 420-25-11-093

Wayne State University/Detroit Medical Center Program
Sponsor: Wayne State University/Detroit Medical Center
Children's Hospital of Michigan
Harper-Hutzel Hospital
Sinai-Grace Hospital
Prgm Director: Wilbur L Smith, MD
4201 St Antoine, DRH 3L8
Detroit, MI 48201
Tel: 313 745-3430   *Fax:* 313 577-8600
Length: 4 Yrs   *ACGME Approved/Offered Positions:* 44
Program ID: 420-25-21-096

Flint

Michigan State University (Flint) Program
Sponsor: Michigan State University/Flint Area Medical Education
Genesys Regional Medical Center-Health Park
Hurley Medical Center
McLaren Regional Medical Center
Prgm Director: Ureddi R Mullangi, MD*
One Hurley Plaza-7W
Flint, MI 48503
Tel: 810 232-7000   *Fax:* 810 232-7020
E-mail: umullangi@msufame.msu.edu
Length: 4 Yrs   *ACGME Approved/Offered Positions:* 12
Program ID: 420-25-31-100

Grand Rapids

Grand Rapids Medical Education and Research Center/Michigan State University Program
Sponsor: Grand Rapids Medical Education and Research Center
Saint Mary's Health Care (Grand Rapids)
Spectrum Health-Blodgett Hospital
Spectrum Health-Butterworth Hospital
Prgm Director: Charles R Luttenton, MD
Diagnostic Radiology Residency
1000 Monroe NW
Grand Rapids, MI 49503
Tel: 616 732-6232   *Fax:* 616 732-6228
E-mail: raddoc11@comcast.net
Length: 4 Yrs   *ACGME Approved/Offered Positions:* 12
Program ID: 420-25-21-099

Pontiac

St Joseph Mercy-Oakland Program
Sponsor: St Joseph Mercy-Oakland
Prgm Director: James Denier, MD
Department of Radiology, H-23
44405 Woodward Avenue
Pontiac, MI 48341
Tel: 248 858-3233   *Fax:* 248 858-3244
E-mail: denierja@trinity-health.org
Length: 4 Yrs   *ACGME Approved/Offered Positions:* 14
Program ID: 420-25-32-101

Royal Oak

William Beaumont Hospital Program
Sponsor: William Beaumont Hospital
Prgm Director: Matthias J Kirsch, MD
Department of Radiology
3601 West Thirteen Mile Road
Royal Oak, MI 48073
Tel: 248 898-6047   *Fax:* 248 898-2496
Length: 4 Yrs   *ACGME Approved/Offered Positions:* 40
Program ID: 420-25-12-102

Southfield

Providence Hospital and Medical Centers Program
Sponsor: Providence Hospital and Medical Centers
Prgm Director: Roger L Gonda, MD
16001 West Nine Mile Road
Department of Radiology
Southfield, MI 48075
Tel: 248 849-2203   *Fax:* 248 849-3931
E-mail: roger.gonda@providence-stjohnhealth.org
Length: 4 Yrs   *ACGME Approved/Offered Positions:* 12
Program ID: 420-25-21-103

Minnesota

Minneapolis

University of Minnesota Program
Sponsor: University of Minnesota Medical School
Hennepin County Medical Center
University of Minnesota Medical Center, Division of Fairview
Veterans Affairs Medical Center (Minneapolis)
Prgm Director: Tim H Emory, MD
Department of Radiology, MMC 292
420 Delaware Street, SE
Minneapolis, MN 55455
Tel: 612 626-5529   *Fax:* 612 626-5580
E-mail: emory002@umn.edu
Length: 4 Yrs   *ACGME Approved/Offered Positions:* 44
Program ID: 420-26-21-104

Note: * indicates a newly appointed program director

Rochester

College of Medicine, Mayo Clinic (Rochester) Program
Sponsor: College of Medicine, Mayo Clinic
Mayo Clinic (Rochester)
Rochester Methodist Hospital
Saint Marys Hospital of Rochester
Prgm Director: Kristen B Thomas, MD*
Department of Radiology
200 First Street, SW
Rochester, MN 55905
Tel: 507 284-0440   *Fax:* 507 293-3680
Length: 4 Yrs   *ACGME Approved/Offered Positions:* 52
Program ID: 420-26-21-105

Mississippi

Jackson

University of Mississippi Medical Center Program
Sponsor: University of Mississippi School of Medicine
University Hospitals and Clinics
Veterans Affairs Medical Center (Jackson)
Prgm Director: Anson L Thaggard, MD*
Department of Radiology
2500 North State Street
Jackson, MS 39216
Tel: 601 984-2695   *Fax:* 601 984-2683
E-mail: bedmonds@radiology.umsmed.edu
Length: 4 Yrs   *ACGME Approved/Offered Positions:* 21
Program ID: 420-27-11-107

Missouri

Columbia

University of Missouri-Columbia Program
Sponsor: University of Missouri-Columbia School of
    Medicine
Harry S Truman Memorial Veterans Hospital
University Hospitals and Clinics
Prgm Director: Yash Sethi, MD
Department of Radiology
One Hospital Drive
Columbia, MO 65212
Tel: 573 882-1026   *Fax:* 573 884-8876
E-mail: SethiY@health.missouri.edu
Length: 4 Yrs   *ACGME Approved/Offered Positions:* 20
Program ID: 420-28-11-108

Kansas City

University of Missouri at Kansas City Program
Sponsor: University of Missouri-Kansas City School of
    Medicine
St Luke's Hospital-Kansas City
Truman Medical Center
Prgm Director: Lisa H Lowe, MD
c/o Daphne Urquhart; Medical Education
4401 Wornall Road
Kansas City, MO 64111
Tel: 816 234-3725   *Fax:* 816 983-6912
E-mail: durquhart@saint-lukes.org
Length: 4 Yrs   *ACGME Approved/Offered Positions:* 24
Program ID: 420-28-21-231

St Louis

St Louis University School of Medicine Program
Sponsor: St Louis University School of Medicine
St Louis University Hospital
Veterans Affairs Medical Center (St Louis)
Prgm Director: B Kirke Bieneman, MD*
3635 Vista Avenue at Grand Blvd
PO Box 15250
St Louis, MO 63110
Tel: 314 268-5781   *Fax:* 314 268-5116
Length: 4 Yrs   *ACGME Approved/Offered Positions:* 24
Program ID: 420-28-21-110

Washington University/B-JH/SLCH Consortium Program
Sponsor: Washington University/B-JH/SLCH Consortium
Barnes-Jewish Hospital
Prgm Director: Jennifer E Gould, MD
510 South Kingshighway
St Louis, MO 63110
Tel: 314 362-2978   *Fax:* 314 747-4671
E-mail: lammersl@mir.wustl.edu
Length: 4 Yrs   *ACGME Approved/Offered Positions:* 72
Program ID: 420-28-11-111

Nebraska

Omaha

Creighton University Program
Sponsor: Creighton University School of Medicine
Creighton University Medical Center (Tenet - SJH)
Prgm Director: James J Phalen, MD
Department of Radiology
601 North 30th Street
Omaha, NE 68131
Tel: 402 449-4753   *Fax:* 402 449-4525
Length: 4 Yrs   *ACGME Approved/Offered Positions:* 12
Program ID: 420-30-21-220

University of Nebraska Medical Center College of Medicine Program
Sponsor: University of Nebraska Medical Center College
    of Medicine
Nebraska Medical Center
Veterans Affairs Medical Center (Omaha)
Prgm Director: Mary Kay Drake, MD
981045 Nebraska Medical Center
Department of Radiology
Omaha, NE 68198
Tel: 402 559-1018   *Fax:* 402 559-1011
Length: 4 Yrs   *ACGME Approved/Offered Positions:* 20
Program ID: 420-30-21-112

New Hampshire

Lebanon

Dartmouth-Hitchcock Medical Center Program
Sponsor: Mary Hitchcock Memorial Hospital
Prgm Director: Jocelyn D Chertoff, MD, MS
One Medical Center Drive
Lebanon, NH 03756
Tel: 603 650-7480   *Fax:* 603 650-5455
Length: 4 Yrs   *ACGME Approved/Offered Positions:* 20
Program ID: 420-32-11-113

New Jersey

Camden

UMDNJ-Robert Wood Johnson Medical School (Camden) Program
Sponsor: Cooper Hospital-University Medical Center
Prgm Director: Joshua D Brody, DO
One Cooper Plaza
B23
Camden, NJ 08103
Tel: 856 342-2383   *Fax:* 856 365-0472
E-mail: brody-joshua@cooperhealth.edu
Length: 4 Yrs   *ACGME Approved/Offered Positions:* 12
Program ID: 420-33-21-244

Livingston

St Barnabas Medical Center Program
Sponsor: St Barnabas Medical Center
Prgm Director: Lyle R Gesner, MD
94 Old Short Hills Road
Livingston, NJ 07039
Tel: 973 322-5267   *Fax:* 973 322-2851
E-mail: lgesner@sbhcs.com
Length: 4 Yrs   *ACGME Approved/Offered Positions:* 16
Program ID: 420-33-21-215

Long Branch

Monmouth Medical Center Program
Sponsor: Monmouth Medical Center
Prgm Director: Richard B Ruchman, MD
Department of Radiology
300 Second Avenue
Long Branch, NJ 07740
Tel: 732 923-6806   *Fax:* 732 923-6216
E-mail: RRuchman@sbhcs.com
Length: 4 Yrs   *ACGME Approved/Offered Positions:* 12
Program ID: 420-33-31-115

Morristown

Atlantic Health (Morristown) Program
Sponsor: Atlantic Health
Morristown Memorial Hospital
Overlook Hospital
Prgm Director: Jeanne R Schwartz, MD
100 Madison Avenue
PO Box 1956
Morristown, NJ 07962
Tel: 973 971-5372   *Fax:* 973 290-7294
Length: 4 Yrs   *ACGME Approved/Offered Positions:* 20
Program ID: 420-33-11-116

New Brunswick

UMDNJ-Robert Wood Johnson Medical School Program
Sponsor: UMDNJ-Robert Wood Johnson Medical School
Robert Wood Johnson University Hospital
St Peter's University Hospital
Prgm Director: Judith K Amorosa, MD, FACR
Department of Radiology
One Robert Wood Johnson Place
New Brunswick, NJ 08903
Tel: 732 235-7721   *Fax:* 732 235-6889
E-mail: amorosa@umdnj.edu
Length: 4 Yrs   *ACGME Approved/Offered Positions:* 20
Program ID: 420-33-21-228

Programs

Newark

Newark Beth Israel Medical Center Program
Sponsor: Newark Beth Israel Medical Center
Prgm Director: Vivian Rivera, MD
201 Lyons Avenue at Osborne Terrace
Newark, NJ 07112
Tel: 973 926-7960   *Fax:* 973 926-7688
E-mail: kdargon@sbhcs.com
Length: 4 Yrs   *ACGME Approved/Offered Positions:* 8
Program ID: 420-33-31-118

UMDNJ-New Jersey Medical School Program
Sponsor: UMDNJ-New Jersey Medical School
UMDNJ-University Hospital
Prgm Director: Stephen R Baker, MD
Department of Radiology, Room C-318
150 Bergen Street
Newark, NJ 07103
Tel: 973 972-5188   *Fax:* 973 972-7429
Length: 4 Yrs   *ACGME Approved/Offered Positions:* 18
Program ID: 420-33-21-226

New Mexico

Albuquerque

University of New Mexico Program
Sponsor: University of New Mexico School of Medicine
University of New Mexico Hospital
Prgm Director: Jennifer Pohl, PhD, MD
Department of Radiology
MSC10 5530, 1 University of New Mexico
Albuquerque, NM 87131
Tel: 505 272-0932   *Fax:* 505 272-5821
E-mail: raderas@salud.unm.edu
Length: 5 Yrs   *ACGME Approved/Offered Positions:* 21
Program ID: 420-34-21-120

New York

Albany

Albany Medical Center Program
Sponsor: Albany Medical Center
Veterans Affairs Medical Center (Albany)
Prgm Director: Paul R Silk, MD
Department of Radiology MC113
43 New Scotland Avenue
Albany, NY 12208
Tel: 518 262-3371   *Fax:* 518 262-8203
Length: 4 Yrs   *ACGME Approved/Offered Positions:* 20
Program ID: 420-35-11-121

Bronx

Albert Einstein College of Medicine (Jacobi) Program
Sponsor: Albert Einstein College of Medicine of Yeshiva
University
North Bronx Healthcare Network-Jacobi Medical Center
Prgm Director: Melvin Zelefsky, MD
1300 Morris Park Avenue
Bronx, NY 10461
Tel: 718 918-4595   *Fax:* 718 918-7535
E-mail: angela.trotta@nbhn.net
Length: 4 Yrs   *ACGME Approved/Offered Positions:* 16
Program ID: 420-35-21-251

Albert Einstein College of Medicine Program
Sponsor: Albert Einstein College of Medicine of Yeshiva
University
Montefiore Medical Center-Henry and Lucy Moses
Division
Prgm Director: Mordecai Koenigsberg, MD
Dept of Radiology
111 East 210th Street
Bronx, NY 10467
Tel: 718 920-5506
E-mail: eofrias@montefiore.org
Length: 4 Yrs   *ACGME Approved/Offered Positions:* 36
Program ID: 420-35-21-126

Bronx-Lebanon Hospital Center Program
Sponsor: Bronx-Lebanon Hospital Center
Prgm Director: Helen T Morehouse, MD
1650 Grand Concourse
Bronx, NY 10457
Tel: 718 518-5272   *Fax:* 718 518-5224
Length: 4 Yrs   *ACGME Approved/Offered Positions:* 12
Program ID: 420-35-12-128

Brooklyn

Long Island College Hospital Program
Sponsor: Long Island College Hospital
Prgm Director: Deborah L Reede, MD
339 Hicks Street
Brooklyn, NY 11201
Tel: 718 780-1793   *Fax:* 718 780-1611
Length: 4 Yrs   *ACGME Approved/Offered Positions:* 14
Program ID: 420-35-11-131

Maimonides Medical Center Program
Sponsor: Maimonides Medical Center
Prgm Director: Steven Shankman, MD
4802 Tenth Avenue
Brooklyn, NY 11219
Tel: 718 283-7117   *Fax:* 718 635-8411
E-mail: csmith@maimonidesmed.org
Length: 4 Yrs   *ACGME Approved/Offered Positions:* 16
Program ID: 420-35-21-221

SUNY Health Science Center at Brooklyn Program
Sponsor: SUNY Health Science Center at Brooklyn
Kings County Hospital Center
University Hospital-SUNY Health Science Center at
Brooklyn
Prgm Director: John Amodio, MD*
Box 45
450 Clarkson Avenue
Brooklyn, NY 11203
Tel: 718 270-6730
E-mail: john.amodio@downstate.edu
Length: 4 Yrs   *ACGME Approved/Offered Positions:* 32
Program ID: 420-35-21-143

East Meadow

Nassau University Medical Center Program
Sponsor: Nassau University Medical Center
Prgm Director: Nalini Kanth, MD
Department of Radiology
2201 Hempstead Turnpike
East Meadow, NY 11554
Tel: 516 572-6785   *Fax:* 516 572-5941
E-mail: nkanth@numc.edu
Length: 4 Yrs   *ACGME Approved/Offered Positions:* 16
Program ID: 420-35-11-123

Great Neck

NSLIJHS-Albert Einstein College of Medicine at Long Island Jewish Medical Center Program
Sponsor: North Shore-Long Island Jewish Health System
Long Island Jewish Medical Center
Prgm Director: Lawrence P Davis, MD
270-05 76th Avenue
New Hyde Park, NY 11040
Tel: 718 470-7235   *Fax:* 718 343-3893
E-mail: eacobacc@lij.edu
Length: 4 Yrs   *ACGME Approved/Offered Positions:* 18
Program ID: 420-35-21-132

NSLIJHS-North Shore University Hospital/NYU School of Medicine Program
Sponsor: North Shore-Long Island Jewish Health System
North Shore University Hospital
Prgm Director: James B Naidich, MD
Department of Radiology
300 Community Drive
Manhasset, NY 11030
Tel: 516 562-4797   *Fax:* 516 562-4794
E-mail: jnaidich@yahoo.com
Length: 4 Yrs   *ACGME Approved/Offered Positions:* 21
Program ID: 420-35-31-124

Mineola

Winthrop-University Hospital Program
Sponsor: Winthrop-University Hospital
Prgm Director: Jonathan Luchs, MD
259 First Street
Mineola, NY 11501
Tel: 516 663-3682   *Fax:* 516 663-8467
Length: 4 Yrs   *ACGME Approved/Offered Positions:* 16
Program ID: 420-35-21-240

New York

Albert Einstein College of Medicine at Beth Israel Medical Center Program
Sponsor: Beth Israel Medical Center
Prgm Director: Marlene Rackson, MD
First Avenue at 16th street
New York, NY 10003
Tel: 212 420-4654   *Fax:* 212 420-2510
E-mail: mrackson@bethisraelny.org
Length: 4 Yrs   *ACGME Approved/Offered Positions:* 24
Program ID: 420-35-21-127

Harlem Hospital Center Program
Sponsor: Harlem Hospital Center
Lincoln Medical and Mental Health Center
New York Presbyterian Hospital (Columbia Campus)
Prgm Director: Roberta C Locko, MD
506 Lenox Avenue
New York, NY 10037
Tel: 212 939-4901   *Fax:* 212 939-4836
Length: 4 Yrs   *ACGME Approved/Offered Positions:* 12
Program ID: 420-35-21-214

Lenox Hill Hospital Program
Sponsor: Lenox Hill Hospital
Prgm Director: Neal F Epstein, MD
Department of Radiology
100 E 77th Street
New York, NY 10021
Tel: 212 434-2522   *Fax:* 212 434-2253
Length: 4 Yrs   *ACGME Approved/Offered Positions:* 16
Program ID: 420-35-21-218

Note: * indicates a newly appointed program director

Mount Sinai School of Medicine Program

Sponsor: Mount Sinai School of Medicine
Mount Sinai Medical Center
Prgm Director: Kathleen P Halton, MD
Department of Radiology Box 1234
One Gustave L Levy Place
New York, NY 10029
Tel: 212 241-4013   *Fax:* 212 241-4234
Length: 4 Yrs   *ACGME Approved/Offered Positions:* 32
Program ID: 420-35-21-135

New York Medical College at St Vincent's Hospital and Medical Center of New York Program

Sponsor: New York Medical College
St Vincent Catholic Medical Centers (Manhattan)
Prgm Director: Steven R Parmett, MD*
170 West 12th Street
New York, NY 10011
Tel: 212 604-2416   *Fax:* 212 604-2929
Length: 4 Yrs   *ACGME Approved/Offered Positions:* 14
Program ID: 420-35-12-141

New York Presbyterian Hospital (Columbia Campus) Program

Sponsor: New York Presbyterian Hospital
New York Presbyterian Hospital (Columbia Campus)
Prgm Director: Anna Rozenshtein, MD
HP-3-320
180 Fort Washington Avenue
New York, NY 10032
Tel: 212 305-6495   *Fax:* 212 305-5777
Length: 4 Yrs   *ACGME Approved/Offered Positions:* 24
Program ID: 420-35-11-138

New York Presbyterian Hospital (Cornell Campus) Program

Sponsor: New York Presbyterian Hospital
Memorial Sloan-Kettering Cancer Center
New York Presbyterian Hospital (Cornell Campus)
Prgm Director: Kevin W Mennitt, MD*
525 East 68th Street
New York, NY 10065
Tel: 212 746-3655   *Fax:* 212 746-8596
E-mail: kem9003@med.cornell.edu
Length: 4 Yrs   *ACGME Approved/Offered Positions:* 40
Program ID: 420-35-21-129

New York University School of Medicine Program

Sponsor: New York University School of Medicine
Bellevue Hospital Center
Manhattan VA Harbor Health Care System
NYU Hospitals Center
Prgm Director: Michael M Ambrosino, MD
Department of Radiology
462 First Avenue
New York, NY 10016
Tel: 212 263-6369   *Fax:* 212 263-7666
Length: 4 Yrs   *ACGME Approved/Offered Positions:* 40
Program ID: 420-35-21-137

St Luke's-Roosevelt Hospital Center Program

Sponsor: St Luke's-Roosevelt Hospital Center
Prgm Director: Nolan J Kagetsu, MD
1000 Tenth Avenue, 4th Floor, Rm 4C-12
Dept of Radiology
New York, NY 10019
Tel: 212 523-7048   *Fax:* 212 523-6019
Length: 4 Yrs   *ACGME Approved/Offered Positions:* 24
Program ID: 420-35-21-224

Rochester

Rochester General Hospital Program

Sponsor: Rochester General Hospital
Prgm Director: James J Montesinos, MD
Department of Radiology
1425 Portland Avenue
Rochester, NY 14621
Tel: 585 922-3220   *Fax:* 585 922-3518
Length: 4 Yrs   *ACGME Approved/Offered Positions:* 16
Program ID: 420-35-12-145

University of Rochester Program

Sponsor: Strong Memorial Hospital of the University of Rochester
Prgm Director: John C Wandtke, MD
601 Elmwood Avenue
PO Box 648
Rochester, NY 14642
Tel: 585 275-7493   *Fax:* 585 273-3549
E-mail: iona_mackey@urmc.rochester.edu
Length: 4 Yrs   *ACGME Approved/Offered Positions:* 36
Program ID: 420-35-11-146

Staten Island

New York Medical College (Richmond) Program

Sponsor: New York Medical College
Richmond University Medical Center
Maimonides Medical Center
Regional Radiology
Prgm Director: Kikkeri Vinaya, MD
Department of Radiology
355 Bard Avenue
Staten Island, NY 10310
Tel: 718 818-3153   *Fax:* 718 818-4180
E-mail: kvinaya@rumcsi.org
Length: 4 Yrs   *ACGME Approved/Offered Positions:* 8
Program ID: 420-35-21-229

Staten Island University Hospital Program

Sponsor: Staten Island University Hospital
Prgm Director: Mary M Salvatore, MD
475 Seaview Avenue
Staten Island, NY 10305
Tel: 718 226-3518   *Fax:* 718 226-8335
E-mail: msalvatore@siuh.edu
Length: 4 Yrs   *ACGME Approved/Offered Positions:* 16
Program ID: 420-35-12-254

Stony Brook

SUNY at Stony Brook Program

Sponsor: University Hospital - SUNY at Stony Brook
Prgm Director: William H Moore, MD*
Dept of Radiology
School of Medicine, Stony Brook University
Stony Brook, NY 11794
Tel: 631 444-3580   *Fax:* 631 444-7538
Length: 4 Yrs   *ACGME Approved/Offered Positions:* 20
Program ID: 420-35-21-222

Syracuse

SUNY Upstate Medical University Program

Sponsor: SUNY Upstate Medical University
Prgm Director: Rolf A Grage, MD
750 East Adams Street
Syracuse, NY 13210
Tel: 315 464-7434   *Fax:* 315 464-2570
E-mail: Jonesae@upstate.edu
Length: 4 Yrs   *ACGME Approved/Offered Positions:* 24
Program ID: 420-35-21-147

Valhalla

New York Medical College at Westchester Medical Center Program

Sponsor: New York Medical College
Westchester Medical Center
Prgm Director: Susan Rachlin, MD
Macy Pavilion, Room 1319
Department of Radiology
Valhalla, NY 10595
Tel: 914 493-8550   *Fax:* 914 493-7407
E-mail: linkowskir@wcmc.com
Length: 4 Yrs   *ACGME Approved/Offered Positions:* 20
Program ID: 420-35-21-136

North Carolina

Chapel Hill

University of North Carolina Hospitals Program

Sponsor: University of North Carolina Hospitals
Prgm Director: Jeffrey K Smith, MD, PhD
CB 7510
Chapel Hill, NC 27599
Tel: 919 966-2885   *Fax:* 919 966-1994
E-mail: jksmith@med.unc.edu
Length: 4 Yrs   *ACGME Approved/Offered Positions:* 32
Program ID: 420-36-11-148

Durham

Duke University Hospital Program

Sponsor: Duke University Hospital
Prgm Director: Charles M Maxfield, MD
Department of Radiology
Box 3808
Durham, NC 27710
Tel: 919 684-7585   *Fax:* 919 684-7151
E-mail: mitzi.chambers@duke.edu
Length: 4 Yrs   *ACGME Approved/Offered Positions:* 48
Program ID: 420-36-31-149

Winston-Salem

Wake Forest University School of Medicine Program

Sponsor: Wake Forest University Baptist Medical Center
Prgm Director: Rita I Freimanis, MD
Department of Radiology
Medical Center Blvd
Winston-Salem, NC 27157
Tel: 336 716-8048   *Fax:* 336 716-2029
Length: 4 Yrs   *ACGME Approved/Offered Positions:* 40
Program ID: 420-36-11-150

Ohio

Canton

Aultman/Mercy/NEOUCOM Program

Sponsor: Aultman Hospital
Mercy Medical Center (Canton)
Prgm Director: Benedict Y Kim, DO
Department of Radiology
2600 Sixth Street, SW
Canton, OH 44710
Tel: 330 363-6267   *Fax:* 330 363-2485
Length: 4 Yrs   *ACGME Approved/Offered Positions:* 16
Program ID: 420-38-21-232

Programs

Cincinnati

University Hospital/University of Cincinnati College of Medicine Program

Sponsor: University Hospital Inc
Cincinnati Children's Hospital Medical Center
Prgm Director: Robert D Wissman, MD
234 Goodman Street
Mail Location 761
Cincinnati, OH 45219
Tel: 513 584-6016   *Fax:* 513 584-0431
E-mail: Robert.Wissman@healthall.com
Length: 4 Yrs   *ACGME Approved/Offered Positions:* 32
Program ID: 420-38-21-152

Cleveland

Case Western Reserve University (MetroHealth) Program

Sponsor: MetroHealth Medical Center
Prgm Director: Melissa T Myers, MD
Department of Radiology
2500 MetroHealth Drive
Cleveland, OH 44109
Tel: 216 778-4016   *Fax:* 216 778-4375
E-mail: mbutler@metrohealth.org
Length: 4 Yrs   *ACGME Approved/Offered Positions:* 20
Program ID: 420-38-21-242

Cleveland Clinic Foundation Program

Sponsor: Cleveland Clinic Foundation
Prgm Director: Tan-Lucien Mohammed, MD
9500 Euclid Avenue
Mailcode Hb6
Cleveland, OH 44195
Tel: 216 444-2136   *Fax:* 216 636-5030
Length: 4 Yrs   *ACGME Approved/Offered Positions:* 32
Program ID: 420-38-12-154

University Hospitals Case Medical Center Program

Sponsor: University Hospitals Case Medical Center
Prgm Director: Mark R Robbin, MD
11100 Euclid Avenue
Cleveland, OH 44106
Tel: 216 844-3113   *Fax:* 216 844-5922
E-mail: mark.robbin@uhhospitals.org
Length: 4 Yrs   *ACGME Approved/Offered Positions:* 36
Program ID: 420-38-21-153

Columbus

Ohio State University Hospital Program

Sponsor: Ohio State University Hospital
Prgm Director: Greg Christoforidis, MD*
1654 Upham Drive
610 Means Hall
Columbus, OH 43210
Tel: 614 293-8369
E-mail: greg.christoforidis@osumc.edu
Length: 4 Yrs   *ACGME Approved/Offered Positions:* 28
Program ID: 420-38-21-156

Toledo

University of Toledo Program

Sponsor: University of Toledo
St Vincent Mercy Medical Center
University Medical Center (Toledo)
Prgm Director: Lee S Woldenberg, MD
Department of Radiology
Mail Stop 1200 Univ Med Ctr, 3000 Arlington Avenue
Toledo, OH 43614
Tel: 419 383-3428   *Fax:* 419 383-6422
E-mail: wendy.gobbell@utoledo.edu
Length: 4 Yrs   *ACGME Approved/Offered Positions:* 16
Program ID: 420-38-21-157

Oklahoma

Oklahoma City

Integris Baptist Medical Center Program

Sponsor: Integris Baptist Medical Center
Prgm Director: Kerri J Kirchhoff, MD
Graduate Medical Education
3300 Northwest Expressway, Room 100-4394
Oklahoma City, OK 73112
Tel: 405 552-0926   *Fax:* 405 552-5102
E-mail: annette.kezbers@integrisok.com
Length: 4 Yrs   *ACGME Approved/Offered Positions:* 17
Program ID: 420-39-12-158

University of Oklahoma Health Sciences Center Program

Sponsor: University of Oklahoma College of Medicine
OU Medical Center - Presbyterian Tower
Veterans Affairs Medical Center (Oklahoma City)
Prgm Director: Jay S Hiller, MD
Dept of Radiological Sciences
PO Box 26901
Oklahoma City, OK 73190
Tel: 405 270-5165   *Fax:* 405 297-5973
E-mail: jay-hiller@ouhsc.edu
Length: 4 Yrs   *ACGME Approved/Offered Positions:* 24
Program ID: 420-39-21-159

Oregon

Portland

Oregon Health & Science University Program

Sponsor: Oregon Health & Science University Hospital
Veterans Affairs Medical Center (Portland)
Prgm Director: Jim C Anderson, MD
Diagnostic Radiology, L340
3181 SW Sam Jackson Park Rd
Portland, OR 97239
Tel: 503 494-5266   *Fax:* 503 494-4982
E-mail: gaddisg@ohsu.edu
Length: 4 Yrs   *ACGME Approved/Offered Positions:* 20
Program ID: 420-40-31-160

Pennsylvania

Bryn Mawr

Bryn Mawr Hospital Program

Sponsor: Bryn Mawr Hospital
Prgm Director: Vikram S Dravid, MD
130 S Bryn Mawr Avenue
Department of Radiology
Bryn Mawr, PA 19010
Tel: 610 526-3436   *Fax:* 610 526-4590
Length: 4 Yrs   *ACGME Approved/Offered Positions:* 16
Program ID: 420-41-21-162

Danville

Geisinger Health System Program

Sponsor: Geisinger Health System
Geisinger Medical Center
Prgm Director: Anne P Dunne, MD
Department of Radiology 2007
100 North Academy Avenue
Danville, PA 17822
Tel: 570 271-6203   *Fax:* 570 271-5976
E-mail: twcordell@geisinger.edu
Length: 4 Yrs   *ACGME Approved/Offered Positions:* 16
Program ID: 420-41-21-163

Darby

Mercy Catholic Medical Center Program

Sponsor: Mercy Catholic Medical Center Inc
Mercy Fitzgerald Hospital
Mercy Philadelphia Hospital
Prgm Director: Betsy A Izes, MD
1500 Lansdowne Avenue
Darby, PA 19023
Tel: 610 237-4355   *Fax:* 610 237-2599
Length: 4 Yrs   *ACGME Approved/Offered Positions:* 10
Program ID: 420-41-21-170

Hershey

Penn State University/Milton S Hershey Medical Center Program

Sponsor: Milton S Hershey Medical Center
Prgm Director: Donald Flemming, MD
500 University Drive, Dept of Radiology, H066
PO Box 850
Hershey, PA 17033
Tel: 717 531-8704   *Fax:* 717 531-0922
Length: 4 Yrs   *ACGME Approved/Offered Positions:* 28
Program ID: 420-41-21-164

Philadelphia

Albert Einstein Healthcare Network Program

Sponsor: Albert Einstein Medical Center
Prgm Director: William Herring, MD, FACR
5501 Old York Road
Philadelphia, PA 19141
Tel: 215 456-6226   *Fax:* 215 456-1749
E-mail: radiology@einstein.edu
Length: 4 Yrs   *ACGME Approved/Offered Positions:* 24
Program ID: 420-41-21-165

Drexel University College of Medicine/Hahnemann University Hospital Program

Sponsor: Drexel University College of
Medicine/Hahnemann University
Hahnemann University Hospital (Tenet Health System)
Prgm Director: Robert Koenigsberg, DO, MSc
3rd Floor, North Tower MS 206
Broad and Vine Streets
Philadelphia, PA 19102
Tel: 215 762-8804   *Fax:* 215 762-2350
E-mail: Robert.Koenigsberg@drexelmed.edu
Length: 4 Yrs   *ACGME Approved/Offered Positions:* 24
Program ID: 420-41-21-169

Pennsylvania Hospital of the University of Pennsylvania Health System Program

Sponsor: Pennsylvania Hospital (UPHS)
Prgm Director: Michael B Love, MD
Department of Radiology
800 Spruce Street
Philadelphia, PA 19107
Tel: 215 829-5699   *Fax:* 215 829-7482
Length: 4 Yrs   *ACGME Approved/Offered Positions:* 20
Program ID: 420-41-31-171

Temple University Hospital Program

Sponsor: Temple University Hospital
Prgm Director: Beverly L Hershey, MD
3401 North Broad Street
Philadelphia, PA 19140
Tel: 215 707-2640   *Fax:* 215 707-5851
E-mail: hersheb@tuhs.temple.edu
Length: 4 Yrs   *ACGME Approved/Offered Positions:* 28
Program ID: 420-41-11-173

Note: * indicates a newly appointed program director

Thomas Jefferson University Program

Sponsor: Thomas Jefferson University Hospital
Prgm Director: Levon Nazarian, MD
132 S 10th Street
Suite 780 Main Bldg
Philadelphia, PA 19107
Tel: 215 955-4916   *Fax:* 215 955-5329
E-mail: levon.nazarian@jefferson.edu
Length: 4 Yrs   *ACGME Approved/Offered Positions:* 36
Program ID: 420-41-11-174

University of Pennsylvania Program

Sponsor: University of Pennsylvania Health System
Prgm Director: Mary H Scanlon, MD
3400 Spruce Street
Philadelphia, PA 19104
Tel: 215 662-2832   *Fax:* 215 662-3093
E-mail: resprog@rad.upenn.edu
Length: 4 Yrs   *ACGME Approved/Offered Positions:* 44
Program ID: 420-41-21-175

Pittsburgh

Allegheny General Hospital Program

Sponsor: Allegheny General Hospital
Prgm Director: Melanie B Fukui, MD
Department of Diagnostic Radiology
320 East North Avenue
Pittsburgh, PA 15212
Tel: 412 359-8674   *Fax:* 412 359-6912
E-mail: lfink1@wpahs.org
Length: 4 Yrs   *ACGME Approved/Offered Positions:* 29
Program ID: 420-41-21-176

University of Pittsburgh Medical Center Medical Education Program

Sponsor: Univ of Pittsburgh Medical Center Medical
  Education
Mercy Hospital of Pittsburgh
UPMC Presbyterian Shadyside
Prgm Director: Philip D Orons, DO
Medical Arts Building, Suite 503
3708 Fifth Avenue
Pittsburgh, PA 15213
Tel: 412 647-7338   *Fax:* 412 647-1137
E-mail: oronspd@upmc.edu
Length: 4 Yrs   *ACGME Approved/Offered Positions:* 60
Program ID: 420-41-21-177

Puerto Rico

San Juan

University of Puerto Rico Program

Sponsor: University of Puerto Rico School of Medicine
University Hospital
University of Puerto Rico Hospital at Carolina
Prgm Director: Angel A Gomez, MD, MPH*
PO Box 365067
Medical Sciences Campus
San Juan, PR 00936
Tel: 787 758-2525   *Fax:* 787 777-3855
E-mail: skeletalrad@gmail.com
Length: 4 Yrs   *ACGME Approved/Offered Positions:* 16
Program ID: 420-42-21-182

Rhode Island

Providence

Brown University Program

Sponsor: Rhode Island Hospital-Lifespan
Prgm Director: Martha B Mainiero, MD
Department of Radiology
593 Eddy Street
Providence, RI 02903
Tel: 401 444-5184   *Fax:* 401 444-5017
Length: 4 Yrs   *ACGME Approved/Offered Positions:* 28
Program ID: 420-43-21-183

South Carolina

Charleston

Medical University of South Carolina Program

Sponsor: Medical University of South Carolina College of
  Medicine
MUSC Medical Center
Ralph H Johnson VA Medical Center (Charleston)
Prgm Director: Leonie Gordon, MD
Department of Radiology
96 Jonathan Lucas St, MSC 323
Charleston, SC 29425
Tel: 843 792-7179   *Fax:* 843 792-9319
Length: 4 Yrs   *ACGME Approved/Offered Positions:* 32
Program ID: 420-45-21-184

Tennessee

Knoxville

University of Tennessee Medical Center at Knoxville Program

Sponsor: University of Tennessee Graduate School of
  Medicine
University of Tennessee Memorial Hospital
Prgm Director: Kathleen Hudson, MD, MEd
1924 Alcoa Highway
Knoxville, TN 37920
Tel: 865 305-8685   *Fax:* 865 305-9025
Length: 4 Yrs   *ACGME Approved/Offered Positions:* 20
Program ID: 420-47-21-236

Memphis

Baptist Memorial Hospital Program

Sponsor: Baptist Memorial Hospital
Prgm Director: John A Ellzey, MD
Department of Radiology, Attn: Ginger Tubbs
6019 Walnut Grove Road
Memphis, TN 38120
Tel: 901 226-3001   *Fax:* 901 226-3159
Length: 4 Yrs   *ACGME Approved/Offered Positions:* 24
Program ID: 420-47-12-186

University of Tennessee/Methodist Healthcare Program

Sponsor: University of Tennessee College of Medicine
Methodist Healthcare - Memphis Hospitals
Regional Medical Center at Memphis
Veterans Affairs Medical Center (Memphis)
Prgm Director: Robert E Laster Jr, MD
Department of Radiology
1265 Union Avenue
Memphis, TN 38104
Tel: 901 516-8529   *Fax:* 901 516-7490
E-mail: barnsl@methodisthealth.org
Length: 4 Yrs   *ACGME Approved/Offered Positions:* 36
Program ID: 420-47-21-187

Nashville

Vanderbilt University Program

Sponsor: Vanderbilt University Medical Center
Veterans Affairs Medical Center (Nashville)
Prgm Director: Thomas S Dina, MD
1161 21st Avenue South
CCC-1121 Medical Center North
Nashville, TN 37232
Tel: 615 322-3780   *Fax:* 615 322-3764
E-mail: radprogram@vanderbilt.edu
Length: 4 Yrs   *ACGME Approved/Offered Positions:* 29
Program ID: 420-47-21-189

Texas

Dallas

Baylor University Medical Center Program

Sponsor: Baylor University Medical Center
Prgm Director: Kenneth L Ford III, MD
Department of Radiology
3500 Gaston Avenue
Dallas, TX 75246
Tel: 214 820-3795   *Fax:* 214 820-7577
E-mail: radres@baylorhealth.edu
Length: 4 Yrs   *ACGME Approved/Offered Positions:* 28
Program ID: 420-48-22-190

University of Texas Southwestern Medical School Program

Sponsor: University of Texas Southwestern Medical
  School
Dallas County Hospital District-Parkland Memorial
  Hospital
Dallas VA Medical Center
Prgm Director: Diane M Twickler, MD
5323 Harry Hines Boulevard
Dallas, TX 75390
Tel: 214 648-9107   *Fax:* 214 648-2678
E-mail: Dianna.Otterstad@UTSouthwestern.edu
Length: 4 Yrs   *ACGME Approved/Offered Positions:* 52
Program ID: 420-48-21-192

El Paso

Texas Tech University Health Sciences Center Paul L Foster School of Medicine Program

Sponsor: Texas Tech University Hlth Sci Ctr Paul L
  Foster Sch of Med
R E Thomason General Hospital / Texas Tech University
  HSC
Prgm Director: Arvin E Robinson, MD, MPH
4800 Alberta Avenue
El Paso, TX 79905
Tel: 915 545-6845   *Fax:* 915 545-0420
Length: 4 Yrs   *ACGME Approved/Offered Positions:* 8
Program ID: 420-48-12-257

Galveston

University of Texas Medical Branch Hospitals Program

Sponsor: University of Texas Medical Branch Hospitals
Prgm Director: Leonard E Swischuk, MD
Department of Radiology
301 University Boulevard
Galveston, TX 77555
Tel: 409 747-2849   *Fax:* 409 772-7120
E-mail: femcdani@utmb.edu
Length: 4 Yrs   *ACGME Approved/Offered Positions:* 24
Program ID: 420-48-11-194

Houston

Baylor College of Medicine Program

Sponsor: Baylor College of Medicine
Harris County Hospital District-Ben Taub General
  Hospital
Prgm Director: Pedro J Diaz-Marchan, MD
Department of Radiology
One Baylor Plaza
Houston, TX 77030
Tel: 713 798-6362   *Fax:* 713 798-8359
E-mail: lburlin@bcm.edu
Length: 4 Yrs   *ACGME Approved/Offered Positions:* 44
Program ID: 420-48-21-195

Programs

University of Texas at Houston Program

Sponsor: University of Texas Health Science Center at Houston
Lyndon B Johnson General Hospital
Memorial Hermann Hospital
University of Texas M D Anderson Cancer Center
Prgm Director: Sandra A Oldham, MD
Department of Diagnostic Radiology
6431 Fannin Street, Suite 2.026
Houston, TX 77030
Tel: 713 500-7640   *Fax:* 713 500-7647
Length: 4 Yrs   *ACGME Approved/Offered Positions:* 52
Program ID: 420-48-21-196

Lackland AFB

San Antonio Uniformed Services Health Education Consortium Program

Sponsor: San Antonio Uniformed Services Health Education Consortium
Brooke Army Medical Center
Wilford Hall Medical Center (AETC)
Prgm Director: Liem T Mansfield COL, MD
Radiology Residency Program - DOR
3851 Roger Brooke Drive, Room 133-2
Fort Sam Houston, TX 78234
Tel: 210 916-3290   *Fax:* 210 916-9256
E-mail: liem.mansfield@amedd.army.mil
Length: 4 Yrs   *ACGME Approved/Offered Positions:* 40
Program ID: 420-48-21-248
Uniformed Services Program

San Antonio

University of Texas Health Science Center at San Antonio Program

Sponsor: University of Texas School of Medicine at San Antonio
Audie L Murphy Memorial Veterans Hospital (San Antonio)
University Health System
Prgm Director: Rajeev Suri, MD*
Department of Radiology
7703 Floyd Curl Drive
San Antonio, TX 78229
Tel: 210 567-6482   *Fax:* 210 567-5541
Length: 4 Yrs   *ACGME Approved/Offered Positions:* 40
Program ID: 420-48-21-197

Temple

Texas A&M College of Medicine-Scott and White Program

Sponsor: Scott and White Memorial Hospital
Prgm Director: James B Schnitker, MD
2401 South 31st Street
Temple, TX 76508
Tel: 254 724-4507   *Fax:* 254 724-6588
Length: 4 Yrs   *ACGME Approved/Offered Positions:* 24
Program ID: 420-48-11-198

Utah

Salt Lake City

University of Utah Program

Sponsor: University of Utah Medical Center
Veterans Affairs Medical Center (Salt Lake City)
Prgm Director: H Christian Davidson, MD
Department of Radiology
30 North 1900 East, #1A71
Salt Lake City, UT 84132
Tel: 801 581-7553   *Fax:* 801 581-2414
Length: 4 Yrs   *ACGME Approved/Offered Positions:* 24
Program ID: 420-49-21-199

Vermont

Burlington

University of Vermont Program

Sponsor: Fletcher Allen Health Care
Prgm Director: Kristen DeStigter, MD
Patrick 113, FAHC, MCHV Campus
111 Colchester Avenue
Burlington, VT 05401
Tel: 802 847-0794   *Fax:* 802 847-4822
E-mail: Kristen.Destigter@vtmednet.org
Length: 4 Yrs   *ACGME Approved/Offered Positions:* 20
Program ID: 420-50-31-200

Virginia

Charlottesville

University of Virginia Program

Sponsor: University of Virginia Medical Center
Prgm Director: Spencer B Gay, MD
PO Box 800170
Lee Street
Charlottesville, VA 22908
Tel: 434 924-9372   *Fax:* 434 924-8698
E-mail: kr3s@virginia.edu
Length: 4 Yrs   *ACGME Approved/Offered Positions:* 41
Program ID: 420-51-11-201

Norfolk

Eastern Virginia Medical School Program

Sponsor: Eastern Virginia Medical School
DePaul Medical Center
Sentara Norfolk General Hospital
Prgm Director: Lester S Johnson, MD, PhD
Department of Radiology
PO Box 1980
Norfolk, VA 23501
Tel: 757 446-8990   *Fax:* 757 446-8441
Length: 4 Yrs   *ACGME Approved/Offered Positions:* 16
Program ID: 420-51-21-202

Portsmouth

Naval Medical Center (Portsmouth) Program

Sponsor: Naval Medical Center (Portsmouth)
Prgm Director: Raymond E Bozman, MD
620 John Paul Jones Circle
Portsmouth, VA 23708
Tel: 757 953-1198   *Fax:* 757 953-7327
E-mail: bridget.wakefield@med.navy.mil
Length: 4 Yrs   *ACGME Approved/Offered Positions:* 28
Program ID: 420-51-13-252
Uniformed Services Program

Richmond

Virginia Commonwealth University Health System Program

Sponsor: Virginia Commonwealth University Health System
Hunter Holmes McGuire VA Medical Center (Richmond)
Medical College of Virginia Hospitals
Prgm Director: Lakshmana D Narla, MD
PO Box 980615
1250 E Marshall Street, Rm 3-406
Richmond, VA 23298
Tel: 804 828-3524   *Fax:* 804 628-2015
E-mail: klrobb@vcu.edu
Length: 4 Yrs   *ACGME Approved/Offered Positions:* 36
Program ID: 420-51-21-203

Washington

Seattle

University of Washington Program

Sponsor: University of Washington School of Medicine
Harborview Medical Center
Seattle Children's Hospital
University of Washington Medical Center
VA Puget Sound Health Care System
Prgm Director: Angelisa M Paladin, MD
1959 NE Pacific Street
Box 357115
Seattle, WA 98195
Tel: 206 685-8307   *Fax:* 206 543-6317
Length: 4 Yrs   *ACGME Approved/Offered Positions:* 44
Program ID: 420-54-21-205

Virginia Mason Medical Center Program

Sponsor: Virginia Mason Medical Center
Prgm Director: Felicia P Cummings, MD
Graduate Medical Education
925 Seneca Street, H8-GME
Seattle, WA 98111
Tel: 206 583-6079   *Fax:* 206 583-2307
E-mail: Joanne.VanderDoes@vmmc.org
Length: 4 Yrs   *ACGME Approved/Offered Positions:* 12
Program ID: 420-54-12-206

Spokane

Spokane Medical Centers Program

Sponsor: Inland Empire Hospital Services Association
Sacred Heart Medical Center
Prgm Director: Terri H Lewis, MD
101 West 8th Avenue
PO Box 2555
Spokane, WA 99220
Tel: 509 474-3021   *Fax:* 509 474-2891
E-mail: buchols@shmc.org
Length: 4 Yrs   *ACGME Approved/Offered Positions:* 9
Program ID: 420-54-21-207

Tacoma

Madigan Army Medical Center Program

Sponsor: Madigan Army Medical Center
Prgm Director: Mohammad Naeem, MBBS, MD
MCHJ-R
Bldg 9040A Jackson Ave
Tacoma, WA 98431
Tel: 253 968-5604   *Fax:* 253 968-3140
E-mail: mohammad.naeem@us.army.mil
Length: 4 Yrs   *ACGME Approved/Offered Positions:* 20
Program ID: 420-54-21-239
Uniformed Services Program

West Virginia

Morgantown

West Virginia University Program

Sponsor: West Virginia University School of Medicine
West Virginia University Hospitals
Prgm Director: Robert J Tallaksen, MD
Robert C Byrd Health Science Ctr North
PO Box 9235
Morgantown, WV 26506
Tel: 304 293-3092   *Fax:* 304 293-3899
E-mail: rtallaksen@hsc.wvu.edu
Length: 4 Yrs   *ACGME Approved/Offered Positions:* 16
Program ID: 420-55-21-208

Note: * indicates a newly appointed program director

Wisconsin

Madison

University of Wisconsin Program

Sponsor: University of Wisconsin Hospital and Clinics
Prgm Director: David H Kim, MD
E3/311 Clinical Sciences Center
600 Highland Avenue
Madison, WI 53792
Tel: 608 263-8310   *Fax:* 608 263-8297
E-mail: ARichgels2@uwhealth.org
Length: 4 Yrs   *ACGME Approved/Offered Positions:* 28
Program ID: 420-56-21-210

Milwaukee

Aurora Health Care Program

Sponsor: Aurora Health Care
St Luke's Medical Center
Prgm Director: Sean R Amoli, MD
2900 West Oklahoma Avenue
Milwaukee, WI 53215
Tel: 414 649-6298   *Fax:* 414 649-5296
E-mail: camille.dykas@aurora.org
Length: 4 Yrs   *ACGME Approved/Offered Positions:* 20
Program ID: 420-56-12-213

Medical College of Wisconsin Affiliated Hospitals Program

Sponsor: Medical College of Wisconsin Affiliated
   Hospitals, Inc
Clement J Zablocki Veterans Affairs Medical Center
Froedtert Memorial Lutheran Hospital
Prgm Director: Guillermo F Carrera, MD
Department of Radiology
9200 West Wisconsin Avenue
Milwaukee, WI 53226
Tel: 414 805-3750   *Fax:* 414 259-9290
Length: 4 Yrs   *ACGME Approved/Offered Positions:* 32
Program ID: 420-56-21-211

Wheaton Franciscan Healthcare-St Joseph Program

Sponsor: Wheaton Franciscan Healthcare-St Joseph
Prgm Director: David W Litzau, MD*
5000 West Chambers Street
Milwaukee, WI 53210
Tel: 414 447-2196   *Fax:* 414 874-4533
Length: 4 Yrs   *ACGME Approved/Offered Positions:* 12
Program ID: 420-56-22-212

Rheumatology (Internal Medicine)

Alabama

Birmingham

University of Alabama Medical Center Program

Sponsor: University of Alabama Hospital
Cooper Green Hospital
Veterans Affairs Medical Center (Birmingham)
Prgm Director: W Winn Chatham, MD
1530 3rd Avenue South
FOT 802
Birmingham, AL 35294
Tel: 205 934-4212   *Fax:* 205 934-4198
Length: 2 Yrs   *ACGME Approved/Offered Positions:* 6
Program ID: 150-01-21-088

Arizona

Tucson

University of Arizona Program

Sponsor: University of Arizona College of Medicine
Southern Arizona VA Health Care Center (Tucson)
University Medical Center
Prgm Director: Berchman A Vaz, MD, PhD
1501 North Campbell Avenue
Room 8303
Tucson, AZ 85724
Tel: 520 694-0622   *Fax:* 520 694-0662
E-mail: terrib@email.arizona.edu
Length: 2 Yrs   *ACGME Approved/Offered Positions:* 4
Program ID: 150-03-21-076

Arkansas

Little Rock

University of Arkansas for Medical Sciences Program

Sponsor: University of Arkansas College of Medicine
Central Arkansas Veterans Healthcare System
UAMS Medical Center
Prgm Director: Robert A Ortmann, MD*
4301 West Markham St
Little Rock, AR 72205
Tel: 501 526-7049   *Fax:* 501 603-1380
Length: 2 Yrs   *ACGME Approved/Offered Positions:* 4
Program ID: 150-04-21-145

California

La Jolla

Scripps Clinic/Scripps Green Hospital Program

Sponsor: Scripps Clinic/Scripps Green Hospital
Prgm Director: Ken D Pischel, MD, PhD
10666 N Torrey Pines Road
La Jolla, CA 92037
Tel: 858 554-8819   *Fax:* 858 554-6763
E-mail: nobles.kathleen@scrippshealth.org
Length: 2 Yrs   *ACGME Approved/Offered Positions:* 2
Program ID: 150-05-21-042

Loma Linda

Loma Linda University Program

Sponsor: Loma Linda University Medical Center
Jerry L Pettis Memorial Veterans Hospital
Prgm Director: Edwin H Krick, MD
Department of Internal Medicine
PO Box 2000
Loma Linda, CA 92354
Tel: 909 558-4911   *Fax:* 909 558-0490
E-mail: dacosta@llu.edu
Length: 2 Yrs   *ACGME Approved/Offered Positions:* 2
Program ID: 150-05-21-090

Los Angeles

Cedars-Sinai Medical Center Program

Sponsor: Cedars-Sinai Medical Center
Los Angeles County-Harbor-UCLA Medical Center
VA Greater Los Angeles Healthcare System
Prgm Director: Michael H Weisman, MD, FACR
Department of Internal Medicine
8700 Beverly Boulevard, Suite B131
Los Angeles, CA 90048
Tel: 310 423-2170   *Fax:* 310 423-6898
Length: 2 Yrs   *ACGME Approved/Offered Positions:* 4
Program ID: 150-05-11-078

UCLA Medical Center Program

Sponsor: UCLA David Geffen School of Medicine/UCLA
   Medical Center
Los Angeles County-Harbor-UCLA Medical Center
UCLA Medical Center
VA Greater Los Angeles Healthcare System
Prgm Director: Ernest Brahn, MD
Center for the Health Sciences
10833 Le Conte Avenue
Los Angeles, CA 90024
Tel: 310 825-5671   *Fax:* 310 206-9707
Length: 2 Yrs   *ACGME Approved/Offered Positions:* 10
Program ID: 150-05-11-091

University of Southern California/ LAC+USC Medical Center Program

Sponsor: University of Southern California/LAC+USC
   Medical Center
LAC+USC Medical Center
LAC-Rancho Los Amigos National Rehabilitation Center
USC University Hospital
Prgm Director: Francisco P Quismorio Jr, MD
2011 Zonal Avenue, HMR 711
Los Angeles, CA 90033
Tel: 323 442-1946   *Fax:* 323 442-2874
E-mail: rheum@usc.edu
Length: 2 Yrs   *ACGME Approved/Offered Positions:* 6
Program ID: 150-05-21-031

Orange

University of California (Irvine) Program

Sponsor: University of California (Irvine) Medical
   Center
VA Long Beach Healthcare System
Prgm Director: Brian S Andrews, MD, PhD
101 The City Drive South
Bldg 53, Room 219
Orange, CA 92868
Tel: 714 456-6602   *Fax:* 714 456-6164
Length: 2 Yrs   *ACGME Approved/Offered Positions:* 3
Program ID: 150-05-21-108

Programs

Sacramento

University of California (Davis) Health System Program

Sponsor: University of California (Davis) Health System
University of California (Davis) Medical Center
VA Northern California Health Care System
Prgm Director: Stanley M Naguwa, MD
451 E Health Sciences Drive
Suite 6510
Davis, CA 95616
Tel: 530 752-2884   *Fax:* 530 754-6407
Length: 2 Yrs   *ACGME Approved/Offered Positions:* 2
Program ID: 150-05-21-153

San Diego

University of California (San Diego) Program

Sponsor: University of California (San Diego) Medical Center
Veterans Affairs Medical Center (San Diego)
Prgm Director: Robert A Terkeltaub, MD
3350 La Jolla Village Drive (111K)
San Diego, CA 92161
Tel: 858 552-8585   *Fax:* 858 552-7425
E-mail: raifellow@ucsd.edu
Length: 2 Yrs   *ACGME Approved/Offered Positions:* 4
Program ID: 150-05-21-123

San Francisco

University of California (San Francisco) Program

Sponsor: University of California (San Francisco) School of Medicine
San Francisco General Hospital Medical Center
UCSF and Mount Zion Medical Centers
Veterans Affairs Medical Center (San Francisco)
Prgm Director: David I Daikh, MD, PhD
Rheumatology Office U384
533 Parnassus Avenue
San Francisco, CA 94143
Tel: 415 750-2104   *Fax:* 415 750-6920
Length: 2 Yrs   *ACGME Approved/Offered Positions:* 8
Program ID: 150-05-21-109

Stanford

Stanford University Program

Sponsor: Stanford Hospital and Clinics
Santa Clara Valley Medical Center
Veterans Affairs Palo Alto Health Care System
Prgm Director: Mark C Genovese, MD*
Department of Medicine
1000 Welch Road, Suite 203
Palo Alto, CA 94305
Tel: 650 498-4528   *Fax:* 650 723-9656
Length: 2 Yrs   *ACGME Approved/Offered Positions:* 4
Program ID: 150-05-21-016

Sylmar

UCLA-Olive View Program

Sponsor: Olive View/UCLA Medical Center
VA Greater Los Angeles Healthcare System
Prgm Director: Andrew L Wong, MD
Department of Medicine 2B182
14445 Olive View Drive, 2B182
Sylmar, CA 91342
Tel: 818 364-3205   *Fax:* 818 364-4573
E-mail: alunwong@ucla.edu
Length: 2 Yrs   *ACGME Approved/Offered Positions:* 2
Program ID: 150-05-21-092

Note: * indicates a newly appointed program director

Colorado

Aurora

University of Colorado Denver Program

Sponsor: University of Colorado Denver School of Medicine
Denver Health Medical Center
University of Colorado Hospital
Veterans Affairs Medical Center (Denver)
Prgm Director: Sterling G West, MD
1775 N Ursula Street, Room 3102
PO Box 6511, Mail Stop B115
Aurora, CO 80045
Tel: 303 724-7610   *Fax:* 303 724-7610
E-mail: helen.martinez@uchsc.edu
Length: 2 Yrs   *ACGME Approved/Offered Positions:* 5
Program ID: 150-07-21-036

Connecticut

Farmington

University of Connecticut Program

Sponsor: University of Connecticut School of Medicine
Univ of Connecticut Health Center/John Dempsey Hospital
Prgm Director: Santhanan Lakshminarayanan, MD
Department of Medicine
263 Farmington Avenue
Farmington, CT 06030
Tel: 860 679-3605   *Fax:* 860 679-1287
Length: 2 Yrs   *ACGME Approved/Offered Positions:* 2
Program ID: 150-08-31-001

New Haven

Yale-New Haven Medical Center Program

Sponsor: Yale-New Haven Hospital
Veterans Affairs Medical Center (West Haven)
Prgm Director: Janine Evans, MD*
300 Cedar Street, S525 TAC Building
PO Box 208031
New Haven, CT 06520
Tel: 203 737-2771   *Fax:* 203 785-7053
Length: 2 Yrs   *ACGME Approved/Offered Positions:* 6
Program ID: 150-08-21-017

District of Columbia

Washington

George Washington University Program

Sponsor: George Washington University School of Medicine
George Washington University Hospital (UHS)
Prgm Director: Rodolfo V Curiel, MD
Department of Medicine, Suite 3-416
2150 Pennsylvania Avenue, NW
Washington, DC 20037
Tel: 202 741-2488   *Fax:* 202 741-2490
E-mail: rcuriel@mfa.gwu.edu
Length: 2 Yrs   *ACGME Approved/Offered Positions:* 2
Program ID: 150-10-21-079

Georgetown University Hospital Program

Sponsor: Georgetown University Hospital
Veterans Affairs Medical Center (Washington, DC)
Prgm Director: Virginia D Steen, MD
Dept of Medicine, Rheumatology
3800 Reservoir Road, NW
Washington, DC 20007
Tel: 202 444-1532   *Fax:* 202 444-7797
E-mail: ah@gunet.georgetown.edu
Length: 2 Yrs   *ACGME Approved/Offered Positions:* 4
Program ID: 150-10-21-060

Georgetown University Hospital/Washington Hospital Center Program

Sponsor: Washington Hospital Center
Prgm Director: Arthur Weinstein, MD
Department of Medicine
110 Irving Street, NW #2A-66
Washington, DC 20010
Tel: 202 877-6274   *Fax:* 202 877-6130
Length: 2 Yrs   *ACGME Approved/Offered Positions:* 4
Program ID: 150-10-11-094

Florida

Gainesville

University of Florida Program

Sponsor: University of Florida College of Medicine
North Florida/South Georgia Veterans Health System
Shands Hospital at the University of Florida
Prgm Director: Eric S Sobel, MD, PhD
Department of Medicine
PO Box 100221
Gainesville, FL 32610
Tel: 352 273-5345   *Fax:* 352 392-8483
Length: 2 Yrs   *ACGME Approved/Offered Positions:* 4
Program ID: 150-11-21-025

Miami

Jackson Memorial Hospital/Jackson Health System Program

Sponsor: Jackson Memorial Hospital/Jackson Health System
University of Miami Hospital
Veterans Affairs Medical Center (Miami)
Prgm Director: Carlos J Lozada, MD
1120 NW 14th Street, Suite 972
Miami, FL 33136
Tel: 305 243-7545   *Fax:* 305 243-7546
Length: 2 Yrs   *ACGME Approved/Offered Positions:* 4
Program ID: 150-11-21-125

Tampa

University of South Florida Program

Sponsor: University of South Florida College of Medicine
James A Haley Veterans Hospital
Tampa General Hospital
Prgm Director: Joanne Valeriano-Marcet, MD
12901 Bruce B Downs Blvd, MDC 81
Division of Rheumatology
Tampa, FL 33612
Tel: 813 974-2681   *Fax:* 813 974-5229
E-mail: kharding@health.usf.edu
Length: 2 Yrs   *ACGME Approved/Offered Positions:* 4
Program ID: 150-11-21-026

Georgia

Atlanta

Emory University Program

Sponsor: Emory University School of Medicine
Crawford Long Hospital of Emory University
Emory University Hospital
Grady Health System
Veterans Affairs Medical Center (Atlanta)
Prgm Director: Jonathan Waltuck, MD
Rheumatology Division
1365 Clifton Road, Suite 4333
Atlanta, GA 30322
Tel: 404 778-5339   *Fax:* 404 778-3217
Length: 2 Yrs   *ACGME Approved/Offered Positions:* 6
Program ID: 150-12-21-095

Augusta

Medical College of Georgia Program
Sponsor: Medical College of Georgia
Veterans Affairs Medical Center (Augusta)
Prgm Director: Bruce E Goeckeritz, MD
1120 15th St, BI 5083
Augusta, GA 30912
Tel: 706 721-2981   *Fax:* 706 721-6314
Length: 2 Yrs   *ACGME Approved/Offered Positions:* 3
Program ID: 150-12-21-002

Illinois

Chicago

McGaw Medical Center of Northwestern University Program
Sponsor: McGaw Medical Center of Northwestern
   University
Jesse Brown Veterans Affairs Medical Center
Northwestern Memorial Hospital
Prgm Director: Calvin Brown, MD*
240 E Huron Street
McGaw Pavilion Suite M300
Chicago, IL 60611
Tel: 312 503-8003   *Fax:* 312 503-0994
Length: 2 Yrs   *ACGME Approved/Offered Positions:* 4
Program ID: 150-16-21-051

Rush University Medical Center Program
Sponsor: Rush University Medical Center
John H Stroger Hospital of Cook County
Prgm Director: Augustine M Manadan, MD*
1725 W Harrison Street, Suite 1017
Chicago, IL 60612
Tel: 312 942-8268   *Fax:* 312 563-2267
E-mail: rheumatology@rush.edu
Length: 2 Yrs   *ACGME Approved/Offered Positions:* 5
Program ID: 150-16-11-096

University of Chicago Program
Sponsor: University of Chicago Medical Center
Prgm Director: Tammy O Utset, MD, MPH
5841 S Maryland Avenue
MC 0930
Chicago, IL 60637
Tel: 773 834-1584   *Fax:* 773 702-8702
Length: 2 Yrs   *ACGME Approved/Offered Positions:* 4
Program ID: 150-16-21-138

University of Illinois College of Medicine at Chicago Program
Sponsor: University of Illinois College of Medicine at
   Chicago
Jesse Brown Veterans Affairs Medical Center
Michael Reese Hospital and Medical Center
University of Illinois Hospital and Clinics
Prgm Director: William Swedler, MD
Suite A312, CMW (M/C 733)
1819 West Polk Street
Chicago, IL 60612
Tel: 312 413-9310   *Fax:* 312 413-9271
Length: 2 Yrs   *ACGME Approved/Offered Positions:* 4
Program ID: 150-16-21-097

Maywood

Loyola University Program
Sponsor: Loyola University Medical Center
Edward Hines, Jr Veterans Affairs Hospital
Prgm Director: Elaine M Adams, MD
2160 S First Avenue
Bldg 54 Room 121
Maywood, IL 60153
Tel: 708 216-3313   *Fax:* 708 216-1085
E-mail: rsramek@lumc.edu
Length: 2 Yrs   *ACGME Approved/Offered Positions:* 2
Program ID: 150-16-21-003

Indiana

Indianapolis

Indiana University School of Medicine Program
Sponsor: Indiana University School of Medicine
Clarian Indiana University Hospital
Clarian Riley Hospital for Children
Richard L Roudebush Veterans Affairs Medical Center
William N Wishard Memorial Hospital
Prgm Director: Steven T Hugenberg, MD
1110 W Michigan St
LO 545
Indianapolis, IN 46202
Tel: 317 274-7724   *Fax:* 317 274-7792
E-mail: nbaxter@iupui.edu
Length: 2 Yrs   *ACGME Approved/Offered Positions:* 4
Program ID: 150-17-21-110

Iowa

Iowa City

University of Iowa Hospitals and Clinics Program
Sponsor: University of Iowa Hospitals and Clinics
Prgm Director: Jacob Ijdo, MD, PhD*
Department of Internal Medicine
200 Hawkins Drive
Iowa City, IA 52242
Tel: 319 384-6175
Length: 2 Yrs   *ACGME Approved/Offered Positions:* 4
Program ID: 150-18-21-067

Kansas

Kansas City

University of Kansas School of Medicine Program
Sponsor: University of Kansas School of Medicine
University of Kansas Hospital
Veterans Affairs Medical Center (Kansas City)
Prgm Director: Daniel J Stechschulte Sr, MD
Department of Internal Medicine
3901 Rainbow Blvd
Kansas City, KS 66160
Tel: 913 588-6008   *Fax:* 913 588-3987
E-mail: khinshaw@kumc.edu
Length: 2 Yrs   *ACGME Approved/Offered Positions:* 4
Program ID: 150-19-21-080

Kentucky

Lexington

University of Kentucky College of Medicine Program
Sponsor: University of Kentucky College of Medicine
University of Kentucky Hospital
Prgm Director: Kristine M Lohr, MD, MS
KY Clinic J515
740 South Limestone St
Lexington, KY 40536
Tel: 859 323-6700   *Fax:* 859 257-8258
E-mail: gjpark2@uky.edu
Length: 2 Yrs   *ACGME Approved/Offered Positions:* 3
Program ID: 150-20-21-156

Louisiana

New Orleans

Louisiana State University Program
Sponsor: Louisiana State University School of Medicine
Children's Hospital (New Orleans)
LSU Baptist Multi-Specialty Clinic
Medical Center of Louisiana at New Orleans
Ochsner Medical Center-Kenner
Touro Infirmary
Prgm Director: Luis R Espinoza, MD
2820 Napoleon Avenue, Suite 890
New Orleans, LA 70115
Tel: 504 896-1440   *Fax:* 504 899-8496
Length: 2 Yrs   *ACGME Approved/Offered Positions:* 3
Program ID: 150-21-13-157

Ochsner Clinic Foundation Program
Sponsor: Ochsner Clinic Foundation
Prgm Director: Robert J Quinet, MD
1514 Jefferson Highway
New Orleans, LA 70121
Tel: 504 842-4920   *Fax:* 504 842-5244
E-mail: segilbert@ochsner.org
Length: 2 Yrs   *ACGME Approved/Offered Positions:* 4
Program ID: 150-21-22-106

Shreveport

Louisiana State University (Shreveport) Program
Sponsor: LSU Health Sciences Center-University
   Hospital
Overton Brooks Veterans Affairs Medical Center
Prgm Director: Samina Hayat, MD
Louisiana State University Health Sciences Center
1501 Kings Highway, PO Box 33932
Shreveport, LA 71103
Tel: 318 675-5930   *Fax:* 318 675-6980
Length: 2 Yrs   *ACGME Approved/Offered Positions:* 6
Program ID: 150-21-21-063

Maryland

Baltimore

Johns Hopkins University Program
Sponsor: Johns Hopkins University School of Medicine
Johns Hopkins Bayview Medical Center
Johns Hopkins Hospital
Prgm Director: Allan C Gelber, MD, MPH
5200 Eastern Avenue, Mason F Lord Building
Center Tower, Suite 4100
Baltimore, MD 21224
Tel: 410 550-2018   *Fax:* 410 550-2072
E-mail: agelber@jhmi.edu
Length: 2 Yrs   *ACGME Approved/Offered Positions:* 8
Program ID: 150-23-11-052

University of Maryland Program
Sponsor: University of Maryland Medical System
Veterans Affairs Medical Center (Baltimore)
Prgm Director: Raymond H Flores, MD
10 South Pine Street
Suite 834
Baltimore, MD 21201
Tel: 410 706-6474   *Fax:* 410 706-0231
Length: 2 Yrs   *ACGME Approved/Offered Positions:* 4
Program ID: 150-23-21-131

Bethesda

National Capital Consortium (Walter Reed) Program

Sponsor: National Capital Consortium
Walter Reed Army Medical Center
Prgm Director: Jon D Roebuck, MD
6900 Georgia Ave NW
Rheumatology, Ward 77
Washington, DC 20307
Tel: 202 782-6735   *Fax:* 202 782-0594
E-mail: Jonathan.roebuck@amedd.army.mil
Length: 2 Yrs   *ACGME Approved/Offered Positions:* 6
Program ID: 150-10-11-093
Uniformed Services Program

National Institutes of Health Clinical Center Program

Sponsor: Clinical Center at the National Institutes of Health
Prgm Director: Mark F Gourley, MD
NIH Clinical Center
Building 10, Room 6N216
Bethesda, MD 20892
Tel: 301 594-0529   *Fax:* 301 451-5590
E-mail: howeken@mail.nih.gov
Length: 2 Yrs   *ACGME Approved/Offered Positions:* 8
Program ID: 150-23-21-141

Massachusetts

Boston

Boston University Medical Center Program

Sponsor: Boston Medical Center
Veterans Affairs Medical Center (Boston)
Prgm Director: Robert W Simms, MD
Arthritis Center
715 Albany St, E-5
Boston, MA 02118
Tel: 617 638-4486   *Fax:* 617 638-5226
Length: 2 Yrs   *ACGME Approved/Offered Positions:* 5
Program ID: 150-24-21-111

Brigham and Women's Hospital Program

Sponsor: Brigham and Women's Hospital
Beth Israel Deaconess Medical Center
Prgm Director: Simon M Helfgott, MD
B-3 Rheumatology
45 Francis Street
Boston, MA 02115
Tel: 617 732-5323   *Fax:* 617 732-5505
E-mail: shelfgott@partners.org
Length: 2 Yrs   *ACGME Approved/Offered Positions:* 9
Program ID: 150-24-21-004

Massachusetts General Hospital Program

Sponsor: Massachusetts General Hospital
Prgm Director: Margaret Seton, MD
Rheumatology Unit, MGH
55 Fruit Street - Bulfinch 165
Boston, MA 02114
Tel: 617 726-2870   *Fax:* 617 726-2872
Length: 2 Yrs   *ACGME Approved/Offered Positions:* 4
Program ID: 150-24-11-038

Tufts Medical Center Program

Sponsor: Tufts Medical Center
Prgm Director: Timothy E McAlindon, MD, MPH
800 Washington St, Box 406
Boston, MA 02111
Tel: 617 636-5645   *Fax:* 617 636-1542
E-mail: tmcalindon@tuftsmedicalcenter.org
Length: 2 Yrs   *ACGME Approved/Offered Positions:* 2
Program ID: 150-24-21-005

Worcester

University of Massachusetts Program

Sponsor: University of Massachusetts Medical School
Boston VA Healthcare System (Brockton-West Roxbury)
UMass Memorial Health Care (Memorial Campus)
UMass Memorial Health Care (University Campus)
Prgm Director: Nancy Y Liu, MD
55 Lake Avenue North
Worcester, MA 01655
Tel: 508 856-6246   *Fax:* 508 856-1180
Length: 2 Yrs   *ACGME Approved/Offered Positions:* 4
Program ID: 150-24-21-006

Michigan

Ann Arbor

University of Michigan Program

Sponsor: University of Michigan Hospitals and Health Centers
Veterans Affairs Medical Center (Ann Arbor)
Prgm Director: Rory M Marks, MB, BS
Room 3918 Taubman Center, Box 5358
Division of Rheumatology
Ann Arbor, MI 48109
Tel: 734 936-9539   *Fax:* 734 763-1253
E-mail: rmarks@umich.edu
Length: 2 Yrs   *ACGME Approved/Offered Positions:* 8
Program ID: 150-25-21-053

Detroit

Wayne State University/Detroit Medical Center Program

Sponsor: Wayne State University/Detroit Medical Center
Detroit Receiving Hospital and University Health Center
Harper-Hutzel Hospital
Veterans Affairs Medical Center (Detroit)
Prgm Director: Jose L Granda, MD, PhD
University Health Center - Suite 4H
4201 St Antoine
Detroit, MI 48201
Tel: 313 577-1133   *Fax:* 313 577-1938
Length: 2 Yrs   *ACGME Approved/Offered Positions:* 4
Program ID: 150-25-21-030

Minnesota

Minneapolis

University of Minnesota Program

Sponsor: University of Minnesota Medical School
Hennepin County Medical Center
Regions Hospital
University of Minnesota Medical Center, Division of Fairview
Veterans Affairs Medical Center (Minneapolis)
Prgm Director: Anne G Minenko, MD*
Division of Rheumatic and Autoimmune Diseases
420 Delaware Street SE, MMC 108
Minneapolis, MN 55455
Tel: 612 624-6843
Length: 2 Yrs   *ACGME Approved/Offered Positions:* 4
Program ID: 150-26-21-082

Rochester

College of Medicine, Mayo Clinic (Rochester) Program

Sponsor: College of Medicine, Mayo Clinic
Mayo Clinic (Rochester)
Prgm Director: Thomas G Mason II, MD
Siebens, 5th Floor
200 First Street SW
Rochester, MN 55905
Tel: 507 284-3126   *Fax:* 507 284-0999
Length: 2 Yrs   *ACGME Approved/Offered Positions:* 6
Program ID: 150-26-21-032

Mississippi

Jackson

University of Mississippi Medical Center Program

Sponsor: University of Mississippi School of Medicine
University Hospitals and Clinics
Veterans Affairs Medical Center (Jackson)
Prgm Director: Robert W McMurray, MD
Division of Rheumatology
2500 N State St
Jackson, MS 39216
Tel: 601 984-5540   *Fax:* 601 984-5535
E-mail: vmajithia@medicine.umsmed.edu
Length: 2 Yrs   *ACGME Approved/Offered Positions:* 4
Program ID: 150-27-21-151

Missouri

Columbia

University of Missouri-Columbia Program

Sponsor: University of Missouri-Columbia School of Medicine
Harry S Truman Memorial Veterans Hospital
University Hospitals and Clinics
Prgm Director: Chokkalingam Siva, MD*
CE326, Clinical Support & Education Building
Five Hospital Drive
Columbia, MO 65212
Tel: 573 884-8786   *Fax:* 573 882-1380
Length: 2 Yrs   *ACGME Approved/Offered Positions:* 4
Program ID: 150-28-21-054

St Louis

St Louis University School of Medicine Program

Sponsor: St Louis University School of Medicine
Cardinal Glennon Children's Hospital
St Louis University Hospital
Prgm Director: Terry L Moore, MD
Room 211A Doisy Hall
1402 S Grand Blvd
St Louis, MO 63104
Tel: 314 977-8838   *Fax:* 314 977-8818
Length: 2 Yrs   *ACGME Approved/Offered Positions:* 4
Program ID: 150-28-21-064

Washington University/B-JH/SLCH Consortium Program

Sponsor: Washington University/B-JH/SLCH Consortium
Barnes-Jewish Hospital
Veterans Affairs Medical Center (St Louis)
Prgm Director: Richard D Brasington Jr, MD
Division of Rheumatology, Box 8045
660 South Euclid Avenue
St Louis, MO 63110
Tel: 314 454-7279   *Fax:* 314 454-5164
Length: 2 Yrs   *ACGME Approved/Offered Positions:* 6
Program ID: 150-28-21-112

Note: * indicates a newly appointed program director

Nebraska

Omaha

University of Nebraska Medical Center College of Medicine Program

Sponsor: University of Nebraska Medical Center College of Medicine
Nebraska Medical Center
Veterans Affairs Medical Center (Omaha)
Prgm Director: James R O'Dell, MD
983025 Nebraska Medical Center
Omaha, NE 68198
Tel: 402 559-7288   *Fax:* 402 559-6788
E-mail: eblaszak@unmc.edu
Length: 2 Yrs   *ACGME Approved/Offered Positions:* 4
Program ID: 150-30-13-154

New Hampshire

Lebanon

Dartmouth-Hitchcock Medical Center Program

Sponsor: Mary Hitchcock Memorial Hospital
Veterans Affairs Medical Center (White River Junction)
Prgm Director: Lin A Brown, MD
Department of Medicine
One Medical Center Drive
Lebanon, NH 03756
Tel: 603 650-7700   *Fax:* 603 650-4961
E-mail: Lin.A.Brown@hitchcock.org
Length: 2 Yrs   *ACGME Approved/Offered Positions:* 3
Program ID: 150-32-21-107

New Jersey

Camden

UMDNJ-Robert Wood Johnson Medical School (Camden) Program

Sponsor: Cooper Hospital-University Medical Center
Prgm Director: Gerald F Falasca, MD
One Cooper Plaza
401 N Haddon Avenue
Camden, NJ 08103
Tel: 856 968-7019   *Fax:* 856 482-5621
E-mail: hanneman-lori@cooperhealth.edu
Length: 2 Yrs   *ACGME Approved/Offered Positions:* 2
Program ID: 150-33-21-132

New Brunswick

UMDNJ-Robert Wood Johnson Medical School Program

Sponsor: UMDNJ-Robert Wood Johnson Medical School
Robert Wood Johnson University Hospital
Prgm Director: Naomi Schlesinger, MD
Dept of Medicine, Div of Rheumatology
PO Box 19, MEB-484
New Brunswick, NJ 08903
Tel: 732 235-8378   *Fax:* 732 235-7238
Length: 2 Yrs   *ACGME Approved/Offered Positions:* 2
Program ID: 150-33-21-019

New Mexico

Albuquerque

University of New Mexico Program

Sponsor: University of New Mexico School of Medicine
University of New Mexico Hospital
Veterans Affairs Medical Center (Albuquerque)
Prgm Director: Arthur D Bankhurst, MD
School of Medicine
Department of Medicine
Albuquerque, NM 87131
Tel: 505 272-4761   *Fax:* 505 272-3624
Length: 2 Yrs   *ACGME Approved/Offered Positions:* 4
Program ID: 150-34-21-100

New York

Albany

Albany Medical Center Program

Sponsor: Albany Medical Center
Veterans Affairs Medical Center (Albany)
Prgm Director: L Frank Cavaliere, MD
Department of Rheumatology, MC-100
47 New Scotland Avenue
Albany, NY 12208
Tel: 518 262-6858   *Fax:* 518 262-6873
E-mail: Brozowml@mail.amc.edu
Length: 2 Yrs   *ACGME Approved/Offered Positions:* 3
Program ID: 150-35-31-020

Bronx

Albert Einstein College of Medicine Program

Sponsor: Albert Einstein College of Medicine of Yeshiva University
Montefiore Medical Center-Henry and Lucy Moses Division
Montefiore Medical Center-Weiler Division
North Bronx Healthcare Network-Jacobi Medical Center
North Bronx Healthcare Network-North Central Bronx Hospital
Prgm Director: Chaim Putterman, MD
Montefiore Medical Center
1300 Morris Park Avenue, Forchheimer 701N
Bronx, NY 10461
Tel: 718 430-4266   *Fax:* 718 430-4268
Length: 2 Yrs   *ACGME Approved/Offered Positions:* 6
Program ID: 150-35-21-072

Brooklyn

SUNY Health Science Center at Brooklyn Program

Sponsor: SUNY Health Science Center at Brooklyn
Kings County Hospital Center
University Hospital-SUNY Health Science Center at Brooklyn
Veterans Affairs Medical Center (Brooklyn)
Prgm Director: Deana Lazaro, MD
450 Clarkson Ave, Box 42
Brooklyn, NY 11203
Tel: 718 270-1662   *Fax:* 718 270-1562
E-mail: deana.lazaro@downstate.edu
Length: 2 Yrs   *ACGME Approved/Offered Positions:* 4
Program ID: 150-35-21-009

Buffalo

University at Buffalo Program

Sponsor: University at Buffalo School of Medicine
Erie County Medical Center
Kaleida Health System (Buffalo General Hospital)
Prgm Director: Arik Zaider, MD
Department of Medicine
462 Grider Street
Buffalo, NY 14215
Tel: 716 898-5762   *Fax:* 716 961-6960
E-mail: azaider@buffalo.edu
Length: 2 Yrs   *ACGME Approved/Offered Positions:* 2
Program ID: 150-35-31-007

Great Neck

NSLIJHS-North Shore University Hospital/NYU School of Medicine Program

Sponsor: North Shore-Long Island Jewish Health System
Long Island Jewish Medical Center
North Shore University Hospital
Prgm Director: Maria-Louise Barilla-LaBarca, MD*
Department of Medicine
300 Community Drive
Manhasset, NY 11030
Tel: 516 708-2550   *Fax:* 516 708-2597
Length: 2 Yrs   *ACGME Approved/Offered Positions:* 2
Program ID: 150-35-21-121

Mineola

Winthrop-University Hospital Program

Sponsor: Winthrop-University Hospital
Nassau University Medical Center
Prgm Director: Steven E Carsons, MD
259 First Street
Mineola, NY 11501
Tel: 516 663-2097   *Fax:* 516 663-2946
Length: 2 Yrs   *ACGME Approved/Offered Positions:* 3
Program ID: 150-35-21-142

New York

Mount Sinai School of Medicine Program

Sponsor: Mount Sinai School of Medicine
Mount Sinai Medical Center
Prgm Director: Leslie D Kerr, MD
Annenberg 21-56
One Gustave L Levy Place
New York, NY 10029
Tel: 212 241-3038   *Fax:* 212 987-5584
Length: 2 Yrs   *ACGME Approved/Offered Positions:* 2
Program ID: 150-35-31-114

New York Presbyterian Hospital (Columbia Campus) Program

Sponsor: New York Presbyterian Hospital
New York Presbyterian Hospital (Columbia Campus)
Prgm Director: Edward Dwyer, MD
622 W 168th St
PH8E-101
New York, NY 10032
Tel: 212 342-3684   *Fax:* 212 305-4943
Length: 2 Yrs   *ACGME Approved/Offered Positions:* 4
Program ID: 150-35-11-039

New York Presbyterian Hospital (Cornell Campus) Program

Sponsor: New York Presbyterian Hospital
Hospital for Special Surgery
Memorial Sloan-Kettering Cancer Center
New York Presbyterian Hospital (Cornell Campus)
Prgm Director: Anne R Bass, MD*
525 East 68th Street
New York, NY 10021
Tel: 212 774-7043   *Fax:* 212 774-2258
E-mail: bassA@hss.edu
Length: 2 Yrs   *ACGME Approved/Offered Positions:* 6
Program ID: 150-35-21-122

New York University School of Medicine Program

Sponsor: New York University School of Medicine
Bellevue Hospital Center
Manhattan VA Harbor Health Care System
NYU Hospital for Joint Diseases
Prgm Director: Michael H Pillinger, MD
301 East 17th Street, Rm 1410
New York, NY 10003
Tel: 212 598-6119   *Fax:* 212 598-6582
E-mail: michael.pillinger@nyumc.org
Length: 2 Yrs   *ACGME Approved/Offered Positions:* 9
Program ID: 150-35-21-083

Rochester

University of Rochester Program

Sponsor: Strong Memorial Hospital of the University of
   Rochester
Prgm Director: Christopher T Ritchlin, MD
601 Elmwood Avenue
Box 695
Rochester, NY 14642
Tel: 585 273-4670   *Fax:* 585 442-3214
Length: 2 Yrs   *ACGME Approved/Offered Positions:* 3
Program ID: 150-35-11-127

Stony Brook

SUNY at Stony Brook Program

Sponsor: University Hospital - SUNY at Stony Brook
Veterans Affairs Medical Center (Northport)
Prgm Director: Peter M Rumore, MD
HSC T-16, 040
Stony Brook, NY 11794
Tel: 631 444-8366   *Fax:* 631 444-3475
Length: 2 Yrs   *ACGME Approved/Offered Positions:* 4
Program ID: 150-35-21-010

Syracuse

SUNY Upstate Medical University Program

Sponsor: SUNY Upstate Medical University
Veterans Affairs Medical Center (Syracuse)
Prgm Director: Andras Perl, MD, PhD
750 East Adams Street
Syracuse, NY 13210
Tel: 315 464-4194   *Fax:* 315 464-4176
E-mail: crolicke@upstate.edu
Length: 2 Yrs   *ACGME Approved/Offered Positions:* 2
Program ID: 150-35-21-074

Valhalla

New York Medical College at Westchester Medical Center Program

Sponsor: New York Medical College
Sound Shore Medical Center of Westchester
Westchester Medical Center
Prgm Director: Julia Y Ash, MD
Westchester Medical Center
Munger Pavilion G73
Valhalla, NY 10595
Tel: 914 594-4444   *Fax:* 914 594-4977
Length: 2 Yrs   *ACGME Approved/Offered Positions:* 2
Program ID: 150-35-11-040

North Carolina

Chapel Hill

University of North Carolina Hospitals Program

Sponsor: University of North Carolina Hospitals
Prgm Director: Beth L Jonas, MD
CB 7280
3330 Thurston Bldg
Chapel Hill, NC 27599
Tel: 919 966-4191   *Fax:* 919 966-1739
Length: 2 Yrs   *ACGME Approved/Offered Positions:* 4
Program ID: 150-36-21-102

Durham

Duke University Hospital Program

Sponsor: Duke University Hospital
Veterans Affairs Medical Center (Durham)
Prgm Director: Lisa G Criscione-Schreiber, MD*
Box 2978
Durham, NC 27710
Tel: 919 668-1466   *Fax:* 919 681-8298
Length: 2 Yrs   *ACGME Approved/Offered Positions:* 6
Program ID: 150-36-21-103

Winston-Salem

Wake Forest University School of Medicine Program

Sponsor: Wake Forest University Baptist Medical Center
Prgm Director: Kenneth S O'Rourke, MD
Medical Center Boulevard
Winston-Salem, NC 27157
Tel: 336 716-4209   *Fax:* 336 716-9821
E-mail: korourke@wfubmc.edu
Length: 2 Yrs   *ACGME Approved/Offered Positions:* 3
Program ID: 150-36-21-011

Ohio

Cincinnati

University Hospital/University of Cincinnati College of Medicine Program

Sponsor: University Hospital Inc
Christ Hospital
Veterans Affairs Medical Center (Cincinnati)
Prgm Director: Avis E Ware, MD
Division of Immunology
PO Box 670563
Cincinnati, OH 45267
Tel: 513 558-4701   *Fax:* 513 558-3799
Length: 2 Yrs   *ACGME Approved/Offered Positions:* 6
Program ID: 150-38-12-149

Cleveland

Case Western Reserve University (MetroHealth) Program

Sponsor: MetroHealth Medical Center
Prgm Director: Stanley P Ballou, MD
2500 MetroHealth Drive
Cleveland, OH 44109
Tel: 216 778-4765   *Fax:* 216 778-8376
E-mail: mbecker@metrohealth.org
Length: 2 Yrs   *ACGME Approved/Offered Positions:* 2
Program ID: 150-38-31-152

Cleveland Clinic Foundation Program

Sponsor: Cleveland Clinic Foundation
Prgm Director: Abby Abelson, MD
9500 Euclid Avenue
Desk A50
Cleveland, OH 44195
Tel: 216 444-3876   *Fax:* 216 445-7569
E-mail: abelsoa@ccf.org
Length: 2 Yrs   *ACGME Approved/Offered Positions:* 6
Program ID: 150-38-12-117

University Hospitals Case Medical Center Program

Sponsor: University Hospitals Case Medical Center
Veterans Affairs Medical Center (Cleveland)
Prgm Director: Ali D Askari, MD
11100 Euclid Avenue
Foley Building - Room 201
Cleveland, OH 44106
Tel: 216 844-2289   *Fax:* 216 844-2288
E-mail: Aliaskari_99@yahoo.com
Length: 2 Yrs   *ACGME Approved/Offered Positions:* 5
Program ID: 150-38-21-115

Columbus

Ohio State University Hospital Program

Sponsor: Ohio State University Hospital
Prgm Director: Kevin V Hackshaw, MD
Davis Medical Research Center
480 Medical Center Drive
Columbus, OH 43210
Tel: 614 293-8093
E-mail: Kevin.Hackshaw@osumc.edu
Length: 2 Yrs   *ACGME Approved/Offered Positions:* 4
Program ID: 150-38-21-144

Oklahoma

Oklahoma City

University of Oklahoma Health Sciences Center Program

Sponsor: University of Oklahoma College of Medicine
OU Medical Center
Veterans Affairs Medical Center (Oklahoma City)
Prgm Director: Leslie S Staudt, MD
PO Box 26901
Oklahoma City, OK 73126
Tel: 405 271-7217   *Fax:* 405 271-7256
E-mail: leslie-staudt@ouhsc.edu
Length: 2 Yrs   *ACGME Approved/Offered Positions:* 4
Program ID: 150-39-21-056

Oregon

Portland

Oregon Health & Science University Program

Sponsor: Oregon Health & Science University Hospital
Veterans Affairs Medical Center (Portland)
Prgm Director: James Rosenbaum, MD
Division of Arthritis & Rheumatic Diseases
3181 SW Sam Jackson Park Rd OP09
Portland, OR 97239
Tel: 503 494-5023   *Fax:* 503 494-6875
Length: 2 Yrs   *ACGME Approved/Offered Positions:* 2
Program ID: 150-40-31-118

Note: * indicates a newly appointed program director

Pennsylvania

Danville

Geisinger Health System Program
Sponsor: Geisinger Health System
Prgm Director: Thomas M Harrington, MD
Department of Rheumatology - MC1341
100 North Academy Avenue
Danville, PA 17822
Tel: 570 271-6416   *Fax:* 570 271-5845
Length: 2 Yrs   *ACGME Approved/Offered Positions:* 4
Program ID: 150-41-11-104

Philadelphia

Albert Einstein Healthcare Network Program
Sponsor: Albert Einstein Medical Center
St Christopher's Hospital for Children (Tenet Health System)
Prgm Director: Lawrence H Brent, MD
Korman Building, Suite 103
5501 Old York Road
Philadelphia, PA 19141
Tel: 215 456-7380   *Fax:* 215 456-3898
E-mail: brentlh@hotmail.com
Length: 2 Yrs   *ACGME Approved/Offered Positions:* 2
Program ID: 150-41-11-033

Drexel University College of Medicine/Hahnemann University Hospital Program
Sponsor: Drexel University College of Medicine/Hahnemann University
Abington Memorial Hospital
Hahnemann University Hospital (Tenet Health System)
St Christopher's Hospital for Children (Tenet Health System)
Prgm Director: Carolyn R O'Connor, MD
245 N 15th Street
MS 426
Philadelphia, PA 19102
Tel: 215 762-8114   *Fax:* 215 246-5913
E-mail: Carolyn.O'Connor@drexelmed.edu
Length: 2 Yrs   *ACGME Approved/Offered Positions:* 4
Program ID: 150-41-21-084

Temple University Hospital Program
Sponsor: Temple University Hospital
St Christopher's Hospital for Children (Tenet Health System)
Prgm Director: Audrey B Uknis, MD
Department of Rheumatology
3322 N Broad Steet
Philadelphia, PA 19140
Tel: 215 707-0791   *Fax:* 215 707-6932
Length: 2 Yrs   *ACGME Approved/Offered Positions:* 3
Program ID: 150-41-21-023

Thomas Jefferson University Program
Sponsor: Thomas Jefferson University Hospital
Prgm Director: Chris T Derk, MD, MS
Division of Rheumatology
Room 613 Curtis Building
Philadelphia, PA 19107
Tel: 215 955-9723   *Fax:* 215 923-7885
E-mail: chris.derk@jefferson.edu
Length: 2 Yrs   *ACGME Approved/Offered Positions:* 2
Program ID: 150-41-21-024

University of Pennsylvania Program
Sponsor: University of Pennsylvania Health System
Prgm Director: Sharon L Kolasinski, MD
Suite 504 Maloney Bldg
3600 Spruce Street
Philadelphia, PA 19104
Tel: 215 349-5066   *Fax:* 215 662-4500
Length: 2 Yrs   *ACGME Approved/Offered Positions:* 6
Program ID: 150-41-21-015

Pittsburgh

University of Pittsburgh Medical Center Medical Education Program
Sponsor: Univ of Pittsburgh Medical Center Medical Education
UPMC Presbyterian Shadyside
Prgm Director: Chester V Oddis, MD
3500 Terrace Street
S703 Biomedical Science Tower
Pittsburgh, PA 15261
Tel: 412 383-8861   *Fax:* 412 383-8864
E-mail: cvo5@pitt.edu
Length: 2 Yrs   *ACGME Approved/Offered Positions:* 6
Program ID: 150-41-21-027

Puerto Rico

San Juan

University of Puerto Rico Program
Sponsor: University of Puerto Rico School of Medicine
University Hospital
Prgm Director: Luis M Vilá, MD
University Hospital
Box 365067
San Juan, PR 00936
Tel: 787 758-2525   *Fax:* 787 764-6839
Length: 2 Yrs   *ACGME Approved/Offered Positions:* 4
Program ID: 150-42-21-085

Rhode Island

Providence

Brown University Program
Sponsor: Rhode Island Hospital-Lifespan
Veterans Affairs Medical Center (Providence)
Prgm Director: Edward V Lally, MD
Department of Medicine-Division of Rheumatology
2 Dudley Street, Suite 370
Providence, RI 02905
Tel: 401 444-2248   *Fax:* 401 444-3558
E-mail: KPoland@lifespan.org
Length: 2 Yrs   *ACGME Approved/Offered Positions:* 2
Program ID: 150-43-12-155

Roger Williams Medical Center Program
Sponsor: Roger Williams Medical Center
Rhode Island Hospital-Lifespan
Veterans Affairs Medical Center (Providence)
Prgm Director: Bernard Zimmermann, MD
Roger Williams Medical Center
825 Chalkstone Avenue
Providence, RI 02908
Tel: 401 456-2393   *Fax:* 401 456-6768
E-mail: umgmarsha@yahoo.com
Length: 2 Yrs   *ACGME Approved/Offered Positions:* 3
Program ID: 150-43-31-028

South Carolina

Charleston

Medical University of South Carolina Program
Sponsor: Medical University of South Carolina College of Medicine
MUSC Medical Center
Ralph H Johnson VA Medical Center (Charleston)
Prgm Director: Marcy B Bolster, MD
96 Jonathan Lucas Street
Suite 912
Charleston, SC 29425
Tel: 843 792-3484   *Fax:* 843 792-7121
E-mail: granger@musc.edu
Length: 2 Yrs   *ACGME Approved/Offered Positions:* 6
Program ID: 150-45-21-075

Tennessee

Memphis

University of Tennessee Program
Sponsor: University of Tennessee College of Medicine
LeBonheur Children's Medical Center
Methodist Healthcare - Memphis Hospitals
Regional Medical Center at Memphis
University of Tennessee Medical Center
Veterans Affairs Medical Center (Memphis)
Prgm Director: Laura Carbone, MD*
Division of Rheumatology
956 Court Avenue, Room A318
Memphis, TN 38163
Tel: 901 448-5479   *Fax:* 901 448-7265
E-mail: lcarbone@utmem.edu
Length: 2 Yrs   *ACGME Approved/Offered Positions:* 4
Program ID: 150-47-21-105

Nashville

Vanderbilt University Program
Sponsor: Vanderbilt University Medical Center
Veterans Affairs Medical Center (Nashville)
Prgm Director: Howard A Fuchs, MD
Division of Rheumatology
Medical Center North, T 3219
Nashville, TN 37232
Tel: 615 322-4746   *Fax:* 615 322-6248
E-mail: howard.fuchs@vanderbilt.edu
Length: 2 Yrs   *ACGME Approved/Offered Positions:* 3
Program ID: 150-47-31-012

Texas

Dallas

University of Texas Southwestern Medical School Program
Sponsor: University of Texas Southwestern Medical School
Dallas County Hospital District-Parkland Memorial Hospital
Dallas VA Medical Center
Prgm Director: Nancy J Olsen, MD
Department of Internal Medicine
5323 Harry Hines Blvd
Dallas, TX 75390
Tel: 214 648-9049   *Fax:* 214 648-7995
E-mail: nancy.olsen@utsouthwestern.edu
Length: 2 Yrs   *ACGME Approved/Offered Positions:* 6
Program ID: 150-48-21-070

Programs

Galveston

University of Texas Medical Branch Hospitals Program

Sponsor: University of Texas Medical Branch Hospitals
Prgm Director: Emilio B Gonzalez, MD
301 University Boulevard
Rheumatology, Rt 1165
Galveston, TX 77555
Tel: 409 772-2863 *Fax:* 409 772-7355
E-mail: ebgonzal@utmb.edu
Length: 2 Yrs *ACGME Approved/Offered Positions:* 2
Program ID: 150-48-21-147

Houston

Baylor College of Medicine Program

Sponsor: Baylor College of Medicine
Harris County Hospital District-Ben Taub General
  Hospital
Methodist Hospital (Houston)
Michael E DeBakey VA Medical Center - Houston
Prgm Director: Sandra Sessoms, MD
1709 Dryden, Suite 5.75
Attn: Kiesha Sloan
Houston, TX 77030
Tel: 713 441-3982
E-mail: jg17@bcm.edu
Length: 2 Yrs *ACGME Approved/Offered Positions:* 4
Program ID: 150-48-21-058

University of Texas at Houston Program

Sponsor: University of Texas Health Science Center at
  Houston
Lyndon B Johnson General Hospital
Memorial Hermann Hospital
Prgm Director: Filemon K Tan, MD, PhD
6431 Fannin St, MSB 5.270
Division of Rheumatology
Houston, TX 77030
Tel: 713 500-6900 *Fax:* 713 500-0580
Length: 2 Yrs *ACGME Approved/Offered Positions:* 6
Program ID: 150-48-31-130

Lackland AFB

San Antonio Uniformed Services Health Education Consortium Program

Sponsor: San Antonio Uniformed Services Health
  Education Consortium
Wilford Hall Medical Center (AETC)
Brooke Army Medical Center
Prgm Director: Jay B Higgs, MD
3851 Roger Brooke Drive
Fort Sam Houston, TX 78234
Tel: 210 916-0797 *Fax:* 210 916-5222
E-mail: jay.higgs@amedd.army.mil
Length: 2 Yrs *ACGME Approved/Offered Positions:* 4
Program ID: 150-48-12-065
Uniformed Services Program

San Antonio

University of Texas Health Science Center at San Antonio Program

Sponsor: University of Texas School of Medicine at San
  Antonio
Audie L Murphy Memorial Veterans Hospital (San
  Antonio)
University Health System
Prgm Director: Michael Fischbach, MD
7703 Floyd Curl Drive
MC 7868
San Antonio, TX 78229
Tel: 210 567-4658 *Fax:* 210 567-4721
E-mail: fischbach@uthscsa.edu
Length: 2 Yrs *ACGME Approved/Offered Positions:* 2
Program ID: 150-48-21-041

Utah

Salt Lake City

University of Utah Program

Sponsor: University of Utah Medical Center
Veterans Affairs Medical Center (Salt Lake City)
Prgm Director: Michael J Battistone, MD
50 N Medical Drive, 4B210
Salt Lake City, UT 84132
Tel: 801 581-4333 *Fax:* 801 581-6069
Length: 2 Yrs *ACGME Approved/Offered Positions:* 3
Program ID: 150-49-21-148

Vermont

Burlington

University of Vermont Program

Sponsor: Fletcher Allen Health Care
Prgm Director: Sheldon M Cooper, MD*
D-305 Given Bldg
89 Beaumont Avenue
Burlington, VT 05405
Tel: 802 656-2144 *Fax:* 802 656-3854
E-mail: sheldon.cooper@uvm.edu
Length: 2 Yrs *ACGME Approved/Offered Positions:* 2
Program ID: 150-50-21-120

Virginia

Charlottesville

University of Virginia Program

Sponsor: University of Virginia Medical Center
Prgm Director: Wael N Jarjour, MD
Department of Medicine
PO Box 800412
Charlottesville, VA 22908
Tel: 434 924-5214 *Fax:* 434 924-9578
E-mail: rheumfellowship@hscmail.mcc.virginia.edu
Length: 2 Yrs *ACGME Approved/Offered Positions:* 4
Program ID: 150-51-21-013

Richmond

Virginia Commonwealth University Health System Program

Sponsor: Virginia Commonwealth University Health
  System
Hunter Holmes McGuire VA Medical Center (Richmond)
Medical College of Virginia Hospitals
Prgm Director: W Neal Roberts Jr, MD
PO Box 980263
Richmond, VA 23298
Tel: 804 828-9685 *Fax:* 804 828-0283
Length: 2 Yrs *ACGME Approved/Offered Positions:* 3
Program ID: 150-51-21-014

Washington

Seattle

University of Washington Program

Sponsor: University of Washington School of Medicine
Harborview Medical Center
University of Washington Medical Center
VA Puget Sound Health Care System
Prgm Director: Gregory C Gardner, MD
Division of Rheumatology, Box 356428
1959 NE Pacific Street
Seattle, WA 98195
Tel: 206 543-3414 *Fax:* 206 685-9397
Length: 2 Yrs *ACGME Approved/Offered Positions:* 5
Program ID: 150-54-21-059

Wisconsin

Madison

University of Wisconsin Program

Sponsor: University of Wisconsin Hospital and Clinics
William S Middleton Veterans Hospital
Prgm Director: Kevin M McKown, MD
600 Highland Avenue
Room H6/363 CSC
Madison, WI 53792
Tel: 608 265-8688 *Fax:* 608 262-6743
Length: 2 Yrs *ACGME Approved/Offered Positions:* 2
Program ID: 150-56-21-087

Milwaukee

Medical College of Wisconsin Affiliated Hospitals Program

Sponsor: Medical College of Wisconsin Affiliated
  Hospitals, Inc
Clement J Zablocki Veterans Affairs Medical Center
Froedtert Memorial Lutheran Hospital
Prgm Director: Mary E Cronin, MD
Rheumatology
9200 West Wisconsin Avenue
Milwaukee, WI 53226
Tel: 414 456-7024 *Fax:* 414 456-6205
Length: 2 Yrs *ACGME Approved/Offered Positions:* 3
Program ID: 150-56-31-029

Note: * indicates a newly appointed program director

Selective Pathology (Pathology)

California

Los Angeles

University of Southern California/ LAC+USC Medical Center Program

Sponsor: University of Southern California/LAC+USC Medical Center
Kenneth Norris Jr Cancer Hospital and Research Institute
LAC+USC Medical Center
Prgm Director: Parakrama T Chandrasoma, MD
1200 North State Street, CT 7A7E
Los Angeles, CA 90033
Tel: 323 409-4606   *Fax:* 323 409-5927
E-mail: norona@usc.edu
Length: 1 Yr   *ACGME Approved/Offered Positions:* 7
Program ID: 301-05-31-053

Connecticut

Hartford

Hartford Hospital Program

Sponsor: Hartford Hospital
Prgm Director: Srinivas R Mandavilli, MD
80 Seymour Street
PO Box 5037
Hartford, CT 06102
Tel: 860 545-3369   *Fax:* 860 545-2204
Length: 1 Yr   *ACGME Approved/Offered Positions:* 5
Program ID: 301-08-22-028

New Haven

Yale-New Haven Medical Center Program

Sponsor: Yale-New Haven Hospital
Prgm Director: Marie E Robert, MD
310 Cedar Street
PO Box 208023
New Haven, CT 06520
Tel: 203 785-5003   *Fax:* 203 737-1064
Length: 1 Yr   *ACGME Approved/Offered Positions:* 1
Program ID: 301-08-21-037

District of Columbia

Washington

Armed Forces Institute of Pathology Program

Sponsor: Armed Forces Institute of Pathology
Prgm Director: Teri J Franks, MD
6825 NW 16th Street
Washington, DC 20306
Tel: 202 782-1780   *Fax:* 202 782-5017
Length: 1 Yr   *ACGME Approved/Offered Positions:* 2
Program ID: 301-10-13-023
Uniformed Services Program

Georgia

Atlanta

Emory University Program

Sponsor: Emory University School of Medicine
Emory University Hospital
Prgm Director: Sanjay Logani, MD
Department of Pathology and Laboratory Medicine H175
1364 Clifton Road, NE
Atlanta, GA 30322
Tel: 404 712-8851   *Fax:* 404 727-3133
Length: 1 Yr   *ACGME Approved/Offered Positions:* 3
Program ID: 301-12-21-054

Emory University Program B

Sponsor: Emory University School of Medicine
Emory University Hospital
Prgm Director: Sharon W Weiss, MD
Department of Pathology and Laboratory Medicine H175
1364 Clifton Road, NE
Atlanta, GA 30322
Tel: 404 712-0708   *Fax:* 404 712-4454
E-mail: mmojonn@emory.edu
Length: 1 Yr   *ACGME Approved/Offered Positions:* 1
Program ID: 301-12-21-056

Emory University Program C

Sponsor: Emory University School of Medicine
Emory University Hospital
Prgm Director: Charles A Parkos, MD, PhD
Department of Pathology and Laboratory Medicine H175
1364 Clifton Road, NE
Atlanta, GA 30322
Tel: 404 712-8536   *Fax:* 404 712-3321
E-mail: cparkos@emory.edu
Length: 1 Yr   *ACGME Approved/Offered Positions:* 1
Program ID: 301-12-31-057

Illinois

Chicago

University of Illinois College of Medicine at Chicago Program

Sponsor: University of Illinois College of Medicine at Chicago
University of Illinois Hospital and Clinics
Prgm Director: Robert Folberg, MD
840 S Wood Street
110 CSN
Chicago, IL 60612
Tel: 312 996-2829   *Fax:* 312 355-3190
Length: 1 Yr   *ACGME Approved/Offered Positions:* 2
Program ID: 301-16-21-026

Kansas

Kansas City

University of Kansas School of Medicine Program

Sponsor: University of Kansas School of Medicine
University of Kansas Medical Center
Prgm Director: Ossama Tawfik, MD
3901 Rainbow Boulevard
Kansas City, KS 66160
Tel: 913 588-7076   *Fax:* 913 588-7073
Length: 1 Yr   *ACGME Approved/Offered Positions:* 2
Program ID: 301-19-12-075

Maryland

Baltimore

Johns Hopkins University Program

Sponsor: Johns Hopkins University School of Medicine
Johns Hopkins Hospital
Prgm Director: Serena Bagnasco, MD
711 Pathology Building
600 N Wolfe Street
Baltimore, MD 21287
Tel: 410 500-0812   *Fax:* 410 502-0811
Length: 1 Yr   *ACGME Approved/Offered Positions:* 1
Program ID: 301-23-21-024

Johns Hopkins University Program A

Sponsor: Johns Hopkins University School of Medicine
Johns Hopkins Hospital
Prgm Director: Jonathan T Epstein, MD
Department of Pathology, Urology, and Oncology
401 N Broadway Street, Weinberg Room 2242
Baltimore, MD 21231
Tel: 410 955-5043   *Fax:* 443 287-3318
Length: 1 Yr   *ACGME Approved/Offered Positions:* 2
Program ID: 301-23-21-058

Massachusetts

Boston

Beth Israel Deaconess Medical Center/Harvard Medical School Program

Sponsor: Beth Israel Deaconess Medical Center
Prgm Director: James L Connolly, MD
330 Brookline Avenue
Boston, MA 02215
Tel: 617 667-4344
E-mail: jallin@bidmc.harvard.edu
Length: 1 Yr   *ACGME Approved/Offered Positions:* 5
Program ID: 301-24-11-027

Brigham and Women's Hospital Program

Sponsor: Brigham and Women's Hospital
Prgm Director: Christopher P Crum, MD
Division of Women's & Perinatal Pathology
75 Francis Street
Boston, MA 02115
Tel: 617 732-7530
Length: 1 Yr   *ACGME Approved/Offered Positions:* 3
Program ID: 301-24-11-003

Worcester

University of Massachusetts Program

Sponsor: University of Massachusetts Medical School
UMass Memorial Health Care (Memorial Campus)
UMass Memorial Health Care (University Campus)
Prgm Director: Ashraf Khan, MBBS, MD*
Department of Pathology
Three Biotech, One Innovation Drive
Worcester, MA 01605
Tel: 508 793-6142   *Fax:* 508 793-6110
Length: 1 Yr   *ACGME Approved/Offered Positions:* 2
Program ID: 301-24-21-061

Michigan

Ann Arbor

University of Michigan Program
Sponsor: University of Michigan Hospitals and Health Centers
Prgm Director: Barbara McKenna, MD
1500 E Medical Center Drive
Room 2G332 UH
Ann Arbor, MI 48109
Tel: 734 936-6770   *Fax:* 734 763-4095
Length: 1 Yr   *ACGME Approved/Offered Positions:* 3
Program ID: 301-25-31-074

Minnesota

Rochester

College of Medicine, Mayo Clinic (Rochester) Program
Sponsor: College of Medicine, Mayo Clinic
Mayo Clinic (Rochester)
Rochester Methodist Hospital
Saint Marys Hospital of Rochester
Prgm Director: Marie-Christine Aubry, MD
Surgical Pathology Fellowship Program
200 First Street, SW
Rochester, MN 55905
Tel: 507 284-1196   *Fax:* 507 538-3267
E-mail: pathologyeducation@mayo.edu
Length: 1 Yr   *ACGME Approved/Offered Positions:* 12
Program ID: 301-26-12-039

College of Medicine, Mayo Clinic (Rochester) Program A
Sponsor: College of Medicine, Mayo Clinic
Mayo Clinic (Rochester)
Saint Marys Hospital of Rochester
Prgm Director: Marie-Christine Aubry, MD
Pulmonary Pathology Fellowship Program
200 First Street, SW
Rochester, MN 55905
Tel: 507 293-3839   *Fax:* 507 538-3267
E-mail: pathologyeducation@mayo.edu
Length: 1 Yr   *ACGME Approved/Offered Positions:* 2
Program ID: 301-26-21-040

College of Medicine, Mayo Clinic (Rochester) Program B
Sponsor: College of Medicine, Mayo Clinic
Mayo Clinic (Rochester)
Rochester Methodist Hospital
Saint Marys Hospital of Rochester
Prgm Director: Thomas C Smyrk, MD
200 First Street, SW
Rochester, MN 55905
Tel: 507 538-6453   *Fax:* 507 538-3267
E-mail: pathologyeducation@mayo.edu
Length: 1 Yr   *ACGME Approved/Offered Positions:* 2
Program ID: 301-26-31-062

College of Medicine, Mayo Clinic (Rochester) Program C
Sponsor: College of Medicine, Mayo Clinic
Mayo Clinic (Rochester)
Prgm Director: William D Edwards, MD
200 First Street SW
Rochester, MN 55905
Tel: 507 538-6453   *Fax:* 507 538-3267
E-mail: pathologyeducation@mayo.edu
Length: 1 Yr   *ACGME Approved/Offered Positions:* 2
Program ID: 301-26-21-068

College of Medicine, Mayo Clinic (Rochester) Program D
Sponsor: College of Medicine, Mayo Clinic
Mayo Clinic (Rochester)
Saint Marys Hospital of Rochester
Prgm Director: Andrew L Folpe, MD
200 First Street, SW
Rochester, MN 55905
Tel: 507 284-1196   *Fax:* 507 538-3267
Length: 1 Yr   *ACGME Approved/Offered Positions:* 2
Program ID: 301-26-13-077

Missouri

St Louis

Washington University/B-JH/SLCH Consortium Program
Sponsor: Washington University/B-JH/SLCH Consortium
Barnes-Jewish Hospital
Prgm Director: Louis P Dehner, MD
660 S Euclid Avenue
Campus Box 8118
St Louis, MO 63110
Tel: 314 362-0104   *Fax:* 314 362-8950
E-mail: huettner@path.wustl.edu
Length: 1 Yr   *ACGME Approved/Offered Positions:* 7
Program ID: 301-28-31-025

New York

Buffalo

University at Buffalo (Roswell Park Cancer Institute) Program
Sponsor: University at Buffalo School of Medicine
Roswell Park Cancer Institute
Prgm Director: Charles M LeVea, MD, PhD
Elm & Carlton Street
Buffalo, NY 14263
Tel: 716 845-7678   *Fax:* 716 845-3427
E-mail: charles.levea@roswellpark.org
Length: 1 Yr   *ACGME Approved/Offered Positions:* 6
Program ID: 301-35-31-016

New York

Memorial Sloan-Kettering Cancer Center Program
Sponsor: Memorial Sloan-Kettering Cancer Center
Prgm Director: Maureen F Zakowski, MD
Pathology Department
1275 York Avenue
New York, NY 10065
Tel: 212 639-5946   *Fax:* 212 639-6318
Length: 1 Yr   *ACGME Approved/Offered Positions:* 17
Program ID: 301-35-21-011

Memorial Sloan-Kettering Cancer Center Program A
Sponsor: Memorial Sloan-Kettering Cancer Center
Prgm Director: William D Travis, MD
Department of Pathology
1275 York Avenue
New York, NY 10065
Tel: 212 639-3325   *Fax:* 212 717-3576
E-mail: travisw@mskcc.org
Length: 1 Yr   *ACGME Approved/Offered Positions:* 1
Program ID: 301-35-12-059

New York University School of Medicine/Hospital for Joint Diseases Program
Sponsor: New York University School of Medicine
NYU Hospital for Joint Diseases
Prgm Director: German C Steiner, MD
301 East 17th Street
New York, NY 10003
Tel: 212 598-6231   *Fax:* 212 598-6057
Length: 1 Yr   *ACGME Approved/Offered Positions:* 1
Program ID: 301-35-21-005

Office of the Chief Medical Examiner-City of New York Program
Sponsor: Office of Chief Medical Examiner - City of New York
Prgm Director: Barbara A Sampson, MD, PhD
520 First Avenue
New York, NY 10016
Tel: 212 447-2335   *Fax:* 212 447-2334
Length: 1 Yr   *ACGME Approved/Offered Positions:* 2
Program ID: 301-35-31-033

Pennsylvania

Hershey

Penn State University/Milton S Hershey Medical Center Program
Sponsor: Milton S Hershey Medical Center
Prgm Director: Francesca M Ruggiero, MD
500 University Drive, H160
Hershey, PA 17033
Tel: 717 531-8246   *Fax:* 717 531-7741
E-mail: fruggiero@hmc.psu.edu
Length: 1 Yr   *ACGME Approved/Offered Positions:* 1
Program ID: 301-41-13-069

Philadelphia

Pennsylvania Hospital of the University of Pennsylvania Health System Program
Sponsor: Pennsylvania Hospital (UPHS)
Prgm Director: Tunde A Farkas, MD*
800 Spruce Street
Philadelphia, PA 19107
Tel: 215 829-6992   *Fax:* 215 829-7564
Length: 1 Yr   *ACGME Approved/Offered Positions:* 2
Program ID: 301-41-32-042

Pennsylvania Hospital of the University of Pennsylvania Health System Program A
Sponsor: Pennsylvania Hospital (UPHS)
Prgm Director: Tunde A Farkas, MD*
Department of Pathology
8th and Spruce Streets
Philadelphia, PA 19107
Tel: 215 829-6992   *Fax:* 215 829-7564
Length: 1 Yr   *ACGME Approved/Offered Positions:* 1
Program ID: 301-41-12-063

Thomas Jefferson University Program
Sponsor: Thomas Jefferson University Hospital
Fox Chase Cancer Center
Prgm Director: Douglas B Flieder, MD
Fox Chase Cancer Center
333 Cottman Avenue
Philadelphia, PA 19111
Tel: 215 728-4092   *Fax:* 215 728-2899
E-mail: Douglas.Flieder@fccc.edu
Length: 1 Yr   *ACGME Approved/Offered Positions:* 3
Program ID: 301-41-21-018

Note: * indicates a newly appointed program director

University of Pennsylvania Program

Sponsor: University of Pennsylvania Health System
Prgm Director: Antonia R Sepulveda, MD, PhD
3400 Spruce Street, 6 Founders
Philadelphia, PA 19104
Tel: 215 615-4361   *Fax:* 215 614-1988
Length: 1 Yr   *ACGME Approved/Offered Positions:* 8
Program ID: 301-41-31-029

University of Pennsylvania Program A

Sponsor: University of Pennsylvania Health System
Prgm Director: Emma E Furth, MD
3400 Spruce Street, 6 Founders
Philadelphia, PA 19104
Tel: 215 662-3211
Length: 1 Yr   *ACGME Approved/Offered Positions:* 1
Program ID: 301-41-23-032

Pittsburgh

University of Pittsburgh Med Center Medical Education (Presbyterian Shadyside Hospital) Program A

Sponsor: Univ of Pittsburgh Medical Center Medical Education
UPMC Presbyterian Shadyside
Prgm Director: Alyssa M Krasinskas, MD
200 Lothrop Street, PUH-A610
Pittsburgh, PA 15213
Tel: 412 647-0282   *Fax:* 412 647-6251
E-mail: krasinskasam@upmc.edu
Length: 1 Yr   *ACGME Approved/Offered Positions:* 1
Program ID: 301-41-31-043

University of Pittsburgh Med Center Medical Education (Presbyterian Shadyside Hospital) Program B

Sponsor: Univ of Pittsburgh Medical Center Medical Education
UPMC Presbyterian Shadyside
Prgm Director: Rajiv Dhir, MD
5230 Centre Avenue
Pittsburgh, PA 15232
Tel: 412 623-1321   *Fax:* 412 623-4014
E-mail: dhirr@upmc.edu
Length: 1 Yr   *ACGME Approved/Offered Positions:* 1
Program ID: 301-41-31-049

University of Pittsburgh Med Center Medical Education (Presbyterian Shadyside Hospital) Program D

Sponsor: Univ of Pittsburgh Medical Center Medical Education
UPMC Presbyterian Shadyside
Prgm Director: Uma Rao, MD
5230 Centre Avenue, Room WG29
Pittsburgh, PA 15232
Tel: 412 623-2319   *Fax:* 412 682-6450
E-mail: raoumn@upmc.edu
Length: 1 Yr   *ACGME Approved/Offered Positions:* 1
Program ID: 301-41-13-051

University of Pittsburgh Med Center Medical Education (Presbyterian Shadyside Hospital) Program E

Sponsor: Univ of Pittsburgh Medical Center Medical Education
UPMC Presbyterian Shadyside
Prgm Director: Samuel A Yousem, MD
Presbyterian Campus - PUH-A610
200 Lothrop Street
Pittsburgh, PA 15213
Tel: 412 647-3238   *Fax:* 412 647-3399
Length: 1 Yr   *ACGME Approved/Offered Positions:* 1
Program ID: 301-41-12-052

University of Pittsburgh Medical Center Medical Education Program

Sponsor: Univ of Pittsburgh Medical Center Medical Education
UPMC Presbyterian Shadyside
Prgm Director: Sheldon I Bastacky, MD
3708 Fifth Avenue, Medical Arts Building
Suite 503
Pittsburgh, PA 15213
Tel: 412 647-9612   *Fax:* 412 647-3455
E-mail: bastackysi@upmc.edu
Length: 1 Yr   *ACGME Approved/Offered Positions:* 5
Program ID: 301-41-11-030

University of Pittsburgh Medical Center Medical Education Program B

Sponsor: Univ of Pittsburgh Medical Center Medical Education
UPMC Presbyterian Shadyside
Prgm Director: Erin R Ochoa, MD*
E733 MUH
200 Lothrop Street
Pittsburgh, PA 15213
Tel: 412 647-9568   *Fax:* 412 647-5237
E-mail: ochoaer@upmc.edu
Length: 1 Yr   *ACGME Approved/Offered Positions:* 1
Program ID: 301-41-13-036

University of Pittsburgh Medical Center Medical Education Program C

Sponsor: Univ of Pittsburgh Medical Center Medical Education
UPMC Presbyterian Shadyside
Prgm Director: Leon Barnes Jr, MD
Department of Pathology
200 Lothrop Street
Pittsburgh, PA 15213
Tel: 412 647-3732   *Fax:* 412 647-6251
Length: 1 Yr   *ACGME Approved/Offered Positions:* 1
Program ID: 301-41-21-064

University of Pittsburgh Medical Center Medical Education/Magee-Women's Hospital Program F

Sponsor: Univ of Pittsburgh Medical Center Medical Education
Magee-Womens Hospital of UPMC
Prgm Director: David J Dabbs, MD
300 Halket Street
Pittsburgh, PA 15213
Tel: 412 641-4651   *Fax:* 412 641-3069
Length: 1 Yr   *ACGME Approved/Offered Positions:* 3
Program ID: 301-41-23-035

Tennessee

Nashville

Vanderbilt University Program

Sponsor: Vanderbilt University Medical Center
Prgm Director: Agnes B Fogo, MD
Division of Renal Pathology/Electron Microscopy
C-2317 Medical Center North
Nashville, TN 37232
Tel: 615 322-3114   *Fax:* 615 322-4840
E-mail: agnes.fogo@vanderbilt.edu
Length: 1 Yr   *ACGME Approved/Offered Positions:* 2
Program ID: 301-47-13-038

Texas

Houston

Methodist Hospital (Houston) Program

Sponsor: Methodist Hospital (Houston)
Prgm Director: Patricia Chevez-Barrios, MD
6565 Fannin St, M227
Houston, TX 77030
Tel: 713 441-6484   *Fax:* 713 793-1603
E-mail: ljozwiak@tmhs.org
Length: 1 Yr   *ACGME Approved/Offered Positions:* 1
Program ID: 301-48-32-045

Methodist Hospital (Houston) Program A

Sponsor: Methodist Hospital (Houston)
Prgm Director: Mary R Schwartz, MD
6565 Fannin St, M227
Houston, TX 77030
Tel: 713 441-6482   *Fax:* 713 793-1603
E-mail: ljozwiak@tmhs.org
Length: 1 Yr   *ACGME Approved/Offered Positions:* 5
Program ID: 301-48-31-044

Methodist Hospital (Houston) Program B

Sponsor: Methodist Hospital (Houston)
Prgm Director: Chung-Che Chung, MD, PhD
Department of Pathology
6565 Fannin St, M227
Houston, TX 77030
Tel: 713 441-4458   *Fax:* 713 441-3489
E-mail: ljozwiak@tmhs.org
Length: 1 Yr   *ACGME Approved/Offered Positions:* 2
Program ID: 301-48-12-067

University of Texas M D Anderson Cancer Center Program

Sponsor: University of Texas M D Anderson Cancer Center
Prgm Director: Aysegul Sahin, MD
1515 Holcomb Blvd, Pathology/Fellowship, Box 085
Houston, TX 77030
Tel: 713 794-1500   *Fax:* 713 745-0789
Length: 1 Yr   *ACGME Approved/Offered Positions:* 14
Program ID: 301-48-21-010

University of Texas M D Anderson Cancer Center Program A

Sponsor: University of Texas M D Anderson Cancer Center
Prgm Director: Anais Malpica, MD
Pathology/Fellowship Unit #085
1515 Holcombe Boulevard
Houston, TX 77030
Tel: 713 794-1501   *Fax:* 713 792-5529
Length: 1 Yr   *ACGME Approved/Offered Positions:* 1
Program ID: 301-48-12-031

University of Texas M D Anderson Cancer Center Program B

Sponsor: University of Texas M D Anderson Cancer Center
Prgm Director: Russell R Broaddus, MD, PhD
Department of Pathology, Unit 085
1515 Holcombe Boulevard
Houston, TX 77030
Tel: 713 745-2794   *Fax:* 713 745-0789
Length: 1 Yr   *ACGME Approved/Offered Positions:* 2
Program ID: 301-48-13-065

University of Texas M D Anderson Cancer Center Program C

Sponsor: University of Texas M D Anderson Cancer Center
Prgm Director: Alexander Lazar, MD, PhD
Department of Pathology
1515 Holcombe Boulevard
Houston, TX 77030
Tel: 713 563-1843   *Fax:* 713 563-1848
Length: 1 Yr   *ACGME Approved/Offered Positions:* 1
Program ID: 301-48-31-066

Programs

University of Texas M D Anderson Cancer Center Program D

Sponsor: University of Texas M D Anderson Cancer Center
Prgm Director: Adel K El-Nagger, MD, PhD
1515 Holcombe Boulevard
Pathology, Unit 085
Houston, TX 77030
Tel: 713 792-3109   *Fax:* 713 792-5532
Length: 1 Yr   *ACGME Approved/Offered Positions:* 2
Program ID: 301-48-31-070

University of Texas M D Anderson Cancer Center Program E

Sponsor: University of Texas M D Anderson Cancer Center
Prgm Director: Asif Rashid, MD, PhD
Pathology, Unit 085
1515 Holcombe Boulevard
Houston, TX 77030
Tel: 713 745-1101   *Fax:* 713 745-0789
Length: 1 Yr   *ACGME Approved/Offered Positions:* 2
Program ID: 301-48-12-071

University of Texas M D Anderson Cancer Center Program F

Sponsor: University of Texas M D Anderson Cancer Center
Prgm Director: Aysegul Sahin, MD
1515 Holcombe Boulevard
Houston, TX 77030
Tel: 713 792-3108   *Fax:* 713 745-0789
Length: 1 Yr   *ACGME Approved/Offered Positions:* 2
Program ID: 301-48-21-072

University of Texas M D Anderson Cancer Center Program G

Sponsor: University of Texas M D Anderson Cancer Center
Prgm Director: Patricia Troncoso, MD
Department of Pathology, Unit 085
1515 Holcombe Boulevard
Houston, TX 77030
Tel: 713 794-5449   *Fax:* 713 745-0789
Length: 1 Yr   *ACGME Approved/Offered Positions:* 2
Program ID: 301-48-13-073

Virginia

Richmond

Virginia Commonwealth University Health System Program

Sponsor: Virginia Commonwealth University Health System
Medical College of Virginia Hospitals
Prgm Director: Ema A Dragoescu, MD*
PO Box 980662
Richmond, VA 23298
Tel: 804 628-0354   *Fax:* 804 828-8733
Length: 1 Yr   *ACGME Approved/Offered Positions:* 1
Program ID: 301-51-12-034

Washington

Seattle

PhenoPath Laboratories Program

Sponsor: PhenoPath Laboratories
Prgm Director: Allen M Gown, MD
551 N 34th St, Suite 100
Seattle, WA 98103
Tel: 206 374-9000   *Fax:* 206 374-9009
E-mail: hchilds@phenopath.com
Length: 1 Yr   *ACGME Approved/Offered Positions:* 1
Program ID: 301-54-21-022

Note: * indicates a newly appointed program director

University of Washington Program

Sponsor: University of Washington School of Medicine
University of Washington Medical Center
Prgm Director: Benjamin Hoch, MD*
Box 356100
1959 NE Pacific Street
Seattle, WA 98195
Tel: 206 598-3540   *Fax:* 206 598-4928
E-mail: residency@pathology.washington.edu
Length: 1 Yr   *ACGME Approved/Offered Positions:* 1
Program ID: 301-54-12-046

University of Washington Program A

Sponsor: University of Washington School of Medicine
University of Washington Medical Center
Prgm Director: Melissa P Upton, MD
Box 356100
1959 NE Pacific Street
Seattle, WA 98195
Tel: 206 598-0006   *Fax:* 206 598-4928
E-mail: residency@pathology.washington.edu
Length: 1 Yr   *ACGME Approved/Offered Positions:* 1
Program ID: 301-54-21-048

University of Washington Program B

Sponsor: University of Washington School of Medicine
University of Washington Medical Center
Prgm Director: Charles E Alpers, MD
Box 356100
1959 NE Pacific Street
Seattle, WA 98195
Tel: 206 598-6409   *Fax:* 206 598-4928
E-mail: residency@pathology.washington.edu
Length: 1 Yr   *ACGME Approved/Offered Positions:* 1
Program ID: 301-54-13-047

University of Washington Program C

Sponsor: University of Washington School of Medicine
University of Washington Medical Center
Prgm Director: Rochelle L Garcia, MD
Box 356100
1959 NE Pacific Street
Seattle, WA 98195
Tel: 206 598-4933   *Fax:* 206 598-7321
E-mail: residency@pathology.washington.edu
Length: 1 Yr   *ACGME Approved/Offered Positions:* 4
Program ID: 301-54-13-060

University of Washington Program D

Sponsor: University of Washington School of Medicine
Seattle Cancer Care Alliance
University of Washington Medical Center
Prgm Director: Rochelle L Garcia, MD
Box 356100
1959 NE Pacific Street
Seattle, WA 98195
Tel: 206 598-4933   *Fax:* 206 598-7321
E-mail: residency@u.washington.edu
Length: 1 Yr   *ACGME Approved/Offered Positions:* 1
Program ID: 301-54-21-076

Sleep Medicine

Alabama

Birmingham

University of Alabama Medical Center Program

Sponsor: University of Alabama Hospital
Children's Hospital of Alabama
Sleep Disorder Center of Alabama
University of Alabama at Birmingham/Highlands
Prgm Director: Christopher M Makris, MD, MPH
Pediatric Pulmonology and Sleep Medicine
619 19th Street South
Birmingham, AL 35294
Tel: 205 939-9583   *Fax:* 205 975-5983
Length: 1 Yr   *ACGME Approved/Offered Positions:* 3
Program ID: 520-01-32-066

California

Los Angeles

UCLA-VA Greater Los Angeles Program

Sponsor: VA Greater Los Angeles Healthcare System
Olive View/UCLA Medical Center
Prgm Director: Silverio M Santiago, MD
11301 Wilshire Blvd
Los Angeles, CA 90073
Tel: 310 268-3021   *Fax:* 310 268-4712
Length: 1 Yr   *ACGME Approved/Offered Positions:* 3
Program ID: 520-05-14-060

Sacramento

University of California (Davis) Health System Program

Sponsor: University of California (Davis) Health System
Mercy General Hospital (Mercy Healthcare Sacramento)
University of California (Davis) Medical Center
VA Northern California Health Care System
Prgm Director: Kimberly A Hardin, MD, MS
4150 V Street
Sacramento, CA 95817
Tel: 916 734-3464   *Fax:* 916 734-7924
Length: 1 Yr   *ACGME Approved/Offered Positions:* 1
Program ID: 520-05-14-094

Stanford

Stanford University Program

Sponsor: Stanford Hospital and Clinics
Prgm Director: Anstella Robinson, MD*
Stanford Sleep Disorders Clinic
401 Quarry Road, Suite 3301
Stanford, CA 94305
Tel: 650 725-5911   *Fax:* 650 725-0725
E-mail: alopez1@stanford.edu
Length: 1 Yr   *ACGME Approved/Offered Positions:* 8
Program ID: 520-05-40-013

Colorado

Aurora

University of Colorado Denver Program
Sponsor: University of Colorado Denver School of Medicine
Children's Hospital (The)
National Jewish Medical and Research Center
University of Colorado Hospital
Veterans Affairs Medical Center (Denver)
Prgm Director: Sheila C Tsai, MD*
National Jewish Health
1400 Jackson Street
Denver, CO 80206
Tel: 303 398-1081   *Fax:* 303 398-1780
Length: 1 Yr   *ACGME Approved/Offered Positions:* 2
Program ID: 520-07-14-103

Connecticut

New Haven

Yale-New Haven Medical Center Program
Sponsor: Yale-New Haven Hospital
Prgm Director: Francoise J Roux, MD, PhD
20 York Street
New Haven, CT 06520
Tel: 203 785-3207   *Fax:* 203 785-3826
Length: 1 Yr   *ACGME Approved/Offered Positions:* 1
Program ID: 520-08-14-046

Norwalk

Norwalk Hospital Program
Sponsor: Norwalk Hospital
Prgm Director: Mary B O'Malley, MD, PhD
34 Maple Street
Sleep Disorders Center
Norwalk, CT 06612
Tel: 203 852-2129   *Fax:* 203 852-2945
Length: 1 Yr   *ACGME Approved/Offered Positions:* 2
Program ID: 520-08-14-047

District of Columbia

Washington

George Washington University Program
Sponsor: George Washington University School of Medicine
George Washington University Hospital (UHS)
Prgm Director: Samuel Potolicchio, MD
2150 Pennsylvania Avenue NW
Suite 7-404
Washington, DC 20037
Tel: 202 741-2715   *Fax:* 202 741-2721
E-mail: spotolicchio@mfa.gwu.edu
Length: 1 Yr   *ACGME Approved/Offered Positions:* 1
Program ID: 520-10-18-091

Florida

Gainesville

University of Florida Program
Sponsor: University of Florida College of Medicine
North Florida/South Georgia Veterans Health System
Shands Hospital at the University of Florida
Prgm Director: Richard B Berry, MD
1600 SW Archer Road
Gainesville, FL 32610
Tel: 352 392-2666   *Fax:* 352 379-4155
Length: 1 Yr   *ACGME Approved/Offered Positions:* 1
Program ID: 520-11-14-065

Miami

Jackson Memorial Hospital/Jackson Health System Program
Sponsor: Jackson Memorial Hospital/Jackson Health System
University of Miami Hospital and Clinics
Veterans Affairs Medical Center (Miami)
Prgm Director: Dalia Lorenzo, MD
1120 NW 14th Street
CRB 1387
Miami, FL 33136
Tel: 305 575-7000   *Fax:* 305 243-6546
E-mail: dlorenzo@med.miami.edu
Length: 1 Yr   *ACGME Approved/Offered Positions:* 4
Program ID: 520-11-18-112

Tampa

University of South Florida Program
Sponsor: University of South Florida College of Medicine
James A Haley Veterans Hospital
Tampa General Hospital
University Community Hospital
Prgm Director: William M Anderson, MD
13000 Bruce B Downs Blvd
Pulmonary & Critical Care Med Sect (111C)
Tampa, FL 33612
Tel: 813 972-7543   *Fax:* 813 979-3606
E-mail: peggy.boyd2@va.gov
Length: 1 Yr   *ACGME Approved/Offered Positions:* 2
Program ID: 520-11-14-101

Illinois

Chicago

McGaw Medical Center of Northwestern University Program
Sponsor: McGaw Medical Center of Northwestern University
Children's Memorial Hospital
Northwestern Memorial Hospital
Prgm Director: Pyllis C Zee, MD, PhD
251 East Huron Street
Chicago, IL 60611
Tel: 312 908-8549   *Fax:* 312 908-5073
Length: 1 Yr   *ACGME Approved/Offered Positions:* 3
Program ID: 520-16-18-053

Rush University Medical Center Program
Sponsor: Rush University Medical Center
Prgm Director: Maria I Crisostomo, MD
Sleep Disorders Service & Research Center
1653 W Congress Parkway
Chicago, IL 60612
Tel: 312 942-5440   *Fax:* 312 942-8961
Length: 1 Yr   *ACGME Approved/Offered Positions:* 2
Program ID: 520-16-14-015

University of Chicago Program
Sponsor: University of Chicago Medical Center
Prgm Director: Babak Mokhlesi, MD, MS
5841 South Maryland Avenue
MC 0999, Room N 701
Chicago, IL 60637
Tel: 773 702-2181   *Fax:* 773 702-6113
Length: 1 Yr   *ACGME Approved/Offered Positions:* 3
Program ID: 520-16-14-081

Iowa

Iowa City

University of Iowa Hospitals and Clinics Program
Sponsor: University of Iowa Hospitals and Clinics
Prgm Director: Mark E Dyken, MD
200 Hawkins Drive
Iowa City, IA 52242
Tel: 319 356-2538   *Fax:* 319 356-4505
Length: 1 Yr   *ACGME Approved/Offered Positions:* 2
Program ID: 520-18-18-052

Kentucky

Louisville

University of Louisville Program
Sponsor: University of Louisville School of Medicine
Kosair Children's Hospital (Norton Healthcare, Inc)
Norton Hospital
University of Louisville Hospital
Prgm Director: David Gozal, MD
332 W Broadway
Ste 1100
Louisville, KY 40202
Tel: 502 852-2323   *Fax:* 502 852-2215
Length: 1 Yr   *ACGME Approved/Offered Positions:* 2
Program ID: 520-20-32-061

Louisiana

Shreveport

Louisiana State University (Shreveport) Program
Sponsor: LSU Health Sciences Center-University Hospital
Overton Brooks Veterans Affairs Medical Center
Prgm Director: Andrew Chesson Jr, MD
1501 Kings Highway
Shreveport, LA 71130
Tel: 318 675-5241   *Fax:* 318 675-5244
E-mail: achess@lsuhsc.edu
Length: 1 Yr   *ACGME Approved/Offered Positions:* 2
Program ID: 520-21-18-086

Maryland

Baltimore

Johns Hopkins University/Bayview Medical Center Program
Sponsor: Johns Hopkins University School of Medicine
Johns Hopkins Bayview Medical Center
Johns Hopkins Hospital
Prgm Director: Alan R Schwartz, MD
5501 Hopkins Bayview Circle
Baltimore, MD 21224
Tel: 410 550-0574   *Fax:* 410 550-3374
Length: 1 Yr   *ACGME Approved/Offered Positions:* 6
Program ID: 520-23-14-018

University of Maryland Program
Sponsor: University of Maryland Medical System
Veterans Affairs Medical Center (Baltimore)
Prgm Director: Steven Scharf, MD, PhD
22 S Greene Street
Baltimore, MD 21201
Tel: 410 706-4771   *Fax:* 410 706-0345
Length: 1 Yr   *ACGME Approved/Offered Positions:* 2
Program ID: 520-23-14-089

Programs

Bethesda

National Capital Consortium (Walter Reed) Program

Sponsor: National Capital Consortium
Children's National Medical Center
Prgm Director: Mark W MIller, MD*
Bldg 2, Room 7636
6900 Georgia Ave NW
Washington, DC 20307
Tel: 301 295-4532
E-mail: MWMiller@med.navy.mil
Length: 1 Yr   *ACGME Approved/Offered Positions:* 1
Program ID: 520-23-14-075
Uniformed Services Program

Massachusetts

Boston

Beth Israel Deaconess Medical Center Program

Sponsor: Beth Israel Deaconess Medical Center
Children's Hospital
Prgm Director: Robert J Thomas, MD
KSB 23
330 Brookline Avenue
Boston, MA 02215
Tel: 617 667-5864   *Fax:* 617 667-4849
Length: 1 Yr   *ACGME Approved/Offered Positions:* 6
Program ID: 520-24-14-054

Boston University Medical Center Program

Sponsor: Boston Medical Center
Veterans Affairs Medical Center (Boston)
Prgm Director: Sanford H Auerbach, MD
72 East Concord St, C3
Boston, MA 02118
Tel: 617 638-7967   *Fax:* 617 638-5354
E-mail: sauerbac@bu.edu
Length: 1 Yr   *ACGME Approved/Offered Positions:* 2
Program ID: 520-24-18-079

Brigham and Women's Hospital Program

Sponsor: Brigham and Women's Hospital
Prgm Director: Lawrence J Epstein, MD
affiliated with Brigham and Women's Hospital
1505 Commonwealth Avenue
Boston, MA 02135
Tel: 617 783-1441   *Fax:* 617 783-1458
Length: 1 Yr   *ACGME Approved/Offered Positions:* 2
Program ID: 520-24-14-039

Children's Hospital Program

Sponsor: Children's Hospital
Beth Israel Deaconess Medical Center
Prgm Director: Sanjeev Kothare, MD
300 Longwood Avenue
Boston, MA 02115
Tel: 617 355-6663   *Fax:* 617 730-0463
Length: 1 Yr   *ACGME Approved/Offered Positions:* 2
Program ID: 520-24-32-111

Worcester

St Vincent Hospital Program

Sponsor: St Vincent Hospital
UMass Memorial Health Care (University Campus)
Prgm Director: Jayant Phadke, MD
123 Summer Street
Worcester, MA 01608
Tel: 508 363-6066   *Fax:* 508 363-6373
E-mail: jayant.phadke@stvincenthospital.com
Length: 1 Yr   *ACGME Approved/Offered Positions:* 1
Program ID: 520-24-14-100

Michigan

Ann Arbor

University of Michigan Program

Sponsor: University of Michigan Hospitals and Health Centers
Prgm Director: Flavia B Consens, MD
C728 Med Inn Building, Box 5845
1500 E Medical Center Drive
Ann Arbor, MI 48109
Tel: 734 647-9064   *Fax:* 734 647-9065
Length: 1 Yr   *ACGME Approved/Offered Positions:* 7
Program ID: 520-25-18-009

Detroit

Henry Ford Hospital Program

Sponsor: Henry Ford Hospital
Children's Hospital of Michigan
Prgm Director: David W Hudgel, MD
2799 W Grand Boulevard, CFP-3
Detroit, MI 48202
Tel: 313 916-5174   *Fax:* 313 916-5150
Length: 1 Yr   *ACGME Approved/Offered Positions:* 3
Program ID: 520-25-14-055

Wayne State University/Detroit Medical Center Program

Sponsor: Wayne State University/Detroit Medical Center
Children's Hospital of Michigan
Harper-Hutzel Hospital
Veterans Affairs Medical Center (Detroit)
Prgm Director: Safwan Badr, MD
Harper University Hospital
3990 John R St, 3 Hudson
Detroit, MI 48323
Tel: 313 745-6033
Length: 1 Yr   *ACGME Approved/Offered Positions:* 4
Program ID: 520-25-14-028

Minnesota

Minneapolis

Hennepin County Medical Center Program

Sponsor: Hennepin County Medical Center
Prgm Director: Conrad Iber, MD*
701 Park Avenue South
Dept of Medicine Sleep Fellowship - G5
Minneapolis, MN 55415
Tel: 612 873-2625   *Fax:* 612 904-4680
E-mail: wendy.yates@hcmed.org
Length: 1 Yr   *ACGME Approved/Offered Positions:* 2
Program ID: 520-26-14-025

Rochester

College of Medicine, Mayo Clinic (Rochester) Program

Sponsor: College of Medicine, Mayo Clinic
Mayo Clinic (Rochester)
Prgm Director: Michael H Silber, MBChB
200 1st Street SW
Rochester, MN 55905
Tel: 507 266-7456   *Fax:* 507 266-7772
Length: 1 Yr   *ACGME Approved/Offered Positions:* 4
Program ID: 520-26-14-010

Mississippi

Jackson

University of Mississippi Medical Center Program

Sponsor: University of Mississippi School of Medicine
University Hospitals and Clinics
Prgm Director: Alp S Baran, MD
Department of Psychiatry and Human Behavior
Attn: Carol Porter, 2500 North State Street
Jackson, MS 39216
Tel: 601 815-1368   *Fax:* 601 815-7623
E-mail: lcporter@psychiatry.umsmed.edu
Length: 1 Yr   *ACGME Approved/Offered Positions:* 1
Program ID: 520-27-40-037

Missouri

Columbia

University of Missouri-Columbia Program

Sponsor: University of Missouri-Columbia School of Medicine
University Hospitals and Clinics
Prgm Director: Pradeep K Sahota, MD
CE507, CE&S Building, Department of Neurology
Five Hospital Drive
Columbia, MO 65212
Tel: 573 882-3135   *Fax:* 573 884-4249
Length: 1 Yr   *ACGME Approved/Offered Positions:* 1
Program ID: 520-28-18-050

Kansas City

University of Missouri at Kansas City Program

Sponsor: University of Missouri-Kansas City School of Medicine
Children's Mercy Hospital
St Luke's Hospital-Kansas City
Prgm Director: Ann M Romaker, MD
2411 Holmes
Kansas City, MO 64108
Tel: 816 756-2466   *Fax:* 816 756-5015
E-mail: mvanderliest@saint-lukes.org
Length: 1 Yr   *ACGME Approved/Offered Positions:* 2
Program ID: 520-28-14-040

St Louis

Washington University/B-JH/SLCH Consortium Program

Sponsor: Washington University/B-JH/SLCH Consortium
Washington University School of Medicine
Prgm Director: Stephen P Duntley, MD
212 N Kingshighway
Suite 237
St Louis, MO 63108
Tel: 314 747-3809   *Fax:* 314 747-3828
Length: 1 Yr   *ACGME Approved/Offered Positions:* 2
Program ID: 520-28-18-049

Note: * indicates a newly appointed program director

Nebraska

Omaha

University of Nebraska Medical Center College of Medicine Program

Sponsor: University of Nebraska Medical Center College of Medicine
Children's Hospital
Nebraska Medical Center
Prgm Director: Teri J Barkoukis, MD
Pulmonary, Critical Care, Sleep & Allergy Section
Box 985300 Nebraska Medical Center
Omaha, NE 68198
Tel: 402 559-4087   *Fax:* 402 559-8210
E-mail: tjbarkoukis@unmc.edu
Length: 1 Yr   *ACGME Approved/Offered Positions:* 2
Program ID: 520-30-14-001

New Hampshire

Lebanon

Dartmouth-Hitchcock Medical Center Program

Sponsor: Mary Hitchcock Memorial Hospital
Prgm Director: Glen P Greenough, MD
Sleep Disorders Center
One Medical Center Drive
Lebanon, NH 03756
Tel: 603 650-7534   *Fax:* 603 650-7820
E-mail: glen.greenough@hitchcock.org
Length: 1 Yr   *ACGME Approved/Offered Positions:* 2
Program ID: 520-32-40-004

New Jersey

South Orange

Seton Hall University School of Health and Medical Sciences Program

Sponsor: Seton Hall University School of Health and Medical Sciences
JFK Medical Center
Prgm Director: Sudhansu Chokroverty, MD*
400 South Orange Ave
South Orange, NJ 07079
Tel: 732 321-7338   *Fax:* 732 632-1584
Length: 1 Yr   *ACGME Approved/Offered Positions:* 2
Program ID: 520-33-18-072

New Mexico

Albuquerque

University of New Mexico Program

Sponsor: University of New Mexico School of Medicine
University of New Mexico Hospital
Prgm Director: Amanda Beck, MD, PhD
MSC 10-5550
Albuquerque, NM 87131
Tel: 505 272-6110   *Fax:* 505 272-6112
E-mail: afinkenhoefer@salud.unm.edu
Length: 1 Yr   *ACGME Approved/Offered Positions:* 2
Program ID: 520-34-14-029

New York

Bronx

Albert Einstein College of Medicine Program

Sponsor: Albert Einstein College of Medicine of Yeshiva University
Montefiore Medical Center-Henry and Lucy Moses Division
Prgm Director: David Appel, MD
111 E 210th Street
Attn: Dr I Ahmed- Neurology Department/Sleep Medicine
Bronx, NY 10467
Tel: 718 920-4841   *Fax:* 718 798-4352
E-mail: thorpy@aecom.yu.edu
Length: 1 Yr   *ACGME Approved/Offered Positions:* 2
Program ID: 520-35-18-030

Buffalo

University at Buffalo Program

Sponsor: University at Buffalo School of Medicine
University at Buffalo Physician Practices (UBPP)
Veterans Affairs Western New York Hospital
Prgm Director: Eric Ten Brock, MD
Department of Medicine
100 High Street
Buffalo, NY 14203
Tel: 716 859-2271   *Fax:* 716 859-1491
Length: 1 Yr   *ACGME Approved/Offered Positions:* 2
Program ID: 520-35-14-036

Great Neck

NSLIJHS-North Shore University Hospital/NYU School of Medicine Program

Sponsor: North Shore-Long Island Jewish Health System
Long Island Jewish Medical Center
North Shore University Hospital
Schneider Children's Hospital at Long Island Jewish Med Ctr
Prgm Director: Harly E Greenberg, MD
410 Lakeville Road
Suite 107
New Hyde Park, NY 11042
Tel: 516 465-3899   *Fax:* 516 616-4124
Length: 1 Yr   *ACGME Approved/Offered Positions:* 1
Program ID: 520-35-14-023

Mineola

Winthrop-University Hospital Program

Sponsor: Winthrop-University Hospital
Prgm Director: Michael D Weinstein, MD
259 First Street
Mineola, NY 11501
Tel: 516 663-2004   *Fax:* 516 663-4888
E-mail: mweinstein@winthrop.org
Length: 1 Yr   *ACGME Approved/Offered Positions:* 1
Program ID: 520-35-14-056

New York

New York Medical College Program

Sponsor: New York Medical College
St Vincent Catholic Medical Centers (Manhattan)
Clinilabs
Prgm Director: Stephen Lund, MD
423 West 55th Street
4th Floor
New York, NY 10019
Tel: 212 994-4570   *Fax:* 212 994-5101
E-mail: slund@clinilabs.com
Length: 1 Yr   *ACGME Approved/Offered Positions:* 5
Program ID: 520-35-40-108

New York University School of Medicine Program

Sponsor: New York University School of Medicine
Bellevue Hospital Center
Manhattan VA Harbor Health Care System
Sleep Medicine Associates of New York City
Prgm Director: David M Rapoport, MD
New Bellevue Hospital
462 First Avenue, Room 7N2
New York, NY 10016
Tel: 212 263-8423   *Fax:* 212 562-4677
E-mail: david.rapoport@nyumc.org
Length: 1 Yr   *ACGME Approved/Offered Positions:* 2
Program ID: 520-35-14-074

Stony Brook

University Hospital - SUNY at Stony Brook Program

Sponsor: University Hospital - SUNY at Stony Brook
Veterans Affairs Medical Center (Northport)
Prgm Director: Avram R Gold, MD*
Pulmonary/Critical Care/Sleep Division
HSC T-17 Room 040
Stony Brook, NY 11794
Tel: 631 444-3869   *Fax:* 631 444-7502
E-mail: iris.kleinman@stonybrook.edu
Length: 1 Yr   *ACGME Approved/Offered Positions:* 2
Program ID: 520-35-14-058

North Carolina

Chapel Hill

University of North Carolina Hospitals Program

Sponsor: University of North Carolina Hospitals
Prgm Director: Bradley V Vaughn, MD
3114 Bioinformatics Building, Dept Neurology
CB 7025, UNC
Chapel Hill, NC 27599
Tel: 919 966-3707   *Fax:* 919 966-2922
Length: 1 Yr   *ACGME Approved/Offered Positions:* 2
Program ID: 520-36-18-038

Durham

Duke University Hospital Program

Sponsor: Duke University Hospital
Veterans Affairs Medical Center (Durham)
Prgm Director: Aatif M Husain, MD
Box 3678, 202 Bell Building
Durham, NC 27710
Tel: 919 684-8485   *Fax:* 919 684-8955
E-mail: neurology@mc.duke.edu
Length: 1 Yr   *ACGME Approved/Offered Positions:* 2
Program ID: 520-36-18-016

Ohio

Cincinnati

Cincinnati Children's Hospital Medical Center/University of Cincinnati College of Medicine Program

Sponsor: Cincinnati Children's Hospital Medical Center
Prgm Director: Narong Simakajornboon, MD
Division of Pulmonary Medicine
3333 Burnet Avenue, MLC 2021
Cincinnati, OH 45229
Tel: 513 636-9735   *Fax:* 513 636-4615
E-mail: rose.alden@cchmc.org
Length: 1 Yr   *ACGME Approved/Offered Positions:* 2
Program ID: 520-38-32-017

Cleveland

Cleveland Clinic Foundation Program
Sponsor: Cleveland Clinic Foundation
Prgm Director: Nancy Foldvary-Schaefer, DO
9500 Euclid Avenue
Sleep Disorders Center/FA20
Cleveland, OH 44195
Tel: 216 445-2990   *Fax:* 216 445-6205
E-mail: foldvan@ccf.org
Length: 1 Yr   *ACGME Approved/Offered Positions:* 6
Program ID: 520-38-18-032

University Hospitals Case Medical Center Program
Sponsor: University Hospitals Case Medical Center
MetroHealth Medical Center
Veterans Affairs Medical Center (Cleveland)
Prgm Director: Kingman P Strohl, MD
11100 Euclid Avenue
Cleveland, OH 44106
Tel: 216 844-3201   *Fax:* 216 844-8708
Length: 1 Yr   *ACGME Approved/Offered Positions:* 4
Program ID: 520-38-14-026

Columbus

Ohio State University Hospital Program
Sponsor: Ohio State University Hospital
Nationwide Children's Hospital
Prgm Director: Ulysses J Magalang, MD
410 West Tenth Avenue
125 Doan Hall
Columbus, OH 43210
Tel: 614 247-7707   *Fax:* 614 293-4799
E-mail: magalang.1@osu.edu
Length: 1 Yr   *ACGME Approved/Offered Positions:* 1
Program ID: 520-38-14-045

Toledo

University of Toledo Program
Sponsor: University of Toledo
University Medical Center (Toledo)
Prgm Director: Jeffrey Hammersley, MD
3000 Arlington Avenue
Mail Stop 1186
Toledo, OH 43614
Tel: 419 383-3543   *Fax:* 419 383-6243
Length: 1 Yr   *ACGME Approved/Offered Positions:* 1
Program ID: 520-38-14-073

Oregon

Portland

Oregon Health & Science University Program
Sponsor: Oregon Health & Science University Hospital
Veterans Affairs Medical Center (Portland)
Prgm Director: Daniel O'Hearn, MD
3181 SW Sam Jackson Park Road
Portland, OR 97239
Tel: 503 494-6668   *Fax:* 503 494-6670
Length: 1 Yr   *ACGME Approved/Offered Positions:* 2
Program ID: 520-40-14-105

Pennsylvania

Philadelphia

Drexel University College of Medicine/Hahnemann University Hospital Program
Sponsor: Drexel University College of Medicine/Hahnemann University
Crozer-Chester Medical Center
Drexel Sleep Center
Hahnemann University Hospital (Tenet Health System)
St Christopher's Hospital for Children (Tenet Health System)
Prgm Director: Joanne E Getsy, MD
245 North 15th Street
MS 107
Philadelphia, PA 19102
Tel: 215 762-7011   *Fax:* 215 762-8728
E-mail: Crystal.White@drexelmed.edu
Length: 1 Yr   *ACGME Approved/Offered Positions:* 2
Program ID: 520-41-14-033

Temple University Hospital Program
Sponsor: Temple University Hospital
Prgm Director: Wissam Chatila, MD
3401 North Broad St
Philadelphia, PA 19140
Tel: 215 707-3053   *Fax:* 215 707-6867
Length: 1 Yr   *ACGME Approved/Offered Positions:* 4
Program ID: 520-41-14-048

Thomas Jefferson University Program
Sponsor: Thomas Jefferson University Hospital
Alfred I duPont Hospital for Children
Prgm Director: Karl Doghramji, MD, BS
211 South Ninth Street
Suite 500
Philadelphia, PA 19107
Tel: 215 955-6175   *Fax:* 215 955-9783
Length: 1 Yr   *ACGME Approved/Offered Positions:* 2
Program ID: 520-41-40-031

University of Pennsylvania Program
Sponsor: University of Pennsylvania Health System
Children's Hospital of Philadelphia
Veterans Affairs Medical Center (Philadelphia)
Prgm Director: Ilene M Rosen, MD, MSCE
Division of Sleep Medicine
3624 Market Street, Suite 205
Philadelphia, PA 19104
Tel: 215 349-5420   *Fax:* 215 615-4874
Length: 1 Yr   *ACGME Approved/Offered Positions:* 4
Program ID: 520-41-14-051

Pittsburgh

University of Pittsburgh Medical Center Medical Education Program
Sponsor: Univ of Pittsburgh Medical Center Medical Education
Children's Hospital of Pittsburgh of UPMC
UPMC Presbyterian Shadyside
Veterans Affairs Medical Center (Pittsburgh)
Prgm Director: Charles W Atwood Jr, MD
200 Lothrop Street
1212 Scaife Hall
Pittsburgh, PA 15213
Tel: 412 692-2880   *Fax:* 412 692-2260
Length: 1 Yr   *ACGME Approved/Offered Positions:* 2
Program ID: 520-41-14-041

Rhode Island

Providence

Brown University Program
Sponsor: Rhode Island Hospital-Lifespan
Prgm Director: Richard P Millman, MD
593 Eddy Street, APC 701
Providence, RI 02903
Tel: 401 444-2670   *Fax:* 401 444-8447
Length: 1 Yr   *ACGME Approved/Offered Positions:* 1
Program ID: 520-43-14-088

Tennessee

Nashville

Vanderbilt University Program
Sponsor: Vanderbilt University Medical Center
Prgm Director: Beth A Malow, MD, MSc
Department of Neurology
1161 21st Avenue South, A-0118 MCN
Nashville, TN 37232
Tel: 615 322-0283   *Fax:* 615 936-0223
Length: 1 Yr   *ACGME Approved/Offered Positions:* 2
Program ID: 520-47-18-002

Texas

Houston

Baylor College of Medicine Program
Sponsor: Baylor College of Medicine
Harris County Hospital District-Ben Taub General Hospital
Michael E DeBakey VA Medical Center - Houston
Texas Children's Hospital
Prgm Director: Amir Sharafkhaneh, MD
One Baylor Plaza
Department of Medicine/Pulmonary Medicine
Houston, TX 77030
Tel: 713 794-7318   *Fax:* 713 794-7316
E-mail: amirs@bcm.tmc.edu
Length: 1 Yr   *ACGME Approved/Offered Positions:* 4
Program ID: 520-48-14-102

Lackland AFB

San Antonio Uniformed Services Health Education Consortium Program
Sponsor: San Antonio Uniformed Services Health Education Consortium
Wilford Hall Medical Center (AETC)
Prgm Director: LTC William C Frey, MD
59th Medical Wing, Lackland AFB
2200 Bergquist Dr
San Antonio, TX 78236
Tel: 210 916-5396   *Fax:* 210 916-0709
E-mail: william.frey@amedd.army.mil
Length: 1 Yr   *ACGME Approved/Offered Positions:* 4
Program ID: 520-48-14-085
Uniformed Services Program

Note: * indicates a newly appointed program director

Utah

Salt Lake City

University of Utah Program
Sponsor: University of Utah Medical Center
LDS Hospital
Primary Children's Medical Center
Prgm Director: Thomas V Cloward, MD
LDS Hospital
325 8th Avenue and C Street
Salt Lake City, UT 84143
Tel: 801 408-3617   *Fax:* 801 408-5110
Length: 1 Yr   *ACGME Approved/Offered Positions:* 2
Program ID: 520-49-14-059

Vermont

Burlington

University of Vermont Program
Sponsor: Fletcher Allen Health Care
Prgm Director: Hrayr Attarian, MD
111 Colchester Avenue Patrick 5
Burlington, VT 05401
Tel: 802 847-5338
Length: 1 Yr   *ACGME Approved/Offered Positions:* 1
Program ID: 520-50-18-080

Washington

Seattle

University of Washington Program
Sponsor: University of Washington School of Medicine
Harborview Medical Center
Seattle Children's Hospital
University of Washington Medical Center
Prgm Director: Vishesh Kapur, MD, MPH
1959 Pacific Ave
Box 359803
Seattle, WA 98195
Tel: 206 744-5703   *Fax:* 206 731-5657
E-mail: lsarmas@u.washington.edu
Length: 1 Yr   *ACGME Approved/Offered Positions:* 1
Program ID: 520-54-14-083

Wisconsin

Madison

University of Wisconsin Program
Sponsor: University of Wisconsin Hospital and Clinics
UW Health/University of Wisconsin Medical Foundation
   (UWMF)
William S Middleton Veterans Hospital
Prgm Director: Steven R Barczi, MD
600 Highland Avenue, K4/926
Madison, WI 53792
Tel: 608 280-7000   *Fax:* 608 280-7291
Length: 1 Yr   *ACGME Approved/Offered Positions:* 1
Program ID: 520-56-14-005

Milwaukee

Medical College of Wisconsin Affiliated Hospitals Program
Sponsor: Medical College of Wisconsin Affiliated
   Hospitals, Inc
Children's Hospital of Wisconsin
Clement J Zablocki Veterans Affairs Medical Center
Froedtert Memorial Lutheran Hospital
Prgm Director: Rose A Franco, MD
9200 West Wisconsin Avenue
Milwaukee, WI 53226
Tel: 414 456-7040   *Fax:* 414 456-6211
E-mail: rquirk@mcw.edu
Length: 1 Yr   *ACGME Approved/Offered Positions:* 4
Program ID: 520-56-28-071

Spinal Cord Injury Medicine (Physical Medicine and Rehabilitation)

California

Orange

University of California (Irvine) Program
Sponsor: University of California (Irvine) Medical
   Center
Long Beach Memorial Medical Center
VA Long Beach Healthcare System
Prgm Director: Sophia Chun, MD*
SCI/D HCG (07/128) VA Long Beach Health Care Syste
5901 East Seventh Street
Long Beach, CA 90822
Tel: 562 826-5701   *Fax:* 562 826-5718
E-mail: sophia.chun@va.gov
Length: 1 Yr   *ACGME Approved/Offered Positions:* 1
Program ID: 345-05-21-014

Stanford

Stanford University Program
Sponsor: Stanford Hospital and Clinics
Santa Clara Valley Medical Center
Veterans Affairs Palo Alto Health Care System
Prgm Director: Vandana Punj, MD
3801 Miranda Avenue
SCIM Service (128)
Palo Alto, CA 94304
Tel: 650 493-5000   *Fax:* 650 849-0321
E-mail: vandana.punj@va.gov
Length: 1 Yr   *ACGME Approved/Offered Positions:* 3
Program ID: 345-05-21-007

Florida

Miami

Jackson Memorial Hospital/Jackson Health System Program
Sponsor: Jackson Memorial Hospital/Jackson Health
   System
Veterans Affairs Medical Center (Miami)
Prgm Director: Diana D Cardenas, MD, MHA*
PO Box 016960 (D-461)
Miami, FL 33101
Tel: 305 243-9516   *Fax:* 305 243-4650
E-mail: cdavis@med.miami.edu
Length: 1 Yr   *ACGME Approved/Offered Positions:* 2
Program ID: 345-11-21-018

Tampa

University of South Florida/James A Haley Veterans Hospital Program
Sponsor: University of South Florida College of Medicine
James A Haley Veterans Hospital
Prgm Director: Steven G Scott, DO
13000 Bruce B Downs Boulevard
RMS 117
Tampa, FL 33612
Tel: 813 972-7506   *Fax:* 813 978-5852
E-mail: steven.scott@va.gov
Length: 1 Yr   *ACGME Approved/Offered Positions:* 1
Program ID: 345-11-21-016

Programs

Illinois

Chicago

McGaw Medical Center of Northwestern University Program

Sponsor: McGaw Medical Center of Northwestern University
Northwestern Memorial Hospital
Rehabilitation Institute of Chicago
Prgm Director: David Chen, MD
345 East Superior Street, Room 1146
Chicago, IL 60611
Tel: 312 238-0764   *Fax:* 312 238-2512
Length: 1 Yr   *ACGME Approved/Offered Positions:* 1
Program ID: 345-16-12-020

Maryland

Baltimore

Johns Hopkins University Program

Sponsor: Johns Hopkins University School of Medicine
Good Samaritan Hospital of Maryland
Johns Hopkins Hospital
Kennedy Krieger Institute
Prgm Director: Cristina L Sadowsky, MD
Kennedy Krieger Institute
707 North Broadway, Suite 518
Baltimore, MD 21205
Tel: 443 923-9211   *Fax:* 443 923-9215
Length: 1 Yr   *ACGME Approved/Offered Positions:* 1
Program ID: 345-23-21-026

Sinai Hospital Program

Sponsor: Sinai Hospital of Baltimore
Kennedy Krieger Institute
University of Maryland Medical System
University of Maryland-Kernan Hospital
Prgm Director: Peter H Gorman, MD, MS
2200 Kernan Drive
Baltimore, MD 21207
Tel: 410 448-6261   *Fax:* 410 448-6617
E-mail: pgorman@kernan.umm.edu
Length: 1 Yr   *ACGME Approved/Offered Positions:* 1
Program ID: 345-23-12-025

Massachusetts

Boston

Harvard Medical School/Spaulding Rehabilitation Hospital Program

Sponsor: Spaulding Rehabilitation Hospital
Boston VA Healthcare System (Brockton-West Roxbury)
Prgm Director: Sunil Sabharwal, MD
1400 VFW Parkway
West Roxbury, MA 02132
Tel: 617 323-7700   *Fax:* 617 363-5553
E-mail: Sunil.Sabharwal2@med.va.gov
Length: 1 Yr   *ACGME Approved/Offered Positions:* 1
Program ID: 345-24-21-002

Michigan

Ann Arbor

University of Michigan Program

Sponsor: University of Michigan Hospitals and Health Centers
Prgm Director: Anthony Chiodo, MD
325 E Eishenhower
Suite 100
Ann Arbor, MI 48108
Tel: 734 615-6722   *Fax:* 734 615-1770
E-mail: twileyr@med.umich.edu
Length: 1 Yr   *ACGME Approved/Offered Positions:* 1
Program ID: 345-25-32-023

New Jersey

Newark

UMDNJ-New Jersey Medical School Program

Sponsor: UMDNJ-New Jersey Medical School
Kessler Institute for Rehabilitation
Veterans Affairs New Jersey Health Care System
Prgm Director: Steven Kirshblum, MD
30 Bergen Street, ADMC 101
PO Box 1709
Newark, NJ 07103
Tel: 973 972-3606   *Fax:* 973 972-5148
E-mail: SKirshblum@kessler-rehab.com
Length: 1 Yr   *ACGME Approved/Offered Positions:* 2
Program ID: 345-33-21-003

New York

New York

Mount Sinai School of Medicine Program

Sponsor: Mount Sinai School of Medicine
Elmhurst Hospital Center-Mount Sinai Services
Mount Sinai Medical Center
NYU Hospitals Center
Veterans Affairs Medical Center (Bronx)
Prgm Director: Thomas N Bryce, MD*
Department of Rehabilitation Medicine, Box 1240
One Gustave L Levy Place
New York, NY 10029
Tel: 212 241-6321   *Fax:* 212 348-5901
Length: 1 Yr   *ACGME Approved/Offered Positions:* 1
Program ID: 345-35-12-015

Ohio

Cleveland

Case Western Reserve University (MetroHealth) Program

Sponsor: MetroHealth Medical Center
Cleveland Clinic Foundation
Veterans Affairs Medical Center (Cleveland)
Prgm Director: Greg A Nemunaitis, MD
Spinal Cord Injury Medicine
2500 MetroHealth Drive
Cleveland, OH 44109
Tel: 216 778-3207   *Fax:* 216 778-7393
E-mail: rkarim@metrohealth.org
Length: 1 Yr   *ACGME Approved/Offered Positions:* 2
Program ID: 345-38-13-024

Pennsylvania

Pittsburgh

University of Pittsburgh Medical Center Medical Education Program

Sponsor: Univ of Pittsburgh Medical Center Medical Education
UPMC Presbyterian Shadyside
UPMC South Side
Prgm Director: John A Horton III, MD
3471 Fifth Ave, Room 201 Kaufmann Bldg
Pittsburgh, PA 15213
Tel: 412 648-6138   *Fax:* 412 692-4410
E-mail: kirleyj@upmc.edu
Length: 1 Yr   *ACGME Approved/Offered Positions:* 1
Program ID: 345-41-13-017

Texas

Dallas

University of Texas Southwestern Medical School Program

Sponsor: University of Texas Southwestern Medical School
Dallas County Hospital District-Parkland Memorial Hospital
Dallas VA Medical Center
Prgm Director: Lance L Goetz, MD
VA North Texas Health Care System
4500 S Lancanster Road (128)
Dallas, TX 75216
Tel: 214 857-1757   *Fax:* 214 857-1759
E-mail: Terri.Isbell@UTSouthwestern.edu
Length: 1 Yr   *ACGME Approved/Offered Positions:* 2
Program ID: 345-48-21-012

Houston

Baylor College of Medicine Program

Sponsor: Baylor College of Medicine
Memorial Hermann Hospital
Michael E DeBakey VA Medical Center - Houston
The Institute for Rehabilitation and Research
Prgm Director: Sally A Holmes, MD
PM&R Alliance Education Office
1333 Moursund St, Suite A-220
Houston, TX 77030
Tel: 713 799-5033   *Fax:* 713 797-5982
E-mail: PMandR@bcm.edu
Length: 1 Yr   *ACGME Approved/Offered Positions:* 1
Program ID: 345-48-13-021

University of Texas at Houston Program

Sponsor: University of Texas Health Science Center at Houston
Memorial Hermann Hospital
Michael E DeBakey VA Medical Center - Houston
The Institute for Rehabilitation and Research
Prgm Director: Juan M Latorre, MD
1333 Moursund, Suite A-220
Houston, TX 77030
Tel: 713 797-5938   *Fax:* 713 799-7052
E-mail: pmandr@bcm.edu
Length: 1 Yr   *ACGME Approved/Offered Positions:* 1
Program ID: 345-48-21-009

Note: * indicates a newly appointed program director

Virginia

Richmond

Virginia Commonwealth University Health System Program

Sponsor: Virginia Commonwealth University Health System
Hunter Holmes McGuire VA Medical Center (Richmond)
Medical College of Virginia Hospitals
Prgm Director: David R Gater Jr, MD, PhD
1201 Broad Rock Boulevard
Richmond, VA 23249
Tel: 804 675-5455   *Fax:* 804 675-5223
E-mail: David.Gater@va.gov
Length: 1 Yr   *ACGME Approved/Offered Positions:* 3
Program ID: 345-51-21-004

Washington

Seattle

University of Washington Program

Sponsor: University of Washington School of Medicine
Harborview Medical Center
Seattle Children's Hospital
University of Washington Medical Center
VA Puget Sound Health Care System
Prgm Director: Steven A Stiens, MD, MA
SCI Svc(128), Puget Sound Hlth Care
1660 Columbian Way South
Seattle, WA 98108
Tel: 206 764-2372   *Fax:* 206 764-2799
E-mail: steven.stiens@va.gov
Length: 1 Yr   *ACGME Approved/Offered Positions:* 1
Program ID: 345-54-21-006

Wisconsin

Milwaukee

Medical College of Wisconsin Affiliated Hospitals Program

Sponsor: Medical College of Wisconsin Affiliated Hospitals, Inc
Clement J Zablocki Veterans Affairs Medical Center
Prgm Director: Kevin T White, MD
SCI Service (128)
5000 W National Avenue
Milwaukee, WI 53295
Tel: 414 384-2000   *Fax:* 414 382-5155
E-mail: kevin.white2@va.gov
Length: 1 Yr   *ACGME Approved/Offered Positions:* 2
Program ID: 345-56-13-013

Sports Medicine (Emergency Medicine)

New York

Great Neck

NSLIJHS-North Shore University Hospital/NYU School of Medicine Program

Sponsor: North Shore-Long Island Jewish Health System
Long Island Jewish Medical Center
North Shore University Hospital
Prgm Director: John Munyak, MD
Department of Emergency Medicine
300 Community Drive
Manhasset, NY 11030
Tel: 516 562-2925   *Fax:* 516 562-3569
E-mail: emergencysports@yahoo.com
Length: 1 Yr   *ACGME Approved/Offered Positions:* 1
Program ID: 116-35-12-007

Rochester

University of Rochester Program

Sponsor: Strong Memorial Hospital of the University of Rochester
Prgm Director: Kenneth R Veenema, MD, MBA
Box 655
601 Elmwood Avenue
Rochester, NY 14642
Tel: 585 341-9257   *Fax:* 585 340-3051
Length: 1 Yr   *ACGME Approved/Offered Positions:* 1
Program ID: 116-35-31-004

Ohio

Dayton

Wright State University Program

Sponsor: Wright State University Boonshoft School of Medicine
Kettering Medical Center
Prgm Director: James M Tytko, MD
3490 Far Hills Avenue
Dayton, OH 45429
Tel: 937 395-3920   *Fax:* 937 395-3940
E-mail: james.tytko@khnetwork.org
Length: 1 Yr   *ACGME Approved/Offered Positions:* 2
Program ID: 116-38-12-003

Pennsylvania

Danville

Geisinger Health System Program

Sponsor: Geisinger Health System
Geisinger Medical Center
Geisinger Wyoming Valley Medical Center
Prgm Director: David S Ross, MD
1000 East Mountain Boulevard
MC 37-51
Wilkes Barre, PA 18711
Tel: 570 819-5661   *Fax:* 570 826-7878
E-mail: sajenkins@geisinger.edu
Length: 1 Yr   *ACGME Approved/Offered Positions:* 2
Program ID: 116-41-13-006

Pittsburgh

Allegheny General Hospital Program

Sponsor: Allegheny General Hospital
Prgm Director: Edward D Snell, MD
1307 Federal Street
2nd Floor
Pittsburgh, PA 15212
Tel: 412 359-6501   *Fax:* 412 359-6265
Length: 1 Yr   *ACGME Approved/Offered Positions:* 2
Program ID: 116-41-21-001

Sports Medicine (Family Medicine)

Alabama

Birmingham

St Vincent's East Program

Sponsor: St Vincent's East
St Vincent's Hospital
Prgm Director: Tracy Ray, MD
Attn: Becky Oxford
2660 10th Ave South, Suite 505
Birmingham, AL 35205
Tel: 205 939-3000   *Fax:* 205 314-2567
Length: 1 Yr   *ACGME Approved/Offered Positions:* 3
Program ID: 127-01-12-109

Huntsville

University of Alabama Medical Center (Huntsville) Program

Sponsor: University of Alabama Hospital
Huntsville Hospital
Prgm Director: Darla R Cowart, MD
301 Governors Drive SW
Huntsville, AL 35801
Tel: 256 551-4632   *Fax:* 256 551-4633
E-mail: francisp@uasomh.uab.edu
Length: 1 Yr   *ACGME Approved/Offered Positions:* 1
Program ID: 127-01-21-002

Mobile

University of South Alabama Program

Sponsor: University of South Alabama Hospitals
University of South Alabama Medical Center
Prgm Director: Michael M Linder, MD
1504 Springhill Avenue
Suite 3414
Mobile, AL 36604
Tel: 251 434-3482   *Fax:* 251 434-3495
Length: 1 Yr   *ACGME Approved/Offered Positions:* 1
Program ID: 127-01-13-124

Tuscaloosa

Tuscaloosa College of Community Health Science Program

Sponsor: Tuscaloosa College of Community Health Sciences
DCH Regional Medical Center
Prgm Director: James B Robinson, MD
850 5th Avenue East
Tuscaloosa, AL 35401
Tel: 205 339-0171   *Fax:* 205 333-8681
E-mail: lupton@cchs.ua.edu
Length: 1 Yr   *ACGME Approved/Offered Positions:* 3
Program ID: 127-01-12-122

Arizona

Phoenix

St Joseph's Hospital and Medical Center Program

Sponsor: St Joseph's Hospital and Medical Center
Carl T Hayden VA Medical Center
Del E Webb Memorial Hospital
Walter O Boswell Memorial Hospital
Prgm Director: Steven M Erickson, MD
PO Box 872104
Tempe, AZ 85287
Tel: 480 965-9771   *Fax:* 480 965-8224
E-mail: Steven.Erickson@asu.edu
Length: 1 Yr   *ACGME Approved/Offered Positions:* 1
Program ID: 127-03-13-120

Tucson

University of Arizona Program

Sponsor: University of Arizona College of Medicine
University of Arizona Campus Health Services
University of Arizona/UPHK Graduate Medical Ed Consortium
Prgm Director: Stephen R Paul, MD, MA
Campus Health Service
PO Box 210095
Tucson, AZ 85721
Tel: 520 626-6363   *Fax:* 520 626-2416
E-mail: paul@health.arizona.edu
Length: 1 Yr   *ACGME Approved/Offered Positions:* 3
Program ID: 127-03-12-083

California

Camp Pendleton

Naval Hospital (Camp Pendleton) Program

Sponsor: Naval Hospital (Camp Pendleton)
Prgm Director: Keith A Stuessi, MD
Sports Medicine Fellowship
Camp Pendleton, CA 92055
Tel: 760 763-6605   *Fax:* 760 763-7266
E-mail: keith.stuessi@med.navy.mil
Length: 1 Yr   *ACGME Approved/Offered Positions:* 2
Program ID: 127-05-21-068
Uniformed Services Program

Fontana

Kaiser Permanente Southern California (Fontana) Program

Sponsor: Kaiser Permanente Southern California
Kaiser Foundation Hospital (Fontana)
Prgm Director: Aaron Rubin, MD
9985 Sierra Avenue
Fontana, CA 92335
Tel: 909 427-6375   *Fax:* 909 427-5619
E-mail: aaron.L.rubin@kp.org
Length: 1 Yr   *ACGME Approved/Offered Positions:* 3
Program ID: 127-05-21-003

Los Angeles

Kaiser Permanente Southern California (Los Angeles) Program

Sponsor: Kaiser Permanente Southern California
Kaiser Foundation Hospital (Los Angeles)
Prgm Director: Joseph P Luftman, MD
Division of Sports Medicine
4950 Sunset Blvd, Suite 4B
Los Angeles, CA 90027
Tel: 323 783-5814   *Fax:* 323 783-4030
E-mail: joseph.p.luftman@kp.org
Length: 1 Yr   *ACGME Approved/Offered Positions:* 2
Program ID: 127-05-12-069

UCLA Medical Center Program

Sponsor: UCLA David Geffen School of Medicine/UCLA Medical Center
UCLA Medical Center
Prgm Director: John P DiFiori, MD
50-080 CHS
10833 Le Conte Ave
Los Angeles, CA 90095
Tel: 310 794-0795   *Fax:* 310 794-8079
E-mail: jdifiori@mednet.ucla.edu
Length: 1 Yr   *ACGME Approved/Offered Positions:* 3
Program ID: 127-05-21-018

Sacramento

University of California (Davis) Health System Program

Sponsor: University of California (Davis) Health System
University Health Services (Tang Center)
University of California (Davis) Medical Center
Prgm Director: David Cosca, MD
Sports Medicine
2805 J Street, Suite 300
Sacramento, CA 95816
Tel: 916 734-6805   *Fax:* 916 734-6806
Length: 1 Yr   *ACGME Approved/Offered Positions:* 1
Program ID: 127-05-31-082

San Diego

University of California (San Diego) Program

Sponsor: University of California (San Diego) Medical Center
Prgm Director: Kenneth S Taylor, MD
Division of Family Medicine
9333 Genesee Ave Suite 200
San Diego, CA 92121
Tel: 858 657-8592   *Fax:* 858 657-8625
E-mail: maskins@ucsd.edu
Length: 1 Yr   *ACGME Approved/Offered Positions:* 2
Program ID: 127-05-31-004

San Jose

San Jose-O'Connor Hospital Program

Sponsor: O'Connor Hospital
Prgm Director: Michael J Henehan, DO
455 O'Connor Drive, Suite 250
San Jose, CA 95128
Tel: 408 283-7767   *Fax:* 408 283-7608
E-mail: mhenehan@stanford.edu
Length: 1 Yr   *ACGME Approved/Offered Positions:* 3
Program ID: 127-05-21-093

Torrance

Los Angeles County-Harbor-UCLA Medical Center Program

Sponsor: Los Angeles County-Harbor-UCLA Medical Center
Kaiser Permanente Medical Center (Harbor City)
Prgm Director: Bernadette M Pendergraph, MD
1403 W Lomita Blvd, #102
Harbor City, CA 90710
Tel: 310 257-4991   *Fax:* 310 326-7205
E-mail: bpendergraph@labiomed.org
Length: 1 Yr   *ACGME Approved/Offered Positions:* 2
Program ID: 127-05-21-070

Note: * indicates a newly appointed program director

Colorado

Aurora

University of Colorado Denver (University Hospital) Program

Sponsor: University of Colorado Denver School of Medicine
Children's Hospital (The)
HealthONE Rose Medical Center
University of Colorado Hospital
Prgm Director: John C Hill, DO
AOL, L15, Mail Stop F496
PO Box 6511
Aurora, CO 80045
Tel: 303 724-9755   *Fax:* 303 724-9746
E-mail: john.hill@ucdenver.edu
Length: 1 Yr   *ACGME Approved/Offered Positions:* 2
Program ID: 127-07-31-055

Connecticut

Farmington

University of Connecticut Program

Sponsor: University of Connecticut School of Medicine
St Francis Hospital and Medical Center
Univ of Connecticut Health Center/John Dempsey Hospital
Prgm Director: Thomas H Trojian, MD
99 Woodland Street
Hartford, CT 06105
Tel: 860 714-6520   *Fax:* 860 714-8079
E-mail: tdaniel@stfranciscare.org
Length: 1 Yr   *ACGME Approved/Offered Positions:* 2
Program ID: 127-08-13-067

Delaware

Wilmington

Christiana Care Health Services Program

Sponsor: Christiana Care Health Services Inc
Prgm Director: Tony S Reed, MD
1400 N Washington St
Wilmington, DE 19801
Tel: 302 255-1350   *Fax:* 302 255-1355
Length: 1 Yr   *ACGME Approved/Offered Positions:* 2
Program ID: 127-09-13-110

Florida

Daytona Beach

Halifax Medical Center Program

Sponsor: Halifax Medical Center
Prgm Director: John A Shelton Jr, MD
Family Medicine Residency Program
303 North Clyde Morris Blvd
Daytona Beach, FL 32114
Tel: 386 254-4167   *Fax:* 386 258-4867
E-mail: residency.coordinator@halifax.org
Length: 1 Yr   *ACGME Approved/Offered Positions:* 1
Program ID: 127-11-21-036

Gainesville

University of Florida Program

Sponsor: University of Florida College of Medicine
Alachua County School Board
Santa Fe Community College Athletic Training Department
Shands Hospital at the University of Florida
University Athletic Association, Inc
Prgm Director: James R Clugston, MD, MS
PO Box 117500
1 Fletcher Drive
Gainesville, FL 32611
Tel: 352 392-1161   *Fax:* 352 392-9625
Length: 1 Yr   *ACGME Approved/Offered Positions:* 2
Program ID: 127-11-12-114

Jacksonville

College of Medicine, Mayo Clinic (Jacksonville) Program

Sponsor: College of Medicine, Mayo Clinic
Mayo Clinic Florida Hospital
Mayo Clinic (Jacksonville)
Prgm Director: Walter C Taylor III, MD
4500 San Pablo Road
Jacksonville, FL 32224
Tel: 904 953-0427   *Fax:* 904 953-0430
E-mail: sayward.jennifer@mayo.edu
Length: 1 Yr   *ACGME Approved/Offered Positions:* 1
Program ID: 127-11-13-072

St. Petersburg

Bayfront Medical Center Program

Sponsor: Bayfront Medical Center
Prgm Director: Arnold M Ramirez, MD
700 Sixth Street South
St Petersburg, FL 33701
Tel: 727 893-6891   *Fax:* 727 553-7340
E-mail: fp.web@bayfront.org
Length: 1 Yr   *ACGME Approved/Offered Positions:* 2
Program ID: 127-11-21-041

Georgia

Albany

Phoebe Putney Memorial Hospital (Southwest Georgia) Program

Sponsor: Phoebe Putney Memorial Hospital
Prgm Director: Nicholas I Kilmer, MD*
2336 Dawson Road, Suite 2200
Albany, GA 31707
Tel: 229 312-8797   *Fax:* 229 312-8743
Length: 1 Yr   *ACGME Approved/Offered Positions:* 1
Program ID: 127-12-31-075

Hawaii

Honolulu

University of Hawaii Program

Sponsor: University of Hawaii John A Burns School of Medicine
University Health Services Manoa
University of Hawaii Athletic Training Room
Prgm Director: Andrew W Nichols, MD
University of Hawaii at Manoa
651 Ilalo Street, MEB
Honolulu, HI 96813
Tel: 808 692-0994   *Fax:* 808 956-5834
E-mail: sportmed@hawaii.edu
Length: 1 Yr   *ACGME Approved/Offered Positions:* 1
Program ID: 127-14-31-074

Idaho

Boise

Family Medicine Residency of Idaho Program

Sponsor: Family Medicine Residency of Idaho
Boise State University Health and Wellness Center
Idaho Sports Medicine Institute
Orthopaedic Sugery Center of Idaho
St Alphonsus Regional Medical Center
Treasure Valley Hospital
Prgm Director: Scot B Scheffel, MD
Primary Care Sports Medicine Program
777 North Raymond
Boise, ID 83704
Tel: 208 367-6040   *Fax:* 208 367-6123
E-mail: holly.taniguchi@fmridaho.org
Length: 1 Yr   *ACGME Approved/Offered Positions:* 1
Program ID: 127-15-21-057

Illinois

Belleville

St Louis University School of Medicine (Belleville) Program

Sponsor: St Louis University School of Medicine
St Elizabeth's Hospital
St Louis University Hospital
Prgm Director: L Tyler Wadsworth, MD
180 South 3rd Street, Suite 400
Belleville, IL 62220
Tel: 618 641-5800   *Fax:* 618 641-5825
E-mail: lwadswor@slu.edu
Length: 1 Yr   *ACGME Approved/Offered Positions:* 2
Program ID: 127-16-12-097

Berwyn

MacNeal Hospital Program

Sponsor: MacNeal Hospital
Prgm Director: Roy G Henderson, MD, MPH
3231 South Euclid Avenue
Berwyn, IL 60402
Tel: 708 783-3539   *Fax:* 708 783-3656
E-mail: rhenders@macneal.com
Length: 1 Yr   *ACGME Approved/Offered Positions:* 1
Program ID: 127-16-21-040

Carbondale

Southern Illinois University (Carbondale) Program

Sponsor: Southern Illinois University School of Medicine
Memorial Hospital of Carbondale
Prgm Director: Scott Schonewolf, DO
305 W Jackson, Suite 200
Carbondale, IL 62901
Tel: 618 536-6621
E-mail: sschonewolf@siumed.edu
Length: 1 Yr   *ACGME Approved/Offered Positions:* 1
Program ID: 127-16-21-085

Chicago

Resurrection Medical Center Program

Sponsor: Resurrection Medical Center
Prgm Director: Cherise N Russo, DO
Resurrection Family Practice Center
7447 W Talcott Avenue, Suite 182
Chicago, IL 60631
Tel: 773 990-7648   *Fax:* 773 594-7975
E-mail: Cherise.Russo@reshealthcare.org
Length: 1 Yr   *ACGME Approved/Offered Positions:* 2
Program ID: 127-16-12-089

Rush University Medical Center/Copley Memorial Hospital Program
Sponsor: Rush University Medical Center
Prgm Director: Kathleen Weber, MD
800 South Wells Street
Suite 120
Chicago, IL 60607
Tel: 312 432-2565   *Fax:* 312 786-0023
E-mail: phyllis_j_velez@rush.edu
Length: 1 Yr   *ACGME Approved/Offered Positions:* 1
Program ID: 127-16-31-113

Park Ridge

Advocate Lutheran General Hospital Program
Sponsor: Advocate Lutheran General Hospital
Prgm Director: William W Briner Jr, MD
1775 West Dempster Street, 6 South
Park Ridge, IL 60068
Tel: 847 723-7979   *Fax:* 847 723-5615
Length: 1 Yr   *ACGME Approved/Offered Positions:* 2
Program ID: 127-16-21-006

Quincy

Southern Illinois University (Quincy) Program
Sponsor: Southern Illinois University School of Medicine
Blessing Hospital
Midwest Orthopedics Specialists
Prgm Director: James M Daniels, MD, MPH
612 North 11th Street, Suite B
Quincy, IL 62301
Tel: 217 224-9484   *Fax:* 217 224-7950
E-mail: lsavage@siumed.edu
Length: 1 Yr   *ACGME Approved/Offered Positions:* 1
Program ID: 127-16-22-079

Indiana

Indianapolis

Indiana University School of Medicine Program
Sponsor: Indiana University School of Medicine
Clarian Methodist Hospital of Indiana
Prgm Director: Kevin B Gebke, MD
1110 West Michigan St
Long Hospital, 2nd Floor
Indianapolis, IN 46202
Tel: 317 278-0118   *Fax:* 317 274-4444
E-mail: kgebke@iupui.edu
Length: 1 Yr   *ACGME Approved/Offered Positions:* 2
Program ID: 127-17-21-021

South Bend

Memorial Hospital of South Bend Program
Sponsor: Memorial Hospital of South Bend
St Joseph's Regional Medical Center (South Bend)
Prgm Director: Mark E Lavallee, MD
111 West Jefferson Boulevard, Suite 100
South Bend, IN 46601
Tel: 574 289-4764   *Fax:* 574 239-6461
E-mail: mlavallee@memorialsb.org
Length: 1 Yr   *ACGME Approved/Offered Positions:* 2
Program ID: 127-17-21-042

St Joseph's Regional Medical Center (South Bend) Program
Sponsor: St Joseph's Regional Medical Center (South Bend)
Memorial Hospital of South Bend
Prgm Director: Stephen M Simons, MD
230 E Day Rd Suite 150
Mishawaka, IN 46545
Tel: 574 247-5678   *Fax:* 574 247-5677
E-mail: simonss@sjrmc.com
Length: 1 Yr   *ACGME Approved/Offered Positions:* 1
Program ID: 127-17-31-043

Kansas

Wichita

University of Kansas (Wichita)/Via Christi Regional Medical Center Program
Sponsor: University of Kansas School of Medicine (Wichita)
Via Christi Regional Medical Center-St Joseph
Prgm Director: Mark L Stovak, MD
707 N Emporia
Wichita, KS 67214
Tel: 316 858-3524   *Fax:* 316 691-6792
Length: 1 Yr   *ACGME Approved/Offered Positions:* 2
Program ID: 127-19-31-086

Kentucky

Lexington

University of Kentucky College of Medicine Program
Sponsor: University of Kentucky College of Medicine
University of Kentucky Hospital
Prgm Director: Robert Hosey, MD
K-302 Kentucky Clinic
Lexington, KY 40536
Tel: 859 323-6712   *Fax:* 859 323-6661
Length: 1 Yr   *ACGME Approved/Offered Positions:* 2
Program ID: 127-20-21-052

Louisville

University of Louisville Program
Sponsor: University of Louisville School of Medicine
Jewish Hospital
Prgm Director: Jon A Becker, MD
Family Medicine Residency
201 Abraham Flexner Way, Suite 690
Louisville, KY 40202
Tel: 502 852-5499   *Fax:* 502 852-4944
Length: 1 Yr   *ACGME Approved/Offered Positions:* 2
Program ID: 127-20-31-108

Louisiana

Baton Rouge

Baton Rouge General Medical Center Program
Sponsor: Baton Rouge General Medical Center
Prgm Director: Jeffrey M Burnham, MD
8490 Picardy Avenue
Suite 100
Baton Rouge, LA 70809
Tel: 225 763-4923   *Fax:* 225 763-4906
E-mail: jeffrey.burnham@brgeneral.org
Length: 1 Yr   *ACGME Approved/Offered Positions:* 2
Program ID: 127-21-31-125

Maine

Portland

Maine Medical Center Program
Sponsor: Maine Medical Center
Prgm Director: William W Dexter, MD
Sports Medicine Program
272 Congress Street, 2nd Floor
Portland, ME 04101
Tel: 207 662-7359   *Fax:* 207 874-1918
E-mail: dextew@mmc.org
Length: 1 Yr   *ACGME Approved/Offered Positions:* 2
Program ID: 127-22-21-035

Maryland

Baltimore

University of Maryland Program
Sponsor: University of Maryland Medical System
Union Memorial Hospital
Prgm Director: Valerie E Cothran, MD*
Lower level
Baltimore, MD 21201
Tel: 410 328-5145   *Fax:* 410 328-0639
Length: 1 Yr   *ACGME Approved/Offered Positions:* 2
Program ID: 127-23-21-051

Massachusetts

Boston

Boston University Medical Center Program
Sponsor: Boston Medical Center
Boston University Athletic Department
Boston University Student Health Center
Massachusetts Institute of Technology Medical Department
Prgm Director: Matthew Pecci, MD
One Boston Medical Center Place
Dowling 5 South
Boston, MA 02118
Tel: 617 414-6239   *Fax:* 617 414-3345
Length: 1 Yr   *ACGME Approved/Offered Positions:* 1
Program ID: 127-24-12-091

Worcester

University of Massachusetts (Fitchburg) Program
Sponsor: University of Massachusetts Medical School
UMass Memorial Health Care (Memorial Campus)
Prgm Director: John H Stevenson, MD
275 Nichols Road, 4th Floor
Fitchburg, MA 01420
Tel: 978 878-8379   *Fax:* 978 343-5687
E-mail: stevej01@ummhc.org
Length: 1 Yr   *ACGME Approved/Offered Positions:* 2
Program ID: 127-24-13-080

Note: * indicates a newly appointed program director

Michigan

Ann Arbor

University of Michigan Program
Sponsor: University of Michigan Hospitals and Health Centers
Prgm Director: Robert B Kiningham, MD, MA
L2003 Women's Hospital
1500 East Medical Center Drive
Ann Arbor, MI 48109
Tel: 734 232-6776   *Fax:* 734 615-2687
E-mail: pmber@med.umich.edu
Length: 1 Yr   *ACGME Approved/Offered Positions:* 2
Program ID: 127-25-21-007

Detroit

Henry Ford Hospital Program
Sponsor: Henry Ford Hospital
Prgm Director: Nancy S White, MD
6525 Second Avenue
Detroit, MI 48202
Tel: 313 972-4076   *Fax:* 313 972-4202
E-mail: nwhite1@hfhs.org
Length: 1 Yr   *ACGME Approved/Offered Positions:* 4
Program ID: 127-25-21-064

Kalamazoo

Kalamazoo Center for Medical Studies/Michigan State University Program
Sponsor: Michigan State Univ/Kalamazoo Center for
   Medical Studies
Western Michigan University Sindecuse Health Center
Prgm Director: Robert J Baker, MD, PhD
Medical Studies
1000 Oakland Drive
Kalamazoo, MI 49008
Tel: 269 337-6554   *Fax:* 269 337-6565
E-mail: rollins@kcms.msu.edu
Length: 1 Yr   *ACGME Approved/Offered Positions:* 1
Program ID: 127-25-21-050

Lansing

Sparrow Hospital/Michigan State University Program
Sponsor: Sparrow Hospital
Prgm Director: Randolph Pearson, MD
1200 E Michigan Avenue
Suite 245C
Lansing, MI 48912
Tel: 517 364-5760
Length: 1 Yr   *ACGME Approved/Offered Positions:* 3
Program ID: 127-25-21-001

Royal Oak

William Beaumont Hospital Program
Sponsor: William Beaumont Hospital
William Beaumont Hospital - Troy
Prgm Director: Sami F Rifat, MD
3121 University Drive
Suite 140
Auburn Hills, MI 48326
Tel: 248 373-7286   *Fax:* 248 475-5979
Length: 1 Yr   *ACGME Approved/Offered Positions:* 1
Program ID: 127-25-21-115

Southfield

Providence Hospital and Medical Centers Program
Sponsor: Providence Hospital and Medical Centers
Prgm Director: Scott Eathorne, MD
30055 Northwestern Highway
Suite 30
Farmington Hills, MI 48334
Tel: 248 865-4030   *Fax:* 248 865-4031
E-mail: scott.eathorne@stjohn.org
Length: 1 Yr   *ACGME Approved/Offered Positions:* 1
Program ID: 127-25-21-022

Wayne

Oakwood Annapolis Hospital Program
Sponsor: Oakwood Annapolis Hospital
Prgm Director: Sarah Bancroft-Treadway, MD*
9398 Lilley Road
Plymouth, MI 48170
Tel: 734 467-2482   *Fax:* 734 467-2485
Length: 1 Yr   *ACGME Approved/Offered Positions:* 2
Program ID: 127-25-31-117

Minnesota

Minneapolis

Hennepin County Medical Center Program
Sponsor: Hennepin County Medical Center
Prgm Director: Robert J Johnson, MD
Family Medical Center
5 West Lake Street
Minneapolis, MN 55408
Tel: 612 545-9222   *Fax:* 612 545-9259
E-mail: rjjohnson@hotmail.com
Length: 1 Yr   *ACGME Approved/Offered Positions:* 4
Program ID: 127-26-21-008

Mississippi

Jackson

University of Mississippi Medical Center Program
Sponsor: University of Mississippi School of Medicine
Prgm Director: Steve A Watts, MD
2500 N State Street
Jackson, MS 39216
Tel: 601 815-6654   *Fax:* 601 984-6835
Length: 1 Yr   *ACGME Approved/Offered Positions:* 1
Program ID: 127-27-21-099

Missouri

Kansas City

University of Missouri at Kansas City Program
Sponsor: University of Missouri-Kansas City School of
   Medicine
Truman Medical Center-Lakewood
Prgm Director: Russell D White, MD
7900 Lee's Summit Road
Kansas City, MO 64139
Tel: 816 404-7106   *Fax:* 816 404-7142
E-mail: jockdoc2000@hotmail.com
Length: 1 Yr   *ACGME Approved/Offered Positions:* 2
Program ID: 127-28-13-107

Montana

Billings

Montana Family Medicine Sports Medicine Program
Sponsor: Montana Family Medicine Residency
St Vincent Healthcare
Prgm Director: Roxanne Fahrenwald, MD
123 S 27th Street, Suite B
Billings, MT 59101
Tel: 406 247-3306   *Fax:* 406 247-3307
E-mail: info@mfmr.famed.washington.edu
Length: 1 Yr   *ACGME Approved/Offered Positions:* 1
Program ID: 127-29-11-078

Nevada

Las Vegas

University of Nevada School of Medicine (Las Vegas) Program
Sponsor: University of Nevada School of Medicine
University Medical Center of Southern Nevada
Crovetti Orthopaedics and Sports Medicine
Prgm Director: Michael D Milligan, MD*
2410 Fire Mesa Street, Suite 180
Las Vegas, NV 89128
Tel: 702 992-6875   *Fax:* 702 992-6880
Length: 1 Yr   *ACGME Approved/Offered Positions:* 1
Program ID: 127-31-13-096

Reno

University of Nevada School of Medicine Program
Sponsor: University of Nevada School of Medicine
Ioannis A Lougaris Veterans Affairs Medical Center
MEDSchool Associates North (Reno)
Renown Medical Center
Saint Mary's Regional Medical Center
University of Nevada, Reno - Student Health Center
Prgm Director: Carol L Scott, MD
Student Health Center
Mail Stop 196, Redfield Building
Reno, NV 89557
Tel: 775 784-6598   *Fax:* 775 784-1298
Length: 1 Yr   *ACGME Approved/Offered Positions:* 1
Program ID: 127-31-12-111

New Jersey

Montclair

Mountainside Hospital Program
Sponsor: Mountainside Hospital
Prgm Director: Jeffrey Rosenberg, MD
1 Bay Avenue
Montclair, NJ 07042
Tel: 973 746-7050   *Fax:* 973 259-3569
E-mail: annmarie.jones@mountainsidehosp.com
Length: 1 Yr   *ACGME Approved/Offered Positions:* 1
Program ID: 127-33-31-104

New Brunswick

UMDNJ-Robert Wood Johnson Medical School Program
Sponsor: UMDNJ-Robert Wood Johnson Medical School
St Peter's University Hospital
Prgm Director: Robert Monaco, MD, MPH
Dept of Family Medicine, MEB 278C
One Robert Wood Johnson Place
New Brunswick, NJ 08903
Tel: 732 235-6969   *Fax:* 732 235-6309
Length: 1 Yr   *ACGME Approved/Offered Positions:* 2
Program ID: 127-33-21-030

New Mexico

Albuquerque

University of New Mexico Program
Sponsor: University of New Mexico School of Medicine
University of New Mexico Hospital
Prgm Director: Christopher McGrew, MD
MSC09 5040
1 University of New Mexico
Albuquerque, NM 87131
Tel: 505 272-2165   *Fax:* 505 272-8045
Length: 1 Yr   *ACGME Approved/Offered Positions:* 1
Program ID: 127-34-13-112

New York

Buffalo

University at Buffalo Program
Sponsor: University at Buffalo School of Medicine
Erie County Medical Center
Kaleida Health System (Buffalo General Hospital)
Kaleida Health System (Millard Fillmore Hospital)
Prgm Director: John J Leddy, MD
3435 Main Street, 160 Farber Hall
Buffalo, NY 14214
Tel: 716 829-2070   *Fax:* 716 898-3164
Length: 1 Yr   *ACGME Approved/Offered Positions:* 2
Program ID: 127-35-31-084

Johnson City

United Health Services Hospitals Program
Sponsor: United Health Services Hospitals
Wilson Medical Center (United Health System)
Prgm Director: Donald W Nash, MD
1302 E Main Street
Endicott, NY 13760
Tel: 607 754-1498   *Fax:* 607 754-0290
E-mail: Donald_Nash@uhs.org
Length: 1 Yr   *ACGME Approved/Offered Positions:* 1
Program ID: 127-35-31-088

North Carolina

Charlotte

Carolinas Medical Center Program
Sponsor: Carolinas Medical Center
Prgm Director: Robert Jones, MD
PO Box 32861
CMC-Eastland Family Practice Center
Charlotte, NC 28232
Tel: 704 446-7700   *Fax:* 704 446-7795
E-mail: robert.jones@carolinas.org
Length: 1 Yr   *ACGME Approved/Offered Positions:* 1
Program ID: 127-36-13-098

Concord

Carolinas Medical Center (Northeast-Cabarrus) Program
Sponsor: Carolinas Medical Center-Northeast
Prgm Director: Kevin E Burroughs, MD
270 Copperfield Boulevard
Suite 202
Concord, NC 28025
Tel: 704 721-2060   *Fax:* 704 721-2077
E-mail: jackquelyn.harve@carolinashealthcare.org
Length: 1 Yr   *ACGME Approved/Offered Positions:* 1
Program ID: 127-36-12-101

Durham

Duke University Hospital Program
Sponsor: Duke University Hospital
Prgm Director: Jeffrey R Bytomski, DO
Box 3672
Durham, NC 27710
Tel: 919 684-3591   *Fax:* 919 681-6357
E-mail: bytom001@mc.duke.edu
Length: 1 Yr   *ACGME Approved/Offered Positions:* 2
Program ID: 127-36-13-065

Greensboro

Moses H Cone Memorial Hospital Program
Sponsor: Moses H Cone Memorial Hospital
Prgm Director: Karl B Fields, MD
1125 N Church Street
Greensboro, NC 27401
Tel: 336 832-8132   *Fax:* 336 832-7078
E-mail: martha.delaney@mosescone.com
Length: 1 Yr   *ACGME Approved/Offered Positions:* 3
Program ID: 127-36-21-023

Greenville

Pitt County Memorial Hospital/East Carolina University Program
Sponsor: Pitt County Memorial Hospital
Brody School of Medicine at East Carolina University
Orthopedics East
Prgm Director: Joseph P Garry, MD
Brody School of Medicine 4N-70
600 Moye Boulevard
Greenville, NC 27858
Tel: 252 744-1378   *Fax:* 252 744-3040
E-mail: garryj@ecu.edu
Length: 1 Yr   *ACGME Approved/Offered Positions:* 1
Program ID: 127-36-12-063

Winston-Salem

Wake Forest University School of Medicine Program
Sponsor: Wake Forest University Baptist Medical Center
Prgm Director: Daryl A Rosenbaum, MD
Medical Center Boulevard
Winston-Salem, NC 27157
Tel: 336 716-2794   *Fax:* 336 716-3206
E-mail: drosenba@wfubmc.edu
Length: 1 Yr   *ACGME Approved/Offered Positions:* 2
Program ID: 127-36-21-048

Ohio

Cincinnati

TriHealth (Bethesda North Hospital) Program
Sponsor: TriHealth
Prgm Director: Richard A Okragly Jr, MD
Sports Medicine Fellowship Program
4411 Montgomery Road, Suite 206
Cincinnati, OH 45212
Tel: 513 531-6720   *Fax:* 513 531-2624
Length: 1 Yr   *ACGME Approved/Offered Positions:* 2
Program ID: 127-38-13-090

Cleveland

Fairview Hospital Program
Sponsor: Fairview Hospital
Cleveland Clinic Foundation
Prgm Director: Alfred J Cianflocco, MD
99 Northline Circel
Euclid, OH 44119
Tel: 216 692-7833   *Fax:* 216 692-7802
Length: 1 Yr   *ACGME Approved/Offered Positions:* 2
Program ID: 127-38-21-047

Columbus

Grant Medical Center (OhioHealth) Program
Sponsor: Grant Medical Center (OhioHealth)
Prgm Director: Joel Shaw, MD
285 E State Street, Suite 670
Medical Education Department
Columbus, OH 43215
Tel: 614 566-9041   *Fax:* 614 566-8073
E-mail: bsnyder@ohiohealth.com
Length: 1 Yr   *ACGME Approved/Offered Positions:* 1
Program ID: 127-38-21-009

Ohio State University Hospital Program
Sponsor: Ohio State University Hospital
Prgm Director: James R Borchers, MD, MPH*
2050 Kenny Road
Columbus, OH 43221
Tel: 614 293-3600   *Fax:* 614 293-4399
E-mail: james.borchers@osumc.edu
Length: 1 Yr   *ACGME Approved/Offered Positions:* 2
Program ID: 127-38-21-031

Riverside Methodist Hospitals (OhioHealth) Program
Sponsor: Riverside Methodist Hospitals (OhioHealth)
Prgm Director: Douglas DiOrio, MD
3705 Olentangy River Road
Columbus, OH 43214
Tel: 614 586-4043   *Fax:* 614 586-1237
Length: 1 Yr   *ACGME Approved/Offered Positions:* 2
Program ID: 127-38-13-092

Toledo

Toledo Hospital Program
Sponsor: Toledo Hospital
Prgm Director: Roger J Kruse, MD
2865 N Reynolds Rd #140
Toledo, OH 43615
Tel: 419 578-7590   *Fax:* 419 537-5605
Length: 1 Yr   *ACGME Approved/Offered Positions:* 3
Program ID: 127-38-31-011

Oklahoma

Oklahoma City

University of Oklahoma Health Sciences Center Program
Sponsor: University of Oklahoma College of Medicine
McBride Clinic Orthopedic Hospital
OU Medical Center
Prgm Director: Brian R Coleman, MD
900 NE 10th Street
Oklahoma City, OK 73104
Tel: 405 271-8818   *Fax:* 405 271-4366
Length: 1 Yr   *ACGME Approved/Offered Positions:* 1
Program ID: 127-39-21-012

Note: * indicates a newly appointed program director

Tulsa

University of Oklahoma College of Medicine-Tulsa Program

Sponsor: University of Oklahoma College of Medicine-Tulsa
Eastern Oklahoma Orthopedic Center, Inc
Oklahoma Surgical Hospital
Saint Francis Health System
Prgm Director: Lamont E Cavanagh, MD
Sports Medicine Program
1111 S Saint Louis Ave
Tulsa, OK 74120
Tel: 918 619-4701   *Fax:* 918 619-4707
E-mail: Eilene-Pirtle@ouhsc.edu
Length: 1 Yr   *ACGME Approved/Offered Positions:* 2
Program ID: 127-39-31-013

Oregon

Portland

Oregon Health & Science University Program

Sponsor: Oregon Health & Science University Hospital
Portland State University Training Room
Prgm Director: Charles W Webb, DO
Sports Medicine Fellowship
4411 SW Vermont Street
Portland, OR 97219
Tel: 503 494-1978   *Fax:* 503 494-6015
E-mail: fmres@ohsu.edu
Length: 1 Yr   *ACGME Approved/Offered Positions:* 2
Program ID: 127-40-21-131

Pennsylvania

Bethlehem

St Luke's Hospital Program

Sponsor: St Luke's Hospital
Prgm Director: Kevin N Waninger, MD, MS
2830 Easton Avenue
Bethlehem, PA 18017
Tel: 610 954-3550   *Fax:* 610 954-3693
E-mail: waningk@slhn.org
Length: 1 Yr   *ACGME Approved/Offered Positions:* 2
Program ID: 127-41-12-095

Erie

St Vincent Health Center Program

Sponsor: St Vincent Health Center
Prgm Director: Jonathan D McKrell, MD
2314 Sassafras Street
3rd Floor
Erie, PA 16502
Tel: 814 452-5106   *Fax:* 814 452-5097
Length: 1 Yr   *ACGME Approved/Offered Positions:* 2
Program ID: 127-41-21-061

Philadelphia

Drexel University College of Medicine/Hahnemann University Hospital Program

Sponsor: Drexel University College of Medicine/Hahnemann University
Hahnemann University Hospital (Tenet Health System)
St Christopher's Hospital for Children (Tenet Health System)
Prgm Director: Eugene S Hong, MD
10 Shurs Lane, Suite 203
Philadelphia, PA 19127
Tel: 215 482-4744   *Fax:* 215 482-1095
Length: 1 Yr   *ACGME Approved/Offered Positions:* 2
Program ID: 127-41-31-121

Thomas Jefferson University Program

Sponsor: Thomas Jefferson University Hospital
St Christopher's Hospital for Children (Tenet Health System)
Prgm Director: Marc Harwood, MD
1015 Walnut Street, Suite 401
Philadelphia, PA 19107
Tel: 215 955-2352   *Fax:* 215 955-0640
E-mail: marc.harwood@jefferson.edu
Length: 1 Yr   *ACGME Approved/Offered Positions:* 2
Program ID: 127-41-21-024

University of Pennsylvania Program

Sponsor: University of Pennsylvania Health System
Pennsylvania Hospital (UPHS)
Prgm Director: Gary Dorshimer, MD
727 Delancey Street
Philadelphia, PA 19106
Tel: 215 829-3523   *Fax:* 215 829-6023
Length: 1 Yr   *ACGME Approved/Offered Positions:* 1
Program ID: 127-41-12-118

Pittsburgh

University of Pittsburgh Medical Center Medical Education (Presbyterian Shadyside Hospital) Program

Sponsor: Univ of Pittsburgh Medical Center Medical Education
UPMC Presbyterian Shadyside
UPMC South Side
UPMC St Margaret
Prgm Director: Tanya J Hagen, MD
Dept of Family Medicine
5230 Centre Avenue - Room 519
Pittsburgh, PA 15232
Tel: 412 623-2028   *Fax:* 412 623-6253
E-mail: pcsmfellowship@msx.upmc.edu
Length: 1 Yr   *ACGME Approved/Offered Positions:* 1
Program ID: 127-41-21-014

University of Pittsburgh Medical Center Medical Education (St Margaret Hospital) Program

Sponsor: Univ of Pittsburgh Medical Center Medical Education
UPMC South Side
UPMC St Margaret
Prgm Director: Anne S Boyd, MD
UPMC St Margaret, c/o Room 519 SON Shadyside
5230 Centre Avenue
Pittsburgh, PA 15232
Tel: 412 623-2028   *Fax:* 412 623-6253
E-mail: pcsmfellowship@upmc.edu
Length: 1 Yr   *ACGME Approved/Offered Positions:* 3
Program ID: 127-41-31-025

Upland

Crozer-Chester Medical Center (Keystone Health System) Program

Sponsor: Crozer-Chester Medical Center
Springfield Hospital
Prgm Director: Steven J Collina, MD
1260 E Woodland Avenue, Suite 200
Springfield, PA 19064
Tel: 610 690-4491   *Fax:* 610 328-9391
Length: 1 Yr   *ACGME Approved/Offered Positions:* 2
Program ID: 127-41-21-033

South Carolina

Anderson

AnMed Health (Anderson) Program

Sponsor: AnMed Health
Prgm Director: Scott Stephen Counts, MD
Oglesby Center
2000 East Greenville Street, Suite 3600
Anderson, SC 29621
Tel: 864 224-8100   *Fax:* 864 512-3702
E-mail: Scott.Counts1@anmedhealth.org
Length: 1 Yr   *ACGME Approved/Offered Positions:* 1
Program ID: 127-45-12-105

Columbia

Palmetto Health/University of South Carolina School of Medicine Program

Sponsor: Palmetto Health
Palmetto Health Richland
Prgm Director: Jason J Stacy, MD
3209 Colonial Drive
Columbia, SC 29203
Tel: 803 434-2419   *Fax:* 803 434-8545
E-mail: Cheryl.Haynes@palmettohealth.org
Length: 1 Yr   *ACGME Approved/Offered Positions:* 2
Program ID: 127-45-21-015

Greenville

Greenville Hospital System/University of South Carolina School of Medicine Program

Sponsor: Greenville Hospital System/University of South Carolina
Prgm Director: Kyle J Cassas, MD
877 West Faris Road
Greenville, SC 29605
Tel: 864 455-9022   *Fax:* 864 455-9015
E-mail: kcassas@ghs.org
Length: 1 Yr   *ACGME Approved/Offered Positions:* 2
Program ID: 127-45-21-119

Greenwood

Self Regional Healthcare/Greenwood Program

Sponsor: Self Regional Healthcare
Prgm Director: David P Sealy, MD
155 Academy Avenue
Greenwood, SC 29646
Tel: 864 725-4691   *Fax:* 864 725-4883
E-mail: dsealy@selfregional.org
Length: 1 Yr   *ACGME Approved/Offered Positions:* 2
Program ID: 127-45-12-126

Tennessee

Knoxville

University of Tennessee Medical Center at Knoxville Program

Sponsor: University of Tennessee Graduate School of Medicine
Knoxville Orthopedic Clinic
University of Tennessee Memorial Hospital
University of Tennessee Student Health Services Clinic
Prgm Director: Kenneth M Bielak, MD, MBA
1924 Alcoa Highway
Box U-67
Knoxville, TN 37920
Tel: 865 305-9352   *Fax:* 865 305-6532
E-mail: kbielak@utmck.edu
Length: 1 Yr   *ACGME Approved/Offered Positions:* 1
Program ID: 127-47-21-044

Programs

Texas

Conroe

Conroe Medical Education Foundation Program

Sponsor: Conroe Medical Education Foundation
Prairie View A&M University
Texas Orthopaedic and Sports Medicine
Tomball Regional Hospital
Prgm Director: Scott E Rand, MD
Sports Medicine Fellowship
605 Holderrieth
Tomball, TX 77375
Tel: 281 378-4300   *Fax:* 281 378-4305
Length: 1 Yr   *ACGME Approved/Offered Positions:* 2
Program ID: 127-48-21-102

Fort Worth

John Peter Smith Hospital (Tarrant County Hospital District) Program

Sponsor: John Peter Smith Hospital (Tarrant County
   Hospital District)
Harris Methodist Fort Worth
Huguley Memorial Medical Center
Southern Methodist Memorial Health Center
Prgm Director: James J Barbee, MD
1500 S Main Street
Fort Worth, TX 76104
Tel: 817 927-1200   *Fax:* 817 927-1691
E-mail: jbarbee@jpshealth.org
Length: 1 Yr   *ACGME Approved/Offered Positions:* 6
Program ID: 127-48-21-073

Lubbock

Texas Tech University (Lubbock) Program

Sponsor: Texas Tech University Health Sciences Center
   at Lubbock
Covenant Medical Center
University Medical Center
Prgm Director: Jennifer J Mitchell, BS, MD*
3601 4th Street
MS 8143
Lubbock, TX 79430
Tel: 806 743-7864   *Fax:* 806 743-3955
E-mail: sports.medicine@ttuhsc.edu
Length: 1 Yr   *ACGME Approved/Offered Positions:* 2
Program ID: 127-48-12-081

San Antonio

Christus Santa Rosa Health Care Program

Sponsor: Christus Santa Rosa Health Care Corporation
Sports Medicine Associates
Prgm Director: Eliot J Young, MD*
21 Spurs Lane
Suite 300
San Antonio, TX 78240
Tel: 210 704-2575   *Fax:* 210 704-2545
E-mail: eliot.young@christushealth.org
Length: 1 Yr   *ACGME Approved/Offered Positions:* 1
Program ID: 127-48-13-103

Tyler

University of Texas Health Center at Tyler Program

Sponsor: University of Texas Health Center at Tyler
Mother Frances Hospital Regional Health Care Center
Prgm Director: Catherine M Fieseler, MD*
11937 US Highway 271
Tyler, TX 75708
Tel: 903 590-2182   *Fax:* 903 590-2188
Length: 1 Yr   *ACGME Approved/Offered Positions:* 1
Program ID: 127-48-21-123

Utah

Provo

Utah Valley Regional Medical Center Program

Sponsor: Utah Valley Regional Medical Center
Prgm Director: Brent Rich, MD
1134 North 500 West, Suite 101
Provo, UT 84604
Tel: 801 357-7134   *Fax:* 801 357-2176
E-mail: brent.rich@imail.org
Length: 1 Yr   *ACGME Approved/Offered Positions:* 2
Program ID: 127-49-21-058

Salt Lake City

University of Utah Program

Sponsor: University of Utah Medical Center
Primary Children's Medical Center
Prgm Director: Elizabeth Joy, MD, MPH
375 Chipeta Way, Suite A
Salt Lake City, UT 84108
Tel: 801 585-9075   *Fax:* 801 581-2771
Length: 1 Yr   *ACGME Approved/Offered Positions:* 3
Program ID: 127-49-31-059

Virginia

Fairfax

Virginia Commonwealth University Health System (Falls Church) Program

Sponsor: Virginia Commonwealth University Health
   System
Inova Fair Oaks Hospital
Dewitt Healthcare Network
Reston Hospital Center
Prgm Director: Thomas M Howard, MD
VCU-FFM Sports Medicine Fellowship
3650 Joseph Siewick Drive, Suite 400, 4th Floor
Fairfax, VA 22033
Tel: 703 391-2020   *Fax:* 703 391-1211
E-mail: residency@ffpcs.com
Length: 1 Yr   *ACGME Approved/Offered Positions:* 2
Program ID: 127-51-31-100

Fort Belvoir

National Capital Consortium (DeWitt Healthcare Network) Program

Sponsor: National Capital Consortium
Dewitt Healthcare Network
Malcolm Grow Medical Center
National Naval Medical Center (Bethesda)
Virginia Hospital Center-Arlington
Prgm Director: Kevin deWeber, MD
4301 Jones Bridge Road
Bethesda, MD 20814
Tel: 301 295-9466
Length: 1 Yr   *ACGME Approved/Offered Positions:* 4
Program ID: 127-51-21-037
Uniformed Services Program

Washington

Seattle

University of Washington Program

Sponsor: University of Washington School of Medicine
University of Washington Medical Center
Prgm Director: Kimberly G Harmon, MD
Hall Health Primary Care Center
Box 354410
Seattle, WA 98195
Tel: 206 685-1044   *Fax:* 206 616-6652
E-mail: residency@fammed.washington.edu
Length: 1 Yr   *ACGME Approved/Offered Positions:* 1
Program ID: 127-54-21-039

Spokane

Spokane Medical Centers/University of Washington School of Medicine Program

Sponsor: Inland Empire Hospital Services Association
Deaconess Medical Center
Sacred Heart Medical Center
Prgm Director: Edward Reisman, MD
104 West Fifth Avenue
Suite 200 West
Spokane, WA 99204
Tel: 509 624-2313   *Fax:* 509 459-0686
E-mail: info@fammedspokane.org
Length: 1 Yr   *ACGME Approved/Offered Positions:* 1
Program ID: 127-54-21-127

Wisconsin

Janesville

Mercy Health System Program

Sponsor: Mercy Health System
Prgm Director: Arthur M Altbuch, MD
849 Kellogg Avenue
Janesville, WI 53546
Tel: 608 755-7960   *Fax:* 608 758-7801
E-mail: aaltbuch@mhsjvl.org
Length: 1 Yr   *ACGME Approved/Offered Positions:* 2
Program ID: 127-56-13-094

Milwaukee

Medical College of Wisconsin Affiliated Hospitals Program

Sponsor: Medical College of Wisconsin Affiliated
   Hospitals, Inc
Froedtert Memorial Lutheran Hospital
Wheaton Franciscan Healthcare-St Joseph
Prgm Director: Craig C Young, MD
c/o Dr Craig Young, Box 26099
9200 West Wisconsin Avenue
Milwaukee, WI 53226
Tel: 414 805-7463   *Fax:* 414 805-7499
Length: 1 Yr   *ACGME Approved/Offered Positions:* 1
Program ID: 127-56-21-029

Note: * indicates a newly appointed program director

Surgery-General

Alabama

Birmingham

Baptist Health System Program
Sponsor: Baptist Health System Inc
Baptist Medical Center-Princeton
Trinity Medical Center
Prgm Director: William J Tapscott, MD
701 Princeton Avenue SW
4 East
Birmingham, AL 35211
Tel: 205 783-3191   *Fax:* 205 783-3164
E-mail: william.tapscott@bhsala.com
Length: 5 Yrs   *ACGME Approved/Offered Positions:* 15
Program ID: 440-01-21-020

University of Alabama Medical Center Program
Sponsor: University of Alabama Hospital
Veterans Affairs Medical Center (Birmingham)
Prgm Director: Marshall M Urist, MD
1922 7th Avenue South
Room 217 Kracke Building
Birmingham, AL 35294
Tel: 205 934-3065   *Fax:* 205 975-5867
Length: 5 Yrs   *ACGME Approved/Offered Positions:* 47
Program ID: 440-01-21-022

Mobile

University of South Alabama Program
Sponsor: University of South Alabama Hospitals
Mobile Infirmary Medical Center
University of South Alabama Medical Center
Veterans Affairs Medical Center (Biloxi)
Prgm Director: Clyde N Ellis Jr, MD
2451 Fillingim Street
Department of General Surgery
Mobile, AL 36617
Tel: 251 471-7993   *Fax:* 251 471-7022
Length: 5 Yrs   *ACGME Approved/Offered Positions:* 24
Program ID: 440-01-11-024

Arizona

Phoenix

Banner Good Samaritan Medical Center Program
Sponsor: Banner Good Samaritan Medical Center
Alaska Native Medical Center
Carl T Hayden VA Medical Center
Prgm Director: John J Ferrara, MD
Department of Surgery
925 East McDowell Road
Phoenix, AZ 85006
Tel: 602 239-2282   *Fax:* 602 495-9112
E-mail: carrie.huston@bannerhealth.com
Length: 5 Yrs   *ACGME Approved/Offered Positions:* 34
Program ID: 440-03-22-026

Maricopa Medical Center Program
Sponsor: Maricopa Medical Center
Scottsdale Healthcare - Shea
Prgm Director: Kevin N Foster, MD, MBA
Department of Surgery
2601 E Roosevelt St
Phoenix, AZ 85008
Tel: 602 344-5445   *Fax:* 602 344-5048
E-mail: kim_kascht@medprodoctors.com
Length: 5 Yrs   *ACGME Approved/Offered Positions:* 31
Program ID: 440-03-22-025

St Joseph's Hospital and Medical Center Program
Sponsor: St Joseph's Hospital and Medical Center
Prgm Director: Scott Petersen, MD
350 West Thomas Road
Phoenix, AZ 85013
Tel: 602 406-6540   *Fax:* 602 406-4113
E-mail: Julie.Wall@chw.edu
Length: 5 Yrs   *ACGME Approved/Offered Positions:* 23
Program ID: 440-03-12-420

Scottsdale

College of Medicine, Mayo Clinic (Arizona) Program
Sponsor: College of Medicine, Mayo Clinic
Mayo Clinic (Arizona)
St Joseph's Hospital and Medical Center
Prgm Director: Richard J Gray, MD
5777 East Mayo Boulevard
Phoenix, AZ 85054
Tel: 480 342-2812   *Fax:* 480 342-2170
Length: 5 Yrs   *ACGME Approved/Offered Positions:* 21
Program ID: 440-03-21-402

Tucson

University of Arizona Program
Sponsor: University of Arizona College of Medicine
Southern Arizona VA Health Care Center (Tucson)
Tucson Medical Center
University Medical Center
Prgm Director: James A Warneke, MD
Dept of Surgery, Room 5334
1501 N Campbell Avenue POB 245058
Tucson, AZ 85724
Tel: 520 626-7747   *Fax:* 520 626-2247
E-mail: gisela@surgery.arizona.edu
Length: 5 Yrs   *ACGME Approved/Offered Positions:* 49
Program ID: 440-03-21-027

Arkansas

Little Rock

University of Arkansas for Medical Sciences Program
Sponsor: University of Arkansas College of Medicine
Arkansas Children's Hospital
Central Arkansas Veterans Healthcare System
UAMS Medical Center
Prgm Director: Samuel D Smith, MD*
Department of Surgery, #520
4301 West Markham Street
Little Rock, AR 72205
Tel: 501 686-6627   *Fax:* 501 686-5696
E-mail: massanellicarola@uams.edu
Length: 5 Yrs   *ACGME Approved/Offered Positions:* 37
Program ID: 440-04-21-029

California

Bakersfield

Kern Medical Center Program
Sponsor: Kern Medical Center
Prgm Director: Ray S Chung, MD
1830 Flower Street
Bakersfield, CA 93305
Tel: 661 326-2276   *Fax:* 661 326-2282
E-mail: duclosd@kernmedctr.com
Length: 5 Yrs   *ACGME Approved/Offered Positions:* 12
Program ID: 440-05-31-030

French Camp

San Joaquin General Hospital Program
Sponsor: San Joaquin General Hospital
St Joseph's Medical Center
University of California (Davis) Medical Center
Prgm Director: Ahmed Mahmoud, MD
500 W Hospital Road
French Camp, CA 95231
Tel: 209 468-6620   *Fax:* 209 468-6246
E-mail: amahmoud@sjgh.org
Length: 5 Yrs   *ACGME Approved/Offered Positions:* 12
Program ID: 440-05-12-055

Fresno

University of California (San Francisco)/Fresno Program
Sponsor: UCSF Fresno Medical Education Program
Community Medical Centers (Fresno)
VA Central California Health Care System
Prgm Director: Steven N Parks, MD
155 N Fresno Street, Suite 216
Fresno, CA 93701
Tel: 559 459-3770   *Fax:* 559 459-3719
E-mail: surgery@fresno.ucsf.edu
Length: 5 Yrs   *ACGME Approved/Offered Positions:* 21
Program ID: 440-05-21-032

Loma Linda

Loma Linda University Program
Sponsor: Loma Linda University Medical Center
Jerry L Pettis Memorial Veterans Hospital
Riverside County Regional Medical Center
Prgm Director: Mark E Reeves, MD, PhD
11175 Campus Street
Room 21108
Loma Linda, CA 92354
Tel: 909 558-4289   *Fax:* 909 558-4872
E-mail: mereeves@llu.edu
Length: 5 Yrs   *ACGME Approved/Offered Positions:* 53
Program ID: 440-05-21-034

Los Angeles

Cedars-Sinai Medical Center Program
Sponsor: Cedars-Sinai Medical Center
Prgm Director: Ali Salim, MD
Department of Surgery
8700 Beverly Blvd #8215
Los Angeles, CA 90048
Tel: 310 423-6637   *Fax:* 310 423-8899
E-mail: ali.salim@cshs.org
Length: 5 Yrs   *ACGME Approved/Offered Positions:* 27
Program ID: 440-05-11-037

Kaiser Permanente Southern California (Los Angeles) Program
Sponsor: Kaiser Permanente Southern California
Kaiser Foundation Hospital (Los Angeles)
LAC+USC Medical Center
Prgm Director: J Craig Collins, MD, MBA
4760 Sunset Blvd, 3rd Floor
Department of Surgery
Los Angeles, CA 90027
Tel: 323 783-5442   *Fax:* 323 783-8747
E-mail: michelle.x.deangelis@kp.org
Length: 5 Yrs   *ACGME Approved/Offered Positions:* 23
Program ID: 440-05-12-038

UCLA Medical Center Program

Sponsor: UCLA David Geffen School of Medicine/UCLA
  Medical Center
Olive View/UCLA Medical Center
UCLA Medical Center
VA Greater Los Angeles Healthcare System
Prgm Director: O Joe Hines, MD
72-229 CHS
Box 951749
Los Angeles, CA 90095
Tel: 310 206-9291   *Fax:* 310 267-0369
E-mail: joehines@mednet.ucla.edu
Length: 5 Yrs   *ACGME Approved/Offered Positions:* 51
Program ID: 440-05-21-042

University of Southern California/
LAC+USC Medical Center Program

Sponsor: University of Southern California/LAC+USC
  Medical Center
LAC+USC Medical Center
USC University Hospital
Prgm Director: Jeffrey A Hagen, MD
1510 San Pablo Street, Suite 514
Los Angeles, CA 90033
Tel: 323 442-5759   *Fax:* 323 442-6887
Length: 5 Yrs   *ACGME Approved/Offered Positions:* 64
Program ID: 440-05-11-039

Orange

University of California (Irvine) Program

Sponsor: University of California (Irvine) Medical
  Center
Kaiser Foundation Hospitals (Anaheim)
VA Long Beach Healthcare System
Prgm Director: Matthew O Dolich, MD
Department of Surgery
333 City Blvd West Ste 705
Orange, CA 92868
Tel: 714 456-5890   *Fax:* 714 456-6048
Length: 5 Yrs   *ACGME Approved/Offered Positions:* 38
Program ID: 440-05-21-033

Pasadena

Huntington Memorial Hospital Program

Sponsor: Huntington Memorial Hospital
Prgm Director: Steven G Katz, MD
100 West California Boulevard
PO Box 7013
Pasadena, CA 91109
Tel: 626 397-5160   *Fax:* 626 397-2914
E-mail: jane.larkin@huntingtonhospital.com
Length: 5 Yrs   *ACGME Approved/Offered Positions:* 14
Program ID: 440-05-11-047

Sacramento

University of California (Davis) Health
System Program

Sponsor: University of California (Davis) Health System
Kaiser Foundation Hospital (Sacramento)
Kaiser Foundation Hospital (South Sacramento)
University of California (Davis) Medical Center
Prgm Director: Lynette A Scherer, MD
2315 Stockton Blvd
Room 6309
Sacramento, CA 95817
Tel: 916 734-2724   *Fax:* 916 734-5633
E-mail: gensurg.residency@ucdmc.ucdavis.edu
Length: 5 Yrs   *ACGME Approved/Offered Positions:* 63
Program ID: 440-05-21-031

San Diego

Naval Medical Center (San Diego)
Program

Sponsor: Naval Medical Center (San Diego)
Scripps Clinic/Scripps Green Hospital
Scripps Mercy Hospital
Prgm Director: Alexander B Chao, MD
34800 Bob Wilson Drive
San Diego, CA 92134
Tel: 619 532-9659   *Fax:* 619 532-7673
E-mail: venus.mendoza@med.navy.mil
Length: 5 Yrs   *ACGME Approved/Offered Positions:* 40
Program ID: 440-05-12-013
Uniformed Services Program

University of California (San Diego)
Program

Sponsor: University of California (San Diego) Medical
  Center
Veterans Affairs Medical Center (San Diego)
Prgm Director: David Easter, MD
9500 Gilman Dr, SOM Bldg 1
Mail Code 0739
La Jolla, CA 92093
Tel: 858 822-5604   *Fax:* 858 822-6994
E-mail: crunge@ucsd.edu
Length: 5 Yrs   *ACGME Approved/Offered Positions:* 46
Program ID: 440-05-21-048

San Francisco

University of California (San Francisco)
Program

Sponsor: University of California (San Francisco) School
  of Medicine
California Pacific Medical Center
San Francisco General Hospital Medical Center
UCSF and Mount Zion Medical Centers
Veterans Affairs Medical Center (San Francisco)
Prgm Director: Linda M Reilly, MD
Department of Surgery
513 Parnassus Avenue, Room S321
San Francisco, CA 94143
Tel: 415 476-1239   *Fax:* 415 502-1259
E-mail: educationoffice@ucsfmedicalcenter.org
Length: 5 Yrs   *ACGME Approved/Offered Positions:* 74
Program ID: 440-05-21-052

University of California San Francisco
(East Bay) Program

Sponsor: University of California (San Francisco) School
  of Medicine
Alameda County Medical Center
Kaiser Permanente Medical Center (Oakland)
Kaiser Permanente Medical Center (Walnut Creek)
Prgm Director: Terrence H Liu, MD
Department of Surgery
1411 East 31st Street
Oakland, CA 94602
Tel: 510 437-4718   *Fax:* 510 437-5017
Length: 5 Yrs   *ACGME Approved/Offered Positions:* 48
Program ID: 440-05-21-389

Santa Barbara

Santa Barbara Cottage Hospital Program

Sponsor: Santa Barbara Cottage Hospital
Prgm Director: Kenneth Waxman, MD
PO Box 689
Pueblo at Bath St
Santa Barbara, CA 93102
Tel: 805 569-7316   *Fax:* 805 569-7317
E-mail: Surged@sbch.org
Length: 5 Yrs   *ACGME Approved/Offered Positions:* 15
Program ID: 440-05-12-053

Stanford

Stanford University Program

Sponsor: Stanford Hospital and Clinics
Kaiser Permanente Medical Center (Santa Clara)
Santa Clara Valley Medical Center
Veterans Affairs Palo Alto Health Care System
Prgm Director: Ralph Greco, MD
300 Pasteur Drive, Suite H-3691
Stanford, CA 94305
Tel: 650 725-2181   *Fax:* 650 724-9806
E-mail: Anita.Hagan@stanford.edu
Length: 5 Yrs   *ACGME Approved/Offered Positions:* 57
Program ID: 440-05-21-054

Torrance

Los Angeles County-Harbor-UCLA
Medical Center Program

Sponsor: Los Angeles County-Harbor-UCLA Medical
  Center
Kaiser Permanente Medical Center (Harbor City)
Prgm Director: Christian M de Virgilio, MD
1000 West Carson Street
Box 461
Torrance, CA 90509
Tel: 310 222-2700   *Fax:* 310 533-1841
E-mail: kmiller@labiomed.org
Length: 5 Yrs   *ACGME Approved/Offered Positions:* 46
Program ID: 440-05-21-056

Colorado

Aurora

University of Colorado Denver Program

Sponsor: University of Colorado Denver School of
  Medicine
Denver Health Medical Center
University of Colorado Hospital
Veterans Affairs Medical Center (Denver)
Prgm Director: Mark R Nehler, MD
12631 E 17th Avenue
Campus Box C-302
Aurora, CO 80045
Tel: 303 724-2680
Length: 5 Yrs   *ACGME Approved/Offered Positions:* 58
Program ID: 440-07-21-058

Denver

Exempla St Joseph Hospital Program

Sponsor: Exempla St Joseph Hospital
Denver Health Medical Center
Prgm Director: John T Moore, MD
1835 Franklin Street
Denver, CO 80218
Tel: 303 837-7296   *Fax:* 303 866-8044
E-mail: moorejt@exempla.org
Length: 5 Yrs   *ACGME Approved/Offered Positions:* 28
Program ID: 440-07-22-057

Connecticut

Farmington

University of Connecticut Program

Sponsor: University of Connecticut School of Medicine
Hartford Hospital
St Francis Hospital and Medical Center
Prgm Director: Robert A Kozol, MD
Department of Surgery
263 Farmington Avenue
Farmington, CT 06030
Tel: 860 679-3467   *Fax:* 860 679-1460
Length: 5 Yrs   *ACGME Approved/Offered Positions:* 49
Program ID: 440-08-21-390

Note: * indicates a newly appointed program director

New Haven

Hospital of St Raphael Program
Sponsor: Hospital of St Raphael
Prgm Director: Geoffrey Nadzam, MD
1450 Chapel Street
New Haven, CT 06511
Tel: 203 789-3443   *Fax:* 203 867-5248
Length: 5 Yrs   *ACGME Approved/Offered Positions:* 24
Program ID: 440-08-21-063

Yale-New Haven Medical Center Program
Sponsor: Yale-New Haven Hospital
Bridgeport Hospital
Veterans Affairs Medical Center (West Haven)
Prgm Director: Walter E Longo, MD, MBA
Department of Surgery
333 Cedar Street
New Haven, CT 06520
Tel: 203 785-2616   *Fax:* 203 737-5209
Length: 5 Yrs   *ACGME Approved/Offered Positions:* 45
Program ID: 440-08-21-064

Stamford

Stamford Hospital/Columbia University College of Physicians and Surgeons Program
Sponsor: Stamford Hospital
Prgm Director: Timothy S Hall, MD
30 Shelburne Road
Stamford, CT 06904
Tel: 203 276-7470   *Fax:* 203 276-7089
Length: 5 Yrs   *ACGME Approved/Offered Positions:* 12
Program ID: 440-08-21-364

Waterbury

St Mary's Hospital (Waterbury) Program
Sponsor: St Mary's Hospital
Prgm Director: Michael S Ajemian, MD*
56 Franklin Street
Department of Surgery
Waterbury, CT 06706
Tel: 203 709-6479   *Fax:* 203 709-5877
Length: 5 Yrs   *ACGME Approved/Offered Positions:* 13
Program ID: 440-08-31-065

Waterbury Hospital Health Center Program
Sponsor: Waterbury Hospital Health Center
Prgm Director: Scott H Kurtzman, MD
64 Robbins St
Waterbury, CT 06708
Tel: 203 573-7257   *Fax:* 203 573-6073
E-mail: skurtzman@wtbyhosp.org
Length: 5 Yrs   *ACGME Approved/Offered Positions:* 12
Program ID: 440-08-11-066

Delaware

Wilmington

Christiana Care Health Services Program
Sponsor: Christiana Care Health Services Inc
Prgm Director: Frederick Giberson, MD
4735 Ogletown-Stanton Road
Suite 2121, MAP-2
Newark, DE 19713
Tel: 302 733-4503   *Fax:* 302 733-4513
E-mail: fgiberson@christianacare.org
Length: 5 Yrs   *ACGME Approved/Offered Positions:* 26
Program ID: 440-09-11-067

District of Columbia

Washington

George Washington University Program
Sponsor: George Washington University School of Medicine
George Washington University Hospital (UHS)
Holy Cross Hospital of Silver Spring
Veterans Affairs Medical Center (Washington, DC)
Prgm Director: Paul Lin, MD
Mail Stop AN6B426
2150 Pennsylvania Avenue, NW
Washington, DC 20037
Tel: 202 741-3151   *Fax:* 202 741-3219
E-mail: surmbn@gwumc.edu
Length: 5 Yrs   *ACGME Approved/Offered Positions:* 27
Program ID: 440-10-21-069

Georgetown University Hospital Program
Sponsor: Georgetown University Hospital
Virginia Hospital Center-Arlington
Washington Hospital Center
Prgm Director: A Alfred Chahine, MD*
3800 Reservoir Road NW (3 PHC)
Department of Surgery, Office of Education
Washington, DC 20007
Tel: 202 444-3534   *Fax:* 202 444-7039
E-mail: aac4@gunet.georgetown.edu
Length: 5 Yrs   *ACGME Approved/Offered Positions:* 34
Program ID: 440-10-21-068

Howard University Program
Sponsor: Howard University Hospital
Providence Hospital
Prgm Director: Debra H Ford, MD
Department of Surgery
2041 Georgia Avenue, NW, Room 4-B17
Washington, DC 20060
Tel: 202 865-1446   *Fax:* 202 865-1666
E-mail: berharris@howard.edu
Length: 5 Yrs   *ACGME Approved/Offered Positions:* 33
Program ID: 440-10-21-070

Washington Hospital Center Program
Sponsor: Washington Hospital Center
Prgm Director: Lisa M Boyle, MD*
110 Irving St, NW
Suite G253
Washington, DC 20010
Tel: 202 877-5611   *Fax:* 202 877-3699
Length: 5 Yrs   *ACGME Approved/Offered Positions:* 41
Program ID: 440-10-31-071

Florida

Gainesville

University of Florida Program
Sponsor: University of Florida College of Medicine
North Florida/South Georgia Veterans Health System
Shands Hospital at the University of Florida
Prgm Director: Kevin E Behrns, MD
Department of Surgery
PO Box 100286
Gainesville, FL 32610
Tel: 352 265-0761   *Fax:* 352 265-3292
Length: 5 Yrs   *ACGME Approved/Offered Positions:* 45
Program ID: 440-11-21-072

Jacksonville

College of Medicine, Mayo Clinic (Jacksonville) Program
Sponsor: College of Medicine, Mayo Clinic
Mayo Clinic (Jacksonville)
Prgm Director: C Daniel Smith, MD
4500 San Pablo Road
Jacksonville, FL 32224
Tel: 904 953-0423   *Fax:* 904 953-0430
E-mail: bishop.melissa@mayo.edu
Length: 5 Yrs   *ACGME Approved/Offered Positions:* 13
Program ID: 440-11-21-405

University of Florida College of Medicine Jacksonville Program
Sponsor: University of Florida College of Medicine Jacksonville
Shands Jacksonville Medical Center
Prgm Director: Michael S Nussbaum, MD*
Department of Surgery, Box FC12
653 W 8th St, 3rd Floor Faculty Clinic
Jacksonville, FL 32209
Tel: 904 244-5502   *Fax:* 904 244-6252
E-mail: michael.nussbaum@jax.ufl.edu
Length: 5 Yrs   *ACGME Approved/Offered Positions:* 28
Program ID: 440-11-21-073

Miami

Jackson Memorial Hospital/Jackson Health System Program
Sponsor: Jackson Memorial Hospital/Jackson Health System
Veterans Affairs Medical Center (Miami)
Prgm Director: Danny Sleeman, MD
Department of Surgery, R310
PO Box 016310
Miami, FL 33101
Tel: 305 585-1280   *Fax:* 305 585-6043
E-mail: TSpencer@med.miami.edu
Length: 5 Yrs   *ACGME Approved/Offered Positions:* 54
Program ID: 440-11-21-074

Miami Beach

Mount Sinai Medical Center of Florida Program
Sponsor: Mount Sinai Medical Center of Florida, Inc
Memorial Regional Hospital
Prgm Director: Thomas W Mesko, MD
4300 Alton Road
Miami Beach, FL 33140
Tel: 305 695-1255   *Fax:* 305 674-2781
Length: 5 Yrs   *ACGME Approved/Offered Positions:* 16
Program ID: 440-11-22-075

Orlando

Florida Hospital Medical Center Program
Sponsor: Florida Hospital Medical Center
University of South Florida College of Medicine
Prgm Director: Joseph Portoghese, MD
2501 North Orange Avenue
Suite 411
Orlando, FL 32804
Tel: 407 303-7203   *Fax:* 407 303-2469
E-mail: katherine.newsum@flhosp.org
Length: 5 Yrs   *ACGME Approved/Offered Positions:* 10
Program ID: 440-11-12-416

Orlando Health Program

Sponsor: Orlando Health
M D Anderson Cancer Center Orlando
Orlando Regional Medical Center
Prgm Director: Mark L Friedell, MD
c/o Department of Surgical Education
86 W Underwood Street, Suite 201, MP 100
Orlando, FL 32806
Tel: 407 841-5142   *Fax:* 407 648-3686
Length: 5 Yrs   *ACGME Approved/Offered Positions:* 26
Program ID: 440-11-11-076

Tampa

University of South Florida Program

Sponsor: University of South Florida College of Medicine
H Lee Moffitt Cancer Center
James A Haley Veterans Hospital
Tampa General Hospital
Prgm Director: Charles N Paidas, MD, MBA
12901 Bruce B Downs Blvd
MDC Box 16
Tampa, FL 33612
Tel: 813 974-6159   *Fax:* 813 974-8106
E-mail: wmccrore@health.usf.edu
Length: 5 Yrs   *ACGME Approved/Offered Positions:* 39
Program ID: 440-11-31-078

Georgia

Atlanta

Atlanta Medical Center Program

Sponsor: Atlanta Medical Center
Piedmont Fayette Hospital
Prgm Director: George M Fuhrman, MD
303 Parkway Drive, NE
Dept of Surgery, Box 423
Atlanta, GA 30312
Tel: 404 265-4411   *Fax:* 404 265-4989
E-mail: amcgensurg@gmail.com
Length: 5 Yrs   *ACGME Approved/Offered Positions:* 16
Program ID: 440-12-22-080

Emory University Program

Sponsor: Emory University School of Medicine
Emory University Hospital
Grady Health System
Piedmont Hospital
Prgm Director: Thomas F Dodson, MD
H120 Emory Hospital
1364 Clifton Road, NE
Atlanta, GA 30322
Tel: 404 727-0093   *Fax:* 404 712-0561
E-mail: lynda.watts@emory.edu
Length: 5 Yrs   *ACGME Approved/Offered Positions:* 70
Program ID: 440-12-21-079

Morehouse School of Medicine Program

Sponsor: Morehouse School of Medicine
Grady Health System
Prgm Director: William L Weaver, MD
720 Westview Drive SW
Atlanta, GA 30310
Tel: 404 616-1424   *Fax:* 404 616-6281
Length: 5 Yrs   *ACGME Approved/Offered Positions:* 22
Program ID: 440-12-21-397

Augusta

Medical College of Georgia Program

Sponsor: Medical College of Georgia
Veterans Affairs Medical Center (Augusta)
Prgm Director: John D Mellinger, MD
General Surgery BI-4070
1120 15th Street
Augusta, GA 30912
Tel: 706 721-1423   *Fax:* 706 721-1047
E-mail: jmellinger@mcg.edu
Length: 5 Yrs   *ACGME Approved/Offered Positions:* 28
Program ID: 440-12-31-082

Fort Gordon

Dwight David Eisenhower Army Medical Center Program

Sponsor: Dwight David Eisenhower Army Medical Center
Prgm Director: Peter J Armstrong, MD
Bldg 300, Hospital Rd, General Surgery Service
Fort Gordon, GA 30905
Tel: 706 787-2567   *Fax:* 706 787-2347
E-mail: peter.armstrong@amedd.army.mil
Length: 5 Yrs   *ACGME Approved/Offered Positions:* 18
Program ID: 440-12-21-365
Uniformed Services Program

Macon

Mercer University School of Medicine Program

Sponsor: Medical Center of Central Georgia
Prgm Director: Don K Nakayama, MD, MBA
General Surgery Residency
777 Hemlock Street, Hospital Box #140
Macon, GA 31201
Tel: 478 633-1367   *Fax:* 478 633-5153
E-mail: nakayama.don@mccg.org
Length: 5 Yrs   *ACGME Approved/Offered Positions:* 20
Program ID: 440-12-21-083

Savannah

Mercer University School of Medicine (Savannah) Program

Sponsor: Memorial Health-University Medical Center
Prgm Director: Steven Brower, MD
4700 Waters Avenue, 2nd Floor, GA Ear Institute
Savannah, GA 31404
Tel: 912 350-5900   *Fax:* 912 350-5984
E-mail: browest1@memorialhealth.com
Length: 5 Yrs   *ACGME Approved/Offered Positions:* 15
Program ID: 440-12-31-084

Hawaii

Honolulu

University of Hawaii Program

Sponsor: University of Hawaii John A Burns School of Medicine
Kuakini Medical Center
Queen's Medical Center
Straub Clinic & Hospital
Prgm Director: Danny M Takanishi Jr, MD
1356 Lusitana Street, Sixth Floor
Honolulu, HI 96813
Tel: 808 586-2920   *Fax:* 808 586-3022
E-mail: surgery@hawaii.edu
Length: 5 Yrs   *ACGME Approved/Offered Positions:* 29
Program ID: 440-14-21-085

Tripler AMC

Tripler Army Medical Center Program

Sponsor: Tripler Army Medical Center
Kaiser Foundation Hospital (Moanalua)
Prgm Director: Ronald A Gagliano Jr, MD
Department of Surgery (Attn: MCHK-DSG)
1 Jarrett White Road
Tripler AMC, HI 96859
Tel: 808 433-3435   *Fax:* 808 433-6539
Length: 5 Yrs   *ACGME Approved/Offered Positions:* 25
Program ID: 440-14-12-008
Uniformed Services Program

Illinois

Chicago

McGaw Medical Center of Northwestern University Program

Sponsor: McGaw Medical Center of Northwestern University
Evanston Hospital
Jesse Brown Veterans Affairs Medical Center
Northwestern Memorial Hospital
Prgm Director: Nathaniel J Soper, MD
McGaw Medical Center - Galter 3-150
251 E Huron Street
Chicago, IL 60611
Tel: 312 926-4962   *Fax:* 312 926-7404
E-mail: nsoper@nmh.org
Length: 5 Yrs   *ACGME Approved/Offered Positions:* 53
Program ID: 440-16-21-091

Rush University Medical Center Program

Sponsor: Rush University Medical Center
John H Stroger Hospital of Cook County
Prgm Director: Richard A Prinz, MD
1653 West Congress Parkway
Suite 785 Jelke
Chicago, IL 60612
Tel: 312 942-6379   *Fax:* 312 942-2867
Length: 5 Yrs   *ACGME Approved/Offered Positions:* 63
Program ID: 440-16-21-092

St Joseph Hospital Program

Sponsor: St Joseph Hospital
Northwestern Memorial Hospital
Prgm Director: Mark M Connolly, MD
2900 N Lake Shore Drive
Chicago, IL 60657
Tel: 773 665-6237   *Fax:* 773 665-6232
Length: 5 Yrs   *ACGME Approved/Offered Positions:* 8
Program ID: 440-16-31-086

University of Chicago Program

Sponsor: University of Chicago Medical Center
Evanston Hospital
John H Stroger Hospital of Cook County
MacNeal Hospital
Prgm Director: Mitchell Posner, MD
5841 South Maryland Avenue, MC-5031
Chicago, IL 60637
Tel: 773 834-0156   *Fax:* 773 702-2140
E-mail: cbarr@surgery.bsd.uchicago.edu
Length: 5 Yrs   *ACGME Approved/Offered Positions:* 42
Program ID: 440-16-11-094

University of Illinois College of Medicine at Chicago (Mount Sinai) Program

Sponsor: University of Illinois College of Medicine at Chicago
Mount Sinai Hospital Medical Center of Chicago
Northwestern Memorial Hospital
Prgm Director: Stephen R Wise, MD
Mount Sinai Medical Center
California Avenue at 15th Street
Chicago, IL 60608
Tel: 773 257-6710   *Fax:* 773 257-6548
Length: 5 Yrs   *ACGME Approved/Offered Positions:* 24
Program ID: 440-16-21-385

Note: * indicates a newly appointed program director

University of Illinois College of Medicine at Chicago Program

Sponsor: University of Illinois College of Medicine at Chicago
Advocate Christ Medical Center
Jesse Brown Veterans Affairs Medical Center
University of Illinois Hospital and Clinics
Prgm Director: Gary J Merlotti, MD*
Department of Surgery, M/C 958
840 S Wood Street, Room 518E
Chicago, IL 60612
Tel: 312 996-6765   *Fax:* 312 996-1214
Length: 5 Yrs   *ACGME Approved/Offered Positions:* 46
Program ID: 440-16-21-395

University of Illinois College of Medicine at Chicago/Metropolitan Group Hospitals Program

Sponsor: University of Illinois College of Medicine at Chicago
Advocate Illinois Masonic Medical Center
Advocate Lutheran General Hospital
Mercy Hospital and Medical Center
St Francis Hospital
Prgm Director: Vijay K Maker, MD
Advocate Illinois Masonic Medical Center
836 West Wellington, Room 4807
Chicago, IL 60657
Tel: 773 296-7093   *Fax:* 773 296-5570
E-mail: Helen.Cereceda@advocatehealth.com
Length: 5 Yrs   *ACGME Approved/Offered Positions:* 42
Program ID: 440-16-31-096

Maywood

Loyola University Program

Sponsor: Loyola University Medical Center
Edward Hines, Jr Veterans Affairs Hospital
Prgm Director: Raymond J Joehl, MD
Department of Surgery
2160 South First Avenue
Maywood, IL 60153
Tel: 708 327-2335   *Fax:* 708 327-3489
Length: 5 Yrs   *ACGME Approved/Offered Positions:* 49
Program ID: 440-16-21-099

Peoria

University of Illinois College of Medicine at Peoria Program

Sponsor: University of Illinois College of Medicine at Peoria
OSF St Francis Medical Center
Prgm Director: Norman C Estes, MD
Department of Surgery
624 NE Glen Oak, North Bldg 2nd Floor
Peoria, IL 61603
Tel: 309 655-2383   *Fax:* 309 655-3630
E-mail: lconlee@uic.edu
Length: 5 Yrs   *ACGME Approved/Offered Positions:* 16
Program ID: 440-16-21-101

Springfield

Southern Illinois University Program

Sponsor: Southern Illinois University School of Medicine
Memorial Medical Center
St John's Hospital
Prgm Director: Edward J Alfrey, MD
800 N Rutledge
PO Box 19638
Springfield, IL 62794
Tel: 217 545-8873   *Fax:* 217 545-2529
E-mail: bcarter@siumed.edu
Length: 5 Yrs   *ACGME Approved/Offered Positions:* 26
Program ID: 440-16-21-102

Indiana

Indianapolis

Indiana University School of Medicine Program

Sponsor: Indiana University School of Medicine
Clarian Indiana University Hospital
Clarian Methodist Hospital of Indiana
Richard L Roudebush Veterans Affairs Medical Center
William N Wishard Memorial Hospital
Prgm Director: Keith D Lillemoe, MD
Department of Surgery
545 Barnhill Drive, Emerson Hall 203
Indianapolis, IN 46202
Tel: 317 274-4966   *Fax:* 317 274-8769
Length: 5 Yrs   *ACGME Approved/Offered Positions:* 65
Program ID: 440-17-21-103

Iowa

Des Moines

Central Iowa Health System (Iowa Methodist Medical Center) Program

Sponsor: Central Iowa Health System (Iowa Methodist/Iowa Lutheran)
Broadlawns Medical Center
Veterans Affairs Central Iowa Health Care System
Prgm Director: Richard A Sidwell, MD
1415 Woodland Avenue
Suite 140
Des Moines, IA 50309
Tel: 515 241-4034   *Fax:* 515 241-4080
E-mail: sidwelra@ihs.org
Length: 5 Yrs   *ACGME Approved/Offered Positions:* 19
Program ID: 440-18-22-105

Iowa City

University of Iowa Hospitals and Clinics Program

Sponsor: University of Iowa Hospitals and Clinics
Veterans Affairs Medical Center (Iowa City)
Prgm Director: William J Sharp, MD
Department of Surgery
200 Hawkins Drive, 1516 JCP
Iowa City, IA 52242
Tel: 319 356-1907   *Fax:* 319 384-6306
Length: 5 Yrs   *ACGME Approved/Offered Positions:* 36
Program ID: 440-18-21-107

Kansas

Kansas City

University of Kansas School of Medicine Program

Sponsor: University of Kansas School of Medicine
University of Kansas Hospital
Prgm Director: Kurt P Schropp, MD
Room 4941 Murphy (1048 Olathe during renovation)
3901 Rainbow Blvd, MS 1037
Kansas City, KS 66160
Tel: 913 588-6124   *Fax:* 913 588-6195
E-mail: klaurie@kumc.edu
Length: 5 Yrs   *ACGME Approved/Offered Positions:* 23
Program ID: 440-19-21-108

Wichita

University of Kansas (Wichita) Program

Sponsor: University of Kansas School of Medicine (Wichita)
Via Christi Regional Medical Center-St Francis
Wesley Medical Center
Prgm Director: Jacqueline S Osland, MD
Department of Surgery
929 North St Francis, Room 3082
Wichita, KS 67214
Tel: 316 268-5990   *Fax:* 316 291-7662
E-mail: dawn_fountain@via-christi.org
Length: 5 Yrs   *ACGME Approved/Offered Positions:* 32
Program ID: 440-19-21-387

Kentucky

Lexington

University of Kentucky College of Medicine Program

Sponsor: University of Kentucky College of Medicine
University of Kentucky Hospital
Veterans Affairs Medical Center (Lexington)
Prgm Director: Eric D Endean, MD
General Surgery
800 Rose Street, C215
Lexington, KY 40536
Tel: 859 323-6346   *Fax:* 859 323-6840
Length: 5 Yrs   *ACGME Approved/Offered Positions:* 47
Program ID: 440-20-21-112

Louisville

University of Louisville Program

Sponsor: University of Louisville School of Medicine
Jewish Hospital
Kosair Children's Hospital (Norton Healthcare, Inc)
Norton Hospital
University of Louisville Hospital
Veterans Affairs Medical Center (Louisville)
Prgm Director: William G Cheadle, MD
Department of Surgery
Health Sciences Center
Louisville, KY 40292
Tel: 502 852-6191   *Fax:* 502 852-8915
Length: 5 Yrs   *ACGME Approved/Offered Positions:* 44
Program ID: 440-20-21-113

Louisiana

New Orleans

Louisiana State University Program

Sponsor: Louisiana State University School of Medicine
Earl K Long Medical Center
Medical Center of Louisiana at New Orleans
Our Lady of the Lake Regional Medical Center
University Medical Center (Lafayette)
West Jefferson Medical Center
Prgm Director: John Hunt, MD, MPH
1542 Tulane Avenue
Room 734
New Orleans, LA 70112
Tel: 504 568-4760   *Fax:* 504 568-4633
E-mail: jhunt2@lsuhsc.edu
Length: 5 Yrs   *ACGME Approved/Offered Positions:* 58
Program ID: 440-21-21-114

Programs

Ochsner Clinic Foundation Program
Sponsor: Ochsner Clinic Foundation
Leonard J Chabert Medical Center
Prgm Director: John S Bolton, MD
Department of Surgery
1514 Jefferson Highway
New Orleans, LA 70121
Tel: 504 842-4070   *Fax:* 504 842-3124
E-mail: dladmirault@ochsner.org
Length: 5 Yrs   *ACGME Approved/Offered Positions:* 30
Program ID: 440-21-22-115

Tulane University Program
Sponsor: Tulane University School of Medicine
East Jefferson General Hospital
Tulane University Hospital and Clinics
Prgm Director: James Korndorffer, Jr, MD
1430 Tulane Avenue
Deapartment of Surgery SL22
New Orleans, LA 70112
Tel: 504 988-2306   *Fax:* 504 988-1882
Length: 5 Yrs   *ACGME Approved/Offered Positions:* 21
Program ID: 440-21-21-423

Shreveport

Louisiana State University (Shreveport) Program
Sponsor: LSU Health Sciences Center-University
   Hospital
E A Conway Medical Center
Overton Brooks Veterans Affairs Medical Center
Prgm Director: Donnie F Aultman, MD
1501 Kings Highway
PO Box 33932
Shreveport, LA 71130
Tel: 318 675-6111   *Fax:* 318 675-6141
Length: 5 Yrs   *ACGME Approved/Offered Positions:* 30
Program ID: 440-21-21-117

Maine

Portland

Maine Medical Center Program
Sponsor: Maine Medical Center
Prgm Director: James F Whiting, MD*
Department of Surgery
22 Bramhall Street
Portland, ME 04102
Tel: 207 662-2921   *Fax:* 207 662-6389
E-mail: camerj@mmc.org
Length: 5 Yrs   *ACGME Approved/Offered Positions:* 22
Program ID: 440-22-21-119

Maryland

Baltimore

Johns Hopkins University Program
Sponsor: Johns Hopkins University School of Medicine
Johns Hopkins Bayview Medical Center
Johns Hopkins Hospital
Prgm Director: Pamela A Lipsett, MD
600 North Wolfe Street
655 Blalock
Baltimore, MD 21287
Tel: 410 955-3739   *Fax:* 410 614-9083
Length: 5 Yrs   *ACGME Approved/Offered Positions:* 48
Program ID: 440-23-21-392

Sinai Hospital of Baltimore Program
Sponsor: Sinai Hospital of Baltimore
Prgm Director: Adrian Barbul, MD
2435 W Belvedere Avenue
Hoffberger Professional Building, Suite 42
Baltimore, MD 21215
Tel: 410 601-6412   *Fax:* 410 601-5835
E-mail: jsturdiv@lifebridgehealth.org
Length: 5 Yrs   *ACGME Approved/Offered Positions:* 10
Program ID: 440-23-21-417

St Agnes HealthCare Program
Sponsor: St Agnes Hospital
Prgm Director: Gavin L Henry, MD
900 Caton Avenue
Department of Surgery, Box 207
Baltimore, MD 21229
Tel: 410 368-2730   *Fax:* 410 951-4007
E-mail: ghenry1@stagnes.org
Length: 5 Yrs   *ACGME Approved/Offered Positions:* 20
Program ID: 440-23-22-123

Union Memorial Hospital Program
Sponsor: Union Memorial Hospital
Franklin Square Hospital Center
Prgm Director: Richard F Heitmiller, MD
201 E University Parkway
Baltimore, MD 21218
Tel: 410 554-2063   *Fax:* 410 554-2299
E-mail: Richard.Heitmiller@medstar.net
Length: 5 Yrs   *ACGME Approved/Offered Positions:* 19
Program ID: 440-23-21-127

University of Maryland Program
Sponsor: University of Maryland Medical System
Mercy Medical Center
Veterans Affairs Medical Center (Baltimore)
Prgm Director: Patricia L Turner, MD*
22 South Greene Street
Baltimore, MD 21201
Tel: 410 328-6187   *Fax:* 410 328-5919
E-mail: pturner@smail.umaryland.edu
Length: 5 Yrs   *ACGME Approved/Offered Positions:* 46
Program ID: 440-23-21-128

Bethesda

National Capital Consortium (Bethesda) Program
Sponsor: National Capital Consortium
National Naval Medical Center (Bethesda)
Prgm Director: Philip W Perdue, MD, MPH
Department of General Surgery
8901 Wisconsin Avenue
Bethesda, MD 20889
Tel: 301 295-4435   *Fax:* 301 295-0959
E-mail: philip.perdue@med.navy.mil
Length: 5 Yrs   *ACGME Approved/Offered Positions:* 23
Program ID: 440-23-21-014
Uniformed Services Program

National Capital Consortium Program
Sponsor: National Capital Consortium
Walter Reed Army Medical Center
Prgm Director: COL MC Craig D Shriver, MD
Heaton Pavilion, General Surgery Service/5C
6900 Geogia Avenue NW
Washington, DC 20307
Tel: 202 782-3418   *Fax:* 202 782-4260
E-mail: craig.shriver@us.army.mil
Length: 5 Yrs   *ACGME Approved/Offered Positions:* 26
Program ID: 440-10-11-007
Uniformed Services Program

Massachusetts

Boston

Beth Israel Deaconess Medical Center Program
Sponsor: Beth Israel Deaconess Medical Center
St Vincent Hospital
Prgm Director: Scott Johnson, MD
110 Francis Street, Suite 9B
Boston, MA 02215
Tel: 617 632-9236   *Fax:* 617 632-7424
E-mail: surgedu@bidmc.harvard.edu
Length: 5 Yrs   *ACGME Approved/Offered Positions:* 75
Program ID: 440-24-31-409

Boston University Medical Center Program
Sponsor: Boston Medical Center
Veterans Affairs Medical Center (Boston)
Prgm Director: James G Petros, MD, MPH
Boston Medical Center
88 E Newton St, Room C515
Boston, MA 02118
Tel: 617 638-8442   *Fax:* 617 638-8409
Length: 5 Yrs   *ACGME Approved/Offered Positions:* 45
Program ID: 440-24-21-131

Brigham and Women's Hospital Program
Sponsor: Brigham and Women's Hospital
Prgm Director: Stanley W Ashley, MD
75 Francis Street
CA-034
Boston, MA 02115
Tel: 617 732-6730   *Fax:* 617 739-1728
E-mail: surgeryeducation@partners.org
Length: 5 Yrs   *ACGME Approved/Offered Positions:* 53
Program ID: 440-24-21-135

Caritas St Elizabeth's Medical Center Program
Sponsor: Caritas St Elizabeth's Medical Center of
   Boston
Good Samaritan Medical Center-Cushing Campus
Prgm Director: Alan Hackford, MD
736 Cambridge St
Boston, MA 02135
Tel: 617 789-2990   *Fax:* 617 789-3419
E-mail: vincenza.gelardi@caritaschristi.org
Length: 5 Yrs   *ACGME Approved/Offered Positions:* 23
Program ID: 440-24-21-136

Massachusetts General Hospital Program
Sponsor: Massachusetts General Hospital
Salem Hospital
Prgm Director: Charles M Ferguson, MD
Surgical Residency Office
55 Fruit Street, GRB 425
Boston, MA 02114
Tel: 617 726-2800   *Fax:* 617 724-3499
Length: 5 Yrs   *ACGME Approved/Offered Positions:* 58
Program ID: 440-24-31-132

Tufts Medical Center Program
Sponsor: Tufts Medical Center
Prgm Director: Jeffrey T Cooper, MD
800 Washington Street
Box 437
Boston, MA 02111
Tel: 617 636-5891   *Fax:* 617 636-5498
E-mail: acerulli@tuftsmedicalcenter.org
Length: 5 Yrs   *ACGME Approved/Offered Positions:* 21
Program ID: 440-24-21-134

Note: * indicates a newly appointed program director

Burlington

Lahey Clinic Program
Sponsor: Lahey Clinic
Prgm Director: Harold J Welch, MD
41 Mall Road
Burlington, MA 01805
Tel: 781 744-8193 *Fax:* 781 744-5744
E-mail: harold.j.welch@lahey.org
Length: 5 Yrs *ACGME Approved/Offered Positions:* 19
Program ID: 440-24-21-401

Pittsfield

Berkshire Medical Center Program
Sponsor: Berkshire Medical Center
Prgm Director: Timothy Counihan, MD
Surgical Residency Education
725 North Street
Pittsfield, MA 01201
Tel: 413 447-2741 *Fax:* 413 447-2766
E-mail: tcounihan@bhs1.org
Length: 5 Yrs *ACGME Approved/Offered Positions:* 14
Program ID: 440-24-31-137

Springfield

Baystate Medical Center/Tufts University School of Medicine Program
Sponsor: Baystate Medical Center
Prgm Director: Richard B Wait, MD, PhD
759 Chestnut Street
Springfield, MA 01199
Tel: 413 794-5165 *Fax:* 413 794-1835
E-mail: joy.isotti@bhs.org
Length: 5 Yrs *ACGME Approved/Offered Positions:* 31
Program ID: 440-24-11-138

Worcester

University of Massachusetts Program
Sponsor: University of Massachusetts Medical School
UMass Memorial Health Care (Memorial Campus)
UMass Memorial Health Care (University Campus)
Prgm Director: Anne C Larkin, MD
55 Lake Avenue North
Department of Surgery
Worcester, MA 01655
Tel: 508 856-3744 *Fax:* 508 334-3306
Length: 5 Yrs *ACGME Approved/Offered Positions:* 43
Program ID: 440-24-21-139

Michigan

Ann Arbor

St Joseph Mercy Hospital Program
Sponsor: St Joseph Mercy Hospital
Prgm Director: John C Eggenberger, MD*
PO Box 995
RHB-2111
Ann Arbor, MI 48106
Tel: 734 712-7352 *Fax:* 734 712-2054
Length: 5 Yrs *ACGME Approved/Offered Positions:* 23
Program ID: 440-25-11-140

University of Michigan Program
Sponsor: University of Michigan Hospitals and Health Centers
Foote Hospital, Inc
St Joseph Mercy Hospital
Veterans Affairs Medical Center (Ann Arbor)
Prgm Director: Gerard M Doherty, MD
2207 Taubman Center
1500 E Medical Center Drive
Ann Arbor, MI 48109
Tel: 734 615-4741 *Fax:* 734 936-5725
E-mail: UMHS-surgery.education@med.umich.edu
Length: 5 Yrs *ACGME Approved/Offered Positions:* 39
Program ID: 440-25-21-141

Detroit

Henry Ford Hospital Program
Sponsor: Henry Ford Hospital
Prgm Director: Ann Woodward, MD*
Department of Surgery
2799 W Grand Blvd
Detroit, MI 48202
Tel: 313 916-3657
Length: 5 Yrs *ACGME Approved/Offered Positions:* 37
Program ID: 440-25-12-143

St John Hospital and Medical Center Program
Sponsor: St John Hospital and Medical Center
Prgm Director: Elango Edhayan, MD*
22151 Moross Road, PBI Suite 332
Detroit, MI 48236
Tel: 313 343-7849 *Fax:* 313 343-7378
E-mail: elango.edhayan@stjohn.org
Length: 5 Yrs *ACGME Approved/Offered Positions:* 26
Program ID: 440-25-11-145

Wayne State University/Detroit Medical Center Program
Sponsor: Wayne State University/Detroit Medical Center
Detroit Receiving Hospital and University Health Center
Harper-Hutzel Hospital
Prgm Director: James G Tyburski, MD
6C University Health Center
4201 St Antoine
Detroit, MI 48201
Tel: 313 745-3487 *Fax:* 313 577-5310
E-mail: surgery@med.wayne.edu
Length: 5 Yrs *ACGME Approved/Offered Positions:* 54
Program ID: 440-25-21-148

Grand Rapids

Grand Rapids Medical Education and Research Center/Michigan State University Program
Sponsor: Grand Rapids Medical Education and Research Center
Saint Mary's Health Care (Grand Rapids)
Spectrum Health-Blodgett Hospital
Spectrum Health-Butterworth Hospital
Prgm Director: Marc G Schlatter, MD
221 Michigan Street, NE
Suite 200A
Grand Rapids, MI 49503
Tel: 616 391-1405 *Fax:* 616 391-8611
E-mail: marc.schlatter@spectrum-health.org
Length: 5 Yrs *ACGME Approved/Offered Positions:* 43
Program ID: 440-25-21-410

Kalamazoo

Kalamazoo Center for Medical Studies/Michigan State University Program
Sponsor: Michigan State Univ/Kalamazoo Center for Medical Studies
Borgess Medical Center
Bronson Methodist Hospital
Prgm Director: Michael K McLeod, MD
Department of Surgery
1000 Oakland Drive
Kalamazoo, MI 49008
Tel: 269 337-6260 *Fax:* 269 337-6441
E-mail: gensurg@kcms.msu.edu
Length: 5 Yrs *ACGME Approved/Offered Positions:* 14
Program ID: 440-25-21-400

Lansing

Michigan State University Program
Sponsor: Michigan State University College of Human Medicine
McLaren Regional Medical Center
Sparrow Hospital
Prgm Director: Andrew Saxe, MD*
1200 East Michigan Ave, Suite 655
Lansing, MI 48912
Tel: 517 267-2480 *Fax:* 517 267-2488
Length: 5 Yrs *ACGME Approved/Offered Positions:* 26
Program ID: 440-25-21-386

Pontiac

St Joseph Mercy-Oakland Program
Sponsor: St Joseph Mercy-Oakland
Prgm Director: Robert B Robinson, MD
44405 Woodward Avenue
Pontiac, MI 48341
Tel: 248 858-3234 *Fax:* 248 858-3244
Length: 5 Yrs *ACGME Approved/Offered Positions:* 14
Program ID: 440-25-11-157

Royal Oak

William Beaumont Hospital Program
Sponsor: William Beaumont Hospital
Prgm Director: Charles J Shanley, MD
3601 West 13 Mile Road
Royal Oak, MI 48073
Tel: 248 551-0424 *Fax:* 248 551-5426
E-mail: kcharbeneau@beaumonthospitals.com
Length: 5 Yrs *ACGME Approved/Offered Positions:* 33
Program ID: 440-25-12-158

Saginaw

Synergy Medical Education Alliance Program
Sponsor: Synergy Medical Education Alliance
Covenant HealthCare System-Cooper Campus
Covenant HealthCare System-Harrison Campus
St Mary's of Michigan
Prgm Director: Dennis A Boysen, MD
1000 Houghton, Rm 2061
Saginaw, MI 48602
Tel: 989 583-6827 *Fax:* 989 583-6989
E-mail: kotoole@synergymedical.org
Length: 5 Yrs *ACGME Approved/Offered Positions:* 10
Program ID: 440-25-21-159

Southfield

Providence Hospital and Medical Centers Program
Sponsor: Providence Hospital and Medical Centers
Prgm Director: Vijay K Mittal, MD
16001 West Nine Mile Road
Department of Surgery
Southfield, MI 48075
Tel: 248 849-3073 *Fax:* 248 849-5380
E-mail: Vijay.Mittal@providence-stjohnhealth.org
Length: 5 Yrs *ACGME Approved/Offered Positions:* 24
Program ID: 440-25-21-160

Programs

Minnesota

Minneapolis

Hennepin County Medical Center Program

Sponsor: Hennepin County Medical Center
Abbott-Northwestern Hospital/Allina Health System
Prgm Director: Joan M Van Camp, MD
701 Park Avenue South
Minneapolis, MN 55415
Tel: 612 873-2849   *Fax:* 612 904-4297
E-mail: phyllis.squiers@hcmed.org
Length: 5 Yrs   *ACGME Approved/Offered Positions:* 28
Program ID: 440-26-11-161

University of Minnesota Program

Sponsor: University of Minnesota Medical School
Methodist Hospital
Regions Hospital
University of Minnesota Medical Center, Division of
   Fairview
Prgm Director: Michael A Maddaus, MD
11-134 Phillips-Wangensteen Bldg
516 Delaware Street, SE, MMC 195
Minneapolis, MN 55455
Tel: 612 625-6483   *Fax:* 612 625-4411
E-mail: larso051@tc.umn.edu
Length: 5 Yrs   *ACGME Approved/Offered Positions:* 48
Program ID: 440-26-31-162

Rochester

College of Medicine, Mayo Clinic (Rochester) Program

Sponsor: College of Medicine, Mayo Clinic
Mayo Clinic (Rochester)
Rochester Methodist Hospital
Saint Marys Hospital of Rochester
Prgm Director: David R Farley, MD
200 First Street SW
Rochester, MN 55905
Tel: 507 284-8240   *Fax:* 507 538-7288
Length: 5 Yrs   *ACGME Approved/Offered Positions:* 83
Program ID: 440-26-21-163

Mississippi

Jackson

University of Mississippi Medical Center Program

Sponsor: University of Mississippi School of Medicine
University Hospitals and Clinics
Veterans Affairs Medical Center (Jackson)
Prgm Director: William H Barber IV, MD, PhD
2500 N State Street, L130
Jackson, MS 39216
Tel: 601 984-5080   *Fax:* 601 984-5110
E-mail: wbarber@surgery.umsmed.edu
Length: 5 Yrs   *ACGME Approved/Offered Positions:* 33
Program ID: 440-27-21-165

Keesler AFB

Keesler Medical Center Program

Sponsor: Keesler Medical Center
University Hospitals and Clinics
Veterans Affairs Medical Center (Biloxi)
Prgm Director: Valerie M Pruitt, MD*
81 MDG/81 MSGS/SGCQ
301 Fisher Street, Room 2A228
Keesler AFB, MS 39534
Tel: 228 376-5571   *Fax:* 228 376-0137
E-mail: valerie.pruitt@keesler.af.mil
Length: 5 Yrs   *ACGME Approved/Offered Positions:* 24
Program ID: 440-27-31-002
Uniformed Services Program

Missouri

Columbia

University of Missouri-Columbia Program

Sponsor: University of Missouri-Columbia School of
   Medicine
Harry S Truman Memorial Veterans Hospital
University Hospitals and Clinics
Prgm Director: Debra G Koivunen, MD
One Hospital Drive
4th Floor McHaney Hall
Columbia, MO 65212
Tel: 573 884-2000   *Fax:* 573 884-4611
E-mail: Lynchg@health.missouri.edu
Length: 5 Yrs   *ACGME Approved/Offered Positions:* 25
Program ID: 440-28-21-166

Kansas City

University of Missouri at Kansas City Program

Sponsor: University of Missouri-Kansas City School of
   Medicine
St Luke's Hospital-Kansas City
Truman Medical Center
Veterans Affairs Medical Center (Kansas City)
Prgm Director: Glenn E Talboy Jr, MD
Surgery Administration
2301 Holmes St, 3rd Fl
Kansas City, MO 64108
Tel: 816 404-5345   *Fax:* 816 404-5381
Length: 5 Yrs   *ACGME Approved/Offered Positions:* 24
Program ID: 440-28-21-168

St Louis

St Louis University School of Medicine Program

Sponsor: St Louis University School of Medicine
St John's Mercy Medical Center
St Louis University Hospital
Veterans Affairs Medical Center (St Louis)
Prgm Director: Aaron Scifres, MD
3635 Vista Avenue at Grand Blvd
PO Box 15250
St Louis, MO 63110
Tel: 314 577-8564   *Fax:* 314 268-5194
E-mail: scifresa@slu.edu
Length: 5 Yrs   *ACGME Approved/Offered Positions:* 35
Program ID: 440-28-21-171

Washington University/B-JH/SLCH Consortium Program

Sponsor: Washington University/B-JH/SLCH Consortium
Barnes-Jewish Hospital
Prgm Director: Mary E Klingensmith, MD
660 South Euclid Avenue, Box 8109
St Louis, MO 63110
Tel: 314 362-8028   *Fax:* 314 747-1288
Length: 5 Yrs   *ACGME Approved/Offered Positions:* 60
Program ID: 440-28-21-388

Nebraska

Omaha

Creighton University Program

Sponsor: Creighton University School of Medicine
Creighton University Medical Center (Tenet - SJH)
Veterans Affairs Medical Center (Omaha)
Prgm Director: Robert A Forse, MD, PhD*
601 N 30th Street, Suite 3700
Omaha, NE 68131
Tel: 402 280-4231   *Fax:* 402 280-4534
Length: 5 Yrs   *ACGME Approved/Offered Positions:* 22
Program ID: 440-30-31-175

University of Nebraska Medical Center College of Medicine Program

Sponsor: University of Nebraska Medical Center College
   of Medicine
Nebraska Medical Center
Nebraska Methodist Hospital
Veterans Affairs Medical Center (Omaha)
Prgm Director: Jon S Thompson, MD
983280 Nebraska Medical Center
Omaha, NE 68198
Tel: 402 559-7182   *Fax:* 402 559-6749
Length: 5 Yrs   *ACGME Approved/Offered Positions:* 28
Program ID: 440-30-21-176

Nevada

Las Vegas

University of Nevada School of Medicine (Las Vegas) Program

Sponsor: University of Nevada School of Medicine
University Medical Center of Southern Nevada
Las Vegas Surgery Center
Sahara Surgery Center
VA Southern Nevada Healthcare System
Prgm Director: John Fildes, MD
2040 West Charleston Boulevard
Suite 302
Las Vegas, NV 89102
Tel: 702 671-2273   *Fax:* 702 385-9399
E-mail: sthomas@medicine.nevada.edu
Length: 5 Yrs   *ACGME Approved/Offered Positions:* 19
Program ID: 440-31-21-378

New Hampshire

Lebanon

Dartmouth-Hitchcock Medical Center Program

Sponsor: Mary Hitchcock Memorial Hospital
Veterans Affairs Medical Center (White River Junction)
Prgm Director: Samuel Finlayson, MD, MPH*
One Medical Center Drive
Lebanon, NH 03756
Tel: 603 650-7692
Length: 5 Yrs   *ACGME Approved/Offered Positions:* 34
Program ID: 440-32-21-177

Note: * indicates a newly appointed program director

New Jersey

Camden

UMDNJ-Robert Wood Johnson Medical School (Camden) Program

Sponsor: Cooper Hospital-University Medical Center
Prgm Director: Brian R Kann, MD
Cooper University Hospital
Three Cooper Plaza, Suite 411
Camden, NJ 08103
Tel: 856 342-3012   *Fax:* 856 365-7582
E-mail: cooneycl@umdnj.edu
Length: 5 Yrs   *ACGME Approved/Offered Positions:* 15
Program ID: 440-33-21-179

Livingston

St Barnabas Medical Center Program

Sponsor: St Barnabas Medical Center
Lincoln Medical and Mental Health Center
Prgm Director: Michael A Marano, MD
94 Old Short Hills Road
Department of Surgery
Livingston, NJ 07039
Tel: 973 322-8945   *Fax:* 973 322-2471
Length: 5 Yrs   *ACGME Approved/Offered Positions:* 28
Program ID: 440-33-22-181

Long Branch

Monmouth Medical Center Program

Sponsor: Monmouth Medical Center
Jersey Shore University Medical Center
Newark Beth Israel Medical Center
Prgm Director: Michael A Goldfarb, MD
Room 251 Stanley Wing
300 Second Avenue
Long Branch, NJ 07740
Tel: 732 923-6770   *Fax:* 732 923-6768
E-mail: mmcsurgery@sbhcs.com
Length: 5 Yrs   *ACGME Approved/Offered Positions:* 21
Program ID: 440-33-21-182

Morristown

Atlantic Health (Morristown) Program

Sponsor: Atlantic Health
Morristown Memorial Hospital
Prgm Director: Eric L Lazar, MD, MS
100 Madison Ave
PO Box 1956
Morristown, NJ 07962
Tel: 973 971-5684   *Fax:* 973 290-7350
E-mail: ericlazar@hotmail.com
Length: 5 Yrs   *ACGME Approved/Offered Positions:* 25
Program ID: 440-33-11-183

New Brunswick

UMDNJ-Robert Wood Johnson Medical School Program

Sponsor: UMDNJ-Robert Wood Johnson Medical School
Jersey Shore University Medical Center
Robert Wood Johnson University Hospital
University Medical Center at Princeton
Prgm Director: Stanley Z Trooskin, MD
Surgery, MEB 596
PO Box 19
New Brunswick, NJ 08803
Tel: 732 235-6598   *Fax:* 732 235-8372
E-mail: troosksz@umdnj.edu
Length: 5 Yrs   *ACGME Approved/Offered Positions:* 44
Program ID: 440-33-21-187

Newark

UMDNJ-New Jersey Medical School Program

Sponsor: UMDNJ-New Jersey Medical School
Hackensack University Medical Center
UMDNJ-University Hospital
Veterans Affairs New Jersey Health Care System
Prgm Director: Dorian J Wilson, MD
150 Bergen Street
University Hospital, Room E-401
Newark, NJ 07103
Tel: 973 972-4417   *Fax:* 973 972-6591
E-mail: njms-res-surgery@umdnj.edu
Length: 5 Yrs   *ACGME Approved/Offered Positions:* 56
Program ID: 440-33-21-184

South Orange

Seton Hall University School of Health and Medical Sciences (St Francis) Program

Sponsor: Seton Hall University School of Health and Medical Sciences
St Francis Medical Center
St Joseph's Regional Medical Center
Prgm Director: Peter N Benotti, MD*
601 Hamilton Avenue, Room B-150
Trenton, NJ 08629
Tel: 609 599-5700   *Fax:* 609 599-6233
E-mail: pbenotti@stfrancismedical.org
Length: 5 Yrs   *ACGME Approved/Offered Positions:* 15
Program ID: 440-33-31-189

New Mexico

Albuquerque

University of New Mexico Program

Sponsor: University of New Mexico School of Medicine
Lovelace Sandia Health
University of New Mexico Hospital
Veterans Affairs Medical Center (Albuquerque)
Prgm Director: Timothy Nelson, MD
MSC 10-5610
1 University of New Mexico
Albuquerque, NM 87131
Tel: 505 272-4161   *Fax:* 505 272-8145
E-mail: MTnelson@salud.unm.edu
Length: 5 Yrs   *ACGME Approved/Offered Positions:* 29
Program ID: 440-34-21-190

New York

Albany

Albany Medical Center Program

Sponsor: Albany Medical Center
Veterans Affairs Medical Center (Albany)
Prgm Director: David J Conti, MD
47 New Scotland Avenue
Department of Surgery
Albany, NY 12208
Tel: 518 262-5374   *Fax:* 518 262-5692
Length: 5 Yrs   *ACGME Approved/Offered Positions:* 26
Program ID: 440-35-21-191

Bronx

Albert Einstein College of Medicine Program

Sponsor: Albert Einstein College of Medicine of Yeshiva University
Montefiore Medical Center-Henry and Lucy Moses Division
Montefiore Medical Center-Weiler Division
North Bronx Healthcare Network-Jacobi Medical Center
Prgm Director: Ronald N Kaleya, MD
Department of Surgery
3400 Bainbridge Avenue, MAP Bldg, 4th Floor
Bronx, NY 10467
Tel: 718 920-4800   *Fax:* 718 798-1883
E-mail: rkaleya@montefiore.org
Length: 5 Yrs   *ACGME Approved/Offered Positions:* 63
Program ID: 440-35-21-202

Bronx-Lebanon Hospital Center Program

Sponsor: Bronx-Lebanon Hospital Center
Prgm Director: John M Cosgrove, MD
1650 Grand Concourse
Bronx, NY 10457
Tel: 718 960-1227   *Fax:* 718 960-1370
E-mail: sstaffor@bronxleb.org
Length: 5 Yrs   *ACGME Approved/Offered Positions:* 26
Program ID: 440-35-11-206

New York Medical College (Bronx) Program

Sponsor: New York Medical College
Lincoln Medical and Mental Health Center
Prgm Director: C Gene Cayten, MD, MPH
600 East 233rd Street
Bronx, NY 10466
Tel: 718 920-9522   *Fax:* 718 920-9837
E-mail: gcayten@montefiore.org
Length: 5 Yrs   *ACGME Approved/Offered Positions:* 25
Program ID: 440-35-11-408

Brooklyn

Brookdale University Hospital and Medical Center Program

Sponsor: Brookdale University Hospital and Medical Center
Prgm Director: Prem S Patel, MD, MS
One Brookdale Plaza
Brooklyn, NY 11212
Tel: 718 240-6380   *Fax:* 718 240-6738
Length: 5 Yrs   *ACGME Approved/Offered Positions:* 25
Program ID: 440-35-21-207

Brooklyn Hospital Center Program

Sponsor: Brooklyn Hospital Center
Prgm Director: Stephen S Carryl, MD
121 Dekalb Avenue
Brooklyn, NY 11201
Tel: 718 250-8944   *Fax:* 718 250-6080
E-mail: bjl9003@nyp.org
Length: 5 Yrs   *ACGME Approved/Offered Positions:* 25
Program ID: 440-35-31-208

Maimonides Medical Center Program

Sponsor: Maimonides Medical Center
Coney Island Hospital
Prgm Director: Patrick I Borgen, MD*
4802 Tenth Avenue
Brooklyn, NY 11219
Tel: 718 283-7170   *Fax:* 718 635-7460
E-mail: pborgen@maimonidesmed.org
Length: 5 Yrs   *ACGME Approved/Offered Positions:* 37
Program ID: 440-35-21-221

Programs

New York Methodist Hospital Program

Sponsor: New York Methodist Hospital
Prgm Director: Leslie Wise, MD
506 Sixth Street
PO Box 159008
Brooklyn, NY 11215
Tel: 718 780-3288   *Fax:* 718 780-3154
E-mail: dim9004@nyp.org
Length: 5 Yrs   *ACGME Approved/Offered Positions:* 20
Program ID: 440-35-21-222

SUNY Health Science Center at Brooklyn Program

Sponsor: SUNY Health Science Center at Brooklyn
Kings County Hospital Center
Long Island College Hospital
University Hospital-SUNY Health Science Center at Brooklyn
Veterans Affairs Medical Center (Brooklyn)
Prgm Director: Michael E Zenilman, MD
Department of Surgery
450 Clarkson Ave, Box 40
Brooklyn, NY 11203
Tel: 718 270-1421   *Fax:* 718 270-2826
Length: 5 Yrs   *ACGME Approved/Offered Positions:* 64
Program ID: 440-35-21-237

Buffalo

University at Buffalo Program

Sponsor: University at Buffalo School of Medicine
Erie County Medical Center
Kaleida Health System (Buffalo General Hospital)
Kaleida Health System (Millard Fillmore Hospital)
Veterans Affairs Western New York Hospital
Prgm Director: James M Hassett, MD
Kaleida Health - Buffalo General Hospital Site
100 High Street, C374
Buffalo, NY 14203
Tel: 716 859-1344   *Fax:* 716 859-7760
E-mail: rhn@buffalo.edu
Length: 5 Yrs   *ACGME Approved/Offered Positions:* 53
Program ID: 440-35-21-393

Cooperstown

Bassett Healthcare Program

Sponsor: Bassett Healthcare
Mary Imogene Bassett Hospital
Prgm Director: David C Borgstrom, MD*
One Atwell Road
Cooperstown, NY 13326
Tel: 607 547-3202   *Fax:* 607 547-6553
E-mail: david.borgstrom@bassett.org
Length: 5 Yrs   *ACGME Approved/Offered Positions:* 15
Program ID: 440-35-31-197

East Meadow

Nassau University Medical Center Program

Sponsor: Nassau University Medical Center
South Nassau Communities Hospital
Prgm Director: Elizabeth Cirincione, MD
2201 Hempstead Turnpike
Box 34
East Meadow, NY 11554
Tel: 516 572-6705   *Fax:* 516 572-5140
E-mail: ecirinci@numc.edu
Length: 5 Yrs   *ACGME Approved/Offered Positions:* 26
Program ID: 440-35-12-198

Flushing

New York Hospital Medical Center of Queens/Cornell University Medical College Program

Sponsor: New York Hospital Medical Center of Queens
Prgm Director: James C Maurer, MD
56-45 Main Street
Flushing, NY 11355
Tel: 718 670-1572   *Fax:* 718 670-1864
E-mail: dmdechir@nyp.org
Length: 5 Yrs   *ACGME Approved/Offered Positions:* 28
Program ID: 440-35-11-205

Great Neck

NSLIJHS Program

Sponsor: North Shore-Long Island Jewish Health System
Long Island Jewish Medical Center
North Shore University Hospital
Prgm Director: Corrado P Marini, MD
300 Community Drive
Manhasset, NY 11030
Tel: 718 470-4534
Length: 5 Yrs   *ACGME Approved/Offered Positions:* 68
Program ID: 440-35-13-411

Jamaica

New York Medical College (Brooklyn-Queens) Program

Sponsor: New York Medical College
Caritas Health Care (Brooklyn-Queens)
Prgm Director: Sambasiva Kamineni, MD
St John's Queens Hospital, Dept of Surgery
90-02 Queens Boulevard
Elmhurst, NY 11373
Tel: 718 558-1953   *Fax:* 718 558-1431
E-mail: skamineni@bqhcny.org
Length: 5 Yrs   *ACGME Approved/Offered Positions:* 13
Program ID: 440-35-21-210

New Rochelle

New York Medical College (Sound Shore) Program

Sponsor: New York Medical College
Sound Shore Medical Center of Westchester
Danbury Hospital
Prgm Director: Burton L Herz, MD
16 Guion Place
New Rochelle, NY 10802
Tel: 914 365-3998   *Fax:* 914 365-5440
Length: 5 Yrs   *ACGME Approved/Offered Positions:* 21
Program ID: 440-35-21-201

New York

Albert Einstein College of Medicine at Beth Israel Medical Center Program

Sponsor: Beth Israel Medical Center
Prgm Director: I Michael Leitman, MD
First Avenue at 16th Street
New York, NY 10003
Tel: 212 844-8570   *Fax:* 212 844-8440
E-mail: mleitman@chpnet.org
Length: 5 Yrs   *ACGME Approved/Offered Positions:* 32
Program ID: 440-35-11-204

Harlem Hospital Center Program

Sponsor: Harlem Hospital Center
Woodhull Medical and Mental Health Center
Prgm Director: Soji F Oluwole, MD
506 Lenox Ave
New York, NY 10037
Tel: 212 939-1639   *Fax:* 212 939-3536
E-mail: so5@columbia.edu
Length: 5 Yrs   *ACGME Approved/Offered Positions:* 25
Program ID: 440-35-11-214

Lenox Hill Hospital Program

Sponsor: Lenox Hill Hospital
Prgm Director: Paresh C Shah, MD
100 East 77th Street
8-Achelis
New York, NY 10075
Tel: 212 434-2150   *Fax:* 212 434-2083
E-mail: Pcshah@lenoxhill.net
Length: 5 Yrs   *ACGME Approved/Offered Positions:* 24
Program ID: 440-35-11-217

Mount Sinai School of Medicine Program

Sponsor: Mount Sinai School of Medicine
Elmhurst Hospital Center-Mount Sinai Services
Mount Sinai Medical Center
Prgm Director: Celia M Divino, MD
Department of Surgery
5 East 98th Street, Box 1259
New York, NY 10029
Tel: 212 241-5499   *Fax:* 212 410-0111
Length: 5 Yrs   *ACGME Approved/Offered Positions:* 50
Program ID: 440-35-21-225

New York Medical College at St Vincent's Hospital and Medical Center of New York Program

Sponsor: New York Medical College
St Vincent Catholic Medical Centers (Manhattan)
Metropolitan Hospital Center
Richmond University Medical Center
Prgm Director: Christopher B Mills, MD
170 West 12th Street
Cronin 802
New York, NY 10011
Tel: 212 604-8344   *Fax:* 212 604-8355
E-mail: cmills@svcmcny.org
Length: 5 Yrs   *ACGME Approved/Offered Positions:* 53
Program ID: 440-35-21-234

New York Presbyterian Hospital (Columbia Campus) Program

Sponsor: New York Presbyterian Hospital
New York Presbyterian Hospital (Columbia Campus)
Overlook Hospital
Prgm Director: Tracey D Arnell, MD, BA*
Milstein Hospital 7GS-313
177 Fort Washington Avenue
New York, NY 10032
Tel: 212 305-3038   *Fax:* 212 305-8321
Length: 5 Yrs   *ACGME Approved/Offered Positions:* 52
Program ID: 440-35-21-229

New York Presbyterian Hospital (Cornell Campus) Program

Sponsor: New York Presbyterian Hospital
Jamaica Hospital Medical Center
Memorial Sloan-Kettering Cancer Center
New York Presbyterian Hospital (Cornell Campus)
Prgm Director: Thomas J Fahey III, MD
525 East 68th Street, Box207
New York, NY 10065
Tel: 212 746-5380   *Fax:* 212 746-8802
E-mail: mat9052@med.cornell.edu
Length: 5 Yrs   *ACGME Approved/Offered Positions:* 62
Program ID: 440-35-21-211

New York University School of Medicine Program

Sponsor: New York University School of Medicine
Bellevue Hospital Center
Manhattan VA Harbor Health Care System
NYU Hospitals Center
Prgm Director: Russell S Berman, MD
550 First Avenue
NB 15 N1
New York, NY 10016
Tel: 212 263-2982   *Fax:* 212 263-8216
E-mail: russell.berman@nyumc.org
Length: 5 Yrs   *ACGME Approved/Offered Positions:* 61
Program ID: 440-35-21-394

Note: * indicates a newly appointed program director

St Luke's-Roosevelt Hospital Center Program

Sponsor: St Luke's-Roosevelt Hospital Center
Prgm Director: James McGinty Jr, MD
1000 Tenth Avenue, Suite 2B
New York, NY 10019
Tel: 212 523-7780   *Fax:* 212 523-6495
E-mail: mbolte@chpnet.org
Length: 5 Yrs   *ACGME Approved/Offered Positions:* 36
Program ID: 440-35-21-383

Rochester

University of Rochester Program

Sponsor: Strong Memorial Hospital of the University of
  Rochester
Highland Hospital of Rochester
Prgm Director: Thomas J Watson, MD*
601 Elmwood Avenue
Department of Surgery Box SURG
Rochester, NY 14642
Tel: 585 275-1509   *Fax:* 585 273-1011
Length: 5 Yrs   *ACGME Approved/Offered Positions:* 45
Program ID: 440-35-21-240

Staten Island

Staten Island University Hospital Program

Sponsor: Staten Island University Hospital
Prgm Director: Gene F Coppa, MD
475 Seaview Avenue
Staten Island, NY 10305
Tel: 718 226-9508   *Fax:* 718 226-8365
Length: 5 Yrs   *ACGME Approved/Offered Positions:* 23
Program ID: 440-35-11-236

Stony Brook

SUNY at Stony Brook Program

Sponsor: University Hospital - SUNY at Stony Brook
Veterans Affairs Medical Center (Northport)
Winthrop-University Hospital
Prgm Director: Scriven Richard, MD*
Health Science Center 19-020
Nicolls Road
Stony Brook, NY 11794
Tel: 631 444-1791   *Fax:* 631 444-7689
E-mail: richard.scriven@stonybrook.edu
Length: 5 Yrs   *ACGME Approved/Offered Positions:* 51
Program ID: 440-35-21-242

Syracuse

SUNY Upstate Medical University Program

Sponsor: SUNY Upstate Medical University
Crouse Hospital
Veterans Affairs Medical Center (Syracuse)
Prgm Director: John Fortune, MD*
Department of Surgery
750 E Adams Street
Syracuse, NY 13210
Tel: 315 464-6289   *Fax:* 315 464-6233
E-mail: thomasr@upstate.edu
Length: 5 Yrs   *ACGME Approved/Offered Positions:* 40
Program ID: 440-35-21-244

Valhalla

New York Medical College at Westchester Medical Center Program

Sponsor: New York Medical College
St Vincent's Medical Center
Westchester Medical Center
Prgm Director: John A Savino, MD
Department of Surgery
Munger Pavillion
Valhalla, NY 10595
Tel: 914 493-7614   *Fax:* 914 594-4359
Length: 5 Yrs   *ACGME Approved/Offered Positions:* 28
Program ID: 440-35-21-227

North Carolina

Chapel Hill

University of North Carolina Hospitals Program

Sponsor: University of North Carolina Hospitals
Wake Medical Center
Prgm Director: Mark J Koruda, MD
Department of Surgery
4029 Burnett-Womack Bldg, CB 7081
Chapel Hill, NC 27599
Tel: 919 966-8436   *Fax:* 919 966-8440
E-mail: koruda@med.unc.edu
Length: 5 Yrs   *ACGME Approved/Offered Positions:* 48
Program ID: 440-36-21-245

Charlotte

Carolinas Medical Center Program

Sponsor: Carolinas Medical Center
Prgm Director: Frederick L Greene, MD
Department of General Surgery
PO Box 32861
Charlotte, NC 28232
Tel: 704 355-3176   *Fax:* 704 355-5619
E-mail: general.surgery@carolinashealthcare.org
Length: 5 Yrs   *ACGME Approved/Offered Positions:* 22
Program ID: 440-36-12-246

Durham

Duke University Hospital Program

Sponsor: Duke University Hospital
Veterans Affairs Medical Center (Durham)
Prgm Director: Bryan M Clary, MD
PO Box 3443
Durham, NC 27710
Tel: 919 684-6553   *Fax:* 919 681-8856
E-mail: carla.thompson@duke.edu
Length: 5 Yrs   *ACGME Approved/Offered Positions:* 60
Program ID: 440-36-21-247

Greenville

Pitt County Memorial Hospital/East Carolina University Program

Sponsor: Pitt County Memorial Hospital
Brody School of Medicine at East Carolina University
Prgm Director: Carl E Haisch, MD*
Department of Surgery
600 Moye Blvd
Greenville, NC 27834
Tel: 252 744-5262   *Fax:* 252 744-3156
E-mail: surgeryed@ecu.edu
Length: 5 Yrs   *ACGME Approved/Offered Positions:* 24
Program ID: 440-36-11-248

Wilmington

New Hanover Regional Medical Center Program

Sponsor: New Hanover Regional Medical Center
Prgm Director: Thomas V Clancy, MD
2131 South 17th Street
PO Box 9025
Wilmington, NC 28402
Tel: 910 343-2516   *Fax:* 910 763-4630
E-mail: thomas.clancy@seahec.net
Length: 5 Yrs   *ACGME Approved/Offered Positions:* 11
Program ID: 440-36-31-249

Winston-Salem

Wake Forest University School of Medicine Program

Sponsor: Wake Forest University Baptist Medical Center
Prgm Director: J Wayne Meredith, MD
Medical Center Blvd
Winston-Salem, NC 27157
Tel: 336 716-7579   *Fax:* 336 716-5414
Length: 5 Yrs   *ACGME Approved/Offered Positions:* 42
Program ID: 440-36-31-250

North Dakota

Grand Forks

University of North Dakota Program

Sponsor: Univ of North Dakota School of Medicine and
  Health Sciences
Altru Health System Hospital
MeritCare Health System
Veterans Affairs Medical and Regional Office Center
  (Fargo)
Prgm Director: Robert P Sticca, MD
Dept of Surgery Rm 5107
501 North Columbia Road Stop 9037
Grand Forks, ND 58203
Tel: 701 777-3067   *Fax:* 701 777-2609
E-mail: landersn@medicine.nodak.edu
Length: 5 Yrs   *ACGME Approved/Offered Positions:* 17
Program ID: 440-37-21-379

Ohio

Akron

Akron General Medical Center/NEOUCOM Program

Sponsor: Akron General Medical Center
Prgm Director: Robert A Marley, MD
400 Wabash Avenue
Akron, OH 44307
Tel: 330 344-7708   *Fax:* 330 344-0019
Length: 5 Yrs   *ACGME Approved/Offered Positions:* 13
Program ID: 440-38-11-252

Summa Health System/NEOUCOM Program

Sponsor: Summa Health System
Akron City Hospital (Summa Health System)
Prgm Director: William F Fallon Jr, MD, MBA*
525 E Market Street
Jacqueline Williams/Program Coordinator
Akron, OH 44304
Tel: 330 375-3648
E-mail: fallonw@summa-health.org
Length: 5 Yrs   *ACGME Approved/Offered Positions:* 17
Program ID: 440-38-21-251

Programs

Cincinnati

Jewish Hospital of Cincinnati Program
Sponsor: Jewish Hospital of Cincinnati
Prgm Director: Elliott J Fegelman, MD
Department of Surgery
4777 E Galbraith Road
Cincinnati, OH 45236
Tel: 513 686-5466   *Fax:* 513 686-5469
E-mail: elliott.fegelman@healthall.com
Length: 5 Yrs   *ACGME Approved/Offered Positions:* 14
Program ID: 440-38-31-254

TriHealth (Good Samaritan Hospital) Program
Sponsor: TriHealth
TriHealth - Bethesda North Hospital
TriHealth - Good Samaritan Hospital
Prgm Director: Richard E Welling, MD
375 Dixmyth Avenue
Cincinnati, OH 45220
Tel: 513 872-3220   *Fax:* 513 221-5865
Length: 5 Yrs   *ACGME Approved/Offered Positions:* 24
Program ID: 440-38-31-253

University Hospital/University of Cincinnati College of Medicine Program
Sponsor: University Hospital Inc
Christ Hospital
Veterans Affairs Medical Center (Cincinnati)
Prgm Director: Timothy A Pritts, MD, PhD*
231 Albert Sabin Way ML 0558
Cincinnati, OH 45267
Tel: 513 558-4206   *Fax:* 513 558-3474
E-mail: prittsta@ucmail.uc.edu
Length: 5 Yrs   *ACGME Approved/Offered Positions:* 60
Program ID: 440-38-21-255

Cleveland

Cleveland Clinic Foundation Program
Sponsor: Cleveland Clinic Foundation
Prgm Director: Allan Siperstein, MD
Department of Surgery A80
9500 Euclid Avenue
Cleveland, OH 44195
Tel: 216 444-5664   *Fax:* 216 445-7653
E-mail: surged@ccf.org
Length: 5 Yrs   *ACGME Approved/Offered Positions:* 46
Program ID: 440-38-22-257

Fairview Hospital Program
Sponsor: Fairview Hospital
Cleveland Clinic Foundation
Prgm Director: Richard C Treat, MD
Department of Surgery
18101 Lorain Avenue
Cleveland, OH 44111
Tel: 216 476-7155   *Fax:* 216 476-7883
E-mail: julie.callahan@fairviewhospital.org
Length: 5 Yrs   *ACGME Approved/Offered Positions:* 20
Program ID: 440-38-22-258

Huron Hospital Program
Sponsor: Huron Hospital
Cleveland Clinic Foundation
Hillcrest Hospital
Robinson Memorial Hospital
Prgm Director: Raphael S Chung, MD, MBA
13951 Terrace Road
East Cleveland, OH 44112
Tel: 216 761-4223   *Fax:* 216 761-3499
Length: 5 Yrs   *ACGME Approved/Offered Positions:* 14
Program ID: 440-38-22-259

University Hospitals Case Medical Center Program
Sponsor: University Hospitals Case Medical Center
MetroHealth Medical Center
Veterans Affairs Medical Center (Cleveland)
Prgm Director: Julian Kim, MD
Case Medical Center
11100 Euclid Avenue - Lakeside Room 7109
Cleveland, OH 44106
Tel: 216 844-8247   *Fax:* 216 844-2888
Length: 5 Yrs   *ACGME Approved/Offered Positions:* 62
Program ID: 440-38-21-399

Columbus

Mount Carmel Program
Sponsor: Mount Carmel
Prgm Director: Thomas H Hartranft, MD
Department of Surgery
793 W State Street - MSB 3rd Floor
Columbus, OH 43222
Tel: 614 234-5983   *Fax:* 614 234-2772
E-mail: lbadurina@mchs.com
Length: 5 Yrs   *ACGME Approved/Offered Positions:* 20
Program ID: 440-38-32-263

Ohio State University Hospital Program
Sponsor: Ohio State University Hospital
Arthur G James Cancer Hospital and Research Institute
Prgm Director: Mark W Arnold, MD
395 W 12th Ave, Room 654
Columbus, OH 43210
Tel: 614 293-8704   *Fax:* 614 293-4063
Length: 5 Yrs   *ACGME Approved/Offered Positions:* 44
Program ID: 440-38-21-264

Riverside Methodist Hospitals (OhioHealth) Program
Sponsor: Riverside Methodist Hospitals (OhioHealth)
Prgm Director: Oscar R Ruiz, MD
Medical Education Department
3535 Olentangy River Road
Columbus, OH 43214
Tel: 614 566-3202   *Fax:* 614 566-6852
E-mail: banderso@ohiohealth.com
Length: 5 Yrs   *ACGME Approved/Offered Positions:* 19
Program ID: 440-38-12-265

Dayton

Wright State University Program
Sponsor: Wright State University Boonshoft School of Medicine
Good Samaritan Hospital and Health Center
Kettering Medical Center
Miami Valley Hospital
Veterans Affairs Medical Center (Dayton)
Wright - Patterson Medical Center
Prgm Director: Paula M Termuhlen, MD
One Wyoming Street
Suite 7000, Weber Center for Health Education
Dayton, OH 45409
Tel: 937 208-2177   *Fax:* 937 208-2105
Length: 5 Yrs   *ACGME Approved/Offered Positions:* 47
Program ID: 440-38-21-266

Toledo

University of Toledo Program
Sponsor: University of Toledo
St Vincent Mercy Medical Center
University Medical Center (Toledo)
Prgm Director: Frederick D Cason Jr, MD
Dowling Hall, Mailstop 1095
3065 Arlington Avenue
Toledo, OH 43614
Tel: 419 383-6931   *Fax:* 419 383-6636
E-mail: Mary.Burda@utoledo.edu
Length: 5 Yrs   *ACGME Approved/Offered Positions:* 27
Program ID: 440-38-21-269

Youngstown

St Elizabeth Health Center/NEOUCOM Program
Sponsor: St Elizabeth Health Center
Prgm Director: Michael S Kavic, MD
1044 Belmont Avenue
PO Box 1790
Youngstown, OH 44501
Tel: 800 422-3699   *Fax:* 330 480-3640
Length: 5 Yrs   *ACGME Approved/Offered Positions:* 20
Program ID: 440-38-11-270

Western Reserve Care System/NEOUCOM Program
Sponsor: Forum Health/Western Reserve Care System (Youngstown)
Prgm Director: Peter M DeVito, MD
500 Gypsy Lane
PO Box 240
Youngstown, OH 44501
Tel: 330 884-3472   *Fax:* 330 884-5690
Length: 5 Yrs   *ACGME Approved/Offered Positions:* 13
Program ID: 440-38-21-271

Oklahoma

Oklahoma City

University of Oklahoma Health Sciences Center Program
Sponsor: University of Oklahoma College of Medicine
OU Medical Center
Veterans Affairs Medical Center (Oklahoma City)
Prgm Director: M Alex Jacocks, MD
Williams Pavilion Building
PO Box 26901 - Room WP2140
Oklahoma City, OK 73190
Tel: 405 271-6308   *Fax:* 405 271-3919
E-mail: rhea-sulzycki@ouhsc.edu
Length: 5 Yrs   *ACGME Approved/Offered Positions:* 30
Program ID: 440-39-21-273

Tulsa

University of Oklahoma College of Medicine-Tulsa Program
Sponsor: University of Oklahoma College of Medicine-Tulsa
St John Medical Center
Prgm Director: Thomas A Broughan, MD
Department of Surgery
4502 E 41st Street
Tulsa, OK 74135
Tel: 918 744-3650   *Fax:* 918 744-3651
Length: 5 Yrs   *ACGME Approved/Offered Positions:* 19
Program ID: 440-39-21-274

Oregon

Portland

Oregon Health & Science University Program
Sponsor: Oregon Health & Science University Hospital
Kaiser Foundation Hospitals-Northwest Region
Legacy Emanuel Hospital and Health Center
Legacy Good Samaritan Hospital and Medical Center
St Vincent Hospital and Medical Center
Three Rivers Community Hospital
Veterans Affairs Medical Center (Portland)
Prgm Director: Karen Deveney, MD
3181 SW Sam Jackson Pk Rd, L223
Portland, OR 97239
Tel: 503 494-7758   *Fax:* 503 494-5615
Length: 5 Yrs   *ACGME Approved/Offered Positions:* 77
Program ID: 440-40-21-278

Note: * indicates a newly appointed program director

Pennsylvania

Abington

Abington Memorial Hospital Program
Sponsor: Abington Memorial Hospital
Prgm Director: John S Kukora, MD
1200 Old York Road
Abington, PA 19001
Tel: 215 481-7464   *Fax:* 215 481-2159
Length: 5 Yrs   *ACGME Approved/Offered Positions:* 24
Program ID: 440-41-12-279

Allentown

Lehigh Valley Hospital Network/Pennsylvania State University Program
Sponsor: Lehigh Valley Hospital Network
Prgm Director: Michael M Badellino, MD, MPH
Department of Surgery
Cedar Crest and I-78, PO Box 689
Allentown, PA 18105
Tel: 610 402-8966   *Fax:* 610 402-1667
Length: 5 Yrs   *ACGME Approved/Offered Positions:* 23
Program ID: 440-41-21-280

Bethlehem

St Luke's Hospital Program
Sponsor: St Luke's Hospital
Prgm Director: Brian A Hoey, MD
General Surgery Residency
801 Ostrum Street
Bethlehem, PA 18015
Tel: 610 954-2255   *Fax:* 610 954-2220
Length: 5 Yrs   *ACGME Approved/Offered Positions:* 10
Program ID: 440-41-21-398

Danville

Geisinger Health System Program
Sponsor: Geisinger Health System
Geisinger Wyoming Valley Medical Center
Prgm Director: William E Strodel, MD*
Department of General Surgery
100 North Academy Avenue
Danville, PA 17822
Tel: 570 214-7711   *Fax:* 570 271-6928
E-mail: gensurgresidency@geisinger.edu
Length: 5 Yrs   *ACGME Approved/Offered Positions:* 22
Program ID: 440-41-21-283

Darby

Mercy Catholic Medical Center Program
Sponsor: Mercy Catholic Medical Center Inc
Mercy Fitzgerald Hospital
Mercy Philadelphia Hospital
Prgm Director: Prashanth Ramachandra, MD
Dept of Surgery, MS 082
1500 Lansdowne Avenue
Darby, PA 19023
Tel: 610 237-4950   *Fax:* 610 237-4329
Length: 5 Yrs   *ACGME Approved/Offered Positions:* 12
Program ID: 440-41-31-297

Easton

Easton Hospital Program
Sponsor: Easton Hospital (Northampton Hospital Corporation)
Prgm Director: Harjeet P Kohli, MD
250 S 21st Street
Department of Surgery
Easton, PA 18042
Tel: 610 250-4375   *Fax:* 610 250-4851
Length: 5 Yrs   *ACGME Approved/Offered Positions:* 14
Program ID: 440-41-31-284

Harrisburg

PinnacleHealth Hospitals Program
Sponsor: PinnacleHealth Hospitals
Prgm Director: Raymond Kostin, MD
Brady 9
205 South Front Street
Harrisburg, PA 17104
Tel: 717 231-8755   *Fax:* 717 231-8756
E-mail: dlaudenslager@pinnaclehealth.org
Length: 5 Yrs   *ACGME Approved/Offered Positions:* 12
Program ID: 440-41-21-384

Hershey

Penn State University/Milton S Hershey Medical Center Program
Sponsor: Milton S Hershey Medical Center
Prgm Director: Timothy R Shope, MD*
500 University Drive
PO Box 850 H051
Hershey, PA 17033
Tel: 717 531-7462
E-mail: tshope@hmc.psu.edu
Length: 5 Yrs   *ACGME Approved/Offered Positions:* 36
Program ID: 440-41-21-287

Johnstown

Conemaugh Valley Memorial Hospital Program
Sponsor: Conemaugh Valley Memorial Hospital
Prgm Director: Russell D Dumire, MD
1086 Franklin Street
GS G54
Johnstown, PA 15905
Tel: 814 534-1660   *Fax:* 814 534-1680
Length: 5 Yrs   *ACGME Approved/Offered Positions:* 14
Program ID: 440-41-11-288

Philadelphia

Albert Einstein Healthcare Network Program
Sponsor: Albert Einstein Medical Center
Prgm Director: H Hank Simms, MD
5501 Old York Road
Klein Building, Suite 510
Philadelphia, PA 19141
Tel: 215 456-6930   *Fax:* 215 456-3529
E-mail: joness@einstein.edu
Length: 5 Yrs   *ACGME Approved/Offered Positions:* 23
Program ID: 440-41-11-291

Drexel University College of Medicine/Hahnemann University Hospital Program
Sponsor: Drexel University College of Medicine/Hahnemann University
Hahnemann University Hospital (Tenet Health System)
St Peter's University Hospital
Prgm Director: William C Meyers, MD, MBA
245 North 15th Street
Mail Stop 413
Philadelphia, PA 19102
Tel: 215 762-3585   *Fax:* 215 762-6275
E-mail: wmeyers@drexelmed.edu
Length: 5 Yrs   *ACGME Approved/Offered Positions:* 41
Program ID: 440-41-21-295

Temple University Hospital Program
Sponsor: Temple University Hospital
Crozer-Chester Medical Center
Jeanes Hospital
Prgm Director: Amy J Goldberg, MD
3401 North Broad Street
Broad & Ontario Streets
Philadelphia, PA 19140
Tel: 215 707-3632   *Fax:* 215 707-9398
E-mail: templesur@tuhs.temple.edu
Length: 5 Yrs   *ACGME Approved/Offered Positions:* 47
Program ID: 440-41-21-300

Thomas Jefferson University Program
Sponsor: Thomas Jefferson University Hospital
Frankford Hospitals (Torresdale Campus)
Prgm Director: Karen Chojnacki, MD*
1015 Walnut Street
Suite 620
Philadelphia, PA 19107
Tel: 215 955-6864   *Fax:* 215 955-2878
E-mail: karen.chojnacki@jefferson.edu
Length: 5 Yrs   *ACGME Approved/Offered Positions:* 40
Program ID: 440-41-21-301

University of Pennsylvania Program
Sponsor: University of Pennsylvania Health System
Pennsylvania Hospital (UPHS)
Presbyterian Medical Center (UPHS)
Prgm Director: Jon B Morris, MD
3400 Spruce Street
Philadelphia, PA 19104
Tel: 215 662-6156   *Fax:* 215 662-7983
E-mail: lori.pray@uphs.upenn.edu
Length: 5 Yrs   *ACGME Approved/Offered Positions:* 71
Program ID: 440-41-21-302

Pittsburgh

Allegheny General Hospital Program
Sponsor: Allegheny General Hospital
Prgm Director: Charles F Cobb, MD
320 East North Avenue
Division of General Surgery
Pittsburgh, PA 15212
Tel: 412 359-6907   *Fax:* 412 359-3212
E-mail: smorello@wpahs.org
Length: 5 Yrs   *ACGME Approved/Offered Positions:* 32
Program ID: 440-41-12-303

University of Pittsburgh Medical Center Medical Education (Mercy) Program
Sponsor: Univ of Pittsburgh Medical Center Medical Education
Mercy Hospital of Pittsburgh
Prgm Director: Kurt R Stahlfeld, MD
Department of Surgery
1400 Locust Street
Pittsburgh, PA 15219
Tel: 412 232-8097   *Fax:* 412 232-8096
E-mail: stahlfeldk@upmc.edu
Length: 5 Yrs   *ACGME Approved/Offered Positions:* 20
Program ID: 440-41-12-305

University of Pittsburgh Medical Center Medical Education Program
Sponsor: Univ of Pittsburgh Medical Center Medical Education
UPMC Presbyterian Shadyside
UPMC St Margaret
Veterans Affairs Medical Center (Pittsburgh)
Prgm Director: Kenneth K Lee, MD
Room F675 PUH
200 Lothrop Street
Pittsburgh, PA 15213
Tel: 412 647-0457   *Fax:* 412 647-1999
E-mail: mrozinskim2@upmc.edu
Length: 5 Yrs   *ACGME Approved/Offered Positions:* 58
Program ID: 440-41-21-304

Programs

Sayre

Guthrie/Robert Packer Hospital Program
Sponsor: Robert Packer Hospital
Prgm Director: Thomas J VanderMeer, MD
One Guthrie Square
Sayre, PA 18840
Tel: 570 882-3585   *Fax:* 570 882-3599
E-mail: vandermeer_thomas@guthrie.org
Length: 5 Yrs   *ACGME Approved/Offered Positions:* 19
Program ID: 440-41-12-309

Wynnewood

Lankenau Hospital Program
Sponsor: Lankenau Hospital
Prgm Director: Barry D Mann, MD
100 Lancaster Avenue
422 Lankenau Medical Office Building South
Wynnewood, PA 19096
Tel: 610 645-2169   *Fax:* 610 645-3354
E-mail: KelleyCa@mlhs.org
Length: 5 Yrs   *ACGME Approved/Offered Positions:* 14
Program ID: 440-41-11-296

York

York Hospital Program
Sponsor: York Hospital
Prgm Director: Thomas R Scott, MD
1001 South George Street
York, PA 17405
Tel: 717 851-3569   *Fax:* 717 851-4513
Length: 5 Yrs   *ACGME Approved/Offered Positions:* 17
Program ID: 440-41-12-310

Puerto Rico

San Juan

University of Puerto Rico Program
Sponsor: University of Puerto Rico School of Medicine
I Gonzalez Martinez Oncologic Hospital
University Hospital
VA Caribbean Healthcare System
Prgm Director: Juan J Lojo, MD
Medical Sciences Campus
GPO Box 365067
San Juan, PR 00936
Tel: 787 763-2440   *Fax:* 787 758-1119
E-mail: jjlojomd@onelinkpr.net
Length: 5 Yrs   *ACGME Approved/Offered Positions:* 43
Program ID: 440-42-21-313

Rhode Island

Providence

Brown University Program
Sponsor: Rhode Island Hospital-Lifespan
Miriam Hospital-Lifespan
Veterans Affairs Medical Center (Providence)
Prgm Director: David T Harrington, MD
593 Eddy Street
APC 4
Providence, RI 02903
Tel: 401 444-5180   *Fax:* 401 444-6681
E-mail: prichardson@lifespan.org
Length: 5 Yrs   *ACGME Approved/Offered Positions:* 46
Program ID: 440-43-21-314

South Carolina

Charleston

Medical University of South Carolina Program
Sponsor: Medical University of South Carolina College of Medicine
MUSC Medical Center
Prgm Director: Thomas E Brothers, MD
96 Jonathan Lucas, PO Box 250613
Charleston, SC 29425
Tel: 843 792-3072   *Fax:* 843 792-8286
Length: 5 Yrs   *ACGME Approved/Offered Positions:* 46
Program ID: 440-45-21-315

Columbia

Palmetto Health/University of South Carolina School of Medicine Program
Sponsor: Palmetto Health
Palmetto Health Richland
William Jennings Bryan Dorn Veterans Hospital
Prgm Director: Richard M Bell, MD
University of South Carolina
Two Richland Medical Park, #402
Columbia, SC 29203
Tel: 803 256-2657   *Fax:* 803 933-9545
Length: 5 Yrs   *ACGME Approved/Offered Positions:* 17
Program ID: 440-45-21-316

Greenville

Greenville Hospital System/University of South Carolina School of Medicine Program
Sponsor: Greenville Hospital System/University of South Carolina
Prgm Director: Dane E Smith, MD
Department of Surgery
701 Grove Road
Greenville, SC 29605
Tel: 864 455-7886   *Fax:* 864 455-1320
E-mail: mostrowski@ghs.org
Length: 5 Yrs   *ACGME Approved/Offered Positions:* 24
Program ID: 440-45-11-317

Spartanburg

Spartanburg Regional Healthcare System Program
Sponsor: Spartanburg Regional Healthcare System
Prgm Director: Richard K Orr, MD, MPH
101 E Wood Street
Spartanburg, SC 29303
Tel: 864 560-6285   *Fax:* 864 560-6063
E-mail: slipsey@srhs.com
Length: 5 Yrs   *ACGME Approved/Offered Positions:* 18
Program ID: 440-45-31-318

Tennessee

Chattanooga

University of Tennessee College of Medicine at Chattanooga Program
Sponsor: University of Tennessee College of Medicine-Chattanooga
Erlanger Medical Center
Prgm Director: Joseph B Cofer, MD
979 East Third Street, Suite 401
Chattanooga, TN 37403
Tel: 423 778-7695   *Fax:* 423 778-2950
Length: 5 Yrs   *ACGME Approved/Offered Positions:* 28
Program ID: 440-47-11-320

Johnson City

East Tennessee State University Program
Sponsor: James H Quillen College of Medicine
Johnson City Medical Center/Mountain States Health Alliance
Veterans Affairs Medical Center (Mountain Home)
Wellmont Health System - Bristol Regional Medical Center
Wellmont Health System - Holston Valley
Prgm Director: Mark A Lockett, MD
Department of Surgery
Box 70575
Johnson City, TN 37614
Tel: 423 439-6267   *Fax:* 423 439-6259
E-mail: lockett@etsu.edu
Length: 5 Yrs   *ACGME Approved/Offered Positions:* 34
Program ID: 440-47-21-377

Knoxville

University of Tennessee Medical Center at Knoxville Program
Sponsor: University of Tennessee Graduate School of Medicine
University of Tennessee Memorial Hospital
Prgm Director: Mitchell H Goldman, MD
University Memorial Hospital
1924 Alcoa Highway, Box U-11
Knoxville, TN 37920
Tel: 865 305-9230   *Fax:* 865 305-6958
E-mail: gmiya@utmck.edu
Length: 5 Yrs   *ACGME Approved/Offered Positions:* 28
Program ID: 440-47-11-321

Memphis

University of Tennessee Program
Sponsor: University of Tennessee College of Medicine
Baptist Memorial Hospital
Methodist Healthcare - Memphis Hospitals
Regional Medical Center at Memphis
Veterans Affairs Medical Center (Memphis)
Prgm Director: Frances E Pritchard, MD
910 Madison Ave
2nd Floor
Memphis, TN 38163
Tel: 901 448-7635   *Fax:* 901 448-7306
E-mail: fpritchard@utmem.edu
Length: 5 Yrs   *ACGME Approved/Offered Positions:* 51
Program ID: 440-47-21-324

Nashville

Vanderbilt University Program
Sponsor: Vanderbilt University Medical Center
Veterans Affairs Medical Center (Nashville)
Prgm Director: John L Tarpley, MD
D-4314 MCN
1161 21st Avenue, South
Nashville, TN 37232
Tel: 615 343-6642   *Fax:* 615 322-0689
E-mail: john.tarpley@vanderbilt.edu
Length: 5 Yrs   *ACGME Approved/Offered Positions:* 58
Program ID: 440-47-21-327

Note: * indicates a newly appointed program director

Texas

Austin

University of Texas Medical Branch (Austin) Program

Sponsor: University of Texas Medical Branch Hospitals
University Medical Center at Brackenridge
Prgm Director: Carlos Brown, MD
601 East 15th Street
Austin, TX 78701
Tel: 512 324-7390   *Fax:* 512 324-7399
E-mail: surgeryres@seton.org
Length: 5 Yrs   *ACGME Approved/Offered Positions:* 15
Program ID: 440-48-13-424

Dallas

Baylor University Medical Center Program

Sponsor: Baylor University Medical Center
John Peter Smith Hospital (Tarrant County Hospital District)
Texas Health Presbyterian Dallas
Prgm Director: Ronald C Jones, MD
3500 Gaston Avenue
Dallas, TX 75246
Tel: 214 820-2468   *Fax:* 214 820-4538
Length: 5 Yrs   *ACGME Approved/Offered Positions:* 45
Program ID: 440-48-21-328

Methodist Health System Dallas Program

Sponsor: Methodist Health System Dallas
Prgm Director: Ernest L Dunn, MD
1441 N Beckley Avenue
PO Box 655999
Dallas, TX 75265
Tel: 214 947-2303   *Fax:* 214 947-2361
E-mail: bertaturner@mhd.com
Length: 5 Yrs   *ACGME Approved/Offered Positions:* 15
Program ID: 440-48-12-329

University of Texas Southwestern Medical School Program

Sponsor: University of Texas Southwestern Medical School
Dallas County Hospital District-Parkland Memorial Hospital
Dallas VA Medical Center
University Hospitals St Paul
Prgm Director: R James Valentine, MD
Department of Surgery
5323 Harry Hines Boulevard
Dallas, TX 75390
Tel: 214 648-3514   *Fax:* 214 648-7969
E-mail: james.valentine@utsouthwestern.edu
Length: 5 Yrs   *ACGME Approved/Offered Positions:* 95
Program ID: 440-48-21-331

El Paso

Texas Tech University Health Sciences Center Paul L Foster School of Medicine Program

Sponsor: Texas Tech University Hlth Sci Ctr Paul L Foster Sch of Med
R E Thomason General Hospital / Texas Tech University HSC
Prgm Director: Steve H Dougherty, MD
Paul L Foster School of Medicine
4800 Alberta Ave
El Paso, TX 79905
Tel: 915 545-6855   *Fax:* 915 545-6864
Length: 5 Yrs   *ACGME Approved/Offered Positions:* 18
Program ID: 440-48-11-332

William Beaumont Army Medical Center Program

Sponsor: William Beaumont Army Medical Center
Swedish Medical Center HealthONE
Prgm Director: Jason M Johnson, DO*
General Surgery Service
5005 N Piedras Street
El Paso, TX 79920
Tel: 915 569-2698   *Fax:* 915 569-2602
E-mail: jason.johnson35@us.army.mil
Length: 5 Yrs   *ACGME Approved/Offered Positions:* 16
Program ID: 440-48-12-009
Uniformed Services Program

Fort Sam Houston

San Antonio Uniformed Services Health Education Consortium (BAMC) Program

Sponsor: San Antonio Uniformed Services Health Education Consortium
Brooke Army Medical Center
Wilford Hall Medical Center (AETC)
Prgm Director: Col Thomas E Le Voyer, MD
3851 Roger Brooke Drive
Fort Sam Houston, TX 78234
Tel: 210 916-0439   *Fax:* 210 916-6658
Length: 5 Yrs   *ACGME Approved/Offered Positions:* 29
Program ID: 440-48-22-010
Uniformed Services Program

Galveston

University of Texas Medical Branch Hospitals Program

Sponsor: University of Texas Medical Branch Hospitals
St Joseph Medical Center
Prgm Director: Kristene K Gugliuzza, MD
Department of Surgery
301 University Boulevard
Galveston, TX 77555
Tel: 409 772-2412   *Fax:* 409 777-7364
Length: 5 Yrs   *ACGME Approved/Offered Positions:* 28
Program ID: 440-48-11-333

Houston

Baylor College of Medicine Program

Sponsor: Baylor College of Medicine
Harris County Hospital District-Ben Taub General Hospital
Michael E DeBakey VA Medical Center - Houston
St Luke's Episcopal Hospital
Prgm Director: Francis C Brunicardi, MD
One Baylor Plaza, Room 404D
Houston, TX 77030
Tel: 713 798-6078   *Fax:* 713 798-8941
E-mail: holmesly@bcm.edu
Length: 5 Yrs   *ACGME Approved/Offered Positions:* 63
Program ID: 440-48-21-334

Methodist Hospital (Houston) Program

Sponsor: Methodist Hospital (Houston)
Memorial Hermann Hospital
Prgm Director: Barbara L Bass, MD
6550 Fannin Street, Smith Tower 1661
Department of Surgery
Houston, TX 77030
Tel: 713 441-5132   *Fax:* 713 790-6300
E-mail: MLJohnson@tmhs.org
Length: 5 Yrs   *ACGME Approved/Offered Positions:* 28
Program ID: 440-48-22-335

University of Texas at Houston Program

Sponsor: University of Texas Health Science Center at Houston
Lyndon B Johnson General Hospital
Memorial Hermann Hospital
Prgm Director: John R Potts III, MD
Department of Surgery
6431 Fannin St, Room 4.162
Houston, TX 77030
Tel: 713 500-7216   *Fax:* 713 500-7239
E-mail: Kathalyn.Gonzalez@uth.tmc.edu
Length: 5 Yrs   *ACGME Approved/Offered Positions:* 54
Program ID: 440-48-21-337

Lubbock

Texas Tech University (Lubbock) Program

Sponsor: Texas Tech University Health Sciences Center at Lubbock
University Medical Center
Prgm Director: Ari O Halldorsson, MD
Department of Surgery
3601 4th Street
Lubbock, TX 79430
Tel: 806 743-2370   *Fax:* 806 743-1475
E-mail: kristen.brake@ttuhsc.edu
Length: 5 Yrs   *ACGME Approved/Offered Positions:* 18
Program ID: 440-48-21-363

San Antonio

University of Texas Health Science Center at San Antonio Program

Sponsor: University of Texas School of Medicine at San Antonio
Audie L Murphy Memorial Veterans Hospital (San Antonio)
Christus Santa Rosa Health Care Corporation
University Health System
Wilford Hall Medical Center (AETC)
Prgm Director: Daniel L Dent, MD
7703 Floyd Curl Drive, MSC 7737
San Antonio, TX 78229
Tel: 210 567-5711   *Fax:* 210 567-2347
E-mail: kleffnere@uthscsa.edu
Length: 5 Yrs   *ACGME Approved/Offered Positions:* 76
Program ID: 440-48-21-338

Temple

Texas A&M College of Medicine-Scott and White Program

Sponsor: Scott and White Memorial Hospital
Central Texas Veterans Affairs Healthcare System
Prgm Director: Mohsen M Shabahang, MD, PhD
2401 S 31st Street
Temple, TX 76508
Tel: 254 724-2366   *Fax:* 254 724-9186
E-mail: lbillingsley@swmail.sw.org
Length: 5 Yrs   *ACGME Approved/Offered Positions:* 31
Program ID: 440-48-21-339

Utah

Salt Lake City

University of Utah Program

Sponsor: University of Utah Medical Center
LDS Hospital
Prgm Director: James McGreevy, MD
50 N Medical Drive
Salt Lake City, UT 84132
Tel: 801 581-6803   *Fax:* 801 581-7122
Length: 5 Yrs   *ACGME Approved/Offered Positions:* 37
Program ID: 440-49-21-340

Programs

Vermont

Burlington

University of Vermont Program
Sponsor: Fletcher Allen Health Care
Prgm Director: Kennith H Sartorelli, MD
Surgery Education Office, Fletcher House 309
111 Colchester Avenue
Burlington, VT 05401
Tel: 802 847-2566   *Fax:* 802 847-9528
Length: 5 Yrs   *ACGME Approved/Offered Positions:* 20
Program ID: 440-50-21-341

Virginia

Charlottesville

University of Virginia Program
Sponsor: University of Virginia Medical Center
Veterans Affairs Medical Center (Salem)
Prgm Director: Bruce D Schirmer, MD
PO Box 800681
2nd Floor Link, Rm 2004
Charlottesville, VA 22908
Tel: 434 924-9307   *Fax:* 434 243-5791
Length: 5 Yrs   *ACGME Approved/Offered Positions:* 51
Program ID: 440-51-21-342

Falls Church

Inova Fairfax Hospital/Inova Fairfax Hospital for Children Program
Sponsor: Inova Fairfax Hospital
Prgm Director: H David Reines, MD
3300 Gallows Road
Falls Church, VA 22042
Tel: 703 776-3564   *Fax:* 703 776-2338
E-mail: hdavid.reines@inova.org
Length: 5 Yrs   *ACGME Approved/Offered Positions:* 15
Program ID: 440-51-21-412

Norfolk

Eastern Virginia Medical School Program
Sponsor: Eastern Virginia Medical School
Children's Hospital of the King's Daughters
Sentara Bayside Hospital
Sentara Leigh Hospital
Sentara Norfolk General Hospital
Prgm Director: L D Britt, MD, MPH
6th Floor, Hofheimer Hall
825 Fairfax Avenue
Norfolk, VA 23507
Tel: 757 446-8950   *Fax:* 757 446-8951
Length: 5 Yrs   *ACGME Approved/Offered Positions:* 37
Program ID: 440-51-21-343

Portsmouth

Naval Medical Center (Portsmouth) Program
Sponsor: Naval Medical Center (Portsmouth)
Sentara Norfolk General Hospital
Prgm Director: Beth R Jaklic, MD
Department of General Surgery (Code 04GS)
620 John Paul Jones Circle
Portsmouth, VA 23708
Tel: 757 953-2992   *Fax:* 757 953-0845
Length: 5 Yrs   *ACGME Approved/Offered Positions:* 24
Program ID: 440-51-32-015
Uniformed Services Program

Richmond

Virginia Commonwealth University Health System Program
Sponsor: Virginia Commonwealth University Health
System
Hunter Holmes McGuire VA Medical Center (Richmond)
Medical College of Virginia Hospitals
Prgm Director: Brian J Kaplan, MD
PO Box 980135
Richmond, VA 23298
Tel: 804 828-2755   *Fax:* 804 828-5595
E-mail: fheath@vcu.edu
Length: 5 Yrs   *ACGME Approved/Offered Positions:* 40
Program ID: 440-51-21-344

Roanoke

Carilion Clinic Program
Sponsor: Carilion Clinic
Carilion Roanoke Memorial Hospital
Prgm Director: Robert S Smith, MD*
Belleview Avenue at Jefferson Street
PO Box 13367
Roanoke, VA 24033
Tel: 540 986-8681   *Fax:* 540 857-5299
E-mail: rssmith@carilion.com
Length: 5 Yrs   *ACGME Approved/Offered Positions:* 27
Program ID: 440-51-31-345

Washington

Seattle

Swedish Medical Center/First Hill Program
Sponsor: Swedish Medical Center
Harborview Medical Center
Prgm Director: Michael J Hart, MD
747 Broadway
Surgery Residency Program, Suite WW 739
Seattle, WA 98122
Tel: 206 386-2123   *Fax:* 206 860-6540
Length: 5 Yrs   *ACGME Approved/Offered Positions:* 21
Program ID: 440-54-32-347

University of Washington Program
Sponsor: University of Washington School of Medicine
Harborview Medical Center
University of Washington Medical Center
VA Puget Sound Health Care System
Prgm Director: Karen D Horvath, MD
1959 NE Pacific Street
Box 356410
Seattle, WA 98195
Tel: 206 543-3687   *Fax:* 206 543-8136
Length: 5 Yrs   *ACGME Approved/Offered Positions:* 69
Program ID: 440-54-21-348

Virginia Mason Medical Center Program
Sponsor: Virginia Mason Medical Center
Harborview Medical Center
Prgm Director: Richard C Thirlby, MD
925 Seneca St
H8-GME
Seattle, WA 98111
Tel: 206 583-6079   *Fax:* 206 583-2307
Length: 5 Yrs   *ACGME Approved/Offered Positions:* 31
Program ID: 440-54-12-349

Tacoma

Madigan Army Medical Center Program
Sponsor: Madigan Army Medical Center
Prgm Director: Tommy A Brown, MD
General Surgery Service
MCHJ-SGY
Tacoma, WA 98431
Tel: 253 968-2200   *Fax:* 253 968-0232
E-mail: tommy.brown@us.army.mil
Length: 5 Yrs   *ACGME Approved/Offered Positions:* 18
Program ID: 440-54-12-011
Uniformed Services Program

West Virginia

Charleston

Charleston Area Medical Center/West Virginia University (Charleston Division) Program
Sponsor: Charleston Area Medical Center/West Virginia
University
Prgm Director: John A DeLuca, MD
3110 Mac Corkle Ave
Charleston, WV 25304
Tel: 304 347-1338   *Fax:* 304 388-9958
Length: 5 Yrs   *ACGME Approved/Offered Positions:* 19
Program ID: 440-55-11-351

Huntington

Marshall University School of Medicine Program
Sponsor: Marshall University School of Medicine
Cabell Huntington Hospital
St Mary's Hospital
Veterans Affairs Medical Center (Huntington)
Prgm Director: David A Denning, MD
1600 Medical Center Dr, Suite 2500
Huntington, WV 25701
Tel: 304 691-1280   *Fax:* 304 691-1287
E-mail: cremeans16@marshall.edu
Length: 5 Yrs   *ACGME Approved/Offered Positions:* 18
Program ID: 440-55-21-366

Morgantown

West Virginia University Program
Sponsor: West Virginia University School of Medicine
West Virginia University Hospitals
Prgm Director: Cynthia F Graves, MD
Health Sciences Center N, Room 7700
PO Box 9238
Morgantown, WV 26506
Tel: 304 293-5169   *Fax:* 304 293-8881
E-mail: cgraves@hsc.wvu.edu
Length: 5 Yrs   *ACGME Approved/Offered Positions:* 21
Program ID: 440-55-21-352

Wisconsin

La Crosse

Gundersen Lutheran Medical Foundation Program
Sponsor: Gundersen Lutheran Medical Foundation
Gundersen Clinic Ltd
Gundersen Lutheran Medical Center
Prgm Director: Thomas H Cogbill, MD
1836 South Avenue
Mail Code C05-001
La Crosse, WI 54601
Tel: 608 775-2431   *Fax:* 608 775-4460
Length: 5 Yrs   *ACGME Approved/Offered Positions:* 10
Program ID: 440-56-12-354

Note: * indicates a newly appointed program director

Madison

University of Wisconsin Program
Sponsor: University of Wisconsin Hospital and Clinics
William S Middleton Veterans Hospital
Prgm Director: Eugene F Foley, MD*
600 Highland Avenue
K4/758 Clinical Science Center
Madison, WI 53792
Tel: 608 263-2521   *Fax:* 608 263-7652
E-mail: foleyc@surgery.wisc.edu
Length: 5 Yrs   *ACGME Approved/Offered Positions:* 36
Program ID: 440-56-21-355

Marshfield

Marshfield Clinic-St Joseph's Hospital Program
Sponsor: Marshfield Clinic-St Joseph's Hospital
Prgm Director: Ronald F Martin, MD*
Marshfield Clinic
1000 North Oak Avenue
Marshfield, WI 54449
Tel: 800 541-2895   *Fax:* 715 389-4454
Length: 5 Yrs   *ACGME Approved/Offered Positions:* 10
Program ID: 440-56-31-356

Milwaukee

Medical College of Wisconsin Affiliated Hospitals Program
Sponsor: Medical College of Wisconsin Affiliated Hospitals, Inc
Clement J Zablocki Veterans Affairs Medical Center
Froedtert Memorial Lutheran Hospital
Prgm Director: Alonzo P Walker, MD
Department of Surgery
9200 West Wisconsin Avenue
Milwaukee, WI 53226
Tel: 414 805-8632   *Fax:* 414 454-0152
E-mail: jsimonso@mcw.edu
Length: 5 Yrs   *ACGME Approved/Offered Positions:* 39
Program ID: 440-56-21-357

Surgical Critical Care (General Surgery)

Alabama

Birmingham

University of Alabama Medical Center Program
Sponsor: University of Alabama Hospital
Prgm Director: Donald A Reiff, MD
Department of Surgery
701 South 19th Street (Suite 112)
Birmingham, AL 35294
Tel: 205 996-4044   *Fax:* 205 975-3035
Length: 1 Yr   *ACGME Approved/Offered Positions:* 2
Program ID: 442-01-21-079

Arizona

Phoenix

Maricopa Medical Center Program
Sponsor: Maricopa Medical Center
Mayo Clinic (Arizona)
Prgm Director: Patrick J O'Neill, MD, PhD
2601 East Roosevelt Street
Phoenix, AZ 85008
Tel: 602 344-5637   *Fax:* 602 344-0793
E-mail: Patrick_ONeill@medprodoctors.com
Length: 1 Yr   *ACGME Approved/Offered Positions:* 2
Program ID: 442-03-31-118

California

Fresno

University of California (San Francisco)/Fresno Program
Sponsor: UCSF Fresno Medical Education Program
Community Medical Centers (Fresno)
Prgm Director: Krista L Kaups, MD
2823 Fresno Street
Department of Surgery 1st Floor
Fresno, CA 93721
Tel: 559 459-3770   *Fax:* 559 459-3719
Length: 1 Yr   *ACGME Approved/Offered Positions:* 1
Program ID: 442-05-21-067

Los Angeles

Cedars-Sinai Medical Center Program
Sponsor: Cedars-Sinai Medical Center
Prgm Director: Daniel R Margulies, MD
8700 Beverly Boulevard
Department of Surgery, Room 8215
Los Angeles, CA 90048
Tel: 310 423-5874   *Fax:* 310 423-0139
E-mail: daniel.margulies@cshs.org
Length: 1 Yr   *ACGME Approved/Offered Positions:* 2
Program ID: 442-05-21-046

Childrens Hospital Los Angeles Program
Sponsor: Childrens Hospital Los Angeles
LAC+USC Medical Center
Prgm Director: Henri R Ford, MD
4650 Sunset Boulevard
Mailstop 72
Los Angeles, CA 90027
Tel: 323 361-2104   *Fax:* 323 361-3534
Length: 1 Yr   *ACGME Approved/Offered Positions:* 1
Program ID: 442-05-31-114

University of Southern California/ LAC+USC Medical Center Program
Sponsor: University of Southern California/LAC+USC Medical Center
LAC+USC Medical Center
USC University Hospital
Prgm Director: Kenji Inaba, MD, MS
Division of Trauma & Critical Care, Room 10-750
1200 N State Street
Los Angeles, CA 90033
Tel: 323 409-8597
E-mail: kinaba@surgery.usc.edu
Length: 1 Yr   *ACGME Approved/Offered Positions:* 3
Program ID: 442-05-31-058

Orange

University of California (Irvine) Program
Sponsor: University of California (Irvine) Medical Center
Prgm Director: Marianne Cinat, MD
333 City Blvd West
Suite 705, Route 81
Orange, CA 92868
Tel: 714 456-5840   *Fax:* 714 456-6048
E-mail: mjanczak@uci.edu
Length: 1 Yr   *ACGME Approved/Offered Positions:* 2
Program ID: 442-05-21-003

Sacramento

University of California (Davis) Health System Program
Sponsor: University of California (Davis) Health System
University of California (Davis) Medical Center
Prgm Director: Christine S Cocanour, MD
Department of Surgery
2315 Stockton Blvd, Rm 4206
Sacramento, CA 95817
Tel: 916 734-7330   *Fax:* 916 734-7755
E-mail: christine.cocanour@ucdmc.ucdavis.edu
Length: 1 Yr   *ACGME Approved/Offered Positions:* 2
Program ID: 442-05-21-017

San Diego

University of California (San Diego) Program
Sponsor: University of California (San Diego) Medical Center
Prgm Director: Raul Coimbra, MD, PhD
200 West Arbor Drive, #8896
San Diego, CA 92103
Tel: 619 543-7200   *Fax:* 619 543-7202
Length: 1 Yr   *ACGME Approved/Offered Positions:* 2
Program ID: 442-05-21-052

San Francisco

University of California (San Francisco) Program
Sponsor: University of California (San Francisco) School of Medicine
San Francisco General Hospital Medical Center
UCSF and Mount Zion Medical Centers
Prgm Director: Andre R Campbell, MD
1001 Potrero Avenue
San Francisco, CA 94110
Tel: 415 206-4627
Length: 1 Yr   *ACGME Approved/Offered Positions:* 1
Program ID: 442-05-21-075

Stanford

Stanford University Program
Sponsor: Stanford Hospital and Clinics
Prgm Director: David A Spain, MD
300 Pasteur Drive
Suite H3680
Stanford, CA 94305
Tel: 650 723-0173   *Fax:* 650 725-0791
E-mail: dspain@stanford.edu
Length: 1 Yr   *ACGME Approved/Offered Positions:* 1
Program ID: 442-05-21-112

Colorado

Aurora

University of Colorado Denver Program
Sponsor: University of Colorado Denver School of
  Medicine
Denver Health Medical Center
University of Colorado Hospital
Prgm Director: Catherine C Cothren, MD
777 Bannock Street MC 0206
Denver, CO 80204
Tel: 303 436-6558   *Fax:* 303 436-6572
Length: 1 Yr   *ACGME Approved/Offered Positions:* 2
Program ID: 442-07-13-094

Connecticut

Farmington

University of Connecticut Program
Sponsor: University of Connecticut School of Medicine
Hartford Hospital
Prgm Director: Karyn L Butler, MD*
Surgical Critical Care Division
80 Seymour Street
Hartford, CT 06102
Tel: 860 545-4291   *Fax:* 860 545-3266
Length: 1 Yr   *ACGME Approved/Offered Positions:* 4
Program ID: 442-08-21-020

New Haven

Yale-New Haven Medical Center Program
Sponsor: Yale-New Haven Hospital
Prgm Director: Lewis J Kaplan, MD
Section of Trauma and Surgical Critical Care
330 Cedar Street, BB310
New Haven, CT 06520
Tel: 203 737-5684   *Fax:* 203 785-3950
E-mail: lewis.kaplan@yale.edu
Length: 1 Yr   *ACGME Approved/Offered Positions:* 2
Program ID: 442-08-21-045

Delaware

Wilmington

Christiana Care Health Services Program
Sponsor: Christiana Care Health Services Inc
Alfred I duPont Hospital for Children
Prgm Director: Gerard J Fulda, MD
4755 Ogletown-Stanton Road
Room 2325
Newark, DE 19718
Tel: 302 733-4260   *Fax:* 302 733-4264
E-mail: gfulda@christianacare.org
Length: 1 Yr   *ACGME Approved/Offered Positions:* 2
Program ID: 442-09-21-093

District of Columbia

Washington

Washington Hospital Center Program
Sponsor: Washington Hospital Center
Prgm Director: Jack A Sava, MD*
110 Irving Street, NW, Room G253
Washington, DC 20010
Tel: 202 877-7259   *Fax:* 202 877-7258
Length: 1 Yr   *ACGME Approved/Offered Positions:* 3
Program ID: 442-10-21-048

Florida

Gainesville

University of Florida Program
Sponsor: University of Florida College of Medicine
Shands Hospital at the University of Florida
Prgm Director: Larry C Martin, MD
1600 SW Archer Road
PO Box 100286
Gainesville, FL 32610
Tel: 352 273-5670   *Fax:* 352 273-5684
Length: 1 Yr   *ACGME Approved/Offered Positions:* 2
Program ID: 442-11-13-125

Jacksonville

University of Florida College of Medicine Jacksonville Program
Sponsor: University of Florida College of Medicine
  Jacksonville
Shands Jacksonville Medical Center
Prgm Director: Miren Schinco, MD
653-2 West 8th Street, Box FC12
Faculty Clinic, 3rd Floor
Jacksonville, FL 32209
Tel: 904 244-3903   *Fax:* 904 244-3870
E-mail: heidi.weschler@jax.ufl.edu
Length: 1 Yr   *ACGME Approved/Offered Positions:* 3
Program ID: 442-11-13-108

Miami

Jackson Memorial Hospital/Jackson Health System Program
Sponsor: Jackson Memorial Hospital/Jackson Health
  System
Prgm Director: Juan Asensio, MD
1800 NW 10th Avenue
Suite T215
Miami, FL 33136
Tel: 305 355-1118   *Fax:* 305 326-7065
Length: 1 Yr   *ACGME Approved/Offered Positions:* 6
Program ID: 442-11-21-004

Orlando

Orlando Health Program
Sponsor: Orlando Health
Orlando Regional Medical Center
Prgm Director: Michael L Cheatham, MD
86 W Underwood Street
Suite 201, MP 100
Orlando, FL 32806
Tel: 407 841-5296   *Fax:* 407 648-3686
Length: 1 Yr   *ACGME Approved/Offered Positions:* 2
Program ID: 442-11-21-068

Tampa

University of South Florida Program
Sponsor: University of South Florida College of Medicine
Tampa General Hospital
Prgm Director: Suneel Khetarpal, MD
2 Columbia Drive
Room G 417
Tampa, FL 33606
Tel: 813 844-7968   *Fax:* 813 844-4049
E-mail: ebeilman@health.usf.edu
Length: 1 Yr   *ACGME Approved/Offered Positions:* 1
Program ID: 442-11-21-104

Georgia

Atlanta

Emory University Program
Sponsor: Emory University School of Medicine
Grady Health System
Prgm Director: Grace S Rozycki, MD, MBA
69 Jesse Hill Jr Drive, SE
Glenn Memorial Bldg, Suite 302
Atlanta, GA 30303
Tel: 404 616-3553   *Fax:* 404 616-7333
E-mail: grozyck@emory.edu
Length: 1 Yr   *ACGME Approved/Offered Positions:* 2
Program ID: 442-12-21-069

Macon

Mercer University School of Medicine Program
Sponsor: Medical Center of Central Georgia
Prgm Director: Dennis W Ashley, MD
777 Hemlock Street, Hospital Box 103
Macon, GA 31201
Tel: 478 633-1199   *Fax:* 478 633-6195
Length: 1 Yr   *ACGME Approved/Offered Positions:* 2
Program ID: 442-12-12-119

Hawaii

Honolulu

University of Hawaii Program
Sponsor: University of Hawaii John A Burns School of
  Medicine
Queen's Medical Center
Prgm Director: Mihae Yu, MD
1356 Lusitana Street, 6th Floor
Honolulu, HI 96813
Tel: 808 586-2920   *Fax:* 808 586-3022
E-mail: mihaey@hawaii.edu
Length: 1 Yr   *ACGME Approved/Offered Positions:* 2
Program ID: 442-14-21-036

Illinois

Chicago

John H Stroger Hospital of Cook County Program
Sponsor: John H Stroger Hospital of Cook County
Prgm Director: Krishnan Sriram, MD
Division of Surgical Critical Care
1901 West Harrison St, Room 3350
Chicago, IL 60612
Tel: 312 864-3133   *Fax:* 312 864-9633
E-mail: ksriram41@hotmail.com
Length: 1 Yr   *ACGME Approved/Offered Positions:* 2
Program ID: 442-16-12-087

Note: * indicates a newly appointed program director

McGaw Medical Center of Northwestern University Program

Sponsor: McGaw Medical Center of Northwestern University
Children's Memorial Hospital
Northwestern Memorial Hospital
Prgm Director: Michael B Shapiro, MD
201 East Huron Street, Galter 10-105
Department of Surgery
Chicago, IL 60611
Tel: 312 695-4835   *Fax:* 312 695-1462
Length: 1 Yr   *ACGME Approved/Offered Positions:* 2
Program ID: 442-16-12-123

McGaw Medical Center of Northwestern University/Children's Memorial Hospital Program

Sponsor: McGaw Medical Center of Northwestern University
Children's Memorial Hospital
Prgm Director: Anthony Chin, MD, MS*
Pediatric Surgery #63
2300 Children's Plaza
Chicago, IL 60614
Tel: 773 880-4912   *Fax:* 773 880-4588
Length: 1 Yr   *ACGME Approved/Offered Positions:* 2
Program ID: 442-16-31-077

University of Illinois College of Medicine at Chicago/Metropolitan Group Hospitals Program

Sponsor: University of Illinois College of Medicine at Chicago
Advocate Illinois Masonic Medical Center
Prgm Director: Richard J Fantus, MD
836 West Wellington Avenue
Room 4813 Center Court
Chicago, IL 60657
Tel: 773 296-7033   *Fax:* 773 296-7199
E-mail:
IMMC-SurgicalCriticalCare@advocatehealth.com
Length: 1 Yr   *ACGME Approved/Offered Positions:* 1
Program ID: 442-16-21-060

Maywood

Loyola University Program

Sponsor: Loyola University Medical Center
Edward Hines, Jr Veterans Affairs Hospital
Prgm Director: John M Santaniello, MD
2160 South First Avenue
EMS 110, Room 3274
Maywood, IL 60153
Tel: 708 327-2680   *Fax:* 708 327-3474
E-mail: jsantan@lumc.edu
Length: 1 Yr   *ACGME Approved/Offered Positions:* 1
Program ID: 442-16-21-102

Indiana

Indianapolis

Indiana University School of Medicine Program

Sponsor: Indiana University School of Medicine
Clarian Indiana University Hospital
Clarian Methodist Hospital of Indiana
William N Wishard Memorial Hospital
Prgm Director: Mark Falimirski, MD
1030 W Michigan St
C5226
Indianapolis, IN 46202
Tel: 317 278-8112
E-mail: mfalimir@iupui.edu
Length: 1 Yr   *ACGME Approved/Offered Positions:* 3
Program ID: 442-17-12-115

Iowa

Iowa City

University of Iowa Hospitals and Clinics Program

Sponsor: University of Iowa Hospitals and Clinics
Prgm Director: Kent Choi, MD, MS
200 Hawkins Drive
Iowa City, IA 52242
Tel: 319 384-6326   *Fax:* 319 356-3392
Length: 1 Yr   *ACGME Approved/Offered Positions:* 1
Program ID: 442-18-13-117

Kentucky

Lexington

University of Kentucky College of Medicine Program

Sponsor: University of Kentucky College of Medicine
University of Kentucky Hospital
Prgm Director: Paul A Kearney, MD
800 Rose Street
Department of Surgery, C207
Lexington, KY 40536
Tel: 859 323-6346   *Fax:* 859 323-6840
E-mail: pakear0@uky.edu
Length: 1 Yr   *ACGME Approved/Offered Positions:* 1
Program ID: 442-20-21-076

Louisville

University of Louisville Program

Sponsor: University of Louisville School of Medicine
University of Louisville Hospital
Prgm Director: Glen A Franklin, MD
Department of Surgery
Louisville, KY 40292
Tel: 502 852-1895   *Fax:* 502 852-8915
Length: 1 Yr   *ACGME Approved/Offered Positions:* 2
Program ID: 442-20-21-059

Louisiana

New Orleans

Louisiana State University Program

Sponsor: Louisiana State University School of Medicine
Medical Center of Louisiana at New Orleans
Prgm Director: John Patrick Hunt, MD
533 Bolivar Street
Room 508
New Orleans, LA 70112
Tel: 504 940-8407   *Fax:* 504 568-4633
Length: 1 Yr   *ACGME Approved/Offered Positions:* 2
Program ID: 442-21-13-090

Maryland

Baltimore

Johns Hopkins University Program

Sponsor: Johns Hopkins University School of Medicine
Johns Hopkins Hospital
Prgm Director: Pamela A Lipsett, MD
Dept of Surgery, Osler 603
600 N Wolfe Street
Baltimore, MD 21287
Tel: 410 955-3739   *Fax:* 410 614-9083
E-mail: plipsett@jhmi.edu
Length: 1 Yr   *ACGME Approved/Offered Positions:* 2
Program ID: 442-23-31-009

University of Maryland Program

Sponsor: University of Maryland Medical System
Prgm Director: William C Chiu, MD
Division of Surgical Critical Care
22 South Greene Street, T3R32
Baltimore, MD 21201
Tel: 410 328-3587   *Fax:* 410 328-8925
E-mail: sjordan@umm.edu
Length: 1 Yr   *ACGME Approved/Offered Positions:* 8
Program ID: 442-23-21-032

Massachusetts

Boston

Beth Israel Deaconess Medical Center Program

Sponsor: Beth Israel Deaconess Medical Center
Prgm Director: Carl J Hauser, MD*
110 Francis Street, Suite 9B
Boston, MA 02215
Tel: 617 632-7364   *Fax:* 617 632-9917
E-mail: mmarion@bidmc.harvard.edu
Length: 1 Yr   *ACGME Approved/Offered Positions:* 1
Program ID: 442-24-21-042

Boston University Medical Center Program

Sponsor: Boston Medical Center
Prgm Director: Suresh Agarwal, MD*
88 E Newton Street, C515
Boston, MA 02118
Tel: 617 414-8085   *Fax:* 617 414-8060
E-mail: Suresh.Agarwal@bmc.org
Length: 1 Yr   *ACGME Approved/Offered Positions:* 2
Program ID: 442-24-21-011

Brigham and Women's Hospital Program

Sponsor: Brigham and Women's Hospital
Prgm Director: Selwyn O Rogers Jr, MD, MPH
75 Francis Street
Boston, MA 02115
Tel: 617 732-8042   *Fax:* 617 582-6047
E-mail: srogers@partners.org
Length: 1 Yr   *ACGME Approved/Offered Positions:* 2
Program ID: 442-24-12-083

Children's Hospital Program

Sponsor: Children's Hospital
Prgm Director: Jay M Wilson, MD
300 Longwood Avenue, Fegan 3
Boston, MA 02115
Tel: 617 355-6019   *Fax:* 617 730-0477
Length: 1 Yr   *ACGME Approved/Offered Positions:* 2
Program ID: 442-24-31-082

Massachusetts General Hospital Program

Sponsor: Massachusetts General Hospital
Prgm Director: Hasan B Alam, MD
55 Fruit Street, CRP 810
Boston, MA 02114
Tel: 617 643-2433   *Fax:* 617 726-9121
Length: 1 Yr   *ACGME Approved/Offered Positions:* 2
Program ID: 442-24-21-054

Worcester

University of Massachusetts Program

Sponsor: University of Massachusetts Medical School
UMass Memorial Health Care (University Campus)
Prgm Director: Timothy A Emhoff, MD
Division of Trauma and Critical Care
55 Lake Avenue North
Worcester, MA 01655
Tel: 508 856-1168   *Fax:* 508 856-4224
E-mail: timothy.emhoff@umassmed.edu
Length: 1 Yr   *ACGME Approved/Offered Positions:* 2
Program ID: 442-24-21-012

Programs

Michigan

Ann Arbor

University of Michigan Program
Sponsor: University of Michigan Hospitals and Health
Centers
Prgm Director: Lena M Napolitano, MD
1500 E Medical Center Drive
1C421 University Hospital
Ann Arbor, MI 48109
Tel: 734 615-4775   *Fax:* 734 936-9657
Length: 1 Yr   *ACGME Approved/Offered Positions:* 7
Program ID: 442-25-21-013

Detroit

Henry Ford Hospital Program
Sponsor: Henry Ford Hospital
Prgm Director: Mary-Margaret Brandt, MD
Department of Surgery, CFP
2799 W Grand Blvd
Detroit, MI 48202
Tel: 313 916-3057   *Fax:* 313 916-8007
E-mail: mbrandt1@hfhs.org
Length: 1 Yr   *ACGME Approved/Offered Positions:* 3
Program ID: 442-25-21-026

Wayne State University/Detroit Medical Center Program
Sponsor: Wayne State University/Detroit Medical Center
Children's Hospital of Michigan
Detroit Receiving Hospital and University Health Center
Prgm Director: Marc L Cullen, MD
3901 Beaubien Boulevard
3rd Floor Carls Building
Detroit, MI 48201
Tel: 313 745-5839   *Fax:* 313 966-7696
Length: 1 Yr   *ACGME Approved/Offered Positions:* 1
Program ID: 442-25-31-027

Grand Rapids

Grand Rapids Medical Education and Research Center/Michigan State University Program
Sponsor: Grand Rapids Medical Education and Research
Center
Spectrum Health-Butterworth Hospital
Prgm Director: Bruce W Bonnell, MD
Surgical Critical Care Fellowship
221 Michigan Street NE, Suite 200A
Grand Rapids, MI 49503
Tel: 616 391-1691   *Fax:* 616 391-8611
Length: 1 Yr   *ACGME Approved/Offered Positions:* 2
Program ID: 442-25-21-014

Lansing

Michigan State University Program
Sponsor: Michigan State University College of Human
Medicine
Sparrow Hospital
Prgm Director: Chet A Morrison, MD
Surgical Critical Care
1200 E Michigan Avenue, Suite 655
Lansing, MI 48912
Tel: 517 267-2460   *Fax:* 517 267-2488
E-mail: chetmmd@pol.net
Length: 1 Yr   *ACGME Approved/Offered Positions:* 1
Program ID: 442-25-21-116

Minnesota

Minneapolis

University of Minnesota Program
Sponsor: University of Minnesota Medical School
Hennepin County Medical Examiner
North Memorial Health Care
Regions Hospital
University of Minnesota Medical Center, Division of
Fairview
Prgm Director: Jeffrey G Chipman, MD*
Department of Surgery, MMC11
420 Delaware Street, SE
Minneapolis, MN 55455
Tel: 612 625-7911   *Fax:* 612 626-0439
E-mail: chipm001@umn.edu
Length: 1 Yr   *ACGME Approved/Offered Positions:* 4
Program ID: 442-26-21-022

Rochester

College of Medicine, Mayo Clinic (Rochester) Program
Sponsor: College of Medicine, Mayo Clinic
Mayo Clinic (Rochester)
Saint Marys Hospital of Rochester
Prgm Director: Michael P Bannon, MD
Department of Surgery
200 First Street, SW
Rochester, MN 55905
Tel: 507 255-6365   *Fax:* 507 255-9872
E-mail: richardson.dianne@mayo.edu
Length: 1 Yr   *ACGME Approved/Offered Positions:* 2
Program ID: 442-26-21-034

Missouri

Columbia

University of Missouri-Columbia Program
Sponsor: University of Missouri-Columbia School of
Medicine
University Hospitals and Clinics
Prgm Director: Stephen L Barnes, MD*
One Hospital Drive
4th Floor McHaney Hall
Columbia, MO 65212
Tel: 573 884-8214   *Fax:* 573 884-3691
E-mail: barnesste@health.missouri.edu
Length: 1 Yr   *ACGME Approved/Offered Positions:* 1
Program ID: 442-28-21-016

Kansas City

University of Missouri at Kansas City Program
Sponsor: University of Missouri-Kansas City School of
Medicine
Children's Mercy Hospital
Prgm Director: Daniel J Ostlie, MD
2401 Gillham Road
Kansas City, MO 64108
Tel: 816 234-3575   *Fax:* 816 983-6885
Length: 1 Yr   *ACGME Approved/Offered Positions:* 1
Program ID: 442-28-21-071

St Louis

St Louis University School of Medicine Program
Sponsor: St Louis University School of Medicine
St John's Mercy Medical Center
St Louis University Hospital
Prgm Director: Catherine Wittgen, MD
3635 Vista Ave at Grand Blvd
PO Box 15250
St Louis, MO 63110
Tel: 314 577-8310   *Fax:* 314 268-5194
E-mail: wittgenc@slu.edu
Length: 1 Yr   *ACGME Approved/Offered Positions:* 1
Program ID: 442-28-21-023

Washington University/B-JH/SLCH Consortium Program
Sponsor: Washington University/B-JH/SLCH Consortium
Barnes-Jewish Hospital
Prgm Director: Craig M Coopersmith, MD
660 S Euclid Avenue
Box 8109
St Louis, MO 63110
Tel: 314 362-9342   *Fax:* 314 362-1602
Length: 1 Yr   *ACGME Approved/Offered Positions:* 2
Program ID: 442-28-21-051

Nevada

Las Vegas

University of Nevada School of Medicine (Las Vegas) Program
Sponsor: University of Nevada School of Medicine
University Medical Center of Southern Nevada
Prgm Director: John J Fildes, MD
2040 West Charleston Blvd
Suite 302
Las Vegas, NV 89102
Tel: 702 671-2273   *Fax:* 702 385-9399
E-mail: sthomas@medicine.nevada.edu
Length: 1 Yr   *ACGME Approved/Offered Positions:* 2
Program ID: 442-31-12-107

New Jersey

Camden

UMDNJ-Robert Wood Johnson Medical School (Camden) Program
Sponsor: Cooper Hospital-University Medical Center
Prgm Director: Steven E Ross, MD
Department of Surgery
3 Cooper Plaza, Suite 411
Camden, NJ 08103
Tel: 856 342-3341   *Fax:* 856 342-2817
Length: 1 Yr   *ACGME Approved/Offered Positions:* 2
Program ID: 442-33-21-031

Newark

UMDNJ-New Jersey Medical School Program
Sponsor: UMDNJ-New Jersey Medical School
UMDNJ-University Hospital
Prgm Director: Alicia M Mohr, MD*
New Jersey Trauma Center
150 Bergen Street, M-243
Newark, NJ 07103
Tel: 973 972-8294   *Fax:* 973 972-7441
E-mail: mohr@umdnj.edu
Length: 1 Yr   *ACGME Approved/Offered Positions:* 2
Program ID: 442-33-21-049

Note: * indicates a newly appointed program director

New York

Bronx

Lincoln Medical and Mental Health Center Program

Sponsor: Lincoln Medical and Mental Health Center
Prgm Director: Samuel P Kigongo, MD
234 East 149th Street
Department of Surgery
Bronx, NY 10451
Tel: 718 579-5900   *Fax:* 718 579-4620
E-mail: gonzalro@nychhc.org
Length: 1 Yr   *ACGME Approved/Offered Positions:* 1
Program ID: 442-35-31-033

Great Neck

NSLIJHS-North Shore University Hospital/NYU School of Medicine Program

Sponsor: North Shore-Long Island Jewish Health System
North Shore University Hospital
Prgm Director: Matthew A Bank, MD
300 Community Drive
Manhasset, NY 11030
Tel: 516 562-2993   *Fax:* 516 562-1576
E-mail: mbank@nshs.edu
Length: 1 Yr   *ACGME Approved/Offered Positions:* 1
Program ID: 442-35-31-100

Rochester

University of Rochester Program

Sponsor: Strong Memorial Hospital of the University of
 Rochester
Prgm Director: Nicole Stassen, MD*
601 Elmwood Avenue
Box Surg
Rochester, NY 14642
Tel: 585 275-3376   *Fax:* 585 276-1992
Length: 1 Yr   *ACGME Approved/Offered Positions:* 2
Program ID: 442-35-21-025

Stony Brook

SUNY at Stony Brook Program

Sponsor: University Hospital - SUNY at Stony Brook
Prgm Director: Marc J Shapiro, MD, MS
Division of GS/Trauma/Surgical Critical Care/Burn
Health Sciences Center, T18-040
Stony Brook, NY 11794
Tel: 631 444-1045   *Fax:* 631 444-6176
Length: 1 Yr   *ACGME Approved/Offered Positions:* 2
Program ID: 442-35-21-084

Valhalla

New York Medical College at Westchester Medical Center Program

Sponsor: New York Medical College
Westchester Medical Center
Prgm Director: John A Savino, MD
Department of Surgery
Munger Pavillion
Valhalla, NY 10595
Tel: 914 594-4352   *Fax:* 914 594-4359
E-mail: o_mateo-rodriguez@nymc.edu
Length: 1 Yr   *ACGME Approved/Offered Positions:* 4
Program ID: 442-35-11-035

North Carolina

Chapel Hill

University of North Carolina Hospitals Program

Sponsor: University of North Carolina Hospitals
Prgm Director: Renae E Stafford, MD, MPH
4008 Burnett-Womack Bldg
CB 7228
Chapel Hill, NC 27599
Tel: 919 966-4389   *Fax:* 919 966-0369
E-mail: renae_stafford@med.unc.edu
Length: 1 Yr   *ACGME Approved/Offered Positions:* 2
Program ID: 442-36-21-028

Durham

Duke University Hospital Program

Sponsor: Duke University Hospital
Prgm Director: Steven N Vaslef, MD, PhD
DUMC, Box 102345
Durham, NC 27710
Tel: 919 684-3636   *Fax:* 919 664-4392
E-mail: vasle001@mc.duke.edu
Length: 1 Yr   *ACGME Approved/Offered Positions:* 1
Program ID: 442-36-21-037

Greenville

Pitt County Memorial Hospital/East Carolina University Program

Sponsor: Pitt County Memorial Hospital
Prgm Director: Eric A Toschlog, MD
600 Moye Boulevard
Greenville, NC 27834
Tel: 252 847-5715   *Fax:* 252 847-8208
E-mail: etoschlo@pcmh.com
Length: 1 Yr   *ACGME Approved/Offered Positions:* 1
Program ID: 442-36-13-105

Winston-Salem

Wake Forest University School of Medicine Program

Sponsor: Wake Forest University Baptist Medical Center
Prgm Director: Preston R Miller, MD
Medical Center Boulevard
Winston-Salem, NC 27157
Tel: 336 716-0549   *Fax:* 336 716-9758
Length: 1 Yr   *ACGME Approved/Offered Positions:* 2
Program ID: 442-36-13-121

Ohio

Cincinnati

University Hospital/University of Cincinnati College of Medicine Program

Sponsor: University Hospital Inc
Prgm Director: Betty J Tsuei, MD
231 Albert Sabin Way
PO Box 670558
Cincinnati, OH 45267
Tel: 513 558-5661   *Fax:* 513 558-3136
E-mail: betty.tsuei@uc.edu
Length: 1 Yr   *ACGME Approved/Offered Positions:* 2
Program ID: 442-38-21-063

Cleveland

University Hospitals Case Medical Center Program

Sponsor: University Hospitals Case Medical Center
MetroHealth Medical Center
Prgm Director: Charles J Yowler, MD
2500 MetroHealth Drive
Cleveland, OH 44109
Tel: 216 778-5627
Length: 1 Yr   *ACGME Approved/Offered Positions:* 1
Program ID: 442-38-21-070

Columbus

Nationwide Children's Hospital/Ohio State University Program

Sponsor: Nationwide Children's Hospital
Prgm Director: Brian D Kenney, MD, MPH
700 Children's Drive, #ED379
Columbus, OH 43205
Tel: 614 722-3919   *Fax:* 614 722-3903
Length: 1 Yr   *ACGME Approved/Offered Positions:* 1
Program ID: 442-38-31-088

Ohio State University Hospital Program

Sponsor: Ohio State University Hospital
Prgm Director: Charles H Cook, MD
N-747 Doan Hall
410 W Tenth Avenue
Columbus, OH 43210
Tel: 614 293-4695   *Fax:* 614 293-4063
E-mail: anna.patterson@osumc.edu
Length: 1 Yr   *ACGME Approved/Offered Positions:* 4
Program ID: 442-38-21-021

Dayton

Wright State University Program

Sponsor: Wright State University Boonshoft School of
 Medicine
Children's Medical Center
Miami Valley Hospital
Prgm Director: Harry Linne Anderson, III, MD
Miami Valley Hospital
One Wyoming Street, Suite 7000 WCHE Building
Dayton, OH 45409
Tel: 937 208-2951   *Fax:* 937 208-2105
E-mail: harry.anderson@wright.edu
Length: 1 Yr   *ACGME Approved/Offered Positions:* 2
Program ID: 442-38-31-122

Oregon

Portland

Oregon Health & Science University Program

Sponsor: Oregon Health & Science University Hospital
Prgm Director: Martin A Schreiber, MD, BA
3181 SW Sam Jackson Park Rd, L611
Portland, OR 97239
Tel: 503 494-5300   *Fax:* 503 494-6519
Length: 1 Yr   *ACGME Approved/Offered Positions:* 3
Program ID: 442-40-21-064

Programs

Pennsylvania

Allentown

Lehigh Valley Hospital Network/Pennsylvania State University Program

Sponsor: Lehigh Valley Hospital Network
Prgm Director: Michael Badellino, MD, MPH
Cedar Crest & I-78
PO Box 689
Allentown, PA 18105
Tel: 610 402-8966   *Fax:* 610 402-1667
Length: 1 Yr   *ACGME Approved/Offered Positions:* 1
Program ID: 442-41-31-047

Hershey

Penn State University/Milton S Hershey Medical Center Program

Sponsor: Milton S Hershey Medical Center
Prgm Director: Daniel E Carney, MD, PhD
500 University Drive, MC H075
Hershey, PA 17033
Tel: 717 531-3563   *Fax:* 717 531-3784
E-mail: dcarney@hmc.psu.edu
Length: 1 Yr   *ACGME Approved/Offered Positions:* 1
Program ID: 442-41-21-041

Philadelphia

University of Pennsylvania Program

Sponsor: University of Pennsylvania Health System
Prgm Director: Patrick M Reilly, MD
3440 Market Street
Suite 101
Philadelphia, PA 19104
Tel: 215 662-7323   *Fax:* 215 349-5917
Length: 1 Yr   *ACGME Approved/Offered Positions:* 5
Program ID: 442-41-21-056

Pittsburgh

University of Pittsburgh Medical Center Medical Education Program

Sponsor: Univ of Pittsburgh Medical Center Medical Education
UPMC Presbyterian Shadyside
Prgm Director: Samuel Tisherman, MD
Department of Critical Care Medicine
3550 Terrace Street, 655 Scaife Hall
Pittsburgh, PA 15261
Tel: 412 647-3135   *Fax:* 412 647-8060
E-mail: tishermansa@upmc.edu
Length: 1 Yr   *ACGME Approved/Offered Positions:* 4
Program ID: 442-41-21-005

University of Pittsburgh Medical Center Medical Education Program A

Sponsor: Univ of Pittsburgh Medical Center Medical Education
Children's Hospital of Pittsburgh of UPMC
Prgm Director: Kelly A Miller, MD*
3705 Fifth Avenue
Pittsburgh, PA 15213
Tel: 412 692-5053   *Fax:* 412 692-8299
Length: 1 Yr   *ACGME Approved/Offered Positions:* 1
Program ID: 442-41-13-103

Rhode Island

Providence

Brown University Program

Sponsor: Rhode Island Hospital-Lifespan
Prgm Director: Charles A Adams Jr, MD
593 Eddy Street
(APC 435)
Providence, RI 02903
Tel: 401 444-5180   *Fax:* 401 444-6681
E-mail: prichardson@lifespan.org
Length: 1 Yr   *ACGME Approved/Offered Positions:* 1
Program ID: 442-43-21-044

South Carolina

Charleston

Medical University of South Carolina Program

Sponsor: Medical University of South Carolina College of Medicine
MUSC Medical Center
Prgm Director: Christian T Minshall, MD, PhD
96 Jonathan Lucas Street, Suite 420
PO Box 250613
Charleston, SC 29425
Tel: 843 792-3072   *Fax:* 843 792-3315
E-mail: wethersf@musc.edu
Length: 1 Yr   *ACGME Approved/Offered Positions:* 1
Program ID: 442-45-12-113

Columbia

Palmetto Health/University of South Carolina School of Medicine Program

Sponsor: Palmetto Health
Prgm Director: James Morrison, MD
Two Richland Medical Park
Suite 402
Columbia, SC 29203
Tel: 803 256-2657   *Fax:* 803 933-9545
E-mail: james.morrison@uscmed.sc.edu
Length: 1 Yr   *ACGME Approved/Offered Positions:* 1
Program ID: 442-45-11-095

Tennessee

Chattanooga

University of Tennessee College of Medicine at Chattanooga Program

Sponsor: University of Tennessee College of Medicine-Chattanooga
Erlanger Medical Center
Prgm Director: Robert A Maxwell, MD
Chattanooga Unit, Department of Surgery
979 East Third Street, Suite 401
Chattanooga, TN 37403
Tel: 423 778-7695   *Fax:* 423 778-2950
E-mail: cindy.schultz@universitysurgical.com
Length: 1 Yr   *ACGME Approved/Offered Positions:* 2
Program ID: 442-47-21-091

Knoxville

University of Tennessee Medical Center at Knoxville Program

Sponsor: University of Tennessee Graduate School of Medicine
University of Tennessee Memorial Hospital
Prgm Director: Blaine L Enderson, MD
1924 Alcoa Highway, U-11
Knoxville, TN 37920
Tel: 865 305-9230   *Fax:* 865 305-6958
E-mail: gmiya@utmck.edu
Length: 1 Yr   *ACGME Approved/Offered Positions:* 1
Program ID: 442-47-21-043

Memphis

University of Tennessee Program

Sponsor: University of Tennessee College of Medicine
Methodist Healthcare - Memphis Hospitals
Regional Medical Center at Memphis
Prgm Director: Martin A Croce, MD
910 Madison Avenue
Suite 220
Memphis, TN 38163
Tel: 901 448-8140   *Fax:* 901 448-8472
E-mail: npearson@utmem.edu
Length: 1 Yr   *ACGME Approved/Offered Positions:* 4
Program ID: 442-47-21-024

Nashville

Vanderbilt University Program

Sponsor: Vanderbilt University Medical Center
Prgm Director: Addison K May, MD
1211 21st Avenue South, 404 MAB
Nashville, TN 37212
Tel: 615 936-0177   *Fax:* 615 936-0185
E-mail: addison.may@vanderbilt.edu
Length: 1 Yr   *ACGME Approved/Offered Positions:* 4
Program ID: 442-47-21-007

Texas

Dallas

University of Texas Southwestern Medical School Program

Sponsor: University of Texas Southwestern Medical School
Dallas County Hospital District-Parkland Memorial Hospital
Prgm Director: Heidi Frankel, MD
Division of Burn/Trauma and Critical Care
5323 Harry Hines Blvd E5.514
Dallas, TX 75390
Tel: 214 648-5469   *Fax:* 214 648-2213
E-mail: criticalcare@utsouthwestern.edu
Length: 1 Yr   *ACGME Approved/Offered Positions:* 4
Program ID: 442-48-21-001

Fort Sam Houston

San Antonio Uniformed Services Health Education Consortium (BAMC) Program

Sponsor: San Antonio Uniformed Services Health Education Consortium
Brooke Army Medical Center
University of Texas Health Science Center
Prgm Director: Brian Eastridge, MD
3851 Roger Brooke Drive
Fort Sam Houston, TX 78234
Tel: 210 916-7104
E-mail: brian.eastridge@amedd.army.mil
Length: 1 Yr   *ACGME Approved/Offered Positions:* 3
Program ID: 442-48-22-008
Uniformed Services Program

Note: * indicates a newly appointed program director

Galveston

University of Texas Medical Branch Hospitals Program
Sponsor: University of Texas Medical Branch Hospitals
Shriners Hospitals for Children (Galveston Burns Institute)
Prgm Director: David N Herndon, MD
Shriners Burn Hospital
815 Market Street
Galveston, TX 77550
Tel: 409 770-6731   *Fax:* 409 770-6919
Length: 1 Yr   *ACGME Approved/Offered Positions:* 2
Program ID: 442-48-31-098

Houston

Baylor College of Medicine Program
Sponsor: Baylor College of Medicine
Harris County Hospital District-Ben Taub General Hospital
Michael E DeBakey VA Medical Center - Houston
Prgm Director: Samir S Awad, MD
Michael E DeBakey Department of Surgery
One Baylor Plaza, Room 404D
Houston, TX 77030
Tel: 713 798-6078   *Fax:* 713 798-8941
Length: 1 Yr   *ACGME Approved/Offered Positions:* 2
Program ID: 442-48-21-120

University of Texas at Houston Program
Sponsor: University of Texas Health Science Center at Houston
Memorial Hermann Hospital
Prgm Director: Ernest A Gonzalez, MD
6431 Fannin St, MSB 4.284
Houston, TX 77030
Tel: 713 500-7220   *Fax:* 713 500-7268
E-mail: Ernest.A.Gonzalez@uth.tmc.edu
Length: 1 Yr   *ACGME Approved/Offered Positions:* 3
Program ID: 442-48-21-038

San Antonio

University of Texas Health Science Center at San Antonio Program
Sponsor: University of Texas School of Medicine at San Antonio
Brooke Army Medical Center
University of Texas Health Science Center
Wilford Hall Medical Center (AETC)
Prgm Director: Ronald Stewart, MD
7703 Floyd Curl Drive
Dept of Surgery/Trauma
San Antonio, TX 78229
Tel: 210 567-3623   *Fax:* 210 567-0003
Length: 1 Yr   *ACGME Approved/Offered Positions:* 3
Program ID: 442-48-12-081

Utah

Salt Lake City

University of Utah Program
Sponsor: University of Utah Medical Center
LDS Hospital
Veterans Affairs Medical Center (Salt Lake City)
Prgm Director: Edward J Kimball, MD, MSc
Dept of Surgery, 3B 110
50 North Medical Drive
Salt Lake City, UT 84132
Tel: 801 581-4623   *Fax:* 801 581-4655
E-mail: edward.kimball@hsc.utah.edu
Length: 1 Yr   *ACGME Approved/Offered Positions:* 1
Program ID: 442-49-12-092

Virginia

Charlottesville

University of Virginia Program
Sponsor: University of Virginia Medical Center
Prgm Director: Robert G Sawyer, MD*
PO Box 800709
Charlottesville, VA 22908
Tel: 434 982-1632
Length: 1 Yr   *ACGME Approved/Offered Positions:* 1
Program ID: 442-51-13-097

Norfolk

Eastern Virginia Medical School Program
Sponsor: Eastern Virginia Medical School
Children's Hospital of the King's Daughters
Sentara Norfolk General Hospital
Prgm Director: Rebecca C Britt, MD
825 Fairfax Avenue, Suite 610
Norfolk, VA 23507
Tel: 757 446-8950   *Fax:* 757 446-8951
E-mail: brittama@evms.edu
Length: 1 Yr   *ACGME Approved/Offered Positions:* 1
Program ID: 442-51-13-089

Richmond

Virginia Commonwealth University Health System Program
Sponsor: Virginia Commonwealth University Health System
Medical College of Virginia Hospitals
Prgm Director: Rao R Ivatury, MD
1200 East Broad, 15th Floor
West Hospital
Richmond, VA 23298
Tel: 804 827-1207   *Fax:* 804 827-0285
E-mail: rivatury@hsc.vcu.edu
Length: 1 Yr   *ACGME Approved/Offered Positions:* 2
Program ID: 442-51-31-085

Washington

Seattle

University of Washington Program
Sponsor: University of Washington School of Medicine
Harborview Medical Center
VA Puget Sound Health Care System
Prgm Director: Ronald V Maier, MD
Dept of Surgery, Box 359796
325 Ninth Avenue
Seattle, WA 98104
Tel: 206 744-3564   *Fax:* 206 744-8582
Length: 1 Yr   *ACGME Approved/Offered Positions:* 3
Program ID: 442-54-21-050

Wisconsin

Milwaukee

Medical College of Wisconsin Affiliated Hospitals Program
Sponsor: Medical College of Wisconsin Affiliated Hospitals, Inc
Clement J Zablocki Veterans Affairs Medical Center
Froedtert Memorial Lutheran Hospital
Prgm Director: Karen J Brasel, MD, MPH
9200 W Wisconsin Avenue
Milwaukee, WI 53226
Tel: 414 805-8624   *Fax:* 414 805-8641
Length: 1 Yr   *ACGME Approved/Offered Positions:* 3
Program ID: 442-56-21-010

Thoracic Surgery

Alabama

Birmingham

University of Alabama Medical Center Program
Sponsor: University of Alabama Hospital
Veterans Affairs Medical Center (Birmingham)
Prgm Director: William L Holman, MD
1900 University Blvd
THT, Room 760
Birmingham, AL 35294
Tel: 205 934-3853   *Fax:* 205 975-6618
E-mail: wholman@uab.edu
Length: 2 Yrs   *ACGME Approved/Offered Positions:* 2
Program ID: 460-01-21-007

Arizona

Tucson

University of Arizona Program
Sponsor: University of Arizona College of Medicine
University Medical Center
Prgm Director: Jack G Copeland III, MD*
1501 N Campbell Avenue
PO Box 245071
Tucson, AZ 85724
Tel: 520 626-5340   *Fax:* 520 626-5333
Length: 2 Yrs   *ACGME Approved/Offered Positions:* 2
Program ID: 460-03-21-106

California

Loma Linda

Loma Linda University Program
Sponsor: Loma Linda University Medical Center
Prgm Director: Anees J Razzouk, MD, MS
11175 Campus Street
Suite 21121
Loma Linda, CA 92354
Tel: 909 558-4354   *Fax:* 909 558-0348
Length: 3 Yrs   *ACGME Approved/Offered Positions:* 3
Program ID: 460-05-21-102

Los Angeles

Cedars-Sinai Medical Center Program
Sponsor: Cedars-Sinai Medical Center
Prgm Director: Wen Cheng, MD
8700 Beverly Blvd
Suite 6215
Los Angeles, CA 90048
Tel: 310 423-3851   *Fax:* 310 423-0127
E-mail: ChengW@cshs.org
Length: 2 Yrs   *ACGME Approved/Offered Positions:* 2
Program ID: 460-05-31-118

UCLA Medical Center Program
Sponsor: UCLA David Geffen School of Medicine/UCLA Medical Center
UCLA Medical Center
VA Greater Los Angeles Healthcare System
Prgm Director: Mary Maish, MD, MPH*
RM-64-124
10833 Le Conte Avenue
Los Angeles, CA 90095
Tel: 310 794-7333
Length: 2 Yrs   *ACGME Approved/Offered Positions:* 4
Program ID: 460-05-21-013

University of Southern California/ LAC+USC Medical Center Program

Sponsor: University of Southern California/LAC+USC
    Medical Center
Childrens Hospital Los Angeles
Huntington Memorial Hospital
LAC+USC Medical Center
USC University Hospital
Prgm Director: Winfield J Wells, MD
USC Cardiothoracic Surgery
1520 San Pablo Street, Suite 4300
Los Angeles, CA 90033
Tel: 323 442-6878   *Fax:* 323 442-6199
Length: 3 Yrs   *ACGME Approved/Offered Positions:* 5
Program ID: 460-05-22-011

Sacramento

University of California (Davis) Health System Program

Sponsor: University of California (Davis) Health System
University of California (Davis) Medical Center
Prgm Director: J Nilas Young, MD
Division of Thoracic Surgery
2221 Stockton Blvd, Suite 2112
Sacramento, CA 95817
Tel: 916 734-3861   *Fax:* 916 734-3066
Length: 2 Yrs   *ACGME Approved/Offered Positions:* 2
Program ID: 460-05-21-112

San Diego

University of California (San Diego) Program

Sponsor: University of California (San Diego) Medical
    Center
Rady Children's Hospital
Veterans Affairs Medical Center (San Diego)
Prgm Director: Patricia A Thistlethwaite, MD, PhD
Division of Cardiothoracic Surgery
200 West Arbor Drive
San Diego, CA 92103
Tel: 619 543-7777   *Fax:* 619 543-2652
Length: 2 Yrs   *ACGME Approved/Offered Positions:* 2
Program ID: 460-05-21-109

San Francisco

University of California (San Francisco) Program

Sponsor: University of California (San Francisco) School
    of Medicine
UCSF and Mount Zion Medical Centers
Veterans Affairs Medical Center (San Francisco)
Prgm Director: Scot H Merrick, MD
500 Parnassus Avenue
Suite MU-405
San Francisco, CA 94143
Tel: 415 353-8890   *Fax:* 415 353-4716
E-mail: guadalupe.romero@ucsfmedctr.org
Length: 3 Yrs   *ACGME Approved/Offered Positions:* 3
Program ID: 460-05-21-015

Stanford

Stanford University Program

Sponsor: Stanford Hospital and Clinics
Lucile Salter Packard Children's Hospital at Stanford
Veterans Affairs Palo Alto Health Care System
Prgm Director: Robert C Robbins, MD
Department of Cardiothoracic Surgery
Falk Cardiovascular Research Building
Stanford, CA 94305
Tel: 650 725-5895   *Fax:* 650 725-3846
E-mail: corrine.sanchez@stanford.edu
Length: 3 Yrs   *ACGME Approved/Offered Positions:* 6
Program ID: 460-05-21-016

Colorado

Aurora

University of Colorado Denver Program

Sponsor: University of Colorado Denver School of
    Medicine
University of Colorado Hospital
Veterans Affairs Medical Center (Denver)
Prgm Director: David A Fullerton, MD
12631 East 17th Avenue, Room 6602
PO Box 6511, MS C310
Aurora, CO 80045
Tel: 303 724-2798   *Fax:* 303 724-2806
E-mail: david.fullerton@uchsc.edu
Length: 3 Yrs   *ACGME Approved/Offered Positions:* 3
Program ID: 460-07-21-017

Connecticut

New Haven

Yale-New Haven Medical Center Program

Sponsor: Yale-New Haven Hospital
Veterans Affairs Medical Center (West Haven)
Prgm Director: John A Elefteriades, MD
333 Cedar Street
Cardiothoracic Surgery, FMB121
New Haven, CT 06520
Tel: 203 785-2704   *Fax:* 203 785-3346
E-mail: john.elefteriades@yale.edu
Length: 2 Yrs   *ACGME Approved/Offered Positions:* 4
Program ID: 460-08-21-018

District of Columbia

Washington

George Washington University Program

Sponsor: George Washington University School of
    Medicine
Children's National Medical Center
George Washington University Hospital (UHS)
Veterans Affairs Medical Center (Washington, DC)
Prgm Director: Pendleton Alexander, MD
2150 Pennsylvania Avenue, Suite 6B
Washington, DC 20037
Tel: 202 745-8626   *Fax:* 202 745-8385
Length: 2 Yrs   *ACGME Approved/Offered Positions:* 4
Program ID: 460-10-21-019

Florida

Gainesville

University of Florida Program

Sponsor: University of Florida College of Medicine
North Florida/South Georgia Veterans Health System
Shands Hospital at the University of Florida
Prgm Director: Curtis G Tribble, MD
Division of Thoracic Surgery
PO Box 100286
Gainesville, FL 32610
Tel: 352 273-5501   *Fax:* 352 273-5513
E-mail: douglas.newburg@surgery.ufl.edu
Length: 3 Yrs   *ACGME Approved/Offered Positions:* 3
Program ID: 460-11-21-020

Miami

Jackson Memorial Hospital/Jackson Health System Program

Sponsor: Jackson Memorial Hospital/Jackson Health
    System
Mount Sinai Medical Center of Florida, Inc
Veterans Affairs Medical Center (Miami)
Prgm Director: Tomas A Salerno, MD
Cardiothoracic Surgery R-114
1611 NW 12th Avenue ET 3072
Miami, FL 33136
Tel: 305 585-5271   *Fax:* 305 547-2185
E-mail: tsalerno@med.miami.edu
Length: 2 Yrs   *ACGME Approved/Offered Positions:* 4
Program ID: 460-11-21-021

Georgia

Atlanta

Emory University Program

Sponsor: Emory University School of Medicine
Crawford Long Hospital of Emory University
Emory University Hospital
Prgm Director: Robert A Guyton, MD
1365A Clifton Road, NE
Room A2223
Atlanta, GA 30322
Tel: 404 778-3836   *Fax:* 404 778-5039
Length: 3 Yrs   *ACGME Approved/Offered Positions:* 9
Program ID: 460-12-21-022

Illinois

Chicago

McGaw Medical Center of Northwestern University Program

Sponsor: McGaw Medical Center of Northwestern
    University
Northwestern Memorial Hospital
Prgm Director: Patrick M McCarthy, MD
201 East Huron Street
Galter 11-140
Chicago, IL 60611
Tel: 312 695-3114   *Fax:* 312 695-0178
Length: 3 Yrs   *ACGME Approved/Offered Positions:* 3
Program ID: 460-16-21-025

Rush University Medical Center Program

Sponsor: Rush University Medical Center
John H Stroger Hospital of Cook County
Prgm Director: Robert S Higgins, MD
1653 West Congress Parkway
714 Jelke
Chicago, IL 60612
Tel: 312 942-6370   *Fax:* 312 942-6052
E-mail: Robert_Higgins@rush.edu
Length: 2 Yrs   *ACGME Approved/Offered Positions:* 4
Program ID: 460-16-21-027

University of Illinois College of Medicine at Chicago Program

Sponsor: University of Illinois College of Medicine at
    Chicago
John H Stroger Hospital of Cook County
University of Illinois Hospital and Clinics
Prgm Director: Malek G Massad, MD
840 South Wood Street
Room 417 CSB (MC 958)
Chicago, IL 60612
Tel: 312 996-4942   *Fax:* 312 996-2013
E-mail: mmassad@uic.edu
Length: 2 Yrs   *ACGME Approved/Offered Positions:* 2
Program ID: 460-16-21-029

Note: * indicates a newly appointed program director

Maywood

Loyola University Program
Sponsor: Loyola University Medical Center
Edward Hines, Jr Veterans Affairs Hospital
Prgm Director: Jeffrey P Schwartz, MD
Foster G McGaw Hospital
2160 South First Avenue, Bldg 110, Room 6243
Maywood, IL 60153
Tel: 708 327-2503   *Fax:* 708 327-2382
E-mail: jschwa1@lumc.edu
Length: 2 Yrs   *ACGME Approved/Offered Positions:* 4
Program ID: 460-16-31-030

Indiana

Indianapolis

Indiana University School of Medicine Program
Sponsor: Indiana University School of Medicine
Clarian Indiana University Hospital
Clarian Methodist Hospital of Indiana
Clarian Riley Hospital for Children
Prgm Director: John W Brown, MD
Emerson Hall 215
545 Barnhill Drive
Indianapolis, IN 46202
Tel: 317 274-7150   *Fax:* 317 274-2940
Length: 3 Yrs   *ACGME Approved/Offered Positions:* 6
Program ID: 460-17-21-031

Iowa

Iowa City

University of Iowa Hospitals and Clinics Program
Sponsor: University of Iowa Hospitals and Clinics
Prgm Director: Mark D Iannettoni, MD, MBA
200 Hawkins Drive
SE514 GH
Iowa City, IA 52242
Tel: 319 356-1133   *Fax:* 319 356-3891
E-mail: mark-iannettoni@uiowa.edu
Length: 2 Yrs   *ACGME Approved/Offered Positions:* 4
Program ID: 460-18-21-032

Kentucky

Lexington

University of Kentucky College of Medicine Program
Sponsor: University of Kentucky College of Medicine
Veterans Affairs Medical Center (Lexington)
Prgm Director: Mark Plunkett, MD*
740 South Limestone, A301
Kentucky Clinic
Lexington, KY 40536
Tel: 859 323-6494   *Fax:* 859 257-4682
Length: 2 Yrs   *ACGME Approved/Offered Positions:* 2
Program ID: 460-20-21-115

Maryland

Baltimore

Johns Hopkins University Program
Sponsor: Johns Hopkins University School of Medicine
Johns Hopkins Hospital
Prgm Director: William A Baumgartner, MD
Blalock 618
600 North Wolfe Street
Baltimore, MD 21287
Tel: 410 955-5248   *Fax:* 410 955-3809
Length: 3 Yrs   *ACGME Approved/Offered Positions:* 6
Program ID: 460-23-11-037

University of Maryland Program
Sponsor: University of Maryland Medical System
Prgm Director: Bartley P Griffith, MD
N4W94, 22 S Greene St
Baltimore, MD 21201
Tel: 410 328-3822   *Fax:* 410 328-2750
Length: 2 Yrs   *ACGME Approved/Offered Positions:* 2
Program ID: 460-23-11-038

Massachusetts

Boston

Beth Israel Deaconess Medical Center Program
Sponsor: Beth Israel Deaconess Medical Center
Children's Hospital
Prgm Director: Malcom M DeCamp Jr, MD
185 Pilgrim Road
Deaconess 201
Boston, MA 02215
Tel: 617 632-8386   *Fax:* 617 632-8253
E-mail: mdecamp@bidmc.harvard.edu
Length: 2 Yrs   *ACGME Approved/Offered Positions:* 2
Program ID: 460-24-21-041

Boston University Medical Center Program
Sponsor: Boston Medical Center
Children's Hospital
Prgm Director: Benedict D Daly, MD
Dept of Cardiothoracic Surgery
88 E Newton Street
Boston, MA 02118
Tel: 617 638-7350   *Fax:* 617 638-7228
E-mail: benedict.daly@bmc.org
Length: 3 Yrs   *ACGME Approved/Offered Positions:* 3
Program ID: 460-24-21-039

Brigham and Women's Hospital/Children's Hospital Program
Sponsor: Brigham and Women's Hospital
Children's Hospital
Prgm Director: Raphael Bueno, MD
75 Francis Street
Boston, MA 02115
Tel: 617 732-8148   *Fax:* 617 582-6171
E-mail: surgeryeducation@partners.org
Length: 2 Yrs   *ACGME Approved/Offered Positions:* 8
Program ID: 460-24-22-043

Massachusetts General Hospital Program
Sponsor: Massachusetts General Hospital
Children's Hospital
Prgm Director: Douglas J Mathisen, MD
55 Fruit Street
Blake 1570
Boston, MA 02114
Tel: 617 726-6826   *Fax:* 617 726-7667
E-mail: dmathisen@partners.org
Length: 2 Yrs   *ACGME Approved/Offered Positions:* 6
Program ID: 460-24-11-040

Tufts Medical Center Program
Sponsor: Tufts Medical Center
Lahey Clinic
Prgm Director: Kenneth G Warner, MD
800 Washington Street, Box 266
Boston, MA 02111
Tel: 617 636-0033   *Fax:* 617 636-7616
Length: 2 Yrs   *ACGME Approved/Offered Positions:* 2
Program ID: 460-24-21-042

Michigan

Ann Arbor

University of Michigan Program
Sponsor: University of Michigan Hospitals and Health Centers
Veterans Affairs Medical Center (Ann Arbor)
Prgm Director: Richard G Ohye, MD
5144 CVC/SPC 5864
1500 E Medical Center Dr
Ann Arbor, MI 48109

Tel: 734 936-4978   *Fax:* 734 763-7353
Length: 2 Yrs   *ACGME Approved/Offered Positions:* 6
Program ID: 460-25-21-044

Minnesota

Minneapolis

University of Minnesota Program
Sponsor: University of Minnesota Medical School
Abbott-Northwestern Hospital/Allina Health System
Mercy Hospital (Minneapolis)
University of Minnesota Medical Center, Division of Fairview
Veterans Affairs Medical Center (Minneapolis)
Prgm Director: Herbert B Ward, MD, PhD*
Mayo Mail Code 207
420 Delaware St SE
Minneapolis, MN 55455
Tel: 612 625-3902   *Fax:* 612 625-1683
E-mail: wardx020@umn.edu
Length: 3 Yrs   *ACGME Approved/Offered Positions:* 6
Program ID: 460-26-21-046

Rochester

College of Medicine, Mayo Clinic (Rochester) Program
Sponsor: College of Medicine, Mayo Clinic
Saint Marys Hospital of Rochester
Prgm Director: Joseph A Dearani, MD
200 First St SW
Rochester, MN 55905
Tel: 507 255-7069   *Fax:* 507 255-7378
Length: 3 Yrs   *ACGME Approved/Offered Positions:* 6
Program ID: 460-26-21-047

Mississippi

Jackson

University of Mississippi Medical Center Program
Sponsor: University of Mississippi School of Medicine
University Hospitals and Clinics
Veterans Affairs Medical Center (Jackson)
Prgm Director: Giorgio M Aru, MD
2500 North State Street
Jackson, MS 39216
Tel: 601 984-5170   *Fax:* 601 984-5198
Length: 2 Yrs   *ACGME Approved/Offered Positions:* 2
Program ID: 460-27-11-048

Missouri

St Louis

St Louis University School of Medicine Program

Sponsor: St Louis University School of Medicine
Cardinal Glennon Children's Hospital
St Louis University Hospital
Prgm Director: Keith S Naunheim, MD
3635 Vista Avenue at Grand Blvd
PO Box 15250
St Louis, MO 63110
Tel: 314 577-8360   *Fax:* 314 577-8315
Length: 2 Yrs   *ACGME Approved/Offered Positions:* 2
Program ID: 460-28-21-052

Washington University/B-JH/SLCH Consortium Program

Sponsor: Washington University/B-JH/SLCH Consortium
Barnes-Jewish Hospital
St Louis Children's Hospital
St Luke's Hospital
Prgm Director: Marc R Moon, MD
Cardiothoracic Surgery, Box 8234
660 S Euclid Avenue
St Louis, MO 63110
Tel: 314 362-0993   *Fax:* 314 362-0328
Length: 2 Yrs   *ACGME Approved/Offered Positions:* 6
Program ID: 460-28-21-051

New Jersey

New Brunswick

UMDNJ-Robert Wood Johnson Medical School Program

Sponsor: UMDNJ-Robert Wood Johnson Medical School
Robert Wood Johnson University Hospital
Prgm Director: Peter M Scholz, MD
Division of Cardiothoracic Surgery
PO Box 19, MEB 524
New Brunswick, NJ 08903
Tel: 732 235-7806   *Fax:* 732 235-8727
Length: 3 Yrs   *ACGME Approved/Offered Positions:* 3
Program ID: 460-33-21-110

New Mexico

Albuquerque

University of New Mexico Program

Sponsor: University of New Mexico School of Medicine
University of New Mexico Hospital
Veterans Affairs Medical Center (Albuquerque)
Prgm Director: Jorge A Wernly, MD
1 University of New Mexico
MSC 10 5610, ACC 2
Albuquerque, NM 87131
Tel: 505 272-6901   *Fax:* 505 272-6909
E-mail: jwernly@salud.unm.edu
Length: 2 Yrs   *ACGME Approved/Offered Positions:* 2
Program ID: 460-34-21-055

New York

Albany

Albany Medical Center Program

Sponsor: Albany Medical Center
Prgm Director: Riivo Ilves, MD
47 New Scotland Avenue, MC 61
Albany, NY 12208
Tel: 518 262-4880   *Fax:* 518 262-5999
E-mail: ilvesr@mail.amc.edu
Length: 2 Yrs   *ACGME Approved/Offered Positions:* 2
Program ID: 460-35-11-056

Bronx

Albert Einstein College of Medicine Program

Sponsor: Albert Einstein College of Medicine of Yeshiva University
Montefiore Medical Center-Henry and Lucy Moses Division
Montefiore Medical Center-Weiler Division
Prgm Director: Abelardo DeAnda, MD
Montefiore Medical Center
111 East 210th Street
Bronx, NY 10467
Tel: 718 920-7732   *Fax:* 718 652-4517
Length: 2 Yrs   *ACGME Approved/Offered Positions:* 4
Program ID: 460-35-21-058

Brooklyn

SUNY Health Science Center at Brooklyn Program

Sponsor: SUNY Health Science Center at Brooklyn
Maimonides Medical Center
University Hospital-SUNY Health Science Center at Brooklyn
Prgm Director: Wilson Ko, MD*
c/o Maimonides Medical Center
4802 10th Avenue
Brooklyn, NY 11219
Tel: 718 270-1981   *Fax:* 718 270-3843
E-mail: wilson.ko@downstate.edu
Length: 2 Yrs   *ACGME Approved/Offered Positions:* 2
Program ID: 460-35-11-066

Great Neck

NSLIJHS-Albert Einstein College of Medicine at Long Island Jewish Medical Center Program

Sponsor: North Shore-Long Island Jewish Health System
Long Island Jewish Medical Center
Prgm Director: Frank Manetta, MD
Cardiovascular & Thoracic Surgery Dept Rm 2123
270-05 76th Avenue
New Hyde Park, NY 11040
Tel: 718 470-7464   *Fax:* 718 343-1438
E-mail: fmanetta@lij.edu
Length: 2 Yrs   *ACGME Approved/Offered Positions:* 2
Program ID: 460-35-21-062

New York

Mount Sinai School of Medicine Program

Sponsor: Mount Sinai School of Medicine
Mount Sinai Medical Center
Prgm Director: David Adams, MD*
One Gustave L Levy Place
Box 1028
New York, NY 10029
Tel: 212 659-6820   *Fax:* 212 659-6818
E-mail: david.adams@mountsinai.org
Length: 3 Yrs   *ACGME Approved/Offered Positions:* 3
Program ID: 460-35-11-064

New York Presbyterian Hospital (Columbia Campus) Program

Sponsor: New York Presbyterian Hospital
New York Presbyterian Hospital (Columbia Campus)
Prgm Director: Craig R Smith, MD
177 Fort Washington Avenue
MHB 7GN-435
New York, NY 10032
Tel: 212 305-8312   *Fax:* 212 342-1602
Length: 2 Yrs   *ACGME Approved/Offered Positions:* 4
Program ID: 460-35-21-059

New York Presbyterian Hospital (Cornell Campus) Program

Sponsor: New York Presbyterian Hospital
Memorial Sloan-Kettering Cancer Center
New York Presbyterian Hospital (Cornell Campus)
Prgm Director: Karl H Krieger, MD
525 E 68th St, Suite M436
Mail Box 110
New York, NY 10021
Tel: 212 746-5152   *Fax:* 212 746-8828
E-mail: jtorres@med.cornell.edu
Length: 2 Yrs   *ACGME Approved/Offered Positions:* 6
Program ID: 460-35-11-060

New York University School of Medicine Program

Sponsor: New York University School of Medicine
Bellevue Hospital Center
NYU Hospitals Center
Prgm Director: Aubrey C Galloway Jr, MD
530 First Avenue, Suite 9-V
New York, NY 10016
Tel: 212 263-7185   *Fax:* 212 263-2246
E-mail: Aubrey.Galloway@nyumc.org
Length: 3 Yrs   *ACGME Approved/Offered Positions:* 6
Program ID: 460-35-21-065

Rochester

University of Rochester Program

Sponsor: Strong Memorial Hospital of the University of Rochester
Prgm Director: George L Hicks Jr, MD
601 Elmwood Avenue
Rochester, NY 14642
Tel: 585 275-5384   *Fax:* 585 244-7171
Length: 2 Yrs   *ACGME Approved/Offered Positions:* 4
Program ID: 460-35-21-067

North Carolina

Chapel Hill

University of North Carolina Hospitals Program

Sponsor: University of North Carolina Hospitals
Prgm Director: Michael R Mill, MD
101 Manning Drive
Chapel Hill, NC 27514
Tel: 919 966-3381   *Fax:* 919 966-3475
Length: 3 Yrs   *ACGME Approved/Offered Positions:* 3
Program ID: 460-36-11-069

Charlotte

Carolinas Medical Center Program

Sponsor: Carolinas Medical Center
Prgm Director: Francis Robicsek, MD, PhD
1000 Blythe Boulevard
PO Box 32861
Charlotte, NC 28203
Tel: 704 355-4712   *Fax:* 704 355-6227
E-mail: mary.mcconnell@carolinashealthcare.org
Length: 2 Yrs   *ACGME Approved/Offered Positions:* 4
Program ID: 460-36-12-070

Note: * indicates a newly appointed program director

Durham

Duke University Hospital Program
Sponsor: Duke University Hospital
Prgm Director: Thomas A D'Amico, MD
Box 3496
Duke South, Room 3589
Durham, NC 27710
Tel: 919 684-4891   *Fax:* 919 684-8508
Length: 3 Yrs   *ACGME Approved/Offered Positions:* 9
Program ID: 460-36-21-071

Winston-Salem

Wake Forest University School of Medicine Program
Sponsor: Wake Forest University Baptist Medical Center
Prgm Director: Neal D Kon, MD
Medical Center Blvd
Winston-Salem, NC 27157
Tel: 336 716-2124   *Fax:* 336 716-3348
E-mail: nkon@wfubmc.edu
Length: 2 Yrs   *ACGME Approved/Offered Positions:* 2
Program ID: 460-36-11-072

Ohio

Cincinnati

University Hospital/University of Cincinnati College of Medicine Program
Sponsor: University Hospital Inc
TriHealth - Good Samaritan Hospital
Prgm Director: Walter H Merrill, MD
231 Albert B Sabin Way, ML 0558
Cincinnati, OH 45267
Tel: 513 584-1387   *Fax:* 513 584-1745
E-mail: walter.merrill@uc.edu
Length: 3 Yrs   *ACGME Approved/Offered Positions:* 3
Program ID: 460-38-22-119

Cleveland

Cleveland Clinic Foundation Program
Sponsor: Cleveland Clinic Foundation
Prgm Director: Joseph F Sabik III, MD
Dept of Thoracic & Cardiovascular Surgery
9500 Euclid Avenue, F24
Cleveland, OH 44195
Tel: 216 444-6788   *Fax:* 216 445-3294
E-mail: sabikj@ccf.org
Length: 3 Yrs   *ACGME Approved/Offered Positions:* 6
Program ID: 460-38-12-075

Columbus

Ohio State University Hospital Program
Sponsor: Ohio State University Hospital
Arthur G James Cancer Hospital and Research Institute
Nationwide Children's Hospital
Prgm Director: Benjamin Sun, MD
410 W 10th Ave
N 8th Floor, Doan Hall
Columbus, OH 43210
Tel: 614 293-4558   *Fax:* 614 293-7221
Length: 2 Yrs   *ACGME Approved/Offered Positions:* 4
Program ID: 460-38-21-077

Oklahoma

Oklahoma City

University of Oklahoma Health Sciences Center Program
Sponsor: University of Oklahoma College of Medicine
Edmond Medical Center
OU Medical Center - Presbyterian Tower
Veterans Affairs Medical Center (Oklahoma City)
Prgm Director: Marvin D Peyton, MD
920 Stanton L Young Blvd, WP2230
Oklahoma City, OK 73104
Tel: 405 271-5789   *Fax:* 405 271-3288
E-mail: Thoracic-Surgery@ouhsc.edu
Length: 2 Yrs   *ACGME Approved/Offered Positions:* 2
Program ID: 460-39-21-078

Oregon

Portland

Oregon Health & Science University Program
Sponsor: Oregon Health & Science University Hospital
Veterans Affairs Medical Center (Portland)
Prgm Director: Paul H Schipper, MD*
Oregon Health & Science University
3181 SW Sam Jackson Park Road
Portland, OR 97239
Tel: 503 494-7820   *Fax:* 503 494-7829
Length: 2 Yrs   *ACGME Approved/Offered Positions:* 2
Program ID: 460-40-21-079

Pennsylvania

Hershey

Penn State University/Milton S Hershey Medical Center Program
Sponsor: Milton S Hershey Medical Center
Prgm Director: Walter E Pae Jr, MD, BA
500 University Drive
PO Box 850
Hershey, PA 17033
Tel: 717 531-8329   *Fax:* 717 531-3664
E-mail: wpae@hmc.psu.edu
Length: 2 Yrs   *ACGME Approved/Offered Positions:* 2
Program ID: 460-41-11-080

Philadelphia

Drexel University College of Medicine/Hahnemann University Hospital Program
Sponsor: Drexel University College of
    Medicine/Hahnemann University
Hahnemann University Hospital (Tenet Health System)
St Christopher's Hospital for Children (Tenet Health
    System)
University of Pennsylvania Health System
Prgm Director: John W Entwistle III, MD, PhD
Dept of CT Surgery, MS 111
245 N 15th Street
Philadelphia, PA 19102
Tel: 215 762-7802   *Fax:* 215 762-1858
E-mail: john.entwistle@drexelmed.edu
Length: 3 Yrs   *ACGME Approved/Offered Positions:* 3
Program ID: 460-41-21-104

University of Pennsylvania Program
Sponsor: University of Pennsylvania Health System
Prgm Director: Michael A Acker, MD
Division of Cardiothoracic Surgery
3400 Spruce Street, 6 Silverstein
Philadelphia, PA 19104
Tel: 215 349-8305   *Fax:* 215 349-5798
Length: 2 Yrs   *ACGME Approved/Offered Positions:* 6
Program ID: 460-41-21-082

Pittsburgh

Allegheny General Hospital Program
Sponsor: Allegheny General Hospital
Prgm Director: George J Magovern Jr, MD
320 E North Avenue
14th Floor, South Tower
Pittsburgh, PA 15212
Tel: 412 359-3715   *Fax:* 412 359-3878
E-mail: gmagover@wpahs.org
Length: 2 Yrs   *ACGME Approved/Offered Positions:* 4
Program ID: 460-41-31-084

University of Pittsburgh Medical Center Medical Education Program
Sponsor: Univ of Pittsburgh Medical Center Medical
    Education
UPMC Passavant
UPMC Presbyterian Shadyside
Veterans Affairs Medical Center (Pittsburgh)
Prgm Director: James D Luketich, MD
Suite C800 PUH
200 Lothrop Street
Pittsburgh, PA 15213
Tel: 412 647-2911   *Fax:* 412 648-6356
Length: 2 Yrs   *ACGME Approved/Offered Positions:* 8
Program ID: 460-41-21-085

South Carolina

Charleston

Medical University of South Carolina Program
Sponsor: Medical University of South Carolina College of
    Medicine
MUSC Medical Center
Ralph H Johnson VA Medical Center (Charleston)
Prgm Director: Fred A Crawford Jr, MD
25 Courtenay Drive, Suite 7018
MSC 295
Charleston, SC 29425
Tel: 843 876-4840   *Fax:* 843 876-4866
Length: 3 Yrs   *ACGME Approved/Offered Positions:* 6
Program ID: 460-45-21-087

Tennessee

Memphis

University of Tennessee Program
Sponsor: University of Tennessee College of Medicine
Baptist Memorial Hospital
LeBonheur Children's Medical Center
Methodist Healthcare - Memphis Hospitals
Veterans Affairs Medical Center (Memphis)
Prgm Director: Darryl S Weiman, MD, JD
910 Madison Avenue, 2nd Floor
Memphis, TN 38163
Tel: 901 448-5914   *Fax:* 901 448-7306
E-mail: rpipkin@utmem.edu
Length: 2 Yrs   *ACGME Approved/Offered Positions:* 4
Program ID: 460-47-21-088

Nashville
Vanderbilt University Program
Sponsor: Vanderbilt University Medical Center
Prgm Director: Joe B Putnam Jr, MD
609 Oxford House
Nashville, TN 37232
Tel: 615 343-9202   *Fax:* 615 322-3079
E-mail: bill.putnam@vanderbilt.edu
Length: 3 Yrs   ACGME Approved/Offered Positions: 3
Program ID: 460-47-31-089

Texas
Dallas
University of Texas Southwestern Medical School Program
Sponsor: University of Texas Southwestern Medical School
Children's Medical Center of Dallas
Dallas County Hospital District-Parkland Memorial Hospital
Dallas VA Medical Center
University Hospitals St Paul
Prgm Director: Michael E Jessen, MD
5323 Harry Hines Boulevard
Dallas, TX 75390
Tel: 214 645-7721   *Fax:* 214 645-7701
Length: 3 Yrs   ACGME Approved/Offered Positions: 6
Program ID: 460-48-21-090

Galveston
University of Texas Medical Branch Hospitals Program
Sponsor: University of Texas Medical Branch Hospitals
Texas Children's Hospital
Prgm Director: Vincent R Conti, MD
Division of Cardiothoracic Surgery
301 University Blvd
Galveston, TX 77555
Tel: 409 772-1203   *Fax:* 409 772-1421
Length: 2 Yrs   ACGME Approved/Offered Positions: 2
Program ID: 460-48-21-091

Houston
Baylor College of Medicine Program
Sponsor: Baylor College of Medicine
Harris County Hospital District-Ben Taub General Hospital
Methodist Hospital (Houston)
Michael E DeBakey VA Medical Center - Houston
Texas Children's Hospital
University of Texas M D Anderson Cancer Center
Prgm Director: Joseph S Coselli, MD
One Baylor Plaza, BCM 390
Houston, TX 77030
Tel: 832 355-9910   *Fax:* 832 355-9920
Length: 2 Yrs   ACGME Approved/Offered Positions: 6
Program ID: 460-48-21-092

Texas Heart Institute Program
Sponsor: Texas Heart Institute
St Luke's Episcopal Hospital
Texas Children's Hospital
University of Texas M D Anderson Cancer Center
Prgm Director: Denton A Cooley, MD
PO Box 20345
Houston, TX 77225
Tel: 832 355-4932   *Fax:* 832 355-3424
Length: 2 Yrs   ACGME Approved/Offered Positions: 6
Program ID: 460-48-21-093

Texas Heart Institute/Baylor College of Medicine Program
Sponsor: Baylor College of Medicine
Michael E DeBakey VA Medical Center - Houston
St Luke's Episcopal Hospital
Texas Heart Institute
Prgm Director: Denton A Cooley, MD
6770 Bertner Avenue, C550
Houston, TX 77030
Tel: 832 355-4932   *Fax:* 832 355-3424
E-mail: ctprograms@bcm.edu
Length: 3 Yrs   ACGME Approved/Offered Positions: 12
Program ID: 460-48-13-124

University of Texas M D Anderson Cancer Center/Methodist Hospital (Houston) Program
Sponsor: University of Texas M D Anderson Cancer Center
Methodist Hospital (Houston)
Prgm Director: Ara A Vaporciyan, MD
1515 Holcombe Boulevard
Box 445
Houston, TX 77030
Tel: 713 563-9161   *Fax:* 713 794-4901
Length: 2 Yrs   ACGME Approved/Offered Positions: 2
Program ID: 460-48-13-121

San Antonio
University of Texas Health Science Center at San Antonio Program
Sponsor: University of Texas School of Medicine at San Antonio
Audie L Murphy Memorial Veterans Hospital (San Antonio)
University Health System
Prgm Director: John H Calhoon, MD
7703 Floyd Curl Drive MC 7841
Division of Cardiothoracic Surgery
San Antonio, TX 78229
Tel: 210 567-6863   *Fax:* 210 567-2877
Length: 2 Yrs   ACGME Approved/Offered Positions: 3
Program ID: 460-48-21-094

Utah
Salt Lake City
University of Utah Program
Sponsor: University of Utah Medical Center
Intermountain Medical Center
Primary Children's Medical Center
Prgm Director: David A Bull, MD
50 North Medical Drive
Salt Lake City, UT 84132
Tel: 801 581-5311   *Fax:* 801 585-3936
Length: 2 Yrs   ACGME Approved/Offered Positions: 4
Program ID: 460-49-21-095

Virginia
Charlottesville
University of Virginia Program
Sponsor: University of Virginia Medical Center
Prgm Director: Irving L Kron, MD
Division Thoracic Cardiovascular Surgery
Box 800679
Charlottesville, VA 22908
Tel: 434 924-2158   *Fax:* 434 982-3885
Length: 2 Yrs   ACGME Approved/Offered Positions: 5
Program ID: 460-51-11-096

Washington
Seattle
University of Washington Program
Sponsor: University of Washington School of Medicine
University of Washington Medical Center
VA Puget Sound Health Care System
Prgm Director: Edward D Verrier, MD
Division of Thoracic Surgery
Box 356310, 1959 NE Pacific St
Seattle, WA 98195
Tel: 206 685-3370   *Fax:* 206 616-9063
Length: 2 Yrs   ACGME Approved/Offered Positions: 4
Program ID: 460-54-21-098

Wisconsin
Madison
University of Wisconsin Program
Sponsor: University of Wisconsin Hospital and Clinics
William S Middleton Veterans Hospital
Prgm Director: Niloo M Edwards, MD, BA
600 Highland Avenue, CSC H4/358
Madison, WI 53792
Tel: 608 263-0439   *Fax:* 608 263-0547
E-mail: edwards@surgery.wisc.edu
Length: 2 Yrs   ACGME Approved/Offered Positions: 3
Program ID: 460-56-21-100

Milwaukee
Medical College of Wisconsin Affiliated Hospitals Program
Sponsor: Medical College of Wisconsin Affiliated Hospitals, Inc
Clement J Zablocki Veterans Affairs Medical Center
Froedtert Memorial Lutheran Hospital
Prgm Director: Mario Gasparri, MD
Froedtert Memorial Lutheran Hospital
9200 W Wisconsin Avenue - FEC 5460
Milwaukee, WI 53226
Tel: 414 456-6904   *Fax:* 414 456-6204
E-mail: magasp@yahoo.com
Length: 2 Yrs   ACGME Approved/Offered Positions: 2
Program ID: 460-56-21-101

Note: * indicates a newly appointed program director

Thoracic Surgery-Integrated

California

Stanford

Stanford University Program
Sponsor: Stanford Hospital and Clinics
Lucile Salter Packard Children's Hospital at Stanford
Prgm Director: Robert C Robbins, MD
Department of Cardiothoracic Surgery
Falk Cardiovascular Research Building
Stanford, CA 94305
Tel: 650 725-5895   *Fax:* 650 725-3846
E-mail: corrine.sanchez@stanford.edu
Length: 6 Yrs   *ACGME Approved/Offered Positions:* 6
Program ID: 461-05-21-016

Pennsylvania

Philadelphia

University of Pennsylvania Program
Sponsor: University of Pennsylvania Health System
Chestnut Hill Hospital
Presbyterian Medical Center (UPHS)
Prgm Director: Michael A Acker, MD
Division of Cardiothoracic Surgery
3400 Spruce Street, 6 Silverstein
Philadelphia, PA 19104
Tel: 215 349-8305   *Fax:* 215 349-5798
Length: 6 Yrs   *ACGME Approved/Offered Positions:* 10
Program ID: 461-41-21-082

South Carolina

Charleston

Medical University of South Carolina Program
Sponsor: Medical University of South Carolina College of
   Medicine
MUSC Medical Center
Ralph H Johnson VA Medical Center (Charleston)
Prgm Director: Fred A Crawford Jr, MD
96 Jonathan Lucas Street
409 CSB PO Box 250612
Charleston, SC 29425
Tel: 843 792-5897   *Fax:* 843 792-9783
Length: 6 Yrs   *ACGME Approved/Offered Positions:* 6
Program ID: 461-45-21-087

Transitional Year

Alabama

Birmingham

Baptist Medical Center Program
Sponsor: Baptist Health System Inc
Baptist Medical Center-Princeton
Trinity Medical Center
Prgm Director: Tiffany Lewis, MD
817 Princeton Avenue SW
Suite 106
Birmingham, AL 35211
Tel: 205 783-7663   *Fax:* 205 783-7399
Length: 1 Yr   *ACGME Approved/Offered Positions:* 16
Sponsoring Spec: DR, GS, IM
Program ID: 999-01-00-001

Arizona

Scottsdale

College of Medicine, Mayo Clinic (Arizona) Program
Sponsor: College of Medicine, Mayo Clinic
Mayo Clinic (Arizona)
Mayo Clinic Hospital
Prgm Director: Mark K Edwin, MD
5777 E Mayo Blvd
2W - Medical Education
Phoenix, AZ 85054
Tel: 480 342-2205   *Fax:* 480 342-2027
E-mail: boord.beth@mayo.edu
Length: 1 Yr   *ACGME Approved/Offered Positions:* 6
Sponsoring Spec: FP, GS, IM
Program ID: 999-03-00-226

Tucson

Tucson Hospitals Medical Education Program
Sponsor: Tucson Hospitals Medical Education Program
   Inc
Southern Arizona VA Health Care Center (Tucson)
Tucson Medical Center
Prgm Director: Tyler J Kent, MD
PO Box 42195
Tucson, AZ 85733
Tel: 520 324-5096   *Fax:* 520 324-5231
Length: 1 Yr   *ACGME Approved/Offered Positions:* 12
Sponsoring Spec: GS, IM
Program ID: 999-03-00-006

California

Bakersfield

Kern Medical Center Program
Sponsor: Kern Medical Center
Prgm Director: Jennifer J Abraham, MD, MEd
1830 Flower Street
Bakersfield, CA 93305
Tel: 661 326-5463   *Fax:* 661 326-2950
E-mail: transitionalyear@kernmedctr.com
Length: 1 Yr   *ACGME Approved/Offered Positions:* 6
Sponsoring Spec: EM, GS, IM
Program ID: 999-05-00-222

Colton

Arrowhead Regional Medical Center Program
Sponsor: Arrowhead Regional Medical Center
Prgm Director: Martha L Melendez, MD*
400 N Pepper Avenue
Colton, CA 92324
Tel: 909 580-6227   *Fax:* 909 580-6308
Length: 1 Yr   *ACGME Approved/Offered Positions:* 12
Sponsoring Spec: FP, GS
Program ID: 999-05-00-009

French Camp

San Joaquin General Hospital Program
Sponsor: San Joaquin General Hospital
Prgm Director: Sheela Kapre, MD*
500 West Hospital Road
French Camp, CA 95231
Tel: 209 468-6611   *Fax:* 209 468-6246
E-mail: skapre@sjgh.org
Length: 1 Yr   *ACGME Approved/Offered Positions:* 4
Sponsoring Spec: FP, IM
Program ID: 999-05-00-243

San Diego

Naval Medical Center (San Diego) Program
Sponsor: Naval Medical Center (San Diego)
Prgm Director: Eric T Stedje-Larsen, MD, BA
34800 Bob Wilson Drive
San Diego, CA 92134
Tel: 619 532-7935   *Fax:* 619 532-5507
E-mail: eric.stedje-larsen@med.navy.mil
Length: 1 Yr   *ACGME Approved/Offered Positions:* 27
Sponsoring Spec: GS, IM, PD
Program ID: 999-05-00-151
Uniformed Services Program

Scripps Mercy Hospital Program
Sponsor: Scripps Mercy Hospital
Prgm Director: David J Shaw, MD, MBA
Department of Graduate Medical Education
4077 Fifth Avenue, MER 35
San Diego, CA 92103
Tel: 619 260-7220   *Fax:* 619 260-7305
Length: 1 Yr   *ACGME Approved/Offered Positions:* 18
Sponsoring Spec: IM, PD
Program ID: 999-05-00-010

San Jose

Santa Clara Valley Medical Center Program
Sponsor: Santa Clara Valley Medical Center
Prgm Director: Jen M Eng, MD
Department of Medicine, 4th Fl
751 S Bascom Avenue
San Jose, CA 95128
Tel: 408 885-6305   *Fax:* 408 885-4046
Length: 1 Yr   *ACGME Approved/Offered Positions:* 16
Sponsoring Spec: IM, PD
Program ID: 999-05-00-013

Torrance

Los Angeles County-Harbor-UCLA Medical Center Program
Sponsor: Los Angeles County-Harbor-UCLA Medical
   Center
Prgm Director: Darrell W Harrington, MD
1000 W Carson Street
Torrance, CA 90509
Tel: 310 222-2903   *Fax:* 310 782-8599
E-mail: molivas@dhs.lacounty.gov
Length: 1 Yr   *ACGME Approved/Offered Positions:* 24
Sponsoring Spec: EM, GS, IM, PD
Program ID: 999-05-00-239

Programs

Travis AFB

David Grant Medical Center Program
Sponsor: David Grant Medical Center
University of California (Davis) Medical Center
Prgm Director: Jessica T Servey, MD
60th Medical Group/SGOL
101 Bodin Circle
Travis AFB, CA 94535
Tel: 707 423-3735   *Fax:* 707 423-3501
E-mail: jessica.servey@travis.af.mil
Length: 1 Yr   *ACGME Approved/Offered Positions:* 4
Sponsoring Spec: FP, GS
Program ID: 999-05-00-008
Uniformed Services Program

Colorado

Denver

Colorado Health Foundation Presbyterian-St Luke's Medical Center Program
Sponsor: Colorado Health Foundation Presbyterian-St Luke's Med Ctr
Prgm Director: Brian G Dwinnell, MD
1719 E 19th Avenue 5C-East
Denver, CO 80218
Tel: 303 869-2268   *Fax:* 303 869-2258
E-mail: bdwinnell@coloradohealth.org
Length: 1 Yr   *ACGME Approved/Offered Positions:* 12
Sponsoring Spec: EM, IM
Program ID: 999-07-00-017

Connecticut

Bridgeport

St Vincent's Medical Center Program
Sponsor: St Vincent's Medical Center
Prgm Director: Catherine E Apaloo, MD
2800 Main St
Bridgeport, CT 06606
Tel: 203 576-5576   *Fax:* 203 576-5022
E-mail: mededucation@svhs-ct.org
Length: 1 Yr   *ACGME Approved/Offered Positions:* 6
Sponsoring Spec: DR, IM
Program ID: 999-08-00-018

New Haven

Hospital of St Raphael Program
Sponsor: Hospital of St Raphael
Prgm Director: Ernest D Moritz, MD
1450 Chapel St
New Haven, CT 06511
Tel: 203 789-3989   *Fax:* 203 789-3222
E-mail: spane@srhs.org
Length: 1 Yr   *ACGME Approved/Offered Positions:* 9
Sponsoring Spec: GS, IM
Program ID: 999-08-00-020

Delaware

Wilmington

Christiana Care Health Services Program
Sponsor: Christiana Care Health Services Inc
Prgm Director: Brian M Aboff, MD
Christiana Hospital
4755 Ogletown-Stanton Road
Newark, DE 19718
Tel: 302 733-6344   *Fax:* 302 733-6386
E-mail: transition.residency@christianacare.org
Length: 1 Yr   *ACGME Approved/Offered Positions:* 9
Sponsoring Spec: FP, IM
Program ID: 999-09-00-021

Florida

Jacksonville

College of Medicine, Mayo Clinic (Jacksonville) Program
Sponsor: College of Medicine, Mayo Clinic
Mayo Clinic (Jacksonville)
Mayo Clinic Florida Hospital
Prgm Director: Gary M Lee, MD
4500 San Pablo Road
Jacksonville, FL 32224
Tel: 904 953-0426   *Fax:* 904 953-0430
E-mail: mgsm.jack.fl.transyear@mayo.edu
Length: 1 Yr   *ACGME Approved/Offered Positions:* 9
Sponsoring Spec: DR, IM
Program ID: 999-11-00-228

Georgia

Atlanta

Emory University Program
Sponsor: Emory University School of Medicine
Emory University Hospital
Grady Health System
Veterans Affairs Medical Center (Atlanta)
Prgm Director: Kimberly D Manning, MD
Thomas K Glenn Memorial Bldg
69 Jesse Hill Jr Dr SE
Atlanta, GA 30303
Tel: 404 778-0263   *Fax:* 404 525-2957
E-mail: trchamb@emory.edu
Length: 1 Yr   *ACGME Approved/Offered Positions:* 24
Sponsoring Spec: DR, IM
Program ID: 999-12-00-026

Columbus

The Medical Center Program
Sponsor: The Medical Center Inc
Prgm Director: Gregory A Foster, MD*
Department of Medical Education
710 Center Street, Box 100
Columbus, GA 31902
Tel: 706 571-1430   *Fax:* 706 571-1604
E-mail: greg.foster@crhs.net
Length: 1 Yr   *ACGME Approved/Offered Positions:* 5
Sponsoring Spec: FP, GS
Program ID: 999-12-00-229

Fort Gordon

Dwight David Eisenhower Army Medical Center Program
Sponsor: Dwight David Eisenhower Army Medical Center
Prgm Director: Keith Fincher, MD
Attn: MCHF-GME
Transitional Year Program
Fort Gordon, GA 30905
Tel: 706 787-4657   *Fax:* 706 787-1745
E-mail: roger.fincher@us.army.mil
Length: 1 Yr   *ACGME Approved/Offered Positions:* 10
Sponsoring Spec: GS, IM
Program ID: 999-12-00-029
Uniformed Services Program

Hawaii

Honolulu

University of Hawaii Program
Sponsor: University of Hawaii John A Burns School of Medicine
Kuakini Medical Center
Queen's Medical Center
Prgm Director: Cynthia S Hew, MD
1356 Lusitana Street, 7th Floor
Honolulu, HI 96813
Tel: 808 586-7477   *Fax:* 808 586-7486
E-mail: uhtrans@hawaii.edu
Length: 1 Yr   *ACGME Approved/Offered Positions:* 10
Sponsoring Spec: GS, IM
Program ID: 999-14-00-031

Tripler AMC

Tripler Army Medical Center Program
Sponsor: Tripler Army Medical Center
Prgm Director: Mary J Edwards, MD*
Medical Education Office (Attn: MCHK-HE-ME)
1 Jarrett White Road
Tripler AMC, HI 96859
Tel: 808 433-3792   *Fax:* 808 433-6539
Length: 1 Yr   *ACGME Approved/Offered Positions:* 17
Sponsoring Spec: GS, IM, OBG, PD
Program ID: 999-14-00-030
Uniformed Services Program

Illinois

Berwyn

MacNeal Hospital Program
Sponsor: MacNeal Hospital
Prgm Director: Katherine M Tynus, MD
3249 S Oak Park Ave
Berwyn, IL 60402
Tel: 708 783-3400   *Fax:* 708 783-3341
Length: 1 Yr   *ACGME Approved/Offered Positions:* 16
Sponsoring Spec: FP, IM
Program ID: 999-16-00-032

Chicago

Louis A Weiss Memorial Hospital Program
Sponsor: Louis A Weiss Memorial Hospital
Prgm Director: Shehzad Ali, MD
4646 North Marine Drive
Chicago, IL 60640
Tel: 773 564-5225   *Fax:* 773 564-5226
Length: 1 Yr   *ACGME Approved/Offered Positions:* 8
Sponsoring Spec: GS, IM
Program ID: 999-16-00-035

Note: * indicates a newly appointed program director

Resurrection Medical Center Program

Sponsor: Resurrection Medical Center
Prgm Director: Gary Fahrenbach, MD*
Medical Education Office
7435 W Talcott Ave
Chicago, IL 60631
Tel: 773 792-5144   *Fax:* 773 990-7635
Length: 1 Yr   *ACGME Approved/Offered Positions:* 14
Sponsoring Spec: EM, FP
Program ID: 999-16-00-207

St Joseph Hospital Program

Sponsor: St Joseph Hospital
Prgm Director: Stephen Grohmann, MD
2900 N Lake Shore Drive
Chicago, IL 60657
Tel: 773 665-3023   *Fax:* 773 665-3384
E-mail: hhayes01@reshealthcare.org
Length: 1 Yr   *ACGME Approved/Offered Positions:* 6
Sponsoring Spec: GS, IM
Program ID: 999-16-00-033

Swedish Covenant Hospital Program

Sponsor: Swedish Covenant Hospital
Prgm Director: Michael J Plunkett, MD
5145 N California Ave
Chicago, IL 60625
Tel: 773 989-3808   *Fax:* 773 989-1648
E-mail: meded@schosp.org
Length: 1 Yr   *ACGME Approved/Offered Positions:* 8
Sponsoring Spec: FP, GS
Program ID: 999-16-00-231

Evanston

McGaw Medical Center of Northwestern University (Evanston) Program

Sponsor: McGaw Medical Center of Northwestern
    University
Evanston Hospital
Glenbrook Hospital
Prgm Director: Liza G Icayan, MD
2650 Ridge Avenue
Evanston, IL 60201
Tel: 847 570-2376   *Fax:* 847 570-2905
E-mail: licayan@northshore.org
Length: 1 Yr   *ACGME Approved/Offered Positions:* 10
Sponsoring Spec: EM, IM
Program ID: 999-16-00-037

St Francis Hospital of Evanston Program

Sponsor: St Francis Hospital
Prgm Director: Marko J Jachtorowycz, MD
Department of Medical Education
355 Ridge Avenue, Room 1042
Evanston, IL 60202
Tel: 847 316-3111   *Fax:* 847 316-3307
E-mail: marko-j@att.net
Length: 1 Yr   *ACGME Approved/Offered Positions:* 10
Sponsoring Spec: IM, OBG
Program ID: 999-16-00-038

Oak Park

West Suburban Medical Center Program

Sponsor: West Suburban Medical Center
Prgm Director: Malcolm A Deam, MD
GME, Suite L-700
3 Erie Court
Oak Park, IL 60302
Tel: 708 763-6908   *Fax:* 708 763-6655
E-mail: imtyws@reshealthcare.org
Length: 1 Yr   *ACGME Approved/Offered Positions:* 8
Sponsoring Spec: FP, IM
Program ID: 999-16-00-154

Indiana

Indianapolis

Indiana University School of Medicine/Methodist Hospital Program

Sponsor: Indiana University School of Medicine
Clarian Methodist Hospital of Indiana
Prgm Director: John R Black, MD
I-65 @ 21st Street
PO Box 1367
Indianapolis, IN 46206
Tel: 317 962-8881   *Fax:* 317 962-6904
E-mail: cferguson@clarian.org
Length: 1 Yr   *ACGME Approved/Offered Positions:* 12
Sponsoring Spec: EM, FP, GS, IM, PD
Program ID: 999-17-00-040

St Vincent Hospital and Health Care Center Program

Sponsor: St Vincent Hospitals and Health Care Center
Prgm Director: Lannie J Cation, MD
2001 W 86th Street
Medical Education / 3 North
Indianapolis, IN 46260
Tel: 317 338-2281   *Fax:* 317 338-6359
Length: 1 Yr   *ACGME Approved/Offered Positions:* 18
Sponsoring Spec: FP, IM
Program ID: 999-17-00-041

Muncie

Ball Memorial Hospital Program

Sponsor: Ball Memorial Hospital
Prgm Director: Gerard T Costello, MD
2401 University Ave
Muncie, IN 47303
Tel: 765 741-1095   *Fax:* 765 751-1451
E-mail: vdubois@chsmail.org
Length: 1 Yr   *ACGME Approved/Offered Positions:* 8
Sponsoring Spec: FP, IM
Program ID: 999-17-00-157

Iowa

Des Moines

Broadlawns Medical Center Program

Sponsor: Broadlawns Medical Center
Central Iowa Health System (Iowa Methodist/Iowa
    Lutheran)
Prgm Director: Nicholas J Galioto, MD
1801 Hickman Road
Des Moines, IA 50314
Tel: 515 282-2386   *Fax:* 515 282-2332
E-mail: residencyprograms@broadlawns.org
Length: 1 Yr   *ACGME Approved/Offered Positions:* 4
Sponsoring Spec: FP, IM, PD
Program ID: 999-18-00-042

Central Iowa Health System (Iowa Methodist Medical Center) Program

Sponsor: Central Iowa Health System (Iowa
    Methodist/Iowa Lutheran)
Prgm Director: Steven R Craig, MD
1415 Woodland Avenue, Suite 140
Des Moines, IA 50309
Tel: 515 241-6266   *Fax:* 515 241-4080
E-mail: craigsr@ihs.org
Length: 1 Yr   *ACGME Approved/Offered Positions:* 5
Sponsoring Spec: GS, IM, PD
Program ID: 999-18-00-220

Louisiana

New Orleans

Tulane University Program

Sponsor: Tulane University School of Medicine
Medical Center of Louisiana at New Orleans
Tulane University Hospital and Clinics
Veterans Affairs Medical Center (New Orleans)
Prgm Director: Edwin W Dennard, MD, JD
Transitional Residency Program
1430 Tulane Avenue
New Orleans, LA 70112
Tel: 504 988-2841   *Fax:* 504 988-4701
E-mail: amiester@tulane.edu
Length: 1 Yr   *ACGME Approved/Offered Positions:* 18
Sponsoring Spec: IM, PD
Program ID: 999-21-00-047

Maryland

Baltimore

Harbor Hospital Center Program

Sponsor: Harbor Hospital Center
Prgm Director: Richard B Williams, MD
3001 S Hanover Street
Baltimore, MD 21225
Tel: 410 350-3565   *Fax:* 410 354-0186
E-mail: terry.kus@medstar.net
Length: 1 Yr   *ACGME Approved/Offered Positions:* 6
Sponsoring Spec: GS, IM
Program ID: 999-23-00-050

Maryland General Hospital Program

Sponsor: Maryland General Hospital
Prgm Director: William C Anthony, MD, MBA
827 Linden Avenue
Suite 3B
Baltimore, MD 21201
Tel: 410 225-8790   *Fax:* 410 225-8910
E-mail: razu@marylandgeneral.org
Length: 1 Yr   *ACGME Approved/Offered Positions:* 12
Sponsoring Spec: IM, OPH
Program ID: 999-23-00-049

Bethesda

National Capital Consortium (Walter Reed) Program

Sponsor: National Capital Consortium
National Naval Medical Center (Bethesda)
Walter Reed Army Medical Center
Prgm Director: mary M Klote, MD
Dept of Clinical Investigations
717 Gouldman Lane
Great Falls, VA 22066
Tel: 202 782-7858   *Fax:* 202 782-7093
Length: 1 Yr   *ACGME Approved/Offered Positions:* 30
Sponsoring Spec: IM, OBG
Program ID: 999-10-00-024
Uniformed Services Program

Massachusetts

Boston

Caritas Carney Hospital Program

Sponsor: Caritas Carney Hospital
Prgm Director: Michael Barza, MD
2100 Dorchester Ave
Boston, MA 02124
Tel: 617 296-4012   *Fax:* 617 474-3855
Length: 1 Yr   *ACGME Approved/Offered Positions:* 7
Sponsoring Spec: IM
Program ID: 999-24-00-159

Programs

Tufts Medical Center/Lemuel Shattuck Hospital Program
Sponsor: Tufts Medical Center
Lahey Clinic
Lemuel Shattuck Hospital
Prgm Director: Salah Alrakawi, MD
170 Morton Street
Jamaica Plain, MA 02130
Tel: 617 971-3338   *Fax:* 617 971-3852
Length: 1 Yr   *ACGME Approved/Offered Positions:* 6
Sponsoring Spec: GS, IM
Program ID: 999-24-00-199

Brockton

Tufts Medical Center Program
Sponsor: Tufts Medical Center
Brockton Hospital
Prgm Director: Burton J Polansky, MD
680 Centre St
Brockton, MA 02302
Tel: 508 941-7221   *Fax:* 508 941-6334
Length: 1 Yr   *ACGME Approved/Offered Positions:* 9
Sponsoring Spec: GS, IM
Program ID: 999-24-00-158

Cambridge

Cambridge Health Alliance Program
Sponsor: Cambridge Health Alliance
Prgm Director: Slava V Gaufberg, MD*
1493 Cambridge Street
Cambridge, MA 02139
Tel: 617 665-1021
E-mail: transint@cha.harvard.edu
Length: 1 Yr   *ACGME Approved/Offered Positions:* 7
Sponsoring Spec: IM, P
Program ID: 999-24-00-054

Framingham

MetroWest Medical Center/Harvard Medical School Program
Sponsor: MetroWest Medical Center-Framingham Union Hospital
Prgm Director: Matthias M Nurnberger, MD
Department of Medical Education
115 Lincoln Street
Framingham, MA 01702
Tel: 508 383-1555   *Fax:* 508 872-4794
Length: 1 Yr   *ACGME Approved/Offered Positions:* 12
Sponsoring Spec: IM, PD
Program ID: 999-24-00-160

Newton

Newton-Wellesley Hospital Program
Sponsor: Newton-Wellesley Hospital
Prgm Director: Janet C Larson, MD
Department of Medicine
2014 Washington Street
Newton, MA 02462
Tel: 617 243-6467   *Fax:* 617 243-6701
E-mail: jlarson2@partners.org
Length: 1 Yr   *ACGME Approved/Offered Positions:* 5
Sponsoring Spec: GS, IM
Program ID: 999-24-00-246

Michigan

Ann Arbor

St Joseph Mercy Hospital Program
Sponsor: St Joseph Mercy Hospital
Prgm Director: John M Watt, MD
5301 E Huron River Drive, RHC-3009
PO Box 995
Ann Arbor, MI 48106
Tel: 734 712-5563   *Fax:* 734 712-5583
E-mail: typrog@trinity-health.org
Length: 1 Yr   *ACGME Approved/Offered Positions:* 12
Sponsoring Spec: GS, IM
Program ID: 999-25-00-056

Dearborn

Oakwood Hospital Program
Sponsor: Oakwood Hospital
Prgm Director: Lyle D Victor, MD, MBA
18101 Oakwood Blvd
Dearborn, MI 48124
Tel: 313 436-2581   *Fax:* 313 436-2071
E-mail: dawn.beutner@oakwood.org
Length: 1 Yr   *ACGME Approved/Offered Positions:* 18
Sponsoring Spec: DR, IM
Program ID: 999-25-00-057

Detroit

Detroit Medical Center Program
Sponsor: Detroit Medical Center Corporation
Children's Hospital of Michigan
Detroit Receiving Hospital and University Health Center
Harper-Hutzel Hospital
Sinai-Grace Hospital
Prgm Director: Kenneth L Bergsman, MD
6071 West Outer Drive
Detroit, MI 48235
Tel: 313 966-4946   *Fax:* 313 966-1738
Length: 1 Yr   *ACGME Approved/Offered Positions:* 28
Sponsoring Spec: EM, FP, IM
Program ID: 999-25-00-060

Henry Ford Hospital Program
Sponsor: Henry Ford Hospital
Henry Ford Macomb - Warren Campus
Wyandotte Hospital
Prgm Director: Anna L Lukowski, MD, BS
2799 W Grand Blvd
CFP-1
Detroit, MI 48202
Tel: 313 916-2889   *Fax:* 313 916-4460
E-mail: alukows2@hfhs.org
Length: 1 Yr   *ACGME Approved/Offered Positions:* 21
Sponsoring Spec: EM, IM
Program ID: 999-25-00-058

St John Hospital and Medical Center Program
Sponsor: St John Hospital and Medical Center
Prgm Director: Adonis N Lorenzana, MD
Medical Education Building
22101 Moross Road
Detroit, MI 48236
Tel: 313 343-3878   *Fax:* 313 343-7840
E-mail: anne.dwyer@stjohn.org
Length: 1 Yr   *ACGME Approved/Offered Positions:* 8
Sponsoring Spec: EM, IM
Program ID: 999-25-00-059

Wayne State University Program
Sponsor: Wayne State University School of Medicine
Crittenton Hospital Medical Center
Veterans Affairs Medical Center (Detroit)
Prgm Director: Maryjean Schenk, MD
540 East Canfield Avenue
Scott Hall, Room 1241
Detroit, MI 48201
Tel: 248 601-4900   *Fax:* 248 601-4994
E-mail: pmorris@med.wayne.edu
Length: 1 Yr   *ACGME Approved/Offered Positions:* 12
Program ID: 999-25-00-253

Flint

Hurley Medical Center/Michigan State University Program
Sponsor: Hurley Medical Center
Prgm Director: Ghassan I Bachuwa, MD, MS
Two Hurley Plaza
Suite 212
Flint, MI 48503
Tel: 810 257-9682   *Fax:* 810 762-7245
Length: 1 Yr   *ACGME Approved/Offered Positions:* 8
Sponsoring Spec: IM, PD
Program ID: 999-25-00-062

Grand Rapids

Grand Rapids Medical Education and Research Center/Michigan State University Program
Sponsor: Grand Rapids Medical Education and Research Center
Saint Mary's Health Care (Grand Rapids)
Spectrum Health-Butterworth Hospital
Prgm Director: Sohail Qadir, MD
Transitional Year Residency Program
25 Michigan NE, Suite 2200
Grand Rapids, MI 49503
Tel: 616 391-3245   *Fax:* 616 391-3130
E-mail: transyear@spectrum-health.org
Length: 1 Yr   *ACGME Approved/Offered Positions:* 20
Sponsoring Spec: EM, IM
Program ID: 999-25-00-190

Kalamazoo

Kalamazoo Center for Medical Studies/Michigan State University Program
Sponsor: Michigan State Univ/Kalamazoo Center for Medical Studies
Borgess Medical Center
Bronson Methodist Hospital
Prgm Director: Joseph A D'Ambrosio, MD, DMD
Transitional Year Program
1000 Oakland Drive
Kalamazoo, MI 49008
Tel: 269 337-6371   *Fax:* 269 337-6380
E-mail: trans@kcms.msu.edu
Length: 1 Yr   *ACGME Approved/Offered Positions:* 8
Sponsoring Spec: FP, IM
Program ID: 999-25-00-065

Pontiac

St Joseph Mercy-Oakland Program
Sponsor: St Joseph Mercy-Oakland
Prgm Director: Jeffrey P Yanez, MD
44405 Woodward Avenue
Pontiac, MI 48341
Tel: 248 858-6233   *Fax:* 248 858-3244
Length: 1 Yr   *ACGME Approved/Offered Positions:* 6
Sponsoring Spec: GS, IM
Program ID: 999-25-00-067

Note: * indicates a newly appointed program director

Royal Oak

William Beaumont Hospital Program

Sponsor: William Beaumont Hospital
Prgm Director: Barbara J Cingel, MD*
3601 West 13 Mile Road
Royal Oak, MI 48073
Tel: 248 551-2678
E-mail: bcingel@beaumont.edu
Length: 1 Yr *ACGME Approved/Offered Positions:* 16
Sponsoring Spec: EM, IM
Program ID: 999-25-00-178

Southfield

Providence Hospital and Medical Centers Program

Sponsor: Providence Hospital and Medical Centers
Prgm Director: Bruce L Kaplan, DO
16001 W Nine Mile, PO Box 2043
Southfield, MI 48037
Tel: 248 849-5663   *Fax:* 248 849-5324
E-mail: dia.harrison@providence-stjohnhealth.org
Length: 1 Yr *ACGME Approved/Offered Positions:* 10
Sponsoring Spec: GS, IM
Program ID: 999-25-00-068

Minnesota

Minneapolis

Hennepin County Medical Center Program

Sponsor: Hennepin County Medical Center
Prgm Director: Meghan M Walsh, MD, MPH*
Medical Administration O7 OMD
701 Park Avenue, S
Minneapolis, MN 55415
Tel: 612 873-9644   *Fax:* 612 904-4401
E-mail: meghan.walsh@hcmed.org
Length: 1 Yr *ACGME Approved/Offered Positions:* 14
Sponsoring Spec: EM, IM
Program ID: 999-26-00-069

Missouri

St Louis

St John's Mercy Medical Center Program

Sponsor: St John's Mercy Medical Center
Prgm Director: Joan Shaffer, MD
615 S New Ballas Rd
St Louis, MO 63141
Tel: 314 251-6930   *Fax:* 314 251-4288
E-mail: pericm@mercy.net
Length: 1 Yr *ACGME Approved/Offered Positions:* 12
Sponsoring Spec: GS, IM
Program ID: 999-28-00-071

New Jersey

Livingston

St Barnabas Medical Center Program

Sponsor: St Barnabas Medical Center
Prgm Director: Henry Rosenberg, MD
94 Old Short Hills Rd
Suite 501 East Wing
Livingston, NJ 07039
Tel: 973 322-5777   *Fax:* 973 322-8720
E-mail: hrosenberg@sbhcs.com
Length: 1 Yr *ACGME Approved/Offered Positions:* 9
Sponsoring Spec: IM, PD
Program ID: 999-33-00-073

Morristown

Atlantic Health Program

Sponsor: Atlantic Health
Morristown Memorial Hospital
Overlook Hospital
Prgm Director: David Kuo, MD
Overlook Hospital
99 Beauvoir Avenue
Summit, NJ 07901
Tel: 908 522-2934   *Fax:* 908 522-0804
E-mail: diana.valcarcel@atlantichealth.org
Length: 1 Yr *ACGME Approved/Offered Positions:* 6
Sponsoring Spec: IM, PD
Program ID: 999-33-00-240

New York

Brooklyn

Maimonides Medical Center Program

Sponsor: Maimonides Medical Center
Coney Island Hospital
Prgm Director: Muthukumar Muthusamy, MD
4802 10th Avenue
Brooklyn, NY 11219
Tel: 718 283-6510   *Fax:* 718 283-8909
E-mail: awoloszyn@maimonidesmed.org
Length: 1 Yr *ACGME Approved/Offered Positions:* 10
Sponsoring Spec: AN, GS, IM
Program ID: 999-35-00-204

Cooperstown

Bassett Healthcare Program

Sponsor: Bassett Healthcare
Prgm Director: Eric L Knight, MD, MPH
One Atwell Road
Cooperstown, NY 13326
Tel: 607 547-6522   *Fax:* 607 547-6612
E-mail: medical.education@bassett.org
Length: 1 Yr *ACGME Approved/Offered Positions:* 9
Sponsoring Spec: GS, IM
Program ID: 999-35-00-080

Flushing

Flushing Hospital Medical Center Program

Sponsor: Flushing Hospital Medical Center
Prgm Director: Roberto Cantu Jr, MD
4500 Parsons Boulevard
Flushing, NY 11355
Tel: 718 670-3135   *Fax:* 718 670-4449
E-mail: FlshngTrans@aol.com
Length: 1 Yr *ACGME Approved/Offered Positions:* 10
Sponsoring Spec: IM, OBG, PD
Program ID: 999-35-00-196

New York Hospital Medical Center of Queens/Cornell University Medical College Program

Sponsor: New York Hospital Medical Center of Queens
Prgm Director: Anthony Somogyi, MD
56-45 Main Street
Flushing, NY 11355
Tel: 718 670-1507   *Fax:* 718 460-1352
E-mail: vmv9002@nyp.org
Length: 1 Yr *ACGME Approved/Offered Positions:* 12
Sponsoring Spec: GS, IM
Program ID: 999-35-00-225

Johnson City

United Health Services Hospitals Program

Sponsor: United Health Services Hospitals
Wilson Medical Center (United Health System)
Prgm Director: James DellaValle, MD
Medical Education Dept
33-57 Harrison Street
Johnson City, NY 13790
Tel: 607 763-8141   *Fax:* 607 763-5484
Length: 1 Yr *ACGME Approved/Offered Positions:* 7
Sponsoring Spec: FP, IM
Program ID: 999-35-00-081

New Rochelle

New York Medical College (Sound Shore) Program

Sponsor: New York Medical College
Sound Shore Medical Center of Westchester
Prgm Director: Stephen Jesmajian, MD
16 Guion Place
New Rochelle, NY 10802
Tel: 914 365-3681   *Fax:* 914 365-5489
Length: 1 Yr *ACGME Approved/Offered Positions:* 4
Sponsoring Spec: GS, IM
Program ID: 999-35-00-216

New York

Memorial Sloan-Kettering Cancer Center Program

Sponsor: Memorial Sloan-Kettering Cancer Center
Prgm Director: Barbara C Egan, MD
1275 York Avenue, Box 420
Bobst Building, Room C1292
New York, NY 10021
Tel: 212 639-3210   *Fax:* 646 422-2135
E-mail: typrogram@mskcc.org
Length: 1 Yr *ACGME Approved/Offered Positions:* 12
Sponsoring Spec: GS, IM
Program ID: 999-35-00-241

New York Medical College at St Vincent's Hospital and Medical Center of New York Program

Sponsor: New York Medical College
St Vincent Catholic Medical Centers (Manhattan)
Prgm Director: Margaret D Smith, MD
Department of Medicine
170 West 12th Street
New York, NY 10011
Tel: 212 604-2124   *Fax:* 212 604-3225
Length: 1 Yr *ACGME Approved/Offered Positions:* 20
Sponsoring Spec: GS, IM
Program ID: 999-35-00-083

Syracuse

St Joseph's Hospital Health Center Program

Sponsor: St Joseph's Hospital Health Center
Prgm Director: Matthew L Picone, MD, MS
301 Prospect Ave
Syracuse, NY 13203
Tel: 315 448-5537   *Fax:* 315 448-6313
E-mail: matthew.picone@sjhsyr.org
Length: 1 Yr *ACGME Approved/Offered Positions:* 8
Sponsoring Spec: EM, FP
Program ID: 999-35-00-084

Programs

North Dakota

Fargo

University of North Dakota Program

Sponsor: Univ of North Dakota School of Medicine and Health Sciences
MeritCare Health System
Prgm Director: David J Theige, MD
Medical & Academic Education
PO Box MC
Fargo, ND 58122
Tel: 701 234-5934   *Fax:* 701 234-7230
Length: 1 Yr   *ACGME Approved/Offered Positions:* 8
Sponsoring Spec: IM, P
Program ID: 999-37-00-086

Ohio

Akron

Akron General Medical Center/NEOUCOM Program

Sponsor: Akron General Medical Center
Prgm Director: Joseph Finocchio, MD
400 Wabash Avenue
Akron, OH 44307
Tel: 330 344-6140   *Fax:* 330 535-9270
E-mail: kstith@agmc.org
Length: 1 Yr   *ACGME Approved/Offered Positions:* 4
Sponsoring Spec: EM, IM
Program ID: 999-38-00-088

Summa Health System/NEOUCOM Program

Sponsor: Summa Health System
Akron City Hospital (Summa Health System)
Prgm Director: Troy W Bishop, MD*
525 E Market St
Medical Education/Mary Yanik
Akron, OH 44304
Tel: 330 375-3736   *Fax:* 330 375-3760
Length: 1 Yr   *ACGME Approved/Offered Positions:* 10
Sponsoring Spec: EM, IM
Program ID: 999-38-00-087

Canton

Aultman Hospital/NEOUCOM Program

Sponsor: Aultman Hospital
Prgm Director: Jennifer L Bolyard, MD
2600 Sixth St, SW
Canton, OH 44710
Tel: 330 363-6293   *Fax:* 330 588-2605
Length: 1 Yr   *ACGME Approved/Offered Positions:* 4
Sponsoring Spec: FP, IM
Program ID: 999-38-00-191

Columbus

Mount Carmel Program

Sponsor: Mount Carmel
Prgm Director: James N Parsons, MD
793 W State St
Columbus, OH 43222
Tel: 614 234-1079   *Fax:* 614 234-2772
Length: 1 Yr   *ACGME Approved/Offered Positions:* 5
Sponsoring Spec: GS, IM
Program ID: 999-38-00-093

Riverside Methodist Hospitals (OhioHealth) Program

Sponsor: Riverside Methodist Hospitals (OhioHealth)
Prgm Director: Kevin L Schroeder, MD
Medical Education Department
3535 Olentangy River Road
Columbus, OH 43214
Tel: 614 566-4462
Length: 1 Yr   *ACGME Approved/Offered Positions:* 12
Sponsoring Spec: FP, IM
Program ID: 999-38-00-095

Kettering

Kettering Medical Center Program

Sponsor: Kettering Medical Center
Prgm Director: John A Shrader, MD
3535 Southern Boulevard
Kettering, OH 45429
Tel: 937 395-8693   *Fax:* 937 395-8399
E-mail: john.shrader@khnetwork.org
Length: 1 Yr   *ACGME Approved/Offered Positions:* 10
Sponsoring Spec: EM, FP, IM
Program ID: 999-38-00-096

Toledo

Mercy Health Partners/St Vincent Mercy Medical Center Program

Sponsor: St Vincent Mercy Medical Center
St Charles Mercy Hospital
Prgm Director: Hamid Riaz, MD
2200 Jefferson Avenue
Toledo, OH 43604
Tel: 419 251-1395   *Fax:* 419 242-9806
Length: 1 Yr   *ACGME Approved/Offered Positions:* 8
Sponsoring Spec: EM, FP, GS
Program ID: 999-38-00-165

Youngstown

St Elizabeth Health Center Program

Sponsor: St Elizabeth Health Center
Prgm Director: William M Quirk III, MD
1044 Belmont Avenue, Box 1790
Youngstown, OH 44501
Tel: 330 480-2994   *Fax:* 330 480-6601
E-mail: larissa_mcelrath@hmis.org
Length: 1 Yr   *ACGME Approved/Offered Positions:* 4
Sponsoring Spec: GS, IM
Program ID: 999-38-00-250

Oregon

Portland

Legacy Emanuel Hospital and Health Center Program

Sponsor: Legacy Emanuel Hospital and Health Center
Legacy Good Samaritan Hospital and Medical Center
Prgm Director: Darcy Deering, MD
2801 N Gantenbein Avenue
Room 4100A
Portland, OR 97227
Tel: 503 413-4692   *Fax:* 503 413-2144
E-mail: ddeering@lhs.org
Length: 1 Yr   *ACGME Approved/Offered Positions:* 8
Sponsoring Spec: GS, IM
Program ID: 999-40-00-101

Pennsylvania

Allentown

Lehigh Valley Hospital Network/Pennsylvania State University Program

Sponsor: Lehigh Valley Hospital Network
Prgm Director: Marc Shalaby, MD
Cedar Crest and I-78
PO Box 689
Allentown, PA 18105
Tel: 610 402-8048   *Fax:* 610 402-1675
Length: 1 Yr   *ACGME Approved/Offered Positions:* 14
Sponsoring Spec: GS, IM
Program ID: 999-41-00-103

Bethlehem

St Luke's Hospital Program

Sponsor: St Luke's Hospital
Prgm Director: Gloria T Fioravanti, DO
Department of Medicine
801 Ostrum Street
Bethlehem, PA 18015
Tel: 610 954-4644   *Fax:* 610 954-4920
E-mail: www.imresidency@slhn.org
Length: 1 Yr   *ACGME Approved/Offered Positions:* 4
Sponsoring Spec: IM, OBG
Program ID: 999-41-00-104

Darby

Mercy Catholic Medical Center Program

Sponsor: Mercy Catholic Medical Center Inc
Mercy Fitzgerald Hospital
Mercy Philadelphia Hospital
Prgm Director: Joanne Connaughton, MD*
1500 Lansdowne Avenue
Darby, PA 19023
Tel: 610 237-7337   *Fax:* 610 237-5093
Length: 1 Yr   *ACGME Approved/Offered Positions:* 10
Sponsoring Spec: GS, IM
Program ID: 999-41-00-106

Johnstown

Conemaugh Valley Memorial Hospital Program

Sponsor: Conemaugh Valley Memorial Hospital
Prgm Director: Jack L DePriest, MD
1086 Franklin Street
Johnstown, PA 15905
Tel: 814 534-9408   *Fax:* 814 534-3290
E-mail: geckenr@conemaugh.org
Length: 1 Yr   *ACGME Approved/Offered Positions:* 8
Sponsoring Spec: FP, IM, PTH
Program ID: 999-41-00-108

Philadelphia

Albert Einstein Healthcare Network Program

Sponsor: Albert Einstein Medical Center
Prgm Director: Glenn Eiger, MD
5401 Old York Road, Suite 363
Philadelphia, PA 19141
Tel: 215 456-4940   *Fax:* 215 456-7926
Length: 1 Yr   *ACGME Approved/Offered Positions:* 20
Sponsoring Spec: EM, IM
Program ID: 999-41-00-224

Note: * indicates a newly appointed program director

Pittsburgh

University of Pittsburgh Med Center Medical Education (Presbyterian Shadyside Hospital) Program

Sponsor: Univ of Pittsburgh Medical Center Medical Education
UPMC Presbyterian Shadyside
Prgm Director: Gary H Tabas, MD
5230 Centre Ave
209 School of Nursing
Pittsburgh, PA 15232
Tel: 412 623-2395   *Fax:* 412 623-6621
E-mail: ty@msx.upmc.edu
Length: 1 Yr   *ACGME Approved/Offered Positions:* 6
Sponsoring Spec: FP, IM
Program ID: 999-41-00-117

University of Pittsburgh Medical Center Medical Education (Mercy) Program

Sponsor: Univ of Pittsburgh Medical Center Medical Education
Mercy Hospital of Pittsburgh
Prgm Director: Anthony J Pinevich, MD, MBA
Department of Medicine
1400 Locust Street
Pittsburgh, PA 15219
Tel: 800 637-2946   *Fax:* 412 232-5689
Length: 1 Yr   *ACGME Approved/Offered Positions:* 15
Sponsoring Spec: AN, DR, IM
Program ID: 999-41-00-114

University of Pittsburgh Medical Center Medical Education Program

Sponsor: Univ of Pittsburgh Medical Center Medical Education
Veterans Affairs Medical Center (Pittsburgh)
Prgm Director: Julie B McCausland, MD, MS*
200 Lothrop Street, Room N713
UPMC Montefiore
Pittsburgh, PA 15213
Tel: 412 692-4700
E-mail: mccauslandjb@upmc.edu
Length: 1 Yr   *ACGME Approved/Offered Positions:* 10
Sponsoring Spec: AN, DR, EM, IM, N, PD, PTH
Program ID: 999-41-00-115

Western Pennsylvania Hospital/Temple University Program

Sponsor: Western Pennsylvania Hospital
Prgm Director: Mary Lynn Sealey, MD
4800 Friendship Avenue
Pittsburgh, PA 15224
Tel: 412 578-6902   *Fax:* 412 578-7212
Length: 1 Yr   *ACGME Approved/Offered Positions:* 10
Sponsoring Spec: GS, IM
Program ID: 999-41-00-234

Upland

Crozer-Chester Medical Center Program

Sponsor: Crozer-Chester Medical Center
Prgm Director: Dina F Capalongo, DO
Dept of Medicine, 3 East
One Medical Center Blvd
Upland, PA 19013
Tel: 610 874-6114   *Fax:* 610 447-6373
E-mail: tyccmc@crozer.org
Length: 1 Yr   *ACGME Approved/Offered Positions:* 14
Sponsoring Spec: IM, PD
Program ID: 999-41-00-212

West Reading

Reading Hospital and Medical Center Program

Sponsor: Reading Hospital and Medical Center
Prgm Director: Benjamin J Lloyd, MD
PO Box 16052
Reading, PA 19612
Tel: 610 988-8470   *Fax:* 610 988-9003
Length: 1 Yr   *ACGME Approved/Offered Positions:* 6
Sponsoring Spec: FP, IM, OBG
Program ID: 999-41-00-119

Puerto Rico

Ponce

Damas Hospital/Ponce School of Medicine Program

Sponsor: Damas Hospital
Hospital Episcopal San Lucas
Prgm Director: Alejandra N Santiago, MD
2225 Ponce BYP, Ste 407
Ponce, PR 00717
Tel: 787 840-8686   *Fax:* 787 984-2986
Length: 1 Yr   *ACGME Approved/Offered Positions:* 12
Sponsoring Spec: IM, OBG
Program ID: 999-42-00-249

Hospital Episcopal San Lucas/Ponce School of Medicine Program

Sponsor: Hospital Episcopal San Lucas
Prgm Director: Olga Rodriguez, MD
917 Tito Castro Ave
PO Box 336810
Ponce, PR 00733
Tel: 787 843-3031   *Fax:* 787 841-7165
E-mail: orodriguez@psm.edu
Length: 1 Yr   *ACGME Approved/Offered Positions:* 12
Sponsoring Spec: IM, OBG
Program ID: 999-42-00-125

San Juan

San Juan City Hospital Program

Sponsor: San Juan City Hospital
University Hospital
Prgm Director: Ana L Bermudez, MD, MPH
PMB 498
PO Box 70344
San Juan, PR 00936
Tel: 787 766-0205   *Fax:* 787 767-7011
Length: 1 Yr   *ACGME Approved/Offered Positions:* 10
Sponsoring Spec: EM, IM
Program ID: 999-42-00-213

South Carolina

Charleston

Trident Medical Center/Medical University of South Carolina Program

Sponsor: Trident Medical Center
MUSC Medical Center
Prgm Director: Terrence E Steyer, MD
9298 Medical Plaza Drive
Charleston, SC 29406
Tel: 843 876-7103   *Fax:* 843 818-2990
E-mail: tyres@musc.edu
Length: 1 Yr   *ACGME Approved/Offered Positions:* 6
Sponsoring Spec: DR, FP
Program ID: 999-45-00-252

Spartanburg

Spartanburg Regional Healthcare System Program

Sponsor: Spartanburg Regional Healthcare System
Prgm Director: Joseph Walton, MD
101 E Wood Street
Spartanburg, SC 29303
Tel: 864 560-6929   *Fax:* 864 560-7015
E-mail: bstowell@srhs.com
Length: 1 Yr   *ACGME Approved/Offered Positions:* 6
Sponsoring Spec: FP, GS
Program ID: 999-45-00-182

South Dakota

Sioux Falls

University of South Dakota Program

Sponsor: University of South Dakota School of Medicine
Avera McKennan Hospital and University Health Center
Sanford USD Medical Center
Prgm Director: Turi A McNamee, MD
1400 West 22nd Street
Sioux Falls, SD 57105
Tel: 605 357-1306   *Fax:* 605 357-1311
E-mail: mary.sutter@usd.edu
Length: 1 Yr   *ACGME Approved/Offered Positions:* 6
Sponsoring Spec: FP, IM
Program ID: 999-46-00-230

Tennessee

Chattanooga

University of Tennessee College of Medicine at Chattanooga Program

Sponsor: University of Tennessee College of Medicine-Chattanooga
Erlanger Medical Center
Prgm Director: Mukta Panda, MD
975 E Third Street, Box 94
Chattanooga, TN 37403
Tel: 423 778-6670   *Fax:* 423 778-2611
E-mail: UTTrans@erlanger.org
Length: 1 Yr   *ACGME Approved/Offered Positions:* 8
Sponsoring Spec: GS, IM, OBG, OPH, PD
Program ID: 999-47-00-129

Knoxville

University of Tennessee Medical Center at Knoxville Program

Sponsor: University of Tennessee Graduate School of Medicine
University of Tennessee Memorial Hospital
Prgm Director: Daphne M Norwood, MD, MPH
1924 Alcoa Highway
Knoxville, TN 37920
Tel: 865 305-9340   *Fax:* 865 305-6849
Length: 1 Yr   *ACGME Approved/Offered Positions:* 10
Sponsoring Spec: FP, IM
Program ID: 999-47-00-130

Memphis

University of Tennessee/Methodist Healthcare-Memphis Hospitals Program

Sponsor: University of Tennessee College of Medicine
Methodist Healthcare - Memphis Hospitals
Prgm Director: Catherine J Clarke, MD
1265 Union Avenue
Memphis, TN 38104
Tel: 901 516-8255   *Fax:* 901 516-8254
E-mail: clarkec@methodisthealth.org
Length: 1 Yr   *ACGME Approved/Offered Positions:* 12
Sponsoring Spec: GS, IM
Program ID: 999-47-00-131

Programs

Texas

Austin

University of Texas Medical Branch (Austin) Program

Sponsor: University of Texas Medical Branch Hospitals
University Medical Center at Brackenridge
Dell Children's Medical Center of Central Texas
Prgm Director: David H Harshaw, MD*
CEC @ Brackenridge, Transitional Residency Program
1400 N IH 35, Suite C2.161
Austin, TX 78701
Tel: 512 234-7000   *Fax:* 512 324-8020
Length: 1 Yr   *ACGME Approved/Offered Positions:* 6
Sponsoring Spec: IM, PD
Program ID: 999-48-00-133

El Paso

Texas Tech University Health Sciences Center Paul L Foster School of Medicine Program

Sponsor: Texas Tech University Hlth Sci Ctr Paul L
   Foster Sch of Med
R E Thomason General Hospital / Texas Tech University
   HSC
Prgm Director: John M MacKay Jr, MD*
Regional Academic Center at El Paso
4800 Alberta Avenue
El Paso, TX 79905
Tel: 915 545-7333   *Fax:* 915 545-7338
E-mail: john.mackay@ttuhsc.edu
Length: 1 Yr   *ACGME Approved/Offered Positions:* 4
Sponsoring Spec: EM, GS, IM
Program ID: 999-48-00-221

William Beaumont Army Medical Center Program

Sponsor: William Beaumont Army Medical Center
Prgm Director: Craig L Maddox, MD, MS*
Office of Graduate Medical Education
5005 North Piedras Street
El Paso, TX 79920
Tel: 915 569-2743   *Fax:* 915 569-2653
Length: 1 Yr   *ACGME Approved/Offered Positions:* 14
Sponsoring Spec: GS, IM
Program ID: 999-48-00-137
Uniformed Services Program

Fort Sam Houston

San Antonio Uniformed Services Health Education Consortium Program

Sponsor: San Antonio Uniformed Services Health
   Education Consortium
Brooke Army Medical Center
Wilford Hall Medical Center (AETC)
Prgm Director: Michael W Hilliard, MD
3851 Roger Brooke Drive
Fort Sam Houston, TX 78234
Tel: 210 916-2203   *Fax:* 210 916-3833
Length: 1 Yr   *ACGME Approved/Offered Positions:* 24
Program ID: 999-48-00-254
Uniformed Services Program

Fort Worth

John Peter Smith Hospital (Tarrant County Hospital District) Program

Sponsor: John Peter Smith Hospital (Tarrant County
   Hospital District)
Prgm Director: Donald K Nelms, MD
1500 South Main Street
Fort Worth, TX 76104
Tel: 817 927-1255   *Fax:* 817 927-1405
E-mail: dnelms@jpshealth.org
Length: 1 Yr   *ACGME Approved/Offered Positions:* 12
Sponsoring Spec: FP, OBG, ORS
Program ID: 999-48-00-168

Houston

Methodist Hospital (Houston) Program

Sponsor: Methodist Hospital (Houston)
Prgm Director: Ethan A Natelson, MD
6565 Fannin Street
SM1001
Houston, TX 77030
Tel: 713 441-5154   *Fax:* 713 790-6615
Length: 1 Yr   *ACGME Approved/Offered Positions:* 16
Sponsoring Spec: FP, GS
Program ID: 999-48-00-140

University of Texas at Houston Program

Sponsor: University of Texas Health Science Center at
   Houston
Lyndon B Johnson General Hospital
Memorial Hermann Hospital
Prgm Director: Christine E Koerner, MD
Lyndon B Johnson General Hospital
5656 Kelley Street
Houston, TX 77026
Tel: 713 566-4646   *Fax:* 713 566-4655
Length: 1 Yr   *ACGME Approved/Offered Positions:* 15
Sponsoring Spec: GS, IM, OBG, PD
Program ID: 999-48-00-219

Utah

Salt Lake City

Intermountain Medical Center Program

Sponsor: Intermountain Medical Center
Prgm Director: Scott M Stevens, MD
5121 South Cottonwood Street
Murray, UT 84157
Tel: 800 548-6672   *Fax:* 801 507-3799
E-mail: kris.bjerregaard@imail.org
Length: 1 Yr   *ACGME Approved/Offered Positions:* 12
Sponsoring Spec: GS, IM
Program ID: 999-49-00-142

Virginia

Falls Church

Georgetown University Hospital Program

Sponsor: Georgetown University Hospital
Inova Fairfax Hospital
Prgm Director: Shirley K Kalwaney, MD
Department of Medicine
3300 Gallows Rd
Falls Church, VA 22042
Tel: 703 776-2896   *Fax:* 703 776-3020
Length: 1 Yr   *ACGME Approved/Offered Positions:* 12
Sponsoring Spec: IM, PD
Program ID: 999-51-00-205

Newport News

Riverside Regional Medical Center Program

Sponsor: Riverside Regional Medical Center
Children's Hospital of the King's Daughters
Prgm Director: Patrick G Haggerty, MD
500 J Clyde Morris Boulevard
Department of Medical Education
Newport News, VA 23601
Tel: 757 594-2041   *Fax:* 757 594-3245
Length: 1 Yr   *ACGME Approved/Offered Positions:* 12
Sponsoring Spec: FP, OBG
Program ID: 999-51-00-170

Portsmouth

Naval Medical Center (Portsmouth) Program

Sponsor: Naval Medical Center (Portsmouth)
Prgm Director: Ashley A Schroeder, MD
620 John Paul Jones Circle
Dept of Graduate Medical Education
Portsmouth, VA 23708
Tel: 757 953-0669   *Fax:* 757 953-5116
E-mail: ashley.schroeder@med.navy.mil
Length: 1 Yr   *ACGME Approved/Offered Positions:* 25
Sponsoring Spec: GS, IM, ORS
Program ID: 999-51-00-193
Uniformed Services Program

Roanoke

Carilion Clinic Program

Sponsor: Carilion Clinic
Carilion Roanoke Memorial Hospital
Prgm Director: James M Sherman, MD
Carilion Clinic
PO Box 13367
Roanoke, VA 24033
Tel: 540 981-7776   *Fax:* 540 857-5296
E-mail: transitionalresidency@carilion.com
Length: 1 Yr   *ACGME Approved/Offered Positions:* 12
Sponsoring Spec: GS, IM
Program ID: 999-51-00-143

Washington

Seattle

Virginia Mason Medical Center Program

Sponsor: Virginia Mason Medical Center
Prgm Director: Larry K Dipboye, MD, MA
Graduate Medical Education, H8-GME
925 Seneca Street
Seattle, WA 98111
Tel: 206 583-6079   *Fax:* 206 583-2307
E-mail: Joanne.VanderDoes@vmmc.org
Length: 1 Yr   *ACGME Approved/Offered Positions:* 12
Sponsoring Spec: GS, IM
Program ID: 999-54-00-144

Spokane

Deaconess Medical Center (Spokane) Program

Sponsor: Inland Empire Hospital Services Association
Deaconess Medical Center
Prgm Director: Darryl Potyk, MD
800 W 5th Ave
PO Box 248
Spokane, WA 99210
Tel: 509 473-7159   *Fax:* 509 473-7797
E-mail: potykd@empirehealth.org
Length: 1 Yr   *ACGME Approved/Offered Positions:* 8
Sponsoring Spec: FP, IM
Program ID: 999-54-00-169

Note: * indicates a newly appointed program director

Spokane Medical Centers Program

Sponsor: Inland Empire Hospital Services Association
Sacred Heart Medical Center
Prgm Director: Lawrence G Schrock, MD
101 West 8th Avenue
PO Box 2555
Spokane, WA 99220
Tel: 509 474-3020   *Fax:* 509 474-5316
Length: 1 Yr   *ACGME Approved/Offered Positions:* 10
Sponsoring Spec: FP, IM
Program ID: 999-54-00-145

Tacoma

Madigan Army Medical Center Program

Sponsor: Madigan Army Medical Center
Prgm Director: Matthew W Short, MD*
Graduate Medical Education Office
Attn: MCHJ-EDME
Tacoma, WA 98431
Tel: 253 968-1511   *Fax:* 253 968-5926
Length: 1 Yr   *ACGME Approved/Offered Positions:* 22
Sponsoring Spec: IM, OBG
Program ID: 999-54-00-146
Uniformed Services Program

West Virginia

Morgantown

West Virginia University Program

Sponsor: West Virginia University School of Medicine
West Virginia University Hospitals
Prgm Director: Mary Warden, MD
PO Box 9001-A
Robert C Byrd Health Sciences Center
Morgantown, WV 26506
Tel: 304 293-2463   *Fax:* 304 293-5160
E-mail: lbrownlee@hsc.wvu.edu
Length: 1 Yr   *ACGME Approved/Offered Positions:* 13
Sponsoring Spec: GS, IM, PD
Program ID: 999-55-00-248

Wisconsin

La Crosse

Gundersen Lutheran Medical Foundation Program

Sponsor: Gundersen Lutheran Medical Foundation
Gundersen Clinic Ltd
Gundersen Lutheran Medical Center
Prgm Director: Gregory P Thompson, MD
1836 South Avenue, C03-006
La Crosse, WI 54601
Tel: 608 775-6650   *Fax:* 608 775-4457
E-mail: gpthomps@gundluth.org
Length: 1 Yr   *ACGME Approved/Offered Positions:* 12
Sponsoring Spec: GS, IM
Program ID: 999-56-00-147

Marshfield

Marshfield Clinic-St Joseph's Hospital Program

Sponsor: Marshfield Clinic-St Joseph's Hospital
Prgm Director: Wayne E Thorne, MD
1000 North Oak Avenue
Marshfield, WI 54449
Tel: 800 541-2895   *Fax:* 715 387-5163
Length: 1 Yr   *ACGME Approved/Offered Positions:* 4
Sponsoring Spec: GS, IM, PD
Program ID: 999-56-00-183

Milwaukee

Aurora Health Care Program

Sponsor: Aurora Health Care
St Luke's Medical Center
Prgm Director: Richard J Battiola, MD
2801 W Kinnickinnic River Parkway
Physican Office Building, Suite 730
Milwaukee, WI 53215
Tel: 414 649-3323   *Fax:* 414 649-5158
E-mail: richard.battiola@aurora.org
Length: 1 Yr   *ACGME Approved/Offered Positions:* 17
Sponsoring Spec: FP, IM
Program ID: 999-56-00-148

Wheaton Franciscan Healthcare-St Joseph Program

Sponsor: Wheaton Franciscan Healthcare-St Joseph
Prgm Director: Kesavan Kutty, MD
5000 West Chambers Street
Milwaukee, WI 53210
Tel: 414 447-2245
Length: 1 Yr   *ACGME Approved/Offered Positions:* 12
Sponsoring Spec: DR, IM
Program ID: 999-56-00-184

Transplant Hepatology (Internal Medicine)

Arizona

Phoenix

College of Medicine, Mayo Clinic (Arizona) Program

Sponsor: College of Medicine, Mayo Clinic
Mayo Clinic Hospital
Prgm Director: David D Douglas, MD
2W, Med Ed
5777 E Mayo Blvd
Phoenix, AZ 85054
Tel: 480 342-1272
Length: 1 Yr   *ACGME Approved/Offered Positions:* 2
Program ID: 158-03-14-014

California

San Francisco

University of California (San Francisco) Program

Sponsor: University of California (San Francisco) School
of Medicine
UCSF and Mount Zion Medical Centers
Prgm Director: Nathan M Bass, MBChB, PhD
513 Parnassus Avenue
Room S-357
San Francisco, CA 94143
Tel: 415 476-3143   *Fax:* 415 476-0659
E-mail: nathan.bass@ucsf.edu
Length: 1 Yr   *ACGME Approved/Offered Positions:* 2
Program ID: 158-05-14-001

Colorado

Aurora

University of Colorado Denver Program

Sponsor: University of Colorado Denver School of
Medicine
University of Colorado Hospital
Prgm Director: Gregory T Everson, MD
12631 E 17th Ave Box B158
PO Box 6511
Aurora, CO 80045
Tel: 303 724-1858   *Fax:* 303 724-1891
E-mail: amanda.bauer@ucdenver.edu
Length: 1 Yr   *ACGME Approved/Offered Positions:* 2
Program ID: 158-07-14-029

Florida

Gainesville

University of Florida Program

Sponsor: University of Florida College of Medicine
Shands Hospital at the University of Florida
Prgm Director: Roberto J Firpi, MD
1600 SW Archer Rd Room M440 MSB
Gainesville, FL 32610
Tel: 352 392-7353   *Fax:* 352 392-7393
E-mail: firpirj@medicine.ufl.edu
Length: 1 Yr   *ACGME Approved/Offered Positions:* 1
Program ID: 158-11-14-018

Programs

Jacksonville

College of Medicine, Mayo Clinic (Jacksonville) Program

Sponsor: College of Medicine, Mayo Clinic
Mayo Clinic (Jacksonville)
Mayo Clinic Florida Hospital
Prgm Director: Andrew P Keaveny, MD*
4500 San Pablo Road
Graduate Medical Education Davis 172 West
Jacksonville, FL 32224
Tel: 904 953-0487   *Fax:* 904 953-0430
E-mail: spier.lori@mayo.edu
Length: 1 Yr   *ACGME Approved/Offered Positions:* 2
Program ID: 158-11-14-011

Illinois

Chicago

McGaw Medical Center of Northwestern University Program

Sponsor: McGaw Medical Center of Northwestern
   University
Children's Memorial Hospital
Northwestern Memorial Hospital
Prgm Director: Richard Green, MD
645 N Michigan Avenue
Suite 1058-A
Chicago, IL 60611
Tel: 312 695-0254   *Fax:* 312 695-9194
E-mail: r-green2@northwestern.edu
Length: 1 Yr   *ACGME Approved/Offered Positions:* 1
Program ID: 158-16-14-015

University of Chicago Program

Sponsor: University of Chicago Medical Center
Prgm Director: Donald Jensen, MD
5841 S Maryland Avenue
Chicago, IL 60637
Tel: 773 702-2395   *Fax:* 773 834-1288
E-mail: lkaczmar@medicine.bsd.uchicago.edu
Length: 1 Yr   *ACGME Approved/Offered Positions:* 1
Program ID: 158-16-14-023

University of Illinois College of Medicine at Chicago Program

Sponsor: University of Illinois College of Medicine at
   Chicago
University of Illinois Hospital and Clinics
Prgm Director: Jamie Berkes, MD*
840 S Wood St, 1029 CSB Bldg
Chicago, IL 60612
Tel: 312 413-5882   *Fax:* 312 996-1334
E-mail: creason3@uic.edu
Length: 1 Yr   *ACGME Approved/Offered Positions:* 1
Program ID: 158-16-14-033

Massachusetts

Boston

Beth Israel Deaconess Medical Center Program

Sponsor: Beth Israel Deaconess Medical Center
Prgm Director: Nezam Afdhal, MD
330 Brookline Avenue
LMOB/Suite 8E
Boston, MA 02215
Tel: 617 632-1070   *Fax:* 617 632-1054
E-mail: nafdhal@bidmc.harvard.edu
Length: 1 Yr   *ACGME Approved/Offered Positions:* 1
Program ID: 158-24-14-003

Massachusetts General Hospital Program

Sponsor: Massachusetts General Hospital
Prgm Director: Raymond T Chung, MD
GI Unit, GRJ 724
55 Fruit Street
Boston, MA 02114
Tel: 617 724-7562
E-mail: rtchung@partners.org
Length: 1 Yr   *ACGME Approved/Offered Positions:* 2
Program ID: 158-24-14-008

Michigan

Ann Arbor

University of Michigan Program

Sponsor: University of Michigan Hospitals and Health
   Centers
Prgm Director: Robert J Fontana, MD*
1500 E Medical Center Drive
3912 Taubman Center, SPC 5362
Ann Arbor, MI 48109
Tel: 734 936-4780   *Fax:* 734 936-7392
E-mail: cerdmann@umich.edu
Length: 1 Yr   *ACGME Approved/Offered Positions:* 2
Program ID: 158-25-14-013

Detroit

Henry Ford Hospital Program

Sponsor: Henry Ford Hospital
Prgm Director: Stuart Gordon, MD
2799 West Grand Boulevard
Detroit, MI 48202
Tel: 313 916-8632   *Fax:* 313 916-5960
Length: 1 Yr   *ACGME Approved/Offered Positions:* 1
Program ID: 158-25-14-031

Minnesota

Minneapolis

University of Minnesota Program

Sponsor: University of Minnesota Medical School
University of Minnesota Medical Center, Division of
   Fairview
Prgm Director: Charmaine A Stewart, MD*
MMC 36
406 Harvard St, SE
Minneapolis, MN 55455
Tel: 612 626-2636   *Fax:* 612 625-5620
E-mail: stewa560@umn.edu
Length: 1 Yr   *ACGME Approved/Offered Positions:* 1
Program ID: 158-26-14-017

Rochester

College of Medicine, Mayo Clinic (Rochester) Program

Sponsor: College of Medicine, Mayo Clinic
Mayo Clinic (Rochester)
Rochester Methodist Hospital
Prgm Director: John J Poterucha, MD
200 First Street, SW
Rochester, MN 55905
Tel: 507 266-4056
Length: 1 Yr   *ACGME Approved/Offered Positions:* 3
Program ID: 158-26-14-006

New York

New York

Mount Sinai School of Medicine Program

Sponsor: Mount Sinai School of Medicine
Mount Sinai Medical Center
Prgm Director: Meena Bansal, MD
1425 Madison Avenue, Room 11-70
New York, NY 10029
Tel: 212 659-9519   *Fax:* 212 849-2574
Length: 1 Yr   *ACGME Approved/Offered Positions:* 4
Program ID: 158-35-14-002

New York Presbyterian Hospital Program

Sponsor: New York Presbyterian Hospital
New York Presbyterian Hospital (Columbia Campus)
Prgm Director: Robert S Brown Jr, MD, MPH*
Center for Liver Disease and Transplantation
PH-14 622 W 168th Street
New York, NY 10032
Tel: 212 305-0915   *Fax:* 212 305-4343
Length: 1 Yr   *ACGME Approved/Offered Positions:* 2
Program ID: 158-35-14-019

Valhalla

New York Medical College at Westchester Medical Center Program

Sponsor: New York Medical College
Prgm Director: Leona Kim-Schluger, MD
Munger Pavilion
Suite 206
Valhalla, NY 10595
Tel: 914 493-7337   *Fax:* 914 594-4317
E-mail: KimL@wcmc.com
Length: 1 Yr   *ACGME Approved/Offered Positions:* 1
Program ID: 158-35-14-022

North Carolina

Durham

Duke University Hospital Program

Sponsor: Duke University Hospital
Prgm Director: Andrew J Muir, MD, MHSc
Division of Gastroenterology
DUMC Box 3913
Durham, NC 27710
Tel: 919 684-2819   *Fax:* 919 684-8857
E-mail: muir0002@mc.duke.edu
Length: 1 Yr   *ACGME Approved/Offered Positions:* 1
Program ID: 158-36-14-037

Ohio

Cincinnati

University Hospital Inc Program

Sponsor: University Hospital Inc
Prgm Director: Stephen D Zucker, MD
Mail Location 0595
231 Albert B Sabin Way
Cincinnati, OH 45267
Tel: 513 558-3944   *Fax:* 513 558-1744
E-mail: zuckersd@email.uc.edu
Length: 1 Yr   *ACGME Approved/Offered Positions:* 1
Program ID: 158-38-14-025

Note: * indicates a newly appointed program director

Pennsylvania

Philadelphia

Thomas Jefferson University Program

Sponsor: Thomas Jefferson University Hospital
Prgm Director: Victor J Navarro, MD
Suite 480 Main
132 South 10th Street
Philadelphia, PA 19107
Tel: 215 955-5271   *Fax:* 215 503-2146
E-mail: victor.navarro@jefferson.edu
Length: 1 Yr   *ACGME Approved/Offered Positions:* 1
Program ID: 158-41-14-028

Pittsburgh

University of Pittsburgh Medical Center Medical Education Program

Sponsor: Univ of Pittsburgh Medical Center Medical
   Education
UPMC Presbyterian Shadyside
Prgm Director: Kapil Chopra, MD
200 Lothrop Street
Pittsburgh, PA 15213
Tel: 412 647-4932   *Fax:* 412 647-9268
E-mail: gibsonh@upmc.edu
Length: 1 Yr   *ACGME Approved/Offered Positions:* 1
Program ID: 158-41-14-021

Texas

Dallas

Baylor University Medical Center Program

Sponsor: Baylor University Medical Center
Prgm Director: Robert Perrillo, MD
3500 Gaston Avenue
1st Floor Roberts, Medical Education
Dallas, TX 75246
Tel: 214 820-2234   *Fax:* 214 820-7272
E-mail: roberper@baylorhealth.edu
Length: 1 Yr   *ACGME Approved/Offered Positions:* 2
Program ID: 158-48-14-007

Virginia

Richmond

Virginia Commonwealth University Health System Program

Sponsor: Virginia Commonwealth University Health
   System
Hunter Holmes McGuire VA Medical Center (Richmond)
Medical College of Virginia Hospitals
Prgm Director: Arun Sanyal, MD, MBBS
1200 East Broad Street
PO Box 980341
Richmond, VA 23298
Tel: 804 828-6314   *Fax:* 804 828-2992
Length: 1 Yr   *ACGME Approved/Offered Positions:* 2
Program ID: 158-51-14-005

Washington

Seattle

University of Washington Program

Sponsor: University of Washington School of Medicine
University of Washington Medical Center
Prgm Director: David J Kearney, MD
1959 NE Pacific Street
Box 356424
Seattle, WA 98195
Tel: 206 277-1445   *Fax:* 206 764-2232
E-mail: kearney@u.washington.edu
Length: 1 Yr   *ACGME Approved/Offered Positions:* 2
Program ID: 158-54-14-030

Wisconsin

Madison

University of Wisconsin Program

Sponsor: University of Wisconsin Hospital and Clinics
Prgm Director: Michael Lucey, MD
600 Highland Avenue
H6/516 CSC
Madison, WI 53792
Tel: 608 263-7322
E-mail: mrl@medicine.wisc.edu
Length: 1 Yr   *ACGME Approved/Offered Positions:* 1
Program ID: 158-56-14-024

Undersea and Hyperbaric Medicine (Emergency Medicine)

California

San Diego

University of California (San Diego) Program

Sponsor: University of California (San Diego) Medical
   Center
Paradise Valley Hospital
Prgm Director: Karen B Van Hoesen, MD
200 West Arbor Drive, #8676
San Diego, CA 92103
Tel: 619 543-6463   *Fax:* 619 543-3115
Length: 1 Yr   *ACGME Approved/Offered Positions:* 2
Program ID: 119-05-31-002

Louisiana

New Orleans

Louisiana State University Program

Sponsor: Louisiana State University School of Medicine
Medical Center of Louisiana at New Orleans
West Jefferson Medical Center
Prgm Director: Paul G Harch, MD
1816 Industrial Boulevard
Harvey, LA 70058
Tel: 504 366-7638   *Fax:* 504 366-1029
Length: 1 Yr   *ACGME Approved/Offered Positions:* 5
Program ID: 119-21-13-004

Minnesota

Minneapolis

Hennepin County Medical Center Program

Sponsor: Hennepin County Medical Center
Prgm Director: Bob Collier, MD
701 Park Avenue South
Mail Code 825
Minneapolis, MN 55415
Tel: 612 873-3174   *Fax:* 612 904-4241
Length: 1 Yr   *ACGME Approved/Offered Positions:* 1
Program ID: 119-26-31-005

Pennsylvania

Philadelphia

University of Pennsylvania Program

Sponsor: University of Pennsylvania Health System
Prgm Director: Stephen R Thom, MD, PhD
Room 1, John Morgan Building
3620 Hamilton Walk
Philadelphia, PA 19104
Tel: 215 898-9102   *Fax:* 215 573-7037
Length: 1 Yr   *ACGME Approved/Offered Positions:* 2
Program ID: 119-41-21-001

Programs

Texas

Dallas

University of Texas Southwestern Medical School Program
Sponsor: University of Texas Southwestern Medical School
Harris Methodist Fort Worth
Texas Health Presbyterian Dallas
Prgm Director: Jeffery Stone, DO
7232 Greenville Avenue
Dallas, TX 75231
Tel: 214 345-4651   *Fax:* 214 345-4647
E-mail: julierogness@texashealth.org
Length: 1 Yr   *ACGME Approved/Offered Positions:* 1
Program ID: 119-48-12-003

Undersea and Hyperbaric Medicine (Preventive Medicine)

North Carolina

Durham

Duke University Hospital Program
Sponsor: Duke University Hospital
Prgm Director: John J Freiberger, MD, MPH
DUMC 3823
Durham, NC 27710
Tel: 919 684-6726   *Fax:* 919 684-6002
Length: 1 Yr   *ACGME Approved/Offered Positions:* 2
Program ID: 398-36-12-001

Urology

Alabama

Birmingham

University of Alabama Medical Center Program
Sponsor: University of Alabama Hospital
Children's Hospital of Alabama
St Vincent's Hospital
University of Alabama at Birmingham/Highlands
Veterans Affairs Medical Center (Birmingham)
Prgm Director: Peter N Kolettis, MD
FOT 1105
1530 3rd Avenue South
Birmingham, AL 35294
Tel: 205 934-1461   *Fax:* 205 934-1470
E-mail: sevans@uab.edu
Length: 4 Yrs   *ACGME Approved/Offered Positions:* 12
Program ID: 480-01-11-014

Arizona

Scottsdale

College of Medicine, Mayo Clinic (Arizona) Program
Sponsor: College of Medicine, Mayo Clinic
Mayo Clinic (Arizona)
Mayo Clinic Hospital
Phoenix Children's Hospital
Prgm Director: Scott K Swanson, MD
5777 East Mayo Boulevard
Phoenix, AZ 85054
Tel: 480 342-2839   *Fax:* 480 342-2799
E-mail: roller.verna@mayo.edu
Length: 4 Yrs   *ACGME Approved/Offered Positions:* 8
Program ID: 480-03-12-182

Tucson

University of Arizona Program
Sponsor: University of Arizona College of Medicine
Southern Arizona VA Health Care Center (Tucson)
Tucson Medical Center
University Medical Center
University of Arizona/UPHK Graduate Medical Ed Consortium
Prgm Director: Jonathan R Walker, MD
1501 North Campbell Avenue
PO Box 245077
Tucson, AZ 85724
Tel: 520 626-6895   *Fax:* 520 626-4933
E-mail: rebalder@email.arizona.edu
Length: 4 Yrs   *ACGME Approved/Offered Positions:* 6
Program ID: 480-03-21-015

Arkansas

Little Rock

University of Arkansas for Medical Sciences Program
Sponsor: University of Arkansas College of Medicine
Arkansas Children's Hospital
Central Arkansas Veterans Healthcare System
UAMS Medical Center
Prgm Director: Nabil K Bissada, MBChB
4301 W Markham Street, Slot 540
Little Rock, AR 72205
Tel: 501 686-7642   *Fax:* 501 686-5277
E-mail: bissadanabilk@uams.edu
Length: 4 Yrs   *ACGME Approved/Offered Positions:* 6
Program ID: 480-04-21-016

Note: * indicates a newly appointed program director

California

Loma Linda

Loma Linda University Program

Sponsor: Loma Linda University Medical Center
Arrowhead Regional Medical Center
Jerry L Pettis Memorial Veterans Hospital
Riverside County Regional Medical Center
Prgm Director: Herbert C Ruckle, MD
111234 Anderson Street
Room A560
Loma Linda, CA 92354
Tel: 909 558-4196   *Fax:* 909 558-4806
E-mail: jmcnamara@ahs.llumc.edu
Length: 4 Yrs   *ACGME Approved/Offered Positions:* 9
Program ID: 480-05-21-019

Los Angeles

Kaiser Permanente Southern California (Los Angeles) Program

Sponsor: Kaiser Permanente Southern California
Kaiser Foundation Hospital (Los Angeles)
Kaiser Foundation Hospital (Bellflower)
Prgm Director: Stephen G Williams, MD
4733 Sunset Blvd, 3rd Floor
Los Angeles, CA 90027
Tel: 323 783-5865   *Fax:* 323 783-4771
E-mail: stephen.g.williams@kp.org
Length: 4 Yrs   *ACGME Approved/Offered Positions:* 8
Program ID: 480-05-12-020

UCLA Medical Center Program

Sponsor: UCLA David Geffen School of Medicine/UCLA
   Medical Center
Los Angeles County-Harbor-UCLA Medical Center
Olive View/UCLA Medical Center
UCLA Medical Center
VA Greater Los Angeles Healthcare System
Prgm Director: Bernard Churchill, MD
Room 66-124 CHS
Box 951738
Los Angeles, CA 90095
Tel: 310 206-8177   *Fax:* 310 206-5343
Length: 4 Yrs   *ACGME Approved/Offered Positions:* 12
Program ID: 480-05-21-022

University of Southern California/ LAC+USC Medical Center Program

Sponsor: University of Southern California/LAC+USC
   Medical Center
Childrens Hospital Los Angeles
Kenneth Norris Jr Cancer Hospital and Research
   Institute
LAC+USC Medical Center
Prgm Director: Eila C Skinner, MD
USC/Norris Cancer Center
1441 Eastlake Avenue, Suite 7416
Los Angeles, CA 90089
Tel: 323 865-3705   *Fax:* 323 865-0120
E-mail: skinner@hsc.usc.edu
Length: 4 Yrs   *ACGME Approved/Offered Positions:* 12
Program ID: 480-05-21-021

Orange

University of California (Irvine) Program

Sponsor: University of California (Irvine) Medical
   Center
Kaiser Foundation Hospitals (Anaheim)
VA Long Beach Healthcare System
Prgm Director: Regina M Hovey, MD
333 City Blvd West
Suite 2100, Rte 81
Orange, CA 92868
Tel: 714 456-7128   *Fax:* 714 456-5062
E-mail: gaumua@uci.edu
Length: 4 Yrs   *ACGME Approved/Offered Positions:* 8
Program ID: 480-05-21-018

Sacramento

University of California (Davis) Health System Program

Sponsor: University of California (Davis) Health System
Kaiser Foundation Hospital (Sacramento)
University of California (Davis) Medical Center
VA Northern California Health Care System
Prgm Director: Roger K Low, MD
4860 Y Street, Suite 3500
Sacramento, CA 95817
Tel: 916 734-2893   *Fax:* 916 734-8094
E-mail: mmontelongo@ucdavis.edu
Length: 4 Yrs   *ACGME Approved/Offered Positions:* 8
Program ID: 480-05-21-017

San Diego

Naval Medical Center (San Diego) Program

Sponsor: Naval Medical Center (San Diego)
Prgm Director: Brian K Auge, MD
34800 Bob Wilson Drive
Bldg 3, Suite 200
San Diego, CA 92134
Tel: 619 532-7200   *Fax:* 619 532-7234
E-mail: brian.auge@med.navy.mil
Length: 4 Yrs   *ACGME Approved/Offered Positions:* 6
Program ID: 480-05-11-009
Uniformed Services Program

University of California (San Diego) Program

Sponsor: University of California (San Diego) Medical
   Center
Rady Children's Hospital
Veterans Affairs Medical Center (San Diego)
Prgm Director: Christopher J Kane, MD
200 West Arbor Drive
San Diego, CA 92103
Tel: 619 543-5904   *Fax:* 619 543-6573
Length: 4 Yrs   *ACGME Approved/Offered Positions:* 8
Program ID: 480-05-21-024

San Francisco

University of California (San Francisco) Program

Sponsor: University of California (San Francisco) School
   of Medicine
San Francisco General Hospital Medical Center
UCSF and Mount Zion Medical Centers
Veterans Affairs Medical Center (San Francisco)
Prgm Director: Jack W McAninch, MD
1001 Potrero Avenue
Room 3A20
San Francisco, CA 94110
Tel: 415 476-3372   *Fax:* 415 206-5153
E-mail: jwmcaninch@urology.ucsf.edu
Length: 4 Yrs   *ACGME Approved/Offered Positions:* 12
Program ID: 480-05-21-025

Stanford

Stanford University Program

Sponsor: Stanford Hospital and Clinics
Lucile Salter Packard Children's Hospital at Stanford
Santa Clara Valley Medical Center
Veterans Affairs Palo Alto Health Care System
Prgm Director: Harcharan Gill, MD
Department of Urology, S-287
300 Pasteur Drive
Stanford, CA 94305
Tel: 650 723-4537   *Fax:* 650 723-4055
E-mail: hgill@stanford.edu
Length: 4 Yrs   *ACGME Approved/Offered Positions:* 12
Program ID: 480-05-31-026

Colorado

Aurora

University of Colorado Denver Program

Sponsor: University of Colorado Denver School of
   Medicine
Children's Hospital (The)
Denver Health Medical Center
University of Colorado Hospital
Veterans Affairs Medical Center (Denver)
Prgm Director: Randall B Meacham, MD
12631 East 17th Ave
Room L15-5602, M/S C-319
Aurora, CO 80045
Tel: 303 724-2714   *Fax:* 303 724-2818
E-mail: beth.musser@uchsc.edu
Length: 4 Yrs   *ACGME Approved/Offered Positions:* 8
Program ID: 480-07-21-027

Connecticut

Farmington

University of Connecticut Program

Sponsor: University of Connecticut School of Medicine
Connecticut Children's Medical Center
Hartford Hospital
St Francis Hospital and Medical Center
Univ of Connecticut Health Center/John Dempsey
   Hospital
Prgm Director: Peter C Albertsen, MD
263 Farmington Avenue, MC 3802
Farmington, CT 06030
Tel: 860 679-7580   *Fax:* 860 679-6109
E-mail: deraleau@uchc.edu
Length: 4 Yrs   *ACGME Approved/Offered Positions:* 12
Program ID: 480-08-21-028

New Haven

Yale-New Haven Medical Center Program

Sponsor: Yale-New Haven Hospital
Veterans Affairs Medical Center (West Haven)
Waterbury Hospital Health Center
Prgm Director: Robert M Weiss, MD
PO Box 208041
800 Howard Avenue
New Haven, CT 06520
Tel: 203 785-2815   *Fax:* 203 785-4043
Length: 4 Yrs   *ACGME Approved/Offered Positions:* 8
Program ID: 480-08-11-029

District of Columbia

Washington

George Washington University Program

Sponsor: George Washington University School of
   Medicine
Children's National Medical Center
George Washington University Hospital (UHS)
Inova Fairfax Hospital
Prgm Director: Thomas Jarrett, MD
2150 Pennsylvania Avenue, NW
3-417
Washington, DC 20037
Tel: 202 741-3100   *Fax:* 202 741-3113
E-mail: jengland@mfa.gwu.edu
Length: 4 Yrs   *ACGME Approved/Offered Positions:* 8
Program ID: 480-10-21-031

Programs

Georgetown University Hospital Program
Sponsor: Georgetown University Hospital
Children's National Medical Center
Sibley Memorial Hospital
Veterans Affairs Medical Center (Washington, DC)
Washington Hospital Center
Prgm Director: John H Lynch, MD
Department of Urology
3800 Reservoir Road, NW, 1PHC
Washington, DC 20007
Tel: 202 444-4688   *Fax:* 202 444-7573
Length: 4 Yrs   *ACGME Approved/Offered Positions:* 12
Program ID: 480-10-21-030

Florida

Gainesville

University of Florida Program
Sponsor: University of Florida College of Medicine
North Florida/South Georgia Veterans Health System
Shands Hospital at the University of Florida
Prgm Director: Marc S Cohen, MD
1600 SW Archer Road, Rm N2-16
Box 100247
Gainesville, FL 32610
Tel: 352 273-6815   *Fax:* 352 273-7515
E-mail: cohenms@urology.ufl.edu
Length: 4 Yrs   *ACGME Approved/Offered Positions:* 8
Program ID: 480-11-21-034

Jacksonville

College of Medicine, Mayo Clinic (Jacksonville) Program
Sponsor: College of Medicine, Mayo Clinic
Mayo Clinic (Jacksonville)
Mayo Clinic Florida Hospital
Prgm Director: Gregory A Broderick, MD
4500 San Pablo Road
Jacksonville, FL 32224
Tel: 904 953-0487   *Fax:* 904 953-0430
E-mail: ja-urologyresidency@mayo.edu
Length: 4 Yrs   *ACGME Approved/Offered Positions:* 4
Program ID: 480-11-21-179

Miami

Jackson Memorial Hospital/Jackson Health System Program
Sponsor: Jackson Memorial Hospital/Jackson Health System
University of Miami Hospital
Veterans Affairs Medical Center (Miami)
Prgm Director: Angelo E Gousse, MD
Department of Urology
PO Box 016960 (M814)
Miami, FL 33101
Tel: 305 243-3670   *Fax:* 305 243-2919
Length: 4 Yrs   *ACGME Approved/Offered Positions:* 12
Program ID: 480-11-21-036

Tampa

University of South Florida Program
Sponsor: University of South Florida College of Medicine
H Lee Moffitt Cancer Center
James A Haley Veterans Hospital
Nemours Children's Clinic
Tampa General Hospital
Prgm Director: Jorge L Lockhart, MD
2 Tampa General Circle
STC 7th Floor
Tampa, FL 33606
Tel: 813 259-8702   *Fax:* 813 259-8706
E-mail: erobert@health.usf.edu
Length: 4 Yrs   *ACGME Approved/Offered Positions:* 12
Program ID: 480-11-21-169

Georgia

Atlanta

Emory University Program
Sponsor: Emory University School of Medicine
Emory University Hospital
Grady Health System
Veterans Affairs Medical Center (Atlanta)
Prgm Director: Chad W Ritenour, MD
1365 Clifton Road, NE
Suite B1400
Atlanta, GA 30322
Tel: 404 778-4615   *Fax:* 404 778-4231
E-mail: Jenny.Alff@emoryhealthcare.org
Length: 4 Yrs   *ACGME Approved/Offered Positions:* 12
Program ID: 480-12-21-039

Augusta

Medical College of Georgia Program
Sponsor: Medical College of Georgia
Dwight David Eisenhower Army Medical Center
Veterans Affairs Medical Center (Augusta)
Prgm Director: Martha K Terris, MD
Section of Urology
Room BA8415B
Augusta, GA 30912
Tel: 706 721-2519   *Fax:* 706 721-2548
E-mail: mterris@mcg.edu
Length: 4 Yrs   *ACGME Approved/Offered Positions:* 8
Program ID: 480-12-21-040

Hawaii

Tripler AMC

Tripler Army Medical Center Program
Sponsor: Tripler Army Medical Center
Kaiser Foundation Hospital (Moanalua)
Prgm Director: Gregory P Thibault, MD
Urology Service (MCHK-DSU)
1 Jarrett White Road
Honolulu, HI 96859
Tel: 808 433-2972   *Fax:* 808 433-7194
E-mail: gregory.thibault@amedd.army.mil
Length: 4 Yrs   *ACGME Approved/Offered Positions:* 4
Program ID: 480-14-32-005
Uniformed Services Program

Illinois

Chicago

McGaw Medical Center of Northwestern University Program
Sponsor: McGaw Medical Center of Northwestern University
Children's Memorial Hospital
Jesse Brown Veterans Affairs Medical Center
Northwestern Memorial Hospital
Prgm Director: Stephanie J Kielb, MD
Northwestern University
303 East Chicago Avenue, Tarry 16-703
Chicago, IL 60611
Tel: 312 695-6124   *Fax:* 312 695-1482
E-mail: k-ross@northwestern.edu
Length: 4 Yrs   *ACGME Approved/Offered Positions:* 12
Program ID: 480-16-21-045

Rush University Medical Center Program
Sponsor: Rush University Medical Center
Prgm Director: Charles F McKiel Jr, MD
1653 W Congress Parkway
Suite 348 Professional Building
Chicago, IL 60612
Tel: 312 942-6447   *Fax:* 312 942-4005
Length: 4 Yrs   *ACGME Approved/Offered Positions:* 4
Program ID: 480-16-31-046

University of Chicago Program
Sponsor: University of Chicago Medical Center
Evanston Hospital
Mount Sinai Hospital Medical Center of Chicago
Prgm Director: Glenn S Gerber, MD
5841 South Maryland Avenue, MC 6038
Chicago, IL 60637
Tel: 773 702-6326   *Fax:* 773 702-1001
Length: 4 Yrs   *ACGME Approved/Offered Positions:* 8
Program ID: 480-16-21-047

University of Illinois College of Medicine at Chicago Program
Sponsor: University of Illinois College of Medicine at Chicago
Advocate Christ Medical Center
Jesse Brown Veterans Affairs Medical Center
University of Illinois Hospital and Clinics
Prgm Director: Craig Niederberger, MD
840 S Wood Street
MC 955
Chicago, IL 60612
Tel: 312 996-9330   *Fax:* 312 413-0495
Length: 4 Yrs   *ACGME Approved/Offered Positions:* 8
Program ID: 480-16-21-174

Maywood

Loyola University Program
Sponsor: Loyola University Medical Center
Edward Hines, Jr Veterans Affairs Hospital
Prgm Director: Thomas M Turk, MD
2160 South First Avenue
A-353100
Maywood, IL 60153
Tel: 708 216-8152   *Fax:* 708 216-6585
E-mail: uromail@lumc.edu
Length: 4 Yrs   *ACGME Approved/Offered Positions:* 12
Program ID: 480-16-21-166

Note: * indicates a newly appointed program director

Springfield

Southern Illinois University Program

Sponsor: Southern Illinois University School of Medicine
Memorial Medical Center
St John's Hospital
Prgm Director: Patrick H McKenna, MD
301 North 8th Street - Room 4B143C
PO Box 19665
Springfield, IL 62794
Tel: 217 545-8860   *Fax:* 217 545-7305
E-mail: urologyres@siumed.edu
Length: 4 Yrs   *ACGME Approved/Offered Positions:* 8
Program ID: 480-16-21-050

Indiana

Indianapolis

Indiana University School of Medicine Program

Sponsor: Indiana University School of Medicine
Clarian Indiana University Hospital
Clarian Methodist Hospital of Indiana
Clarian Riley Hospital for Children
Richard L Roudebush Veterans Affairs Medical Center
William N Wishard Memorial Hospital
Prgm Director: Chandru P Sundaram, MD*
Department of Urology
535 Barnhill Drive, Suite 420
Indianapolis, IN 46202
Tel: 317 278-3098   *Fax:* 317 274-0174
E-mail: sundaram@iupui.edu
Length: 4 Yrs   *ACGME Approved/Offered Positions:* 16
Program ID: 480-17-21-051

Iowa

Iowa City

University of Iowa Hospitals and Clinics Program

Sponsor: University of Iowa Hospitals and Clinics
Veterans Affairs Medical Center (Iowa City)
Prgm Director: Bernard Fallon, MD, MBA
200 Hawkins Drive
Iowa City, IA 52242
Tel: 319 356-2905   *Fax:* 319 353-8564
Length: 4 Yrs   *ACGME Approved/Offered Positions:* 12
Program ID: 480-18-21-052

Kansas

Kansas City

University of Kansas School of Medicine Program

Sponsor: University of Kansas School of Medicine
Children's Mercy Hospital
University of Kansas Hospital
Veterans Affairs Medical Center (Kansas City)
Prgm Director: James B Thrasher, MD
3901 Rainbow Blvd
Kansas City, KS 66160
Tel: 913 588-6152   *Fax:* 913 588-0603
E-mail: chightower@kumc.edu
Length: 4 Yrs   *ACGME Approved/Offered Positions:* 12
Program ID: 480-19-21-053

Kentucky

Lexington

University of Kentucky College of Medicine Program

Sponsor: University of Kentucky College of Medicine
Cincinnati Children's Hospital Medical Center
St Joseph Hospital
University of Kentucky Hospital
Veterans Affairs Medical Center (Lexington)
Prgm Director: Stephen E Strup, MD
800 Rose Street MS-283
Lexington, KY 40536
Tel: 859 323-6679   *Fax:* 859 323-1944
E-mail: pjroge2@email.uky.edu
Length: 4 Yrs   *ACGME Approved/Offered Positions:* 8
Program ID: 480-20-21-054

Louisville

University of Louisville Program

Sponsor: University of Louisville School of Medicine
Jewish Hospital
Kosair Children's Hospital (Norton Healthcare, Inc)
Norton Hospital
University of Louisville Hospital
Veterans Affairs Medical Center (Louisville)
Prgm Director: Anthony J Casale, MD
Department of Urology
234 East Gray Street, Suite 660
Louisville, KY 40202
Tel: 502 629-4224   *Fax:* 502 629-4223
Length: 4 Yrs   *ACGME Approved/Offered Positions:* 8
Program ID: 480-20-21-186

Louisiana

New Orleans

Ochsner Clinic Foundation/Louisiana State University Program

Sponsor: Ochsner Clinic Foundation
Children's Hospital (New Orleans)
East Jefferson General Hospital
Medical Center of Louisiana at New Orleans
Prgm Director: J Christian Winters, MD
1514 Jefferson Highway
AT-4W
New Orleans, LA 70121
Tel: 504 842-5263   *Fax:* 504 842-2009
E-mail: kprice@ochsner.org
Length: 4 Yrs   *ACGME Approved/Offered Positions:* 8
Program ID: 480-21-21-176

Tulane University Program

Sponsor: Tulane University School of Medicine
Children's Hospital (New Orleans)
Medical Center of Louisiana at New Orleans
Tulane University Hospital and Clinics
Tulane-Lakeside Hospital
Veterans Affairs Medical Center (New Orleans)
Prgm Director: Raju Thomas, MD
Department of Urology
1430 Tulane Avenue, SL-42
New Orleans, LA 70112
Tel: 504 988-2794   *Fax:* 504 988-5059
Length: 4 Yrs   *ACGME Approved/Offered Positions:* 5
Program ID: 480-21-21-058

Shreveport

Louisiana State University (Shreveport) Program

Sponsor: LSU Health Sciences Center-University Hospital
Overton Brooks Veterans Affairs Medical Center
Willis-Knighton Medical Center
Prgm Director: Dennis D Venable, MD
1501 Kings Highway
PO Box 33932
Shreveport, LA 71130
Tel: 318 675-5600   *Fax:* 318 675-5665
E-mail: dvenablemd@aol.com
Length: 4 Yrs   *ACGME Approved/Offered Positions:* 8
Program ID: 480-21-21-059

Maryland

Baltimore

Johns Hopkins University Program

Sponsor: Johns Hopkins University School of Medicine
Johns Hopkins Bayview Medical Center
Johns Hopkins Hospital
Prgm Director: Ronald Rodriguez, MD, PhD
Johns Hopkins Hospital
600 N Wolfe St Marburg Bldg Rm 205
Baltimore, MD 21287
Tel: 410 614-6662   *Fax:* 410 287-1010
E-mail: rrodriguez@jhmi.edu
Length: 4 Yrs   *ACGME Approved/Offered Positions:* 12
Program ID: 480-23-21-060

University of Maryland Program

Sponsor: University of Maryland Medical System
Baltimore Washington Medical Center
Johns Hopkins Hospital
Veterans Affairs Medical Center (Baltimore)
Prgm Director: Michael Naslund, MD, MBA
Division of Urology, ste 500
29 S Greene Street
Baltimore, MD 21201
Tel: 410 328-0801   *Fax:* 410 328-0595
E-mail: sjacobs@smail.umaryland.edu
Length: 4 Yrs   *ACGME Approved/Offered Positions:* 8
Program ID: 480-23-21-062

Bethesda

National Capital Consortium (Walter Reed) Program

Sponsor: National Capital Consortium
National Naval Medical Center (Bethesda)
Uniformed Svcs Univ of Health Sci Hebert School of Medicine
Walter Reed Army Medical Center
Prgm Director: Robert C Dean, MD
Department of Surgery
6900 Geogia Avenue NW
Washington, DC 20307
Tel: 202 782-6406   *Fax:* 202 782-4118
E-mail: Robert.Dean@us.army.mil
Length: 4 Yrs   *ACGME Approved/Offered Positions:* 8
Program ID: 480-10-21-004
Uniformed Services Program

Programs

Massachusetts

Boston

Boston University Medical Center Program

Sponsor: Boston Medical Center
Children's Hospital
Veterans Affairs Medical Center (Boston)
Prgm Director: Robert D Oates, MD
720 Harrison Avenue, Suite 606
Boston, MA 02118
Tel: 617 638-8485   *Fax:* 617 638-8483
E-mail: robert.oates@bmc.org
Length: 4 Yrs   *ACGME Approved/Offered Positions:* 8
Program ID: 480-24-21-063

Brigham and Women's Hospital/Harvard Medical School Program

Sponsor: Brigham and Women's Hospital
Beth Israel Deaconess Medical Center
Boston VA Healthcare System (Brockton-West Roxbury)
Children's Hospital
Prgm Director: Jerome P Richie, MD
45 Francis Street, ASB2-3
Boston, MA 02115
Tel: 617 732-6227   *Fax:* 617 566-3475
E-mail: surgeryeducation@partners.org
Length: 4 Yrs   *ACGME Approved/Offered Positions:* 12
Program ID: 480-24-21-064

Massachusetts General Hospital/Harvard Medical School Program

Sponsor: Massachusetts General Hospital
Children's Hospital
Prgm Director: W Scott McDougal, MD
55 Fruit Street
GRB 1102
Boston, MA 02114
Tel: 617 726-3010   *Fax:* 617 726-6131
E-mail: cmurphy3@partners.org
Length: 4 Yrs   *ACGME Approved/Offered Positions:* 12
Program ID: 480-24-11-161

Burlington

Lahey Clinic Program

Sponsor: Lahey Clinic
Children's Hospital
Prgm Director: John A Libertino, MD
41 Mall Road
Burlington, MA 01805
Tel: 781 744-2511   *Fax:* 781 744-5635
Length: 4 Yrs   *ACGME Approved/Offered Positions:* 12
Program ID: 480-24-22-065

Michigan

Ann Arbor

University of Michigan Program

Sponsor: University of Michigan Hospitals and Health
  Centers
Veterans Affairs Medical Center (Ann Arbor)
Prgm Director: Gary J Faerber, MD
1500 East Medical Center Drive
TC 3875 SPC 5330
Ann Arbor, MI 48109
Tel: 734 936-5801   *Fax:* 734 936-9127
Length: 4 Yrs   *ACGME Approved/Offered Positions:* 16
Program ID: 480-25-21-066

Detroit

Henry Ford Hospital Program

Sponsor: Henry Ford Hospital
Children's Hospital of Michigan
Veterans Affairs Medical Center (Detroit)
Prgm Director: Jack S Elder, MD
Vattikuti Urology Institute, K-9
2799 West Grand Boulevard
Detroit, MI 48202
Tel: 313 916-2626   *Fax:* 313 916-2956
E-mail: jelder1@hfhs.org
Length: 4 Yrs   *ACGME Approved/Offered Positions:* 8
Program ID: 480-25-11-067

Wayne State University Program

Sponsor: Wayne State University School of Medicine
Grand Rapids Medical Education and Research Center
Karmanos Cancer Hospital
Oakwood Hospital
St John Hospital and Medical Center
Prgm Director: Jeffrey Triest, MD*
4201 St Antoine, UHC 7C
Detroit, MI 48201
Tel: 313 577-5222   *Fax:* 313 577-5217
E-mail: cchampagne@med.wayne.edu
Length: 4 Yrs   *ACGME Approved/Offered Positions:* 8
Program ID: 480-25-12-185

Royal Oak

William Beaumont Hospital Program

Sponsor: William Beaumont Hospital
Prgm Director: Jay B Hollander, MD
3535 W 13 Mile Road
Suite 438
Royal Oak, MI 48073
Tel: 248 551-9238   *Fax:* 248 551-8107
E-mail: jhollander@beaumont.edu
Length: 4 Yrs   *ACGME Approved/Offered Positions:* 8
Program ID: 480-25-12-071

Minnesota

Minneapolis

University of Minnesota Program

Sponsor: University of Minnesota Medical School
Children's Hospitals and Clinics of Minnesota - St Paul
University of Minnesota Medical Center, Division of
  Fairview
Veterans Affairs Medical Center (Minneapolis)
Prgm Director: Aseem R Shukla, MD*
MMC 394
420 Delaware Street, SE
Minneapolis, MN 55455
Tel: 612 625-9117   *Fax:* 612 626-7005
E-mail: shukl011@umn.edu
Length: 4 Yrs   *ACGME Approved/Offered Positions:* 12
Program ID: 480-26-21-072

Rochester

College of Medicine, Mayo Clinic (Rochester) Program

Sponsor: College of Medicine, Mayo Clinic
Rochester Methodist Hospital
Saint Marys Hospital of Rochester
Prgm Director: Douglas A Husmann, MD
Gonda 7
200 First Street SW
Rochester, MN 55905
Tel: 507 284-1330   *Fax:* 507 284-4951
E-mail: wagner.jean@mayo.edu
Length: 4 Yrs   *ACGME Approved/Offered Positions:* 20
Program ID: 480-26-21-073

Mississippi

Jackson

University of Mississippi Medical Center Program

Sponsor: University of Mississippi School of Medicine
Mississippi Baptist Medical Center
University Hospitals and Clinics
Veterans Affairs Medical Center (Jackson)
Prgm Director: Charles R Pound, MD
2500 N State Street
Jackson, MS 39216
Tel: 601 984-5185   *Fax:* 601 984-5190
Length: 4 Yrs   *ACGME Approved/Offered Positions:* 8
Program ID: 480-27-21-075

Missouri

Columbia

University of Missouri-Columbia Program

Sponsor: University of Missouri-Columbia School of
  Medicine
Harry S Truman Memorial Veterans Hospital
University Hospitals and Clinics
Prgm Director: Durwood E Neal Jr, MD
Division of Urology - M562-DCO80.00
One Hospital Drive
Columbia, MO 65212
Tel: 537 882-1151   *Fax:* 537 884-7453
E-mail: HoskinsT@health.missouri.edu
Length: 4 Yrs   *ACGME Approved/Offered Positions:* 8
Program ID: 480-28-21-076

St Louis

St Louis University School of Medicine Program

Sponsor: St Louis University School of Medicine
Cardinal Glennon Children's Hospital
St John's Mercy Medical Center
St Louis ConnectCare
St Louis University Hospital
Prgm Director: James M Cummings, MD
3635 Vista Avenue at Grand Blvd
PO Box 15250
St Louis, MO 63110
Tel: 314 577-8790   *Fax:* 314 268-5183
E-mail: cummings@slu.edu
Length: 4 Yrs   *ACGME Approved/Offered Positions:* 4
Program ID: 480-28-21-078

Washington University/B-JH/SLCH Consortium Program

Sponsor: Washington University/B-JH/SLCH Consortium
Barnes-Jewish Hospital
St Louis Children's Hospital
Veterans Affairs Medical Center (St Louis)
Prgm Director: Steven B Brandes, MD
4960 Children's Place
Campus Box 8242
St Louis, MO 63110
Tel: 314 362-8212   *Fax:* 314 361-2203
Length: 4 Yrs   *ACGME Approved/Offered Positions:* 12
Program ID: 480-28-21-079

Note: * indicates a newly appointed program director

Nebraska

Omaha

University of Nebraska Medical Center College of Medicine Program

Sponsor: University of Nebraska Medical Center College of Medicine
Children's Hospital
Nebraska Medical Center
Nebraska Methodist Hospital
Veterans Affairs Medical Center (Omaha)
Prgm Director: George P Hemstreet III, MD, PhD
Department of Surgery, Section of Urologic Surgery
982360 Nebraska Medical Center
Omaha, NE 68198
Tel: 402 559-4292   *Fax:* 402 559-6529
E-mail: cabboud@unmc.edu
Length: 4 Yrs   *ACGME Approved/Offered Positions:* 8
Program ID: 480-30-21-081

New Hampshire

Lebanon

Dartmouth-Hitchcock Medical Center Program

Sponsor: Mary Hitchcock Memorial Hospital
Concord Hospital
Veterans Affairs Medical Center (White River Junction)
Prgm Director: E Ann Gormley, MD
One Medical Center Drive
Lebanon, NH 03756
Tel: 603 650-6033   *Fax:* 603 650-4985
E-mail: ann.gormley@hitchcock.org
Length: 4 Yrs   *ACGME Approved/Offered Positions:* 8
Program ID: 480-32-21-082

New Jersey

New Brunswick

UMDNJ-Robert Wood Johnson Medical School Program

Sponsor: UMDNJ-Robert Wood Johnson Medical School
Cooper Hospital-University Medical Center
Robert Wood Johnson University Hospital
University Medical Center at Princeton
Prgm Director: Robert E Weiss, MD
One Robert Wood Johnson Place, CN19
MEB 584
New Brunswick, NJ 08903
Tel: 732 235-6813   *Fax:* 732 235-8959
Length: 4 Yrs   *ACGME Approved/Offered Positions:* 8
Program ID: 480-33-21-173

Newark

UMDNJ-New Jersey Medical School Program

Sponsor: UMDNJ-New Jersey Medical School
Hackensack University Medical Center
St Barnabas Medical Center
UMDNJ-University Hospital
Veterans Affairs New Jersey Health Care System
Prgm Director: Mark L Jordan, MD
185 South Orange Avenue, MSB G-536
Newark, NJ 07103
Tel: 973 972-4488   *Fax:* 973 972-3892
E-mail: jordanml@umdnj.edu
Length: 4 Yrs   *ACGME Approved/Offered Positions:* 8
Program ID: 480-33-21-083

New Mexico

Albuquerque

University of New Mexico Program

Sponsor: University of New Mexico School of Medicine
University of New Mexico Hospital
Veterans Affairs Medical Center (Albuquerque)
Prgm Director: Anthony Y Smith, MD
Dept of Surgery/Urology - MSC10 5610
1 University of New Mexico
Albuquerque, NM 87131
Tel: 505 272-5505   *Fax:* 505 272-3699
E-mail: aysmith@salud.unm.edu
Length: 4 Yrs   *ACGME Approved/Offered Positions:* 8
Program ID: 480-34-21-084

New York

Albany

Albany Medical Center Program

Sponsor: Albany Medical Center
St Peter's Hospital
Veterans Affairs Medical Center (Albany)
Prgm Director: Barry A Kogan, MD
South Clinical Campus, Division of Urology
23 Hackett Boulevard, Mail Code 208
Albany, NY 12208
Tel: 518 262-3296   *Fax:* 518 262-6050
Length: 4 Yrs   *ACGME Approved/Offered Positions:* 8
Program ID: 480-35-21-085

Bronx

Albert Einstein College of Medicine Program

Sponsor: Albert Einstein College of Medicine of Yeshiva University
Montefiore Medical Center-Henry and Lucy Moses Division
Montefiore Medical Center-Weiler Division
Prgm Director: Arnold Melman, MD
111 E 210th Street
Bronx, NY 10467
Tel: 718 920-5402   *Fax:* 718 547-2902
E-mail: amelman@montefiore.org
Length: 4 Yrs   *ACGME Approved/Offered Positions:* 8
Program ID: 480-35-21-089

Brooklyn

Brookdale University Hospital and Medical Center Program

Sponsor: Brookdale University Hospital and Medical Center
Prgm Director: Frederick A Gulmi, MD
Linden Blvd and Brookdale Plaza
Brooklyn, NY 11212
Tel: 718 240-5324   *Fax:* 718 240-6605
Length: 4 Yrs   *ACGME Approved/Offered Positions:* 4
Program ID: 480-35-31-091

Maimonides Medical Center Program

Sponsor: Maimonides Medical Center
Coney Island Hospital
Prgm Director: Ridwan Shabsigh, MD
4802 10th Avenue
Brooklyn, NY 11219
Tel: 718 283-7634   *Fax:* 718 635-7167
E-mail: rshabsigh@maimonidesmed.org
Length: 4 Yrs   *ACGME Approved/Offered Positions:* 4
Program ID: 480-35-21-099

SUNY Health Science Center at Brooklyn Program

Sponsor: SUNY Health Science Center at Brooklyn
Kings County Hospital Center
Long Island College Hospital
Memorial Sloan-Kettering Cancer Center
Veterans Affairs Medical Center (Brooklyn)
Prgm Director: Richard J Macchia, MD
Department of Urology, Box 79
445 Lenox Road
Brooklyn, NY 11203
Tel: 718 270-2554   *Fax:* 718 270-3848
E-mail: richard.macchia@downstate.edu
Length: 4 Yrs   *ACGME Approved/Offered Positions:* 12
Program ID: 480-35-21-107

Buffalo

University at Buffalo Program

Sponsor: University at Buffalo School of Medicine
Erie County Medical Center
Kaleida Health System (Buffalo General Hospital)
Kaleida Health System (Millard Fillmore Hospital)
Kaleida Health System (Women and Children's Hosp of Buffalo)
Veterans Affairs Western New York Hospital
Prgm Director: Gerald Sufrin, MD
100 High Street
Suite B451
Buffalo, NY 14203
Tel: 716 859-3760   *Fax:* 716 859-4015
E-mail: wrscales@buffalo.edu
Length: 4 Yrs   *ACGME Approved/Offered Positions:* 12
Program ID: 480-35-21-087

Great Neck

NSLIJHS Program

Sponsor: North Shore-Long Island Jewish Health System
Long Island Jewish Medical Center
Schneider Children's Hospital at Long Island Jewish Med Ctr
Prgm Director: Louis R Kavoussi, MD
450 Lakeville Road
New Hyde Park, NY 11042
Tel: 516 734-8567   *Fax:* 516 734-8538
E-mail: bhyde@nshs.edu
Length: 4 Yrs   *ACGME Approved/Offered Positions:* 8
Program ID: 480-35-21-098

New York

Albert Einstein College of Medicine at Beth Israel Medical Center Program

Sponsor: Beth Israel Medical Center
Prgm Director: Harris M Nagler, MD
Phillips Ambulatory Care Center
10 Union Square East, Suite 3A
New York, NY 10003
Tel: 212 844-8920   *Fax:* 212 844-8921
Length: 4 Yrs   *ACGME Approved/Offered Positions:* 4
Program ID: 480-35-11-090

Lenox Hill Hospital Program

Sponsor: Lenox Hill Hospital
Memorial Sloan-Kettering Cancer Center
Prgm Director: Elizabeth Kavaler, MD*
100 East 77th Street
New York, NY 10021
Tel: 212 570-6800
Length: 4 Yrs   *ACGME Approved/Offered Positions:* 4
Program ID: 480-35-11-096

Mount Sinai School of Medicine Program

Sponsor: Mount Sinai School of Medicine
Elmhurst Hospital Center-Mount Sinai Services
Mount Sinai Medical Center
Queens Hospital Center
Veterans Affairs Medical Center (Bronx)
Prgm Director: Simon J Hall, MD
Box 1272
One Gustave L Levy Place
New York, NY 10029
Tel: 212 241-8714   *Fax:* 212 876-3246
E-mail: bonnie.fultz@mountsinai.org
Length: 4 Yrs   *ACGME Approved/Offered Positions:* 12
Program ID: 480-35-21-102

New York Presbyterian Hospital (Columbia Campus) Program

Sponsor: New York Presbyterian Hospital
New York Presbyterian Hospital (Columbia Campus)
St Luke's-Roosevelt Hospital Center
Prgm Director: Mitchell C Benson, BS, MD
Department of Urology, HIP 11
161 Fort Washington Avenue
New York, NY 10032
Tel: 212 305-5201   *Fax:* 212 305-0113
E-mail: mcb2@columbia.edu
Length: 4 Yrs   *ACGME Approved/Offered Positions:* 12
Program ID: 480-35-21-092

New York Presbyterian Hospital (Cornell Campus) Program

Sponsor: New York Presbyterian Hospital
Memorial Sloan-Kettering Cancer Center
New York Presbyterian Hospital (Cornell Campus)
Prgm Director: Peter Schlegel, MD
525 East 68th Street, Box 94
New York, NY 10021
Tel: 212 746-5491   *Fax:* 212 746-8425
E-mail: jbbrady@med.cornell.edu
Length: 4 Yrs   *ACGME Approved/Offered Positions:* 12
Program ID: 480-35-21-093

New York University School of Medicine Program

Sponsor: New York University School of Medicine
Bellevue Hospital Center
Manhattan VA Harbor Health Care System
NYU Hospitals Center
Prgm Director: Victor W Nitti, MD
Department of Urology
150 East 32nd Street
New York, NY 10016
Tel: 646 825-6343   *Fax:* 646 825-6397
E-mail: sabine.gay@nyumc.org
Length: 4 Yrs   *ACGME Approved/Offered Positions:* 12
Program ID: 480-35-21-104

Rochester

University of Rochester Program

Sponsor: Strong Memorial Hospital of the University of
Rochester
Rochester General Hospital
Unity Hospital (Unity Health System)
Prgm Director: William C Hulbert Jr, MD
601 Elmwood Avenue, Box 656
Rochester, NY 14642
Tel: 585 273-1904   *Fax:* 585 273-1070
Length: 4 Yrs   *ACGME Approved/Offered Positions:* 8
Program ID: 480-35-21-108

Stony Brook

SUNY at Stony Brook Program

Sponsor: University Hospital - SUNY at Stony Brook
Veterans Affairs Medical Center (Northport)
Prgm Director: Wayne C Waltzer, MD
HSC-T9-040
Stony Brook, NY 11794
Tel: 631 444-1916   *Fax:* 631 444-7620
Length: 4 Yrs   *ACGME Approved/Offered Positions:* 4
Program ID: 480-35-21-175

Syracuse

SUNY Upstate Medical University Program

Sponsor: SUNY Upstate Medical University
Crouse Hospital
Fletcher Allen Health Care
Fox Chase Cancer Center
Veterans Affairs Medical Center (Syracuse)
Prgm Director: Imad Nsouli, MD
Department of Urology
750 E Adams Street
Syracuse, NY 13210
Tel: 315 425-2636   *Fax:* 315 425-2639
Length: 4 Yrs   *ACGME Approved/Offered Positions:* 4
Program ID: 480-35-21-109

Valhalla

New York Medical College at Westchester Medical Center Program

Sponsor: New York Medical College
Lincoln Medical and Mental Health Center
Metropolitan Hospital Center
St Vincent Catholic Medical Centers (Manhattan)
Westchester Medical Center
Prgm Director: Muhammad S Choudhury, MD
Munger Pavilion, Room 460
Valhalla, NY 10595
Tel: 914 594-4300   *Fax:* 914 594-4394
E-mail: Muhammad_Choudhury@nymc.edu
Length: 4 Yrs   *ACGME Approved/Offered Positions:* 8
Program ID: 480-35-21-103

North Carolina

Chapel Hill

University of North Carolina Hospitals Program

Sponsor: University of North Carolina Hospitals
Carolinas Medical Center
Prgm Director: Culley C Carson III, MD
2113 Physicians Office Bldg CB 7235
170 Manning Dr
Chapel Hill, NC 27599
Tel: 919 966-2574   *Fax:* 919 966-0098
E-mail: lmwest@med.unc.edu
Length: 4 Yrs   *ACGME Approved/Offered Positions:* 8
Program ID: 480-36-21-110

Durham

Duke University Hospital Program

Sponsor: Duke University Hospital
Veterans Affairs Medical Center (Asheville)
Veterans Affairs Medical Center (Durham)
Prgm Director: Glenn M Preminger, MD
PO Box 3167
Durham, NC 27710
Tel: 919 681-5506   *Fax:* 919 681-5507
E-mail: gladys.walker@duke.edu
Length: 4 Yrs   *ACGME Approved/Offered Positions:* 12
Program ID: 480-36-21-112

Winston-Salem

Wake Forest University School of Medicine Program

Sponsor: Wake Forest University Baptist Medical Center
The Urology Center, PA
Prgm Director: Dean G Assimos, MD
Department of Urology
Medical Center Boulevard
Winston-Salem, NC 27157
Tel: 336 716-5702   *Fax:* 336 716-5711
E-mail: dewolfe@wfubmc.edu
Length: 4 Yrs   *ACGME Approved/Offered Positions:* 10
Program ID: 480-36-21-113

Ohio

Akron

Akron General Medical Center Program

Sponsor: Akron General Medical Center
Akron City Hospital (Summa Health System)
Children's Hospital Medical Center of Akron
Prgm Director: Phillip F Nasrallah, MD
300 Locust Street Suite 260
Akron, OH 44302
Tel: 330 543-8212   *Fax:* 330 543-8621
E-mail: mdague@chmca.org
Length: 4 Yrs   *ACGME Approved/Offered Positions:* 8
Program ID: 480-38-21-164

Cincinnati

University Hospital/University of Cincinnati College of Medicine Program

Sponsor: University Hospital Inc
Cincinnati Children's Hospital Medical Center
TriHealth - Good Samaritan Hospital
Veterans Affairs Medical Center (Cincinnati)
Prgm Director: James F Donovan Jr, MD
231 Albert Sabin Way
Mail Location 0589
Cincinnati, OH 45267
Tel: 513 558-0983   *Fax:* 513 558-3575
E-mail: perri.wright@uc.edu
Length: 4 Yrs   *ACGME Approved/Offered Positions:* 8
Program ID: 480-38-21-117

Cleveland

Cleveland Clinic Foundation Program

Sponsor: Cleveland Clinic Foundation
Prgm Director: Steven C Campbell, MD, PhD
Urology
9500 Euclid Avenue, A100
Cleveland, OH 44195
Tel: 216 445-7242   *Fax:* 216 445-2267
E-mail: nolderm@ccf.org
Length: 4 Yrs   *ACGME Approved/Offered Positions:* 20
Program ID: 480-38-22-119

University Hospitals Case Medical Center Program

Sponsor: University Hospitals Case Medical Center
MetroHealth Medical Center
Veterans Affairs Medical Center (Cleveland)
Prgm Director: Edward Cherullo, MD*
11100 Euclid Avenue
Cleveland, OH 44106
Tel: 216 844-7490   *Fax:* 216 844-1900
E-mail: edward.cherullo@uhhospitals.org
Length: 4 Yrs   *ACGME Approved/Offered Positions:* 12
Program ID: 480-38-21-118

Note: * indicates a newly appointed program director

Columbus

Ohio State University Hospital Program
Sponsor: Ohio State University Hospital
Prgm Director: Robert R Bahnson, MD
4960 Cramblett Medical Clinic
456 West 10th Avenue
Columbus, OH 43210
Tel: 614 293-4889   *Fax:* 614 293-3565
Length: 4 Yrs   *ACGME Approved/Offered Positions:* 12
Program ID: 480-38-21-120

Toledo

University of Toledo Program
Sponsor: University of Toledo
St Vincent Mercy Medical Center
Toledo Hospital
University Medical Center (Toledo)
Prgm Director: Steven H Selman, MD
Health Science Campus
3045 Arlington Avenue, DH-2178
Toledo, OH 43614
Tel: 419 383-3505   *Fax:* 419 383-3785
Length: 4 Yrs   *ACGME Approved/Offered Positions:* 8
Program ID: 480-38-21-122

Oklahoma

Oklahoma City

University of Oklahoma Health Sciences Center Program
Sponsor: University of Oklahoma College of Medicine
OU Medical Center
OU Medical Center - Children's Hospital
Veterans Affairs Medical Center (Oklahoma City)
Prgm Director: Daniel J Culkin, MD, MBA
920 Stanton L Young Blvd, WP3150
PO Box 26901
Oklahoma City, OK 73104
Tel: 405 271-6900   *Fax:* 405 271-3118
E-mail: beverly-shipman@ouhsc.edu
Length: 4 Yrs   *ACGME Approved/Offered Positions:* 12
Program ID: 480-39-21-123

Oregon

Portland

Oregon Health & Science University Program
Sponsor: Oregon Health & Science University Hospital
Kaiser Foundation Hospitals-Northwest Region
Veterans Affairs Medical Center (Portland)
Prgm Director: Michael J Conlin, MD
3303 SW Bond Avenue, CH10U
Portland, OR 97239
Tel: 503 494-8470   *Fax:* 503 346-1501
E-mail: taylorme@ohsu.edu
Length: 4 Yrs   *ACGME Approved/Offered Positions:* 8
Program ID: 480-40-21-124

Pennsylvania

Danville

Geisinger Health System Program
Sponsor: Geisinger Health System
Prgm Director: Daniel B Rukstalis, MD
100 North Academy Avenue
Danville, PA 17822
Tel: 570 271-6328   *Fax:* 570 271-6955
E-mail: urology_residency@geisinger.edu
Length: 4 Yrs   *ACGME Approved/Offered Positions:* 4
Program ID: 480-41-11-125

Hershey

Penn State University/Milton S Hershey Medical Center Program
Sponsor: Milton S Hershey Medical Center
Lehigh Valley Hospital Network
Prgm Director: Ross M Decter, MD
Division of Urology - MCH055
500 University Drive
Hershey, PA 17033
Tel: 717 531-8848   *Fax:* 717 531-4475
Length: 4 Yrs   *ACGME Approved/Offered Positions:* 8
Program ID: 480-41-21-127

Philadelphia

Temple University Hospital Program
Sponsor: Temple University Hospital
Abington Memorial Hospital
Fox Chase Cancer Center
St Christopher's Hospital for Children (Tenet Health System)
Prgm Director: Jack H Mydlo, MD
3401 North Broad Street
Zone C - Suite 330
Philadelphia, PA 19140
Tel: 215 707-2333   *Fax:* 215 707-4758
Length: 4 Yrs   *ACGME Approved/Offered Positions:* 8
Program ID: 480-41-21-132

Thomas Jefferson University Program
Sponsor: Thomas Jefferson University Hospital
Alfred I duPont Hospital for Children
Bryn Mawr Hospital
Veterans Affairs Medical Center (Wilmington)
Prgm Director: Patrick J Shenot, MD
1025 Walnut St, Ste 1112
Philadelphia, PA 19107
Tel: 215 955-6961   *Fax:* 215 923-1884
Length: 4 Yrs   *ACGME Approved/Offered Positions:* 8
Program ID: 480-41-21-133

University of Pennsylvania Program
Sponsor: University of Pennsylvania Health System
Children's Hospital of Philadelphia
Pennsylvania Hospital (UPHS)
Presbyterian Medical Center (UPHS)
Veterans Affairs Medical Center (Philadelphia)
Prgm Director: Alan J Wein, MD, PhD
3400 Spruce Street
9 Penn Tower
Philadelphia, PA 19104
Tel: 215 662-6755   *Fax:* 215 662-3955
Length: 4 Yrs   *ACGME Approved/Offered Positions:* 16
Program ID: 480-41-21-134

Pittsburgh

University of Pittsburgh Medical Center Medical Education Program
Sponsor: Univ of Pittsburgh Medical Center Medical Education
Children's Hospital of Pittsburgh of UPMC
UPMC Presbyterian Shadyside
Veterans Affairs Medical Center (Pittsburgh)
Prgm Director: Stephen V Jackman, MD
Kaufmann Building, Suite 700
3471 Fifth Avenue
Pittsburgh, PA 15213
Tel: 412 692-4095   *Fax:* 412 692-4101
E-mail: peitztl@upmc.edu
Length: 4 Yrs   *ACGME Approved/Offered Positions:* 12
Program ID: 480-41-21-135

Puerto Rico

San Juan

University of Puerto Rico Program
Sponsor: University of Puerto Rico School of Medicine
Hospital Pavia
University Hospital
University Pediatric Hospital
VA Caribbean Healthcare System
Prgm Director: Antonio Puras-Baez, MD
Department of Surgery
Medical Sciences Campus, PO Box 365067
San Juan, PR 00936
Tel: 787 767-7072   *Fax:* 787 766-0088
Length: 4 Yrs   *ACGME Approved/Offered Positions:* 8
Program ID: 480-42-31-138

Rhode Island

Providence

Brown University Program
Sponsor: Rhode Island Hospital-Lifespan
Memorial Hospital of Rhode Island
Miriam Hospital-Lifespan
Veterans Affairs Medical Center (Providence)
Prgm Director: Anthony A Caldamone, MD
Division of Urology
2 Dudley Street, Suite 174
Providence, RI 02905
Tel: 401 444-5795   *Fax:* 401 444-6947
Length: 4 Yrs   *ACGME Approved/Offered Positions:* 9
Program ID: 480-43-31-139

South Carolina

Charleston

Medical University of South Carolina Program
Sponsor: Medical University of South Carolina College of Medicine
MUSC Medical Center
Ralph H Johnson VA Medical Center (Charleston)
Prgm Director: Harry S Clarke Jr, MD, PhD
96 Jonathan Lucas Street, Suite 644 CSB
PO Box 250620
Charleston, SC 29425
Tel: 843 792-9308   *Fax:* 843 792-8523
Length: 4 Yrs   *ACGME Approved/Offered Positions:* 8
Program ID: 480-45-21-140

Tennessee

Knoxville

University of Tennessee Medical Center at Knoxville Program
Sponsor: University of Tennessee Graduate School of Medicine
East Tennessee Children's Hospital (Knoxville)
University of Tennessee Memorial Hospital
Prgm Director: Frederick A Klein, MD
1924 Alcoa Highway, Box U-11
Knoxville, TN 37920
Tel: 865 305-9230   *Fax:* 865 305-6958
E-mail: gmiya@utmck.edu
Length: 4 Yrs   *ACGME Approved/Offered Positions:* 4
Program ID: 480-47-11-181

Programs

Memphis

University of Tennessee Program
Sponsor: University of Tennessee College of Medicine
LeBonheur Children's Medical Center
Methodist Healthcare - Memphis Hospitals
Regional Medical Center at Memphis
Veterans Affairs Medical Center (Memphis)
Prgm Director: Robert Wake, MD*
910 Madison Ave
Room 409
Memphis, TN 38163
Tel: 901 448-1026   *Fax:* 901 448-1122
E-mail: pphelan@utmem.edu
Length: 4 Yrs   *ACGME Approved/Offered Positions:* 8
Program ID: 480-47-21-141

Nashville

Vanderbilt University Program
Sponsor: Vanderbilt University Medical Center
Veterans Affairs Medical Center (Nashville)
Prgm Director: Harriette M Scarpero, MD
A-1302 Medical Center North
21st & Garland Streets
Nashville, TN 37232
Tel: 615 343-5604   *Fax:* 615 322-8990
E-mail: derenda.gold@vanderbilt.edu
Length: 4 Yrs   *ACGME Approved/Offered Positions:* 16
Program ID: 480-47-21-142

Texas

Dallas

University of Texas Southwestern Medical School Program
Sponsor: University of Texas Southwestern Medical School
Baylor University Medical Center
Children's Medical Center of Dallas
Dallas County Hospital District-Parkland Memorial Hospital
Dallas VA Medical Center
University Hospitals Zale Lipshy
Prgm Director: Gary Lemack, MD
5323 Harry Hines Blvd, J8-148
Dallas, TX 75390
Tel: 214 648-2277   *Fax:* 214 648-4789
Length: 4 Yrs   *ACGME Approved/Offered Positions:* 16
Program ID: 480-48-21-143

Galveston

University of Texas Medical Branch Hospitals Program
Sponsor: University of Texas Medical Branch Hospitals
Prgm Director: Eduardo Orihuela, MD
Division of Urology, Route 0540
301 University Boulevard
Galveston, TX 77555
Tel: 409 772-2091   *Fax:* 409 772-5144
Length: 4 Yrs   *ACGME Approved/Offered Positions:* 4
Program ID: 480-48-11-144

Houston

Baylor College of Medicine Program
Sponsor: Baylor College of Medicine
Harris County Hospital District-Ben Taub General Hospital
Methodist Hospital (Houston)
Michael E DeBakey VA Medical Center - Houston
St Luke's Episcopal Hospital
Texas Children's Hospital
Prgm Director: Michael Coburn, MD
Scott Department of Urology
6620 Main Street, Suite 1325
Houston, TX 77030
Tel: 713 798-3498   *Fax:* 713 798-5553
E-mail: colleenk@bcm.edu
Length: 4 Yrs   *ACGME Approved/Offered Positions:* 16
Program ID: 480-48-21-145

University of Texas at Houston Program
Sponsor: University of Texas Health Science Center at Houston
Lyndon B Johnson General Hospital
Memorial Hermann Hospital
University of Texas M D Anderson Cancer Center
Prgm Director: Ouida L Westney, MD
6431 Fannin St, Suite 6018
Houston, TX 77030
Tel: 713 500-7328   *Fax:* 713 500-7319
E-mail: Ouida.L.Westney@uth.tmc.edu
Length: 4 Yrs   *ACGME Approved/Offered Positions:* 12
Program ID: 480-48-21-146

Lackland AFB

San Antonio Uniformed Services Health Education Consortium Program
Sponsor: San Antonio Uniformed Services Health Education Consortium
Brooke Army Medical Center
Wilford Hall Medical Center (AETC)
Prgm Director: Richard D Cespedes, MD
Department of Urology/SGO2U
2200 Bergquist Drive, Suite 1
Lackland AFB, TX 78236
Tel: 210 292-5755   *Fax:* 210 292-7199
E-mail: richard.cespedes@lackland.af.mil
Length: 4 Yrs   *ACGME Approved/Offered Positions:* 8
Program ID: 480-48-21-170
Uniformed Services Program

Lubbock

Texas Tech University (Lubbock) Program
Sponsor: Texas Tech University Health Sciences Center at Lubbock
University Medical Center
Prgm Director: Jonathan S Vordermark, MD
Department of Urology
3601 4th Street, Stop 7260
Lubbock, TX 79430
Tel: 806 743-1810   *Fax:* 806 743-1335
Length: 4 Yrs   *ACGME Approved/Offered Positions:* 4
Program ID: 480-48-31-184

San Antonio

University of Texas Health Science Center at San Antonio Program
Sponsor: University of Texas School of Medicine at San Antonio
Audie L Murphy Memorial Veterans Hospital (San Antonio)
Christus Santa Rosa Health Care Corporation
Methodist Healthcare
University Health System
Prgm Director: Joseph W Basler, MD, PhD
4502 Medical Drive
San Antonio, TX 78229
Tel: 210 567-6866   *Fax:* 210 567-6868
E-mail: Paynee@uthscsa.edu
Length: 4 Yrs   *ACGME Approved/Offered Positions:* 16
Program ID: 480-48-21-147

Temple

Texas A&M College of Medicine-Scott and White Program
Sponsor: Scott and White Memorial Hospital
Central Texas Veterans Affairs Healthcare System
Prgm Director: K Scott Coffield, MD
Scott & White Clinic
2401 South 31st Street
Temple, TX 76508
Tel: 254 724-1695   *Fax:* 254 724-6317
E-mail: cstone@swmail.sw.org
Length: 4 Yrs   *ACGME Approved/Offered Positions:* 8
Program ID: 480-48-21-148

Utah

Salt Lake City

University of Utah Program
Sponsor: University of Utah Medical Center
Intermountain Medical Center
Primary Children's Medical Center
Veterans Affairs Medical Center (Salt Lake City)
Prgm Director: Blake D Hamilton, MD
Division of Urology
30 North 1900 East
Salt Lake City, UT 84132
Tel: 801 213-2780   *Fax:* 801 585-2891
E-mail: elizabeth.lignell@hsc.utah.edu
Length: 4 Yrs   *ACGME Approved/Offered Positions:* 8
Program ID: 480-49-21-149

Virginia

Charlottesville

University of Virginia Program
Sponsor: University of Virginia Medical Center
Augusta Health Care, Inc
Prgm Director: Alan D Jenkins, MD*
PO Box 800422
Charlottesville, VA 22908
Tel: 434 924-5677   *Fax:* 434 243-9544
Length: 4 Yrs   *ACGME Approved/Offered Positions:* 8
Program ID: 480-51-21-151

Note: * indicates a newly appointed program director

Norfolk

Eastern Virginia Medical School Program

Sponsor: Eastern Virginia Medical School
Children's Hospital of the King's Daughters
Sentara Leigh Hospital
Sentara Norfolk General Hospital
Prgm Director: Kurt A McCammon, MD
400 W Brambleton Avenue
Suite 100
Norfolk, VA 23510
Tel: 757 457-5175   *Fax:* 757 626-0768
E-mail: mccammka@evms.edu
Length: 4 Yrs   *ACGME Approved/Offered Positions:* 8
Program ID: 480-51-21-153

Richmond

Virginia Commonwealth University Health System Program

Sponsor: Virginia Commonwealth University Health
System
Hunter Holmes McGuire VA Medical Center (Richmond)
Medical College of Virginia Hospitals
Prgm Director: Baruch M Grob, MD*
Box 980118
Richmond, VA 23298
Tel: 804 828-5320   *Fax:* 804 828-2157
E-mail: dhenson@mcvh-vcu.edu
Length: 4 Yrs   *ACGME Approved/Offered Positions:* 8
Program ID: 480-51-21-154

Washington

Seattle

University of Washington Program

Sponsor: University of Washington School of Medicine
Harborview Medical Center
Seattle Children's Hospital
University of Washington Medical Center
VA Puget Sound Health Care System
Prgm Director: Byron D Joyner, MD
4800 Sand Point Way
Box 359300, W-7729
Seattle, WA 98105
Tel: 206 987-4030   *Fax:* 206 987-3925
Length: 4 Yrs   *ACGME Approved/Offered Positions:* 10
Program ID: 480-54-21-155

Tacoma

Madigan Army Medical Center Program

Sponsor: Madigan Army Medical Center
Prgm Director: Andrew C Peterson, MD
Attn: MCHJ-SU
Urology Service
Tacoma, WA 98431
Tel: 253 968-2300   *Fax:* 253 968-2895
Length: 4 Yrs   *ACGME Approved/Offered Positions:* 4
Program ID: 480-54-11-007
Uniformed Services Program

West Virginia

Morgantown

West Virginia University Program

Sponsor: West Virginia University School of Medicine
West Virginia University Hospitals
Prgm Director: Stanley Zaslau, MD, MBA
PO Box 9238
Morgantown, WV 26506
Tel: 304 293-2706   *Fax:* 304 293-4711
E-mail: jahunt@hsc.wvu.edu
Length: 4 Yrs   *ACGME Approved/Offered Positions:* 4
Program ID: 480-55-21-157

Wisconsin

Madison

University of Wisconsin Program

Sponsor: University of Wisconsin Hospital and Clinics
Meriter Hospital
St Mary's Hospital
William S Middleton Veterans Hospital
Prgm Director: John V Kryger, MD
600 Highland Ave, Rm G5/339 CSC
Madison, WI 53792
Tel: 608 263-1358   *Fax:* 608 262-6453
E-mail: kryger@urology.wisc.edu
Length: 4 Yrs   *ACGME Approved/Offered Positions:* 8
Program ID: 480-56-21-158

Milwaukee

Medical College of Wisconsin Affiliated Hospitals Program

Sponsor: Medical College of Wisconsin Affiliated
Hospitals, Inc
Children's Hospital of Wisconsin
Clement J Zablocki Veterans Affairs Medical Center
Froedtert Memorial Lutheran Hospital
Prgm Director: Peter Langenstroer, MD, MS
Department of Urology
9200 W Wisconsin Avenue
Milwaukee, WI 53226
Tel: 414 805-7088   *Fax:* 414 805-0771
E-mail: tjanik@mcw.edu
Length: 4 Yrs   *ACGME Approved/Offered Positions:* 12
Program ID: 480-56-21-159

Vascular and Interventional Radiology (Radiology-Diagnostic)

Alabama

Birmingham

University of Alabama Medical Center Program

Sponsor: University of Alabama Hospital
Prgm Director: Rachel F Oser, MD*
Room H623
619 South 19th Street
Birmingham, AL 35249
Tel: 205 975-4850   *Fax:* 205 975-5257
Length: 1 Yr   *ACGME Approved/Offered Positions:* 4
Program ID: 427-01-21-054

Arizona

Tucson

University of Arizona Program

Sponsor: University of Arizona College of Medicine
University Medical Center
Prgm Director: Stephen H Smyth, MD
1501 North Campbell Avenue
PO Box 245067
Tucson, AZ 85724
Tel: 520 626-6794   *Fax:* 520 626-2955
Length: 1 Yr   *ACGME Approved/Offered Positions:* 1
Program ID: 427-03-21-074

Arkansas

Little Rock

University of Arkansas for Medical Sciences Program

Sponsor: University of Arkansas College of Medicine
Central Arkansas Veterans Healthcare System
UAMS Medical Center
Prgm Director: William C Culp, MD
Department of Radiology, Slot 556
4301 West Markham Street
Little Rock, AR 72205
Tel: 501 686-6910   *Fax:* 501 686-6900
E-mail: culpwilliamc@uams.edu
Length: 1 Yr   *ACGME Approved/Offered Positions:* 2
Program ID: 427-04-21-007

California

Loma Linda

Loma Linda University Program

Sponsor: Loma Linda University Medical Center
Jerry L Pettis Memorial Veterans Hospital
Prgm Director: Jason C Smith, MD
11234 Anderson Street
Loma Linda, CA 92354
Tel: 909 558-7814   *Fax:* 909 558-0202
E-mail: pthomas@llu.edu
Length: 1 Yr   *ACGME Approved/Offered Positions:* 3
Program ID: 427-05-21-026

Programs

Los Angeles

UCLA Medical Center Program
Sponsor: UCLA David Geffen School of Medicine/UCLA
  Medical Center
Santa Monica-UCLA Medical Center
UCLA Medical Center
VA Greater Los Angeles Healthcare System
Prgm Director: Stephen Kee, MD
Department of Radiology
757 Westwood Plaza, Suite 1633C
Los Angeles, CA 90095
Tel: 310 267-8768   *Fax:* 310 267-3631
Length: 1 Yr   *ACGME Approved/Offered Positions:* 5
Program ID: 427-05-21-063

University of Southern California/ LAC+USC Medical Center Program
Sponsor: University of Southern California/LAC+USC
  Medical Center
Kaiser Foundation Hospital (Los Angeles)
Kenneth Norris Jr Cancer Hospital and Research
  Institute
LAC+USC Medical Center
USC University Hospital
Prgm Director: Michael D Katz, MD
1500 San Pablo Street, Second Floor Imaging
Los Angeles, CA 90033
Tel: 323 226-4218   *Fax:* 323 224-7830
Length: 1 Yr   *ACGME Approved/Offered Positions:* 4
Program ID: 427-05-21-013

Orange

University of California (Irvine) Program
Sponsor: University of California (Irvine) Medical
  Center
University of California (Irvine) College of Medicine
Prgm Director: Duane J Vajgrt, MD
101 The City Drive South
Rte 140
Orange, CA 92868
Tel: 714 456-6579   *Fax:* 714 456-6832
E-mail: djvajgrt@uci.edu
Length: 1 Yr   *ACGME Approved/Offered Positions:* 4
Program ID: 427-05-11-089

Sacramento

University of California (Davis) Health System Program
Sponsor: University of California (Davis) Health System
University of California (Davis) Medical Center
Prgm Director: Wayne L Monsky, MD, PhD
Lawrence Ellison Bldg
4860 Y Street, Ste 3100
Sacramento, CA 95817
Tel: 916 703-2177
Length: 1 Yr   *ACGME Approved/Offered Positions:* 2
Program ID: 427-05-31-082

San Diego

University of California (San Diego) Program
Sponsor: University of California (San Diego) Medical
  Center
Naval Medical Center (San Diego)
Prgm Director: Anne C Roberts, MD
Department of Radiology, #7756
9300 Campus Point Drive
La Jolla, CA 92037
Tel: 858 657-6650   *Fax:* 858 657-6699
E-mail: keverhart@ucsd.edu
Length: 1 Yr   *ACGME Approved/Offered Positions:* 3
Program ID: 427-05-21-058

San Francisco

University of California (San Francisco) Program
Sponsor: University of California (San Francisco) School
  of Medicine
Prgm Director: Jeanne M LaBerge, MD, MS
Room M-361, Box 0628
505 Parnassus Avenue
San Francisco, CA 94143
Tel: 415 353-1300   *Fax:* 415 353-8570
E-mail: kimberly.morrell@radiology.ucsf.edu
Length: 1 Yr   *ACGME Approved/Offered Positions:* 3
Program ID: 427-05-21-009

Stanford

Stanford University Program
Sponsor: Stanford Hospital and Clinics
Prgm Director: Nishita Kothary, MD
Room H3651
300 Pasteur Drive
Stanford, CA 94305
Tel: 650 725-5202   *Fax:* 650 725-0533
E-mail: kothary@stanford.edu
Length: 1 Yr   *ACGME Approved/Offered Positions:* 3
Program ID: 427-05-21-081

Torrance

Los Angeles County-Harbor-UCLA Medical Center Program
Sponsor: Los Angeles County-Harbor-UCLA Medical
  Center
Prgm Director: Irwin Walot, MD
1000 W Carson Street
Torrance, CA 90509
Tel: 310 222-2808   *Fax:* 310 222-5688
E-mail: drwalot@cox.net
Length: 1 Yr   *ACGME Approved/Offered Positions:* 1
Program ID: 427-05-13-105

Colorado

Aurora

University of Colorado Denver Program
Sponsor: University of Colorado Denver School of
  Medicine
Denver Health Medical Center
University of Colorado Hospital
Prgm Director: Rajan K Gupta, MD*
Interventional Radiology, Mail Stop L954
Leprino Office Bldg 12401 East 17th Ave
Aurora, CO 80045
Tel: 303 724-1981   *Fax:* 303 724-1983
Length: 1 Yr   *ACGME Approved/Offered Positions:* 3
Program ID: 427-07-21-049

Connecticut

New Haven

Yale-New Haven Medical Center Program
Sponsor: Yale-New Haven Hospital
Veterans Affairs Medical Center (West Haven)
Prgm Director: Jeffrey S Pollak, MD
20 York Street, SP 2-213
New Haven, CT 06504
Tel: 203 785-7026   *Fax:* 203 737-1077
Length: 1 Yr   *ACGME Approved/Offered Positions:* 4
Program ID: 427-08-21-032

Delaware

Wilmington

Christiana Care Health Services Program
Sponsor: Christiana Care Health Services Inc
Prgm Director: Mark J Garcia, MD, FSIR
4755 Ogletown-Stanton Road
PO Box 6001
Newark, DE 19718
Tel: 302 733-5582   *Fax:* 302 733-5589
Length: 1 Yr   *ACGME Approved/Offered Positions:* 2
Program ID: 427-09-21-096

District of Columbia

Washington

George Washington University Program A
Sponsor: George Washington University School of
  Medicine
George Washington University Hospital (UHS)
Prgm Director: Anthony C Venbrux, MD
900 23rd Street, NW
Washington, DC 20037
Tel: 202 994-5190   *Fax:* 202 994-5210
Length: 1 Yr   *ACGME Approved/Offered Positions:* 1
Program ID: 427-10-21-070

Georgetown University Hospital Program
Sponsor: Georgetown University Hospital
Washington Hospital Center
Prgm Director: Filip Banovac, MD*
3800 Reservoir Road, NW, Dept of Radiology
Interventional Radiology
Washington, DC 20007
Tel: 202 444-3454   *Fax:* 202 444-1804
E-mail: fb2@gunet.georgetown.edu
Length: 1 Yr   *ACGME Approved/Offered Positions:* 3
Program ID: 427-10-31-069

Florida

Gainesville

University of Florida Program
Sponsor: University of Florida College of Medicine
North Florida/South Georgia Veterans Health System
Shands Hospital at the University of Florida
Prgm Director: Darren W Postoak, MD
PO Box 100374
Gainesville, FL 32610
Tel: 352 265-0291   *Fax:* 352 265-0279
E-mail: postod@radiology.ufl.edu
Length: 1 Yr   *ACGME Approved/Offered Positions:* 4
Program ID: 427-11-21-033

Jacksonville

College of Medicine, Mayo Clinic (Jacksonville) Program
Sponsor: College of Medicine, Mayo Clinic
Mayo Clinic (Jacksonville)
Prgm Director: Anthony B Adelson, MD*
4500 San Pablo Road
Jacksonville, FL 32224
Tel: 904 953-9755   *Fax:* 904 953-0430
Length: 1 Yr   *ACGME Approved/Offered Positions:* 1
Program ID: 427-11-12-112

Note: * indicates a newly appointed program director

University of Florida College of Medicine Jacksonville Program

Sponsor: University of Florida College of Medicine Jacksonville
Shands Jacksonville Medical Center
Prgm Director: Daniel Siragusa, MD
Radiology Dept, Box C90
655 West Eighth Street
Jacksonville, FL 32209
Tel: 904 244-4885   *Fax:* 904 244-3382
E-mail: vascinterventionalrad.gme@jax.ufl.edu
Length: 1 Yr   *ACGME Approved/Offered Positions:* 2
Program ID: 427-11-21-086

Miami

Jackson Memorial Hospital/Jackson Health System Program

Sponsor: Jackson Memorial Hospital/Jackson Health System
University of Miami Hospital and Clinics
Prgm Director: Govindarajan Narayanan, MD*
Department of Radiology - West Wing #279
1611 NW 12th Avenue
Miami, FL 33136
Tel: 305 585-7500   *Fax:* 305 325-8591
E-mail: gnarayanan@med.miami.edu
Length: 1 Yr   *ACGME Approved/Offered Positions:* 5
Program ID: 427-11-31-028

Tampa

University of South Florida Program

Sponsor: University of South Florida College of Medicine
Tampa General Hospital
Prgm Director: Bruce R Zwiebel, MD
MDC Box 17
Tampa, FL 33612
Tel: 813 844-4570   *Fax:* 813 844-4032
E-mail: bzwieb@tampabay.rr.com
Length: 1 Yr   *ACGME Approved/Offered Positions:* 3
Program ID: 427-11-21-092

University of South Florida Program A

Sponsor: University of South Florida College of Medicine
Baptist Hospital of Miami
Prgm Director: James F Benenati, MD
8900 N Kendall Drive
Miami, FL 33176
Tel: 786 596-5990   *Fax:* 786 596-2999
E-mail: JamesB@baptisthealth.net
Length: 1 Yr   *ACGME Approved/Offered Positions:* 5
Program ID: 427-11-21-025

Georgia

Atlanta

Emory University Program

Sponsor: Emory University School of Medicine
Children's Healthcare of Atlanta at Egleston
Emory University Hospital
Grady Health System
Prgm Director: Gail L Peters, MD*
1364 Clifton Rd NE
Atlanta, GA 30322
Tel: 404 712-7033   *Fax:* 404 712-7970
E-mail: gpeter2@emory.edu
Length: 1 Yr   *ACGME Approved/Offered Positions:* 5
Program ID: 427-12-21-022

Illinois

Chicago

McGaw Medical Center of Northwestern University Program

Sponsor: McGaw Medical Center of Northwestern University
Northwestern Memorial Hospital
Prgm Director: Scott A Resnick, MD
Department of Radiology - Feinberg
251 East Huron St
Chicago, IL 60611
Tel: 312 926-5113   *Fax:* 312 926-0826
Length: 1 Yr   *ACGME Approved/Offered Positions:* 8
Program ID: 427-16-21-034

Rush University Medical Center Program

Sponsor: Rush University Medical Center
Prgm Director: Hector Ferral, MD
1653 W Congress Parkway
Chicago, IL 60612
Tel: 312 942-3265   *Fax:* 312 942-7244
Length: 1 Yr   *ACGME Approved/Offered Positions:* 3
Program ID: 427-16-21-023

University of Chicago Program

Sponsor: University of Chicago Medical Center
Prgm Director: Jonathan Lorenz, MD
MC 2026
5841 S Maryland Avenue
Chicago, IL 60637
Tel: 773 702-3550   *Fax:* 773 834-6237
E-mail: mvelligan@radiology.bsd.uchicago.edu
Length: 1 Yr   *ACGME Approved/Offered Positions:* 3
Program ID: 427-16-21-059

University of Illinois College of Medicine at Chicago Program

Sponsor: University of Illinois College of Medicine at Chicago
University of Illinois Hospital and Clinics
Prgm Director: James T Bui, MD
1740 W Taylor Street
Department of Radiology (MC 931)
Chicago, IL 60612
Tel: 312 996-0242   *Fax:* 312 996-0511
E-mail: jtbui@uic.edu
Length: 1 Yr   *ACGME Approved/Offered Positions:* 2
Program ID: 427-16-31-099

Peoria

University of Illinois College of Medicine at Peoria Program

Sponsor: University of Illinois College of Medicine at Peoria
OSF St Francis Medical Center
Prgm Director: H Bob Smouse, MD
530 NE Glen Oak Avenue
Peoria, IL 61637
Tel: 309 624-3355   *Fax:* 309 655-7365
Length: 1 Yr   *ACGME Approved/Offered Positions:* 2
Program ID: 427-16-21-094

Indiana

Indianapolis

Indiana University School of Medicine Program

Sponsor: Indiana University School of Medicine
Clarian Indiana University Hospital
Clarian Methodist Hospital of Indiana
Richard L Roudebush Veterans Affairs Medical Center
William N Wishard Memorial Hospital
Prgm Director: David M Agarwal, MD
Department of Radiology, IUH 0279
550 North University Boulevard
Indianapolis, IN 46202
Tel: 317 278-7785   *Fax:* 317 278-7793
E-mail: dagarwal@iupui.edu
Length: 1 Yr   *ACGME Approved/Offered Positions:* 5
Program ID: 427-17-21-010

Iowa

Iowa City

University of Iowa Hospitals and Clinics Program

Sponsor: University of Iowa Hospitals and Clinics
Prgm Director: Laurie L Fajardo, MD, MBA*
200 Hawkins Drive
3955 JPP
Iowa City, IA 52242
Tel: 319 356-3372   *Fax:* 319 356-2220
E-mail: l-fajardo@uiowa.edu
Length: 1 Yr   *ACGME Approved/Offered Positions:* 2
Program ID: 427-18-21-065

Kansas

Kansas City

University of Kansas School of Medicine Program

Sponsor: University of Kansas School of Medicine
University of Kansas Hospital
Prgm Director: Philip L Johnson, MD
Department of Radiology MS4032
3901 Rainbow Blvd
Kansas City, KS 66160
Tel: 913 588-6880   *Fax:* 913 588-7899
E-mail: pjohnson@kumc.edu
Length: 1 Yr   *ACGME Approved/Offered Positions:* 1
Program ID: 427-19-13-103

Maryland

Baltimore

Johns Hopkins University Program

Sponsor: Johns Hopkins University School of Medicine
Johns Hopkins Bayview Medical Center
Johns Hopkins Hospital
Prgm Director: Christos S Georgiades, MD, PhD
Interventional Radiology
600 N Wolfe St, Blalock 544
Baltimore, MD 21287
Tel: 410 614-2648   *Fax:* 410 955-0233
Length: 1 Yr   *ACGME Approved/Offered Positions:* 7
Program ID: 427-23-21-011

University of Maryland Program

Sponsor: University of Maryland Medical System
Veterans Affairs Medical Center (Baltimore)
Prgm Director: Ziv J Haskal, MD*
22 S Greene Street
Baltimore, MD 21201
Tel: 410 328-3477   *Fax:* 410 326-0641
E-mail: ziv2@mac.com
Length: 1 Yr   *ACGME Approved/Offered Positions:* 3
Program ID: 427-23-21-053

Massachusetts

Boston

Beth Israel Deaconess Medical Center Program

Sponsor: Beth Israel Deaconess Medical Center
Prgm Director: Dmitry J Rabkin, MD, PhD
330 Brookline Avenue
WCC-308
Boston, MA 02215
Tel: 617 754-2523   *Fax:* 617 754-2651
E-mail: drabkin@bidmc.harvard.edu
Length: 1 Yr   *ACGME Approved/Offered Positions:* 5
Program ID: 427-24-31-042

Boston University Medical Center Program

Sponsor: Boston Medical Center
Prgm Director: Ducksoo Kim, MD
East Newton Campus
One Boston Medical Center Place
Boston, MA 02118
Tel: 617 414-5135   *Fax:* 617 414-5135
E-mail: ducksoo.kim@bmc.org
Length: 1 Yr   *ACGME Approved/Offered Positions:* 1
Program ID: 427-24-21-050

Brigham and Women's Hospital/Harvard Medical School Program

Sponsor: Brigham and Women's Hospital
Prgm Director: Chieh-Min Fan, MD
Department of Radiology
75 Francis St
Boston, MA 02115
Tel: 617 732-4763   *Fax:* 617 277-8331
E-mail: cfan@partners.org
Length: 1 Yr   *ACGME Approved/Offered Positions:* 3
Program ID: 427-24-21-005

Massachusetts General Hospital/Harvard Medical School Program

Sponsor: Massachusetts General Hospital
Prgm Director: Ronald S Arellano, MD
55 Fruit Street
Division of Vascular Radiology, GRB 290
Boston, MA 02114
Tel: 617 726-8396   *Fax:* 617 726-4891
Length: 1 Yr   *ACGME Approved/Offered Positions:* 7
Program ID: 427-24-21-041

Tufts Medical Center Program

Sponsor: Tufts Medical Center
Prgm Director: Neil J Halin, DO
800 Washington Street, Box 299
Boston, MA 02111
Tel: 617 636-5947   *Fax:* 617 636-1449
Length: 1 Yr   *ACGME Approved/Offered Positions:* 2
Program ID: 427-24-21-104

Worcester

University of Massachusetts Program

Sponsor: University of Massachusetts Medical School
UMass Memorial Health Care (Memorial Campus)
UMass Memorial Health Care (University Campus)
Prgm Director: David A Phillips, MD
55 Lake Avenue North
Worcester, MA 01655
Tel: 508 856-5740   *Fax:* 508 856-1860
E-mail: boisvern@ummhc.org
Length: 1 Yr   *ACGME Approved/Offered Positions:* 1
Program ID: 427-24-31-052

Michigan

Ann Arbor

University of Michigan Program

Sponsor: University of Michigan Hospitals and Health Centers
Veterans Affairs Medical Center (Ann Arbor)
Prgm Director: Kyung J Cho, MD
Department of Radiology, Room #UH-B1-D530
1500 East Medical Center Drive
Ann Arbor, MI 48109
Tel: 734 936-4466   *Fax:* 734 232-5055
Length: 1 Yr   *ACGME Approved/Offered Positions:* 5
Program ID: 427-25-21-035

Detroit

Henry Ford Hospital Program

Sponsor: Henry Ford Hospital
Prgm Director: David W McVinnie, MD
Department of Diagnostic Radiology
2799 West Grand Boulevard, E-328
Detroit, MI 48202
Tel: 313 916-7952   *Fax:* 313 916-8857
Length: 1 Yr   *ACGME Approved/Offered Positions:* 2
Program ID: 427-25-21-055

Wayne State University/Detroit Medical Center Program

Sponsor: Wayne State University/Detroit Medical Center
Harper-Hutzel Hospital
Prgm Director: Monte L Harvill, MD
Harper University Hospital-Department of Radiology
3990 John R Street
Detroit, MI 48201
Tel: 313 745-8408   *Fax:* 313 966-2742
E-mail: sowens@dmc.org
Length: 1 Yr   *ACGME Approved/Offered Positions:* 2
Program ID: 427-25-31-083

Royal Oak

William Beaumont Hospital Program

Sponsor: William Beaumont Hospital
Prgm Director: William J Romano, MD
3601 West 13 Mile Road
Royal Oak, MI 48073
Tel: 248 898-2197   *Fax:* 248 898-4063
E-mail: wromano@beaumont.edu
Length: 1 Yr   *ACGME Approved/Offered Positions:* 3
Program ID: 427-25-21-080

Minnesota

Minneapolis

University of Minnesota Program

Sponsor: University of Minnesota Medical School
University of Minnesota Medical Center, Division of Fairview
Veterans Affairs Medical Center (Minneapolis)
Prgm Director: David W Hunter, MD
Interventional Radiology, MMC 292
420 Delaware St SE
Minneapolis, MN 55455
Tel: 612 626-5570   *Fax:* 612 626-5580
E-mail: murr0300@umn.edu
Length: 1 Yr   *ACGME Approved/Offered Positions:* 4
Program ID: 427-26-21-008

Rochester

College of Medicine, Mayo Clinic (Rochester) Program

Sponsor: College of Medicine, Mayo Clinic
Mayo Clinic (Rochester)
Saint Marys Hospital of Rochester
Prgm Director: Sanjay Misra, MD*
200 First Street SW
Rochester, MN 55905
Tel: 507 255-7208   *Fax:* 507 255-7872
Length: 1 Yr   *ACGME Approved/Offered Positions:* 2
Program ID: 427-26-21-064

Missouri

St Louis

Washington University/B-JH/SLCH Consortium Program

Sponsor: Washington University/B-JH/SLCH Consortium
Barnes-Jewish Hospital
Prgm Director: Jennifer E Gould, MD
510 S Kingshighway Blvd
St Louis, MO 63110
Tel: 314 362-2900   *Fax:* 314 362-2276
E-mail: gouldj@wustl.edu
Length: 1 Yr   *ACGME Approved/Offered Positions:* 6
Program ID: 427-28-21-001

Nebraska

Omaha

University of Nebraska Medical Center College of Medicine Program

Sponsor: University of Nebraska Medical Center College of Medicine
Nebraska Medical Center
Prgm Director: Dick Slater, MD*
981045 Nebraska Medical Center
Omaha, NE 68198
Tel: 402 559-1018   *Fax:* 402 559-1011
Length: 1 Yr   *ACGME Approved/Offered Positions:* 1
Program ID: 427-30-21-014

Note: * indicates a newly appointed program director

New Hampshire

Lebanon

Dartmouth-Hitchcock Medical Center Program

Sponsor: Mary Hitchcock Memorial Hospital
Veterans Affairs Medical Center (White River Junction)
Prgm Director: Eric K Hoffer, MD
One Medical Center Drive
Lebanon, NH 03756
Tel: 603 650-7230   *Fax:* 603 650-5455
Length: 1 Yr   *ACGME Approved/Offered Positions:* 2
Program ID: 427-32-21-067

New Jersey

New Brunswick

UMDNJ-Robert Wood Johnson Medical School Program

Sponsor: UMDNJ-Robert Wood Johnson Medical School
Robert Wood Johnson University Hospital
Prgm Director: John L Nosher, MD
Department of Radiology, MEB #404
One Robert Wood Johnson Place, PO Box 19
New Brunswick, NJ 08903
Tel: 732 235-7721   *Fax:* 732 235-6889
E-mail: lakatofs@umdnj.edu
Length: 1 Yr   *ACGME Approved/Offered Positions:* 1
Program ID: 427-33-21-087

New Mexico

Albuquerque

University of New Mexico Program

Sponsor: University of New Mexico School of Medicine
University of New Mexico Hospital
Veterans Affairs Medical Center (Albuquerque)
Prgm Director: Kevin T Williams, MD
Department of Radiology
MSC10 5530, 1 University of New Mexico
Albuquerque, NM 87131
Tel: 505 272-0932   *Fax:* 505 272-5821
E-mail: raderas@salud.unm.edu
Length: 1 Yr   *ACGME Approved/Offered Positions:* 1
Program ID: 427-34-21-091

New York

Albany

Albany Medical Center Program

Sponsor: Albany Medical Center
Prgm Director: Gary P Siskin, MD
Department of Radiology, MC-113
43 New Scotland Avenue
Albany, NY 12208
Tel: 518 262-5149   *Fax:* 518 262-4210
Length: 1 Yr   *ACGME Approved/Offered Positions:* 3
Program ID: 427-35-31-073

Bronx

Albert Einstein College of Medicine Program

Sponsor: Albert Einstein College of Medicine of Yeshiva University
Montefiore Medical Center-Henry and Lucy Moses Division
Montefiore Medical Center-Weiler Division
Prgm Director: Jacob Cynamon, MD
Dept of Radiology
111 East 210th Street
Bronx, NY 10467
Tel: 718 920-5506   *Fax:* 718 920-4854
E-mail: eofrias@montefiore.org
Length: 1 Yr   *ACGME Approved/Offered Positions:* 2
Program ID: 427-35-32-027

Brooklyn

SUNY Health Science Center at Brooklyn Program

Sponsor: SUNY Health Science Center at Brooklyn
Kings County Hospital Center
Lutheran Medical Center
Prgm Director: Salvatore J Sclafani, MD
c/o Kings County Hospital Center Radiology Dept
451 Clarkson Avenue
Brooklyn, NY 11203
Tel: 718 245-4447
E-mail: sclafans@nychhc.org
Length: 1 Yr   *ACGME Approved/Offered Positions:* 1
Program ID: 427-35-12-109

Great Neck

NSLIJHS-Albert Einstein College of Medicine at Long Island Jewish Medical Center Program

Sponsor: North Shore-Long Island Jewish Health System
Long Island Jewish Medical Center
Prgm Director: David N Siegel, MD
270-05 76th Avenue
New Hyde Park, NY 11042
Tel: 718 470-7175   *Fax:* 718 343-7463
E-mail: eacobacc@lij.edu
Length: 1 Yr   *ACGME Approved/Offered Positions:* 1
Program ID: 427-35-31-024

New York

Albert Einstein College of Medicine at Beth Israel Medical Center Program

Sponsor: Beth Israel Medical Center
Prgm Director: Joseph N Shams, MD
Department of Radiology
1st Avenue at 16th Street
New York, NY 10003
Tel: 212 420-2546   *Fax:* 212 420-2557
E-mail: jshams@chpnet.org
Length: 1 Yr   *ACGME Approved/Offered Positions:* 1
Program ID: 427-35-31-095

Mount Sinai School of Medicine Program

Sponsor: Mount Sinai School of Medicine
Mount Sinai Medical Center
Prgm Director: Joshua L Weintraub, MD
One Gustave L Levy Place
New York, NY 10029
Tel: 212 241-4888   *Fax:* 212 241-4234
Length: 1 Yr   *ACGME Approved/Offered Positions:* 4
Program ID: 427-35-21-048

New York Presbyterian Hospital (Columbia Campus) Program

Sponsor: New York Presbyterian Hospital
New York Presbyterian Hospital (Columbia Campus)
Prgm Director: Jonathan Susman, MD, BA
177 Fort Washington Ave, MHB 4-100
Interventional Radiology
New York, NY 10032
Tel: 212 305-7094   *Fax:* 212 305-6184
E-mail: js1138@columbia.edu
Length: 1 Yr   *ACGME Approved/Offered Positions:* 3
Program ID: 427-35-21-021

New York Presbyterian Hospital (Cornell Campus) Program

Sponsor: New York Presbyterian Hospital
Memorial Sloan-Kettering Cancer Center
New York Presbyterian Hospital (Cornell Campus)
Prgm Director: David W Trost, MD
525 East 68th Street
New York, NY 10021
Tel: 212 746-2603   *Fax:* 212 746-8463
E-mail: cornell@med.edu
Length: 1 Yr   *ACGME Approved/Offered Positions:* 5
Program ID: 427-35-21-039

New York University School of Medicine Program

Sponsor: New York University School of Medicine
Bellevue Hospital Center
Manhattan VA Harbor Health Care System
Prgm Director: Timothy Clark, MD
560 First Avenue
New York, NY 10016
Tel: 212 263-5898   *Fax:* 212 263-7914
Length: 1 Yr   *ACGME Approved/Offered Positions:* 3
Program ID: 427-35-21-090

St Luke's-Roosevelt Hospital Center Program

Sponsor: St Luke's-Roosevelt Hospital Center
St Luke's-Roosevelt Hospital Center-Roosevelt Division
St Luke's-Roosevelt Hospital Center-St Luke's Division
Prgm Director: James E Silberzweig, MD
Department of Radiology, 4th Floor
1000 Tenth Avenue
New York, NY 10019
Tel: 212 636-3379   *Fax:* 212 636-3380
E-mail: azitaalexj@aol.com
Length: 1 Yr   *ACGME Approved/Offered Positions:* 2
Program ID: 427-35-21-072

Rochester

University of Rochester Program

Sponsor: Strong Memorial Hospital of the University of Rochester
Prgm Director: Talia Sasson, MD
601 Elmwood Avenue
Box 648
Rochester, NY 14642
Tel: 585 273-5476   *Fax:* 585 273-1033
Length: 1 Yr   *ACGME Approved/Offered Positions:* 2
Program ID: 427-35-21-051

Syracuse

SUNY Upstate Medical University Program

Sponsor: SUNY Upstate Medical University
Prgm Director: Frank Vogel, MD, PhD
750 East Adams Street
Department of Radiology, Room 3416
Syracuse, NY 13210
Tel: 315 464-7439   *Fax:* 315 464-2570
E-mail: vogelf@upstate.edu
Length: 1 Yr   *ACGME Approved/Offered Positions:* 1
Program ID: 427-35-13-114

Programs

North Carolina

Chapel Hill

University of North Carolina Hospitals Program

Sponsor: University of North Carolina Hospitals
Prgm Director: Charles T Burke, MD
Division of Radiology CB 7510
Chapel Hill, NC 27599
Tel: 919 966-2992   *Fax:* 919 843-8740
Length: 1 Yr   *ACGME Approved/Offered Positions:* 3
Program ID: 427-36-21-030

Durham

Duke University Hospital Program

Sponsor: Duke University Hospital
Prgm Director: Paul V Suhocki, MD
Box 3808, Room 1502
Durham, NC 27710
Tel: 919 684-7284   *Fax:* 919 684-7148
Length: 1 Yr   *ACGME Approved/Offered Positions:* 3
Program ID: 427-36-21-088

Winston-Salem

Wake Forest University School of Medicine Program

Sponsor: Wake Forest University Baptist Medical Center
Prgm Director: Michael A Bettmann, MD
Medical Center Boulevard
Winston-Salem, NC 27157
Tel: 336 716-2463   *Fax:* 336 716-2488
Length: 1 Yr   *ACGME Approved/Offered Positions:* 3
Program ID: 427-36-21-015

Ohio

Cincinnati

University Hospital/University of Cincinnati College of Medicine Program

Sponsor: University Hospital Inc
Prgm Director: Ross L Ristagno, MD*
234 Goodman
PO Box 0761
Cincinnati, OH 45267
Tel: 513 584-2146   *Fax:* 513 584-0431
Length: 1 Yr   *ACGME Approved/Offered Positions:* 2
Program ID: 427-38-31-110

Cleveland

Case Western Reserve University (MetroHealth) Program

Sponsor: MetroHealth Medical Center
Prgm Director: David Rosenblum, DO
2500 MetroHealth Drive
Cleveland, OH 44109
Tel: 216 778-4020   *Fax:* 216 778-4375
E-mail: mbutler@metrohealth.org
Length: 1 Yr   *ACGME Approved/Offered Positions:* 1
Program ID: 427-38-21-093

Cleveland Clinic Foundation Program

Sponsor: Cleveland Clinic Foundation
Prgm Director: Abraham Levitin, MD
Department of Radiology, Desk HB6
9500 Euclid Avenue
Cleveland, OH 44195
Tel: 216 444-2244   *Fax:* 216 445-1492
E-mail: abelevitin@aol.com
Length: 1 Yr   *ACGME Approved/Offered Positions:* 3
Program ID: 427-38-21-002

Columbus

Ohio State University Hospital Program

Sponsor: Ohio State University Hospital
Prgm Director: Hooman Khabiri, MD
630 Means Hall
1654 Upham Drive
Columbus, OH 43210
Tel: 614 293-8315   *Fax:* 614 293-6935
E-mail: hooman.khabiri@osumc.edu
Length: 1 Yr   *ACGME Approved/Offered Positions:* 2
Program ID: 427-38-21-100

Oklahoma

Oklahoma City

University of Oklahoma Health Sciences Center Program

Sponsor: University of Oklahoma College of Medicine
OU Medical Center - Children's Hospital
OU Medical Center - Presbyterian Tower
Veterans Affairs Medical Center (Oklahoma City)
Prgm Director: Feroz Maqbool, MD
PO Box 26307
Oklahoma City, OK 73126
Tel: 405 271-5125   *Fax:* 405 271-3462
Length: 1 Yr   *ACGME Approved/Offered Positions:* 2
Program ID: 427-39-21-036

Oregon

Portland

Oregon Health & Science University Program

Sponsor: Oregon Health & Science University Hospital
Veterans Affairs Medical Center (Portland)
Prgm Director: John A Kaufman, MD
3181 SW Sam Jackson Park Road
Portland, OR 97239
Tel: 503 494-7660   *Fax:* 503 494-7664
Length: 1 Yr   *ACGME Approved/Offered Positions:* 3
Program ID: 427-40-21-097

Pennsylvania

Hershey

Penn State University/Milton S Hershey Medical Center Program

Sponsor: Milton S Hershey Medical Center
Prgm Director: Harjit Singh, MD
Department of Radiology
PO Box 850
Hershey, PA 17033
Tel: 717 531-5416   *Fax:* 717 531-4445
Length: 1 Yr   *ACGME Approved/Offered Positions:* 2
Program ID: 427-41-21-004

Philadelphia

Thomas Jefferson University Program

Sponsor: Thomas Jefferson University Hospital
Prgm Director: Carin Gonsalves, MD
132 South 10th Street
766 Main Building
Philadelphia, PA 19107
Tel: 215 955-6609   *Fax:* 215 923-6754
Length: 1 Yr   *ACGME Approved/Offered Positions:* 4
Program ID: 427-41-21-040

University of Pennsylvania Program

Sponsor: University of Pennsylvania Health System
Prgm Director: Alexander M Nemeth, MD, MFA
1 Silverstein
3400 Spruce Street
Philadelphia, PA 19104
Tel: 215 615-3591   *Fax:* 215 662-7448
E-mail: alexander.nemeth@uphs.upenn.edu
Length: 1 Yr   *ACGME Approved/Offered Positions:* 8
Program ID: 427-41-21-016

Pittsburgh

Allegheny General Hospital Program

Sponsor: Allegheny General Hospital
Western Pennsylvania Hospital
Prgm Director: Gordon K McLean, MD
4800 Friendship Avenue
Pittsburgh, PA 15224
Tel: 412 578-1787   *Fax:* 412 578-4064
E-mail: gkmclean2@wpahs.org
Length: 1 Yr   *ACGME Approved/Offered Positions:* 2
Program ID: 427-41-31-044

Rhode Island

Providence

Brown University Program

Sponsor: Rhode Island Hospital-Lifespan
Rhode Island Vascular Institute
Prgm Director: Sun Ho Ahn, MD*
593 Eddy Street
Providence, RI 02903
Tel: 401 444-5184   *Fax:* 401 444-5017
Length: 1 Yr   *ACGME Approved/Offered Positions:* 3
Program ID: 427-43-21-066

South Carolina

Charleston

Medical University of South Carolina Program

Sponsor: Medical University of South Carolina College of Medicine
MUSC Medical Center
Prgm Director: Christopher Hannegan, MD*
25 Courtenay Drive
Room 3304, MSC 226
Charleston, SC 29401
Tel: 843 876-5556
Length: 1 Yr   *ACGME Approved/Offered Positions:* 3
Program ID: 427-45-21-056

Tennessee

Memphis

University of Tennessee/Methodist Healthcare Program

Sponsor: University of Tennessee College of Medicine
Regional Medical Center at Memphis
Veterans Affairs Medical Center (Memphis)
Prgm Director: James S Williams, MD, PhD
Room F150C Chandler
865 Jefferson
Memphis, TN 38163
Tel: 901 448-8248   *Fax:* 901 448-1248
E-mail: scottwillaims@utmem.edu
Length: 1 Yr   *ACGME Approved/Offered Positions:* 3
Program ID: 427-47-21-019

Note: * indicates a newly appointed program director

Nashville

Vanderbilt University Program
Sponsor: Vanderbilt University Medical Center
Prgm Director: Peter R Bream Jr, MD
21st and Garland Avenue
R1318 MCN
Nashville, TN 37232
Tel: 615 322-3906   *Fax:* 615 322-3764
E-mail: radprogram@vanderbilt.edu
Length: 1 Yr   *ACGME Approved/Offered Positions:* 2
Program ID: 427-47-21-060

Texas

Dallas

Baylor University Medical Center Program
Sponsor: Baylor University Medical Center
Prgm Director: Chet Rees, MD
3500 Gaston Avenue
Dallas, TX 75246
Tel: 214 820-2312   *Fax:* 214 820-2380
E-mail: stellama@baylorhealth.edu
Length: 1 Yr   *ACGME Approved/Offered Positions:* 2
Program ID: 427-48-21-043

University of Texas Southwestern Medical School Program
Sponsor: University of Texas Southwestern Medical
 School
Dallas County Hospital District-Parkland Memorial
 Hospital
Prgm Director: Bart L Dolmatch, MD
Dept of Radiology
5323 Harry Hines Blvd
Dallas, TX 75390-8834
Tel: 214 645-8990   *Fax:* 214 645-8998
E-mail: bart.dolmatch@utsouthwestern.edu
Length: 1 Yr   *ACGME Approved/Offered Positions:* 3
Program ID: 427-48-21-003

Galveston

University of Texas Medical Branch Hospitals Program
Sponsor: University of Texas Medical Branch Hospitals
Prgm Director: Orhan S Ozkan, MD
301 University Boulevard
Galveston, TX 77555
Tel: 409 772-4884   *Fax:* 409 772-1815
E-mail: oozkan@utmb.edu
Length: 1 Yr   *ACGME Approved/Offered Positions:* 3
Program ID: 427-48-21-098

Houston

University of Texas at Houston Program
Sponsor: University of Texas Health Science Center at
 Houston
Memorial Hermann Hospital
St Luke's Episcopal Hospital
University of Texas M D Anderson Cancer Center
Prgm Director: Stephen E McRae, MD
1515 Holcombe Boulevard, Unit 325
Houston, TX 77030
Tel: 713 563-1809   *Fax:* 713 563-7889
E-mail: smcrae@mdanderson.org
Length: 1 Yr   *ACGME Approved/Offered Positions:* 4
Program ID: 427-48-21-078

San Antonio

University of Texas Health Science Center at San Antonio Program
Sponsor: University of Texas School of Medicine at San
 Antonio
Audie L Murphy Memorial Veterans Hospital (San
 Antonio)
University Health System
Prgm Director: Rajeev Suri, MD
7703 Floyd Curl Drive, MS 7800
San Antonio, TX 78229
Tel: 210 567-5564   *Fax:* 210 567-6418
E-mail: suri@uthscsa.edu
Length: 1 Yr   *ACGME Approved/Offered Positions:* 3
Program ID: 427-48-21-031

Temple

Texas A&M College of Medicine-Scott and White Program
Sponsor: Scott and White Memorial Hospital
Prgm Director: Mark L Montgomery, MD
2401 South 31st Street
Temple, TX 76502
Tel: 254 724-2415   *Fax:* 254 724-0502
Length: 1 Yr   *ACGME Approved/Offered Positions:* 1
Program ID: 427-48-21-113

Utah

Salt Lake City

University of Utah Program
Sponsor: University of Utah Medical Center
Veterans Affairs Medical Center (Salt Lake City)
Prgm Director: James G Carlisle, MD
30 North 1900 East
Salt Lake City, UT 84132
Tel: 801 581-7553   *Fax:* 801 581-2414
Length: 1 Yr   *ACGME Approved/Offered Positions:* 2
Program ID: 427-49-21-045

Vermont

Burlington

University of Vermont Program
Sponsor: Fletcher Allen Health Care
Prgm Director: Anant Bhave, MD, MS
MCHV Campus Radiology Dept-Patrick One-Rm 113
111 Colchester Avenue
Burlington, VT 05401
Tel: 802 847-0794   *Fax:* 802 847-4822
Length: 1 Yr   *ACGME Approved/Offered Positions:* 2
Program ID: 427-50-21-062

Virginia

Charlottesville

University of Virginia Program
Sponsor: University of Virginia Medical Center
Prgm Director: John F Angle, MD
PO Box 800170
UVA Health Science Center
Charlottesville, VA 22908
Tel: 434 982-1576   *Fax:* 434 982-5753
Length: 1 Yr   *ACGME Approved/Offered Positions:* 5
Program ID: 427-51-21-057

Richmond

Virginia Commonwealth University Health System Program
Sponsor: Virginia Commonwealth University Health
 System
Medical College of Virginia Hospitals
Prgm Director: Daniel A Leung, MD
PO Box 980615
1250 East Marshall Street, Room 3-406
Richmond, VA 23298
Tel: 804 828-2842   *Fax:* 804 628-2015
Length: 1 Yr   *ACGME Approved/Offered Positions:* 2
Program ID: 427-51-13-111

Washington

Seattle

University of Washington Program
Sponsor: University of Washington School of Medicine
Harborview Medical Center
University of Washington Medical Center
VA Puget Sound Health Care System
Prgm Director: Todd Kooy, MD*
Dept of Radiology, Box 357115
1959 NE Pacific St, RR215
Seattle, WA 98195
Tel: 206 543-5972   *Fax:* 206 543-6317
Length: 1 Yr   *ACGME Approved/Offered Positions:* 4
Program ID: 427-54-21-047

Wisconsin

Madison

University of Wisconsin Program
Sponsor: University of Wisconsin Hospital and Clinics
Gundersen Clinic Ltd
Prgm Director: Foluke Otitoju, MD*
E3/3 Clinical Science Center
600 Highland Avenue
Madison, WI 53792
Tel: 608 261-1393   *Fax:* 608 262-6214
E-mail: fotitoju@uwhealth.org
Length: 1 Yr   *ACGME Approved/Offered Positions:* 2
Program ID: 427-56-21-017

Milwaukee

Medical College of Wisconsin Affiliated Hospitals Program
Sponsor: Medical College of Wisconsin Affiliated
 Hospitals, Inc
Clement J Zablocki Veterans Affairs Medical Center
Froedtert Memorial Lutheran Hospital
Prgm Director: Robert A Hieb, MD
9200 West Wisconsin Avenue
Suite 2803
Milwaukee, WI 53226
Tel: 414 805-3125   *Fax:* 414 476-7503
E-mail: rhieb@mcw.edu
Length: 1 Yr   *ACGME Approved/Offered Positions:* 3
Program ID: 427-56-31-018

Programs

Vascular Neurology (Neurology)

Alabama

Birmingham

University of Alabama Medical Center Program
Sponsor: University of Alabama Hospital
Prgm Director: James H Halsey, MD
1813 6th Avenue South
RWUH Suite M-226
Birmingham, AL 35249
Tel: 205 975-7533   *Fax:* 205 975-6785
E-mail: jhalsey@uab.edu
Length: 1 Yr   *ACGME Approved/Offered Positions:* 2
Program ID: 188-01-12-051

Mobile

University of South Alabama Program
Sponsor: University of South Alabama Hospitals
University of South Alabama Medical Center
Prgm Director: J Ivan Lopez, MD*
2451 Fillingim Street
10th Floor - Suite I
Mobile, AL 36617
Tel: 251 660-5506   *Fax:* 251 660-5924
E-mail: ilopez@usouthal.edu
Length: 1 Yr   *ACGME Approved/Offered Positions:* 1
Program ID: 188-01-12-036

Arizona

Phoenix

College of Medicine, Mayo Clinic (Arizona) Program
Sponsor: College of Medicine, Mayo Clinic
Mayo Clinic Hospital
Prgm Director: Timothy Ingall, MB, BS
5777 East Mayo Boulevard
Phoenix, AZ 85054
Tel: 480 301-8100   *Fax:* 480 301-8451
E-mail: siemon.dana@mayo.edu
Length: 1 Yr   *ACGME Approved/Offered Positions:* 1
Program ID: 188-03-21-044

St Joseph's Hospital and Medical Center Program
Sponsor: St Joseph's Hospital and Medical Center
Prgm Director: Joni M Clark, MD*
350 W Thomas Road
Phoenix, AZ 85013
Tel: 602 406-4786   *Fax:* 602 406-4608
E-mail: ann.chowdhury@chw.edu
Length: 1 Yr   *ACGME Approved/Offered Positions:* 1
Program ID: 188-03-13-031

California

Los Angeles

UCLA Medical Center Program
Sponsor: UCLA David Geffen School of Medicine/UCLA
Medical Center
Prgm Director: David S Liebeskind, MD
710 Westwood Plaza
Los Angeles, CA 90095
Tel: 310 794-6379   *Fax:* 310 267-2063
E-mail: dliebeskind@mednet.ucla.edu
Length: 1 Yr   *ACGME Approved/Offered Positions:* 2
Program ID: 188-05-12-007

San Diego

University of California (San Diego) Program
Sponsor: University of California (San Diego) Medical
Center
Alvarado Hospital Medical Center
Scripps Mercy Hospital
Sharp Memorial Hospital
Thornton Hospital
Veterans Affairs Medical Center (San Diego)
Prgm Director: Patrick D Lyden, MD
200 West Arbor Drive
OPC, 3rd Floor, Suite 3
San Diego, CA 92103
Tel: 619 543-7760   *Fax:* 619 543-7771
E-mail: plyden@ucsd.edu
Length: 1 Yr   *ACGME Approved/Offered Positions:* 2
Program ID: 188-05-13-037

San Francisco

University of California (San Francisco) Program
Sponsor: University of California (San Francisco) School
of Medicine
UCSF and Mount Zion Medical Centers
Prgm Director: S Claiborne Johnston, MD, PhD
Department of Neurology, Box 0114
505 Parnassus Avenue, M-798
San Francisco, CA 94143
Tel: 415 502-7487   *Fax:* 415 476-3428
Length: 1 Yr   *ACGME Approved/Offered Positions:* 2
Program ID: 188-05-31-042

Stanford

Stanford University Program
Sponsor: Stanford Hospital and Clinics
Prgm Director: Gregory W Albers, MD
701 Welch Road, Suite B325
Palo Alto, CA 94304
Tel: 650 723-4448   *Fax:* 650 723-4451
Length: 1 Yr   *ACGME Approved/Offered Positions:* 2
Program ID: 188-05-33-006

Colorado

Aurora

University of Colorado Denver Program
Sponsor: University of Colorado Denver School of
Medicine
Children's Hospital (The)
Denver Health Medical Center
University of Colorado Hospital
Veterans Affairs Medical Center (Denver)
Prgm Director: Richard L Hughes, MD
4200 E 9th Avenue B183
Denver, CO 80262
Tel: 303 315-0139   *Fax:* 303 315-8720
Length: 1 Yr   *ACGME Approved/Offered Positions:* 1
Program ID: 188-07-12-059

Connecticut

Farmington

University of Connecticut/Hartford Hospital Program
Sponsor: University of Connecticut School of Medicine
Hartford Hospital
Univ of Connecticut Health Center/John Dempsey
Hospital
Prgm Director: Nora Lee, MD
80 Seymour Street
Hartford, CT 06102
Tel: 860 545-3621   *Fax:* 860 545-5003
Length: 1 Yr   *ACGME Approved/Offered Positions:* 1
Program ID: 188-08-13-049

Florida

Jacksonville

University of Florida College of Medicine Jacksonville Program
Sponsor: University of Florida College of Medicine
Jacksonville
Shands Jacksonville Medical Center
Prgm Director: Scott Silliman, MD
580 West 8th Street
Tower 1, 9th Floor
Jacksonville, FL 32209
Tel: 904 244-9696   *Fax:* 904 244-9481
E-mail: shands.vascular@jax.ufl.edu
Length: 1 Yr   *ACGME Approved/Offered Positions:* 2
Program ID: 188-11-12-039

Miami

Jackson Memorial Hospital/Jackson Health System Program
Sponsor: Jackson Memorial Hospital/Jackson Health
System
Prgm Director: Jose G Romano, MD*
Department of Neurology
1150 NW 14th Street, PAC Suite 609
Miami, FL 33136
Tel: 305 243-2336   *Fax:* 305 243-7081
E-mail: acampo2@med.miami.edu
Length: 1 Yr   *ACGME Approved/Offered Positions:* 2
Program ID: 188-11-31-029

Tampa

University of South Florida Program
Sponsor: University of South Florida College of Medicine
Tampa General Hospital
Prgm Director: Michael A Sloan, MD, MS
Department of Neurology
2 Tampa General Circle
Tampa, FL 33606
Tel: 813 259-8577   *Fax:* 813 259-8551
Length: 1 Yr   *ACGME Approved/Offered Positions:* 2
Program ID: 188-11-13-057

Note: * indicates a newly appointed program director

Georgia

Atlanta

Emory University Program
Sponsor: Emory University School of Medicine
Emory University Hospital
Grady Health System
Prgm Director: Marc I Chimowitz, MB, ChB
Department of Neurology
101 Woodruff Circle Suite 6000
Atlanta, GA 30322
Tel: 404 727-5004   *Fax:* 404 727-3157
E-mail: mfranke@emory.edu
Length: 1 Yr   *ACGME Approved/Offered Positions:* 2
Program ID: 188-12-31-023

Augusta

Medical College of Georgia Program
Sponsor: Medical College of Georgia
Veterans Affairs Medical Center (Augusta)
Prgm Director: Fenwick T Nichols III, MD
1120 15th Street
Department of Neurology/BI-3078
Augusta, GA 30912
Tel: 706 721-1990   *Fax:* 706 721-1962
Length: 1 Yr   *ACGME Approved/Offered Positions:* 2
Program ID: 188-12-21-011

Illinois

Chicago

McGaw Medical Center of Northwestern University Program
Sponsor: McGaw Medical Center of Northwestern
   University
Northwestern Memorial Hospital
Prgm Director: Mark J Alberts, MD
710 North Lake Shore Drive
Abbott Hall, Room 1114
Chicago, IL 60611
Tel: 312 908-5095   *Fax:* 312 503-3593
Length: 1 Yr   *ACGME Approved/Offered Positions:* 2
Program ID: 188-16-21-052

Rush University Medical Center Program
Sponsor: Rush University Medical Center
Prgm Director: Shyam Prabhakaran, MD, MS
1725 West Harrison Street
Suite 1121
Chicago, IL 60612
Tel: 312 563-2518   *Fax:* 312 563-2206
Length: 1 Yr   *ACGME Approved/Offered Positions:* 1
Program ID: 188-16-12-047

University of Illinois College of Medicine at Chicago Program
Sponsor: University of Illinois College of Medicine at
   Chicago
University of Illinois Hospital and Clinics
Prgm Director: Sean Ruland, DO
Department of Neurology
912 South Wood, Room 855N M/C 796
Chicago, IL 60612
Tel: 312 996-6906   *Fax:* 312 996-4169
Length: 1 Yr   *ACGME Approved/Offered Positions:* 2
Program ID: 188-16-13-027

Maywood

Loyola University Program
Sponsor: Loyola University Medical Center
Prgm Director: Jose Biller, MD*
McGuire Center, Suite 2700
2160 South First Avenue
Maywood, IL 60153
Tel: 708 216-2662   *Fax:* 708 216-5617
E-mail: dshannon@lumc.edu
Length: 1 Yr   *ACGME Approved/Offered Positions:* 1
Program ID: 188-16-12-032

Indiana

Indianapolis

Indiana University School of Medicine Program
Sponsor: Indiana University School of Medicine
Clarian Indiana University Hospital
William N Wishard Memorial Hospital
Prgm Director: Askiel Bruno, MD
Neurology Department
1050 Wishard Blvd RG 6105
Indianapolis, IN 46202
Tel: 317 274-4297   *Fax:* 317 630-7906
Length: 1 Yr   *ACGME Approved/Offered Positions:* 1
Program ID: 188-17-12-013

Iowa

Iowa City

University of Iowa Hospitals and Clinics Program
Sponsor: University of Iowa Hospitals and Clinics
Veterans Affairs Medical Center (Iowa City)
Prgm Director: Enrique C Leira, MD
Department of Neurology
200 Hawkins Drive
Iowa City, IA 52242
Tel: 319 356-8755   *Fax:* 319 384-7199
Length: 1 Yr   *ACGME Approved/Offered Positions:* 2
Program ID: 188-18-12-043

Kansas

Kansas City

University of Kansas School of Medicine Program
Sponsor: University of Kansas School of Medicine
St Luke's Hospital-Kansas City
University of Kansas Hospital
Prgm Director: Gary Gronseth, MD*
3901 Rainbow Boulevard
Mailstop 2012
Kansas City, KS 66160
Tel: 913 588-6972   *Fax:* 913 588-1811
E-mail: ggronseth@kumc.edu
Length: 1 Yr   *ACGME Approved/Offered Positions:* 1
Program ID: 188-19-31-046

Maryland

Baltimore

Johns Hopkins University Program
Sponsor: Johns Hopkins University School of Medicine
Johns Hopkins Hospital
Prgm Director: Robert J Wityk, MD
Phipps 126b
600 North Wolfe Street
Baltimore, MD 21287
Tel: 410 955-2228   *Fax:* 410 614-9807
Length: 1 Yr   *ACGME Approved/Offered Positions:* 2
Program ID: 188-23-12-024

University of Maryland Program
Sponsor: University of Maryland Medical System
University of Maryland-Kernan Hospital
Veterans Affairs Medical Center (Baltimore)
Prgm Director: Barney Stern, MD
Department of Neurology
22 South Greene Street, Room N4W46
Baltimore, MD 21201
Tel: 410 328-3372   *Fax:* 410 328-5899
E-mail: BStern@som.umaryland.edu
Length: 1 Yr   *ACGME Approved/Offered Positions:* 2
Program ID: 188-23-13-045

Massachusetts

Boston

Beth Israel Deaconess Medical Center/Harvard Medical School Program
Sponsor: Beth Israel Deaconess Medical Center
Prgm Director: Louis R Caplan, MD
Department of Neurology
330 Brookline Avenue, Palmer 127
Boston, MA 02215
Tel: 617 632-8911   *Fax:* 617 632-8920
Length: 1 Yr   *ACGME Approved/Offered Positions:* 2
Program ID: 188-24-22-004

Boston University Medical Center Program
Sponsor: Boston Medical Center
Prgm Director: Viken L Babikian, MD
72 East Concord Street, C-329
Boston, MA 02118
Tel: 617 638-5309   *Fax:* 617 638-5354
E-mail: babikian@bu.edu
Length: 1 Yr   *ACGME Approved/Offered Positions:* 2
Program ID: 188-24-31-010

Massachusetts General Hospital/Brigham and Women's Hospital/Harvard Medical School Program
Sponsor: Massachusetts General Hospital
Brigham and Women's Hospital
Prgm Director: Jonathan Rosand, MD, MS
185 Cambridge St, CPZN6818
Richard B Simches Research Building
Boston, MA 02114
Tel: 617 724-2698   *Fax:* 617 643-3293
E-mail: vsagar1@partners.org
Length: 1 Yr   *ACGME Approved/Offered Positions:* 6
Program ID: 188-24-21-018

Worcester

University of Massachusetts Program
Sponsor: University of Massachusetts Medical School
UMass Memorial Health Care (University Campus)
Prgm Director: Majaz Moonis, MD
55 Lake Avenue North
Worcester, MA 01655
Tel: 508 856-3083   *Fax:* 508 856-3180
Length: 1 Yr   *ACGME Approved/Offered Positions:* 2
Program ID: 188-24-31-050

Michigan

Ann Arbor

University of Michigan Program
Sponsor: University of Michigan Hospitals and Health Centers
Prgm Director: Devin L Brown, MD, MS
1500 E Medical Center Drive
CVC - Stroke SPC 5855
Ann Arbor, MI 48109
Tel: 734 936-9075   *Fax:* 734 232-4447
Length: 1 Yr   *ACGME Approved/Offered Positions:* 2
Program ID: 188-25-21-040

Detroit

Henry Ford Hospital Program
Sponsor: Henry Ford Hospital
Prgm Director: Brian Silver, MD
2799 West Grand Boulevard, K-11
Detroit, MI 48202
Tel: 313 916-9107   *Fax:* 313 916-3014
E-mail: bsilver1@hfhs.org
Length: 1 Yr   *ACGME Approved/Offered Positions:* 2
Program ID: 188-25-12-030

Wayne State University/Detroit Medical Center Program
Sponsor: Wayne State University/Detroit Medical Center
Detroit Receiving Hospital and University Health Center
Harper-Hutzel Hospital
Prgm Director: Renee Van Stavern, MD*
4201 St Antoine 9C-UHC
Detroit, MI 48201
Tel: 313 577-1244
Length: 1 Yr   *ACGME Approved/Offered Positions:* 2
Program ID: 188-25-21-003

Lansing

Sparrow Hospital/Michigan State University Program
Sponsor: Sparrow Hospital
Michigan State University Clinical Center
Prgm Director: Mounzer Kassab, MD*
A217 Clinical Center
138 Service Road
East Lansing, MI 48824
Tel: 517 432-9277   *Fax:* 517 432-9414
E-mail: mounzer.kassab@hc.msu.edu
Length: 1 Yr   *ACGME Approved/Offered Positions:* 2
Program ID: 188-25-12-028

Minnesota

Minneapolis

University of Minnesota/Hennepin County Medical Center Program
Sponsor: University of Minnesota Medical School
Hennepin County Medical Center
University of Minnesota Medical Center, Division of Fairview
Prgm Director: David C Anderson, MD
Department of Neurology (P5)
701 Park Avenue South
Minneapolis, MN 55415
Tel: 612 873-2430   *Fax:* 612 904-4270
Length: 1 Yr   *ACGME Approved/Offered Positions:* 3
Program ID: 188-26-13-034

Missouri

St Louis

Washington University/B-JH/SLCH Consortium Program
Sponsor: Washington University/B-JH/SLCH Consortium
Barnes-Jewish Hospital
The Rehabilitation Institute of St Louis
Prgm Director: Jin-Moo Lee, MD, PhD
660 S Euclid Avenue, Box 8111
St Louis, MO 63110
Tel: 314 747-1138   *Fax:* 314 362-9462
E-mail: leejm@wustl.edu
Length: 1 Yr   *ACGME Approved/Offered Positions:* 2
Program ID: 188-28-12-020

New Jersey

Newark

UMDNJ-New Jersey Medical School Program
Sponsor: UMDNJ-New Jersey Medical School
UMDNJ-University Hospital
Prgm Director: Jawad F Kirmani, MD
90 Bergen Street
DOC 8100
Newark, NJ 07103
Tel: 973 972-7852   *Fax:* 973 972-9960
E-mail: kirmanjf@umdnj.edu
Length: 1 Yr   *ACGME Approved/Offered Positions:* 2
Program ID: 188-33-13-005

New York

Albany

Albany Medical Center Program
Sponsor: Albany Medical Center
Prgm Director: Gary L Bernardini, MD, PhD
47 New Scotland Avenue
MC70
Albany, NY 12208
Tel: 518 262-5226   *Fax:* 518 262-6261
Length: 1 Yr   *ACGME Approved/Offered Positions:* 1
Program ID: 188-35-12-063

Buffalo

University at Buffalo Program
Sponsor: University at Buffalo School of Medicine
Kaleida Health System (Millard Fillmore Hospital)
Prgm Director: Frederick E Munschauer III, MD
The Jacobs Neurological Institute
100 High Street
Buffalo, NY 14203
Tel: 716 859-3496   *Fax:* 716 859-7573
E-mail: ejtamoga@buffalo.edu
Length: 1 Yr   *ACGME Approved/Offered Positions:* 2
Program ID: 188-35-12-022

New York

Mount Sinai School of Medicine Program
Sponsor: Mount Sinai School of Medicine
Maimonides Medical Center
Mount Sinai Medical Center
Prgm Director: Stanley Tuhrim, MD
1 Gustave L Levy Place
Box 1137
New York, NY 10029
Tel: 212 241-4562   *Fax:* 212 241-4561
E-mail: stanley.tuhrim@msnyuhealth.org
Length: 1 Yr   *ACGME Approved/Offered Positions:* 2
Program ID: 188-35-21-001

New York Presbyterian Hospital (Columbia Campus) Program
Sponsor: New York Presbyterian Hospital
New York Presbyterian Hospital (Columbia Campus)
Prgm Director: Randolph S Marshall, MD, MS*
710 West 168th Street
New York, NY 10032
Tel: 212 305-8389   *Fax:* 212 305-3741
E-mail: rsm2@columbia.edu
Length: 1 Yr   *ACGME Approved/Offered Positions:* 2
Program ID: 188-35-31-012

New York Presbyterian Hospital (Cornell Campus) Program
Sponsor: New York Presbyterian Hospital
Prgm Director: Alan Z Segal, MD
525 East 68th Street F610
New York, NY 10021
Tel: 212 746-0225   *Fax:* 212 746-8790
E-mail: azs2001@med.cornell.edu
Length: 1 Yr   *ACGME Approved/Offered Positions:* 2
Program ID: 188-35-31-054

Rochester

University of Rochester Program
Sponsor: Strong Memorial Hospital of the University of Rochester
Prgm Director: Curtis Benesch, MD, MPH*
601 Elmwood Avenue
Box 681
Rochester, NY 14642
Tel: 585 275-2530   *Fax:* 585 273-1026
E-mail: curtis_benesch@urmc.rochester.edu
Length: 1 Yr   *ACGME Approved/Offered Positions:* 1
Program ID: 188-35-12-016

Stony Brook

SUNY at Stony Brook Program
Sponsor: University Hospital - SUNY at Stony Brook
Prgm Director: Candice J Perkins, MD
Department of Neurology
Health Sciences Center, Tower 12, Room 020
Stony Brook, NY 11794
Tel: 631 444-7878   *Fax:* 631 632-2451
Length: 1 Yr   *ACGME Approved/Offered Positions:* 1
Program ID: 188-35-21-026

Syracuse

SUNY Upstate Medical University Program
Sponsor: SUNY Upstate Medical University
Prgm Director: Yahia M Lodi, MD
750 East Adams Street
Syracuse, NY 13210
Tel: 315 464-5014   *Fax:* 315 464-5015
Length: 1 Yr   *ACGME Approved/Offered Positions:* 3
Program ID: 188-35-13-053

North Carolina

Chapel Hill

University of North Carolina Hospitals Program
Sponsor: University of North Carolina Hospitals
Prgm Director: Souvik Sen, MD, MS
CB 7025, Room 7001C
University of North Carolina
Chapel Hill, NC 27599
Tel: 919 843-2579   *Fax:* 919 843-3252
Length: 1 Yr   *ACGME Approved/Offered Positions:* 1
Program ID: 188-36-31-058

Note: * indicates a newly appointed program director

Ohio

Cincinnati

University Hospital/University of Cincinnati College of Medicine Program

Sponsor: University Hospital Inc
Prgm Director: Dawn Kleindorfer, MD*
260 Stetson Street, Suite 2300
Cincinnati, OH 45267
Tel: 513 558-5478   *Fax:* 513 558-4887
Length: 1 Yr   *ACGME Approved/Offered Positions:* 2
Program ID: 188-38-13-019

Cleveland

Cleveland Clinic Foundation Program

Sponsor: Cleveland Clinic Foundation
Prgm Director: Rishi Gupta, MD*
Cerebrovascular Center/S80
9500 Euclid Avenue
Cleveland, OH 44195
Tel: 216 445-9897   *Fax:* 216 636-2061
E-mail: guptar@ccf.org
Length: 1 Yr   *ACGME Approved/Offered Positions:* 2
Program ID: 188-38-12-009

University Hospitals Case Medical Center Program

Sponsor: University Hospitals Case Medical Center
Prgm Director: Michael DeGeorgia, MD
11100 Euclid Avenue
Cleveland, OH 44006
Tel: 216 844-5550   *Fax:* 216 844-5066
E-mail: kristen.stacy@uhhospitals.org
Length: 1 Yr   *ACGME Approved/Offered Positions:* 2
Program ID: 188-38-13-061

Oregon

Portland

Oregon Health & Science University Program

Sponsor: Oregon Health & Science University Hospital
Veterans Affairs Medical Center (Portland)
Prgm Director: Helmi L Lutsep, MD
3181 SW Sam Jackson Park Road, CR 131
Portland, OR 97239
Tel: 503 494-7225   *Fax:* 503 494-4690
Length: 1 Yr   *ACGME Approved/Offered Positions:* 1
Program ID: 188-40-21-048

Pennsylvania

Philadelphia

Thomas Jefferson University Program

Sponsor: Thomas Jefferson University Hospital
Prgm Director: Rodney D Bell, MD
Department of Neurology
900 Walnut St, Suite 2-00
Philadelphia, PA 19107
Tel: 215 955-6488   *Fax:* 215 923-6792
Length: 1 Yr   *ACGME Approved/Offered Positions:* 3
Program ID: 188-41-31-038

University of Pennsylvania Program

Sponsor: University of Pennsylvania Health System
Prgm Director: Steven Messe, MD
3400 Spruce Street, 3 W Gates
Philadelphia, PA 19104
Tel: 215 662-3363   *Fax:* 215 614-1927
E-mail: messe@mail.med.upenn.edu
Length: 1 Yr   *ACGME Approved/Offered Positions:* 2
Program ID: 188-41-21-056

Pittsburgh

Allegheny General Hospital Program

Sponsor: Allegheny General Hospital
Prgm Director: Ashis H Tayal, MD
420 East North Avenue, Suite 206
East Wing Office Building
Pittsburgh, PA 15212
Tel: 412 359-8841   *Fax:* 412 359-8878
Length: 1 Yr   *ACGME Approved/Offered Positions:* 1
Program ID: 188-41-21-060

University of Pittsburgh Medical Center Medical Education Program

Sponsor: Univ of Pittsburgh Medical Center Medical Education
Prgm Director: Ken Uchino, MD
200 Lothrop Street PUH C-400
Pittsburgh, PA 15218
Tel: 412 648-9165   *Fax:* 412 624-3661
E-mail: barefootj@upmc.edu
Length: 1 Yr   *ACGME Approved/Offered Positions:* 2
Program ID: 188-41-11-002

South Carolina

Charleston

Medical University of South Carolina Program

Sponsor: Medical University of South Carolina College of Medicine
MUSC Medical Center
Prgm Director: Robert J Adams, MD
96 Jonathan Lucas Street
Suite 309, MSC 606
Charleston, SC 29425
Tel: 843 792-3221   *Fax:* 843 792-8626
Length: 1 Yr   *ACGME Approved/Offered Positions:* 1
Program ID: 188-45-13-065

Tennessee

Memphis

University of Tennessee Program

Sponsor: University of Tennessee College of Medicine
Regional Medical Center at Memphis
Prgm Director: Elias A Giraldo, MD, MS
Department of Neurology
855 Monroe Avenue, Room 415
Memphis, TN 38163
Tel: 901 448-7674   *Fax:* 901 448-7440
Length: 1 Yr   *ACGME Approved/Offered Positions:* 2
Program ID: 188-47-12-055

Nashville

Vanderbilt University Program

Sponsor: Vanderbilt University Medical Center
Prgm Director: Howard Kirshner, MD
Department of Neurology
A-0118 Vanderbilt Medical Center North
Nashville, TN 37232
Tel: 615 936-1354   *Fax:* 615 936-1286
E-mail: howard.kirshner@vanderbilt.edu
Length: 1 Yr   *ACGME Approved/Offered Positions:* 2
Program ID: 188-47-31-035

Texas

Dallas

University of Texas Southwestern Medical School Program

Sponsor: University of Texas Southwestern Medical School
Dallas County Hospital District-Parkland Memorial Hospital
University Hospitals Zale Lipshy
Prgm Director: Mark D Johnson, MD
5323 Harry Hines Boulevard
Mail Code 8897
Dallas, TX 75390
Tel: 214 648-7811   *Fax:* 214 648-9311
Length: 1 Yr   *ACGME Approved/Offered Positions:* 2
Program ID: 188-48-31-008

Houston

University of Texas at Houston Program

Sponsor: University of Texas Health Science Center at Houston
Memorial Hermann Hospital
Prgm Director: Sean I Savitz, MD*
6431 Fannin Street
7.044/MSB
Houston, TX 77030
Tel: 713 500-7066   *Fax:* 713 500-0692
E-mail: sean.i.savitz@uth.tmc.edu
Length: 1 Yr   *ACGME Approved/Offered Positions:* 3
Program ID: 188-48-31-014

Virginia

Charlottesville

University of Virginia Program

Sponsor: University of Virginia Medical Center
Prgm Director: E Clarke Haley Jr, MD*
McKim Hall, UVA
PO Box 800394
Charlottesville, VA 22908
Tel: 434 924-8041   *Fax:* 434 982-1726
Length: 1 Yr   *ACGME Approved/Offered Positions:* 1
Program ID: 188-51-31-017

Washington

Seattle

University of Washington Program

Sponsor: University of Washington School of Medicine
Harborview Medical Center
Prgm Director: David Tirschwell, MD, MSc
325 Ninth Avenue
Box 359775
Seattle, WA 98104
Tel: 206 744-3251   *Fax:* 206 744-8787
E-mail: tirsch@u.washington.edu
Length: 1 Yr   *ACGME Approved/Offered Positions:* 1
Program ID: 188-54-13-041

Programs

Wisconsin

Madison

University of Wisconsin Program
Sponsor: University of Wisconsin Hospital and Clinics
William S Middleton Veterans Hospital
Prgm Director: Matthew Jensen, MD
H6/574 CSC, 600 Highland Avenue
Madison, WI 53792
Tel: 608 263-5420   *Fax:* 608 263-0412
E-mail: jensen@neurology.wisc.edu
Length: 1 Yr   *ACGME Approved/Offered Positions:* 1
Program ID: 188-56-21-064

Vascular Surgery (General Surgery)

Alabama

Birmingham

University of Alabama Medical Center Program
Sponsor: University of Alabama Hospital
Prgm Director: William D Jordan Jr, MD
1808 7th Avenue South, BDB 503
Birmingham, AL 35294
Tel: 205 934-2003   *Fax:* 205 934-0024
E-mail: wdjordan@uab.edu
Length: 2 Yrs   *ACGME Approved/Offered Positions:* 2
Program ID: 450-01-21-105

Arizona

Tucson

University of Arizona Program
Sponsor: University of Arizona College of Medicine
University Medical Center
Prgm Director: Joseph L Mills, MD
1501 North Campbell Avenue, Room 4404
PO Box 245072
Tucson, AZ 85724
Tel: 520 626-6670   *Fax:* 520 626-4008
E-mail: dejonghe@email.arizona.edu
Length: 2 Yrs   *ACGME Approved/Offered Positions:* 2
Program ID: 450-03-21-032

Arkansas

Little Rock

University of Arkansas for Medical Sciences Program
Sponsor: University of Arkansas College of Medicine
Central Arkansas Veterans Healthcare System
UAMS Medical Center
Prgm Director: John F Eidt, MD
Department of Surgery, # 520-2
4301 West Markham Street
Little Rock, AR 72205
Tel: 501 686-6176   *Fax:* 501 686-5328
E-mail: jfeidt@uams.edu
Length: 2 Yrs   *ACGME Approved/Offered Positions:* 2
Program ID: 450-04-21-055

California

La Jolla

Scripps Clinic/Scripps Green Hospital/UCSD Program
Sponsor: Scripps Clinic/Scripps Green Hospital
Kaiser Foundation Hospital (San Diego)
Veterans Affairs Medical Center (San Diego)
Prgm Director: Giacomo A DeLaria, MD
10666 N Torrey Pines Road
La Jolla, CA 92037
Tel: 858 554-8988   *Fax:* 858 554-6135
Length: 2 Yrs   *ACGME Approved/Offered Positions:* 2
Program ID: 450-05-21-091

Loma Linda

Loma Linda University Program
Sponsor: Loma Linda University Medical Center
Jerry L Pettis Memorial Veterans Hospital
Prgm Director: Ahmed M Abou-Zamzam Jr, MD
11175 Campus Street, CP 21123
Loma Linda, CA 92354
Tel: 909 558-4354   *Fax:* 909 558-0348
E-mail: azamzam@llu.edu
Length: 2 Yrs   *ACGME Approved/Offered Positions:* 2
Program ID: 450-05-21-010

Los Angeles

UCLA Medical Center Program
Sponsor: UCLA David Geffen School of Medicine/UCLA
   Medical Center
UCLA Medical Center
Prgm Director: Peter F Lawrence, MD
Gonda (Goldschmied) Vascular Center
200 UCLA Medical Plaza, Suite 510-6
Los Angeles, CA 90095
Tel: 310 267-0182   *Fax:* 310 267-0189
E-mail: pflawrence@mednet.ucla.edu
Length: 2 Yrs   *ACGME Approved/Offered Positions:* 2
Program ID: 450-05-21-011

University of Southern California/ LAC+USC Medical Center Program
Sponsor: University of Southern California/LAC+USC
   Medical Center
Huntington Memorial Hospital
USC University Hospital
Prgm Director: Fred A Weaver, MD
1520 San Pablo Street, Suite 4300
Los Angeles, CA 90033
Tel: 323 442-6835   *Fax:* 323 442-5735
Length: 2 Yrs   *ACGME Approved/Offered Positions:* 2
Program ID: 450-05-21-094

San Francisco

University of California (San Francisco) Program
Sponsor: University of California (San Francisco) School
   of Medicine
UCSF and Mount Zion Medical Centers
Prgm Director: Darren B Schneider, MD
Box 0222, A-581
400 Parnassus Avenue
San Francisco, CA 94143
Tel: 415 353-4366   *Fax:* 415 353-4370
E-mail: darren.schneider@ucsfmedctr.org
Length: 2 Yrs   *ACGME Approved/Offered Positions:* 2
Program ID: 450-05-21-033

Stanford

Stanford University Program
Sponsor: Stanford Hospital and Clinics
Veterans Affairs Palo Alto Health Care System
Prgm Director: Ronald L Dalman, MD
Division of Vascular Surgery
300 Pasteur Drive, Suite H3642
Stanford, CA 94305
Tel: 650 723-3639   *Fax:* 650 498-6044
Length: 2 Yrs   *ACGME Approved/Offered Positions:* 2
Program ID: 450-05-21-021

Note: * indicates a newly appointed program director

Torrance

Los Angeles County-Harbor-UCLA Medical Center Program
Sponsor: Los Angeles County-Harbor-UCLA Medical Center
Long Beach Memorial Medical Center
Prgm Director: Rodney A White, MD
1000 West Carson Street, Box 11
Torrance, CA 90509
Tel: 310 222-2704   *Fax:* 310 787-1889
E-mail: rawhite@ucla.edu
Length: 2 Yrs   *ACGME Approved/Offered Positions:* 2
Program ID: 450-05-21-067

Connecticut

Farmington

University of Connecticut Program
Sponsor: University of Connecticut School of Medicine
Hartford Hospital
Prgm Director: A David Drezner, MD
80 Seymour Street, Dept of Surgery, B501C
PO Box 5037
Hartford, CT 06102
Tel: 860 545-2840   *Fax:* 860 545-1568
E-mail: ddrezne@harthosp.org
Length: 2 Yrs   *ACGME Approved/Offered Positions:* 2
Program ID: 450-08-21-070

New Haven

Yale-New Haven Medical Center Program
Sponsor: Yale-New Haven Hospital
Veterans Affairs Medical Center (West Haven)
Prgm Director: Bauer E Sumpio, MD, PhD
Farnam Memorial Building 137
333 Cedar Street
New Haven, CT 06510
Tel: 203 785-2561   *Fax:* 203 785-7609
Length: 2 Yrs   *ACGME Approved/Offered Positions:* 2
Program ID: 450-08-21-084

District of Columbia

Washington

Georgetown University Hospital/Washington Hospital Center Program
Sponsor: Washington Hospital Center
Georgetown University Hospital
Veterans Affairs Medical Center (Washington, DC)
Prgm Director: Anton N Sidawy, MD, MPH
110 Irving Street, NW
Washington, DC 20010
Tel: 202 745-8295   *Fax:* 202 745-8293
E-mail: ansidawy@aol.com
Length: 2 Yrs   *ACGME Approved/Offered Positions:* 2
Program ID: 450-10-13-099

Florida

Gainesville

University of Florida Program
Sponsor: University of Florida College of Medicine
North Florida/South Georgia Veterans Health System
Shands Hospital at the University of Florida
Prgm Director: Thomas S Huber, MD, PhD
1600 SW Archer Road, Room NG-45
Division of Vascular Surgery, Box 100128
Gainesville, FL 32610
Tel: 352 273-5484   *Fax:* 352 273-5515
E-mail: huber@surgery.ufl.edu
Length: 2 Yrs   *ACGME Approved/Offered Positions:* 3
Program ID: 450-11-21-044

Tampa

University of South Florida Program
Sponsor: University of South Florida College of Medicine
Tampa General Hospital
Prgm Director: Murray L Shames, MD
USF Health South, 7th Floor
2 Tampa General Circle
Tampa, FL 33606
Tel: 813 259-0958   *Fax:* 813 259-0606
E-mail: mshames@health.usf.edu
Length: 2 Yrs   *ACGME Approved/Offered Positions:* 2
Program ID: 450-11-21-031

Georgia

Atlanta

Atlanta Medical Center Program
Sponsor: Atlanta Medical Center
Southern Regional Health System
Prgm Director: David Rosenthal, MD
315 Boulevard NE, Suite 412
Atlanta, GA 30312
Tel: 404 524-0095   *Fax:* 404 658-9558
Length: 2 Yrs   *ACGME Approved/Offered Positions:* 2
Program ID: 450-12-21-079

Emory University Program
Sponsor: Emory University School of Medicine
Emory University Hospital
Veterans Affairs Medical Center (Atlanta)
Prgm Director: Elliot L Chaikof, MD, PhD*
Vascular Surgery Section
101 Woodruff Circle, Room 5105
Atlanta, GA 30322
Tel: 404 727-8413   *Fax:* 404 727-3396
Length: 2 Yrs   *ACGME Approved/Offered Positions:* 4
Program ID: 450-12-21-012

Illinois

Chicago

McGaw Medical Center of Northwestern University Program
Sponsor: McGaw Medical Center of Northwestern University
Jesse Brown Veterans Affairs Medical Center
Northwestern Memorial Hospital
Prgm Director: Mark K Eskandari, MD
676 N Saint Clair St
Suite 650
Chicago, IL 60611
Tel: 312 695-4857   *Fax:* 312 695-4955
Length: 2 Yrs   *ACGME Approved/Offered Positions:* 4
Program ID: 450-16-21-001

Rush University Medical Center Program
Sponsor: Rush University Medical Center
Prgm Director: Walter J McCarthy III, MD
1653 West Congress Parkway
714 Jelke South Center
Chicago, IL 60612
Tel: 312 942-8272   *Fax:* 312 942-6052
E-mail: walter_mccarthy@rush.edu
Length: 2 Yrs   *ACGME Approved/Offered Positions:* 2
Program ID: 450-16-21-057

University of Chicago Program
Sponsor: University of Chicago Medical Center
Prgm Director: Hisham Bassiouny, MD
5841 S Maryland Avenue, MC 5028
Room J-555
Chicago, IL 60637
Tel: 773 702-6128   *Fax:* 773 702-0863
Length: 2 Yrs   *ACGME Approved/Offered Positions:* 2
Program ID: 450-16-11-023

Maywood

Loyola University Program
Sponsor: Loyola University Medical Center
Edward Hines, Jr Veterans Affairs Hospital
Prgm Director: Bernadette Aulivola, MD*
2160 S First Avenue
EMS 110, Room 3215
Maywood, IL 60153
Tel: 708 327-2686   *Fax:* 708 327-3492
Length: 2 Yrs   *ACGME Approved/Offered Positions:* 2
Program ID: 450-16-21-002

Springfield

Southern Illinois University Program
Sponsor: Southern Illinois University School of Medicine
Memorial Medical Center
St John's Hospital
Prgm Director: Kim J Hodgson, MD
800 N Rutledge, Suite D346
PO Box 19638
Springfield, IL 62794
Tel: 217 545-8856   *Fax:* 217 545-2563
E-mail: rlloyd@siumed.edu
Length: 2 Yrs   *ACGME Approved/Offered Positions:* 2
Program ID: 450-16-21-034

Indiana

Indianapolis

Indiana University School of Medicine Program
Sponsor: Indiana University School of Medicine
Clarian Methodist Hospital of Indiana
Richard L Roudebush Veterans Affairs Medical Center
Prgm Director: Michael C Dalsing, MD
1120 South Dr
224 Fesler Hall
Indianapolis, IN 46202
Tel: 317 962-0283   *Fax:* 317 962-0289
Length: 2 Yrs   *ACGME Approved/Offered Positions:* 2
Program ID: 450-17-31-095

Iowa

Iowa City

University of Iowa Hospitals and Clinics Program

Sponsor: University of Iowa Hospitals and Clinics
Veterans Affairs Medical Center (Iowa City)
Prgm Director: W John Sharp, MD*
Department of Surgery
200 Hawkins Drive
Iowa City, IA 52242
Tel: 319 356-8242
Length: 2 Yrs   *ACGME Approved/Offered Positions:* 2
Program ID: 450-18-21-048

Kansas

Kansas City

University of Kansas School of Medicine Program

Sponsor: University of Kansas School of Medicine
Dwight D Eisenhower Veterans Affairs Medical Center
Hutchinson Hospital
University of Kansas Hospital
Prgm Director: James H Thomas, MD
3901 Rainbow Blvd
4959 Murphy, MS 1037
Kansas City, KS 66160
Tel: 913 588-6101   *Fax:* 913 588-7583
E-mail: jthomas@kumc.edu
Length: 2 Yrs   *ACGME Approved/Offered Positions:* 2
Program ID: 450-19-21-060

Kentucky

Lexington

University of Kentucky College of Medicine Program

Sponsor: University of Kentucky College of Medicine
University of Kentucky Hospital
Veterans Affairs Medical Center (Lexington)
Prgm Director: David J Minion, MD, BS
Vascular Surgery
800 Rose Street, C246
Lexington, KY 40536
Tel: 859 323-6346   *Fax:* 859 323-6840
E-mail: djmini@uky.edu
Length: 2 Yrs   *ACGME Approved/Offered Positions:* 2
Program ID: 450-20-21-062

Louisiana

New Orleans

Louisiana State University Program

Sponsor: Louisiana State University School of Medicine
Our Lady of the Lake Regional Medical Center
West Jefferson Medical Center
Prgm Director: Malachi G Sheahan III, MD
Department of Surgery
533 Bolivar Street
New Orleans, LA 70112
Tel: 504 568-2728   *Fax:* 504 568-4633
E-mail: surgdhp@lsuhsc.edu
Length: 2 Yrs   *ACGME Approved/Offered Positions:* 2
Program ID: 450-21-21-058

Ochsner Clinic Foundation Program

Sponsor: Ochsner Clinic Foundation
Leonard J Chabert Medical Center
Prgm Director: W Charles Sternbergh III, MD
1514 Jefferson Highway
New Orleans, LA 70121
Tel: 504 842-4053   *Fax:* 504 842-5017
E-mail: dladmirault@ochsner.org
Length: 2 Yrs   *ACGME Approved/Offered Positions:* 2
Program ID: 450-21-22-024

Maryland

Baltimore

Johns Hopkins University Program

Sponsor: Johns Hopkins University School of Medicine
Johns Hopkins Hospital
Prgm Director: Bruce A Perler, MD, MBA
600 North Wolfe Street/Harvey 611
Baltimore, MD 21287
Tel: 410 955-2618   *Fax:* 410 614-2079
Length: 2 Yrs   *ACGME Approved/Offered Positions:* 2
Program ID: 450-23-31-086

University of Maryland Program

Sponsor: University of Maryland Medical System
Baltimore Washington Medical Center
Maryland General Hospital
Mercy Medical Center
Veterans Affairs Medical Center (Baltimore)
Prgm Director: William R Flinn, MD
22 South Greene Street
Room N4W66
Baltimore, MD 21201
Tel: 410 328-5840   *Fax:* 410 328-0717
Length: 2 Yrs   *ACGME Approved/Offered Positions:* 4
Program ID: 450-23-21-080

Bethesda

National Capital Consortium (Walter Reed) Program

Sponsor: National Capital Consortium
Walter Reed Army Medical Center
Prgm Director: Charles J Fox, MD*
Vascular Surgery Service, Wd 64, Bldg 2
6900 Georgia Avenue NW
Washington, DC 20307
Tel: 202 782-6537   *Fax:* 202 782-3198
E-mail: charles.fox@us.army.mil
Length: 2 Yrs   *ACGME Approved/Offered Positions:* 2
Program ID: 450-10-11-022
Uniformed Services Program

Massachusetts

Boston

Beth Israel Deaconess Medical Center Program

Sponsor: Beth Israel Deaconess Medical Center
Prgm Director: Frank B Pomposelli Jr, MD
110 Francis Street
Suite 5B
Boston, MA 02215
Tel: 617 632-9955   *Fax:* 617 632-7977
Length: 2 Yrs   *ACGME Approved/Offered Positions:* 2
Program ID: 450-24-21-040

Boston University Medical Center Program

Sponsor: Boston Medical Center
Quincy Medical Center
Prgm Director: Palma Shaw, MD
88 East Newton Street
Boston, MA 02118
Tel: 617 638-8488   *Fax:* 617 638-8469
E-mail: palma.shaw@bmc.org
Length: 2 Yrs   *ACGME Approved/Offered Positions:* 2
Program ID: 450-24-21-026

Brigham and Women's Hospital Program

Sponsor: Brigham and Women's Hospital
Prgm Director: Michael Belkin, MD
75 Francis St
Department of Surgery
Boston, MA 02115
Tel: 617 732-6816   *Fax:* 617 730-2876
E-mail: surgeryeducation@partners.org
Length: 2 Yrs   *ACGME Approved/Offered Positions:* 2
Program ID: 450-24-21-003

Massachusetts General Hospital Program

Sponsor: Massachusetts General Hospital
Prgm Director: Christopher J Kwolek, MD*
15 Parkman Street
WAC 440
Boston, MA 02114
Tel: 617 724-6101   *Fax:* 617 643-0418
E-mail: ckwolek@partners.org
Length: 2 Yrs   *ACGME Approved/Offered Positions:* 4
Program ID: 450-24-21-004

Tufts Medical Center Program

Sponsor: Tufts Medical Center
Prgm Director: Mark D Iafrati, MD
NEMC #437
800 Washington Street
Boston, MA 02111
Tel: 617 636-5019   *Fax:* 617 636-5936
E-mail: miafrati@tuftsmedicalcenter.org
Length: 2 Yrs   *ACGME Approved/Offered Positions:* 2
Program ID: 450-24-21-005

Worcester

University of Massachusetts Program

Sponsor: University of Massachusetts Medical School
UMass Memorial Health Care (University Campus)
Prgm Director: Louis Messina, MD
55 Lake Avenue North
S3-822
Worcester, MA 01655
Tel: 508 856-5599   *Fax:* 508 856-8329
E-mail: Louis.Messina@umassmemorial.org
Length: 2 Yrs   *ACGME Approved/Offered Positions:* 2
Program ID: 450-24-21-013

Michigan

Ann Arbor

University of Michigan Program

Sponsor: University of Michigan Hospitals and Health
 Centers
Prgm Director: Thomas W Wakefield, MD
1500 E Medical Center Drive
2210 Taubman Center
Ann Arbor, MI 48109
Tel: 734 936-5847   *Fax:* 734 647-9867
E-mail: thomasww@med.umich.edu
Length: 2 Yrs   *ACGME Approved/Offered Positions:* 2
Program ID: 450-25-21-035

Note: * indicates a newly appointed program director

Detroit

Henry Ford Hospital Program

Sponsor: Henry Ford Hospital
Prgm Director: Tim Nypaver, MD
2799 W Grand Boulevard
Detroit, MI 48202
Tel: 313 916-3153   *Fax:* 313 916-3023
E-mail: tnypave1@hfhs.org
Length: 2 Yrs   *ACGME Approved/Offered Positions:* 2
Program ID: 450-25-12-014

Wayne State University/Detroit Medical Center Program

Sponsor: Wayne State University/Detroit Medical Center
Harper-Hutzel Hospital
William Beaumont Hospital
Prgm Director: O W Brown, MD, JD
Harper Hospital
3990 John R Street
Detroit, MI 48201
Tel: 313 745-8637   *Fax:* 313 993-0244
E-mail: mduchene@dmc.org
Length: 2 Yrs   *ACGME Approved/Offered Positions:* 4
Program ID: 450-25-21-066

Grand Rapids

Grand Rapids Medical Education and Research Center/Michigan State University Program

Sponsor: Grand Rapids Medical Education and Research
Center
Saint Mary's Health Care (Grand Rapids)
Spectrum Health-Blodgett Hospital
Spectrum Health-Butterworth Hospital
Prgm Director: M Ashraf Mansour, MD
Vascular Surgery Fellowship
221 Michigan NE, Suite 200A
Grand Rapids, MI 49503
Tel: 616 391-1691   *Fax:* 616 391-8611
Length: 2 Yrs   *ACGME Approved/Offered Positions:* 2
Program ID: 450-25-31-109

Minnesota

Rochester

College of Medicine, Mayo Clinic (Rochester) Program

Sponsor: College of Medicine, Mayo Clinic
Saint Marys Hospital of Rochester
Prgm Director: Thomas C Bower, MD
200 First Street, SW
Rochester, MN 55905
Tel: 507 255-7062   *Fax:* 507 255-7378
Length: 2 Yrs   *ACGME Approved/Offered Positions:* 6
Program ID: 450-26-21-042

Missouri

Columbia

University of Missouri-Columbia Program

Sponsor: University of Missouri-Columbia School of
Medicine
University Hospitals and Clinics
Prgm Director: Walter K Nichols, MD
MA202 Medical Sciences Building
One Hospital Drive
Columbia, MO 65212
Tel: 573 884-1348   *Fax:* 573 884-5049
Length: 2 Yrs   *ACGME Approved/Offered Positions:* 2
Program ID: 450-28-21-049

St Louis

St Louis University School of Medicine Program

Sponsor: St Louis University School of Medicine
St John's Mercy Medical Center
St Louis University Hospital
Prgm Director: Donald L Jacobs, MD
3635 Vista Avenue at Grand Blvd
PO Box 15250
St Louis, MO 63110
Tel: 314 577-8310   *Fax:* 314 577-8635
Length: 2 Yrs   *ACGME Approved/Offered Positions:* 2
Program ID: 450-28-21-027

Washington University/B-JH/SLCH Consortium Program

Sponsor: Washington University/B-JH/SLCH Consortium
Barnes-Jewish Hospital
Barnes-Jewish West County Hospital
Prgm Director: Gregorio A Sicard, MD
One Barnes-Jewish Hospital Plaza
Suite 5103
St Louis, MO 63110
Tel: 314 362-7841   *Fax:* 314 454-3923
E-mail: swapd@wudosis.wustl.edu
Length: 2 Yrs   *ACGME Approved/Offered Positions:* 4
Program ID: 450-28-21-050

New Hampshire

Lebanon

Dartmouth-Hitchcock Medical Center Program

Sponsor: Mary Hitchcock Memorial Hospital
Prgm Director: Mark F Fillinger, MD
One Medical Center Drive
Lebanon, NH 03756
Tel: 603 650-8677   *Fax:* 603 650-4973
E-mail: Mark.Fillinger@hitchcock.org
Length: 2 Yrs   *ACGME Approved/Offered Positions:* 3
Program ID: 450-32-21-059

New Jersey

Englewood

Mount Sinai School of Medicine (Englewood) Program

Sponsor: Mount Sinai School of Medicine
Englewood Hospital and Medical Center
Prgm Director: Herbert Dardik, MD
350 Engle Street
Englewood, NJ 07631
Tel: 201 894-3141   *Fax:* 201 227-5551
Length: 2 Yrs   *ACGME Approved/Offered Positions:* 2
Program ID: 450-35-21-089

New Brunswick

UMDNJ-Robert Wood Johnson Medical School Program

Sponsor: UMDNJ-Robert Wood Johnson Medical School
Robert Wood Johnson University Hospital
Prgm Director: Alan M Graham, MD
One Robert Wood Johnson Pl, MEB-541
New Brunswick, NJ 08903
Tel: 732 235-8770   *Fax:* 732 235-8538
E-mail: grahamal@umdnj.edu
Length: 2 Yrs   *ACGME Approved/Offered Positions:* 2
Program ID: 450-33-21-037

Newark

Newark Beth Israel Medical Center Program

Sponsor: Newark Beth Israel Medical Center
St Barnabas Medical Center
Prgm Director: Bruce J Brener, MD
201 Lyons Avenue
Department of Surgery L3
Newark, NJ 07112
Tel: 973 926-7330   *Fax:* 973 923-8757
E-mail: bbrener@sbhcs.com
Length: 2 Yrs   *ACGME Approved/Offered Positions:* 2
Program ID: 450-33-21-087

UMDNJ-New Jersey Medical School Program

Sponsor: UMDNJ-New Jersey Medical School
Clara Maass Medical Center, Inc
Hackensack University Medical Center
St Michael's Medical Center (A Member of Catholic Hlth
East)
UMDNJ-University Hospital
Prgm Director: Brajesh K Lal, MD*
UMDNJ-New Jersey Medical School
90 Bergen Street, Suite 7600
Newark, NJ 07103
Tel: 973 972-6295   *Fax:* 973 972-0092
E-mail: lalbk@umdnj.edu
Length: 2 Yrs   *ACGME Approved/Offered Positions:* 4
Program ID: 450-33-21-036

New York

Albany

Albany Medical Center Program

Sponsor: Albany Medical Center
Prgm Director: Paul B Kreienberg, MD
Vascular Institute (MC157)
43 New Scotland Avenue
Albany, NY 12208
Tel: 518 262-5640   *Fax:* 518 262-6720
Length: 2 Yrs   *ACGME Approved/Offered Positions:* 4
Program ID: 450-35-21-061

Bronx

Albert Einstein College of Medicine Program

Sponsor: Albert Einstein College of Medicine of Yeshiva
University
Montefiore Medical Center-Henry and Lucy Moses
Division
Prgm Director: William Suggs, MD
Montefiore Medical Center
111 E 210 Street
Bronx, NY 10467
Tel: 718 920-6338   *Fax:* 718 231-9811
Length: 2 Yrs   *ACGME Approved/Offered Positions:* 2
Program ID: 450-35-21-015

Brooklyn

Maimonides Medical Center Program

Sponsor: Maimonides Medical Center
Prgm Director: Enrico Ascher, MD
4802 Tenth Avenue
Brooklyn, NY 11219
Tel: 718 283-7957
Length: 2 Yrs   *ACGME Approved/Offered Positions:* 2
Program ID: 450-35-21-076

Programs

Buffalo

University at Buffalo Program

Sponsor: University at Buffalo School of Medicine
Kaleida Health System (Millard Fillmore Hospital)
Veterans Affairs Western New York Hospital
Prgm Director: Linda M Harris, MD
3 Gates Circle
Department of Surgery
Buffalo, NY 14209
Tel: 716 887-4807 *Fax:* 716 887-4220
Length: 2 Yrs *ACGME Approved/Offered Positions:* 2
Program ID: 450-35-21-069

Great Neck

NSLIJHS Program

Sponsor: North Shore-Long Island Jewish Health System
Long Island Jewish Medical Center
North Shore University Hospital
Prgm Director: Kambhampaty V Krishnasastry, MD
1999 Marcus Avenue
Lake Success, NY 11042
Tel: 516 562-4863 *Fax:* 516 562-1521
Length: 2 Yrs *ACGME Approved/Offered Positions:* 4
Program ID: 450-35-31-082

New York

Mount Sinai School of Medicine Program

Sponsor: Mount Sinai School of Medicine
Mount Sinai Medical Center
Veterans Affairs Medical Center (Bronx)
Prgm Director: Victoria J Teodorescu, MD
One Gustave L Levy Place, Box 1259
New York, NY 10029
Tel: 212 241-5871 *Fax:* 212 411-0111
E-mail: victoria.teodorescu@mssm.edu
Length: 2 Yrs *ACGME Approved/Offered Positions:* 4
Program ID: 450-35-21-038

New York Presbyterian Hospital (Columbia and Cornell Campus) Program

Sponsor: New York Presbyterian Hospital
New York Presbyterian Hospital (Cornell Campus)
New York Presbyterian Hospital (Columbia Campus)
Prgm Director: James Mckinsey, MD*
525 East 68th Street
F 172
New York, NY 10021
Tel: 212 342-3255 *Fax:* 212 342-3252
E-mail: jfm2111@columbia.edu
Length: 2 Yrs *ACGME Approved/Offered Positions:* 4
Program ID: 450-35-21-092

New York University School of Medicine Program

Sponsor: New York University School of Medicine
Bellevue Hospital Center
Manhattan VA Harbor Health Care System
Prgm Director: Patrick J Lamparello Jr, MD
530 First Avenue
Suite 6F
New York, NY 10016
Tel: 212 263-7311 *Fax:* 212 263-7722
Length: 2 Yrs *ACGME Approved/Offered Positions:* 4
Program ID: 450-35-21-045

Rochester

University of Rochester Program

Sponsor: Strong Memorial Hospital of the University of
  Rochester
Prgm Director: Karl A Illig, MD
601 Elmwood Ave
Rochester, NY 14642
Tel: 585 275-6772 *Fax:* 585 756-7752
E-mail: Karl_Illig@urmc.rochester.edu
Length: 2 Yrs *ACGME Approved/Offered Positions:* 2
Program ID: 450-35-21-006

Staten Island

Staten Island University Hospital Program

Sponsor: Staten Island University Hospital
Prgm Director: Gary ' Giangola, MD*
475 Seaview Avuenue
Staten Island, NY 10305
Tel: 718 226-9508 *Fax:* 718 226-8365
E-mail: ggiangola@siuh.edu
Length: 2 Yrs *ACGME Approved/Offered Positions:* 2
Program ID: 450-35-13-107

Stony Brook

SUNY at Stony Brook Program

Sponsor: University Hospital - SUNY at Stony Brook
Veterans Affairs Medical Center (Northport)
Winthrop-University Hospital
Prgm Director: John J Ricotta, MD
Dept of Surgery, HSC 18-040
Stony Brook, NY 11794
Tel: 631 444-7875 *Fax:* 631 444-8947
Length: 2 Yrs *ACGME Approved/Offered Positions:* 2
Program ID: 450-35-21-051

North Carolina

Chapel Hill

University of North Carolina Hospitals Program

Sponsor: University of North Carolina Hospitals
Prgm Director: Mark A Farber, MD*
Campus Box 7212
3024 Burnett Womack Building
Chapel Hill, NC 27599
Tel: 919 966-3391 *Fax:* 919 966-2898
E-mail: mark_farber@med.unc.edu
Length: 2 Yrs *ACGME Approved/Offered Positions:* 2
Program ID: 450-36-21-007

Charlotte

Carolinas Medical Center Program

Sponsor: Carolinas Medical Center
Prgm Director: Timothy S Roush, MD, MPH
1000 Blythe Boulevard, CHI, Suite 300
PO Box 32861
Charlotte, NC 28232
Tel: 704 355-9431 *Fax:* 704 355-6227
E-mail: troush@sanger-clinic.com
Length: 2 Yrs *ACGME Approved/Offered Positions:* 2
Program ID: 450-36-21-008

Durham

Duke University Hospital Program

Sponsor: Duke University Hospital
Prgm Director: Cynthia K Shortell, MD
DUMC Box 3538, Room 7682A - HAFS Building
Erwin Road
Durham, NC 27710
Tel: 919 681-2915 *Fax:* 919 668-5284
E-mail: sherry.davi@duke.edu
Length: 2 Yrs *ACGME Approved/Offered Positions:* 2
Program ID: 450-36-13-114

Winston-Salem

Wake Forest University School of Medicine Program

Sponsor: Wake Forest University Baptist Medical Center
Prgm Director: Kimberley J Hansen, MD
Division of Surgical Sciences
Wake Forest University School of Medicine
Winston-Salem, NC 27157
Tel: 336 713-5256 *Fax:* 336 716-2934
E-mail: kjhansen@wfubmc.edu
Length: 2 Yrs *ACGME Approved/Offered Positions:* 4
Program ID: 450-36-21-073

Ohio

Cincinnati

TriHealth (Good Samaritan Hospital) Program

Sponsor: TriHealth
TriHealth - Good Samaritan Hospital
Prgm Director: Patrick Muck, MD
375 Dixmyth Avenue
3rd Floor/Tower
Cincinnati, OH 45220
Tel: 513 872-3220
E-mail: patrick_muck@trihealth.com
Length: 2 Yrs *ACGME Approved/Offered Positions:* 2
Program ID: 450-38-31-043

University Hospital/University of Cincinnati College of Medicine Program

Sponsor: University Hospital Inc
Christ Hospital
Veterans Affairs Medical Center (Cincinnati)
Prgm Director: Amy B Reed, MD
PO Box 670558
231 Albert Sabin Way
Cincinnati, OH 45267
Tel: 513 558-5367 *Fax:* 513 558-2967
E-mail: amy.reed@uc.edu
Length: 2 Yrs *ACGME Approved/Offered Positions:* 2
Program ID: 450-38-31-078

Cleveland

Cleveland Clinic Foundation Program

Sponsor: Cleveland Clinic Foundation
Hillcrest Hospital
Marymount Hospital
Veterans Affairs Medical Center (Cleveland)
Prgm Director: Daniel G Clair, MD
Dept of Vascular Surgery
9500 Euclid Ave, Desk S40
Cleveland, OH 44195
Tel: 216 444-4766 *Fax:* 216 444-9324
Length: 2 Yrs *ACGME Approved/Offered Positions:* 6
Program ID: 450-38-22-046

University Hospitals Case Medical Center Program

Sponsor: University Hospitals Case Medical Center
Prgm Director: John Blebea, MD*
University Hospitals of Cleveland Case Medical Ctr
11100 Euclid Avenue
Cleveland, OH 44106
Tel: 216 844-3013 *Fax:* 216 844-7716
E-mail: john.blebea@uhhospitals.org
Length: 2 Yrs *ACGME Approved/Offered Positions:* 2
Program ID: 450-38-21-071

Note: * indicates a newly appointed program director

Columbus

Ohio State University Hospital Program
Sponsor: Ohio State University Hospital
Prgm Director: Patrick S Vaccaro, MD
1654 Upham Drive
Means Hall N325
Columbus, OH 43210
Tel: 614 293-8536   *Fax:* 614 293-8902
Length: 2 Yrs   *ACGME Approved/Offered Positions:* 2
Program ID: 450-38-21-056

Toledo

Toledo Hospital (Jobst Vascular Center) Program
Sponsor: Toledo Hospital
Prgm Director: Anthony J Comerota, MD
Jobst Vascular Center
2109 Hughes Dr, Suite 400
Toledo, OH 43606
Tel: 419 291-2088   *Fax:* 419 479-6980
E-mail: peggy.mauer@promedica.org
Length: 2 Yrs   *ACGME Approved/Offered Positions:* 4
Program ID: 450-38-21-100

Oregon

Portland

Oregon Health & Science University Program
Sponsor: Oregon Health & Science University Hospital
Legacy Emanuel Hospital and Health Center
Prgm Director: Timothy K Liem, MD
Division of Vascular Surgery, OP-11
3181 SW Sam Jackson Park Road
Portland, OR 97239
Tel: 503 494-7593   *Fax:* 503 494-4324
E-mail: liemt@ohsu.edu
Length: 2 Yrs   *ACGME Approved/Offered Positions:* 2
Program ID: 450-40-21-009

Pennsylvania

Danville

Geisinger Health System Program
Sponsor: Geisinger Health System
Geisinger Medical Center
Prgm Director: James R Elmore, MD
Vascular Surgery
100 North Academy Avenue
Danville, PA 17822
Tel: 570 271-6369   *Fax:* 570 271-5840
E-mail: jelmore@geisinger.edu
Length: 2 Yrs   *ACGME Approved/Offered Positions:* 2
Program ID: 450-41-21-072

Hershey

Penn State University/Milton S Hershey Medical Center Program
Sponsor: Milton S Hershey Medical Center
Prgm Director: David C Han, MD, MS
Vascular Surgery MC H053
500 University Drive
Hershey, PA 17033
Tel: 717 531-8866   *Fax:* 717 531-4151
Length: 2 Yrs   *ACGME Approved/Offered Positions:* 2
Program ID: 450-41-21-065

Philadelphia

Pennsylvania Hospital of the University of Pennsylvania Health System Program
Sponsor: Pennsylvania Hospital (UPHS)
Prgm Director: Keith D Calligaro, MD
800 Spruce Street
Philadelphia, PA 19107
Tel: 215 829-5000   *Fax:* 215 627-0578
Length: 2 Yrs   *ACGME Approved/Offered Positions:* 2
Program ID: 450-41-31-074

Temple University Hospital Program
Sponsor: Temple University Hospital
Prgm Director: Andrew B Roberts, MD*
3401 North Broad Street, Parkinson Pavilion #447
Section of Vascular Surgery
Philadelphia, PA 19140
Tel: 215 707-9850   *Fax:* 215 707-5901
E-mail: andrew.roberts@tuhs.temple.edu
Length: 2 Yrs   *ACGME Approved/Offered Positions:* 2
Program ID: 450-41-21-054

Thomas Jefferson University Program
Sponsor: Thomas Jefferson University Hospital
Methodist Hospital
Prgm Director: Paul J DiMuzio, MD
111 South 11th Street
Gibbon Building, Suite 6350
Philadelphia, PA 19107
Tel: 215 955-8304
Length: 2 Yrs   *ACGME Approved/Offered Positions:* 2
Program ID: 450-41-12-112

University of Pennsylvania Program
Sponsor: University of Pennsylvania Health System
Prgm Director: Edward Y Woo, MD
3400 Spruce Street, 4 Silverstein
Philadelphia, PA 19104
Tel: 215 662-7836   *Fax:* 215 662-4871
E-mail: megan.kavanagh@uphs.upenn.edu
Length: 2 Yrs   *ACGME Approved/Offered Positions:* 2
Program ID: 450-41-21-052

Pittsburgh

Allegheny General Hospital Program
Sponsor: Allegheny General Hospital
Prgm Director: Satish Muluk, MD
320 East North Avenue
Pittsburgh, PA 15212
Tel: 412 359-6907   *Fax:* 412 359-3212
E-mail: smorello@wpahs.org
Length: 2 Yrs   *ACGME Approved/Offered Positions:* 2
Program ID: 450-41-31-111

University of Pittsburgh Medical Center Medical Education Program
Sponsor: Univ of Pittsburgh Medical Center Medical Education
UPMC Passavant
UPMC Presbyterian Shadyside
UPMC St Margaret
Prgm Director: Michel S Makaroun, MD
A1011 PUH
200 Lothrop Street
Pittsburgh, PA 15213
Tel: 412 802-3028   *Fax:* 412 291-1669
Length: 2 Yrs   *ACGME Approved/Offered Positions:* 8
Program ID: 450-41-21-088

South Carolina

Greenville

Greenville Hospital System/University of South Carolina School of Medicine Program
Sponsor: Greenville Hospital System/University of South Carolina
Prgm Director: Eugene M Langan III, MD
Academic Department of Surgery
701 Grove Road
Greenville, SC 29605
Tel: 864 455-7886   *Fax:* 864 455-1320
E-mail: elangan@ghs.org
Length: 2 Yrs   *ACGME Approved/Offered Positions:* 4
Program ID: 450-45-12-093

Tennessee

Chattanooga

University of Tennessee College of Medicine at Chattanooga Program
Sponsor: University of Tennessee College of Medicine-Chattanooga
Erlanger Medical Center
Memorial Hospital
Parkridge Medical Center
Prgm Director: L Richard Sprouse, MD
Department of Surgery
979 East 3rd Street, Suite 401
Chattanooga, TN 37403
Tel: 423 778-7695   *Fax:* 423 778-2950
E-mail: same
Length: 2 Yrs   *ACGME Approved/Offered Positions:* 2
Program ID: 450-47-21-113

Knoxville

University of Tennessee Medical Center at Knoxville Program
Sponsor: University of Tennessee Graduate School of Medicine
University of Tennessee Memorial Hospital
Prgm Director: Michael B Freeman, MD
Department of Surgery
1924 Alcoa Hwy, Box U-11
Knoxville, TN 37920
Tel: 865 305-9230   *Fax:* 865 305-8894
E-mail: gmiya@utmck.edu
Length: 2 Yrs   *ACGME Approved/Offered Positions:* 2
Program ID: 450-47-21-075

Memphis

University of Tennessee Program
Sponsor: University of Tennessee College of Medicine
Baptist Memorial Hospital
Veterans Affairs Medical Center (Memphis)
Prgm Director: H Edward Garrett Jr, MD
Department of Surgery
910 Madison Avenue, Suite 203
Memphis, TN 38163
Tel: 901 448-5914   *Fax:* 901 448-7306
Length: 2 Yrs   *ACGME Approved/Offered Positions:* 2
Program ID: 450-47-21-041

Nashville

Vanderbilt University Program
Sponsor: Vanderbilt University Medical Center
Prgm Director: Thomas C Naslund, MD
Department of Vascular Surgery
1161 21st Avenue South, D-5237 MCN
Nashville, TN 37232
Tel: 615 322-2343   *Fax:* 615 343-4251
Length: 2 Yrs   *ACGME Approved/Offered Positions:* 2
Program ID: 450-47-21-047

Programs

Texas

Dallas

Baylor University Medical Center Program

Sponsor: Baylor University Medical Center
Prgm Director: Gregory J Pearl, MD
Department of Vascular Surgery
3500 Gaston Avenue
Dallas, TX 75246
Tel: 214 820-4543   *Fax:* 214 820-4538
Length: 2 Yrs   *ACGME Approved/Offered Positions:* 4
Program ID: 450-48-21-028

University of Texas Southwestern Medical School Program

Sponsor: University of Texas Southwestern Medical School
Dallas County Hospital District-Parkland Memorial Hospital
Dallas VA Medical Center
University Hospitals Zale Lipshy
Prgm Director: G Patrick Clagett, MD
5909 Harry Hines Blvd
Dallas, TX 75390
Tel: 214 645-0548   *Fax:* 214 645-0546
Length: 2 Yrs   *ACGME Approved/Offered Positions:* 3
Program ID: 450-48-21-029

Houston

Baylor College of Medicine Program

Sponsor: Baylor College of Medicine
Harris County Hospital District-Ben Taub General Hospital
Memorial Hermann Hospital
Methodist Hospital (Houston)
Michael E DeBakey VA Medical Center - Houston
St Joseph Medical Center
St Luke's Episcopal Hospital
Prgm Director: Peter H Lin, MD
1709 Dryden Rd, Suite 1500
Houston, TX 77030
Tel: 713 798-8629   *Fax:* 713 798-8333
E-mail: plin@bcm.edu
Length: 2 Yrs   *ACGME Approved/Offered Positions:* 4
Program ID: 450-48-21-016

University of Texas at Houston Program

Sponsor: University of Texas Health Science Center at Houston
Memorial Hermann Hospital
Prgm Director: Hazim J Safi, MD
Department of Cardiothoracic and Vascular Surgery
6410 Fannin St, Suite 450
Houston, TX 77030
Tel: 713 500-5304
E-mail: harold.d.heidemann@uth.tmc.edu
Length: 2 Yrs   *ACGME Approved/Offered Positions:* 2
Program ID: 450-48-13-104

Temple

Texas A&M College of Medicine-Scott and White Program

Sponsor: Scott and White Memorial Hospital
Central Texas Veterans Affairs Healthcare System
Prgm Director: Ruth L Bush, MD, MPH
Division of Vascular Surgery
2401 South 31st Street
Temple, TX 76508
Tel: 254 724-6571   *Fax:* 254 724-1731
E-mail: rsims@swmail.sw.org
Length: 2 Yrs   *ACGME Approved/Offered Positions:* 2
Program ID: 450-48-31-115

Note: * indicates a newly appointed program director

Utah

Salt Lake City

University of Utah Program

Sponsor: University of Utah Medical Center
Veterans Affairs Medical Center (Salt Lake City)
Prgm Director: Larry W Kraiss, MD
30 North 1900 East
Rm 3C344
Salt Lake City, UT 84132
Tel: 801 581-8301   *Fax:* 801 581-3433
E-mail: larry.kraiss@hsc.utah.edu
Length: 2 Yrs   *ACGME Approved/Offered Positions:* 2
Program ID: 450-49-21-085

Virginia

Charlottesville

University of Virginia Program

Sponsor: University of Virginia Medical Center
Prgm Director: Kenneth J Cherry Jr, MD
Section of Vascular Surgery UHE Room 4070
PO Box 800679, 1215 Lane Road
Charlottesville, VA 22908
Tel: 434 243-7052   *Fax:* 434 982-3885
Length: 2 Yrs   *ACGME Approved/Offered Positions:* 2
Program ID: 450-51-21-083

Norfolk

Eastern Virginia Medical School Program

Sponsor: Eastern Virginia Medical School
DePaul Medical Center
Sentara Norfolk General Hospital
Prgm Director: Jean M Panneton, MD
600 Gresham Drive
Suite 8620, Sentara Heart Hospital
Norfolk, VA 23507
Tel: 757 622-2649   *Fax:* 757 961-6440
E-mail: pannetjm@evms.edu
Length: 2 Yrs   *ACGME Approved/Offered Positions:* 4
Program ID: 450-51-21-018

Richmond

Virginia Commonwealth University Health System Program

Sponsor: Virginia Commonwealth University Health System
Bon Secours St Mary's Hospital
Medical College of Virginia Hospitals
Prgm Director: Mark M Levy, MD
1200 E Broad St
PO Box 980108
Richmond, VA 23298
Tel: 804 828-3211   *Fax:* 804 828-2744
E-mail: mmlevy@vcu.edu
Length: 2 Yrs   *ACGME Approved/Offered Positions:* 2
Program ID: 450-51-21-039

Washington

Seattle

University of Washington Program

Sponsor: University of Washington School of Medicine
University of Washington Medical Center
VA Puget Sound Health Care System
Prgm Director: Benjamin W Starnes, MD
325 9th Ave
Box 359796
Seattle, WA 98104
Tel: 206 744-3033   *Fax:* 206 744-6794
E-mail: starnes@u.washington.edu
Length: 2 Yrs   *ACGME Approved/Offered Positions:* 2
Program ID: 450-54-21-019

Wisconsin

Madison

University of Wisconsin Program

Sponsor: University of Wisconsin Hospital and Clinics
William S Middleton Veterans Hospital
Prgm Director: John R Hoch, MD
600 Highland Avenue, G5/325
Madison, WI 53792
Tel: 608 265-4420   *Fax:* 608 265-1148
Length: 2 Yrs   *ACGME Approved/Offered Positions:* 2
Program ID: 450-56-22-106

Milwaukee

Medical College of Wisconsin Affiliated Hospitals Program

Sponsor: Medical College of Wisconsin Affiliated Hospitals, Inc
Froedtert Memorial Lutheran Hospital
Prgm Director: Gary R Seabrook, MD
9200 W Wisconsin Avenue
Milwaukee, WI 53226
Tel: 414 805-9172   *Fax:* 414 805-9170
Length: 2 Yrs   *ACGME Approved/Offered Positions:* 2
Program ID: 450-56-21-020

Vascular Surgery-Integrated

Arkansas

Little Rock

University of Arkansas for Medical Sciences Program
Sponsor: University of Arkansas College of Medicine
Central Arkansas Veterans Healthcare System
UAMS Medical Center
Prgm Director: John F Eidt, MD
Department of Surgery, #520-2
4301 West Markham Street
Little Rock, AR 72205
Tel: 501 686-6176   *Fax:* 501 686-5328
Length: 5 Yrs   *ACGME Approved/Offered Positions:* 5
Program ID: 451-04-21-055

California

Stanford

Stanford University Program
Sponsor: Stanford Hospital and Clinics
Veterans Affairs Palo Alto Health Care System
Prgm Director: Ronald L Dalman, MD
Division of Vascular Surgery
300 Pastuer Drive, Suite H3642
Stanford, CA 94305
Tel: 650 723-3639   *Fax:* 650 498-6044
Length: 5 Yrs   *ACGME Approved/Offered Positions:* 5
Program ID: 451-05-21-021

Connecticut

New Haven

Yale-New Haven Medical Center Program
Sponsor: Yale-New Haven Hospital
Veterans Affairs Medical Center (West Haven)
Prgm Director: Bauer E Sumpio, MD
Farnam Memorial Building 137
333 Cedar Street
New Haven, CT 06510
Tel: 203 785-2561   *Fax:* 203 785-7609
Length: 5 Yrs   *ACGME Approved/Offered Positions:* 5
Program ID: 451-08-21-084

Florida

Tampa

University of South Florida Program
Sponsor: University of South Florida College of Medicine
James A Haley Veterans Hospital
Tampa General Hospital
Veterans Affairs Medical Center (Bay Pines)
Prgm Director: Murray L Shames, MD
USF Health South - 7th Floor
2 Tampa General Circle
Tampa, FL 33606
Tel: 813 259-0958   *Fax:* 813 259-0606
E-mail: mshames@health.usf.edu
Length: 5 Yrs   *ACGME Approved/Offered Positions:* 5
Program ID: 451-11-21-031

Indiana

Indianapolis

Indiana University School of Medicine Program
Sponsor: Indiana University School of Medicine
Clarian Indiana University Hospital
Clarian Methodist Hospital of Indiana
Richard L Roudebush Veterans Affairs Medical Center
William N Wishard Memorial Hospital
Prgm Director: Michael C Dalsing, MD
1120 South Drive
224 Fesler Hall
Indianapolis, IN 46202
Tel: 317 962-0283   *Fax:* 317 962-0289
Length: 5 Yrs   *ACGME Approved/Offered Positions:* 5
Program ID: 451-17-31-095

Massachusetts

Worcester

University of Massachusetts Program
Sponsor: University of Massachusetts Medical School
UMass Memorial Health Care (Memorial Campus)
UMass Memorial Health Care (University Campus)
Prgm Director: Louis Messina, MD
55 Lake Avenue, North
S3-822
Worcester, MA 01655
Tel: 508 856-5599   *Fax:* 508 856-8329
E-mail: Louis.Messina@umassmemorial.org
Length: 5 Yrs   *ACGME Approved/Offered Positions:* 5
Program ID: 451-24-21-013

Michigan

Ann Arbor

University of Michigan Program
Sponsor: University of Michigan Hospitals and Health Centers
Veterans Affairs Medical Center (Ann Arbor)
Prgm Director: Thomas W Wakefield, MD
1500 E Medical Center Drive
2210 Taubman Center
Ann Arbor, MI 48109
Tel: 734 936-5847   *Fax:* 734 647-9867
E-mail: thomasww@med.umich.edu
Length: 5 Yrs   *ACGME Approved/Offered Positions:* 5
Program ID: 451-25-21-035

New Hampshire

Lebanon

Dartmouth-Hitchcock Medical Center Program
Sponsor: Mary Hitchcock Memorial Hospital
Prgm Director: Mark F Fillinger, MD
One Medical Center Drive
Lebanon, NH 03756
Tel: 603 650-8677   *Fax:* 603 650-4973
E-mail: Mark.Fillinger@hitchcock.org
Length: 5 Yrs   *ACGME Approved/Offered Positions:* 5
Program ID: 451-32-21-059

New York

New York

Mount Sinai School of Medicine Program
Sponsor: Mount Sinai School of Medicine
Mount Sinai Medical Center
Prgm Director: Victoria J Teodorescu, MD
One Gustave L Levy Place, Box 1259
New York, NY 10029
Tel: 212 241-5871   *Fax:* 212 410-0111
Length: 5 Yrs   *ACGME Approved/Offered Positions:* 10
Program ID: 451-35-21-038

Rochester

University of Rochester Program
Sponsor: Strong Memorial Hospital of the University of Rochester
Prgm Director: Karl A Illig, MD
601 Elmwood Ave
Rochester, NY 14642
Tel: 585 275-6772   *Fax:* 585 756-7752
E-mail: Karl_Illig@urmc.rochester.edu
Length: 5 Yrs   *ACGME Approved/Offered Positions:* 5
Program ID: 451-35-21-006

Stony Brook

SUNY at Stony Brook Program
Sponsor: University Hospital - SUNY at Stony Brook
Prgm Director: John J Ricotta, MD
Dept of Surgery, HSC 18-040
Stony Brook, NY 11794
Tel: 631 444-7875   *Fax:* 631 444-8947
Length: 5 Yrs   *ACGME Approved/Offered Positions:* 5
Program ID: 451-35-21-051

North Carolina

Chapel Hill

University of North Carolina Hospitals Program
Sponsor: University of North Carolina Hospitals
University of North Carolina School of Medicine
Prgm Director: Mark A Farber, MD*
Campus Box 7212
3024 Burnett Womack Building
Chapel Hill, NC 27599
Tel: 919 966-3391   *Fax:* 919 966-2898
Length: 5 Yrs   *ACGME Approved/Offered Positions:* 5
Program ID: 451-36-21-007

Ohio

Cincinnati

TriHealth (Good Samaritan Hospital) Program
Sponsor: TriHealth
TriHealth - Bethesda North Hospital
TriHealth - Good Samaritan Hospital
Prgm Director: Patrick Muck, MD
375 Dixmyth Avenue
3rd Floor/Tower
Cincinnati, OH 45220
Tel: 513 872-3220
Length: 5 Yrs   *ACGME Approved/Offered Positions:* 5
Program ID: 451-38-31-043

University Hospital/University of Cincinnati College of Medicine Program

Sponsor: University Hospital Inc
Christ Hospital
Veterans Affairs Medical Center (Cincinnati)
Prgm Director: Amy B Reed, MD
PO Box 670558
231 Albert Sabin Way
Cincinnati, OH 45267
Tel: 513 558-5367   *Fax:* 513 558-2967
Length: 5 Yrs   *ACGME Approved/Offered Positions:* 5
Program ID: 451-38-31-078

Cleveland

Cleveland Clinic Foundation Program

Sponsor: Cleveland Clinic Foundation
Hillcrest Hospital
Marymount Hospital
Veterans Affairs Medical Center (Cleveland)
Prgm Director: Daniel G Clair, MD
Department of Vascular Surgery
9500 Euclid Avenue, Desk S40
Cleveland, OH 44195
Tel: 216 444-4766   *Fax:* 216 444-9324
Length: 5 Yrs   *ACGME Approved/Offered Positions:* 5
Program ID: 451-38-22-046

Pennsylvania

Pittsburgh

University of Pittsburgh Medical Center Medical Education Program

Sponsor: Univ of Pittsburgh Medical Center Medical
  Education
UPMC Passavant
UPMC Presbyterian Shadyside
UPMC St Margaret
Prgm Director: Michel S Makaroun, MD
A1011 PUH
200 Lothrop Street
Pittsburgh, PA 15213
Tel: 412 802-3028
Length: 5 Yrs   *ACGME Approved/Offered Positions:* 10
Program ID: 451-41-21-088

Note: * indicates a newly appointed program director

Section IV

New and Withdrawn Programs

New Programs

The following programs were accredited by the Accreditation Council for Graduate Medical Education with an effective date between January 1 and December 31, 2008.

Addiction Psychiatry (Psychiatry)

University of Massachusetts Program
Worcester, MA
Effective date: 7/1/2008
Program ID: 401-24-13-063

Baylor College of Medicine Program
Houston, TX
Effective date: 7/1/2008
Program ID: 401-48-31-064

Adolescent Medicine (Pediatrics)

Medical College of Wisconsin Affiliated Hospitals Program
Milwaukee, WI
Effective date: 7/1/2008
Program ID: 321-56-21-034

Adult Cardiothoracic Anesthesiology

UCLA Medical Center Program
Los Angeles, CA
Effective date: 7/1/2008
Program ID: 041-05-12-037

University of California (San Diego) Program
San Diego, CA
Effective date: 7/1/2008
Program ID: 041-05-12-041

Loma Linda University Program
Loma Linda, CA
Effective date: 7/1/2008
Program ID: 041-05-12-045

Jackson Memorial Hospital/Jackson Health System Program
Miami, FL
Effective date: 7/1/2008
Program ID: 041-11-13-047

University of Florida Program
Gainesville, FL
Effective date: 7/1/2008
Program ID: 041-11-31-044

Tufts Medical Center Program
Boston, MA
Effective date: 7/1/2008
Program ID: 041-24-13-031

Washington University/B-JH/SLCH Consortium Program
St Louis, MO
Effective date: 7/1/2008
Program ID: 041-28-13-019

UMDNJ-Robert Wood Johnson Medical School Program
New Brunswick, NJ
Effective date: 7/1/2008
Program ID: 041-33-21-046

University of Rochester Program
Rochester, NY
Effective date: 7/1/2008
Program ID: 041-35-21-038

Vanderbilt University Program
Nashville, TN
Effective date: 7/1/2008
Program ID: 041-47-12-025

University of Texas Medical Branch Hospitals Program
Galveston, TX
Effective date: 7/1/2008
Program ID: 041-48-31-040

University of Washington Program
Seattle, WA
Effective date: 7/1/2008
Program ID: 041-54-21-042

Allergy and Immunology

Winthrop-University Hospital Program
Mineola, NY
Effective date: 7/1/2008
Program ID: 020-35-31-126

Ohio State University Hospital Program
Columbus, OH
Effective date: 7/1/2008
Program ID: 020-38-21-128

Anesthesiology

Louisiana State University Program
New Orleans, LA
Effective date: 7/1/2008
Program ID: 040-21-31-199

Blood Banking/Transfusion Medicine (Pathology)

Dartmouth-Hitchcock Medical Center Program
Lebanon, NH
Effective date: 7/1/2008
Program ID: 305-32-12-088

Cardiovascular Disease (Internal Medicine)

Kaiser Permanente Medical Group (Northern California)/San Francisco Program
San Francisco, CA
Effective date: 7/1/2008
Program ID: 141-05-12-286

College of Medicine, Mayo Clinic (Jacksonville) Program
Jacksonville, FL
Effective date: 7/1/2008
Program ID: 141-11-13-284

Kettering Medical Center Program
Kettering, OH
Effective date: 7/1/2008
Program ID: 141-38-31-281

Child and Adolescent Psychiatry (Psychiatry)

University of Vermont Program
Burlington, VT
Effective date: 7/1/2008
Program ID: 405-50-31-195

New / Withdrawn Programs

Child Neurology (Neurology)

University of Iowa Hospitals and Clinics Program
Iowa City, IA
Effective date: 7/1/2008
Program ID: 185-18-31-106

University of New Mexico Program
Albuquerque, NM
Effective date: 7/1/2008
Program ID: 185-34-13-105

Clinical Cardiac Electrophysiology (Internal Medicine)

University of Florida College of Medicine Jacksonville Program
Jacksonville, FL
Effective date: 7/1/2008
Program ID: 154-11-31-127

Medical College of Georgia Program
Augusta, GA
Effective date: 7/1/2008
Program ID: 154-12-21-125

Clinical Neurophysiology (Neurology)

Albany Medical Center Program
Albany, NY
Effective date: 7/1/2008
Program ID: 187-35-13-118

NSLIJHS-Albert Einstein College of Medicine at Long Island Jewish Medical Center Program
Manhasset, NY
Effective date: 7/1/2008
Program ID: 187-35-31-119

Colon and Rectal Surgery

Southern Illinois University Program
Springfield, IL
Effective date: 9/19/2008
Program ID: 060-16-21-068

University of Chicago Program
Chicago, IL
Effective date: 9/19/2008
Program ID: 060-16-31-066

Indiana University School of Medicine Program
Mooresville, IN
Effective date: 9/19/2008
Program ID: 060-17-13-065

Congenital Cardiac Surgery (Thoracic Surgery)

University of Colorado Denver Program
Aurora, CO
Effective date: 7/1/2008
Program ID: 466-07-21-006

Emory University Program
Atlanta, GA
Effective date: 7/1/2008
Program ID: 466-12-31-008

Children's Memorial Hospital/McGaw Medical Center of Northwestern University Program
Chicago, IL
Effective date: 7/1/2008
Program ID: 466-16-12-009

Nationwide Children's Hospital/Ohio State University Program
Columbus, OH
Effective date: 7/1/2008
Program ID: 466-38-31-004

University of Pennsylvania/Children's Hospital of Philadelphia Program
Philadelphia, PA
Effective date: 7/1/2008
Program ID: 466-41-21-002

Texas Heart Institute/Baylor College of Medicine Program
Houston, TX
Effective date: 7/1/2008
Program ID: 466-48-13-007

Critical Care Medicine (Internal Medicine)

Baystate Medical Center/Tufts University School of Medicine Program
Springfield, MA
Effective date: 7/1/2008
Program ID: 142-24-21-161

Geisinger Health System Program
Danville, PA
Effective date: 7/1/2008
Program ID: 142-41-12-164

Cytopathology (Pathology)

Dartmouth-Hitchcock Medical Center Program
Lebanon, NH
Effective date: 7/1/2008
Program ID: 307-32-21-101

Dermatology

Tufts Medical Center Program
Boston, MA
Effective date: 7/1/2008
Program ID: 080-24-21-141

University of Texas Medical Branch Hospitals Program
Austin, TX
Effective date: 7/1/2008
Program ID: 080-48-12-140

Dermatopathology (Dermatology)

University of Massachusetts Program
Worcester, MA
Effective date: 7/1/2008
Program ID: 100-24-21-089

Tufts Medical Center Program
Newton, MA
Effective date: 7/1/2008
Program ID: 100-24-31-091

St Louis University School of Medicine Program
St Louis, MO
Effective date: 7/1/2008
Program ID: 100-28-12-088

Memorial Sloan-Kettering Cancer Center Program
New York, NY
Effective date: 7/1/2008
Program ID: 100-35-31-087

Oregon Health & Science University Program
Portland, OR
Effective date: 7/1/2008
Program ID: 100-40-13-090

Thomas Jefferson University Program
Philadelphia, PA
Effective date: 7/1/2008
Program ID: 100-41-13-086

Developmental-Behavioral Pediatrics (Pediatrics)

Childrens Hospital Los Angeles Program
Los Angeles, CA
Effective date: 7/1/2008
Program ID: 336-05-31-044

University of Michigan Program
Ann Arbor, MI
Effective date: 7/1/2008
Program ID: 336-25-12-045

College of Medicine, Mayo Clinic (Rochester) Program
Rochester, MN
Effective date: 7/1/2008
Program ID: 336-26-21-042

Children's Hospital Medical Center of Akron/NEOUCOM Program
Akron, OH
Effective date: 7/1/2008
Program ID: 336-38-13-043

Emergency Medicine

St Louis University School of Medicine Program
St Louis, MO
Effective date: 7/1/2008
Program ID: 110-28-31-201

University Hospitals Case Medical Center Program
Cleveland, OH
Effective date: 7/1/2008
Program ID: 110-38-13-200

Lehigh Valley Hospital Network/Pennsylvania State University Hospital Program
Bethlehem, PA
Effective date: 7/1/2008
Program ID: 110-41-21-199

Endocrinology, Diabetes, and Metabolism (Internal Medicine)

University of Arizona Program
Tucson, AZ
Effective date: 7/1/2008
Program ID: 143-03-21-185

University of Florida College of Medicine Jacksonville Program
Jacksonville, FL
Effective date: 7/1/2008
Program ID: 143-11-45-188

Union Memorial Hospital Program
Baltimore, MD
Effective date: 7/1/2008
Program ID: 143-23-31-187

Endovascular Surgical Neuroradiology (Neurology)

University of Minnesota Program
Minneapolis, MN
Effective date: 7/1/2008
Program ID: 182-26-12-001

Family Medicine

Saints Mary and Elizabeth Medical Center Program
Chicago, IL
Effective date: 7/1/2008
Program ID: 120-16-12-693

Foot and Ankle Orthopaedics (Orthopaedic Surgery)

Penn State University/Milton S Hershey Medical Center Program
Hershey, PA
Effective date: 8/1/2008
Program ID: 262-41-13-012

Forensic Pathology (Pathology)

University of Colorado Denver Program
Denver, CO
Effective date: 7/1/2008
Program ID: 310-07-31-097

University of Puerto Rico Program
San Juan, PR
Effective date: 7/1/2008
Program ID: 310-42-21-095

Forensic Psychiatry (Psychiatry)

University of Missouri-Columbia Program
Columbia, MO
Effective date: 7/1/2008
Program ID: 406-28-31-054

University of Pennsylvania Program
Philadelphia, PA
Effective date: 7/1/2008
Program ID: 406-41-12-059

Gastroenterology (Internal Medicine)

University of California (San Francisco)/Fresno Program
Fresno, CA
Effective date: 7/1/2008
Program ID: 144-05-12-235

Mount Sinai School of Medicine (Elmhurst) Program
Elmhurst, NY
Effective date: 7/1/2008
Program ID: 144-35-31-234

Geriatric Medicine (Family Medicine)

Wright State University/Dayton Community Hospitals Program
Dayton, OH
Effective date: 7/1/2008
Program ID: 125-38-31-072

Geriatric Medicine (Internal Medicine)

Bridgeport Hospital Program
Stratford, CT
Effective date: 7/1/2008
Program ID: 151-08-13-161

Summa Health System/NEOUCOM Program
Akron, OH
Effective date: 7/1/2008
Program ID: 151-38-21-160

University of Texas at Houston Program
Houston, TX
Effective date: 7/1/2008
Program ID: 151-48-31-162

Charleston Area Medical Center/West Virginia University (Charleston Division) Program
Charleston, WV
Effective date: 7/1/2008
Program ID: 151-55-12-151

Geriatric Psychiatry (Psychiatry)

University of Tennessee Program
Memphis, TN
Effective date: 7/1/2008
Program ID: 407-47-12-074

Hand Surgery (Orthopaedic Surgery)

University of California Irvine/ Kaiser Permanente Southern California (Orange County) Program
Orange, CA
Effective date: 8/1/2008
Program ID: 263-05-12-075

Hand Surgery (Plastic Surgery)

University of Mississippi Medical Center Program
Jackson, MS
Effective date: 7/1/2008
Program ID: 363-27-13-028

Hematology (Pathology)

University of Maryland Program
Baltimore, MD
Effective date: 7/1/2008
Program ID: 311-23-31-106

Hematology and Oncology (Internal Medicine)

Johns Hopkins University Program
Baltimore, MD
Effective date: 7/1/2008
Program ID: 155-23-21-154

University of Tennessee Medical Center at Knoxville Program
Knoxville, TN
Effective date: 7/1/2008
Program ID: 125-47-13-071

Hospice and Palliative Medicine

University of Alabama Hospital Program
Birmingham, AL
Effective date: 7/1/2009
Program ID: 540-01-14-027

College of Medicine, Mayo Clinic Program
Phoenix, AZ
Effective date: 7/1/2008
Program ID: 540-03-14-014

Stanford Hospital and Clinics Program
Stanford, CA
Effective date: 7/1/2008
Program ID: 540-05-14-019

Cedars-Sinai Medical Center Program
Los Angeles, CA
Effective date: 7/1/2008
Program ID: 540-05-14-030

University of California (San Francisco) School of Medicine Program
San Francisco, CA
Effective date: 7/1/2008
Program ID: 540-05-14-056

Scripps Mercy Hospital Program
San Diego, CA
Effective date: 7/1/2008
Program ID: 540-05-14-060

George Washington University School of Medicine Program
Washington, DC
Effective date: 7/1/2008
Program ID: 540-10-14-044

University of South Florida College of Medicine Program
Tampa, FL
Effective date: 7/1/2008
Program ID: 540-11-14-025

McGaw Medical Center of Northwestern University Program
Chicago, IL
Effective date: 7/1/2008
Program ID: 540-16-14-026

Rush University Medical Center Program
Chicago, IL
Effective date: 7/1/2008
Program ID: 540-16-14-042

Indiana University School of Medicine Program
Indianapolis, IN
Effective date: 7/1/2008
Program ID: 540-17-14-002

Mercy Medical Center-North Iowa Program
Mason City, IA
Effective date: 7/1/2008
Program ID: 540-18-12-012

University of Kansas School of Medicine Program
Kansas City, KS
Effective date: 7/1/2008
Program ID: 540-19-14-036

University of Louisville School of Medicine Program
Louisville, KY
Effective date: 7/1/2008
Program ID: 540-20-14-032

University of Kentucky College of Medicine Program
Lexington, KY
Effective date: 7/1/2008
Program ID: 540-20-14-059

Massachusetts General Hospital Program
Boston, MA
Effective date: 7/1/2008
Program ID: 540-24-14-046

Henry Ford Hospital Program
Detroit, MI
Effective date: 7/1/2008
Program ID: 540-25-14-017

University of Michigan Hospitals and Health Centers Program
Ann Arbor, MI
Effective date: 7/1/2008
Program ID: 540-25-14-033

Wayne State University/Detroit Medical Center Program
Detroit, MI
Effective date: 7/1/2008
Program ID: 540-25-14-058

University of Minnesota Medical School Program
Minneapolis, MN
Effective date: 7/1/2008
Program ID: 540-26-12-023

College of Medicine, Mayo Clinic Program
Rochester, MN
Effective date: 7/1/2008
Program ID: 540-26-14-037

Mary Hitchcock Memorial Hospital Program
Lebanon, NH
Effective date: 7/1/2008
Program ID: 540-32-04-047

Albert Einstein College of Medicine of Yeshiva University Program
Bronx, NY
Effective date: 7/1/2008
Program ID: 540-35-12-015

Beth Israel Medical Center Program
New York, NY
Effective date: 7/1/2008
Program ID: 540-35-12-039

Strong Memorial Hospital of the University of Rochester Program
Rochester, NY
Effective date: 7/1/2008
Program ID: 540-35-14-001

University at Buffalo School of Medicine Program
Buffalo, NY
Effective date: 7/1/2008
Program ID: 540-35-14-009

Mount Sinai School of Medicine Program
New York, NY
Effective date: 7/1/2008
Program ID: 540-35-14-043

North Shore-Long Island Jewish Health System Program
Manhasset, NY
Effective date: 7/1/2008
Program ID: 540-35-14-049

Duke University Hospital Program
Durham, NC
Effective date: 7/1/2008
Program ID: 540-36-14-021

MetroHealth Medical Center Program
Cleveland, OH
Effective date: 7/1/2008
Program ID: 540-38-14-003

Summa Health System Program
Akron, OH
Effective date: 7/1/2008
Program ID: 540-38-14-005

Cleveland Clinic Foundation Program
Cleveland, OH
Effective date: 7/1/2008
Program ID: 540-38-14-006

Wright State University Boonshoft School of Medicine Program
Dayton, OH
Effective date: 7/1/2008
Program ID: 540-38-14-022

Children's Hospital Medical Center of Akron Program
Akron, OH
Effective date: 7/1/2008
Program ID: 540-38-32-038

Oregon Health & Science University Hospital Program
Portland, OR
Effective date: 7/1/2008
Program ID: 540-40-14-004

Lancaster General Hospital Program
Lancaster, PA
Effective date: 7/1/2008
Program ID: 540-41-12-008

Univ of Pittsburgh Medical Center Medical Education Program Program
Pittsburgh, PA
Effective date: 7/1/2008
Program ID: 540-41-14-011

University of Pennsylvania Health System Program
Philadelphia, PA
Effective date: 7/1/2008
Program ID: 540-41-14-048

Children's Hospital of Philadelphia Program
Philadelphia, PA
Effective date: 7/1/2008
Program ID: 540-41-32-013

University of Tennessee College of Medicine-Chattanooga Program
Chattanooga, TN
Effective date: 7/1/2008
Program ID: 540-47-14-051

Vanderbilt University Medical Center Program
Nashville, TN
Effective date: 7/1/2008
Program ID: 540-47-14-053

University of Texas Medical School at San Antonio Program
San Antonio, TX
Effective date: 7/1/2008
Program ID: 540-48-14-024

University of Texas MD Anderson Cancer Center Program
Houston, TX
Effective date: 7/1/2008
Program ID: 540-48-43-034

University of Utah Medical Center Program
Salt Lake City, UT
Effective date: 7/1/2009
Program ID: 540-49-04-054

Virginia Commonwealth University Health System Program
Richmond, VA
Effective date: 7/1/2008
Program ID: 540-51-14-018

Medical College of Wisconsin Affiliated Hospitals, Inc Program
Milwaukee, WI
Effective date: 7/1/2008
Program ID: 540-56-14-010

University of Wisconsin Hospital and Clinics Program
Madison, WI
Effective date: 7/1/2008
Program ID: 540-56-14-016

Marshfield Clinic-St Joseph's Hospital Program
Marshfield, WI
Effective date: 7/1/2008
Program ID: 540-56-14-040

Infectious Disease (Internal Medicine)

University of California (San Francisco)/Fresno
Fresno, CA
Effective date: 7/1/2008
Program ID: 146-05-21-211

Orlando Health Program
Orlando, FL
Effective date: 7/1/2008
Program ID: 146-11-12-210

Internal Medicine

Florida Hospital Medical Center Program
Orlando, FL
Effective date: 7/1/2008
Program ID: 140-11-31-539

Leonard J Chabert Medical Center Program
Houma, LA
Effective date: 7/1/2008
Program ID: 140-21-21-537

Internal Medicine/Pediatrics

Jackson Memorial Hospital/Jackson Health System Program
Miami, FL
Effective date: 7/1/2008
Program ID: 700-11-14-086

Interventional Cardiology (Internal Medicine)

College of Medicine, Mayo Clinic (Arizona) Program
Phoenix, AZ
Effective date: 7/1/2008
Program ID: 152-03-31-153

Jefferson Medical College/Christiana Care Health Services Program
Newark, DE
Effective date: 7/1/2008
Program ID: 152-09-21-155

New York Methodist Hospital Program
Brooklyn, NY
Effective date: 7/1/2008
Program ID: 152-35-12-154

Medical Biochemical Genetics (Medical Genetics)

National Institutes of Health Clinical Center Program
Bethesda, MD
Effective date: 7/1/2008
Program ID: 131-23-12-001

Wayne State University Program
Detroit, MI
Effective date: 7/1/2008
Program ID: 131-25-21-002

Cincinnati Children's Hospital Medical Center/University of Cincinnati College of Medicine Program
Cincinnati, OH
Effective date: 7/1/2008
Program ID: 131-38-13-003

Baylor College of Medicine Program
Houston, TX
Effective date: 7/1/2008
Program ID: 131-48-31-004

Medical Genetics

Boston University Medical Center Program
Boston, MA
Effective date: 7/1/2008
Program ID: 130-24-31-074

Medical Toxicology (Emergency Medicine)

Albert Einstein Healthcare Network Program
Philadelphia, PA
Effective date: 7/1/2008
Program ID: 118-41-31-030

Molecular Genetic Pathology (Medical Genetics and Pathology)

Cedars-Sinai Medical Center Program
Los Angeles, CA
Effective date: 7/1/2008
Program ID: 190-05-21-025

University of Chicago Program
Chicago, IL
Effective date: 7/1/2008
Program ID: 190-16-31-027

Washington University/B-JH/SLCH Consortium Program
St Louis, MO
Effective date: 7/1/2008
Program ID: 190-28-13-026

University of New Mexico Program
Albuquerque, NM
Effective date: 7/1/2008
Program ID: 190-34-12-024

Mount Sinai School of Medicine Program
New York, NY
Effective date: 4/8/2008
Program ID: 190-35-12-020

Musculoskeletal Radiology (Radiology-Diagnostic)

Cedars-Sinai Medical Center Program
Los Angeles, CA
Effective date: 7/1/2008
Program ID: 426-05-21-015

Neonatal-Perinatal Medicine (Pediatrics)

College of Medicine, Mayo Clinic (Rochester) Program
Rochester, MN
Effective date: 7/1/2008
Program ID: 329-26-21-125

Nephrology (Internal Medicine)

Loma Linda University Program
Loma Linda, CA
Effective date: 7/1/2008
Program ID: 148-05-31-195

Jefferson Medical College/Christiana Care Health Services Program
Newark, DE
Effective date: 7/1/2008
Program ID: 148-09-12-196

Neurological Surgery

University of California (Irvine) Program
Orange, CA
Effective date: 7/1/2008
Program ID: 160-05-12-127

University of Texas at Houston Program
Houston, TX
Effective date: 7/1/2008
Program ID: 160-48-31-126

Neurology

University of Arizona/UPHK Graduate Medical Education Consortium Program
Tucson, AZ
Effective date: 7/1/2008
Program ID: 180-03-31-159

UMDNJ-Robert Wood Johnson Medical School (Camden) Program
Camden, NJ
Effective date: 7/1/2008
Program ID: 180-33-13-158

Albert Einstein Healthcare Network Program
Philadelphia, PA
Effective date: 7/1/2008
Program ID: 180-41-33-162

Methodist Hospital (Houston) Program
Houston, TX
Effective date: 7/1/2008
Program ID: 180-48-12-160

Neuromuscular Medicine (Neurology)

University of California (Irvine) Program
Orange, CA
Effective date: 7/1/2008
Program ID: 183-05-31-020

Jackson Memorial Hospital/Jackson Health System Program
Miami, FL
Effective date: 7/1/2008
Program ID: 183-11-12-021

University of Kansas School of Medicine Program
Kansas City, KS
Effective date: 7/1/2008
Program ID: 183-19-12-017

Beth Israel Deaconess Medical Center/Harvard Medical School Program
Boston, MA
Effective date: 7/1/2008
Program ID: 183-24-13-019

Washington University/B-JH/SLCH Consortium Program
St Louis, MO
Effective date: 7/1/2008
Program ID: 183-28-21-018

Nuclear Medicine

Ohio State University Hospital Program
Columbus, OH
Effective date: 7/1/2008
Program ID: 200-38-31-117

Nuclear Radiology (Radiology-Diagnostic)

Cedars-Sinai Medical Center Program
Los Angeles, CA
Effective date: 7/1/2008
Program ID: 425-05-21-073

University of Minnesota Program
Minneapolis, MN
Effective date: 7/1/2008
Program ID: 425-26-12-072

Oncology (Internal Medicine)

University of Nevada School of Medicine (Las Vegas) Program
Las Vegas, NV
Effective date: 7/1/2008
Program ID: 147-31-13-199

Ophthalmology

University of Arizona/UPHK Graduate Medical Education Consortium Program
Tucson, AZ
Effective date: 7/1/2008
Program ID: 240-03-13-181

New / Withdrawn Programs

Orthopaedic Sports Medicine (Orthopaedic Surgery)

University of South Alabama Program
Mobile, AL
Effective date: 8/1/2008
Program ID: 268-01-21-112

University of South Florida Program
Tampa, FL
Effective date: 8/1/2008
Program ID: 268-11-21-128

Atlanta Sports Medicine Foundation Program
Atlanta, GA
Effective date: 8/1/2008
Program ID: 268-12-31-126

Brown University Program
Providence, RI
Effective date: 8/1/2008
Program ID: 268-43-13-125

Texas Tech University (Lubbock) Program
Lubbock, TX
Effective date: 8/1/2008
Program ID: 268-48-31-122

Orthopaedic Surgery of the Spine (Orthopaedic Surgery)

Texas Back Institute Program
Plano, TX
Effective date: 8/1/2008
Program ID: 267-48-31-030

Otolaryngology

Dartmouth-Hitchcock Medical Center Program
Lebanon, NH
Effective date: 7/1/2008
Program ID: 280-32-12-136

Pain Medicine

Children's Hospital Program
Boston, MA
Effective date: 7/1/2008
Program ID: 530-24-04-003

Vanderbilt University Program
Nashville, TN
Effective date: 7/1/2008
Program ID: 530-47-04-001

Pediatric Anesthesiology (Anesthesiology)

Nationwide Children's Hospital/Ohio State University Program
Columbus, OH
Effective date: 7/1/2008
Program ID: 042-38-21-061

University of Oklahoma Health Sciences Center Program
Oklahoma City, OK
Effective date: 7/1/2008
Program ID: 042-39-12-060

Pediatric Cardiology (Pediatrics)

Newark Beth Israel Medical Center Program
Newark, NJ
Effective date: 7/1/2008
Program ID: 325-33-13-080

University of Texas at Houston Program
Houston, TX
Effective date: 7/1/2008
Program ID: 325-48-21-083

Pediatric Critical Care Medicine (Pediatrics)

University of California (San Diego) Program
San Diego, CA
Effective date: 7/1/2008
Program ID: 323-05-12-084

University of Missouri at Kansas City Program
Kansas City, MO
Effective date: 7/1/2008
Program ID: 323-28-21-085

Pediatric Emergency Medicine (Emergency Medicine)

Orlando Health Program
Orlando, FL
Effective date: 7/1/2008
Program ID: 114-11-12-022

Oregon Health & Science University Program
Portland, OR
Effective date: 7/1/2008
Program ID: 114-40-21-019

Pediatric Endocrinology (Pediatrics)

University of Arizona Program
Tucson, AZ
Effective date: 7/1/2008
Program ID: 326-03-13-089

Pediatric Gastroenterology (Pediatrics)

SUNY at Stony Brook Program
Stony Brook, NY
Effective date: 7/1/2008
Program ID: 332-35-13-072

University of Texas at Houston Program
Houston, TX
Effective date: 7/1/2008
Program ID: 332-48-31-073

University of Washington Program
Seattle, WA
Effective date: 7/1/2008
Program ID: 332-54-21-071

Pediatric Hematology/Oncology (Pediatrics)

Phoenix Children's Hospital/Maricopa Medical Center Program
Phoenix, AZ
Effective date: 7/1/2008
Program ID: 327-03-13-079

University of Arkansas for Medical Sciences Program
Little Rock, AR
Effective date: 7/1/2008
Program ID: 327-04-31-086

University of Texas Health Science Center at San Antonio Program
San Antonio, TX
Effective date: 7/1/2008
Program ID: 327-48-12-087

Pediatric Nephrology (Pediatrics)

University of Alabama Medical Center Program
Birmingham, AL
Effective date: 7/1/2008
Program ID: 328-01-12-076

Grand Rapids Medical Education and Research Center/Michigan State University Program
Grand Rapids, MI
Effective date: 7/1/2008
Program ID: 328-25-13-075

University of Pittsburgh Medical Center Medical Education Program
Pittsburgh, PA
Effective date: 7/1/2008
Program ID: 328-41-21-077

Pediatric Orthopaedics (Orthopaedic Surgery)

University of Michigan Program
Ann Arbor, MI
Effective date: 8/1/2008
Program ID: 265-25-12-047

Pediatric Otolaryngology (Otolaryngology)

University of Colorado Denver Program
Aurora, CO
Effective date: 7/1/2008
Program ID: 288-07-12-008

Pediatric Pulmonology (Pediatrics)

University of California (San Diego) Program
San Diego, CA
Effective date: 7/1/2008
Program ID: 330-05-13-064

Pediatric Radiology (Radiology-Diagnostic)

University of Minnesota Program
Minneapolis, MN
Effective date: 7/1/2008
Program ID: 424-26-21-064

Albert Einstein College of Medicine Program
Bronx, NY
Effective date: 7/1/2008
Program ID: 424-35-13-065

Pediatric Rehabilitation Medicine (Physical Medicine and Rehabilitation)

University of Alabama Medical Center Program
Birmingham, AL
Effective date: 7/1/2008
Program ID: 346-01-13-012

Pediatric Rheumatology (Pediatrics)

Albert Einstein College of Medicine Program
Bronx, NY
Effective date: 7/1/2008
Program ID: 331-35-21-032

Nationwide Children's Hospital/Ohio State University Program
Columbus, OH
Effective date: 7/1/2008
Program ID: 331-38-13-033

Pediatric Sports Medicine (Pediatrics)

University Hospitals Case Medical Center Program
Cleveland, OH
Effective date: 7/1/2008
Program ID: 333-38-13-012

Nationwide Children's Hospital/Ohio State University Program
Westerville, OH
Effective date: 7/1/2008
Program ID: 333-38-31-013

Pediatric Surgery (General Surgery)

Stanford University Program
Stanford, CA
Effective date: 7/1/2008
Program ID: 445-05-31-048

Pediatric Transplant Hepatology (Pediatrics)

Emory University School of Medicine Program
Atlanta, GA
Effective date: 7/1/2008
Program ID: 338-12-32-004

Cincinnati Children's Hospital Medical Center Program
Cincinnati, OH
Effective date: 7/1/2008
Program ID: 338-38-32-002

Univ of Pittsburgh Medical Center Medical Education Program Program
Pittsburgh, PA
Effective date: 7/1/2008
Program ID: 338-41-32-001

Pediatric Urology (Urology)

Medical College of Wisconsin Affiliated Hospitals/Children's Hospital of Wisconsin Program
Milwaukee, WI
Effective date: 7/1/2008
Program ID: 485-56-12-026

Plastic Surgery

College of Medicine, Mayo Clinic (Arizona) Program
Phoenix, AZ
Effective date: 7/1/2008
Program ID: 360-03-31-142

Temple University Hospital Program
Philadelphia, PA
Effective date: 7/1/2008
Program ID: 360-41-12-143

Procedural Dermatology (Dermatology)

UCLA Medical Center Program
Los Angeles, CA
Effective date: 7/1/2008
Program ID: 081-05-12-039

University of Minnesota Program
Minneapolis, MN
Effective date: 7/1/2008
Program ID: 081-26-21-040

Dermatologic Surgicenter (Philadelphia) Program
Philadelphia, PA
Effective date: 7/1/2008
Program ID: 081-41-31-038

Psychiatry

Berkshire Medical Center Program
Pittsfield, MA
Effective date: 7/1/2008
Program ID: 400-24-13-302

Baystate Medical Center/Tufts University School of Medicine Program
Springfield, MA
Effective date: 7/1/2008
Program ID: 400-24-31-303

Psychosomatic Medicine (Psychiatry)

University of Colorado Denver Program
Aurora, CO
Effective date: 7/1/2008
Program ID: 409-07-21-042

Jackson Memorial Hospital/Jackson Health System Program
Miami, FL
Effective date: 7/1/2008
Program ID: 409-11-13-039

Louisiana State University Program
New Orleans, LA
Effective date: 7/1/2008
Program ID: 409-21-13-043

Vanderbilt University Program
Nashville, TN
Effective date: 7/1/2008
Program ID: 409-47-31-040

University of Texas Health Science Center at San Antonio Program
San Antonio, TX
Effective date: 7/1/2008
Program ID: 409-48-12-041

Pulmonary Disease (Internal Medicine)

University of Tennessee Medical Center at Knoxville Program
Knoxville, TN
Effective date: 7/1/2008
Program ID: 149-47-31-207

Pulmonary Disease and Critical Care Medicine (Internal Medicine)

University of South Alabama Program
Mobile, AL
Effective date: 7/1/2008
Program ID: 156-01-12-145

College of Medicine, Mayo Clinic (Jacksonville) Program
Jacksonville, FL
Effective date: 7/1/2008
Program ID: 156-11-13-147

University of Florida College of Medicine Jacksonville Program
Jacksonville, FL
Effective date: 7/1/2008
Program ID: 156-11-31-148

Radiation Oncology

City of Hope National Medical Center Program
Duarte, CA
Effective date: 7/1/2008
Program ID: 430-05-13-139

Radiology-Diagnostic

University of Arizona/UPHK Graduate Medical Education Consortium Program
Tucson, AZ
Effective date: 7/1/2008
Program ID: 420-03-13-258

Louisiana State University Program
New Orleans, LA
Effective date: 7/1/2008
Program ID: 420-21-31-259

Texas Tech University Health Sciences Center Paul L Foster School of Medicine Program
El Paso, TX
Effective date: 7/1/2008
Program ID: 420-48-12-257

Selective Pathology (Pathology)

University of Michigan Program
Ann Arbor, MI
Effective date: 7/1/2008
Program ID: 301-25-31-074

Sleep Medicine

Jackson Memorial Hospital/Jackson Health System Program
Miami, FL
Effective date: 7/1/2008
Program ID: 520-11-18-112

St Vincent Hospital Program
Worcester, MA
Effective date: 7/1/2008
Program ID: 520-24-14-100

University Hospital - SUNY at Stony Brook Program
Stony Brook, NY
Effective date: 7/1/2008
Program ID: 520-35-14-058

New York University School of Medicine Program
New York, NY
Effective date: 7/1/2008
Program ID: 520-35-14-074

University of Toledo Program
Toledo, OH
Effective date: 7/1/2008
Program ID: 520-38-14-073

Oregon Health & Science University Hospital Program
Portland, OR
Effective date: 7/1/2008
Program ID: 520-40-14-105

Sports Medicine (Family Medicine)

Tuscaloosa College of Community Health Science Program
Tuscaloosa, AL
Effective date: 7/1/2008
Program ID: 127-01-12-122

University of South Alabama Program
Mobile, AL
Effective date: 7/1/2008
Program ID: 127-01-13-124

Baton Rouge General Medical Center Program
Baton Rouge, LA
Effective date: 7/1/2008
Program ID: 127-21-31-125

Self Regional Healthcare/Greenwood Program
Greenwood, SC
Effective date: 7/1/2008
Program ID: 127-45-12-126

University of Texas Health Center at Tyler Program
Tyler, TX
Effective date: 7/1/2008
Program ID: 127-48-21-123

Spokane Medical Centers/University of Washington School of Medicine Program
Spokane, WA
Effective date: 7/1/2008
Program ID: 127-54-21-127

Surgery-General

University of Texas Medical Branch (Austin) Program
Austin, TX
Effective date: 7/1/2008
Program ID: 440-48-13-424

Surgical Critical Care (General Surgery)

Mercer University School of Medicine Program
Macon, GA
Effective date: 7/1/2008
Program ID: 442-12-12-119

McGaw Medical Center of Northwestern University Program
Chicago, IL
Effective date: 7/1/2008
Program ID: 442-16-12-123

Wake Forest University School of Medicine Program
Winston-Salem, NC
Effective date: 7/1/2008
Program ID: 442-36-13-121

Wright State University Program
Dayton, OH
Effective date: 7/1/2008
Program ID: 442-38-31-122

Baylor College of Medicine Program
Houston, TX
Effective date: 7/1/2008
Program ID: 442-48-21-120

Thoracic Surgery-Integrated

Stanford University Program
Stanford, CA
Effective date: 7/1/2008
Program ID: 461-05-21-016

University of Pennsylvania Program
Philadelphia, PA
Effective date: 7/1/2008
Program ID: 461-41-21-082

Transitional Year

Wayne State University Program
Detroit, MI
Effective date: 7/1/2008
Program ID: 999-25-00-253

San Antonio Uniformed Services Health Education Consortium Program
Fort Sam Houston, TX
Effective date: 7/1/2008
Program ID: 999-48-00-254

Transplant Hepatology (Internal Medicine)

McGaw Medical Center of Northwestern University Program
Chicago, IL
Effective date: 7/1/2008
Program ID: 158-16-14-015

Henry Ford Hospital Program
Detroit, MI
Effective date: 7/1/2008
Program ID: 158-25-14-031

Duke University Hospital Program
Durham, NC
Effective date: 7/1/2008
Program ID: 158-36-14-037

Univ of Pittsburgh Medical Center Medical Education Program
Pittsburgh, PA
Effective date: 7/1/2008
Program ID: 158-41-14-021

Undersea and Hyperbaric Medicine (Emergency Medicine)

Louisiana State University Program
Harvey, LA
Effective date: 7/1/2008
Program ID: 119-21-13-004

Hennepin County Medical Center Program
Minneapolis, MN
Effective date: 7/1/2008
Program ID: 119-26-31-005

Urology

University of Louisville Program
Louisville, KY
Effective date: 12/3/2008
Program ID: 480-20-21-186

Vascular and Interventional Radiology (Radiology-Diagnostic)

College of Medicine, Mayo Clinic (Jacksonville) Program
Jacksonville, FL
Effective date: 7/1/2008
Program ID: 427-11-12-112

SUNY Upstate Medical University Program
Syracuse, NY
Effective date: 7/1/2008
Program ID: 427-35-13-114

Texas A&M College of Medicine-Scott and White Program
Temple, TX
Effective date: 7/1/2008
Program ID: 427-48-21-113

Vascular Neurology (Neurology)

University of Alabama Medical Center Program
Birmingham, AL
Effective date: 7/1/2008
Program ID: 188-01-12-051

University of Colorado Denver Program
Denver, CO
Effective date: 7/1/2008
Program ID: 188-07-12-059

University of Connecticut/Hartford Hospital Program
Hartford, CT
Effective date: 7/1/2008
Program ID: 188-08-13-049

University of South Florida Program
Tampa, FL
Effective date: 7/1/2008
Program ID: 188-11-13-057

Rush University Medical Center Program
Chicago, IL
Effective date: 7/1/2008
Program ID: 188-16-12-047

University of Massachusetts Program
Worcester, MA
Effective date: 7/1/2008
Program ID: 188-24-31-050

Albany Medical Center Program
Albany, NY
Effective date: 7/1/2008
Program ID: 188-35-12-063

SUNY Upstate Medical University Program
Syracuse, NY
Effective date: 7/1/2008
Program ID: 188-35-13-053

New York Presbyterian Hospital (Cornell Campus) Program
New York, NY
Effective date: 7/1/2008
Program ID: 188-35-31-054

University of North Carolina Hospitals Program
Chapel Hill, NC
Effective date: 7/1/2008
Program ID: 188-36-31-058

University Hospitals Case Medical Center Program
Cleveland, OH
Effective date: 7/1/2008
Program ID: 188-38-13-061

Oregon Health & Science University Program
Portland, OR
Effective date: 7/1/2008
Program ID: 188-40-21-048

University of Pennsylvania Program
Philadelphia, PA
Effective date: 7/1/2008
Program ID: 188-41-21-056

Allegheny General Hospital Program
Pittsburgh, PA
Effective date: 7/1/2008
Program ID: 188-41-21-060

Medical University of South Carolina Program
Charleston, SC
Effective date: 7/1/2008
Program ID: 188-45-13-065

Vanderbilt University Program
Nashville, TN
Effective date: 7/1/2008
Program ID: 188-47-31-035

University of Wisconsin Program
Madison, WI
Effective date: 7/1/2008
Program ID: 188-56-21-064

Vascular Surgery (General Surgery)

Texas A&M College of Medicine-Scott and White Program
Temple, TX
Effective date: 7/1/2008
Program ID: 450-48-31-115

Vascular Surgery-Integrated

Stanford University Program
Stanford, CA
Effective date: 7/1/2008
Program ID: 451-05-21-021

Indiana University School of Medicine Program
Indianapolis, IN
Effective date: 7/1/2008
Program ID: 451-17-31-095

University of Massachusetts Program
Worcester, MA
Effective date: 7/1/2008
Program ID: 451-24-21-013

University of Rochester Program
Rochester, NY
Effective date: 7/1/2008
Program ID: 451-35-21-006

Mount Sinai School of Medicine Program
New York, NY
Effective date: 7/1/2008
Program ID: 451-35-21-038

Withdrawn Programs

The accreditation of the following programs was withdrawn or voluntarily withdrawn with an effective date between January 1 and December 31, 2008.

Addiction Psychiatry

UMDNJ-Robert Wood Johnson Medical School Program
Piscataway, NJ
Program ID: 401-33-21-041

Adolescent Medicine

West Virginia University Program
Morgantown, WV
Program ID: 321-55-31-023

Adult Cardiothoracic Anesthesiology

University of Kansas School of Medicine Program
Kansas City, KS
Program ID: 041-19-13-027

Adult Reconstructive Orthopaedics

Jackson Memorial Hospital/Jackson Health System Program
Miami, FL
Program ID: 261-11-13-038

University of Pittsburgh Medical Center Medical Education Program
Pittsburgh, PA
Program ID: 261-41-21-023

Anesthesiology

University of South Florida Program
Tampa, FL
Program ID: 040-11-21-178

Cardiovascular Disease

Michael Reese Hospital/University of Illinois College of Medicine at Chicago Program
Chicago, IL
Program ID: 141-16-21-028

Clinical Cardiac Electrophysiology

University of North Carolina Hospitals Program
Chapel Hill, NC
Program ID: 154-36-21-053

Clinical Neurophysiology

Southern Illinois University Program
Springfield, IL
Program ID: 187-16-31-008

University of Oklahoma Health Sciences Center Program
Oklahoma City, OK
Program ID: 187-39-21-090

Colon and Rectal Surgery

Western Pennsylvania/Allegheny General Hospital Program
Pittsburgh, PA
Program ID: 060-41-21-056

Critical Care Medicine

University of Connecticut Program
Hartford, CT
Program ID: 045-08-21-035

University of Illinois College of Medicine at Chicago Program
Chicago, IL
Program ID: 045-16-21-076

University at Buffalo Program
Buffalo, NY
Program ID: 045-35-12-080

Cytopathology

University Hospital/University of Cincinnati College of Medicine Program
Cincinnati, OH
Program ID: 307-38-21-035

Emergency Medicine

University of Arizona/UPHK Graduate Medical Education Consortium Program
Tucson, AZ
Program ID: 110-03-12-194

Family Medicine

Northeast Alabama Regional Medical Center Program
Anniston, AL
Program ID: 120-01-21-636

Physicians Medical Center Carraway Program
Birmingham, AL
Program ID: 120-01-31-019

University of Southern California School of Medicine
Los Angeles, CA
Program ID: 120-05-22-674

Saints Mary and Elizabeth Medical Center (St Mary of Nazareth Hospital Center) Program
Chicago, IL
Program ID: 120-16-11-104

Saints Mary and Elizabeth Medical Center (St Elizabeth's Hospital) Program
Chicago, IL
Program ID: 120-16-21-428

Methodist Hospitals Program
Gary, IN
Program ID: 120-17-21-493

Forensic Pathology

Eastern Virginia Medical School Program
Norfolk, VA
Program ID: 310-51-12-083

New / Withdrawn Programs

Forensic Psychiatry

Louisiana State University Program
New Orleans, LA
Program ID: 406-21-21-024

New Hampshire Department of Corrections/Dartmouth-Hitchcock Medical Center Program
Concord, NH
Program ID: 406-32-21-031

Virginia Commonwealth University Health System Program
Richmond, VA
Program ID: 406-51-21-044

Gastroenterology

Johns Hopkins University/Bayview Medical Center Program
Baltimore, MD
Program ID: 144-23-11-140

Western Pennsylvania Hospital/Temple University Program
Pittsburgh, PA
Program ID: 144-41-11-046

Geriatric Medicine

Louisiana State University (Kenner) Program
Kenner, LA
Program ID: 125-21-12-057

NSLIJHS-North Shore University Hospital/NYU School of Medicine Program
Manhasset, NY
Program ID: 151-35-21-084

Geriatric Psychiatry

Rush University Medical Center Program
Chicago, IL
Program ID: 407-16-13-072

Louisiana State University Program
New Orleans, LA
Program ID: 407-21-21-011

University of Missouri-Columbia Program
Columbia, MO
Program ID: 407-28-31-064

Virginia Commonwealth University Health System Program
Richmond, VA
Program ID: 407-51-21-051

Hematology

Johns Hopkins University Program
Baltimore, MD
Program ID: 145-23-11-064

Infectious Disease

Mount Sinai School of Medicine (Cabrini) Program
New York, NY
Program ID: 146-35-31-097

Internal Medicine

Physicians Medical Center Carraway Program
Birmingham, AL
Program ID: 140-01-31-021

Michael Reese Hospital/University of Illinois College of Medicine at Chicago Program
Chicago, IL
Program ID: 140-16-11-117

Mount Sinai School of Medicine (Cabrini) Program
New York, NY
Program ID: 140-35-31-266

San Antonio Uniformed Services Health Education Consortium (WHMC) Program
Lackland AFB, TX
Program ID: 140-48-12-003

Internal Medicine/Pediatrics

New York Medical College at St Vincent's Hospital and Medical Center of New York Program
New York, NY
Program ID: 700-35-14-082

Albert Einstein Healthcare Network Program
Philadelphia, PA
Program ID: 700-41-14-069

Musculoskeletal Radiology

University of Oklahoma Health Sciences Center Program
Oklahoma City, OK
Program ID: 426-39-12-010

Neonatal-Perinatal Medicine

University of Arizona Program
Tucson, AZ
Program ID: 329-03-13-123

Neuroradiology

SUNY at Stony Brook Program
Stony Brook, NY
Program ID: 423-35-21-053

Neurotology

McGaw Medical Center of Northwestern University Program
Chicago, IL
Program ID: 286-16-21-101

Nuclear Medicine

University of Connecticut (Danbury) Program
Danbury, CT
Program ID: 200-08-21-103

University of Rochester Program
Rochester, NY
Program ID: 200-35-11-057

Oncology

Johns Hopkins University Program
Baltimore, MD
Program ID: 147-23-11-067

Orthopaedic Sports Medicine

Tufts Medical Center Program
Boston, MA
Program ID: 268-24-31-059

Wayne State University/Detroit Medical Center Program
Warren, MI
Program ID: 268-25-21-065

Otolaryngology

SUNY at Stony Brook Program
Stony Brook, NY
Program ID: 280-35-31-128

Pain Medicine

SUNY at Stony Brook Program
Stony Brook, NY
Program ID: 530-35-04-067

Pathology-Anatomic and Clinical

Cook County Hospital Program
Chicago, IL
Program ID: 300-16-21-088

Pediatric Anesthesiology

University of Rochester Program
Rochester, NY
Program ID: 042-35-21-027

Children's Hospital (Columbus) Program
Columbus, OH
Program ID: 042-38-31-016

Pediatric Cardiology

University of Chicago Program
Chicago, IL
Program ID: 325-16-11-074

Tulane University Program
New Orleans, LA
Program ID: 325-21-21-064

Cleveland Clinic Foundation Program
Cleveland, OH
Program ID: 325-38-31-075

Pediatric Critical Care Medicine

Naval Medical Center (San Diego) Program
San Diego, CA
Program ID: 323-05-21-042

Medical College of Georgia Program
Augusta, GA
Program ID: 323-12-21-010

Advocate Christ Medical Center Program
Oak Lawn, IL
Program ID: 323-16-21-073

Pediatric Endocrinology

University of Illinois College of Medicine at Chicago Program
Chicago, IL
Program ID: 326-16-31-062

SUNY Upstate Medical University Program
Syracuse, NY
Program ID: 326-35-21-088

Pediatric Hematology/Oncology

University of New Mexico Program
Albuquerque, NM
Program ID: 327-34-21-070

Pediatric Nephrology

SUNY at Stony Brook Program
Stony Brook, NY
Program ID: 328-35-21-033

University Hospitals Case Medical Center Program
Cleveland, OH
Program ID: 328-38-21-054

Pediatric Pulmonology

University of New Mexico Program
Albuquerque, NM
Program ID: 330-34-21-039

Pediatric Radiology

Alfred I duPont Hospital for Children Program
Wilmington, DE
Program ID: 424-09-31-057

Pediatric Sports Medicine

University of Texas Health Science Center at San Antonio Program
San Antonio, TX
Program ID: 333-48-21-002

Pediatric Urology

St Louis University School of Medicine Program
St Louis, MO
Program ID: 485-28-31-028

Pediatrics

Long Island College Hospital Program
Brooklyn, NY
Program ID: 320-35-11-154

New York Medical College at St Vincent's Hospital and Medical Center of New York Program
New York, NY
Program ID: 320-35-11-170

Universidad Central del Caribe Program
Bayamon, PR
Program ID: 320-42-21-255

Plastic Surgery

Loma Linda University Program
Loma Linda, CA
Program ID: 360-05-21-133

Stanford University Program
Palo Alto, CA
Program ID: 360-05-31-013

Georgetown University Hospital Program
Washington, DC
Program ID: 360-10-21-017

McGaw Medical Center of Northwestern University Program
Chicago, IL
Program ID: 360-16-21-025

Southern Illinois University Program
Springfield, IL
Program ID: 360-16-21-030

University of Kansas School of Medicine Program
Kansas City, KS
Program ID: 360-19-11-032

University of Kentucky College of Medicine Program
Lexington, KY
Program ID: 360-20-21-033

University of Michigan Program
Ann Arbor, MI
Program ID: 360-25-21-042

University of Missouri-Columbia Program
Columbia, MO
Program ID: 360-28-21-049

University of Nevada School of Medicine (Las Vegas) Program
Las Vegas, NV
Program ID: 360-31-21-138

Wake Forest University School of Medicine Program
Winston-Salem, NC
Program ID: 360-36-11-074

University Hospitals Case Medical Center Program
Cleveland, OH
Program ID: 360-38-21-078

Temple University Hospital Program
Philadelphia, PA
Program ID: 360-41-21-088

Baylor College of Medicine Program
Houston, TX
Program ID: 360-48-31-099

University of Wisconsin Program
Madison, WI
Program ID: 360-56-21-109

Medical College of Wisconsin Affiliated Hospitals Program
Milwaukee, WI
Program ID: 360-56-21-110

Preventive Medicine

University of Arizona Program
Phoenix, AZ
Program ID: 380-03-21-007

Maryland State Department of Health and Mental Hygiene Program
Baltimore, MD
Program ID: 380-23-88-100

University of Pittsburgh Graduate School of Public Health Program
Pittsburgh, PA
Program ID: 380-41-77-087

Procedural Dermatology

Dermatologic Surgicenter (Philadelphia) Program
Philadelphia, PA
Program ID: 081-41-31-012

Psychiatry

Mount Sinai School of Medicine (Cabrini) Program
New York, NY
Program ID: 400-35-31-137

Psychosomatic Medicine

University of Iowa Hospitals and Clinics Program
Iowa City, IA
Program ID: 409-18-21-004

Pulmonary Disease

University of South Alabama Program
Mobile, AL
Program ID: 149-01-11-048

College of Medicine, Mayo Clinic (Jacksonville) Program
Jacksonville, FL
Program ID: 149-11-21-205

Mount Sinai School of Medicine (Cabrini) Program
New York, NY
Program ID: 149-35-31-096

Radiology-Diagnostic

University of Pittsburgh Medical Center Medical Education (Mercy) Program
Pittsburgh, PA
Program ID: 420-41-11-178

Western Pennsylvania Hospital/Temple University Program
Pittsburgh, PA
Program ID: 420-41-21-241

Sleep Medicine

St Christopher's Hospital for Children Program
Philadelphia, PA
Program ID: 520-41-32-003

University of Texas Southwestern Medical School Program
Dallas, TX
Program ID: 520-48-40-006

Sports Medicine

North Colorado Medical Center Program
Greeley, CO
Program ID: 127-07-21-106

University of Texas Southwestern Medical School Program
Dallas, TX
Program ID: 127-48-13-116

Marshall University School of Medicine Program
Huntington, WV
Program ID: 127-55-31-062

Surgery-General

Physicians Medical Center Carraway Program
Birmingham, AL
Program ID: 440-01-12-021

New / Withdrawn Programs

Mount Sinai School of Medicine (Cabrini) Program
New York, NY
Program ID: 440-35-21-209

Western Pennsylvania Hospital/Temple University Program
Pittsburgh, PA
Program ID: 440-41-12-308

Thoracic Surgery

National Capital Consortium Program
Washington, DC
Program ID: 460-10-11-003

University of Louisville Program
Louisville, KY
Program ID: 460-20-21-105

Thomas Jefferson University Program
Philadelphia, PA
Program ID: 460-41-21-081

West Virginia University Program
Morgantown, WV
Program ID: 460-55-11-099

Transitional Year

Physicians Medical Center Carraway Program
Birmingham, AL
Program ID: 999-01-00-002

Banner Good Samaritan Medical Center Program
Phoenix, AZ
Program ID: 999-03-00-004

National Capital Consortium (Bethesda) Program
Bethesda, MD
Program ID: 999-23-00-051

Presbyterian Medical Center of the University of Pennsylvania Health System Program
Philadelphia, PA
Program ID: 999-41-00-113

York Hospital Program
York, PA
Program ID: 999-41-00-120

Frankford Hospitals Program A
Philadelphia, PA
Program ID: 999-41-00-247

Universidad Central del Caribe Program
Bayamon, PR
Program ID: 999-42-00-121

San Antonio Uniformed Services Health Education Consortium (BAMC) Program
Fort Sam Houston, TX
Program ID: 999-48-00-138

San Antonio Uniformed Services Health Education Consortium (WHMC) Program
Lackland AFB, TX
Program ID: 999-48-00-192

Urology

Wayne State University/Detroit Medical Center Program
Detroit, MI
Program ID: 480-25-31-069

Vascular and Interventional Radiology

SUNY at Stony Brook Program
Stony Brook, NY
Program ID: 427-35-21-084

University Hospitals Case Medical Center Program
Cleveland, OH
Program ID: 427-38-21-012

Temple University Hospital Program
Philadelphia, PA
Program ID: 427-41-21-076

George Washington University Program
Alexandria, VA
Program ID: 427-51-21-020

Vascular Neurology

University of Wisconsin Program
Madison, WI
Program ID: 188-56-13-025

Section V

Graduate Medical Education Teaching Institutions

Section V lists hospitals and organizations that sponsor graduate medical education (GME) programs or participate in GME. *Sponsoring institutions* assume final responsibility for a GME program. Most GME programs are sponsored by specific clinical departments within a hospital, another health care institution such as a medical school, or an educational consortium. *Major participating institutions* include hospitals or other sites recognized by at least one residency review committee as providing a major portion of required GME. Hospitals and other institutions that provide rotations of less than one-sixth of the program length or less than a total of 6 months are not listed in the *Directory*.

All institutions that sponsor GME programs or participate in GME are listed in alphabetical order by state and city. Each listing includes the institution name, address, and identification code. Also provided are codes of medical schools affiliated with each institution (where applicable) and abbreviations for the specialty and subspecialty programs affiliated with each institution. (A key for specialty and subspecialty abbreviation codes is provided on the inside back cover of this *Directory*).

Candidates seeking a residency should refer to the list of programs in Section III. Applications for a residency position should be addressed to the program director rather than to an institution.

Relationships Between Hospitals and Medical Schools (Medical School Affiliation)

Hospitals that sponsor an accredited program are not required to have a formal relationship with a medical school. Where such a relationship exists, the affiliation is identified by the dean of the medical school as M (major), G (graduate only), or L (limited). The medical school associated with the code number in this listing is identified in Appendix D.

Major affiliation (M) signifies that an institution is an important part of the teaching program of the medical school and is a major unit in the clinical clerkship program. Major teaching institutions provide clerkship experience in two or more of the major specialties: internal medicine, surgery, pediatrics, and obstetrics-gynecology. An institution responsible for most of the teaching in a single specialty, such as psychiatry or pediatrics, may also be considered a major affiliation. In a major teaching institution, medical students serve clinical clerkships regularly on inpatient services, under the direct supervision of medical school faculty. A major teaching institution may or may not be used for medical school residencies.

Graduate affiliation (G) indicates that the institution is affiliated with the medical school only for its graduate programs and that one or more of the following arrangements is in effect:

1. House staff of the GME programs are selected by officials of a medical school department or by a joint committee of the institution teaching staff and medical school faculty.
2. Medical school faculty (other than the institution's attending staff) are regularly scheduled to participate in the teaching programs of the institution. No graduate affiliation is indicated if medical school faculty participation at the institution is limited to an occasional lecture or consultation visit, or if the institution's residents attend medical school teaching conferences only as visitors.
3. A contractual arrangement (with or without financial commitment) specifies the medical school participation in the organization and supervision of the GME program in the institution.
4. There is some degree of exchange of residents between this institution and the principal teaching institution of the medical school.

Limited affiliation (L) signifies that the institution is affiliated with the medical school's teaching program only for brief and/or unique rotations of students or residents.

Alabama

Birmingham

Alabama Allergy and Asthma Center
10 Old Montgomery Highway
Suite 100
Birmingham, AL 35209
Major participating institution for programs in: AI
Institution ID: 01-8058

American Red Cross Blood Services-Alabama Region
1130 22nd Street South
Birmingham, AL 35203-0605
Med Sch Affil: G-00102
Major participating institution for programs in: BBK
Institution ID: 01-8004

American Sports Medicine Institute
2660 10th Avenue South
Suite 505
Birmingham, AL 35205-1626
www.asmi.org
Med Sch Affil: G-00102
Programs sponsored in: OFA, OSM
Institution ID: 01-8009

Baptist Health System Inc
Buchanan Building Suite 9-B
800 Montclair Road
Birmingham, AL 35213
www.bhsala.com
Med Sch Affil: G-00102
Programs sponsored in: DR, GS, IM, PTH, TY
Institution ID: 01-0519

Baptist Medical Center-Princeton
701 Princeton Ave, S W
Birmingham, AL 35211
Med Sch Affil: G-00102
Major participating institution for programs in: DR,
GS, IM, PTH, TY
Institution ID: 01-0187

Brookwood Medical Center
2010 Brookwood Medical Center Drive
Birmingham, AL 35209
Major participating institution for programs in: HSO,
OSM
Institution ID: 01-8023

Children's Hospital of Alabama
1600 Seventh Avenue, South
Birmingham, AL 35233-0010
Med Sch Affil: M-00102
Major participating institution for programs in: ADL,
CCP, CHN, CHP, MDG, MG, MPD, NPM, NS, ORS, OTO,
PD, PDE, PDI, PDP, PDS, PEM, PG, PHO, PMG, PN, PRD,
PS, RPM, SME, U
Institution ID: 01-0497

Cooper Green Hospital
1515 Sixth Avenue, South
Birmingham, AL 35233-9990
Med Sch Affil: M-00102
Major participating institution for programs in: ID,
MDG, NEP, NPM, OPH, PRD, RHU
Institution ID: 01-0511

Department of Youth Services (VACCA)
8950 Roebuck Boulevard
Birmingham, AL 35206
Major participating institution for programs in: ADL
Institution ID: 01-8038

Dermatology Associates
2100 16th Avenue South, Suite 202
Birmingham, AL 35205
www.totalskinandbeauty.com
Programs sponsored in: PRD
Institution ID: 01-8015

Dermatopathology Services, PC
3918 Montclair Road
Birmingham, AL 35213
Major participating institution for programs in: DMP
Institution ID: 01-8031

Eastern Pulmonary and Sleep Medicine
100 Pilot Medical Drive
Suite 100
Birmingham, AL 35235-3412
Major participating institution for programs in: AI
Institution ID: 01-8059

Eye Foundation Hospital
1720 University Blvd
Birmingham, AL 35233-6805
Med Sch Affil: M-00102
Major participating institution for programs in: OPH
Institution ID: 01-0502

Family Court of Jefferson County
120 2nd Court North
Birmingham, AL 35204
Major participating institution for programs in: ADL
Institution ID: 01-8027

Glenwood Mental Health Services, Inc
150 Glenwood Lane
Birmingham, AL 35242
Major participating institution for programs in: CHP
Institution ID: 01-8028

Jefferson County Coroner/Medical Examiner's Office
1515 Sixth Ave, S
Birmingham, AL 35233-0605
Med Sch Affil: G-00102
Major participating institution for programs in: FOP
Institution ID: 01-0531

Pediatric and Adult Asthma & Allergy, PC
2700 10th Avenue South
Suite 401
Birmingham, AL 35205-1250
Major participating institution for programs in: AI
Institution ID: 01-8060

Sleep Disorder Center of Alabama
790 Montclair Road
Suite 200
Birmingham, AL 35213
Major participating institution for programs in: SME
Institution ID: 01-8040

St Vincent's East
50 Medical Park Dr
Birmingham, AL 35235-9990
http://ehs.com
Med Sch Affil: L-00102
Programs sponsored in: FP, FSM
Institution ID: 01-0515

St Vincent's Hospital
810 St Vincent's Drive
PO Box 12407
Birmingham, AL 35202-2407
Med Sch Affil: G-00102
Major participating institution for programs in: FSM,
OFA, OSM, U
Institution ID: 01-0196

Trinity Medical Center
800 Montclair Road
Birmingham, AL 35213
Med Sch Affil: G-00102
Major participating institution for programs in: DR,
GS, IM, PTH, TY
Institution ID: 01-0307

University of Alabama at Birmingham/Highlands
1201 11th Avenue South
Birmingham, AL 35205-0605
Major participating institution for programs in: HSO,
OFA, ORS, OTO, PMM, PS, SME, U
Institution ID: 01-7003

University of Alabama Hospital
619 S 19th Street
Birmingham, AL 35249-6505
www.health.uab.edu
Med Sch Affil: M-00102
Programs sponsored in: ACA, ADL, AI, AN, BBK, CCA,
CCP, CCS, CD, CHN, CHP, CN, D, DMP, DR, EM, END,
FOP, FP, FSM, GE, GS, HMP, HO, HPM, HSO, IC, ICE, ID,
IM, IMG, MDG, MG, MGP, MPD, N, NEP, NM, NP, NPM,
NS, OBG, OPH, ORS, OTO, P, PCC, PCP, PD, PDE, PDI,
PDP, PDS, PEM, PG, PHO, PM, PMG, PMM, PN, PRD, PS,
PTH, RHU, RNR, RO, RPM, SME, TS, U, VIR, VN, VS
Institution ID: 01-0498

University of Alabama School of Medicine
306 Medical Education Bldg
1813 Sixth Ave
Birmingham, AL 35294-3293
http://medicine.uab.edu/
Major participating institution for programs in: PMG,
MDG
Institution ID: 01-0527

Veterans Affairs Medical Center (Birmingham)
700 S 19th St
Birmingham, AL 35233-6805
Med Sch Affil: M-00102
Major participating institution for programs in: AI,
CD, CN, D, DMP, DR, END, GE, GS, HO, ID, IM, IMG,
MDG, N, NEP, NM, NS, OPH, OTO, P, PCC, PRD, PS, PTH,
RHU, TS, U
Institution ID: 01-0500

Huntsville

Huntsville Hospital
101 Sivley Road
Huntsville, AL 35801-9990
Med Sch Affil: M-00102
Major participating institution for programs in: FP,
FSM
Institution ID: 01-0507

Mobile

Alta Pointe Health Systems
2400 Gordon Smith Drive
Mobile, AL 36617
Major participating institution for programs in: P
Institution ID: 01-8041

Infirmary West
5600 Girby Road
Mobile, AL 36693-3398
Med Sch Affil: M-00106
Major participating institution for programs in: CD,
DR, GE, ID, N, ORS, OSM, PCC, PTH
Institution ID: 01-8010

Mobile Infirmary Medical Center
PO Box 2226
Mobile, AL 36652-2144
Major participating institution for programs in: GS,
ID, ORS
Institution ID: 01-0508

University of South Alabama Hospitals
2451 Fillingim Street
Mobile, AL 36617-2293
www.southalabama.edu/usahealthsystem/
Med Sch Affil: M-00106
Programs sponsored in: CD, DR, FP, FSM, GE, GS, ID,
IM, MPD, N, OBG, ORS, OSM, P, PCC, PD, PTH, VN
Institution ID: 01-0406

University of South Alabama Medical Center
2451 Fillingim Street
Mobile, AL 36617-2293
Major participating institution for programs in: CD, DR, FP, FSM, GE, GS, ID, IM, MPD, N, ORS, P, PCC, PTH, VN
Institution ID: 01-8013

USA Children's and Women's Hospital
1700 Center St
Mobile, AL 36604-3391
Med Sch Affil: M-00106
Major participating institution for programs in: FP, ID, MPD, OBG, ORS, OSM, PD
Institution ID: 01-8011

Montgomery

Baptist Medical Center South
2105 East South Boulevard
PO Box 11010
Montgomery, AL 36111-0010
Med Sch Affil: M-00102
Major participating institution for programs in: FP, IM
Institution ID: 01-0309

Baptist Outreach Services
301 Brown Springs Road
PO Box 244001
Montgomery, AL 36124-0124
Programs sponsored in: FP
Institution ID: 01-8012

Phenix City

Jack Hughston Memorial Hospital
4401 Riverchase Drive
Phenix City, AL 36867
Major participating institution for programs in: OSM
Institution ID: 01-8053

Pinson

Department of Youth Service (Chalkville)
5849 Old Springville Road
Pinson, AL 35126
Major participating institution for programs in: ADL
Institution ID: 01-8039

Selma

Vaughan Regional Medical Center
1015 Medice Center Parkway
Selma, AL 36701-9990
Major participating institution for programs in: FP
Institution ID: 01-0512

Tuscaloosa

DCH Regional Medical Center
809 University Blvd, E
Tuscaloosa, AL 35403-9990
Med Sch Affil: M-00102
Major participating institution for programs in: FP, FSM
Institution ID: 01-0510

Tuscaloosa College of Community Health Sciences
Box 870377
Tuscaloosa, AL 35487-0377
http://cchs.ua.edu/fmr/index.html
Programs sponsored in: FP, FSM
Institution ID: 01-8025

Alaska

Anchorage

Alaska Native Medical Center
4315 Diplomacy Drive
Anchorage, AK 99508
Major participating institution for programs in: GS
Institution ID: 02-0102

Providence Hospital
3200 Providence Dr
PO Box 196604
Anchorage, AK 99519-6604
www.akfmr.org
Med Sch Affil: L-05404
Programs sponsored in: FP
Institution ID: 02-8001

Arizona

Phoenix

Banner Good Samaritan Medical Center
1111 E McDowell Rd
Phoenix, AZ 85006
www.bannerhealth.com
Med Sch Affil: M-00301
Programs sponsored in: CD, END, ETX, FP, GE, GS, IC, IM, IMG, MPD, OBG, ORS, P, PCC
Institution ID: 03-0345

Carl T Hayden VA Medical Center
7th St and Indian School Rd
Phoenix, AZ 85012
Med Sch Affil: L-00301
Major participating institution for programs in: CD, END, FSM, GE, GS, IM, IMG, MPD, PCC
Institution ID: 03-0504

GSRMC/VA Medical Center
1111 East McDowell/650 E Indian School Rd
Phoenix, AZ 85012
Major participating institution for programs in: PDE
Institution ID: 03-8103

Maricopa County Forensic Science Center
701 W Jefferson
Phoenix, AZ 85007
Major participating institution for programs in: NP
Institution ID: 03-8092

Maricopa Medical Center
2601 East Roosevelt St
Phoenix, AZ 85008
http://maricopa.gov/medcenter/mmc.html
Med Sch Affil: M-00301, G-02608
Programs sponsored in: CCS, CHP, DR, EM, GS, IM, OBG, P
Major participating institution for programs in: D, MPD, PD
Institution ID: 03-0253

Mayo Clinic Hospital
5777 E Mayo Boulevard
Phoenix, AZ 85054
Med Sch Affil: M-02608
Major participating institution for programs in: AN, CCA, CD, CN, D, FP, GE, HO, HPM, IC, ICE, IM, N, ORS, OTO, PMM, PS, PUD, THP, TY, U, VN
Institution ID: 03-8029

National Institutes of Health (NIH), Phoenix Branch
4212 N 16th St
Phoenix, AZ 85012
Major participating institution for programs in: PDE
Institution ID: 03-8104

Orthopaedic Clinic Association
2222 E Highland Ave
Ste 300
Phoenix, AZ 85016-4872
Major participating institution for programs in: OSM
Institution ID: 03-8093

Phoenix Baptist Hospital and Med Ctr/Vanguard Health System
2000 W Bethany Home Road
Phoenix, AZ 85015
www.baptistresidency.org
Med Sch Affil: L-00301
Programs sponsored in: FP
Institution ID: 03-0517

Phoenix Children's Hospital
1919 E Thomas Rd
Phoenix, AZ 85016-7710
www.phoenixchildrens.com
Med Sch Affil: L-00301
Programs sponsored in: PD, PDE, PEM, PHO
Major participating institution for programs in: D, DR, ETX, MPD, NS, ORS, PS, U
Institution ID: 03-8015

St Joseph's Hospital and Medical Center
350 West Thomas Road
Phoenix, AZ 85013-6604
www.ichosestjoes.com
Med Sch Affil: M-00301, G-04815
Programs sponsored in: CHN, CN, DR, ESS, FP, FPG, FSM, GS, IM, N, NP, NS, PD, PTH, RNR, VN
Major participating institution for programs in: DR, GS, IC, NS, OBG, ORS, PS
Institution ID: 03-0136

St Luke's Medical Center
1800 E Van Buren St
Phoenix, AZ 85006
Major participating institution for programs in: IC
Institution ID: 03-0523

Translational Genomics Research Institute
445 N 5th Street
Phoenix, AZ 85004
Major participating institution for programs in: PHO
Institution ID: 03-8085

Scottsdale

Mayo Clinic (Arizona)
13400 E Shea Boulevard
Scottsdale, AZ 85259-2184
Med Sch Affil: M-02608, L-00301
Major participating institution for programs in: CCA, CCS, CD, CN, D, GE, GS, HO, IM, N, PMM, PUD, TY, U
Institution ID: 03-8019

Scottsdale Healthcare - Shea
9003 East Shea Boulevard
Scottsdale, AZ 85260-6771
Major participating institution for programs in: FP, GS
Institution ID: 03-8024

Scottsdale Healthcare-Osborn
7400 E Osborn Road
Scottsdale, AZ 85251-6403
www.shc.org/fpres
Med Sch Affil: M-00301
Programs sponsored in: FP
Major participating institution for programs in: ORS
Institution ID: 03-0512

Sun City

Walter O Boswell Memorial Hospital
10401 W Thunderbird Blvd
PO Box 1690
Sun City, AZ 85372-6771
Major participating institution for programs in: FPG, FSM
Institution ID: 03-8026

Teaching Institutions

Sun City West

Del E Webb Memorial Hospital
14502 W Meeker Blvd
PO Box 5169
Sun City West, AZ 85357-6771
Major participating institution for programs in: FPG, FSM
Institution ID: 03-8027

Tempe

Arizona State University (Tempe)
PO Box 872203
Tempe, AZ 85287
Major participating institution for programs in: ORS
Institution ID: 03-8047

Tucson

Arizona Poison and Drug Information Center
1501 N Campbell Avenue
Tucson, AZ 85724
Major participating institution for programs in: ETX
Institution ID: 03-8037

Arizona Telemedicine Network
2800 East Ajo Way
Tucson, AZ 85713
Major participating institution for programs in: DR
Institution ID: 03-8060

Desert Dialysis Center
2022 E Prince Rd
Tucson, AZ 85719
Major participating institution for programs in: NEP
Institution ID: 03-8034

Southern Arizona VA Health Care Center (Tucson)
3601 South Sixth Ave
Tucson, AZ 85723-6604
Med Sch Affil: M-00301
Major participating institution for programs in: CD, DR, END, GE, GS, IC, ID, IM, IMG, MGP, N, NEP, NS, OPH, P, PCC, PTH, RHU, TY, U
Institution ID: 03-0501

Tucson Hospitals Medical Education Program Inc
5301 E Grant Road
Box 42195
Tucson, AZ 85733-6604
Programs sponsored in: TY
Institution ID: 03-0497

Tucson Medical Center
5301 East Grant Road
Tucson, AZ 85712-6604
Med Sch Affil: M-00301
Major participating institution for programs in: GS, IM, N, NS, PD, PDP, TY, U
Institution ID: 03-0235

University Medical Center
1501 North Campbell Avenue
PO Box 245128
Tucson, AZ 85724-4405
Med Sch Affil: M-00301
Major participating institution for programs in: AN, CD, CHP, DR, EM, EMP, END, ETX, FP, GE, GS, HMP, HO, IC, ID, IM, IMG, MGP, N, NEP, NS, OBG, OPH, ORS, P, PCC, PD, PDE, PDP, PTH, RHU, RNR, RO, TS, U, VIR, VS
Institution ID: 03-0506

University of Arizona Campus Health Services
1224 E Lowell St
PO Box 210095
Tucson, AZ 85721
Major participating institution for programs in: FSM
Institution ID: 03-8101

University of Arizona College of Medicine
1501 North Campbell Avenue
PO Box 245085
Tucson, AZ 85724-5085
www.medicine.arizona.edu/gme
Programs sponsored in: AN, CD, CHP, DR, EM, EMP, END, ETX, FP, FSM, GE, GS, HMP, HO, IC, ID, IM, IMG, MGP, N, NEP, NS, OBG, OPH, ORS, OSM, P, PCC, PD, PDE, PDP, PTH, RHU, RNR, RO, TS, U, VIR, VS
Institution ID: 03-0509

University of Arizona/UPHK Graduate Medical Ed Consortium
2800 E Ajo Way
Tucson, AZ 85713
Med Sch Affil: M-00301
Programs sponsored in: DR, IM, N, OPH, P
Major participating institution for programs in: END, FP, FSM, GE, IC, ID, NEP, PCC, U
Institution ID: 03-0246

University Orthopaedic Specialists
1555 E River Rd
Tucson, AZ 85718
Major participating institution for programs in: ORS
Institution ID: 03-8094

Arkansas

Benton

Arkansas Health Center
6701 Highway 67
Benton, AR 72015
Major participating institution for programs in: PYG
Institution ID: 04-0484

El Dorado

Medical Center of South Arkansas (Union Medical Center)
700 W Grove Street
El Dorado, AR 71730-3591
Major participating institution for programs in: FP
Institution ID: 04-0476

Fayetteville

Washington Regional Medical Center
3215 N North Hills Blvd
Fayetteville, AR 72703-3591
Major participating institution for programs in: FP
Institution ID: 04-0473

Fort Smith

Sparks Regional Medical Center
1311 South I St
PO Box 17006
Fort Smith, AR 72917-3591
Major participating institution for programs in: FP
Institution ID: 04-0467

Jonesboro

St Bernards Regional Medical Center
224 E Matthews Street
Jonesboro, AR 72401-3591
Major participating institution for programs in: FP
Institution ID: 04-0478

Little Rock

American Red Cross Blood Services
Greater Ozarks-AR Region Lowery Blood Center
401 S Monroe
Little Rock, AR 72205
Major participating institution for programs in: BBK
Institution ID: 04-8035

Arkansas Children's Hospital
800 Marshall Street
Little Rock, AR 72202
Med Sch Affil: M-00401
Major participating institution for programs in: AN, BBK, CCP, CHN, CHP, DBP, DR, EM, GS, HSO, MPD, NPM, NS, OPH, ORS, OTO, PAN, PD, PDC, PDE, PDP, PDR, PDS, PEM, PHO, PM, U
Institution ID: 04-0284

Arkansas State Hospital (DBHS)
Division of Behavioral Health Services (DBHS)
305 S Palm Street
Little Rock, AR 72205-3591
Med Sch Affil: G-00401
Major participating institution for programs in: CHP, P, PFP
Institution ID: 04-0307

Baptist Health Rehabilitation Institute of Arkansas
9601 Interstate 630, Exit 7
Little Rock, AR 72205-7249
Med Sch Affil: L-00401
Major participating institution for programs in: PM
Institution ID: 04-8015

Central Arkansas Veterans Healthcare System
4300 West 7th Street
Little Rock, AR 72205
Med Sch Affil: M-00401
Major participating institution for programs in: ADP, AN, CD, D, DR, END, FP, GE, GS, HMP, HO, HSO, IC, ICE, ID, IM, IMG, MPD, N, NEP, NM, NS, OFA, OPH, ORS, OTO, P, PCC, PCP, PM, PTH, PYG, RHU, RNR, U, VIR, VS, VSI
Institution ID: 04-0349

Dennis Developmental Center
1301 Wolfe Street
Little Rock, AR 72202
Major participating institution for programs in: DBP
Institution ID: 04-8047

UAMS Medical Center
4301 W Markham Street, Slot 719
Little Rock, AR 72205
Med Sch Affil: M-00401
Major participating institution for programs in: ADP, AN, BBK, CD, CHN, CHP, D, DMP, DR, EM, END, FP, GE, GS, HMP, HO, HSO, IC, ICE, ID, IM, IMG, MPD, N, NEP, NM, NPM, NS, OBG, OFA, OPH, ORS, OTO, P, PCC, PCP, PDI, PDP, PFP, PM, PTH, PYG, RHU, RNR, U, VIR, VS, VSI
Institution ID: 04-0261

UAMS-Area Health Education Centers
4301 W Markham Street, Slot 599
Little Rock, AR 72205-7199
www.uams.edu/ahec/ahec1.htm
Programs sponsored in: FP
Institution ID: 04-8018

University of Arkansas College of Medicine
4301 W Markham Street, Slot 550
Little Rock, AR 72205
www.uams.edu
Med Sch Affil: M-00401
Programs sponsored in: ADP, AN, BBK, CCP, CD, CHN, CHP, D, DBP, DMP, DR, EM, END, FP, GE, GS, HMP, HO, HSO, IC, ICE, ID, IM, IMG, MPD, N, NEP, NM, NPM, NS, OBG, OFA, OPH, ORS, OTO, P, PAN, PCC, PCP, PD, PDC, PDE, PDI, PDP, PDR, PDS, PEM, PFP, PHO, PM, PTH, PYG, RHU, RNR, U, VIR, VS, VSI
Institution ID: 04-9501

Pine Bluff

Jefferson Regional Medical Center
1515 W 42nd Ave
Pine Bluff, AR 71603-3591
Major participating institution for programs in: FP
Institution ID: 04-0465

Springdale

Northwest Medical Center
609 West Maple Street
Springdale, AR 72764
Major participating institution for programs in: FP
Institution ID: 04-8023

Texarkana

Christus St Michael Health System
Sixth and Hazel Sts
Texarkana, AR 75502
Major participating institution for programs in: FP
Institution ID: 04-7012

California

Altadena

Five Acres - The Boys & Girls Aid Society LA
760 Mountain View Street
798-6793
Altadena, CA 91001
Major participating institution for programs in: CHP
Institution ID: 05-8237

Anaheim

Kaiser Foundation Hospitals (Anaheim)
Anaheim Medical Center
441 Lakeview Avenue
Anaheim, CA 92807-4162
Med Sch Affil: G-00515
Major participating institution for programs in: D, FP, GS, HSO, NS, ORS, OTO, PS, U
Institution ID: 05-8043

Bakersfield

Bakersfield Memorial Hospital
420 34th Street
Bakersfield, CA 93301
Major participating institution for programs in: IC
Institution ID: 05-8126

Good Samaritan Hospital Southwest
5201 White Lane
Bakersfield, CA 93309
Major participating institution for programs in: CHP
Institution ID: 05-8212

Kern County Mental Health Department
3300 Truxtun Avenue, Suite 100
Bakersfield, CA 93301
Major participating institution for programs in: CHP, P
Institution ID: 05-8193

Kern Medical Center
1700 Mount Vernon
Department of Medical Education
Bakersfield, CA 93305-4007
www.kernmedicalcenter.com
Med Sch Affil: L-00518, L-00514
Programs sponsored in: CHP, EM, FP, GS, IM, OBG, P, TY
Major participating institution for programs in: CHN
Institution ID: 05-0120

Baldwin Park

Kaiser Foundation Hospital (Baldwin Park)
1011 Baldwin Park Boulevard
Baldwin Park, CA 91706
Major participating institution for programs in: HO
Institution ID: 05-8117

Bellflower

Kaiser Foundation Hospital (Bellflower)
9400 Rosecrans Avenue
Bellflower, CA 90706-2246
Med Sch Affil: G-00515
Major participating institution for programs in: HO, OBG, PS, U
Institution ID: 05-8046

Berkeley

University Health Services (Tang Center)
2222 Bancroft Way
Berkeley, CA 94720
Major participating institution for programs in: FSM
Institution ID: 05-8222

University of California School of Public Health
19 Earl Warren Hall
Berkeley, CA 94720-7360
Med Sch Affil: L-00502
Major participating institution for programs in: GPM, IPM
Institution ID: 05-0376

Camp Pendleton

Naval Hospital (Camp Pendleton)
Box 555191
Camp Pendleton, CA 92055-5191
Med Sch Affil: L-00518, G-02312
Programs sponsored in: FP, FSM
Institution ID: 05-0320

Chula Vista

Scripps Mercy Hospital (Chula Vista)
435 H Street (CV112)
Chula Vista, CA 91910-1537
http://medicine.ucsd.edu/scrippsfp
Med Sch Affil: G-00518
Programs sponsored in: FP
Institution ID: 05-8098

Colton

Arrowhead Regional Medical Center
400 North Pepper Avenue
Colton, CA 92324-1819
www.arrowheadmedcenter.org
Med Sch Affil: L-00512, L-00514, G-00515
Programs sponsored in: FP, FPG, TY
Major participating institution for programs in: CCA, GPM, ORS, U
Institution ID: 05-0207

Daly City

Seton Medical Center
1900 Sullivan Ave
Daly City, CA 94015-1200
Med Sch Affil: L-00502
Major participating institution for programs in: RO
Institution ID: 05-0494

Davis

Sutter Davis Hospital
2000 Sutter Place
Davis, CA 95617-0231
Major participating institution for programs in: FP
Institution ID: 05-0728

Downey

LAC-Rancho Los Amigos National Rehabilitation Center
7601 E Imperial Highway
Downey, CA 90242
Med Sch Affil: M-00506, G-01401, G-00515
Major participating institution for programs in: RHU
Institution ID: 05-0504

Duarte

City of Hope National Medical Center
1500 E Duarte Rd
Duarte, CA 91010-1495
Med Sch Affil: L-01902, L-00518, L-00506, G-00515
Programs sponsored in: HMP, RO
Major participating institution for programs in: END, HO, RO
Institution ID: 05-0233

Fontana

Kaiser Foundation Hospital (Fontana)
9961 Sierra Ave
Fontana, CA 92335-1084
Med Sch Affil: L-00514, L-00512
Major participating institution for programs in: FP, FPG, FSM, OBG
Institution ID: 05-0576

French Camp

San Joaquin General Hospital
Administration Office
500 W Hospital Rd
French Camp, CA 95231
www.sjgeneralhospital.com
Med Sch Affil: G-00519
Programs sponsored in: FP, GS, IM, TY
Institution ID: 05-0281

Fresno

Community Medical Centers (Fresno)
PO Box 1232
2823 Fresno Street
Fresno, CA 93721
Major participating institution for programs in: CCS, CD, EM, FP, GE, GS, ID, IM, OBG, P, PD, PUD
Institution ID: 05-8127

Fresno County Health Services
1221 Fulton
Fresno, CA 93725
Major participating institution for programs in: P
Institution ID: 05-8129

UCSF Fresno Medical Education Program
155 N Fresno Street
Fresno, CA 93701-2302
www.fresno.ucsf.edu
Programs sponsored in: CCS, CD, EM, FP, GE, GS, ID, IM, OBG, P, PD, PUD
Institution ID: 05-9501

University Psychiatry Associates
2027 Divisadero Street
Suite 227
Fresno, CA 93701
Major participating institution for programs in: P
Institution ID: 05-8226

VA Central California Health Care System
2615 E Clinton Ave
Fresno, CA 93703-1084
Med Sch Affil: M-00502
Major participating institution for programs in: CD, GE, GS, ID, IM, P, PUD
Institution ID: 05-0581

Glendale

Glendale Adventist Medical Center
1509 Wilson Terrace
Medical Education - Claudia Kanne, CHC, MBA
Glendale, CA 91206-4007
gamcpo.ah.org
Med Sch Affil: L-00512, L-00514
Programs sponsored in: FP
Institution ID: 05-0116

Teaching Institutions

Glendale Memorial Hospital and Health Center
1420 South Central Avenue
Glendale, CA 91204
Major participating institution for programs in: CRS
Institution ID: 05-8206

Hanford

Central Valley General Hospital
1025 Douty Street
Hanford, CA 93230
Major participating institution for programs in: FP
Institution ID: 05-0720

Hanford Community Medical Center
450 Greenfield Avenue
Hanford, CA 93230
Major participating institution for programs in: FP
Institution ID: 05-0719

Harbor City

Kaiser Permanente Medical Center (Harbor City)
25825 S Vermont Ave
Harbor City, CA 90710
Major participating institution for programs in: FSM, GS
Institution ID: 05-8145

Irvine

University of California (Irvine) College of Medicine
Irvine Hall Bldg
Irvine, CA 92717
Major participating institution for programs in: AI, GPM, RO, VIR
Institution ID: 05-0741

La Jolla

Scripps Clinic
10666 N Torrey Pines Road, Rm 403 C
La Jolla, CA 92037
Med Sch Affil: L-00518
Major participating institution for programs in: GPM, NO, OSM, PRD
Institution ID: 05-0225

Scripps Clinic/Scripps Green Hospital
10666 N Torrey Pines Road
La Jolla, CA 92037-2128
http://scrippsclinic.org
Programs sponsored in: AI, CD, END, GE, HMP, HO, IC, IM, PRD, RHU, VS
Major participating institution for programs in: GS
Institution ID: 05-8106

The Scripps Research Institute
10650 N Torrey Pines Road
La Jolla, CA 92037
Major participating institution for programs in: HO
Institution ID: 05-8211

University of California San Diego Cancer Center
3855 Health Sciences Drive
La Jolla, CA 92093
Major participating institution for programs in: PHO
Institution ID: 05-8205

La Mesa

Grossmont Hospital
5555 Grossmont Center Drive
PO Box 158
La Mesa, CA 91944-1084
Major participating institution for programs in: OSM
Institution ID: 05-0566

Laguna Hills

The Sports Clinic Orthopedic Medical Associates, Inc
23961 Calle de la Magdalena
Laguna Hills, CA 92653
Programs sponsored in: OSM
Institution ID: 05-8207

LaJolla

Thornton Hospital
9350 Campus Point Drive
LaJolla, CA 92037
Major participating institution for programs in: VN
Institution ID: 05-8204

Loma Linda

Jerry L Pettis Memorial Veterans Hospital
11201 Benton Street
Loma Linda, CA 92357-6009
Med Sch Affil: M-00512
Major participating institution for programs in: CD, D, FP, GE, GPM, GS, IM, MPD, N, NEP, OPH, ORS, OTO, P, PCC, PM, PMM, PTH, RHU, U, VIR, VS
Institution ID: 05-0748

Loma Linda University Medical Center
11234 Anderson Street
House Staff Office CP 21005
Loma Linda, CA 92354
www.llu.edu/llumc/residency/train.htm
Med Sch Affil: M-00512, L-02312, G-00515
Programs sponsored in: ACA, AN, CCA, CCP, CD, CHN, CN, D, DR, EM, FP, GE, GPM, GS, IM, MPD, N, NEP, NPM, NS, OBG, OPH, ORS, OTO, P, PAN, PCC, PD, PDR, PE, PM, PMM, PRD, PSI, PTH, RHU, RNR, RO, TS, U, VIR, VS
Institution ID: 05-0238

Long Beach

Long Beach Memorial Medical Center
2801 Atlantic Ave, PO Box 1428
Long Beach, CA 90801-1428
http://memorialcare.org
Med Sch Affil: M-00515, L-00514
Programs sponsored in: FP, OSM
Major participating institution for programs in: CD, EM, IC, IM, NMN, OBG, PCC, PD, PDP, PM, PMG, PS, PTH, RO, SCI, VN
Institution ID: 05-0195

Miller Children's Hospital
2801 Atlantic Avenue
Long Beach, CA 90801
Major participating institution for programs in: PDP
Institution ID: 05-0794

Southern California Center for Sports Medicine
2760 Atlantic Avenue
Long Beach, CA 90806-1219
Major participating institution for programs in: OSM
Institution ID: 05-8062

St Mary Medical Center
1050 Linden Ave
Long Beach, CA 90813-1495
www.stmarymed.com
Med Sch Affil: L-00514
Programs sponsored in: IM
Institution ID: 05-0267

Surgery Center of Long Beach
2880 Atlantic Ave, Suite 160
Long Beach, CA 90806
Major participating institution for programs in: OSM
Institution ID: 05-8239

VA Long Beach Healthcare System
5901 E Seventh Street
Long Beach, CA 90822-5201
Med Sch Affil: M-00515
Major participating institution for programs in: AI, CD, D, DR, END, GE, GS, HO, ID, IM, IMG, N, NEP, OPH, ORS, OTO, P, PCC, PM, PTH, RHU, RO, SCI, U
Institution ID: 05-0186

Los Angeles

California Hospital Medical Center
1401 S Grand Avenue
Los Angeles, CA 90015
www.chmcla.org
Med Sch Affil: G-00506, G-00515
Programs sponsored in: FP
Major participating institution for programs in: OBG
Institution ID: 05-0231

Cedars-Sinai Medical Center
8700 Beverly Blvd
Los Angeles, CA 90048
www.cedars-sinai.edu/gme
Med Sch Affil: M-00514, G-00515, G-04815
Programs sponsored in: ADP, AN, BBK, CCM, CCS, CD, CHP, CRS, DR, END, GS, HMP, HPM, IC, ICE, IM, MG, MGP, MSR, NEP, NR, NS, OBG, P, PCC, PTH, PYM, RHU, RNR, TS
Major participating institution for programs in: CD, CN, GE, HO, ID
Institution ID: 05-0545

Childrens Hospital Los Angeles
4650 Sunset Boulevard
Los Angeles, CA 90027-6062
http://chla.usc.edu
Med Sch Affil: M-00506, G-00515
Programs sponsored in: ADL, CCP, CCS, CHN, CHS, DBP, PAN, PD, PDC, PDE, PDI, PDP, PDR, PDS, PEM, PG, PHO, PP, PPR
Major participating institution for programs in: AI, MEM, NM, NPM, NS, ORS, TS, U
Institution ID: 05-0344

County of Los Angeles-Department of Coroner
1104 North Mission Road
Los Angeles, CA 90033-5700
http://coroner.co.la.ca.us
Programs sponsored in: FOP
Institution ID: 05-0553

Hollenbeck Palms
573 South Boyle Street
Los Angeles, CA 90033
Major participating institution for programs in: IMG
Institution ID: 05-8199

Hospital of the Good Samaritan
1225 Wilshire Boulevard
Los Angeles, CA 90017-2395
Med Sch Affil: L-00506
Major participating institution for programs in: IC, ICE
Institution ID: 05-0118

House Ear Clinic, Inc
2100 West Third Street, Suite 111
Los Angeles, CA 90057
Programs sponsored in: NO
Institution ID: 05-8107

Kaiser Foundation Hospital (Los Angeles)
Los Angeles, CA 90027-1207
Med Sch Affil: M-00514
Major participating institution for programs in: AI, CD, DR, FP, FPG, FSM, GE, GS, IC, ICE, IM, N, NEP, OBG, PD, RO, U, VIR
Institution ID: 05-0285

Kenneth Norris Jr Cancer Hospital and Research Institute
1441 Eastlake Avenue
Los Angeles, CA 90033-4496
Med Sch Affil: M-00506
Major participating institution for programs in: AN, CRS, HEM, NM, ON, PMM, RO, SP, U, VIR
Institution ID: 05-0793

Kerlan-Jobe Orthopaedic Clinic
6801 Park Terrace Drive, Suite 500
Los Angeles, CA 90045-3000
www.kerlanjobe.com
Programs sponsored in: OSM
Institution ID: 05-8067

LAC+USC Medical Center
1200 North State Street
Room 1112
Los Angeles, CA 90033-1084
Med Sch Affil: M-00506, G-01401
Major participating institution for programs in: ACA, AI, AN, CCS, CD, CHN, CHP, CN, CRS, D, DR, EM, END, GE, GS, HEM, HMP, HSO, HSP, IC, ICE, ID, IM, IMG, MPD, N, NEP, NM, NO, NP, NPM, NS, OBG, ON, OPH, ORS, OTO, P, PCC, PCP, PD, PDC, PDI, PFP, PMM, PS, PTH, RHU, RNR, RO, SP, TS, U, VIR
Institution ID: 05-0557

Orthopaedic Hospital
2400 South Flower Street
Los Angeles, CA 90007
http://orthohospital.org
Med Sch Affil: M-00506
Programs sponsored in: OP
Institution ID: 05-0347

Ronald L Moy Dermatology Clinic
100 UCLA Medical Plaza, Suite 590
Los Angeles, CA 90024
Programs sponsored in: PRD
Institution ID: 05-8187

SCA Surgery Center
6801 Park Terrace Drive
Suite 300
Los Angeles, CA 90045
Major participating institution for programs in: OSM
Institution ID: 05-8232

Shriners Hospitals for Children (Los Angeles)
3160 Geneva St
Los Angeles, CA 90020-2481
Med Sch Affil: L-00514
Major participating institution for programs in: HSO, ORS
Institution ID: 05-0367

St Vincent Medical Center
2131 W 3rd St
Los Angeles, CA 90057-7360
Med Sch Affil: L-00506
Major participating institution for programs in: NO
Institution ID: 05-0382

Twin Towers Correctional Facility-Jail Mental Health Service
450 Bauchet Street, Room M4127
Los Angeles, CA 90012
Major participating institution for programs in: PFP
Institution ID: 05-8195

UCLA David Geffen School of Medicine/UCLA Medical Center
10833 Le Conte Avenue
Los Angeles, CA 90095-1722
www.medsch.ucla.edu/residencies/
Med Sch Affil: L-02312
Programs sponsored in: ACA, AI, AN, BBK, CCP, CD, CHN, CHP, CN, D, DBP, DMP, DR, EM, END, FP, FSM, GE, GPM, GS, HMP, HO, HSO, IC, ICE, ID, IM, IMG, MGP, MPD, N, NEP, NM, NP, NPM, NS, OBG, OPH, ORS, OSM, OTO, P, PCC, PCP, PD, PDC, PDE, PDI, PDR, PG, PHO, PMM, PN, PPR, PRD, PS, PTH, PYG, RHU, RNR, RO, TS, U, VIR, VN, VS
Institution ID: 05-9503

UCLA Medical Center
10833 Le Conte Avenue
Los Angeles, CA 90095
Med Sch Affil: M-00514, G-00515
Major participating institution for programs in: ACA, AI, AN, BBK, CCP, CD, CHN, CN, D, DMP, DR, EM, END, FSM, GE, GS, HMP, HO, HSO, IC, ICE, ID, IM, MEM, MG, MGP, MPD, N, NEP, NM, NP, NPM, NS, OBG, ORS, OTO, PCC, PCP, PD, PDC, PDE, PDI, PDR, PEM, PG, PHO, PMM, PN, PPR, PRD, PS, PTH, RHU, RNR, RO, TS, U, VIR, VS
Institution ID: 05-0555

UCLA Neuropsychiatric Hospital
760 Westwood Plaza, Room B 8-248
Los Angeles, CA 90024-0231
Med Sch Affil: M-00514
Major participating institution for programs in: CHP, P, PYG
Institution ID: 05-0722

UCLA School of Public Health
16-035 CHS
Box 951772
Los Angeles, CA 90095-1772
Major participating institution for programs in: GPM
Institution ID: 05-0514

University of Southern California/LAC+USC Medical Center
1200 North State Street
Room 1102
Los Angeles, CA 90033-1084
Med Sch Affil: M-00506
Programs sponsored in: ACA, AI, AN, CCS, CD, CHP, CN, CRS, D, DR, EM, END, GE, GS, HEM, HMP, HSO, HSP, IC, ICE, ID, IM, IMG, MPD, N, NEP, NM, NP, NPM, NS, OBG, ON, OPH, ORS, OTO, P, PCC, PCP, PD, PDI, PFP, PMM, PS, PSI, PTH, RHU, RNR, RO, SP, TS, U, VIR, VS
Institution ID: 05-8116

USC Orthopaedic Surgery Associates
1520 San Pablo Street #2000
Los Angeles, CA 90033
Programs sponsored in: OSM
Institution ID: 05-8209

USC University Hospital
1500 San Pablo Street
Los Angeles, CA 90033-1219
Med Sch Affil: M-00506
Major participating institution for programs in: ACA, AN, CCS, CN, CRS, END, GE, GS, HEM, HSO, ICE, ID, IMG, NEP, NM, NS, OPH, ORS, OSM, OTO, PCC, PMM, RHU, RNR, TS, VIR, VS
Institution ID: 05-8065

VA Greater Los Angeles Healthcare System
11301 Wilshire Boulevard
Los Angeles, CA 90073-2128
www.va.gov
Programs sponsored in: AI, CD, END, ICE, ID, IM, NM, P, PFP, PM, PMM, SME
Major participating institution for programs in: CCM, CD, CN, D, DR, END, GE, GS, HPM, ICE, IM, IMG, N, NEP, NS, OPH, ORS, OTO, PCC, PRD, PTH, PYG, PYM, RHU, RNR, TS, U, VIR
Institution ID: 05-8105

Vista Del Mar Child & Family Services
3200 Motor Avenue
Los Angeles, CA 90034
Major participating institution for programs in: CHP
Institution ID: 05-8220

White Memorial Medical Center
1720 Cesar E Chavez Avenue
Department of Medical Education
Los Angeles, CA 90033-2481
www.whitememorial.com
Med Sch Affil: L-00512
Programs sponsored in: FP, IM, OBG, PD
Institution ID: 05-0353

Madera

Children's Hospital Central California
9300 Valley Children's Place
Madera, CA 93638-8761
Med Sch Affil: M-00502
Major participating institution for programs in: PD
Institution ID: 05-7058

Martinez

Contra Costa Regional Medical Center
2500 Alhambra Avenue
Martinez, CA 94553-1495
http://cchealth.org
Med Sch Affil: G-00519
Programs sponsored in: FP
Institution ID: 05-0271

Kaiser Permanente - Martinez Medical Offices
200 Muir Road
Martinez, CA 94553
Major participating institution for programs in: GPM
Institution ID: 05-8236

Mather

VA Northern California Health Care System
10535 Hospital Way
Mather, CA 95655
Major participating institution for programs in: AI, CN, D, END, ETX, FP, HO, ID, IMG, N, NEP, OTO, PCC, PRD, PTH, RHU, SME, U
Institution ID: 05-8118

Merced

Mercy Medical Center Merced
315 East 13th Street
Merced, CA 95340
www.mercymercedCARES.org
Med Sch Affil: G-00519
Programs sponsored in: FP
Institution ID: 05-0715

Milpitas

Alliance Occupational Medicine
315 S Abbott Avenue
Milpitas, CA 95035
Major participating institution for programs in: GPM
Institution ID: 05-8215

Mission Viejo

Mission Hospital Regional Medical Center
27700 Medical Center Drive
Mission Viejo, CA 92691
Major participating institution for programs in: PS
Institution ID: 05-8188

Teaching Institutions

Modesto

Doctors Medical Center
1441 Florida Avenue
PO Box 4138
Modesto, CA 95352-4138
Major participating institution for programs in: FP
Institution ID: 05-8099

Stanislaus County Health Services
830 Scenic Drive
Modesto, CA 95350-4138
http://fpnetwork.ucdavis.edu
Programs sponsored in: FP
Institution ID: 05-8102

Moreno Valley

Riverside County Regional Medical Center
26520 Cactus Avenue
Office of Graduate Medical Education, Rm A1005
Moreno Valley, CA 92555-1495
www.riversidecountyfpresidency.com
Med Sch Affil: M-00512, L-00514, G-00515
Programs sponsored in: FP
Major participating institution for programs in: D, EM, GE, GS, IM, MPD, OPH, OTO, U
Institution ID: 05-0260

Napa

Napa State Hospital
2100 Napa-Vallejo Highway
Napa, CA 94558-6293
Major participating institution for programs in: PFP
Institution ID: 05-0205

National City

Paradise Valley Hospital
2400 East Fourth Street
National City, CA 91950-2099
Major participating institution for programs in: UME
Institution ID: 05-7068

Northridge

Northridge Hospital Medical Center
18300 Roscoe Blvd
Northridge, CA 91325-0231
www.northridgefp.org
Med Sch Affil: L-00514
Programs sponsored in: FP
Institution ID: 05-0726

Norwalk

Metropolitan State Hospital
11400 Norwalk Boulevard
Norwalk, CA 90650-5693
Major participating institution for programs in: CHP, PFP
Institution ID: 05-0299

Oakland

Alameda County Medical Center
1411 East 31st Street
Oakland, CA 94602-2180
www.acmedctr.org
Med Sch Affil: L-00502
Programs sponsored in: EM, IM
Major participating institution for programs in: GS, OPH, ORS, PCC
Institution ID: 05-0413

Children's Hospital-Oakland
747 52nd Street
Oakland, CA 94609-1809
www.choresidency.org
Med Sch Affil: M-00502
Programs sponsored in: PD, PDI, PDP, PEM, PHO
Major participating institution for programs in: CCP, PAN
Institution ID: 05-0110

Kaiser Permanente Medical Center (Oakland)
280 West MacArthur Boulevard
Oakland, CA 94611-5693
Med Sch Affil: L-00502, G-00519
Major participating institution for programs in: GS, IM, OBG, ORS, OTO, PD
Institution ID: 05-0296

Kaiser Permanente Medical Group (Northern California)
1800 Harrison St, 21st Floor
Oakland, CA 94612-2298
http://residency.kp.org/ncal
Programs sponsored in: CD, IM, OBG, OTO, PD
Institution ID: 05-8090

Orange

Children's Hospital of Orange County
455 S Main Street
Academic Affairs Office
Orange, CA 92868
www.choc.org
Med Sch Affil: G-00515
Programs sponsored in: PD, PHO
Major participating institution for programs in: CCP, CHN, END, NPM, NS, ORS, OTO
Institution ID: 05-0547

St Joseph Hospital (Orange)
1100 West La Veta
Orange, CA 92868
Major participating institution for programs in: ORS
Institution ID: 05-8173

University of California (Irvine) Medical Center
200 East Manchester Street
Suite 130
Orange, CA 92868-1084
uci.edu
Med Sch Affil: M-00515
Programs sponsored in: AI, AN, CCS, CD, CHN, CHP, CN, D, DR, EM, END, FP, GE, GPM, GS, HO, HSO, IC, ID, IM, IMG, MG, N, NEP, NMN, NPM, NR, NS, OBG, OPH, ORS, OTO, P, PCC, PCP, PD, PDP, PM, PMG, PMM, PS, PSI, PTH, RHU, RO, SCI, U, VIR
Institution ID: 05-0564

Palo Alto

Lucile Salter Packard Children's Hospital at Stanford
725 Welch Road
Palo Alto, CA 94304-1084
Med Sch Affil: M-00511
Major participating institution for programs in: ADL, AI, BBK, CCP, CHN, CHP, CN, DBP, HSO, NPM, NS, OBG, OTO, PAN, PD, PDC, PDE, PDI, PDP, PDR, PDS, PG, PHO, PN, PPR, TS, TSI, U
Institution ID: 05-0572

Stanford Blood Center
800 Welch Road, Room 280
Palo Alto, CA 94394
Major participating institution for programs in: BBK
Institution ID: 05-8192

Veterans Affairs Palo Alto Health Care System
3801 Miranda Avenue
Palo Alto, CA 94304-1207
Med Sch Affil: M-00511
Major participating institution for programs in: AN, CCA, CCM, CD, CHN, D, DR, END, GE, GS, HSO, IM, IMG, NM, NS, OAR, OPH, ORS, OTO, P, PCC, PCP, PM, PMM, PTH, PYG, RHU, SCI, TS, U, VS, VSI
Institution ID: 05-0273

Panorama City

Kaiser Permanente Panorama City Medical Center
13652 Cantara St
Panorama City, CA 91402
Major participating institution for programs in: FP
Institution ID: 05-0575

Pasadena

Congress Medical Associates
39 Congress Street, Suite 201
Pasadena, CA 91105
Programs sponsored in: OSM
Institution ID: 05-8200

Hathaway-Sycamores Child & Family Services
210 S DeLacey Ave #110
Pasadena, CA 91101-2074
Major participating institution for programs in: CHP
Institution ID: 05-8221

Huntington Memorial Hospital
100 W California Blvd
Pasadena, CA 91105-7013
http://huntingtonhospital.com
Med Sch Affil: M-00506
Programs sponsored in: GS, IM
Major participating institution for programs in: TS, VS
Institution ID: 05-0474

Kaiser Permanente Southern California
Physician Education
100 S Los Robles, Suite 550
Pasadena, CA 91101
http://residency.kp.org/scal/
Programs sponsored in: AI, CD, DR, FP, FPG, FSM, GE, GS, IC, ICE, IM, N, NEP, OBG, OSM, PD, RO, U
Major participating institution for programs in: GPM, HSO, PS
Institution ID: 05-8072

Patton

Patton State Hospital
3102 E Highland Avenue
Patton, CA 92369-4007
Major participating institution for programs in: GPM
Institution ID: 05-0149

Pomona

Pomona Valley Hospital Medical Center
1798 North Garey Avenue
Pomona, CA 91767-2298
www.pvhmc.org
Programs sponsored in: FP
Institution ID: 05-8094

Redding

Mercy Medical Center
2175 Rosaline Avenue
PO Box 496009
Redding, CA 96049-6009
www.mercy.org
Med Sch Affil: G-00519
Programs sponsored in: FP
Institution ID: 05-0745

Redwood City

Kaiser Permanente Medical Center (Redwood City)
1150 Veterans Blvd
Redwood City, CA 94063-1994
Med Sch Affil: L-00511
Major participating institution for programs in: OTO
Institution ID: 05-8029

Riverside

Kaiser Foundation Hospital (Riverside)
10800 Magnolia Avenue
Riverside, CA 92505-3000
Med Sch Affil: G-00515
Major participating institution for programs in: FP
Institution ID: 05-8066

Sacramento

California Department of Public Health
1615 Capitol Ave Ste 720
PO Box 997377, MS 0500
Sacramento, CA 95899-7377
www.dhs.ca.gov/ps/cdic/cdcb/pds/pmrp
Programs sponsored in: GPM
Institution ID: 05-0202

Kaiser Foundation Hospital (Sacramento)
2025 Morse Avenue
Sacramento, CA 95825-1084
Med Sch Affil: M-00519
Major participating institution for programs in: GS, OBG, U
Institution ID: 05-0578

Kaiser Foundation Hospital (South Sacramento)
6600 Bruceville Road
Sacramento, CA 95823-2246
Major participating institution for programs in: EM, GS
Institution ID: 05-8048

Laser & Skin Surgery Center of Northern California
3835 J Street
Sacramento, CA 95816
Major participating institution for programs in: PRD
Institution ID: 05-8213

Mercy General Hospital (Mercy Healthcare Sacramento)
4001 J Street
Sacramento, CA 95819
Major participating institution for programs in: FP, SME
Institution ID: 05-0489

Methodist Hospital of Sacramento
7500 Hospital Drive
Sacramento, CA 95823-0037
www.calweb.com/~mhsfpres/
Programs sponsored in: FP
Institution ID: 05-8089

Sacramento County Correctional Health Services
9616 Micron Avenue
Suite 850
Sacramento, CA 95827
Major participating institution for programs in: PFP
Institution ID: 05-8252

Sacramento County Health and Human Services
3701 Branch Center Road
Room 210
Sacramento, CA 95827
Major participating institution for programs in: CHP, MP, P
Institution ID: 05-8190

Shriners Hospitals for Children (Sacramento)
2425 Stockton Boulevard
Sacramento, CA 95817-1495
Med Sch Affil: M-00519
Major participating institution for programs in: HSO, ORS, PDR
Institution ID: 05-0239

Sutter General Hospital
2801 L St
Sacramento, CA 95816-1495
Med Sch Affil: M-00519
Major participating institution for programs in: FP
Institution ID: 05-0241

Sutter Health
2200 River Plaza Drive
Sacramento, CA 95833
www.sutterhealth.org
Programs sponsored in: FP
Institution ID: 05-8085

University of California (Davis) Health System
4610 X Street
Suite 4202, Education Building
Sacramento, CA 95817
www.ucdmc.ucdavis.edu/gme/
Programs sponsored in: ACA, AI, AN, CCS, CD, CHP, CN, D, DBP, DR, EM, END, ETX, FP, FPP, FSM, GE, GS, HMP, HO, HSO, IC, ID, IM, IMG, MP, N, NEP, NM, NPM, NS, OBG, OPH, ORS, OTO, P, PAN, PCC, PCP, PD, PDE, PDR, PFP, PHO, PM, PMM, PRD, PS, PTH, PYM, RHU, RNR, RO, SME, TS, U, VIR
Institution ID: 05-8115

University of California (Davis) Medical Center
2315 Stockton Blvd
Sacramento, CA 95817
Med Sch Affil: M-00519, G-02312
Major participating institution for programs in: ACA, AI, AN, CCS, CD, CHP, CN, D, DBP, DR, EM, END, ETX, FP, FPP, FSM, GE, GPM, GS, HMP, HO, HSO, IC, ID, IM, IMG, MP, N, NEP, NM, NPM, NS, OBG, OPH, ORS, OTO, P, PAN, PCC, PCP, PD, PDE, PFP, PHO, PM, PMM, PRD, PS, PTH, PYM, RHU, RNR, RO, SME, TS, TY, U, VIR
Institution ID: 05-0436

Salinas

Natividad Medical Center
1441 Constitution Boulevard, Building 300
Salinas, CA 93906-4007
www.natividad.com/res
Med Sch Affil: M-00502
Programs sponsored in: FP
Major participating institution for programs in: UP
Institution ID: 05-0160

San Diego

Alvarado Hospital Medical Center
6655 Alvarado Rd
San Diego, CA 92120-0037
Major participating institution for programs in: OSM, VN
Institution ID: 05-8086

California Poison Control System (CPSC)-San Diego
135 Dickinson Street
San Diego, CA 92103-8925
Major participating institution for programs in: PTX
Institution ID: 05-8110

Docere Foundation
6719 Alvarado Road
Suite 200
San Diego, CA 92120
Programs sponsored in: OSM
Institution ID: 05-8201

Graduate School of Public Health
San Diego State University
5500 Campanile Drive
San Diego, CA 92182-4162
Med Sch Affil: G-00518
Major participating institution for programs in: GPM
Institution ID: 05-8030

Kaiser Foundation Hospital (San Diego)
4647 Zion Avenue
San Diego, CA 92120-6009
Med Sch Affil: G-00518
Major participating institution for programs in: NO, NS, OBG, OSM, OTO, VS
Institution ID: 05-0760

Naval Medical Center (San Diego)
34800 Bob Wilson Dr
San Diego, CA 92134-5000
www.nmcsd.med.navy.mil
Med Sch Affil: M-02312, M-00518, L-02012
Programs sponsored in: AN, CD, D, DR, EM, GE, GS, ID, IM, OBG, OPH, ORS, OTO, P, PCC, PD, PTH, TY, U
Major participating institution for programs in: FP, NEP, PTX, UP, VIR
Institution ID: 05-0386

Rady Children's Hospital
3020 Children's Way
San Diego, CA 92123-1772
Med Sch Affil: M-00518
Major participating institution for programs in: AI, CCP, CHN, CHP, MG, MPD, NPM, NS, ORS, PD, PDC, PDE, PDI, PDP, PE, PG, PHO, PN, PS, PTX, TS, U, UP
Institution ID: 05-0533

San Diego County Medical Examiner
5555 Overland Avenue
Suite 1411
San Diego, CA 92123-1270
www.co.san-diego.ca.us/cnty/cntydepts/safety/medical/index.html
Programs sponsored in: FOP
Institution ID: 05-8061

San Diego Hospice and Palliative Care Center
4311 Third Avenue
San Diego, CA 92103-1407
Major participating institution for programs in: HPM
Institution ID: 05-8138

San Diego Sports Medicine and Orthopaedic Center
6719 Alvarado Road
Suite 200
San Diego, CA 92120
Major participating institution for programs in: OSM
Institution ID: 05-8202

Scripps Mercy Hospital
Department of Graduate Medical Education (MER35)
4077 Fifth Avenue
San Diego, CA 92103-2180
www.scrippsmercy.com
Med Sch Affil: M-00518
Programs sponsored in: HPM, IM, TY
Major participating institution for programs in: GS, PTX, VN
Institution ID: 05-0397

Sharp HealthCare
8695 Spectrum Center CT
San Diego, CA 92123-1489
Major participating institution for programs in: ORS
Institution ID: 05-8076

Sharp Memorial Hospital
7901 Frost Street
San Diego, CA 92123-2788
Major participating institution for programs in: VN
Institution ID: 05-0366

Teaching Institutions

University of California (San Diego) Medical Center
200 W Arbor Drive
San Diego, CA 92103
Med Sch Affil: M-00518, G-00515
Programs sponsored in: ACA, AI, AN, CCP, CCS, CD, CHN, CHP, CN, D, DR, EM, END, FP, FPP, FSM, GE, GPM, GS, HO, HSO, IC, ICE, ID, IM, IMG, MG, MPD, N, NEP, NM, NO, NP, NPM, NS, OBG, OPH, ORS, OTO, P, PCC, PD, PDC, PDE, PDI, PDP, PE, PG, PHO, PMM, PN, PS, PTH, PTX, PYG, RHU, RNR, TS, U, UME, UP, VIR, VN
Major participating institution for programs in: OSM, P, PCC
Institution ID: 05-0434

Veterans Affairs Medical Center (San Diego)
3350 La Jolla Village Drive
San Diego, CA 92161-1084
Med Sch Affil: M-00518
Major participating institution for programs in: ACA, AI, AN, CD, CHN, D, DR, END, GE, GS, HO, HSO, IC, ICE, IM, IMG, MPD, N, NEP, NM, NO, NP, NS, OPH, ORS, OSM, OTO, P, PCC, PMM, PS, PTH, PTX, PYG, RHU, RNR, TS, U, VN, VS
Institution ID: 05-0589

San Francisco

Blood Centers of the Pacific
270 Masonic Avenue
San Francisco, CA 94118-4496
www.bloodcenters.org
Programs sponsored in: BBK
Institution ID: 05-0767

California Pacific Medical Center
2333 Buchanan Street
San Francisco, CA 94115
http://cpmc.org
Med Sch Affil: L-00502
Programs sponsored in: CD, GE, HSP, IM, OPH, P, PCC, RO
Major participating institution for programs in: CN, GS
Institution ID: 05-0432

Center for Occupational Psychiatry
690 Market Street, Suite 706
San Francisco, CA 94104-2128
Major participating institution for programs in: PFP
Institution ID: 05-8109

Department of Public Health (San Francisco)
101 Grove Street
San Francisco, CA 94102
Major participating institution for programs in: CHP, GPM
Institution ID: 05-8175

Edgewood Center for Children & Families
1801 Vicente Street
San Francisco, CA 94116
Major participating institution for programs in: CHP
Institution ID: 05-8186

Kaiser Permanente Medical Center (San Francisco)
2425 Geary Boulevard
San Francisco, CA 94115-1428
Med Sch Affil: L-00502
Major participating institution for programs in: CD, IM, IPM, OBG, OTO
Institution ID: 05-0204

San Francisco General Hospital Medical Center
1001 Potrero Avenue
Suite 2A5
San Francisco, CA 94110-5693
Med Sch Affil: M-00502
Major participating institution for programs in: AN, CCS, CD, CRS, D, DMP, DR, EM, END, FP, GE, GS, HSO, ID, IM, IPM, NEP, OBG, OPH, ORS, OTO, P, PCC, PCP, PD, PDM, PS, PTH, PTX, RHU, U
Institution ID: 05-0334

St Francis Memorial Hospital
900 Hyde Street
San Francisco, CA 94109-4007
Major participating institution for programs in: RO
Institution ID: 05-0162

St Mary's Hospital and Medical Center
450 Stanyan Street
San Francisco, CA 94117
www.chw.edu
Med Sch Affil: L-00502
Programs sponsored in: IM, ORS
Institution ID: 05-0163

Treasure Island Job Corps
655 H Avenue, Building 442
Treasure Island
San Francisco, CA 94130
Major participating institution for programs in: ADL
Institution ID: 05-8253

UCSF and Mount Zion Medical Centers
500 Parnassus Avenue, Box 0296
San Francisco, CA 94143-0296
Med Sch Affil: M-00502
Major participating institution for programs in: ADL, AN, BBK, CCA, CCM, CCP, CCS, CD, CHN, CN, CRS, D, DMP, DR, EM, END, GE, GPM, GS, HMP, HO, HSO, IC, ICE, ID, IM, IMG, IPM, MG, N, NEP, NM, NP, NPM, NS, OBG, OPH, ORS, OSM, OTO, PAN, PCC, PD, PDC, PDE, PDI, PDM, PDP, PG, PHO, PMM, PN, PPR, PRD, PS, PTH, RHU, RNR, RO, THP, TS, U, UP, VN, VS
Institution ID: 05-0554

UCSF Med Ctr/Langley Porter Psychiatric Hosp and Clinics
500 Parnassus Avenue, Box 0296
San Francisco, CA 94143-0296
Med Sch Affil: M-00502
Major participating institution for programs in: EM, P, PFP, PYG
Institution ID: 05-0122

University of California (San Francisco) School of Medicine
500 Parnassus Avenue
MU 250 East
San Francisco, CA 94143-0474
www.medschool.ucsf.edu/gme
Med Sch Affil: M-00502
Programs sponsored in: ADL, AN, CCA, CCM, CCP, CCS, CD, CHN, CHP, CN, CRS, D, DMP, DR, EM, END, FP, GE, GPM, GS, HMP, HO, HPM, HSO, IC, ICE, ID, IM, IMG, IPM, MGP, N, NEP, NM, NP, NPM, NS, OBG, OPH, ORS, OSM, OTO, P, PAN, PCC, PCP, PD, PDC, PDE, PDI, PDM, PDP, PDR, PFP, PG, PHO, PMM, PN, PPR, PRD, PS, PTH, PTX, PYG, RHU, RNR, RO, THP, TS, U, UP, VIR, VN, VS
Institution ID: 05-0737

Veterans Affairs Medical Center (San Francisco)
4150 Clement Street
San Francisco, CA 94121
Med Sch Affil: M-00502
Major participating institution for programs in: CD, CN, D, DMP, DR, END, GE, GS, IC, ID, IM, IMG, IPM, NEP, OPH, ORS, OTO, P, PDM, PMM, PTH, PYG, RHU, RNR, TS, U
Institution ID: 05-0113

San Jose

Kaiser Santa Teresa
250 Hospital Parkway
San Jose, CA 95119-2298
Major participating institution for programs in: CHP
Institution ID: 05-8092

O'Connor Hospital
2105 Forest Avenue
San Jose, CA 95128-1471
Programs sponsored in: FP, FSM
Institution ID: 05-0178

Santa Clara Valley Medical Center
751 S Bascom Ave
San Jose, CA 95128-2180
Med Sch Affil: M-00511
Programs sponsored in: DR, IM, OBG, TY
Major participating institution for programs in: CHN, D, END, GS, N, NEP, OPH, ORS, OTO, PD, PM, RHU, SCI, U, UP
Institution ID: 05-0438

San Mateo

San Mateo County Behavioral Health and Recovery Services
Psychiatry Residency Training Program
222 West 39th Avenue
San Mateo, CA 94403-2116
www.smhealth.org/psychresidency
Programs sponsored in: P
Institution ID: 05-8194

San Mateo Medical Center
San Mateo County Mental Health Services
222 West 39th Avenue
San Mateo, CA 94403
Major participating institution for programs in: P
Institution ID: 05-0585

San Quentin

California Department of Corrections
San Quentin, CA 94964
Major participating institution for programs in: PFP
Institution ID: 05-8108

Santa Ana

Western Medical Center
1001 N Tustin Ave
Santa Ana, CA 92705-6009
Med Sch Affil: G-00515
Major participating institution for programs in: FP
Institution ID: 05-0747

Santa Barbara

Santa Barbara Cottage Hospital
PO Box 689
Santa Barbara, CA 93102-0689
www.sbch.org
Med Sch Affil: L-00506
Programs sponsored in: DR, GS, IM
Institution ID: 05-0381

Santa Clara

Kaiser Permanente Medical Center (Santa Clara)
700 Lawrence Expressway
Santa Clara, CA 95051-5173
Med Sch Affil: L-00511
Major participating institution for programs in: CHP, EM, GS, IM, OBG, P
Institution ID: 05-0571

Santa Monica

Santa Monica Orthopaedic and Sports Medicine Group
2020 Santa Monica Blvd
Suite 400
Santa Monica, CA 90404
Programs sponsored in: OSM
Institution ID: 05-8189

Santa Monica-UCLA Medical Center
1250 16th Street
Santa Monica, CA 90404-1200
Med Sch Affil: M-00514
Major participating institution for programs in: CN,
DBP, FP, HSO, IC, OP, PMM, VIR
Institution ID: 05-0439

Santa Rosa

Sutter Medical Center of Santa Rosa
3325 Chanate Road
Santa Rosa, CA 95404-4007
http://sutterhealth.org
Med Sch Affil: M-00502
Major participating institution for programs in: FP
Institution ID: 05-0152

Santa Rose

Santa Rosa Consortium
3324 Chanate Road
Santa Rose, CA 95404
Programs sponsored in: FP
Institution ID: 05-8249

Signal Hill

Willow Medical Center
2704 East Willow Street
Signal Hill, CA 90755
Major participating institution for programs in: D
Institution ID: 05-8208

Stanford

Stanford Hospital and Clinics
Dept of Graduate Medical Education, Room-HC435
300 Pasteur Dr
Stanford, CA 94305-5207
Med Sch Affil: M-00511, L-00502
Programs sponsored in: ACA, ADL, AI, AN, BBK, CCA,
CCM, CCP, CCS, CD, CHN, CHP, CN, D, DBP, DMP, DR,
EM, END, GE, GS, HEM, HMP, HPM, HSO, IC, ICE, ID,
IM, IMG, MG, MGP, N, NEP, NM, NO, NP, NPM, NS, OAR,
OBG, ON, OPH, ORS, OSM, OTO, P, PAN, PCC, PCP, PD,
PDC, PDE, PDI, PDP, PDR, PDS, PG, PHO, PM, PMM, PN,
PPR, PTH, PSI, PYG, RHU, RNR, RO, SCI, SME, TS, TSI,
U, UP, VIR, VN, VS, VSI
Major participating institution for programs in: MGP
Institution ID: 05-0129

Stockton

St Joseph's Medical Center
PO Box 213008
1800 North California Street
Stockton, CA 95213-2000
Major participating institution for programs in: GS
Institution ID: 05-8112

Sylmar

Olive View/UCLA Medical Center
14445 Olive View Drive
Sylmar, CA 91342
Programs sponsored in: HO, IM, MEM, NEP, RHU
Major participating institution for programs in: CD,
D, DR, EM, FP, GS, HSO, ID, OBG, OPH, OTO, P, PFP,
SME, U
Institution ID: 05-0216

Torrance

Los Angeles County-Harbor-UCLA Medical Center
1000 W Carson Street
Torrance, CA 90509-7360
www.harbor-ucla.org
Med Sch Affil: M-00514, G-00515, G-04815
Programs sponsored in: AN, CCP, CD, CHN, CHP, D, DR,
EM, END, FP, FSM, GS, HO, IC, ICE, ID, IM, N, NEP,
NPM, NR, OBG, ORS, P, PCC, PD, PDE, PDI, PEM, PTH,
RNR, TY, VIR, VS
Major participating institution for programs in: ADP,
IM, MG, NS, OPH, OTO, RHU, U
Institution ID: 05-0385

Travis AFB

David Grant Medical Center
60 MDG/SGT
101 Bodin Circle
Travis AFB, CA 94535-1800
Med Sch Affil: M-00519, G-02312
Programs sponsored in: DR, FP, TY
Institution ID: 05-0499

Van Nuys

Southern California Orthopedic Institute
6815 Noble Ave
Van Nuys, CA 91405-3730
www.scoi.com
Programs sponsored in: OSM
Major participating institution for programs in: HSP
Institution ID: 05-8070

Ventura

Ventura County Medical Center
Office of Medical Education
3291 Loma Vista Rd
Ventura, CA 93003-5693
www.venturafpr.com
Programs sponsored in: FP
Institution ID: 05-0324

Walnut Creek

Kaiser Permanente Medical Center (Walnut Creek)
1425 South Main Street
Walnut Creek, CA 94596
Major participating institution for programs in: GS
Institution ID: 05-0761

Whittier

Presbyterian Intercommunity Hospital
12401 E Washington Blvd
Whittier, CA 90602-1099
www.pih.net
Med Sch Affil: L-00514, G-00506
Programs sponsored in: FP
Institution ID: 05-0762

Woodland Hills

Kaiser Foundation Hospital (Woodland Hills)
5601 DeSoto Ave
Woodland Hills, CA 91365-3000
Med Sch Affil: G-00514
Major participating institution for programs in: FP,
FPG
Institution ID: 05-8068

Colorado

Aspen

Aspen Sports Medicine Foundation
100 East Main Street
Suite 101
Aspen, CO 81611-3798
www.orthop.com
Programs sponsored in: OSM
Institution ID: 07-8013

Aurora

Children's Hospital (The)
13123 E 16th Avenue
Aurora, CO 80045
Med Sch Affil: M-00702
Major participating institution for programs in: ACA,
ADL, AI, BBK, CCP, CHN, CHP, CHS, FSM, HSO, MG,
NPM, NS, ORS, OTO, PAN, PD, PDC, PDE, PDI, PDO,
PDP, PDR, PDS, PEM, PG, PHO, PM, PP, RNR, RPM,
SME, U, VN
Institution ID: 07-0378

Colorado Foundation for Medical Care
2851 South Parker Road
Suite 1000
Aurora, CO 80014
Major participating institution for programs in: GPM
Institution ID: 07-8034

University of Colorado Denver School of Medicine
Mail Stop C293
13001 E 17th Place
Aurora, CO 80045
www.uchsc.edu/gme
Med Sch Affil: M-00702, L-02312
Programs sponsored in: ACA, ADL, ADP, AI, AN, BBK,
CCP, CCS, CD, CHN, CHP, CHS, D, DMP, DR, END, FOP,
FP, FSM, GE, GS, HO, HSO, IC, ICE, ID, IM, IMG, MG, N,
NEP, NM, NMN, NPM, NS, OBG, OPH, ORS, OTO, P, PAN,
PCC, PD, PDC, PDE, PDI, PDO, PDP, PDR, PDS, PEM,
PFP, PG, PHO, PM, PMM, PP, PPM, PTH, PYG, PYM,
RHU, RNR, RO, RPM, SME, THP, TS, U, VIR, VN
Institution ID: 07-0313

University of Colorado Hospital
12605 East 16th Avenue
Aurora, CO 80045
Major participating institution for programs in: ACA,
ADP, AI, AN, BBK, CCS, CD, CHN, CHP, D, DMP, DR, EM,
END, FP, FSM, GE, GS, HO, HSO, IC, ICE, ID, IM, IMG,
MG, N, NEP, NM, NMN, NS, OBG, OPH, ORS, OTO, P,
PCC, PM, PMM, PTH, PYM, RHU, RNR, RO, SME, THP,
TS, U, VIR, VN
Institution ID: 07-8022

Colorado Springs

Penrose-St Francis Health Services
Department of Pathology
2222 North Nevada Ave
Colorado Springs, CO 80907
www.penrosepathologyresidency.org
Programs sponsored in: PTH
Institution ID: 07-0327

Denver

Bonfils Blood Center
717 Yosemite Street
Denver, CO 80230
bonfils.org
Med Sch Affil: L-00702
Programs sponsored in: BBK
Institution ID: 07-8025

Teaching Institutions

Colorado Department of Corrections
3600 Havana St
PO Box 392005
Denver, CO 80239
Major participating institution for programs in: PFP
Institution ID: 07-8026

Colorado Department of Public Health and Environment
4200 Cherry Creek Drive South
EDO-A5
Denver, CO 80246
Major participating institution for programs in: GPM
Institution ID: 07-8037

Colorado Health Foundation Presbyterian-St Luke's Med Ctr
1719 East 19th Avenue, 5 C-East
Denver, CO 80218-1281
www.health1.org
Programs sponsored in: TY
Institution ID: 07-0277

Colorado Mental Health Institute at Fort Logan
3520 West Oxford Avenue
Denver, CO 80236
Major participating institution for programs in: CHP
Institution ID: 07-0469

Colorado School of Public Health
4200 E 9th Avenue, #B119
Denver, CO 80262
Programs sponsored in: GPM
Institution ID: 07-8050

Denver Health Medical Center
777 Bannock Street, MC 0108
Denver, CO 80204-4507
http://dhha.org
Med Sch Affil: M-00702, L-02312
Programs sponsored in: EM, ETX
Major participating institution for programs in: ADP, AN, CCS, CD, CHP, D, DR, FP, GPM, GS, HSO, ICE, ID, IM, N, NEP, NS, OBG, OPH, ORS, OTO, P, PD, PFP, PM, PTH, PYG, RHU, U, VIR, VN
Institution ID: 07-0280

Denver Office of the Medical Examiner
660 Bannock Street
Denver, CO 80204
Major participating institution for programs in: FOP
Institution ID: 07-8048

Dermatopathology Services LLC
240 Josephine St
Suite 204
Denver, CO 80206
Major participating institution for programs in: DMP
Institution ID: 07-8046

Exempla St Joseph Hospital
1835 Franklin Street
Denver, CO 80218-3798
http://exempla.org
Programs sponsored in: FP, GS, IM, OBG
Major participating institution for programs in: ACA, ICE
Institution ID: 07-0451

HealthONE Rose Medical Center
4567 E Ninth Avenue
Denver, CO 80220-3941
Med Sch Affil: G-00702
Major participating institution for programs in: FP, FSM, OBG
Institution ID: 07-0269

Kaiser Permanente Health Care Group (Denver)
19th Avenue and Lafayette Street
Denver, CO 80218
Major participating institution for programs in: GPM
Institution ID: 07-8027

National Jewish Medical and Research Center
1400 Jackson Street
Denver, CO 80206-1281
Med Sch Affil: M-00702, G-02312
Major participating institution for programs in: AI, PCC, PYM, SME
Institution ID: 07-0287

University of Colorado Denver
4200 East 9th Avenue
Denver, CO 80262
Major participating institution for programs in: CCP, GPM
Institution ID: 07-8035

Veterans Affairs Medical Center (Denver)
1055 Clermont St
Denver, CO 80220-1722
Med Sch Affil: M-00702
Major participating institution for programs in: ADP, CD, D, DMP, DR, GPM, GS, HSO, IC, ID, IM, IMG, N, NEP, NS, OPH, ORS, OTO, P, PM, PTH, PYG, RHU, SME, TS, U, VN
Institution ID: 07-0157

Englewood

HealthONE Swedish Medical Center
501 E Hampden Ave
Englewood, CO 80110-1420
Med Sch Affil: G-00702
Major participating institution for programs in: FP, PM, GS
Institution ID: 07-8020

Fort Collins

Health District of Northern Larimer County
120 Bristlecone Drive
Fort Collins, CO 80524
Major participating institution for programs in: GPM
Institution ID: 07-8038

Poudre Valley Hospital
1024 Lemay Ave
Fort Collins, CO 80524-3798
www.pvhs.org
Programs sponsored in: FP
Institution ID: 07-0705

Ft Collins

Centers for Disease Control and Prevention
3150 Rampart Rd
Ft Collins, CO 80522
Major participating institution for programs in: GPM
Institution ID: 07-8051

Ft Lupton

Plan de Salud del Valle, Inc
1115 2nd Street
Ft. Lupton, CO 80621
Major participating institution for programs in: GPM
Institution ID: 07-8040

Golden

Jefferson County Health and Environment
1801 19th Street
Golden, CO 80401
Major participating institution for programs in: GPM
Institution ID: 07-8039

Panorama Orthopedics & Spine Center
660 Golden Ridge Road, Suite 250
Golden, CO 80401
Programs sponsored in: OSM
Institution ID: 07-8047

Grand Junction

St Mary's Hospital and Medical Center
Seventh St and Patterson Rd
PO Box 1628
Grand Junction, CO 81502-3798
www.stmarygj.org
Programs sponsored in: FP
Institution ID: 07-0713

Greeley

North Colorado Medical Center
1801 16th Street
Greeley, CO 80631-1281
http://NCMCGreeley.com
Programs sponsored in: FP
Institution ID: 07-0348

Greenwood Village

Steadman Hawkins Clinic (Denver)
8200 E Belleview Avenue
Suite 615
Greenwood Village, CO 80111
Programs sponsored in: OSM
Institution ID: 07-8032

Tri-County Health Dept
Suite 301
Greenwood Village, CO 80111
Major participating institution for programs in: GPM
Institution ID: 07-8041

Lafayette

Clinica Campesina
1345 Plaza Court North #1A
Lafayette, CO 80026
Major participating institution for programs in: GPM
Institution ID: 07-8036

Pueblo

Colorado Mental Health Institute at Pueblo
1600 W 24th Street
Pueblo, CO 81003-1499
Major participating institution for programs in: PFP
Institution ID: 07-8024

St Mary-Corwin Medical Center
1008 Minnequa Avenue
Pueblo, CO 81004-3798
www.s-co-familymed.com
Programs sponsored in: FP
Institution ID: 07-0360

Vail

Steadman Hawkins Clinic
181 West Meadow Drive
Suite 400
Vail, CO 81657
www.shsmf.org
Programs sponsored in: OSM
Institution ID: 07-8018

Vail Valley Medical Center
181 W Meadow Dr
Vail, CO 81657-1420
Major participating institution for programs in: OSM
Institution ID: 07-8017

Westminster

St Anthony Hospital Central
2551 West 84th Avenue
Westminster, CO 80030-1420
Major participating institution for programs in: FP, OSM
Institution ID: 07-8023

St Anthony Hospital North
2551 West 84th Avenue
Westminster, CO 80031
www.stanthonyfamilymed.org
Med Sch Affil: G-00702
Programs sponsored in: FP
Major participating institution for programs in: OSM
Institution ID: 07-0351

Wray

Wray Community District Hospital
1017 West 7th Street
Wray, CO 80758-1420
Major participating institution for programs in: FP
Institution ID: 07-8016

Connecticut

Bridgeport

Bridgeport Hospital
267 Grant Street, Box 5000
Bridgeport, CT 06610-0729
www.bpthosp.org/gme
Med Sch Affil: M-00801
Programs sponsored in: CD, DR, GE, IC, IM, IMG, OBG, PUD
Major participating institution for programs in: EM, GS, MG, PS
Institution ID: 08-0359

St Vincent's Medical Center
2800 Main Street
Bridgeport, CT 06606-0729
www.stvincents.org
Med Sch Affil: M-00801, L-03509, G-03501
Programs sponsored in: DR, IM, TY
Major participating institution for programs in: GPM, GS, PCC
Institution ID: 08-0341

Cheshire

Connecticut, Dept of Corrections: Manson Youth Facility
42 Jarvis Street
Cheshire, CT 06410
Major participating institution for programs in: CHP
Institution ID: 08-8023

Danbury

Danbury Hospital
24 Hospital Ave
Danbury, CT 06810-0729
Http://danhosp.org
Med Sch Affil: M-00801, M-03509, G-00802
Programs sponsored in: CD, IM, OBG, PTH
Major participating institution for programs in: AN, CHP, GS, P
Institution ID: 08-0363

Derby

Griffin Hospital
130 Division Street
Derby, CT 06418-1499
www.griffinhealth.org
Med Sch Affil: M-00801
Programs sponsored in: GPM, IM, IPM
Institution ID: 08-0172

Fairfield

Jewish Home for the Elderly
175 Jefferson St
Fairfield, CT 06825
Major participating institution for programs in: PYG
Institution ID: 08-8039

Farmington

Connecticut Red Cross Blood Services
209 Farmington Avenue
Farmington, CT 06032
Med Sch Affil: G-00802
Major participating institution for programs in: BBK
Institution ID: 08-0723

Univ of Connecticut Health Center/John Dempsey Hospital
263 Farmington Avenue
Farmington, CT 06030-2947
Med Sch Affil: M-00802
Major participating institution for programs in: AN, CD, CHP, DR, END, ETX, FSM, GE, GPM, HO, ID, IM, IMG, MG, N, NEP, NPM, OBG, ORS, OSM, OTO, P, PCC, PMG, RHU, U, VN
Institution ID: 08-0501

University of Connecticut School of Medicine
263 Farmington Avenue
Farmington, CT 06030-1925
www.uchc.edu
Programs sponsored in: AN, CCS, CD, CHP, D, DR, EM, END, ETX, FP, FSM, GE, GPM, GS, HO, HSO, IC, ID, IM, IMG, MG, N, NEP, NPM, OBG, ORS, OSM, OTO, P, PCC, PD, PDE, PDP, PE, PMG, RHU, U, VN, VS
Institution ID: 08-0445

Greenwich

Greenwich Hospital
5 Perryridge Road
Greenwich, CT 06830-2700
www.greenhosp.org
Med Sch Affil: M-00801
Programs sponsored in: IM
Institution ID: 08-0257

Hamden

Hamden Health Care Center
1270 Sherman Lane
Hamden, CT 06514
Major participating institution for programs in: PYG
Institution ID: 08-8038

Hartford

Capital Region Education Council Polaris Center
111 Charter Oak Avenue
Hartford, CT 06106
Major participating institution for programs in: CHP
Institution ID: 08-8024

Connecticut Children's Medical Center
282 Washington Street
Hartford, CT 06106-3316
Med Sch Affil: M-00802, G-03201
Major participating institution for programs in: CHP, EM, HSO, MG, NPM, ORS, OTO, PD, PDE, PDP, PE, PMG, U
Institution ID: 08-0407

Hartford Hospital
80 Seymour Street
PO Box 5037
Hartford, CT 06102
http://harthosp.org
Med Sch Affil: M-00802, L-03201
Programs sponsored in: CHP, DR, HMP, P, PCP, PTH, PYM, SP
Major participating institution for programs in: AN, CCS, CD, EM, END, ETX, GE, GS, HO, HSO, IC, ID, IM, N, OBG, ORS, OTO, P, U, VN, VS
Institution ID: 08-0275

Hartford Surgery Center, LLC
100 Retreat Ave
Hartford, CT 06106
Major participating institution for programs in: HSO
Institution ID: 08-8042

Institute of Living
400 Washington Street
Hartford, CT 06106-3392
Med Sch Affil: M-00802
Major participating institution for programs in: CHP, P
Institution ID: 08-0400

St Francis Hospital and Medical Center
114 Woodland Street
Hartford, CT 06105-1299
www.saintfranciscare.com
Med Sch Affil: M-00802
Programs sponsored in: CRS, OBG
Major participating institution for programs in: AN, CD, D, DR, END, FP, FSM, GE, GS, HO, ID, IM, IMG, ORS, OTO, PCC, PMG, U
Institution ID: 08-0490

Middletown

Connecticut Valley Hospital
PO Box 351 Silver Street
Middletown, CT 06457-2700
Major participating institution for programs in: PFP
Institution ID: 08-0214

Middlesex Hospital
28 Crescent Street
Middletown, CT 06457-1499
http://midhosp.org
Med Sch Affil: L-00802
Programs sponsored in: FP
Institution ID: 08-0135

Riverview Hospital for Children
River Rd
Box 621
Middletown, CT 06457-2742
Major participating institution for programs in: CHP, PFP
Institution ID: 08-8015

New Britain

Hospital for Central Connecticut
100 Grand Street
New Britain, CT 06050-0729
Med Sch Affil: M-00802
Major participating institution for programs in: END, GE, ID, IM, OBG, OTO, PCC
Institution ID: 08-0372

New Haven

APT Foundation, Inc Substance Abuse Treatment
1 Long Wharf
New Haven, CT 06511
Major participating institution for programs in: ADP
Institution ID: 08-8036

Connecticut Mental Health Center
34 Park St
New Haven, CT 06519
Med Sch Affil: M-00801
Major participating institution for programs in: ADP, P, PFP
Institution ID: 08-0715

Hospital of St Raphael
1450 Chapel St
New Haven, CT 06511-2700
www.srhs.org
Med Sch Affil: M-00801
Programs sponsored in: CD, DR, GS, IM, IMG, NEP, TY
Major participating institution for programs in: GE, ID, OTO, P, PS
Institution ID: 08-0244

Teaching Institutions

Yale Law School
Jerome N Frank Legal Services Org
127 Wall Street
New Haven, CT 06511
Major participating institution for programs in: PFP
Institution ID: 08-8019

Yale University Health Service
17 Hillhouse Avenue
New Haven, CT 06520-8034
Med Sch Affil: G-00801
Major participating institution for programs in: P
Institution ID: 08-0716

Yale University School of Public Health
60 College Street
PO Box 208034
New Haven, CT 06520-8034
Major participating institution for programs in: GPM,
IPM
Institution ID: 08-0505

Yale-New Haven Hospital
20 York Street
New Haven, CT 06510-3202
ynhh.org
Med Sch Affil: M-00801
Programs sponsored in: ADP, AI, AN, BBK, CCA, CCP,
CCS, CD, CHP, D, DBP, DMP, DR, EM, END, GE, GPM, GS,
HEM, HMP, HSP, IC, ICE, ID, IM, IMG, MG, MM, MPD, N,
NEP, NM, NMN, NPM, NR, NS, OBG, ON, OPH, ORS, OTO,
P, PAN, PCC, PCP, PD, PDC, PDE, PDI, PDP, PDS, PEM,
PFP, PG, PHO, PN, PS, PSI, PTH, PYG, PYM, RHU, RNR,
RO, SME, SP, TS, U, VIR, VS, VSI
Major participating institution for programs in: DR,
GE, IM
Institution ID: 08-0433

New London

Lawrence and Memorial Hospitals
365 Montauk Avenue
New London, CT 06320
Major participating institution for programs in: GPM,
RO
Institution ID: 08-0442

Newington

VA Connecticut-Newington
555 Willard Avenue
Newington, CT 06111
Major participating institution for programs in: D,
IMG
Institution ID: 08-0493

Norwalk

Norwalk Hospital
34 Maple Street
Norwalk, CT 06856-2700
Med Sch Affil: M-00801, L-01642
Programs sponsored in: DR, GE, IM, PUD, SME
Institution ID: 08-0206

Norwich

William W Backus Hospital
326 Washington Street
Norwich, CT 06360-2742
Major participating institution for programs in: RO
Institution ID: 08-7004

Plainville

Wheeler Clinic
91 Northwest Drive
Plainville, CT 06062
Major participating institution for programs in: CHP
Institution ID: 08-8032

Stamford

Stamford Hospital
Shelburne Rd at W Broad St
PO Box 9317
Stamford, CT 06904-9317
stamhealth.org
Med Sch Affil: M-03501
Programs sponsored in: FP, GS, IM, OBG
Institution ID: 08-0456

Wallingford

Masonicare
22 Masonic Ave
Wallingford, CT 06492
Major participating institution for programs in: PYG
Institution ID: 08-8040

Waterbury

St Mary's Hospital
56 Franklin Street
Waterbury, CT 06706-9317
http://stmh.org
Med Sch Affil: M-00802, M-00801
Programs sponsored in: GS, IM
Institution ID: 08-0458

Waterbury Hospital Health Center
64 Robbins St
Waterbury, CT 06721-1499
Med Sch Affil: M-00801
Programs sponsored in: GS
Major participating institution for programs in: IM, U
Institution ID: 08-0131

West Haven

Hebrew Home and Hospital
1 Abrahms Boulevard
West Haven, CT 06117
Major participating institution for programs in: IMG
Institution ID: 08-8022

Veterans Affairs Medical Center (West Haven)
950 Campbell Avenue
West Haven, CT 06516-2700
Med Sch Affil: M-00801
Major participating institution for programs in: ADP,
CD, DR, END, GE, GPM, GS, HMP, IC, ID, IM, IMG, N,
NEP, NM, NMN, NR, NS, ON, OPH, ORS, OTO, P, PTH,
PYG, PYM, RHU, RNR, TS, U, VIR, VS, VSI
Institution ID: 08-0199

Delaware

Dover

Community Mental Health Clinic - Dover
805 River Road
Dover, DE 19901
Major participating institution for programs in: P
Institution ID: 09-8004

New Castle

Delaware Psychiatric Center
1901 North DuPont Highway
Springer Building
New Castle, DE 19720-1668
Programs sponsored in: P
Institution ID: 09-0297

Wilmington

Alfred I duPont Hospital for Children
1600 Rockland Road
PO Box 269
Wilmington, DE 19899-0269
http://nemours.org
Med Sch Affil: M-04102, L-04113, L-04114
Programs sponsored in: RPM
Major participating institution for programs in: AI,
CCP, CCS, MPD, OP, OTO, PAN, PD, PEM, PG, PPM, PPR,
SME, U, UP
Institution ID: 09-0340

Christiana Care Health Services Inc
501 West 14th Street
PO Box 1668
Wilmington, DE 19899-1668
www.christianacare.org
Med Sch Affil: M-04102, L-04113
Programs sponsored in: CCS, DR, EFM, EM, FP, FSM,
GS, MEM, OBG, TY, VIR
Major participating institution for programs in: CD,
IC, IM, MPD, NEP, NPM, OPH, OSM, P, PMM
Institution ID: 09-0247

Community Mental Health Clinic - Wilmington
809 Washington Street
Wilmington, DE 19801
Major participating institution for programs in: P
Institution ID: 09-8005

St Francis Hospital
7th and Clayton Sts, Suite 209
Wilmington, DE 19805-0269
www.sffp.org
Med Sch Affil: M-04113
Programs sponsored in: FP
Institution ID: 09-0709

Veterans Affairs Medical Center (Wilmington)
1601 Kirkwood Highway
Wilmington, DE 19805
Med Sch Affil: M-04102
Major participating institution for programs in: OPH,
U
Institution ID: 09-0462

District of Columbia

Washington

Andromeda Transcultural Health
1400 Decatur St, NW
Washington, DC 20011
Major participating institution for programs in: P
Institution ID: 10-8034

Armed Forces Institute of Pathology
6825 16th Street, NW
Washington, DC 20306-6000
www.afip.org
Med Sch Affil: L-01001, L-03843, L-01643, L-02307,
L-02803, G-03201, G-02301, G-02012, G-01003
Programs sponsored in: NP, SP
Major participating institution for programs in: FOP
Institution ID: 10-0392

Children's National Medical Center
111 Michigan Ave, NW
Washington, DC 20010-2970
www.dcchildrens.com
Med Sch Affil: M-01001, L-01002, G-02312, G-01003,
G-02301
Programs sponsored in: ADL, CCP, CHN, CHP, NDN,
NPM, PD, PDC, PDI, PDO, PDP, PDR, PDS, PEM, PHO,
PN, UP
Major participating institution for programs in: AN,
CN, D, MBG, NS, ORS, OTO, PAN, PMG, SME, TS, U
Institution ID: 10-0441

DMH Assessment Center
300 Indiana Avenue, NW
4th Floor
Washington, DC 20002
Major participating institution for programs in: PFP
Institution ID: **10-8030**

George Washington University Hospital (UHS)
900 23rd Street NW
Washington, DC 20037
Med Sch Affil: M-01001, G-01002, G-02312
Major participating institution for programs in: AN, CCA, CCM, CD, CHN, DR, EM, END, GE, GS, HO, IC, ICE, ID, IM, IMG, N, NDN, NEP, NPM, NS, OBG, OPH, ORS, OTO, P, PCC, PCP, PTH, PYM, RHU, RNR, SME, TS, U, VIR
Institution ID: **10-0249**

George Washington University School of Medicine
2300 Eye Street, NW
Suite 707
Washington, DC 20037-4799
www.gwumc.edu
Programs sponsored in: AN, CCA, CCM, CD, CN, DR, EM, END, ETX, GE, GS, HO, HPM, IC, ICE, ID, IM, IMG, N, NEP, NS, OBG, OPH, ORS, OTO, P, PAN, PCC, PCP, PTH, PYM, RHU, RNR, SME, TS, U, VIR
Institution ID: **10-9501**

Georgetown University Hospital
3800 Reservoir Road, NW
Washington, DC 20007
www.georgetownuniversityhospital.org
Med Sch Affil: M-01002, G-01001, G-02312
Programs sponsored in: AN, CN, DR, END, GE, GS, HMP, HO, ID, IM, MPD, N, NEP, NPM, NS, OBG, ORS, OTO, P, PCC, PCP, PD, PFP, PSI, PTH, PYM, RHU, RNR, RO, TY, U, VIR
Major participating institution for programs in: CD, CHN, EM, ICE, VS
Institution ID: **10-0470**

Howard University Hospital
2041 Georgia Ave, NW
6th Towers Building Suite 6000
Washington, DC 20060-6000
http://huhosp.org
Med Sch Affil: M-01003, G-01002
Programs sponsored in: CD, D, END, FP, GE, GS, HEM, ID, IM, N, OBG, ON, OPH, ORS, P, PTH, PUD
Institution ID: **10-0475**

National Capital Poison Center
3201 New Mexico Avenue, Suite 310
Washington, DC 20016
Major participating institution for programs in: ETX
Institution ID: **10-8028**

National Rehabilitation Hospital
102 Irving Street, NW, Room 2159
Washington, DC 20010-5100
http://nrhrehab.org
Med Sch Affil: G-02312
Programs sponsored in: PM
Major participating institution for programs in: PMM
Institution ID: **10-0720**

Providence Hospital
1150 Varnum St, NE
Washington, DC 20017
http://provhosp.org
Med Sch Affil: L-01001, G-01002, G-01003
Programs sponsored in: FP, IM
Major participating institution for programs in: GS, OBG, ORS, P
Institution ID: **10-0412**

Sibley Memorial Hospital
5255 Loughboro Rd, NW
Washington, DC 20016
Med Sch Affil: L-01001, L-01002
Major participating institution for programs in: ORS, U
Institution ID: **10-0479**

St Elizabeth's Hospital-DC Department of Mental Health
Barton Hall, 2nd Floor
2700 Martin Luther King Avenue, SE
Washington, DC 20032-6000
Med Sch Affil: L-01001, L-01003
Programs sponsored in: P
Major participating institution for programs in: PFP
Institution ID: **10-0471**

University of the District of Columbia
4200 Connecticut Avenue, NW
Washington, DC 20008
Major participating institution for programs in: P
Institution ID: **10-8032**

US Soldiers' and Airmen's Home
3700 North Capital Street
Washington, DC 20317
Major participating institution for programs in: PYG
Institution ID: **10-8026**

Veterans Affairs Medical Center (Washington, DC)
50 Irving St, NW
Washington, DC 20422-0269
Med Sch Affil: M-01002, M-01001, M-01003, G-02312
Major participating institution for programs in: CD, D, END, GE, GS, HO, HPM, ICE, ID, IM, IMG, N, NEP, OPH, ORS, OTO, P, PCC, PTH, RHU, TS, U, VS
Institution ID: **10-0291**

Walter Reed Army Medical Center
6900 Georgia Ave, NW
Bldg 2, 2nd Fl, Rm 2B
Washington, DC 20307
Med Sch Affil: M-01002, M-02312, L-01003, L-01001
Major participating institution for programs in: AI, AN, CCA, CCM, CD, CHN, CHP, CN, D, DR, END, FPP, GE, GS, HO, HSO, ID, IM, N, NEP, NM, NS, OBG, OPH, ORS, OTO, P, PCC, PD, PDE, PDI, PFP, PG, PHO, PM, PMM, PTH, PYG, RHU, RO, TY, U, VS
Institution ID: **10-0242**

Washington Hospital Center
110 Irving St NW
6A-126A
Washington, DC 20010
http://gme.whcenter.org
Med Sch Affil: M-01001, M-02312, G-01003, G-01002
Programs sponsored in: CCS, CD, CRS, D, EM, GE, GS, HO, IC, ICE, ID, IM, IMD, NEP, NM, OBG, OMO, OPH, PCC, PMM, PTH, RHU, VS
Major participating institution for programs in: AN, CCM, END, GS, NS, OBG, ORS, OTO, PYM, RO, U, VIR
Institution ID: **10-0377**

Washington School of Psychiatry
5028 Wisconsin Avenue, NW
Suite 400
Washington, DC 20016
Major participating institution for programs in: P
Institution ID: **10-0715**

Florida

Apopka

Florida Living Nursing Center Inc
3355 East Semoran Blvd
Apopka, FL 32703
Major participating institution for programs in: FPG
Institution ID: **11-9086**

Atlantis

JFK Medical Center
5301 Congress Avenue
Atlantis, FL 33462
Major participating institution for programs in: IM
Institution ID: **11-9025**

Bay Pines

Veterans Affairs Medical Center (Bay Pines)
1000 Bay Pines Blvd
Bay Pines, FL 33744
Med Sch Affil: M-01104
Major participating institution for programs in: IMG, PS, PYG, VSI
Institution ID: **11-0302**

Bradenton

Manatee Glens
2020 26th Ave E
Bradenton, FL 34208
Major participating institution for programs in: CHP
Institution ID: **11-9070**

Brooksville

Hernando Correctional Institution
16415 Spring Hill Drive
Brooksville, FL 34604-8167
Major participating institution for programs in: PFP
Institution ID: **11-9021**

Clearwater

Morton Plant Hospital
323 Jeffords Street
Box 210
Clearwater, FL 34617-0210
Med Sch Affil: L-01104
Major participating institution for programs in: FP
Institution ID: **11-8101**

Coral Gables

Doctors' Hospital (Baptist Health of South Florida)
5000 University Drive
Coral Gables, FL 33146
http://baptisthealth.net
Med Sch Affil: L-01102
Programs sponsored in: OSM
Institution ID: **11-7024**

UHZ Sports Medicine Institute
1150 Campo Sano Avenue
Coral Gables, FL 33146
Major participating institution for programs in: OSM
Institution ID: **11-8111**

Daytona Beach

Halifax Medical Center
303 N Clyde Morris Blvd
Daytona Beach, FL 32114
www.halifax.org
Med Sch Affil: L-01104
Programs sponsored in: FP, FSM
Institution ID: **11-0165**

Eglin AFB

US Air Force Regional Hospital
96th MDOS/SGOF Family Medicine Residency
307 Boatner Road, Suite 114
Eglin AFB, FL 32542-1282
Med Sch Affil: L-02312
Programs sponsored in: FP
Institution ID: **11-0722**

Fort Lauderdale

Broward County Medical Examiner's Office
5301 SW 31st Avenue
Fort Lauderdale, FL 33312
www.co.broward.fl.us/medical
Programs sponsored in: FOP
Institution ID: 11-0524

Gainesville

Alachua County School Board
620 E University Ave
Gainesville, FL 32601
Major participating institution for programs in: FSM
Institution ID: 11-9120

North Florida Regional Medical Center
6500 Newberry Road
Gainesville, FL 32605
Major participating institution for programs in: OBG
Institution ID: 11-9122

North Florida/South Georgia Veterans Health System
1601 Archer Road
Gainesville, FL 32602
Med Sch Affil: M-01103
Major participating institution for programs in: ACA, AN, CN, D, DR, END, GE, GS, HO, IC, ID, IM, IMG, N, NEP, NP, NS, OPH, ORS, OTO, P, PCC, PMM, PS, PTH, RHU, SME, TS, U, VIR, VS
Institution ID: 11-0525

Santa Fe Community College Athletic Training Department
3000 NW 83rd Street
Gainesville, FL 32606
Major participating institution for programs in: FSM
Institution ID: 11-9083

Shands at AGH
801 SW Second Ave
Gainesville, FL 32601
Med Sch Affil: M-01103
Major participating institution for programs in: ACA, FP, ORS
Institution ID: 11-0523

Shands Hospital at the University of Florida
PO Box 100326
Gainesville, FL 32610-0326
Med Sch Affil: M-01103
Major participating institution for programs in: ACA, AN, CCA, CCP, CCS, CD, CHP, CN, D, DMP, DR, EM, END, FSM, GE, GS, HMP, HO, HSO, IC, ICE, ID, IM, IMG, MG, N, NEP, NP, NPM, NS, OBG, OMO, OPH, ORS, OTO, P, PCC, PCP, PD, PDC, PDE, PDP, PDS, PFP, PG, PHO, PMM, PN, PS, PTH, RHU, RNR, RO, SME, THP, TS, U, VIR, VS
Institution ID: 11-0461

University Athletic Association, Inc
PO Box 14485
Gainesville, FL 32604
Major participating institution for programs in: FSM
Institution ID: 11-9084

University of Florida College of Medicine
PO Box 100215
Gainesville, FL 32610
www.med.ufl.edu
Med Sch Affil: M-01103, L-01104
Programs sponsored in: ACA, AN, CCA, CCP, CCS, CD, CHP, CN, D, DMP, DR, EM, END, FP, FSM, GE, GS, HMP, HO, HSO, IC, ICE, ID, IM, IMG, MG, N, NEP, NP, NPM, NS, OBG, OMO, OPH, ORS, OTO, P, PCC, PCP, PD, PDC, PDE, PDP, PDS, PFP, PG, PHO, PMM, PN, PS, PTH, RHU, RNR, RO, SME, THP, TS, U, VIR, VS
Institution ID: 11-9501

Hollywood

Joe Di Maggio Children's Hospital
1150 N 35th Ave
Hollywood, FL 33021
Major participating institution for programs in: PS
Institution ID: 11-8108

Memorial Regional Hospital
3501 Johnson St
Hollywood, FL 33021
Med Sch Affil: L-01102
Major participating institution for programs in: GS, PS
Institution ID: 11-0276

Jacksonville

Baptist Medical Center
800 Prudential Drive
Jacksonville, FL 32207
Med Sch Affil: G-02608, G-01103
Major participating institution for programs in: ON
Institution ID: 11-0119

Duval County Health Department
Main Office
515 W 6th Street
Jacksonville, FL 32206
Major participating institution for programs in: ID
Institution ID: 11-9073

Mayo Clinic (Jacksonville)
4500 San Pablo Road
Jacksonville, FL 32224
Med Sch Affil: M-02608, G-01103
Major participating institution for programs in: CCA, CD, CHN, CN, D, DR, END, FP, FSM, GE, GS, HO, ID, IM, N, ORS, PCC, PMM, RO, THP, TY, U, VIR
Institution ID: 11-8093

Mayo Clinic Florida Hospital
4500 San Pablo Road
Jacksonville, FL 32224
Major participating institution for programs in: AN, CCA, CD, CHN, END, FP, FSM, GE, HO, ID, IM, N, PCC, PMM, THP, TY, U
Institution ID: 11-9093

Naval Hospital (Jacksonville)
2080 Child Street
Jacksonville, FL 32214-5227
www.navalhospitaljax.com
Med Sch Affil: L-02312, L-01103
Programs sponsored in: FP
Institution ID: 11-0256

Nemours Children's Clinic
807 Childrens Way
PO Box 5720
Jacksonville, FL 32247-5720
www.nemours.org
Med Sch Affil: L-01103
Major participating institution for programs in: CHN, ORS, PDE, U
Institution ID: 11-0478

Shands Jacksonville Medical Center
655 West Eighth Street
Jacksonville, FL 32209
Med Sch Affil: M-01103
Major participating institution for programs in: CCS, CD, DR, EM, END, GE, GS, IC, ICE, ID, IM, N, NEP, OBG, ON, OPH, ORS, PCC, PCP, PD, PDI, PE, PTH, VIR, VN
Institution ID: 11-0486

St Luke's Hospital
4201 Belfort Rd
Jacksonville, FL 32216
Med Sch Affil: M-02608
Major participating institution for programs in: DR
Institution ID: 11-0215

St Vincent's Medical Center
2627 Riverside Avenue
Jacksonville, FL 32204
www.jaxhealth.com
Med Sch Affil: L-01104, G-01103
Programs sponsored in: FP
Institution ID: 11-0148

UF Pediatric Multispecialty Center
820 Prudential Drive
Suite 405
Jacksonville, FL 32207
Major participating institution for programs in: PD
Institution ID: 11-9076

University of Florida College of Medicine Jacksonville
653-1 West 8th Street
Jacksonville, FL 32209
www.hscj.ufl.edu
Med Sch Affil: L-02312
Programs sponsored in: CCS, CD, DR, EM, END, GE, GS, IC, ICE, ID, IM, N, NEP, OBG, ON, OPH, ORS, PCC, PCP, PD, PDE, PDI, PE, PTH, VIR, VN
Institution ID: 11-9502

Wolfson Children's Hospital
800 Prudential Drive
Jacksonville, FL 32207
Major participating institution for programs in: CHN, PAN, PD, PDE, PDI, PE
Institution ID: 11-8106

Lakeland

Lakeland Regional Medical Center
1324 Lakeland Hills Boulevard
Lakeland, FL 33805
Major participating institution for programs in: ORS
Institution ID: 11-8127

Leesburg

Florida Heart and Vascular Center
511 Medical Plaza Drive
Leesburg, FL 34748
Major participating institution for programs in: IC
Institution ID: 11-9069

Miami

Baptist Hospital of Miami
8900 N Kendall Dr
Miami, FL 33176
Med Sch Affil: L-01102
Major participating institution for programs in: VIR
Institution ID: 11-0511

Bascom Palmer Eye Institute-Anne Bates Leach Eye Hospital
900 NW 17th St
Miami, FL 33136
Med Sch Affil: M-01102
Major participating institution for programs in: HSO, NO, OPH, OTO
Institution ID: 11-0701

DaVita Dialysis Center (Florida)
601 Hawaii Street (Corporate Office in CA)
Suite 106
Miami, FL 33136
Major participating institution for programs in: NEP
Institution ID: 11-9108

Jackson Memorial Hospital/Jackson Health System
1611 NW 12th Avenue
Miami, FL 33136
www.um-jmh.org
Med Sch Affil: M-01102, L-02312
Programs sponsored in: ACA, ADP, AN, CCA, CCM, CCP, CCS, CD, CHP, CRS, D, DR, END, FP, GE, GS, HMP, HO, HSO, IC, ICE, ID, IM, IMG, MG, MPD, N, NEP, NM, NMN, NO, NPM, NS, OBG, OMO, OPH, ORS, OSS, OTO, P, PAN, PCC, PCP, PD, PDC, PDE, PDI, PDP, PFP, PG, PM, PMM, PN, PP, PS, PTH, PYG, PYM, PYN, RHU, RNR, RO, SCI, SME, TS, U, VIR, VN
Institution ID: 11-0314

Mercy Hospital
3663 South Miami Avenue
Miami, FL 33133
Major participating institution for programs in: ICE
Institution ID: 11-7013

Miami Children's Hospital
3100 SW 62nd Avenue
Miami, FL 33155
www.mch.com
Med Sch Affil: L-03508, L-01102
Programs sponsored in: ADL, CCP, CN, PD, PDR, PEM
Major participating institution for programs in: HSO, MG, NS, OMO, PAN
Institution ID: 11-0311

Miami-Dade County Office of Medical Examiner
Number 1 on Bob Hope Road
Miami, FL 33136-1133
www.miamidade.gov/medexam
Programs sponsored in: FOP
Institution ID: 11-0496

South Florida Evaluation and Treatment Center
200 NW 7th avenue
Miami, FL 33127
Major participating institution for programs in: PFP
Institution ID: 11-9075

University of Miami Hospital
1400 NW 12th Ave
Miami, FL 33136
Med Sch Affil: L-01102
Major participating institution for programs in: CD, GE, ICE, OMO, ORS, OTO, PS, RHU, U
Institution ID: 11-0707

University of Miami Hospital and Clinics
1475 NW 12th Avenue
Miami, FL 33136-1002
Med Sch Affil: M-01102
Programs sponsored in: IM
Major participating institution for programs in: OTO, PCP, RNR, SME, VIR
Institution ID: 11-0721

University of Miami Sylvester Comprehensive Cancer Center
1475 NW 12th Avenue
Miami, FL 33136
Major participating institution for programs in: AN, D, OBG, PMM, RO
Institution ID: 11-9014

Veterans Affairs Medical Center (Miami)
1201 NW 16th Street (128)
Miami, FL 33125
Med Sch Affil: M-01102
Major participating institution for programs in: AN, CCA, CCM, CD, D, END, GE, GS, HSO, IC, ICE, IM, IMG, N, NS, ORS, P, PCC, PM, PMM, PS, PYG, PYN, RHU, SCI, SME, TS, U
Institution ID: 11-0515

Miami Beach

Mount Sinai Medical Center of Florida, Inc
4300 Alton Road
Miami Beach, FL 33140
www.msmc.com
Med Sch Affil: L-01104, L-01102
Programs sponsored in: CD, DR, GS, IC, IM, PTH
Major participating institution for programs in: GE, P, PYG, TS
Institution ID: 11-0101

Naples

Physicians Regional Medical Center (Naples)
6101 Pine Ridge Road
Naples, FL 34119
Major participating institution for programs in: CRS
Institution ID: 11-8105

Orlando

Arnold Palmer Hospital for Children
92 West Miller Street
Orlando, FL 32806
Major participating institution for programs in: OP, ORS, PD, PE
Institution ID: 11-8095

Florida Hospital Medical Center
601 E Rollins
Orlando, FL 32803
www.floridahospitalresidency.com
Med Sch Affil: L-00512, L-01104
Programs sponsored in: EM, FP, FPG, GS, IM
Major participating institution for programs in: CRS, ORS
Institution ID: 11-0513

M D Anderson Cancer Center Orlando
1400 South Orange Avenue
Orlando, FL 32806
Major participating institution for programs in: GS
Institution ID: 11-9074

Orlando Health
1414 Kuhl Ave, MP 7
Orlando, FL 32806
www.orlandoregional.org
Programs sponsored in: CCS, CRS, EM, GS, HO, ID, IM, OBG, OP, ORS, PD, PE, PTH
Institution ID: 11-8132

Orlando Regional Medical Center
1414 Kuhl Avenue
Orlando, FL 32806-2134
Med Sch Affil: L-01103, G-02608
Major participating institution for programs in: CCS, CRS, EM, GS, HO, ID, IM, OBG, OP, ORS, PTH
Institution ID: 11-0258

Winnie Palmer Hospital for Women and Babies
83 W Miller Street
Orlando, FL 32806
Major participating institution for programs in: OBG
Institution ID: 11-9023

Pensacola

Naval Aerospace Medical Institute
340 Hulse Road
Pensacola, FL 32508
Major participating institution for programs in: GPM
Institution ID: 11-9067

Naval Hospital (Pensacola)
6000 W Highway 98
Pensacola, FL 32512-0003
http://psaweb.med.navy.mil/Default.htm
Med Sch Affil: G-02312
Programs sponsored in: FP
Institution ID: 11-0159

Naval Operational Medicine Institute
220 Hovey Rd
Pensacola, FL 32508-1047
www.nomi.navy.mil
Programs sponsored in: GPM
Institution ID: 11-0108

Sacred Heart Hospital of Pensacola
5151 North Ninth Avenue
PO Box 2700
Pensacola, FL 32513-2700
Med Sch Affil: G-01103
Major participating institution for programs in: OBG, PD
Institution ID: 11-0396

St Petersburg

All Children's Hospital
801 6th Street South
PO Box 31020
St. Petersburg, FL 33731-8920
Med Sch Affil: M-01104
Major participating institution for programs in: AI, AI, CHP, HMP, MPD, NPM, NS, OTO, PD, PDE, PP
Institution ID: 11-0182

Bayfront Medical Center
701 6th St, S
St. Petersburg, FL 33701-4891
http://bayfront.md
Med Sch Affil: L-01104
Programs sponsored in: FP, FSM, OBG
Institution ID: 11-0440

Sunrise

Health South Sunrise Rehabilitation Hospital
4399 Nob Hill Road
Sunrise, FL 33351-5899
Major participating institution for programs in: IMG
Institution ID: 11-8109

Sunrise Health & Rehabilitation Center
4800 Nob Hill Rd
Sunrise, FL 33351-4722
Major participating institution for programs in: IMG
Institution ID: 11-9110

Tallahassee

Florida State University College of Medicine
1115 West Call Street
Tallahassee, FL 32306-4300
Programs sponsored in: OBG, PD
Institution ID: 11-9505

Tallahassee Memorial HealthCare
1300 Miccosukee Road
Tallahassee, FL 32308-5054
www.tmh.org
Med Sch Affil: L-01104
Programs sponsored in: FP
Institution ID: 11-0522

Tampa

Allergy Asthma and Immunology Associates of Tampa Bay
13801 Bruce B Downs Blvd
Suite 502
Tampa, FL 33613
Major participating institution for programs in: AI
Institution ID: 11-9016

Teaching Institutions

H Lee Moffitt Cancer Center
12901 Magnolia Drive
Tampa, FL 33612
Med Sch Affil: M-01104
Major participating institution for programs in: AI, D, DMP, DR, END, GS, HMP, HO, ID, NEP, NS, OBG, OTO, PCC, PCP, PS, PTH, RO, U
Institution ID: 11-8003

Hillsborough County Medical Examiner Department
401 S Morgan St
Tampa, FL 33602
Major participating institution for programs in: FOP
Institution ID: 11-8094

Hillsborough County Sheriff's Office
1201 Orient Road/520 Falkenburg Road
Tampa, FL 33619
Major participating institution for programs in: PFP
Institution ID: 11-9022

James A Haley Veterans Hospital
13000 Bruce B Downs Blvd
Tampa, FL 33612
Med Sch Affil: M-01104
Major participating institution for programs in: ADP, AI, CD, D, DMP, DR, END, GE, GPM, GS, HO, IC, ID, IM, IMG, MPD, N, NEP, NS, OPH, ORS, OTO, P, PCC, PCP, PM, PMM, PTH, PYG, RHU, RO, SCI, SME, U, VSI
Institution ID: 11-0521

Shriners Hospitals for Children (Tampa)
12502 Pine Drive
Tampa, FL 33612-9411
http://shrinershq.org
Med Sch Affil: L-01104
Major participating institution for programs in: ORS
Institution ID: 11-8002

St Joseph's Hospital
3001 W Dr Martin Luther King Blvd
Tampa, FL 33607
Major participating institution for programs in: ORS
Institution ID: 11-0520

Tampa General Hospital
PO Box 1289
Tampa, FL 33601
Major participating institution for programs in: AI, CCS, CD, CHP, D, DR, EM, END, GE, GS, HO, IC, ICE, ID, IM, IMG, MPD, N, NEP, NPM, NS, OBG, OPH, ORS, OTO, P, PCC, PD, PFP, PM, PMM, PP, PS, PTH, RHU, SME, U, VIR, VN, VS, VSI
Institution ID: 11-8104

University Community Hospital
3100 E Fletcher Ave
Tampa, FL 33613-4688
Major participating institution for programs in: ORS, SME
Institution ID: 11-9013

University of South Florida College of Medicine
12901 Bruce B Downs Blvd
Tampa, FL 33612
www.hsc.usf.edu
Med Sch Affil: M-01104
Programs sponsored in: ADP, AI, CCS, CD, CHP, D, DMP, DR, EM, END, FOP, FP, GE, GPM, GS, HMP, HO, HPM, IC, ICE, ID, IM, IMG, MPD, N, NEP, NPM, NS, OBG, OPH, ORS, OSM, OTO, P, PCC, PCP, PD, PDE, PFP, PM, PMM, PP, PS, PSI, PTH, PYG, RHU, RO, SCI, SME, U, VIR, VN, VS, VSI
Major participating institution for programs in: GS
Institution ID: 11-0184

University of South Florida College of Public Health
13201 Bruce B Downs Blvd
Tampa, FL 33612
Major participating institution for programs in: GPM
Institution ID: 11-8097

University Psychiatry Center
3515 E Fletcher Avenue
Tampa, FL 33613
Major participating institution for programs in: CHP, P, PFP, PYG
Institution ID: 11-8016

West Palm Beach

Palm Beach County Public Health Department
PO Box 29
826 Evernia Street
West Palm Beach, FL 33402
http://pbchd.com
Programs sponsored in: GPM
Institution ID: 11-0729

West Palm Beach VA Medical Center
7305 North Military Trail
West Palm Beach, FL 33410-6400
Major participating institution for programs in: GPM, IM
Institution ID: 11-8120

Weston

Cleveland Clinic Florida
2950 Cleveland Clinic Blvd
Weston, FL 33331
www.clevelandclinic.org/florida//
Med Sch Affil: L-01104
Programs sponsored in: CD, CRS, GE, IM, IMG, N, NEP, PS
Major participating institution for programs in: CN
Institution ID: 11-8092

Cleveland Clinic Hospital
3100 Weston Blvd
Weston, FL 33331
Major participating institution for programs in: NR
Institution ID: 11-8091

Winter Park

Mayflower Retirement Community
1620 Mayflower Court
Winter Park, FL 32792
Major participating institution for programs in: FPG
Institution ID: 11-9087

Zephyrhills

Zephyrhills Correctional Institution
2739 Gall Boulevard
Zephyrhills, FL 33541-9701
Major participating institution for programs in: PFP
Institution ID: 11-9020

Georgia

Albany

Phoebe Putney Memorial Hospital
417 Third Avenue
PO Box 1828
Albany, GA 31701
www.phoebeputney.com
Med Sch Affil: L-01222, L-01201
Programs sponsored in: FP, FSM
Institution ID: 12-0315

Atlanta

Atlanta Medical Center
303 Parkway Drive, NE
Box 423
Atlanta, GA 30312
www.amc-gme.com
Med Sch Affil: M-01201, L-01222
Programs sponsored in: FP, GS, IM, ORS, VS
Institution ID: 12-0198

Atlanta Sports Medicine Foundation, Inc
3200 Downwood Circle, NW
Suite 500
Atlanta, GA 30327
Programs sponsored in: OSM
Institution ID: 12-8066

Centers for Disease Control and Prevention
1600 Clifton Road, Mail Stop E-92
Atlanta, GA 30333
www.cdc.gov
Med Sch Affil: L-01221, G-02312
Programs sponsored in: GPM
Major participating institution for programs in: ETX, GPM, PDI
Institution ID: 12-0491

Children's Healthcare of Atlanta
1001 Johnson Ferry Rd, NE
Atlanta, GA 30363
http://CHOA.org
Med Sch Affil: L-02101, G-01205, G-01221
Programs sponsored in: OP
Major participating institution for programs in: ORS
Institution ID: 12-0111

Children's Healthcare of Atlanta at Egleston
1405 Clifton Road, NE
Atlanta, GA 30322
Med Sch Affil: M-01205, G-01221
Major participating institution for programs in: CCP, CHN, CHS, MG, NPM, PAN, PD, PDC, PDE, PDI, PDP, PDR, PDS, PEM, PG, PHO, PN, PTP, RNR, UP, VIR
Institution ID: 12-0481

Children's Healthcare of Atlanta at Scottish Rite
1101 Johnson Ferry Road NE
Atlanta, GA 30342-1600
Major participating institution for programs in: ORS, PD, PHO, UP
Institution ID: 12-8043

Crawford Long Hospital of Emory University
550 Peachtree St, NE
Atlanta, GA 30365
Med Sch Affil: M-01205
Major participating institution for programs in: ACA, CD, IC, ICE, INM, MP, NEP, NS, OBG, OTO, PMM, RHU, RO, TS
Institution ID: 12-0173

Emory University Hospital
1364 Clifton Road, NE
Atlanta, GA 30322
Med Sch Affil: M-01205
Major participating institution for programs in: ACA, AN, AR, BBK, CCA, CD, CHN, CHS, CN, D, DMP, DR, END, GE, GS, HMP, HO, IC, ICE, ID, IM, INM, MGP, MM, MP, N, NEP, NM, NP, NR, NS, OPH, ORS, OSM, OTO, P, PCC, PCP, PM, PMM, PS, PTH, PYM, RHU, RNR, SP, TS, TY, U, VIR, VN, VS
Institution ID: 12-0139

Emory University School of Medicine
1648 Pierce Drive, NE
Suite 327
Atlanta, GA 30322
www.emory.edu/WHSC/MED/index.html
Med Sch Affil: M-01205, L-04802
Programs sponsored in: ACA, ADP, AN, AR, BBK, CCA, CCP, CCS, CD, CHN, CHP, CHS, CN, D, DMP, DR, EM, END, ETX, FOP, FP, GE, GPM, GS, HMP, HO, IC, ICE, ID, IM, IMG, INM, MG, MGP, MM, MP, N, NEP, NM, NP, NPM, NR, NS, OBG, OPH, ORS, OSM, OTO, P, PAN, PCC, PCP, PD, PDC, PDE, PDI, PDP, PDR, PDS, PEM, PFP, PG, PHO, PM, PMM, PN, PS, PTH, PTP, PYG, PYM, RHU, RNR, RO, SP, TS, TY, U, UP, VIR, VN, VS
Institution ID: 12-0490

Emory University School of Medicine (Briarcliff)
1256 Briarcliff Road NE 317 S
Atlanta, GA 30306
Major participating institution for programs in: CHP
Institution ID: 12-8059

Fulton County Medical Examiner's Office
430 Pryor Street, SW
Atlanta, GA 30312
Med Sch Affil: L-01205
Major participating institution for programs in: FOP
Institution ID: 12-0496

Georgia Colon & Rectal Surgical Clinic
5555 Peachtree Dunwoody Road, Suite 206
Atlanta, GA 30342
www.gcrsa.com
Programs sponsored in: CRS
Institution ID: 12-8031

Georgia Dept of Human Resources-Division of Public Health
2 Peachtree Street
7th Floor
Atlanta, GA 30303
Med Sch Affil: G-01221
Major participating institution for programs in: GPM
Institution ID: 12-8015

Georgia Poison Control Center-Grady Health System
80 Butler Street
PO Box 26066
Atlanta, GA 30335-3801
Major participating institution for programs in: ETX
Institution ID: 12-8037

Grady Health System
80 Jesse Hill Jr Drive SW
PO Box 26189
Atlanta, GA 30303
Med Sch Affil: M-01221, M-01205
Major participating institution for programs in: ADP, AN, AR, CCA, CCS, CD, CHN, CHP, CN, D, DR, EM, END, FP, GE, GPM, GS, HO, IM, INM, MM, MP, N, NEP, NM, NPM, NR, NS, OBG, OPH, ORS, OTO, P, PCP, PD, PDE, PEM, PFP, PMM, PS, PTH, PYM, RHU, RNR, RO, TY, U, VIR, VN
Institution ID: 12-0483

Morehouse School of Medicine
720 Westview Drive, SW
Atlanta, GA 30310-1495
www.msm.edu
Med Sch Affil: M-01221
Programs sponsored in: FP, GPM, GS, IM, OBG, P, PD
Institution ID: 12-0499

Northside Hospital
1000 Johnson Ferry Road, NE
Atlanta, GA 30342-1611
Major participating institution for programs in: CRS
Institution ID: 12-0497

Piedmont Hospital
1968 Peachtree Road, NW
Atlanta, GA 30309
Med Sch Affil: G-01205
Major participating institution for programs in: GS
Institution ID: 12-0317

Rollins School of Public Health of Emory University
1518 Clifton Road, NE
Atlanta, GA 30322
Major participating institution for programs in: GPM
Institution ID: 12-8033

Saint Joseph's Hospital of Atlanta
5665 Peachtree Dunwoody Road, NE
Atlanta, GA 30342-1764
Major participating institution for programs in: CRS
Institution ID: 12-0254

The Shepherd Center
2020 Peachtree Road
Atlanta, GA 30309
Major participating institution for programs in: PM
Institution ID: 12-8035

Wesley Woods Geriatric Hospital
1812 Clifton Road, NE
Atlanta, GA 30329
Med Sch Affil: G-01205
Major participating institution for programs in: CN, IMG, PYG
Institution ID: 12-7032

Augusta

Medical College of Georgia
1120 Fifteenth Street
(AE-3042)
Augusta, GA 30912-5000
www.mcg.edu
Programs sponsored in: AI, AN, BBK, CD, CHN, CHP, CN, D, DR, EM, END, FP, GE, GS, HO, ICE, ID, IM, N, NEP, NPM, NS, OBG, OPH, ORS, OTO, P, PCC, PD, PDC, PE, PMM, PS, PTH, RHU, RNR, U, VN
Institution ID: 12-9503

Medical College of Georgia Cardiovascular Center
1003 Chafee Avenue
Augusta, GA 30912
Major participating institution for programs in: ICE
Institution ID: 12-8054

University Hospital
1350 Walton Way
Augusta, GA 30901-2629
Med Sch Affil: M-01201
Major participating institution for programs in: OBG
Institution ID: 12-0428

Veterans Affairs Medical Center (Augusta)
1 Freedom Way
Augusta, GA 30904-6285
Med Sch Affil: M-01201
Major participating institution for programs in: CD, D, DR, END, GE, GS, HO, ID, IM, NEP, NS, OPH, ORS, OTO, P, PCC, PS, PTH, RHU, U, VN
Institution ID: 12-0272

Columbus

Hughston Foundation
6262 Veterans Parkway
PO Box 9517
Columbus, GA 31908-9517
Programs sponsored in: OSM
Institution ID: 12-8023

Hughston Orthopedic Hospital
100 Frist Court
PO Box 7188
Columbus, GA 31908-7188
Med Sch Affil: G-02312
Major participating institution for programs in: OSM
Institution ID: 12-0501

The Hughston Clinic
6262 Veterans Parkway
Columbus, GA 31909
Major participating institution for programs in: OSM
Institution ID: 12-8051

The Medical Center Inc
710 Center Street
PO Box 951
Columbus, GA 31902
www.columbusregional.com
Med Sch Affil: L-01222, L-01221, L-01201
Programs sponsored in: FP, TY
Institution ID: 12-0209

Decatur

Dekalb Medical Center
2701 North Decatur Road
Decatur, GA 30033-5995
Med Sch Affil: L-04802
Major participating institution for programs in: CRS
Institution ID: 12-8029

Georgia Regional Hospital at Atlanta
3073 Panthersville Rd
Decatur, GA 30037-0407
Med Sch Affil: M-01221
Major participating institution for programs in: P, PFP
Institution ID: 12-8017

Veterans Affairs Medical Center (Atlanta)
1670 Clairmont Road
Decatur, GA 30033
Med Sch Affil: M-01205
Major participating institution for programs in: ADP, CD, D, END, GE, GPM, IC, IM, IMG, INM, MP, NM, OTO, P, PDI, PM, PYM, RHU, RO, TY, U, VS
Institution ID: 12-0293

Duluth

Emory Johns Creek Hospital
6325 West Johns Crossing
Duluth, GA 30097
Major participating institution for programs in: FP
Institution ID: 12-8053

East Point

Tenet-South Fulton Medical Center
1170 Cleveland Ave
East Point, GA 30344
Major participating institution for programs in: FP, OBG
Institution ID: 12-8039

Fayetteville

Piedmont Fayette Hospital
1279 Highway 54W
Suite 300
Fayetteville, GA 30214
Major participating institution for programs in: GS
Institution ID: 12-8049

Fort Benning

Martin Army Community Hospital
Attn: MCXB-FRT
7950 Martin Loop
Fort Benning, GA 31905-5637
Med Sch Affil: L-02312
Programs sponsored in: FP
Institution ID: 12-0357

Fort Gordon

Dwight David Eisenhower Army Medical Center
Building 300
Fort Gordon, GA 30905-5650
www.ddeamc.amedd.army.mil/
Med Sch Affil: M-02312, L-01201
Programs sponsored in: FP, GS, IM, ORS, TY
Major participating institution for programs in: U
Institution ID: 12-0492

Lawrenceville

Gwinnett Medical Center
1000 Medical Center Boulevard
Lawrenceville, GA 30245
Major participating institution for programs in: CRS
Institution ID: 12-8030

Teaching Institutions

Macon

Central Georgia Rehabilitation Hospital
3351 Northside Drive
Macon, GA 31210
Major participating institution for programs in: FPG
Institution ID: 12-8078

Central Georgia Senior Health, Inc
5330 Zebulon Road
Macon, GA 31210
Major participating institution for programs in: FPG
Institution ID: 12-8072

Medical Center of Central Georgia
777 Hemlock
PO Box 6000 / Hospital Box 51
Macon, GA 31208
www.mccg.org
Med Sch Affil: M-01222
Programs sponsored in: CCS, FP, FPG, GS, IM, OBG, PD
Institution ID: 12-0266

Oaks at Peake Nursing Home
6190 Peake Road
Macon, GA 31220
Major participating institution for programs in: FPG
Institution ID: 12-8071

Riverdale

Southern Regional Health System
11 Upper Riverdale Rd
Riverdale, GA 30274-2600
Major participating institution for programs in: VS
Institution ID: 12-8068

Rome

Floyd Medical Center
Turner McCall Blvd
PO Box 233
Rome, GA 30165
www.floyd.org
Med Sch Affil: L-01222, L-01201
Programs sponsored in: FP
Institution ID: 12-0402

Savannah

Memorial Health-University Medical Center
PO Box 23089
Savannah, GA 31404-3089
www.memorialhealth.com
Med Sch Affil: M-01222, L-01201
Programs sponsored in: DR, FP, GS, IM, OBG, PD
Institution ID: 12-0362

Waycross

Satilla Regional Medical Center
410 Darling Avenue
PO Box 139
Waycross, GA 31502-0139
Major participating institution for programs in: FP
Institution ID: 12-8027

Hawaii

Ewa Beach

Kahi Mohala Hospital
91-2301 Ft Weaver Road
Ewa Beach, HI 96706
Major participating institution for programs in: CHP
Institution ID: 14-8012

Honolulu

DOH AMHD Community Mental Health Centers
1250 Punchbowl Street
Room 256
Honolulu, HI 96813
Major participating institution for programs in: P
Institution ID: 14-8019

DOH CAMHD FCLB at HYCF
3627 Kilauea Avenue
Honolulu, HI 96816
Major participating institution for programs in: CHP
Institution ID: 14-8026

Hawaii Health Systems Corporation
3675 Kilauea Avenue
Honolulu, HI 96816
Major participating institution for programs in: PYG
Institution ID: 14-8020

Kaiser Foundation Hospital (Moanalua)
3288 Moanalua, N Frontage Rd
Honolulu, HI 96819
Med Sch Affil: M-01401, G-00502
Major participating institution for programs in: GS, PTH, U
Institution ID: 14-0431

Kapiolani Medical Center for Women and Children
1319 Punahou St
Honolulu, HI 96826
Med Sch Affil: M-01401
Major participating institution for programs in: CHP, CPP, DBP, NPM, OBG, PD
Institution ID: 14-0371

Kuakini Medical Center
347 N Kuakini St
Honolulu, HI 96817
Med Sch Affil: M-01401
Major participating institution for programs in: GS, IMG, TY
Institution ID: 14-0425

Queen's Medical Center
1301 Punchbowl Street
Honolulu, HI 96813
Med Sch Affil: M-01401
Major participating institution for programs in: ADP, CCS, CHP, GS, IM, IMG, OBG, ORS, P, PTH, PYG, TY
Institution ID: 14-0429

Shriners Hospitals for Children (Honolulu)
1310 Punahou Street
Honolulu, HI 96826-1099
www.shriners.com/shc/honolulu/index.html
Med Sch Affil: L-01401
Programs sponsored in: OP
Major participating institution for programs in: DBP
Institution ID: 14-0300

Straub Clinic & Hospital
888 S King St
Honolulu, HI 96813
Med Sch Affil: L-01401
Major participating institution for programs in: GS
Institution ID: 14-0440

University Health Services Manoa
1960 East West Road
Honolulu, HI 96822
Major participating institution for programs in: FSM
Institution ID: 14-8023

University of Hawaii Athletic Training Room
1377 Lower Campus Road
Honolulu, HI 96822
Major participating institution for programs in: FSM
Institution ID: 14-8024

University of Hawaii John A Burns School of Medicine
1356 Lusitana Street, Suite 510
Honolulu, HI 96813
Med Sch Affil: M-01401
Programs sponsored in: ADP, CCS, CHP, CPP, DBP, FP, FSM, GS, IM, IMG, NPM, OBG, ORS, P, PD, PTH, PYG, TY
Institution ID: 14-0439

VA Pacific Islands Health Care System (Honolulu)
PO Box 50188
Honolulu, HI 96850
Med Sch Affil: M-01401
Major participating institution for programs in: IMG, P, PYG
Institution ID: 14-0444

Kaneohe

Hawaii State Hospital
45-710 Keaahala Road
Kaneohe, HI 96744
Med Sch Affil: M-01401
Major participating institution for programs in: ADP, P
Institution ID: 14-0268

Tripler AMC

Tripler Army Medical Center
Medical Education Office (Attn: MCHK-HE-ME)
1 Jarrett White Road
Tripler AMC, HI 96859-5000
www.tamc.amedd.army.mil/
Med Sch Affil: M-01401, M-02312
Programs sponsored in: CHP, DR, FP, GS, IM, OBG, ORS, OTO, P, PD, TY, U
Major participating institution for programs in: ADP, DBP, NPM
Institution ID: 14-0426

Wahiawa

Wahiawa General Hospital
128 Lehua St, Box 508
Wahiawa, HI 96786
Med Sch Affil: M-01401
Major participating institution for programs in: FP
Institution ID: 14-8014

Idaho

Boise

Boise State University Health and Wellness Center
1910 University Drive
Boise, ID 83706
Major participating institution for programs in: FSM
Institution ID: 15-8007

Family Medicine Residency of Idaho
777 N Raymond St
Boise, ID 83704
www.fmridaho.org
Med Sch Affil: L-05404
Programs sponsored in: FP, FSM
Institution ID: 15-0714

Idaho Sports Medicine Institute
1188 University Drive
Boise, ID 83706
Major participating institution for programs in: FSM
Institution ID: 15-8008

Orthopaedic Sugery Center of Idaho
1450 West River
Boise, ID 83702
Major participating institution for programs in: FSM
Institution ID: 15-8009

St Alphonsus Regional Medical Center
1055 N Curtis Road
Boise, ID 83706
Med Sch Affil: L-05404
Major participating institution for programs in: FP, FSM
Institution ID: 15-0713

St Luke's Regional Medical Center
190 E Bannock Street
Boise, ID 83712
Med Sch Affil: L-05404
Major participating institution for programs in: FP
Institution ID: 15-0711

Treasure Valley Hospital
8800 West Emerald Street
Boise, ID 83704
Major participating institution for programs in: FSM
Institution ID: 15-8004

Veterans Affairs Medical Center (Boise)
500 W Fort Street
Boise, ID 83702
Med Sch Affil: M-05404
Major participating institution for programs in: IM, P
Institution ID: 15-0712

Caldwell

Saint Alphonsus Medical Group
315 Elm Street
Caldwell, ID 83605
Major participating institution for programs in: FP
Institution ID: 15-8005

West Valley Medical Center
1717 Arlington
Caldwell, ID 83605
Major participating institution for programs in: FP
Institution ID: 15-0710

Pocatello

Idaho State University
Kasiska College of Health Professions
921 South 8th Avenue, Stop 8090
Pocatello, ID 83209-8090
www.isu.edu/departments/chp/
Programs sponsored in: FP
Institution ID: 15-8001

Portneuf Regional Medical Center
651 Memorial Drive
Pocatello, ID 83201
Major participating institution for programs in: FP
Institution ID: 15-8002

Illinois

Aurora

Rush-Copley Medical Center
2000 Ogden Avenue
Aurora, IL 60504-4206
Med Sch Affil: G-01601
Major participating institution for programs in: FP
Institution ID: 16-7005

Belleville

St Elizabeth's Hospital
211 S Third Street
Belleville, IL 62222
Med Sch Affil: M-02834
Major participating institution for programs in: FP, FSM
Institution ID: 16-0787

Berwyn

MacNeal Hospital
3249 S Oak Park Avenue
Berwyn, IL 60402
www.macneal.com
Med Sch Affil: L-01601, L-01602, G-01611, G-01642
Programs sponsored in: FP, FSM, TY
Major participating institution for programs in: GS, OBG, P
Institution ID: 16-0453

Carbondale

Memorial Hospital of Carbondale
404 W Main St
Carbondale, IL 62901
Med Sch Affil: M-01645
Major participating institution for programs in: FP, FSM
Institution ID: 16-0508

Chicago

Advocate Illinois Masonic Medical Center
836 West Wellington Avenue
Chicago, IL 60657-5193
www.advocatehealth.com/immc/
Med Sch Affil: M-01601, M-01611, M-01642
Programs sponsored in: AN, CD, DR, ICE, IM, OBG
Major participating institution for programs in: CCS, DBP, EM, FP, GS, PTH
Institution ID: 16-0411

Children's Memorial Hospital
2300 Children's Plaza
Room 105
Chicago, IL 60614
Med Sch Affil: M-01606, L-01643, G-01611
Major participating institution for programs in: AI, CCP, CCS, CHN, CHP, CHS, MG, NPM, NS, ORS, OTO, P, PAN, PD, PDC, PDE, PDI, PDP, PDR, PDS, PEM, PG, PHO, PN, PP, PPR, PTP, RNR, RPM, SME, THP, U, UP
Institution ID: 16-0264

Cook County Medical Examiner's Office
2121 W Harrison
Chicago, IL 60612
Major participating institution for programs in: NP
Institution ID: 16-8111

HCA Chicago Lakeshore Hospital
4840 N Marine Dr
Chicago, IL 60640
Med Sch Affil: L-01602
Major participating institution for programs in: CHP
Institution ID: 16-8028

Illinois Poison Center
222 South Riverside Plaza, Suite 1900
Chicago, IL 60606
Major participating institution for programs in: ETX
Institution ID: 16-8068

Jackson Park Hospital
7531 South Stony Island Avenue
Chicago, IL 60649-3913
www.jacksonpark.com
Programs sponsored in: FP
Institution ID: 16-0354

Jesse Brown Veterans Affairs Medical Center
820 South Damen Avenue
PO Box 8195
Chicago, IL 60612
Med Sch Affil: M-01611
Major participating institution for programs in: ADP, AN, CD, D, END, GE, GS, HO, IC, ID, IM, IMD, IMG, N, NEP, OPH, ORS, OTO, P, PCC, PM, RHU, U, VS
Institution ID: 16-0220

John H Stroger Hospital of Cook County
1901 West Harrison Street
Chicago, IL 60612
www.cookcountygov.com/agencyDetail.php?AgencyID=5
3
Med Sch Affil: M-01601, M-01642, M-01611, L-01602, L-01606, G-01643
Programs sponsored in: AN, CCS, CD, CRS, D, DR, EM, ETX, GE, GPM, HO, IM, NPM, OBG, OPH, PCC, PD, PMM
Major participating institution for programs in: AI, CN, END, FP, GS, IC, ID, NEP, ORS, OTO, PS, RHU, TS
Institution ID: 16-0164

LaRabida Children's Hospital and Research Center
East 65th Street at Lake Michigan
Chicago, IL 60649-1395
Major participating institution for programs in: DBP, PPR
Institution ID: 16-0774

Louis A Weiss Memorial Hospital
4646 N Marine Dr
Chicago, IL 60640
http://weisshospital.com
Med Sch Affil: M-01602
Programs sponsored in: IM, TY
Major participating institution for programs in: OAR, OPH, ORS
Institution ID: 16-0123

McGaw Medical Center of Northwestern University
645 N Michigan Avenue
Suite 1058
Chicago, IL 60611
http://gme.northwestern.edu
Med Sch Affil: M-01606
Programs sponsored in: ACA, ADP, AI, AN, CCA, CCP, CCS, CD, CHN, CHP, CHS, CN, D, DMP, DR, EM, END, FP, GE, GS, HMP, HO, HPM, IC, ICE, ID, IM, IMD, IMG, N, NEP, NMN, NP, NPM, NS, OBG, OPH, ORS, OTO, P, PAN, PCC, PCP, PD, PDC, PDE, PDI, PDP, PDR, PDS, PEM, PG, PHO, PM, PMM, PN, PP, PPR, PRD, PSI, PTH, PTP, PYG, RHU, RNR, RO, RPM, SCI, SME, THP, TS, TY, U, UP, VIR, VN, VS
Major participating institution for programs in: CRS
Institution ID: 16-9502

Mercy Hospital and Medical Center
2525 S Michigan Avenue
Chicago, IL 60616-2477
www.mercy-chicago.org
Med Sch Affil: M-01643, M-01611, L-01606
Programs sponsored in: IM, OBG
Major participating institution for programs in: DR, EM, GS, PCC
Institution ID: 16-0329

Michael Reese Hospital and Medical Center
2929 S Ellis Avenue
Chicago, IL 60616-3390
Med Sch Affil: M-01611, G-01602
Major participating institution for programs in: RHU
Institution ID: 16-0112

Mount Sinai Hospital Medical Center of Chicago
California Ave at 15th St
Chicago, IL 60608-1797
www.sinai.org
Med Sch Affil: M-01642, L-01606, G-01611, G-01602
Programs sponsored in: FP, OBG, PD
Major participating institution for programs in: CD, END, GS, ID, IM, P, PS, PUD, U
Institution ID: 16-0339

Teaching Institutions

Northwestern Memorial Hospital
251 East Huron, Suite 3-708
Chicago, IL 60611
Med Sch Affil: M-01606
Major participating institution for programs in: ACA, ADP, AI, AN, CCA, CCS, CD, CHN, CN, D, DMP, DR, EM, END, GE, GS, HMP, HO, IC, ICE, ID, IM, IMD, IMG, N, NMN, NP, NPM, NS, OBG, OPH, ORS, OTO, P, PCC, PCP, PM, PMM, PRD, PTH, PYG, RHU, RNR, RO, SCI, SME, THP, TS, U, VIR, VN, VS
Institution ID: 16-0286

Office of the Medical Examiner of Cook County
2121 West Harrison Street
Chicago, IL 60612-3705
Med Sch Affil: G-01643
Programs sponsored in: FOP
Institution ID: 16-0502

Provident Hospital of Cook County
500 E 51st St
Chicago, IL 60615
Major participating institution for programs in: FP
Institution ID: 16-0201

Rehabilitation Institute of Chicago
345 E Superior St
Chicago, IL 60611
Med Sch Affil: M-01606
Major participating institution for programs in: PM, RPM, SCI
Institution ID: 16-0491

Resurrection Medical Center
7435 W Talcott Avenue
Chicago, IL 60631
www.reshealth.org
Med Sch Affil: M-01643
Programs sponsored in: EM, FP, FSM, IM, TY
Major participating institution for programs in: DR, OBG
Institution ID: 16-0121

Rush University Medical Center
1653 W Congress Pkwy
Chicago, IL 60612-3833
www.rush.edu
Med Sch Affil: M-01601
Programs sponsored in: AI, AN, CD, CHP, CN, D, DR, END, FP, FSM, GE, GS, HO, HPM, IC, ICE, ID, IM, IMG, MP, MPD, N, NEP, NM, NS, OBG, OPH, ORS, OSM, OSS, OTO, P, PCC, PD, PDC, PM, PMM, PS, PTH, RHU, RNR, RO, SME, TS, U, VIR, VN, VS
Major participating institution for programs in: CD, CHP, HO
Institution ID: 16-0278

Saints Mary and Elizabeth Medical Center
St Mary of Nazareth Hospital Center
2233 W Division Street
Chicago, IL 60622
Programs sponsored in: FP
Institution ID: 16-8043

Schwab Rehabilitation Hospital and Care Network
1401 S California Blvd
Chicago, IL 60608
www.schwabrehab.org
Programs sponsored in: PM
Institution ID: 16-0480

Shriners Hospitals for Children (Chicago)
2211 N Oak Park Avenue
Chicago, IL 60707-3392
Med Sch Affil: L-01606, G-01601, G-01611, G-01643
Major participating institution for programs in: ORS, OSS
Institution ID: 16-0312

St Joseph Hospital
2900 N Lake Shore Drive
Chicago, IL 60657
reshealthcare.org
Med Sch Affil: L-01606, L-01602, G-01643, G-01611
Programs sponsored in: FP, GS, IM, OBG, TY
Institution ID: 16-0310

Swedish Covenant Hospital
5145 N California Ave
Chicago, IL 60625-3642
www.swedishcovenant.org
Med Sch Affil: M-01642
Programs sponsored in: FP, TY
Institution ID: 16-0342

University of Chicago Comer Children's Hospital
5721 South Maryland Avenue
MC-8016
Chicago, IL 60637
Med Sch Affil: M-01602
Major participating institution for programs in: CCP, PAN, PD, PDE, PDI, PDP, PDS, PHO, PPR
Institution ID: 16-0763

University of Chicago Medical Center
5841 South Maryland Avenue
M/C 1052
Chicago, IL 60637
Med Sch Affil: M-01602, G-01611
Programs sponsored in: ACA, AN, AR, BBK, CCA, CCP, CD, CHN, CHP, CN, CRS, D, DBP, DMP, DR, EM, END, GE, GS, HMP, HO, HSO, IC, ICE, ID, IM, IMG, MG, MGP, MPD, N, NEP, NPM, NS, OAR, OBG, OMO, OPH, ORS, OSM, OTO, P, PAN, PCC, PCP, PD, PDE, PDI, PDP, PDS, PG, PHO, PMM, PPR, PS, PTH, RHU, RNR, RO, SME, THP, U, VIR, VS
Major participating institution for programs in: ID
Institution ID: 16-0465

University of Illinois College of Medicine at Chicago
1853 W Polk Street, M/C 784
Chicago, IL 60612
www.uic.edu/com/gme/
Programs sponsored in: ADP, AN, BBK, CCS, CD, CHP, CN, D, DR, EM, END, FP, GE, GPM, GS, HMP, HO, IC, ID, IM, IMG, MEM, MPD, N, NEP, NMN, NPM, NS, OBG, OPH, ORS, OSM, OTO, P, PAN, PCC, PD, PMM, PS, PTH, RHU, SP, THP, TS, U, VIR, VN
Institution ID: 16-0762

University of Illinois Hosp-Illinois Eye and Ear Infirmary
1855 W Taylor St
Chicago, IL 60612
Med Sch Affil: M-01611, L-01643
Major participating institution for programs in: OPH, OTO
Institution ID: 16-0337

University of Illinois Hospital and Clinics
1740 W Taylor St, Suite 1400
Chicago, IL 60612
Med Sch Affil: M-01611, L-01602
Major participating institution for programs in: ADP, AN, BBK, CD, CHP, CN, CRS, D, DBP, DR, EM, END, ETX, FP, GE, GPM, GS, HMP, HO, IC, ID, IM, IMG, MEM, MPD, N, NEP, NMN, NPM, NS, OBG, ORS, P, PAN, PCC, PD, PMM, PS, PTH, RHU, RO, SP, THP, TS, U, VIR, VN
Institution ID: 16-0447

University of Illinois School of Public Health
1603 West Taylor St
Chicago, IL 60612-7260
Major participating institution for programs in: GPM
Institution ID: 16-0769

Women's Treatment Center
140 N Ashland Street
Chicago, IL 60607
Major participating institution for programs in: ADP
Institution ID: 16-8108

Danville

Veterans Affairs Medical Center (Danville)
1900 E Main Street
Danville, IL 61832
Med Sch Affil: M-01611
Major participating institution for programs in: IM
Institution ID: 16-0766

Decatur

Decatur Memorial Hospital
2300 N Edward St
Decatur, IL 62526
Med Sch Affil: G-01645
Major participating institution for programs in: FP
Institution ID: 16-0158

Dixon

Katherine Shaw Bethea Hospital
403 East 1st St
Dixon, IL 61021
Major participating institution for programs in: FP
Institution ID: 16-8042

Elk Grove Village

Alexian Brothers Medical Center
800 Biester Field Road
Elk Grove Village, IL 60007
Major participating institution for programs in: NS
Institution ID: 16-8110

Evanston

Evanston Hospital
2650 Ridge Ave
Evanston, IL 60201
Med Sch Affil: M-01606, G-01642
Major participating institution for programs in: D, DR, EM, FP, GS, IM, NEP, NPM, NS, OBG, OPH, ORS, OTO, P, PTH, TY, U
Institution ID: 16-0145

St Francis Hospital
355 Ridge Avenue
Evanston, IL 60202
www.reshealth.org
Med Sch Affil: M-01611, L-01602, G-01643
Programs sponsored in: DR, IM, OBG, TY
Major participating institution for programs in: EM, GS
Institution ID: 16-0168

Glenview

Glenbrook Hospital
2100 Pfingsten Road
Glenview, IL 60025
Major participating institution for programs in: FP, IM, TY
Institution ID: 16-8024

Hines

Edward Hines, Jr Veterans Affairs Hospital
Fifth Avenue & Roosevelt Road
PO Box 5000
Hines, IL 60141
Med Sch Affil: M-01643, L-01642
Major participating institution for programs in: CCS, CD, D, END, GE, GS, HO, ID, IM, IMG, MPD, N, NEP, NM, NS, OPH, ORS, OTO, P, PCC, PM, PS, PTH, RHU, RO, TS, U, VS
Institution ID: 16-0259

Hinsdale

Adventist Hinsdale Hospital
120 North Oak Street
Hinsdale, IL 60521
www.keepingyouwell.org/hfmr
Med Sch Affil: L-01601, L-00512
Programs sponsored in: FP
Institution ID: 16-0369

LaGrange

Adventist La Grange Memorial Hospital
5101 South Willow Springs Road
LaGrange, IL 60525
www.keepingyouwell.org
Med Sch Affil: L-01602, L-01601
Programs sponsored in: FP
Major participating institution for programs in: RO
Institution ID: 16-0175

Maywood

Loyola University Medical Center
2160 S First Avenue
Maywood, IL 60153-5585
http://luhs.org
Med Sch Affil: M-01643
Programs sponsored in: ACA, AN, CCS, CD, CN, D, DR,
END, FP, GE, GS, HMP, HO, IC, ICE, ID, IM, IMG, MPD,
N, NEP, NM, NPM, NS, OBG, OPH, ORS, OTO, P, PCC,
PCP, PD, PM, PMM, PS, PTH, RHU, RO, TS, U, VN, VS
Institution ID: 16-0498

Melrose Park

Gottlieb Memorial Hospital
701 West North Avenue
Melrose Park, IL 60160
Major participating institution for programs in: OBG
Institution ID: 16-0505

Westlake Community Hospital
1225 Lake Street
Melrose Park, IL 60160
Med Sch Affil: G-01643
Major participating institution for programs in: IM
Institution ID: 16-7049

North Chicago

Chicago Medical School/Rosalind Franklin Univ of Med & Sci
3333 Green Bay Road
North Chicago, IL 60064
www.rosalindfranklin.edu
Med Sch Affil: M-01642
Programs sponsored in: CD, END, ID, IM, P, PUD
Institution ID: 16-0748

Veterans Affairs Medical Center (North Chicago)
North Chicago, IL 60064
Med Sch Affil: M-01642
Major participating institution for programs in: CD,
END, ID, IM, P, PUD
Institution ID: 16-0460

Oak Forest

Oak Forest Hospital of Cook County
15900 S Cicero Ave
Oak Forest, IL 60452
Med Sch Affil: G-01602, G-01601
Major participating institution for programs in: PM
Institution ID: 16-0732

Oak Lawn

Advocate Christ Medical Center
4440 W 95th Street
Oak Lawn, IL 60453
www.advocatehealth.com
Med Sch Affil: M-01611, M-01642
Programs sponsored in: EM, FP, PD, PDC
Major participating institution for programs in: CD,
END, GS, IC, IM, N, NS, OBG, PD, PS, U
Institution ID: 16-0303

Oak Park

Rush Oak Park Hospital
520 S Maple Ave
Oak Park, IL 60304
Major participating institution for programs in: AI
Institution ID: 16-8054

West Suburban Medical Center
3 Erie Court
Oak Park, IL 60302-2599
www.wshmc.org
Programs sponsored in: FP, IM, TY
Institution ID: 16-0454

Park Ridge

Advocate Lutheran General Hospital
1775 W Dempster St
Park Ridge, IL 60068-1174
http://advocatehealth.com
Med Sch Affil: M-01611, M-01642, G-01643
Programs sponsored in: CCP, CD, FP, FSM, GE, HO, IM,
IMG, NPM, OBG, P, PD
Major participating institution for programs in: ADP,
CRS, EM, GS, NS, PTH
Institution ID: 16-0484

Peoria

Methodist Medical Center of Illinois
221 NE Glen Oak Ave
Peoria, IL 61636
Med Sch Affil: M-01611
Major participating institution for programs in: FP,
FPG, NS
Institution ID: 16-0390

OSF St Francis Medical Center
530 NE Glen Oak Ave
Peoria, IL 61637
Med Sch Affil: M-01611
Major participating institution for programs in: DR,
EM, GS, IM, MPD, N, NS, OBG, PD, RNR, VIR
Institution ID: 16-0398

University of Illinois College of Medicine at Peoria
One Illini Drive, Box 1649
Peoria, IL 61656
www.uicomp.uic.edu/
Programs sponsored in: DR, EM, FP, FPG, GS, IM, MPD,
N, NS, OBG, PD, RNR, VIR
Institution ID: 16-0751

Quincy

Blessing Hospital
Broadway at 11th St
Quincy, IL 62301
Med Sch Affil: G-01645
Major participating institution for programs in: FP,
FSM
Institution ID: 16-7127

Rockford

Swedish American Hospital
1400 Charles St
Rockford, IL 61104
Med Sch Affil: M-01611
Major participating institution for programs in: FP
Institution ID: 16-0446

University of Illinois College of Medicine at Rockford
1601 Parkview Avenue
Rockford, IL 61107-1897
www.rockford.uic.edu
Programs sponsored in: FP
Institution ID: 16-0504

Springfield

Memorial Medical Center
800 N Rutledge St
Springfield, IL 62781
Med Sch Affil: M-01645
Major participating institution for programs in: CHP,
CRS, D, DR, END, FP, GS, HSP, ID, IM, MP, N, OBG, ORS,
OTO, P, PUD, U, VS
Institution ID: 16-0509

Southern Illinois University School of Medicine
801 N Rutledge
PO Box 19620
Springfield, IL 62794-9620
www.siumed.edu
Med Sch Affil: M-01645
Programs sponsored in: CHP, CRS, D, DR, END, FP,
FSM, GS, HSP, ID, IM, MP, N, OBG, ORS, OTO, P, PD, PSI,
PUD, U, VS
Institution ID: 16-0512

Springfield Clinic Outpatient Facility
700 N First Street
Springfield, IL 62781
Major participating institution for programs in: CRS
Institution ID: 16-8077

St John's Hospital
800 E Carpenter Street
Springfield, IL 62769
Med Sch Affil: M-01645
Major participating institution for programs in: CHP,
CRS, D, DR, END, FP, GS, HSP, ID, IM, MP, N, OBG, ORS,
OTO, P, PD, PUD, U, VS
Institution ID: 16-0503

Urbana

Carle Foundation Hospital
611 West Park Street
Urbana, IL 61801
http://carle.com
Med Sch Affil: M-01611
Programs sponsored in: FP, FPG
Major participating institution for programs in: GPM,
IM
Institution ID: 16-0146

Provena Covenant Medical Center
1400 W Park Street
Urbana, IL 61801
Med Sch Affil: M-01611
Major participating institution for programs in: IM
Institution ID: 16-0768

University of Illinois College of Medicine at Urbana
611 West Park Street
Urbana, IL 61801
www.med.uiuc.edu/residency/internalmed
Programs sponsored in: IM
Institution ID: 16-0752

Teaching Institutions

Wheaton

Marianjoy Rehabilitation Hospital
26 West 171 Roosevelt Road
Wheaton, IL 60187
www.marianjoy.org
Med Sch Affil: G-01643, G-01601
Programs sponsored in: PM
Institution ID: 16-8025

Indiana

Evansville

Deaconess Hospital
600 Mary Street
Evansville, IN 47747
www.deaconess.com
Med Sch Affil: L-01720
Programs sponsored in: FP
Institution ID: 17-0708

Fort Wayne

Fort Wayne Medical Education Program
750 Broadway Suite 250
Fort Wayne, IN 46802
www.fwmep.edu
Programs sponsored in: FP, ORS
Institution ID: 17-0446

Lutheran Hospital of Indiana
7950 W Jefferson Boulevard
Fort Wayne, IN 46804
Med Sch Affil: L-01720
Major participating institution for programs in: FP, ORS
Institution ID: 17-0228

Parkview Memorial Hospital
2200 Randallia Dr
Fort Wayne, IN 46805
Med Sch Affil: L-01720
Major participating institution for programs in: FP, ORS
Institution ID: 17-0447

St Joseph Hospital
700 Broadway
Fort Wayne, IN 46802
Med Sch Affil: L-01720
Major participating institution for programs in: FP, ORS
Institution ID: 17-0422

Indianapolis

Central Indiana Regional Blood Center
3450 N Meridian St
Indianapolis, IN 46208
Major participating institution for programs in: BBK
Institution ID: 17-8008

Clarian Indiana University Hospital
550 N University Boulevard
Indianapolis, IN 46202
Med Sch Affil: M-01720
Major participating institution for programs in: AN, BBK, CCS, CFS, CHN, CN, CPP, D, DMP, DR, EM, GS, HO, HSO, ID, IM, MG, MN, MPD, N, NEP, NM, NS, OBG, OPH, ORS, OTO, P, PCC, PCP, PM, PMM, PS, PYN, RHU, RNR, RO, TS, U, VIR, VN, VSI
Institution ID: 17-0444

Clarian Methodist Hospital of Indiana
I-65 at 21st Street
PO Box 1367
Indianapolis, IN 46206-1367
Med Sch Affil: M-01720
Major participating institution for programs in: BBK, CCS, CD, DR, EM, EMP, ETX, FP, FSM, GS, IC, ICE, IM, MPD, NS, OBG, ORS, OSM, P, PCP, TS, TY, U, VIR, VS, VSI
Institution ID: 17-0217

Clarian Pathology Laboratory
350 West 11th Street
Indianapolis, IN 46202
Major participating institution for programs in: BBK, HMP, MM, NP, PCP, PP, PTH
Institution ID: 17-8015

Clarian Riley Hospital for Children
702 Barnhill Drive
Indianapolis, IN 46202-1367
Med Sch Affil: M-01720
Major participating institution for programs in: ADL, AN, CCP, CFS, CHN, CHP, CN, CPP, D, DR, IM, MG, MPD, N, NPM, NS, ORS, OTO, P, PAN, PD, PDC, PDE, PDP, PDR, PDS, PG, PHO, PMM, PP, PPR, PS, RHU, RNR, TS, U, UP
Institution ID: 17-8005

Community Hospital North
7150 Clearvista Drive
Indianapolis, IN 46256
Major participating institution for programs in: FP
Institution ID: 17-8024

Community Hospitals of Indianapolis
1500 N Ritter Ave
Indianapolis, IN 46219
www.eCommunity.com
Med Sch Affil: M-01720
Programs sponsored in: FP
Institution ID: 17-0710

Indiana Hand Center
8501 Harcourt Rd
Indianapolis, IN 46260
Major participating institution for programs in: HSO
Institution ID: 17-8007

Indiana University School of Medicine
Fairbanks Hall, Suite 6200
340 West 10th Street
Indianapolis, IN 46202-3082
www.medicine.iu.edu/home.html
Med Sch Affil: M-01720
Programs sponsored in: ADL, ADP, AN, BBK, CCP, CCS, CD, CFS, CHN, CHP, CN, CPP, CRS, D, DMP, DR, EM, EMP, END, ETX, FOP, FP, FSM, GE, GS, HMP, HO, HPM, HSO, IC, ICE, ID, IM, IMG, MG, MM, MN, MPD, N, NEP, NM, NP, NPM, NS, OBG, OPH, ORS, OSM, OTO, P, PAN, PCC, PCP, PD, PDC, PDE, PDP, PDR, PDS, PG, PHO, PM, PMM, PP, PPR, PS, PTH, PYG, PYN, RHU, RNR, RO, TS, TY, U, UP, VIR, VN, VS, VSI
Institution ID: 17-9501

Larue D Carter Memorial Hospital
2601 Cold Spring Road
Indianapolis, IN 46222
Med Sch Affil: M-01720
Major participating institution for programs in: CHP, P
Institution ID: 17-0189

MAPS/Dermatology Inc
1801 N Senate Blvd
Suite 745
Indianapolis, IN 46202
Major participating institution for programs in: DMP
Institution ID: 17-8018

Rehabilitation Hospital of Indiana (Indianapolis)
4141 Shore Drive
Indianapolis, IN 46254-2607
Major participating institution for programs in: PM
Institution ID: 17-8009

Richard L Roudebush Veterans Affairs Medical Center
1481 W Tenth Street
Indianapolis, IN 46202
Med Sch Affil: M-01720
Major participating institution for programs in: ADP, AN, D, DMP, END, GE, GS, HSO, IC, ICE, IM, IMG, MN, MPD, NS, OPH, ORS, OTO, P, PMM, PS, PYG, PYN, RHU, RNR, RO, U, VIR, VS, VSI
Institution ID: 17-0414

St Francis Hospital - Beech Grove
8111 S Emerson Ave
Indianapolis, IN 46237
www.stfrancishospitals.org/directory/residency
Med Sch Affil: L-01720
Programs sponsored in: FP
Major participating institution for programs in: CRS
Institution ID: 17-0125

St Francis Hospital - Indianapolis
8111 South Emerson Avenue
Indianapolis, IN 46237
Major participating institution for programs in: CRS
Institution ID: 17-7020

St Vincent Hospitals and Health Care Center
2001 W 86th Street
Indianapolis, IN 46260
http://stvincent.org
Med Sch Affil: M-01720
Programs sponsored in: CD, FP, FPG, IC, ICE, IFP, IM, OBG, PD, PRD, TY
Major participating institution for programs in: HPM, HSO, PS, UP
Institution ID: 17-0421

Westpark Healthcare Center
1316 North Tibbs Avenue
Indianapolis, IN 46222
Major participating institution for programs in: IMG
Institution ID: 17-8023

William N Wishard Memorial Hospital
Indiana University
1001 W Tenth St
Indianapolis, IN 46202
Med Sch Affil: M-01720
Major participating institution for programs in: ADP, AN, CCS, CFS, D, DMP, DR, EM, END, ETX, GE, GS, HSO, IM, IMG, MM, MN, MPD, N, NS, OBG, OPH, ORS, OTO, P, PCC, PCP, PMM, PS, PYN, RHU, RNR, U, VIR, VN, VSI
Institution ID: 17-0141

Mooresville

St Francis Hospital - Mooresville
1201 Hadley Road
Mooresville, IN 46158
Major participating institution for programs in: CRS
Institution ID: 17-0716

Muncie

Ball Memorial Hospital
Cardinal Health System
2401 University Avenue
Muncie, IN 47303
www.ballhospital.org
Med Sch Affil: L-01720
Programs sponsored in: FP, IM, PTH, TY
Institution ID: 17-0150

New Albany

Floyd Memorial Hospital
1850 State Street
New Albany, IN 47150
Major participating institution for programs in: PCC, RO
Institution ID: 17-8013

South Bend

Memorial Hospital of South Bend
615 N Michigan Street
South Bend, IN 46601
http://qualityoflife.org
Med Sch Affil: L-01720
Programs sponsored in: FP, FSM
Major participating institution for programs in: FSM
Institution ID: 17-0335

St Joseph's Regional Medical Center (South Bend)
801 E LaSalle Street
PO Box 1935
South Bend, IN 46634-1935
www.sjmed.com
Med Sch Affil: L-01720
Programs sponsored in: FP, FSM
Major participating institution for programs in: FSM
Institution ID: 17-0419

Terre Haute

Union Hospital, Inc
1513 N 6 1/2 St
Terre Haute, IN 47807
www.mcrh.org
Med Sch Affil: L-01720
Programs sponsored in: FP
Institution ID: 17-0709

Iowa

Cedar Rapids

Cedar Rapids Medical Education Foundation
1026 A Avenue NE
Cedar Rapids, IA 52402
www.CRMEF.org
Programs sponsored in: FP
Institution ID: 18-8002

Mercy Medical Center
701 Tenth St, SE
Cedar Rapids, IA 52403
Med Sch Affil: L-01803
Major participating institution for programs in: FP
Institution ID: 18-0452

St Luke's Methodist Hospital
1026 A Avenue, NE
PO Box 3026
Cedar Rapids, IA 52406-3026
Med Sch Affil: L-01803
Major participating institution for programs in: EM, FP
Institution ID: 18-0417

Davenport

Genesis Health System
1227 E Rusholme
Davenport, IA 52803
www.fmcdocs.org
Programs sponsored in: FP
Institution ID: 18-9501

Genesis Medical Center
1227 E Rusholme
Davenport, IA 52803
Med Sch Affil: L-01803
Major participating institution for programs in: FP
Institution ID: 18-8001

Des Moines

Broadlawns Medical Center
1801 Hickman Road
Des Moines, IA 50314-1597
www.broadlawns.org
Med Sch Affil: L-01803
Programs sponsored in: FP, TY
Major participating institution for programs in: GS
Institution ID: 18-0240

Central Iowa Health System (Iowa Methodist/Iowa Lutheran)
1415 Woodland Avenue
Suite 140
Des Moines, IA 50309-1453
www.ihsmeded.org
Med Sch Affil: M-01803
Programs sponsored in: FP, GS, IM, PD, TY
Major participating institution for programs in: TY
Institution ID: 18-0130

Mercy Hospital Medical Center
1111 6th Avenue
Des Moines, IA 50314
Med Sch Affil: G-02608
Programs sponsored in: FP, FPG
Institution ID: 18-0356

Veterans Affairs Central Iowa Health Care System
3600 30th Street
Des Moines, IA 50310-5774
Med Sch Affil: L-01803
Major participating institution for programs in: GS, IM
Institution ID: 18-0226

Iowa City

University of Iowa Hospitals and Clinics
C123 GH, Graduate Medical Education Office
200 Hawkins Drive
Iowa City, IA 52242-1009
www.uihealthcare.com/index.html
Med Sch Affil: M-01803
Programs sponsored in: AI, AN, BBK, CCA, CCP, CCS, CD, CHN, CHP, CN, D, DBP, DR, EM, END, FP, FPG, FPP, GE, GPM, GS, HMP, HO, HSO, IC, ICE, ID, IM, INM, MG, MGP, MM, MP, N, NEP, NM, NO, NPM, NS, OBG, OPH, ORS, OSM, OTO, P, PCC, PCP, PD, PDC, PDE, PDO, PDP, PDR, PG, PHO, PMM, PTH, PYG, RHU, RNR, RO, SME, TS, U, VIR, VN, VS
Institution ID: 18-0415

Veterans Affairs Medical Center (Iowa City)
Highway 6 West
Iowa City, IA 52240
Med Sch Affil: M-01803
Major participating institution for programs in: D, GE, GS, HO, IC, INM, MP, N, NM, NS, OPH, ORS, P, PMM, PTH, U, VN, VS
Institution ID: 18-0319

Mason City

Mercy Medical Center-North Iowa
1000 4th Street, SW
Mason City, IA 50401
www.mercynorthiowa.com/career/famres/index.shtml
Med Sch Affil: L-01803
Programs sponsored in: FP, HPM
Institution ID: 18-0705

Pella

Pella Regional Health Center
404 Jefferson Street
Pella, IA 50219
Major participating institution for programs in: FP
Institution ID: 18-8003

Sioux City

Mercy Medical Center (Sioux City)
801 Fifth St, Box 3168
Sioux City, IA 51101
Med Sch Affil: L-01803
Major participating institution for programs in: FP
Institution ID: 18-0709

Siouxland Medical Education Foundation
2501 Pierce Street
Sioux City, IA 51104
www.siouxlandresidencyfp.org
Programs sponsored in: FP
Institution ID: 18-0708

St Luke's Regional Medical Center
2720 Stone Park Blvd
Sioux City, IA 51104
Med Sch Affil: L-01803
Major participating institution for programs in: FP
Institution ID: 18-0710

Waterloo

Allen Memorial Hospital
1825 Logan Avenue
Waterloo, IA 50703
Med Sch Affil: L-01803
Major participating institution for programs in: FP
Institution ID: 18-0713

Covenant Medical Center
3421 W Ninth Street
Waterloo, IA 50702-5499
Med Sch Affil: L-01803
Major participating institution for programs in: FP
Institution ID: 18-0714

Northeast Iowa Medical Education Foundation
2055 Kimball Avenue
Waterloo, IA 50702
www.familypracticecenter.org
Programs sponsored in: FP
Institution ID: 18-0712

Kansas

Hutchinson

Hutchinson Hospital
1703 East 23rd Street
Hutchinson, KS 67502
Major participating institution for programs in: VS
Institution ID: 19-8033

Junction City

Geary Community Hospital
1102 St Mary's Rd
Box 490
Junction City, KS 66441
Med Sch Affil: G-01902
Major participating institution for programs in: FP
Institution ID: 19-8003

Kansas City

Kansas City Presbyterian Manor
7850 Freeman
Kansas City, KS 66101
Major participating institution for programs in: IMG
Institution ID: 19-8016

KVC Psychiatric Hospital
4300 Brenner Drive
Kansas City, KS 66104
Major participating institution for programs in: CHP
Institution ID: 19-8035

Teaching Institutions

Southview Home Care
1701 South 45th Street
Kansas City, KS 66106
Major participating institution for programs in: IMG
Institution ID: 19-8031

University of Kansas Hospital
3901 University Boulevard
Mail Stop 3011
Kansas City, KS 66160-7220
Major participating institution for programs in: AI,
AN, CD, CHP, CN, D, DBP, DR, END, FP, GE, GS, IC, ICE,
ID, IM, IMG, N, NEP, NS, OBG, OPH, ORS, OTO, P, PCC,
PCP, PD, PM, PTH, RHU, RO, U, VIR, VN, VS
Institution ID: 19-8034

University of Kansas Medical Center
39th and Rainbow Blvd
Kansas City, KS 66103
Med Sch Affil: G-01902
Major participating institution for programs in: ADP,
CHN, MP, NMN, SP
Institution ID: 19-0488

University of Kansas School of Medicine
3901 Rainbow Blvd
Kansas City, KS 66160-7100
www.kumc.edu
Med Sch Affil: G-01902
Programs sponsored in: ADP, AI, AN, CD, CHP, CN, D,
DBP, DR, END, FP, GE, GS, HO, HPM, IC, ICE, ID, IM,
IMG, MP, N, NEP, NMN, NS, OBG, OPH, ORS, OTO, P,
PCC, PCP, PD, PM, PSI, PTH, RHU, RO, SP, U, VIR, VN,
VS
Institution ID: 19-9501

Wyandot Mental Health Center, Inc
3615 Eaton Street
Kansas City, KS 66103
Major participating institution for programs in: P
Institution ID: 19-8022

Leavenworth

Dwight D Eisenhower Veterans Affairs Medical Center
4401 S Fourth St
Leavenworth, KS 66048
Med Sch Affil: M-01902
Major participating institution for programs in: P, VS
Institution ID: 19-0406

Leawood

Kansas City Orthopaedic Institute
3651 College Blvd
Leawood, KS 66209
Major participating institution for programs in: OSM
Institution ID: 19-8028

Olathe

Aberdeen Village
17500 W 119th Street
Olathe, KS 66061
Major participating institution for programs in: IMG
Institution ID: 19-8030

Overland Park

Menorah Medical Center
5721 W 119th St
Overland Park, KS 66209
Major participating institution for programs in: OSM
Institution ID: 19-8018

Salina

Salina Regional Health Center
400 S Santa Fe Avenue
PO Box 5080
Salina, KS 67402-5080
Major participating institution for programs in: FP
Institution ID: 19-0518

Shawnee Mission

Johnson County Mental Health Center
6000 Lamar
Shawnee Mission, KS 66202
Major participating institution for programs in: ADP,
P
Institution ID: 19-8015

Topeka

Colmery-O'Neil Veterans Affairs Medical Center
2200 Gage Blvd
Topeka, KS 66622
Major participating institution for programs in: N
Institution ID: 19-0498

Wichita

University of Kansas School of Medicine (Wichita)
1010 N Kansas
Wichita, KS 67214-3199
http://wichita.kumc.edu/
Med Sch Affil: M-01902
Programs sponsored in: AN, DR, FP, FSM, GS, IM, MPD,
OBG, ORS, P, PD
Institution ID: 19-0511

Veterans Affairs Medical Center (Wichita)
5500 E Kellogg
Wichita, KS 67218-1607
Med Sch Affil: M-01902
Major participating institution for programs in: IM,
MPD, ORS
Institution ID: 19-0196

Via Christi Regional Medical Center-Good Shepherd
8901 E Orme
Wichita, KS 67207
Major participating institution for programs in: P
Institution ID: 19-8001

Via Christi Regional Medical Center-St Francis
929 N St Francis Avenue
Wichita, KS 67214-3882
Med Sch Affil: M-01902
Major participating institution for programs in: AN,
FP, GS, IM, MPD, ORS, P
Institution ID: 19-0132

Via Christi Regional Medical Center-St Joseph
3600 E Harry Street
Wichita, KS 67218-3713
Med Sch Affil: M-01902
Major participating institution for programs in: FP,
FSM, P
Institution ID: 19-0306

Wesley Medical Center
550 N Hillside
Wichita, KS 67214-4976
Med Sch Affil: M-01902
Major participating institution for programs in: AN,
DR, FP, GS, IM, MPD, OBG, ORS, PD
Institution ID: 19-0500

Kentucky

Edgewood

St Elizabeth Medical Center
One Medical Village Dr
Edgewood, KY 41017
www.StElizabeth.com
Med Sch Affil: L-03841, G-02012
Programs sponsored in: FP
Institution ID: 20-0463

Glasgow

T J Samson Community Hospital
1301 N Race Street
Glasgow, KY 42141-3483
Med Sch Affil: G-02002
Major participating institution for programs in: FP
Institution ID: 20-7044

Hazard

ARH Regional Medical Center (Hazard)
100 Medical Center Drive
Hazard, KY 41701
Med Sch Affil: G-02012
Major participating institution for programs in: FP
Institution ID: 20-7045

Lexington

Cardinal Hill Hospital
2050 Versailles Road
Lexington, KY 40504
Med Sch Affil: G-02012
Major participating institution for programs in: PM
Institution ID: 20-0525

Central Baptist Hospital
1740 S Nicholasville Rd
Lexington, KY 40503
Major participating institution for programs in: OBG
Institution ID: 20-0248

Hospice of the Bluegrass
2312 Alexandria Way
Lexington, KY 40504
Major participating institution for programs in: HPM
Institution ID: 20-8031

Ridge Behavioral Health System
3050 Rio Dosa Dr
Lexington, KY 40509
www.ridgebhs.com
Major participating institution for programs in: CPP
Institution ID: 20-8006

Shriners Hospitals for Children (Lexington)
1900 Richmond Rd
Lexington, KY 40502-1298
Med Sch Affil: L-03843, G-02012
Major participating institution for programs in: ORS
Institution ID: 20-0284

St Joseph Hospital
1 St Joseph Drive
Lexington, KY 40504
Med Sch Affil: L-02012
Major participating institution for programs in: U
Institution ID: 20-0261

University of Kentucky College of Medicine
800 Rose Street
Lexington, KY 40536
www.uky.edu
Med Sch Affil: M-02012
Programs sponsored in: AN, CCS, CD, CHN, CHP, CPP, DR, EM, END, FP, FSM, GE, GPM, GS, HO, HPM, IC, ID, IM, MPD, N, NEP, NPM, NS, OBG, OPH, ORS, OSM, OTO, P, PCC, PCP, PD, PM, PMM, PSI, PTH, RHU, RO, TS, U, VS
Institution ID: 20-0513

University of Kentucky Hospital
800 Rose Street
Lexington, KY 40536-0084
Med Sch Affil: M-02012
Major participating institution for programs in: AN, CCS, CD, CHN, CHP, CPP, DR, EM, END, FP, FP, FSM, GE, GS, HO, IC, ID, IM, MPD, N, NEP, NPM, NS, OBG, OPH, ORS, OSM, OTO, P, PCP, PD, PM, PMM, PTH, RHU, RO, U, VS
Institution ID: 20-0505

Veterans Affairs Medical Center (Lexington)
1101 Veteran's Drive (Cooper Drive Division)
Lexington, KY 40502
Med Sch Affil: M-02012
Major participating institution for programs in: CD, GE, GS, HO, IC, ID, IM, MPD, N, NEP, OPH, ORS, P, PCC, PCP, PM, PTH, TS, U, VS
Institution ID: 20-0352

Louisville

American Red Cross Blood Services (Louisville Region)
510 E Chestnut Street
Louisville, KY 40202
Major participating institution for programs in: BBK
Institution ID: 20-8020

Caritas Medical Center
1850 Bluegrass Avenue
Louisville, KY 40215
Major participating institution for programs in: CHP
Institution ID: 20-8036

Central State Hospital
10510 LaGrange Road
Louisville, KY 40223
Major participating institution for programs in: ADP
Institution ID: 20-0495

Child Psychiatric Services (Bingham Child Guidance Clinic)
Univ of Louisville Sch of Med
200 E Chestnut St
Louisville, KY 40202
Med Sch Affil: L-02002
Major participating institution for programs in: CHP
Institution ID: 20-0500

Frazier Rehabilitation Institute
220 Abraham Flexner Way
Louisville, KY 40202-1887
Med Sch Affil: M-02002
Major participating institution for programs in: PM
Institution ID: 20-0515

James Graham Brown Medical Center
529 S Jackson Street
Louisville, KY 40292
Major participating institution for programs in: HO
Institution ID: 20-8005

Jewish Hospital
217 East Chestnut Street
Louisville, KY 40202
Med Sch Affil: M-02002
Major participating institution for programs in: CD, CRS, END, FP, FPG, FSM, GE, GS, HSS, IC, ICE, OAR, ORS, PCC, U
Institution ID: 20-0136

Kosair Children's Hospital (Norton Healthcare, Inc)
PO Box 35070
231 East Chestnut Street
Louisville, KY 40232-5070
Med Sch Affil: M-02002
Major participating institution for programs in: BBK, CCP, CHN, CHP, EM, GS, MPD, NPM, NS, ORS, OTO, PD, PDI, PDS, PEM, PG, SME, U
Institution ID: 20-0345

Norton Audubon Hospital
One Audubon Plaza
Louisville, KY 40217
Major participating institution for programs in: OAR
Institution ID: 20-8027

Norton Hospital
200 East Chestnut Street
Louisville, KY 40217
Med Sch Affil: M-02002
Major participating institution for programs in: BBK, CRS, END, GE, GS, N, NEP, NS, OAR, OTO, P, PCC, SME, U
Institution ID: 20-0235

Norton Medical Pavilion-Norton Healthcare, Inc
PO Box 35070
315 E Broadway
Louisville, KY 40232
Med Sch Affil: L-02012
Major participating institution for programs in: ORS
Institution ID: 20-8007

Office of Chief Medical Examiner
810 Barret Avenue
Louisville, KY 40204
Major participating institution for programs in: FOP
Institution ID: 20-8008

Seven Counties Services (Louisville)
2105 Crums Lane
Louisville, KY 40216
Major participating institution for programs in: ADP, CHP
Institution ID: 20-8026

University Neurologists, PSC
601 S Floyd Street
Suite 503
Louisville, KY 40202
Major participating institution for programs in: CHN, N
Institution ID: 20-8028

University of Louisville Hospital
530 South Jackson Street
Louisville, KY 40202
Med Sch Affil: M-02002
Major participating institution for programs in: AN, BBK, CCS, CD, CHN, CRS, D, DR, EM, END, FP, FPG, GE, GS, HO, HSS, IC, ICE, ID, IM, MPD, N, NEP, NPM, NS, OAR, OBG, OPH, ORS, OTO, P, PCC, PCP, PMM, PS, PTH, RO, SME, U
Institution ID: 20-0283

University of Louisville School of Medicine
Abell Administration Center, #518
323 E Chestnut Street
Louisville, KY 40202
www.louisville.edu/medschool/gme
Med Sch Affil: M-02002
Programs sponsored in: ADP, AN, BBK, CCP, CCS, CD, CHN, CHP, CRS, D, DR, EM, END, FOP, FP, FPG, FSM, GE, GS, HO, HPM, HSS, IC, ICE, ID, IM, MPD, N, NEP, NPM, NS, OAR, OBG, OPH, ORS, OTO, P, PCC, PCP, PD, PDI, PDS, PEM, PG, PM, PMM, PS, PTH, RO, SME, U
Institution ID: 20-0507

Veterans Affairs Medical Center (Louisville)
800 Zorn Avenue
Louisville, KY 40206
Med Sch Affil: M-02002
Major participating institution for programs in: ADP, AN, CD, CRS, D, DR, END, FPG, GE, GS, HO, HSS, IC, ICE, ID, IM, MPD, NEP, OPH, OTO, P, PCC, PM, U
Institution ID: 20-0179

Madisonville

Regional Medical Center of Hopkins County
900 Hospital Dr
Madisonville, KY 42431
Med Sch Affil: L-02012, L-02002
Major participating institution for programs in: FP
Institution ID: 20-0520

Trover Clinic Foundation
200 Clinic Drive
Madisonville, KY 42431
www.troverfoundation.org
Programs sponsored in: FP
Institution ID: 20-8021

Morehead

St Claire Medical Center
222 Medical Circle
Morehead, KY 40351-1180
Med Sch Affil: M-02012
Major participating institution for programs in: FP
Institution ID: 20-8011

Louisiana

Alexandria

Rapides Regional Medical Center
211 Fourth St
Box 30101
Alexandria, LA 71306
Med Sch Affil: G-02106
Major participating institution for programs in: FP
Institution ID: 21-8028

Veterans Affairs Medical Center (Alexandria)
Quarters 21-A
PO Box 69004
Alexandria, LA 71306-9004
Med Sch Affil: G-02101
Major participating institution for programs in: OPH
Institution ID: 21-0100

Baton Rouge

Baton Rouge General Medical Center
3600 Florida Blvd
PO Box 2511
Baton Rouge, LA 70821
www.brgeneral.org
Med Sch Affil: G-02105
Programs sponsored in: FP, FSM
Major participating institution for programs in: EM
Institution ID: 21-7005

Teaching Institutions

Earl K Long Medical Center
5825 Airline Highway
Baton Rouge, LA 70805-2498
www.lsuhsc.edu
Med Sch Affil: M-02105
Programs sponsored in: EM, IM, OBG
Major participating institution for programs in: D, GS,
IMD, OPH, ORS, OTO
Institution ID: 21-0491

Our Lady of the Lake Regional Medical Center
5000 Hennessy Blvd
Baton Rouge, LA 70808
Major participating institution for programs in: EM,
GS, OTO, VS
Institution ID: 21-8059

Woman's Hospital
9050 Airline Highway
Baton Rouge, LA 70815
Major participating institution for programs in: OBG
Institution ID: 21-8062

Bogalusa

LSU Health Science Center-Bogalusa Medical Center
433 Plaza Street
Bogalusa, LA 70427
Major participating institution for programs in: FP,
OPH
Institution ID: 21-0714

Bridge City

LSU Health Science Center Juvenile Justice Program
3225 River Road
Bridge City, LA 70094
Major participating institution for programs in: CHP
Institution ID: 21-8090

Houma

Leonard J Chabert Medical Center
1978 Industrial Blvd
Houma, LA 70363
Programs sponsored in: IM
Major participating institution for programs in: FP,
GE, GS, OBG, OPH, ORS, VS
Institution ID: 21-0735

Jackson

Eastern Louisiana Mental Health System
PO Box 888
Jackson, LA 70748
Major participating institution for programs in: PFP
Institution ID: 21-8104

Kenner

Ochsner Medical Center-Kenner
180 West Esplanade Avenue
Kenner, LA 70065
Med Sch Affil: G-02105
Major participating institution for programs in: AI,
FP, GE, ID, IM, IMD, MPD, NEP, ORS, RHU
Institution ID: 21-8030

Lafayette

Hospice of Acadiana
2600 Johnston Street #200
Lafayette, LA 70503
Major participating institution for programs in: FPG
Institution ID: 21-8089

Lafayette General Medical Center
1214 Coolidge
PO Box 52009
Lafayette, LA 70505
Major participating institution for programs in: FPG
Institution ID: 21-8038

Oakwood of Acadiana/River Oaks Retirement Manor
2500 East Simcoe Street
Lafayette, LA 70501
Major participating institution for programs in: FPG
Institution ID: 21-8091

Rehabilitation Hospital of Acadiana Long Term Acute Care
310 Youngsville Highway
Lafayette, LA 70508
Major participating institution for programs in: FPG
Institution ID: 21-8061

University Medical Center (Lafayette)
2390 W Congress, Box 69300
Lafayette, LA 70596-9300
www.umcip.lsumc.edu
Med Sch Affil: M-02105
Programs sponsored in: FP, FPG, IM
Major participating institution for programs in: GS,
OBG, OTO
Institution ID: 21-0380

Lake Charles

Lake Charles Memorial Hospital
1700 Oak Park Boulevard
Lake Charles, LA 70601
Med Sch Affil: G-02105, G-02106
Major participating institution for programs in: FP
Institution ID: 21-8019

Mandeville

Southeast Louisiana Hospital
PO Box 3850
Mandeville, LA 70470
Major participating institution for programs in: CHP
Institution ID: 21-0490

Marrero

West Jefferson Medical Center
1101 Medical Center Boulevard
Marrero, LA 70072
Major participating institution for programs in: AN,
GS, N, NS, PS, PTH, UME, VS
Institution ID: 21-8040

Metairie

East Jefferson General Hospital
4200 Houma Blvd
Metairie, LA 70006
www.ejgh.org
Programs sponsored in: FP
Major participating institution for programs in: AN,
GS, NPM, U
Institution ID: 21-8021

Houma Outpatient Surgery Center
3717 Houma Boulevard
Suite 300
Metairie, LA 70006
Major participating institution for programs in: PS
Institution ID: 21-8055

Jefferson Parish Human Services Authority
3101 W Napolean Ave, Suite 210
Metairie, LA 70001
Major participating institution for programs in: P
Institution ID: 21-8050

Louisiana Office of Public Health
1450 L and A Road
Metairie, LA 70001
Major participating institution for programs in: GPM
Institution ID: 21-8064

Tulane-Lakeside Hospital
4700 I-10 Service Road W
Metairie, LA 70001
Major participating institution for programs in: PS, U
Institution ID: 21-8063

Monroe

E A Conway Medical Center
PO Box 1881
4864 Jackson Street
Monroe, LA 71210-1881
www.conway.lsumc.edu/resident/homepage.htm
Med Sch Affil: G-02106
Programs sponsored in: FP
Major participating institution for programs in: GS, N,
OBG
Institution ID: 21-0344

Swanson Center for Youth
4701 South Grand Street
Monroe, LA 71020
Major participating institution for programs in: PFP
Institution ID: 21-8074

New Orleans

Children's Hospital (New Orleans)
200 Henry Clay Avenue
New Orleans, LA 70118
Med Sch Affil: M-02105, L-00106, G-02101
Major participating institution for programs in: AI,
AN, CHN, CHP, DR, MPD, NPM, NS, OP, ORS, PD, PDE,
PDI, PG, PHO, RHU, U
Institution ID: 21-0731

DePaul/Tulane Behavioral Health Center
1040 Calhoun St
New Orleans, LA 70118
www.depaultulane.com/
Major participating institution for programs in: CPP
Institution ID: 21-8031

Kindred Hospital
3601 Coliseum Street
New Orleans, LA 70115
Major participating institution for programs in: PCC
Institution ID: 21-8105

Louisiana State University School of Medicine
2020 Gravier Street
7th Floor Suite B
New Orleans, LA 70112
www.lsuhsc.edu
Med Sch Affil: L-00106
Programs sponsored in: AI, AN, CCS, CD, CHN, CHP,
CN, D, DR, EM, FP, GE, GS, ID, IM, IMD, MEM, MPD, N,
NEP, NPM, NS, OBG, OP, OPH, ORS, OTO, P, PCC, PD,
PDE, PG, PHO, PM, PMM, PS, PTH, PYM, RHU, UME, VS
Institution ID: 21-9502

LSU Baptist Multi-Specialty Clinic
2820 Napoleon Avenue
New Orleans, LA 70115
Major participating institution for programs in: RHU
Institution ID: 21-8076

Medical Center of Louisiana at New Orleans
2021 Perdido Street
New Orleans, LA 70112-1396
Med Sch Affil: M-02105
Major participating institution for programs in: AI,
AN, CCS, CD, CHN, CHP, CN, CPP, D, DMP, DR, EM, END,
GE, GS, HO, ID, IM, IMD, MG, MPD, N, NEP, NS, OBG,
ORS, P, PCC, PM, PMM, PN, PS, PTH, PYM, RHU, TY, U,
UME
Institution ID: 21-0727

Mercy Family Center (Metairie)
110 Veteran Blvd, Suite 425
New Orleans, LA 70124
Major participating institution for programs in: CHP
Institution ID: 21-8045

Metropolitan Human Services District
400 Poydras Street
Suite 1800
New Orleans, LA 70130
Major participating institution for programs in: P
Institution ID: 21-8082

New Orleans Adolescent Hospital
210 State Street
New Orleans, LA 70118
Major participating institution for programs in: CHP
Institution ID: 21-8017

Ochsner Clinic Foundation
1514 Jefferson Highway
New Orleans, LA 70121
www.ochsner.org
Med Sch Affil: M-02105, L-00106, G-02101
Programs sponsored in: ACA, AN, CD, CRS, DR, END,
GE, GS, IC, ID, IM, OBG, ON, ORS, OSM, RHU, U, VS
Major participating institution for programs in: AI,
CPP, D, HMP, MPD, NEP, NS, OPH, OTO, P, PCC, PCP, PD,
PM, PMM, PS, PTH
Institution ID: 21-0381

Odyssey House Louisiana
1125 North Tonti Street
New Orleans, LA 70119
Major participating institution for programs in: P
Institution ID: 21-8083

Touro Infirmary
1401 Foucher Street
New Orleans, LA 70115-3593
Med Sch Affil: M-02101, G-02105
Major participating institution for programs in: CD,
ID, IM, IMD, N, OBG, PM, RHU
Institution ID: 21-0193

Tulane Hospital for Children
1415 Tulane Avenue
New Orleans, LA 70112
Major participating institution for programs in: CPP,
MPD, PD, PDI, PN
Institution ID: 21-8027

**Tulane Univ School of Public Health and
Tropical Medicine**
1440 Tulane Avenue
New Orleans, LA 70112
Major participating institution for programs in: GPM,
IPM
Institution ID: 21-0493

Tulane University Hospital and Clinics
Tulane University School of Medicine
1430 Tulane Avenue SL-97
New Orleans, LA 70112
Med Sch Affil: M-02101
Major participating institution for programs in: AI,
AN, CD, CHP, CPP, D, DMP, DR, END, GE, GS, HMP, HO,
ID, IM, MG, MN, MP, MPD, N, NEP, NS, OBG, OPH, ORS,
OTO, P, PCC, PCP, PDI, PFP, PS, PTH, PYN, TY, U
Institution ID: 21-0485

Tulane University School of Medicine
Office of Graduate Medical Education
1430 Tulane Avenue SL-97
New Orleans, LA 70112
www.som.tulane.edu/gme
Med Sch Affil: M-02101, M-02105, L-02312
Programs sponsored in: AI, AN, CD, CHP, CPP, D, DMP,
DR, END, GE, GPM, GS, HMP, HO, ID, IM, IPM, MG, MN,
MP, MPD, N, NEP, NS, OBG, OPH, ORS, OTO, P, PCC,
PCP, PD, PDI, PFP, PN, PS, PTH, PYN, TY, U
Institution ID: 21-9501

**Veterans Affairs Medical Center (New
Orleans)**
1601 Perdido Street
Suite 1300
New Orleans, LA 70112
Med Sch Affil: M-02105
Major participating institution for programs in: AI,
CD, CPP, D, END, GE, GPM, HO, IM, IMD, MPD, N, NS,
OPH, P, PM, PMM, TY, U
Institution ID: 21-0234

Pineville

Huey P Long Regional Medical Center
352 Hospital Boulevard
Pineville, LA 71360
Med Sch Affil: M-02101, G-02105
Major participating institution for programs in: OBG
Institution ID: 21-0430

Pinecrest Developmental Center
100 Pinecrest Drive
Pineville, LA 71360
Major participating institution for programs in: PFP
Institution ID: 21-8071

Plaquemine

Dow Chemical Company
21145 Highway 1
Plaquemine, LA 70764
Major participating institution for programs in: GPM
Institution ID: 21-8084

Shreveport

Brentwood Behavioral Health Company
1006 Highland Avenue
Shreveport, LA 71101
Major participating institution for programs in: CHP
Institution ID: 21-8024

Caddo Correctional Center
1101 Forum Drive
Shreveport, LA 71101
Major participating institution for programs in: PFP
Institution ID: 21-8070

Christus Schumpert Health System
One Saint Mary Place
Shreveport, LA 71101
Med Sch Affil: L-02106
Major participating institution for programs in: CRS,
FP
Institution ID: 21-0460

First Judicial District Court
501 Texas Street
Shreveport, LA 71101
Major participating institution for programs in: PFP
Institution ID: 21-8075

**Lousiana State University School of
Medicine in Shreveport**
PO Box 33932
1501 Kings Hwy
Shreveport, LA 71130-3932
www.sh.lsuhsc.edu/medschool/
Programs sponsored in: EFM
Institution ID: 21-9503

**LSU Health Sciences Center-University
Hospital**
1501 Kings Highway
PO Box 33932
Shreveport, LA 71130-3932
www.sh.lsuhsc.edu
Med Sch Affil: M-02106
Programs sponsored in: AI, AN, CCM, CD, CHP, CRS,
DR, EM, END, FP, GE, GS, HO, ID, IM, MPD, N, NEP,
NPM, NS, OBG, OPH, ORS, OTO, P, PCC, PCP, PD, PFP,
PMM, PTH, PYM, RHU, SME, U
Major participating institution for programs in: EFM
Institution ID: 21-0722

**Overton Brooks Veterans Affairs Medical
Center**
510 E Stoner Avenue
Shreveport, LA 71101
Med Sch Affil: M-02106
Major participating institution for programs in: AN,
CD, END, GE, GS, ID, IM, NS, OPH, ORS, OTO, P, PCC,
RHU, SME, U
Institution ID: 21-0497

**Shriners Hospitals for Children
(Shreveport)**
3100 Samford Ave
Shreveport, LA 71103
Med Sch Affil: L-02106
Major participating institution for programs in: ORS
Institution ID: 21-0410

Willis-Knighton Medical Center
2600 Greenwood Road
PO Box 32600
Shreveport, LA 71103-2600
Med Sch Affil: L-02106
Major participating institution for programs in: CRS,
GE, NEP, NS, U
Institution ID: 21-0459

Vivian

North Caddo Medical Center
1000 South Spruce Street
Vivian, LA 71082-3232
Major participating institution for programs in: FP
Institution ID: 21-8034

Maine

Augusta

Maine General Medical Center
6 E Chestnut Street
Augusta, ME 04330
Major participating institution for programs in: FP,
FPG
Institution ID: 22-0100

**Maine-Dartmouth Family Medicine
Residency**
15 East Chestnut St
Augusta, ME 04330
www.mainedartmouth.org
Programs sponsored in: FP, FPG
Institution ID: 22-0114

Bangor

Eastern Maine Medical Center
Family Medicine Residency Program
895 Union Street - Suite 12
Bangor, ME 04401-3010
www.emmcfprp.org/
Med Sch Affil: M-02407
Programs sponsored in: FP
Institution ID: 22-0191

The Acadia Hospital
268 Stillwater Avenue
PO Box 422
Bangor, ME 04402
Major participating institution for programs in: P
Institution ID: 22-8003

Lewiston

Central Maine Medical Center
76 High St
Lewiston, ME 04240
www.cmhc.org
Med Sch Affil: L-02405
Programs sponsored in: FP
Institution ID: 22-0116

Teaching Institutions

Portland

Maine Medical Center
22 Bramhall St
Portland, ME 04102
www.mmc.org
Med Sch Affil: M-05002
Programs sponsored in: AN, CD, CHP, DR, EM, FP, FSM, GS, ID, IM, IMG, MPD, NEP, OBG, P, PCC, PD
Major participating institution for programs in: NS, PS
Institution ID: 22-0384

New England Rehabilitation Hospital
335 Brighton Medical
Portland, ME 04102
Major participating institution for programs in: IMG
Institution ID: 22-8002

Southern Maine Dialysis Facility
1600 Congress St
Portland, ME 04102
Major participating institution for programs in: NEP
Institution ID: 22-8005

Westbook

Spring Harbor Hospital
123 Andover Road
Westbook, ME 04092
Major participating institution for programs in: CHP
Institution ID: 22-8001

Maryland

Andrews AFB

Malcolm Grow Medical Center
89th Medical Group/SGA
1050 West Perimeter Road
Andrews AFB, MD 20762-6600
Med Sch Affil: M-02312
Major participating institution for programs in: FP, FPP, FSM, P
Institution ID: 23-0216

Baltimore

Franklin Square Hospital Center
9000 Franklin Square Dr
Baltimore, MD 21237-3998
www.franklinsquare.org
Med Sch Affil: M-02301, L-02307
Programs sponsored in: FP, IM, OBG
Major participating institution for programs in: GS
Institution ID: 23-0122

Franklin Woods Center
9200 Franklin Square Drive
Baltimore, MD 21237
Major participating institution for programs in: IMG
Institution ID: 23-8034

Good Samaritan Hospital of Maryland
5601 Loch Raven Blvd
Russell Morgan Building, Suite 502
Baltimore, MD 21239-2995
www.goodsam-md.org
Med Sch Affil: M-02307
Programs sponsored in: IM
Major participating institution for programs in: ORS, PM, SCI
Institution ID: 23-0522

Greater Baltimore Medical Center
6701 North Charles Street
Baltimore, MD 21204
www.gbmc.org
Med Sch Affil: M-02307, L-02301
Programs sponsored in: CRS, IM
Major participating institution for programs in: NS, OBG, OPH, OTO
Institution ID: 23-0507

Harbor Hospital Center
3001 S Hanover Street
Baltimore, MD 21225-1250
www.harborhospital.org
Med Sch Affil: L-02301, L-02307
Programs sponsored in: IM, TY
Institution ID: 23-0459

Johns Hopkins Bayview Medical Center
4940 Eastern Avenue
Baltimore, MD 21224
Med Sch Affil: M-02307, L-02301
Major participating institution for programs in: AI, D, DR, EM, GS, ICE, IM, IMG, N, NEP, OBG, ORS, OTO, P, PCC, PS, PYG, RHU, SME, U, VIR
Institution ID: 23-0118

Johns Hopkins Bloomberg School of Public Health
615 N Wolfe St
Baltimore, MD 21205
http://jhsph.edu
Med Sch Affil: L-02307
Programs sponsored in: GPM
Institution ID: 23-0503

Johns Hopkins Hospital
600 N Wolfe Street, Billings 129
Baltimore, MD 21287-1629
Med Sch Affil: M-02307, L-01001, G-02301, G-02312
Major participating institution for programs in: ACA, ADL, AI, AN, BBK, CCA, CCP, CCS, CD, CFS, CHN, CHP, CN, D, DMP, DR, EM, END, ESN, GE, GPM, GS, HMP, HO, IC, ICE, ID, IM, IMG, MDG, MG, MGP, MM, N, NDN, NEP, NM, NMN, NO, NP, NPM, NS, OBG, OPH, ORS, OTO, P, PAN, PCC, PCP, PD, PDC, PDE, PDI, PDP, PDR, PDS, PEM, PG, PHO, PM, PMG, PMM, PN, PS, PTH, PYG, RHU, RNR, RO, SCI, SME, SP, TS, U, UP, VIR, VN, VS
Institution ID: 23-0191

Johns Hopkins University School of Medicine
733 North Broadway
Suite 100
Baltimore, MD 21205-2196
Med Sch Affil: M-02307
Programs sponsored in: ACA, ADL, AI, AN, BBK, CCA, CCP, CCS, CD, CFS, CHN, CHP, CN, D, DMP, DR, EM, END, ESN, GE, GS, HMP, HO, IC, ICE, ID, IM, IMG, MDG, MG, MGP, MM, N, NDN, NEP, NM, NMN, NO, N, NPM, NS, OBG, OPH, ORS, OTO, P, PAN, PCC, PCP, PD, PDC, PDE, PDI, PDP, PDR, PDS, PEM, PG, PHO, PM, PMG, PMM, PN, PS, PSI, PTH, PYG, RHU, RNR, RO, RPM, SCI, SME, SP, TS, U, UP, VIR, VN, VS
Institution ID: 23-0703

Kennedy Krieger Institute
707 North Broadway
Baltimore, MD 21205
Major participating institution for programs in: NDN, RPM, SCI
Institution ID: 23-8020

Maryland General Hospital
827 Linden Ave
Baltimore, MD 21201-4681
www.marylandgeneral.org
Med Sch Affil: L-02301
Programs sponsored in: IM, OPH, TY
Major participating institution for programs in: VS
Institution ID: 23-0147

Medical Services Div of Circuit Court for Baltimore City
111 North Calvert
Baltimore, MD 21202
Major participating institution for programs in: PFP
Institution ID: 23-8052

Mercy Medical Center
301 St Paul Place
Baltimore, MD 21202-2102
www.mdmercy.com
Med Sch Affil: M-02301
Programs sponsored in: OFA
Major participating institution for programs in: EMP, GS, MEM, OBG, P, VS
Institution ID: 23-0195

National Institute on Aging (Clinical Research Branch)
3001 S Hanover St
Baltimore, MD 21225
Major participating institution for programs in: HO
Institution ID: 23-8035

Office of the Chief Medical Examiner
111 Penn Street
Baltimore, MD 21201
Med Sch Affil: L-02307, G-02301
Programs sponsored in: FOP
Major participating institution for programs in: FOP
Institution ID: 23-0499

R Adams Cowley Shock Trauma Center/University of Maryland
22 South Greene Street
Baltimore, MD 21201
Major participating institution for programs in: NS
Institution ID: 23-0707

Sinai Hospital of Baltimore
2401 W Belvedere Avenue
Baltimore, MD 21215-5271
http://lifebridgehealth.org
Med Sch Affil: M-02307, L-02301, G-02312
Programs sponsored in: GS, OBG, OPH, PD, PM, PMM, SCI
Major participating institution for programs in: IM, ORS
Institution ID: 23-0160

St Agnes Hospital
900 South Caton Avenue
Baltimore, MD 21229-5299
www.stagnes.org
Med Sch Affil: M-02307, L-02301
Programs sponsored in: GS, IM
Institution ID: 23-0320

Union Memorial Hospital
201 E University Parkway
Baltimore, MD 21218-2895
www.unionmemorial.org/gme
Med Sch Affil: M-02301, L-02312, L-02307, G-01001
Programs sponsored in: END, GS, HSO, IM, OAR, OFA, ORS, OSM
Major participating institution for programs in: FP, FSM, HSO, PS
Institution ID: 23-0287

University of Maryland Medical System
22 South Greene Street, Box 353
Baltimore, MD 21201-1595
www.umm.edu
Med Sch Affil: M-02301, G-02307
Programs sponsored in: ACA, ADP, AN, CCA, CCP, CCS, CD, CHP, CN, D, DBP, DR, EM, EMP, END, FP, FSM, GE, GPM, GS, HMP, HO, IC, ICE, ID, IEC, IM, IMG, MEM, MPD, N, NEP, NM, NPM, NR, NS, OBG, OPH, ORS, OSS, OTO, OTR, P, PCC, PCP, PD, PDI, PFP, PG, PMM, PTH, PYG, PYM, RHU, RNR, RO, SME, TS, U, VIR, VN, VS
Major participating institution for programs in: CFS, GE, GPM, PDS, PS, SCI
Institution ID: 23-0247

University of Maryland-Kernan Hospital
2200 Kernan Drive
Baltimore, MD 21207-6697
Med Sch Affil: L-02301
Major participating institution for programs in: PDI, PMM, SCI, VN
Institution ID: 23-0238

Veterans Affairs Medical Center (Baltimore)
10 N Greene St
Baltimore, MD 21201-1524
Med Sch Affil: M-02301, G-02307
Major participating institution for programs in: ADP, CD, D, END, GE, GS, IC, ID, IEC, IM, IMG, MPD, N, NM, NS, ORS, OSS, OTO, P, PCC, PM, PTH, PYG, PYM, RHU, SME, U, VIR, VN, VS
Institution ID: 23-0265

Walter P Carter Mental Health Center
630 W Fayette Street
Baltimore, MD 21201
Med Sch Affil: M-02301
Major participating institution for programs in: P
Institution ID: 23-0713

Bethesda

Clinical Center at the National Institutes of Health
Building 10, Room 6-2551
10 Center Drive
Bethesda, MD 20892-1158
www.training.nih.gov
Med Sch Affil: L-01001, L-02312, G-01002
Programs sponsored in: AI, BBK, CCM, D, END, HEM, HMP, ID, MBG, MG, ON, P, PCP, PDE, PMG, PTH, RHU
Major participating institution for programs in: CCA, CN, GE, NS, ORS, PYM, RNR
Institution ID: 23-0204

National Cancer Institute
Building 10, Rm B3-B69
9000 Rockville Pike
Bethesda, MD 20892
Med Sch Affil: G-02307, G-02312
Major participating institution for programs in: RO
Institution ID: 23-8012

National Capital Consortium
F Edward Hebert School of Medicine
4301 Jones Bridge Road
Bethesda, MD 20814-4799
www.usuhs.mil/gme/NCC.htm
Programs sponsored in: AI, AN, CCA, CCM, CD, CHN, CHP, CN, D, DR, END, FOP, FP, FPP, FSM, GE, GPM, GS, HO, HSO, ID, IM, MP, N, NEP, NM, NPM, NS, OBG, OPH, ORS, OTO, P, PCC, PD, PDE, PDI, PFP, PG, PHO, PM, PMM, PTH, PYG, RHU, RO, SME, TY, U, VS
Institution ID: 10-8020

National Naval Medical Center (Bethesda)
8901 Wisconsin Avenue
Bethesda, MD 20889-5600
Med Sch Affil: M-01002, M-02312, L-01001, G-01003
Major participating institution for programs in: AN, CD, D, DR, END, FSM, GE, GS, ID, IM, NEP, NPM, NS, OBG, ON, OPH, ORS, OTO, P, PCC, PD, PDE, PMM, PTH, RO, TY, U
Institution ID: 23-0275

Uniformed Svsc Univ of Health Sci Hebert School of Medicine
4301 Jones Bridge Road
Bethesda, MD 20814-4799
Major participating institution for programs in: GPM, PFP, U
Institution ID: 23-0714

Cheverly

Prince George's Hospital Center
3001 Hospital Drive
Cheverly, MD 20785
Med Sch Affil: L-02312, G-01001, G-01003
Programs sponsored in: IM
Major participating institution for programs in: OBG
Institution ID: 23-0142

Glen Burnie

Baltimore Washington Medical Center
301 Hospital Drive
Glen Burnie, MD 21061
Major participating institution for programs in: U, VS
Institution ID: 23-8025

Jessup

Clifton T Perkins Hospital Center
8450 Dorsey Run Road
PO Box 1000
Jessup, MD 20794-1000
Med Sch Affil: L-02301, G-02312
Major participating institution for programs in: PFP
Institution ID: 23-8015

Maryland Correctional Institute-Women
7943 Brockbridge Road
Jessup, MD 20794
Major participating institution for programs in: PFP
Institution ID: 23-8046

Lanham

Concentra Medical Centers (Maryland)
4451 G Parliment Place
Lanham, MD 20706
Major participating institution for programs in: GPM
Institution ID: 23-8047

Rockville

National Medical Advisory Services
2301 Research Boulevard
Suite 210
Rockville, MD 20850
Major participating institution for programs in: GPM
Institution ID: 23-8048

Silver Spring

Holy Cross Hospital of Silver Spring
1500 Forest Glen Rd
Silver Spring, MD 20910-1484
Med Sch Affil: M-01001, G-02312
Major participating institution for programs in: GS, OBG, OTO
Institution ID: 23-0710

Walter Reed Army Institute of Research
Attn: MCMR-UWZ
503 Robert Grant Ave, Room 1W38
Silver Spring, MD 20910-7500
http://wrair-www.army.mil/
Med Sch Affil: G-02312
Major participating institution for programs in: GPM, MP
Institution ID: 10-0485

Tacoma Park

Washington Adventist Hospital
7600 Carroll Ave
Tacoma Park, MD 20912
Major participating institution for programs in: IC, ICE
Institution ID: 23-0222

Towson

Sheppard Pratt Health System
6501 North Charles Street
Towson, MD 21204
Med Sch Affil: M-02301
Major participating institution for programs in: CHP, P
Institution ID: 23-0397

Massachusetts

Bedford

Edith Nourse Rogers Memorial Veterans Hospital (Bedford)
Bedford, MA 01730
Med Sch Affil: L-02405
Major participating institution for programs in: ADP, IMG, P
Institution ID: 24-0443

Belmont

McLean Hospital
115 Mill Street
Belmont, MA 02478-9106
Med Sch Affil: M-02401
Programs sponsored in: PYG
Major participating institution for programs in: ADP, CHP, P
Institution ID: 24-0230

Boston

Beth Israel Deaconess Medical Center
Graduate Medical Education Office ES 217
330 Brookline Avenue
Boston, MA 02215
www.bidmc.harvard.edu/
Med Sch Affil: M-02401
Programs sponsored in: ACA, AN, AR, CCA, CCS, CD, DMP, DR, EM, END, GE, GS, HMP, HO, HSO, HSP, IC, ICE, ID, IM, IMG, MM, N, NEP, NMN, NR, OBG, OSS, PCP, PMM, PTH, RNR, SME, SP, THP, TS, VIR, VN, VS
Major participating institution for programs in: BBK, CHN, CN, D, ETX, IMD, MG, MGP, NDN, NM, OMO, ORS, OSM, OTO, P, PCC, PMM, PS, RHU, RO, SME, U
Institution ID: 24-8076

Boston Medical Center
One Boston Medical Center Place
Boston, MA 02118-2393
www.bmc.org
Med Sch Affil: M-02405
Programs sponsored in: ADP, AI, AN, CCS, CD, CHN, D, DMP, DR, EM, END, FP, FSM, GE, GPM, GS, HO, IC, ICE, ID, IM, IMG, MG, N, NEP, OBG, OPH, ORS, OSM, OTO, P, PCC, PCP, PM, PRD, PTH, PYM, RHU, RNR, SME, TS, U, VIR, VN, VS
Major participating institution for programs in: DBP, PD, PDI, PEM, PMG, RO
Institution ID: 24-8077

Boston University Athletic Department
285 Babcock Street
Boston, MA 02215
Major participating institution for programs in: FSM
Institution ID: 24-8111

Boston University School of Public Health
80 East Concord Street
Boston, MA 02118
Major participating institution for programs in: GPM
Institution ID: 24-0449

Boston University Student Health Center
881 Commonwealth Avenue
Boston, MA 02115
Major participating institution for programs in: FSM
Institution ID: 24-8110

Brigham and Women's Hospital
75 Francis St
Boston, MA 02115
www.partners.org
Med Sch Affil: M-02401, G-03515
Programs sponsored in: ACA, AI, AN, AR, BBK, CCA,
CCS, CD, CN, CTR, DR, EM, END, GE, GS, HMP, HO, HSO,
IC, ICE, IM, MDG, MGP, MPD, NEP, NM, NMN, NP, OBG,
P, PCP, PMM, PS, PSI, PTH, PYM, RHU, RNR, RO, SME,
SP, TS, U, VIR, VS
Major participating institution for programs in: ADP,
AI, DMP, ID, IMD, N, NS, ORS, OTO, PCC, PMM, PP, PPR,
VN
Institution ID: 24-0438

Caritas Carney Hospital
2100 Dorchester Ave
Boston, MA 02124
www.caritaschristi.org
Med Sch Affil: M-02407, L-02405
Programs sponsored in: IM, TY
Major participating institution for programs in: P
Institution ID: 24-0239

Caritas St Elizabeth's Medical Center of Boston
736 Cambridge Street
Boston, MA 02135
www.semc.org
Med Sch Affil: M-02407, M-02416
Programs sponsored in: AN, CD, GS, HO, IC, ICE, IM, P,
PCC, PMM
Major participating institution for programs in: GE, N,
OBG, OTO
Institution ID: 24-0211

Children's Hospital
300 Longwood Avenue
Boston, MA 02115-5737
www.childrenshospital.org
Med Sch Affil: M-02401, L-03515, L-02312, L-02416,
G-03201, G-02405
Programs sponsored in: ADL, AI, CCP, CCS, CHN, CHP,
CN, DBP, ETX, MG, NDN, NPM, NS, OP, OSM, PAN, PD,
PDC, PDE, PDI, PDP, PDR, PDS, PEM, PG, PHO, PMG,
PMM, PN, PP, PPR, PSM, SME, UP
Major participating institution for programs in: AI,
BBK, END, ETX, HMP, HPM, HSO, HSP, ID, MDG, MG,
MGP, MPD, NM, NMN, NP, NR, NS, OMO, ORS, PAN,
PMM, PS, RNR, SME, TS, U
Institution ID: 24-0152

Dana-Farber Cancer Institute
44 Binney Street
Boston, MA 02115
Med Sch Affil: M-02401
Major participating institution for programs in: HO,
HPM, MGP, NM, PHO, PTH, PYM, RO
Institution ID: 24-0726

Erich Lindemann Mental Health Center
25 Staniford Street
Government Center
Boston, MA 02114
Major participating institution for programs in: P,
PFP
Institution ID: 24-0757

Faulkner Hospital
1153 Centre St
Boston, MA 02130
Med Sch Affil: M-02407, L-02401, G-02405
Major participating institution for programs in: HSO,
P, PYM
Institution ID: 24-0472

Harvard Sch of Public Health Occ Med Physician Activities
677 Huntington Avenue
Kresge Bldg, Room 1005
Boston, MA 02115
Major participating institution for programs in: GPM
Institution ID: 24-8121

Harvard School of Public Health
677 Huntington Avenue
Boston, MA 02115
www.hsph.harvard.edu
Programs sponsored in: GPM
Institution ID: 24-0124

Hearth - Ending Elder Homelessness
1640 Washington St
Boston, MA 02118
Major participating institution for programs in: PYG
Institution ID: 24-8117

Massachusetts Eye and Ear Infirmary
243 Charles Street
Boston, MA 02114-3096
www.meei.harvard.edu
Med Sch Affil: M-02401, G-02405
Programs sponsored in: NO, OPH, OTO
Institution ID: 24-0155

Massachusetts General Hospital
Bulfinch Building, 2nd Floor
55 Fruit Street
Boston, MA 02114
www.mgh.harvard.edu
Med Sch Affil: M-02401, G-02405
Programs sponsored in: ACA, ADP, AI, AN, CCA, CCP,
CCS, CD, CHN, CHP, CN, D, DR, END, GE, GS, HMP,
HPM, HSO, IC, ICE, ID, IM, IMD, MPD, N, NP, NS, OMO,
ORS, OSM, P, PCC, PCP, PD, PDE, PDP, PDR, PFP, PG,
PMM, PTH, PYM, RHU, RNR, THP, TS, U, VIR, VN, VS
Major participating institution for programs in: BBK,
CD, DMP, EM, HO, HSO, MDG, MGP, NEP, NMN, OBG,
PM, PS, RO
Institution ID: 24-0394

New England Baptist Hospital
125 Parker Hill Avenue
Department of Orthopedics
Boston, MA 02120
www.nebh.org
Med Sch Affil: L-02407, G-02416, G-02405
Programs sponsored in: OSM
Major participating institution for programs in: HSO,
ORS, OSM
Institution ID: 24-0522

Northeastern University Health and Counseling Services
360 Huntington Ave
Boston, MA 02115
Major participating institution for programs in: PSM
Institution ID: 24-8127

Office of the Chief Medical Examiner
Eastern Massachusetts Office
720 Albany Street
Boston, MA 02118-2518
Programs sponsored in: FOP
Major participating institution for programs in: PP,
PTH
Institution ID: 24-8006

Shriners Hospitals for Children (Boston)
51 Blossom Street
Boston, MA 02114-2699
Med Sch Affil: G-02401
Major participating institution for programs in: HSP
Institution ID: 24-8073

Spaulding Rehabilitation Hospital
125 Nashua Street
Boston, MA 02114-1198
www.spauldingrehab.org
Med Sch Affil: L-02407, G-02401
Programs sponsored in: PM, PMM, SCI
Major participating institution for programs in: P
Institution ID: 24-8036

Tufts Medical Center
800 Washington Street
Boston, MA 02111
www.tufts-nemc.org
Med Sch Affil: M-02407, G-02405
Programs sponsored in: ACA, AN, CD, CHN, CHP, CN,
CPP, D, DBP, DMP, DR, END, GE, GS, HO, HSO, IC, ICE,
ID, IM, MG, N, NEP, NPM, NS, OBG, OPH, ORS, OTO, P,
PAN, PCC, PD, PM, PPR, PTH, RHU, RO, TS, TY, VIR, VS
Major participating institution for programs in: D,
RNR
Institution ID: 24-0378

Bridgewater

Bridgewater State Hospital
20 Administration Road
Bridgewater, MA 02324
Major participating institution for programs in: PFP
Institution ID: 24-7010

Brockton

Boston VA Healthcare System (Brockton-West Roxbury)
940 Belmont Street
Brockton, MA 02401-5596
Med Sch Affil: M-02401
Programs sponsored in: P
Major participating institution for programs in: CD,
HSO, IC, ICE, NM, PYM, RHU, SCI, U
Institution ID: 24-0172

Brockton Hospital
680 Centre St
Brockton, MA 02402
Med Sch Affil: M-02405
Major participating institution for programs in: TY
Institution ID: 24-0225

Good Samaritan Medical Center-Cushing Campus
235 N Pearl St
Brockton, MA 02401-1794
Med Sch Affil: L-02407
Major participating institution for programs in: GS
Institution ID: 24-8014

Burlington

Lahey Clinic
41 Mall Road
Burlington, MA 01805
www.lahey.org
Med Sch Affil: M-02407, L-02401, G-02405
Programs sponsored in: CD, CRS, DR, END, GE, GS, IC,
ICE, IM, PCC, PS, U
Major participating institution for programs in: AN,
CN, N, NS, OBG, OPH, ORS, OTO, TS, TY
Institution ID: 24-0163

Cambridge

Cambridge Court Clinic
40 Thorndike St
Cambridge, MA 02141
Major participating institution for programs in: PFP
Institution ID: 24-8093

Cambridge Health Alliance
1493 Cambridge Street
Cambridge, MA 02139
www.challiance.org
Med Sch Affil: M-02401, M-02407
Programs sponsored in: CHP, FP, IM, P, PYG, PYM, TY
Major participating institution for programs in: ADP,
ETX, GPM
Institution ID: 24-0367

Massachusetts Institute of Technology Medical Department

Medical Department
77 Massachusetts Avenue
Cambridge, MA 02139
Major participating institution for programs in: FSM
Institution ID: 24-8112

Massachusetts Institute of Technology Mental Health Services

77 Massachusetts Ave
E23-368
Cambridge, MA 02139
Major participating institution for programs in: P
Institution ID: 24-8104

Mount Auburn Hospital

330 Mount Auburn St
Cambridge, MA 02138
www.mtauburnhospital.org
Med Sch Affil: M-02401
Programs sponsored in: DR, IM
Major participating institution for programs in: P
Institution ID: 24-0375

Youville Hospital & Rehabilitation Center

1575 Cambridge Street
Cambridge, MA 02138
Major participating institution for programs in: PYG
Institution ID: 24-8099

Dorchester

Harbor Health Services, Inc

398 Neponset Avenue
Dorchester, MA 02122
Major participating institution for programs in: IMG
Institution ID: 24-8107

Upham's Corner Health Center

500 Columbia Road
Dorchester, MA 02125
Major participating institution for programs in: IMG
Institution ID: 24-8102

Framingham

MetroWest Medical Center-Framingham Union Hospital

115 Lincoln Street
Framingham, MA 01702
www.mwmc.com
Med Sch Affil: M-02407, L-02416, L-02405, G-02401
Programs sponsored in: IM, TY
Institution ID: 24-0162

Groton

Seven Hills at Groton

22 Hillside Ave
Groton, MA 01450
Major participating institution for programs in: NDN
Institution ID: 24-8115

Jamaica Plain

Lemuel Shattuck Hospital

170 Morton Street
Jamaica Plain, MA 02130-3787
Med Sch Affil: M-02407
Major participating institution for programs in: P, TY
Institution ID: 24-0401

Massachusetts Mental Health Center

180 Morton Street
Jamaica Plain, MA 02130
Med Sch Affil: M-02401
Major participating institution for programs in: P
Institution ID: 24-0255

Lawrence

Greater Lawrence Family Health Center Inc

34 Haverhill Street
Lawrence, MA 01841-2884
http://lawrencefpr.org
Med Sch Affil: L-02416
Programs sponsored in: FP
Institution ID: 24-8072

Lawrence General Hospital

One General Street
Lawrence, MA 01841
Med Sch Affil: L-02407
Major participating institution for programs in: FP
Institution ID: 24-0330

Leominster

Health Alliance Hospital-Leominster

60 Hospital Road
Leominster, MA 01420
Major participating institution for programs in: FP
Institution ID: 24-0366

Newton

Caris Cohen Dx

320 Needham Street
Newton, MA 02464
Major participating institution for programs in: DMP
Institution ID: 24-8113

Newton-Wellesley Hospital

2014 Washington St
Newton, MA 02462
http://nwh.org
Med Sch Affil: M-02407
Programs sponsored in: TY
Major participating institution for programs in: AN, ORS, P, PMM
Institution ID: 24-0448

Pittsfield

Berkshire Medical Center

725 North Street
Pittsfield, MA 01201
www.berkshirehealthsystems.org
Med Sch Affil: M-02416
Programs sponsored in: GS, IM, P, PTH
Institution ID: 24-0180

Brien Center for Mental Health

333 East Street
Pittsfield, MA 01021
Major participating institution for programs in: P
Institution ID: 24-8108

Quincy

Quincy Medical Center

Quincy, MA 02169
Major participating institution for programs in: VS
Institution ID: 24-8088

Salem

Salem Hospital

81 Highland Avenue
Salem, MA 01970
www.nsmc.partners.org
Med Sch Affil: L-02407, L-02405
Programs sponsored in: IM
Major participating institution for programs in: GS
Institution ID: 24-0287

Springfield

Baystate Medical Center

759 Chestnut St
Springfield, MA 01199
www.baystatehealth.com
Med Sch Affil: M-02407, L-02416, G-02405
Programs sponsored in: AN, BBK, CCA, CCM, CD, DR, EM, END, GS, HO, IC, ICE, ID, IM, IMG, MPD, NEP, OBG, P, PCP, PD, PDE, PE, PMM, PTH
Institution ID: 24-0309

Behavioral Health Network, Inc

417 Liberty Street
Springfield, MA 01104
Major participating institution for programs in: P
Institution ID: 24-8119

Shriners Hospitals for Children (Springfield)

516 Carew Street
Springfield, MA 01104-2396
Med Sch Affil: G-02405, G-03503
Major participating institution for programs in: ORS
Institution ID: 24-0388

Stockbridge

Austen Riggs Center

25 Main Street
PO Box 962
Stockbridge, MA 01262-0962
www.austenriggs.org
Programs sponsored in: P
Institution ID: 24-0435

Stoughton

New England Sinai Hospital and Rehabilitation Center

150 York Street
Stoughton, MA 02072
Med Sch Affil: L-02407
Major participating institution for programs in: PM
Institution ID: 24-8035

Waltham

Boston Outpatient Surgical Suites

840 Winter Street
Waltham, MA 02451
Major participating institution for programs in: OSM
Institution ID: 24-8106

West Roxbury

Veterans Affairs Medical Center (Boston)

1400 VFW Parkway
West Roxbury, MA 02132
Med Sch Affil: M-02405, L-02407
Major participating institution for programs in: ADP, CD, D, DR, GE, GS, HO, ID, IM, N, OPH, ORS, OTO, P, PCC, PM, PYM, RHU, SME, U
Institution ID: 24-0257

Westboro

Westboro State Hospital

288 Lyman Street
Westboro, MA 01581-0288
Major participating institution for programs in: CHP
Institution ID: 24-0442

Woburn

New England Rehabilitation Hospital

Two Rehabilitation Way
Woburn, MA 01801-6098
Major participating institution for programs in: PM
Institution ID: 24-8079

Teaching Institutions

Worcester

Central Massachusetts Magnetic Imaging Center, Inc
367 Plantation St
Worcester, MA 01655
Major participating institution for programs in: RNR
Institution ID: 24-8129

Community Healthlink
72 Jaques Avenue
Worcester, MA 01610
Major participating institution for programs in: ADP
Institution ID: 24-8128

St Vincent Hospital
Worcester Medical Center
123 Summer Street
Worcester, MA 01608-1320
http://stvincenthospital.com
Med Sch Affil: M-02416
Programs sponsored in: CD, DR, IC, IM, SME
Major participating institution for programs in: CCA, GS
Institution ID: 24-0361

UMass Memorial Health Care (Hahnemann Campus)
291 Lincoln Street
Worcester, MA 01605
Major participating institution for programs in: D, DMP, HSO, ORS, OSM, PS
Institution ID: 24-8091

UMass Memorial Health Care (Memorial Campus)
119 Belmont Street, J4
Worcester, MA 01605
Med Sch Affil: M-02416
Major participating institution for programs in: DR, END, FP, FSM, GS, HO, ID, IM, NEP, NPM, OBG, ORS, PCP, PTH, RHU, RNR, SP, VIR, VSI
Institution ID: 24-0113

UMass Memorial Health Care (University Campus)
55 Lake Avenue North
Worcester, MA 01605
Med Sch Affil: M-02416, G-02312
Major participating institution for programs in: ADP, AN, CCA, CCS, CD, CHP, CN, D, DR, EM, END, ETX, GE, GPM, GS, HO, IC, ICE, ID, IM, MPD, N, NEP, ORS, OSM, PCC, PCP, PD, PS, PTH, PYN, RHU, RNR, SME, SP, VIR, VN, VS, VSI
Institution ID: 24-0724

UMASS Memorial Medical Group Sleep Disorders Center
85 Prescott Street, Suite 302
Worcester, MA 01605-2610
Major participating institution for programs in: CN
Institution ID: 24-8118

University of Massachusetts Medical School
55 Lake Avenue North
Worcester, MA 01655
http://umassmed.edu/gme
Programs sponsored in: ADP, AN, CCA, CCS, CD, CHP, CN, D, DMP, DR, EM, END, ETX, FP, FSM, GE, GPM, GS, HMP, HO, HSO, IC, ICE, ID, IM, MPD, N, NEP, NPM, OBG, ORS, OSM, P, PCC, PCP, PD, PFP, PS, PSI, PTH, PYN, RHU, RNR, SP, VIR, VN, VS, VSI
Institution ID: 24-9501

Worcester State Hospital
305 Belmont St
Worcester, MA 01604
Med Sch Affil: G-02416
Major participating institution for programs in: PFP
Institution ID: 24-0135

Michigan

Ann Arbor

St Joseph Mercy Hospital
5301 E Huron River Drive - GME Office
PO Box 995
Ann Arbor, MI 48106-2172
www.stjoesannarbormeded.com/
Med Sch Affil: M-02501, L-02507
Programs sponsored in: GS, IM, OBG, TY
Major participating institution for programs in: EM, GS
Institution ID: 25-0487

University of Michigan Hospitals and Health Centers
2500 Green Road
Suite 700
Ann Arbor, MI 48109-0748
www.med.umich.edu
Med Sch Affil: M-02501
Programs sponsored in: ACA, ADP, AI, AN, BBK, CCA, CCP, CCS, CD, CHN, CHP, CHS, CN, D, DBP, DMP, DR, EM, END, FP, FSM, GE, GS, HMP, HO, HPM, IC, ICE, ID, IM, IMG, MG, MGP, MPD, N, NEP, NM, NO, NPM, NS, OBG, OP, OPH, ORS, OSM, OTO, P, PAN, PCC, PCP, PD, PDC, PDE, PDI, PDP, PDR, PDS, PE, PFP, PG, PHO, PM, PMM, PN, PPR, PRD, PSI, PTH, PYG, PYM, RHU, RNR, RO, SCI, SME, SP, THP, TS, U, VIR, VN, VS, VSI
Institution ID: 25-0256

University of Michigan School of Public Health
109 Observatory Street
Ann Arbor, MI 48109-2029
www.sph.umich.edu
Programs sponsored in: GPM
Institution ID: 25-0526

Veterans Affairs Medical Center (Ann Arbor)
2215 Fuller Road
Ann Arbor, MI 48105
Med Sch Affil: M-02501, L-03843
Major participating institution for programs in: ADP, CD, END, GE, GS, IC, ID, IM, IMG, MPD, N, NEP, NM, OPH, OTO, P, PMM, PYG, PYM, RHU, TS, U, VIR, VSI
Institution ID: 25-0498

Chelsea

Chelsea Community Hospital
775 S Main Street
Chelsea, MI 48118
Med Sch Affil: L-02501
Major participating institution for programs in: FP
Institution ID: 25-0555

Chesterfield

Village of East Harbor
33875 Kiely Dr
Chesterfield, MI 48047
Major participating institution for programs in: IMG
Institution ID: 25-9049

Commerce

Huron Valley-Sinai Hospital
One William Carls Drive
Commerce, MI 48382-2201
Med Sch Affil: G-02507
Major participating institution for programs in: RO
Institution ID: 25-8003

Dearborn

Henry Ford Village
15101 Ford Road
Dearborn, MI 48216
Major participating institution for programs in: PYG
Institution ID: 25-9089

Oakwood Hospital
18101 Oakwood Blvd
Medical Education
Dearborn, MI 48123-2500
www.oakwood.org
Med Sch Affil: M-02507, L-02501
Programs sponsored in: DR, IM, IMG, OBG, TY
Major participating institution for programs in: FP, OSM, OTO, U
Institution ID: 25-0366

Detroit

Children's Hospital of Michigan
3901 Beaubien
Detroit, MI 48201
Med Sch Affil: M-02507
Programs sponsored in: CCP, NPM, PD, PDC, PDI, PEM, PG, PHO, PN
Major participating institution for programs in: AI, CCS, CHN, CHP, CN, DR, ETX, MBG, MG, MPD, NS, ORS, PAN, PDR, PDS, PMG, PP, PPM, RNR, SME, TY, U
Institution ID: 25-0456

Chrysler Corporation, LLC (Occupational Medicine Clinic)
Jefferson N Assembly Plant
2101 Conner Avenue
Detroit, MI 48215
Major participating institution for programs in: GPM
Institution ID: 25-9065

Detroit Medical Center Corporation
Corporate Offices 1 South Brush
3990 John R Street
Detroit, MI 48201
Programs sponsored in: IM, ORS, OSM, TY
Institution ID: 25-9016

Detroit Receiving Hospital and University Health Center
Detroit, MI 48201
Med Sch Affil: M-02507
Major participating institution for programs in: AI, CCS, CHN, EM, END, GE, GS, HMP, ID, IMG, MBG, MG, MPD, N, NEP, NS, ORS, PCC, PTH, PYG, RHU, TY, VN
Institution ID: 25-0131

Elwood Geriatric Village
1881 E Grand Blvd
Detroit, MI 48211
Major participating institution for programs in: IMG
Institution ID: 25-9047

Harper-Hutzel Hospital
Detroit, MI 48201
Med Sch Affil: M-02507
Major participating institution for programs in: AN, CD, CHN, DR, END, GE, GS, HMP, HO, IC, ID, MG, MPD, N, NEP, NPM, NS, OBG, OPH, PCC, PMG, PS, PTH, RHU, RNR, SME, TY, VIR, VN, VS
Institution ID: 25-0151

Hartford Nursing and Rehabilitation Center
6700 W Outer Dr
Detroit, MI 48235
Major participating institution for programs in: IMG
Institution ID: 25-9048

Henry Ford Center for Senior Independence
78200 W Outer Dr
Suite 240
Detroit, MI 48235
Major participating institution for programs in: PYG
Institution ID: 25-9088

Henry Ford Hospital

2799 West Grand Blvd
Department of Medical Education, CFP 046
Detroit, MI 48202-2689
www.henryford.com
Med Sch Affil: M-02507, M-03806, L-01642
Programs sponsored in: ACA, AI, AN, CCM, CCS, CD, CN, CRS, D, DR, EM, END, FP, FSM, GE, GS, HO, HPM, IC, ICE, ID, IEC, IM, MEM, MG, MSR, N, NEP, NS, OBG, OPH, ORS, OSM, OTO, P, PCC, PCP, PMM, PTH, RNR, RO, SME, THP, TY, U, VIR, VN, VS
Major participating institution for programs in: GPM
Institution ID: 25-0331

Jefferson Avenue Research Clinic

2761 East Jefferson
Detroit, MI 48207
Major participating institution for programs in: ADP
Institution ID: 25-9094

Karmanos Cancer Hospital

4100 John R Street - 4 HWCRC
Detroit, MI 48201
Major participating institution for programs in: HO, NEP, OTO, PMM, RO, U
Institution ID: 25-9015

Moroun Nursing Home

8045 E Jefferson Ave
Detroit, MI 48207
Major participating institution for programs in: PYG
Institution ID: 25-9092

Rehabilitation Institute

261 Mack Boulevard
Detroit, MI 48201
Med Sch Affil: M-02507
Major participating institution for programs in: PM, PPM, PYG
Institution ID: 25-0210

Sinai-Grace Hospital

6071 West Outer Drive
Detroit, MI 48235
Med Sch Affil: M-02507
Major participating institution for programs in: ADP, DR, EM, IM, OBG, P, RO, TY
Institution ID: 25-0291

St John Hospital and Medical Center

22101 Moross Road
Detroit, MI 48236-2172
http://stjohn.org/gme
Med Sch Affil: M-02507
Programs sponsored in: CD, EM, FP, GS, IC, ID, IM, NEP, OBG, PD, PTH, TY
Major participating institution for programs in: U
Institution ID: 25-0486

University Psychiatric Centers

2751 East Jefferson
Detroit, MI 48207
Major participating institution for programs in: P
Institution ID: 25-9020

Veterans Affairs Medical Center (Detroit)

4646 John R Street
Detroit, MI 48201
Med Sch Affil: M-02507
Major participating institution for programs in: ADP, D, GE, IMG, OTO, P, PYG, RHU, SME, TY, U
Institution ID: 25-0108

Wayne County Medical Examiner's Office

1300 East Warren
Detroit, MI 48207
Programs sponsored in: FOP
Institution ID: 25-0520

Wayne State University School of Medicine

540 East Canfield
Detroit, MI 48201
Programs sponsored in: D, FP, OTO, TY, U
Institution ID: 25-9504

Wayne State University/Detroit Medical Center

4201 St Antoine, Suite 9C, UHC
Detroit, MI 48201-2403
www.dmc.org/gme/
Med Sch Affil: M-02507
Programs sponsored in: ADP, AI, AN, CCS, CD, CHN, CHP, CN, DR, EM, END, ETX, GE, GS, HMP, HO, HPM, IC, ID, IM, IMG, MBG, MG, MPD, N, NEP, NS, OBG, OPH, P, PAN, PCC, PCP, PDR, PDS, PM, PMG, PMM, PP, PPM, PS, PTH, PYG, RHU, RNR, RO, SME, VIR, VN, VS
Institution ID: 25-9501

East Lansing

Michigan State University Clinical Center

138 Service Road
East Lansing, MI 48824-1303
Med Sch Affil: M-02512
Major participating institution for programs in: END, FPG, IC, ID, N, VN
Institution ID: 25-0532

Farmington Hills

Weisberg Cancer Treatment Center

31995 Northwestern Highway
Farmington Hills, MI 48334
Major participating institution for programs in: RO
Institution ID: 25-9096

Ferndale

Kingswood Hospital

10300 W Eight Mile Road
Ferndale, MI 48220
Major participating institution for programs in: P
Institution ID: 25-8398

Flint

Hamilton Community Health Network

4001 N Saginaw
Flint, MI 48502
Major participating institution for programs in: MPD
Institution ID: 25-9022

Hurley Medical Center

One Hurley Plaza
Flint, MI 48503-5993
http://hurleymc.com
Med Sch Affil: M-02512, G-02501
Programs sponsored in: IM, IMG, MPD, OBG, PD, TY
Major participating institution for programs in: DR, ORS, PE
Institution ID: 25-0304

McLaren Regional Medical Center

401 S Ballenger Highway
Flint, MI 48532
www.mclaren.org
Med Sch Affil: M-02512
Programs sponsored in: FP, IM, ORS
Major participating institution for programs in: DR, GS, HO, PM
Institution ID: 25-0412

Michigan State University/Flint Area Medical Education

One Hurley Plaza
Flint, MI 48503-5902
www.msufame.msu.edu
Med Sch Affil: M-02512
Programs sponsored in: DR
Institution ID: 25-0562

Willowbrook Manor Nursing Home

G-4436 Beecher Road
Flint, MI 48532
Major participating institution for programs in: HO
Institution ID: 25-9090

Grand Blanc

Genesys Regional Medical Center

One Genesys Parkway
Grand Blanc, MI 48439-8066
www.genesys.org
Med Sch Affil: G-02512
Programs sponsored in: EM, FP
Institution ID: 25-8007

Genesys Regional Medical Center-Health Park

One Genesys Parkway
Grand Blanc, MI 48439
Major participating institution for programs in: DR
Institution ID: 25-0480

Grand Rapids

Grand Rapids Medical Education and Research Center

1000 Monroe, NW
Grand Rapids, MI 49503
www.grmerc.net
Med Sch Affil: M-02512
Programs sponsored in: CCS, CRS, DR, EM, FP, GS, IM, MPD, OBG, ORS, PD, PHO, PN, PS, TY, VS
Major participating institution for programs in: U
Institution ID: 25-0460

Saint Mary's Health Care (Grand Rapids)

200 Jefferson Avenue, SE
Grand Rapids, MI 49503
Med Sch Affil: M-02512
Major participating institution for programs in: CRS, DR, FP, GS, IM, OBG, ORS, PS, TY, VS
Institution ID: 25-0473

Spectrum Health-Blodgett Hospital

1840 Wealthy Street, SE
Grand Rapids, MI 49506
Major participating institution for programs in: CRS, DR, GS, ORS, PS, VS
Institution ID: 25-0395

Spectrum Health-Butterworth Hospital

100 Michigan Street, NE
Grand Rapids, MI 49503
Major participating institution for programs in: CCS, CRS, DR, EM, GS, IM, MPD, OBG, ORS, PD, PHO, PN, PS, TY, VS
Institution ID: 25-0341

Van Andel Research Institute

333 Bostwick Avenue NE
Grand Rapids, MI 49503
Major participating institution for programs in: PHO
Institution ID: 25-9021

Grosse Pointe

William Beaumont Hospital-Grosse Pointe

Department of Medical Education
468 Cadieux Road
Grosse Pointe, MI 48230
www.bonsecoursmi.com
Med Sch Affil: M-02507
Major participating institution for programs in: FP
Institution ID: 25-0103

Howell

St Joseph Mercy (Livingston) Hospital

620 Byron Road
Howell, MI 48843
Programs sponsored in: FP
Institution ID: 25-9017

Teaching Institutions

Jackson

Foote Hospital, Inc
205 N East Avenue
Jackson, MI 49201
Major participating institution for programs in: GS
Institution ID: 25-7017

Kalamazoo

Borgess Medical Center
1521 Gull Road
Kalamazoo, MI 49048
Med Sch Affil: M-02512
Major participating institution for programs in: EM,
FP, GS, IC, IM, MPD, ORS, P, TY
Institution ID: 25-0490

Bronson Methodist Hospital
601 John Street
Kalamazoo, MI 49007-5345
Med Sch Affil: M-02512
Major participating institution for programs in: EM,
FP, GS, IM, MPD, ORS, PD, TY
Institution ID: 25-0458

K Valley Orthopaedics
315 Turwill Lane
Kalamazoo, MI 49007
Major participating institution for programs in: FSM
Institution ID: 25-9019

**Michigan State Univ/Kalamazoo Center
for Medical Studies**
1000 Oakland Drive
Kalamazoo, MI 49008
http://kcms.msu.edu
Med Sch Affil: M-02512
Programs sponsored in: EM, FP, FSM, GS, IM, MPD,
ORS, P, PD, TY
Institution ID: 25-0538

Midwest Orthopaedic Surgery
940 John Street
Kalamazoo, MI 49001
Major participating institution for programs in: ORS
Institution ID: 25-9028

**Western Michigan University Sindecuse
Health Center**
1903 West Michigan Ave
Kalamazoo, MI 49008
Major participating institution for programs in: FSM
Institution ID: 25-9018

Lansing

**Clinton-Eaton-Ingham Community Mental
Health Center**
812 East Jolly Road
Lansing, MI 48910
Major participating institution for programs in: P
Institution ID: 25-9013

Ingham County Health Department
Human Services Bldg
5303 S Cedar
Lansing, MI 48911
Major participating institution for programs in: ID
Institution ID: 25-9051

Ingham Regional Medical Center
401 W Greenlawn
Lansing, MI 48910
Med Sch Affil: M-02512
Major participating institution for programs in: EM,
HO, ICE, PM
Institution ID: 25-0183

**Michigan State University College of
Human Medicine**
Suite 640 Sparrow Professional Building
1200 E Michigan Avenue
Lansing, MI 48912-1316
www.chm.msu.edu/chmhome/graded.htm
Med Sch Affil: M-02512
Programs sponsored in: CCS, CD, CHP, END, GS, HO, IC,
ICE, ID, IM, NPM, P, PD, PM
Institution ID: 25-9502

Mid Michigan Physicians PC
1540 Lake Lansing Rd
#201
Lansing, MI 48912
Major participating institution for programs in: END
Institution ID: 25-9056

Sparrow Hospital
1215 E Michigan Ave
PO Box 30480
Lansing, MI 48909-7980
http://sparrow.org
Med Sch Affil: M-02512
Programs sponsored in: EM, FP, FPG, FSM, N, OBG, VN
Major participating institution for programs in: CCS,
CD, END, GS, HO, ICE, ID, IM, NPM, P, PD, PM
Institution ID: 25-0290

Livonia

University Psychiatric Centers - Livonia
16836 Newburgh Road
Newburgh Professional Park
Livonia, MI 48154
Major participating institution for programs in: CHP
Institution ID: 25-9095

Madison Heights

**Michigan Orthopaedic Specialty
Hospital, The**
30671 Stephenson Highway
Madison Heights, MI 48071
Med Sch Affil: M-02507
Major participating institution for programs in: OSM
Institution ID: 25-0105

Marquette

Marquette General Hospital
420 W Magnetic Street
Marquette, MI 49855-2794
www.mgh.org
Med Sch Affil: M-02512
Programs sponsored in: FP
Major participating institution for programs in: P
Institution ID: 25-0549

Midland

MidMichigan Medical Center-Midland
4005 Orchard Drive
Midland, MI 48670
www.midmichigan.org
Med Sch Affil: G-02512
Programs sponsored in: FP
Institution ID: 25-0322

Northville

Hawthorn Center Hospital
18471 Haggerty Rd
Northville, MI 48167
Med Sch Affil: G-02507
Major participating institution for programs in: CHP
Institution ID: 25-0247

Pontiac

Oakland Physicians Medical Center
461 W Huron
Pontiac, MI 48341-1651
www.nomc/org
Med Sch Affil: M-02507
Programs sponsored in: FP, OBG
Institution ID: 25-0222

St Joseph Mercy-Oakland
44405 Woodward Avenue
Pontiac, MI 48341-2985
www.stjoesoakland.com
Med Sch Affil: M-02507
Programs sponsored in: DR, GS, IM, TY
Major participating institution for programs in: FP,
OBG
Institution ID: 25-0478

Rochester

Crittenton Hospital Medical Center
1101 West University Drive
Rochester, MI 48307-1831
Major participating institution for programs in: FP,
OTO, TY
Institution ID: 25-0199

Royal Oak

William Beaumont Hospital
Medical Administration
3601 West Thirteen Mile Road
Royal Oak, MI 48073
www.beaumont.edu/gme
Med Sch Affil: M-02507, L-02501
Programs sponsored in: BBK, CD, CRS, DR, EM, FP,
FSM, GE, GS, HMP, IC, ICE, ID, IM, IMG, MPD, MSR,
NM, OAR, OBG, ON, OPH, ORS, OSM, OSS, PCH, PCP,
PD, PM, PTH, RNR, RO, TY, U, VIR
Major participating institution for programs in: PS,
VS
Institution ID: 25-0396

Saginaw

**Covenant HealthCare System-Cooper
Campus**
700 Cooper Street
Saginaw, MI 48602
Major participating institution for programs in: EM,
FP, GS, IM
Institution ID: 25-0314

**Covenant HealthCare System-Harrison
Campus**
1447 N Harrison Street
Saginaw, MI 48602
Major participating institution for programs in: FP,
GS, IM, OBG
Institution ID: 25-0200

St Mary's of Michigan
800 S Washington Avenue
Saginaw, MI 48601
Med Sch Affil: M-02512
Major participating institution for programs in: EM,
GS, IM
Institution ID: 25-0276

Synergy Medical Education Alliance
1000 Houghton Avenue
Saginaw, MI 48602
www.synergymedical.org
Med Sch Affil: M-02512
Programs sponsored in: EM, FP, GS, IM, OBG
Major participating institution for programs in: OBG
Institution ID: 25-0525

Saline

Center for Forensic Psychiatry
8303 Platt Road
Saline, MI 48176
Major participating institution for programs in: PFP
Institution ID: 25-8006

Southfield

Providence Hospital and Medical Centers
16001 West 9 Mile Rd
Fourth Floor Fisher Center
Southfield, MI 48075
www.realmedicine.org/providencegme
Med Sch Affil: M-02507, G-02501
Programs sponsored in: CD, DR, FP, FSM, GE, GS, HO, IC, IM, NO, OBG, TY
Major participating institution for programs in: ORS, OSM, PS
Institution ID: 25-0197

Taylor

Concentra Medical Centers (Michigan)
21107 Eureka Road
Taylor, MI 48180
Major participating institution for programs in: GPM
Institution ID: 25-9066

Oakwood Heritage Hospital
10000 Telegraph
Taylor, MI 48160
Major participating institution for programs in: D
Institution ID: 25-9024

Traverse City

Munson Medical Center
1105 Sixth St
Traverse City, MI 49684
http://munsonhealthcare.org
Med Sch Affil: G-02512
Programs sponsored in: FP
Institution ID: 25-0251

Troy

William Beaumont Hospital - Troy
44201 Dequindre Road
Troy, MI 48085-1117
Major participating institution for programs in: EM, FP, FSM
Institution ID: 25-0551

Warren

Henry Ford Macomb - Warren Campus
13355 E Ten Mile Road
Warren, MI 48089
Major participating institution for programs in: TY
Institution ID: 25-9011

St John Macomb-Oakland Hospital
11800 East 12 mile Rd
Warren, MI 48093
Major participating institution for programs in: GE
Institution ID: 25-9025

Wayne

Oakwood Annapolis Hospital
33155 Annapolis Avenue
Wayne, MI 48184-2493
www.oakwood.org
Programs sponsored in: FP, FSM
Institution ID: 25-8399

Wyandotte

Wyandotte Hospital
2333 Biddle Ave
Wyandotte, MI 48192
Major participating institution for programs in: TY
Institution ID: 25-8418

Minnesota

Bloomington

HealthPartners Hospice of the Lakes & Palliative Care
8170 33rd Avenue South
Mailstop 26602A
Bloomington, MN 55440
Major participating institution for programs in: PYG
Institution ID: 26-8093

TRIA Orthopaedic Center
8100 Northland Drive
Bloomington, MN 55431
Major participating institution for programs in: HSO, OSM
Institution ID: 26-8091

Coon Rapids

Mercy Hospital (Minneapolis)
4050 Coon Rapids Blvd Northwest
Coon Rapids, MN 55433
Major participating institution for programs in: TS
Institution ID: 26-8040

Duluth

Duluth Graduate Medical Education Council
Duluth Family Medicine Residency Program
330 North Eighth Avenue East
Duluth, MN 55805
Programs sponsored in: FP
Institution ID: 26-0500

St Luke's Hospital
915 East First Street
Duluth, MN 55805
www.slhduluth.com
Med Sch Affil: M-02607
Major participating institution for programs in: FP
Institution ID: 26-0209

St Mary's Medical Center
407 E Third St
Duluth, MN 55805
Med Sch Affil: M-02607
Major participating institution for programs in: FP
Institution ID: 26-0346

Eden Prairie

Park Nicollet Clinic-Alexander Center
Suite 300, 11455 Viking Drive
Eden Prairie, MN 55344
Major participating institution for programs in: DBP
Institution ID: 26-8037

Mankato

Immanuel St Joseph's-Mayo Health System
1025 Marsh Street
PO Box 8673
Mankato, MN 56002-8673
Med Sch Affil: L-02604
Major participating institution for programs in: FP
Institution ID: 26-8030

Minneaplis

The Orthopaedic Center
8100 Northland Drive
Minneaplis, MN 55431
www.theorthoctr.com
Programs sponsored in: OSM
Institution ID: 26-8036

Minneapolis

Abbott-Northwestern Hospital/Allina Health System
800 E 28th Street-11135
Minneapolis, MN 55407
www.anwim.umn.edu
Med Sch Affil: L-02604
Programs sponsored in: IM
Major participating institution for programs in: CD, CRS, GS, IC, PCP, PTH, TS
Institution ID: 26-0343

Allina Hospitals & Clinics
710 East 24th Street
Minneapolis, MN 55404
www.unitedhospital.com/ufmr
Programs sponsored in: FP
Institution ID: 26-8031

Augustana Care Corporation
1007 East 14th Street
Minneapolis, MN 55404
Major participating institution for programs in: IMG
Institution ID: 26-8085

Benedictine Health Center of Minneapolis
618 East 17th Street
Minneapolis, MN 55404
Major participating institution for programs in: IMG
Institution ID: 26-8086

Children's Hospitals and Clinics of Minnesota - Minneapolis
2525 Chicago Avenue, S
Minneapolis, MN 55404
Med Sch Affil: L-04601, L-02604
Major participating institution for programs in: PEM
Institution ID: 26-0740

HealthPartners Institute for Medical Education
Attention: Carl Patow, MD, MPH
8170 33rd Avenue South - Mail Stop 21110T
Minneapolis, MN 55425
www.ime.healthpartners
Programs sponsored in: EM, ETX, GPM
Institution ID: 26-8034

Hennepin County Medical Center
701 Park Ave S
Office of the Medical Director MC #01
Minneapolis, MN 55415-1829
www.hcmc.org
Med Sch Affil: M-02604
Programs sponsored in: CCM, EM, FP, FSM, GS, IM, IMG, MEM, P, SME, TY, UME
Major participating institution for programs in: AN, CN, D, DBP, DR, END, ENR, ETX, GE, HSO, IMD, MPD, N, NEP, NS, OBG, OPH, ORS, OTO, PCP, PD, PG, PM, PTH, PYG, RHU, RNR, VN
Institution ID: 26-0402

Hennepin County Medical Examiner
530 Chicago Avenue
Minneapolis, MN 55415-1518
Programs sponsored in: FOP
Major participating institution for programs in: CCS
Institution ID: 26-0733

Teaching Institutions

KDWB University Pediatrics Family Center
STAR Center for Family Health
McNamara Alumni Center, 200 Oaks St SE, Suite 160
Minneapolis, MN 55455-2022
Major participating institution for programs in: CHP
Institution ID: 26-8062

Minnesota Sports Medicine
701 25th Ave S, #150
Minneapolis, MN 55454
www.mnsportsmed.org
Programs sponsored in: OSM
Institution ID: 26-8024

Twin Cities Spine Center
913 East 26th Street
Suite 600
Minneapolis, MN 55404-4515
www.tcspine.com
Programs sponsored in: OSS
Institution ID: 26-8032

University of Minnesota Medical Center, Division of Fairview
500 Harvard St SE
Minneapolis, MN 55455
Major participating institution for programs in: ADL, ADP, AI, AN, BBK, CCP, CCS, CD, CHP, CN, CRS, D, DBP, DR, END, ENR, FP, GE, GS, HMP, HO, HSO, IC, ICE, ID, IM, IMD, IMG, MGP, MPD, N, NEP, NPM, NR, NS, OAR, OBG, OPH, ORS, OSM, OTO, P, PCC, PCP, PD, PDC, PDE, PDI, PDP, PDR, PG, PHO, PM, PN, PS, PTH, PYG, PYM, RHU, RNR, RO, THP, TS, U, VIR, VN
Institution ID: 26-0254

University of Minnesota Medical School
MMC 293
420 Delaware Street, SE
Minneapolis, MN 55455
www.med.umn.edu/
Med Sch Affil: M-02604
Programs sponsored in: ADL, ADP, AI, AN, BBK, CCP, CCS, CD, CHP, CN, CRS, D, DBP, DR, END, ENR, FP, GE, GS, HMP, HO, HPM, HSO, IC, ICE, ID, IM, IMD, IMG, MGP, MPD, N, NEP, NPM, NR, NS, OAR, OBG, OP, OPH, ORS, OTO, P, PCC, PCP, PD, PDC, PDE, PDI, PDP, PDR, PEM, PG, PHO, PM, PN, PRD, PS, PTH, PYG, PYM, RHU, RNR, RO, RPM, THP, TS, U, VIR, VN
Institution ID: 26-9501

University of Minnesota School of Public Health
Box 197, Mayo Bldg, Rm A-304
420 Delaware St, SE
Minneapolis, MN 55455-0381
Med Sch Affil: G-02608
Major participating institution for programs in: GPM
Institution ID: 26-0495

Veterans Affairs Medical Center (Minneapolis)
One Veterans Drive
Minneapolis, MN 55417
Med Sch Affil: M-02604
Major participating institution for programs in: ADP, CN, CRS, D, DR, END, GE, HSO, IC, ICE, ID, IM, IMD, MPD, N, NS, OAR, OPH, ORS, OTO, P, PM, PS, PTH, PYG, PYM, RHU, RO, TS, U, VIR
Institution ID: 26-0119

Minnetonka

Hennepin County Home School
14300 County Road 62
Minnetonka, MN 55345
Major participating institution for programs in: CHP
Institution ID: 26-8061

Robbinsdale

North Memorial Health Care
3300 Oakdale Avenue, N
Robbinsdale, MN 55422-2900
Med Sch Affil: G-02604
Major participating institution for programs in: CCS, CRS, FP
Institution ID: 26-0498

Rochester

College of Medicine, Mayo Clinic
200 First Street, SW
Rochester, MN 55905
www.mayo.edu
Med Sch Affil: M-02608, L-02012, L-04802
Programs sponsored in: ACA, ADP, AI, AN, AR, BBK, CCA, CCM, CCS, CD, CHN, CHP, CN, CRS, D, DBP, DMP, DR, EM, END, FP, FSM, GE, GPM, GS, HMP, HO, HPM, HSO, IC, ICE, ID, IM, IMG, MG, MGP, MM, N, NEP, NP, NPM, NR, NS, OAR, OBG, OMO, OPH, ORS, OTO, P, PAN, PCC, PCP, PD, PDC, PDE, PDI, PG, PHO, PM, PMM, PRD, PS, PTH, PUD, PYG, PYM, RHU, RNR, RO, RPM, SME, SP, THP, TS, TY, U, VIR, VN, VS
Institution ID: 26-0173

Comfort Home Health Care
2746 Superior Drive NW
Rochester, MN 55901
Major participating institution for programs in: IMG
Institution ID: 26-8081

Federal Medical Center (Federal Bureau of Prisons)
2110 East Center Street
Rochester, MN 55904
Major participating institution for programs in: ID
Institution ID: 26-8067

Mayo Clinic (Rochester)
200 First Street, SW
Rochester, MN 55905
Major participating institution for programs in: AI, AN, AR, BBK, CCA, CCM, CCS, CD, CHN, CHP, CN, CRS, D, DBP, DMP, DR, END, FP, GE, GPM, GS, HMP, HO, HPM, HSO, ICE, ID, IM, IMG, MG, MGP, MM, N, NEP, NP, NR, NS, OAR, OBG, OMO, OPH, ORS, OTO, P, PCC, PD, PDC, PDE, PG, PHO, PM, PRD, PS, PTH, PYG, RHU, RNR, RO, RPM, SME, SP, THP, VIR
Institution ID: 26-0737

Rochester Methodist Hospital
201 W Center St
Rochester, MN 55902-3084
Med Sch Affil: M-02608
Major participating institution for programs in: AN, AR, CCA, CRS, DR, FP, GS, HO, HPM, HSO, ID, NEP, NPM, OAR, OBG, OMO, OPH, ORS, OTO, P, PMM, PS, PTH, PYM, RNR, SP, THP, U
Institution ID: 26-0483

Saint Marys Hospital of Rochester
1216 Second Street, SW
Rochester, MN 55902-1970
Med Sch Affil: M-02608
Major participating institution for programs in: ACA, ADP, AN, AR, CCA, CCM, CCS, CD, CHN, CHP, CN, CRS, DR, EM, END, FP, GE, GS, HPM, HSO, IC, ICE, ID, IM, IMG, N, NEP, NPM, NS, OAR, OMO, OPH, ORS, OTO, P, PAN, PCC, PCP, PD, PDC, PDE, PDI, PG, PHO, PM, PS, PTH, PYM, RNR, RPM, SP, TS, U, VIR, VS
Institution ID: 26-0317

Samaritan Bethany Heights
1530 Assisi Drive NW
Rochester, MN 55901
Major participating institution for programs in: IMG
Institution ID: 26-8083

Samaritan Bethany Home on Eighth
24 Eighth Street NW
Rochester, MN 55901
Major participating institution for programs in: IMG
Institution ID: 26-8084

St Cloud

CentraCare Clinic (River Campus)
1200 Sixth Avenue North
St. Cloud, MN 56303
Major participating institution for programs in: FP
Institution ID: 26-8048

St Cloud Hospital
1406 Sixth Ave, N
St Cloud, MN 56303
Med Sch Affil: G-02608
Major participating institution for programs in: FP
Institution ID: 26-7010

St Louis Park

Methodist Hospital
6500 Excelsior Blvd
PO Box 650
St Louis Park, MN 55440
Med Sch Affil: G-02604
Major participating institution for programs in: CCM, FP, GS, OSM, PYG
Institution ID: 26-0135

Park Nicollet Clinic
3800 Park Nicollet Blvd
St. Louis Park, MN 55416
Major participating institution for programs in: FP
Institution ID: 26-8046

St Paul

American Red Cross Blood Services-St Paul Region
100 S Robert St
St Paul, MN 55107
Med Sch Affil: G-02604
Major participating institution for programs in: BBK
Institution ID: 26-0736

Bethesda Hospital
559 Capitol Blvd
St. Paul, MN 55103
Major participating institution for programs in: PYG
Institution ID: 26-8092

Children's Hospitals and Clinics of Minnesota - St Paul
345 N Smith Avenue
St Paul, MN 55102
Med Sch Affil: L-02604
Major participating institution for programs in: FP, MPD, NPM, PD, PEM, U
Institution ID: 26-0497

Gillette Children's Hospital
200 East University Avenue
St. Paul, MN 55101
Major participating institution for programs in: HSO, OP, ORS, RPM
Institution ID: 26-0492

HealthEast St John's Hospital
559 Capitol Boulevard
St. Paul, MN 55103
Med Sch Affil: G-02604
Major participating institution for programs in: FP
Institution ID: 26-0130

HealthEast St Joseph's Hospital
559 Capitol Boulevard
St. Paul, MN 55103
Med Sch Affil: G-02604
Major participating institution for programs in: FP
Institution ID: 26-0357

HealthPartners St Paul Clinic
205 S Wabasha
St. Paul, MN 55107
Major participating institution for programs in: GPM
Institution ID: 26-8047

Regions Hospital
640 Jackson Street
St. Paul, MN 55101-2595
Med Sch Affil: M-02604
Major participating institution for programs in: CCS,
EM, ETX, GPM, GS, IM, IMD, IMG, MPD, OBG, OPH,
ORS, OTO, P, PM, PS, RHU
Institution ID: 26-0184

United Hospital
333 N Smith Avenue
St Paul, MN 55102
Med Sch Affil: L-02604
Major participating institution for programs in: CN,
CRS, FP, RO
Institution ID: 26-0311

Wilder Child Guidance
919 Lafond Avenue
St. Paul, MN 55104-2198
Major participating institution for programs in: CHP
Institution ID: 26-8060

William Mitchell College of Law
875 Summit Avenue
St. Paul, MN 55105-3076
Major participating institution for programs in: CHP
Institution ID: 26-8058

Wyoming

University of Minnesota Physicians Radiation Therapy Center
Radiation Therapy Center
5160 Fairview Blvd, Suite 1100
Wyoming, MN 55092
Major participating institution for programs in: RO
Institution ID: 26-8094

Mississippi

Biloxi

Veterans Affairs Medical Center (Biloxi)
400 Veterans Avenue
Biloxi, MS 39531-2410
Med Sch Affil: L-00106, G-02101
Major participating institution for programs in: GS,
OPH, OTO, P
Institution ID: 27-0425

Jackson

Mississippi Baptist Medical Center
1225 North State Street
Jackson, MS 39202
Med Sch Affil: G-02701
Major participating institution for programs in: FP, U
Institution ID: 27-0374

Mississippi Sports Medicine & Orthopaedic Center
1325 East Fortification Street
Jackson, MS 39202
www.msmoc.com
Programs sponsored in: OSM
Institution ID: 27-8001

St Dominic-Jackson Memorial Hospital
969 Lakeland Drive
Jackson, MS 39216
Med Sch Affil: L-02701
Major participating institution for programs in: HSP,
IC
Institution ID: 27-0433

University Hospitals and Clinics
2500 North State Street
Jackson, MS 39216-4505
Med Sch Affil: M-02701
Major participating institution for programs in: AI,
AN, CD, CHN, CHP, CN, DR, EM, END, FP, GE, GS, HO,
HSO, HSP, IC, ID, IM, MPD, N, NEP, NS, OBG, OPH, ORS,
OTO, P, PCC, PCP, PD, PHO, PMM, PS, PTH, RHU, SME,
TS, U
Institution ID: 27-0427

University of Mississippi School of Medicine
2500 North State Street
Jackson, MS 39216-4505
www.umc.edu
Programs sponsored in: AI, AN, CD, CHN, CHP, CN, DR,
EM, END, FP, FSM, GE, GS, HO, HSO, HSP, IC, ID, IM,
MPD, N, NEP, NS, OBG, OPH, ORS, OTO, P, PCC, PCP,
PD, PHO, PMM, PS, PTH, RHU, SME, TS, U
Institution ID: 27-9501

Veterans Affairs Medical Center (Jackson)
1500 East Woodrow Wilson Drive
Jackson, MS 39216
Med Sch Affil: M-02701
Major participating institution for programs in: AI,
CD, DR, END, GE, GS, HO, HSO, HSP, IC, ID, IM, MPD, N,
NEP, NS, OPH, ORS, OTO, P, PCC, PS, RHU, TS, U
Institution ID: 27-0430

Keesler AFB

Keesler Medical Center
81st Medical Group/SG
301 Fisher St, Rm 5A166
Keesler AFB, MS 39534-2576
www.keesler.af.mil/81MDG/medical.asp?menu=info.mnu
Med Sch Affil: M-02312
Programs sponsored in: GS, IM
Institution ID: 27-0371

Tupelo

North Mississippi Medical Center
830 S Gloster St
Tupelo, MS 38801-4934
www. nmhs.net
Med Sch Affil: G-02701
Programs sponsored in: FP
Institution ID: 27-7005

Missouri

Berkeley

St Louis County Medical Examiner's Office
6039 Helen Avenue
Berkeley, MO 63134
Major participating institution for programs in: FOP
Institution ID: 28-8174

Chesterfield

St Luke's Hospital
232 S Woods Mill Rd
Chesterfield, MO 63017
www.stlukes-stl.com
Med Sch Affil: M-02803
Programs sponsored in: IM
Major participating institution for programs in: TS
Institution ID: 28-0203

Columbia

Boone Hospital Center
1600 E Broadway
Columbia, MO 65201
Med Sch Affil: L-02803
Major participating institution for programs in: NS
Institution ID: 28-7035

Dialysis Clinics, Inc
330 Lemone Industrial Boulevard
Columbia, MO 65201
Major participating institution for programs in: NEP
Institution ID: 28-9004

Harry S Truman Memorial Veterans Hospital
800 Hospital Drive
Columbia, MO 65201
Med Sch Affil: M-02803
Major participating institution for programs in: CD,
D, DR, END, GE, GS, ID, IM, MPD, N, NEP, OPH, ORS,
OTO, P, PCC, PM, PSI, PTH, RHU, U
Institution ID: 28-0178

Howard A Rusk (HealthSouth) Rehabilitation Center
315 Business Loop 70W
Columbia, MO 65201
Major participating institution for programs in: PM
Institution ID: 28-8187

Mid-Missouri Mental Health Center
3 Hospital Dr
Columbia, MO 65201
Med Sch Affil: M-02803
Major participating institution for programs in: P
Institution ID: 28-8013

Surgery Center of Columbia
305 N Keene St #107
Columbia, MO 65201
Major participating institution for programs in: NS
Institution ID: 28-9024

University Hospitals and Clinics
One Hospital Drive, DC031
Columbia, MO 65212
Med Sch Affil: M-02803
Major participating institution for programs in: AN,
CCS, CD, CHP, D, DR, END, FP, FPG, GE, GS, HO, ID, IM,
MG, MPD, N, NEP, NM, NPM, NS, OBG, OPH, ORS, OTO,
P, PCC, PD, PDR, PM, PSI, PTH, RHU, RNR, SME, U, VS
Institution ID: 28-0176

University of Missouri-Columbia School of Medicine
MA101 Medical Sciences Building
One Hospital Drive, DC018.00
Columbia, MO 65212
www.muhealth.org/~medicine/
Programs sponsored in: AN, CCS, CD, CHP, D, DR, END,
FP, FPG, GE, GS, HO, ID, IM, MG, MPD, N, NEP, NM,
NPM, NS, OBG, OPH, ORS, OTO, P, PCC, PD, PDR, PFP,
PM, PSI, PTH, RHU, RNR, SME, U, VS
Institution ID: 28-0709

Fulton

Fulton State Hospital
600 E 5th
Fulton, MO 65251
Major participating institution for programs in: PFP
Institution ID: 28-7014

Gladstone

Allergy and Asthma Specialists of Kansas City
6000 N Oak Trafficway
Suite 102
Gladstone, MO 64118-5176
Major participating institution for programs in: AI
Institution ID: 28-8188

Teaching Institutions

Hannibal

Midwest Orthopedics Specialists
PO Box 935
Hannibal, MO 63401
Major participating institution for programs in: FSM
Institution ID: 28-9018

Kansas City

Children's Mercy Hospital
2401 Gillham Road
Kansas City, MO 64108
www.childrens-mercy.org
Med Sch Affil: M-02846, L-02803, L-01902, G-03006
Programs sponsored in: CHN, RPM
Major participating institution for programs in: AI,
CCP, CCS, D, DBP, MPD, NPM, ORS, PD, PDE, PDI, PDR,
PDS, PEM, PG, PHO, PN, PP, SME, U
Institution ID: 28-0426

Office of the Jackson County Medical Examiner
660 East 24th Street
Kansas City, MO 64108
Programs sponsored in: FOP
Institution ID: 28-8178

Research Medical Center
2316 E Meyer Boulevard
Kansas City, MO 64132-1199
Med Sch Affil: M-02846, L-01902
Programs sponsored in: FP
Major participating institution for programs in: ID
Institution ID: 28-0175

St Luke's Hospital-Kansas City
4401 Wornall Road
Kansas City, MO 64111
Med Sch Affil: M-02846, G-01902
Major participating institution for programs in: AN,
CCM, CD, DR, GE, GS, HO, IC, ICE, ID, IM, MPD, OBG,
ORS, OTO, PCC, PSI, SME, VN
Institution ID: 28-0337

Truman Medical Center
2301 Holmes Street
Kansas City, MO 64108
Med Sch Affil: M-02846
Major participating institution for programs in: AI,
AN, CCM, CD, DR, EM, GE, GS, HO, ID, IM, MPD, NPM,
OBG, OPH, ORS, OSM, OTO, P, PCC, PTH
Institution ID: 28-0263

Truman Medical Center-Lakewood
7900 Lee's Summit Road
Kansas City, MO 64139-1241
Med Sch Affil: M-02846
Major participating institution for programs in: FP,
FPG, FSM
Institution ID: 28-8012

University of Missouri-Kansas City School of Medicine
2411 Holmes
Kansas City, MO 64108-2792
www.med.umkc.edu/
Programs sponsored in: AI, AN, CCM, CCP, CCS, CD,
DBP, DR, EM, FP, FPG, FSM, GE, GS, HO, IC, ICE, ID, IM,
MPD, NPM, OBG, OPH, ORS, OSM, P, PCC, PD, PDE, PDI,
PDR, PDS, PEM, PG, PHO, PN, PP, PTH, SME
Institution ID: 28-0453

Veterans Affairs Medical Center (Kansas City)
4801 Linwood Boulevard
Kansas City, MO 64128
Major participating institution for programs in: ADP,
CD, CN, D, DR, END, GE, GS, HO, ID, IM, IMG, MP, N,
NEP, NS, OPH, ORS, OTO, P, PCC, PSI, PTH, RHU, U
Institution ID: 28-0218

Western Missouri Mental Health Center
600 E 22nd St
Kansas City, MO 64108
Med Sch Affil: M-02846
Major participating institution for programs in: P
Institution ID: 28-0433

Springfield

Cox Medical Center
1423 N Jefferson
A100
Springfield, MO 65802
Programs sponsored in: FP
Institution ID: 28-8169

St Louis

Anheuser-Busch Institute
1755 S Grand Boulevard
St Louis, MO 63104
Major participating institution for programs in: D,
DMP, OPH
Institution ID: 28-7025

Barnes Jewish Center Behavioral Health
1430 Olive St
Suite 400
St. Louis, MO 63101
Major participating institution for programs in: CHP
Institution ID: 28-9006

Barnes-Jewish Hospital
One Barnes-Jewish Hospital Plaza
St Louis, MO 63110
Med Sch Affil: M-02802, L-02803
Major participating institution for programs in: ACA,
AI, AN, BBK, CCA, CCS, CD, CHN, CN, CRS, D, DMP, DR,
EM, END, ESN, GE, GS, HMP, HO, HSO, HSP, IC, ICE, ID,
IM, IMG, MG, MGP, N, NEP, NM, NP, NS, OBG, OPH, ORS,
OSM, OSS, OTO, P, PCC, PCP, PM, PMG, PMM, PP, PS,
PTH, RHU, RNR, RO, SP, TS, U, VIR, VN, VS
Institution ID: 28-0146

Barnes-Jewish West County Hospital
12634 Olive Street Road
St Louis, MO 63141-6354
Med Sch Affil: G-02802
Major participating institution for programs in: AI,
CRS, OSM, VS
Institution ID: 28-8173

Cardinal Glennon Children's Hospital
1465 South Grand Boulevard
St Louis, MO 63104
Med Sch Affil: M-02834
Major participating institution for programs in: AI,
AN, CCA, CHN, DMP, EM, MPD, NPM, NS, OPH, ORS,
OTO, PD, PEM, PP, PPR, PS, PTH, RHU, TS, U
Institution ID: 28-0444

Hawthorn Children's Psychiatric Hospital
1901 Pennsylvania Ave
St. Louis, MO 63133
Major participating institution for programs in: CHP
Institution ID: 28-8015

Metropolitan St Louis Psychiatric Center
5351 Delmar
St Louis, MO 63116
Med Sch Affil: M-02802
Major participating institution for programs in: P
Institution ID: 28-0214

Quest Diagnostics, Inc
11636 Administration Drive
St. Louis, MO 63146
Major participating institution for programs in: PCP
Institution ID: 28-9028

Shriners Hospitals for Children (St Louis)
2001 S Lindberg Blvd
St Louis, MO 63131
Med Sch Affil: L-02803, G-02802
Major participating institution for programs in: OP,
ORS
Institution ID: 28-0164

SLU Care (the Ambulatory Practices of the UMG)
3660 Vista Avenue
St. Louis, MO 63110
Major participating institution for programs in: NEP
Institution ID: 28-9029

St John's Mercy Medical Center
615 South New Ballas Road/GME
St Louis, MO 63141
www.sjmmcgme.com
Med Sch Affil: M-02834, L-02803
Programs sponsored in: FP, IM, OBG, TY
Major participating institution for programs in: CCM,
CCS, EM, GS, ORS, OTO, PCC, U, VS
Institution ID: 28-0231

St Louis Children's Hospital
One Children's Place
St Louis, MO 63110-1077
Med Sch Affil: M-02802
Major participating institution for programs in: AI,
CCP, CHN, DMP, EM, MG, NMN, NPM, NS, OP, OTO, PAN,
PCP, PD, PDC, PDE, PDI, PDP, PDR, PDS, PEM, PG,
PHO, PMG, PN, PP, PPR, TS, U
Institution ID: 28-0145

St Louis City Medical Examiner Office
1300 Clark Avenue
St. Louis, MO 63103
Major participating institution for programs in: FOP
Institution ID: 28-9011

St Louis ConnectCare
5535 Delmar Boulevard
St Louis, MO 63112-3095
Med Sch Affil: L-02802
Major participating institution for programs in: IM, N,
U
Institution ID: 28-0250

St Louis University Hospital
3635 Vista Avenue at Grand Blvd
PO Box 15250
St. Louis, MO 63110-0250
Med Sch Affil: M-02834
Major participating institution for programs in: AI,
AN, CCM, CCS, CD, CHN, CN, DMP, DR, END, FSM, GE,
GS, HMP, HO, IC, ICE, ID, IM, IMG, MPD, N, NEP, NM,
NS, ORS, OTO, P, PCC, PCP, PPR, PS, PTH, PYG, RHU,
TS, U, VS
Institution ID: 28-0167

St Louis University School of Medicine
1402 South Grand Boulevard
Suite 260
St Louis, MO 63104
Med Sch Affil: M-02803
Programs sponsored in: AI, AN, CCA, CCM, CCS, CD,
CHN, CN, D, DMP, DR, EM, END, FOP, FP, FSM, GE, GS,
HMP, HO, IC, ICE, ID, IM, IMG, MPD, N, NEP, NM, NPM,
NS, OBG, OPH, ORS, OTO, P, PCC, PCP, PD, PEM, PP,
PPR, PS, PTH, PYG, RHU, TS, U, VS
Institution ID: 28-9501

St Mary's Health Center
6420 Clayton Road
St Louis, MO 63117
http://stmarysintmed.com
Med Sch Affil: M-02834
Programs sponsored in: IM
Major participating institution for programs in: EM,
N, OBG, PS, PTH
Institution ID: 28-0442

The Rehabilitation Institute of St Louis
4455 Duncan Avenue
St Louis, MO 63110
Major participating institution for programs in: PM, VN
Institution ID: 28-8179

Veterans Affairs Medical Center (St Louis)
915 North Grand Avenue
St Louis, MO 63125
Med Sch Affil: M-02834, M-02802
Major participating institution for programs in: AI, CD, CN, DR, END, GE, GS, IC, IM, IMG, N, NEP, NM, OPH, OSM, OTO, P, PYG, RHU, U
Institution ID: 28-0354

Washington University School of Medicine
660 S Euclid
St Louis, MO 63110
Med Sch Affil: M-02803, M-02802
Major participating institution for programs in: AI, CD, NS, PCC, PDE, SME
Institution ID: 28-0440

Washington University/B-JH/SLCH Consortium
Washington University School of Medicine
660 South Euclid Avenue, Campus Box 8033
St Louis, MO 63110-1039
http://medicine.wustl.edu/gme
Programs sponsored in: ACA, AI, AN, BBK, CCA, CCP, CCS, CD, CHN, CHP, CN, CRS, D, DMP, DR, EM, END, ESN, GE, GS, HMP, HO, HSO, HSP, IC, ICE, ID, IM, IMG, MG, MGP, N, NEP, NM, NMN, NP, NPM, NS, OBG, OP, OPH, ORS, OSM, OSS, OTO, P, PAN, PCC, PCP, PD, PDC, PDE, PDI, PDP, PDR, PDS, PEM, PG, PHO, PM, PMG, PMM, PN, PP, PPR, PS, PTH, RHU, RNR, RO, SME, SP, TS, U, VIR, VN, VS
Institution ID: 28-9502

Windsor
Royal Oaks Hospital
307 N Main
Windsor, MO 65360
Med Sch Affil: L-02803
Major participating institution for programs in: CHP
Institution ID: 28-8177

Montana
Billings
Billings Clinic
2800 Tenth Ave, N
PO Box 37000
Billings, MT 59107-7000
www.billingsclinic.org
Med Sch Affil: L-05404
Major participating institution for programs in: FP
Institution ID: 29-8002

Montana Family Medicine Residency
123 South 27th Street
Suite B
Billings, MT 59101
www.mfmr.org
Programs sponsored in: FP, FSM
Institution ID: 29-8001

St Vincent Healthcare
PO Box 35200
Billings, MT 59107
Med Sch Affil: L-05404
Major participating institution for programs in: FP, FSM
Institution ID: 29-7001

Nebraska
Grand Island
St Francis Medical Center (Grand Island)
2620 W Faidley Ave
Box 9804
Grand Island, NE 68802
Med Sch Affil: G-03005
Major participating institution for programs in: FP
Institution ID: 30-7009

Kearney
Good Samaritan Hospital (Kearney)
31st St and Central Ave
PO Box 1990
Kearney, NE 68848
Med Sch Affil: G-03005
Major participating institution for programs in: FP
Institution ID: 30-7004

Lincoln
BryanLGH Medical Center East
1600 S 48th Street
Lincoln, NE 68506
Med Sch Affil: L-03005
Major participating institution for programs in: FP
Institution ID: 30-0329

BryanLGH Medical Center West
2300 S 16th Street
Lincoln, NE 68502
Med Sch Affil: L-03005
Major participating institution for programs in: FP
Institution ID: 30-0332

Lincoln Medical Education Partnership
4600 Valley Road
Suite 210
Lincoln, NE 68510-4891
www.lmep.com
Programs sponsored in: FP
Institution ID: 30-0706

St Elizabeth Regional Medical Center
555 South 70th Street
Lincoln, NE 68510
Med Sch Affil: L-03005, G-03006
Major participating institution for programs in: FP
Institution ID: 30-0278

Norfolk
Faith Regional Health Services
PO Box 869
2700 Norfolk Avenue
Norfolk, NE 68702-0869
Major participating institution for programs in: FP
Institution ID: 30-8006

North Platte
Great Plains Regional Medical Center
601 W Leota Street
Box 1167
North Platte, NE 69103
Med Sch Affil: G-03005
Major participating institution for programs in: FP
Institution ID: 30-8004

Offutt AFB
Ehrling Bergquist Hospital
55 MDG/SGA
2501Capehart Road
Offutt AFB, NE 68113-2160
Med Sch Affil: M-03005, L-03006
Major participating institution for programs in: AI, FP
Institution ID: 30-0708

Omaha
Alegent Health Bergan Mercy Health System
7500 Mercy Rd
Omaha, NE 68124
Med Sch Affil: M-03006, G-03005
Major participating institution for programs in: OBG, ORS
Institution ID: 30-0452

Alegent Health Immanuel Medical Center
6901 N 72nd Street
Omaha, NE 68122
Major participating institution for programs in: CHP, P, PYG
Institution ID: 30-0365

Boys Town National Research Hospital
555 North 30th Street
Omaha, NE 68131
Major participating institution for programs in: OTO
Institution ID: 30-8003

Children's Hospital
8301 Dodge Street
Omaha, NE 68114
Med Sch Affil: M-03006, M-03005
Major participating institution for programs in: MPD, NS, ORS, PD, PDI, PDR, PG, SME, U
Institution ID: 30-0390

Creighton Psychiatric Clinic
3528 Dodge St
Omaha, NE 68131
Major participating institution for programs in: CHP
Institution ID: 30-8012

Creighton University Medical Center (Tenet - SJH)
601 North 30th Street
Omaha, NE 68131-2197
Med Sch Affil: M-03006, M-03005
Major participating institution for programs in: AI, AN, CD, DR, END, FP, GS, IC, ID, IM, N, NM, OBG, P, PCC, PDI, PTH
Institution ID: 30-0709

Creighton University School of Medicine
2500 California Plaza
Omaha, NE 68178
http://medicine.creighton.edu/
Programs sponsored in: ADP, AI, CD, CHP, CRS, DR, END, FP, GS, IC, ID, IM, OBG, P, PCC, PTH, PYG
Institution ID: 30-9502

Douglas County Hospital
4102 Woolworth Ave
Omaha, NE 68105
Major participating institution for programs in: ID
Institution ID: 30-0458

Nebraska Medical Center
987400 Nebraska Medical Center
Omaha, NE 68198-7400
http://nebraskamed.com
Programs sponsored in: FP
Major participating institution for programs in: ADP, AN, CD, CHP, DR, EM, END, GE, GS, HMP, HO, IC, ICE, ID, IMG, MPD, N, NEP, NM, NS, OBG, OPH, ORS, OTO, P, PCC, PD, PG, PMM, PS, PTH, PYG, RHU, SME, U, VIR
Institution ID: 30-0453

Nebraska Methodist Hospital
8303 Dodge St
Omaha, NE 68114-4199
Med Sch Affil: M-03005
Major participating institution for programs in: GS, NS, OBG, OTO, U
Institution ID: 30-0294

Teaching Institutions

Renal Advantage Inc (Ames)
5084 Ames Avenue
Omaha, NE 68104
Major participating institution for programs in: NEP
Institution ID: 30-8015

Renal Advantage, Inc (Center Street)
4411 Center Street
Ste A
Omaha, NE 68107
Major participating institution for programs in: NEP
Institution ID: 30-8018

University of Nebraska Medical Center College of Medicine
985524 Nebraska Medical Center
Omaha, NE 68198-5524
Med Sch Affil: M-03005, M-03006
Programs sponsored in: AN, CD, DR, EM, END, FP, GE, GS, HMP, HO, IC, ICE, IM, IMG, MPD, N, NEP, NM, NS, OBG, OPH, ORS, OTO, PCC, PD, PDI, PDR, PG, PMM, PS, PTH, RHU, SME, U, VIR
Institution ID: 30-0710

Veterans Affairs Medical Center (Omaha)
4101 Woolworth Avenue
Omaha, NE 68105
Med Sch Affil: M-03006, M-03005
Major participating institution for programs in: ADP, AI, CD, DR, END, GE, GS, HO, IC, ICE, ID, IM, MPD, N, NEP, OPH, ORS, OTO, P, PCC, PTH, RHU, U
Institution ID: 30-0447

Scottsbluff

Regional West Medical Center
4021 Avenue B
Scottsbluff, NE 69361-4695
Med Sch Affil: M-03005
Major participating institution for programs in: FP
Institution ID: 30-8005

Nevada
Henderson

Crovetti Orthopaedics and Sports Medicine
880 Seven Hills Drive
Henderson, NV 89052
Major participating institution for programs in: FSM
Institution ID: 31-8040

Las Vegas

Harmony Healthcare
1710 W Charleston Blvd
Las Vegas, NV 89102
Major participating institution for programs in: P
Institution ID: 31-8025

Las Vegas Surgery Center
870 S Rancho Drive
Las Vegas, NV 89106
Major participating institution for programs in: GS, PSI
Institution ID: 31-8027

Nevada Cancer Institute
1 Breakthrough Way
10441 N Twain Avenue
Las Vegas, NV 89135
Major participating institution for programs in: IM
Institution ID: 31-8028

Sahara Surgery Center
2401 Paseo Del Prado
Las Vegas, NV 89102
Major participating institution for programs in: GS, PSI
Institution ID: 31-8021

Southern Nevada Adult Mental Health Services
1650 Community College Drive
Las Vegas, NV 89146
Major participating institution for programs in: P
Institution ID: 31-8036

Specialty Surgery Center
7250 Cathedral Rock Drive
Las Vegas, NV 89128
Major participating institution for programs in: PSI
Institution ID: 31-8030

Sunrise Hospital and Medical Center
3186 Maryland Parkway
PO Box 98530
Las Vegas, NV 89193-8530
Med Sch Affil: M-03101
Major participating institution for programs in: PD, PSI
Institution ID: 31-8014

University Medical Center of Southern Nevada
1800 West Charleston Boulevard
Las Vegas, NV 89102
Med Sch Affil: M-03101
Major participating institution for programs in: CCS, EM, FP, FSM, GS, IM, OBG, ON, P, PD, PSI
Institution ID: 31-0100

VA Southern Nevada Healthcare System
1700 Vegas Drive
Las Vegas, NV 89106
Major participating institution for programs in: GS, P
Institution ID: 31-8016

Reno

Circle of Life Hospice, Inc
1575 Delucchi Lane
Suite 214
Reno, NV 89506
Major participating institution for programs in: IMG
Institution ID: 31-8020

Ioannis A Lougaris Veterans Affairs Medical Center
1000 Locust Street
Reno, NV 89520
Med Sch Affil: M-03101
Major participating institution for programs in: FP, FSM, IM, IMG, P
Institution ID: 31-0110

Jan Evans Juvenile Justice Center
650 Ferrari McLeod Boulevard
Reno, NV 89512
Major participating institution for programs in: CHP
Institution ID: 31-8026

MEDSchool Associates North (Reno)
401 W Second St
Suite 215
Reno, NV 89503
Major participating institution for programs in: CHP, FSM, IMG
Institution ID: 31-8018

Northern Nevada Child and Adolescent Services
2655 Enterprise Road
Reno, NV 89512
Major participating institution for programs in: CHP
Institution ID: 31-8029

Renown Medical Center
77 Pringle Way
Reno, NV 89520
Med Sch Affil: M-03101
Major participating institution for programs in: CHP, FP, FSM, IM, IMG, P
Institution ID: 31-7004

Saint Mary's Regional Medical Center
235 West 6th Street
Reno, NV 89503
Major participating institution for programs in: FSM
Institution ID: 31-7003

University of Nevada School of Medicine
1664 N Virginia Street, Mail Stop 332
Pennington Building
Reno, NV 89557-0046
www.unr.edu/med/
Med Sch Affil: G-00515
Programs sponsored in: CCS, CHP, EM, FP, FSM, GS, IM, IMG, OBG, ON, P, PD, PSI
Institution ID: 31-0111

University of Nevada, Reno - Student Health Center
MS/196
Reno, NV 89577
Major participating institution for programs in: FSM, P
Institution ID: 31-8051

Washoe County School District
PO Box 30425
Reno, NV 89520-3425
Major participating institution for programs in: CHP
Institution ID: 31-8039

West Hills Hospital
1240 E Ninth Street
Reno, NV 89512
Major participating institution for programs in: CHP, P
Institution ID: 31-8013

Willow Springs Center
690 Edison Way
Reno, NV 89502
Major participating institution for programs in: CHP
Institution ID: 31-8033

Sparks

Northern Nevada Adult Mental Health Services
Sparks, NV 89431
Med Sch Affil: G-03101
Major participating institution for programs in: P
Institution ID: 31-7002

New Hampshire
Concord

Concord Hospital
250 Pleasant Street
Concord, NH 03301
http://concordhospital.org
Med Sch Affil: M-03201
Programs sponsored in: FP
Major participating institution for programs in: GPM, U
Institution ID: 32-8002

New Hampshire Hospital
36 Clinton Street
Concord, NH 03301
Major participating institution for programs in: CHP
Institution ID: 32-8008

Lebanon

Mary Hitchcock Memorial Hospital
One Medical Center Drive
Lebanon, NH 03756-0001
www.dhmc.org/dept/gme
Programs sponsored in: ADP, AN, BBK, CCA, CCM, CD,
CHP, CN, D, DMP, DR, END, GE, GPM, GS, HMP, HO,
HPM, IC, ICE, ID, IM, MP, N, NEP, NPM, NS, OBG, ORS,
OTO, P, PCC, PCP, PD, PMM, PS, PTH, PYG, RHU, RNR,
SME, U, VIR, VS, VSI
Major participating institution for programs in: OTO
Institution ID: 32-8001

Nashua

Southern New Hampshire Medical Center
8 Prospect Street
PO Box 2014
Nashua, NH 03061
Major participating institution for programs in: OBG
Institution ID: 32-8007

New Jersey

Atlantic City

AtlantiCare Regional Medical Center
1925 Pacific Avenue
Department of Medical Education
Atlantic City, NJ 08401
www.AtlantiCare.org
Med Sch Affil: G-04115
Programs sponsored in: IM
Major participating institution for programs in: P
Institution ID: 33-0168

Belleville

Clara Maass Medical Center, Inc
1 Clara Maass Drive
Belleville, NJ 07109
Major participating institution for programs in: VS
Institution ID: 33-9029

Browns Mills

Deborah Heart and Lung Center
Trenton Road
Browns Mills, NJ 08015
Med Sch Affil: G-03306, G-04101, G-03305
Major participating institution for programs in: CD,
PCC
Institution ID: 33-0513

Camden

Cooper Hospital-University Medical Center
One Cooper Plaza
Camden, NJ 08103
http://cooperhealth.org
Med Sch Affil: M-03306, L-04113
Programs sponsored in: AN, CCM, CCP, CCS, CD, D, DR,
EM, GE, GS, HO, IC, ICE, ID, IM, N, NEP, OBG, OTR, P,
PCC, PD, PE, PRD, PS, RHU
Major participating institution for programs in: OSM,
PTH, U
Institution ID: 33-0465

Our Lady of Lourdes Medical Center
1600 Haddon Ave
Camden, NJ 08103
Major participating institution for programs in: GE
Institution ID: 33-0166

West Jersey Health System (Camden)
Mt Ephraim and Atlantic Avenues
Camden, NJ 08104
Med Sch Affil: M-04102
Major participating institution for programs in: OBG
Institution ID: 33-0719

Cherry Hill

DaVita Dialysis Center
1030 North Kings Highway
Suite 100
Cherry Hill, NJ 08034
Major participating institution for programs in: NEP
Institution ID: 33-9021

Kennedy Memorial Hospitals-University Med Ctr-Cherry Hill
c/o UMDNJ-School of Osteopathic Medicine
One Medical Center Drive, Office of GME, Suite 214
Cherry Hill, NJ 08084
Major participating institution for programs in: P
Institution ID: 33-9003

East Orange

Veterans Affairs New Jersey Health Care System
385 Tremont Avenue
East Orange, NJ 07018-1095
Med Sch Affil: M-03306, M-03305
Major participating institution for programs in: AI,
CD, D, END, GE, GS, ID, IM, N, NEP, OPH, OTO, P, PCC,
PM, PTH, PYG, RO, SCI, U
Institution ID: 33-0187

Edison

JFK Medical Center
65 James Street
Edison, NJ 08818-3059
www.Solarishs.org
Med Sch Affil: G-03306
Programs sponsored in: FP, PM
Major participating institution for programs in: CCM,
CN, CRS, N, SME
Institution ID: 33-0714

Elizabeth

Trinitas Hospital
225 Williamson Street
Elizabeth, NJ 07207
Major participating institution for programs in: IM, P
Institution ID: 33-0417

Englewood

Englewood Hospital and Medical Center
350 Engle Street
Englewood, NJ 07631
Med Sch Affil: M-04101, M-03547
Major participating institution for programs in: CCA,
CCM, IM, VS
Institution ID: 33-0259

Flemington

Hunterdon Medical Center
2100 Wescott Dr
Flemington, NJ 08822
www.hunterfpr.org
Med Sch Affil: L-03306
Programs sponsored in: FP
Institution ID: 33-0444

Freehold

CentraState Medical Center
901 West Main Street
Freehold, NJ 07728
Major participating institution for programs in: FP,
FPG
Institution ID: 33-8024

Hackensack

Hackensack University Medical Center
30 Prospect Avenue
Hackensack, NJ 07601
Med Sch Affil: M-03305
Major participating institution for programs in: AN,
CD, GS, ID, IM, IMG, MPD, NEP, NS, OBG, OTO, P, PCC,
PD, PS, PTH, U, VS
Institution ID: 33-0219

Skin Laser and Surgery Specialists of New York/New Jersey
20 Prospect Avenue, Suite 702
Hackensack, NJ 07601
Programs sponsored in: PRD
Institution ID: 33-8037

Hoboken

Hoboken Municipal Hospital
308 Willow Avenue
Hoboken, NJ 07030-3889
Med Sch Affil: G-03305
Major participating institution for programs in: FP
Institution ID: 33-0226

Jersey City

Jersey City Medical Center
355 Grand Street
Jersey City, NJ 07302
Med Sch Affil: M-03547, G-03305
Major participating institution for programs in: IM,
OBG, OPH
Institution ID: 33-0189

Livingston

St Barnabas Medical Center
94 Old Short Hills Rd
Livingston, NJ 07039
www.saintbarnabas.com
Med Sch Affil: M-03547
Programs sponsored in: AN, DR, GS, IM, OBG, PTH, TY
Major participating institution for programs in: NEP,
PD, U, VS
Institution ID: 33-0416

Long Branch

Monmouth Medical Center
300 Second Ave
Long Branch, NJ 07740
www.sbhcs.com/education/mmced/index.html
Med Sch Affil: M-04115, G-04101
Programs sponsored in: DR, GS, IM, OBG, ORS, PD
Major participating institution for programs in: PTH
Institution ID: 33-0335

Marlton

West Jersey Health System
401 Route 73N
50 Lake Center Drive
Marlton, NJ 08053
www.virtua.org
Programs sponsored in: FP
Institution ID: 33-8021

Montclair

Mountainside Hospital
1 Bay Avenue
Montclair, NJ 07042
Med Sch Affil: L-03306, G-03305
Programs sponsored in: FP, FSM, IM
Institution ID: 33-0217

Morristown

Affiliated Dermatologists and Dermatologic Surgeons
182 South Street, Suite 1
Morristown, NJ 07960
www.youthfullook.com
Programs sponsored in: PRD
Institution ID: 33-8025

Atlantic Health
475 South Steet
Morristown, NJ 07960
http://atlantichealth.org
Programs sponsored in: DR, EM, FP, GS, IM, OBG, PD, PE, TY
Institution ID: 33-8020

Morristown Memorial Hospital
Atlantic Health System
100 Madison Avenue
Morristown, NJ 07962-1956
Med Sch Affil: M-03305
Major participating institution for programs in: DR, EM, GS, IM, OBG, ORS, PD, PE, TY
Institution ID: 33-0236

Mount Holly

Virtua-Memorial Hospital Burlington County
175 Madison Ave
Mount Holly, NJ 08060-2099
Med Sch Affil: L-03306
Major participating institution for programs in: FP
Institution ID: 33-0171

Neptune

Jersey Shore University Medical Center
1945 Corlies Avenue
Neptune, NJ 07753
www.meridianhealth.com
Med Sch Affil: M-03306
Programs sponsored in: IM, IMG, OBG, PD, PSM
Major participating institution for programs in: END, GS, ID, ORS, P
Institution ID: 33-0220

New Brunswick

Robert Wood Johnson University Hospital
One Robert Wood Johnson Pl
New Brunswick, NJ 08901
Med Sch Affil: M-03306, L-04113, G-03305
Major participating institution for programs in: ACA, AN, CCP, CD, D, DR, END, FP, FPG, GE, GS, HMP, HO, IC, ID, IM, N, NEP, NPM, OBG, ORS, PCC, PD, PHO, PMM, PTH, RHU, RO, TS, U, VIR, VS
Institution ID: 33-0141

St Peter's University Hospital
254 Easton Avenue
New Brunswick, NJ 08901
www.saintpetersuh.com
Med Sch Affil: M-03306
Programs sponsored in: IM, OBG, PD
Major participating institution for programs in: DR, FSM, GS, ORS, PM
Institution ID: 33-0107

UMDNJ-Robert Wood Johnson Medical School
125 Paterson Street
New Brunswick, NJ 08903
http://rwjms.umdnj.edu
Med Sch Affil: M-03306
Programs sponsored in: ACA, AN, CCP, CD, CHP, CRS, D, DR, END, FP, FPG, FSM, GE, GPM, GS, HMP, HO, IC, ID, IM, N, NEP, NPM, OBG, ORS, P, PCC, PD, PHO, PMM, PTH, PYG, RHU, RO, TS, U, VIR, VS
Institution ID: 33-0522

Newark

Newark Beth Israel Medical Center
201 Lyons Ave
Newark, NJ 07112
Med Sch Affil: M-03547, L-03305
Programs sponsored in: CD, DR, EM, HO, IC, ID, IM, MPD, NEP, OBG, PCC, PD, PDC, PEM, VS
Major participating institution for programs in: CHP, GS
Institution ID: 33-0424

Newark Regional Medical Examiner Office
325 Norfolk Street
Newark, NJ 07103
Programs sponsored in: FOP
Institution ID: 33-8023

St Michael's Medical Center (A Member of Catholic Hlth East)
268 Dr Martin Luther King Jr Blvd
Newark, NJ 07102
Med Sch Affil: G-03305
Major participating institution for programs in: AN, CCM, CD, GE, HO, IC, ID, IM, PUD, VS
Institution ID: 33-0418

UMDNJ-New Jersey Medical School
30 Bergen Street ADMC 1107
PO Box 1709
Newark, NJ 07101-1709
www.umdnj.edu/njmsweb/
Med Sch Affil: M-03305, G-02312
Programs sponsored in: AI, AN, CCS, CD, CHN, CHP, D, DMP, DR, EM, END, FP, GE, GS, HSO, ID, IM, IMG, MG, MPD, N, NEP, NMN, NS, OBG, OMO, OPH, ORS, OTO, P, PCC, PD, PDI, PM, PS, PTH, SCI, U, VN, VS
Institution ID: 33-9502

UMDNJ-University Behavioral Health Care
183 South Orange Avenue
Newark, NJ 07101
Med Sch Affil: G-03305
Major participating institution for programs in: CHP, P
Institution ID: 33-8015

UMDNJ-University Hospital
150 Bergen Street, D 217
Newark, NJ 07103-2406
Med Sch Affil: M-03305
Major participating institution for programs in: AI, AN, CCS, CD, CHN, CHP, D, DMP, DR, EM, END, GE, GS, HSO, ID, IM, MG, MPD, N, NEP, NS, OBG, OMO, OPH, ORS, OTO, P, PCC, PD, PDI, PS, PTH, RO, U, VN, VS
Institution ID: 33-0274

Paramus

Bergen Regional Medical Center
230 East Ridgewood Avenue
Paramus, NJ 07652-4131
www.bergenregional.com
Med Sch Affil: G-03305
Programs sponsored in: P
Institution ID: 33-0109

Paterson

St Joseph's Regional Medical Center
703 Main Street
Paterson, NJ 07503-2691
Med Sch Affil: M-03547, L-03306, G-03305
Major participating institution for programs in: AN, CD, FP, GE, GS, HO, IC, IM, NEP, OBG, ORS, PD, PUD
Institution ID: 33-0319

Perth Amboy

Raritan Bay Medical Center-Perth Amboy Division
530 New Brunswick Ave
Perth Amboy, NJ 08861
www.rbmc.org
Programs sponsored in: IM
Major participating institution for programs in: OBG
Institution ID: 33-0144

Phillipsburg

Warren Hospital
185 Roseberry St
Phillipsburg, NJ 08865
www.warrenfp.com
Med Sch Affil: L-03306
Programs sponsored in: FP
Institution ID: 33-0138

Piscataway

UMDNJ-University Behavioral HealthCare
671 Hoes Lane
Piscataway, NJ 08854
Med Sch Affil: M-03306
Major participating institution for programs in: CHP, P, PYG
Institution ID: 33-0717

Plainfield

Muhlenberg Regional Medical Center
Park Ave & Randolph Road
Plainfield, NJ 07061
www.solarishs.org
Med Sch Affil: M-03306
Programs sponsored in: IM
Institution ID: 33-0137

Princeton

University Medical Center at Princeton
253 Witherspoon Street
Princeton, NJ 08542
Med Sch Affil: M-03306
Major participating institution for programs in: GS, IM, PCC, PYG, U
Institution ID: 33-0452

Somerville

Somerset Medical Center
110 Rehill Avenue
Somerville, NJ 08876
www.somersetmedicalcenter.com
Med Sch Affil: L-03306
Programs sponsored in: FP
Institution ID: 33-0356

South Orange

Seton Hall University School of Health and Medical Sciences
School of Health & Medical Sciences
400 South Orange Avenue
South Orange, NJ 07079-2689
http://gradmeded.shu.edu/
Programs sponsored in: CCM, CD, CN, GE, GS, HO, IC, ID, IM, N, ORS, P, PUD, SME
Institution ID: 33-9501

Stratford

UMDNJ-School of Osteopathic Medicine
One Medical Center Drive
Office of Graduate Medical Education, Suite 162
Stratford, NJ 08084
http://som.umdnj.edu
Programs sponsored in: P
Institution ID: 33-9004

Summit

Overlook Hospital
Atlantic Health System
99 Beauvoir Avenue at Sylvan Road
Summit, NJ 07902
Med Sch Affil: L-03501, G-03305
Major participating institution for programs in: CRS, DR, FP, GS, IM, OBG, TY
Institution ID: 33-0240

Trenton

Ann Klein Forensic Center
Stuyvesant Avenue
PO Box 7717
Trenton, NJ 08628
Major participating institution for programs in: PFP
Institution ID: 33-8038

Capital Health System - Mercer Campus
446 Belleview Avenue
Trenton, NJ 08618-4597
Major participating institution for programs in: FP
Institution ID: 33-0228

Capital Health System-Fuld Campus
750 Brunswick Avenue
Trenton, NJ 08638
www.capitalhealth.com
Med Sch Affil: G-03306
Programs sponsored in: IM
Major participating institution for programs in: FP
Institution ID: 33-0150

St Francis Medical Center
601 Hamilton Ave
Trenton, NJ 08629
Major participating institution for programs in: GS, IM
Institution ID: 33-0415

Voorhees

Virtua-West Jersey Hospital Voorhees
101 Carnie Blvd
Voorhees, NJ 08043
Med Sch Affil: L-04113
Major participating institution for programs in: FP
Institution ID: 33-8018

West Orange

Kessler Institute for Rehabilitation
1199 Pleasant Valley Way
West Orange, NJ 07052-1419
Med Sch Affil: M-03305
Major participating institution for programs in: PM, SCI
Institution ID: 33-0726

Woodbury

Underwood-Memorial Hospital
509 N Broad Street
Woodbury, NJ 08096
www.umhospital.org
Med Sch Affil: L-04113
Programs sponsored in: FP
Institution ID: 33-7079

New Mexico

Albuquerque

Lovelace Sandia Health
5400 Gibson Boulevard, SE
Albuquerque, NM 87108
Med Sch Affil: G-03401
Major participating institution for programs in: GS
Institution ID: 34-0196

New Mexico Orthopaedics Fellowship Foundation
201 Cedar SE
Suite 6600
Albuquerque, NM 87106
Programs sponsored in: OSM
Institution ID: 34-8021

Office of the Medical Investigator
University of New Mexico
School of Medicine
Albuquerque, NM 87131
Med Sch Affil: G-03401
Major participating institution for programs in: FOP
Institution ID: 34-0508

Presbyterian Healthcare Services
5901 Harper Drive, NE
PO Box 26666
Albuquerque, NM 87125-6666
Major participating institution for programs in: OTO, PCP
Institution ID: 34-0507

Sandia National Laboratories
2101 Louisiana Boulevard
Albuquerque, NM 87110
Major participating institution for programs in: GPM
Institution ID: 34-8022

University of New Mexico Hospital
University Hospital
2211 Lomas Blvd, NE
Albuquerque, NM 87106
Med Sch Affil: M-03401
Major participating institution for programs in: ADP, AN, BBK, CCM, CD, CHN, CHP, CN, D, DR, EM, END, FP, FSM, GE, GS, HMP, HO, HSO, ID, IM, IMG, MGP, N, NEP, NPM, NS, OBG, ORS, OSM, OTO, OTR, P, PAN, PCC, PD, PMM, PTH, PYG, RHU, RNR, SME, TS, U, VIR
Institution ID: 34-0498

University of New Mexico School of Medicine
MSC09 5300
2500 Marble NE
Albuquerque, NM 87131-0001
http://hsc.unm.edu/gme/
Med Sch Affil: M-03401
Programs sponsored in: ADP, AN, BBK, CCM, CD, CHN, CHP, CN, D, DR, EM, END, FOP, FP, FSM, GE, GS, HMP, HO, HSO, ID, IM, IMG, MGP, N, NEP, NPM, NS, OBG, ORS, OSM, OTO, OTR, P, PAN, PCC, PCP, PD, PMM, PTH, PYG, RHU, RNR, SME, TS, U, VIR
Institution ID: 34-0510

Veterans Affairs Medical Center (Albuquerque)
1501 San Pedro Dr SE
Albuquerque, NM 87108
Med Sch Affil: M-03401
Major participating institution for programs in: ADP, CCM, CD, CHN, D, END, GE, GS, HO, ID, IM, IMG, N, NEP, NS, ORS, OTO, P, PCC, PTH, PYG, RHU, RNR, TS, U, VIR
Institution ID: 34-0499

Las Cruces

Memorial Medical Center
2450 South Telshor Boulevard
Las Cruces, NM 88011
www.mmclc.org
Med Sch Affil: M-03401
Programs sponsored in: FP
Institution ID: 34-8014

Roswell

Eastern New Mexico Medical Center
405 W Country Club Road
Roswell, NM 88201
Med Sch Affil: G-03401
Major participating institution for programs in: FP
Institution ID: 34-8016

Santa Fe

St Vincent Hospital
455 St Michael's Dr
PO Box 2107
Santa Fe, NM 87505
Med Sch Affil: G-03401
Major participating institution for programs in: FP
Institution ID: 34-8015

Taos

Taos Orthopaedic Institute and Research Foundation
1219 Gusdorf Road Suite A
Taos, NM 87571
www.taosortho.com
Programs sponsored in: OSM
Institution ID: 34-8019

New York

Albany

Albany Medical Center
43 New Scotland Avenue
Mailcode 50
Albany, NY 12208
www.amc.edu
Med Sch Affil: M-03503
Programs sponsored in: AN, CD, CN, DR, EM, END, FP, GE, GS, HMP, IC, IM, MPD, N, NPM, NS, OBG, OPH, ORS, OTO, P, PCC, PD, PM, PS, PSI, PTH, RHU, TS, U, VIR, VN, VS
Institution ID: 35-0345

Albany Medical Center South Clinical Campus
25 Hackett Blvd
Albany, NY 12208
Med Sch Affil: G-03503
Major participating institution for programs in: OTO, PS, PSI
Institution ID: 35-0515

Capital District Psychiatric Center
75 New Scotland Ave
Albany, NY 12208
Med Sch Affil: M-03503
Major participating institution for programs in: P
Institution ID: 35-0815

New York State Department of Health
Corning Tower, Room 649
Empire State Plaza
Albany, NY 12237
www.albany.edu/sph/residencies/pmr_main.htm
Programs sponsored in: GPM
Institution ID: 35-0456

St Peter's Hospital
315 S Manning Blvd
Albany, NY 12208
Med Sch Affil: M-03503
Major participating institution for programs in: FP, OBG, ORS, OTO, PSI, U
Institution ID: 35-0103

SUNY at Albany School of Public Health
2 University Place
Albany, NY 12003
Major participating institution for programs in: GPM
Institution ID: 35-8036

Teaching Institutions

Veterans Affairs Medical Center (Albany)
113 Holland Avenue
Albany, NY 12208
Med Sch Affil: M-03503
Major participating institution for programs in: CD,
DR, GE, GS, IM, MPD, OPH, ORS, OTO, P, PCC, PM, PSI,
PTH, RHU, U
Institution ID: 35-0151

Bay Shore

Southside Hospital
301 East Main Street
Bay Shore, NY 11706-8458
http://southsidehospital.org
Med Sch Affil: L-03548
Major participating institution for programs in: FP,
PM
Institution ID: 35-0556

Binghamton

Binghamton General Hospital
10-42 Mitchell Avenue
Binghamton, NY 13903
Major participating institution for programs in: FPG,
IM
Institution ID: 35-8068

Binghamton Psychiatric Center
425 Robinson Street
Binghamton, NY 13901
Major participating institution for programs in: PYG
Institution ID: 35-0261

Briarwood

Silvercrest Extended Care Facility
144-45 87th Avenue
Briarwood, NY 11435
Major participating institution for programs in: IMG
Institution ID: 35-8072

Bronx

Albert Einstein College of Medicine of Yeshiva University
1300 Morris Park Avenue
Belfer Room 312
Bronx, NY 10461
www.aecom.yu.edu
Med Sch Affil: M-03546
Programs sponsored in: ACA, ADL, ADP, AI, AN, AR,
CCM, CCP, CD, CHN, CHP, CN, D, DBP, DMP, DR, EM,
END, FP, GE, GS, HMP, HO, HPM, IC, ICE, ID, IM, IMG,
MG, MSR, N, NEP, NM, NP, NPM, NS, OBG, OPH, ORS,
OTO, P, PCC, PCP, PD, PDE, PDI, PDP, PDR, PEM, PFP,
PG, PHO, PM, PN, PPR, PS, PTH, PYG, PYM, RHU, RNR,
RO, SME, TS, U, VIR, VS
Institution ID: 35-0745

Bronx Children's Psychiatric Center
1000 Waters Place
Bronx, NY 10461
Major participating institution for programs in: CHP
Institution ID: 35-8039

Bronx Psychiatric Center
1500 Waters Place
Bronx, NY 10461
Med Sch Affil: M-03546
Major participating institution for programs in: P,
PFP
Institution ID: 35-0542

Bronx-Lebanon Hospital Center
1650 Grand Concourse
Bronx, NY 10457
www.bronx-leb.org/
Med Sch Affil: M-03546
Programs sponsored in: ADP, CHP, DR, FP, GS, IM, OBG,
OPH, P, PD, PUD
Major participating institution for programs in: ADP,
CD
Institution ID: 35-0352

Lincoln Medical and Mental Health Center
234 Eugenio Mario De Hostos Boulevard (149th) St
Bronx, NY 10451-9998
Med Sch Affil: M-03520
Programs sponsored in: CCS, EM, IM, OBG, P, PD
Major participating institution for programs in: D,
DR, GS, GS, U
Institution ID: 35-0437

Melrose-On-Track(MOT) Clinic
260 East 161st Street
Bronx, NY 10451
Major participating institution for programs in: ADP
Institution ID: 35-8103

Montefiore Medical Center - North Division
600 E 233rd St
Bronx, NY 10466
Med Sch Affil: M-03509, G-03508
Major participating institution for programs in: CD,
D, GE, HO, IM, IMG, NEP, OBG, OPH
Institution ID: 35-0401

Montefiore Medical Center-Henry and Lucy Moses Division
Bronx, NY 10467
Med Sch Affil: M-03546
Major participating institution for programs in: ACA,
ADL, ADP, AN, BBK, CCM, CCP, CD, CHN, CHP, CN, D,
DMP, DR, EM, END, FP, GE, GS, HMP, HO, HPM, IC, ICE,
ID, IM, IMG, MG, N, NEP, NM, NP, NS, OBG, OPH, ORS,
OTO, P, PCC, PCP, PD, PDE, PDI, PDP, PDR, PEM, PG,
PHO, PM, PN, PPR, PS, PTH, PYG, PYM, RHU, RNR, RO,
SME, TS, U, VIR, VS
Institution ID: 35-0526

Montefiore Medical Center-Weiler Division
Bronx, NY 10461
Med Sch Affil: M-03546
Major participating institution for programs in: ACA,
AI, AN, AR, CCM, CD, CHN, D, DMP, GS, HO, IC, MG,
MSR, N, NEP, NM, NPM, OBG, OPH, ORS, PDE, PDI, PM,
PTH, PYM, RHU, RO, TS, U, VIR
Institution ID: 35-0543

North Bronx Healthcare Network-Jacobi Medical Center
Bronx, NY 10461
Med Sch Affil: M-03546
Major participating institution for programs in: CHN,
D, DR, EM, END, GE, GS, HO, IEC, IM, N, NEP, OBG,
OPH, ORS, OTO, PCC, PD, PEM, PM, PS, RHU
Institution ID: 35-0179

North Bronx Healthcare Network-North Central Bronx Hospital
Bronx, NY 10467-2490
Major participating institution for programs in: D,
END, IM, NEP, OPH, RHU
Institution ID: 35-0784

Sound View Throgs Neck Community Mental Health Center
2527 Glebe Avenue
Bronx, NY 10461
Major participating institution for programs in: ADP
Institution ID: 35-8104

St Barnabas Hospital
183rd St and Third Ave
Bronx, NY 10457
www.stbarnabashospital.org
Med Sch Affil: L-03520
Programs sponsored in: IM, PD
Major participating institution for programs in: GE
Institution ID: 35-0348

Veterans Affairs Medical Center (Bronx)
130 West Kingsbridge Road
Bronx, NY 10468
Med Sch Affil: M-03547
Major participating institution for programs in: ADP,
CCM, CD, GE, IM, OPH, OTO, P, PM, PS, PTH, PYG, PYM,
SCI, U, VS
Institution ID: 35-0247

Brooklyn

Brookdale University Hospital and Medical Center
Linden Blvd at Brookdale Plaza
Brooklyn, NY 11212-3198
http://brookdalehospital.org
Med Sch Affil: M-03508
Programs sponsored in: AN, CHP, GS, HO, IM, NEP, P,
PD, U
Major participating institution for programs in: CD,
GE, ICE, OPH, ORS, P
Institution ID: 35-0307

Brooklyn Children's Center
1819 Bergen Street
Brooklyn, NY 11233
Major participating institution for programs in: CHP
Institution ID: 35-8102

Brooklyn Hospital Center
121 DeKalb Avenue
Brooklyn, NY 11201
TBH.org
Med Sch Affil: M-03520, L-03508, G-03519
Programs sponsored in: EM, FP, GE, GS, HO, IM, OBG,
PD, PUD
Major participating institution for programs in: CD
Institution ID: 35-0202

Coney Island Hospital
2601 Ocean Parkway
Brooklyn, NY 11235
Med Sch Affil: L-03508
Programs sponsored in: IM
Major participating institution for programs in: CD,
GE, GS, HO, ID, OBG, OPH, PD, TY, U
Institution ID: 35-0469

Interfaith Medical Center
1545 Atlantic Avenue
Brooklyn, NY 11213
www.interfaithmedical.com
Med Sch Affil: L-03508
Programs sponsored in: IM, PUD
Major participating institution for programs in: GE
Institution ID: 35-0347

Kings County Hospital Center
451 Clarkson Ave
Brooklyn, NY 11203
Med Sch Affil: M-03508
Major participating institution for programs in: ADL,
AI, AN, CD, CHN, CHP, CN, D, DMP, DR, EM, END, FP,
GE, GS, HO, IM, IMG, MEM, MP, N, NP, OBG, OPH, ORS,
OTO, P, PD, PDE, PDI, PDP, PG, PM, PP, PTH, RHU, RNR,
RO, U, VIR
Institution ID: 35-0109

Kingsboro Psychiatric Center
681 Clarkson Ave
Brooklyn, NY 11203
Med Sch Affil: L-03508
Major participating institution for programs in: PYG
Institution ID: 35-0231

Kingsbrook Jewish Medical Center
585 Schenectady Ave
Brooklyn, NY 11203-1891
http://kingsbrook.org
Med Sch Affil: G-03508
Programs sponsored in: IM, ORS, PM
Major participating institution for programs in: MP, PYG
Institution ID: 35-0387

Leading Edge Radiation Oncology Services
8715 5th Avenue
Brooklyn, NY 11209
Major participating institution for programs in: RO
Institution ID: 35-8188

Long Island College Hospital
Department of GME
339 Hicks Street
Brooklyn, NY 11201-5541
Med Sch Affil: M-03508
Programs sponsored in: AI, DR, GE, IM, NEP, OBG
Major participating institution for programs in: AN, CD, GS, HO, ID, N, OPH, ORS, OTO, PD, RO, U
Institution ID: 35-0439

Lutheran Medical Center
150 55th St
Brooklyn, NY 11220
http://lutheranmedicalcenter.com
Med Sch Affil: L-03508
Programs sponsored in: FP, IM, OBG
Major participating institution for programs in: IMG, VIR
Institution ID: 35-0449

Maimonides Medical Center
4802 Tenth Ave
Brooklyn, NY 11219
www.maimonidesmed.org
Med Sch Affil: M-03508
Programs sponsored in: AN, CCM, CD, DR, EM, GE, GS, HO, IC, ID, IM, IMG, NEP, OBG, ORS, P, PD, PE, PUD, TY, U, VS
Major participating institution for programs in: DR, N, PDE, TS, VN
Institution ID: 35-0366

Millennium Dialysis Center
1408 Ocean Avenue
Brooklyn, NY 11230
Major participating institution for programs in: NEP
Institution ID: 35-8135

New York Methodist Hospital
506 Sixth Street
Brooklyn, NY 11215
Med Sch Affil: L-03520, L-03508
Programs sponsored in: AN, CD, EM, GE, GS, HO, IC, IM, IMG, OBG, PCC, PD, RO
Institution ID: 35-0267

SUNY Health Science Center at Brooklyn
GME Office
450 Clarkson Avenue, Box 51
Brooklyn, NY 11203-2098
www.hscbklyn.edu/
Programs sponsored in: ADL, AI, AN, CCA, CD, CHN, CHP, CN, D, DMP, DR, EM, END, FP, GE, GS, HO, IC, ICE, ID, IM, IMG, MEM, MP, N, NEP, NP, OBG, OPH, ORS, OTO, P, PCC, PD, PDE, PDI, PDP, PG, PM, PN, PP, PRD, PTH, PYG, RHU, RNR, RO, TS, U, VIR
Institution ID: 35-9502

University Hospital-SUNY Health Science Center at Brooklyn
445 Lenox Road
Box 23
Brooklyn, NY 11203
Med Sch Affil: M-03508
Major participating institution for programs in: ADL, AI, AN, CCA, CD, CHN, CN, D, DMP, DR, EM, END, FP, GE, GS, HO, IC, ICE, ID, IM, IMG, MEM, MP, N, NEP, NP, OBG, OTO, PD, PDE, PDI, PDP, PG, PM, PN, PP, PRD, PTH, PYG, RHU, RNR, RO, TS
Institution ID: 35-0541

Veterans Affairs Medical Center (Brooklyn)
800 Poly Place
Brooklyn, NY 11209-7104
Med Sch Affil: M-03508, G-03519
Major participating institution for programs in: CD, D, END, GE, GS, HO, IM, IMG, MEM, MP, NEP, OPH, ORS, OTO, PRD, PTH, PYG, RHU, U
Institution ID: 35-0331

Woodhull Medical and Mental Health Center
760 Broadway
Brooklyn, NY 11206-5317
Med Sch Affil: L-03508
Programs sponsored in: IM, PD
Major participating institution for programs in: END, GE, GS
Institution ID: 35-0825

Wyckoff Heights Medical Center
374 Stockholm Street
Brooklyn, NY 11237
wyckoffhospital.org
Med Sch Affil: L-03520
Programs sponsored in: FP, IM
Major participating institution for programs in: GE, HO, OBG, OPH, PD, PUD
Institution ID: 35-0412

Buffalo

Buffalo Psychiatric Center
Del-Nor Day Treatment Center
737 Delaware Avenue
Buffalo, NY 14209
Major participating institution for programs in: P, PYG
Institution ID: 35-0344

Erie County Medical Center
462 Grider Street
Buffalo, NY 14215
Med Sch Affil: M-03506
Major participating institution for programs in: AN, CD, EM, END, FP, FSM, GE, GS, HEM, HSO, ID, IM, MN, MPD, NEP, ORS, OSM, OTO, P, PM, PMM, PPM, PYG, RHU, U
Institution ID: 35-0413

Kaleida Health System (Buffalo General Hospital)
Buffalo, NY 14203
Med Sch Affil: M-03506
Major participating institution for programs in: ACA, AI, AN, CRS, EM, FP, FSM, GPM, GS, IM, IPM, MN, MPD, N, NM, NS, OAR, ORS, OTO, P, PCC, PM, PPM, PTH, RHU, U
Institution ID: 35-0482

Kaleida Health System (Millard Fillmore Hospital)
3 Gates Circle
Buffalo, NY 14209-9986
Med Sch Affil: M-03506
Major participating institution for programs in: ACA, AN, CD, CN, END, FP, FSM, GS, HSO, IMG, N, NS, OBG, ORS, OSM, OTO, P, PTH, PYG, U, VN, VS
Institution ID: 35-0330

Kaleida Health System (Women and Children's Hosp of Buffalo)
219 Bryant Street
Buffalo, NY 14222
Med Sch Affil: M-03506
Programs sponsored in: PDR
Major participating institution for programs in: AI, AN, CCP, CHN, CHP, CN, D, EM, MPD, NPM, NS, OBG, OPH, ORS, OTO, P, PAN, PD, PDE, PDS, PEM, PG, PHO, PN, PPM, U
Institution ID: 35-0223

Mercy Hospital of Buffalo
565 Abbott Rd
Buffalo, NY 14220
Med Sch Affil: L-03506
Major participating institution for programs in: IM, NM
Institution ID: 35-0126

Roswell Park Cancer Institute
Elm & Carlton Streets
Buffalo, NY 14263
www.roswellpark.org
Med Sch Affil: M-03506
Major participating institution for programs in: AN, D, GPM, HEM, ID, NM, NS, ON, OTO, PMM, RO, SP
Institution ID: 35-0451

Sisters of Charity Hospital
2157 Main St
Buffalo, NY 14214
Med Sch Affil: L-03506
Major participating institution for programs in: IM, OBG, PPM
Institution ID: 35-0157

University at Buffalo Affiliated Physician Practices (UBAPP)
117 Cary Hall
3435 Main Street
Buffalo, NY 14213
Major participating institution for programs in: FP, OPH, ORS, PG
Institution ID: 35-8176

University at Buffalo Physician Practices (UBPP)
117 Cary Hall
3435 Main Street
Buffalo, NY 14214
Major participating institution for programs in: FP, HEM, PYG, SME
Institution ID: 35-8175

University at Buffalo School of Medicine
3435 Main St
117 Cary Hall
Buffalo, NY 14214
http://wings.buffalo.edu/smbs/GME/
Med Sch Affil: M-03506, L-03515
Programs sponsored in: ACA, AI, AN, CCP, CD, CHN, CHP, CN, CRS, D, EM, END, FP, FSM, GE, GPM, GS, HEM, HPM, HSO, ID, IM, IMG, IPM, MN, MPD, N, NEP, NM, NPM, NS, OAR, OBG, ON, OPH, ORS, OSM, OTO, P, PAN, PCC, PD, PDE, PDS, PEM, PG, PHO, PM, PMM, PN, PPM, PTH, PYG, RHU, RO, SME, SP, U, VN, VS
Institution ID: 35-9501

Veterans Affairs Western New York Hospital
Buffalo, NY 14215
Med Sch Affil: M-03506
Major participating institution for programs in: ACA, AN, CD, CN, D, END, GE, GS, HEM, ID, IM, IMG, NEP, NM, OPH, OTO, P, PCC, PM, PPM, PYG, SME, U, VS
Institution ID: 35-0466

Cheektowaga

Center for Hospice and Palliative Care/Hospice Buffalo
225 Como Park Blvd
Cheektowaga, NY 14227
Major participating institution for programs in: HPM
Institution ID: 35-8143

Commack

Gurwin Jewish Geriatric Center
68 Hauppauge Road
Commack, NY 11725
Major participating institution for programs in: IMG
Institution ID: 35-8097

Cooperstown

Bassett Healthcare
Office of Medical Education
1 Atwell Road
Cooperstown, NY 13326
www.bassett.edu
Med Sch Affil: M-03503, M-03501, M-03201, M-03545
Programs sponsored in: GS, IM, TY
Institution ID: 35-8049

Mary Imogene Bassett Hospital
One Atwell Rd
Cooperstown, NY 13326-1394
Med Sch Affil: M-03501
Major participating institution for programs in: GS, IM
Institution ID: 35-0134

Dobbs Ferry

Children's Village (Dobbs Ferry)
Childrens Village
Dobbs Ferry, NY 10522
Major participating institution for programs in: CHP
Institution ID: 35-8071

East Meadow

Nassau University Medical Center
2201 Hempstead Turnpike
East Meadow, NY 11554-1854
www.numc.edu
Med Sch Affil: M-03548
Programs sponsored in: AN, DR, END, GE, GS, IM, NEP, OBG, ON, OPH, P, PD, PM, PS, PTH
Major participating institution for programs in: RHU
Institution ID: 35-0162

Elmhurst

Elmhurst Hospital Center-Mount Sinai Services
79-01 Broadway
Elmhurst, NY 11373
Med Sch Affil: M-03547, G-03519
Major participating institution for programs in: CD, CHP, D, EM, GE, GS, HSO, ID, IM, MPD, NEP, NS, OBG, OPH, ORS, OTO, P, PCC, PD, PM, PS, PYG, SCI, U
Institution ID: 35-0271

Far Rockaway

St John's Episcopal Hospital-South Shore
327 Beach 19th Street
Far Rockaway, NY 11691
www.ehs.org/sshr/ml/resmed.html
Med Sch Affil: G-03508
Programs sponsored in: IM
Major participating institution for programs in: MP, PM
Institution ID: 35-0244

Flushing

Eye Care Center
161-10 Union Turnpike
Flushing, NY 11366
Major participating institution for programs in: OPH
Institution ID: 35-8142

Flushing Hospital Medical Center
45th Avenue at Parsons Blvd
Flushing, NY 11355
www.flushinghospital.org
Med Sch Affil: G-03508
Programs sponsored in: IM, IMG, OBG, PD, TY
Major participating institution for programs in: ADP, P, PYM
Institution ID: 35-0364

New York Hospital Medical Center of Queens
56-45 Main St
Flushing, NY 11355-5095
www.gmeatnyhq.org
Med Sch Affil: M-03520
Programs sponsored in: CD, EM, GE, GS, ID, IM, IMG, NEP, PCC, RO, TY
Major participating institution for programs in: OBG, ORS
Institution ID: 35-0349

Forest Hills

Forest Hills Hospital
102-01 66th Rd
Forest Hills, NY 11375
www.nslij.com
Major participating institution for programs in: IM
Institution ID: 35-0568

Glen Cove

North Shore University Hospital at Glen Cove
101 St Andrews Lane
Glen Cove, NY 11542
Med Sch Affil: L-03548
Major participating institution for programs in: FP, PM
Institution ID: 35-0409

Glen Oaks

Hillside Hospital (Long Island Jewish Medical Center)
75-59 263rd St
Glen Oaks, NY 11004
Major participating institution for programs in: P, PYG
Institution ID: 35-0299

Great Neck

North Shore-Long Island Jewish Health System
145 Community Drive
Great Neck, NY 11021
www.northshorelij.com
Med Sch Affil: M-03546
Programs sponsored in: ADL, ADP, AI, CCP, CCS, CD, CHN, CHP, CN, CRS, DBP, DR, EM, END, ESM, ETX, FP, GE, GS, HO, HPM, IC, ID, IEC, IM, IMG, N, NEP, NM, NPM, OBG, OPH, ORS, P, PCC, PCP, PD, PDC, PDE, PDI, PDR, PDS, PEM, PG, PHO, PM, PPR, PTH, PYG, PYM, RHU, RNR, SME, TS, U, UP, VIR, VS
Institution ID: 35-8024

Harrison

St Vincent Catholic Medical Centers (Westchester)
240 North St
Harrison, NY 10528
Major participating institution for programs in: P
Institution ID: 35-0490

Hauppauge

Suffolk County Department of Health Services
225 Rabro Drive, E
Hauppauge, NY 11788
Med Sch Affil: G-03548
Major participating institution for programs in: GPM
Institution ID: 35-8021

Holliswood

Holliswood Hospital
87-37 Palermo Street
Holliswood, NY 11423
Major participating institution for programs in: CHP
Institution ID: 35-8133

Jamaica

Caritas Health Care (Brooklyn-Queens)
152-11 89th Avenue
Jamaica, NY 11432
Med Sch Affil: L-03508
Major participating institution for programs in: CD, FP, GS, ID, IM, IMG, OBG, OPH, ORS, P, PUD
Institution ID: 35-0558

Jamaica Hospital Medical Center
89th Ave and Van Wyck Expwy
Jamaica, NY 11418
http://jamaicahospital.org/
Med Sch Affil: L-03520, G-03508, G-03519
Programs sponsored in: FP, IM, OBG, P, PYM
Major participating institution for programs in: GS, HSO, ORS, PD, PM
Institution ID: 35-0216

Queens Hospital Center
82-68 164th Street
D-116
Jamaica, NY 11432
Med Sch Affil: M-03547
Major participating institution for programs in: D, IM, NEP, OBG, OPH, PCC, U
Institution ID: 35-0220

Johnson City

United Health Services Hospitals
33-57 Harrison Street
Johnson City, NY 13790
www.uhs.net
Programs sponsored in: FP, FPG, FSM, IM, TY
Institution ID: 35-0463

Wilson Medical Center (United Health System)
33-57 Harrison Street
Johnson City, NY 13790
Major participating institution for programs in: FP, FPG, FSM, IM, TY
Institution ID: 35-0110

Kingston

Kingston Hospital
396 Broadway
Kingston, NY 12401
Major participating institution for programs in: FP
Institution ID: 35-0435

Manhasset

North Shore University Hospital
300 Community Drive
Manhasset, NY 11030
Med Sch Affil: M-03519
Major participating institution for programs in: ADP,
CCS, CD, CN, CRS, DR, EM, END, ESM, ETX, GE, GS, HO,
IC, ID, IM, N, NEP, NM, OBG, OPH, ORS, PCC, PDI, PS,
PTH, PYM, RHU, RNR, SME, VS
Institution ID: 35-0467

Schneider Children's Hospital at North Shore University Hosp
North Shore-Long Island Jewish Health System
300 Community Drive
Manhasset, NY 11030-3876
Major participating institution for programs in: ADL,
NPM, PD, PDI, UP
Institution ID: 35-8064

Mineola

Long Island Regional Poison and Drug Information Center
259 First Street
Mineola, NY 11501
Major participating institution for programs in: ETX
Institution ID: 35-8092

Nassau County Department of Health
240 Old Country Road
Mineola, NY 11501
Major participating institution for programs in: GPM
Institution ID: 35-8022

Winthrop-University Hospital
259 First Street
Mineola, NY 11501
www.winthrop.org
Med Sch Affil: M-03548
Programs sponsored in: AI, CD, DR, END, GE, HO, IC,
ID, IM, IMG, NEP, OBG, PCC, PD, PDE, PDP, PTH, RHU,
SME
Major participating institution for programs in: AN,
CRS, GS, ORS, PS, VS
Institution ID: 35-0375

Mount Vernon

Mount Vernon Hospital
12 North Seventh Avenue
Mount Vernon, NY 10550-2026
Med Sch Affil: L-03509
Programs sponsored in: IM
Institution ID: 35-0255

New Hampton

Mid-Hudson Forensic Psychiatric Center
PO Box 159, Route 17 M
New Hampton, NY 10928
Major participating institution for programs in: PFP
Institution ID: 35-8054

New Hyde Park

Long Island Jewish Medical Center
270-05 76th Avenue
New Hyde Park, NY 11040
Med Sch Affil: M-03546, L-03508
Programs sponsored in: MEM
Major participating institution for programs in: ADL,
AI, CD, CHN, CHP, CN, CRS, DR, EM, END, ESM, GE, GS,
HO, IC, ID, IEC, IM, IMG, N, NEP, NM, OBG, OPH, ORS,
OTO, PCC, PCP, PDR, PM, PTH, PYG, PYM, RHU, RNR,
SME, TS, U, UP, VIR, VS
Institution ID: 35-0232

Schneider Children's Hospital at Long Island Jewish Med Ctr
North Shore-Long Island Jewish Health System
269-01 76th Avenue
New Hyde Park, NY 11040
Major participating institution for programs in: ADL,
CCP, CHN, DBP, ETX, NPM, PD, PDC, PDI, PDS, PEM,
PG, PHO, PPR, SME, U
Institution ID: 35-8061

New Rochelle

Sound Shore Medical Center of Westchester
16 Guion Place
New Rochelle, NY 10802
Med Sch Affil: M-03509
Major participating institution for programs in: CD,
END, GE, GS, HO, IM, RHU, TY
Institution ID: 35-0104

New York

Academy of Dermatopathology
145 E 32nd Street
10th Fl
New York, NY 10016
Major participating institution for programs in: DMP
Institution ID: 35-8052

Barnard College Student Health Services
3009 Broadway
Lower Level, Brooks Hall
New York, NY 10027
Major participating institution for programs in: ADL
Institution ID: 35-8124

Bellevue Hospital Center
462 First Avenue
New York, NY 10016
Med Sch Affil: M-03519
Major participating institution for programs in: ACA,
ADP, AN, CCA, CD, CHN, CHP, D, DBP, DMP, DR, EM,
END, ETX, GE, GS, HMP, HO, HSO, HSP, ICE, ID, IM,
IMG, MSR, N, NEP, NO, NP, NPM, NRN, NS, OBG, OPH,
ORS, OTO, P, PCC, PCP, PD, PDC, PDE, PDI, PDR, PEM,
PFP, PM, PMM, PP, PS, PTH, PYG, PYM, PYN, RHU, RNR,
SME, TS, U, VIR, VS
Institution ID: 35-0235

Beth Israel Medical Center
First Avenue at 16th Street
New York, NY 10003
http://intranet.chpnet.org/bimc/index.html
Med Sch Affil: M-03546
Programs sponsored in: ADP, AR, CD, DR, EM, END, FP,
GE, GS, HMP, HO, HPM, HSO, IC, ICE, ID, IM, N, NEP,
OAR, OBG, P, PCC, PMM, PYG, PYM, RNR, U, VIR
Major participating institution for programs in: D,
IMG, OTO, PTH
Institution ID: 35-0284

Cabrini Medical Center
227 East 19th Street
New York, NY 10003
Med Sch Affil: M-03547
Major participating institution for programs in: END
Institution ID: 35-0410

Clinilabs
423 West 55th St, F4
New York, NY 10019
Major participating institution for programs in: SME
Institution ID: 35-8116

Columbia University School of Public Health
617 West 168th Street
New York, NY 10032
Med Sch Affil: L-03501
Major participating institution for programs in: GPM
Institution ID: 35-0766

Goldwater Memorial Hospital
F D Roosevelt Island
New York, NY 10044
Med Sch Affil: L-03508, G-03519
Major participating institution for programs in: IMG
Institution ID: 35-0122

Harlem Hospital Center
506 Lenox Ave
New York, NY 10037
www.ci.nyc.ny.us/html/hhc/html/facilities/harlem.shtml
Med Sch Affil: M-03501
Programs sponsored in: CHP, DR, GE, GS, ID, IM, NEP,
P, PD, PUD
Institution ID: 35-0195

Hospital for Special Surgery
535 East 70th Street
New York, NY 10021
www.hss.edu
Med Sch Affil: M-03520
Programs sponsored in: HSO, OAR, OFA, OP, ORS, OSM,
OSS, OTR
Major participating institution for programs in: OMO,
OSM, PMM, PPR, RHU
Institution ID: 35-0459

Jewish Home and Hospital Lifecare System
120 West 106th Street
New York, NY 10025
Major participating institution for programs in: IMG
Institution ID: 35-8127

Kirby Forensic Psychiatric Center
Ward's Island
New York, NY 10035
Major participating institution for programs in: PFP
Institution ID: 35-8123

Laser and Skin Surgery Center of New York
317 East 34th Street
New York, NY 10016
Programs sponsored in: PRD
Major participating institution for programs in: PRD
Institution ID: 35-8095

Lenox Hill Hospital
100 E 77th St
New York, NY 10021-1896
www.lenoxhillhospital.org
Med Sch Affil: M-03519, L-03508, G-02416
Programs sponsored in: CD, DR, GE, GS, HO, IC, IM,
NEP, OAR, OBG, ORS, OSM, PTH, PUD, U
Major participating institution for programs in: CN,
OTO, P
Institution ID: 35-0334

Manhattan Eye, Ear & Throat Hospital
210 East 64th Street
New York, NY 10021
Med Sch Affil: M-03519
Major participating institution for programs in: OPH
Institution ID: 35-0367

Manhattan Psychiatric Center
Ward's Island Complex
New York, NY 10035
Med Sch Affil: L-03519
Major participating institution for programs in: P,
PYG
Institution ID: 35-0239

Manhattan VA Harbor Health Care System
423 E 23rd St
New York, NY 10010
Med Sch Affil: M-03519
Major participating institution for programs in: CD,
D, DMP, DR, GE, GS, IC, ICE, ID, IM, IMG, N, NEP, NO,
NRN, NS, OPH, P, PM, PYM, PYN, RHU, RNR, SME, U,
VIR, VS
Institution ID: 35-0392

Teaching Institutions

Memorial Sloan-Kettering Cancer Center

1275 York Ave
New York, NY 10065
www.mskcc.org
Med Sch Affil: M-03520, L-03508, L-00102, L-03515, G-03519
Programs sponsored in: CCM, DMP, GE, HMP, HO, ID, MG, NM, OMO, PCP, PMM, PUD, PYM, RO, SP, TY
Major participating institution for programs in: AN, CN, D, DR, END, GS, N, NS, PDE, PHO, PMM, PRD, RHU, RNR, TS, U, VIR
Institution ID: 35-0125

Metropolitan Hospital Center

1901 First Avenue
New York, NY 10029
Med Sch Affil: M-03509
Major participating institution for programs in: AN, D, EM, GE, GS, HO, ID, IM, N, NEP, OBG, OPH, P, PCC, PD, PM, U
Institution ID: 35-0163

Mid-Hudson Family Health Inst/The Inst for Fam Health

16 East 16th Street
New York, NY 10008
www.fpinstitute.org
Programs sponsored in: FP
Institution ID: 35-0432

Mount Sinai Medical Center

1425 Madison Avenue
New York, NY 10029
Med Sch Affil: M-03547, G-03519
Programs sponsored in: CPP
Major participating institution for programs in: ACA, ADL, ADP, AI, AN, CCA, CCM, CD, CHP, CN, CRS, D, DMP, DR, EM, END, GE, GPM, GS, HO, HPM, HSP, IC, ICE, ID, IM, IMG, MDG, MG, MGP, MPD, N, NEP, NM, NP, NPM, NS, OBG, OPH, ORS, OTO, P, PCC, PCP, PD, PDC, PDE, PDI, PDP, PEM, PG, PM, PMG, PMM, PN, PRD, PS, PTH, PYG, PYM, RHU, RNR, RO, SCI, THP, TS, U, VIR, VN, VS, VSI
Institution ID: 35-0376

Mount Sinai School of Medicine

One Gustave L Levy Place
Box 1076
New York, NY 10029-6574
www.mssm.edu
Med Sch Affil: M-03547
Programs sponsored in: ACA, ADL, ADP, AI, AN, CCA, CCM, CD, CHP, CN, CRS, D, DMP, DR, EM, END, FP, GE, GPM, GS, HO, HPM, HSO, IC, ICE, ID, IM, IMG, MDG, MG, MGP, MPD, N, NEP, NM, NP, NPM, NS, OBG, OPH, ORS, OTO, P, PCC, PCP, PD, PDC, PDE, PDI, PDP, PEM, PG, PM, PMG, PMM, PN, PRD, PS, PTH, PYG, PYM, RHU, RNR, RO, SCI, THP, TS, U, VIR, VN, VS, VSI
Institution ID: 35-9503

New York Blood Center

310 E 67th St
New York, NY 10065
http://nybloodcenter.org
Programs sponsored in: BBK
Institution ID: 35-0807

New York City Department of Health and Mental Hygiene

125 Worth Street
New York, NY 10013
www.nyc.gov/health
Programs sponsored in: GPM
Institution ID: 35-0394

New York City Poison Control Center

455 1st Ave
Room 123
New York, NY 10016
Major participating institution for programs in: ETX
Institution ID: 35-8091

New York Downtown Hospital

83 Gold Street
New York, NY 10038-2649
www.downtownhospital.org
Med Sch Affil: M-03519
Programs sponsored in: IM, OBG
Institution ID: 35-0270

New York Eye and Ear Infirmary

310 E 14th St
New York, NY 10003
http://nyee.edu
Med Sch Affil: M-03509
Programs sponsored in: OPH
Major participating institution for programs in: OTO
Institution ID: 35-0230

New York Presbyterian Hospital

622 West 168th Street
New York, NY 10032
www.nyp.org/
Programs sponsored in: ACA, ADL, ADP, AI, AN, CCA, CCP, CD, CHN, CHP, CN, CRS, D, DR, EM, END, FP, GE, GPM, GS, HMP, HO, HSO, IC, ICE, ID, IM, IMG, MG, N, NEP, NM, NP, NPM, NR, NS, OBG, OPH, ORS, OSM, OTO, P, PAN, PCC, PCP, PD, PDC, PDE, PDI, PDP, PDR, PDS, PEM, PFP, PG, PHO, PM, PMM, PPR, PRD, PS, PTH, PYG, PYM, PYN, RHU, RNR, RO, THP, TS, U, VIR, VN, VS
Institution ID: 35-8051

New York Presbyterian Hospital (Columbia Campus)

622 West 168th Street
New York, NY 10032
Med Sch Affil: M-03501
Major participating institution for programs in: ADP, AI, AN, BBK, CCA, CCP, CD, CHN, CN, CRS, D, DR, EM, END, FP, GE, GS, HMP, HO, HSO, IC, ICE, ID, IM, MG, N, NEP, NM, NP, NPM, NR, NS, OBG, OPH, ORS, OSM, OTO, P, PAN, PCC, PD, PDC, PDE, PDI, PDP, PDR, PDS, PEM, PFP, PG, PHO, PM, PMM, PS, PTH, PYG, PYN, RHU, RNR, RO, THP, TS, U, VIR, VN, VS
Institution ID: 35-0269

New York Presbyterian Hospital (Cornell Campus)

525 E 68th Street
New York, NY 10021
Med Sch Affil: M-03520
Major participating institution for programs in: AN, CCP, CD, CHN, CHP, CN, CRS, D, DR, EM, END, GE, GS, HO, IC, ICE, ID, IM, IMG, MG, N, NEP, NM, NPM, NS, OBG, OP, OPH, ORS, OTO, P, PCC, PCP, PD, PDE, PEM, PG, PM, PMM, PS, PYM, RHU, RNR, RO, TS, U, VIR, VS
Institution ID: 35-0262

New York State Psychiatric Institute

1051 Riverside Drive
New York, NY 10032
Med Sch Affil: M-03501
Major participating institution for programs in: ADP, P, PFP, PYN
Institution ID: 35-0353

New York University School of Medicine

550 First Avenue
New York, NY 10016
www.med.nyu.edu/
Med Sch Affil: M-03519
Programs sponsored in: ACA, ADP, AN, CCA, CD, CHN, CHP, CN, D, DBP, DMP, DR, EM, END, ETX, GE, GS, HMP, HO, HSO, HSP, IC, ICE, ID, IM, IMG, MSR, N, NEP, NO, NP, NPM, NR, NRN, NS, OBG, OP, OPH, ORS, OSM, OSS, OTO, P, PCC, PCP, PD, PDC, PDE, PDI, PDR, PEM, PFP, PHO, PM, PMM, PP, PRD, PS, PTH, PYG, PYM, PYN, RHU, RNR, RO, SME, SP, TS, U, VIR, VS
Institution ID: 35-0450

North General Hospital

1879 Madison Avenue
New York, NY 10035
Med Sch Affil: M-03547
Major participating institution for programs in: IM, P
Institution ID: 35-0808

NYU Hospital for Joint Diseases

301 East 17th Street
New York, NY 10003-3899
www.med.nyu.edu/hjd/
Med Sch Affil: M-03519
Major participating institution for programs in: CN, HSO, MSR, OP, ORS, OSM, OSS, PMM, RHU, SP
Institution ID: 35-0289

NYU Hospitals Center

550 First Ave
New York, NY 10016
Major participating institution for programs in: ACA, AN, CCA, CD, CHN, D, DMP, DR, EM, ETX, GE, GS, HMP, HO, HSO, HSP, ICE, IM, IMG, MSR, N, NEP, NO, NR, NS, OBG, ORS, OSM, OSS, OTO, P, PD, PDC, PDE, PDI, PHO, PMM, PRD, PS, PTH, PYG, PYM, RO, SCI, TS, U
Institution ID: 35-8060

Office of Chief Medical Examiner - City of New York

520 First Avenue
New York, NY 10016
Programs sponsored in: FOP, SP
Institution ID: 35-0528

Rusk Institute of Rehabilitation Medicine

400 E 34th St, R R615
New York, NY 10016
Med Sch Affil: M-03519
Major participating institution for programs in: PM, PYG
Institution ID: 35-0145

Ryan Chelsea Clinton Community Health Center

645 Tenth Ave
New York, NY 10036-2904
Major participating institution for programs in: IM
Institution ID: 35-8118

Sleep Medicine Associates of New York City

11 E 26th Street
New York, NY 10016
Major participating institution for programs in: SME
Institution ID: 35-8126

St Luke's-Roosevelt Hospital Center

1111 Amsterdam Avenue
New York, NY 10025
www.wehealny.org
Med Sch Affil: M-03501
Programs sponsored in: AN, CD, CHP, CRS, D, DR, EM, END, GE, GS, HO, HSO, IC, ICE, ID, IM, IMG, NEP, NM, OBG, OPH, ORS, P, PCC, PMM, PTH, PYM, VIR
Major participating institution for programs in: HMP, NS, PYG, U
Institution ID: 35-8013

St Luke's-Roosevelt Hospital Center-Roosevelt Division

1000 Tenth Avenue
New York, NY 10019
Med Sch Affil: M-03501
Major participating institution for programs in: CHP, CRS, EM, NM, OBG, OFA, P, VIR
Institution ID: 35-0211

St Luke's-Roosevelt Hospital Center-St Luke's Division

1111 Amsterdam Avenue
New York, NY 10025
Med Sch Affil: M-03501
Major participating institution for programs in: AN, CHP, EM, NM, OBG, P, VIR
Institution ID: 35-0135

St Vincent Catholic Medical Centers (Manhattan)
170 West 12th Street
New York, NY 10011
Med Sch Affil: M-03509, L-03508
Major participating institution for programs in: AN, CCM, CD, CHP, DR, END, GE, GS, HO, IC, ID, IM, IMG, N, NEP, NM, NS, OBG, OPH, ORS, OTO, P, PCC, PFP, PM, PMM, PTH, PYG, SME, TY, U
Institution ID: 35-0241

University Medical Practice Associates
1790 Broadway
3rd Floor
New York, NY 10019
Major participating institution for programs in: IM
Institution ID: 35-8178

University Pain Center (New York Med Coll at St Vincent's)
95 University Place
New York, NY 10003
Major participating institution for programs in: PMM
Institution ID: 35-8105

Visiting Nurse Service of New York
1250 Broadway
New York, NY 10001
Major participating institution for programs in: HPM
Institution ID: 35-8145

Westside Pulmonary
1090 Amsterdam Ave
#5A
New York, NY 10025
Major participating institution for programs in: IM
Institution ID: 35-8179

Niagara Falls

Niagara Falls Memorial Medical Center
621 10th Street
Niagara Falls, NY 14302
Med Sch Affil: L-03506
Major participating institution for programs in: FP, OSM
Institution ID: 35-0448

Northport

Veterans Affairs Medical Center (Northport)
79 Middleville Rd
Northport, NY 11768-2290
http://nop-b12websrv1/
Med Sch Affil: M-03548
Major participating institution for programs in: CN, D, END, GE, GS, HO, ID, IM, IMG, MN, N, NEP, OPH, PCC, PM, RHU, SME, U, VS
Institution ID: 35-0441

Oceanside

South Nassau Communities Hospital
One Healthy Way
Oceanside, NY 11572
www.southnassau.org
Med Sch Affil: L-03548
Programs sponsored in: FP
Major participating institution for programs in: GS, OBG, PTH
Institution ID: 35-0277

Olean

Olean General Hospital
515 Main Street
Olean, NY 14760
Major participating institution for programs in: FP
Institution ID: 35-7243

Orangeburg

Rockland Children's Psychiatric Center
595 Convent Rd
Orangeburg, NY 10962
Major participating institution for programs in: CHP
Institution ID: 35-8042

Rockland Psychiatric Center
140 Old Orangeburg Road
Orangeburg, NY 10962
Major participating institution for programs in: PYG
Institution ID: 35-0351

Port Jefferson

St Charles Hospital and Rehabilitation Center
200 Belle Terre Rd
Port Jefferson, NY 11777
Major participating institution for programs in: PM
Institution ID: 35-0298

Portchester

Pathology Associates
100 Midland Avenue
Portchester, NY 10583
Major participating institution for programs in: DMP
Institution ID: 35-8132

Queens Village

Creedmoor Psychiatric Center
79-25 Winchester Blvd
Queens Village, NY 11427
Programs sponsored in: P
Institution ID: 35-0193

Rochester

Highland Hospital of Rochester
1000 South Avenue
Rochester, NY 14620
Med Sch Affil: M-03545
Major participating institution for programs in: CCM, FP, GS, IM, IMG, MPD, OBG, ORS, RO
Institution ID: 35-0397

Monroe Community Hospital
435 E Henrietta Road
Rochester, NY 14620
Med Sch Affil: M-03545
Major participating institution for programs in: IMG
Institution ID: 35-0562

Rochester General Hospital
1425 Portland Ave
Rochester, NY 14621-3095
www.viahealth.org
Med Sch Affil: M-03545
Programs sponsored in: DR, IM, OBG
Major participating institution for programs in: ADL, MPD, NS, OPH, PD, PS, U
Institution ID: 35-0388

Rochester Psychiatric Center
1111 Elmwood Avenue
Rochester, NY 14620
Med Sch Affil: L-03545
Major participating institution for programs in: PFP, PYG
Institution ID: 35-0309

Strong Memorial Hospital of the University of Rochester
601 Elmwood Avenue, Box 601
Rochester, NY 14642
www.urmc.rochester.edu
Med Sch Affil: M-03545
Programs sponsored in: ACA, ADL, AI, AN, CCA, CCM, CCP, CCS, CD, CHN, CHP, CN, D, DBP, DR, EM, END, ESM, FP, GE, GPM, GS, HMP, HO, HPM, HSO, IC, ICE, ID, IM, IMG, MPD, MSR, N, NEP, NMN, NPM, NS, OBG, OFA, OPH, ORS, OSM, OTO, P, PCC, PCP, PD, PDC, PDI, PDP, PDR, PE, PFP, PG, PHO, PM, PMM, PN, PRD, PS, PTH, PYG, RHU, RNR, RO, TS, U, VIR, VN, VS, VSI
Institution ID: 35-0493

Unity Hospital (Unity Health System)
1555 Long Pond Road
Rochester, NY 14626-4182
Major participating institution for programs in: IM, PFP, U
Institution ID: 35-8059

Unity St Mary's Campus (Unity Health System)
1555 Long Pond Road
Rochester, NY 14626
www.unityhealth.org
Med Sch Affil: M-03545
Programs sponsored in: IM
Institution ID: 35-0372

Schenectady

Ellis Hospital
1101 Nott St
Schenectady, NY 12308
Med Sch Affil: G-03503
Programs sponsored in: FP
Major participating institution for programs in: ORS
Institution ID: 35-0474

Smithtown

Long Island Skin Cancer & Dermatologic Surgery
994 Jericho Turnpike
Smithtown, NY 11787
Major participating institution for programs in: PRD
Institution ID: 35-8192

Staten Island

Regional Radiology
360 Bard Ave
Staten Island, NY 10310
Major participating institution for programs in: DR
Institution ID: 35-8154

Richmond University Medical Center
355 Bard Avenue
Staten Island, NY 10310
Med Sch Affil: M-03508
Major participating institution for programs in: CD, DR, GS, HO, IM, NEP, OBG, OPH, P, PD
Institution ID: 35-0458

South Beach Psychiatric Center
777 Seaview Avenue
Staten Island, NY 10305
Major participating institution for programs in: CHP
Institution ID: 35-8058

Staten Island University Hospital
475 Seaview Ave
Staten Island, NY 10305-3498
www.siuh.edu
Med Sch Affil: M-03508, G-03305
Programs sponsored in: CD, DR, GS, HO, IM, IMG, OBG, VS
Major participating institution for programs in: AN, CD, IC, ORS, PM
Institution ID: 35-0156

Teaching Institutions

Stony Brook

University Hospital - SUNY at Stony Brook
School of Medicine Health Sciences Center
Level 4, Room 158
Stony Brook, NY 11794-8432
www.stonybrookhospital.com
Med Sch Affil: M-03548
Programs sponsored in: AN, AR, BBK, CCS, CD, CHN, CHP, CN, CRS, D, DR, EM, END, FP, GE, GPM, GS, HO, HSO, IC, ID, IM, IMG, MN, MPD, MSR, N, NEP, NPM, OBG, OPH, ORS, P, PCC, PD, PDE, PDI, PG, PM, PTH, PYG, RHU, SME, U, VN, VS, VSI
Major participating institution for programs in: OPH, PDP
Institution ID: 35-0560

Syracuse

Crouse Hospital
736 Irving Avenue
Syracuse, NY 13210
Med Sch Affil: M-03515
Major participating institution for programs in: GS, HSO, ID, N, NS, OBG, OPH, ORS, OTO, PD, PDI, U
Institution ID: 35-0566

St Joseph's Hospital Health Center
301 Prospect Ave
Syracuse, NY 13203
www.sjhsyr.org
Med Sch Affil: M-03515
Programs sponsored in: FP, TY
Major participating institution for programs in: NS, OBG
Institution ID: 35-0445

SUNY Upstate Medical University
750 East Adams Street, UH-1814
Syracuse, NY 13210
www.upstate.edu/gme
Programs sponsored in: AN, BBK, CD, CHP, CN, DR, EM, END, GE, GS, HMP, HO, HSO, ID, IM, IMG, N, NEP, NR, NS, OBG, OPH, ORS, OSS, OTO, P, PCC, PCP, PD, PDI, PE, PFP, PM, PMM, PTH, PYM, RHU, RNR, RO, RPM, U, VIR, VN
Institution ID: 35-0174

Veterans Affairs Medical Center (Syracuse)
800 Irving Avenue
Syracuse, NY 13210
Med Sch Affil: M-03515
Major participating institution for programs in: CD, CN, END, GE, GS, ID, IMG, N, NEP, NS, OPH, ORS, OTO, P, PCC, PM, PMM, PYM, RHU, U
Institution ID: 35-0183

Upton

Brookhaven National Laboratory Occupational Medicine Clinic
Occ Med Clinical-Building 490
PO Box 5000
Upton, NY 11973
Major participating institution for programs in: GPM
Institution ID: 35-8180

Utica

St Elizabeth Hospital
2209 Genesee Street
Utica, NY 13501
www.stem.org
Programs sponsored in: FP
Institution ID: 35-0759

Valhalla

New York Medical College
Office of Clinical Affairs and GME
Admininstration Building, Room 143
Valhalla, NY 10595
www.nymc.edu
Med Sch Affil: M-03509
Programs sponsored in: AN, CCM, CCS, CD, CHP, D, DR, EM, END, FP, GE, GS, HO, IC, ID, IM, IMG, N, NEP, NM, NPM, NS, OBG, OPH, ORS, OTO, P, PCC, PD, PDP, PFP, PG, PM, PMM, PTH, PUD, PYG, PYM, RHU, RNR, SME, THP, TY, U
Institution ID: 35-0782

Westchester Medical Center
Valhalla, NY 10595
Med Sch Affil: M-03509
Major participating institution for programs in: AN, BBK, CCS, CD, CHP, DR, EM, END, GE, GS, HO, IC, ID, IM, N, NEP, NPM, NS, OBG, OPH, ORS, OTO, OTR, P, PCC, PD, PDP, PG, PS, PTH, PYM, RHU, RNR, U
Institution ID: 35-0301

West Brentwood

Pilgrim Psychiatric Center
998 Crooked Hill Road
West Brentwood, NY 11717-1087
Major participating institution for programs in: PYG
Institution ID: 35-0461

West Point

Keller Army Community Hospital
John A Feagin, Jr Sports Medicine Fellowship
Keller Army Community Hospital, 900 Washington Road
West Point, NY 10996-1197
Programs sponsored in: OSM
Institution ID: 35-7271

West Seneca

Western New York Children's Psychiatric Center
1010 East & West Road
West Seneca, NY 14224
Major participating institution for programs in: CHP
Institution ID: 35-8035

White Plains

New York Presbyterian Hospital (Westchester Division)
21 Bloomingdale Road
White Plains, NY 10605
Med Sch Affil: M-03520
Major participating institution for programs in: CHP, PYG
Institution ID: 35-0378

Woodbury

Cold Spring Hills Center for Nursing and Rehabilitation
378 Syosset-Woodbury Road
Woodbury, NY 11797
Major participating institution for programs in: IMG
Institution ID: 35-8067

Yonkers

St Josephs Medical Center
127 South Broadway
Yonkers, NY 10701-4080
Med Sch Affil: M-03509
Major participating institution for programs in: FP
Institution ID: 35-0442

North Carolina

Asheville

CarePartners
68 Sweeten Creek Road
Asheville, NC 28803-2318
Major participating institution for programs in: FPG
Institution ID: 36-8036

Deerfield Episcopal Retirement Community, Inc
1617 Hendersonville Road
Asheville, NC 28803-3454
Major participating institution for programs in: FPG
Institution ID: 36-8037

Mission Hospitals - Memorial Campus
509 Biltmore Ave
Asheville, NC 28801
Med Sch Affil: L-03601
Major participating institution for programs in: FP, FPG, OBG
Institution ID: 36-0114

Mountain Area Health Education Center
501 Biltmore Avenue
Asheville, NC 28801-4601
www.mahec.net
Programs sponsored in: FP, FPG, OBG
Institution ID: 36-0732

Veterans Affairs Medical Center (Asheville)
Riceville and Tunnel Rds
Asheville, NC 28805
Med Sch Affil: L-03607
Major participating institution for programs in: ORS, U
Institution ID: 36-0740

Butner

John Umstead Hospital
1003 12th Street
Butner, NC 27509-1626
Med Sch Affil: G-03607
Major participating institution for programs in: CHP, PYG
Institution ID: 36-0507

Camp Lejeune

Naval Hospital-Camp Lejeune
100 Brewster Boulevard
Camp Lejeune, NC 28547-2538
http://lej-www.med.navy.mil
Programs sponsored in: FP
Institution ID: 36-0509

Chapel Hill

Office of the Chief Medical Examiner
Chapel Hill, NC 27599-7580
Major participating institution for programs in: FOP
Institution ID: 36-0514

University of North Carolina Hospitals
101 Manning Drive, Rm 1107G West Wing
Office of Graduate Medical Education
Chapel Hill, NC 27514
www.unchealthcare.org/
Med Sch Affil: M-03601, L-03607
Programs sponsored in: AI, AN, BBK, CCP, CCS, CD, CHN, CHP, D, DBP, DR, EM, END, FOP, FP, GE, GPM, GS, HMP, HO, IC, ID, IM, IMG, MG, MGP, MPD, N, NEP, NM, NP, NPM, NS, OBG, OPH, ORS, OTO, P, PAN, PCC, PCP, PD, PDE, PDP, PE, PFP, PHO, PM, PMM, PN, PS, PTH, RHU, RNR, RO, SME, TS, U, VIR, VN, VS, VSI
Institution ID: 36-0478

University of North Carolina School of Medicine
CB 7000-125 MacNider Bldg
Chapel Hill, NC 27599-7000
Med Sch Affil: M-03601
Major participating institution for programs in: GPM, VSI
Institution ID: 36-0511

University of North Carolina School of Public Health
2105B McGavran-Greenberg Hall
CB 7400, School of Public Health
Chapel Hill, NC 27599-7400
Med Sch Affil: L-03607
Major participating institution for programs in: GPM
Institution ID: 36-9502

Charlotte

Carolinas Medical Center
1000 Blythe Boulevard
PO Box 32861
Charlotte, NC 28232-2861
www.carolinashealthcare.org/education/
Med Sch Affil: M-03601
Programs sponsored in: EM, ETX, FP, FSM, GS, IM, OBG, ORS, OTR, PD, PE, PM, TS, VS
Institution ID: 36-0291

Carolinas Rehabilitation
1100 Blythe Blvd
Charlotte, NC 28203
Major participating institution for programs in: PM
Institution ID: 36-8012

Carolinas Medical Center: Mercy
2001 Vail Avenue
Charlotte, NC 28207
Major participating institution for programs in: FP
Institution ID: 36-8066

Concord

Carolinas Medical Center-Northeast
920 Church Street, N
Concord, NC 28025
www.northeastmedical.org
Programs sponsored in: FP, FSM
Institution ID: 36-8016

Durham

Duke University Hospital
Box 3708
Durham, NC 27710
www.gme.duke.edu
Programs sponsored in: ACA, AI, AN, CCA, CCP, CCS, CD, CHN, CHP, CN, D, DMP, DR, EM, END, FP, FSM, GE, GPM, GS, HMP, HO, HPM, HSO, IC, ICE, ID, IM, IMG, MG, MM, MP, MPD, N, NEP, NM, NMN, NP, NPM, NR, NS, OAR, OBG, OFA, OPH, ORS, OSM, OTO, P, PAN, PCC, PCP, PD, PDC, PDI, PDP, PDR, PHO, PMM, PPR, PS, PTH, PYG, RHU, RNR, RO, SME, THP, TS, U, UM, VIR, VS
Institution ID: 36-0222

Durham Regional Hospital
3643 North Roxboro Street
Durham, NC 27704
Med Sch Affil: M-03607, L-03601
Major participating institution for programs in: NS, ORS, PS
Institution ID: 36-0440

Veterans Affairs Medical Center (Durham)
508 Fulton Street
Durham, NC 27705
Med Sch Affil: M-03607
Major participating institution for programs in: AN, CCA, D, DMP, END, GE, GS, HMP, HPM, ICE, ID, IM, IMG, MP, N, NS, OPH, ORS, OTO, P, PCC, PMM, PS, PTH, PYG, RHU, RO, SME, U
Institution ID: 36-0473

Fayetteville

Cape Fear Valley Medical Center
1320 Medical Drive
Fayetteville, NC 28304
www.southernregionalahec.org
Major participating institution for programs in: FP,
Institution ID: 36-0731

Southern Regional Area Health Education Center
1601 Owen Drive
Fayetteville, NC 28304-3482
www.southernregionalahec.org
Programs sponsored in: FP
Institution ID: 36-8020

Fort Bragg

Womack Army Medical Center
Attn: MCXC-GME (Mr Raymond Sanders)
2817 Reilly Rd
Fort Bragg, NC 28310
Med Sch Affil: G-02312
Programs sponsored in: FP
Institution ID: 36-0101

Greensboro

Moses H Cone Memorial Hospital
1200 North Elm Street
Greensboro, NC 27401-1020
www.mosescone.com
Programs sponsored in: FP, FSM, IM
Major participating institution for programs in: PD
Institution ID: 36-0486

The Urology Center, PA
509 North Elam Avenue
Greensboro, NC 27403
Major participating institution for programs in: U
Institution ID: 36-8026

Greenville

Brody School of Medicine at East Carolina University
600 Moye Boulevard
Greenville, NC 27834
Major participating institution for programs in: FSM
Institution ID: 36-8030

Orthopedics East
622 Medical Drive
Greenville, NC 27834
Major participating institution for programs in: FSM
Institution ID: 36-9501

Pitt County Memorial Hospital
Graduate Medical Education Office
2100 Stantonsburg Road, PO Box 6028
Greenville, NC 27835-6028
www.uhseast.com
Med Sch Affil: M-03608
Programs sponsored in: CCS, CD, CHP, D, EM, FP, FPG, FPP, FSM, GS, HO, IC, ID, IM, MEM, MP, MPD, NEP, NPM, OBG, P, PCC, PCP, PD, PM, PTH
Institution ID: 36-0738

Hendersonville

Margaret R Pardee Memorial Hospital
715 Fleming St
Hendersonville, NC 28739
Major participating institution for programs in: FP
Institution ID: 36-8015

Hillsborough

Duke HomeCare & Hospice
1001 Corporate Drive
Hillsborough, NC 27278
Major participating institution for programs in: HPM
Institution ID: 36-8019

Monroe

Carolinas Medical Center Union
600 Hospital Drive
PO Box 5003
Monroe, NC 28111
Major participating institution for programs in: FP
Institution ID: 36-8052

Raleigh

Central Regional Hospital (Raleigh Campus)
820 South Boylan Avenue
Raleigh, NC 27603-2176
Med Sch Affil: M-03601
Major participating institution for programs in: CHP, P, PFP
Institution ID: 36-0377

Wake Medical Center
3000 New Bern Avenue
Raleigh, NC 27610
Med Sch Affil: M-03601, L-02312
Major participating institution for programs in: EM, GS, OBG, ORS, OTO, PD, PE
Institution ID: 36-0498

Salisbury

WG (Bill) Hefner VA Medical Center
1601 Brenner Avenue
Salisbury, NC 28144
Major participating institution for programs in: FP, GS, IM, OBG
Institution ID: 36-8028

Wilmington

New Hanover Regional Medical Center
2131 S 17th St
PO Box 9025
Wilmington, NC 28402-9025
www.nhhn.org
Med Sch Affil: M-03601
Programs sponsored in: FP, GS, IM, OBG
Institution ID: 36-0288

Winston-Salem

Carolinas Pain Institute
145 Kimel Park Drive, Suite 330
Winston-Salem, NC 27103
Major participating institution for programs in: PMM
Institution ID: 36-8029

Forsyth Memorial Hospital
3333 Silas Creek Parkway
Winston-Salem, NC 27103
Med Sch Affil: M-03605
Major participating institution for programs in: FP, NPM, OBG, PMM
Institution ID: 36-0242

North Carolina

Skin Surgery Center (Winston-Salem)
125 Sunnynoll Court, Suite 100
Winston-Salem, NC 27106
http://skinsurgeryecenter.net
Programs sponsored in: PRD
Institution ID: 36-8021

Wake Forest University Baptist Medical Center
Medical Center Blvd
Winston-Salem, NC 27157-1088
www.wfubmc.edu
Med Sch Affil: M-03605
Programs sponsored in: AI, AN, AR, CCA, CCM, CCS, CD, CHN, CHP, CN, D, DMP, DR, EM, END, FOP, FP, FSM, GE, GS, HMP, HO, HSO, IC, ICE, ID, IM, IMG, MSR, N, NEP, NM, NPM, NR, NS, OBG, OPH, ORS, OSM, OTO, P, PCC, PCP, PD, PE, PMM, PSI, PTH, RHU, RNR, RO, TS, U, VIR, VS
Institution ID: 36-0480

North Dakota

Bismarck

Medcenter One Hospital
300 North 7th Street
PO Box 5525
Bismarck, ND 58506-5525
Med Sch Affil: M-03701
Major participating institution for programs in: FP
Institution ID: 37-0159

St Alexius Medical Center
900 E Broadway
PO Box 5510
Bismarck, ND 58506-5510
Med Sch Affil: M-03701
Major participating institution for programs in: GS, IM, P
Institution ID: 37-0395

Fargo

MeritCare Health System
720 4th Street, North
Fargo, ND 58122
Med Sch Affil: M-03701
Major participating institution for programs in: GS, IM, P, TY
Institution ID: 37-0396

Veterans Affairs Medical and Regional Office Center (Fargo)
2101 Elm St
Fargo, ND 58102
Med Sch Affil: M-03701
Programs sponsored in: FP
Major participating institution for programs in: FP
Institution ID: 37-0403

Grand Forks

Altru Health System Hospital
1200 S Columbia Road
PO Box 6002
Grand Forks, ND 58206-6002
Med Sch Affil: M-03701
Programs sponsored in: FP
Institution ID: 37-0108

Univ of North Dakota School of Medicine and Health Sciences
501 North Columbia Road
Box 9037
Grand Forks, ND 58202-9037
www.medicine.nodak.edu/
Med Sch Affil: M-03701, L-02312
Programs sponsored in: FP, GS, IM, P, TY
Institution ID: 37-0400

Minot

Trinity Health
Burdick Expwy at Main Street
PO Box 5020
Minot, ND 58702-5020
Med Sch Affil: M-03701
Major participating institution for programs in: FP
Institution ID: 37-0409

Ohio

Akron

Akron City Hospital (Summa Health System)
525 E Market St
Akron, OH 44309
Med Sch Affil: M-03844, L-03840
Major participating institution for programs in: EM, FP, GS, HPM, IM, IMG, OBG, OPH, ORS, PS, PTH, TY, U
Institution ID: 38-0215

Akron General Medical Center
400 Wabash Avenue
Akron, OH 44307
http://agmc.org
Med Sch Affil: M-03844, L-03840
Programs sponsored in: EM, FP, GS, IM, OBG, ORS, TY, U
Institution ID: 38-0124

Bath Manor Care Center
2330 Smith Road
Akron, OH 44333
Major participating institution for programs in: P, PS
Institution ID: 38-9030

Child Guidance and Family Solutions
County of Summit, ADM Board
100 West Cedar Street, Suite 300
Akron, OH 44308
Major participating institution for programs in: CHP
Institution ID: 38-9022

Children's Hospital Medical Center of Akron
Department of Medical Education
One Perkins Square
Akron, OH 44308-1062
www.akronchildrens.org
Med Sch Affil: M-03844
Programs sponsored in: CHP, DBP, HPM, PD, PDR, PEM, PHO, PP, PSM
Major participating institution for programs in: ORS, PAN, PS, U
Institution ID: 38-0371

Summa Health System
525 E Market Street
PO Box 2090
Akron, OH 44304-2090
http://summa-health.org
Programs sponsored in: EM, FP, GS, HPM, IM, IMG, OBG, OPH, ORS, PS, PTH, TY
Institution ID: 38-8066

Windsong Care Center
120 Brookmont Road
Akron, OH 44313
Major participating institution for programs in: PM
Institution ID: 38-9029

Barberton

Barberton Citizens Hospital
155 Fifth Street, NE
Barberton, OH 44203
www.barbhosp.com
Med Sch Affil: M-03844
Programs sponsored in: FP
Institution ID: 38-0184

Bellefontaine

Mary Rutan Hospital
205 Palmer Avenue
Bellefontaine, OH 43311
Med Sch Affil: L-03840
Major participating institution for programs in: FP
Institution ID: 38-8069

Canton

Aultman Hospital
2600 Sixth St, SW
Canton, OH 44710
www.aultman.com
Med Sch Affil: M-03844
Programs sponsored in: DR, FP, OBG, TY
Major participating institution for programs in: IM
Institution ID: 38-0148

Canton Medical Education Foundation
2600 Sixth Street, SW
Canton, OH 44710
Programs sponsored in: IM
Institution ID: 38-8059

Mercy Medical Center (Canton)
1320 Timken Mercy Drive, NW
Canton, OH 44708
www.healthall.com
Med Sch Affil: M-03844
Major participating institution for programs in: DR, IM
Institution ID: 38-0426

Cincinnati

Christ Hospital
2139 Auburn Avenue
Cincinnati, OH 45219-2989
www.healthall.com
Med Sch Affil: M-03841, L-03840
Major participating institution for programs in: GS, NS, OBG, OSS, RHU, VS, VSI
Institution ID: 38-0492

Cincinnati Children's Hospital Medical Center
ML-3013
3333 Burnet Avenue
Cincinnati, OH 45229-3039
www.cincinnatichildrens.org
Med Sch Affil: M-03841, G-03515
Programs sponsored in: ADL, CCP, CHN, CHP, CN, CPP, DBP, MBG, MG, NDN, NPM, OP, OSS, PAN, PD, PDC, PDE, PDI, PDO, PDP, PDR, PDS, PEM, PG, PHO, PMG, PN, PP, PPR, PSM, PTP, RPM, SME, UP
Major participating institution for programs in: AI, DR, MPD, NS, ORS, OTO, PS, PSI, U
Institution ID: 38-0302

Cincinnati Sports Medicine & Orthopaedic Center
10663 Montgomery Road - First Floor
Cincinnati, OH 45242
www.cincinnatisportsmed.com
Programs sponsored in: OSM
Institution ID: 38-8058

Drake Center Inc
151 W Galbraith
Cincinnati, OH 45216
Major participating institution for programs in: PM
Institution ID: 38-0368

Episcopal Retirement Homes
3870 Virginia Ave
Cincinnati, OH 45227-3427
Major participating institution for programs in: FPG
Institution ID: 38-9045

Teaching Institution

Hoxworth Blood Center
3130 Highland Avenue
PO Box 670055
Cincinnati, OH 45267-0055
www.hoxworth.org
Programs sponsored in: BBK
Institution ID: 38-0763

Jewish Hospital of Cincinnati
4777 East Galbraith Road
Cincinnati, OH 45236
www.health-alliance.com/jewish
Med Sch Affil: L-03841
Programs sponsored in: GS, IM
Institution ID: 38-0428

Maple Knoll Village
11100 Springfield Pike
Cincinnati, OH 45246
Major participating institution for programs in: FPG, IM
Institution ID: 38-9047

Mercy Hospital Anderson
7500 State Road
Cincinnati, OH 45255
Programs sponsored in: OSM
Institution ID: 38-8100

TriHealth
Good Samaritan Hospital Campus
375 Dixmyth Avenue
Cincinnati, OH 45220-2489
www.trihealth.com
Programs sponsored in: FP, FSM, GS, IM, OBG, VS, VSI
Institution ID: 38-8079

TriHealth - Bethesda North Hospital
10500 Montgomery Road
Cincinnati, OH 45242
Med Sch Affil: L-03841
Major participating institution for programs in: FP, GS, OBG, VSI
Institution ID: 38-0464

TriHealth - Good Samaritan Hospital
375 Dixmyth Avenue
Cincinnati, OH 45220-2489
Med Sch Affil: M-03841
Major participating institution for programs in: GS, IM, NS, OBG, TS, U, VS, VSI
Institution ID: 38-0346

University Hospital Inc
234 Goodman Street
ML 0796
Cincinnati, OH 45219-2316
www.med.uc.edu/residency
Med Sch Affil: M-03841, L-02012
Programs sponsored in: ADP, AI, AN, CCA, CCS, CD, CN, D, DMP, DR, EM, END, ETX, FPP, GE, GPM, GS, HO, HSO, IC, ID, IM, MPD, N, NEP, NR, NS, OBG, OPH, ORS, OTO, P, PCC, PFP, PM, PMM, PPM, PS, PSI, PTH, RHU, RNR, RO, THP, TS, U, VIR, VN, VS, VSI
Major participating institution for programs in: CHN, CN, CPP, FPG
Institution ID: 38-0405

University Institute for Psychiatry and Law
Univ of Cincinnati, Coll of Med
231 Albert Sabin Way, PO Box 0559
Cincinnati, OH 45267-0559
Major participating institution for programs in: PFP
Institution ID: 38-8074

University of Cincinnati College of Medicine
PO Box 670555
231 Albert Sabin Way
Cincinnati, OH 45267
Med Sch Affil: M-03841
Major participating institution for programs in: NDN, OSM, OSS, PP
Institution ID: 38-0521

Veterans Affairs Medical Center (Cincinnati)
3200 Vine Street
Cincinnati, OH 45220-2288
Med Sch Affil: M-03841
Major participating institution for programs in: ADP, AI, CD, END, GE, GS, HO, ID, IM, N, NEP, OPH, ORS, OTO, P, PCC, PM, RHU, RO, U, VS, VSI
Institution ID: 38-0329

Wellington Orthopaedic and Sports Medicine (Blue Ash Office)
4701 Creek Road #110
Cincinnati, OH 45242
Major participating institution for programs in: OSM
Institution ID: 38-9044

Cleveland

American Red Cross
3747 Euclid Ave
Cleveland, OH 44115-2501
Programs sponsored in: BBK
Institution ID: 38-8064

Cleveland Clinic Foundation
9500 Euclid Avenue
Cleveland, OH 44195-5242
www.clevelandclinic.org
Med Sch Affil: M-04114, M-03840, L-03806
Programs sponsored in: ACA, AI, AN, CCA, CD, CHN, CHP, CN, CRS, D, DMP, DR, END, ESN, GE, GS, HMP, HO, HPM, HSO, IC, ICE, ID, IM, IMG, MM, MSR, N, NEP, NMN, NR, NS, OPH, ORS, OSM, OTO, P, PAN, PCC, PCP, PD, PDI, PG, PHO, PMM, PS, PTH, PYM, RHU, RNR, RO, SME, TS, U, VIR, VN, VS, VSI
Major participating institution for programs in: BBK, CD, EM, FSM, GS, OBG, PDE, PM, SCI
Institution ID: 38-0393

Cuyahoga County Coroner's Office
11001 Cedar Avenue
Cleveland, OH 44106
www.cuyahogacounty.us
Programs sponsored in: FOP
Institution ID: 38-0198

Fairview Hospital
18101 Lorain Avenue
Cleveland, OH 44111-5656
www.fairviewhospital.org
Med Sch Affil: L-03806
Programs sponsored in: FP, FSM, GS, IM
Institution ID: 38-0209

Hospice of the Western Reserve
300 East 185th Street
Cleveland, OH 44119
Major participating institution for programs in: HPM
Institution ID: 38-9035

Mental Health Services (Cleveland)
3518 W 25th St
Cleveland, OH 44109
Major participating institution for programs in: P
Institution ID: 38-8086

MetroHealth Medical Center
2500 MetroHealth Drive
GME - A107
Cleveland, OH 44109-1998
www.metrohealth.org
Med Sch Affil: M-03806, L-03840
Programs sponsored in: ADL, AN, CD, DR, EM, FP, FPG, GE, HPM, ICE, IM, MPD, NPM, OBG, P, PCC, PCP, PD, PM, PTH, RHU, SCI, VIR
Major participating institution for programs in: CCS, D, EM, GS, HO, HSO, ID, MDG, NEP, NS, OPH, ORS, OTO, PG, PSI, SME, U
Institution ID: 38-0173

Northcoast Behavioral Health (Cleveland)
1708 Aiken St
Cleveland, OH 44109
Major participating institution for programs in: PFP
Institution ID: 38-0391

St Vincent Charity Hospital/St Luke's Medical Center
2351 East 22nd Street
Cleveland, OH 44115
www.stvincentresidency.org
Med Sch Affil: L-03806
Programs sponsored in: IM
Institution ID: 38-0411

University Hospitals Case Medical Center
11100 Euclid Avenue
Lakeside Building Room 6223
Cleveland, OH 44106
www.uhhs.com/
Med Sch Affil: M-03806
Programs sponsored in: ADP, AN, CCA, CCP, CCS, CD, CHN, CHP, CN, D, DBP, DMP, DR, EM, END, FP, FPP, GE, GS, HMP, HO, IC, ICE, ID, IM, IMG, MDG, MG, MPD, N, NEP, NMN, NPM, NR, NS, OBG, OPH, ORS, OTO, P, PAN, PCC, PCP, PD, PDC, PDE, PDI, PDP, PEM, PFP, PG, PHO, PMG, PMM, PPR, PSI, PSM, PTH, PYG, PYM, RHU, RNR, RO, SME, U, VN, VS
Major participating institution for programs in: ADL, BBK, EM
Institution ID: 38-0373

Veterans Affairs Medical Center (Cleveland)
10701 East Boulevard
Cleveland, OH 44106
Med Sch Affil: M-03806
Major participating institution for programs in: ADP, CD, D, END, GE, GS, IC, ICE, ID, IM, IMG, MDG, N, NEP, OPH, ORS, OTO, P, PCC, PMM, PSI, PYG, RHU, SCI, SME, U, VS, VSI
Institution ID: 38-0390

Columbus

American Red Cross-Central Ohio Region
995 E Broad St
Columbus, OH 43205
Major participating institution for programs in: BBK
Institution ID: 38-8063

Arthur G James Cancer Hospital and Research Institute
300 West 10th Avenue
Columbus, OH 43210
Med Sch Affil: M-03840
Major participating institution for programs in: GS, HO, NM, OTO, PCC, TS
Institution ID: 38-8020

Grant Medical Center (OhioHealth)
285 E State Street
Suite 670
Columbus, OH 43215-1898
www.ohiohealth.com
Programs sponsored in: CRS, FP, FSM
Major participating institution for programs in: ORS, PS, PSI
Institution ID: 38-0317

Mount Carmel
Medical Staff Building, 3rd Floor
793 West State Street
Columbus, OH 43222-1560
www.mountcarmelhealth.com
Med Sch Affil: M-03840
Programs sponsored in: FP, GS, IM, ORS, TY
Major participating institution for programs in: CRS, OBG, PS, PSI
Institution ID: 38-0245

Teaching Institutions

Nationwide Children's Hospital
700 Children's Drive
Columbus, OH 43205-2696
www.columbuschildrens.com
Med Sch Affil: M-03840, G-03843
Programs sponsored in: CCP, CCS, CHN, CHS, DBP, MG,
NPM, OP, PAN, PD, PDC, PDE, PDI, PDP, PDR, PDS,
PEM, PG, PHO, PN, PP, PPR, PSM, RPM, UP
Major participating institution for programs in: AI,
CHP, CN, EM, FP, MPD, NM, NMN, NS, OPH, ORS, OTO,
PS, PSI, SME, TS
Institution ID: 38-0491

Ohio State University Hospital
410 W Tenth Avenue
125 Doan Hall
Columbus, OH 43210-1228
http://medicalcenter.osu.edu/
Med Sch Affil: M-03840
Programs sponsored in: AI, AN, BBK, CCS, CD, CHP, CN,
D, DMP, DR, EM, END, FP, FSM, GE, GS, HMP, HO, IC,
ICE, ID, IM, IMG, MPD, N, NEP, NM, NMN, NO, NR, NS,
OBG, OPH, ORS, OSM, OTO, P, PCC, PCP, PM, PMM, PS,
PSI, PTH, RHU, RNR, RO, SME, TS, U, VIR, VS
Major participating institution for programs in: CHN,
CRS, DBP, MG, NPM, PPR
Institution ID: 38-0123

Ohio State University Hospitals, East
1492 E Broad Street
Columbus, OH 43205
Med Sch Affil: M-03840
Major participating institution for programs in: FP, N,
NEP, OSM
Institution ID: 38-0584

Riverside Methodist Hospitals (OhioHealth)
Medical Education Department
3535 Olentangy River Road
Columbus, OH 43214
www.ohiohealth.com
Programs sponsored in: FP, FPG, FSM, GS, IM, OBG, TY
Major participating institution for programs in: ORS,
PS, PSI
Institution ID: 38-0383

Veterans Affairs Medical Center (Columbus)
543 Taylor Ave
Columbus, OH 43203
Major participating institution for programs in: D,
OPH
Institution ID: 38-8099

Wexner Heritage Village
1151 College Avenue
Columbus, OH 43209
Major participating institution for programs in: IMG
Institution ID: 38-9038

Dayton

Children's Medical Center
One Children's Plaza
Dayton, OH 45404
Med Sch Affil: M-03845
Major participating institution for programs in: CCS,
MPD, ORS, PD, PS
Institution ID: 38-0536

Good Samaritan Hospital and Health Center
2222 Philadelphia Drive
Dayton, OH 45406
Med Sch Affil: M-03845, L-03840
Major participating institution for programs in: CHP,
EM, FP, GS, HO, ID, IM, P, PS
Institution ID: 38-0315

Miami Valley Hospital
One Wyoming St
Dayton, OH 45409
Med Sch Affil: M-03845
Programs sponsored in: FP
Major participating institution for programs in: CCS,
EM, GE, GS, ID, IM, MPD, OBG, ORS, P, PS
Institution ID: 38-0431

Office of the Montgomery County Coroner
361 West Third Street
Dayton, OH 45402
www.siscom.net/~mcco
Programs sponsored in: FOP
Institution ID: 38-8060

Veterans Affairs Medical Center (Dayton)
4100 West Third Street
Dayton, OH 45428
Med Sch Affil: M-03845, L-03840
Major participating institution for programs in: CD,
D, FPG, GE, GS, HO, ID, IM, MPD, OPH, P
Institution ID: 38-0453

Wright State Dermatology (Elizabeth Place)
One Elizabeth Place
Suite 200
Dayton, OH 45408-1445
Major participating institution for programs in: D
Institution ID: 38-9027

Wright State University Boonshoft School of Medicine
PO Box 927
Dayton, OH 45401-0927
www.med.wright.edu
Med Sch Affil: M-03845
Programs sponsored in: CCS, CHP, D, EM, ESM, FP,
FPG, GE, GPM, GS, HO, HPM, ID, IM, MPD, OBG, ORS, P,
PD, PS
Institution ID: 38-0756

East Cleveland

Huron Hospital
13951 Terrace Road
East Cleveland, OH 44112-4399
www.huronhospital.org
Programs sponsored in: GS, IM
Institution ID: 38-0170

Garfield Heights

Marymount Hospital
12300 McCracken Road
Garfield Heights, OH 44125-2975
Major participating institution for programs in: VS,
VSI
Institution ID: 38-0425

Kettering

Dayton Skin Surgery Center
500 Lincoln Park Drive
Suite 200
Kettering, OH 45429
Programs sponsored in: PRD
Institution ID: 38-9020

Kettering Medical Center
3535 Southern Blvd
Kettering, OH 45429
www.kmcnetwork.org/meded/
Med Sch Affil: M-03845
Programs sponsored in: CD, IM, TY
Major participating institution for programs in: CHP,
EM, ESM, GS, P, PS
Institution ID: 38-0515

Maumee

St Luke's Hospital
5901 Monclova Road
Maumee, OH 43537
Programs sponsored in: FP
Major participating institution for programs in: EM
Institution ID: 38-0370

Mayfield Heights

Hillcrest Hospital
6780 Mayfield Road
Mayfield Heights, OH 44124-2202
Major participating institution for programs in: GS,
IM, VS, VSI
Institution ID: 38-0483

Oregon

St Charles Mercy Hospital
2600 Navaree Avenue
Oregon, OH 43616
Major participating institution for programs in: FP, TY
Institution ID: 38-0221

Ravenna

Robinson Memorial Hospital
6847 Chestnut Street
PO Box 1204
Ravenna, OH 44266-1204
Med Sch Affil: L-03844
Major participating institution for programs in: GS
Institution ID: 38-0264

Richmond Hts

UHHS Richmond Hts Hospital
27100 Chardon Rd
Richmond Hts, OH 44143
Major participating institution for programs in: P
Institution ID: 38-9057

Rootstown

Northeastern Ohio Universities College of Medicine
4209 State Route 44
PO Box 95
Rootstown, OH 44272
www.neoucom.edu
Med Sch Affil: M-03844
Programs sponsored in: P
Institution ID: 38-0755

Sylvania

Flower Hospital
5200 Harroun Rd
Sylvania, OH 43560
www.promedica.org
Programs sponsored in: FP
Institution ID: 38-0362

Toledo

Northcoast Behavioral Healthcare (Toledo Campus)
930 S Detroit Ave
Toledo, OH 43614-2701
Major participating institution for programs in: P
Institution ID: 38-0531

St Vincent Mercy Medical Center
2213 Cherry Street
Toledo, OH 43608
www.mercyweb.org
Med Sch Affil: M-03843
Programs sponsored in: EM, FP, IM, TY
Major participating institution for programs in: DR,
GS, ID, NEP, OBG, ORS, OTR, PD, U
Institution ID: 38-0180

Toledo Children's Hospital
2142 North Cove Blvd
Toledo, OH 43606
Major participating institution for programs in: PD
Institution ID: 38-8094

Toledo Hospital
2142 North Cove Boulevard
Toledo, OH 43606
www.promedica.org
Programs sponsored in: FP, FSM, VS
Major participating institution for programs in: OBG, U
Institution ID: 38-0218

University Medical Center (Toledo)
3000 Arlington Ave
Toledo, OH 43699
Med Sch Affil: M-03843
Major participating institution for programs in: CD, CHP, DR, EM, GS, IC, ICE, ID, IM, N, NEP, OBG, ORS, OTR, P, PCC, PM, PTH, SME, U
Institution ID: 38-0533

University of Toledo
3045 Arlington Avenue
Toledo, OH 43614
www.meduohio.edu
Programs sponsored in: AN, CD, CHP, DR, EM, GS, IC, ICE, ID, IM, N, NEP, OBG, ORS, OTR, P, PCC, PD, PM, PTH, SME, U
Major participating institution for programs in: FP
Institution ID: 38-9501

West Chester

Heritagespring of West Chester
7235 Heritage Spring Dr
West Chester, OH 45069
Major participating institution for programs in: FPG
Institution ID: 38-9049

Westerville

Mount Carmel St Ann's Hospital
500 S Cleveland Ave
Westerville, OH 43081
Med Sch Affil: L-03840
Major participating institution for programs in: OBG
Institution ID: 38-0321

Wilmington

Clinton Memorial Hospital
610 W Main Street
Wilmington, OH 45177-2194
www.cmhregional.com
Med Sch Affil: G-03841
Programs sponsored in: FP
Institution ID: 38-8067

Wright - Patterson AFB

Wright - Patterson Medical Center
88th Medical Group
4881 Sugar Maple Drive
Wright - Patterson AFB, OH 45433-5529
Med Sch Affil: M-03845, M-02312
Major participating institution for programs in: GS, IM, OBG, P, PD
Institution ID: 38-0336

Youngstown

Forum Health/Western Reserve Care System (Youngstown)
500 Gypsy Lane
Youngstown, OH 44501
www.forumhealth.org
Programs sponsored in: FP, GS, IM, PTH
Institution ID: 38-8061

Northside Medical Center
500 Gypsy Lane
Youngstown, OH 44501
Med Sch Affil: M-03844
Major participating institution for programs in: IM, PTH
Institution ID: 38-8056

St Elizabeth Health Center
Humility of Mary Health Partners
1044 Belmont Avenue, PO Box 1790
Youngstown, OH 44501-1790
www.hmpartners.org
Med Sch Affil: M-03844
Programs sponsored in: FP, GS, IM, TY
Institution ID: 38-0145

Oklahoma

Bartlesville

Jane Phillips Episcopal-Memorial Medical Center
3500 E Frank Phillips Blvd
Bartlesville, OK 74006
Med Sch Affil: L-03901
Major participating institution for programs in: FP
Institution ID: 39-0496

Edmond

Edmond Medical Center
One South Bryant Avenue
Edmond, OK 73034
Major participating institution for programs in: TS
Institution ID: 39-8038

Enid

Integris Bass Baptist Health Center
600 South Monroe
PO Box 3168
Enid, OK 73701
Med Sch Affil: G-03901
Major participating institution for programs in: FP
Institution ID: 39-0488

St Mary's Regional Medical Center
305 S Fifth Street
Box 232
Enid, OK 73702
Med Sch Affil: G-03901
Major participating institution for programs in: FP
Institution ID: 39-0489

Lawton

Comanche County Memorial Hospital
3401 Gore Boulevard
PO Box 129
Lawton, OK 73502-0129
Major participating institution for programs in: FP
Institution ID: 39-8023

Southwestern Medical Center
5602 SW Lee Blvd
PO Box 7290
Lawton, OK 73506-7290
Major participating institution for programs in: FP
Institution ID: 39-8024

Norman

Central Oklahoma Community Mental Health Center
909 E Alameda
PO Box 400
Norman, OK 73070
Major participating institution for programs in: P
Institution ID: 39-8040

Griffin Memorial Hospital
PO Box 151
900 E Main St
Norman, OK 73070
Med Sch Affil: G-03901
Programs sponsored in: P
Institution ID: 39-0286

Oklahoma City

Deaconess Hospital
5501 N Portland
Oklahoma City, OK 73112
Major participating institution for programs in: FP
Institution ID: 39-8017

Integris Baptist Medical Center
Graduate Medical Education
3300 Northwest Expressway, 100-4394
Oklahoma City, OK 73112-4481
www.integrisgme.org
Med Sch Affil: G-03901
Programs sponsored in: DR, FP, HSO
Major participating institution for programs in: AN
Institution ID: 39-0475

McBride Clinic Orthopedic Hospital
9600 Broadway Extension
Oklahoma City, OK 73114
Major participating institution for programs in: FSM, ORS
Institution ID: 39-8041

McGee Eye Institute
608 Stanton L Young Blvd
Oklahoma City, OK 73104
Major participating institution for programs in: OPH
Institution ID: 39-8019

North Care Center (Oklahoma City)
4436 NW 50th Street
Oklahoma City, OK 73112
Major participating institution for programs in: CHP
Institution ID: 39-8039

Office of the Chief Medical Examiner-State of Oklahoma
901 North Stonewall
Oklahoma City, OK 73117
Programs sponsored in: FOP
Institution ID: 39-0485

OU Medical Center
PO Box 26307
Oklahoma City, OK 73126
Major participating institution for programs in: AN, CD, D, END, FP, FSM, GE, GS, HSO, ICE, ID, IM, MG, MGP, NEP, NS, OBG, ORS, OTO, P, PCC, PMM, PS, PTH, RHU, RO, U
Institution ID: 39-8027

OU Medical Center - Children's Hospital
PO Box 26307
Oklahoma City, OK 73126
Major participating institution for programs in: AN, CHP, DBP, MG, MPD, NM, NPM, OPH, PAN, PD, PDE, PDR, PDS, PS, U, UP, VIR
Institution ID: 39-0130

OU Medical Center - Presbyterian Tower
PO Box 26307
Oklahoma City, OK 73126
Major participating institution for programs in: DR, HO, IC, IMG, MPD, N, NM, TS, VIR
Institution ID: 39-0312

St Anthony Hospital
608 NW 9th Street, Suite 1000
Oklahoma City, OK 73102
www.saintafmr.com
Med Sch Affil: G-03901
Programs sponsored in: FP
Major participating institution for programs in: P
Institution ID: 39-0115

Teaching Institutions

University of Oklahoma College of Medicine
Biomedical Sciences Bldg, Rm 357
PO Box 26901
Oklahoma City, OK 73126-0901
www.medicine.ouhsc.edu
Med Sch Affil: M-03901
Programs sponsored in: AN, CD, CHP, D, DBP, DR, END,
FP, FSM, GE, GS, HO, IC, ICE, ID, IM, IMG, MG, MGP,
MPD, N, NEP, NM, NPM, NS, OBG, OPH, ORS, OTO, P,
PAN, PCC, PD, PDE, PDR, PDS, PMM, PS, PTH, RHU, RO,
TS, U, UP, VIR
Institution ID: 39-0477

Veterans Affairs Medical Center (Oklahoma City)
921 NE 13th Street
Oklahoma City, OK 73104
Med Sch Affil: M-03901
Major participating institution for programs in: CD,
D, DR, END, GE, GS, HO, IC, ICE, ID, IM, IMG, MPD, N,
NEP, NM, NS, OPH, ORS, OTO, P, PCC, PS, RHU, RO, TS,
U, VIR
Institution ID: 39-0471

Spencer

Integris Mental Health Center - Spencer
2601 N Spencer Road
Spencer, OK 73084
Major participating institution for programs in: CHP
Institution ID: 39-8046

Tulsa

Eastern Oklahoma Orthopedic Center, Inc
6475 S Yale Ave, #301
Tulsa, OK 74136
Major participating institution for programs in: FSM
Institution ID: 39-8044

Hillcrest Medical Center
1120 S Utica Ave
Tulsa, OK 74104
Med Sch Affil: M-03901
Major participating institution for programs in: EM,
FP, OBG
Institution ID: 39-0117

In His Image Inc
7600 S Lewis
Tulsa, OK 74136
www.inhisimage.org
Programs sponsored in: FP
Institution ID: 39-8016

Laureate Psychiatric Clinic and Hospital
6655 S Yale
Tulsa, OK 74136
Med Sch Affil: G-03901
Major participating institution for programs in: P
Institution ID: 39-8015

Oklahoma Surgical Hospital
2408 E 81st Street
Tulsa, OK 74137
Major participating institution for programs in: FSM
Institution ID: 39-8045

Saint Francis Health System
6161 S Yale Avenue
Tulsa, OK 74136-1902
Med Sch Affil: M-03901
Major participating institution for programs in: EM,
FSM, MPD, OBG, PD
Institution ID: 39-0479

St John Medical Center
1923 S Utica Street
Tulsa, OK 74104
Med Sch Affil: M-03901
Major participating institution for programs in: EM,
GS, IM, MPD, OBG
Institution ID: 39-0447

University of Oklahoma College of Medicine-Tulsa
Suite 2-B-30
4502 East 41st Street
Tulsa, OK 74135-2553
Med Sch Affil: M-03901
Programs sponsored in: EM, FP, FPP, FSM, GS, IM,
MPD, OBG, P, PD
Institution ID: 39-9501

Women's Health Care Specialists
4444 E 41st Street
Third Floor, Suite B
Tulsa, OK 74135-2512
Major participating institution for programs in: OBG
Institution ID: 39-8043

Oregon

Grants Pass

Three Rivers Community Hospital
500 SW Ramsey Avenue
Grants Pass, OR 97527
Major participating institution for programs in: GS
Institution ID: 40-8014

Klamath Falls

Sky Lakes Medical Center
2865 Daggett Avenue
Klamath Falls, OR 97601-1180
Med Sch Affil: L-04002
Major participating institution for programs in: FP
Institution ID: 40-8004

Milwaukie

Providence Milwaukie Hospital
10150 SE 32nd Avenue
Milwaukie, OR 97222-6593
Major participating institution for programs in: FP
Institution ID: 40-8006

Portland

Kaiser Foundation Hospitals-Northwest Region
500 NE Multnomah St
Portland, OR 97232-2099
Med Sch Affil: M-04002
Major participating institution for programs in: GE,
GS, PTH, U
Institution ID: 40-0707

Legacy Emanuel Hospital and Health Center
2801 North Gantenbein Avenue, Rm 4100
Portland, OR 97227-1623
www.legacyhealth.org/body.cfm?id=58
Med Sch Affil: M-04002
Programs sponsored in: IM, TY
Major participating institution for programs in: GS,
ORS, PDS, PE, VS
Institution ID: 40-0229

Legacy Good Samaritan Hospital and Medical Center
1015 NW 22nd Avenue R200
Portland, OR 97210-3090
Med Sch Affil: M-04002
Major participating institution for programs in: GS,
IM, IMG, OPH, TY
Institution ID: 40-0102

Oregon Health & Science University Hospital
3181 SW Sam Jackson Park Rd, L579
Portland, OR 97239-3098
http://ohsu.edu
Med Sch Affil: M-04002
Programs sponsored in: ADP, AN, CCA, CCM, CCS, CD,
CHN, CHP, D, DMP, DR, EM, END, ETX, FP, FSM, GE,
GPM, GS, HMP, HO, HPM, HSP, ICE, ID, IM, IMG, MG,
MGP, N, NDN, NEP, NM, NP, NPM, NS, OBG, OPH, ORS,
OTO, P, PAN, PCC, PCP, PD, PDC, PDE, PDR, PDS, PE,
PFP, PHO, PMM, PS, PTH, PYG, PYM, RHU, RNR, RO,
SME, TS, U, VIR, VN, VS
Major participating institution for programs in: OP
Institution ID: 40-0109

Oregon State Hospital
1225 Northeast 2nd Ave
Portland, OR 97232
Med Sch Affil: L-04002
Major participating institution for programs in: PFP
Institution ID: 40-0143

Portland State University Training Room
930 SW Hall
Portland, OR 97201
Major participating institution for programs in: FSM
Institution ID: 40-8020

Progressive Rehabilitation Services
1815 SW Marlow, #110
Portland, OR 97225
Major participating institution for programs in: GPM
Institution ID: 40-8015

Providence Health System, Portland Service Area
Regional Graduate Medical Education
10150 SE 32nd Avenue
Portland, OR 97222
Programs sponsored in: FP, IM
Institution ID: 40-8013

Providence Portland Medical Center
4805 NE Glisan
Portland, OR 97213-2967
Med Sch Affil: G-04002
Major participating institution for programs in: IM
Institution ID: 40-0398

Shriners Hospitals for Children (Portland)
3101 SW Sam Jackson Park Road
Portland, OR 97239-5090
Med Sch Affil: L-04002
Programs sponsored in: OP
Major participating institution for programs in: HSP,
MG
Institution ID: 40-0325

St Vincent Hospital and Medical Center
9205 Southwest Barnes Road
Portland, OR 97225
Med Sch Affil: M-04002
Major participating institution for programs in: EM,
GS, IM, OBG
Institution ID: 40-0133

Veterans Affairs Medical Center (Portland)
3710 SW US Veterans Hospital Road
PO Box 1034
Portland, OR 97207
Med Sch Affil: M-04002
Major participating institution for programs in: ADP,
AN, CD, D, DR, END, GE, GS, HO, HSP, ICE, ID, IM, IMG,
N, NDN, NEP, NS, OPH, ORS, OTO, P, PCC, PMM, PTH,
PYG, PYM, RHU, RNR, SME, TS, U, VIR, VN
Institution ID: 40-0171

Pennsylvania

Abington

Abington Memorial Hospital
1200 Old York Road
Abington, PA 19001-3788
www.amh.org
Med Sch Affil: M-04113
Programs sponsored in: FP, GS, IM, IMG, OBG
Major participating institution in: GE, ICE, IID, ORS, OTO, PS, RHU, RO, U
Institution ID: 41-0455

Allentown

Lehigh Valley Hospital Network
Cedar Crest Blvd & I-78
Allentown, PA 18105-1556
www.lvhn.org
Med Sch Affil: M-04115, M-04114, M-04113
Programs sponsored in: CCS, CD, CRS, EM, FP, GS, IM, OBG, PS, TY
Major participating institution for programs in: HO, U
Institution ID: 41-0724

Sacred Heart Hospital
421 Chew St
Allentown, PA 18102
www.shh.org
Med Sch Affil: M-04113
Programs sponsored in: FP, FPG
Institution ID: 41-9015

St Luke's Hospital (Allentown)
1736 Hamilton Street
Allentown, PA 18104
Programs sponsored in: OBG
Institution ID: 41-0220

Altoona

Altoona Regional Health System (Altoona Hospital Campus)
620 Howard Ave
Altoona, PA 16601
www.altoonaregional.org
Programs sponsored in: FP
Institution ID: 41-9040

Bala Cynwyd

Penn Home Care and Hospice Services
150 Monument Road
Suite 300
Bala Cynwyd, PA 19004
www.heritagevalley.org
Programs sponsored in: HPM
Institution ID: 41-0747

Beaver

HVHS, The Medical Center, Beaver
1000 Dutch Ridge Road
Beaver, PA 15009
www.heritagevalley.org
Programs sponsored in: EM, CD
Institution ID: 41-9022

Bethlehem

Lehigh Valley Hospital (Muhlenberg)
2545 Schoenersville Road
Bethlehem, PA 18017
Major participating institution for programs in: FP
Institution ID: 41-0505

St Luke's Hospital
801 Ostrum St
Bethlehem, PA 18015
www.slhhn.org
Med Sch Affil: M-04113
Programs sponsored in: EM, FP, FSM, GS, IM, OBG, ORS, TY
Institution ID: 41-0234

Bridgeville

Mayview State Hospital
1601 Mayview Road
Bridgeville, PA 15017
Major participating institution for programs in: PFP
Institution ID: 41-9057

Bryn Mawr

Bryn Mawr Hospital
130 S Bryn Mawr Ave
3rd Floor - H Wing - Suite 319
Bryn Mawr, PA 19010-3160
www.mainlinehealth.org
Med Sch Affil: M-04102, G-04101
Programs sponsored in: DR, FP
Major participating institution for programs in: ORS, PS, U
Institution ID: 41-0274

Conshohocken

Institute for Dermatopathology
20 Ash Street, Suite 310
Conshohocken, PA 19428
www.mercyhealth.org
Major participating institution for programs in: DMP
Institution ID: 41-9071

Danville

Geisinger Health System
100 North Academy Avenue
Danville, PA 17822-1384
www.geisinger.edu
Med Sch Affil: M-04102, L-04115, L-04114
Programs sponsored in: CCM, CD, D, DMP, DR, EM, ESM, FP, GE, GS, IC, ICE, IM, MPD, NEP, OBG, OPH, ORS, OTO, PCP, PD, PRD, RHU, U, VS
Institution ID: 41-8029

Geisinger Medical Center
100 N Academy Avenue
Danville, PA 17822-1334
Med Sch Affil: G-04101
Programs sponsored in: DR, ETX, GS, IM, TY
Institution ID: 41-0414

Darby

Mercy Fitzgerald Hospital
1500 S Lansdowne Avenue
Darby, PA 19023
Med Sch Affil: G-04101
Major participating institution for programs in: DR, ETX, GS, IM, TY
Institution ID: 41-8036

Drexel Hill

Crozer Keystone Health System-Delaware County Mem Hosp
501 N Lansdowne Ave
Drexel Hill, PA 19026-1186
Med Sch Affil: L-04115, G-04113
Major participating institution for programs in: FP
Institution ID: 41-0505

Easton

Easton Hospital (Northampton Hospital Corporation)
250 S 21st Street
Easton, PA 18042-3892
www.easton-hospital.com
Med Sch Affil: M-04115, G-04101
Programs sponsored in: GS, IM
Institution ID: 41-0420

Erie

Hamot Medical Center
201 State St
Erie, PA 16550
www.Hamot.org
Med Sch Affil: M-04115, L-04114
Programs sponsored in: HSO, ORS
Major participating institution for programs in: CRS
Institution ID: 41-0452

Shriners Hospitals for Children (Erie)
1645 W 8th St
Erie, PA 16505
ORS
Major participating institution for programs in: HSO, ORS
Institution ID: 41-0526

St Vincent Health Center
232 W 25th St
Erie, PA 16544-0002
www.saintvincenthealth.com
Programs sponsored in: CRS, FP, FSM
Institution ID: 41-0191

Fort Washington

Brooke Glen Behavioral Hospital
7170 Lafayette Avenue
Fort Washington, PA 19034-2301
Major participating institution for programs in: CHP
Institution ID: 41-9070

Harrisburg

PinnacleHealth Hospitals
111 S Front Street
PO Box 8700
Harrisburg, PA 17105-8700
www.pinnaclehealth.org
Med Sch Affil: L-04114
Programs sponsored in: GS, IM
Institution ID: 41-0463

PinnacleHealth System-Harrisburg Hospital
111 S Front Street
PO Box 8700
Harrisburg, PA 17105-8700
Med Sch Affil: L-04114, G-04101
Major participating institution for programs in: ETX, OBG
Institution ID: 41-0356

Pennsylvania Psychiatric Institute
2501 North Third Street
Harrisburg, PA 17110-2908
Major participating institution for programs in: P
Institution ID: 41-9036

Teaching Institutions

Hershey

Milton S Hershey Medical Center
Penn State Milton S Hershey Medical Center
500 University Drive, PO Box 850
Hershey, PA 17033-0850
www.hmc.psu.edu
Med Sch Affil: M-04114, G-04101
Programs sponsored in: AI, AN, BBK, CCP, CCS, CD, CHP, CN, CRS, D, DMP, DR, EM, END, ETX, FP, GE, GS, HO, IC, ICE, ID, IM, MPD, N, NEP, NMN, NPM, NS, OBG, OFA, OPH, ORS, OSM, OTO, P, PAN, PCC, PD, PHO, PMM, PS, PTH, RNR, SP, TS, U, VIR, VS
Institution ID: 41-0528

Johnstown

Conemaugh Valley Memorial Hospital
1086 Franklin St
Johnstown, PA 15905
www.conemaugh.org
Med Sch Affil: M-04113
Programs sponsored in: FP, GS, IM, PTH, TY
Institution ID: 41-0236

Lancaster

Lancaster General Hospital
555 N Duke Street
PO Box 3555
Lancaster, PA 17604-3555
www.lancastergeneral.org
Med Sch Affil: L-04113, L-04114
Programs sponsored in: FP, FPG, HPM
Institution ID: 41-0107

Latrobe

Latrobe Area Hospital
One Mellon Way
Latrobe, PA 15650-1096
http://LAH.com
Med Sch Affil: M-04102
Programs sponsored in: FP
Institution ID: 41-0130

Lebanon

Veterans Affairs Medical Center (Lebanon)
1700 S Lincoln Ave
Lebanon, PA 17042
Med Sch Affil: M-04114
Major participating institution for programs in: OPH
Institution ID: 41-7070

Good Samaritan Hospital
4th and Walnut Streets
PO Box 1281
Lebanon, PA 17042-1281
Med Sch Affil: G-04114
Major participating institution for programs in: FP
Institution ID: 41-0450

Malvern

Devereux Beneto Center
555 Sugartown Road
PO Box 275
Malvern, PA 19355
Major participating institution for programs in: CHP
Institution ID: 41-9017

Manayunk

Drexel Sleep Center
10 Shurs Lane
Suite 205
Manayunk, PA 19127
Major participating institution for programs in: SME
Institution ID: 41-9012

McKeesport

UPMC McKeesport
1500 Fifth Avenue
McKeesport, PA 15132
Med Sch Affil: M-04112, L-04113
Major participating institution for programs in: FP, IM, P, PM
Institution ID: 41-0497

Monroeville

Western Pennsylvania Hospital/Forbes Regional Campus
2570 Haymaker Road
Monroeville, PA 15146
www.wpahs.org
Med Sch Affil: L-04115
Programs sponsored in: FP
Major participating institution for programs in: IC
Institution ID: 41-0524

Norristown

Montgomery Hospital
1301 Powell Street
PO Box 992
Norristown, PA 19404-0992
www.montgomeryhospital.com
Med Sch Affil: M-04113, L-04115
Programs sponsored in: FP
Institution ID: 41-0495

Norristown State Hospital
1001 Sterigere Street
Norristown, PA 19401
Major participating institution for programs in: PFP
Institution ID: 41-0282

Philadelphia

Albert Einstein Medical Center
5501 Old York Road
Philadelphia, PA 19141-3098
www.einstein.edu
Programs sponsored in: CD, DR, EM, ETX, GE, GS, IC, ID, IM, IMG, N, NEP, OBG, ORS, P, PCC, PD, PYG, RHU, TY
Major participating institution for programs in: CHP, N
Institution ID: 41-0450

American Red Cross Blood Services-Penn-Jersey Region
Musser Blood Center
700 Spring Garden Street
Philadelphia, PA 19123-3594
Major participating institution for programs in: BBK
Institution ID: 41-8003

Belmont Center for Comprehensive Treatment
4200 Monument Ave
Philadelphia, PA 19131
Major participating institution for programs in: P, PYG
Institution ID: 41-0283

Chestnut Hill Hospital
8835 Germantown Ave
Graduate Medical Education Office
Philadelphia, PA 19118
www.chh.org
Med Sch Affil: M-04101, G-04115
Programs sponsored in: FP
Major participating institution for programs in: TSI
Institution ID: 41-0358

Children's Hospital of Philadelphia
One Children's Center
34th St and Civic Center Blvd
Philadelphia, PA 19104-4399
www.chop.edu
Med Sch Affil: M-04101, G-04102, G-04115, G-04113, G-03305
Programs sponsored in: ADL, AI, CCP, CHN, CHP, CHS, DBP, ETX, HPM, MG, NPM, OP, PAN, PD, PDC, PDE, PDI, PDM, PDO, PDP, PDR, PDS, PEM, PG, PHO, PMG, PN, PP, PPR, UP
Major participating institution for programs in: ACA, AN, EM, ETX, HMP, IMD, MM, MPD, NS, ORS, OTO, PAN, PD, PS, RNR, SME, U
Institution ID: 41-0189

Dermatologic Surgicenter (Philadelphia)
1200 Locust Street
Philadelphia, PA 19107
Programs sponsored in: PRD
Institution ID: 41-8052

Drexel University College of Medicine/Hahnemann University
Broad and Vine Streets
Mail Stop 623 - 4th Floor, South Tower
Philadelphia, PA 19102
www.drexel.edu/med/gme
Programs sponsored in: AN, CD, CHP, CN, D, DMP, DR, EM, ETX, FP, FSM, GE, GS, HMP, HO, IC, ICE, ID, IM, N, NEP, OBG, OPH, ORS, P, PCC, PCP, PE, PTH, RHU, RNR, RO, SME, TS
Institution ID: 41-9503

Episcopal Hospital (TUHS)
100 E Lehigh Ave
Philadelphia, PA 19125-1098
Med Sch Affil: M-04102
Major participating institution for programs in: P
Institution ID: 41-0529

Fox Chase Cancer Center
333 Cottman Avenue
Philadelphia, PA 19111
http://fccc.edu
Med Sch Affil: M-04113, G-04115
Programs sponsored in: RO
Major participating institution for programs in: HO, OTO, SP, U
Institution ID: 41-0166

Frankford Hospitals (Torresdale Campus)
Knights and Red Lion Rds
Philadelphia, PA 19114
www.frankfordhospitals.org
Med Sch Affil: M-04102, G-04101
Major participating institution for programs in: GS, IC
Institution ID: 41-0424

Friends Hospital
4641 Roosevelt Blvd
Philadelphia, PA 19124-2399
Med Sch Affil: G-04101
Major participating institution for programs in: CHP, P
Institution ID: 41-7107

Hahnemann University Hospital (Tenet Health System)
Broad and Vine Streets
Mail Stop 300
Philadelphia, PA 19102-1192
Med Sch Affil: M-04102, M-04115
Major participating institution for programs in: AN, CD, CHN, CN, D, DMP, DR, EM, ETX, FP, FSM, GE, GS, HMP, HO, IC, ICE, ID, IM, N, NEP, NPM, OBG, OPH, ORS, P, PCC, PCP, PE, PTH, RHU, RNR, RO, SME, TS
Institution ID: 41-0484

Jeanes Hospital
7600 Central Avenue
Philadelphia, PA 19111
Major participating institution for programs in: GS
Institution ID: 41-8067

Jefferson Medical College
1025 Walnut Street
Room 112
Philadelphia, PA 19107-5083
Programs sponsored in: CCP, CD, IC, IM, MPD, NEP, NPM, PD, PEM, PG, PPR
Institution ID: 41-9510

Magee Rehabilitation Hospital
Six Franklin Plaza
Philadelphia, PA 19102
Med Sch Affil: G-04101, G-04102
Major participating institution for programs in: PM
Institution ID: 41-0508

Mercy Philadelphia Hospital
5301 Cedar Avenue
Philadelphia, PA 19143
Med Sch Affil: M-04115
Major participating institution for programs in: DR, EM, ETX, GS, IM, TY
Institution ID: 41-0499

Methodist Hospital
2301 S Broad St
Philadelphia, PA 19148
Med Sch Affil: M-04102
Major participating institution for programs in: EM, VS
Institution ID: 41-0306

Moss Rehabilitation Hospital
1200 West Tabor Road
Philadelphia, PA 19141
Med Sch Affil: G-04113
Major participating institution for programs in: FPG, PM
Institution ID: 41-0515

Northwestern Human Services of Philadelphia
11082 Knights Road
Philadelphia, PA 19154
Major participating institution for programs in: CHP, P
Institution ID: 41-8055

Pennsylvania Hospital (UPHS)
800 Spruce Street
Philadelphia, PA 19107-6192
http://pahosp.com
Med Sch Affil: M-04101
Programs sponsored in: DR, IM, OBG, OSM, PTH, SP, VS
Major participating institution for programs in: CRS, FSM, GS, NS, ORS, OTO, P, PMM, PS, U
Institution ID: 41-0235

Philadelphia Prison System
7901 State Road
Philadelphia, PA 19136
Major participating institution for programs in: PFP
Institution ID: 41-9065

Presbyterian Medical Center (UPHS)
51 N 39th Street
Philadelphia, PA 19104-2699
Med Sch Affil: M-04101
Major participating institution for programs in: ACA, AI, AN, FP, GE, GS, HSO, IC, ICE, IMD, MPD, OAR, OPH, ORS, TSI, U
Institution ID: 41-0323

Shriners Hospitals for Children (Philadelphia)
3551 North Broad Street
Philadelphia, PA 19140-4105
Med Sch Affil: G-04115, G-04113
Major participating institution for programs in: HSO
Institution ID: 41-0110

St Christopher's Hospital for Children (Tenet Health System)
Erie Avenue at Front Street
Philadelphia, PA 19134-1095
Med Sch Affil: M-04115, G-04113, G-04102
Programs sponsored in: CHN, NPM, PAN, PD, PDE, PDI, PDR, PDS, PG, PHO, PP
Major participating institution for programs in: CHP, ETX, FSM, N, ORS, OTO, PD, PE, PS, RHU, SME, TS, U
Institution ID: 41-0380

Temple University Hospital
3401 N Broad St
Philadelphia, PA 19140
www.temple.edu/tuhs/
Med Sch Affil: M-04113
Programs sponsored in: AN, CD, CN, DR, EM, END, GE, GS, HO, IC, ICE, ID, IM, IMG, MSR, N, NEP, NS, OBG, OPH, ORS, OTO, P, PCC, PM, PMM, PS, PTH, RHU, RNR, SME, U, VS
Institution ID: 41-0413

Thomas Jefferson University Hospital
111 S 11th St
Philadelphia, PA 19107
www.jeffersonhospital.org
Med Sch Affil: M-04102, G-04115
Programs sponsored in: AI, AN, AR, BBK, CD, CHP, CN, CRS, D, DMP, DR, EM, END, FP, FPG, FSM, GE, GS, HMP, HO, HSO, IC, ICE, ID, IM, MSR, N, NEP, NM, NS, OAR, OBG, OP, OPH, ORS, OSM, OTO, P, PAN, PCC, PCP, PM, PMM, PPM, PTH, PYM, RHU, RNR, RO, SME, SP, THP, U, UP, VIR, VN, VS
Institution ID: 41-0224

University of Pennsylvania Health System
3400 Spruce Street
1 Maloney Bldg
Philadelphia, PA 19104
www.uphs.upenn.edu/gme/
Med Sch Affil: M-04101, L-04114
Programs sponsored in: ACA, ADP, AI, AN, AR, BBK, CCA, CCS, CD, CN, CRS, CTR, D, DMP, DR, EM, END, FP, FSM, GE, GPM, GS, HMP, HO, HPM, HSO, IC, ICE, ID, IM, IMD, IMG, MDG, MGP, MM, MPD, MSR, N, NEP, NM, NP, NR, NS, OAR, OBG, OPH, ORS, OTO, P, PCC, PCP, PFP, PM, PMM, PS, PTH, PYG, PYM, RHU, RNR, RO, SME, SP, TS, TSI, U, UME, VIR, VN, VS
Major participating institution for programs in: CHN, ETX, NPM, PDM, TS
Institution ID: 41-0106

Veterans Affairs Medical Center (Philadelphia)
University and Woodland Avenues
Philadelphia, PA 19104
Med Sch Affil: M-04101, L-04115
Major participating institution for programs in: AN, D, DMP, END, ICE, IMD, IMG, MDG, OPH, ORS, OTO, P, PDM, PFP, PM, PYG, PYM, RO, SME, U
Institution ID: 41-0285

Wills Eye Institute
840 Walnut Street
Suite 800
Philadelphia, PA 19107-5109
www.willseye.org
Major participating institution for programs in: OPH
Institution ID: 41-0494

Pittsburgh

Allegheny County Behavior Assessment Unit
Court of Common Plea Criminal Division
564 Forbes Ave, 4th Floor
Pittsburgh, PA 15219
Major participating institution for programs in: PFP
Institution ID: 41-9061

Allegheny County Medical Examiner's Office
542 Fourth Avenue
Pittsburgh, PA 15219
http://webmaster.coroner.county.allegheny.pa.us
Programs sponsored in: FOP
Institution ID: 41-0531

Allegheny General Hospital
320 E North Avenue
Pittsburgh, PA 15212-4772
http://wpahs.org
Med Sch Affil: M-04115, G-04112
Programs sponsored in: CD, CHP, CN, DR, EM, ESM, GE, GS, HSO, IC, IM, MEM, N, NEP, NS, OBG, ORS, P, PCC, PCP, PTH, RNR, RO, TS, VIR, VN, VS
Major participating institution for programs in: AN, HO, PMM
Institution ID: 41-0465

Asbury Health Center
700 Bower Hill Road
Pittsburgh, PA 15243
Major participating institution for programs in: IMG
Institution ID: 41-9046

Canterbury Place
310 Fisk Street
Pittsburgh, PA 15201
Major participating institution for programs in: IMG
Institution ID: 41-9042

Charles Morris Center Nursing & Rehabilitation
200 JHF Drive
Pittsburgh, PA 15217
Major participating institution for programs in: IMG
Institution ID: 41-9043

Children's Hospital of Pittsburgh of UPMC
3705 5th Avenue
Pittsburgh, PA 15213-2583
Med Sch Affil: M-04112
Major participating institution for programs in: ADL, AI, BBK, CCP, CCS, CHN, CPP, DBP, HSO, MG, MPD, NDN, NP, NPM, NS, ORS, PAN, PD, PDC, PDE, PDI, PDO, PDP, PDR, PDS, PEM, PG, PHO, PN, PP, PPR, PTP, RNR, SME, U, UP
Institution ID: 41-0161

Family Hospice and Palliative Care
50 Moffett Street
Pittsburgh, PA 15243
Major participating institution for programs in: HPM
Institution ID: 41-9049

Heritage Shadyside
5700 Phillips Ave
Pittsburgh, PA 15217
Major participating institution for programs in: IMG
Institution ID: 41-9044

Institute for Transfusion Medicine
812 Fifth Ave
Pittsburgh, PA 15219
Major participating institution for programs in: BBK
Institution ID: 41-8030

Jefferson Regional Medical Center
565 Coal Valley Road
PO Box 18119
Pittsburgh, PA 15236
Major participating institution for programs in: HSO
Institution ID: 41-9009

Magee-Womens Hospital of UPMC
300 Halket Street
Pittsburgh, PA 15213
Med Sch Affil: M-04112
Major participating institution for programs in: CPP, MG, NPM, OBG, PCP, PDI, PG, PP, PS, PSI, PTH, SP
Institution ID: 41-0208

Teaching Institutions

Mercy Hospital of Pittsburgh

1400 Locust Street
Pittsburgh, PA 15219-5166
www.pmhs.org/gme
Med Sch Affil: M-04102, G-04112
Major participating institution for programs in: AN, DR, EM, GS, PM, TY
Institution ID: 41-0196

Pittsburgh Poison Center

Children's Hospital of Pittsburgh
Birmingham Towers, Suite 700
Pittsburgh, PA 15203
Major participating institution for programs in: ETX
Institution ID: 41-8051

Univ of Pittsburgh Medical Center Medical Education

3600 Forbes Avenue
Iroquois Building, Suite 300
Pittsburgh, PA 15213
www.upmc.com
Med Sch Affil: M-04112
Programs sponsored in: ADL, ADP, AI, AN, BBK, CCA, CCM, CCP, CCS, CD, CHN, CHP, CN, CPP, D, DBP, DMP, DR, EM, END, ETX, FP, FPG, FPP, FSM, GE, GS, HMP, HO, HPM, HSO, HSP, IC, ICE, ID, IM, IMG, MG, MGP, MPD, N, NDN, NEP, NO, NP, NPM, NS, OBG, OPH, ORS, OSM, OTO, P, PAN, PCC, PCP, PD, PDC, PDE, PDI, PDO, PDP, PDR, PDS, PEM, PFP, PG, PHO, PM, PMM, PN, PP, PPR, PS, PSI, PTH, PTP, PYG, RHU, RNR, RO, SCI, @LIST PRGNUM = Institution ID: 41-8024

UPMC Passavant

9100 Babcock Boulevard
Pittsburgh, PA 15237
Major participating institution for programs in: TS, VS, VSI
Institution ID: 41-9035

UPMC Presbyterian Shadyside

200 Lothrop Street
Suite N739 MUH
Pittsburgh, PA 15213
Major participating institution for programs in: AI, AN, BBK, CCA, CCM, CCS, CD, CHN, CN, CPP, D, DMP, DR, EM, END, FP, FSM, GE, GS, HMP, HO, HSO, HSP, IC, ICE, ID, IM, IMG, MGP, MPD, N, NDN, NEP, NO, NP, NS, OPH, ORS, OSM, OTO, PCC, PCP, PM, PRD, PS, PSI, PTH, PYG, RHU, RNR, RO, SCI, SME, SP, THP, TS, TY, U, VS, VSI
Institution ID: 41-8048

UPMC South Side

2000 Mary Street
RMB North Suite 101
Pittsburgh, PA 15203
Major participating institution for programs in: FSM, ORS, OSM, PM, SCI
Institution ID: 41-8062

UPMC St Margaret

815 Freeport Road
Pittsburgh, PA 15215-3399
Med Sch Affil: M-04112
Major participating institution for programs in: FP, FPG, FPP, FSM, GS, OSM, PMM, VS, VSI
Institution ID: 41-0324

UPMC Western Psychiatric Institute and Clinic

3811 O'Hara St
Pittsburgh, PA 15213
Med Sch Affil: M-04112
Major participating institution for programs in: ADP, CHP, CPP, FPP, P, PFP, PYG
Institution ID: 41-0462

Veterans Affairs Medical Center (Pittsburgh)

University Drive
Pittsburgh, PA 15240
Med Sch Affil: M-04112
Major participating institution for programs in: ADP, CCA, CCM, CPP, D, GE, GS, IM, IMG, OPH, ORS, PYG, SME, TS, TY, U
Institution ID: 41-0296

Western Pennsylvania Hospital

4800 Friendship Ave
Pittsburgh, PA 15224
http://westpennhospital.org
Med Sch Affil: M-04112, M-04113
Programs sponsored in: AN, CD, FP, HO, IC, IM, OBG, PMM, PUD, TY
Major participating institution for programs in: GE, VIR
Institution ID: 41-0122

Zitelli and Brodland PC

5200 Centre Ave, Suite 303
Pittsburgh, PA 15232
Programs sponsored in: PRD
Institution ID: 41-8068

Sayre

Robert Packer Hospital

One Guthrie Square
Sayre, PA 18840-1698
www.guthrie.org
Med Sch Affil: L-04115
Programs sponsored in: FP, GS, IM
Institution ID: 41-0352

Scranton

Mercy Hospital

746 Jefferson Ave
Scranton, PA 18501
Med Sch Affil: M-04113
Major participating institution for programs in: IM
Institution ID: 41-0717

Moses Taylor Hospital

700 Quincy Ave
Scranton, PA 18510
Med Sch Affil: M-04113
Major participating institution for programs in: IM
Institution ID: 41-0718

Scranton-Temple Residency Program Inc

746 Jefferson Avenue
Scranton, PA 18510
www.strpweb.org
Programs sponsored in: IM
Institution ID: 41-0719

Springfield

Springfield Hospital

190 W Sproul Rd
Springfield, PA 19064
Major participating institution for programs in: FSM
Institution ID: 41-9005

Upland

Crozer-Chester Medical Center

One Medical Center Blvd
Professional Office Bldg #1 Suite 302
Upland, PA 19013-3995
www.crozer.org
Med Sch Affil: M-04113, G-04102, G-04101
Programs sponsored in: FP, FSM, IM, OBG, PD, TY
Major participating institution for programs in: CN, GS, IMG, SME
Institution ID: 41-0511

Washington

Washington Hospital

155 Wilson Ave
Washington, PA 15301
www.washingtonhospital.org
Med Sch Affil: L-04112
Programs sponsored in: FP
Major participating institution for programs in: IC
Institution ID: 41-0385

West Reading

Reading Hospital and Medical Center

6th Ave and Spruce St
PO Box 16052
West Reading, PA 19612-6052
www.readinghospital.org
Med Sch Affil: M-04113, M-04114, G-04101
Programs sponsored in: FP, IM, OBG, TY
Institution ID: 41-0305

Wexford

Hand and UpperEx Center (Wexford Office)

6001 Stonewood Drive
Wexford, PA 15090
Major participating institution for programs in: HSO, HSP
Institution ID: 41-9008

Wilkes-Barre

Geisinger Wyoming Valley Medical Center

100 East Mountain Drive
Wilkes-Barre, PA 18711
Major participating institution for programs in: CCM, ESM, FP, GS
Institution ID: 41-8060

Veterans Affairs Medical Center (Wilkes-Barre)

1111 East End Boulevard
Wilkes-Barre, PA 18711
Med Sch Affil: G-04115
Major participating institution for programs in: OPH
Institution ID: 41-0517

Wyoming Valley Health Care System

North River and Auburn Streets
Wilkes-Barre, PA 18764
www.wvhcs.org
Programs sponsored in: FP
Institution ID: 41-8035

Williamsport

Susquehanna Health System

777 Rural Avenue
Williamsport, PA 17701
www.shscares.org
Programs sponsored in: FP
Institution ID: 41-0147

Wynnewood

Lankenau Hospital

100 Lancaster Ave
Wynnewood, PA 19096-3498
www.mainlinehealth.org
Med Sch Affil: M-04102, G-04113, G-04101
Programs sponsored in: CD, GE, GS, HO, IC, ICE, IM, NEP, OBG
Major participating institution for programs in: ID, OPH, OSM
Institution ID: 41-0403

York

Orthopaedic and Spine Specialists
1855 Powder Mill Road
York, PA 17402
Major participating institution for programs in: PMM
Institution ID: 41-8047

York Hospital
1001 South George Street
PO Box 15198
York, PA 17405
www.wellspan.org
Med Sch Affil: M-04114, M-04101, L-02301
Programs sponsored in: EM, FP, GS, IM, OBG
Institution ID: 41-0142

Puerto Rico

Bayamon

Hospital Universitario Dr Ramon Ruiz Arnau
Avenida Laurel-Santa Juanita
Bayamon, PR 00619
Med Sch Affil: M-04203
Major participating institution for programs in: IM
Institution ID: 42-7019

Universidad Central del Caribe School of Medicine
PO Box 60327
Bayamon, PR 00960-6032
www.uccaribe.edu
Programs sponsored in: IM
Institution ID: 42-9501

Carolina

University of Puerto Rico Hospital at Carolina
65th Infantry Ave, Km 8.3 Road 3
Km 8.3 Road 3
Carolina, PR 00985
Major participating institution for programs in: AN, CHP, DR, EM, FP, FPG, IM, IMG, P
Institution ID: 42-8015

Cidra

First Hospital Panamericano
State Road 787, KM 1.5
PO Box 1398
Cidra, PR 00739
Med Sch Affil: M-04203, L-04202, L-04201
Major participating institution for programs in: CHP, P
Institution ID: 42-8021

Manati

Hospital Dr Alejandro Otero Lopez
PO Box 1142
Manati, PR 00674-1142
www.haol.homestead.com
Med Sch Affil: L-04203
Programs sponsored in: FP
Institution ID: 42-8016

Mayaguez

Advanced Cardiology Center Corp/Ponce SOM Consortium
410 Hostos Avenue/Ramon E Betances Univ Hospital
Mayaguez, PR 00680
Major participating institution for programs in: IM
Institution ID: 42-8026

ASSMCA (Mayaguez)
Western Region
410 Ave de Hostos Suite 7
Mayaguez, PR 00680
Major participating institution for programs in: CHP
Institution ID: 42-8042

Bella Vista Hospital
State Road 349
PO Box 1750
Mayaguez, PR 00681
Programs sponsored in: FP
Institution ID: 42-8022

Dr Ramon E Betances Hospital-Mayaguez Medical Center
Mayaguez Medical Center
410 Hostos Ave
Mayaguez, PR 00680
Med Sch Affil: G-04202
Programs sponsored in: IM
Institution ID: 42-0467

Ponce School Mental Health Clinics
Mayaguez Medical Center
Mayaguez, PR 00738
Major participating institution for programs in: P
Institution ID: 42-8039

Ponce

Damas Hospital
2213 Ponce By Pass
Ponce, PR 00717-1318
www.hospitaldamas.com
Med Sch Affil: M-04202
Programs sponsored in: IM, TY
Institution ID: 42-0289

Dr Pila Hospital
Avenida Las Americas
PO Box 331910
Ponce, PR 00733-1910
Med Sch Affil: M-04202
Programs sponsored in: FP
Institution ID: 42-7016

Hospital Episcopal San Lucas
917 Tito Castro Ave
PO Box 336810
Ponce, PR 00733-6810
www.ssepr.com
Med Sch Affil: M-04202
Programs sponsored in: EM, IM, OBG, PD, TY
Major participating institution for programs in: CHP, TY
Institution ID: 42-0194

Playa Medical Center
Ave Hostos #1058
Ponce, PR 00731
Major participating institution for programs in: IM
Institution ID: 42-8030

Ponce School of Medicine
PO Box 7004
Ponce, PR 00732-7004
www.psm.edu
Programs sponsored in: CHP, P
Major participating institution for programs in: IM
Institution ID: 42-9505

San German

Hospital de la Concepcion
Oficina de Educacion Medica
PO Box 285
San German, PR 00683
www.hospitalconcepcion.org
Med Sch Affil: M-04202
Programs sponsored in: IM
Institution ID: 42-0478

San Juan

Cardiovascular Center of Puerto Rico and the Caribbean
PO Box 366528
San Juan, PR 00936
Major participating institution for programs in: AN, CD
Institution ID: 42-8029

HealthSouth Rehabilitation Hospital
Puerto Rico Medical Center
PMB 340 PO Box 70344
San Juan, PR 00936-0344
Major participating institution for programs in: PM
Institution ID: 42-8024

Hospital Pavia
1462 Asia Street
Aptdo 11137, Santurce
San Juan, PR 00910
Med Sch Affil: L-04201
Major participating institution for programs in: U
Institution ID: 42-7006

I Gonzalez Martinez Oncologic Hospital
Puerto Rico Medical Center
PO Box 1811
San Juan, PR 00919
Med Sch Affil: L-04201
Major participating institution for programs in: GS, ORS
Institution ID: 42-0205

Institute of Forensic Sciences of Puerto Rico
Box 11878, Caparra Heights Station
San Juan, PR 00922-1878
Med Sch Affil: L-04201
Major participating institution for programs in: FOP
Institution ID: 42-0461

San Jorge Children"s Hospital
258 San Jorge Street
San Juan, PR 00912
Major participating institution for programs in: PD
Institution ID: 42-8052

San Juan City Hospital
PMB 498
PO Box 70344
San Juan, PR 00936-8344
www.ms4c.org/obgyn/pr-2.shtml
Med Sch Affil: M-04203, M-04201
Programs sponsored in: HEM, IM, OBG, ON, PD, PUD, TY
Major participating institution for programs in: CHN, N, ORS, OTO
Institution ID: 42-0320

University Hospital
Puerto Rico Medical Center
PO Box 2116
San Juan, PR 00922
Med Sch Affil: M-04201
Major participating institution for programs in: AN, CD, CHN, D, DR, END, FP, GE, GS, HO, ID, IM, IMG, N, NEP, NM, NMN, NS, OBG, OPH, ORS, OTO, PM, PTH, PUD, RHU, TY, U
Institution ID: 42-0178

University of Puerto Rico School of Medicine
Medical Sciences Campus
PO Box 365067
San Juan, PR 00936-5067
http://rcm.upr.edu
Med Sch Affil: M-04201
Programs sponsored in: AN, CCP, CD, CHN, CHP, D, DR, EM, END, FOP, FP, FPG, GE, GS, HO, ID, IM, IMG, N, NEP, NM, NMN, NPM, NS, OBG, OPH, ORS, OTO, P, PD, PHO, PM, PTH, PUD, RHU, U
Institution ID: 42-0464

Teaching Institutions

University Pediatric Hospital
PO Box 191079
San Juan, PR 00919-1079
Med Sch Affil: M-04201
Major participating institution for programs in: AN,
CCP, CHN, CHP, NPM, NS, ORS, P, PD, PHO, PM, U
Institution ID: 42-0477

VA Caribbean Healthcare System
10 Casia Street
San Juan, PR 00921-3201
http://152.130.130.32/
Med Sch Affil: M-04203, M-04201
Programs sponsored in: CCM, CD, GE, ID, IM, NEP,
PCC, PM
Major participating institution for programs in: AN,
FPG, GS, HEM, ID, IMG, N, NM, ON, OPH, ORS, OTO, P,
PUD, U
Institution ID: 42-0265

Rhode Island

East Providence

Emma Pendleton Bradley Hospital
1011 Veterans Memorial Parkway
East Providence, RI 02915-5099
Med Sch Affil: M-04301
Major participating institution for programs in: CHP
Institution ID: 43-0432

Pawtucket

Memorial Hospital of Rhode Island
111 Brewster Street
Pawtucket, RI 02860
www.MHRI.org
Med Sch Affil: M-04301
Programs sponsored in: FP, IM
Major participating institution for programs in: DBP,
ID, PCC, U
Institution ID: 43-0436

Rhode Island Foundation for Colon and Rectal Diseases
334 East Avenue
Pawtucket, RI 02860
www.ricolorectalclinic.com
Programs sponsored in: CRS
Institution ID: 43-8015

Providence

Butler Hospital
345 Blackstone Blvd
Providence, RI 02906
www.butler.org
Med Sch Affil: M-04301
Programs sponsored in: P, PYG, PYN
Institution ID: 43-0483

Miriam Hospital-Lifespan
164 Summit Avenue
Providence, RI 02906
Med Sch Affil: M-04301
Major participating institution for programs in: CCM,
CD, CRS, EM, GS, HO, IC, ID, IM, NEP, ORS, OSM, P,
PTH, PYG, U
Institution ID: 43-0232

Providence Community Health Center
375 Allens Ave
Providence, RI 02905-5010
Major participating institution for programs in: D
Institution ID: 43-8014

Rhode Island Hospital-Lifespan
593 Eddy St
Aldrich Building, Room 120
Providence, RI 02903
Med Sch Affil: M-04301, G-02405
Programs sponsored in: CCM, CCS, CD, CHP, CN, CPP,
CRS, D, DBP, DR, EM, END, GE, GS, HO, HSO, IC, ICE,
ID, IM, IMG, MPD, N, NEP, NP, NS, OP, OPH, ORS, OSM,
PCC, PD, PDE, PDI, PDS, PEM, PG, PHO, PS, PTH, RHU,
SME, U, VIR
Major participating institution for programs in: HO,
ID, OTO, P, PP, PYN, RHU, RO
Institution ID: 43-0281

Rhode Island Vascular Institute
690 Eddy Street
Providence, RI 02903
Major participating institution for programs in: VIR
Institution ID: 43-8016

Roger Williams Medical Center
825 Chalkstone Avenue
Providence, RI 02908
http://rwmc.org
Med Sch Affil: M-02405
Programs sponsored in: D, DMP, HO, ID, IM, PUD, RHU
Major participating institution for programs in: CRS,
END, PCC
Institution ID: 43-0438

Veterans Affairs Medical Center (Providence)
Providence, RI 02908
Med Sch Affil: M-04301
Major participating institution for programs in: CD,
D, END, GE, GS, NEP, OPH, ORS, P, PCC, PS, PYG, RHU,
U
Institution ID: 43-0439

Women and Infants Hospital of Rhode Island
101 Dudley Street
Providence, RI 02905-2499
www.womenandinfants.com
Med Sch Affil: M-04301
Programs sponsored in: NPM, OBG, PP
Major participating institution for programs in: CRS,
PD, PDE, PDI, PDS
Institution ID: 43-0334

South Carolina

Anderson

AnMed Health
800 N Fant St
Anderson, SC 29621
www.AnMed.com
Med Sch Affil: L-04501, L-04504
Programs sponsored in: FP, FSM
Institution ID: 45-0732

Charleston

Charleston Center of Charleston County
5 Charleston Center Drive
Charleston, SC 29401
Major participating institution for programs in: ADP
Institution ID: 45-8034

Charleston/Dorchester Community Mental Health Center
960 Morrison Drive
Charleston, SC 29403
Major participating institution for programs in: PFP
Institution ID: 45-8020

Dee Norton Lowcountry Children's Center
1061 King Street
Charleston, SC 29403
Major participating institution for programs in: CHP
Institution ID: 45-8037

Medical University of South Carolina College of Medicine
169 Ashley Avenue (Room 202 - Main Hospital)
PO Box 250333
Charleston, SC 29425
www.musc.edu/gme
Med Sch Affil: M-04501
Programs sponsored in: ACA, ADP, AN, CCS, CD, CHP,
CN, D, DBP, DMP, DR, EM, END, FOP, GE, GS, HMP, HO,
IC, ICE, ID, IM, MP, MPD, N, NEP, NM, NPM, NS, OBG,
OPH, ORS, OTO, P, PCC, PCP, PD, PDC, PDE, PFP, PHO,
PRD, PS, PTH, PYG, PYN, RHU, RNR, RO, TS, TSI, U, VIR,
VN
Institution ID: 45-9501

MUSC Medical Center
171 Ashley Avenue
Charleston, SC 29425-0950
Med Sch Affil: M-04501, L-04504
Major participating institution for programs in: ACA,
ADP, AN, CCS, CD, CHP, CN, D, DBP, DMP, DR, EM,
END, FOP, FP, GE, GS, HMP, HO, IC, ICE, ID, IM, MP,
MPD, N, NEP, NM, NPM, OBG, OPH, ORS, OTO, P, PCC,
PCP, PD, PDC, PDE, PHO, PRD, PS, PTH, PYN, RHU,
RNR, RO, TS, TSI, TY, U, VIR, VN
Institution ID: 45-0152

Ralph H Johnson VA Medical Center (Charleston)
109 Bee Street
Charleston, SC 29401
Med Sch Affil: M-04501
Major participating institution for programs in: ADP,
CD, D, DR, END, GE, IC, ID, IM, MP, N, NEP, OPH, ORS,
OTO, P, PYG, PYN, RHU, TS, TSI, U
Institution ID: 45-0485

Trident Medical Center
9330 Medical Plaza Drive
Charleston, SC 29406-9195
www.tridenthealthsystem.com
Programs sponsored in: FP, TY
Major participating institution for programs in: PS
Institution ID: 45-8009

Columbia

Palmetto Health
PO Box 2266
Columbia, SC 29202-2266
www.palmettohealth.org
Programs sponsored in: CCS, CHP, EM, END, FP, FSM,
GS, IM, IMG, MPD, OBG, OPH, ORS, P, PD, PFP, PUD,
PYG
Institution ID: 45-8005

Palmetto Health Baptist
Taylor at Marion Street
Columbia, SC 29220
Med Sch Affil: M-04504
Major participating institution for programs in: P,
PYG
Institution ID: 45-8006

Palmetto Health Richland
Five Richland Medical Park
Columbia, SC 29203
Med Sch Affil: M-04504, L-04501
Major participating institution for programs in: EM,
END, FP, FSM, GS, IM, IMG, MPD, OBG, OPH,
ORS, P, PD, PUD
Institution ID: 45-0366

South Carolina Department of Mental Health (SCDMH)
7901 Farrow Road
Columbia, SC 29203
Major participating institution for programs in: PFP
Institution ID: 45-8026

University of South Carolina School of Medicine
Neuropsychiatry Speciality Clinic
15 Medical Park, Suite 141
Columbia, SC 29203
Major participating institution for programs in: CHP, P, PFP, PYG
Institution ID: 45-8021

University of South Carolina School of Medicine
6439 Garners Ferry Road
VA Bldg 3
Columbia, SC 29208
www.med.sc.edu
Med Sch Affil: M-04504
Programs sponsored in: GPM
Institution ID: 45-8001

William Jennings Bryan Dorn Veterans Hospital
6439 Garners Ferry Rd
Columbia, SC 29209-1639
Med Sch Affil: M-04504
Major participating institution for programs in: END, FP, GS, IM, IMG, MPD, OPH, ORS, P, PUD
Institution ID: 45-0735

Florence

McLeod Regional Medical Center
555 E Cheves Street
Florence, SC 29506
www.mcleodhealth.org
Med Sch Affil: L-04504, L-04501
Programs sponsored in: FP
Institution ID: 45-0239

Greenville

Greenville Hospital System/University of South Carolina
701 Grove Road
Greenville, SC 29605
www.ghs.org
Med Sch Affil: M-04504, L-04501
Programs sponsored in: DBP, FP, FSM, GS, IM, MPD, OBG, ORS, PD, VS
Major participating institution for programs in: OSM
Institution ID: 45-0367

Shriners Hospitals for Children (Greenville)
950 W Faris Road
Greenville, SC 29605-4277
Med Sch Affil: L-03607
Major participating institution for programs in: ORS
Institution ID: 45-0174

Steadman Hawkins Clinic of the Carolinas
200 Patewood Drive
Suite C100
Greenville, SC 29615
Programs sponsored in: OSM
Institution ID: 45-8027

Greenwood

Greenwood Genetic Center
101 Gregor Mendel Circle
Greenwood, SC 29646
www.ggc.org
Programs sponsored in: MG
Institution ID: 45-8004

Self Regional Healthcare
1325 Spring St
Greenwood, SC 29646
www.selfregional.org
Med Sch Affil: L-04504, L-04501
Programs sponsored in: FP, FSM
Major participating institution for programs in: MG
Institution ID: 45-7024

Mt Pleasant

Hollings Cancer Center-Mt Pleasant
1200 B Johnnie Dodds Avenue
Mt Pleasant, SC 29464
Major participating institution for programs in: RO
Institution ID: 45-8025

Seneca

Oconee Memorial Hospital
298 Memorial Drive
Seneca, SC 29672
Major participating institution for programs in: FP
Institution ID: 45-8007

Spartanburg

Spartanburg Regional Healthcare System
101 E Wood Street
Spartanburg, SC 29303
www.srhs.org
Med Sch Affil: L-04504, L-04501
Programs sponsored in: FP, GS, TY
Institution ID: 45-0162

South Dakota

Rapid City

Rapid City Regional Hospital
353 Fairmont Blvd
PO Box 6000
Rapid City, SD 57709
www.rcrh.org
Med Sch Affil: M-04601
Programs sponsored in: FP
Institution ID: 46-8005

Sioux Falls

Avera McKennan Hospital and University Health Center
800 E 21st Street
PO Box 5045
Sioux Falls, SD 57117-5045
Med Sch Affil: M-04601
Major participating institution for programs in: CHP, FP, IM, P, TY
Institution ID: 46-0125

Center for Family Medicine
1115 E 20th Street
Sioux Falls, SD 57105
www.siouxfallsfpr.org/
Programs sponsored in: FP
Institution ID: 46-0219

Children's Home Society
801 N Sycamore Ave
Sioux Falls, SD 57110
Major participating institution for programs in: CHP
Institution ID: 46-8008

Royal C Johnson Veterans Affairs Medical Center
2501 W 22nd Street
PO Box 5046
Sioux Falls, SD 57117
Med Sch Affil: M-04601
Major participating institution for programs in: IM, P, PTH
Institution ID: 46-0218

Sanford USD Medical Center
1305 West 18th Street
Sioux Falls, SD 57117
Major participating institution for programs in: TY
Institution ID: 46-8006

Sioux Valley Hospital University of SD Medical Center
1305 West 18th Street
PO Box 5039
Sioux Falls, SD 57117-5039
Med Sch Affil: M-04601
Major participating institution for programs in: CHP, FP, IM, PTH
Institution ID: 46-0212

University of South Dakota School of Medicine
1400 W 22nd St
Sioux Falls, SD 57105-1570
www.usd.edu/med/residencies/
Programs sponsored in: CHP, IM, P, PTH, TY
Institution ID: 46-9501

Tennessee

Bristol

Wellmont Health System - Bristol Regional Medical Center
1 Medical Park Boulevard
Bristol, TN 37620
Med Sch Affil: M-04720
Major participating institution for programs in: FP, GS, PCC
Institution ID: 47-0491

Chattanooga

Erlanger Medical Center
975 E Third Street
Chattanooga, TN 37403
Med Sch Affil: M-04706
Major participating institution for programs in: CCS, EM, FP, FPG, GS, HPM, IM, OBG, ORS, PS, TY, VS
Institution ID: 47-0330

Hospice of Chattanooga
4411 Oakwood Drive
Chattanooga, TN 37416
Major participating institution for programs in: HPM
Institution ID: 47-8052

Memorial Hospital
2525 DeSales Ave
Chattanooga, TN 37404
Med Sch Affil: M-04720
Major participating institution for programs in: VS
Institution ID: 47-7001

Parkridge Medical Center
2333 McCallie Avenue
Chattanooga, TN 37404
Major participating institution for programs in: VS
Institution ID: 47-8038

T C Thompson Children's Hospital Medical Center
910 Blackford Street
Chattanooga, TN 37403
Med Sch Affil: M-04706
Major participating institution for programs in: ORS, PD
Institution ID: 47-0313

University of Tennessee College of Medicine-Chattanooga

960 East Third Street
Suite 100
Chattanooga, TN 37403
www.utcomchatt.org
Med Sch Affil: M-04706
Programs sponsored in: CCS, EM, FP, FPG, GS, HPM, IM, OBG, ORS, PD, PS, TY, VS
Institution ID: 47-0490

Jackson

Jackson-Madison County General Hospital

708 W Forest Ave
Jackson, TN 38305
Med Sch Affil: G-04706
Major participating institution for programs in: FP
Institution ID: 47-0480

Sports, Orthopedics, and Spine Educational Foundation

569 Skyline Drive, Suite 100
Sports, Orthopedics & Spine, 569 Skyline Dr
Jackson, TN 38301
Programs sponsored in: OSM
Institution ID: 47-8040

Johnson City

James H Quillen College of Medicine

East Tennessee State University
PO Box 70694
Johnson City, TN 37614-1704
www.etsu.edu
Med Sch Affil: M-04720
Programs sponsored in: CD, FP, GS, ID, IM, MP, OBG, ON, P, PCC, PD, PTH
Institution ID: 47-0492

Johnson City Medical Center/Mountain States Health Alliance

400 State of Franklin Road
Johnson City, TN 37604
Med Sch Affil: M-04720
Major participating institution for programs in: CD, FP, GS, ID, IM, MP, OBG, ON, P, PCC, PD, PTH
Institution ID: 47-0499

Woodridge Hospital/Mountain States Health Alliance

403 State of Franklin Road
Johnson City, TN 37604
Med Sch Affil: M-04720
Major participating institution for programs in: P
Institution ID: 47-0493

Kingsport

Wellmont Health System - Holston Valley

130 West Ravine Road
Kingsport, TN 37662
Med Sch Affil: M-04720
Major participating institution for programs in: FP, GS, IM
Institution ID: 47-0379

Knoxville

East Tennessee Children's Hospital (Knoxville)

2018 Clinch Avenue
Knoxville, TN 37916
Major participating institution for programs in: U
Institution ID: 47-8036

Knoxville Orthopedic Clinic

1128 Weisgarber Rd
Knoxville, TN 37909
Major participating institution for programs in: FSM
Institution ID: 47-8022

University of Tennessee Graduate School of Medicine

1924 Alcoa Highway, Box 94
Knoxville, TN 37920-6999
http://gsm.utmck.edu
Med Sch Affil: M-04706
Programs sponsored in: AN, CCS, CD, DR, FP, FPG, FSM, GS, IM, NM, OBG, PCP, PTH, PUD, TY, U, VS
Institution ID: 47-0448

University of Tennessee Memorial Hospital

1924 Alcoa Highway
Knoxville, TN 37920
Major participating institution for programs in: AN, CCS, CD, DR, FP, FPG, FSM, GS, IM, NM, OBG, PCP, PTH, PUD, TY, U, VS
Institution ID: 47-8023

University of Tennessee Student Health Services Clinic

1818 Andy Holt Drive
Knoxville, TN 37996-2800
Major participating institution for programs in: FSM
Institution ID: 47-8051

Memphis

Baptist Memorial Hospital

6019 Walnut Grove Road
Memphis, TN 38120
www.baptistonline.org
Med Sch Affil: M-04706
Programs sponsored in: DR
Major participating institution for programs in: DMP, GS, OBG, OTO, PTH, TS, VS
Institution ID: 47-0382

Campbell Clinics & Surgery Center

1211 Union Avenue
Suite 510
Memphis, TN 38104
Med Sch Affil: M-04706
Major participating institution for programs in: OP, ORS, OSM
Institution ID: 47-0401

LeBonheur Children's Medical Center

50 N Dunlap
Memphis, TN 38103
Med Sch Affil: M-04706
Major participating institution for programs in: AI, CCP, CHN, CHP, CN, MPD, NS, OP, ORS, PD, PDC, PDE, PDI, PDS, PEM, PN, PP, PPR, RHU, TS, U, UP
Institution ID: 47-0186

Methodist Healthcare - Memphis Hospitals

1265 Union Avenue
Memphis, TN 38104
Med Sch Affil: M-04706
Major participating institution for programs in: CCS, CD, CHN, CN, D, DMP, DR, END, GE, GS, HO, ID, IM, MPD, N, NEP, NS, OPH, ORS, OTO, PCC, PS, PTH, RHU, TS, TY, U
Institution ID: 47-0113

Regional Medical Center at Memphis

877 Jefferson Avenue
Memphis, TN 38103
Med Sch Affil: M-04706
Major participating institution for programs in: AI, CCS, CD, CHN, CN, D, DMP, DR, END, GE, GS, ID, IM, MPD, N, NEP, NPM, NS, OBG, OPH, ORS, OSM, OTO, P, PCC, PDC, PP, PPR, PS, PTH, RHU, U, VIR, VN
Institution ID: 47-0241

St Francis Hospital

5959 Park Avenue
PO Box 171808
Memphis, TN 38187
Med Sch Affil: G-04706
Major participating institution for programs in: CHP, FP, PYG
Institution ID: 47-0478

St Jude Children's Research Hospital

262 Danny Thomas Place
Memphis, TN 38105-3678
Med Sch Affil: M-04706, L-00102
Major participating institution for programs in: CHN, HMP, PDC, PDI, PHO, PP, PPR, PTH
Institution ID: 47-0482

University of Tennessee College of Medicine

910 Madison Avenue, Suite 1031
Memphis, TN 38163
www.utmem.edu/gme
Med Sch Affil: M-04706
Programs sponsored in: AI, CCP, CCS, CD, CHN, CHP, CN, D, DMP, DR, END, FP, GE, GS, HMP, HO, ID, IM, MPD, N, NEP, NPM, NS, OBG, OP, OPH, ORS, OSM, OTO, P, PCC, PD, PDC, PDE, PDI, PDS, PEM, PHO, PN, PP, PPR, PS, PTH, PYG, RHU, TS, TY, U, UP, VIR, VN, VS
Institution ID: 47-0474

University of Tennessee Department of Pathology

930 Madison Avenue, Suite 800
Memphis, TN 38163
Major participating institution for programs in: DMP, PP, PTH
Institution ID: 47-8049

University of Tennessee Medical Center

951 Court Avenue
Memphis, TN 38103
Med Sch Affil: M-04706
Major participating institution for programs in: CHP, P, PTH, PYG, RHU
Institution ID: 47-0269

Veterans Affairs Medical Center (Memphis)

1030 Jefferson Avenue
Memphis, TN 38104
Med Sch Affil: M-04706
Major participating institution for programs in: AI, CD, CHN, CN, D, DR, END, GE, GS, ID, IM, MPD, N, NEP, NS, OPH, ORS, OTO, P, PCC, PTH, PYG, RHU, TS, U, VIR, VS
Institution ID: 47-0280

Mountain Home

Veterans Affairs Medical Center (Mountain Home)

Mountain Home, TN 37684
Med Sch Affil: M-04720
Major participating institution for programs in: CD, GS, ID, IM, MP, ON, P, PCC, PTH
Institution ID: 47-0498

Murfreesboro

Alvin C York Veterans Affairs Medical Center

Alvin C York Campus
3400 Lebanon Rd
Murfreesboro, TN 37139
Med Sch Affil: M-04707
Major participating institution for programs in: GPM, IM, P
Institution ID: 47-0501

Middle Tennessee Medical Center

400 North Highland Avenue
Murfreesboro, TN 37130
Major participating institution for programs in: OBG
Institution ID: 47-8035

Nashville

Baptist Hospital
2000 Church St
Nashville, TN 37236
Med Sch Affil: M-04706, L-04707, G-04705
Major participating institution for programs in: IM, OSM
Institution ID: 47-0163

Comprehensive Care Center
345 24th Avenue North Suite 103
Nashville, TN 37203
Major participating institution for programs in: ID
Institution ID: 47-8045

Medical Examiner's Office, TN and Nashville and Davidson Co
850 R S Gass Boulevard
Nashville, TN 37216
www.forensicmed.com
Programs sponsored in: FOP
Institution ID: 47-8029

Meharry Medical College School of Medicine
1005 Dr D B Todd, Jr Boulevard
Nashville, TN 37208
http://mmc.edu
Programs sponsored in: FP, GPM, IM, OBG, P
Major participating institution for programs in: HO
Institution ID: 47-9501

Metropolitan Nashville General Hospital
1818 Albion Street
Nashville, TN 37208
Med Sch Affil: M-04707, G-04705
Major participating institution for programs in: FP, GPM, IM, OBG
Institution ID: 47-0408

Middle Tennessee Mental Health Institute
221 Stewarts Ferry Pike
Nashville, TN 37214
Med Sch Affil: M-04707, G-04705
Major participating institution for programs in: P
Institution ID: 47-0502

Monroe Carell, Jr Children's Hospital at Vanderbilt
2200 Children's Way
Nashville, TN 37232
Major participating institution for programs in: PDS
Institution ID: 47-8037

St Thomas Hospital
4220 Harding Road
PO Box 380
Nashville, TN 37202
Med Sch Affil: M-04705
Major participating institution for programs in: NO
Institution ID: 47-0262

Vanderbilt University Medical Center
1161 21st Avenue S
D-3300 MCN
Nashville, TN 37232-2104
www.mc.vanderbilt.edu
Med Sch Affil: M-04705, L-02012
Programs sponsored in: ACA, ADP, AI, AN, CCA, CCP, CCS, CD, CHN, CHP, CN, D, DBP, DR, EM, END, GE, GS, HMP, HO, HPM, HSO, IC, ICE, ID, IM, IMG, MG, MGP, MPD, N, NEP, NM, NO, NP, NPM, NS, OBG, OMO, OPH, ORS, OSM, OTO, P, PAN, PCC, PD, PDC, PDE, PDI, PDP, PDR, PDS, PE, PG, PHO, PMM, PN, PS, PSM, PTH, PYM, RHU, RNR, RO, SME, SP, TS, U, UP, VIR, VN, VS
Institution ID: 47-0467

Veterans Affairs Medical Center (Nashville)
1310 24th Ave, South
Nashville, TN 37212-2637
Med Sch Affil: M-04705
Major participating institution for programs in: AI, D, DR, END, GE, GS, HMP, HO, IC, ICE, IM, IMG, N, NM, NS, OPH, ORS, OTO, P, PCC, RHU, U
Institution ID: 47-0461

Texas

Abilene

Hendrick Medical Center/Health System
1900 Pine Street
Abilene, TX 79601-2316
Major participating institution for programs in: FP
Institution ID: 48-7002

Amarillo

Baptist-St Anthony's Health System
1600 Wallace
PO Box 98721
Amarillo, TX 79176-0950
Major participating institution for programs in: FP, FPG
Institution ID: 48-7005

Don and Cybil Harrington Cancer Center
1500 Wallace Blvd
Amarillo, TX 79106
Major participating institution for programs in: OBG
Institution ID: 48-8039

Northwest Texas Health Care System
PO Box 1110
Amarillo, TX 79175
Med Sch Affil: M-04815
Major participating institution for programs in: FP, IM, OBG, PD
Institution ID: 48-0566

Texas Tech University Health Sciences Center at Amarillo
1400 S Coulter St.
Suite 4100
Amarillo, TX 79106
www.ama.ttuhsc.edu/AMAHome.html
Med Sch Affil: M-04815
Programs sponsored in: FP, FPG, IM, OBG, PD
Institution ID: 48-0520

Veterans Affairs Medical Center (Amarillo)
6010 Amarillo Boulevard, West
Amarillo, TX 79106
Med Sch Affil: M-04815
Major participating institution for programs in: D, FPG, IM
Institution ID: 48-0584

Austin

Austin Medical Education Program of Seton Healthcare Network
Seton Healthcare Network - Executive Offices
1201 W 38th Street
Austin, TX 78705
www.amepgme.net
Med Sch Affil: M-04802
Programs sponsored in: CHP, FP, P
Institution ID: 48-0451

Austin State Hospital
4110 Guadalupe
Austin, TX 78751-4296
Major participating institution for programs in: CHP
Institution ID: 48-0388

Central Texas Veterans Hlth Care System Facilities (Austin)
2901 Montopolis Drive
Austin, TX 78741
Major participating institution for programs in: D, IM, N
Institution ID: 48-8079

Dell Children's Medical Center of Central Texas
4900 Mueller Boulevard
Austin, TX 78723
Major participating institution for programs in: PD, TY
Institution ID: 48-8157

Seton Medical Center
1201 West 38th Street
Austin, TX 78705-1056
Major participating institution for programs in: GS, N
Institution ID: 48-8130

Seton Shoal Creek Hospital
3501 Mills Avenue
Austin, TX 78731
Major participating institution for programs in: P
Institution ID: 48-8042

Specially For Children-Neurology
1301 Barbara Jordan Blvd.
Ste 200
Austin, TX 78723
Major participating institution for programs in: CHP
Institution ID: 48-8179

Texas Department of State Health Services
1100 W 49th St
Austin, TX 78756
www.dshs.state.tx.us
Med Sch Affil: L-04802
Programs sponsored in: GPM
Institution ID: 48-0458

University Medical Center at Brackenridge
601 E 15th Street
Austin, TX 78701
Major participating institution for programs in: D, FP, GS, IM, N, OBG, P, TY
Institution ID: 48-0563

Baytown

San Jacinto Methodist Hospital
4401 Garth Rd
Baytown, TX 77521-3159
www.methodisthealth.com/sanjacinto/residency
Programs sponsored in: FP
Institution ID: 48-0579

Big Spring

Veterans Affairs Medical Center (Big Spring)
300 Veterans Boulevard
Big Spring, TX 79720
Med Sch Affil: G-04815
Major participating institution for programs in: OPH
Institution ID: 48-0557

Brooks City-Base

USAF School of Aerospace Medicine
USAFSAM/CC
2601 Louis Bauer Drive
Brooks City-Base, TX 78235-5130
www.brooks.af.mil
Programs sponsored in: GPM
Institution ID: 48-0493

Teaching Institutions

Bryan

Family Practice Foundation of the Brazos Valley
Texas A&M Family Medicine Residency
1301 Memorial Drive #200
Bryan, TX 77802
www.brazosfm.com
Med Sch Affil: L-04802
Programs sponsored in: FP
Institution ID: 48-8062

St Joseph Regional Health Center
2801 Franciscan Drive
Bryan, TX 77802-2544
Med Sch Affil: G-04816
Major participating institution for programs in: FP
Institution ID: 48-8063

Columbus

Columbus Community Hospital
110 Shult Drive
Columbus, TX 78934
Major participating institution for programs in: FP
Institution ID: 48-8128

Conroe

Conroe Medical Education Foundation
704 Old Montgomery Road
Conroe, TX 77301
www.lonestarfamily.org
Programs sponsored in: FP, FSM
Institution ID: 48-0590

Conroe Regional Medical Center
504 Medical Center Blvd
Conroe, TX 77304
Major participating institution for programs in: FP
Institution ID: 48-0574

Corpus Christi

Christus Spohn Memorial Hospital
2606 Hospital Boulevard
Corpus Christi, TX 78405
www.ccfprp.com
Med Sch Affil: G-04813
Programs sponsored in: EM, FP, FPG
Major participating institution for programs in: PD
Institution ID: 48-0257

Driscoll Children's Hospital
3533 S Alameda, PO Drawer 6530
Corpus Christi, TX 78466-6530
www.driscollchildrens.org
Med Sch Affil: M-04816, M-04802, G-04815
Programs sponsored in: PD
Major participating institution for programs in: PAN
Institution ID: 48-0157

Retama Manor Nursing Center
2322 Morgan
Corpus Christi, TX 78405
Major participating institution for programs in: FPG
Institution ID: 48-8218

Dallas

Baylor Institute for Rehabilitation
3505 Gaston Avenue
Dallas, TX 75246
Major participating institution for programs in: PM
Institution ID: 48-8030

Baylor University Medical Center
3500 Gaston Avenue
Dallas, TX 75246
www.baylorhealth.com/
Med Sch Affil: L-04812
Programs sponsored in: CD, CRS, DR, GE, GS, IC, ICE, IM, NEP, NR, OBG, OFA, ON, PM, PTH, THP, VIR, VS
Major participating institution for programs in: ACA, PS, PSI, U
Institution ID: 48-0351

Carter BloodCare
9000 Harry Hines Blvd
Dallas, TX 75235
Med Sch Affil: G-04812
Major participating institution for programs in: BBK
Institution ID: 48-8061

Children's Medical Center of Dallas
1935 Motor Street
Dallas, TX 75235
Med Sch Affil: M-04812
Major participating institution for programs in: AI, CCA, CCP, CHN, CHP, CN, D, ETX, HSP, MG, NMN, NS, OTO, PAN, PD, PDC, PDE, PDI, PDR, PDS, PEM, PG, PHO, PN, PP, PPR, TS, U, UP
Institution ID: 48-0360

Dallas County Hospital District-Parkland Memorial Hospital
5201 Harry Hines Blvd
Dallas, TX 75235
Med Sch Affil: M-04812
Major participating institution for programs in: AI, AN, CCA, CCS, CD, CHN, CN, CRS, D, DMP, DR, EM, END, ETX, FP, GE, GS, HMP, HO, HSP, IC, ICE, ID, IM, IMG, MG, MM, N, NEP, NM, NP, NPM, NR, NS, OBG, OPH, ORS, OTO, P, PCC, PCP, PDI, PDR, PDS, PG, PM, PMM, PS, PSI, PTH, PYG, PYM, RHU, RNR, SCI, TS, U, VIR, VN, VS
Institution ID: 48-0400

Dallas Nephrology Associates
3601 Swiss Avenue
Dallas, TX 75204
Major participating institution for programs in: NEP
Institution ID: 48-8215

Dallas VA Medical Center
4500 S Lancaster Rd
Dallas, TX 75216
Med Sch Affil: M-04812
Major participating institution for programs in: ACA, ADP, AN, CCA, CD, D, DMP, DR, END, GE, GS, HO, HSP, IC, ICE, ID, IM, IMG, NEP, NR, NS, OPH, ORS, OTO, P, PCC, PFP, PM, PMM, PSI, PYG, PYM, RHU, SCI, TS, U, VS
Institution ID: 48-0290

Medical City Hospital of Dallas
7777 Forest Lane
Dallas, TX 75230
Major participating institution for programs in: OFA
Institution ID: 48-8139

Methodist Charlton Medical Center
3500 W Wheatland Road
Dallas, TX 75237
Major participating institution for programs in: FP
Institution ID: 48-0575

Methodist Health System Dallas
1441 North Beckley Avenue
PO Box 655999
Dallas, TX 75265-5999
www.methodisthealthsystem.org
Med Sch Affil: L-04812
Programs sponsored in: FP, GS, IM, OBG
Major participating institution for programs in: AN
Institution ID: 48-0407

Southern Methodist Memorial Health Center
6211 Bishop Blvd
PO Box 750195
Dallas, TX 75275-0195
Major participating institution for programs in: FSM
Institution ID: 48-8230

Texas Health Presbyterian Dallas
8200 Walnut Hill Lane
Dallas, TX 75231
www.texashealth.org/phdgradmed
Med Sch Affil: L-04812
Programs sponsored in: CRS, IM
Major participating institution for programs in: GS, OFA, P, UME
Institution ID: 48-0519

Texas Scottish Rite Hospital for Children
2222 Welborn St
Dallas, TX 75219
Med Sch Affil: L-03515, G-04812, G-04815
Major participating institution for programs in: OP, ORS, PPR, UP
Institution ID: 48-0341

University Hospitals St Paul
Graduate Medical Education Dept
5909 Harry Hines Blvd
Dallas, TX 75235
Med Sch Affil: M-04812
Major participating institution for programs in: ACA, AI, FP, GS, HSP, ICE, IM, PCC, PS, PSI, RNR, TS
Institution ID: 48-0103

University Hospitals Zale Lipshy
5323 Harry Hines Boulevard
Dallas, TX 75390-9265
Med Sch Affil: M-04812
Major participating institution for programs in: AI, AN, CHN, HSP, NP, NS, OTO, P, PM, PYM, U, VN, VS
Institution ID: 48-8034

University of Texas Southwestern Medical School
5323 Harry Hines Blvd
Room B5.100/Mail Code 9005
Dallas, TX 75390-9002
www.swmed.edu
Med Sch Affil: M-04812
Programs sponsored in: ACA, ADP, AI, AN, BBK, CCA, CCP, CCS, CD, CHN, CHP, CN, D, DMP, DR, EM, END, ETX, FOP, FP, GE, GS, HMP, HO, HSP, IC, ICE, ID, IM, IMG, MG, MM, N, NEP, NM, NMN, NP, NPM, NR, NS, OBG, OP, OPH, ORS, OTO, P, PAN, PCC, PCP, PD, PDC, PDE, PDI, PDR, PDS, PEM, PFP, PG, PHO, PM, PMM, PN, PP, PPR, PRD, PS, PSI, PTH, PYG, PYM, RHU, RNR, RO, SCI, TS, U, UME, UP, VIR, VN, VS
Institution ID: 48-0316

World Craniofacial Foundation
7777 Forest Lane, Suite C-616
Dallas, TX 75230
http://worldcf.org
Programs sponsored in: CFS
Institution ID: 48-8071

Denton

Denton Regional Medical Center
3535 Interstate-35
Denton, TX 76210
Major participating institution for programs in: OSS
Institution ID: 48-8207

Denton Surgicare (Baylor Surgical of Denton)
350 South I-35E
Denton, TX 76205
Major participating institution for programs in: OSS
Institution ID: 48-8205

North Texas Hospital
2801 South Mayhill Road
Denton, TX 76208
Major participating institution for programs in: OSS
Institution ID: 48-8202

Texas Back Institute (Clinical Site)
2817 South Mayhill Road
Suite 100
Denton, TX 76208
Major participating institution for programs in: OSS
Institution ID: 48-8199

El Paso

El Paso Psychiatric Center
4615 Alameda
El Paso, TX 79905
Med Sch Affil: M-04815
Major participating institution for programs in: P
Institution ID: 48-0571

R E Thomason General Hospital / Texas Tech University HSC
4815 Alameda Avenue
El Paso, TX 79998
Med Sch Affil: M-04815
Major participating institution for programs in: DR,
EM, FP, GS, IM, OBG, PD, TY
Institution ID: 48-0442

Texas Tech University Hlth Sci Ctr Paul L Foster Sch of Med
4800 Alberta Avenue
El Paso, TX 79905
www.elp.ttuhsc.edu
Med Sch Affil: M-04815
Programs sponsored in: DR, EM, FP, GS, IM, OBG, P,
PD, TY
Major participating institution for programs in: ORS
Institution ID: 48-0550

William Beaumont Army Medical Center
Attn: Graduate Medical Education
5005 North Piedras Street
El Paso, TX 79920-5001
www.wbamc.amedd.army.mil
Med Sch Affil: M-04815, M-02312
Programs sponsored in: GS, IM, ORS, TY
Institution ID: 48-0318

Fort Hood

Carl R Darnall Army Medical Center
MCXI-DCS-ME
36000 Darnall Loop
Fort Hood, TX 76544-4752
www.hood-meddac.army.mil
Med Sch Affil: M-04816, L-04802, G-02312
Programs sponsored in: EM, FP
Major participating institution for programs in: FP,
OBG, OTO
Institution ID: 48-0199

Fort Sam Houston

Brooke Army Medical Center
3851 Roger Brooke Drive
Fort Sam Houston, TX 78234-6200
Med Sch Affil: M-04813, M-02312
Major participating institution for programs in: ADL,
AN, CCA, CCS, CCS, CD, CN, DR, EM, GS, HO, ID, IM,
NM, OBG, OPH, ORS, OTO, PCC, PCP, PTH, RHU, TY, U
Institution ID: 48-0277

Fort Worth

Cook Children's Medical Center
801 Seventh Avenue
Fort Worth, TX 76104
Major participating institution for programs in: ORS,
PAN
Institution ID: 48-0503

Harris Methodist Fort Worth
1301 Pennsylvania Avenue
Fort Worth, TX 76104
Major participating institution for programs in: FSM,
UME
Institution ID: 48-0361

Huguley Memorial Medical Center
11801 S Freeway
Fort Worth, TX 76028
Major participating institution for programs in: FSM
Institution ID: 48-8100

John Peter Smith Hospital (Tarrant County Hospital District)
1500 S Main Street
Fort Worth, TX 76104
www.jpshealthnetwork.org
Med Sch Affil: G-04812
Programs sponsored in: FP, FPG, FSM, OBG, ORS, P, TY
Major participating institution for programs in: GS,
OTO, PMM
Institution ID: 48-0214

Tarrant County Medical Examiner's Office
200 Feliks Gwozds Place
Fort Worth, TX 76104
Programs sponsored in: FOP
Institution ID: 48-8076

Frisco

Baylor Medical Center of Frisco
5601 Warren Parkway
Frisco, TX 75034
Major participating institution for programs in: OSS
Institution ID: 48-8203

Galveston

Shriners Hospitals for Children (Galveston Burns Institute)
815 Market Street
Galveston, TX 77550-2725
Med Sch Affil: L-04804, L-04802
Major participating institution for programs in: CCS,
PSI
Institution ID: 48-8001

University of Texas Medical Branch Hospitals
301 University Blvd
Galveston, TX 77555-0462
www.utmb.edu/
Programs sponsored in: ACA, AI, AN, CCA, CCS, CD,
CHP, D, DMP, DR, EM, END, FP, GE, GPM, GS, IC, ID, IM,
IMG, IPM, MM, MPD, N, NEP, NPM, NS, OBG, ON, OPH,
ORS, OTO, P, PAN, PCC, PCP, PD, PDI, PDM, PDR, PMM,
PS, PSI, PTH, RHU, RNR, RO, TS, TY, U, VIR
Institution ID: 48-0131

University of Texas Medical School at Galveston
5-106 Administration Building
301 University Boulevard, Route 0133
Galveston, TX 77555-0133
Med Sch Affil: M-04802
Major participating institution for programs in: END,
GPM, IPM, OBG
Institution ID: 48-9502

Garland

Baylor Medical Center at Garland
2300 Marie Curie Blvd
Garland, TX 75042
www.baylordallas.edu
Programs sponsored in: FP
Institution ID: 48-8058

Harlingen

Valley Baptist Medical Center
2101 Pease St
PO Box 2588
Harlingen, TX 78551
www.vbmc.org
Med Sch Affil: L-04802, G-04813
Programs sponsored in: FP
Major participating institution for programs in: IM
Institution ID: 48-8060

Houston

Baylor Clinic
One Baylor Plaza
Houston, TX 77030
Major participating institution for programs in: D,
DMP, PRD
Institution ID: 48-8135

Baylor College of Medicine
One Baylor Plaza
022D
Houston, TX 77030
www.bcm.tmc.edu
Med Sch Affil: M-04802, L-02012
Programs sponsored in: ACA, ADL, ADP, AI, AN, BBK,
CCM, CCP, CCS, CD, CHN, CHP, CHS, CN, D, DMP, DR,
END, FP, GE, GS, HMP, HO, HSO, HSP, IC, ICE, ID, IM,
IMG, MBG, MG, MGP, MPD, N, NDN, NEP, NM, NO, NP,
NPM, NS, OBG, OP, OPH, ORS, OSM, OTO, P, PAN, PCC,
PCP, PD, PDC, PDE, PDI, PDO, PDP, PDR, PDS, PEM,
PG, PHO, PM, PMG, PN, PP, PPR, PRD, PSI, PSM, PTH,
RHU, RNR, RO, SCI, SME, TS, U, UP, VS
Institution ID: 48-0211

Harris County Hospital District-Ben Taub General Hospital
PO Box 66769
Houston, TX 77266
Med Sch Affil: M-04804, L-02312
Major participating institution for programs in: AI,
AN, BBK, CCM, CCS, CD, D, DMP, DR, END, FP, GE, GS,
HMP, HO, HSO, HSP, IC, MG, MPD, NEP, NM, NP, NS,
OBG, OPH, ORS, OTO, P, PCC, PCP, PD, PDE, PMG, PSI,
PTH, RHU, RO, SME, TS, U, VS
Institution ID: 48-0363

Harris County Medical Examiner Department
1885 Old Spanish Trail
Houston, TX 77054
www.co.harris.tx.us/me
Programs sponsored in: FOP
Institution ID: 48-8070

Harris County Psychiatric Center
2800 S MacGregor
PO Box 20249
Houston, TX 77225-0249
Med Sch Affil: M-04814
Major participating institution for programs in: CHP,
IMG, P
Institution ID: 48-8044

HCPHES Antoine Health Clinic
5688 West Little York Road
Houston, TX 77091
Major participating institution for programs in: FP
Institution ID: 48-8143

Houston Northwest Medical Center
710 FM 1960 West
Houston, TX 77090
Major participating institution for programs in: CRS
Institution ID: 48-8003

Kelsey-Seybold Main Campus
2727 West Holcombe
Houston, TX 77025
Major participating institution for programs in: FP
Institution ID: 48-8144

Teaching Institutions

Kirby Surgical Center
9300 Kirby Dr #1100
Houston, TX 77054
Major participating institution for programs in: OSM
Institution ID: 48-8241

Lyndon B Johnson General Hospital
5656 Kelly Street
Houston, TX 77026
Med Sch Affil: M-04814
Major participating institution for programs in: ADL,
CN, D, DR, END, FP, GE, GS, HO, ID, IM, IMG, MG, MPD,
N, NEP, OBG, OPH, ORS, OTO, PCC, PCP, PD, PG, PTH,
RHU, TY, U
Institution ID: 48-8045

Memorial Hermann Hospital
6411 Fannin
Houston, TX 77030-1501
Med Sch Affil: L-04804
Major participating institution for programs in: ADL,
AN, BBK, CCA, CCP, CCS, CD, CHN, CHP, CN, D, DMP,
DR, EM, END, FP, GE, GS, IC, ICE, IM, MG, MPD, MSR,
N, NEP, NP, NPM, NS, OBG, OPH, ORS, OSM, OTO, P,
PCC, PD, PDC, PDE, PDI, PDP, PDS, PG, PM, PN, PS,
PTH, RHU, RNR, SCI, TY, U, VIR, VN, VS
Institution ID: 48-0359

Memorial Hermann Hospital System
7737 Southwest Freeway, Suite 200
Houston, TX 77074
http://mhhs.org
Programs sponsored in: FP
Institution ID: 48-8131

Memorial Hermann Northwest Hospital
1635 North Loop West
Houston, TX 77008
Major participating institution for programs in: CRS
Institution ID: 48-8122

Memorial Hermann Southwest Hospital
7600 Beechnut
Houston, TX 77074
Major participating institution for programs in: FP
Institution ID: 48-0443

Methodist Hospital (Houston)
6565 Fannin Street
MGJ9-002
Houston, TX 77030
www.methodisthealth.com
Med Sch Affil: M-04804, L-04814
Programs sponsored in: BBK, FP, GS, HMP, IM, N, NP,
NS, OAR, OBG, OSM, PCP, PS, PTH, SP, TY
Major participating institution for programs in: ACA,
CCA, CD, CN, CRS, DMP, GE, HMP, HO, IC, IMG, MG, N,
NEP, NM, NO, NP, NS, OPH, ORS, OSM, OTO, PCC, PMG,
PSI, RHU, RNR, RO, TS, U, VS
Institution ID: 48-0172

Michael E DeBakey VA Medical Center - Houston
2002 Holcombe Boulevard
Houston, TX 77030
Med Sch Affil: M-04804
Major participating institution for programs in: ADP,
AN, CCS, CD, CN, D, END, GE, GS, HO, HSO, HSP, IC,
IMG, MPD, N, NEP, NM, NS, OPH, ORS, OSM, OTO, P,
PCC, PCP, PM, PRD, PTH, RHU, RNR, RO, SCI, SME, TS,
U, VS
Institution ID: 48-0326

NASA Johnson Space Center
Houston, TX 77058
Med Sch Affil: M-04802
Major participating institution for programs in: GPM,
IPM
Institution ID: 48-8067

Shriners Hospitals for Children (Houston)
6977 Main Street
Houston, TX 77030
Med Sch Affil: L-04804, L-04814
Major participating institution for programs in: MG,
OP, PMG
Institution ID: 48-0528

St Joseph Medical Center
1919 LaBranch
Houston, TX 77002
Med Sch Affil: L-04814
Major participating institution for programs in: GS,
MG, OBG, PMG, PS, VS
Institution ID: 48-0206

St Luke's Episcopal Hospital
6720 Bertner Ave
Houston, TX 77030
Med Sch Affil: M-04804, L-04814, L-01602, G-04815
Major participating institution for programs in: ACA,
AN, BBK, CD, CHS, CN, END, FP, GE, GS, HSO, HSP, IC,
ICE, MG, MPD, MSR, N, NEP, NM, NS, OBG, ORS, OSM,
PSI, RNR, RO, TS, U, VIR, VS
Institution ID: 48-0395

Texas Children's Hospital
6621 Fannin Street
Houston, TX 77030
Med Sch Affil: M-04804, L-04814
Major participating institution for programs in: ACA,
ADL, AI, BBK, CCP, CHN, CHP, CHS, CN, END, HMP, HSP,
MBG, MG, MGP, MPD, NDN, NP, NPM, NS, OP, ORS, OTO,
PAN, PD, PDC, PDE, PDI, PDO, PDP, PDR, PDS, PEM,
PG, PHO, PMG, PN, PP, PPR, PSM, PTH, PSI, RNR, SME,
TS, U, UP
Institution ID: 48-0456

Texas Heart Institute
Mail Code 3-117
PO Box 20345
Houston, TX 77225-0345
http://texasheartinstitute.org
Med Sch Affil: L-01602, L-04814, L-02101, G-04815
Programs sponsored in: TS
Major participating institution for programs in: ACA,
TS
Institution ID: 48-0529

Texas Orthopedic Hospital (Houston)
7401 S Main St
Houston, TX 77030
Major participating institution for programs in: HSO
Institution ID: 48-8084

The Institute for Rehabilitation and Research
1333 Moursund
Houston, TX 77030
Med Sch Affil: M-04814, M-04804, L-04802
Major participating institution for programs in: PM,
SCI
Institution ID: 48-0511

The Menninger Clinic (Houston)
PO Box 809045
2801 Gessner
Houston, TX 77280
Major participating institution for programs in: ADP,
CHP
Institution ID: 48-8113

University of Texas Health Science Center at Houston
Suite JJL 310
PO Box 20708
Houston, TX 77030
http://med.uth.tmc.edu/
Med Sch Affil: M-04814, M-04802
Programs sponsored in: ADL, AN, CCA, CCP, CCS, CD,
CHN, CHP, CN, CRS, D, DMP, DR, EM, END, FP, GE,
GPM, GS, HO, IC, ICE, ID, IM, IMG, MG, MPD, MSR, N,
NEP, NPM, NS, OBG, OPH, ORS, OTO, P, PCC, PD, PDC,
PDE, PDI, PDP, PDS, PG, PHO, PM, PMM, PN, PS, PTH,
RHU, RNR, SCI, TY, U, VIR, VN, VS
Institution ID: 48-0547

University of Texas M D Anderson Cancer Center
1515 Holcombe Boulevard
Houston, TX 77030
www.mdanderson.org
Med Sch Affil: M-04802, M-04814, L-02012, L-04804
Programs sponsored in: BBK, DMP, HMP, HPM, MGP,
OMO, PCH, PCP, PMG, PRD, RO, SP, TS
Major participating institution for programs in: AN,
CCA, CCP, CD, D, DR, END, GE, HMP, HO, ID, MGP, MSR,
N, NEP, NP, NS, OTO, PCC, PCP, PDS, PG, PHO, PSI,
RNR, TS, U, VIR
Institution ID: 48-0404

University of Texas Mental Sciences Institute
1300 Moursund Ave
Houston, TX 77030
Med Sch Affil: M-04814
Major participating institution for programs in: CHP
Institution ID: 48-0525

University of Texas School of Public Health
PO Box 20708
Houston, TX 77225-0708
Med Sch Affil: L-04814
Major participating institution for programs in: GPM,
MG, PMG
Institution ID: 48-0560

UTHSC at Houston Physician Practices
Fannin Street
Houston, TX 77030
Major participating institution for programs in: CN,
DMP, ICE
Institution ID: 48-8192

Kerrville

Kerrville State Hospital
721 Thompson Drive
Kerrville, TX 78028
Major participating institution for programs in: PFP
Institution ID: 48-8124

Killeen

Metroplex Pavilion Hospital
2201 South Clear Creek Road
Killeen, TX 76542-9305
Major participating institution for programs in: CHP
Institution ID: 48-8073

Lackland AFB

San Antonio Uniformed Services Health Education Consortium
Wilford Hall Medical Center/GE
2200 Bergquist Drive, Suite 1
Lackland AFB, TX 78236-9908
www.whmc.af.mil/saushec/
Programs sponsored in: ADL, AI, AN, CCA, CCS, CD, D,
DR, EM, END, GE, GS, HO, ID, IM, N, NPM, OBG, OPH,
ORS, OTO, PCC, PCP, PD, PTH, RHU, SME, TY, U
Institution ID: 48-8068

Wilford Hall Medical Center (AETC)
2200 Berquist Dr, Ste 1
Lackland AFB, TX 78236-5300
Med Sch Affil: M-04813, M-02312
Major participating institution for programs in: ADL, AI, AN, CCA, CCS, CD, CN, D, DR, EM, END, GE, GS, HO, ID, IM, N, NEP, NM, NPM, OBG, OPH, ORS, OTO, P, PCC, PCP, PD, PTH, RHU, SME, TY, U
Institution ID: 48-0287

Lubbock

Covenant Medical Center
3615 19th Street
Lubbock, TX 79410
Med Sch Affil: G-04815
Major participating institution for programs in: AN, FP, FSM, PTH
Institution ID: 48-0561

Dialysis Center of Lubbock
16630 Quaker Ave.
Lubbock, TX 79413
Major participating institution for programs in: NEP
Institution ID: 48-8178

Lubbock Heart Hospital
4810 N Loop 289
Lubbock, TX 79416
Major participating institution for programs in: AN
Institution ID: 48-8242

Texas Tech University Health Sciences Center at Lubbock
Graduate Medical Education
3601 4th Street
Lubbock, TX 79430-6211
http://ttuhsc.edu
Med Sch Affil: M-04815
Programs sponsored in: AN, CD, D, FOP, FP, FSM, GS, IM, NEP, OBG, OPH, ORS, OSM, P, PD, PMM, PTH, U
Institution ID: 48-0534

University Medical Center
602 Indiana Avenue
PO Box 5980
Lubbock, TX 79417
Med Sch Affil: M-04815
Major participating institution for programs in: AN, CD, FP, FSM, GS, IM, NEP, OBG, OPH, ORS, P, PD, PMM, PTH, U
Institution ID: 48-0562

McAllen

McAllen Medical Center
301 W Expressway 83
McAllen, TX 78503
Med Sch Affil: G-04813
Major participating institution for programs in: FP
Institution ID: 48-0548

Midland

Midland Memorial Hospital
2200 W Illinois Ave
Midland, TX 79701-9980
Med Sch Affil: M-04815
Major participating institution for programs in: IM
Institution ID: 48-8032

Nacogdoches

Stephen F Austin State University
1936 North Street
Nacogdoches, TX 75962
Major participating institution for programs in: GPM
Institution ID: 48-8069

Odessa

Medical Center Hospital
500 W 4th Street
PO Box 7239
Odessa, TX 79760
Med Sch Affil: M-04815
Major participating institution for programs in: FP, FPG, IM, OBG
Institution ID: 48-0588

Parks Methodist Retirement Village
3301 Faudree Road
Odessa, TX 79765
Major participating institution for programs in: FP
Institution ID: 48-8141

Seabury Center NCU
2443 W 16th Street
Odessa, TX 79763
Major participating institution for programs in: FP
Institution ID: 48-8220

Texas Tech University Health Sciences Center (Permian Basin)
800 W 4th Street
Odessa, TX 79763
http://odessa.ttuhsc.edu/
Med Sch Affil: M-04815
Programs sponsored in: FP, FPG, IM, OBG
Institution ID: 48-0589

Plano

Associated Orthopedic Sports Medicine (Plano)
4031 W Plano Pkwy
Suite 100
Plano, TX 75093
Major participating institution for programs in: OSM
Institution ID: 48-8155

Medical Center of Plano
3901 West 15th Street
Plano, TX 75075
Major participating institution for programs in: OSS
Institution ID: 48-8204

Plano Orthopedic and Sports Medicine Center
5228 West Plano Parkway
Plano, TX 75093
Programs sponsored in: OSM
Institution ID: 48-8137

Presbyterian Hospital of Plano
6200 West Parker Road
Plano, TX 75093
Major participating institution for programs in: OSS
Institution ID: 48-8201

Presbyterian Plano Center for Diagnostics and Surgery
6020 West Parker Road
Plano, TX 75093
Major participating institution for programs in: OSS
Institution ID: 48-8200

Texas Back Institute Research Foundation
6020 West Parker Road
Suite 200
Plano, TX 75093
Programs sponsored in: OSS
Institution ID: 48-8198

Prairie View

Prairie View A&M University
FM 1098 Rd and University Dr
c/o Athletics Owens-Franklin Health Ctr, RM 113
Prairie View, TX 77446
Major participating institution for programs in: FSM
Institution ID: 48-8225

Rockwall

Presbyterian Hospital of Rockwall
3150 Horizon Road
Rockwall, TX 75032
Major participating institution for programs in: OSS
Institution ID: 48-8206

San Antonio

Audie L Murphy Memorial Veterans Hospital (San Antonio)
7400 Merton Minter Boulevard
San Antonio, TX 78229
Med Sch Affil: M-04813
Major participating institution for programs in: AN, CD, CN, D, DR, END, GE, GS, HMP, HO, IC, ID, IM, IMG, N, NEP, NS, OPH, ORS, OTO, P, PCC, PCP, PDE, PFP, PM, PMM, PS, PTH, PYG, PYM, RHU, RO, TS, U, VIR
Institution ID: 48-0530

Baptist Memorial Healthcare System
111 Dallas Street
San Antonio, TX 78205-1230
Med Sch Affil: L-04813
Major participating institution for programs in: CRS, HSO, OSM
Institution ID: 48-0309

Bexar County District Courts
300 Dolorosa Avenue, Suite 4076
San Antonio, TX 78205
Major participating institution for programs in: PFP
Institution ID: 48-8125

Bexar County Juvenile Probation Department
Frank M Tejeda, Jr Juvenile Justice Center
235 E Mitchell Street
San Antonio, TX 78210-3845
Major participating institution for programs in: PFP
Institution ID: 48-8240

Bexar County Medical Examiner's Office
7337 Louis Pasteur Drive
San Antonio, TX 78229-4565
Programs sponsored in: FOP
Institution ID: 48-8027

Cancer Therapy and Research Center at UTHSCSA
7979 Wurzbach
San Antonio, TX 78229
Major participating institution for programs in: RO
Institution ID: 48-8005

Center for Special Surgery at the Texas Center for Athletes
21 Spurs Lane
San Antonio, TX 78240
Major participating institution for programs in: HSO
Institution ID: 48-8158

Child Guidance Center
2135 Babcock Rd
San Antonio, TX 78229
Med Sch Affil: L-04813
Major participating institution for programs in: CHP
Institution ID: 48-0531

Christus Santa Rosa Health Care Corporation
Physician Services, Building D
333 N Santa Rosa St
San Antonio, TX 78207-3198
www.christussantarosa.org/fprp_main.htm
Med Sch Affil: M-04813
Programs sponsored in: CRS, FP, FSM
Major participating institution for programs in: CCP, D, GS, NS, ORS, OSM, OTO, PD, PDE, PN, PS, U
Institution ID: 48-0468

Methodist Healthcare
7700 Floyd Curl Drive
San Antonio, TX 78229-3993
Med Sch Affil: L-04813
Major participating institution for programs in: CRS, HSO, NS, ORS, OSM, OTO, U
Institution ID: 48-8051

Nix Medical Center
414 Navarro St
San Antonio, TX 78205
Med Sch Affil: L-04813
Major participating institution for programs in: OSM
Institution ID: 48-7086

Orthopaedic Surgery Center of San Antonio
400 Concord Plaza, Ste 200
San Antonio, TX 78216
Major participating institution for programs in: OSM
Institution ID: 48-8243

San Antonio Warm Springs Rehabilitation Hospital
5101 Medical Drive
San Antonio, TX 78229
Med Sch Affil: L-04813
Major participating institution for programs in: PM
Institution ID: 48-8056

South Texas Spinal Clinic (San Antonio)
18626 Hardy Oak
Ste 300
San Antonio, TX 78258
Major participating institution for programs in: OSM
Institution ID: 48-8115

Sports Medicine Associates
21 Spurs Lane
Suite 300
San Antonio, TX 78240
Major participating institution for programs in: FSM
Institution ID: 48-8168

St Luke's Baptist Hospital
7930 Floyd Curl Drive
San Antonio, TX 78229
Med Sch Affil: L-04813
Major participating institution for programs in: HSO
Institution ID: 48-8050

The Hand Center (San Antonio)
9150 Huebner, Suite 290
San Antonio, TX 78240
Major participating institution for programs in: HSO
Institution ID: 48-8086

University Health System
4502 Medical Drive
San Antonio, TX 78229
Med Sch Affil: M-04813
Major participating institution for programs in: AN, BBK, CCP, CD, CN, D, DR, END, FP, GE, GS, HMP, HO, IC, ID, IM, NEP, NM, NPM, NS, OBG, OPH, ORS, OTO, P, PCC, PCP, PD, PDE, PM, PMM, PN, PS, PTH, PYM, RHU, RO, TS, U, VIR
Institution ID: 48-0445

University of Texas Health Science Center
Bexar County Hospital District
7703 Floyd Curl Drive
San Antonio, TX 78229-3900
Med Sch Affil: M-04813
Major participating institution for programs in: CCA, CCS, ID, N, OPH, ORS, PFP, PN, PTH, PYG, PYM
Institution ID: 48-0522

University of Texas School of Medicine at San Antonio
7703 Floyd Curl Dr, Mail Stop 7790
Office of the Medical Dean
San Antonio, TX 78229-3900
www.uthscsa.edu/
Med Sch Affil: M-04802, M-04813
Programs sponsored in: AN, BBK, CCP, CCS, CD, CHP, CN, D, DR, END, FP, GE, GS, HMP, HO, HPM, HSO, IC, ID, IM, IMG, N, NEP, NM, NPM, NS, OBG, OPH, ORS, OSM, OTO, P, PCC, PCP, PD, PDE, PFP, PHO, PM, PMM, PN, PS, PTH, PYG, PYM, RHU, RO, TS, U, VIR
Institution ID: 48-9501

Temple

Central Texas Veterans Affairs Healthcare System
1901 S First Street
Temple, TX 76504
Med Sch Affil: M-04816
Major participating institution for programs in: FP, GE, GS, ON, OPH, P, PCC, PS, U, VS
Institution ID: 48-0505

Scott and White Memorial Hospital
The TAMHSC College of Medicine
2401 S 31st St
Temple, TX 76508
http://gme.sw.org
Med Sch Affil: M-04816
Programs sponsored in: AN, CD, CHP, D, DR, EM, FP, GE, GS, HMP, IC, ICE, ID, IM, NEP, OBG, ON, OPH, ORS, P, PCC, PCP, PD, PS, PTH, U, VIR, VS
Institution ID: 48-0140

Texarkana

Wadley Regional Medical Center (Texarkana, TX)
1000 Pine St
PO Box 1878
Texarkana, TX 75504
Major participating institution for programs in: FP
Institution ID: 48-8055

Texas City

Mainland Medical Center
6801 Emmett F Lowery Expressway
Texas City, TX 77591
Major participating institution for programs in: IMG
Institution ID: 48-8138

Tomball

Texas Orthopaedic and Sports Medicine
13635 Michel Road
Tomball, TX 77375
Major participating institution for programs in: FSM
Institution ID: 48-8223

Tomball Regional Hospital
605 Holderreith
Tomball, TX 77375
Major participating institution for programs in: FSM
Institution ID: 48-8089

Tyler

Mother Frances Hospital Regional Health Care Center
800 E Dawson
Tyler, TX 75701
Major participating institution for programs in: FP, FSM
Institution ID: 48-8037

University of Texas Health Center at Tyler
11937 US Highway 271
Tyler, TX 75708-3154
http:// www.uthct.edu
Med Sch Affil: L-04802
Programs sponsored in: FP, FSM, GPM
Institution ID: 48-0587

Waco

Hillcrest Baptist Medical Center
Box 5100
Waco, TX 76708
Med Sch Affil: G-04812
Major participating institution for programs in: FP
Institution ID: 48-0539

McLennan County Medical Education and Research Foundation
1600 Providence Drive
PO Box 3276
Waco, TX 76707-2261
www.wacofpc.org
Programs sponsored in: FP
Institution ID: 48-0533

Providence Health Center
1700 Providence Drive
Waco, TX 76703
Med Sch Affil: L-04816, G-04812
Major participating institution for programs in: FP
Institution ID: 48-0540

Weimar

Colorado-Fayette Medical Center
400 Youens Drive
Weimar, TX 78962
Major participating institution for programs in: FP
Institution ID: 48-8129

Wichita Falls

North Central Texas Medical Foundation
1301 3rd St, Suite 200
Wichita Falls, TX 76301-2213
Programs sponsored in: FP
Institution ID: 48-0555

United Regional Health Care System (URHCS)
1600 Eighth St
Wichita Falls, TX 76301
Med Sch Affil: G-04812
Major participating institution for programs in: FP
Institution ID: 48-0554

Utah

Murray

Valley Mental Health
5965 South 900 East
Murray, UT 84121
Major participating institution for programs in: P
Institution ID: 49-0140

Ogden

McKay-Dee Hospital Center
4403 Harrison Boulevard
Suite A-700
Ogden, UT 84403
www.mckay-dee-residency.com
Programs sponsored in: FP
Institution ID: 49-0304

Provo

Utah Valley Regional Medical Center
1034 North 500 West
Provo, UT 84604-3337
www.utahvalleyhospital.com
Programs sponsored in: FP, FSM
Institution ID: 49-8019

Salt Lake City

Intermountain Medical Center
Administration
PO Box 577000
Salt Lake City, UT 84157
Programs sponsored in: TY
Major participating institution for programs in: CRS,
EM, IC, OBG, TS, U
Institution ID: 49-8025

LDS Hospital
Eight Avenue and C Street
Salt Lake City, UT 84143
www.ldsty.com
Med Sch Affil: M-04901
Major participating institution for programs in: CCS,
CRS, GS, ID, IM, OTO, PCC, RO, SME
Institution ID: 49-0340

Primary Children's Medical Center
100 North Medical Drive
Salt Lake City, UT 84113
Med Sch Affil: M-04901
Major participating institution for programs in: CCP,
CHN, CHP, D, END, FSM, MG, MGP, MPD, NPM, NS, OP,
OTO, PD, PDC, PDI, PEM, PHO, PP, PS, PTH, SME, TS, U
Institution ID: 49-0151

Salt Lake Regional Medical Center
1050 E South Temple
Salt Lake City, UT 84102
Med Sch Affil: L-04901
Major participating institution for programs in: FP
Institution ID: 49-0297

Shriners Hospital for Children (Intermountain Unit)
Fairfax Avenue and Virginia Street
Salt Lake City, UT 84103
Med Sch Affil: G-04901
Major participating institution for programs in: OP
Institution ID: 49-0331

St Mark's Health Care Foundation
dba Utah HealthCare Institute
1250 East 3900 South #260
Salt Lake City, UT 84124
www.utahhealthcare.org
Programs sponsored in: CRS, FP
Institution ID: 49-8021

St Mark's Hospital
3900 South 12000 East
Salt Lake City, UT 84124
Major participating institution for programs in: CRS,
FP
Institution ID: 49-0441

University of Utah Counseling Center
100 Presidents Circle, Room 203
University of Utah
Salt Lake City, UT 84112
Major participating institution for programs in: P
Institution ID: 49-8015

University of Utah Medical Center
30 North 1900 East
Salt Lake City, UT 84132
www.med.utah.edu/som/education/gme/
Med Sch Affil: M-04901, L-04601
Programs sponsored in: AN, CCP, CCS, CD, CHN, CHP,
CN, CPP, D, DR, EM, END, FP, FSM, GE, GPM, GS, HMP,
HO, HPM, HSO, IC, ICE, ID, IM, IMG, MG, MGP, MM,
MPD, N, NEP, NPM, NR, NS, OBG, OP, OPH, ORS, OSM,
OTO, P, PCC, PCP, PD, PDC, PDI, PEM, PHO, PM, PMM,
PP, PS, PTH, RHU, RNR, RO, SME, TS, U, VIR, VS
Major participating institution for programs in: ORS
Institution ID: 49-0247

University of Utah Neuropsychiatric Institute
501 Chipeta Way
Salt Lake City, UT 84108
Med Sch Affil: L-04901
Major participating institution for programs in: CHP,
P
Institution ID: 49-8014

Veterans Affairs Medical Center (Salt Lake City)
500 Foothill Boulevard
Salt Lake City, UT 84148
Med Sch Affil: M-04901
Major participating institution for programs in: CCS,
CD, CHN, D, DR, END, GE, ICE, IM, IMG, MPD, N, NEP,
OPH, OTO, P, PM, PS, RHU, RNR, U, VIR, VS
Institution ID: 49-0251

Vermont

Burlington

Fletcher Allen Health Care
West Pavillion 2-273
111 Colchester Avenue
Burlington, VT 05401-1429
www.fahc.org/gme
Med Sch Affil: M-05002, G-03201
Programs sponsored in: AN, CD, CHP, CN, D, DMP, DR,
END, FP, GE, GS, HO, IC, ICE, ID, IM, N, NEP, NMN,
NPM, NS, OBG, ORS, OTO, P, PCC, PCP, PD, PMM, PRD,
PTH, RHU, RNR, SME, VIR
Major participating institution for programs in: U
Institution ID: 50-0480

White River Junction

Veterans Affairs Medical Center (White River Junction)
N Hartland Road
White River Junction, VT 05001
Med Sch Affil: M-03201
Major participating institution for programs in: ADP,
D, GE, GS, IM, MP, N, P, PCC, PYG, RHU, U, VIR
Institution ID: 50-0249

Virginia

Arlington

Nirschl Orthopedic Clinic
1715 N George Mason Dr
Suite 504
Arlington, VA 22205
Med Sch Affil: G-02312
Major participating institution for programs in: OSM
Institution ID: 51-8023

Virginia Hospital Center-Arlington
1701 N George Mason Dr
Arlington, VA 22205
www.virginiahospitalcenter.com
Med Sch Affil: M-01002, L-02012, G-01001
Programs sponsored in: OSM
Major participating institution for programs in: FSM,
GS, MPD, OBG, ORS
Institution ID: 51-0501

Charlottesville

University of Virginia Medical Center
4008 McKim Hall
PO Box 800136
Charlottesville, VA 22908-0136
www.med.virginia.edu
Med Sch Affil: M-05101
Programs sponsored in: AI, AN, BBK, CCP, CCS, CD,
CHN, CHP, CN, D, DBP, DMP, DR, EM, END, ETX, FP, GE,
GS, HMP, HO, HSP, IC, ICE, ID, IM, IMG, N, NEP, NO, NP,
NPM, NR, NS, OAR, OBG, OPH, ORS, OSM, OSS, OTO, P,
PCC, PCP, PD, PDC, PDE, PDP, PFP, PM, PMM, PN, PS,
PSI, PTH, PYG, RHU, RNR, RO, TS, U, VIR,
VN, VS
Institution ID: 51-0124

UVA HealthSouth Rehabilitation Hospital
515 Ray C Hunt Drive
Charlottesville, VA 22908
Major participating institution for programs in: PM
Institution ID: 51-8065

Chesapeake

Chesapeake General Hospital
736 Battlefield Blvd
Chesapeake, VA 23332
Major participating institution for programs in: OBG
Institution ID: 51-8088

Chesapeake Place
1508 Volvo Pkwy
Chesapeake, VA 23320
Major participating institution for programs in: IMG
Institution ID: 51-8074

Fairfax

Inova Fair Oaks Hospital
3600 Joseph Siewick Drive
Fairfax, VA 22033
Med Sch Affil: G-05104
Major participating institution for programs in: FP,
FSM
Institution ID: 51-8036

Falls Church

Inova Fairfax Hospital
3300 Gallows Road
Falls Church, VA 22042-3300
http://inova.org
Med Sch Affil: M-01001, M-01002, G-01003, G-02312,
G-05104
Programs sponsored in: GS, PD, PEM
Major participating institution for programs in: EM,
FP, FP, GE, NEP, NS, OBG, ORS, OTO, P, PCC, PYM, TY, U
Institution ID: 51-0492

Fishersville

Augusta Health Care, Inc
PO Box 1000
96 Medical Center Drive
Fishersville, VA 22939
Major participating institution for programs in: U
Institution ID: 51-8037

Teaching Institutions

Fort Belvoir

Dewitt Healthcare Network
9501 Farrell Road, Ste GC 11
Fort Belvoir, VA 22060-5901
Med Sch Affil: G-02312
Major participating institution for programs in: FP,
FSM, FSM
Institution ID: 51-0377

Front Royal

Valley Health System
140 West Eleventh Street
Front Royal, VA 22630
www.valleyhealthlink.com
Programs sponsored in: FP
Institution ID: 51-8027

Warren Memorial Hospital
1000 Shenandoah Avenue
Front Royal, VA 22630-3598
Major participating institution for programs in: FP
Institution ID: 51-8029

Hampton

Sentara CarePlex Hospital
3000 Coliseum Drive
Hampton, VA 23666
Major participating institution for programs in: OBG
Institution ID: 51-8080

Veterans Affairs Medical Center (Hampton)
100 Emancipation Drive
Hampton, VA 23667
Med Sch Affil: M-05107
Major participating institution for programs in: D, IM,
OPH, P, PM
Institution ID: 51-0508

Lynchburg

Centra Health Inc
1920 Atherholt Rd
Lynchburg, VA 24501
www.centrahealth.com
Med Sch Affil: G-05101
Programs sponsored in: FP
Institution ID: 51-0716

Midlothian

Bon Secours Richmond Health System
13710 St Francis Boulevard
Midlothian, VA 23114
www.bonsecours.com
Programs sponsored in: FP
Institution ID: 51-8047

Newport News

Riverside Regional Medical Center
500 J Clyde Morris Boulevard
Newport News, VA 23601-1976
http://riversideonline.org
Med Sch Affil: G-05104
Programs sponsored in: FP, OBG, TY
Institution ID: 51-0108

Norfolk

Children's Hospital of the King's Daughters
800 West Olney Road
Norfolk, VA 23507
Med Sch Affil: M-05107
Major participating institution for programs in: CCS,
D, GS, OTO, PD, PDI, PEM, TY, U
Institution ID: 51-0490

DePaul Medical Center
150 Kingsley Lane
Norfolk, VA 23505
Med Sch Affil: M-05107
Major participating institution for programs in: DR,
IM, OBG, VS
Institution ID: 51-0242

Eastern Virginia Medical School
358 Mowbray Arch
PO Box 1980
Norfolk, VA 23501
http://evms.edu
Med Sch Affil: M-05107
Programs sponsored in: CCS, D, DR, EM, END, FP, GS,
ID, IFP, IM, IMG, OBG, OPH, OTO, P, PD, PDI, PEM, PM,
U, VS
Institution ID: 51-0714

Harbor's Edge
One Colley Avenue
Norfolk, VA 23510
Major participating institution for programs in: IMG
Institution ID: 51-8075

Lake Taylor Transitional Care Hospital
1309 Kempsville Road
Norfolk, VA 23502
Major participating institution for programs in: IMG
Institution ID: 51-8063

Sentara Leigh Hospital
830 Kempsville Rd
Norfolk, VA 23502
Med Sch Affil: M-05107
Major participating institution for programs in: GS, U
Institution ID: 51-0713

Sentara Norfolk General Hospital
600 Gresham Drive
Norfolk, VA 23507
Med Sch Affil: M-05107
Major participating institution for programs in: CCS,
D, DR, EM, END, FP, GS, ID, IFP, IM, IMG, OBG, OPH,
OTO, P, PM, U, VS
Institution ID: 51-0276

Portsmouth

Maryview Medical Center
3636 High St
Portsmouth, VA 23701
Med Sch Affil: G-05107
Major participating institution for programs in: FP
Institution ID: 51-0480

Naval Medical Center (Portsmouth)
Graduate Medical Education, Code 14G300
620 John Paul Jones Circle
Portsmouth, VA 23708-2197
www.nmcp.med.navy.mil
Med Sch Affil: M-05107, M-02312
Programs sponsored in: AN, DR, EM, GS, IM, OBG, ORS,
OTO, P, PD, PMM, TY
Major participating institution for programs in: D
Institution ID: 51-0314

Quantico

FBI-Center for Analysis of Violent Crime Forensic Psychiatry
FBI Academy
Quantico, VA 22135
Major participating institution for programs in: PFP
Institution ID: 51-8078

Reston

Reston Hospital Center
1850 Town Center Parkway
Reston, VA 20190
Major participating institution for programs in: FSM,
OSM
Institution ID: 51-8060

Town Center Orthopaedic Associates
1800 Town Center Drive, Suite 111
Reston, VA 20190
Major participating institution for programs in: OSM
Institution ID: 51-8062

Richmond

Bon Secours St Mary's Hospital
5801 Bremo Road
Richmond, VA 23226
Med Sch Affil: G-05104
Major participating institution for programs in: OAR,
ORS, PS, VS
Institution ID: 51-8017

Children's Hospital
2924 Brook Rd
Richmond, VA 23220
Med Sch Affil: G-05104
Major participating institution for programs in: RPM
Institution ID: 51-0291

Chippenham and Johnston-Willis Hospitals (Chippenham Campus)
7101 Jahnke Road
Richmond, VA 23225
Med Sch Affil: G-05104
Major participating institution for programs in: FP
Institution ID: 51-0721

Commonwealth of Virginia Department of Health
Main Street Station, Suite 214
PO Box 2448
Richmond, VA 23218
Major participating institution for programs in: GPM
Institution ID: 51-0184

Hunter Holmes McGuire VA Medical Center (Richmond)
1201 Broad Rock Boulevard
Richmond, VA 23249
Med Sch Affil: M-05104
Major participating institution for programs in: AN,
CD, CHN, CN, D, DR, END, GE, GS, HO, HPM, IC, ICE,
ID, IM, IMG, N, NEP, NS, OPH, ORS, OTO, P, PCC, PM,
PMM, PPM, PS, RHU, RO, SCI, THP, U
Institution ID: 51-0148

MCV-Virginia Treatment Center for Children
PO Box 489
Richmond, VA 23298
Med Sch Affil: G-05104
Major participating institution for programs in: CHP,
P
Institution ID: 51-0494

Medical College of Virginia Hospitals
PO Box 980510
Richmond, VA 23298-0510
Med Sch Affil: M-05104
Major participating institution for programs in: ACA,
AI, AN, CCP, CCS, CD, CHP, CN, D, DR, EM, END, GE, GS,
HMP, HO, IC, ICE, ID, IM, IMG, MG, MPD, N, NEP, NM,
NP, NPM, OAR, OBG, OPH, ORS, OTO, P, PCC, PCP, PD,
PDC, PDI, PHO, PM, PMM, PPM, PRD, PS, PTH, RHU,
RNR, RO, RPM, SCI, SP, THP, U, VIR, VS
Institution ID: 51-0487

Office of Chief Medical Examiner
400 East Jackson St
Richmond, VA 23289-3694
Major participating institution for programs in: FOP
Institution ID: 51-8061

Orthopaedic Research of Virginia
7660 E Parham Road, Suite 207
Richmond, VA 23294
www.orv.com
Programs sponsored in: OSM
Institution ID: 51-8026

Sheltering Arms Hospital
8254 Atlee Rd
Richmond, VA 23069
Major participating institution for programs in: PMM
Institution ID: 51-8051

Tuckahoe Orthopaedic Associates
8919 Three Chopt Rd
Richmond, VA 23229
Major participating institution for programs in: OSM
Institution ID: 51-8021

Virginia Commonwealth University Health System
PO Box 980549
Richmond, VA 23298-0549
www.medschool.vcu.edu/gme
Programs sponsored in: ACA, AI, AN, CCP, CCS, CD, CHN, CHP, CN, D, DR, EM, END, FOP, FP, FSM, GE, GPM, GS, HMP, HO, HPM, IC, ICE, ID, IM, IMG, MG, MGP, MPD, N, NEP, NM, NP, NPM, NS, OAR, OBG, OPH, ORS, OTO, OTR, P, PCC, PCP, PD, PDC, PDI, PHO, PM, PMM, PPM, PRD, PS, PTH, PYM, RHU, RNR, RO, RPM, SCI, SP, THP, U, VIR, VS
Institution ID: 51-8038

Virginia Commonwealth University School of Medicine
Box 980549
Richmond, VA 23298-0549
Med Sch Affil: M-05104, L-02312
Major participating institution for programs in: MGP, OTR, PYM
Institution ID: 51-9501

Roanoke

Blue Ridge Behavioral Healthcare
301 Elm Ave, SW
Roanoke, VA 24016
Major participating institution for programs in: CHP
Institution ID: 51-8057

Carilion Clinic
PO Box 13367
Roanoke, VA 24033-3367
www.carilion.com/residency/index.html
Programs sponsored in: CHP, FP, FPG, GS, IM, OBG, P, PYG, TY
Institution ID: 51-8024

Carilion Roanoke Memorial Hospital
1906 Belleview St
Roanoke, VA 24014
Med Sch Affil: M-05101
Major participating institution for programs in: FP, FPG, GS, OBG, ORS, P, TY
Institution ID: 51-0258

Salem

Veterans Affairs Medical Center (Salem)
1970 Boulevard
Salem, VA 24153
Med Sch Affil: M-05101
Major participating institution for programs in: FPG, GS, IM, P, PYG
Institution ID: 51-0513

Staunton

Commonwealth Center for Children & Adolescents
PO Box 2309
Staunton, VA 24401
Major participating institution for programs in: CHP
Institution ID: 51-8002

Western State Hospital
1301 Richmond Ave
PO Box 2500
Staunton, VA 24402-2500
Major participating institution for programs in: PFP
Institution ID: 51-7023

Virginia Beach

Berger Goldrich Home at Beth Sholom Village
6401 Auburn Drive
Virginia Beach, VA 23464
Major participating institution for programs in: IMG
Institution ID: 51-8076

Oakwood Rehabilitation and Nursing Center
5520 Indian River Road
Virginia Beach, VA 23464
Major participating institution for programs in: IMG
Institution ID: 51-8064

Sentara Bayside Hospital
800 Independence Blvd
Virginia Beach, VA 23455
Major participating institution for programs in: GS
Institution ID: 51-8059

Sentara Virginia Beach General Hospital
1060 First Colonial Rd
Virginia Beach, VA 23454
Med Sch Affil: G-05107
Major participating institution for programs in: EM
Institution ID: 51-0514

Virginia Beach Comprehensive Mental Health Services
3143 Magic Hollow Blvd
Virginia Beach, VA 23452
Major participating institution for programs in: P
Institution ID: 51-8089

Winchester

Winchester Medical Center
1840 Amherst Street
PO Box 3340
Winchester, VA 22601-3340
Major participating institution for programs in: FP
Institution ID: 51-0478

Washington

Bremerton

Naval Hospital (Bremerton)
One Boone Road, Code 00
Family Medicine
Bremerton, WA 98312-1898
http://nh_bremerton.med.navy.mil
Med Sch Affil: L-05404, G-02312
Programs sponsored in: FP
Institution ID: 54-7003

Colville

Mount Carmel Hospital
982 E Columbia St
Box 351
Colville, WA 99114
Major participating institution for programs in: FP
Institution ID: 54-8008

Olympia

St Peter Hospital
413 Lilly Road, NE
Olympia, WA 98506
www.providence.org/swsa
Med Sch Affil: L-05404
Programs sponsored in: FP
Institution ID: 54-8004

Renton

Valley Medical Center
400 S 43rd Street
Renton, WA 98055
www.valleymed.org
Med Sch Affil: L-05404
Programs sponsored in: FP
Institution ID: 54-0519

Seattle

Country Doctor Community Clinic
500 19th Ave East
Seattle, WA 98112
Major participating institution for programs in: ADL
Institution ID: 54-8035

Department of Adult & Juvenile Detention
Youth Services Center
1211 E Alder
Seattle, WA 98122
Major participating institution for programs in: ADL
Institution ID: 54-8061

Fred Hutchinson Cancer Research Center
PO Box 19024, Mail Stop D1-060
1100 Fairview Avenue, North
Seattle, WA 98109-1024
Med Sch Affil: L-05404
Major participating institution for programs in: HO, PHO
Institution ID: 54-8001

Group Health Cooperative
320 Westlake Ave N
Suite 100
Seattle, WA 98109-5233
www.ghc.org
Med Sch Affil: M-05404
Programs sponsored in: FP
Major participating institution for programs in: ADL
Institution ID: 54-0498

Harborview Medical Center
325 Ninth Ave
Seattle, WA 98104
Med Sch Affil: M-05404, L-03515, G-03519
Major participating institution for programs in: AI, AN, CCA, CCM, CCS, CN, DR, END, GE, GPM, GS, HSO, IM, IMG, N, NP, NS, OBG, OPH, ORS, OTO, P, PCP, PM, PS, PTH, PYG, PYM, RHU, RNR, SCI, SME, U, VIR, VN
Institution ID: 54-0405

King County Medical Examiner's Office
Public Health - Seattle & King County
325 9th Avenue, HMC Box 359792
Seattle, WA 98104-2499
www.metrokc.gov/health
Med Sch Affil: L-05404
Programs sponsored in: FOP
Institution ID: 54-0515

Northwest Asthma & Allergy Center
4540 Sandpoint Way NE
Seattle, WA 98105
Major participating institution for programs in: AI
Institution ID: 54-8041

Northwest Colon and Rectal Clinic, PS
1101 Madison, Suite 500
Seattle, WA 98104
www.nwcrc.com
Programs sponsored in: CRS
Institution ID: 54-8005

Northwest Hospital
1550 N 115th St
Seattle, WA 98133
Med Sch Affil: L-05404
Major participating institution for programs in: CRS
Institution ID: 54-8006

Teaching Institutions

PhenoPath Laboratories
551 N 34th Street, Suite 100
Seattle, WA 98103-8675
www.phenopath.com
Programs sponsored in: SP
Institution ID: 54-8015

Puget Sound Blood Center
Medical Division
921 Terry Avenue
Seattle, WA 98104-1256
www.psbc.org
Programs sponsored in: BBK
Institution ID: 54-8012

Seattle Cancer Care Alliance
824 Eastlake Ave East
Seattle, WA 98109-1023
Major participating institution for programs in: GE,
HMP, PTH, RO, SP
Institution ID: 54-8032

Seattle Children's Hospital
4800 Sand Point Way NE, G-0061
Seattle, WA 98105
Med Sch Affil: M-05404
Major participating institution for programs in: ADL,
AI, CCP, CHN, CHP, CHS, DBP, DR, END, HSO, MG, NPM,
NS, ORS, OTO, PAN, PD, PDC, PDE, PDI, PDP, PDR, PDS,
PEM, PG, PHO, PN, PP, PPR, PS, SCI, SME, U, UP
Institution ID: 54-0311

Swedish Medical Center
747 Broadway
Seattle, WA 98122-4307
www.swedish.org
Med Sch Affil: M-05404
Programs sponsored in: FP, FPG, GS
Major participating institution for programs in: CRS,
OBG
Institution ID: 54-0481

University of Washington Center on Human Development (CHDD)
PO Box 357920
Seattle, WA 98195-7920
Major participating institution for programs in: DBP
Institution ID: 54-8023

University of Washington Medical Center
1959 NE Pacific Street, Box 356151
Seattle, WA 98195-6151
Med Sch Affil: M-05404
Major participating institution for programs in: ACA,
AI, AN, AR, BBK, CCA, CD, CHN, CHP, CN, D, DBP, DMP,
DR, END, FP, FSM, GE, GS, HMP, HSO, IC, ICE, ID, IM,
IMG, MG, N, NEP, NM, NP, NPM, NS, OBG, OPH, ORS,
OTO, P, PM, PMM, PPR, PRD, PS, PTH, PYG, PYM, RHU,
RNR, RO, SCI, SME, SP, THP, TS, U, VIR, VS
Institution ID: 54-0209

University of Washington School of Medicine
A-300 Health Sciences Center, Box 356340
1959 NE Pacific Street
Seattle, WA 98195-6340
www.washington.edu/medicine/
Med Sch Affil: M-05404
Programs sponsored in: ACA, ADL, ADP, AI, AN, AR,
CCA, CCM, CCP, CCS, CD, CHN, CHP, CHS, CN, D, DBP,
DMP, DR, END, FP, FSM, GE, GS, HMP, HO, HSO, IC, ICE,
ID, IM, IMG, MG, N, NEP, NM, NP, NPM, NS, OBG, OPH,
ORS, OTO, P, PAN, PCC, PCP, PD, PDC, PDE, PDI, PDP,
PDR, PDS, PEM, PFP, PG, PHO, PM, PMM, PN, PP, PPR,
PRD, PS, PTH, PYG, PYM, RHU, RNR, RO, SCI, SME, SP,
THP, TS, U, UP, VIR, VN, VS
Institution ID: 54-0502

University of Washington School of Public Health
Dean's Office, Box 357230
Seattle, WA 98195-7230
http://depts.washington.edu/sphcm
Med Sch Affil: L-05404
Programs sponsored in: GPM
Major participating institution for programs in: GPM
Institution ID: 54-0505

VA Puget Sound Health Care System
1660 S Columbian Way
Seattle, WA 98108-1597
Med Sch Affil: M-05404
Major participating institution for programs in: ADP,
CCS, DR, END, GE, GS, IM, IMG, N, NS, OPH, ORS, OTO,
P, PM, PMM, PTH, PYG, RHU, RO, SCI, TS, U, VIR, VS
Institution ID: 54-0362

Virginia Mason Medical Center
925 Seneca Street
Mailstop H8-GME
Seattle, WA 98101
www.virginiamason.org/graduate
Med Sch Affil: L-05404
Programs sponsored in: AN, DR, GS, IM, PMM, TY
Major participating institution for programs in: AI,
FP, OTO
Institution ID: 54-0346

Spokane

Deaconess Medical Center
West 800 Fifth Ave
PO Box 248
Spokane, WA 99210-0248
Med Sch Affil: L-05404
Major participating institution for programs in: FP,
FSM, IM, TY
Institution ID: 54-0302

Inland Empire Hospital Services Association
Sacred Heart Medical Center
West 101 Eighth, PO Box 2555
Spokane, WA 99220-2555
www.shmc.org
Programs sponsored in: DR, FP, FSM, IM, TY
Institution ID: 54-0516

Sacred Heart Medical Center
West 101 Eighth, TAF-C9
Spokane, WA 99220
Med Sch Affil: M-05404
Major participating institution for programs in: DR,
FP, FSM, IM, P, TY
Institution ID: 54-0402

Shriners Hospitals for Children (Spokane)
911 W Fifth Avenue
PO Box 2472
Spokane, WA 99210-2472
Major participating institution for programs in: ORS
Institution ID: 54-0198

Tacoma

Madigan Army Medical Center
Attn: MCHJ-CG
9040 Reid St
Tacoma, WA 98431-1100
www.mamc.amedd.army.mil
Med Sch Affil: M-05404, M-02312, L-04002
Programs sponsored in: DBP, DR, EM, FP, GPM, GS, IM,
IMG, N, OBG, OPH, ORS, OTO, PD, PTH, TY, U
Major participating institution for programs in: AI
Institution ID: 54-0393

MultiCare Medical Center
PO Box 5299
Tacoma, WA 98415
www.multicare.org
Programs sponsored in: FP
Institution ID: 54-8013

Tacoma General Hospital
315 South K St
PO Box 5299
Tacoma, WA 98415-0299
Med Sch Affil: L-05404
Major participating institution for programs in: FP
Institution ID: 54-0266

Veterans Affairs Medical Center (Tacoma)
American Lake
Tacoma, WA 98493
Major participating institution for programs in: IMG
Institution ID: 54-8003

Western State Hospital
9601 Steilacoom Blvd, SW
Tacoma, WA 98498-7213
Major participating institution for programs in: PFP
Institution ID: 54-8014

Vancouver

Southwest Washington Medical Center
PO Box 1600
Vancouver, WA 98668
www.swmedctr.com
Med Sch Affil: L-04002
Programs sponsored in: FP
Institution ID: 54-8007

Yakima

Yakima Regional Medical and Heart Center
110 N Ninth Ave
Yakima, WA 98902-3397
Major participating institution for programs in: FP
Institution ID: 54-0509

Yakima Valley Memorial Hospital
2811 Tieton Dr
Yakima, WA 98902
Programs sponsored in: FP
Institution ID: 54-0510

West Virginia

Charleston

Charleston Area Medical Center/West Virginia University
3110 MacCorkle Ave SE
Room 58, WVU Bldg
Charleston, WV 25304
camc.wvu.edu
Med Sch Affil: M-05501, G-05502
Programs sponsored in: FP, GS, IM, IMG, MP, MPD,
OBG, P, PD
Major participating institution for programs in: PYN
Institution ID: 55-0350

Clarksburg

Louis A Johnson Veterans Affairs Medical Center
One Medical Center Drive
Clarksburg, WV 26301-4199
Med Sch Affil: G-05501
Major participating institution for programs in: OPH,
OTO, PCC, PTH
Institution ID: 55-0740

United Hospital Center
3 Hospital Plaza
PO Box 1680
Clarksburg, WV 26302
www.uhcwv.org/
Med Sch Affil: L-05501
Programs sponsored in: FP
Institution ID: 55-0738

Huntington

Cabell Huntington Hospital
1340 Hal Greer Blvd
Huntington, WV 25701
Med Sch Affil: M-05502
Major participating institution for programs in: CD,
END, FP, GS, IM, MPD, OBG, ORS, PD, PUD
Institution ID: 55-0170

Marshall University School of Medicine
1600 Medical Center Dr, Suite 3400
Huntington, WV 25701-3655
http://musom.marshall.edu
Med Sch Affil: M-05502, L-05501
Programs sponsored in: CD, END, FP, GS, IC, IM, MPD,
OBG, ORS, PD, PUD
Institution ID: 55-9501

St Mary's Hospital
2900 First Ave
Huntington, WV 25701
Med Sch Affil: M-05502
Major participating institution for programs in: CD,
END, GS, IC, IM, MPD, PUD
Institution ID: 55-0300

Veterans Affairs Medical Center (Huntington)
1540 Spring Valley Drive
Huntington, WV 25704
Med Sch Affil: M-05502
Major participating institution for programs in: CD,
END, GS, IM, PUD
Institution ID: 55-0742

Martinsburg

City Hospital
Dry Run Rd
PO Box 1418
Martinsburg, WV 25401
Major participating institution for programs in: FP
Institution ID: 55-7031

Veterans Affairs Medical Center (Martinsburg)
State Route 9
Martinsburg, WV 25401
Med Sch Affil: G-05501, G-01001
Major participating institution for programs in: FP,
FPG, OPH
Institution ID: 55-0210

Morgantown

HealthSouth Mountain Regional Rehabilitation Hospital
1160 Van Voorhis
Morgantown, WV 26505
Major participating institution for programs in: PCC
Institution ID: 55-8018

West Virginia University Hospitals
One Medical Center Drive Morgantown
Administration Offices, PO Box 8059
Morgantown, WV 26506
Med Sch Affil: M-05501
Programs sponsored in: FPP, MN, MP, PYN
Major participating institution for programs in: AI,
AN, CD, CHP, CN, D, DR, EM, FP, GE, GPM, GS, HMP, HO,
IC, ID, IM, MPD, N, NEP, NPM, NR, NS, OBG, OPH, ORS,
OTO, P, PCC, PD, PFP, PTH, RNR, TY, U
Institution ID: 55-0426

West Virginia University School of Medicine
WVU Robert C Byrd Health Sciences Center
PO Box 9100-A
Morgantown, WV 26506-9100
www.hsc.wvu.edu/som/gme/
Programs sponsored in: AI, AN, CD, CHP, CN, D, DR,
EM, FP, FPG, GE, GPM, GS, HMP, HO, IC, ID, IM, MPD,
N, NEP, NPM, NR, NS, OBG, OPH, ORS, OTO, P, PCC, PD,
PFP, PTH, RNR, TY, U
Institution ID: 55-9502

Ranson

Jefferson Memorial Hospital
300 S Preston St
Ranson, WV 25438
Med Sch Affil: L-05501
Major participating institution for programs in: FP,
FPG
Institution ID: 55-8016

Weston

William R Sharpe Jr Hospital
936 William Sharp Road
Weston, WV 26452
Major participating institution for programs in: PFP
Institution ID: 55-8032

Wheeling

Wheeling Hospital
One Medical Park
Wheeling, WV 26003
www.wheelinghospital.com
Programs sponsored in: FP
Institution ID: 55-0431

Wisconsin

Appleton

Appleton Medical Center
1818 North Meade Street
Appleton, WI 54911
Med Sch Affil: G-05605
Major participating institution for programs in: FP
Institution ID: 56-0724

St Elizabeth Hospital
1506 South Oneida Street
Appleton, WI 54915
Med Sch Affil: G-05605
Major participating institution for programs in: FP
Institution ID: 56-7001

Baraboo

St Clare Hospital and Health Services
707 14th Street
Baraboo, WI 53913-1597
Med Sch Affil: G-05605
Major participating institution for programs in: FP
Institution ID: 56-8021

Brookfield

Concentra Medical Centers (Wisconsin)
2455 N 124th Street
Brookfield, WI 53005
Major participating institution for programs in: GPM
Institution ID: 56-8060

Delafield

Orthopaedic Associates of Wisconsin
1111 Delafield St, Ste 120
Delafield, WI 53188
Major participating institution for programs in: HSO
Institution ID: 56-8053

Eau Claire

Luther Hospital
1221 Whipple St
Eau Claire, WI 54702-4105
Med Sch Affil: G-05605
Major participating institution for programs in: FP
Institution ID: 56-0399

Sacred Heart Hospital
900 West Clairemont Avenue
Eau Claire, WI 54701
Med Sch Affil: G-05605
Major participating institution for programs in: FP
Institution ID: 56-0716

Janesville

Mercy Health System
1000 Mineral Point Avenue
Janesville, WI 53545
http://mercyhealthsystem.org
Programs sponsored in: FP, FSM
Institution ID: 56-0333

La Crosse

Franciscan Skemp Healthcare-La Crosse Campus
700 West Avenue S
La Crosse, WI 54601-4783
http://franciscanskemp.org
Programs sponsored in: FP
Institution ID: 56-0718

Gundersen Clinic Ltd
1900 South Avenue
La Crosse, WI 54601-9980
Major participating institution for programs in: GS,
IM, TY, VIR
Institution ID: 56-8031

Gundersen Lutheran Medical Center
1900 South Avenue
La Crosse, WI 54601-9980
Med Sch Affil: M-05605
Major participating institution for programs in: GS,
IM, TY
Institution ID: 56-0355

Gundersen Lutheran Medical Foundation
1836 South Avenue/C03-006A
La Crosse, WI 54601-5494
www.gundluth.org/web/meded
Programs sponsored in: GS, IM, TY
Institution ID: 56-8030

Madison

HospiceCare Inc
5395 East Cheryl Parkway
Madison, WI 53711
Major participating institution for programs in: HPM
Institution ID: 56-8057

Mendota Mental Health Institute
301 Troy Drive
Madison, WI 53704
Med Sch Affil: L-05605
Major participating institution for programs in: PFP,
PYG
Institution ID: 56-0437

Meriter Hospital
202 S Park St
Madison, WI 53715-1599
Med Sch Affil: M-05605
Major participating institution for programs in: ADP,
CHP, NEP, NPM, NS, OBG, ORS, PD, PSI, U
Institution ID: 56-8018

St Mary's Hospital
707 S Mills Street
Madison, WI 53715
Med Sch Affil: G-05605
Major participating institution for programs in: FP,
OBG, PSI, U
Institution ID: 56-0450

University of Wisconsin Hospital and Clinics
600 Highland Avenue
Madison, WI 53792
www.uwhospital.org
Med Sch Affil: M-05605
Programs sponsored in: ADP, AI, AN, BBK, CCA, CCP,
CD, CHP, CN, D, DR, EM, END, GE, GS, HEM, HMP, HPM,
IC, ICE, ID, IM, IMD, IMG, MG, N, NEP, NM, NPM, NS,
OBG, ON, OPH, ORS, OSM, OTO, P, PCC, PCP, PD, PDE,
PDP, PHO, PM, PRD, PSI, PSM, PTH, PYG, RHU, RNR,
RO, SME, THP, TS, U, VIR, VN, VS
Institution ID: 56-0176

University of Wisconsin School of Medicine and Public Health
Health Science Learning Center
750 Highland Avenue
Madison, WI 53705
http://fammed.wisc.edu/residency/
Programs sponsored in: FP
Institution ID: 56-9501

UW Health/University of Wisconsin Medical Foundation (UWMF)
555 Zor Shrine Place
Madison, WI 53719
Major participating institution for programs in: SME
Institution ID: 56-8050

William S Middleton Veterans Hospital
2500 Overlook Terrace
Madison, WI 53705
Med Sch Affil: M-05605
Major participating institution for programs in: ADP,
AI, CD, CN, D, GS, HPM, ICE, ID, IM, IMD, IMG, N, NEP,
NS, ON, OPH, OTO, P, PYG, RHU, SME, TS, U, VN, VS
Institution ID: 56-0218

Marshfield

Marshfield Clinic-St Joseph's Hospital
1000 N Oak Ave
Marshfield, WI 54449-5777
www2.marshfieldclinic.org/education/residency/
Med Sch Affil: M-05605
Programs sponsored in: D, GS, HPM, IM, MPD, PD, TY
Major participating institution for programs in: D
Institution ID: 56-0264

Menomonee Falls

Community Memorial Hospital
W180 N8085 Town Hall Road
PO Box 408
Menomonee Falls, WI 53052-0408
Major participating institution for programs in: RO
Institution ID: 56-8029

Milwaukee

AIDS Resource Center of Wisconsin
820 N Plankinton Avenue
Milwaukee, WI 53203-0092
Major participating institution for programs in: ID
Institution ID: 56-8051

Aurora Health Care
3000 W Montana Avenue
Milwaukee, WI 53215
www.aurorahealthcare.org
Programs sponsored in: CD, DR, FP, GE, IC, ICE, IM,
IMG, OBG, TY
Institution ID: 56-8020

Aurora Sinai Medical Center
945 N 12th Street
PO Box 342
Milwaukee, WI 53201
Med Sch Affil: M-05605, G-05606
Major participating institution for programs in: CD,
GE, IC, ICE, IM, IMG, OBG
Institution ID: 56-0303

BloodCenter of Wisconsin
PO Box 2178
Milwaukee, WI 53201-2178
Med Sch Affil: G-05606
Major participating institution for programs in: BBK
Institution ID: 56-0737

Blount Orthopaedic Clinic Ltd
625 East St Paul Avenue
Milwaukee, WI 53202
Major participating institution for programs in: HSO
Institution ID: 56-8048

Children's Hospital of Wisconsin
9000 W Wisconsin Avenue
PO Box 1997
Milwaukee, WI 53201
Med Sch Affil: M-05606, L-05605
Major participating institution for programs in: ADL,
AI, BBK, CCP, CFS, CHN, CHP, CN, D, EM, HSO, HSP,
NPM, NS, ORS, OTO, PAN, PD, PDC, PDE, PDP, PDR,
PDS, PEM, PG, PHO, PPR, PSI, RPM, SME, U, UP
Institution ID: 56-0237

Clement J Zablocki Veterans Affairs Medical Center
5000 West National Avenue
Milwaukee, WI 53295
Med Sch Affil: M-05606
Major participating institution for programs in: AI,
CCA, CCS, CD, CN, D, DR, END, GE, GS, HO, ID, IM,
IMG, MN, N, NEP, NM, NS, OPH, ORS, OTO, P, PCC, PFP,
PM, PMM, PSI, PYG, RHU, RO, SCI, SME, TS, U, VIR
Institution ID: 56-0354

Columbia St Mary's Hospitals
2025 E Newport Avenue
Milwaukee, WI 53211-9682
Med Sch Affil: M-05606
Major participating institution for programs in: FP,
HSO, OBG, P
Institution ID: 56-0167

Froedtert Memorial Lutheran Hospital
9200 West Wisconsin Ave
Milwaukee, WI 53226
Med Sch Affil: M-05606
Major participating institution for programs in: AI,
AN, BBK, CCA, CCS, CD, CHN, CN, D, DR, EM, END,
FSM, GE, GS, HMP, HO, HSO, HPM, HSP, ID, IM, IMG,
MN, N, NEP, NM, NPM, NS, OBG, OPH, ORS, OTO, P, PCC,
PCP, PM, PMM, PSI, PTH, PYG, RHU, RNR, RO, SME, TS,
U, VIR, VS
Institution ID: 56-0739

Medical College of Wisconsin Affiliated Hospitals, Inc
8701 Watertown Plank Road
Milwaukee, WI 53226
http://mcw.edu/gme
Programs sponsored in: ADL, AI, AN, BBK, CCA, CCP,
CCS, CD, CFS, CHN, CHP, CN, D, DR, EM, END, FOP, FP,
FSM, GE, GS, HMP, HO, HPM, HSO, HSP, ID, IM, IMG,
MN, MPD, N, NEP, NM, NPM, NS, OBG, OPH, ORS, OTO,
P, PAN, PCC, PCP, PD, PDC, PDE, PDP, PDR, PDS, PEM,
PFP, PG, PHO, PM, PMM, PPR, PSI, PTH, PYG, RHU,
RNR, RO, RPM, SCI, SME, TS, U, UP, VIR, VS
Institution ID: 56-0441

Milwaukee County Behavioral Health Division
9455 Watertown Plank Rd
Milwaukee, WI 53226
Med Sch Affil: M-05606
Major participating institution for programs in: P,
PFP
Institution ID: 56-0146

St Luke's Medical Center
2900 W Oklahoma Ave
Milwaukee, WI 53215
Med Sch Affil: M-05605, G-05606
Major participating institution for programs in: CD,
DR, FP, GE, IC, ICE, IM, PCC, TY
Institution ID: 56-0337

Wheaton Franciscan Healthcare-St Joseph
5000 W Chambers St
Milwaukee, WI 53210
www.sjmed.com/
Med Sch Affil: M-05606
Programs sponsored in: DR, TY
Major participating institution for programs in: FP,
FSM, ID, OBG
Institution ID: 56-0370

Racine

Wheaton Franciscan Healthcare - All Saints (Racine) Campus
3801 Spring Street
Racine, WI 53405
Med Sch Affil: G-05606
Major participating institution for programs in: FP
Institution ID: 56-8027

Waukesha

Waukesha Memorial Hospital
725 American Ave
Waukesha, WI 53188
Med Sch Affil: G-05606
Major participating institution for programs in: FP,
HSO
Institution ID: 56-0722

Wausau

Wausau Hospital
333 Pine Ridge Blvd
Wausau, WI 54401
Med Sch Affil: G-05605
Major participating institution for programs in: FP
Institution ID: 56-0411

West Allis

Rogers Memorial Hospital
11101 W Lincoln Ave
West Allis, WI 53227
Major participating institution for programs in: CHP,
PYG
Institution ID: 56-8042

Village at Manor Park Continuing Care Retirement Community
3023 S 84th Street
West Allis, WI 53227
Major participating institution for programs in: PYG
Institution ID: 56-8049

West Allis Memorial Hospital
8901 W Lincoln Ave
West Allis, WI 53227
Major participating institution for programs in: OBG
Institution ID: 56-8063

Wyoming

Casper

Wyoming Medical Center
1233 E 2nd St
Casper, WY 82601
Major participating institution for programs in: FP
Institution ID: 57-0100

Cheyenne

Cheyenne Regional Medical Center
300 E 23rd St
Cheyenne, WY 82001
Major participating institution for programs in: FP
Institution ID: 57-0106

Laramie

University of Wyoming College of Health Sciences
Dept 3432
1000 East University Avenue
Laramie, WY 82071
http://uwadmnweb.uwyo.edu/hs/
Programs sponsored in: FP
Institution ID: 57-9501

Teaching Institutions

Appendix A

Combined Specialty Programs

Combined training consists of a coherent educational experience in two or more closely related specialty or subspecialty programs. The educational plan for combined training is approved by the board of each of the specialties to assure that resident physicians completing combined training are eligible for board certification in each of the component specialties. Each specialty or subspecialty program is separately accredited by the Accreditation Council for Graduate Medical Education (ACGME) through its respective Residency Review Committee (RRC). The duration of combined training is longer than any one of its component specialty programs standing alone, and shorter than all of its component specialty programs together.

Applicants to combined specialty programs are encouraged to review requirements for admission to the certification process of each board (see Appendix B).

Note on Combined Internal Medicine/Pediatrics Programs

The American Board of Internal Medicine and American Board of Pediatrics have developed policies regarding board eligibility of residents in programs that are not accredited. Combined internal medicine/pediatrics training initiated June 1, 2007, or after must be undertaken in combined internal medicine/pediatrics programs accredited by the ACGME.

Residents contracted to programs for July 1, 2007 through the NRMP in programs that do not seek or achieve accreditation will be allowed to finish that academic year in the unaccredited program and still have the training count toward the requirements for certification. After the 1 year of training, they must transfer to an accredited program in order to be eligible for certification.

Residents who have entered board-approved internal medicine/pediatrics programs prior to June 1, 2007 will be allowed to complete their training in the approved program and will be eligible for admission to the certification examination in internal medicine and pediatrics, even if the program chooses not to seek accreditation or is unsuccessful in achieving accreditation. The boards will continue to monitor those programs in order to assure compliance with the curricular content required by the ACGME.

ACGME-accredited programs in internal medicine/pediatrics are listed in Section III.

Diagnostic Radiology/Nuclear Medicine/Nuclear Radiology

The American Board of Radiology and the American Board of Nuclear Medicine offer dual certification for candidates who have satisfactorily completed a combined total of 6 years of suitable accredited training in programs approved by both boards and successfully passed the certifying examination of both boards.

To be eligible for dual certification, a resident must obtain residency training in diagnostic radiology and nuclear medicine that must include a) a preparatory clinical year in an ACGME-accredited program and b) 4 years of education in an ACGME-accredited diagnostic radiology program that includes 6 months of nuclear medicine training, followed by c) 1 year of education in a combined nuclear medicine and nuclear radiology program. Certifying examinations of each board cannot be taken until all required years of training in both specialties are satisfactorily completed.Emergency Medicine/Family Medicine

The American Board of Emergency Medicine and the American Board of Family Medicine offer dual certification for candidates (el-

Combined Specialty Programs

	Length(s)	GY1*	# of Prgms	
705 MEM	5	Y	11	Internal Medicine/Emergency Medicine
710 MPM	5	Y	0	Internal Medicine/Physical Medicine and Rehabilitation
715 MP	5	Y	16	Internal Medicine/Psychiatry
720 FPP	5	Y	10	Psychiatry/Family Medicine
725 EMP	5	Y	3	Pediatrics/Emergency Medicine
730 CPP	5	Y	10	Pediatrics/Psychiatry/Child and Adolescent Psychiatry
735 PPM	5	Y	6	Pediatrics/Physical Medicine and Rehabilitation
740 IFP	4	Y	2	Internal Medicine/Family Medicine
745 MN	5	Y	6	Internal Medicine/Neurology
751 IPM	4	Y	7	Internal Medicine/Preventive Medicine
755 PYN	5 6	Y	9	Psychiatry/Neurology
760 NRN	7	Y	1	Neurology/Diagnostic Radiology/Neuroradiology
765 PMG	5	Y	14	Pediatrics/Medical Genetics
766 MDG	5	Y	6	Internal Medicine/Medical Genetics
770 DNN	5	N	0	Diagnostic Radiology/Nuclear Medicine/Nuclear Radiology
775 IEC	6	Y	3	Internal Medicine/Emergency Medicine/Critical Care Medicine
780 INM	4	Y	2	Internal Medicine/Nuclear Medicine
785 IMD	5	Y	7	Internal Medicine/Dermatology
790 PDM	5	Y	3	Pediatrics/Dermatology
795 EFM	5	Y	2	Emergency Medicine/Family Medicine
			118	Total

igible for certification by each Board) who enter and successfully complete the curriculum of the 5-year program.

Emergency Medicine/Family Medicine

The American Board of Emergency Medicine and the American Board of Family Medicine offer dual certification for candidates (eligible for certification by each Board) who enter and successfully complete the curriculum of the 5-year program.

Internal Medicine/Dermatology

The American Board of Internal Medicine and the American Board of Dermatology offer dual certification for candidates who fulfill the requirements of both boards by completing joint training in 5 years. All 5 years should be completed in the same combined program; exceptions must be approved in advance by both boards. Applicants may not take the certifying examinations until all required years in both specialties have been completed.

Data

Unless otherwise noted, all data are for 2008.

Table 1. Internal Medicine/Dermatology Programs

Number of accredited programs	7
Program Data	
Length of accredited training	5
Minimum number of prior years of GME required	0
Offers graduate year 1 positions, available immediately upon medical school completion	Yes
Average number of interviews for program year 1 positions	8.9
Percent new program directors, 2007-2008 academic year (source: ACGME)	
Residents/Fellows	
Total number of active residents/fellows	14
Average number of residents/fellows per program	2.0
Average percent female	71.4%
Average percent international medical graduate (IMG)	
Program Faculty	
Average number of full-time physician faculty	211.2
Average number of part-time physician faculty	6.5
Average percent female full-time physician faculty	30.6%
Average ratio of full-time physician faculty to resident/fellow	55.1

Table 2. Data for Internal Medicine/Dermatology Listed in FREIDA

Number of programs providing data	3
Work Schedule (Program Year 1)	
Average hours on duty per week	40.0
Average maximum consecutive hours on duty	18.0
Average days off duty per week	1.3
Moonlighting allowed within institution	66.7%
Night float system	100.0%
Offers awareness and management of fatigue in residents/fellows	100.0%
Educational Setting (Program Year 1)	
Average hours/week of regularly scheduled lectures/conferences	7.0
Average percent of training in hospital outpatient clinics	44.7%
Average percent of training in nonhospital ambulatory care community settings	8.3%
Educational Benefits	
Curriculum on management of tobacco dependence	33.3%
Program to assess/enhance medical professionalism	66.7%

Debt management/financial counseling	100.0%
Formal program to develop teaching skills	100.0%
Formal mentoring program	100.0%
Formal program to foster interdisciplinary teamwork	33.3%
Continuous quality improvement training	100.0%
International experience	66.7%
Resident/fellow retreats	100.0%
Off-campus electives	100.0%
Hospice/home care experience	100.0%
Cultural competence awareness	100.0%
Instruction in medical Spanish or other non-English language	66.7%
Alternative/complementary medicine curriculum	100.0%
Training in identifying and reporting of domestic violence/abuse	100.0%
MPH/MBA or PhD training	33.3%
Research rotation	66.7%
Educational Features	
Offers additional training or educational experience beyond accredited length	16.7%
Offers a primary care track	33.3%
Offers a rural track	0.0%
Offers a women's health track	33.3%
Offers a hospitalist track	33.3%
Offers a research track/nonaccredited fellowship	33.3%
Offers an other track	66.7%
Resident Evaluation	
Yearly specialty in-service examination required	85.7%
Patient surveys	100.0%
Portfolio system	100.0%
360 degree evaluations	100.0%
Objective structured clinical examinations (OSCE)	33.3%
Program Evaluation	
Program graduation rates	66.7%
Board certification rates	100.0%
In-training examinations	100.0%
Performance-based assessments	100.0%
Employment Policies and Benefits	
Part-time/shared positions	66.7%
On-site child care	33.3%
Subsidized child care	0.0%
Allowance/stipend for professional expenses	66.7%
Leave for educational meetings/conferences	70.0%
Moving allowance	0.0%
Housing stipend	0.0%
On-call meal allowance	100.0%
Free parking	33.3%
PDAs	0.0%
Placement assistance upon completion of program	66.7%
Cross coverage in case of illness/disability	100.0%
Compensation and Leave (Graduate Year 1)	
Average resident/fellow compensation	$46,941
Average number weeks of vacation	3.0
Sick days (paid)	10.0
Maximum number of paid days for family/medical leave	15
Maximum number of unpaid days for family/medical leave	30
Major Medical Benefits	
Major medical insurance for residents	100.0%
Major medical insurance for dependents	100.0%
Outpatient mental health insurance	100.0%
Inpatient mental health insurance	100.0%
Group life insurance	66.7%
Dental insurance	100.0%
Disability insurance	100.0%

Disability insurance for occupationally acquired HIV	66.7%
Medical insurance coverage begins when starting program	100.0%

Internal Medicine/Emergency Medicine

The American Board of Internal Medicine and the American Board of Emergency Medicine offer dual certification for candidates who have completed at least 2½ years of suitable accredited training in each specialty. A combined residency consists of 5 years of balanced education in the two disciplines. It is strongly recommended that the participating residencies be in the same academic health center.

To be eligible for dual certification, the resident must satisfactorily complete 60 months of combined education, which must be verified by the directors of both programs. The certifying examinations cannot be taken until all 5 years are completed.

Data

Unless otherwise noted, all data are for 2008.

Table 1. Internal Medicine/Emergency Medicine Programs

Number of accredited programs	11
Program Data	
Length of accredited training	5
Minimum number of prior years of GME required	0
Offers graduate year 1 positions, available immediately upon medical school completion	Yes
Average number of interviews for program year 1 positions	22.2
Percent new program directors, 2007-2008 academic year (source: ACGME)	
Residents/Fellows	
Total number of active residents/fellows	92
Average number of residents/fellows per program	8.4
Average percent female	32.6%
Average percent international medical graduate (IMG)	7.6%
Program Faculty	
Average number of full-time physician faculty	88.1
Average number of part-time physician faculty	13.8
Average percent female full-time physician faculty	25.2%
Average ratio of full-time physician faculty to resident/fellow	7.5

Table 2. Data for Internal Medicine/Emergency Medicine Listed in FREIDA

Number of programs providing data	7
Work Schedule (Program Year 1)	
Average hours on duty per week	58.9
Average maximum consecutive hours on duty	25.1
Average days off duty per week	1.5
Moonlighting allowed within institution	71.4%
Night float system	71.4%
Offers awareness and management of fatigue in residents/fellows	100.0%
Educational Setting (Program Year 1)	
Average hours/week of regularly scheduled lectures/conferences	5.0
Average percent of training in hospital outpatient clinics	20.0%
Average percent of training in nonhospital ambulatory care community settings	5.7%
Educational Benefits	
Curriculum on management of tobacco dependence	14.3%
Program to assess/enhance medical professionalism	85.7%
Debt management/financial counseling	85.7%

Formal program to develop teaching skills	100.0%
Formal mentoring program	100.0%
Formal program to foster interdisciplinary teamwork	14.3%
Continuous quality improvement training	100.0%
International experience	71.4%
Resident/fellow retreats	85.7%
Off-campus electives	100.0%
Hospice/home care experience	57.1%
Cultural competence awareness	100.0%
Instruction in medical Spanish or other non-English language	42.9%
Alternative/complementary medicine curriculum	28.6%
Training in identifying and reporting of domestic violence/abuse	100.0%
MPH/MBA or PhD training	14.3%
Research rotation	42.9%
Educational Features	
Offers additional training or educational experience beyond accredited length	9.1%
Offers a primary care track	14.3%
Offers a rural track	14.3%
Offers a women's health track	0.0%
Offers a hospitalist track	14.3%
Offers a research track/nonaccredited fellowship	14.3%
Offers an other track	14.3%
Resident Evaluation	
Yearly specialty in-service examination required	92.9%
Patient surveys	71.4%
Portfolio system	100.0%
360 degree evaluations	100.0%
Objective structured clinical examinations (OSCE)	28.6%
Program Evaluation	
Program graduation rates	85.7%
Board certification rates	100.0%
In-training examinations	100.0%
Performance-based assessments	85.7%
Employment Policies and Benefits	
Part-time/shared positions	0.0%
On-site child care	42.9%
Subsidized child care	14.3%
Allowance/stipend for professional expenses	85.7%
Leave for educational meetings/conferences	63.2%
Moving allowance	14.3%
Housing stipend	14.3%
On-call meal allowance	85.7%
Free parking	100.0%
PDAs	85.7%
Placement assistance upon completion of program	28.6%
Cross coverage in case of illness/disability	100.0%
Compensation and Leave (Graduate Year 1)	
Average resident/fellow compensation	$44,981
Average number weeks of vacation	3.5
Sick days (paid)	28.8
Maximum number of paid days for family/medical leave	77
Maximum number of unpaid days for family/medical leave	38
Major Medical Benefits	
Major medical insurance for residents	100.0%
Major medical insurance for dependents	100.0%
Outpatient mental health insurance	71.4%
Inpatient mental health insurance	85.7%
Group life insurance	85.7%
Dental insurance	100.0%
Disability insurance	100.0%
Disability insurance for occupationally acquired HIV	85.7%

Medical insurance coverage begins when starting program	85.7%

Internal Medicine/Emergency Medicine/Critical Care Medicine

The American Board of Internal Medicine and the American Board of Emergency Medicine offer triple certification for candidates who complete a 6-year (72-month) integrated, coherent program of combined training in internal medicine, emergency medicine, and critical care medicine, approved by both boards.

Upon successful completion and verification of the first 5 years of this program, candidates may apply to take the certification examinations in internal medicine and emergency medicine. To meet eligibility for certification in critical care medicine, the candidate must: (1) have satisfactorily completed the 6-year combined program; (2) be certified by the American Board of Internal Medicine; and (3) have met the certification requirements of the American Board of Emergency Medicine.

Internal Medicine/Family Medicine

The American Board of Internal Medicine and the American Board of Family Medicine offer dual certification for candidates who have satisfactorily completed 4 years of combined training in programs approved by both boards.

To be eligible for dual certification, combined residency training in internal medicine and family medicine must include at least 48 months of balanced education in the two disciplines and be verified by the training director(s) of the program. The written certifying examinations cannot be taken until all required years in both specialties are completed.

Data

Unless otherwise noted, all data are for 2008.

Table 1. Internal Medicine/Family Medicine Programs

Number of accredited programs	2
Program Data	
Length of accredited training	4
Minimum number of prior years of GME required	0
Offers graduate year 1 positions, available immediately upon medical school completion	Yes
Average number of interviews for program year 1 positions	6.0
Percent new program directors, 2007-2008 academic year (source: ACGME)	
Residents/Fellows	
Total number of active residents/fellows	19
Average number of residents/fellows per program	9.5
Average percent female	47.4%
Average percent international medical graduate (IMG)	10.5%
Program Faculty	
Average number of full-time physician faculty	48.0
Average number of part-time physician faculty	49.0
Average percent female full-time physician faculty	43.8%
Average ratio of full-time physician faculty to resident/fellow	3.8

Table 2. Data for Internal Medicine/Family Medicine Listed in FREIDA

Number of programs providing data	2
Work Schedule (Program Year 1)	
Average hours on duty per week	52.6
Average maximum consecutive hours on duty	23.2
Average days off duty per week	1.2
Moonlighting allowed within institution	100.0%
Night float system	50.0%
Offers awareness and management of fatigue in residents/fellows	100.0%
Educational Setting (Program Year 1)	
Average hours/week of regularly scheduled lectures/conferences	8.0
Average percent of training in hospital outpatient clinics	18.5%
Average percent of training in nonhospital ambulatory care community settings	11.0%
Educational Benefits	
Curriculum on management of tobacco dependence	50.0%
Program to assess/enhance medical professionalism	100.0%
Debt management/financial counseling	100.0%
Formal program to develop teaching skills	100.0%
Formal mentoring program	100.0%
Formal program to foster interdisciplinary teamwork	0.0%
Continuous quality improvement training	100.0%
International experience	50.0%
Resident/fellow retreats	100.0%
Off-campus electives	100.0%
Hospice/home care experience	50.0%
Cultural competence awareness	100.0%
Instruction in medical Spanish or other non-English language	50.0%
Alternative/complementary medicine curriculum	50.0%
Training in identifying and reporting of domestic violence/abuse	100.0%
MPH/MBA or PhD training	0.0%
Research rotation	0.0%
Educational Features	
Offers additional training or educational experience beyond accredited length	0.0%
Offers a primary care track	50.0%
Offers a rural track	50.0%
Offers a women's health track	50.0%
Offers a hospitalist track	50.0%
Offers a research track/nonaccredited fellowship	0.0%
Offers an other track	50.0%
Resident Evaluation	
Yearly specialty in-service examination required	80.0%
Patient surveys	100.0%
Portfolio system	50.0%
360 degree evaluations	100.0%
Objective structured clinical examinations (OSCE)	100.0%
Program Evaluation	
Program graduation rates	100.0%
Board certification rates	100.0%
In-training examinations	100.0%
Performance-based assessments	100.0%
Employment Policies and Benefits	
Part-time/shared positions	0.0%
On-site child care	50.0%
Subsidized child care	50.0%
Allowance/stipend for professional expenses	100.0%
Leave for educational meetings/conferences	60.0%
Moving allowance	0.0%
Housing stipend	0.0%
On-call meal allowance	100.0%
Free parking	100.0%
PDAs	50.0%
Placement assistance upon completion of program	50.0%
Cross coverage in case of illness/disability	100.0%

Compensation and Leave (Graduate Year 1)

Average resident/fellow compensation	$46,656
Average number weeks of vacation	3.5
Sick days (paid)	30.0
Maximum number of paid days for family/medical leave	9
Maximum number of unpaid days for family/medical leave	30

Major Medical Benefits

Major medical insurance for residents	100.0%
Major medical insurance for dependents	100.0%
Outpatient mental health insurance	100.0%
Inpatient mental health insurance	100.0%
Group life insurance	100.0%
Dental insurance	100.0%
Disability insurance	100.0%
Disability insurance for occupationally acquired HIV	100.0%
Medical insurance coverage begins when starting program	100.0%

Internal Medicine/Medical Genetics

The American Board of Internal Medicine and the American Board of Medical Genetics have approved a pathway leading to admissibility to the certification processes in internal medicine and medical genetics to candidates who have satisfactorily completed 5 years of combined training in internal medicine and medical genetics in an approved training track, beginning with a GY1 in internal medicine. Such training, which must be verified by the program directors of both specialties, is intended to provide educational and practical experiences in each discipline that are equivalent to those in the training programs of the parent specialties.

This combined residency training must be conducted in the same institution and its affiliated hospitals. There should be no interruption in training.

Internal Medicine/Neurology

The American Board of Internal Medicine and the American Board of Psychiatry and Neurology offer dual certification for candidates who have completed 5 years of combined training suitable to both boards. A combined residency in internal medicine and neurology must include at least 5 years of coherent education integral to residencies in the two disciplines. It is strongly recommended that the participating residencies be in the same institution.

To meet eligibility for dual certification, the resident must satisfactorily complete 60 months of training, which must be verified by the directors of both programs. The written certifying examinations cannot be taken until all required years in both specialties are satisfactorily completed.

Data

Unless otherwise noted, all data are for 2008.

Table 1. Internal Medicine/Neurology Programs

Number of accredited programs	6

Program Data

Length of accredited training	5
Minimum number of prior years of GME required	0
Offers graduate year 1 positions, available immediately upon medical school completion	Yes
Average number of interviews for program year 1 positions	3.9
Percent new program directors, 2007-2008 academic year (source: ACGME)	

Residents/Fellows

Total number of active residents/fellows	13
Average number of residents/fellows per program	2.2
Average percent female	46.2%
Average percent international medical graduate (IMG)	23.1%

Program Faculty

Average number of full-time physician faculty	105.8
Average number of part-time physician faculty	9.3
Average percent female full-time physician faculty	28.0%
Average ratio of full-time physician faculty to resident/fellow	35.3

Table 2. Data for Internal Medicine/Neurology Listed in FREIDA

Number of programs providing data	5

Work Schedule (Program Year 1)

Average hours on duty per week	59.6
Average maximum consecutive hours on duty	25.5
Average days off duty per week	1.0
Moonlighting allowed within institution	80.0%
Night float system	80.0%
Offers awareness and management of fatigue in residents/fellows	80.0%

Educational Setting (Program Year 1)

Average hours/week of regularly scheduled lectures/conferences	6.4
Average percent of training in hospital outpatient clinics	26.4%
Average percent of training in nonhospital ambulatory care community settings	5.5%

Educational Benefits

Curriculum on management of tobacco dependence	0.0%
Program to assess/enhance medical professionalism	40.0%
Debt management/financial counseling	60.0%
Formal program to develop teaching skills	80.0%
Formal mentoring program	40.0%
Formal program to foster interdisciplinary teamwork	20.0%
Continuous quality improvement training	80.0%
International experience	40.0%
Resident/fellow retreats	60.0%
Off-campus electives	60.0%
Hospice/home care experience	20.0%
Cultural competence awareness	40.0%
Instruction in medical Spanish or other non-English language	0.0%
Alternative/complementary medicine curriculum	40.0%
Training in identifying and reporting of domestic violence/abuse	60.0%
MPH/MBA or PhD training	0.0%
Research rotation	40.0%

Educational Features

Offers additional training or educational experience beyond accredited length	0.0%
Offers a primary care track	0.0%
Offers a rural track	0.0%
Offers a women's health track	0.0%
Offers a hospitalist track	0.0%
Offers a research track/nonaccredited fellowship	0.0%
Offers an other track	0.0%

Resident Evaluation

Yearly specialty in-service examination required	83.3%
Patient surveys	80.0%
Portfolio system	60.0%
360 degree evaluations	80.0%
Objective structured clinical examinations (OSCE)	80.0%

Program Evaluation

Program graduation rates	100.0%
Board certification rates	100.0%
In-training examinations	100.0%
Performance-based assessments	60.0%

Employment Policies and Benefits

Part-time/shared positions	20.0%
On-site child care	80.0%
Subsidized child care	0.0%
Allowance/stipend for professional expenses	100.0%
Leave for educational meetings/conferences	50.0%
Moving allowance	0.0%
Housing stipend	20.0%
On-call meal allowance	100.0%
Free parking	80.0%
PDAs	20.0%
Placement assistance upon completion of program	40.0%
Cross coverage in case of illness/disability	100.0%

Compensation and Leave (Graduate Year 1)

Average resident/fellow compensation	$45,324
Average number weeks of vacation	3.5
Sick days (paid)	15.6
Maximum number of paid days for family/medical leave	41
Maximum number of unpaid days for family/medical leave	42

Major Medical Benefits

Major medical insurance for residents	100.0%
Major medical insurance for dependents	80.0%
Outpatient mental health insurance	100.0%
Inpatient mental health insurance	100.0%
Group life insurance	60.0%
Dental insurance	40.0%
Disability insurance	80.0%
Disability insurance for occupationally acquired HIV	40.0%
Medical insurance coverage begins when starting program	80.0%

Internal Medicine/Nuclear Medicine

The American Board of Internal Medicine and the American Board of Nuclear Medicine offer a training pathway for candidates who have completed 4 years of combined accredited training in internal medicine and nuclear medicine leading to admissibility to certification in both specialties. To meet eligibility for dual certification, the resident must satisfactorily complete 48 months of combined training that is verified by the directors of both training programs. It is strongly recommended that combined training occur in the same institution. Residents will be eligible for admission to the written certifying examination in internal medicine after successfully completing the R-3 year of training and for the nuclear medicine examination after the R-4 year.

Internal Medicine/Physical Medicine and Rehabilitation

The American Board of Internal Medicine and the American Board of Physical Medicine and Rehabilitation offer dual certification for candidates who have completed at least 2½ years of suitable accredited training in each specialty. A combined residency must include at least 5 years of coherent training integral to residencies in the two disciplines. It is strongly recommended that the participating residencies be in the same institution.

To meet eligibility requirements for dual certification, the resident must satisfactorily complete 60 months of combined education, which must be verified by the directors of both programs. The written certifying examinations cannot be taken until required training in a specialty has been satisfactorily completed. The certi-

fying examination in internal medicine cannot be taken prior to the fall of the fifth year in the combined program.

Internal Medicine/Preventive Medicine

The American Board of Internal Medicine (ABIM) and the American Board of Preventive Medicine (ABPM) offer dual certification for candidates who have completed a minimum of 4 years of accredited training in combined internal medicine/preventive medicine programs that meet the Guidelines for Combined Internal Medicine - Preventive Medicine Residency Training Programs approved by ABPM and ABIM. In addition to satisfactory completion of the combined training programs, applicants for the ABPM certifying examination must have completed the required year of preventive medicine practice to qualify.

Data

Unless otherwise noted, all data are for 2008.

Table 1. Internal Medicine/Preventive Medicine Programs

Number of accredited programs	7

Program Data	
Length of accredited training	4
Minimum number of prior years of GME required	0
Offers graduate year 1 positions, available immediately upon medical school completion	Yes
Average number of interviews for program year 1 positions	8.1
Percent new program directors, 2007-2008 academic year (source: ACGME)	

Residents/Fellows	
Total number of active residents/fellows	28
Average number of residents/fellows per program	4.0
Average percent female	57.1%
Average percent international medical graduate (IMG)	39.3%

Program Faculty	
Average number of full-time physician faculty	30.0
Average number of part-time physician faculty	2.2
Average percent female full-time physician faculty	23.3%
Average ratio of full-time physician faculty to resident/fellow	4.6

Table 2. Data for Internal Medicine/Preventive Medicine Listed in FREIDA

Number of programs providing data	5

Work Schedule (Program Year 1)	
Average hours on duty per week	53.3
Average maximum consecutive hours on duty	23.6
Average days off duty per week	1.0
Moonlighting allowed within institution	100.0%
Night float system	100.0%
Offers awareness and management of fatigue in residents/fellows	100.0%

Educational Setting (Program Year 1)	
Average hours/week of regularly scheduled lectures/conferences	7.4
Average percent of training in hospital outpatient clinics	26.4%
Average percent of training in nonhospital ambulatory care community settings	23.4%

Educational Benefits	
Curriculum on management of tobacco dependence	40.0%
Program to assess/enhance medical professionalism	100.0%
Debt management/financial counseling	80.0%
Formal program to develop teaching skills	40.0%
Formal mentoring program	20.0%
Formal program to foster interdisciplinary teamwork	20.0%

Continuous quality improvement training	40.0%
International experience	60.0%
Resident/fellow retreats	20.0%
Off-campus electives	100.0%
Hospice/home care experience	40.0%
Cultural competence awareness	40.0%
Instruction in medical Spanish or other non-English language	0.0%
Alternative/complementary medicine curriculum	40.0%
Training in identifying and reporting of domestic violence/abuse	20.0%
MPH/MBA or PhD training	100.0%
Research rotation	20.0%

Educational Features

Offers additional training or educational experience beyond accredited length	0.0%
Offers a primary care track	60.0%
Offers a rural track	20.0%
Offers a women's health track	0.0%
Offers a hospitalist track	0.0%
Offers a research track/nonaccredited fellowship	0.0%
Offers an other track	80.0%

Resident Evaluation

Yearly specialty in-service examination required	80.0%
Patient surveys	20.0%
Portfolio system	40.0%
360 degree evaluations	60.0%
Objective structured clinical examinations (OSCE)	40.0%

Program Evaluation

Program graduation rates	100.0%
Board certification rates	100.0%
In-training examinations	100.0%
Performance-based assessments	40.0%

Employment Policies and Benefits

Part-time/shared positions	0.0%
On-site child care	60.0%
Subsidized child care	0.0%
Allowance/stipend for professional expenses	80.0%
Leave for educational meetings/conferences	63.6%
Moving allowance	0.0%
Housing stipend	0.0%
On-call meal allowance	100.0%
Free parking	40.0%
PDAs	80.0%
Placement assistance upon completion of program	80.0%
Cross coverage in case of illness/disability	100.0%

Compensation and Leave (Graduate Year 1)

Average resident/fellow compensation	$43,276
Average number weeks of vacation	2.7
Sick days (paid)	13.1
Maximum number of paid days for family/medical leave	39
Maximum number of unpaid days for family/medical leave	60

Major Medical Benefits

Major medical insurance for residents	100.0%
Major medical insurance for dependents	40.0%
Outpatient mental health insurance	100.0%
Inpatient mental health insurance	100.0%
Group life insurance	100.0%
Dental insurance	100.0%
Disability insurance	100.0%
Disability insurance for occupationally acquired HIV	20.0%
Medical insurance coverage begins when starting program	100.0%

Internal Medicine/Psychiatry

The American Board of Internal Medicine and the American Board of Psychiatry and Neurology offer dual certification in internal medicine and psychiatry. A combined residency must include at least 5 years of coherent education integral to residencies in the two disciplines. Participating residencies must be in the same institution.

To meet eligibility requirements for dual certification, the resident must satisfactorily complete 60 months of combined education, which must be verified by the directors of both programs. The written certifying examinations cannot be taken until all required years of training in both specialties are satisfactorily completed.

Data

Unless otherwise noted, all data are for 2008.

Table 1. Internal Medicine/Psychiatry Programs

Number of accredited programs	16

Program Data

Length of accredited training	5
Minimum number of prior years of GME required	0
Offers graduate year 1 positions, available immediately upon medical school completion	Yes
Average number of interviews for program year 1 positions	10.1
Percent new program directors, 2007-2008 academic year (source: ACGME)	

Residents/Fellows

Total number of active residents/fellows	86
Average number of residents/fellows per program	5.4
Average percent female	45.3%
Average percent international medical graduate (IMG)	34.9%

Program Faculty

Average number of full-time physician faculty	107.9
Average number of part-time physician faculty	12.4
Average percent female full-time physician faculty	21.4%
Average ratio of full-time physician faculty to resident/fellow	14.8

Table 2. Data for Internal Medicine/Psychiatry Listed in FREIDA

Number of programs providing data	10

Work Schedule (Program Year 1)

Average hours on duty per week	56.0
Average maximum consecutive hours on duty	26.3
Average days off duty per week	1.2
Moonlighting allowed within institution	70.0%
Night float system	80.0%
Offers awareness and management of fatigue in residents/fellows	100.0%

Educational Setting (Program Year 1)

Average hours/week of regularly scheduled lectures/conferences	6.1
Average percent of training in hospital outpatient clinics	21.3%
Average percent of training in nonhospital ambulatory care community settings	7.7%

Educational Benefits

Curriculum on management of tobacco dependence	10.0%
Program to assess/enhance medical professionalism	80.0%
Debt management/financial counseling	90.0%
Formal program to develop teaching skills	100.0%
Formal mentoring program	80.0%
Formal program to foster interdisciplinary teamwork	50.0%
Continuous quality improvement training	90.0%
International experience	20.0%
Resident/fellow retreats	90.0%
Off-campus electives	70.0%

Hospice/home care experience	50.0%
Cultural competence awareness	100.0%
Instruction in medical Spanish or other non-English language	20.0%
Alternative/complementary medicine curriculum	60.0%
Training in identifying and reporting of domestic violence/abuse	70.0%
MPH/MBA or PhD training	30.0%
Research rotation	30.0%
Educational Features	
Offers additional training or educational experience beyond accredited length	4.0%
Offers a primary care track	10.0%
Offers a rural track	10.0%
Offers a women's health track	10.0%
Offers a hospitalist track	10.0%
Offers a research track/nonaccredited fellowship	20.0%
Offers an other track	10.0%
Resident Evaluation	
Yearly specialty in-service examination required	87.1%
Patient surveys	80.0%
Portfolio system	40.0%
360 degree evaluations	80.0%
Objective structured clinical examinations (OSCE)	60.0%
Program Evaluation	
Program graduation rates	70.0%
Board certification rates	100.0%
In-training examinations	100.0%
Performance-based assessments	70.0%
Employment Policies and Benefits	
Part-time/shared positions	30.0%
On-site child care	60.0%
Subsidized child care	10.0%
Allowance/stipend for professional expenses	90.0%
Leave for educational meetings/conferences	73.5%
Moving allowance	20.0%
Housing stipend	0.0%
On-call meal allowance	100.0%
Free parking	80.0%
PDAs	50.0%
Placement assistance upon completion of program	50.0%
Cross coverage in case of illness/disability	90.0%
Compensation and Leave (Graduate Year 1)	
Average resident/fellow compensation	$44,341
Average number weeks of vacation	3.2
Sick days (paid)	21.2
Maximum number of paid days for family/medical leave	66
Maximum number of unpaid days for family/medical leave	38
Major Medical Benefits	
Major medical insurance for residents	90.0%
Major medical insurance for dependents	80.0%
Outpatient mental health insurance	90.0%
Inpatient mental health insurance	90.0%
Group life insurance	90.0%
Dental insurance	60.0%
Disability insurance	90.0%
Disability insurance for occupationally acquired HIV	70.0%
Medical insurance coverage begins when starting program	90.0%

Neurology/Diagnostic Radiology/Neuroradiology

The American Board of Psychiatry and Neurology and the American Board of Radiology offer certification in neurology, diagnostic radiology, and neuroradiology. The combined residency must include at least 7 years of coherent training integral to all three residencies. It is recommended that the participating residencies be in the same academic health center.

To meet eligibility requirements for triple certification, the resident must satisfactorily complete 84 months of combined training, which must be verified by the directors of each program. Lacking verification of acceptable clinical competence in the combined program, the resident must satisfactorily complete the standard length of residency training and all other requirements before each certifying examination may be taken. Applicants may not take the certifying examination until all required years of training have been completed. In order to be eligible for the neuroradiology exam, a resident must have completed certification in both diagnostic radiology and neurology.

Pediatrics/Dermatology

The American Board of Pediatrics and the American Board of Dermatology offer dual certification for candidates who fulfill the requirements of both boards by completing joint training in 5 years. All 5 years should be completed in the same combined program; exceptions must be approved in advance by both boards. Applicants may not take the certifying examinations until all required years in both specialties have been completed.

Pediatrics/Emergency Medicine

The American Board of Pediatrics and the American Board of Emergency Medicine offer dual certification for candidates who fulfill the requirements of both boards by completing joint training in 5 years. All 5 years should be completed in the same combined program; exceptions must be approved in advance by both boards. Applicants may not take the certifying examinations until all required years in both specialties have been completed.

Data

Unless otherwise noted, all data are for 2008.

Table 1. Pediatrics/Emergency Medicine Programs	
Number of accredited programs	3
Program Data	
Length of accredited training	5
Minimum number of prior years of GME required	0
Offers graduate year 1 positions, available immediately upon medical school completion	Yes
Average number of interviews for program year 1 positions	7.2
Percent new program directors, 2007-2008 academic year (source: ACGME)	
Residents/Fellows	
Total number of active residents/fellows	27
Average number of residents/fellows per program	9.0
Average percent female	59.3%
Average percent international medical graduate (IMG)	
Program Faculty	
Average number of full-time physician faculty	133.3

Average number of part-time physician faculty	21.7
Average percent female full-time physician faculty	41.5%
Average ratio of full-time physician faculty to resident/fellow	12.9

Table 2. Data for Pediatrics/Emergency Medicine Listed in FREIDA

Number of programs providing data	3

Work Schedule (Program Year 1)

Average hours on duty per week	69.2
Average maximum consecutive hours on duty	26.3
Average days off duty per week	1.4
Moonlighting allowed within institution	66.7%
Night float system	100.0%
Offers awareness and management of fatigue in residents/fellows	100.0%

Educational Setting (Program Year 1)

Average hours/week of regularly scheduled lectures/conferences	4.7
Average percent of training in hospital outpatient clinics	18.3%
Average percent of training in nonhospital ambulatory care community settings	10.0%

Educational Benefits

Curriculum on management of tobacco dependence	0.0%
Program to assess/enhance medical professionalism	100.0%
Debt management/financial counseling	66.7%
Formal program to develop teaching skills	100.0%
Formal mentoring program	100.0%
Formal program to foster interdisciplinary teamwork	33.3%
Continuous quality improvement training	100.0%
International experience	100.0%
Resident/fellow retreats	100.0%
Off-campus electives	100.0%
Hospice/home care experience	33.3%
Cultural competence awareness	100.0%
Instruction in medical Spanish or other non-English language	100.0%
Alternative/complementary medicine curriculum	33.3%
Training in identifying and reporting of domestic violence/abuse	100.0%
MPH/MBA or PhD training	0.0%
Research rotation	33.3%

Educational Features

Offers additional training or educational experience beyond accredited length	0.0%
Offers a primary care track	0.0%
Offers a rural track	0.0%
Offers a women's health track	0.0%
Offers a hospitalist track	0.0%
Offers a research track/nonaccredited fellowship	0.0%
Offers an other track	0.0%

Resident Evaluation

Yearly specialty in-service examination required	100.0%
Patient surveys	66.7%
Portfolio system	100.0%
360 degree evaluations	100.0%
Objective structured clinical examinations (OSCE)	0.0%

Program Evaluation

Program graduation rates	100.0%
Board certification rates	100.0%
In-training examinations	100.0%
Performance-based assessments	100.0%

Employment Policies and Benefits

Part-time/shared positions	0.0%
On-site child care	33.3%
Subsidized child care	0.0%
Allowance/stipend for professional expenses	100.0%
Leave for educational meetings/conferences	33.3%

Moving allowance	0.0%
Housing stipend	0.0%
On-call meal allowance	100.0%
Free parking	100.0%
PDAs	66.7%
Placement assistance upon completion of program	33.3%
Cross coverage in case of illness/disability	100.0%

Compensation and Leave (Graduate Year 1)

Average resident/fellow compensation	$44,407
Average number weeks of vacation	3.5
Sick days (paid)	12.0
Maximum number of paid days for family/medical leave	48
Maximum number of unpaid days for family/medical leave	63

Major Medical Benefits

Major medical insurance for residents	100.0%
Major medical insurance for dependents	100.0%
Outpatient mental health insurance	100.0%
Inpatient mental health insurance	100.0%
Group life insurance	100.0%
Dental insurance	100.0%
Disability insurance	100.0%
Disability insurance for occupationally acquired HIV	100.0%
Medical insurance coverage begins when starting program	66.7%

Pediatrics/Medical Genetics

The American Board of Pediatrics and the American Board of Medical Genetics offer dual certification for candidates who fulfill the requirements of both boards by completing joint training in 5 years. All 5 years should be completed in the same combined program; exceptions must be approved in advance by both boards. Applicants may not take the certifying examinations until all required years in both specialties have been completed.

Pediatrics/Physical Medicine and Rehabilitation

The American Board of Pediatrics and the American Board of Physical Medicine and Rehabilitation permit applicants interested in pediatric rehabilitation to qualify for admission to the certifying examinations of both boards by completing a 5-year combined program. All 5 years should be completed at one academic institution; exceptions must be approved in advance by both boards.

Applicants may not take the certifying examinations until all required years in both specialties have been completed.

Pediatrics/Psychiatry/Child and Adolescent Psychiatry

The American Board of Pediatrics and the American Board of Physical Medicine and Rehabilitation permit applicants interested in pediatric rehabilitation to qualify for admission to the certifying examinations of both boards by completing a 5-year combined program. All 5 years should be completed at one academic institution; exceptions must be approved in advance by both boards.

Applicants may not take the certifying examinations until all required years in both specialties have been completed.

Data

Unless otherwise noted, all data are for 2008.

Table 1. Pediatrics/Psychiatry/Child and Adolescent Psychiatry Programs

Number of accredited programs	10
Program Data	
Length of accredited training	5
Minimum number of prior years of GME required	0
Offers graduate year 1 positions, available immediately upon medical school completion	Yes
Average number of interviews for program year 1 positions	17.3
Percent new program directors, 2007-2008 academic year (source: ACGME)	
Residents/Fellows	
Total number of active residents/fellows	79
Average number of residents/fellows per program	7.9
Average percent female	73.4%
Average percent international medical graduate (IMG)	7.6%
Program Faculty	
Average number of full-time physician faculty	116.3
Average number of part-time physician faculty	11.0
Average percent female full-time physician faculty	31.6%
Average ratio of full-time physician faculty to resident/fellow	10.7

Table 2. Data for Pediatrics/Psychiatry/Child and Adolescent Psychiatry Listed in FREIDA

Number of programs providing data	9
Work Schedule (Program Year 1)	
Average hours on duty per week	63.8
Average maximum consecutive hours on duty	26.2
Average days off duty per week	1.5
Moonlighting allowed within institution	88.9%
Night float system	77.8%
Offers awareness and management of fatigue in residents/fellows	100.0%
Educational Setting (Program Year 1)	
Average hours/week of regularly scheduled lectures/conferences	6.6
Average percent of training in hospital outpatient clinics	26.8%
Average percent of training in nonhospital ambulatory care community settings	13.9%
Educational Benefits	
Curriculum on management of tobacco dependence	11.1%
Program to assess/enhance medical professionalism	100.0%
Debt management/financial counseling	55.6%
Formal program to develop teaching skills	100.0%
Formal mentoring program	77.8%
Formal program to foster interdisciplinary teamwork	33.3%
Continuous quality improvement training	88.9%
International experience	55.6%
Resident/fellow retreats	88.9%
Off-campus electives	88.9%
Hospice/home care experience	22.2%
Cultural competence awareness	100.0%
Instruction in medical Spanish or other non-English language	11.1%
Alternative/complementary medicine curriculum	33.3%
Training in identifying and reporting of domestic violence/abuse	100.0%
MPH/MBA or PhD training	33.3%
Research rotation	11.1%
Educational Features	
Offers additional training or educational experience beyond accredited length	9.1%
Offers a primary care track	0.0%

Offers a rural track	11.1%
Offers a women's health track	0.0%
Offers a hospitalist track	0.0%
Offers a research track/nonaccredited fellowship	22.2%
Offers an other track	0.0%
Resident Evaluation	
Yearly specialty in-service examination required	100.0%
Patient surveys	33.3%
Portfolio system	44.4%
360 degree evaluations	88.9%
Objective structured clinical examinations (OSCE)	44.4%
Program Evaluation	
Program graduation rates	100.0%
Board certification rates	88.9%
In-training examinations	100.0%
Performance-based assessments	88.9%
Employment Policies and Benefits	
Part-time/shared positions	33.3%
On-site child care	44.4%
Subsidized child care	0.0%
Allowance/stipend for professional expenses	88.9%
Leave for educational meetings/conferences	91.7%
Moving allowance	11.1%
Housing stipend	0.0%
On-call meal allowance	100.0%
Free parking	77.8%
PDAs	11.1%
Placement assistance upon completion of program	33.3%
Cross coverage in case of illness/disability	100.0%
Compensation and Leave (Graduate Year 1)	
Average resident/fellow compensation	$46,482
Average number weeks of vacation	3.2
Sick days (paid)	11.0
Maximum number of paid days for family/medical leave	26
Maximum number of unpaid days for family/medical leave	62
Major Medical Benefits	
Major medical insurance for residents	100.0%
Major medical insurance for dependents	100.0%
Outpatient mental health insurance	100.0%
Inpatient mental health insurance	100.0%
Group life insurance	100.0%
Dental insurance	100.0%
Disability insurance	100.0%
Disability insurance for occupationally acquired HIV	55.6%
Medical insurance coverage begins when starting program	100.0%

Psychiatry/Family Medicine

The American Board of Family Medicine and the American Board of Psychiatry and Neurology offer dual certification in family medicine and psychiatry. A combined residency in family medicine and psychiatry must include at least 5 years of coherent training integral to residencies in the two disciplines. It is required that the combined training be under the aegis of the same academic institution.

To meet eligibility for dual certification, the resident must satisfactorily complete 60 months of combined training, which must be verified by the directors of both programs. The certifying examinations may not be taken until all required years of training in both specialties are satisfactorily completed.

Data

Unless otherwise noted, all data are for 2008.

Table 1. Psychiatry/Family Medicine Programs

Number of accredited programs	11

Program Data

Length of accredited training	5
Minimum number of prior years of GME required	0
Offers graduate year 1 positions, available immediately upon medical school completion	Yes
Average number of interviews for program year 1 positions	7.6
Percent new program directors, 2007-2008 academic year (source: ACGME)	

Residents/Fellows

Total number of active residents/fellows	41
Average number of residents/fellows per program	3.7
Average percent female	41.5%
Average percent international medical graduate (IMG)	7.3%

Program Faculty

Average number of full-time physician faculty	43.7
Average number of part-time physician faculty	7.7
Average percent female full-time physician faculty	27.0%
Average ratio of full-time physician faculty to resident/fellow	7.0

Table 2. Data for Psychiatry/Family Medicine Listed in FREIDA

Number of programs providing data	6

Work Schedule (Program Year 1)

Average hours on duty per week	52.0
Average maximum consecutive hours on duty	22.9
Average days off duty per week	1.2
Moonlighting allowed within institution	66.7%
Night float system	83.3%
Offers awareness and management of fatigue in residents/fellows	100.0%

Educational Setting (Program Year 1)

Average hours/week of regularly scheduled lectures/conferences	5.2
Average percent of training in hospital outpatient clinics	17.7%
Average percent of training in nonhospital ambulatory care community settings	13.3%

Educational Benefits

Curriculum on management of tobacco dependence	33.3%
Program to assess/enhance medical professionalism	50.0%
Debt management/financial counseling	50.0%
Formal program to develop teaching skills	100.0%
Formal mentoring program	100.0%
Formal program to foster interdisciplinary teamwork	50.0%
Continuous quality improvement training	100.0%
International experience	33.3%
Resident/fellow retreats	100.0%
Off-campus electives	100.0%
Hospice/home care experience	50.0%
Cultural competence awareness	100.0%
Instruction in medical Spanish or other non-English language	16.7%
Alternative/complementary medicine curriculum	50.0%
Training in identifying and reporting of domestic violence/abuse	50.0%
MPH/MBA or PhD training	16.7%
Research rotation	0.0%

Educational Features

Offers additional training or educational experience beyond accredited length	0.0%
Offers a primary care track	16.7%
Offers a rural track	0.0%
Offers a women's health track	0.0%
Offers a hospitalist track	0.0%
Offers a research track/nonaccredited fellowship	16.7%
Offers an other track	16.7%

Resident Evaluation

Yearly specialty in-service examination required	92.9%
Patient surveys	66.7%
Portfolio system	50.0%
360 degree evaluations	100.0%
Objective structured clinical examinations (OSCE)	50.0%

Program Evaluation

Program graduation rates	83.3%
Board certification rates	100.0%
In-training examinations	100.0%
Performance-based assessments	83.3%

Employment Policies and Benefits

Part-time/shared positions	33.3%
On-site child care	33.3%
Subsidized child care	16.7%
Allowance/stipend for professional expenses	100.0%
Leave for educational meetings/conferences	56.3%
Moving allowance	33.3%
Housing stipend	0.0%
On-call meal allowance	100.0%
Free parking	50.0%
PDAs	83.3%
Placement assistance upon completion of program	66.7%
Cross coverage in case of illness/disability	83.3%

Compensation and Leave (Graduate Year 1)

Average resident/fellow compensation	$49,336
Average number weeks of vacation	3.5
Sick days (paid)	12.5
Maximum number of paid days for family/medical leave	15
Maximum number of unpaid days for family/medical leave	15

Major Medical Benefits

Major medical insurance for residents	100.0%
Major medical insurance for dependents	83.3%
Outpatient mental health insurance	100.0%
Inpatient mental health insurance	100.0%
Group life insurance	100.0%
Dental insurance	83.3%
Disability insurance	66.7%
Disability insurance for occupationally acquired HIV	50.0%
Medical insurance coverage begins when starting program	100.0%

Psychiatry/Neurology

The American Board of Psychiatry and Neurology has established guidelines for combined training in psychiatry and neurology. A combined residency must include one postgraduate year (PGY1) of training that is acceptable to neurology plus a minimum of 5 years of combined residency training. The 5 years of residency training are usually taken at one approved institution but may be taken at no more than two approved institutions.

Data

Unless otherwise noted, all data are for 2008.

Table 1. Psychiatry/Neurology Programs

Number of accredited programs	9

Program Data

Length of accredited training	5/6

Minimum number of prior years of GME required	0
Offers graduate year 1 positions, available immediately upon medical school completion	Yes
Average number of interviews for program year 1 positions	3.7
Percent new program directors, 2007-2008 academic year (source: ACGME)	

Residents/Fellows

Total number of active residents/fellows	12
Average number of residents/fellows per program	1.3
Average percent female	16.7%
Average percent international medical graduate (IMG)	

Program Faculty

Average number of full-time physician faculty	106.6
Average number of part-time physician faculty	83.9
Average percent female full-time physician faculty	37.4%
Average ratio of full-time physician faculty to resident/fellow	46.6

Table 2. Data for Psychiatry/Neurology Listed in FREIDA

Number of programs providing data	7

Work Schedule (Program Year 1)

Average hours on duty per week	56.5
Average maximum consecutive hours on duty	26.5
Average days off duty per week	1.5
Moonlighting allowed within institution	85.7%
Night float system	57.1%
Offers awareness and management of fatigue in residents/fellows	71.4%

Educational Setting (Program Year 1)

Average hours/week of regularly scheduled lectures/conferences	7.6
Average percent of training in hospital outpatient clinics	14.3%
Average percent of training in nonhospital ambulatory care community settings	5.0%

Educational Benefits

Curriculum on management of tobacco dependence	14.3%
Program to assess/enhance medical professionalism	57.1%
Debt management/financial counseling	42.9%
Formal program to develop teaching skills	100.0%
Formal mentoring program	71.4%
Formal program to foster interdisciplinary teamwork	0.0%
Continuous quality improvement training	71.4%
International experience	0.0%
Resident/fellow retreats	71.4%
Off-campus electives	85.7%
Hospice/home care experience	14.3%
Cultural competence awareness	85.7%
Instruction in medical Spanish or other non-English language	57.1%
Alternative/complementary medicine curriculum	57.1%
Training in identifying and reporting of domestic violence/abuse	42.9%
MPH/MBA or PhD training	14.3%
Research rotation	0.0%

Educational Features

Offers additional training or educational experience beyond accredited length	18.2%
Offers a primary care track	0.0%
Offers a rural track	14.3%
Offers a women's health track	0.0%
Offers a hospitalist track	0.0%
Offers a research track/nonaccredited fellowship	42.9%
Offers an other track	0.0%

Resident Evaluation

Yearly specialty in-service examination required	91.7%
Patient surveys	71.4%
Portfolio system	42.9%
360 degree evaluations	85.7%

Objective structured clinical examinations (OSCE)	28.6%

Program Evaluation

Program graduation rates	85.7%
Board certification rates	100.0%
In-training examinations	100.0%
Performance-based assessments	57.1%

Employment Policies and Benefits

Part-time/shared positions	42.9%
On-site child care	71.4%
Subsidized child care	28.6%
Allowance/stipend for professional expenses	100.0%
Leave for educational meetings/conferences	75.0%
Moving allowance	0.0%
Housing stipend	14.3%
On-call meal allowance	85.7%
Free parking	57.1%
PDAs	14.3%
Placement assistance upon completion of program	28.6%
Cross coverage in case of illness/disability	71.4%

Compensation and Leave (Graduate Year 1)

Average resident/fellow compensation	$46,542
Average number weeks of vacation	5.4
Sick days (paid)	29.6
Maximum number of paid days for family/medical leave	71
Maximum number of unpaid days for family/medical leave	46

Major Medical Benefits

Major medical insurance for residents	85.7%
Major medical insurance for dependents	71.4%
Outpatient mental health insurance	85.7%
Inpatient mental health insurance	85.7%
Group life insurance	71.4%
Dental insurance	57.1%
Disability insurance	71.4%
Disability insurance for occupationally acquired HIV	42.9%
Medical insurance coverage begins when starting program	85.7%

Emergency Medicine/Family Medicine

Delaware

Wilmington

Christiana Care Health Services Program

Sponsor: Christiana Care Health Services Inc

Prgm Director: Lisa Maxwell, MD
Robert E O'Connor, MD, MPH
Christiana Care Hlth Services
Family Med Ctr Ste 100-B
1401 Foulk Rd
Wilmington, DE 19803
Tel: 302 477-3320   *Fax:* 320 477-3162
E-mail: dcovey@christianacare.org
Accred Length: 5 Yrs   *Program Size:* 5   *(GY1:* 2)
Program ID: 795-09-44-001

Louisiana

Shreveport

Louisiana State University (Shreveport) Program

Sponsor: Louisiana State University School of Medicine
  in Shreveport
LSU Health Sciences Center-University Hospital

Prgm Director: Michael B Harper, MD
Thomas Swoboda, MD
1501 Kings Hwy
Shreveport, LA 71103
Tel: 318 675-5815
E-mail: mharpe@lsuhsc.edu
Accred Length: 5 Yrs
Program ID: 795-21-44-002

Internal Medicine/ Dermatology

District of Columbia

Washington

Washington Hospital Center Program

Sponsor: Washington Hospital Center

Prgm Director: Alan Moshell, MD
John Hong, MD
Washington Hosp Ctr
2B44
110 Irving St NW
Washington, DC 20010
Tel: 202 877-6654   *Fax:* 202 877-3288
E-mail: senora.grooms@medstar.net
Accred Length: 5 Yrs   *Program Size:* 10   *(GY1:* 2)
Program ID: 785-10-44-005

Illinois

Chicago

McGaw Medical Center of Northwestern University Program

Sponsor: McGaw Medical Center of Northwestern
  University
Jesse Brown Veterans Affairs Medical Center
Northwestern Memorial Hospital

Prgm Director: Anne M Laumann, MD
Diane B Wayne, MD
McGaw Med Ctr Northwestern Univ
Ste 1600
676 N St Clair St
Chicago, IL 60611
Tel: 312 695-7932   *Fax:* 312 695-0664
E-mail: msferruz@nmff.org
Accred Length: 5 Yrs   *Program Size:* 3   *(GY1:* 1)
Program ID: 785-16-44-007

Louisiana

New Orleans

Louisiana State University Program

Sponsor: Louisiana State University School of Medicine
Earl K Long Medical Center
LSU Interim Hospital
Ochsner Medical Center-Kenner
Touro Infirmary
Veterans Affairs Medical Center (New Orleans)

Prgm Director: Jorge Martinez, MD
Lee T Nesbitt, MD
Louisiana State Univ Hlth Sci Ctr
Dept of Derm
450 A South Claiborne Ave Ste 206
New Orleans, LA 70112
Tel:
Accred Length: 5 Yrs   *Program Size:* 1
Program ID: 785-21-44-001

Massachusetts

Boston

Beth Israel Deaconess Medical Center/Massachusetts General Hospital/Harvard Medical School Program

Sponsor: Massachusetts General Hospital
Beth Israel Deaconess Medical Center
Brigham and Women's Hospital

Prgm Director: Eileen Reynolds, MD
Joseph Kvedar, MD
Beth Israel Deaconess Med Ctr
Deaconess 306
185 Pilgrim Rd
Boston, MA 02114
Tel: 617 632-8264   *Fax:* 617 632-8261
E-mail: medinternship@bidmc.harvard.edu
Accred Length: 5 Yrs
Program ID: 785-24-44-010

Minnesota

Minneapolis

University of Minnesota Program

Sponsor: University of Minnesota Medical School
Hennepin County Medical Center
Regions Hospital
University of Minnesota Medical Center-Division of
  Fairview
Veterans Affairs Medical Center (Minneapolis)

Prgm Director: Kimberly Bohjanen, MD
William Browne, MD
Univ of Minnesota Med Sch
4-259 Phillips Wangensteen Bldg
516 Delaware St SE
Minneapolis, MN 55455
Tel: 612 626-4454   *Fax:* 612 624-6678
E-mail: boyer009@umn.edu
Accred Length: 5 Yrs   *Program Size:* 6   *(GY1:* 2)
Program ID: 785-26-44-008

Pennsylvania

Philadelphia

University of Pennsylvania Program

Sponsor: University of Pennsylvania Health System
Children's Hospital of Philadelphia
Presbyterian Medical Center (UPHS)
Veterans Affairs Medical Center (Philadelphia)

Prgm Director: Lisa Bellini, MD
Victoria P Werth, MD
Univ of Pennsylvania
2 Rhoads Pavillion
3600 Spruce St
Philadelphia, PA 19104
Tel: 215 662-3924   *Fax:* 215 662-7919
E-mail: mededu@uphs.upenn.edu
Accred Length: 5 Yrs   *Program Size:* 2   *(GY1:* 1)
Program ID: 785-41-44-002

Wisconsin

Madison

University of Wisconsin Program

Sponsor: University of Wisconsin Hospital and Clinics
William S Middleton Veterans Hospital

Prgm Director: William Aughenbaugh, MD
Bennett S Vogelman, MD
Univ of Wisconsin Hosp & Clinics
IM/Derm Pgm 7th Fl
One S Park St
Madison, WI 53715
Tel: 608 287-2658   *Fax:* 608 287-2676
E-mail: jhanser@dermatology.wisc.edu
Accred Length: 5 Yrs   *Program Size:* 5   (*GY1:* 1)
Program ID: 785-56-44-004

Internal Medicine/ Emergency Medicine

California

Sylmar

UCLA-Olive View Program

Sponsor: Olive View/UCLA Medical Center
Childrens Hospital Los Angeles
UCLA Medical Center

Prgm Director: Pamela Dyne, MD
Soma Wali, MD
UCLA Emergency Med Ctr
924 Westwood Blvd Ste 300
Los Angeles, CA 90024
Tel: 818 364-3108   *Fax:* 818 364-3268
E-mail: pdyne@ucla.edu
Accred Length: 5 Yrs   *Program Size:* 10   (*GY1:* 2)
Program ID: 705-05-44-016

Delaware

Wilmington

Christiana Care Health Services Program

Sponsor: Christiana Care Health Services Inc

Prgm Director: Charles L Reese IV, MD
Christiana Care Hlth Services
Emergency Med/Int Med Pgm
4755 Ogletown-Stanton Rd
Newark, DE 19718-6001
Tel: 302 733-1840   *Fax:* 302 733-1633
E-mail: smullenix@christianacare.org
Accred Length: 5 Yrs   *Program Size:* 15   (*GY1:* 3)
Program ID: 705-09-44-010

Illinois

Chicago

University of Illinois College of Medicine at Chicago Program

Sponsor: University of Illinois College of Medicine at Chicago
University of Illinois Hospital and Clinics

Prgm Director: Carissa J Tyo, MD
Univ of Illinois Med Ctr
Rm 470 MC 724
808 S Wood St
Chicago, IL 60612
Tel: 312 996-5719   *Fax:* 312 413-0289
E-mail: ctyo1@uic.edu
Accred Length: 5 Yrs   *Program Size:* 10   (*GY1:* 2)
Program ID: 705-16-44-012

Louisiana

New Orleans

Louisiana State University Program

Sponsor: Louisiana State University School of Medicine

Prgm Director: Jorge Martinez, MD, JD
Dayton Daberkow II, MD
Louisiana State Univ Hlth Sci Ctr
7th Fl Ste D Box E7-20
2020 Gravier St
New Orleans, LA 70112
Tel: 504 568-5600   *Fax:* 504 568-7884
E-mail: acomea@lsuhsc.edu
Accred Length: 5 Yrs   *Program Size:* 9   (*GY1:* 2)
Program ID: 705-21-44-015

Maryland

Baltimore

University of Maryland Program

Sponsor: University of Maryland Medical System
Mercy Medical Center

Prgm Director: Michael E Winters, MD
Univ of Maryland Med System
6th Fl Ste 200
110 S Paca St
Baltimore, MD 21201
Tel: 410 328-8025   *Fax:* 410 328-8028
E-mail: nvancleave@smail.umaryland.edu
Accred Length: 5 Yrs   *Program Size:* 10   (*GY1:* 2)
Program ID: 705-23-44-014

Michigan

Detroit

Henry Ford Hospital Program

Sponsor: Henry Ford Hospital

Prgm Director: Nikhil Goyal, MD
Kimberly Baker-Genaw, MD
Henry Ford Hosp
Emer Med/Int Med Pgm CFP-259
2799 W Grand Blvd
Detroit, MI 48202-2689
Tel: 313 916-1553   *Fax:* 313 916-7437
E-mail: jowens1@hfhs.org
Accred Length: 5 Yrs   *Program Size:* 10   (*GY1:* 2)
Program ID: 705-25-44-003

Minnesota

Minneapolis

Hennepin County Medical Center Program

Sponsor: Hennepin County Medical Center

Prgm Director: Anne Pereira, MD, MPH
Marc L Martel, MD
Hennepin Cnty Med Ctr
Med Ed R7
701 Park Ave S
Minneapolis, MN 55415
Tel: 612 873-5645   *Fax:* 612 904-4241
E-mail: mary.hirschboeck@hcmed.org
Accred Length: 5 Yrs   *Program Size:* 8   (*GY1:* 2)
Program ID: 705-26-44-020

New York

Brooklyn

SUNY Health Science Center at Brooklyn Program

Sponsor: SUNY Health Science Center at Brooklyn
Kings County Hospital Center
University Hospital-SUNY Health Science Center at Brooklyn
Veterans Affairs Medical Center (Brooklyn)

Prgm Director: Christopher Doty, MD
Jeanne Macrae, MD
SUNY Downstate Med Ctr
Box 1228
450 Clarkson Ave
Brooklyn, NY 11203-2098
Tel: 718 245-3320   *Fax:* 718 245-4799
E-mail: em-im.residency@downstate.edu
Accred Length: 5 Yrs   *Program Size:* 20   *(GY1:* 4)
Program ID: 705-35-44-018

New Hyde Park

NSLIJHS-Albert Einstein College of Medicine at Long Island Jewish Medical Center Program

Sponsor: Long Island Jewish Medical Center

Prgm Director: Barbara Barnett, MD
Long Island Jewish Med Ctr
Int Med/Emergency Med Pgm
270-05 76th Ave
New Hyde Park, NY 11040
Tel: 718 470-7873   *Fax:* 718 962-9113
E-mail: sluciano@nshs.edu
Accred Length: 5 Yrs   *Program Size:* 10   *(GY1:* 2)
Program ID: 705-35-44-011

North Carolina

Greenville

Pitt County Memorial Hospital/East Carolina University Program

Sponsor: Pitt County Memorial Hospital

Prgm Director: Charles K Brown, MD
Brody Sch of Med ECU
Dept of Emergency Med
600 Moye Blvd
Greenville, NC 27834
Tel: 252 744-4184   *Fax:* 252 744-4125
E-mail: dmorgan@pcmh.com
Accred Length: 5 Yrs   *Program Size:* 10   *(GY1:* 2)
Program ID: 705-36-44-019

Pennsylvania

Pittsburgh

Allegheny General Hospital Program

Sponsor: Allegheny General Hospital

Prgm Director: Mara S Aloi, MD
James J Reilly, MD
Allegheny General Hosp
Dept of Emergency Med
320 E North Ave
Pittsburgh, PA 15212-9986
Tel: 412 359-4905   *Fax:* 412 359-4963
E-mail: cadelsbe@wpahs.org
Accred Length: 5 Yrs   *Program Size:* 10   *(GY1:* 2)
Program ID: 705-41-44-006

Internal Medicine/ Emergency Medicine/Critical Care Medicine

Maryland

Baltimore

University of Maryland Program

Sponsor: University of Maryland Medical System
Veterans Affairs Medical Center (Baltimore)

Prgm Director: Michael E Winters, MD
Pamela Amelung, MD
Univ of Maryland Med System
Dept of Med
110 S Paca St
Baltimore, MD 21201
Tel: 410 328-8025   *Fax:* 410 328-8028
Accred Length: 6 Yrs
Program ID: 775-23-44-004

Michigan

Detroit

Henry Ford Hospital Program

Sponsor: Henry Ford Hospital

Prgm Director: Nikhil Goyal, MD
Henry Ford Hosp
Dept of Emergency Med CFP-259
2799 W Grand Blvd
Detroit, MI 48202
Tel: 313 916-1553   *Fax:* 313 916-7437
E-mail: jowens1@hfhs.org
Accred Length: 6 Yrs   *Program Size:* 4
Program ID: 775-25-44-001

New York

Great Neck

NSLIJHS-Albert Einstein College of Medicine at Long Island Jewish Medical Center Program

Sponsor: North Shore-Long Island Jewish Health System
Long Island Jewish Medical Center
North Bronx Healthcare Network-Jacobi Medical Center

Prgm Director: Barbara Barnett, MD
Alan Multz, MD
Long Island Jewish Med Ctr
IM/EM/CCM Pgm
270-05 76th Ave
New Hyde Park, NY 11040
Tel: 718 470-7873   *Fax:* 718 962-7728
E-mail: foti@lij.edu
Accred Length: 6 Yrs
Program ID: 775-35-44-003

Internal Medicine/ Family Medicine

Indiana

Indianapolis

St Vincent Hospital Program

Sponsor: St Vincent Hospitals and Health Care Center

Prgm Director: David M Harsha, MD
Steven P Gerke, MD
St Vincent Hosp & Hlth Care Ctr
Dept of Family Med #160
8414 Naab Rd
Indianapolis, IN 46260
Tel: 317 338-7600   *Fax:* 317 338-7606
E-mail: dmeastma@stvincent.org
Accred Length: 4 Yrs   *Program Size:* 8   *(GY1:* 2)
Program ID: 740-17-44-006

Virginia

Norfolk

Eastern Virginia Medical School Program

Sponsor: Eastern Virginia Medical School
Sentara Norfolk General Hospital

Prgm Director: James G Dixon, MD
Eastern Virginia Med Sch
Dept of Internal Med
825 Fairfax Ave
Norfolk, VA 23507-1912
Tel: 757 446-7356   *Fax:* 757 446-5242
E-mail: brennalm@evms.edu
Accred Length: 4 Yrs   *Program Size:* 11   *(GY1:* 3)
Program ID: 740-51-44-001

Internal Medicine/ Medical Genetics

Alabama

Birmingham

University of Alabama Medical Center Program
Sponsor: University of Alabama Hospital
Children's Hospital of Alabama
Cooper Green Hospital
University of Alabama School of Medicine
Veterans Affairs Medical Center (Birmingham)
Prgm Director: Gustavo R Heudebert, MD
Nathaniel H Robin, MD
Univ of Alabama Med Ctr
720 20th St S
Kaul 230
Birmingham, AL 35294-0024
Tel: 205 996-2916   *Fax:* 205 934-9488
E-mail: saustin@genetics.uab.edu
Accred Length: 5 Yrs   *Program Size:* 2   (*GY1:* 1)
Program ID: 766-01-44-005

Maryland

Baltimore

Johns Hopkins University School of Medicine Program
Sponsor: Johns Hopkins University School of Medicine
Johns Hopkins Hospital
Prgm Director: Charles Weiner, MD
Garry R Cutting, MD
Johns Hopkins Univ Hosp
Inst of Genetic Med Blalock 1010A
600 N Wolfe St
Baltimore, MD 21287
Tel: 443 287-3566   *Fax:* 410 502-2646
E-mail: agilbe13@jhmi.edu
Accred Length: 5 Yrs   *Program Size:* 1
Program ID: 766-23-44-004

Massachusetts

Boston

Brigham and Women's Hospital/Harvard Medical School Program
Sponsor: Brigham and Women's Hospital
Children's Hospital
Massachusetts General Hospital
Prgm Director: Michael F Murray, MD
Brigham & Women's Hosp
NRB 455
77 Ave Louis Pasteur
Boston, MA 02115
Tel: 617 525-4542   *Fax:* 617 525-4705
E-mail: mfmurray@bics.bwh.harvard.edu
Accred Length: 5 Yrs
Program ID: 766-24-44-002

New York

New York

Mount Sinai School of Medicine Program
Sponsor: Mount Sinai School of Medicine
Mount Sinai Medical Center
Prgm Director: Ethylin Jabs, MD
Mount Sinai Med Ctr
Box 1497
One Gustave L Levy Pl
New York, NY 10029
Tel: 212 241-6609   *Fax:* 212 241-8445
E-mail: residency@mssm.edu
Accred Length: 5 Yrs   *Program Size:* 5   (*GY1:* 2)
Program ID: 766-35-44-003

Ohio

Cleveland

University Hospitals Case Medical Center Program
Sponsor: University Hospitals Case Medical Center
MetroHealth Medical Center
Veterans Affairs Medical Center (Cleveland)
Prgm Director: Georgia Wiesner, MD
Arthur Zinn, MD
Univ Hosps Case Med Ctr
Ctr for Human Genetics
11100 Euclid Ave
Cleveland, OH 44106
Tel: 216 844-3936   *Fax:* 216 844-7497
E-mail: shawn.mccandless@uhhs.com
Accred Length: 5 Yrs   *Program Size:* 10   (*GY1:* 2)
Program ID: 766-38-44-001

Pennsylvania

Philadelphia

University of Pennsylvania Program
Sponsor: University of Pennsylvania Health System
Veterans Affairs Medical Center (Philadelphia)
Prgm Director: Reed E Pyeritz, MD, PhD
Lisa Bellini, MD
Univ of Pennsylvania Hlth System
5 Mahoney Bldg
3600 Spruce St
Philadelphia, PA 19104-4283
Tel: 215 662-4740   *Fax:* 215 614-0298
E-mail: reed.pyeritz@uphs.upenn.edu
Accred Length: 5 Yrs
Program ID: 766-41-44-006

Internal Medicine/ Neurology

Indiana

Indianapolis

Indiana University School of Medicine Program
Sponsor: Indiana University School of Medicine
Clarian Indiana University Hospital
Richard L Roudebush Veterans Affairs Medical Center
William N Wishard Memorial Hospital
Prgm Director: James D Fleck, MD
Indiana Univ Med Ctr
Dept of Neurology EH 125
545 Barnhill Dr
Indianapolis, IN 46202-5124
Tel: 317 274-4455   *Fax:* 317 278-4918
E-mail: prcowher@iupui.edu
Accred Length: 5 Yrs   *Program Size:* 5   (*GY1:* 1)
Program ID: 745-17-44-009

Louisiana

New Orleans

Tulane University Program
Sponsor: Tulane University School of Medicine
Tulane University Hospital and Clinics
Prgm Director: Jeffrey Nicholl, MD
Jeffrey G Wiese, MD
Tulane Univ Hlth Sci Ctr
Dept of Neurology TB-52 10th Fl
1430 Tulane Ave
New Orleans, LA 70112-2699
Tel: 504 988-2241   *Fax:* 504 988-3695
E-mail: akivell@tulane.edu
Accred Length: 5 Yrs   *Program Size:* 5   (*GY1:* 1)
Program ID: 745-21-44-005

New York

Buffalo

University at Buffalo Program
Sponsor: University at Buffalo School of Medicine
Erie County Medical Center
Kaleida Health System (Buffalo General Hospital)
Prgm Director: Richard E Ferguson, MD
Ellen P Rich, MD
Jacobs Neurological Inst
Int Med/Neurology Pgm
100 High St
Buffalo, NY 14203
Tel: 716 859-3496   *Fax:* 716 859-7573
E-mail: ejtamoga@buffalo.edu
Accred Length: 5 Yrs
Program ID: 745-35-44-001

Stony Brook

SUNY at Stony Brook Program

Sponsor: University Hospital-SUNY at Stony Brook
Veterans Affairs Medical Center (Northport)

Prgm Director: Cara E Harth, MD
Michael Guido, MD
Stony Brook Univ Med Ctr
Dept of Neurology
HSC T12 Rm 020
Stony Brook, NY 11794-8121
Tel: 631 444-7878   *Fax:* 631 632-2451
E-mail: dboehle@notes.cc.sunysb.edu
Accred Length: 5 Yrs   *Program Size:* 3   (GY1: 1)
Program ID: 745-35-44-004

West Virginia

Morgantown

West Virginia University Program

Sponsor: West Virginia University Hospitals

Prgm Director: Gauri Pawar, MD
Michelle Nuss, MD
Robert C Byrd Hlth Sci Ctr
Dept of Neurology Box 9180
One Medical Center Dr
Morgantown, WV 26506-9180
Tel: 304 293-2342   *Fax:* 304 293-3352
E-mail: bzapotosky@hsc.wvu.edu
Accred Length: 5 Yrs   *Program Size:* 1   (GY1: 1)
Program ID: 745-55-44-002

Wisconsin

Milwaukee

Medical College of Wisconsin Affiliated Hospitals Program

Sponsor: Medical College of Wisconsin Affiliated
Hospitals Inc
Clement J Zablocki Veterans Affairs Medical Center
Froedtert Memorial Lutheran Hospital

Prgm Director: Michael Frank, MD
Doug Woo, MD
Froedtert Memorial Lutheran Hosp
Dept of Med
9200 W Wisconsin Ave
Milwaukee, WI 53226
Tel: 414 805-5254   *Fax:* 414 805-0535
E-mail: jdavies@mcw.edu
Accred Length: 5 Yrs   *Program Size:* 4   (GY1: 1)
Program ID: 745-56-44-016

Internal Medicine/ Nuclear Medicine

Georgia

Atlanta

Emory University School of Medicine Program

Sponsor: Emory University School of Medicine
Crawford Long Hospital of Emory University
Emory University Hospital
Grady Health System
Veterans Affairs Medical Center (Atlanta)

Prgm Director: Joyce D Doyle, MD
Scott C Bartley, MD
Emory Univ Sch of Med
Int Med/Nuclear Med Pgm
69 Jesse Hill Jr Dr SE
Atlanta, GA 30303
Tel: 404 616-7028   *Fax:* 404 525-2957
E-mail: interns@emory.edu
Accred Length: 4 Yrs
Program ID: 780-12-44-001

Iowa

Iowa City

University of Iowa Hospitals and Clinics Program

Sponsor: University of Iowa Hospitals and Clinics
Veterans Affairs Medical Center (Iowa City)

Prgm Director: Scott Vogelgesang, MD
Michael Graham, MD
Univ of Iowa Hosps & Clinics
Dept of Internal Med E323 GH
200 Hawkins Dr
Iowa City, IA 52242-1081
Tel: 319 356-2034   *Fax:* 319 384-8955
E-mail: intmedres@uiowa.edu
Accred Length: 4 Yrs
Program ID: 780-18-44-002

Internal Medicine/ Preventive Medicine

California

San Francisco

Kaiser Foundation/UCSF Program

Sponsor: University of California (San Francisco) School
of Medicine
Kaiser Permanente Medical Center (San Francisco)
San Francisco General Hospital Medical Center
UCSF and Mount Zion Medical Centers
University of California School of Public Health
Veterans Affairs Medical Center (San Francisco)

Prgm Director: Michael Coppolino, MD
George W Rutherford, MD
Kaiser Permanente Med Ctr
Rm M-160
2425 Geary Blvd
San Francisco, CA 94115
Tel: 415 833-3034   *Fax:* 415 833-4983
E-mail: Helen.I.Lee@kp.org
Accred Length: 4 Yrs
Program ID: 751-05-44-011

Connecticut

Derby

Griffin Hospital Program

Sponsor: Griffin Hospital
Yale University School of Public Health

Prgm Director: Haq Nawaz, MD, MPH
Ramin Ahmadi, MD, MPH
Griffin Hosp
Int Med/Prev Med Pgm
130 Division St
Derby, CT 06418
Tel: 203 732-7327   *Fax:* 203 732-7185
E-mail: mbliga@griffinhealth.org
Accred Length: 4 Yrs   *Program Size:* 12   (GY1: 3)
Program ID: 751-08-44-008

Louisiana

New Orleans

Tulane University Program

Sponsor: Tulane University School of Medicine
Tulane Univ School of Public Health and Tropical
Medicine

Prgm Director: Jeffrey G Wiese, MD
Amita Toprani, MD, MPH
Tulane Univ Med Ctr
Preventive Med/IM Res
1430 Tulane Ave TB-50
New Orleans, LA 70112-2699
Tel: 504 988-2841
E-mail: aneumann@tulane.edu
Accred Length: 4 Yrs   *Program Size:* 1   (GY1: 1)
Program ID: 751-21-44-003

New York

Buffalo

University at Buffalo Program

Sponsor: University at Buffalo School of Medicine
Kaleida Health System (Buffalo General Hospital)
Prgm Director: Ellen P Rich, MD
Michael Noe, MD, MPH, MA
Univ at Buffalo
Dept of Med
462 Grider St
Buffalo, NY 14215
Tel: 716 829-2975   *Fax:* 716 829-2979
E-mail: carlli@buffalo.edu
Accred Length: 4 Yrs   *Program Size:* 6   *(GY1:* 2)
Program ID: 751-35-44-004

Texas

Galveston

University of Texas Medical Branch at Galveston Program

Sponsor: University of Texas Medical Branch Hospitals
Prgm Director: Thomas A Blackwell, MD
Nelson Avery, MD
301 Univ Blvd
Preventive Med Residencies
Galveston, TX 77555-1150
Tel: 409 772-5845   *Fax:* 409 747-6129
E-mail: ryschulz@utmb.edu
Accred Length: 4 Yrs   *Program Size:* 1
Program ID: 751-48-44-007

University of Texas Medical Branch Hospitals Program A

Sponsor: University of Texas Medical Branch Hospitals
Prgm Director: Robert Johnson, MD, MPH, MBA
Thomas A Blackwell, MD
Preventive Med Residencies
301 University Blvd
Ewing Hall Ste 1 104
Galveston, TX 77555-1150
Tel: 409 772-5845   *Fax:* 409 747-6129
E-mail: ryschulz@utmb.edu
Accred Length: 4 Yrs   *Program Size:* 5   *(GY1:* 1)
Program ID: 751-48-44-010

University of Texas Medical Branch Hospitals Program

Sponsor: University of Texas Medical Branch Hospitals
NASA Johnson Space Center
University of Texas Medical School at Galveston
Prgm Director: Richard T Jennings, MD, MS
Thomas A Blackwell, MD
Preventive Med Residencies
301 University Blvd
Maurice Ewing Hall Ste 1104
Galveston, TX 77555-1150
Tel: 409 772-5845   *Fax:* 409 747-6129
E-mail: ryschulz@utmb.edu
Accred Length: 4 Yrs   *Program Size:* 3   *(GY1:* 1)
Program ID: 751-48-44-009

Internal Medicine/ Psychiatry

California

Sacramento

University of California (Davis) Health System Program

Sponsor: University of California (Davis) Health System
Sacramento County Health and Human Services
University of California (Davis) Medical Center
Prgm Director: Robert M McCarron, DO
UC Davis Med Ctr
Psychiatry & Behavioral Sci
2230 Stockton Blvd
Sacramento, CA 95817
Tel: 916 734-5514   *Fax:* 916 734-3384
E-mail: marilyn.clark@ucdmc.ucdavis.edu
Accred Length: 5 Yrs   *Program Size:* 6   *(GY1:* 2)
Program ID: 715-05-44-032

Georgia

Atlanta

Emory University School of Medicine Program

Sponsor: Emory University School of Medicine
Crawford Long Hospital of Emory University
Emory University Hospital
Grady Health System
Veterans Affairs Medical Center (Atlanta)
Prgm Director: Kellie Clearo, MD
Raymond Young, MD
Emory Univ Sch of Med
Faculty Office Bldg 4th Fl
49 Jesse Hill Jr Dr SE
Atlanta, GA 30303
Tel: 404 778-1624   *Fax:* 404 778-1602
E-mail: kclearo@emory.edu
Accred Length: 5 Yrs   *Program Size:* 5   *(GY1:* 2)
Program ID: 715-12-44-034

Illinois

Chicago

Rush University Medical Center Program

Sponsor: Rush University Medical Center
Prgm Director: Daniel Rosenthal, MD
Richard Abrams, MD
Rush Univ Med Ctr
4th Fl Mail Box
1653 W Congress Pkwy
Chicago, IL 60612
Tel: 312 942-5015   *Fax:* 312 942-8664
E-mail: zaida_llera@rush.edu
Accred Length: 5 Yrs   *Program Size:* 14
Program ID: 715-16-44-018

Springfield

Southern Illinois University Program

Sponsor: Southern Illinois University School of Medicine
Memorial Medical Center
St John's Hospital
Prgm Director: Andrew J Varney, MD
Jeffrey Bennett, MD
SIU Sch of Med
PO Box 19636
701 N First St
Springfield, IL 62794-9636
Tel: 217 545-0193   *Fax:* 217 545-8156
E-mail: cbrower@siumed.edu
Accred Length: 5 Yrs   *Program Size:* 10   *(GY1:* 2)
Program ID: 715-16-44-009

Iowa

Iowa City

University of Iowa Hospitals and Clinics Program

Sponsor: University of Iowa Hospitals and Clinics
Veterans Affairs Medical Center (Iowa City)
Prgm Director: Ole Behrendtsen, MD, BA
Univ of Iowa Hosp and Clinics
Dept of Int Med E330-2 GH
200 Hawkins Dr
Iowa City, IA 52242-1081
Tel: 319 356-2034   *Fax:* 319 384-8955
E-mail: cynthia-batzkiel@uiowa.edu
Accred Length: 5 Yrs   *Program Size:* 10   *(GY1:* 2)
Program ID: 715-18-44-003

Kansas

Kansas City

University of Kansas Medical Center Program

Sponsor: University of Kansas School of Medicine
University of Kansas Hospital
Veterans Affairs Medical Center (Kansas City)
Prgm Director: Teresa D Long, MD
Barry I Liskow, MD
Univ of Kansas Med Ctr
Dept of Psych
3901 Rainbow Blvd
Kansas City, KS 66160-7341
Tel: 913 588-6412   *Fax:* 913 588-6414
E-mail: sbuckley2@kumc.edu
Accred Length: 5 Yrs   *Program Size:* 7   *(GY1:* 2)
Program ID: 715-19-44-008

Louisiana

New Orleans

Tulane University Program

Sponsor: Tulane University School of Medicine
Tulane University Hospital and Clinics
Prgm Director: L Lee Tynes, MD, PhD
Jeffrey G Wiese, MD
Tulane Univ Hlth Sci Ctr
Dept of Psychiatry Mailbox TB53
1440 Canal St
New Orleans, LA 70112-2715
Tel: 504 988-4272   *Fax:* 504 988-4270
E-mail: psychres@tulane.edu
Accred Length: 5 Yrs   *Program Size:* 7   *(GY1:* 1)
Program ID: 715-21-44-010

Maryland

Bethesda

National Capital Consortium Program
Sponsor: National Capital Consortium
Walter Reed Army Institute of Research

Prgm Director: Scott C Moran, MD
Brian Cuneo, MD
Walter Reed Army Inst of Research
Dept of Psychiatry
4301 Jones Bridge Rd
Bethesda, MD 20814
Tel: 202 782-7104   *Fax:* 202 782-6480
E-mail: leslie.galloway@na.amedd.army.mil
Accred Length: 5 Yrs   *Program Size:* 12   *(GY1:* 3)
Program ID: 715-23-44-021
Uniformed Services Program

New Hampshire

Lebanon

Dartmouth-Hitchcock Medical Center Program
Sponsor: Mary Hitchcock Memorial Hospital
Veterans Affairs Medical Center (White River Junction)

Prgm Director: Ronald L Green, MD
Dartmouth-Hitchcock Med Ctr
Dept of Psychiatry
One Medical Center Dr
Lebanon, NH 03756
Tel: 603 650-4523   *Fax:* 603 650-5842
E-mail: leslie.j.papa@hitchcock.org
Accred Length: 5 Yrs   *Program Size:* 2
Program ID: 715-32-44-016

New York

Brooklyn

SUNY Health Science Center at Brooklyn Program
Sponsor: SUNY Health Science Center at Brooklyn
Kings County Hospital Center
Kingsbrook Jewish Medical Center
St John's Episcopal Hospital-South Shore
University Hospital-SUNY Health Science Center at Brooklyn
Veterans Affairs Medical Center (Brooklyn)

Prgm Director: Stephen Goldfinger, MD
SUNY Health Sci Ctr-Brooklyn
Box 1203
450 Clarkson Ave
Brooklyn, NY 11203-2098
Tel: 718 270-2023   *Fax:* 718 270-8826
E-mail: stephen.goldfinger@downstate.edu
Accred Length: 5 Yrs
Program ID: 715-35-44-033

North Carolina

Durham

Duke University Hospital Program
Sponsor: Duke University Hospital
Veterans Affairs Medical Center (Durham)

Prgm Director: Grace C Thrall, MD
Diana B McNeill, MD
Duke Univ Med Ctr
IM/Psych Pgm
Box 3837
Durham, NC 27710
Tel: 919 684-2258   *Fax:* 919 684-2290
E-mail: psychres@duke.edu
Accred Length: 5 Yrs   *Program Size:* 10   *(GY1:* 2)
Program ID: 715-36-44-012

Greenville

Pitt County Memorial Hospital/East Carolina University Program
Sponsor: Pitt County Memorial Hospital
Brody School of Medicine at East Carolina University

Prgm Director: James G Peden Jr, MD
Brody Sch of Med ECU
Student Admissions Ofc Brody 2N-49
600 Moye Blvd
Greenville, NC 27834
Tel: 252 744-2562   *Fax:* 252 744-1926
E-mail: cowardly@ecu.edu
Accred Length: 5 Yrs   *Program Size:* 10   *(GY1:* 2)
Program ID: 715-36-44-005

South Carolina

Charleston

Medical University of South Carolina Program
Sponsor: Medical University of South Carolina College of Medicine
MUSC Medical Center
Ralph H Johnson VA Medical Center (Charleston)

Prgm Director: Robert P Albanese, MD
Ernest B Clyburn, MD
Med Univ of South Carolina
Dept of Psychiatry PO Box 250861
67 President St
Charleston, SC 29425
Tel: 843 792-0192   *Fax:* 843 792-6894
E-mail: pucalm@musc.edu
Accred Length: 5 Yrs   *Program Size:* 10   *(GY1:* 2)
Program ID: 715-45-44-025

Tennessee

Johnson City

East Tennessee State University Program
Sponsor: James H Quillen College of Medicine
Johnson City Medical Center/Mountain States Health Alliance
Veterans Affairs Medical Center (Mountain Home)

Prgm Director: Hetal K Brahmbhatt, MD
Margaret A Shugart, MD, MS
East Tennessee State Univ
Dept of Psychiatry
PO Box 70567
Johnson City, TN 37614-0567
Tel: 423 439-2225   *Fax:* 423 439-2250
E-mail: adamsj@mail.etsu.edu
Accred Length: 5 Yrs   *Program Size:* 10   *(GY1:* 2)
Program ID: 715-47-44-028

West Virginia

Charleston

Charleston Area Medical Center/West Virginia University (Charleston Division) Program
Sponsor: Charleston Area Medical Center/West Virginia University

Prgm Director: James P Griffith, MD
Robert C Byrd Hlth Sci Ctr
Med/Psych Pgm PO Box 1547
501 Morris St
Charleston, WV 25326-1547
Tel: 304 341-1500   *Fax:* 304 341-1554
E-mail: jgriffith@hsc.wvu.edu
Accred Length: 5 Yrs   *Program Size:* 10   *(GY1:* 2)
Program ID: 715-55-44-014

Morgantown

West Virginia University Program
Sponsor: West Virginia University Hospitals

Prgm Director: Michelle Nuss, MD
Ryan Finkenbine, MD
West Virginia Univ Hosps
Dept of Med/Internal Med
One Medical Center Dr
Morgantown, WV 26501
Tel: 304 293-4239   *Fax:* 304 293-3651
E-mail: chenry@hsc.wvu.edu
Accred Length: 5 Yrs   *Program Size:* 2   *(GY1:* 1)
Program ID: 715-55-44-006

Neurology/Diagnostic Radiology/ Neuroradiology

New York

New York

New York University School of Medicine Program

Sponsor: New York University School of Medicine
Bellevue Hospital Center
Manhattan VA Harbor Health Care System
Prgm Director: Peter K Nelson, MD
New York Univ Hosps Ctr
Dept of Rad/Neurointerventional HE-208
560 First Ave
New York, NY 10016
Tel: 212 263-6008   *Fax:* 212 263-0405
E-mail: nelsop01@popmail.med.nyu.edu
Accred Length: 7 Yrs   *Program Size:* 1
Program ID: 760-35-44-002

Pediatrics/ Dermatology

California

San Francisco

University of California (San Francisco) Program

Sponsor: University of California (San Francisco) School
of Medicine
San Francisco General Hospital Medical Center
UCSF and Mount Zion Medical Centers
Veterans Affairs Medical Center (San Francisco)
Prgm Director: Ilona Frieden, MD
UCSF Med Ctr
Dept of Dermatology
505 Parnassus Ave
San Francisco, CA 94143-0316
Tel: 415 502-5559   *Fax:* 415 476-4009
E-mail: pedsapp@ucsf.edu
Accred Length: 5 Yrs   *Program Size:* 4   *(GY1:* 1)
Program ID: 790-05-44-003

Pennsylvania

Philadelphia

Children's Hospital of Philadelphia Program

Sponsor: Children's Hospital of Philadelphia
University of Pennsylvania Health System
Veterans Affairs Medical Center (Philadelphia)
Prgm Director: Albert C Yan, MD
34th St & Civic Ctr Blvd
Sect of Dermatology - Wood Bldg 1st Fl
Philadelphia, PA 19104
Tel: 215 590-2169   *Fax:* 215 590-4948
E-mail: evenosky@email.chop.edu
Accred Length: 5 Yrs
Program ID: 790-41-44-002

Texas

Galveston

University of Texas Medical Branch Hospitals Program

Sponsor: University of Texas Medical Branch Hospitals
Prgm Director: Cassandra Pruitt, MD
Sharon S Raimer, MD
Univ of Texas Med Branch Hosps
Peds/Dermatology Pgm
301 University Blvd
Galveston, TX 77555-0354
Tel: 409 747-0534   *Fax:* 409 747-0721
E-mail: pdmcclai@utmb.edu
Accred Length: 5 Yrs   *Program Size:* 2
Program ID: 790-48-44-001

Pediatrics/ Emergency Medicine

Arizona

Tucson

University of Arizona Program

Sponsor: University of Arizona College of Medicine
University Medical Center
Prgm Director: Dale P Woolridge, MD
Univ of Arizona Hlth Sci Ctr
Dept of Emergency Med
1501 N Campbell Ave
Tucson, AZ 85724-5057
Tel: 520 626-7233   *Fax:* 520 626-2480
E-mail: donna@aemrc.arizona.edu
Accred Length: 5 Yrs   *Program Size:* 10   *(GY1:* 2)
Program ID: 725-03-44-009

Indiana

Indianapolis

Indiana University School of Medicine/Methodist Hospital Program

Sponsor: Indiana University School of Medicine
Clarian Methodist Hospital of Indiana
Prgm Director: Carey D Chisholm, MD
Jerry L Rushton II, MD, MPH
Clarian Methodist Hosp
Emergency Med/Trauma Ctr
I-65 at 21st St
Indianapolis, IN 46206
Tel: 317 962-5975   *Fax:* 317 963-5394
E-mail: cchisholm@clarian.org
Accred Length: 5 Yrs   *Program Size:* 10   *(GY1:* 2)
Program ID: 725-17-44-005

Maryland

Baltimore

University of Maryland Program

Sponsor: University of Maryland Medical System
Mercy Medical Center
Prgm Director: David Jerrard, MD
Erin Giudice, MD
Univ of Maryland Med System
Dept of Emergency Med 6th Fl Ste 200
110 S Paca St
Baltimore, MD 21201
Tel: 410 328-8025   *Fax:* 410 328-8028
E-mail: nvancleave@smail.umaryland.edu
Accred Length: 5 Yrs   *Program Size:* 10   *(GY1:* 2)
Program ID: 725-23-44-006

Pediatrics/Medical Genetics

Alabama

Birmingham

University of Alabama Medical Center Program

Sponsor: University of Alabama Hospital
Children's Hospital of Alabama
University of Alabama School of Medicine

Prgm Director: Michele H Nichols, MD
Nathaniel H Robin, MD
Univ of Alabama Med Ctr
Peds/Med Genetics
1600 7th Ave S
Birmingham, AL 35233-1711
Tel: 205 939-9589   *Fax:* 205 939-9977
E-mail: lmcpherson@peds.uab.edu
Accred Length: 5 Yrs   *Program Size:* 2
Program ID: 765-01-44-013

California

Orange

University of California (Irvine) Program

Sponsor: University of California (Irvine) Medical
Center
Long Beach Memorial Medical Center
Prgm Director: Maureen Bocian, MD, MS
Khanh-Van Le-Bucklin, MD
UC Irvine Med Ctr
Dept of Pediatrics ZC4482
101 The City Dr S
Orange, CA 92868-3298
Tel: 714 456-5631   *Fax:* 714 456-6660
E-mail: dpeach@uci.edu
Accred Length: 5 Yrs   *Program Size:* 1   *(GY1:* 1)
Program ID: 765-05-44-009

Connecticut

Farmington

University of Connecticut Program

Sponsor: University of Connecticut School of Medicine
Connecticut Children's Medical Center
St Francis Hospital and Medical Center
Univ of Connecticut Health Center/John Dempsey
Hospital
Prgm Director: Robert M Greenstein, MD
Edwin L Zalneraitis, MD
Univ of Connecticut Hlth Ctr
UConn Hlth Partners Bldg
65 Kane St
West Hartford, CT 06119
Tel: 860 523-6470   *Fax:* 860 523-6465
E-mail: greenstein@nso1.uchc.edu
Accred Length: 5 Yrs   *Program Size:* 1   *(GY1:* 1)
Program ID: 765-08-44-004

Maryland

Baltimore

Johns Hopkins University School of Medicine Program

Sponsor: Johns Hopkins University School of Medicine
Johns Hopkins Hospital

Prgm Director: Julia A McMillan, MD
Ronald D Cohn, MD
Pediatric Residency Pgm
Institute of Genetic Med
600 N Wolfe St/CMSC 1004
Baltimore, MD 21287-3914
Tel: 410 955-2727
Accred Length: 5 Yrs   *Program Size:* 3   *(GY1:* 1)
Program ID: 765-23-44-010

Bethesda

National Human Genome Research Institute/Children's National Medical Center Program

Sponsor: Clinical Center at the National Institutes of
Health
Children's National Medical Center

Prgm Director: Maximilian Muenke, MD
Bernhard L Wiedermann, MD
NIH Dept of Hlth & Human Services
Bldg 35 Rm 1B-203 MSC 1852
10 Center Dr
Bethesda, MD 20892-1852
Tel: 301 402-8167   *Fax:* 301 480-7876
E-mail: mmuenke@nhgri.nih.gov
Accred Length: 5 Yrs   *Program Size:* 1
Program ID: 765-23-44-008

Massachusetts

Boston

Children's Hospital Boston Program

Sponsor: Children's Hospital
Boston Medical Center

Prgm Director: Amy Roberts, MD
Theodore Sectish, MD
Children's Hosp Boston
Peds/Med Genetics Pgm
300 Longwood Ave
Boston, MA 02115
Tel: 617 355-6529   *Fax:* 617 713-3808
E-mail: Amy.roberts@cardio.chboston.org
Accred Length: 5 Yrs
Program ID: 765-24-44-017

Michigan

Detroit

Wayne State University/Detroit Medical Center Program

Sponsor: Wayne State University/Detroit Medical Center
Children's Hospital of Michigan
Harper-Hutzel Hospital

Prgm Director: Gerald Feldman, MD, PhD
Anne Mortensen, MD
Children's Hosp of Michigan
Pediatric Ed Dept
3901 Beaubien
Detroit, MI 48201
Tel: 313 577-6298   *Fax:* 313 577-9137
E-mail: genpeds@chom.net
Accred Length: 5 Yrs   *Program Size:* 5   *(GY1:* 1)
Program ID: 765-25-44-012

Missouri

St Louis

Washington University/B-JH/SLCH Consortium Program

Sponsor: Washington University/B-JH/SLCH Consortium
Barnes-Jewish Hospital
St Louis Children's Hospital

Prgm Director: Tyler Reimschisel, MD
Andy White, MD
Washington Univ Med Ctr
Campus Box 8116
One Children's Pl
St Louis, MO 63110
Tel: 314 454-6093
E-mail: Reimschisel_t@kids.wustl.edu
Accred Length: 5 Yrs
Program ID: 765-28-44-015

New York

New York

Mount Sinai School of Medicine Program

Sponsor: Mount Sinai School of Medicine
Mount Sinai Medical Center

Prgm Director: Ethylin Jabs, MD
Joel A Forman, MD
Mount Sinai Med Ctr
Box 1497
One Gustave L Levy Pl
New York, NY 10029-6574
Tel: 212 241-6934   *Fax:* 212 241-4309
E-mail: lorrayne.garcia@mssm.edu
Accred Length: 5 Yrs   *Program Size:* 5   *(GY1:* 1)
Program ID: 765-35-44-001

Ohio

Cincinnati

Cincinnati Children's Hospital Medical Center Program

Sponsor: Cincinnati Children's Hospital Medical Center

Prgm Director: Javier A Gonzalez-del-Rey, MD, MEd
Howard M Saal, MD
Pediatric Pgm
Children's Hosp Med Ctr
3333 Burnet Ave
Cincinnati, OH 45229-3039
Tel: 513 636-4760   *Fax:* 513 636-7297
E-mail: rob.hopkin@cchmc.org
Accred Length: 5 Yrs   *Program Size:* 5   *(GY1:* 1)
Program ID: 765-38-44-011

Cleveland

University Hospitals Case Medical Center Program

Sponsor: University Hospitals Case Medical Center

Prgm Director: Martha Wright, MD
Shawn E McCandless, MD
Rainbow Babies & Children's Hosp
RB&C 865 MS 6002
11100 Euclid Ave
Cleveland, OH 44106
Tel: 216 844-3641   *Fax:* 216 844-7166
E-mail: jacqueline.sherry@uhhs.com
Accred Length: 5 Yrs   *Program Size:* 2
Program ID: 765-38-44-002

Pennsylvania

Philadelphia

Children's Hospital of Philadelphia Program

Sponsor: Children's Hospital of Philadelphia

Prgm Director: Ian Krantz, MD
Children's Hosp of Philadelphia
Div of Human Genetics Rm 1002
3615 Civic Center Blvd
Philadelphia, PA 19104-6145
Tel: 215 590-3856   *Fax:* 215 590-3764
E-mail: harveyr@email.chop.edu
Accred Length: 5 Yrs   *Program Size:* 3
Program ID: 765-41-44-003

Texas

Houston

Baylor College of Medicine Program

Sponsor: Baylor College of Medicine
Harris County Hospital District-Ben Taub General
  Hospital
Methodist Hospital (Houston)
St Joseph Medical Center
Texas Children's Hospital

Prgm Director: V Reid Sutton, MD
Arthur L Beaudet, MD
Texas Children's Hosp
CC-1560
6621 Fannin St
Houston, TX 77030
Tel: 832 822-4292   *Fax:* 832 825-4294
E-mail: vsutton@bcm.edu
Accred Length: 5 Yrs   *Program Size:* 2   *(GY1: 2)*
Program ID: 765-48-44-016

University of Texas at Houston Program

Sponsor: University of Texas M D Anderson Cancer
  Center
Shriners Hospitals for Children (Houston)
University of Texas School of Public Health

Prgm Director: Hope Northrup, MD
Univ of Texas HSC Houston
MSB 3.142
6431 Fannin St
Houston, TX 77030
Tel: 713 500-5760
E-mail: shirlene.edwards@uth.tmc.edu
Accred Length: 5 Yrs
Program ID: 765-48-44-014

Pediatrics/Physical Medicine and Rehabilitation

Colorado

Denver

University of Colorado Denver Program

Sponsor: University of Colorado School of Medicine

Prgm Director: Adam Rosenberg, MD
Amitabh Jha, MD
UCHSC c/o Children's Hosp
Off of Med Education
13123 E 16th Ave
Aurora, CO 80045
Tel: 800 225-6611   *Fax:* 720 777-7258
E-mail: PedResPro@tchden.org
Accred Length: 5 Yrs   *Program Size:* 3
Program ID: 735-07-44-001

Michigan

Detroit

Wayne State University/Detroit Medical Center Program

Sponsor: Wayne State University/Detroit Medical Center
Children's Hospital of Michigan
Rehabilitation Institute

Prgm Director: Charles Pelshaw, MD
Children's Hosp Michigan
3T72
3901 Beaubien Blvd
Detroit, MI 48201-2196
Tel:
E-mail: contact@chom.net
Accred Length: 5 Yrs   *Program Size:* 1   *(GY1: 1)*
Program ID: 735-25-44-024

New York

Buffalo

University at Buffalo Program

Sponsor: University at Buffalo School of Medicine
Erie County Medical Center
Kaleida Health System (Buffalo General Hospital)
Kaleida Health System (Women and Children's Hosp of
  Buffalo)
Sisters of Charity Hospital
Veterans Affairs Western New York Hospital

Prgm Director: Thomas Polisoto, MD
Lorna K Fitzpatrick, MD
Erie Cnty Med Ctr
Rehabilitation Med
462 Grider St
Buffalo, NY 14215
Tel: 716 898-3218   *Fax:* 716 898-3652
E-mail: tpolisot@buffalo.edu
Accred Length: 5 Yrs   *Program Size:* 2   *(GY1: 1)*
Program ID: 735-35-44-023

Ohio

Cincinnati

University of Cincinnati Hospital Group Program

Sponsor: University Hospital Inc

Prgm Director: Mary McMahon, MD
Univ Hosp Univ of Cincinnati
PO Box 670530 Ste 5200
260 Stetson St
Cincinnati, OH 45267-0530
Tel: 513 558-7635   *Fax:* 513 558-4458
E-mail: mary.duke@uc.edu
Accred Length: 5 Yrs   *Program Size:* 6   *(GY1: 1)*
Program ID: 735-38-44-012

Pennsylvania

Philadelphia

Thomas Jefferson University/duPont Hospital for Children Program

Sponsor: Thomas Jefferson University Hospital
Alfred I duPont Hospital for Children

Prgm Director: Steven M Selbst, MD
Christopher Formal, MD
A I duPont Hosp for Children
PO Box 269
1600 Rockland Rd
Wilmington, DE 19899
Tel: 302 651-5874   *Fax:* 302 651-5954
E-mail: cchuidia@nemours.org
Accred Length: 5 Yrs   *Program Size:* 5   *(GY1: 1)*
Program ID: 735-41-44-020

Virginia

Richmond

Virginia Commonwealth University Health System Program

Sponsor: Virginia Commonwealth University Health
  System
Hunter Holmes McGuire VA Medical Center (Richmond)
Medical College of Virginia Hospitals

Prgm Director: William McKinley, MD
Eugenio Monasterio, MD
VCU Health System
PO Box 980661
1300 E Marshall St
Richmond, VA 23298
Tel: 804 828-4233   *Fax:* 804 828-5074
E-mail: wcarlton@mcvh-vcu.edu
Accred Length: 5 Yrs   *Program Size:* 1
Program ID: 735-51-44-022

Pediatrics/ Psychiatry/Child and Adolescent Psychiatry

Hawaii

Honolulu

University of Hawaii Program

Sponsor: University of Hawaii John A Burns School of Medicine
Kapiolani Medical Center for Women and Children

Prgm Director: Cathy K Bell, MD
Courtenay R Matsu, MD
Univ of Hawaii John A Burns Sch of Med
Dept of Psychiatry 4th Fl
1356 Lusitana St
Honolulu, HI 96813
Tel: 808 586-2939   *Fax:* 808 586-2940
E-mail: leet@dop.hawaii.edu
Accred Length: 5 Yrs   *Program Size:* 10   (*GY1:* 2)
Program ID: 730-14-44-007

Indiana

Indianapolis

Indiana University School of Medicine Program

Sponsor: Indiana University School of Medicine
Clarian Indiana University Hospital
Clarian Riley Hospital for Children

Prgm Director: David Dunn, MD
Jerry L Rushton II, MD, MPH
Indiana Univ Sch of Med
Dept of Psychiatry
1111 W 10th St #A212
Indianapolis, IN 46202-5200
Tel: 317 274-7423   *Fax:* 317 274-1248
E-mail: jtsouder@iupui.edu
Accred Length: 5 Yrs   *Program Size:* 10   (*GY1:* 2)
Program ID: 730-17-44-009

Kentucky

Lexington

University of Kentucky College of Medicine Program

Sponsor: University of Kentucky College of Medicine
Ridge Behavioral Health System
University of Kentucky Hospital

Prgm Director: Robert Simon, MD
Univ of Kentucky Med Ctr
Dept of Psychiatry
3470 Blazer Pkwy
Lexington, KY 40509-1810
Tel: 859 323-6861   *Fax:* 859 323-1194
E-mail: lcbroy0@email.uky.edu
Accred Length: 5 Yrs   *Program Size:* 10   (*GY1:* 2)
Program ID: 730-20-44-001

Louisiana

New Orleans

Tulane University Program

Sponsor: Tulane University School of Medicine
DePaul/Tulane Behavioral Health Center
LSU Interim Hospital
Ochsner Clinic Foundation
Tulane Hospital for Children
Tulane University Hospital and Clinics
Veterans Affairs Medical Center (New Orleans)

Prgm Director: Cecile L Many, MD
Tulane Univ Hlth Sci Ctr
Dept of Psych/Neuro TB52
1440 Canal St
New Orleans, LA 70112
Tel: 504 988-7829   *Fax:* 504 988-4264
E-mail: lconners@tulane.edu
Accred Length: 5 Yrs   *Program Size:* 10   (*GY1:* 2)
Program ID: 730-21-44-012

Massachusetts

Boston

Tufts Medical Center Program

Sponsor: Tufts Medical Center

Prgm Director: Joseph J Jankowski, MD
Tufts Med Ctr
800 Washington St # 1007
Boston, MA 02111
Tel: 617 636-7802   *Fax:* 617 636-1277
E-mail: aszetela@tuftsmedicalcenter.org
Accred Length: 5 Yrs   *Program Size:* 10   (*GY1:* 2)
Program ID: 730-24-44-002

New York

New York

Mount Sinai School of Medicine Program

Sponsor: Mount Sinai Medical Center

Prgm Director: John D O'Brien, MD
Mount Sinai Med Ctr
Dept of Psychiatry Box 1230
One Gustave L Levy Pl
New York, NY 10029
Tel: 212 659-8768   *Fax:* 212 659-8710
E-mail: patricia.morrison@mssm.edu
Accred Length: 5 Yrs   *Program Size:* 10   (*GY1:* 2)
Program ID: 730-35-44-004

Ohio

Cincinnati

Cincinnati Children's Hospital Medical Center/University of Cincinnati College of Medicine Program

Sponsor: Cincinnati Children's Hospital Medical Center
University Hospital Inc

Prgm Director: Raymond G Troy, MD
Javier A Gonzalez-del-Rey, MD, MEd
ML 6015 - College Hill Campus
Cincinnati Children's Hospital Med Ctr
5642 Hamilton Ave
Cincinnati, OH 45224
Tel: 513 636-7331   *Fax:* 513 803-0571
E-mail: dee.cannedy@cchmc.org
Accred Length: 5 Yrs   *Program Size:* 16   (*GY1:* 3)
Program ID: 730-38-44-008

Pennsylvania

Pittsburgh

University of Pittsburgh Medical Center Medical Education Program

Sponsor: Univ of Pittsburgh Medical Center Medical Education Program
Children's Hospital of Pittsburgh of UPMC
Magee-Womens Hospital of UPMC
UPMC Presbyterian Shadyside
UPMC Western Psychiatric Institute and Clinic
Veterans Affairs Medical Center (Pittsburgh)

Prgm Director: Erin E Malley, MD
Dena Hofkosh, MD
Western Psychiatric Inst and Clinic
Ste 502
3811 O'Hara St
Pittsburgh, PA 15213-2583
Tel: 412 246-5320   *Fax:* 412 246-5335
E-mail: malleyee@upmc.edu
Accred Length: 5 Yrs   *Program Size:* 10   (*GY1:* 2)
Program ID: 730-41-44-011

Rhode Island

Providence

Brown University Program

Sponsor: Rhode Island Hospital-Lifespan

Prgm Director: Jeffrey I Hunt, MD, MS
Rhode Island Hosp
POB 122
593 Eddy St
Providence, RI 02903
Tel: 401 444-3762   *Fax:* 401 444-8879
E-mail: mspirito@lifespan.org
Accred Length: 5 Yrs   *Program Size:* 15   (*GY1:* 3)
Program ID: 730-43-44-005

Utah

Salt Lake City

University of Utah Program

Sponsor: University of Utah Medical Center

Prgm Director: Douglas Gray, MD
Univ of Utah Sch of Med
Div of Child/Adolescent Psych
650 S Komas Dr Ste 208
Salt Lake City, UT 84108
Tel: 801 581-3936   *Fax:* 801 585-9096
E-mail: Glenda.Evans@hsc.utah.edu
Accred Length: 5 Yrs   *Program Size:* 10   (*GY1:* 2)
Program ID: 730-49-44-006

Psychiatry/Family Medicine

California

Sacramento

University of California (Davis) Health System Program

Sponsor: University of California (Davis) Health System
University of California (Davis) Medical Center

Prgm Director: Jaesu Han, MD
Thomas Balsbaugh, MD
UC Davis Med Ctr
Dept of Psychiatry
2230 Stockton Blvd
Sacramento, CA 95817
Tel: 916 734-5514   *Fax:* 916 734-3384
E-mail: marilyn.clark@ucdmc.ucdavis.edu
Accred Length: 5 Yrs   *Program Size:* 7   (GY1: 2)
Program ID: 720-05-44-004

San Diego

University of California (San Diego) Program

Sponsor: University of California (San Diego) Medical Center

Prgm Director: R Christopher Searles, MD
David P Folsom, MD
UCSD Med Ctr
Dept of Family & Prev Med MC 8809
200 W Arbor Dr
San Diego, CA 92103
Tel: 619 233-8500, ext 1402   *Fax:* 619 687-1067
E-mail: combinedresidency@ucsd.edu
Accred Length: 5 Yrs   *Program Size:* 10   (GY1: 2)
Program ID: 720-05-44-005

Iowa

Iowa City

University of Iowa Hospitals and Clinics Program

Sponsor: University of Iowa Hospitals and Clinics

Prgm Director: Alison C Abreu, MD
Univ of Iowa Hosp & Clinics
Dept of Family Med
200 Hawkins Dr
Iowa City, IA 52242
Tel: 319 384-7507   *Fax:* 319 384-7822
E-mail: linda-hoover@uiowa.edu
Accred Length: 5 Yrs   *Program Size:* 10   (GY1: 2)
Program ID: 720-18-44-009

Maryland

Bethesda

National Capital Consortium Program

Sponsor: National Capital Consortium
Malcolm Grow Medical Center
Walter Reed Army Medical Center

Prgm Director: Jennifer Lange, MD
Douglas C Warren, MD
Malcolm Grow Med Ctr
Ste A-01
1075 W Perimeter Rd
Andrews AFB, MD 20762-6600
Tel: 202 782-7104   *Fax:* 240 857-3011
E-mail: psych-familymedicine@nccpsychiatry.info
Accred Length: 5 Yrs   *Program Size:* 4
Program ID: 720-23-44-012
Uniformed Services Program

North Carolina

Greenville

Pitt County Memorial Hospital/East Carolina University Program

Sponsor: Pitt County Memorial Hospital
Brody School of Medicine at East Carolina University

Prgm Director: Diana J Antonacci, MD
Gary Levine, MD
Pitt County Memorial Hosp
PO 6028
2100 Strantonsburg Rd
Greenville, NC 27835-6028
Tel: 252 744-2663   *Fax:* 252 744-2419
E-mail: antonaccid@ecu.edu
Accred Length: 5 Yrs
Program ID: 720-36-44-015

Ohio

Cincinnati

University of Cincinnati Hospital Group Program

Sponsor: University Hospital Inc

Prgm Director: Lawson Wulsin, MD
Philip M Diller, MD, PhD
Univ Hosp Univ of Cincinnati
Family Med/Psychiatry Pgm ML 0559
231 Albert B Sabin Way
Cincinnati, OH 45267
Tel: 513 558-5192   *Fax:* 513 558-3477
E-mail: Lawson.Wulsin@uc.edu
Accred Length: 5 Yrs   *Program Size:* 7   (GY1: 1)
Program ID: 720-38-44-006

Cleveland

University Hospitals Case Medical Center Program

Sponsor: University Hospitals Case Medical Center

Prgm Director: Alan Cadesky, MD
Susan Stagno, MD
Univ Hosps Case Med Ctr
Dept of Family Med Ste 1200 Bolwell HC
11100 Euclid Ave
Cleveland, OH 44106-5036
Tel: 216 844-5483   *Fax:* 216 844-1030
E-mail: jean.navratil@UHhospitals.org
Accred Length: 5 Yrs   *Program Size:* 2
Program ID: 720-38-44-013

Oklahoma

Tulsa

University of Oklahoma College of Medicine-Tulsa Program

Sponsor: University of Oklahoma College of Medicine-Tulsa

Prgm Director: Ondria C Gleason, MD
Robert M Morse, MD
Univ of Oklahoma Coll of Med-Tulsa
Dept of Psychiatry # 2F05
4502 E 41st St
Tulsa, OK 74135-2512
Tel: 918 660-3518
E-mail: rhonda-wallace@ouhsc.edu
Accred Length: 5 Yrs   *Program Size:* 10   (GY1: 2)
Program ID: 720-39-44-001

Pennsylvania

Pittsburgh

University of Pittsburgh Medical Center Medical Education Program

Sponsor: Univ of Pittsburgh Medical Center Medical Education Program
UPMC St Margaret
UPMC Western Psychiatric Institute and Clinic

Prgm Director: Michael J Travis, MD
William Markle, MD
Univ of Pittsburgh Med Ctr
WPIC E502
3811 O'Hara St
Pittsburgh, PA 15213
Tel: 412 246-5320   *Fax:* 412 246-5335
E-mail: kirchnerks@upmc.edu
Accred Length: 5 Yrs   *Program Size:* 10   (GY1: 2)
Program ID: 720-41-44-015

West Virginia

Morgantown

West Virginia University Program

Sponsor: West Virginia University Hospitals

Prgm Director: George Frederick, MD
Ryan Finkenbine, MD
Robert C Byrd Hlth Sci Ctr
Dept of Family Med Box 9152
One Medical Center Dr
Morgantown, WV 26506
Tel: 304 598-6907   *Fax:* 304 598-6908
E-mail: eddyd@rcbhsc.wvu.edu
Accred Length: 5 Yrs   *Program Size:* 4   (GY1: 1)
Program ID: 720-55-44-010

Psychiatry/Neurology

Florida

Miami

Jackson Memorial Hospital/Jackson Health System Program
Sponsor: Jackson Memorial Hospital/Jackson Health System
Veterans Affairs Medical Center (Miami)
Prgm Director: Richard S Isaacson, MD
Richard M Steinbook, MD
Univ of Miami Jackson Memorial Med Ctr
Dept of Psych/Neurology #603
1150 NW 14th St
Miami, FL 33136
Tel: 305 243-3902   *Fax:* 305 243-6546
E-mail: vmaldona@med.miami.edu
Accred Length: 5 Yrs   *Program Size:* 1   *(GY1:* 1)
Program ID: 755-11-44-009

Indiana

Indianapolis

Indiana University School of Medicine Program
Sponsor: Indiana University School of Medicine
Clarian Indiana University Hospital
Richard L Roudebush Veterans Affairs Medical Center
William N Wishard Memorial Hospital
Prgm Director: Alan D Schmetzer, MD
James D Fleck, MD
Indiana Univ Sch of Med
545 Barnhill Dr EH 125
Indianapolis, IN 46202
Tel: 317 274-4455   *Fax:* 317 278-4918
E-mail: prcowher@iupui.edu
Accred Length: 6 Yrs   *Program Size:* 6   *(GY1:* 1)
Program ID: 755-17-44-003

Louisiana

New Orleans

Tulane University Program
Sponsor: Tulane University School of Medicine
Tulane University Hospital and Clinics
Prgm Director: Patrick T O'Neill, MD
Jeffrey Nicholl, MD
Tulane Univ Sch of Med
Dept of Psych/Neuro TB52
1440 Canal St
New Orleans, LA 70112-2715
Tel: 504 988-2241   *Fax:* 504 988-3695
E-mail: akivell@tulane.edu
Accred Length: 6 Yrs   *Program Size:* 6   *(GY1:* 1)
Program ID: 755-21-44-002

Massachusetts

Worcester

University of Massachusetts Program
Sponsor: University of Massachusetts Medical School
UMass Memorial Health Care (University Campus)
Prgm Director: Sheldon Benjamin, MD
Ann L Mitchell, MD
Univ of Massachusetts Med Sch
Dept of Psychiatry
55 Lake Ave N
Worcester, MA 01655
Tel: 508 856-4087   *Fax:* 508 856-5000
E-mail: vickie.white@umassmed.edu
Accred Length: 6 Yrs   *Program Size:* 4   *(GY1:* 1)
Program ID: 755-24-44-010

New York

New York

New York Presbyterian Hospital (Columbia Campus) Program
Sponsor: New York Presbyterian Hospital
New York Presbyterian Hospital (Columbia Campus)
New York State Psychiatric Institute
Prgm Director: Maria Oquendo, MD
Ford Blair, MD
New York Psychiatric Inst
Dept of Psychiatry
1051 Riverside Dr
New York, NY 10032
Tel: 212 543-5553   *Fax:* 212 543-5356
E-mail: hf2137@columbia.edu
Accred Length: 5 Yrs   *Program Size:* 1   *(GY1:* 1)
Program ID: 755-35-44-011

New York University School of Medicine Program
Sponsor: New York University School of Medicine
Bellevue Hospital Center
Manhattan VA Harbor Health Care System
Prgm Director: Carol A Bernstein, MD
Laura S Boylan, MD
New York Univ Hosps Ctr
NBV 20N11
550 First Ave
New York, NY 10016-9196
Tel: 212 263-6238   *Fax:* 212 263-6497
E-mail: psychiatry.residency@med.nyu.edu
Accred Length: 6 Yrs   *Program Size:* 3
Program ID: 755-35-44-008

Rhode Island

Providence

Brown University (Butler Hospital) Program
Sponsor: Butler Hospital
Rhode Island Hospital-Lifespan
Prgm Director: Stephen P Salloway, MD, MS
Butler Hosp
Dept of Neurology
345 Blackstone Blvd
Providence, RI 02906
Tel: 401 444-6183   *Fax:* 401 444-8781
E-mail: borourke1@lifespan.org
Accred Length: 6 Yrs   *Program Size:* 5   *(GY1:* 1)
Program ID: 755-43-44-005

South Carolina

Charleston

Medical University of South Carolina Program
Sponsor: Medical University of South Carolina College of Medicine
MUSC Medical Center
Ralph H Johnson VA Medical Center (Charleston)
Prgm Director: Ben Weinstein, MD
Paul B Pritchard, MD
Med Univ of South Carolina
Dept of Psych Box 2508
67 President St
Charleston, SC 29425
Tel: 843 792-0192   *Fax:* 843 792-6894
E-mail: pucalm@musc.edu
Accred Length: 5 Yrs   *Program Size:* 2   *(GY1:* 1)
Program ID: 755-45-44-012

West Virginia

Morgantown

West Virginia University Program
Sponsor: West Virginia University Hospitals
Charleston Area Medical Center/West Virginia University
Prgm Director: John Young, MD
Laura Gutmann, MD
Chestnut Ridge Hosp
Behavioral Med/Psych
930 Chestnut Ridge Rd
Morgantown, WV 26505
Tel: 304 293-0768   *Fax:* 304 293-8724
E-mail: sbienekcate@hsc.wvu.edu
Accred Length: 6 Yrs   *Program Size:* 1   *(GY1:* 1)
Program ID: 755-55-44-001

Appendix B

Medical Specialty Board Certification Requirements

This section provides general information about the American Board of Medical Specialties (ABMS®), its member boards, board certification, and maintenance of certification, as well as a brief summary of board certification requirements for each member board. It was developed to answer some of the most commonly asked questions on board certification, such as:

- What are the steps of the certification process?
- Is my training program ACGME- or RCPSC-accredited?
- Does training in nonaccredited programs count toward board certification requirements?
- Can one receive credit for training completed outside the United States?
- Must all training occur in one program? What happens if one changes residencies?
- What is the program's policy on maternity/paternity leave and vacations?
- What impact do absences during residency/fellowship have on board certification?
- How soon after training can one take the boards?
- What training/expertise is necessary beyond residency/fellowship training?
- Does my GME program offer dual certification?
- Is certification with added qualifications available?
- How frequently are the board examinations (written, oral) offered?
- What are the application deadlines for the certification process?
- How long does it take to complete certification?
- What is the pass/fail rate for first-time test-takers? For repeat candidates?
- What is required if I fail to achieve certification within a given period of time? Is additional training necessary?
- How many opportunities does one have to certify?
- Is an unrestricted medical license required?
- What is the impact of a history of substance abuse on board certification?
- What are the repercussions of losing board certification?
- What does the board certification process cost?
- What other costs are associated with certification and maintenance of certification (including travel, lodging, and review courses)?
- What is the impact of choosing not to become board certified?
- What are the requirements for maintenance of certification?
- Is there a "by-experience" route to certification?

Applicants for certification should contact the respective ABMS member board(s) to confirm the current, official policy and requirements. Inquiries should be directed to the to the particular member board executive offices listed in Table 1.

Table 1. Member Boards of the American Board of Medical Specialties

John W. Yunginger, MD
President
American Board of Allergy and Immunology
111 South Independence Mall East, Suite 701
Philadelphia, PA 19106
(215) 592-9466
(215) 592-9411   Fax
E-mail: abai@abai.org
www.abai.org

Mary E. Post, MBA, CAE
Executive Director, Administrative Affairs
American Board of Anesthesiology
4101 Lake Boone Trail, Suite 510
Raleigh, NC 27607-7506
(919) 881-2570
(919) 881-2575   Fax
www.theaba.org

David J. Schoetz, MD
Executive Director
American Board of Colon and Rectal Surgery
20600 Eureka Road, Suite 600
Taylor, MI 48180
(734) 282-9400
(734) 282-9402   Fax
E-mail: admin@abcrs.org
www.abcrs.org

Antoinette F. Hood, MD
Executive Director
American Board of Dermatology
Henry Ford Health System, One Ford Place
Detroit, MI 48202-3450
(313) 874-1088
(313) 872-3221   Fax
E-mail: abderm@hfhs.org
www.abderm.org

Mary Ann Reinhart, PhD
Executive Director
American Board of Emergency Medicine
3000 Coolidge Road
East Lansing, MI 48823-6319
(517) 332-4800
(517) 332-2234   Fax
www.abem.org

James C. Puffer, MD
President and CEO
American Board of Family Medicine
2228 Young Drive
Lexington, KY 40505-4294
(859) 269-5626   Fax
E-mail: general@theabfm.org
www.theabfm.org

Christine K. Cassel, MD
President
American Board of Internal Medicine
510 Walnut Street, Suite 1700
Philadelphia, PA 19106-3699
(800) 441-2246
(215) 446-3470   Fax
E-mail: request@abim.org
www.abim.org

Sharon Robinson, MS
Administrator
American Board of Medical Genetics
9650 Rockville Pike
Bethesda, MD 20814-3998
(301) 634-7315
(301) 634-7320   Fax
E-mail: abmg@abmg.org
www.abmg.org

Kevin B. Weiss, MD
President and CEO
American Board of Medical Specialties
1007 Church Street, Suite 404
Evanston, IL 60201-5913
(847) 491-9091   Fax
www.abms.org

M. Sean Grady, MD
Chairman
American Board of Neurological Surgery
6550 Fannin Street, Suite 2139
Houston, TX 77030-2701
(713) 441-6015
(713) 794-0207   Fax
E-mail: abns@tmhs.org
www.abns.org

Henry D. Royal, MD
Executive Director
American Board of Nuclear Medicine
4555 Forest Park Blvd, Suite 119
St Louis, MO 63108
(314) 367-2225   Fax
E-mail: abnm@abnm.org
www.abnm.org

Norman F. Gant, MD
Executive Director
American Board of Obstetrics and Gynecology
2915 Vine Street, Suite 300
Dallas, TX 75204
(214) 871-1619
(214) 871-1943   Fax
E-mail: info@abog.org
www.abog.org

Denis M. O'Day, MD
Executive Director
American Board of Ophthalmology
111 Presidential Blvd, Suite 241
Bala Cynwyd, PA 19004-1075
(610) 664-1175
(610) 664-6503   Fax
www.abop.org

Shepard R. Hurwitz, MD
Executive Director
American Board of Orthopaedic Surgery
400 Silver Cedar Court
Chapel Hill, NC 27514
(919) 929-7103
(919) 942-8988   Fax
www.abos.org

Robert H. Miller, MD, MBA
Executive Director
American Board of Otolaryngology
5615 Kirby Drive, Suite 600
Houston, TX 77005
(713) 850-0399
(713) 850-1104   Fax
www.aboto.org

Betsy D. Bennett, MD
Executive Vice President
American Board of Pathology
PO Box 25915
Tampa, FL 33622-5915
(813) 286-2444
(813) 289-5279   Fax
E-mail: questions@abpath.org
www.abpath.org

James A. Stockman, III, MD
President and CEO
American Board of Pediatrics
111 Silver Cedar Court
Chapel Hill, NC 27514-1513
(919) 929-0461
(919) 929-9255   Fax
E-mail: abpeds@abpeds.org
www.abp.org

Anthony M. Tarvestad, JD
Executive Director
American Board of Physical Medicine and Rehabilitation
3015 Allegro Park Lane SW
Rochester, MN 55902-4139
(507) 282-1776
(507) 282-9242   Fax
E-mail: office@abpmr.org
www.abpmr.org

R. Barrett Noone, MD
Executive Director
American Board of Plastic Surgery
Seven Penn Center, Suite 400, 1635 Market Street
Philadelphia, PA 19103-2204
(215) 587-9322
(215) 587-9622   Fax
E-mail: info@abplsurg.org
www.abplsurg.org

James R. Vanderploeg, MD, MPH
Executive Director
American Board of Preventive Medicine
111 West Jackson, Suite 1110
Chicago, IL 60604
(312) 939-2276
(312) 939-2218   Fax
E-mail: abpm@theabpm.org
www.theabpm.org

Larry R. Faulkner, MD
President and CEO
American Board of Psychiatry and Neurology
2150 E Lake Cook Road, Suite 900
Buffalo Grove, IL 60089
(847) 229-6500
(847) 229-6600   Fax
www.abpn.com

Robert R. Hattery, Jr., MD
Executive Director
American Board of Radiology
5441 East Williams Blvd, Suite 200
Tucson, AZ 85711
(520) 790-2900
(520) 790-3200   Fax
E-mail: information@theabr.org
www.theabr.org

Frank R. Lewis, Jr., MD
Executive Director
American Board of Surgery
1617 John F Kennedy Blvd, Suite 860
Philadelphia, PA 19103-1847
(215) 568-4000
(215) 563-5718   Fax
www.absurgery.org

William A. Baumgartner, MD
Executive Director
American Board of Thoracic Surgery
633 North St Clair Street, Suite 2320
Chicago, IL 60611
(312) 202-5900
(312) 202-5960   Fax
E-mail: info@abts.org
www.abts.org

Stuart S. Howards, MD
Executive Secretary
American Board of Urology
2216 Ivy Road, Suite 210
Charlottesville, VA 22903
(434) 979-0059
(434) 979-0266   Fax
www.abu.org

The American Board of Medical Specialties (ABMS) and Board Certification

American Board of Medical Specialties
1007 Church Street, Suite 404
Evanston, IL 60201-5913
847 491-9091
847 328-3596 Fax
www.abms.org

Established in 1933, the American Board of Medical Specialties (ABMS®) is a not-for-profit group made up of 24 member boards that certify physicians in a wide variety of medical specialties. The ABMS does not itself certify physicians, but rather is the umbrella organization that establishes standards and provides information, support, and guidance to the member boards. Between 85% and 90% of practicing physicians are certified by a member board of the ABMS.

The vast majority of medical specialties are represented by the 24 ABMS member boards. A few member boards also certify some nonphysician specialists, such as in the areas of radiology and medical genetics. Today, the member boards issue more than 145 specialty and subspecialty certificates (see Table 2). The number of ABMS member board specialties undoubtedly will increase as medicine continues to evolve and new subspecialties are created to focus on particular aspects of patient care.

The ABMS member boards listed below have been approved by ABMS and the AMA Council on Medical Education (AMA CME) through the Liaison Committee for Specialty Boards (LCSB). They oversee the certification process for their particular specialty.

The American Board of:
- Allergy and Immunology
- Anesthesiology
- Colon and Rectal Surgery
- Dermatology
- Emergency Medicine
- Family Medicine
- Internal Medicine
- Medical Genetics
- Neurological Surgery
- Nuclear Medicine
- Obstetrics and Gynecology
- Ophthalmology
- Orthopaedic Surgery
- Otolaryngology
- Pathology
- Pediatrics
- Physical Medicine and Rehabilitation
- Plastic Surgery
- Preventive Medicine
- Psychiatry and Neurology
- Radiology
- Surgery
- Thoracic Surgery
- Urology

The governing body of each ABMS member board is composed of specialists qualified in the particular field represented by that board. These individuals can include teachers in the specialty; those with specialized training or skills in the primary specialty or subspecialties represented by the Board; and those who have demonstrated the expertise, motivation, and ability to assist in the evaluation procedures leading to certification.

ABMS also partners with other organizations that share a like focus for improving the quality of medical education and the accreditation and certification processes. These are called the associate members, and include:
- Accreditation Council for Continuing Medical Education (ACCME)
- Accreditation Council for Graduate Medical Education (ACGME)
- American Hospital Association (AHA)
- American Medical Association (AMA)
- Association of American Medical Colleges (AAMC)
- Council of Medical Specialty Societies (CMSS)
- Educational Commission for Foreign Medical Graduates (ECFMG)
- Federation of State Medical Boards of the United States (FSMB)
- National Board of Medical Examiners (NBME)

The Difference Between Board Certification and State Licensure

Board certification by an ABMS member board is widely recognized by physicians, health care institutions, insurers, and patients as the gold standard and an essential tool to judge a physician's knowledge, experience, and skills for providing quality healthcare within a given specialty.

This wasn't always the case. Until about a century ago, physicians typically were generalists and did everything from treating the flu and delivering babies to performing surgery. The early and mid-1900s saw the rise of specialization in medicine, and physician leaders called for certification to ensure that doctors were well qualified to provide good care in their respective specialties.

As individual medical specialties matured, professionals in the field formed boards that developed and enforced practice standards. Ophthalmology was the first specialty to form a board in 1917, and in 1933, the four existing boards at the time—Dermatology, Obstetrics and Gynecology, Ophthalmology and Otolaryngology—formed ABMS, originally called the Advisory Board of Medical Specialties.

Physicians who are board certified by an ABMS member board have participated in a voluntary process that involves evaluation of their knowledge and skills beyond what is required for them to become licensed physicians. A doctor must have a license to legally practice medicine but need not be board certified. Licensure is the process by which a state or jurisdiction of the United States admits physicians to the practice of medicine.

Other key differences between state licensing and board certification include:
- State licensing is not specialty-specific; it sets only minimum competence requirements to diagnose and treat patients. Board certification represents a physician's commitment to become more knowledgeable about a specific area of medicine.
- Physicians are licensed by the medical board of the state, territory, or Canadian province in which they practice medicine. They must have a license for each state in which they practice. Board certification is a nationwide credential supported by the ABMS member boards. Physicians can be certified by more than one member board and hold certifications in one or more subspecialties.
- To obtain a medical license, a physician must complete medical school and graduate medical education and pass an examination. Once licensed, a physician's competence and professional conduct is monitored by the state medical board, which also typically requires participation in continuing medical education (CME). The CME credits can be earned in a number of ways,

such as attending a lecture or reading or listening to CME-designated material and then taking a test.

- Board certification is awarded to the physician in an individual specialty or specialties; those who want to be board certified in multiple specialties must undergo the process for each of them. It is granted by independent boards—not government-regulated boards—and is not connected to the state or territory where the physician practices. Once certified, physicians participate in a program of continuous professional development linked to maintaining certification involving education, evaluation, and improvement activities that allow them to demonstrate their understanding of current treatments and technologies and their ability to apply these concepts to provide quality patient care in a particular specialty.

Licensure Requirements

In most cases, applicants for certification and maintenance of certification, as well as current diplomates, must hold a full, valid, current, and unrestricted license to practice medicine in the United States, its territories, or Canada. If licenses are held in more than one jurisdiction, all licenses held must meet this requirement. Applicants and diplomates are also required to inform their respective board of any and all restrictions placed on their licenses.

Some boards (American Board of Obstetrics and Gynecology, American Board of Nuclear Medicine [ABNM], and American Board of Psychiatry and Neurology [ABPN]) allow for exceptions for those applicants who do not yet have an unrestricted medical license because they are still in training; in these cases, an educational or institutional license is sufficient, provided that proof of the full, unrestricted medical license is provided to the ABPN within the specified time frame. The ABNM also requires confirmation from the training program the resident is still enrolled at the time of the examination. The ABPN allows consideration of the following exceptions for licensure: Restriction of a physician's medical license does not include medical licenses that, when issued, are limited to a geographic area within a jurisdiction (eg, practice limited to underserved areas), as long as such licenses are not in any way limited due to, because of, or by virtue of a disciplinary, legal, or administrative action against the license holder. At its sole discretion, the ABPN may review instances of licensure restrictions to determine whether such restrictions constitute a violation of the ABPN's licensure requirements.

The American Board of Dermatology requires that candidates hold a currently valid, full, and unrestricted license to practice medicine or osteopathy *in the candidate's state or province of residence* in either the United States or Canada.

Steps in Achieving Certification

For initial certification, doctors are evaluated according to the standards set by the ABMS member board for education and residency training in their specialty and then must pass written and oral examinations.

Certification by an ABMS member board indicates that the physician has:

1. Earned a medical degree (MD, DO, or other approved credential approved by the member board) which includes:
   - Graduation from a medical school in the United States accredited by the Liaison Committee for Medical Education (LCME), sponsored by the AMA and the Association of American Medical Colleges
   - Graduation from a medical school in Canada accredited by the Committee on Accreditation of Canadian Medical Schools (CACMS), with which the LCME collaborates
   - Graduation from an osteopathic school in the United States accredited by the American Osteopathic Association

   - Graduation from a foreign medical school plus a certificate from the Educational Commission for Foreign Medical Graduates (ECFMG)
2. Completed the required accredited education and training; the amount of graduate medical education and training required varies by ABMS member board (see Table 3); similarly, leave of absence policies, for parental or family leave or illness, vary from one board to the next (Table 4).
3. Provided letters of attestation from the program director and/or faculty stating whether an individual has achieved a satisfactory level of competence and is qualified to pursue certification
4. Fulfilled residency requirements
5. Been licensed to practice medicine in at least one US state, territory or Canada
6. Passed rigorous tests administered by an ABMS member board
7. Met other ABMS member board-specific qualifications

Many physicians have a general specialty certification as well as one or more subspecialty certifications. For instance, a physician might hold a general certification in psychiatry as well as two subspecialty certifications, in addiction psychiatry and child and adolescent psychiatry. In addition, a physician can be certified by more than one member board; a doctor can be certified by the American Board of Pediatrics as well as the American Board of Allergy and Immunology.

Maintaining Certification and the Commitment to Lifelong Learning

ABMS Maintenance of Certification® (AMBS MOC®) is the most recent advance in the board certification process (see Table 6). Like medicine and science, certification is evolving. Originally, the physician passed a rigorous one-time exam and was considered board certified for life. Beginning in the 1970s, individual ABMS Member Boards began implementing time-limited recertification; physicians had to pass the certification test every 6 to 10 years (depending on the board) to become recertified. But even this requirement seemed insufficient given the increasing pace of research and technological advances and the drive to improve patient care and safety.

By following ABMS MOC, physicians demonstrate their commitment to live the standards by which medical care is evaluated and demonstrate leadership in the national movement for health care quality and patient safety. Physicians must prove they have practice-related knowledge to provide quality care in the particular specialty. They must also assess the quality of care they provide compared to peers and national benchmarks, then apply best practices to improve care.

ABMS MOC replaces periodic recertification and provides assurances that the physician is committed to lifelong learning and competency in a specialty and/or subspecialty by requiring ongoing measurement of six core competencies, including:

- **Patient Care**—Providing care that is compassionate, appropriate, and effective for the treatment of health problems and to promote health
- **Medical Knowledge**—Demonstrating knowledge about established and evolving biomedical, clinical, and cognate sciences and their application to patient care
- **Practice-based Learning and Improvement**—Ability to investigate and evaluate patient care practices, appraise and assimilate scientific evidence, and improve one's practice of medicine
- **Interpersonal and Communication Skills**—Demonstrating skills that result in effective information exchange and teaming with patients, their families, and professional associates (eg, fostering a therapeutic relationship that is ethically sound; using effective listening skills, with nonverbal and verbal communication; working as both a team member and at times as a leader)

- **Professionalism**—Demonstrating a commitment to carrying out professional responsibilities, adherence to ethical principles, and sensitivity to diverse patient populations
- **Systems-based Practice**—Demonstrating awareness of and responsiveness to the larger context and systems of health care, and the ability to call on system resources to provide optimal care (eg, coordinating care across sites or serving as the primary case manager when the case involves multiple specialties, professions, or sites)

These competencies were adopted by the ABMS and Accreditation Council for Graduate Medical Education (ACGME) in 1999 as those which are crucial for a physician to deliver high-quality patient care. In addition, the competencies are incorporated into the ABMS MOC four-part process that is designed to keep certification continuous.

- Part I—Licensure and Professional Standing. Holding a valid, unrestricted medical license in at least one US state or territory or in Canada
- Part II—Lifelong Learning and Self-Assessment. Participating in continual educational and self-assessment programs that meet specialty-specific standards set by the member boards. This can include everything from rigorous take-home tests to continuing medical education, which provide specific information about new treatments and standards of care.
- Part III—Cognitive Expertise. Proving medical and practice-related knowledge through regular, formal examination.
- Part IV—Practice Performance Assessment. Being continually evaluated to assess care compared to peers and national standards and then improving care based on findings and recommendations. This can be achieved through peer and patient surveys, patient chart reviews by objective sources, etc.

While ABMS guides the process, the member boards set the criteria and curriculum for each specialty. In 2006, all member boards received approval for their ABMS MOC program plans. The boards are currently implementing these plans.

The ongoing monitoring of certification through ABMS MOC will undoubtedly provide information about whether a physician is keeping up with the standards of his or her specialty. It can also have dramatic impact on health care quality because of the frequency of evaluation and the inclusion of a practice assessment component. Amid increasingly urgent calls for comparable, valid measures of performance and physician accountability, ABMS MOC represents measured, thoughtful, and proactive professional involvement in setting quality standards for medical practice.

Use of the Term "Board Eligible"

Because certification is a process of advancement through several individual steps, including examination, the completion of any one step, such as the minimal educational requirements, should not imply that a candidate is now possessed of some special qualification that is more or less equivalent to certification. For this reason, the majority of ABMS boards do not use or sanction the use of the terms "board eligible" or "board qualified." The status of an applicant with a given board is determined by and varies with the current status of his/her credentials.

Exceptions: The American Board of Orthopaedic Surgery recognizes candidates who have successfully completed Part I and are waiting to take Part II as being "board eligible." The American Board of Physical Medicine and Rehabilitation, although it does not accept any use of "board eligible," uses the term "board admissible" to define the status of an applicant who has been accepted by the ABPMR as a candidate to take the examination for which he or she has applied.

Providing Board Certification Information to the Public

Information about a physician's certification status has always been available through the ABMS or an ABMS member board to assure the public of a physician's qualifications. This was one of the original purposes for the organization and remains just as important today.

The ABMS collects information from the member boards and certified physicians, maintains a centralized database, and circulates the information through its licensees for professional use. Plus, many consumers have checked their physician's board certification through the ABMS Web site or have called the ABMS toll-free number.

Board certification information provided by ABMS is relied upon by the majority of health care and credentials verification organizations for privileging and staffing purposes. Insurance companies, law firms, recruiters, and research organizations also reference these data for their purposes. In addition, the public refers to ABMS information to verify certification or locate a specialist in a particular field or geographic region.

Because this information is heavily relied upon, it is essential that data on certified physicians be kept accurate and current. With an increasing number of hospitals, surgicenters, managed care organizations, and insurance carriers requiring board certification, physician information that is inaccurate, dated, or unavailable could cause difficulties during the credentialing, licensure, or hospital privileging processes.

Applicants with a History of Chemical Dependency or Substance Abuse

(*Note:* The following is general information about board policies in this regard. Each board may have specific policies that differ from these general guidelines.)

The Americans with Disabilities Act (ADA) protects individuals with a history of chemical dependency or substance abuse who are not currently abusing alcohol or using drugs illegally. Candidates with a history of chemical dependency or abuse of a controlled substance will not be admitted to board examinations unless they present evidence satisfactory to the board that they have successfully completed the program of treatment prescribed for their condition, and the board is satisfied that they are currently free of such substance abuse or chemical dependency and do not currently pose a direct threat to the health and safety of others. A board may also require attestations from the responsible program administrators and physicians that the applicant has been free of chemical dependency for a period sufficient to establish that the applicant is not currently exhibiting chemical dependency and/or that substance abuse is not an ongoing problem.

Notes

Dermatology—A confirmatory letter from a licensed physician within 1 month of the examination stating that the disorder no longer exists or is currently controlled is also necessary.

Internal Medicine—Documentation of at least 1 year of continuous sobriety from a reliable monitoring source must be submitted to the board for admission to an examination or to receive a certificate.

Psychiatry and Neurology—Restriction of a physician's medical license does not include voluntary participation in an impaired physicians' program or other appropriate, monitored alcohol or chemical substance-abuse recovery program if the physician has not been reported to either the National Practitioner Data Bank or the Data Bank of the Federation of State Medical Boards.

Thoracic Surgery—Documentation of at least 2 years of continuous sobriety from a reliable monitoring source must be submitted to

Certification Requirements

the board for admission to an examination. For candidates who are already in the examination process and develop a chemical dependency as reported to the board, the process will be suspended until the candidate can provide documentation suitable to the board that the condition has been under control for a period of 2 years. At that time, the candidate will be readmitted to the examination process. The requirement to be accepted for examination within 5 years of completion of an approved thoracic surgery residency will not be waived.

Applicants with Disabilities

(*Note:* The following is general information about board policies in this regard. Each board may have specific policies that differ from these general guidelines.)

The ABMS certification boards support the intent of the Americans with Disabilities Act (ADA). Accordingly, the boards will attempt to make reasonable accommodations for applicants with disabilities, and may provide or allow the use of necessary auxiliary aids, services, or testing conditions that do not fundamentally alter the measurement of the skills or knowledge the examination is intended to test.

Candidates are required to notify the respective board of the need for special testing circumstances when applying for examination. This deadline allows the board to request the necessary documentation, review the records, and verify the disability, if necessary. All special arrangements must be made and agreed upon in advance; special arrangements cannot be made at the time the examination is given. Therefore, early notification of the need for special testing circumstances is encouraged.

If necessary, some boards may undertake an independent assessment, at the expense of the board. Documentation and other evidence substantiating the disability may include:

- A report diagnosing the applicant's disability written by a professional appropriately qualified to evaluate the disability
- A history of the disability, including previous settings in which accommodations have been granted
- Diagnostic information about the specified disability using standard nomenclature from sources such as the *International Classification of Diseases* (ICD) and the *Diagnostic and Statistical Manual of Mental Disorders*
- Specific recommended accommodations with a rationale for why each accommodation is needed.

Cheating and Irregular or Unethical Behavior on Examinations

(*Note:* The following is general information about board policies in this regard. Each board may have specific policies that differ from these general guidelines.)

Cheating and irregular or unethical behavior by a candidate before, during, or after a written or oral examination may include:

- Giving or obtaining information or aid
- Looking at others' test material
- Removing examination materials from the test center and/or reproducing these materials or distributing them to others
- Reconstructing examination questions and answers and transferring this information to others after the examination
- Taking notes
- Bringing electronic devices (beepers, pagers, cell phones, etc) into the examination
- Failing to comply with time limits or instructions
- Talking or other disruptive behavior
- Making telephone calls
- Offering any benefit to an agent of the board in return for any right, privilege, or benefit that is not usually granted by the board to other similarly situated candidates or persons

Any irregular or improper behavior that is observed, made apparent by statistical analysis, or uncovered by other means will be considered a subversion of the certification process and may be sufficient to bar a person from qualification, terminate participation in an examination, invalidate the results of a candidate's examination, cause the withholding or revocation of scores or certificates, or merit other appropriate actions, up to and including legal prosecution. In addition, the candidate may be barred from retaking the examination in the future for a period determined by the board (the orthopaedic surgery board, for example, requires a 3-year hiatus, the psychiatry/neurology board up to 5 years), and the board may inform program director(s), licensing bodies, state and national medical associations and specialty societies, impaired physicians advocacy groups, or law enforcement agencies of these actions.

The materials comprising all board examinations are confidential and are the sole property of the respective board. Any unauthorized reproduction, distribution, or use of any of these materials is prohibited. Boards will prosecute copyright violations to the full extent provided by law and seek monetary damages for any loss of examination materials.

A board may withhold a candidate's scores and require that the candidate retake one or more portions of an examination if presented with sufficient evidence that the security of the examination has been compromised, notwithstanding the absence of any evidence of the candidate's personal involvement in such activities.

Table 2. ABMS General and Subspecialty Certificates

American Board of:	General Certificate(s)	Subspecialty Certificate(s)
Allergy and Immunology	Allergy and Immunology	
Anesthesiology	Anesthesiology	• Critical Care Medicine • Hospice and Palliative Medicine • Pain Medicine
Colon and Rectal Surgery	Colon and Rectal Surgery	
Dermatology	Dermatology	• Clinical and Laboratory Dermatological Immunology • Dermatopathology • Pediatric Dermatology
Emergency Medicine	Emergency Medicine	• Hospice and Palliative Medicine • Medical Toxicology • Pediatric Emergency Medicine • Sports Medicine • Undersea and Hyperbaric Medicine
Family Medicine	Family Medicine	• Adolescent Medicine • Geriatric Medicine • Hospice and Palliative Medicine • Sleep Medicine • Sports Medicine
Internal Medicine	Internal Medicine	• Adolescent Medicine • Cardiovascular Disease • Clinical Cardiac Electrophysiology • Critical Care Medicine • Endocrinology, Diabetes and Metabolism • Gastroenterology • Geriatric Medicine • Hematology • Hospice and Palliative Medicine • Infectious Disease • Interventional Cardiology • Medical Oncology • Nephrology • Pulmonary Disease • Rheumatology • Sleep Medicine • Sports Medicine • Transplant Hepatology
Medical Genetics	• Clinical Biochemical Genetics • Clinical Cytogenetics • Clinical Genetics (MD) • Clinical Molecular Genetics	• Medical Biochemical Genetics • Molecular Genetic Pathology
Neurological Surgery	Neurological Surgery	
Nuclear Medicine	Nuclear Medicine	
Obstetrics and Gynecology	Obstetrics and Gynecology	• Critical Care Medicine • Gynecologic Oncology • Hospice and Palliative Medicine • Maternal and Fetal Medicine • Reproductive Endocrinology/Infertility
Ophthalmology	Ophthalmology	

Certification Requirements

American Board of:	General Certificate(s)	Subspecialty Certificate(s)
Orthopaedic Surgery	Orthopaedic Surgery	• Orthopaedic Sports Medicine • Surgery of the Hand
Otolaryngology	Otolaryngology	• Neurotology • Pediatric Otolaryngology • Plastic Surgery Within the Head and Neck (no certificates have yet been awarded) • Sleep Medicine
Pathology	Anatomic Pathology and Clinical Pathology Pathology – Anatomic Pathology – Clinical	• Blood Banking/Transfusion Medicine • Chemical Pathology • Cytopathology • Dermatopathology • Forensic Pathology • Hematology • Medical Microbiology • Molecular Genetic Pathology • Neuropathology • Pediatric Pathology
Pediatrics	Pediatrics	• Adolescent Medicine • Child Abuse Pediatrics • Developmental-Behavioral Pediatrics • Hospice and Palliative Medicine • Medical Toxicology • Neonatal-Perinatal Medicine • Neurodevelopmental Disabilities • Pediatric Cardiology • Pediatric Critical Care Medicine • Pediatric Emergency Medicine • Pediatric Endocrinology • Pediatric Gastroenterology • Pediatric Hematology-Oncology • Pediatric Infectious Diseases • Pediatric Nephrology • Pediatric Pulmonology • Pediatric Rheumatology • Pediatric Transplant Hepatology • Sleep Medicine • Sports Medicine
Physical Medicine and Rehabilitation	Physical Medicine and Rehabilitation	• Hospice and Palliative Medicine • Neuromuscular Medicine • Pain Medicine • Pediatric Rehabilitation Medicine • Spinal Cord Injury Medicine • Sports Medicine
Plastic Surgery	Plastic Surgery	• Plastic Surgery Within the Head and Neck (no certificates have yet been awarded) • Surgery of the Hand
Preventive Medicine	• Aerospace Medicine • Occupational Medicine • Public Health and General Preventive Medicine	• Medical Toxicology • Undersea and Hyperbaric Medicine

American Board of:	General Certificate(s)	Subspecialty Certificate(s)
Psychiatry and Neurology	• Psychiatry • Neurology • Neurology with Special Qualifications in Child Neurology	• Addiction Psychiatry • Child and Adolescent Psychiatry • Clinical Neurophysiology • Forensic Psychiatry • Geriatric Psychiatry • Hospice and Palliative Medicine • Neurodevelopmental Disabilities • Neuromuscular Medicine • Pain Medicine • Psychosomatic Medicine • Sleep Medicine • Vascular Neurology
Radiology	• Diagnostic Radiology • Radiation Oncology • Radiologic Physics	• Hospice and Palliative Medicine • Neuroradiology • Nuclear Radiology • Pediatric Radiology • Vascular and Interventional Radiology
Surgery	• Surgery • Vascular Surgery	• Hospice and Palliative Medicine • Pediatric Surgery • Surgery of the Hand • Surgical Critical Care
Thoracic Surgery	Thoracic Surgery	• Congenital Cardiac Surgery (starting in 2009)
Urology	Urology	• Pediatric Urology

This table lists the approved general and subspecialty certificates that can be issued by an ABMS member board. For the most current list, refer to the ABMS Web site at www.abms.org

Certification Requirements

Table 3. GME requirements for certification by an ABMS member board

American Board of:	Years of ACGME-accredited GME required			Other GME accepted	
	Prerequisite GME	Specialty GME	Total	RCPSC-accredited GME	Non ACGME-accredited GME
Allergy and Immunology	3	2	5	Yes	
Anesthesiology	1	3	4	Yes (for prerequisite GME only)	
Colon and Rectal Surgery	5	1	6		
Dermatology	1	3	4	Yes	
Emergency Medicine	—	3	3	Yes	
Family Medicine	—	3	3	Yes	Yes
Internal Medicine	—	3	3	Yes	
Medical Genetics	2	2	4		Yes
Neurological Surgery	1	5	6		Yes
Nuclear Medicine	1	3	4	Yes	Yes
Obstetrics and Gynecology	—	4	4	Yes	
Ophthalmology	1	3	4	Yes	
Orthopaedic Surgery	—	5	5	Yes	
Otolaryngology	—	5	5		
Pathology	1	3 or 4	4 or 5	Yes	
Pediatrics	—	3	3	Yes	Yes
Physical Medicine and Rehabilitation	1	3	4	Yes	Yes
Plastic Surgery	3	2 or 3	5 or 6	Yes	
Preventive Medicine	1	2	3	Yes	Yes
Psychiatry and Neurology	0 or 1	4 or 3	4	Yes	
Radiology	1	4	5	Yes	
Surgery	—	5	5	Yes	
Thoracic Surgery	0 or 4 or 5	6 or 3 or 2	6 or 7		
Urology	1	4	5		

Table 4. Residency/fellowship leave of absence policies of ABMS certification boards

American Board of:	Absences may not exceed ...	Notes
Allergy and Immunology	2 months over the 24-month allergy/immunology program	Absences should be made up. Program directors who believe that an absence of more than 2 months is justified should send a letter of explanation to the ABAI for review and approval.
Anesthesiology	60 working days (12 weeks) during the Clinical Anesthesia (CA) 1-3 years of training	If a resident's absence exceeds the prescribed limits, the total training time will be lengthened to make up for the additional absence. In the event of an absence of 6 months or longer, the board shall determine the number of months of training the resident will have to complete after resuming the residency program to satisfy the training required for admission to the ABA examination system.
Colon and Rectal Surgery		
Dermatology	6 weeks in any 1 academic year, or a total of 14 weeks over 3 years	Any absence(s) exceeding these limits, including vacation, should be approved only under truly exceptional circumstances. In addition, any resident approved to sit for the certifying examination despite such an absence should have completed each year of training in an above average or excellent manner as recorded on the residency evaluation forms.
Emergency Medicine	6 weeks in an academic year	Leaves of absence, vacation time, sick time, etc, that exceed 6 weeks in an academic year require extension of the residency program. Such leave time cannot be accrued from year to year. Therefore, the Board defines an acceptable year of training as a minimum of 46 weeks.
Family Medicine	1 month per academic year	Vacation periods may not accumulate from one year to another. Annual vacations must be taken in the year of the service for which the vacation is granted. No two vacation periods may be concurrent. Absence from residency education, in excess of 1 month within the academic year, must be made up before the resident advances to the next training level, and the time must be added to the projected date of completion of the required 36 months of training.
Internal Medicine	1 month per year	Up to 1 month per academic year is permitted for time away from training, which includes vacation, illness, parental or family leave, or pregnancy-related disabilities. Training must be extended to make up any absences exceeding 1 month per year of training. Vacation leave is essential and should not be forfeited or postponed in any year of training and cannot be used to reduce the total required training period. The ABIM recognizes that leave policies vary from institution to institution and expects the program director to apply local requirements within these guidelines to ensure trainees have completed the requisite period of training.
Medical Genetics		Residents/fellows may take up to 1 month per year of training for vacation, parental or family leave, or illness (including pregnancy-related disabilities). Training must be extended to make up any absences exceeding 1 month per year of training. Vacation leave is essential and cannot be forfeited.
Neurological Surgery		Left to the program director's discretion and state regulations, as long as ABNS training requirements for certification are met.
Nuclear Medicine		A resident may have a total of 6 weeks per year leave of absence for any cause, including vacation and pregnancy. Any more time must be made up for the resident to be accepted to take the certifying examination.

Certification Requirements

American Board of:	Absences may not exceed . . .	Notes
Obstetrics and Gynecology	8 weeks in any of the first 3 years of GME, or 6 weeks during the fourth year of GME, or a total of 20 weeks over the 4 years of residency	If a resident's absence exceeds the prescribed limits, the total training time will be lengthened to make up for the additional absence.
Ophthalmology		Left to the program director's discretion and state regulations, as long as ABO training requirements for certification are met.
Orthopaedic Surgery	6 weeks per year	
Otolaryngology	6 weeks per year	If a resident's absence exceeds the 6-week per year limit, the program director must submit a plan to the ABOto for approval on how the training will be made up, which may require an extension of the residency. If a longer leave of absence is granted in any year, the required period of GME may be extended accordingly.
Pathology	4 weeks per year	One year of approved training credit toward ABP certification must be 52 weeks in duration, and the resident must document an average of 48 weeks per year of full-time pathology training over the course of the training program. Any additional leave must be made up.
Pediatrics	1 month per year	Standard training for residency and fellowship is 36 months. For general pediatrics, 33 months of clinical training are required. Absences greater than 3 months during the 3 years of training should be made up by additional periods of training. A program director who believes that the candidate is well qualifed and has met all the training requirements may submit a petition to the ABP requesting an exemption to the policy. Residents in combined training may not take more than 1 month of leave per year.
Physical Medicine and Rehabilitation	6 weeks (30 working days) per year	Leave time beyond 6 weeks would need to be made up by arrangement with the program director.
Plastic Surgery	4 weeks per year	The minimum acceptable residency year must include at least 48 weeks of full-time clinical training experience. A leave of absence during training will not be included toward completion of the 48-week requirement. This includes military leave and maternity/paternity leave.
Preventive Medicine		A training or experience year must consist of a minimum of 48 weeks of active service. In the event of maternity leave, an additional 2-week absence from a training year is permissible. Longer authorized interruptions in training periods, with documentation of conformance with approved policies on parental leave, are accepted as determined on an individual case basis provided the combined time to be credited includes at least 48 weeks of on-duty training within an overall period of 2 years.
Psychiatry and Neurology		Training may be completed on a part-time basis, provided that it is no less than half time. Programs may schedule individual leave or vacation time for residents in accordance with the overall institutional policy. Leave or vacation time may not be used to reduce the total amount of required residency training or to make up deficiencies in training. The 36 months of full-time, specialized residency training must be completed in no more than two blocks. If completed in two blocks, the blocks must not be more than 10 years apart.

American Board of:	Absences may not exceed . . .	Notes
Radiology	Diagnostic radiology: 6 calendar weeks (30 working days) per year Radiation oncology: 4 calendar weeks (20 working days) per year	
Surgery	6 weeks for documented medical problems or maternity leave (see Notes)	For documented medical problems or maternity leave, the ABS will accept 46 weeks of surgical training in 1 of the first 3 years of residency and 46 weeks of training in 1 of the last 2 years, for a total of 142 weeks in the first 3 years and 94 weeks in the last 2 years.
Thoracic Surgery		
Urology	15% of the clinical residency training; 20% of the chief resident year	

Certification Requirements

Table 5. Fees

American Board of:	Application Fee	Late Application Fee	Examination Fee	Written Examination Fee	Oral Examination Fee	Cancellation Fee (Written Exam)	Cancellation Fee (Oral Exam)	Returned Check Fee	Written verification of certification status	Hand rescoring of exam	MOC Examination Fee	Annual fee for all diplomates
Allergy and Immunology		$500	$2,700			$800			$75 per name	$100	$3,000	$150
Anesthesiology	$800	$300		$500	$1,950	$200	$750	$50	$35		$1,200	$0
Anesthesiology critical care medicine or pain medicine	$500	$300	$875			$200		$50			$875 (recertification only)	
Colon and Rectal Surgery	$400	$600		$700 ($900 late)	$800 ($1,000 late)			$35			$600 (app fee $350)	$175
Dermatology			$2,200					$35	$35	$35	$150/year	
Emergency Medicine	$385	TBD		TBD	$1,125 ($1,390 late)				TBD	TBD		
Family Medicine	$1,200	Up to $1,900						$50				
Internal Medicine		$400	$1,230								$1,495	
Internal Medicine subspecialties			$1,905*								$1,495	
Medical Genetics	$600	$250	$1,700					$50	$0			$300
Neurological Surgery	$500 $1,000 $2,000	$0		$475	$2,500	Forfeit fee	Forfeit fee	$0	$0	$100	$800	$275
Nuclear Medicine	$500 (nonrefundable)	$500	$2,250 (including application fee)								$1,750	$150
Obstetrics and Gynecology	$735 (written), $805 (oral)	$330, $790	$675	$675	$935						$920 written, $865 oral	
Ophthalmology		$300		$1,650	$1,650				$35		$1,550	
Orthopaedic Surgery	$1,040 (written), $975 (oral)	$350			$980				$25	$100	$975 application, $980 - $1,125 exam	
Otolaryngology		$200	$1,800 - $2,200	$3,050	$1,675				$50	$75		
Pathology							$35					
Pediatrics	$510	$300	$1,250					$50	$50	$200	$990 or $1,430	
Pediatrics subspecialties	$630	$250	$1,370						$25		$990 or $1,430	
Physical Medicine and Rehabilitation	$600	$500		$775	$1,270			$20	$35	$100	$745 Total	$125

American Board of:	Application Fee	Late Application Fee	Examination Fee	Written Examination Fee	Oral Examination Fee	Cancellation Fee (Written Exam)	Cancellation Fee (Oral Exam)	Returned Check Fee	Written verification of certification status	Hand rescoring of exam	MOC Examination Fee	Annual fee for all diplomates
Plastic Surgery	$525	$500		$1,300	$1,725				$35	$210	$1,100	$200
Preventive Medicine	$410 - $705	$200	$1,950			$50		$25	$25		$1,750	
Undersea and Hyperbaric Medicine	$385 - $555		$1,750			$50		$25	$25		$1,550	
Psychiatry and Neurology	$700	$500	$950 - $2,300	Re-exam $950 - $2,300	Re-exam $1,000 - $1,350				$50	$35	$1,500	
Psychiatry and Neurology subspecialties	$700	$500	$1,200	Re-exam $1,200					$50	$35	$1,500	
Radiology			$875 - $2,885			$400	$400	$100	$100	$250 - $275		
Radiation Oncology			$557 - $2885			$400	$400	$100	$100	$250 - $300	$900	
Surgery	$300	$500		$700	$900	$220	$900	$50				
Thoracic Surgery	$475			$1,150	$1,225				$50			$250
Urology		$400		$1,250 (re-exam $700)	$1,300 (re-exam $800)	$200 - $500	$200 - $500	$100	$35		$1,350	$200

* Exceptions: Transplant Hepatology, Interventional Cardiology, and Clinical Cardiac Electrophysiology, which are $2,300.

Table 6. Maintenance of Certification

Note: Unless otherwise indicated, the information shown is for MOC in the specialty; different rules may apply to subspecialty MOC.

American Board of:	CME requirement	Lifelong learning and self-assessment requirements	Cognitive expertise/examination requirements	Practice performance assessment	Notes
Allergy and Immunology	25 allergy/immunology CME credits from accredited organizations each year of the MOC process	A passing score of 80% on the Home Study Examination is required to sit for the Final Examination. Candidates who fail the initial Home Study Examination are entitled to retest. The open-book exam covers basic and clinical science.	MOC candidates must attain an absolute minimum score on the Final Examination to successfully recertify. The exam, administered via computer at test centers across the nation, focuses on clinical science items that can be answered correctly based on clinical experience, without reference to textbooks or journals.	Patient and Physician Peer Assessment Module (PAPPA), through which the candidate's patients and peers rate the physician on professionalism and communication skills via an automated phone survey. Candidates complete the ABIM Communications module and either the Asthma Practice Improvement Module (PIM) or Patient Safety Module.	
Anesthesiology	350 CME credits: At least 250 credits must be ACCME-approved Category 1 credits; the ABA will grant at most 70 LLSA (CME) credits per year. All newly certified diplomates and non-time limited diplomates who enter the MOCA program after January 1, 2008, are required to complete 60 Category 1 credits of either the American Society of Anesthesiologists' (ASA) Self-Education and Evaluation (SEE) program or Anesthesiology Continuing Education (ACE) program once during their 10-year MOCA cycle.		Candidates may satisfy the examination requirement no earlier than the 7th year of their 10-year MOC cycle. To be eligible for examination, completion of at least 200 CME credits and one of the two required Practice Performance Assessments and Improvement Activities is required.	Diplomates should be continually engaged in a self-directed program of practice assessment and performance improvement (PPAI). For MOC, the PPAI process consists of case evaluation and simulation education. Diplomates must complete the two PPAI activities over their 10-year MOCA cycle. Diplomates must complete at least one of the two activities in each of the following segments of their MOCA cycle: Years 1-5 and 6-10. Each activity must be completed at least once in the diplomate's 10-year cycle.	Recertification program to end in 2009. MOC program began in 2004.
Colon and Rectal Surgery	150 Category 1 CME credits every 5 years. CARSEP (Colon and Rectal Surgery Education Program): Twice in 10-year cycle.		Submission of operative log (every 5 years) consisting of cases performed 12 months prior to the end of the 5-year cycle. Written closed-book examination every 10 years.	Evaluation of performance in practice in two areas: (1) Clinical Practice Data, and (2) Communications/Interpersonal Skills	Maintenance of Certification program begins in 2010.

(Continued on next page)

Certification Requirements

American Board of:	CME requirement	Lifelong learning and self-assessment requirements	Cognitive expertise/examination requirements	Practice performance assessment	Notes
Dermatology	40 Category 1 CME credits per year over the 10-year cycle	Three self-assessment examinations at approximately 3-year intervals	The current examination is a clinically focused, take-home, open-book examination that is administered online annually. The examination consists of two modules, one required and one elective, that are tailored to the candidate's practice profile. In 2010 this examination will change to a secure, proctored, closed-book examination administered at testing centers in the US.	Completion of one Quality Assessment/Quality Improvement program, one patient survey, and one peer survey in 10-year cycle.	MOC program began in 2004.
Emergency Medicine		The Lifelong Learning and Self-Assessment (LLSA) component includes an annual set of readings to guide participants in self study of recent emergency medicine literature. Each year, the ABEM will offer an open-book, unproctored LLSA test with 32-40 questions to help reinforce what physicians learn from the readings.	The Continuous Certification (ConCert) examination, a secure examination administered at testing centers in the United States and Canada, takes approximately 5 hours to complete and focuses on what the practicing emergency physician needs to know when treating patients.	Diplomates who are clinically active will be required to attest to ABEM twice during a 10-year certification period that they have participated in an acceptable patient care practice improvement (PI) program at a national, regional, or local level and once that they have participated in a communication/professionalism feedback program. Diplomates will be required to attest that their own clinical practice data and patient feedback data are included in their APP activities. Data that is reported back at either an individual or a group level will be appropriate.	
Family Medicine	300 CME credits	One Self Assessment Module (SAM), composed of an online, 60-question assessment and patient simulation on a specific topic, each year for 6 years	The Part III Cognitive Examination contains multiple-choice (one best answer) questions and tests cognitive knowledge and problem-solving ability relevant to family medicine. The examination, offered in computer-based format only, is a full day in length.	One Performance in Practice Module (PPM) must be completed during the 7-year MC-FP cycle. This online module assists diplomates with a mini-audit focusing on quality indicators for a specific disease entity, development of a quality improvement plan, and a repeat audit to measure improvement.	MOC program began in 2004. If all requirements and deadlines are met, the diplomate is eligible for a 3-year extension to the 7-year certificate.

(Continued on next page)

American Board of:	CME requirement	Lifelong learning and self-assessment requirements	Cognitive expertise/examination requirements	Practice performance assessment	Notes
Internal Medicine		ABIM diplomates must earn at least 20 of the required 100 self-assessment points for Maintenance of Certification in the Self-Evaluation of Medical Knowledge category by completing ABIM medical knowledge modules. These open-book modules test clinical and practical knowledge in a particular field.	The ABIM secure exam is a computer-based multiple choice examination (single best answer format) which takes approximately 8 hours to complete. The exam stresses clinical decision-making, using patient-based case scenarios.	ABIM diplomates must earn at least 20 of the required 100 self-assessment points for Maintenance of Certification in the Self-Evaluation of Practice Performance category. ABIM offers a Web-based tool to fulfill this requirement – the ABIM PIMsm Practice Improvement Module, which enables physicians to conduct a confidential self-evaluation of the medical care that they provide. PIMs help physicians gain knowledge about their practices through analysis of practice data and the development and implementation of a plan to target areas for improvement.	MOC program began in 2006. All ABIM certificates issued in 1990 (1987 for critical care medicine and 1988 for geriatric medicine) and thereafter are valid for 10 years.
Medical Genetics	250 Category 1 CME credits over the 10-year period; at least 50% of the credits must be in genetics. Credits will be audited in years 4-5 and 8-9.	Web-based, open-book, and non-proctored literature modules will be more concise versions of the current literature review. A pre-reading and post-reading test are required to help diplomates assess their acquisition of knowledge. Only the post-reading test will count, and can be taken as often as necessary to pass. A message rather than a score is recorded when diplomates pass the post-reading test. Participation in three of five offered modules must take place during the 10-year cycle. Each module will be accessible for only a 3-year period of time.	The specialty-only certification-type examination will be computerized and proctored at a testing center; it must be passed only once during years 8 to 10 of the 10-year cycle. The examination may be taken again, if necessary, to achieve a passing score. The examination will be available once a year.	Practice improvement activities will assist diplomates in evaluating their practice, identifying areas that may need improvement, and documenting any improvements. Activities are not graded, but participation in three activities during the 10-year cycle is mandatory.	MOC program began in 2007.
Neurological Surgery	150 CME credits every 3 years, including a minimum of 60 Category 1 neurosurgical credits. The remaining 90 may be Category 1 or Category 2; 30 of those may be nonneurosurgical.	Every 3 years, take the web-based educational Self-Assessment in Neurological Surgery (SANS) examination developed and administered by the Congress of Neurological Surgeons.	Secure, proctored, web-based examination given each March at neurosurgical residency programs. Consists of 200 clinically oriented questions. 150 items are General Neurosurgery; three different modules are offered for the other 50: (1) More general neurosurgery, (2) Complex spine surgery, (3) Pediatric neurosurgery. Taken once each 10 years.	Submit details of 10 consecutive current cases selected from a list of procedures that cover the subspecialties. Assessment of physician/patient communication, via a survey of 20 patients. Chief of staff questionnaire covering professionalism, communication skills, and participation in systems-based practice. All three repeated every 3 years.	

(Continued on next page)

(Continued on next page)

Certification Requirements

American Board of:	CME requirement	Lifelong learning and self-assessment requirements	Cognitive expertise/examination requirements	Practice performance assessment	Notes
Nuclear Medicine	50 CME credits every year, of which 25 must be category 1 (including 8 category 1 CME credits from ABNM-approved self-assessment modules); 70% of Category 1 credit must be in nuclear medicine (17.5 credits)	Each diplomate must obtain a minimum of eight self-assessment credits per year.	The examination contains questions on fundamental knowledge, up-to-date practice-related knowledge, and issues such as patient safety.	Applicants must demonstrate evidence of evaluation of performance in practice. The focus of these evaluations includes (1) patient safety, (2) accuracy of interpretation, (3) report turnaround time, (4) practice guidelines and technical standards, and (5) referring physician surveys.	MOC program began in 2007.
Obstetrics and Gynecology	The basic annual board certification process for diplomates results in a minimum of 150 Category 1 CME credits granted by ACOG. Each diplomate may earn up to 210 Category 1 CME credits per 6-year cycle.	Diplomates receive three booklets each year containing 180 questions (60 in GYN, 60 in OB, and 60 in Office Practice) and must answer at least 120 out of 180 questions.	The written maintenance of certification examination will last 3 hours and 45 minutes and have 180 objective multiple choice questions. The examination will be held in computer testing facilities located throughout the US and will first be administered in 2013.	Diplomates must complete ten modules per 6-year cycle. For General OB/GYN, diplomates can chose from OB, GYN, or OP, as well as modules in patient safety, ethics, etc.	MOC program begins in 2008.
Ophthalmology	An average of 30 ACCME-approved Category 1 CME credits per year as of the date of certification and throughout the 10-year MOC cycle, with 3 CME credits in ethics.	The Periodic Ophthalmic Review Tests (PORT) are a series of 50-item, online self-review tests in core ophthalmic knowledge and 10 Practice Emphasis Areas (PEAs). Two PORTs are required: one in core knowledge and one in a PEA of choice.	The Demonstration of Ophthalmic Cognitive Knowledge (DOCK) Examination is required for completion of MOC. DOCK is a secure, proctored, 150-item computer-based examination administered at approximately 250 test centers for a period of 1 month each September; it consists of three 50-item modules, one in core ophthalmic knowledge and two in Practice Emphasis Areas (PEAs) of choice.	The Office Record Review (ORR) is an online self-review of clinical practice in which a diplomate reviews 15 current patient charts; it consists of over 35 ophthalmic diagnoses with specific criteria. The self-review of patient charts via ORR modules is meant to assess the quality of practice through verification of the documentation of appropriate measurements, diagnosis, management, treatment, and follow-up.	MOC program began in 2006.
Orthopaedic Surgery	120 credits of Category 1 CME over two 3-year cycles	As part of the CME requirement, a minimum of 20 CME credits of Self-Assessment Examinations (SAEs) is required.	Secure exam options include a practice-based oral exam or choice of computer exams, which include general, adult reconstruction, sports medicine, surgery of the spine, combined hand (for those who hold a CAQ in Surgery of the Hand), and combined sports (for those who hold a Subspecialty certificate in Orthopaedic Sports Medicine).	Submission of a 3-month case list of surgical cases for the computer exam option or a 6-month surgical case list for the oral exam option. In addition, the Board will obtain peer review of the candidate from colleagues and evaluations from hospital chiefs of staff and others.	

American Board of:	CME requirement	Lifelong learning and self-assessment requirements	Cognitive expertise/examination requirements	Practice performance assessment	Notes
Otolaryngology	Candidates are required to complete a sufficient number of CME credits to meet their state's requirement for licensure for each license held. Sixty percent of the hours must be specifically related to otolaryngology. For candidates in states that do not have specific requirements, 15 CME credits are required.		Core component examination includes knowledge fundamental to the practice of otolaryngology, as well as knowledge of practice environment issues such as quality assurance, safety, regulations, ethics of practice, professionalism, legal and reimbursement issues, and one module, selected by the candidate, which focuses on a specific area.	Neurotology and sleep medicine subspecialty-certified individuals need only participate in the neurotology MOC or sleep medicine program to maintain the primary and subspecialty certificates.	MOC program began in 2002.
Pathology	An average of 35 Category 1 CME credits per year for each two-year period in the MOC cycle; ten of these credits must be obtained from completion of self-assessment modules (SAMs), and 80% of the CME must be directly related to the diplomate's practice. The remainder may be in relevant areas, such as administration or ethics.		The examination will be a closed-book assessment based on knowledge that a competent practitioner would be expected to possess without access to reference material. Initially, the examination will be given in the ABP Examination Center in Tampa, Florida; if future technology permits assurance of examination security, the ABP anticipates administering its computer-based examinations in regional computer testing centers	At the beginning of the fourth and eighth years of each certification period, diplomates must supply four references who can attest to their ability and effectiveness in practice. In addition, each pathologist must document (1) the participation of his/her laboratory in inter-laboratory performance improvement and assessment activities and (2) individual participation in at least one practice improvement and quality assurance activity or program per year. Documentation of both laboratory and individual participation in practice improvement and quality assurance activities must be provided at the end of each 2-year period of the MOC cycle.	Participation in an accredited fellowship during 1 full year of any 2-year period will cover all MOC Part II and Part IV requirements for that period.

(Continued on next page)

Certification Requirements

American Board of:	CME requirement	Lifelong learning and self-assessment requirements	Cognitive expertise/examination requirements	Practice performance assessment	Notes
Pediatrics		Part Two of MOC in General Pediatrics consists of two Internet-based self-assessment exercises: (1) The ABP Knowledge Self-assessment consists of 200 multiple-choice items reflecting the same general content as the secure examination. Because this activity is a self-assessment and is designed to provide practice experience for the examination, there is no passing score for this activity. (2) The Decision Skills Self-assessment consists of 50 multiple-choice items based on patient cases. Each question provides history, physical, and laboratory findings and asks for the most likely diagnosis or for the most appropriate additional study or expected laboratory finding. Unlike the Knowledge Self-assessment, a minimum score is required for this activity. Both assessment exercises must be completed during the calendar year in which they were started to receive credit for MOC. Part Two of MOC in Pediatric Subspecialties consists an Internet-based self-assessment exercise. Participants are required to complete one self-assessment exercise during a 7-year period. This requirement may be met by completing a self-assessment provided by the ABP or an ABP-approved self-assessment provided by an external entity. The ABP's self-assessment focuses on recent literature and is delivered via the Internet. Expert panels of subspecialists select a list of articles, available on the ABP Web site, that focus on recent advances in each subspecialty. The self-assessment exercise consists of multiple-choice questions based on the listed references. Participants may start and stop the assessment exercises as often as they like within the specified year (ie, each assessment will have 365-day validity period). However, a self-assessment must be completed within the stated 365-day period in which it was started in order to receive credit for MOC. A passing score is required for each self-assessment. Participants are allowed as many attempts as necessary to successfully complete the assessment.	Part Three of MOC consists of a secure examination administered at testing centers throughout the US and elsewhere. Approximately 200 questions are included in this half-day, closed-book examination. Pass rates for MOC examinations are relatively high, ranging from 88% to 100%.	Component A: Patient surveys to solicit information about a participant's interpersonal and communication skills and professionalism (once during the 7-year certificate span). There will be no minimum score for this activity. Component B: The Practice Performance component, designed to help physicians learn about quality improvement strategies, collect and analyze practice data over time, and document improved quality of care.	• For certificates expiring in 2009, the examination component has been extended to a 10-year requirement. Additionally, enrollment in MOC will be required. For certificates expiring in 2010 and beyond, all MOC requirements must be completed prior to the ending date of the certificate. • Diplomates are not required to maintain their general pediatric certificates in order to maintain certification in a subspecialty. • MOC program began in 2003.

(Continued on next page)

American Board of:	CME requirement	Lifelong learning and self-assessment requirements	Cognitive expertise/examination requirements	Practice performance assessment	Notes
Physical Medicine and Rehabilitation	A minimum of 500 CME credits during the 10-year MOC cycle	Diplomates with certificates expiring in 2010 and beyond will be required to participate in four ABPMR-approved self-assessments during the 10-year MOC cycle.	Candidates may satisfy the examination requirement no earlier than the 7th year of their 10-year MOC cycle.	Component 4 will contain various assessments designed to address quality improvement in practice. Diplomates with certificates expiring in 2010 and beyond will be required to complete a minimum of one Practice Improvement Project (PIP) during the 10-year MOC cycle. Additional practice assessment tools are in development.	
Plastic Surgery	150 CME credits in 3 years, to include 60 in Category 1, 50 in plastic surgery, and 20 in patient safety	Completion of one Web-based assessment module is required in years 3, 6, and 9 of the 10-year cycle.		Practice Assessment in Plastic Surgery (PA-PS) and a Patient Satisfaction Survey are required in years 3, 6, and 9 of the 10-year cycle.	
Preventive Medicine	45 hours of Category 1 ACCME-approved CME every 3 years	30 hours of ABPM-approved LLSA activities every 3 years	Diplomates may begin taking the multiple-choice, proctored examination 7 years after receiving initial certification and may repeat the examination if necessary to pass it prior to expiration of their certificate.	This component utilizes a quality improvement model with opportunities for assessment of practice performance and improvement activities available in clinical practice, teaching, research, and administration.	MOC program is Enhancing Professional Improvement and Quality (EPIQ).
Psychiatry and Neurology	Completion of 150 specialty- or subspecialty-specific, Category 1, CME credits in each of the two 5-year blocks of the 10-year MOC cycle, for a total of 300 CME credits	Diplomates are required to participate in at least two major, broad-based self-assessment programs during the 10-year MOC cycle, to be completed in years 1-3 of the first 5-year block of the cycle and years 6-8 of the second 5-year block. The self-assessment activities must cover current knowledge and/or current best practices in one or more of the required competency areas in a single assessment or in the sum of several combined assessments, total at least 100 questions, and provide feedback to the diplomate that can be used as the subsequent basis for focused CME, lifelong learning, and/or career development.	The cognitive examinations are multiple-choice, computer-based examinations administered at testing centers throughout the country. MOC cognitive examinations differ from the initial certification examinations in that they are practice-relevant and focus on the clinical applications of knowledge. To prepare for the examinations, a diplomate should keep current with research and developments in the respective field, read specialty-specific journals and practice guidelines, and attend relevant CME programs.	The Performance in Practice (PIP) component is a quality improvement program designed to evaluate whether physicians have shown practice improvement over the 10-year MOC cycle by chart review and second-party external review. Diplomates will be required to complete three PIP Units consisting of both modules in years 1-3, 4-6, and 7-9 of the 10-year cycle.	Diplomates with certificates in addiction psychiatry, clinical neurophysiology, forensic psychiatry, geriatric psychiatry, hospice and palliative medicine, neuromuscular medicine, pain medicine, psychosomatic medicine, sleep medicine, and vascular neurology must also maintain certification in their specialty in order to apply for MOC in the area of subspecialization. Diplomates in neurodevelopmental disabilities must maintain certification in neurology with special qualification in child neurology. If certification in the specialty lapses, certification in the subspecialty is no longer valid. Diplomates in child and adolescent psychiatry do not need to maintain current certification in general psychiatry for their subspecialty certification to remain valid and to maintain certification in child and adolescent psychiatry.

(Continued on next page)

American Board of:	CME requirement	Lifelong learning and self-assessment requirements	Cognitive expertise/examination requirements	Practice performance assessment	Notes
Radiology	A minimum of 200 to 250 ACCME-accredited Category 1 CME credits over the 10-year cycle	Self-assessment modules (SAMs) are educational venues (eg, refresher courses, workshops, reading assignments, online offerings), usually offered by the societies that have been ABR-qualified. All SAMs are also qualified as Category 1 CME and can serve to fill that requirement as well.	Completion of a computer-based examination within the last 3 years of the 10-year MOC cycle.	All diplomates are required to participate in Practice Quality Improvement (PQI) initiatives on an ongoing basis. PQI initiatives should (1) be relevant to your practice; (2) be achievable in your practice setting; (3) produce results that are suited to repeat measurement during your MOC cycle; and (4) be reasonably expected to bring about quality improvement.	The ABR certifies diplomates in diagnostic radiology, radiation oncology, and radiologic physics. Despite having a common structure, requirements vary for the three disciplines. For more information, see www.theabr.org.
Surgery	A minimum of 30 credits of Category 1 and 50 credits overall of CME, to be performed yearly	Over the course of 3 years, one third of Category 1 CME must include a self-assessment activity.	Successful completion of a secure examination at 10-year intervals; diplomates may first take the examination starting 3 years prior to certificate expiration.	Participation in a national, regional, or local surgical outcomes database or quality assessment program. Participation in the CMS Physician Quality Reporting Initiative (PQRI) or ACS case log system meets this requirement. Periodic communication skills assessment based on patient feedback will also be required, but this is not yet finalized.	MOC takes effect the July 1 following certification or recertification. Diplomates report on their MOC activities every 3 years.
Thoracic Surgery	150 credits of Category 1 CME in the broad category of cardiothoracic surgery over each 5 year period (an average of 30 credits per year)	Each diplomate must complete the standard self-assessment exercise (SESATS) 5 years after initial certification and every 10 years thereafter.	During each 10-year MOC cycle, the diplomate must pass a secure, comprehensive written examination of fundamental and practice-related knowledge. Exam content will be derived from recent editions of SESATS and will include all areas of thoracic surgery.	• *Reference letters*—Letters of reference on behalf of the diplomate documenting licensing, hospital privileges, level of clinical activity, and stature within the surgical community will be solicited from responsible members of the staff of the diplomate's principal hospital. • *Peer (and patient) evaluation*—Once during each 10-year MOC cycle each diplomate will be required to submit the names of at least 4 physicians familiar with his/her practice who may serve as peer evaluators. • *Outcome data*—Diplomate must keep a record of a representative sample (at least their five most frequently done procedures) for documentation of clinical activity and outcomes, compare his/her outcomes to national norms, and use this information as a means of practice improvement.	

(Continued on next page)

American Board of:	CME requirement	Lifelong learning and self-assessment requirements	Cognitive expertise/examination requirements	Practice performance assessment	Notes
Urology	90 CME credits in years 4 and 8-9 of the 10-year cycle	Completion of a Practice Assessment Protocol (PAP) is required in years 2, 4, 6, and 8-9 of the 10-year cycle in the diplomate's area of practice. The PAPs, non-graded learning tools based on current clinical guidelines, involve self-review of a small number of sequential cases in a specific area (eg, evaluation of hematuria, treatment of superficial bladder cancer, etc); a comparison of the diplomate's evaluation and management of these cases to accepted practice guidelines; and the successful answering of a short series of questions regarding the clinical guidelines.	Successful completion of a computer-based closed book examination will be required within the 3-year period prior to expiration of the candidate's certification.	Completion of a 6-month electronic practice log is required in years 8-9 of the 10-year cycle.	MOC program began in 2007.

American Board of Allergy and Immunology

111 S Independence Mall East, Suite 701
Philadelphia, PA 19106
215 592-9466
215 592-9411 Fax
E-mail: abai@abai.org
www.abai.org

Examination Schedule

Certification

Examination Date: October 5-9, 2009, 2008
Registration Period: January 1 – March 31, 2009
Fee: $2,700
Cancellation Deadline: June 30, 2009

Recertification

Home Study Examination: January 15 – March 31, 2009
Final Examination: October 5-9, 2009
Registration Period: December 15, 2008 – January 31, 2009
Fee: $3,000
Cancellation Date: March 31, 2009
No applications will be accepted 30 days after the close of registration.

American Board of Anesthesiology

4101 Lake Boone Trail, Suite 510
Raleigh, NC 27607-7506
919 881-2570
919 881-2575 Fax
www.theABA.org

Filing Deadlines and Test Dates

Primary Certification Part 1 Examination

2009 Examination

October 15, 2008—Application cycle begins
December 15, 2008—Standard application deadline
January 15, 2009—Late application deadline
March 15, 2009—Decision deadline
August 3-4, 2009—Examination date

2010 Examination

October 15, 2009—Application cycle begins
December 15, 2009—Standard application deadline
December 31, 2009—Late application deadline
March 15, 2010—Decision deadline
August 2-3, 2010—Examination date

Primary Certification Part 2 (oral) Examination

2009 Examinations

November 30, 2008—Registration deadline
April 20-24, 2009—Examination dates
February 15, 2009—Registration deadline
October 5-9, 2009—Examination dates

2010 Examinations

November 30, 2009—Registration deadline
April 19-23, 2010—Examination dates
February 15, 2010—Registration deadline
September 27-October 1, 2010—Examination dates

Anesthesiology Recertification Examination

2009 Examinations Only - Application cycle open until December 31, 2008

August 31, 2008—Decision deadline
January 3-17, 2009—Examination dates
March 31, 2009—Decision deadline
August 1-15, 2009—Examination dates

Maintenance of Certification in Anesthesiology Examination

2009 Examinations – Continuous Application cycle (24/7/365)

August 31, 2008—Decision deadline
January 3-17, 2009—Examination dates
March 31, 2009—Decision deadline
August 1-15, 2009—Examination dates

2010 Examinations – Continuous Application cycle (24/7/365)

October 31, 2009—Decision deadline
January 16-30, 2010—Examination dates
April 30, 2010—Decision deadline
July 17-31, 2010—Examination dates

Critical Care Medicine and Pain Medicine Certification Examinations

2009 Examinations

January 15, 2009—Application cycle begins
March 15, 2009—Standard application deadline
March 31, 2009—Late application deadline
May 15, 2009—Decision deadline

September 12, 2009—Examination date

2010 Examinations
February 1, 2010—Application cycle begins
March 31, 2010—Standard application deadline
April 15, 2010—Late application deadline
May 15, 2010—Decision deadline
October 23, 2010—Examination date

Critical Care Medicine and Pain Medicine Recertification Examinations

2009 Examination
January 15, 2009—Application cycle begins
March 15, 2009—Standard application deadline
March 31, 2009—Late application deadline
May 15, 2009—Decision deadline
September 19 - October 3, 2009—Examination dates

2010 Examination
February 1, 2010—Application cycle begins
March 31, 2010—Standard application deadline
April 15, 2010—Late application deadline
May 15, 2010—Decision deadline
October 30 – November 13, 2010—Examination dates

Hospice and Palliative Medicine Certification Examination

2009 – No Examination
2010 Examination
February 1, 2010—Application cycle begins
March 31, 2010—Standard application deadline
April 15, 2010—Late application deadline
May 15, 2010—Decision deadline

Note: Examination date to be determined

American Board of Colon and Rectal Surgery

20600 Eureka Rd, Suite 600
Taylor, MI 48180
734 282-9400
734 282-9402 Fax
E-mail: admin@abcrs.org
www.abcrs.org

Application for Examination

Each candidate for examination must complete and submit an Application for Examination, which may be accessed on the ABCRS Web site at www.abcrs.org.

As part of the application process, residents must submit a list of all operative procedures performed during their training period. Case log reporting is completed using the electronic software provided by the Accreditation Council for Graduate Medical Education (ACGME). Login instructions and deadline dates are accessible through the ACGME web site at www.acgme.org. The American Board of Colon and Rectal Surgery will obtain the information directly from the ACGME

Examination Schedule

Applications for the 2010 certification process must be completed and returned at the conclusion of training according to the schedule below:

July 15, 2009	Deadline for receipt of application materials and $400 application fee
July 16 - August 15, 2009	Late applications accepted (late application fee is $600)
August 15, 2009	No applications will be accepted postmarked after this date
September 27, 2009	Credentials Committee reviews applications. Applicants notified of acceptance for examination.
November 15, 2010	Deadline for receipt of $700 Written Examination fee. Instructions on Written Examination procedure sent to candidates.
March 19, 2010	Written Examination held at Pearson Vue Testing Centers
April, 2010	Notification of Written Examination results and Oral Examination information sent to candidates
July 15, 2010	Deadline for receipt of $800 Oral Examination fee; instructions on Oral Examination procedure sent to candidates
September 25, 2010	Oral Examination (Omni Hotel, Chicago, Illinois)
October 2010	Notification of Oral Examination results

American Board of Dermatology

Henry Ford Health System
One Ford Place
Detroit, MI 48202-3450
313 874-1088
313 872-3221 Fax
E-mail: abderm@hfhs.org
www.abderm.org

Examination Schedule

In-Training Examination
April 2, 2009—Online, Training Programs
March 25, 2010—Online, Training Programs
March 24, 2011—Online, Training Progrrams

Recertification Examination
May 1 - June 12, 2009—Online
March 5, 2010—Miami, Florida, in conjunction with the American Academy of Dermatology (AAD) meeting (also in conjunction with 2009 AAD summer meeting)

Certifying Examination
August 3-7, 2009— Tampa, Florida and/or Tucson, Arizona
2010 – TBD

Subspecialty Certification Examination in Dermatopathology
September 16, 2009—Tampa, Florida

Subspecialty Certification Examination in Pediatric Dermatology
No examination in 2009
2010 – TBD

American Board of Emergency Medicine

3000 Coolidge Road
East Lansing, MI 48823-6319
517 332-4800
517 332-2234 Fax
www.abem.org

Important Dates for Residents and Applicants

April 2009	ABEM mails certification applications to graduating residents via emergency medicine program directors
April 15 - June 30, 2009	Physicians return application materials to ABEM, including payment of $385 for the application fee
July 1-31, 2009	Physicians who return application materials to ABEM between these dates pay the application fee plus a late fee
August 1-31, 2009	Physicians who return application materials to ABEM between these dates pay the application fee plus a second late fee
Mid-July 2009	ABEM begins mailing acceptance letters and qualifying examination registration information to candidates as their applications are approved
May 1 – November 5, 2009	Candidates registering online for the qualifying examination between these dates pay an examination fee
November 6 - November 13, 2009	Candidates registering online for the qualifying examination between these dates must pay the examination fee plus a late fee
November 16-21, 2009	ABEM administers the qualifying examination in testing centers
February 22, 2010	ABEM mails the qualifying examination results no later than this date
February 29, 2010	ABEM mails spring and fall oral certification examination assignments for 2010 examinations no later than this date
Spring 2010	Spring Oral Certification Examination
November 2010	2010 Qualifying Examination Dates; registration dates and fees to be determined
Fall 2010	Fall Oral Certification Examination; fees to be determined

Note: Fees subject to change without notice. Please check www.abem.org for the most current exam-related dates and fee information.

American Board of Family Medicine

2228 Young Drive
Lexington, KY 40505-4294
859 269-5626 or 888 995-5700
877 223-7437 (Support Center)
E-mail: general@theabfm.org
www.theabfm.org

Examination Schedule

Certification, Recertification, and Sports Medicine Exams, 2009 Summer Examination

January 29—Online applications available; registration begins ($1,200 fee)
February 28—First deadline to submit the online application ($1,200 fee)
March 31—Second deadline to submit the online application ($1,350 fee)
April 30—Third deadline to submit the online application ($1,500 fee)
May 31—Fourth deadline to submit the online application ($1,650 fee)
June 15—Final deadline to submit the online application ($1,900 fee)
June 15—Final deadline to submit special testing (ADA) documentation
June 25—Last day to clear all application deficiencies
June 25—Last day to approve all special testing (ADA) requests
June 25—Last day to make official name change with the ABFM for exam
June 30—All family medicine residency and sports medicine fellowship training must be completed 48 hours prior to scheduled exam
—Last day to select/change testing date or location 5 days prior to scheduled exam
—Last day to withdraw from testing center without seat fee
July 8-11, 13-18, 20, 22-25—Examination dates

Certification, Recertification and Sports Medicine Exams, 2009 Winter Examination

December 4 and 5—Examination dates (application deadlines to be determined)

In-Training Examination, 2009

November 6—Examination date

Geriatric Certification/Recertification, 2009

Note: Only one Geriatric examination is given per year.
November 16—Examination date (application deadlines to be determined)

Sleep Medicine, 2009

Note: The sleep medicine examination is given biennially.
November 19—Examination dates (application deadlines to be determined)

Hospice and Palliative Medicine, 2010

(Examination and application deadlines to be determined)

Adolescent Medicine, 2010

Note: The adolescent medicine examination is given biennially.
(Examination and application deadlines to be determined)

American Board of Internal Medicine

510 Walnut Street, Suite 1700
Philadelphia, PA 19106-3699
800 441-ABIM (2246)
215 446-3500
215 446-3590 Fax
E-mail: request@abim.org
www.abim.org

Examination Schedule

Internal Medicine

August 11, 12, 14, 17, 18, 20, 24, or 27, 2009—Examination dates
August 25 and 26, 2009—Examination for candidates requiring testing accommodations across multiple days*
February 1, 2009— Registration deadline
February 2, 2009—Late registration (requires late fee)
March 1, 2009—Late registration deadline
June 1, 2009—Cancellation deadline

Cardiovascular Disease

November 4-5, 2009 or November 5-6, 2009—Examination dates

Clinical Cardiac Electrophysiology

October 29, 2009—Examination date

Critical Care Medicine

October 27, 2009—Examination date

Endocrinology, Diabetes, and Metabolism

October 29, 2009—Examination date

Gastroenterology

October 7, 2009—Examination date

Geriatric Medicine

November 16, 2009—Examination date

Hematology

November 11, 2009—Examination date

Hospice and Palliative Medicine

Examination date: NA

Infectious Disease

October 6, 2009—Examination date

Interventional Cardiology

October 20, 2009—Examination date

Medical Oncology

November 12, 2009—Examination date

Nephrology

November 18, 2009—Examination date

Pulmonary Disease

October 26, 2009—Examination date

Rheumatology

October 8, 2009—Examination date

Sleep Medicine

November 19, 2009—Examination date

Transplant Hepatology

Examination date: NA

March 1, 2009—Registration opens
May 1, 2009—Registration deadline
May 2, 2009—Late registration (requires late fee)
June 1, 2009—Late registration deadline
September 1, 2009—Cancellation deadline
November 17 and 18, 2009—Examination for candidates requiring testing accommodations across multiple days*
Fee: $1,905 (except clinical cardiac electrophysiology, interventional cardiology, and transplant hepatology, which are $2,300)
* These testing dates are available *only* to candidates with a documented disability requiring additional testing time, as provided under the Americans with Disabilities Act. Refer to the ABIM policy on Testing Accommodations for Exam Takers with Disabilities at www.abim.org/exam/ada.aspx.

American Board of Medical Genetics

9650 Rockville Pike
Bethesda, MD 20814-3998
301 634-7315
301 634-7320 Fax
ABMG@abmg.org
www.abmg.org

Schedule of Examinations

August 17, 2009—Clinical Genetics and PhD Medical Genetics Examinations
August 18, 2009—Biochemical Genetics Examination
August 19, 2009—General Examination
August 20, 2009—Cytogenetics Examination
August 21, 2009—Molecular Genetics Examination

Deadline for Applications

The electronic portions of the application must be completed online no later than November 28. All required fees, documents, letters of endorsement, and other non-electronic materials must be submitted to the ABMG administrative office and must be postmarked no later than November 28.

Late Submission: Certification Examination Program Application, Password Request Form, and the Notarized Application Statement postmarked between November 29 and December 31, must be accompanied by a late fee (see Fees).

Certification Examination Program Application, Password Request Form, and the Notarized Application Statement postmarked January 1, 2009 or later will be returned to the applicant without review.

Notification of receipt of applications: Applicants will be notified of the receipt of an application via e-mail.

American Board of Neurological Surgery

6550 Fannin Street, Suite 2139
Houston, TX 77030-2701
713 441-6015
713 794-0207 Fax
E-mail: abns@tmhs.org, abns.moc@tmhs.org
www.abns.org

Schedule of Examinations

2009

March 28—Primary examination, at all residency programs
March 28—MOC cognitive examination, at all residency programs
May 19-22—Oral examination (Houston, Texas)
November 10-13—Oral examination (Houston, Texas)

2010

March 27—Primary examination, at all residency programs
March 27—MOC cognitive examination, at all residency programs
May 18-21—Oral examination (Houston, Texas)
November 9-12—Oral examination (Houston, Texas)

American Board of Nuclear Medicine

4555 Forest Park Boulevard, Suite 119
St Louis, MO 63108
314 367-2225
E-mail: abnm@abnm.org
www.ABNM.org

2009 Certification and Maintenance of Certification Exams

Important Dates and Deadlines

October 5 - October 9—Examination dates

April 1 – May 31—Application period

- May 31—Deadline for completing and submitting online application, receipt of supporting documents, and payment of processing fee
- May 31—No applications accepted after midnight (EST)
- July 15—Deadline for paying balance of all fees

Late fees:

- Payments received after **July 15** will be assessed a late fee
- Applications not paid in full by **July 31, 2009,** will be rejected, and no fees (including late fees) will be refunded

American Board of Obstetrics and Gynecology

2915 Vine Street, Suite 300
Dallas, TX 75204
214 871-1619
214 871-1943 Fax
E-mail: info@abog.org
www.abog.org

Important Dates and Deadlines

I. Final Year of Residency (ending on or before the following September 30)

A. July 1—Commence
B. September to November—Apply for basic written examination
C. June—Take basic written examination

II. Practice

A. First year of practice
   No board activities necessary
B. Second year of practice
   July 1 to June 30—Patient case list
   February to March—Apply for general oral examination
C. Third year of practice
   August—Deadline for submission of patient list
   November, December, or January—Take general oral examination

III. Fellowship in Subspecialty

A. First year (fellowship) (July 1-June 30)
   No board activities
B. Second year (fellowship) (July 1-June 30)
   No general board activities
C. Third year (fellowship) (July 1-June 30)
   - No general board activities
   - September to November—Apply for subspecialty written examination
   - June—Take subspecialty written examination
D. Fourth year—First year of practice (July 1-June 30)
   - February to March—Patient case list
   - Apply for the general oral examination
E. Fifth year—Second year of practice (July 1-June 30)
   - August—Deadline for submission of patient list for general oral examination
   - November, December, or January—Take general oral examination
   - May—Apply for subspecialty oral examination
   - January 1 to December 31—Prepare subspecialty patient case list
F. Sixth year—Third year of practice (July 1-June 30)
   - January—Submission of thesis
   - February—Submission of subspecialty patient case list
   - March or April—Take oral subspecialty examination

Recent Resident Graduates

Summary of Dates, Fees, and Late Fees for Accelerated Oral Examination

- July 1 of year written exam taken and passed—Candidate begins collection of cases for case list
- August 1, 2008—Candidate will be notified of pass/fail on written examination by the board office
- August 1, 2008—Candidate must return automated application for oral examination with application fee of $805 by September 12

- September 12, 2008—No applications accepted after this date
- October 1, 2008—Candidates will be notified of acceptance into accelerated process for the 2009 examination
- July 2009—Candidates will be notified to submit properly formatted case lists and examination fee of $935 by August 3
- August 4-14, 2009—Candidates notified by the board in July to submit their properly formatted case lists and examination fee must include a late fee of $330 ($935 plus $330 = $1,265) by August 14
- August 14, 2009—No case lists or examination fees accepted after this date
- November and December 2009 and January 2010—Oral Examination, ABOG Test Center, 2915 Vine Street, Dallas, TX

Fellowship Applicants

Summary of Dates, Fees, and Late Fees for Accelerated Oral Examination

- July 1 of 1st, 2nd, 3rd or 4th fellowship year—Candidate begins collection of cases for case list
- August 1, 2008—Candidate must complete online application for oral examination with application fee of $805 by September 12
- September 12, 2008—No applications accepted after this date
- October 1, 2008—Candidates will be notified of acceptance into accelerated process
- July 2009—Candidates will be notified to submit properly formatted case lists and examination fee of $935 by August 3
- August 4-14, 2009—Candidates notified by the board in July to submit their properly formatted case lists and examination fee must include a late fee of $330 ($935 plus $330 = $1,265) by August 14
- August 14, 2009—No case lists or examination fees accepted after this date
- November and December 2009, and January 2010—Oral Examination, ABOG Test Center, 2915 Vine Street, Dallas, TX

Dates, Deadlines, Fees, and Late Fees for the Written Examination

- September 1, 2008—Application to be completed online at www.abog.org
- November 14, 2008—Application and application fee of $735 must be received in board office
  November 15 to December 15, 2008—Application, application fee ($735), and late fee ($330) (total $1,065) due in board office
- December 16 to December 31, 2008—Application, application fee ($735), and late fee ($790) (total $1,525) due in board office
- December 31, 2008—No applications accepted after this date
- February 2009—Candidates will be notified to submit a $675 examination fee and to make a computer testing center reservation (Pearson-VUE)
- March 23, 2009—No examination fees accepted after this date
- June 29, 2009—Written examination held at various sites
  All correspondence, applications, and information directed to the board must be in English.
All fees must be paid in US currency.

Dates, Deadlines, Fees, and Late Fees for Oral Examination (Does not pertain to the Accelerated Oral Examination)

- February 1, 2009—Application to be completed online at www.abog.org
- February 1 to March 15, 2009—Application, current medical license, and application fee ($805) are due

- March 16 to April 15, 2009—Application, current medical license, and application fee ($805) plus late fee ($330) are due (total $1,135)
- April 16 to April 30, 2009—Application, current medical license, and application fee ($805) plus late fee ($790) are due (total $1,595)
- April 30, 2009—No applications accepted after this date
- July 2009—Candidates notified to submit properly formatted case lists and examination fee ($935) by August 3
- August 4-14, 2009—Candidates notified by the board in July to submit their properly formatted case lists and examination fee ($935) must include a late fee ($330), for a total of $1,265
- August 14, 2009—No case lists or examination fees accepted after this date
- November and December 2009 and January 2010—Oral Examination, ABOG Test Center, 2915 Vine St, Dallas, TX

American Board of Ophthalmology

111 Presidential Boulevard, Suite 241
Bala Cynwyd, PA 19004-1075
610 664-1175
610 664-6503 Fax
www.abop.org

Examination Schedule

Written Qualifying Examination (WQE), 2009
Tuesday, March 31, 2009
- Applications accepted March – August 1, 2008
- Late applications accepted until September 1, 2008

Approved candidates are assigned to one of two Oral Examination options:
- 2009: Washington, DC—Friday, November 13 through Sunday, November 15
  Registration deadline: July 15, 2009
- 2010: San Francisco, CA—Friday, June 4 through Sunday, June 6
  Registration deadline: February 15, 2010

WQE, 2010
Tuesday, March 23, 2010
- Applications accepted March – August 1, 2009
- Late applications accepted until September 1, 2009

Approved candidates are assigned to one of two Oral Examination options:
- 2010: San Francisco, CA—Friday, November 5 through Sunday, November 7
  Registration deadline: July 15, 2010
- 2011: Cambridge, MA—Friday, June 3 through Sunday, June 5
  Registration deadline: February 15, 2011

American Board of Orthopaedic Surgery

400 Silver Cedar Court
Chapel Hill, NC 27514
919 929-7103
919 942-8988 Fax
www.abos.org

2008 Examinations Calendar

Part I (Written) Examination

October 1, 2008—Application forms for 2008 Part I examination available at www.abos.org

December 15, 2008—Electronic submission deadline for completed application; fee payment and registered mail postmark deadline for signed signature page and any other required documents

March 20, 2009—Deadline for candidates to update address information on their profile

March/April—Credentials Committee meets to determine admission to examination

April—Candidates receive scheduling permits, which must be presented at the examination

July 9—Part I examination, Prometric Testing Centers

October—Examination results sent to candidates and program directors

Part II (Oral) Examination

April 1, 2008—Applications and Scribe 6-month case lists for the 2009 Part II examination available at www.abos.org

October 31, 2008—Electronic submission deadline for completed application; fee payment and registered mail postmark deadline for finalized, signed, and notarized Scribe 6-month case lists; application, signed signature page, and required hospital letters

November 15, 2008—Late deadline for application along with $250 late fee

March/April 2009—Credentials Committee meets to determine admission to the examination

April—Letters of notification of admission to examination mailed to candidates; letter states deadline for submission of examination fee

April—Candidates receive list of 12 cases selected with summary sheet and complication sheet for practice-based oral examination

June—Candidates receive examination assignments and admission cards

July 21-23—Part II examination, Chicago

October—Examination results sent to candidates and program directors

American Board of Otolaryngology

5615 Kirby Drive, Suite 600
Houston, TX 77005
713 850-0399
713 850-1104 Fax
www.aboto.org

Important Dates and Fees

Dates	Process	Fee (if paid by credit card)	Late fee
July 10	Resident registry due	None	$210
July 10	Maintenance of Certification updates due	$210	$210
September 1	Medical school transcripts due from new residents	None	$210
September 1	Written applications due with half of exam fee	$1,625	$210
September 18	Last day written applications accepted with late fee		
September 1	OTE applications available	$295 per applicant	$50 each
September 1	OTE site applications available	$405	$210
October 15	Written examination applicants notified of acceptance		
October 15	Oral reexaminee application due	$1,725	$210
October 16	OTE site and candidate applications due		
December 1	Remaining half of written application fee due	$1,625	$210
March 7	Otolaryngology training examination		
April 17	Written qualifying examination		

Certification Requirements

American Board of Pathology

PO Box 25915
Tampa, FL 33622-5915
813 286-2444
813 289-5279 Fax
www.abpath.org

Examination Dates

All examinations are computer based and are administered at the ABP Examination Center in Tampa, Florida.

Anatomic Pathology and Clinical Pathology Examinations

The Spring 2009 primary examinations will begin on Monday, May 18, and will continue until all qualified, registered candidates have been examined. Individuals applying for the Spring primary certification examinations must complete their training by July 1 of the year of application.

The Fall 2009 primary examinations will begin on Monday, October 12, and will continue until all qualified, registered candidates have been examined. Individuals applying for the Fall primary certification examinations must complete their training by November 1 of the year of application.

Subspecialty Examinations

The subspecialty examinations in chemical pathology, medical microbiology, molecular genetic pathology, neuropathology, and pediatric pathology are given every 2 years. Individuals applying for subspecialty examinations must complete their training by October 1 of the year of application.
- Blood Banking/Transfusion Medicine—September 14
- Chemical Pathology—September 15
- Cytopathology—September 1
- Dermatopathology—September 16
- Forensic Pathology—September
- Hematology—September 17
- Medical Microbiology—September 15
- Molecular Genetic Pathology—September 11
- Neuropathology—September 10
- Pediatric Pathology—September 21

Depending on the number of candidates, it may be necessary to give certain subspecialty examinations on multiple days. In that case, each candidate will be notified of his or her examination date at least 6 weeks prior to the examination date listed.

Final Filing and Cutoff Dates

The final filing dates for receipt of applications or registrations are as follows:
- January 4 for Spring primary examinations
- May 1 for Fall primary examinations for initial applicants
- August 15 for Fall primary examinations for those who have been declared qualified by ABP
- May 1 for subspecialty examinations

If the candidate cancels an appearance for the examination after these dates or does not appear for the examination, the entire application-examination fee is forfeited with the following exceptions:
1. Personal illness at the time of the examinations, validated by the candidate's personal physician. In this case, consideration will be given to transferring a major portion of the examination fee to the following examination.
2. Inability to accept the date assignment (primary certification applicants only). Once examination date assignments are mailed, candidates for the primary certification examination have 4 weeks from notification of their assignment to accept. These candidates may request a transfer to a future examina-

tion, in which case the examination fee, minus a $250 transfer fee, will be applied to that examination. There will be a $500 fee assessed for any additional transfer of examination dates. There is no opportunity to change the assignment within a given examination period. If the ABP is not notified within the 4-week period, the assignment will stand.

It is the candidate's responsibility to notify the ABP in writing of any change that may affect a scheduled examination.

American Board of Pediatrics

111 Silver Cedar Court
Chapel Hill, NC 27514-1513
919 929-0461
919 929-9255 Fax
E-mail: abpeds@abpeds.org
www.abp.org

2008 Examinations Schedule

The fees for certification in general pediatrics and the pediatric subspecialties are payable only in US dollars. Application payment for both first-time applicants and re-registrants is required using either a VISA or MasterCard credit card. The American Board of Pediatrics (ABP) reserves the right to make changes in its fees, policies, and procedures at any time and will make every effort to give advance notice when such changes are made. It is the applicant's responsibility to be aware of and to meet all deadlines. All applications must be submitted online.

Certification in the Pediatric Subspecialties

The ABP issues a certificate of special qualifications in the following subspecialties:
- Adolescent medicine
- Child abuse pediatrics
- Pediatric cardiology
- Pediatric critical care medicine
- Developmental-behavioral pediatrics
- Pediatric emergency medicine
- Pediatric endocrinology
- Pediatric gastroenterology
- Pediatric hematology-oncology
- Pediatric infectious diseases
- Neonatal-perinatal medicine
- Pediatric nephrology
- Pediatric pulmonology
- Pediatric rheumatology

The ABP, in collaboration with other ABMS boards, also offers a certificate of added qualifications in the following fields: (*Note:* Physicians must submit an application to the board through which they are certified.)
- Hospice and palliative medicine
- Medical toxicology
- Neurodevelopmental disabilities
- Pediatric transplant hepatology
- Sleep medicine
- Sports medicine

Examinations/Registration Dates: 2009 - Spring 2010

General Pediatrics In-training Examination
Tuesday, July 14, 2009

General Pediatrics
Monday, October 12, 2009
- December 2, 2008 – February 26, 2009—New applicants' regular registration ($1,760)
- February 27 – May 7, 2009—New applicants' late registration ($2,060)
  February 17 – May 7, 2009—Reregistrants' regular registration ($1,760)
- May 8 – May 28, 2009—Reregistrants' late registration ($2,060)
- March 9-14, 2009—Subspecialty in-training examination

Developmental-Behavioral Pediatrics, Pediatric Emergency Medicine, Pediatric Hematology-Oncology, Pediatric Rheumatology

Monday, March 30, 2009
- August 4 – October 1, 2008—New applicants' regular registration ($2,000)
- October 2 – October 31, 2008—New applicants' late registration ($2,300)
- September 15 – November 17, 2008—Reregistrants' regular registration ($2,000)
- November 18 – December 15, 2008—Reregistrants' late registration ($2,300)

Child Abuse Pediatrics, Pediatric Endocrinology, Pediatric Gastroenterology, Pediatric Infectious Diseases

Monday, November 16, 2009
- February 3 – March 31, 2009—New applicants' regular registration ($2,000)
- April 1 – April 30, 2009—New applicants' late registration ($2,300)
- March 17 – May 14, 2009—Reregistrants' regular registration ($2,000)
- May 15, 2008 – June 16, 2009—Reregistrants' late registration ($2,300)

Adolescent Medicine, Pediatric Nephrology, and Neonatal-Perinatal Medicine

Spring 2010
- August 4 – October 1, 2009—New applicants' regular registration (Fees to be determined)
- October 2 – November 3, 2009—New applicants' late registration (Fees to be determined)
- September 15 – November 17, 2009—Reregistrants' regular registration (Fees to be determined)
- November 18 – December 15, 2009—Reregistrants' late registration (Fees to be determined)

Sports Medicine

July 8-11, 13-18, 20, 22-25, 2009
- November 13, 2008 – January 15, 2009—New applicants' regular registration ($2,000)
- January 16 – February 19, 2009—New applicants' late registration ($2,300)
- December 18, 2008 – February 19, 2009—Reregistrants' regular registration ($2,000)
- February 20 – March 17, 2009—Reregistrants' late registration ($2,300)

Sleep Medicine

Tuesday, October 20, 2009
- February 3 – March 31, 2009—New applicants' regular registration ($2,000)
- April 1 – April 30, 2009—New applicants' late registration ($2,300)
- March 17 – May 14, 2009—Reregistrants' regular registration ($2,000)
- May 15 – June 16, 2009— Reregistrants' late registration ($2,300)

American Board of Physical Medicine and Rehabilitation

3015 Allegro Park Lane SW
Rochester, MN 55902-4139
507 282-1776
507 282-9242 Fax
E-mail: office@abpmr.org
www.abpmr.org

Deadlines

The appropriate fees must be postmarked and mailed and the completed application materials for admissibility must be submitted online by January 31 (Part I) or November 15 (Part II) preceding the scheduled examination. This applies to initial applications or reapplications.

An additional $500 nonrefundable late fee will be required for consideration of applications postmarked between February 1 and February 28 (Part I) or November 16 and December 15 (Part II). Applications submitted after February 28 (Part I) or December 16 (Part II) will not be accepted. The postmark applied by the United States Postal Service (or the appropriate national postal service for non-US citizens) is the date of mailing and takes precedence over postmarks applied by in-house mailing equipment.

Fees

Refer to the *Booklet of Information* at the ABPMR Web site for the current fees.

Part I

$1,375, $600 of which is an application processing fee and is not refundable.

Part II

$1,870, $600 of which is an application processing fee and is not refundable.

Late Fee

An additional nonrefundable $500 is required after the January 31 deadline for Part I and after the November 15 deadline for Part II.

Reapplication

Physicians who have initially applied for and failed or did not take either Part I or Part II can apply for admissibility for re-examination or examination during any subsequent examination period. The same requirements will be in effect for reapplication as for initial admissibility. Currently, there is no limit to the number of times a physician may reapply for examinations.

Refunds and Forfeiture of Fees

Except as hereafter provided, no fees paid will be refunded. The board will return the refundable portion of the fee only in the event that

- an applicant withdraws the application prior to the meeting of the board to act thereon, or
- an applicant is declared not admissible to the examination.

Once an applicant has been declared admissible and is a candidate, the fees will be forfeited if the candidate withdraws for any reason, or does not appear for the scheduled examination for which he or she applied.

Dual Specialty Certification

Residents may elect to pursue integrated training in physical medicine and rehabilitation (PM&R) and another specialty by enrolling in a combined training program. The ABPMR currently approves two types of combined training:

- Pediatrics and PM&R
- Internal medicine and PM&R

All three programs require completion of at least 36 months of accredited training in general comprehensive PM&R.

Subspecialty Certification

Hospice and Palliative Medicine

Applications are available on the ABPMR Web site after December 1, and completed applications are due by February 15, of the year the examination will be given.

Neuromuscular Medicine

Applications are available on the ABPMR Web site after December 1, and completed applications are due by February 15, of the year the examination will be given.

Pain Medicine

Applications are available on the ABPMR Web site after January 1, and completed applications are due by February 15, of the year the examination will be given.

Pediatric Rehabilitation Medicine

Applications are available on the ABPMR Web site after February 1, and completed applications are due by March 15, of the year in which the exam will be taken.

Spinal Cord Injury (SCI) Medicine

Applications are available on the ABPMR Web site after February 1, and completed applications are due by March 15, of the year the examination will be given.

Sports Medicine

Applications are available on the ABPMR Web site after December 1, and completed applications are due by February 15, of the year the examination will be given.

American Board of Plastic Surgery

Seven Penn Center, Suite 400
1635 Market St
Philadelphia, PA 19103-2204
215 587-9322
215 587-9622 Fax
E-mail: info@abplsurg.org
www.abplsurg.org

Fee Schedule

Resident Registration/Training Evaluation	$160
Application Registration Fee	$525
Application Registration Late Penalty Fee	$500

Written Examination Fees

Examination Fee	$1,300
Late Penalty Fee	$500
Withdraw Fee (>30 days prior to exam)	$700

Oral Examination Fees

Case List Review Fee	$625
Case List Late Penalty Fee	$500
Examination Fee	$1,100
Late Penalty Fee	$700
Withdrawal Fee (>30 days prior to exam)	$700
Critique Fee	$210

Other Fees

Missing Items Penalty Fee	$100
Written and Oral Examination Reapplication Registration Fee	$525
Credentials Review Fee	$225
Ethics Review Fee	$225
Certificate Fee	$115
Verification of Status Fee	$35
Check Returned for Insufficient Funds Fee	$55
Photocopying Fee	$15
Repeat Examination Fee	(Examination Fees above)
Informal Appeal Fee	$750
Formal Appeal Fee	$1,500
MOC-PS Application Fee	$400
MOC-PS Examination Fee	$1,000
MOC-PS Annual Contribution	$200
MOC-PS Practice Assessment PA-PS	$250

All fees must be submitted in United States currency by check or money order. Foreign currencies, including Canadian, are unacceptable.

Credit Cards are required for all online processes.

Fees are subject to change by the board.

Most fees are nonrefundable.

Diplomate Annual Dues (Lifetime Certificate Holders): $200

An annual dues fee was initiated in 1999. The board office sends out announcements annually. Retired diplomates are excluded from the annual dues request.

Refunds

For the written examination, a refund of the examination fee (less a processing charge of $700) will be granted provided the candidate submits a written request for withdrawal received in the board office at least 30 calendar days prior to the date of the examination.

For the oral examination, a refund of the examination fee (less a processing charge of $700) will be granted provided the candidate

submits a written request for withdrawal received in the board office at least 30 calendar days prior to the date of the examination. For either the written or oral examination, candidates who notify the board office in writing less than 30 calendar days prior to the examination date of their intent to withdraw, or who fail to appear for examination, will forfeit the entire examination fee. The board may waive this rule only if the circumstances warrant.

Important Dates and Deadlines

Written Examination, Computer-Based Test: October 19, 2009

- December 31, 2008—Senior resident's form due - plastic surgery program director for application requests
- January 2009—Senior resident packet and reply form sent to candidates approved before 12/31/07
- February 1—Online application available to senior residents
- March 3—Online reply forms due for candidates approved before 12/31/08
- March 4-10—Online reply forms due with late fee
- April 9—Online applications due senior residents
- April 10-14—Online applications due senior residents with late fee
- July 1—Residency graduation forms due from plastic surgery program directors
- August 1—Online reply forms due for senior residents and those approved after 12/31/08
- August 2-8—Online reply forms due with late fee for senior residents and those approved after 12/31/08
- August—Written exam scheduling permits sent to scheduled candidates
- September 19—Withdraw date with partial refund
- October 19—Written exam CBT
- December 22—Results mailed

Oral Examination, Phoenix, Arizona, November 12-14, 2009

- Fall 2007—Case collection instructions sent for 2008
- September 1, 2008 – March 31, 2009—Case list collection period
- April 24—Case list due with review fee
- April 25-30—Case list due with late fee
- August 4—Announcement packet and reply form sent with notification of five selected cases
- September 2—Online reply forms due
- September 3-8—Online reply forms due with late fee
- October 1—Candidate notification of insufficient case report data
- October 12—Hotel reservation deadline
- October 12—Withdraw date with partial refund
- November 12-14—Oral exam
- January 22, 2010—Oral exam results mailed

Other Important Dates

- March 1—Spring board meeting: requests, documents, and fee due from individuals for special consideration
- September 2—Fall board meeting: requests, documents, and fee due from individuals for special consideration

Certification Requirements

American Board of Preventive Medicine

111 West Jackson Blvd, Suite 1110
Chicago, IL 60606
312 939-2276
312 939-2218 Fax
E-mail: abpm@theabpm.org
www.theabpm.org

Fees

A nonrefundable application fee of $410 is required if the applicant holds an MPH or equivalent masters or doctoral post-graduate degree and has completed an ACGME-accredited residency in the specialty area of preventive medicine in which certification is sought.

A nonrefundable application fee of $705 is required if the applicant is applying through the alternative pathway to certification. A nonrefundable application fee of $590 is required if the applicant is applying through the special pathway for ABPM diplomates.

A late fee will be charged to all applications received after June 1. A list of late fee charges is available on the ABPM Web site at www.theabpm.org.

A nonrefundable re-review fee of $190 is required to reactivate an application within 2 years of the original review.

The examination fee of $1,950 is due with the application fee.

Fees for the Subspecialty of Medical Toxicology

The next offering of Medical Toxicology will be in 2010. Fees are to be determined.

Fees for the Subspecialty of Undersea and Hyperbaric Medicine

A nonrefundable application fee of $385 is required if the applicant is applying through the fellowship pathway ($555 if applying through the practice pathway).

The examination fee of $1,750 is due with the application fee. *Note:* All fees are reviewed annually and are subject to change at the direction of the board. Please contact the board office for the current fee schedule.

Important Dates

- June 1—Deadline for completed application forms, application fees, and reapplication requests to be received in the board office for the examination
- June 1—Deadline for receipt of re-review requests and fees
- July 15—Deadline for receipt of additional information not included with the June 1 application
- August 1—Deadline for completion of all requirements for alternative and special pathway applicants to sit for the examination
- August—Meeting of the board to determine admissibility of applicants to the examination. Letters of notification of admissibility for the examination are sent by email to candidates after the August board meeting. Notification is not given by telephone.
- September—Deadline for completion of requirements for residency pathway applicants to sit for the examination. Requirements must be completed 15 business days prior to the first day of the examination.
- Fall—Annual 1-day computer-based examination at various sites across the United States and several international sites. Current examination dates are listed on the ABPM Web site at www.theabpm.org.
- December/January—Meeting of the board to determine the pass/non-pass score for the examination
- December/January—Results of the certifying examination are mailed to candidates. Notification is not given by telephone.

Special Requirements in Aerospace Medicine, Occupational Medicine, and Public Health and General Preventive Medicine

A period of not less than 1 year of supervised training and instruction, accredited by the ACGME in the specialty area for which certification is being sought, is required.

Subspecialties

Medical Toxicology

Every 2 years the ABPM offers subspecialty certification in medical toxicology to ABPM diplomates who meet the appropriate requirements for medical toxicology. Applications for the 2008 examination cycle will be available from the board office beginning in January 2008 and will be accepted with postmark dates through May 1.

Undersea and Hyperbaric Medicine

ABPM offers subspecialty certification in undersea and hyperbaric medicine in late fall each year to physicians who hold current certification by one of the ABMS member boards and meet the appropriate requirements in undersea and hyperbaric medicine. The American Board of Emergency Medicine (ABEM) also offers subspecialty certification in undersea and hyperbaric medicine. Those physicians certified only by the ABEM must apply through that board.

American Board of Psychiatry and Neurology

2150 E Lake Cook Road, Suite 900
Buffalo Grove, IL 60089
847 229-6500
847 229-6600
www.abpn.com

2009 Examination Schedule and Fees

Visit www.abpn.com for the most current information on examination schedules, fees, and *Information for Applicants* publications, including specific training requirements, applications for examinations, and examinations' content outlines. Most documents are available as .pdf files that can be downloaded and printed.

2009 Examinations	2009 Examination Dates	Application Deadline	Late Deadline	Application Fee	Examination Fee	Late Fee
Psychiatry Part I	June 15-19, June 22-26	October 1, 2008	November 1, 2008	$700	$950	$500
Neurology/Child Neurology Part I (for residents who began training, PGY-2 for neurology, PGY-3 for child neurology, before July 1, 2005)	Sept. 28-Oct 2, Oct. 5-9, Oct. 12-16, 2009	February 1, 2009	March 1, 2009	$700	$950	$500
Psychiatry, Neurology, Child Neurology Part II Orals	January 16-18 (San Antonio, TX) April 3-5 (Boston, MA) June 12-14 (Denver, CO) September 11-13 (Kansas City, MO)	N/A	N/A	N/A	$1,350	N/A
Neurology/Child Neurology (for residents who began training, PGY-2 for neurology, PGY-3 for child neurology, on or after July 1, 2005) (No Part II Orals)	Sept. 28-Oct 2, Oct. 5-9, Oct. 12-16, 2009	February 1, 2009	March 1, 2009	$700	$2,300	$500
Vascular Neurology	April 13-17	November 1, 2008	December 1, 2008	$700	$1,200	$500
Psychosomatic Medicine	April 27-May 1	November 1, 2008	December 1, 2008	$700	$1,200	$500
Clinical Neurophysiology	May 18-22, May 26-29	November 1, 2008	December 1, 2008	$700	$1,200	$500
Forensic Psychiatry	May 18-22, May 26-29	November 1, 2008	December 1, 2008	$700	$1,200	$500
Child and Adolescent Psychiatry Part I (computer)	June 1-5	December 1, 2008	January 2, 2009	$700	$1,025	$500
Child and Adolescent Psychiatry Part II (oral)	November 13-15 (Baltimore, MD)	N/A	N/A	N/A	$1,875	N/A
Neuromuscular Medicine	Aug. 31-Sept. 4, Sept. 8-11	February 1, 2009	March 1, 2009	$700	$1,200	$500
Pain Medicine	September 12	January 2, 2009	February 1, 2009	$700	$1,200	$500
Neurodevelopmental Disabilities	Sept. 21-25	March 1, 2009	April 1, 2009	$700	$1,200	$500
Sleep Medicine	October 20	March 1, 2009	April 1, 2009	$700	$1,200	$500
MOC Psychiatry	March 9-13, March 16-20	September 1, 2008	November 1, 2008	$700	$800	$500
MOC Neurology/Child Neurology	March 23-27	October 1, 2008	November 1, 2008	$700	$800	$500
MOC Child and Adolescent Psychiatry	July 13-17	December 1, 2008	January 2, 2009	$700	$800	$500
MOC Addiction Psychiatry	August 3-7	January 2, 2009	February 1, 2009	$700	$800	$500
MOC Geriatric Psychiatry	August 3-7	January 2, 2009	February 1, 2009	$700	$800	$500
MOC Forensic Psychiatry	August 3-7	January 2, 2009	February 1, 2009	$700	$800	$500
MOC Clinical Neurophysiology	August 17-21	January 2, 2009	February 1, 2009	$700	$800	$500
MOC Pain Medicine	Sept. 19 – Oct. 3	March 1, 2009	April 1, 2009	$700	$800	$500

American Board of Radiology

5441 E Williams Circle, Suite 200
Tucson, AZ 85711
520 790-2900
520 790-3200 Fax
E-mail: information@theabr.org
Note: Refer to the American Board of Radiology Web site
(www.theabr.org) for more details.

Registration Form Deadlines and Exam Information

Diagnostic Radiology: Key Dates for Initial Certification

Oral Examinations, Louisville, KY	May 31 - June 3, 2009
Submission of Registration Forms (to be eligible for Initial Qualification Exam for the following year)	July 1 – September 30, 2009
Initial Qualification Exams administered at Pearson VUE testing centers	September 10-11, 2009

Radiation Oncology: Key Dates for Initial Certification

Oral Examinations, Louisville, KY	May 31 - June 3, 2009
Submission of Registration Forms (to be eligible for Initial Qualification Exam for the following year)	July 1 – September 30, 2009
Initial Qualification Exams administered at Pearson VUE testing centers	July 9 - 11, 2009

Radiologic Physics: Key Dates for Initial Certification

Oral Examinations, Louisville, KY	May 31 - June 3, 2009
Submission of Registration Forms (to be eligible for Initial Qualification Exam for the following year)	July 1 – September 30, 2009
Initial Qualification Exams administered at Pearson VUE testing centers	September 1-3. 2009

Diagnostic Radiology Subspecialties: Key Dates for Initial Certification

Oral Examinations, Louisville, KY	November 8-9, 2009
Submission of Registration Forms	February 1 - April 30, 2009

Note: Diagnostic radiology subspecialties include neuroradiology, nuclear radiology, pediatric radiology, and vascular and interventional radiology.

The exam for hospice and palliative medicine, a subspecialty of radiation oncology, is administered every other year. The next exam will be given in 2010 (exact date TBA).

American Board of Surgery

1617 John F Kennedy Boulevard, Suite 860
Philadelphia, PA 19103-1847
215 568-4000
215 563-5718 Fax
www.absurgery.org

Certification is offered in:
- General surgery
- Vascular surgery
- Hospice and palliative medicine
- Pediatric surgery
- Surgical critical care
- Surgery of the hand

2009 Surgery Qualifying Examination

May 1, 2009—Application deadline
June 1, 2009—Late applications deadline
August 13, 2009—Examination date

2009 Vascular Surgery Qualifying Examination

2009 Pediatric Surgery Qualifying Examination
2009 Surgical Critical Care Certifying Examination
July 1, 2009—Application deadline
July 15, 2009—Late applications deadline
September 22, 2009—Examination date

See www.absurgery.org for additional examination dates and application deadlines, as well as for eligibility requirements, application instructions and examination fees.

American Board of Thoracic Surgery

William A Baumgartner, MD, Executive Director
633 N St Clair Street, Suite 2320
Chicago, IL 60611
312 202-5900
312 202-5960 Fax
E-mail: info@abts.org
www.abts.org

Examination Dates

August 15, 2009—Registration Application
November 30, 2009—Part I (Written) Examination (multiple sites)
May 29-30, 2009—Part II (Oral) Examination (Chicago, IL)

Fees

The following fees are subject to change:

Registration fee (not refundable)	$475
Part I examination fee	$1,150
Part I reexamination fee	$1,150
Part II examination fee	$1,225
Part II reexamination fee	$1,225

   Candidates who do not appear for their scheduled examination (Part I or Part II) or who cancel less than 6 weeks prior to either examination may forfeit their examination fee.

American Board of Urology

Stuart S Howards, MD
Executive Secretary
2216 Ivy Road, Suite 210
Charlottesville, VA 22903
434 979-0059
434 979-0266 Fax
www.abu.org

Examination Dates for 2009-2010

Qualifying (Part 1) Examination

July 28-29, 2009
August 2 or 3. 2010

Certifying (Part 2) Examination

February 21-22, 2009
February 19-20, 2010
All examination dates are subject to change.

Appendix C

Medical Schools in the United States

Note: The following medical schools were accredited by the Liaison Committee on Medical Education (LCME) as of October 2008.

Alabama

00102 University of Alabama School of Medicine
Birmingham, AL 35294
00106 University of South Alabama College of Medicine
Mobile, AL 37788

Arizona

00301 University of Arizona College of Medicine
Tucson, AZ 85724

Arkansas

00401 University of Arkansas for Medical Sciences College of Medicine
Little Rock, AR 77205

California

00502 University of California San Francisco School of Medicine
San Francisco, CA 94143
00506 Keck School of Medicine of the University of Southern California
Los Angeles, CA 90033
00511 Stanford University School of Medicine
Stanford, CA 94305
00512 Loma Linda University School of Medicine
Loma Linda, CA 92350
00514 David Geffen School of Medicine at University of California, Los Angeles
Los Angeles, CA 90024
00515 University of California, Irvine College of Medicine
Irvine, CA 92717
00518 University of California San Diego School of Medicine
La Jolla, CA 92093
00519 University of California Davis School of Medicine
Davis, CA 95616

Colorado

00702 University of Colorado School of Medicine
Denver, CO 80262

Connecticut

00801 Yale University School of Medicine
New Haven, CT 06510
00802 University of Connecticut School of Medicine
Farmington, CT 06032

District of Columbia

01001 George Washington University School of Medicine and Health Sciences
Washington, DC 20037
01002 Georgetown University School of Medicine
Washington, DC 20007
01003 Howard University College of Medicine
Washington, DC 20059

Florida

01102 University of Miami Miller School of Medicine
Miami, FL 33101
01103 University of Florida College of Medicine
Gainesville, FL 32610
01104 University of South Florida College of Medicine
Tampa, FL 33612
01105 Florida State University College of Medicine
Tallahassee, FL 32306-4300
01106 Florida International University College of Medicine
Miami, FL 33199
01107 University of Central Florida College of Medicine
Orlando, FL 32816

Georgia

01201 Medical College of Georgia School of Medicine
Augusta, GA 30912
01205 Emory University School of Medicine
Atlanta, GA 30322
01221 Morehouse School of Medicine
Atlanta, GA 30314
01222 Mercer University School of Medicine
Macon, GA 31207

Hawaii

01401 University of Hawaii at Manoa John A Burns School of Medicine
Honolulu, HI 96822

Illinois

01601 Rush Medical College of Rush University Medical Center
Chicago, IL 60612
01602 University of Chicago Division of Biological Sciences Pritzker School of Medicine
Chicago, IL 60637
01606 Northwestern University Feinberg School of Medicine
Chicago, IL 60611
01611 University of Illinois at Chicago College of Medicine
Chicago, IL 60612
06142 Chicago Medical School at Rosalind Franklin University of Medicine & Science
North Chicago, IL 60064
01643 Loyola University Chicago Stritch School of Medicine
Maywood, IL 60153
01645 Southern Illinois UniversitySchool of Medicine
Springfield, IL 62708

Indiana

01720 Indiana University School of Medicine
Indianapolis, IN 46223

Iowa

1803 University of Iowa Roy J. and Lucille A. Carver College of Medicine
Iowa City, IA 52242

US Medical Schools

Kansas

01902 University of Kansas School of Medicine
Kansas City, KS 66103

Kentucky

02002 University of Louisville School of Medicine
Louisville, KY 40292
02012 University of Kentucky College of Medicine
Lexington, KY 40536

Louisiana

02101 Tulane University School of Medicine
New Orleans, LA 70112
02105 Louisiana State University School of Medicine in New Orleans
New Orleans, LA 70112
02106 Louisiana State University School of Medicine in Shreveport
Shreveport, LA 71130

Maryland

02301 University of Maryland School of Medicine
Baltimore, MD 21201
02307 Johns Hopkins University School of Medicine
Baltimore, MD 21205
02312 Uniformed Services University of the Health Sciences F. Edward Hebert School of Medicine
Bethesda, MD 20014

Massachusetts

02401 Harvard Medical School
Boston, MA 02115
02405 Boston University School of Medicine
Boston, MA 02118
02407 Tufts University School of Medicine
Boston, MA 02111
02416 University of Massachusetts Medical School
Worcester, MA 01605

Michigan

02501 University of Michigan Medical School
Ann Arbor, MI 48109
02507 Wayne State University School of Medicine
Detroit, MI 48201
02512 Michigan State University College of Human Medicine
East Lansing, MI 48824

Minnesota

02604 University of Minnesota Medical School
Minneapolis, MN 55455
02608 Mayo Medical School
Rochester, MN 55905

Mississippi

02701 University of Mississippi
School of Medicine
Jackson, MS 39216

Missouri

02802 Washington University School of Medicine
St Louis, MO 63110
02803 University of Missouri, Columbia School of Medicine
Columbia, MO 65212
02834 Saint Louis University School of Medicine
St Louis, MO 63104
02846 University of Missouri, Kansas City School of Medicine
Kansas City, MO 64108

Nebraska

03005 University of Nebraska College of Medicine
Omaha, NE 68105
03006 Creighton University School of Medicine
Omaha, NE 68178

Nevada

03101 University of Nevada School of Medicine
Reno, NV 89557

New Hampshire

03201 Dartmouth Medical School
Hanover, NH 03756

New Jersey

03305 UMDNJ-New Jersey Medical School
Newark, NJ 07103
03306 UMDNJ-Robert Wood Johnson Medical School
Piscataway, NJ 08854

New Mexico

03401 University of New Mexico School of Medicine
Albuquerque, NM 87131

New York

03501 Columbia University College of Physicians and Surgeons
New York, NY 10032
03503 Albany Medical College
Albany, NY 12208
03506 University of Buffalo SUNY School of Medicine & Biomedical Sciences
Buffalo, NY 14214
03508 SUNY Downstate Medical Center College of Medicine
Brooklyn, NY 11203
03509 New York Medical College
Valhalla, NY 10595
03515 SUNY Upstate Medical University College of Medicine
Syracuse, NY 13210
03519 New York University School of Medicine
New York, NY 10016
03520 Weill Cornell Medical College
New York, NY 10021
03545 University of Rochester School of Medicine and Dentistry
Rochester, NY 14642
03546 Albert Einstein College of Medicine of Yeshiva University
New York, NY 10461
03547 Mount Sinai School of Medicine of New York University
New York, NY 10029
03548 Stony Brook University Medical Center School of Medicine
Stony Brook, NY 11794

North Carolina

03601 University of North Carolina at Chapel Hill School of Medicine
Chapel Hill, NC 27514

03605 Wake Forest University School of Medicine
Winston-Salem, NC 27103

03607 Duke University School of Medicine
Durham, NC 27710

03608 Brody School of Medicine at East Carolina University
Greenville, NC 27834

North Dakota

03701 University of North Dakota School of Medicine and Health Sciences
Grand Forks, ND 58202

Ohio

03806 Case Western Reserve University School of Medicine
Cleveland, OH 44206

03840 Ohio State University College of Medicine and Public Health
Columbus, OH 43210

03841 University of Cincinnati College of Medicine
Cincinnati, OH 45267

03843 University of Toledo College of Medicine
Toledo, OH 43699

03844 Northeastern Ohio Universities College of Medicine
Rootstown, OH 44272

03845 Wright State University Boonshoft School of Medicine
Dayton, OH 45435

Oklahoma

03901 University of Oklahoma College of Medicine
Oklahoma City, OK 73190

Oregon

04002 Oregon Health and Sciences University School of Medicine
Portland, OR 97201

Pennsylvania

04101 University of Pennsylvania School of Medicine
Philadelphia, PA 19104

04102 Jefferson Medical College of Thomas Jefferson University
Philadelphia, PA 19107

04112 University of Pittsburgh School of Medicine
Pittsburgh, PA 15261

04113 Temple University School of Medicine
Philadelphia, PA 19140

04114 Pennsylvania State University College of Medicine
Hershey, PA 17033

04115 Drexel University College of Medicine
Philadelphia, PA 19102

04116 The Commonwealth Medical College
Scranton, PA 18503

Puerto Rico

04201 University of Puerto Rico School of Medicine
San Juan, PR 00936

04202 Ponce School of Medicine
Ponce, PR 00732

04203 Universidad Central del Caribe School of Medicine
Bayamon, PR 00960-6032

04204 San Juan Bautista School of Medicine
Caguas, PR 00726

Rhode Island

04301 Warren Alpert Medical School at Brown University
Providence, RI 02912

South Carolina

04501 Medical University of South Carolina College of Medicine
Charleston, SC 29425

04504 University of South Carolina School of Medicine
Columbia, SC 29208

South Dakota

04601 Sanford School of Medicine of the University of South Dakota
Sioux Falls, SD 57069

Tennessee

04705 Vanderbilt University School of Medicine
Nashville, TN 37232

04706 University of Tennessee Health Science Center College of Medicine
Memphis, TN 38163

04707 Meharry Medical College School of Medicine
Nashville, TN 37208

04720 East Tennessee State University James H. Quillen College of Medicine
Johnson City, TN 37614

Texas

04802 University of Texas Medical School at Galveston
Galveston, TX 77550

04804 Baylor College of Medicine
Houston, TX 77030

04812 University of Texas Southwestern Medical Center at Dallas Southwestern Medical School
Dallas, TX 75235

04813 University of Texas Medical School at San Antonio
San Antonio, TX 78284

04814 University of Texas Medical School at Houston
Houston, TX 77225

04815 Texas Tech University Health Sciences Center School of Medicine
Lubbock, TX 79430

04816 Texas A & M Health Science Center College of Medicine
College Station, TX 77843

04817 Texas Tech University Health Science Center Paul L. Foster School of Medicine
El Paso, TX 79905

Utah

04901 University of Utah School of Medicine
Salt Lake City, UT 84132

Vermont

05002 University of Vermont College of Medicine
Burlington, VT 05405

Virginia

05101 University of Virginia School of Medicine
Charlottesville, VA 22908

05104 Virginia Commonwealth University School of Medicine
Richmond, VA 23298

05107 Eastern Virginia Medical School
Norfolk, VA 23501

US Medical Schools

Washington

05404 University of Washington School of Medicine
Seattle, WA 98195

West Virginia

05501 West Virginia University School of Medicine
Morgantown, WV 26506
05502 Joan C. Edwards School of Medicine at Marshall University
Huntington, WV 25701

Wisconsin

05605 University of Wisconsin School of Medicine and Public Health
Madison, WI 53706
05606 Medical College of Wisconsin
Milwaukee, WI 53226

Appendix D

Graduate Medical Education Glossary

Accreditation Council for Graduate Medical Education (ACGME)—An accrediting agency with the mission of improving health care by assessing and advancing the quality of resident physicians' education through accreditation. The ACGME establishes national standards for graduate medical education by which it approves and continually assesses educational programs under its aegis. The ACGME accredits GME programs through its 28 review committees (26 Residency Review Committees, or RRCs, the Transitional Year Review Committee, and the Institutional Review Committee). The ACGME has five member organizations:

- American Board of Medical Specialties
- American Hospital Association
- American Medical Association
- Association of American Medical Colleges
- Council of Medical Specialty Societies

Each member organization nominates four individuals to the ACGME's Board of Directors. In addition, the Board of Directors includes three public representatives, two resident representatives, and the chair of the Council of Review Committee Chairs. A representative for the federal government also serves on the Board in a non-voting capacity.

Affiliated institution (see "Major participating institution")—Term no longer in use by the AMA or ACGME; it has been replaced by "major participating institution."

American Board of Medical Specialties (ABMS) (see also "Certification")—The umbrella organization for the 24 approved medical specialty boards in the United States. Established in 1933, the ABMS serves to coordinate the activities of its Member Boards and to provide information to the public, the government, the profession, and its members concerning issues of specialization and certification in medicine. The mission of the ABMS is to maintain and improve the quality of medical care in the United States by assisting the member Boards in their efforts to develop and utilize professional and educational standards for the evaluation and certification of physician specialists. See Appendix B for more information.

Annual Survey of Graduate Medical Education Programs—see "National GME Census."

Attending—see "Teaching staff."

Categorical positions (see also "Graduate Year 1" and "Preliminary Positions")—Positions for residents who remain in a given program or specialty until completion of the total year(s) required for admission to specialty board examination.

Certification (see also "American Board of Medical Specialties")—A voluntary process intended to assure the public that a certified medical specialist has successfully completed an approved educational program and an evaluation including an examination process designed to assess the knowledge, experience, and skills requisite to the provision of high-quality patient care in that specialty. Medical specialty boards determine whether candidates have received appropriate preparation in approved residency training programs in accordance with established educational standards, evaluate candidates with comprehensive examinations, and certify those candidates who have satisfied the board requirements. Physicians who are successful in achieving certification are called diplomates of the respective specialty board. The boards also offer a Maintenance of Certification® program for qualified diplomates at intervals of 7 to 10 years. See Appendix B for more information.

Chief resident—A position in the final year of the residency (eg, surgery) or in the year after the residency is completed (eg, internal medicine and pediatrics); the individual in this position plays a significant administrative and teaching role in guiding new residents.

GME Glossary

Combined specialty programs—Combined training consists of a coherent educational experience in two or more closely related specialty or subspecialty programs (listed below; see Appendix A for more information). The educational plan for combined training is approved by the specialty board of each of the specialties to assure that resident physicians completing combined training are eligible for board certification in each of the component specialties. Each specialty or subspecialty program is separately accredited by the Accreditation Council for Graduate Medical Education (ACGME) through its respective Residency Review Committee (RRC). The duration of combined training is longer than any one of its component specialty programs standing alone, and shorter than all of its component specialty programs together. Current combined specialties are:

- Diagnostic radiology/nuclear medicine/nuclear radiology
- Emergency medicine/family medicine
- Family medicine/preventive medicine
- Internal medicine/dermatology
- Internal medicine/emergency medicine
- Internal medicine/emergency medicine/critical care medicine
- Internal medicine/family medicine
- Internal medicine/medical genetics
- Internal medicine/neurology
- Internal medicine/nuclear medicine
- Internal medicine/physical medicine and rehabilitation
- Internal medicine/preventive medicine
- Internal medicine/psychiatry
- Neurology/diagnostic radiology/neuroradiology
- Neurology/nuclear medicine
- Pediatrics/dermatology
- Pediatrics/emergency medicine
- Pediatrics/medical genetics
- Pediatrics/physical medicine and rehabilitation
- Pediatrics/psychiatry/child and adolescent psychiatry
- Psychiatry/family medicine
- Psychiatry/neurology

Note: Combined internal medicine/pediatrics training initiated June 1, 2007, or after must be undertaken in combined medicine/pediatrics programs accredited by the ACGME, which are listed in Section III.

Consortium—A group of healthcare organizations established to pursue joint objectives in patient care, education, research, or other areas. If a consortium is formally established as an ongoing organizational entity with a commitment to graduate medical education, it may serve as a sponsoring institution of one or more GME programs.

Core discipline program—See "General specialty program"

Council on Medical Education—This AMA council formulates policy on medical education by recommending educational policies to the AMA House of Delegates, through the AMA Board of Trustees. The Council is also responsible for recommending the appointments of more than 100 representatives to accrediting bodies and other national organizations.

Designated institutional official—An individual at an institution sponsoring or participating in one or more GME programs who has the authority and responsibility for the oversight and administration of GME programs.

Educational Commission for Foreign Medical Graduates (ECFMG)—A nonprofit organization that assesses the readiness of graduates of foreign medical schools to enter graduate medical education in the United States. ECFMG certification provides assurance to GME program directors, and to the people of the United States, that graduates of foreign medical schools have met minimum standards of eligibility required to enter such programs. Almost all graduates of foreign medical schools must have an ECFMG certificate to participate in GME in the US. This certification does not guarantee that such graduates will be accepted into GME programs in the United States. (For more information on the ECFMG, see Section I.)

Electronic Residency Application Service (ERAS)—A service for medical students/residents through which residency/fellowship applications, letters of recommendation, Medical Student Performance Evaluations (MSPEs), transcripts, and other supporting credentials are transmitted via the Internet from medical schools to residency program directors. For more information about ERAS, a service of the Association of American Medical Colleges (AAMC), consult www.aamc.org/eras or see Section I.

Fellow (also see "Resident or resident physician" and "Intern")—A physician in an ACGME-accredited program that is beyond the requirements for eligibility for first board certification in the discipline. Such physicians may also be termed "residents." The term "fellow" may require modifiers for precision and clarity, eg, "research fellow."

Fifth Pathway—One of several ways that individuals who obtain their undergraduate medical education abroad can enter GME in the United States. The Fifth Pathway is a period of supervised clinical training for students who obtained their premedical education in the United States, received undergraduate medical education in countries that do not grant the MD degree until the completion of 1 year of national service after medical school, and passed Step 1 of the United States Medical Licensing Examination. After these students successfully complete a year of clinical training sponsored by an LCME-accredited US medical school and pass USMLE Step 2, they become eligible for an ACGME-accredited residency. For more information, see Section I. *Note:* The Fifth Pathway is being discontinued as of June 30, 2009.

FREIDA Online® (Fellowship and Residency Electronic Interactive Database Access)—An online information resource, available through the AMA Web site at www.ama-assn.org/go/freida, that assists medical students and residents in selecting GME programs. It includes information on all ACGME-accredited residency programs and combined specialty programs, the majority with expanded listings that provide such information as program benefits (including compensation), resident-to-faculty ratio, work schedule, policies, and educational environment.

General specialty program—A primary specialty (eg, anesthesiology, family practice, internal medicine) that provides resident physicians, under supervision, with the knowledge and skills needed to be practitioners in a specified area of medical practice; sometimes referred to as a "core discipline program." General specialty programs function within an institution and are subject to all ACGME accreditation actions, policies, and procedures. Completing an ACGME-accredited residency in a general specialty program is one of the requirements of certification by a specialty board and is a prerequisite to subspecialty training.

GME Track (see also "National GME Census")—Available at www.aamc.org/gmetrack, this secure Web-based application of the Association of American Medical Colleges includes, among other services, the National GME Census. Through GME Track, residency information is collected for both the AAMC and the AMA.

Graduate medical education (GME) (see also "Postgraduate medical education")—As the second of three major phases of medical education in the US, graduate medical education (GME) prepares physicians for the independent practice of medicine in a medical specialty. GME focuses on the development of clinical skills and professional competencies and on the acquisition of detailed factual knowledge in a medical specialty. GME programs are based in hospitals or other health care institutions and, in most specialties, utilize both inpatient and ambulatory settings. GME programs, including Transitional Year programs, are usually called "residency programs" and the physicians educated in them "residents."

Graduate Medical Education Directory—Annual publication that lists residency/fellowship programs accredited by the ACGME. Known informally as the "Green Book," the *Directory* lists all ACGME-accredited programs, Board-approved combined programs, and the certification requirements of 24 medical specialty boards.

Graduate Year (GY) (see also "Program year" and "Postgraduate year")—Refers to an individual's current year of accredited GME; this may or may not correspond to the program year. For example, a fellow in pediatric cardiology could be in the first program year of the pediatric cardiology program but in his/her fourth graduate year of GME (including the 3 prior years of pediatrics). The AMA does not use the term "postgraduate year" (PGY).

Graduate Year 1 (GY1)—Used in connection with residents and with residency positions to indicate the first year of training after medical school. Individuals in GY1 positions who plan to complete the entire program are counted as enrolled in Graduate Year 1 (GY1), Categorical. Individuals in GY1 positions who are using their first year in a residency program as a prerequisite to enter another specialty or subspecialty program are counted as enrolled in Graduate Year 1 (GY1), Preliminary. Not all specialties offer GY1 positions, and in those specialties with approved GY1 positions, some programs do not offer them. Furthermore, although by definition residents in GY1 positions are not required to have prior GME, some residents who fill such positions may have had previous training.

Institution—A *sponsoring institution* is the institution (eg, a university, medical school, hospital, school of public health, health department, public health agency, organized health care delivery system, medical examiner's office, consortium, or educational foundation) that assumes the ultimate responsibility for a GME program. ACGME-accredited GME programs must operate under the authority and control of a sponsoring institution, which must be appropriately organized for the conduct of GME in a scholarly environment and committed to excellence in both medical education and patient care. A sponsoring institution must be in substantial compliance with the ACGME Institutional Requirements and must ensure that its ACGME-accredited programs are in substantial compliance with the Institutional, Common, and specialty-specific Program Requirements.

A *major participating institution* is an institution to which residents rotate for a required experience of long duration and/or those that require explicit approval by the appropriate RRC prior to utilization. Major participating institutions are listed as part of an accredited program in the *Graduate Medical Education Directory. Note:* Hospitals and other institutions that provide rotations of less than one sixth of the program length or less than a total of 6 months are not listed in the *Directory.*

Intern (see "Resident or resident physician" and "Fellow")—No longer used by the AMA or ACGME. Historically, "intern" was used to designate individuals in the first post-MD year of hospital training; less commonly, it designated individuals in the first year of any residency program. Since 1975, the *Graduate Medical Education Directory* and the ACGME have used "resident," "resident physician," or "fellow" to designate all individuals in ACGME-accredited programs.

International medical graduate (IMG)—A graduate from a medical school outside the US and Canada.

In-training examination (also known as "in-service examination")—Examinations to gauge residents' progress toward meeting a residency program's educational objectives. Certification boards of the American Board of Medical Specialties (ABMS) or medical specialty societies offer in-training examinations on a periodic basis.

Liaison Committee for Specialty Boards (LCSB)—The body that reviews and recommends approval of new examining boards in medical specialties to the ABMS and AMA, which are the sponsors of the LCSB.

Liaison Committee on Medical Education (LCME)—The body that accredits allopathic medicine educational programs in the US and Canada leading to the MD degree. The American Osteopathic Association (AOA) accredits educational programs leading to the doctor of osteopathic medicine (DO) degree.

Licensure—The process by which a state or jurisdiction of the United States admits physicians to the practice of medicine. Licensure is intended to ensure that practicing physicians have appropriate education and training and that they abide by recognized standards of professional conduct while serving their patients. Candidates for first licensure must complete a rigorous examination sequence (the United States Medical Licensing Examination, or USMLE) designed to assess a physician's ability to apply knowledge, concepts, and principles that are important in health and disease and that constitute the basis of safe and effective patient care. All applicants must submit proof of medical education and training and provide details about their work history. Finally, applicants must reveal information regarding past medical history (including the use of habit-forming drugs and emotional or mental illness), arrests, and convictions. For more information, see *State Medical Licensure Requirements and Statistics*, published by the AMA, or visit www.ama-assn.org/go/licensure.

Major participating institution—See "Institution."

Match—See "National Resident Matching Program."

Medical school affiliation—Institutions sponsoring an accredited GME program may have a formal relationship with a medical school. Where such a relationship exists, the affiliation is identified by the dean of the medical school as major (M), graduate only (G), or limited (L). *Major* affiliation signifies that an institution is an important part of the teaching program of the medical school and plays a significant role in the clinical clerkship program. *Graduate only* affiliation indicates that the institution is affiliated with the medical school only for its graduate programs. *Limited* affiliation signifies that the institution is affiliated with the medical school's teaching program only for brief, occasional, and/or unique rotations of students or residents.

Medical school number—Unique 5-digit identifier for each medical school. See Appendix C for a list of LCME-accredited medical schools and medical school numbers.

Medical Student Section (MSS)— A section of the AMA, the AMA-MSS comprises nearly 50,000 members representing students from accredited allopathic and osteopathic schools in the US. For more information, see www.ama-assn.org/go/mss.

National GME Census—Beginning in 2000, the AMA's Annual Survey of Graduate Medical Education Programs was replaced by the National GME Census, a joint effort of the AMA and the Association of American Medical Colleges (AAMC). All programs accredited by the ACGME and combined specialty programs approved by their respective boards are asked to complete this online census, available at www.aamc.org/gmetrack. The census collects data on program characteristics such as clinical and research facilities and the work and learning environment residents can expect, as well as

GME Glossary

biographical data on residents in the programs. Data collected from the census are used in the following AMA publications and products:

- *Graduate Medical Education Directory*
- *Graduate Medical Education Library on CD-ROM*
- FREIDA Online® (Fellowship and Residency Electronic Interactive Database Access)
- Medical Education issue of the *Journal of the American Medical Association*
- *State-level Data for Accredited Graduate Medical Education Programs in the US*
- AMA Physician Masterfile
- AMA Physician Select

National Resident Matching Program (NRMP)—Informally referred to as the "Match," this process matches GME programs and applicants to those programs. Managed by the Association of American Medical Colleges (AAMC), the NRMP system was developed to provide both applicants and residency program directors an opportunity to consider their options for accepting and offering appointments to residency programs, respectively, and to have their decisions announced at a specific time. For more information, consult www.nrmp.org or see Section I.

Participating institution—See "Institution."

Postgraduate medical education (see "Graduate medical education")—The AMA does not use the term "postgraduate medical education" to refer to any stage of physician education. The term is sometimes used in the United Kingdom and Canada to refer to graduate medical education.

Postgraduate year (PGY) (see also "Graduate year")—The AMA does not use this term to describe any part of graduate medical education. The preferred term is graduate year (GY).

Preliminary positions (see also "Graduate Year 1")—Positions for residents who are obtaining training required to enter another program or specialty. Some residents in preliminary positions may move into permanent positions in the second year. Preliminary positions are usually 1 year in length and usually offered for Graduate Year 1. Internal medicine, surgery, and transitional year programs commonly offer preliminary positions.

Program—The unit of GME residency/fellowship training, comprising a series of learning experiences within a GME specialty/subspecialty, which is evaluated for accreditation.

Program director—The individual responsible for maintaining the quality of a specific GME program so that it meets ACGME accreditation standards. Other duties of the program director include preparing a written statement outlining the program's educational goals; providing an accurate statistical and narrative description of the program as requested by the Residency Review Committee (RRC); and providing for the selection, supervision, and evaluation of residents for appointment to and completion of the program.

Program year (see also "Graduate Year")—Refers to the current year of training within a specific program; this may or may not correspond to the graduate year. For example, a fellow in pediatric cardiology could be in the first program year of the pediatric cardiology program but in his/her fourth graduate year of GME (including the 3 prior years of pediatrics).

Resident and Fellow Section (RFS)—A section of the AMA formed in 1974, the AMA-RFS is the largest organization of residents in the United States. For more information, see www.ama-assn.org/go/rfs.

Residency Review Committees (RRCs)—The 28 review committees within the ACGME system (including the Transitional Year Review Committee) that meet periodically to review programs within their specialty and/or subspecialty, propose Program Requirements for new specialties/subspecialties, and revise requirements for existing specialties/subspecialties.

Resident or resident physician (see also "Fellow")—Any individual at any level in an ACGME-accredited GME program, including subspecialty programs. Local usage might refer to these individuals as interns, house officers, housestaff, trainees, fellows, junior faculty, or other comparable terminology. Beginning in 2000, the ACGME has used the term "fellow" to denote physicians in subspecialty programs (versus residents in specialty programs) or in GME programs that are beyond the requirements for eligibility for first board certification in the discipline.

Section on Medical Schools (SMS)—A section of the AMA House of Delegates with representation from deans and faculty of accredited US medical and osteopathic schools. For more information, see www.ama-assn.org/go/sms.

Sponsoring institution—See "Institution."

Subspecialty program—Provides advanced GME in a highly specialized field of study within a specialty, eg, gastroenterology within the field of internal medicine. Many subspecialty programs are subject to ACGME accreditation actions, policies, and procedures. Completing an ACGME-accredited residency/fellowship in a particular subspecialty program may qualify the physician to seek certification by the related subspecialty board. Some subspecialty programs are accredited independently of the related general specialty program and are not dependent on a general specialty program. Other subspecialty programs function only in conjunction with an accredited general specialty program, and the subspecialty program's accreditation status is related to the status of the accredited general specialty program.

Teaching staff—Any individual who has received a formal assignment to teach resident physicians. In some institutions appointment to the medical staff of the hospital constitutes appointment to its teaching staff.

Transitional year program (see also "Preliminary positions")—Broad-based clinical training in an ACGME-accredited graduate year 1 (GY1) residency program that provides a balanced curriculum in multiple clinical disciplines. Developed for the year between medical school graduation and a specialty residency program, the transitional year is designed to facilitate the choice of and/or preparation for a specific specialty; it is not meant to prepare participants for the independent practice of medicine. To sponsor a transitional year program, an institution and its affiliate must conduct two or more ACGME-accredited programs that participate in the transitional year.

United States Medical Licensing Examination (USMLE)—A three-step examination that is required for licensure of all practicing physicians in the US. For more information, see www.usmle.org or refer to *State Medical Licensure Requirements and Statistics*, published annually by the AMA.

Web ADS—The Web Accreditation Data System (ADS) of the ACGME. This Internet-based data collection system contains the current data on file with the ACGME for all sponsoring institutions and programs, which are required to verify and update general information annually via this secure online system. In addition, programs are required to verify the accredited training of all residents and to communicate organizational changes as they occur. See www.acgme.org/ADS for more information.

Appendix E

Listings of Subspecialty and Fellowship Programs

Introduction

In addition to the residency/fellowship programs accredited by the Accreditation Council for Graduate Medical Education (ACGME), a number of medical specialty societies maintain lists of subspecialty and fellowship programs outside the purview of the ACGME accreditation process. *Note:* Inclusion on this list does not reflect AMA approval or recognition of these practice areas.

To propose an additional list of subspecialties/fellowships for this section, contact Fred Donini-Lenhoff at fred.lenhoff@ama-assn.org.

Abdominal Transplant Surgery Fellowships

www.asts.org/FellowshipTraining

The American Society of Transplant Surgeons (ASTS) accredits abdominal transplant surgery programs, through which fellows develop proficiency in the surgical and medical management of patients with end-stage organ diseases amenable to transplantation. Candidates for such training must have satisfactorily completed a residency that satisfies the educational requirements for certification by the American Board of Surgery or the American Board of Urology (or foreign equivalency).

The ASTS is composed of over 1,200 transplant surgeons, physicians, scientists, and allied health professionals dedicated to excellence in transplantation surgery through education and research with respect to all aspects of organ donation and transplantation.

Nearly 70 abdominal transplant surgery fellowships in the United States and Canada are listed on the ASTS Web site.

Information

American Society of Transplant Surgeons
2461 South Clark Street, Suite 640
Arlington, VA 22202
703 414-7870
703 414-7874 Fax
www.asts.org
E-mail: asts@asts.org

Aesthetic Plastic Surgery Fellowships

www.surgery.org/professionals/aserf-fellowship.php

In January 2009, 19 aesthetic plastic surgery fellowships in the United States and Canada were listed on the ASAPS Web site.

Information

American Society for Aesthetic Plastic Surgery (ASAPS)
11081 Winners Circle
Los Alamitos, CA 90720
800 364-2147 or 562 799-2356
562 799-1098 Fax
E-mail: asaps@surgery.org

Breast Fellowships

www.surgonc.org/default.aspx?id=60

The Society of Surgical Oncology (SSO) reviews and approves breast fellowship and general surgical oncology training programs on an ongoing basis. Each fall the Society conducts a Matching Program to match qualified candidates with positions in SSO-approved training programs.

In January 2009, 32 breast fellowships were listed on the SSO's Web site.

Information

Society of Surgical Oncology
85 West Algonquin Road, Suite 550
Arlington Heights, IL 60005
847 427-1400
847 427-9656 Fax
E-mail: webmaster@surgonc.org
www.surgonc.org

Dermatology Fellowships

www.aad.org/members/residents

The American Academy of Dermatology (AAD) is a professional association for physicians in dermatology. The online *Fellowship Directory* of the AAD, which is intended for reference by medical students, residents, and dermatologists, includes dermatology fellowships in the following disciplines or areas:

- Burn
- Clinical dermatology
- Clinical research
- Clinician educator
- Cosmetic
- Dermatopathology
- Dermatopharmacology and epidermolysis bullosa
- HIV
- Immunodermatology
- Immunology
- Laser
- Medical dermatology
- Melanoma translational research
- Mohs surgery
- Oncology/melanoma
- Pediatric dermatology
- Pharmacology
- Phototherapy
- Research

Information

American Academy of Dermatology
PO Box 4014
Schaumburg, IL 60168-4014
866 503-SKIN (7546) or 847 240-1280
847 240-1859 Fax
www.aad.org

Electrodiagnostic Medicine Fellowships

www.aanem.org/education/training/fellowship_listing.cfm

The *Listing of Fellowships in Electrodiagnostic Medicine* from the American Association of Neuromuscular & Electrodiagnostic Medicine (AANEM) is an informational service assembled from data submitted voluntarily by various institutions. The AANEM does not review, evaluate, or provide input regarding the listing. This listing is not necessarily complete, and inclusion of a program does not imply sponsorship or endorsement by the AANEM. This listing is not affiliated with or endorsed by the American Board of Electrodiagnostic Medicine (ABEM) in any way. Completion of any of the listed fellowships does not guarantee satisfaction of the ABEM eligibility requirement of completion of a preceptorship in electrodiagnostic medicine. Any statement included in this listing that completion of the fellowship will enable a candidate to qualify for examination by a particular board should be investigated by the individual applying for the fellowship. Candidates should contact the individual boards for determination of eligibility requirements.

Fellowships in many areas are listed, including:

- Clinical electrodiagnostic medicine
- EMG/neuromuscular
- Electrodiagnostic medicine and electrophysiology of movement disorders
- Epilepsy, neuromuscular disorders
- Neuromuscular diseases
- Spine/neuromuscular

Information

American Association of Neuromuscular & Electrodiagnostic Medicine
2621 Superior Drive NW
Rochester, MN 55901
507 288-0100
507 288-1225 Fax
E-mail: aanem@aanem.org
www.aanem.org

Endocrine Surgery Fellowships

www.endocrinesurgery.org/fellowships/fellowships.html

The Web site of the American Association of Endocrine Surgeons lists 16 endocrine surgery fellowships in the US, Canada, and Australia as of January 2009.

Information

American Association of Endocrine Surgeons
Sally E Carty, MD, FACS, Secretary-Treasurer
497 Scaife Hall, Department of Surgery
University of Pittsburgh School of Medicine
3550 Terrace Street
Pittsburgh PA 15261
412 647-0467
412 648-9551 Fax
E-mail: information@endocrinesurgery.org
www.endocrinesurgery.org

General Internal Medicine Fellowships

www.sgim.org/impak/members_online/members/
fellowship.asp?action=start

Fellowships in general internal medicine are intended to prepare internists for academic careers. The Society of General Internal Medicine maintains a list of fellowship programs.

Information

Society of General Internal Medicine
2501 M Street NW, Suite 575
Washington, DC 20037
800 822-3060 or 202 887-5150
E-mail: membership@sgim.org
www.sgim.org

Advanced Gynecologic Endoscopy Fellowships

www.aagl.org/fellowships.asp?0.6805318

The Fellowship in Gynecologic Endoscopy, an affiliate of the AAGL and the Society of Reproductive Surgeons (SRS), sponsors fellowships in advanced gynecologic endoscopy. These fellowships were created to produce a standardized training program with a research requirement. The fellowship provides an opportunity for gynecologists who have completed their residency to acquire additional skills in minimally invasive gynecologic surgery.

Educational objectives focus on evidence-based medicine, anatomical principles, instrumentation, operative laparoscopy, and operative hysteroscopy. The fellowship offers in-depth experience using state-of-the-art techniques to treat abnormal uterine bleeding, pelvic pain, myomata, endometriosis, adhesive disease, and pelvic relaxation.

This fellowship also aims to further research in the field of minimally invasive gynecology. Fellows are required to complete a scholarly contribution to be presented at the annual meetings of the AAGL and the American Society for Reproductive Medicine.

The Fellowship in Gynecologic Endoscopy actively encourages applications from postgraduate physicians aspiring to develop their surgical skills in minimally invasive gynecology.

Information

Fellowship in Gynecologic Endoscopy
6757 Katella Avenue
Cypress, CA 90630-5105
800 554-2245 or 714 503-6200
714 503-6202 Fax
Email: adominguez@aagl.org
www.aagl.org

Hospitalist and Hospital Medicine Programs

www.hospitalmedicine.org

Hospitalists are physicians whose primary professional focus is the general medical care of hospitalized patients. Their activities include patient care, teaching, research, and leadership related to hospital care.

The term "hospitalist" refers to physicians whose practice emphasizes providing care for hospitalized patients. The term was coined by Drs. Robert Wachter and Lee Goldman in a *New England Journal of Medicine* article in August 1996 (Wachter RM, Goldman L. The emerging role of "hospitalists" in the American health care system. *N Engl J Med* 1996;335:514-7). A review in the *Journal of the American Medical Association* (Wachter, RM, Goldman L: The Hospitalist Movement: 5 Years Later, *JAMA* 287;487-494, Jan 23/30, 2002) further defines the field of hospital medicine. While some doctors have emphasized inpatient care for many years, there has been an explosive growth of such doctors since 1994. There are now more than 12,000 hospitalists in the US according to a study by the American Hospital Association. There are more new jobs available for hospitalists than in any aspect of internal medicine. Hospital medicine is a significant career path option for those trained in general internal medicine, general pediatrics, family practice, and obstetrics.

The majority (85%) of practicing hospitalists are trained in internal medicine, and some (5%) have completed subspecialty fellowships, pulmonary disease and critical care medicine being the most common. Recognizing that many medical students and residents are interested in this field, academic centers have recently begun to develop hospitalist residency and fellowship programs in hospital medicine. Hospitalist tracks are generally part of an internal medicine residency program, but offer additional exposure to the broad range of issues confronting hospital-based physicians, such as end-of-life care, quality improvement, and medical consultation. Fellowship programs tend to emphasize research training, teaching skills, and additional clinical experience.

As of September 2008, 31 fellowships were listed on the Society of Hospital Medicine's Web site (20 internal medicine, six family medicine, and five pediatrics).

Information

Society of Hospital Medicine
190 N Independence Mall West
Philadelphia, PA 19106
800 843-3360
E-mail: gbarnes@hospitalmedicine.org
www.hospitalmedicine.org

Subspecialties & Fellowships

Minimally Invasive and GI Surgery Fellowships

www.fellowshipcouncil.org/directory/index2.php

The Fellowship Council (FC) is an association of minimally invasive and GI surgical fellowship directors formed to address the unique needs of these programs. Programs include minimally invasive surgery, bariatrics, flexible surgical endoscopy, and hepato-biliary/pancreatic and colorectal specialties. The FC is an independent entity that is sponsored by the following surgical societies:

- Society of American Gastrointestinal and Endoscopic Surgeons
- Society for Surgery of the Alimentary Tract
- American Society for Metabolic and Bariatric Surgery
- American Hepato-Pancreato-Biliary Association

It provides a communication forum for disseminating information about fellowship programs, discussing fellowship issues, and communicating the Council's positions to other organizations. It administers a secure electronic match to ensure fair placement of residents into quality programs. The Council has a rigorous accreditation process according to published guidelines for high-quality training. It is also charged with creating training curricula in conjunction with the American Board of Surgery.

In January 2009, 128 fellowships were listed on the Council's Web site.

Information

The Fellowship Council
11300 West Olympic Blvd, Suite 600
Los Angeles, CA 90064
310 437-0555
310 437-0585 Fax
E-mail: info@fellowshipcouncil.org
www.fellowshipcouncil.org

Neurology Fellowship Programs

www.aan.com/education/fellowships/

The online Directory for Fellowship Positions is provided through the efforts of the American Academy of Neurology's Graduate Education Subcommittee (GES), the Association of University Professors of Neurology (AUPN), and the American Neurological Association (ANA). The goals of the GES are to provide opportunities for resident involvement in the Academy, encourage attendance at the annual meeting, and provide information to residents on fellowships.

The mission of the AUPN is to support academic departments of neurology in attracting, educating, and developing the cadre of physicians and physician-scientists needed to diagnose, understand, and treat disorders of the nervous system. Members of the AUPN include heads or chairs of divisions or departments of neurology, directors of residency training programs, directors of clerkship programs, or directors of research programs in accredited medical schools in the United States (or similar medical schools in Canada which take part in the United States Neurology Resident Matching Program).

The American Neurological Association is a professional society of academic neurologists and neuroscientists devoted to advancing the goals of academic neurology; training and educating neurologists and other physicians in the neurologic sciences; and expanding both our understanding of diseases of the nervous system and our ability to treat them.

Child neurology residency positions or fellowships are not listed in the Directory since these positions are residency training that leads to certification by the ABPN with special competence in child neurology, and therefore are not post-residency training. All listings of child neurology programs are available on the ACGME Web site and in the AMA's *Graduate Medical Education Directory* ("Green Book").

The *Directory* lists fellowships that have been submitted by programs covering the following disciplines:

- Advanced clinical neurology
- AIDS
- Alzheimer's disease
- Basic research
- Behavioral neurology
- Cerebrovascular disease/stroke
- Clinical neurophysiology
- Dementia
- EEG
- EMG
- Epilepsy
- Geriatric neurology
- Headache
- Interventional neurology
- Movement disorders
- Multiple sclerosis
- Neuroepidemiology
- Neurogenetics
- Neuroimaging
- Neuroimmunology
- Neurologic critical care
- Neuromuscular disorders
- Neuro-oncology
- Neuro-ophthalmology
- Neuro-otology
- Neuropathology
- Neuropharmacology
- Neurorehabilitation
- Neurovirology
- Pain
- Sleep disorders
- Spine

Information

American Academy of Neurology
Attn: Cheryl Alementi
1080 Montreal Avenue
St Paul, MN 55116
800 879-1960 or 651 695-2737
651 361-4837 Fax
E-mail: calementi@aan.com
www.aan.com

Obstetrics-Gynecology Subspecialty Programs

www.abog.org/app/app.html

The American Board of Obstetrics and Gynecology (ABOG) approves GME fellowship programs in the following subspecialties of obstetrics and gynecology:

- Female pelvic medicine and reconstructive surgery (29 programs)
- Gynecologic oncology (40 programs)
- Maternal-fetal medicine (69 programs)
- Reproductive endocrinology/infertility (38 programs)

An educational program in gynecologic oncology, maternal-fetal medicine, or reproductive endocrinology and infertility must (with rare exceptions) be affiliated with a medical school and be an integral part of a department of obstetrics and gynecology that also conducts an accredited residency program in obstetrics and gynecology. It must function with the approval, but not necessarily under the direction, of the chair of the department. A subspecialty program requires special facilities, services, and personnel, and the activities of the subspecialty fellows and the residents in the core program must be clearly and separately identified.

Institutions may apply for approval of education programs of 3 years' duration. Refer to the General and Special Requirements for Graduate Medical Education for detailed guidelines.

Subspecialty Certification

Fellows who enter a 3-year fellowship program must satisfactorily complete 3 years of training to be admissible to the subspecialty division's written examination. The certification process for all candidates will be identical. Program directors and candidates must be aware that in order to become certified in any subspecialty, the candidate must pass both the written and oral examinations of the principal Board.

It is recommended that continued contact with the broad aspects of obstetrics and gynecology be continued throughout the fellowship, including such mechanisms as participation in lectures, conferences, or night and weekend call. The extent of these activities, however, must not significantly alter the training program as proposed by the program director and approved by the division.

Information

American Board of Obstetrics and Gynecology
2915 Vine St
Dallas, TX 75204
214 871-1619
214 871-1943 Fax
E-mail: LDaniels@abog.org
www.abog.org

Ophthalmology Fellowship Programs

www.aupofcc.org

Formed in 2005, the Association of University Professors of Ophthalmology Fellowship Compliance Committee (AUPO FCC) is a nonprofit organization committed to the establishment of program requirements for ophthalmology fellowship programs. The AUPO FCC offers a voluntary compliance system focused on uniform educational requirements, protection of the public, protection of institutions, protection of trainees, accountability, and enforcement. The compliance process is voluntary and financed by participating fellowship programs, subspecialty societies, and the AUPO. All subspecialties in ophthalmology are encouraged to participate in the AUPO FCC.

The AUPO FCC Web site includes listings of fellowships in AUPO-FCC compliant programs in the following ophthalmic subspecialty areas:

- Cornea, external disease & refractive surgery
- Glaucoma
- Neuro-ophthalmology
- Ophthalmic pathology
- Pediatric ophthalmology & strabismus
- Surgical retina & vitreous
- Uveitis

Information

Association of University Professors of Ophthalmology Fellowship Compliance Committee (AUPO FCC)
655 Beach Street
San Francisco, CA 94109
415 561-8548
415 561-8531 Fax
E-mail: aupo@aao.org
www.aupofcc.org

Palliative Medicine Fellowship Programs

www.aahpm.org/fellowship/directory.html

The American Academy of Hospice and Palliative Medicine (AAHPM) is the professional association for physicians in palliative medicine. The AAHPM's online fellowship directory lists 56 active programs offering 140 fellowship positions, including 20 research slots.

A total of 32 programs have been accredited by the Palliative Medicine Review Committee (PMRC) as being in compliance with the Fellowship Program Standards.

Information

American Academy of Hospice and Palliative Medicine
4700 West Lake Avenue
Glenview, IL 60025
847 375-4712
877 734-8671 Fax
E-mail: info@aahpm.org
www.aahpm.org

Pathology Fellowship Programs

www.pathologytraining.org

The Intersociety Council for Pathology Information (ICPI) is a non-profit educational organization sponsored by national pathology societies to serve as a central source of information about pathology in the practice of medicine and in medical research and education. It publishes annually the *Directory of Pathology Training Programs in the US and Canada*, which includes specialty and subspecialty programs in US and Canada. Other features of the *Directory* include listings of post-sophomore fellowships for medical students and information about careers in pathology, as well as a description of the principal pathology societies. A searchable Web version of the *Directory* is available at www.pathologytraining.org.

Listings of programs in pathology subspecialties include the following:

- Anatomic pathology
- Blood banking/transfusion medicine
- Breast pathology
- Cardiovascular respiratory pathology
- Chemical pathology/clinical chemistry
- Clinical microbiology
- Coagulation
- Cytopathology
- Dermatopathology
- Forensic pathology
- Gastrointestinal pathology/hepatic pathology
- Gentourinary pathology
- Gynecologic, OB-Gyn, and perinatal pathology
- Head and neck pathology
- Hematopathology
- Immunohistochemistry
- Immunopathology/transplantation
- Informatics
- Laboratory medicine
- Molecular diagnostics
- Molecular pathology
- Neuropathology
- Oncologic pathology
- Ophthalmic pathology
- Orthopedic pathology
- Pediatric/developmental/perinatal pathology
- Renal pathology
- Soft tissue pathology
- Surgical/anatomic pathology

The *Directory* is intended for reference by medical students and residents, who can obtain a complimentary copy with a request countersigned by a pathologist or by sending a check for $8 (to cover shipping and handling) to the below address.

The Intersociety Committee also offers a 16-page brochure, *Pathology as a Career in Medicine*.

Information

Intersociety Council for Pathology Information
9650 Rockville Pike
Bethesda, MD 20814-3993
301 634-7200
301 634-7990 Fax
E-mail: icpi@asip.org
www.pathologytraining.org

Spine Programs

www.spine.org/Pages/MedicalEducation/ResidentFellow/

This directory of spine fellowship programs is produced by the North American Spine Society and includes spine fellowships throughout the United States and Canada. Earlier editions of the directory listed orthopedic spine fellowships almost exclusively, but the directory now includes neurosurgical and physical medicine and rehabilitation programs or any other specialty with a spine focus.

Information

North American Spine Society
7075 Veterans Blvd
Burr Ridge, IL 60527
630 230-3600
E-mail: education@spine.org
www.spine.org

Surgical Oncology Fellowships

www.surgonc.org/default.aspx?id=60

The Society of Surgical Oncology (SSO) reviews and approves general surgical oncology and breast fellowship training programs on an ongoing basis. Each fall the Society conducts a Matching Program to match qualified candidates with positions in SSO-approved training programs.

In January 2009, 19 surgical oncology fellowships were listed on the SSO's Web site.

Information

Society of Surgical Oncology
85 West Algonquin Road, Suite 550
Arlington Heights, IL 60005
847 427-1400
847 427-9656 Fax
Email: webmaster@surgonc.org
www.surgonc.org

Trauma Fellowships

www.aast.org/Jobs/fellowships.aspx
www.trauma.org/index.php/resources/fellowships/

The American Association for the Surgery of Trauma (AAST) has compiled lists of trauma and trauma-related fellowships arranged according to compliance with AAST-published guidelines.

In January 2009, 67 trauma and trauma-related fellowships and 11 research fellowships in compliance with the AAST's guidelines were listed on the AAST's Web site.

The site also includes a link to www.trauma.org/index.php/resources/fellowships/, which lists approximately 90 institutions supporting trauma-related fellowships, lectureships, and research positions in the following:

- Trauma Surgery
- Trauma Surgery & Critical Care
- Trauma, Critical Care and Acute Care Surgery
- Trauma Surgery & Injury Control
- Surgical Critical Care
- Orthopaedic Trauma
- Burn & Plastics Trauma
- Trauma Anaesthesia
- Trauma Radiology
- Trauma Research

Information

Sharon Gautschy, Executive Director
American Association for the Surgery of Trauma
633 North Saint Clair Street, Suite 2600
Chicago, IL 60611
800 789-4006 or 312 202-5252
312 202-5063 Fax
E-mail: aast@aast.org
www.aast.org

Appendix F
Medical Licensure Information

This section contains an article on the basics of medical licensure, in addition to information on the licensure policies of state medical boards, published in the 2009 edition of *State Medical Licensure Requirements and Statistics*.

To order your copy of the licensure book, call the AMA at 800 621-8335 or visit www.ama-assn.org/go/licensure.

Obtaining a Medical License: The Basics

By the Federation of State Medical Boards
[Reprinted from *Licensing and Credentialing: What Physicians Need to Know*]

Increasing public demand for protection, coupled with the growth in the number and sophistication of fraudulent practitioners over the past 2 decades, has resulted in stronger and more complex licensing boards and licensing statutes throughout the country. As might be expected, the rate of change differs widely among the states' licensing boards, depending on each jurisdiction's resources and Medical Practice Act, as well as on legislative, media, and public expectations. All medical boards have continued to improve licensure processes, and a trend toward uniformity among licensing boards exists to enhance both the initial licensure process and licensure portability.

Many states have expanded what is considered to be the practice of medicine to address new trends in the medical field that need to be regulated by medical boards. For example, a number of states have passed legislation in recent years that empower medical boards to have jurisdiction over the practice of medicine across state boundaries or treatment decisions made by medical directors of managed care organizations.

Within this context, a physician seeking initial licensure or subsequently applying for a license in other states should anticipate the possibility of delays due to the necessary investigation of credentials and past practice, as well as the need to comply with necessary licensing standards. To assist a physician in the quest for licensure, this article attempts to provide some ground rules. These suggestions will not apply in all cases but generally will help most physicians applying for licensure as well as benefit the licensing board of the state in which the physician wishes to practice.

When contacting a licensing board for the first time, ask for a copy of its current licensing requirements and the average time it takes to process applications. This will provide the physician with a solid idea of when to consider closing an existing practice and/or plan a move as well as with information about the potential problem areas to be addressed in completing an application. While initial licensure requirements for domestic and international medical graduates differ somewhat among states, all states will require proof of prior education and training and proof of the completion of a licensure examination approved by the board. Specifically, all physicians must submit proof of successful completion of all three steps of the United States Medical Licensing Examination (USMLE). However, because some medical students and physicians had completed portions of the National Board of Medical Examiners and Federation Licensing Examination (FLEX) sequences before the implementation of USMLE in 1994, certain combinations of examinations may be considered by medical licensing authorities as comparable to the USMLE.

To send a USMLE or FLEX transcript to state medical boards, visit www.fsmb.org or contact:

Federation of State Medical Boards
PO Box 619850
Dallas, TX 75261-9850
817 868-4000
www.fsmb.org

For info on the USMLE, visit www.usmle.org or see:

USMLE Office of the Secretariat
3750 Market St
Philadelphia, PA 19104-3910
215 590-9700

At the initial contact, the physician should provide the licensing board with a resume or curriculum vitae. This will allow a licensing board to evaluate potential problem areas early in the process. In short, the initial contact should be used to develop a set of reasonable expectations about the duration and complexity of the licensing process in a state to avoid frustration about the time required to obtain licensure. Unreasonable expectations can result in financial jeopardy due to the premature closing of a practice or failure to meet a starting date with an employer in the new state.

A physician should never try to hide derogatory information from a licensing board. It is much better to come forward with the information, assist the board in obtaining records and other necessary data, and provide information about mitigating circumstances that would prevent license denial. Full and frank disclosure of all information requested is by far the best approach to successful licensure. A physician should remember that in most states, making a false statement on an application for licensure is grounds for denial or future restriction.

A physician who is actively involved in the licensing process can often shorten the length of time it takes to obtain a license. Personally contacting and following up with the medical schools, training programs, and appropriate hospitals will motivate these institutions to verify credentials more expeditiously. Following up with the licensing boards in other states where the physician holds or has held a license also may assist in shortening the time for licensure. It is important to note a difference between follow-up and excessive use of phone contact, which often delays the processing of requested verification materials, since the physician's application or request may need to be pulled from the "stack" to answer an inquiry. A short note to the organization processing the request for information 30 days after the initial letter or form was mailed may be a better course to follow than frequent phone contact.

Another option for physicians applying for licensure is the Federation Credentials Verification Service (FCVS). The FCVS was created in 1996 by the Federation of State Medical Boards of the United States to provide a centralized, uniform process for state medical boards—as well as private, governmental and commercial entities—to obtain a verified, primary source record of a physician's core credentials. The FCVS repository of information allows a physician to establish a confidential, lifetime professional portfolio that can be forwarded, at the physician's request, to any entity that has established an agreement with FCVS. Currently, the majority of licensing authorities accept FCVS-verified documents for licensure. For more information on FCVS, call 888 ASK-FCVS (275-3287).

A wise physician will exercise patience and courtesy in the licensing process. State licensing boards and their staff, in most cases, do the best job possible to protect the public with the resources provided them. This requires taking the necessary time to fairly evaluate each application for licensure. In that same context, all actively practicing physicians should be cognizant of state laws;

they may be providing care or performing acts that might not, until recently, have required them to hold a license.

Even for physicians with uncomplicated histories who submit complete and accurate applications, delays in obtaining a medical license may be encountered. Physicians should plan for at least a 60-day period from the time they submit a completed application for license and the actual date licensure is granted. Physicians who are graduates of a medical school outside the United States should anticipate a slightly longer period. All physicians should be cognizant of the fact that, in general, the highest volume of licensure applications is received between the months of April and September. This is the peak period because physicians with families want to relocate before the academic school year starts for their children, residents want and need licensure to begin practicing, and state employees with school-age children often take their earned vacation time during this period. Finally, it is important to remember that hospital credentialing and qualification for medical malpractice insurance are based on possession of full and unrestricted licensure. This too may mean additional time before a physician can actually begin practicing.

Physicians informed about the process and working cooperatively with the licensing board need not find licensing an unpleasant experience. Members of the medical profession should always remember that the business of medical licensing boards is to protect the public from unqualified and unfit physicians. However, licensing boards also strive to ensure a process that protects the legal rights and privileges of physicians. While maintaining this balance often appears bureaucratic and cumbersome, the end result is improved health care for the people of the United States.

State Medical Licensure Requirements and Statistics: Contents

State Medical Licensure Requirements and Statistics, 2009 edition, includes the information shown below. On the following pages are selected tables that are relevant to GME.

To order your copy, call the AMA at 800 621-8335 or visit www.ama-assn.org/go/licensure.

Section I: Licensure Policies and Regulations of State Medical Boards

- Administration of the United States Medical Licensing Examination Steps 1 and 2
- Administration of the United States Medical Licensing Examination Step 3
- Endorsement Policies for Physicians Holding an Initial License
- Additional Requirements for Endorsement of Licenses Held by International Medical Graduates
- Policies About the Special Purpose Examination (SPEX) and Comprehensive Osteopathic Medical Variable-Purpose Examination (COMVEX)
- Initial Licensure of US Medical/Osteopathic School Graduates
- Initial Licensure of Canadian Citizens Who Are Graduates of Accredited Canadian Medical Schools
- Initial Licensure of International Medical Graduates
- Medical Student Clerkship Regulations
- Additional Policies Concerning IMGs and DOs
- Accredited Subspecialties and Nonaccredited Fellowships That Satisfy GME Requirements for Licensure
- Licensure Requirement Exemptions for Eminent Physicians and Medical School Faculty
- Teaching (Visiting Professor) Licenses
- Licensure and Reregistration Fees, Intervals, and Requirements
- Continuing Medical Education for Licensure Reregistration
- Resident/Fellow Physician Licenses
- Resident/Fellow Physician Licenses: Documentation and Verification
- Noneducational Temporary or Limited Licenses, Permits, Certificates, and Registration
- Physician Reentry
- Regulations on the Practice of Telemedicine and Out-of-state Consulting Physicians

Section II: Statistics of State Medical Licensing Boards

- Licenses Issued to Physicians by State Medical Boards, 1975–present
- Full Unrestricted Licenses (Whether Physician's Initial or Subsequent) Issued to MDs and DOs by State Medical Boards
- Initial Licenses Issued to MDs and DOs by State Medical Boards
- Initial Licenses Issued to MDs and DOs by State Medical Boards, 1950-present
- Initial Licenses Issued to International Medical Graduates by State Medical Boards, 1975-present

Section III: Medical Licensing Examinations and Organizations

- The United States Medical Licensing Examination (USMLE)
- The Federation of State Medical Boards (FSMB) of the United States, Inc
- National Board of Medical Examiners (NBME)

- National Board of Osteopathic Medical Examiners (NBOME)

Section IV: Information for International Medical Graduates

- Educational Commission for Foreign Medical Graduates (ECFMG)
- Immigration Overview for International Medical Graduates

Section V: Federal and National Programs and Activities

- Licensure in the United States Armed Forces
- Federal Controlled Substances Registration
- National Practitioner Data Bank and Healthcare Integrity and Protection Data Bank

Section VI: Other Organizations and Programs

- American Board of Medical Specialties
- Accreditation Council for Graduate Medical Education
- Accreditation Council for Continuing Medical Education
- American Medical Association Survey and Data Resources
- American Medical Association Continuing Medical Education
- The Joint Commission
- National Association Medical Staff Services
- National Committee for Quality Assurance
- Administrators in Medicine

Appendixes

- Boards of Medical Examiners in the United States and Possessions
- Boards of Osteopathic Medical Examiners in the United States and Possessions
- Member Boards of the Federation of Medical Licensing Authorities of Canada
- Glossary of Medical Licensure Terms and List of Common Abbreviations
- AMA Policy on Medical Licensure

Administration of the United States Medical Licensing Examination Step 3

In 1990, the Federation of State Medical Boards (FSMB) and the National Board of Medical Examiners (NBME) established the United States Medical Licensing Exami-nation (USMLE), a single examination for assessment of US and international medical school students or graduates seeking initial licensure by US licensing jurisdictions. The USMLE replaced the Federation Licensing Examination (FLEX) and the certification examination of the NBME, as well as the Foreign Medical Graduate Examination in the Medical Sciences (FMGEMS), which was formerly used by the Educational Commission for Foreign Medical Graduates (ECFMG) for certification purposes.

The USMLE is a single examination program with three steps. Each step is complementary to the others; no step can stand alone in the assessment of readiness for medical licensure. For 2009, the fee for the Step 1 examination is $495; Step 2 CK is $495; Step 2 CS is $1,055; and Step 3 is $690.

Many states require US or Canadian medical school graduates to have from 6 to 12 months of accredited US or Canadian graduate medical education (GME) to take USMLE Step 3. In some states, graduates of foreign medical schools are required to have completed more GME (as much as 3 years in several states). A number of states do not require completion of GME to take Step 3 or require only that a physician taking the examination be enrolled in a GME program.

Nearly all medical licensing authorities require completion of Steps 1, 2, and 3 within a 7-year period, or 10 years for those in MD/PhD or similar dual-degree programs (although 21 states may make exceptions in the event of extenuating circumstances, as noted in Table 2). The 7-year period begins when the medical student or graduate first passes Step 1 or Step 2. Ten states allow 10 years for completion of all three steps, and nine states do not impose a time limit for completion. Many states limit the number of attempts allowed to pass each step (particularly Step 3) and require additional education, training, or experience after a given number of failed attempts.

Additional Notes for Specific Licensing Jurisdictions

Alabama—If an applicant fails to achieve a passing score on Step 3 in three administrations, the Board may approve one additional attempt to pass Step 3 after demonstration by the applicant of additional education, experience, or training acceptable to the Board.

Applicants who are "dual degree candidates" (see definition, below) must achieve a passing score on Step 3 in not more than three administrations and complete Steps 1, 2, and 3 within a 10-year period, beginning when the applicant initially passes his or her first step. The Board does not accept scores from a retaking of a previously passed step of the USMLE.

For purposes of the USMLE, dual degree candidates are defined as the following:

- The applicant is pursuing the MD or DO degree and the PhD degree in an institution or program accredited by the LCME and a regional university accrediting body; and
- The applicant is a student in good standing, enrolled in the institution or program; and
- The PhD studies are in a field of biological sciences tested in the USMLE Step 1 content, including, but not limited to, anatomy, biochemistry, physiology, microbiology, pharmacology, pathology, genetics, neuroscience, and molecular biology.

Arizona—No time limit for USMLE Step 3 for applicants who hold a license in another jurisdiction (licensure by endorsement); for initial licensure, the 7-year limit applies.

Ohio—All 3 steps must have been passed within a 7-year period, and the performance achieved on each step must have been recognized by the USMLE as a recommended passing performance. A limited exception to this rule may be granted to an applicant who in conjunction with a medical degree is actively pursuing a doctoral degree in an institution or program accredited by the Liaison Committee on Medical Education and a regional university accrediting body. The applicant must be a student in good standing when enrolled in the institution or program, and the doctoral degree must be in a field of biological sciences tested in the Step 1 content. These fields include, but are not necessarily limited to, anatomy, biochemistry, physiology, microbiology, pharmacology, genetics, neuroscience, and molecular biology. Fields not excepted include, but are not necessarily limited to, business, economics, ethics, history, and other fields not directly related to biological science. A limited exception to this rule may also be granted to an applicant who suffered from a significant health condition which by its severity would necessarily cause a delay to the applicant's medical study. Regardless, all three steps must have been passed within a 10-year period.

Oregon—A waiver is allowed of the three attempt limit for USMLE Step 3 (1 year approved GME after third failed attempt before fourth and final attempt) for applicants who are ABMS certified.

A waiver of the 7-year time limit for completion of USMLE Steps 1, 2, and 3 is allowed for applicants who are ABMS certified, have participated in a combined MD/PhD or DO/PhD program, suffered from a documented significant health condition that by its severity would necessarily cause delay to an applicant's medical study, or have completed continuous GME equivalent to an MD/PhD or DO/PhD program.

Texas—All candidates, except MD/PhD graduates, must pass all examination steps within 7 years. MD/PhD graduates must pass all steps within 2 years of completing the GME required for licensure in Texas. Both of these time limits may be expanded to 10 years if the applicant 1) is ABMS or AOA Bureau of Osteopathic Specialists specialty board certified, or 2) has been issued a faculty temporary license in Texas, has practiced under that permit for at least 12 months, and has been recommended for licensure by the institution at which the faculty temporary license was used.

In addition, although any of the three steps must be passed within three attempts, a fourth attempt is allowed on one step only, and a fifth or sixth attempt is allowed on one step only, as long as the applicant becomes ABMS or AOA board-certified and completes, in Texas, an additional 2 years of GME beyond what is required.

Virgin Islands—The USMLE is not administered; SPEX is used to evaluate physicians' knowledge.

Washington—All applicants who graduated from medical school after 1993, whether within the US or internationally, are required to pass the USMLE to qualify for licensure.

Table 1
Administration of the US Medical Licensing Examination Step 3: Graduate Medical Education Requirements

	Amount of Accredited US or Canadian GME Required to Take USMLE Step 3	
	Graduates of US/Canadian Medical Schools	Graduates of Foreign Medical Schools
Alabama	None (but must be enrolled in GME program)	2 yrs (must be enrolled in third yr of GME program)
Alaska	1 yr	1 yr
Arizona	6 mos	6 mos
Arkansas	None	None
California	None	None
Colorado	1 yr	3 yrs
Connecticut	None	None
Delaware	1 yr	1 yr
DC	1 yr	3 yrs
Florida	None	None
Georgia	1 yr	1-3 yrs
Guam	2 yrs	2 yrs
Hawaii	None (must be enrolled in first yr of GME program)	1 yr (and must be enrolled in second yr of GME program)
Idaho	9 mos	2 yrs, 9 mos
Illinois	1 yr	1 yr
Indiana	1 yr	2 yrs
Iowa	7 mos (or enrollment in approved GME program)	7 mos (or enrollment in approved GME program)
Kansas	1 yr (or enrollment in GME program in Kansas)	3 yrs (2 in US) (or enrollment in GME program in Kansas)
Kentucky	1 yr	1 yr
Louisiana	None	None
Maine	1 yr	1 yr (plus ECFMG certificate)
Maryland	None	None
Massachusetts	1 yr	1 yr
Michigan	6 mos	6 mos
Minnesota	None (but must be enrolled in GME program)	None (but must be enrolled in GME program)
Mississippi	1 yr	1 yr
Missouri	1 yr	3 yrs
Montana	2 yrs	3 yrs
Nebraska	None	None
Nevada	None	None
New Hampshire	1 yr	1 yr
New Jersey	1 yr	1 yr
New Mexico	1 yr	1 yr
New York	None	None
North Carolina	None	3 yrs (none if enrolled in GME program in state)
North Dakota	6 mos	1 yr
Ohio	9 mos	9 mos
Oklahoma	None	None

(continued on next page)

Table 1 (continued)
Administration of the US Medical Licensing Examination Step 3: Graduate Medical Education Requirements

	Amount of Accredited US or Canadian GME Required to Take USMLE Step 3	
	Graduates of US/Canadian Medical Schools	Graduates of Foreign Medical Schools
Oregon	None (but must be enrolled in GME program)	None (but must be enrolled in GME program)
Pennsylvania	None	None
Puerto Rico	None	None
Rhode Island	1 yr	1 yr
South Carolina	1 yr	3 yrs
South Dakota	None	1 yr
Tennessee	1 yr	1 yr
Texas	None	None
Utah	None	None (must be ECFMG-certified)
Vermont	7 mos	7 mos
Virgin Islands	Not applicable	Not applicable
Virginia	None	None
Washington*	1 yr (or enrolled in GME program)	1 yr (or enrolled in GME program)
West Virginia	None	None
Wisconsin	1 yr	1 yr
Wyoming	1 yr	2 yrs (subject to Board discretion)

Abbreviations
USMLE—United States Medical Licensing Examination
ECFMG—Educational Commission for Foreign Medical Graduates
GME—graduate medical education

**Note: All information should be verified with the licensing board;
medical licenses are granted to those physicians meeting all state
requirements—at the discretion of the board.**

Table 2
Administration of the US Medical Licensing Examination Step 3: Time Limits for Completion

	Number of Times Candidates for Licensure May Take USMLE Step 3	Requirements to Repeat Step 3 if Not Passed in Designated Number of Attempts	Time Limit for Completion of All Steps of USMLE	Time Limit for MD/PhD or Dual-Degree Candidates	Time Limit May be Waived in Event of Extenuating Circumstances
Alabama*	3	Further education, training, or experience	7 yrs	10 yrs	No
Alaska	2		7 yrs		No
Arizona*	No limit		7 yrs (initial applicants only)		No
Arkansas	6		7 yrs		
California	4		10 yrs		—
Colorado	No limit		7 yrs	10 yrs	Yes
Connecticut	No limit		7 yrs		No
Delaware	No limit		No limit		No
DC	No limit	After 3 failed attempts, 1 additional yr ACGME- or AOA-approved GME	7 yrs		Yes
Florida	No limit		No limit		—
Georgia	3	1 yr of additional Board-approved training	7 yrs	9 yrs	Yes
Guam	No limit		7 yrs		No
Hawaii	No limit		7 yrs	10 yrs	No
Idaho	2	Remedial training; may be required to be interviewed, evaluated, or examined by the Board	7 yrs	10 yrs	Yes
Illinois	5	Further education, experience, or remedial training	7 yrs		Yes
Indiana	3		10 yrs	10 yrs	No
Iowa	3	After 3 failed attempts, 3 yrs of progressive GME required	10 yrs (If not, ABMS or AOA board certification required)	10 yrs	Yes
Kansas	3	After 3 failed attempts, further education, training, or experience	10 yrs		Yes
Kentucky	4		No limit		No
Louisiana	4	After 3 failed attempts, 6 mos of additional GME	No limit		—
Maine	3		7 yrs		Yes
Maryland	4	After 3 failed attempts, 1 yr additional GME; no more than 3 failures permitted on any 1 step	10 yrs		No
Massachusetts	4	After 3 failed attempts, 1 yr additional GME	7 yrs		Yes
Michigan	No limit	After 5 yrs from first attempt, additional GME in Board-approved program in-state	No limit		—
Minnesota	3 (4 if currently licensed in another state and specialty board certified)		Within 5 yrs of passing Step 2 or by end of training		No
Mississippi	3	After 3 failed attempts, 1 additional yr ACGME- or AOA-approved GME	7 yrs		Yes
Missouri	3		7 yrs		No

(continued on next page)

Table 2 (continued)
Administration of the US Medical Licensing Examination Step 3: Time Limits for Completion

	Number of Times Candidates for Licensure May Take USMLE Step 3	Requirements to Repeat Step 3 if Not Passed in Designated Number of Attempts	Time Limit for Completion of All Steps of USMLE	Time Limit for MD/PhD or Dual-Degree Candidates	Time Limit May be Waived in Event of Extenuating Circumstances
Montana	3		7 yrs		Yes
Nebraska	4		10 yrs		No
Nevada	No limit		7 yrs (all 3 steps and 9 total attempts)	10 yrs	Yes
New Hampshire	3	Further education, training, or experience	No limit		—
New Jersey	5	Further education, training, or experience	7 yrs (if not passed, must repeat entire sequence)		Yes
New Mexico	6 (within 7 yrs of first pass)		7 yrs	10 yrs	Yes
New York	No limit		No limit		—
North Carolina	6		7 yrs	10 yrs	Yes
North Dakota	3		7 yrs	Exception may be granted	No
Ohio*	No limit		7 yrs	10 yrs	Yes
Oklahoma	3		10 yrs	10 yrs	No
Oregon	4	After 3 failed attempts, 1 yr of GME required before 4th attempt	7 yrs	10 yrs	Yes
Pennsylvania	No limit		No limit		Yes
Puerto Rico	No limit		7 yrs		
Rhode Island	3		7 yrs		Yes
South Carolina	3		10 yrs		No
South Dakota	3		7 yrs (Board may grant exceptions if candidate is Board-certified)		No
Tennessee	No limit		7 yrs		No
Texas*	3		7 yrs	10 yrs	No
Utah	3	Remedial training	7 yrs	10 yrs	No
Vermont	3		7 yrs	10 yrs	No
Virgin Islands*	Not applicable		Not applicable		No
Virginia	No limit		10 yrs		Yes (if ABMS certified)
Washington*	3	Remedial training	7 yrs	10 yrs	Yes
West Virginia	3		10 yrs	10 yrs	No
Wisconsin	3		10 yrs		No
Wyoming	No limit		No limit		

Abbreviations

ACGME—Accreditation Council for Graduate Medical Education
AOA—American Osteopathic Association
USMLE—United States Medical Licensing Examination
ECFMG—Educational Commission for Foreign Medical Graduates
GME—graduate medical education

* Refer to introductory text to this table for more information on this state's regulations.

Note: All information should be verified with the licensing board; medical licenses are granted to those physicians meeting all state requirements—at the discretion of the board.

Initial Licensure of US Medical/ Osteopathic School Graduates

All states require a written examination for initial licensure: generally, for MDs, the three-step United States Medical Licensing Examination (USMLE), which has replaced the Federation Licensing Examination (FLEX) and the national board examination of the National Board of Medical Examiners (NBME). Osteopathic physicians take the three-level Comprehensive Osteopathic Medical Licensing Examination (COMLEX-USA) of the National Board of Osteopathic Medical Examiners (NBOME).

To be eligible to take USMLE Step 3, more than half of the state medical boards require graduates of US medical schools to have completed at least 1 year of graduate medical education (GME). Twenty-five boards do not require completion of any GME to take USMLE Step 3 (although in some cases a candidate must be enrolled in a GME program).

To be eligible to take Level 3 of the Comprehensive Osteopathic Medical Licensing Examination (COMLEX), osteopathic physicians must be currently participating in and in good standing with an AOA-accredited internship or ACGME-accredited GME program or must have successfully completed such an internship or program.

All medical and osteopathic boards require completion of at least 1 year of GME before issuing a full, unrestricted license

Table 3
Initial Licensure of US Medical/Osteopathic School Graduates

	Amount of Accredited US or Canadian GME Required	
	...to Take USMLE Step 3 or COMLEX Level 3	...for Licensure
Alabama	None (must be enrolled in GME program)	1 yr
Alaska	1 yr	2 yrs (1 yr if completed medical school before Jan. 1995)
Arizona	6 mos	1 yr
Arizona DO	6 mos of a 1-yr AOA- or ACGME-accredited program	1 yr AOA- or ACGME-accredited GME
Arkansas	None	1 yr
California	None	1 yr (including 4 mos general medicine)
California DO	1-yr AOA- or ACGME-accredited program	1 yr AOA- or ACGME-accredited GME, including at least 4 mos general medicine (unless applicant completed 1 yr of GME before July 1, 1990).
Colorado	1 yr	1 yr
Connecticut	None	2 yrs
Delaware	1 yr	1 yr
DC	1 yr	1 yr
Florida	None	1 yr
Florida DO	6 mos of a 1-yr AOA- or ACGME-accredited program	1 yr AOA-approved rotating internship
Georgia	1 yr	1 yr
Guam	2 yrs	
Hawaii	None (must be enrolled in 1st year of GME prgm)	1 yr
Hawaii DO	None	1 yr AOA- or ACGME-accredited GME
Idaho	9 mos	1 yr
Illinois	1 yr	2 yrs (1 yr if entered GME before Jan. 1988)
Indiana	1 yr (6 mos may be waived)	1 yr
Iowa	7 mos (or enrollment in board-approved program)	1 yr AOA-, ACGME-, RCPSC-, CFPC-accredited GME
Kansas	1 yr (or enrollment in GME program in Kansas)	1 yr
Kentucky	1 yr	2 yrs
Louisiana	None	1 yr allopathic GME
Maine	1 yr	3 yrs (for those graduating after 7/1/2004)
Maine DO	1-yr AOA- or ACGME-accredited program	1 yr AOA- or ACGME-accredited GME
Maryland	None (1 yr if 3 fails on any Step)	1 yr (plus 1 yr GME if candidate failed any part of an exam 3 times)
Massachusetts	1 yr	2 yrs
Michigan	6 mos	2 yrs
Michigan DO	None	1 yr AOA-approved GME
Minnesota	None (must be enrolled in GME program)	1 yr
Mississippi	1 yr	1 yr
Missouri	1 yr	1 yr
Montana	2 yrs	2 yrs
Nebraska	None	1 yr
Nevada	None	3 yrs
Nevada DO	6 mos of a 1-yr AOA- or ACGME-accredited program	3 yrs in AOA-approved or ACGME-accredited prgm (grads after 1995)

(continued on next page)

Table 3 (continued)
Initial Licensure of US Medical/Osteopathic School Graduates

	Amount of Accredited US or Canadian GME Required	
	...to Take USMLE Step 3 or COMLEX Level 3	...for Licensure
New Hampshire	1 yr	2 yrs
New Jersey	1 yr	2 yrs, and contract for year 3, if graduated after July 1, 2003; 1 yr if graduated before July 1, 2003
New Mexico	1 yr	2 yrs
New Mexico DO	6 mos of a 1-yr AOA- or ACGME-accredited program	1 yr
New York	None	1 yr
North Carolina	None	1 yr
North Dakota	6 mos of a 1-yr ACGME- or AOA-accredited program	1 yr
Ohio	9 mos	1 yr
Oklahoma	None	1 yr
Oklahoma DO	6 mos of a 1-yr AOA- or ACGME-accredited program	1 yr AOA-approved rotating internship or equivalent
Oregon	None (must be enrolled in GME program)	1 yr
Pennsylvania	None	2 yrs (1 yr if GME in US before July 1987)
Pennsylvania DO	6 mos of a 1-yr AOA- or ACGME-accredited program	1 yr AOA-approved rotating internship
Puerto Rico	None	1 yr
Rhode Island	1 yr	2 yrs
South Carolina	1 yr	1 yr
South Dakota	None	Completion of residency program
Tennessee	1 yr	1 yr
Tennessee DO	6 mos of a 1-yr AOA- or ACGME-accredited program	1-yr AOA-approved or ACGME-accredited GME
Texas	None	1 yr
Utah	None	2 yrs
Vermont	7 mos	1 yr (Canadian GME accepted if program accredited by RCPSC or CFPC)
Vermont DO	6 mos of a 1-yr AOA- or ACGME-accredited program	1 yr AOA-approved rotating internship or 3-yr AOA- or ACGME-accredited GME program
Virgin Islands	USMLE not offered	1 yr
Virginia	None	1 yr
Washington	1 yr (or enrolled in GME program)	2 yrs (1 yr if completed medical school before July 28, 1985)
Washington DO	6 mos of a 1-yr AOA- or ACGME-accredited program	1 yr AOA-approved or ACGME-accredited GME
West Virginia	None	1 yr
West Virginia DO	1-yr AOA- or ACGME-accredited program	1 yr AOA-approved GME
Wisconsin	1 yr	1 yr
Wyoming	1 yr	1 yr

Abbreviations

USMLE—United States Medical Licensing Examination

COMLEX—Comprehensive Osteopathic Medical Licensing Examination

GME—graduate medical education

RCPSC—Royal College of Physicians and Surgeons of Canada

**Note: All information should be verified with the licensing board;
medical licenses are granted to those physicians meeting all
state requirements—at the discretion of the board.**

Initial Licensure of Canadian Citizens Who Are Graduates of Accredited Canadian Medical Schools

When considering applications for licensure, all state medical boards consider Canadian citizens who have graduated from an accredited Canadian medical school on the same basis as graduates of accredited US medical schools.

Forty-seven licensing boards endorse the Licentiate of the Medical Council of Canada (LMCC) as evidence of passing an acceptable licensing examination (applicants must also pass all other board requirements for licensure).

With the exception of Guam and the Virgin Islands, all licensing boards accept Canadian graduate medical education (GME) as equivalent to GME in a US program accredited by the Accreditation Council for Graduate Medical Education (ACGME). These rules do not uniformly apply to international medical graduates, who should refer to Table 5.

Table 4
Initial Licensure of Canadian Citizens Who Are Graduates of Accredited Canadian Medical Schools

	LMCC Approved for Licensure by Endorsement	GME in Accredited Canadian Programs Accepted as Equivalent to ACGME-accredited GME in the United States	Notes
Alabama	Yes	Yes	
Alaska	Yes	Yes	
Arizona	Yes	Yes	
Arkansas	Yes	Yes	
California	Yes	Yes	
Colorado	Yes	Yes	
Connecticut	Yes	Yes	
Delaware	Yes	Yes	
DC	Yes	Yes	
Florida	No	Yes	
Georgia	Yes	Yes	
Guam	No	No	
Hawaii	No	Yes	
Idaho	Yes	Yes	
Illinois	Yes	Yes	
Indiana	Yes	Yes	
Iowa	Yes	Yes	LMCC must be endorsed by provincial licensing board
Kansas	Yes	Yes	
Kentucky	Yes	Yes	
Louisiana	No	Yes	
Maine	Yes	Yes	LMCC, subject to board approval
Maryland	Yes	Yes	LMCC (although applicants are not licensed by endorsement)
Massachusetts	Yes	Yes	
Michigan	Yes	Yes	
Minnesota	Yes	Yes	
Mississippi	Yes	Yes	
Missouri	Yes	Yes	Only if medical school graduate of Canadian medical school
Montana	Yes	Yes	
Nebraska	Yes	Yes	
Nevada	Yes	Yes	
New Hampshire	Yes	Yes	
New Jersey	No	Yes	LMCC considered only if applicant is licensed in US jurisdiction
New Mexico	Yes	Yes	
New York	Yes	Yes	LMCC considered only if applicant has valid provincial license
North Carolina	Yes	Yes	
North Dakota	Yes	Yes	
Ohio	Yes	Yes	1 yr of GME or its equivalent required

(continued on next page)

Table 4 (continued)

Initial Licensure of Canadian Citizens Who Are Graduates of Accredited Canadian Medical Schools

	LMCC Approved for Licensure by Endorsement	GME in Accredited Canadian Programs Accepted as Equivalent to ACGME-accredited GME in the United States	Notes
Oklahoma	Yes	Yes	
Oregon	Yes	Yes	
Pennsylvania	Yes	Yes	Must have received LMCC after 5/70 and in English
Puerto Rico	No	Yes	LMCC considered only if applicant is licensed in US jurisdiction
Rhode Island	Yes	Yes	
South Carolina	Yes	Yes	
South Dakota	Yes	Yes	
Tennessee	Yes	Yes	
Texas	Yes	Yes	
Utah	Yes	Yes	
Vermont	Yes	Yes	
Virgin Islands	No	No	
Virginia	Yes	Yes	
Washington	Yes	Yes	Must have received LMCC after 12/69
West Virginia	Yes	Yes	
Wisconsin	Yes	Yes	Must have received LMCC after 1/1/78
Wyoming	Yes	Yes	

Abbreviations

ACGME—Accreditation Council for Graduate Medical Education

GME—graduate medical education

LMCC—certification by the Licentiate of the Medical Council of Canada

Note: All information should be verified with the licensing board; licenses based on endorsement are granted to those physicians meeting all state requirements.

Initial Licensure of International Medical Graduates

All international medical graduates (IMGs) must hold a certificate from the Educational Commission for Foreign Medical Graduates (ECFMG) examination before taking Step 3 of the United States Medical Licensing Examination (USMLE).

Nineteen boards maintain and/or use a list of approved/unapproved foreign medical schools for initial licensure decisions; several states use the list of schools from the California board. In addition, about half of the boards require IMG candidates for endorsement of licensure to have graduated from a state-approved foreign medical school.

Forty states will endorse for licensure the Licentiate of the Medical Council of Canada (LMCC) when held by an IMG.

Twenty-one state boards allow IMGs to take USMLE Step 3 before they have had GME in a US or Canadian hospital (although some of these states require that a candidate be enrolled in a GME program). All states, however, require at least 1 year of GME for licensure, and 30 states require 3 years. Candidates are not awarded a license until they undertake the required GME in the United States and meet other board requirements (eg, an ECFMG certificate, personal interview, payment of fees).

Fifth Pathway

In 1971, the AMA established Fifth Pathway, a program for US citizens studying abroad at foreign medical schools. The program requires that participants have

1. Completed, in an accredited US college or university, undergraduate premedical work of a quality acceptable for matriculation in an accredited US medical school, evaluated by measures such as college grade point average and scores on the Medical College Admission Test
2. Studied medicine in a foreign medical school located outside the US, including Puerto Rico, and Canada that is listed in the International Medical Education Directory, available on the ECFMG Web site at www.ecfmg.org and developed and maintained by the Foundation for Advancement of International Medical Education and Research (FAIMERSM), a nonprofit foundation of the ECFMG
3. Completed all formal requirements for a diploma of the foreign medical school except internship and/or social service (Those who have completed all the formal graduation requirements of the foreign medical school, including internship and/or social service, and are consequently eligible to apply for ECFMG certification, are not eligible for the Fifth Pathway.)

If the aforementioned criteria are met, the candidate may substitute the Fifth Pathway program for internship and/or social service in the foreign country. After receiving a Fifth Pathway certificate from an accredited US medical school, these US citizens are eligible to enter the first year of GME in the United States.

In 52 jurisdictions (exceptions are Guam and the Virgin Islands), individuals who hold Fifth Pathway certificates (but not the ECFMG certificate) are eligible for licensure. Fifth Pathway certificate holders must pass Steps 1 and 2 of the USMLE before entering a GME program accredited by the Accreditation Council for Graduate Medical Education (ACGME).

Note: As of June 30, 2009, through action of the AMA Council on Medical Education (CME Report 1-I-07), the Fifth Pathway is discontinued. The Council no longer supports the Fifth Pathway as a mechanism for eligibility to enter the first year of ACGME-accredited graduate medical education programs. The AMA will continue to maintain record of former graduates of Fifth Pathway programs, but will cease to add records of individuals completing a year of supervised clinical education at an LCME-accredited medical school in the US after July 1, 2009, although entrants beginning in January 2009 will be included.

Additional Notes for Specific Licensing Jurisdictions

California—The state maintains lists of both recognized and disapproved schools, available at:

www.mbc.ca.gov/applicant/schools_recognized.html
www.mbc.ca.gov/applicant/schools_unapproved.html

Neither education completed at nor diplomas issued by the 10 schools currently on the disapproved list will be accepted toward meeting the requirements for training and/or licensure in the state. The following list shows the name of medical school and date disapproved.

1. CETEC University, Santo Domingo (closed)
   May 19, 1983
2. CIFAS University, Santo Domingo (closed)
   November 16, 1984
3. UTESA University, Santo Domingo
   July 13, 1985 (disapproval reaffirmed 02-07-97)
4. World University, Santo Domingo (closed)
   December 1, 1989
5. Spartan Health Sciences University, St. Lucia
   June 13, 1985
6. University of Health Sciences Antigua, St. John's
   July 28, 1995
7. Universidad Eugenio Maria de Hostos (UNIREMHOS), Dominican Republic
   November 1, 1996
8. Universidad Federico Henriquez y Carvajal, Dom. Rep.
   July 31, 1998
9. St. Matthew's University, Grand Cayman
   February 18, 2005
10. Kigezi International School of Medicine, Cambridge, England and Uganda
    November 2, 2007

Florida—ECFMG certificate required for licensure if a candidate is not a graduate of a foreign medical school approved by the Florida Board of Medicine (none has yet been approved).

Idaho—No list of approved foreign medical schools is maintained, but for IMGs applying for licensure, such schools must have been in existence for at least 15 years from the date of application for Idaho licensure.

Kansas—Licensure applicants must have graduated from a school approved by the Board. If the school has not been approved by the Board, an applicant may still be eligible for a license if the school has not been disapproved and has been in operation (date instruction started) for not less than 15 years.

Schools approved by the Board are:

1. All schools accredited by the Liaison Committee for Medical Eduction (LCME)
2. Universidad Autonoma de Guadalajara, Mexico
3. Aga Khan, Pakistan
4. American University of the Caribbean, Netherlands Antilles
5. SABA University, Netherlands Antilles (for graduates who matriculated at the school from and after January 1, 2002)

Schools unapproved (neither approved or disapproved) by the Board are:

1. SABA University, Netherlands Antilles (for graduates who matriculated at the school before 2002)

Applicants from any school disapproved by the Board are not eligible for licensure. The schools are:

1. UTESA, Santo Domingo
2. UNIREMBOS, Santo Domingo
3. St. Matthews, British West Indies

Maine—GME taken in Canada or the British Isles (accredited by a national body deemed equivalent to ACGME) may be considered qualifying on an individual basis.

Maryland—In addition to 2 years of ACGME- or AOA-accredited GME required for licensure, 1 year of GME required if a candidate failed any part of an examination three times; no more than three failures permitted.

Mississippi—ABMS board certification required for candidates who completed the Fifth Pathway.

Nevada—A formal list of approved/unapproved medical schools is not maintained, but the board does have an internal list of questionable medical schools.

New Jersey—An individual's educational experience must meet certain eligibility requirements.

North Carolina—Less than 3 years of GME may be accepted if applicant has completed at least 1 year of approved GME and is certified by an ABMS or AOA specialty board.

North Dakota—Three years of US or Canadian GME is required for licensure; if a candidate has not completed 3 years of GME but has met all other licensing requirements and has completed 1 year of GME in the United States or Canada in a board-approved program, and if the board finds that the candidate has other professional experience and training substantially equivalent to the second and third years of GME, the candidate may be deemed eligible for licensure (upon passing SPEX or ABMS board certification).

Oregon—IMG candidates for licensure must have completed at least 3 years of progressive GME in not more than two specialties in not more than two US or Canadian hospitals accredited for such training.

Pennsylvania—The board will grant unrestricted license by endorsement to a candidate who does not meet standard requirements if the candidate has achieved cumulative qualifications that are endorsed by the board as being equivalent to the standard license requirements.

South Carolina—ABMS/AOA board certification required for candidates who completed the Fifth Pathway.

South Dakota—No list of approved/unapproved foreign medical schools is maintained; decisions made on a case-by-case basis.

Table 5
Initial Licensure of International Medical Graduates

	Accepts Fifth Pathway	Maintains/ Uses List of Approved Foreign Med Schools	Endorses Canadian Certificate (LMCC) Held by an IMG	Amount of Accredited US or Canadian GME Required	
				...to Take USMLE Step 3	...for Licensure
Alabama	Yes	Yes	Yes	2 yrs (must be in 3rd yr of GME)	3 yrs
Alaska	Yes	Yes	Yes	1 yr	3 yrs
Arizona	Yes	No	Yes	6 mos	3 yrs
Arkansas	Yes	No	Yes	None	3 yrs (1 yr if currently enrolled in prgm at U of Arkansas for Med Sci)
California*	Yes	Yes	Yes	None	2 yrs (including 4 mos general med)
Colorado	Yes	Yes	Yes/No (case-by-case review)	3 yrs	3 yrs
Connecticut	Yes	Yes (WHO)	Yes	None	2 yrs
Delaware	Yes	No	No	1 yr	3 yrs
DC	Yes	No	Yes	3 yrs	3 yrs
Florida*	Yes	No	No	None	2 yrs
Georgia	Yes	Yes (WHO, CA lists)	Yes	1-3 yrs	3 yrs
Guam	No	No	No	2 yrs	3 yrs
Hawaii	Yes	No	No	1 yr (must be in 2nd yr of pgm)	2 yrs
Idaho*	Yes	No	No	2 yrs, 9 mos	3 yrs
Illinois	Yes	No	Yes	1 yr	1 yr (entered GME pre-1988); 2 yrs (entered GME post-1988)
Indiana	Yes	Yes	Yes	2 yrs	2 yrs
Iowa	Yes	No	Yes (with valid Canadian provincial license and fulfillment of all other licensure requirements)	7 mos (or enrollment in GME pgm approved by board at time of application for Step 3)	2 yrs AOA-, ACGME-, RCPSC-, or CFPC-accredited GME
Kansas*	Yes	Yes	Yes	2 yrs (or enrollment in GME program in Kansas)	2 yrs
Kentucky	Yes	No	Yes	1 yr	2 yrs
Louisiana	Yes	Yes (WHO)	No	None	3 yrs (Fifth Pathway may be counted as 1 yr of required GME)
Maine*	Yes	Yes (IMED)	Yes	1 yr	3 yrs
Maryland*	Yes	No	Yes	None (1 yr if 3 fails on any Step)	2 yrs AOA- or ACGME-accredited GME (as of Oct. 1, 2000)
Massachusetts	Yes	No	Yes	1 yr	3 yrs
Michigan	Yes	No	Yes (with valid Canadian license)	6 mos	2 yrs
Minnesota	Yes	Yes	Yes	None (must be in GME program)	2 yrs
Mississippi*	Yes	No	No	1 yr	3 yrs (or 1 yr plus ABMS certification)
Missouri	Yes	No	No	3 yrs	3 yrs
Montana	Yes	Yes	No	3 yrs	3 yrs (or ABMS or AOA certification)
Nebraska	Yes	No	Yes	None	3 yrs
Nevada*	Yes	No	Yes	None	3 yrs
New Hampshire	Yes	No	Yes	1 yr	2 yrs
New Jersey*	Yes	Yes (WHO)*	No	1 yr	3 yrs (1 yr if medical school completed before July 1, 1985); 2 yrs, and contract for year 3, if graduated after July 1, 2003

(continued on next page)

Table 5 (continued)
Initial Licensure of International Medical Graduates

	Accepts Fifth Pathway	Maintains/ Uses List of Approved Foreign Med Schools	Endorses Canadian Certificate (LMCC) Held by an IMG	Amount of Accredited US or Canadian GME Required	
				...to Take USMLE Step 3	...for Licensure
New Mexico	Yes	Yes (CA list)	No	1 yr	2 yrs
New York	Yes	No	Yes (with valid Canadian provincial license and fulfillment of all other licensure requirements)	None	3 yrs
North Carolina	Yes	No	Yes	None	3 yrs
North Dakota*	Yes	Yes (CA list)	Yes	1 yr (none if enrolled in-state)	3 yrs
Ohio	Yes	No	Yes	9 mos	2 yrs (through the 2nd-yr level)
Oklahoma	Yes	No	Yes	None	2 yrs
Oregon*	Yes	No	Yes	None (must be in GME program)	3 yrs
Pennsylvania*	Yes	No	Yes (if passed after 5/70 and in English)	None	3 yrs (1 yr if GME taken in US before July 1987)
Puerto Rico	Yes		Yes	None	1 yr
Rhode Island	Yes	Yes (WHO)	Yes (with valid Canadian provincial license and fulfillment of all other licensure requirements)	1 yr	3 yrs
South Carolina*	Yes	No	Yes	3 yrs	3 yrs
South Dakota*	Yes	No	Yes	1 yr	Completion of residency (1 yr if US GME taken before 7/87)
Tennessee	Yes	Yes	Yes	1 yr	3 yrs
Texas	Yes	Yes	Yes	None	3 yrs
Utah	Yes	No	No	None	2 yrs
Vermont	Yes	Yes (CA list)	Yes	7 mos	3 yrs
Virgin Islands	No	No	No	Not applicable	1 yr US GME
Virginia	Yes	No	Yes	None	2 yrs
Washington	Yes	No	Yes (if passed after 12/69)	1 yr (or enrollment in GME program)	2 yrs (1 yr if medical school completed before July 28, 1985)
West Virginia	Yes	No	Yes	None	3 yrs (or 1 yr plus ABMS cert.)
Wisconsin	Yes	No	Yes (if passed after 12/77)	1 yr	1 yr
Wyoming*	Yes	No	Yes	2 yrs	2 yrs

Abbreviations

GME—graduate medical education

IMED—*International Medical Education Directory*

IMG—international medical graduate

LMCC—Licentiate of the Medical Council of Canada

USMLE—United States Medical Licensing Examination

WHO—World Health Organization

* Refer to introductory text to this table for more information on this state's regulations.

Note: All information should be verified with the licensing board; licenses are granted to those physicians meeting all state requirements—at the discretion of the board.

Medical Student Clerkship Regulations

For purposes of this publication, a clerkship is defined as clinical education provided to medical students. Twenty states evaluate the quality of clinical clerkships in connection with an application for licensure. In most states, clerkships for US medical students must take place in hospitals affiliated with medical schools accredited by the Liaison Committee on Medical Education (LCME). Eleven of these 20 states have additional and/or more specific bases for evaluation, which are particularly relevant for students of non-LCME-accredited medical schools in the Caribbean, the majority of which complete their clinical clerkships in US hospitals and teaching institutions.

For example, Texas (as noted below) requires that the clerkship(s) must be performed in a hosital or teaching institution sponsoring or participating in a graduate medical education (GME) program accredited, at the time the applicant performed the clerkship, by the ACGME, AOA, or the board in the same subject (eg, the exact same specialty or subspecialty). Required core (or fundamental) clinical clerkships are:

- Internal medicine
- Obstetrics-gynecology
- Pediatrics
- Psychiatry
- Family medicine
- Surgery

Thirteen boards regulate clerkships provided in their states to students of foreign medical schools (including US citizens studying medicine in foreign schools). Of these, Pennsylvania and Puerto Rico forbid such clerkships. For purposes of licensure, 22 states accept only those clerkships completed in hospital departments with ACGME-accredited programs. Nine states have additional regulations.

Additional Notes for Specific Licensing Jurisdictions

California—Students of foreign medical schools may complete up to 18 of 72 required weeks in nonapproved clerkships outside of California.

Florida—Rules on clinical clerkships for international medical graduates adopted by the Florida Board before October 1986 do not apply to any graduate who had already completed a clinical clerkship or who had begun a clinical clerkship, as long as the clerkship was completed within 3 years.

An international medical school must be registered with the Florida Department of Education for its students to perform clinical clerkships in Florida.

Michigan—Specific clerkships are required (only for MDs).

New Jersey—For students from "international" medical schools (ie, non-LCME or AOA-accredited) who complete clinical clerkships in the US, the core clerkships (internal medicine, obstetrics-gynecology, pediatrics, psychiatry, and surgery) must be completed (minimum of 4 weeks in each) at facilities that maintain an ACGME- or AOA-accredited residency program in the specific specialty.

Pennsylvania—Students of foreign medical schools are not permitted to engage in clinical clerkships within Pennsylvania.

Texas—Clerkships must be performed 1) as a student in an accredited medical or osteopathic school or 2) in a hospital or teaching institution sponsoring or participating in a GME program accredited by the ACGME, the AOA, or the board in the same specialty or subspecialty as the medical or osteopathic medical education. The only exception is for applicants who are ABMS or AOA Bureau of Osteopathic Specialists specialty board certified.

Table 6
Medical Student Clerkship Regulations

	Evaluates the Quality of Clinical Clerkships in Connection with a Licensure Application	Regulation of Clerkships Provided to Students of Foreign Medical Schools			
		Regulates Clerkships Provided by Hospitals	Forbids Clerkships for Students of Foreign Med. Schools	Accepts Clerkships Only in Hospital Departments with ACGME-accredited Programs	Has Additional Regulations
Alabama	Yes			Yes	
Alaska					
Arizona					
Arkansas	Yes[†]	Yes		Yes	
California*	Yes[†]	Yes		Yes	Yes
Colorado					
Connecticut	Yes[†]	Yes		Yes	
Delaware	Yes	Yes		Yes	
DC					
Florida*	Yes	Yes		Yes	Yes
Georgia	Yes[†]			Yes	
Guam	Yes			Yes	
Hawaii					
Idaho					
Illinois					
Indiana				Yes	
Iowa					
Kansas					
Kentucky	Yes			Yes	
Louisiana					
Maine				Yes	
Maryland		Yes	Yes		Yes
Massachusetts	Yes[†]	Yes		Yes	Yes
Michigan*					Yes
Minnesota					
Mississippi					
Missouri					
Montana					
Nebraska					
Nevada				Yes	
New Hampshire					
New Jersey*	Yes[†]	Yes		Yes	Yes
New Mexico	Yes[†]				
New York	Yes[†]	Yes		Yes	Yes
North Carolina					
North Dakota					
Ohio					
Oklahoma				Yes	
Oregon	Yes	Yes		Yes	
Pennsylvania*	Yes[†]	Yes	Yes	Yes	

(continued on next page)

Table 6 (continued)
Medical Student Clerkship Regulations

	Evaluates the Quality of Clinical Clerkships in Connection with a Licensure Application	Regulation of Clerkships Provided to Students of Foreign Medical Schools			
		Regulates Clerkships Provided by Hospitals	Forbids Clerkships for Students of Foreign Med. Schools	Accepts Clerkships Only in Hospital Departments with ACGME-accredited Programs	Has Additional Regulations
Puerto Rico	Yes	Yes	Yes		
Rhode Island	Yes			Yes	
South Carolina					
South Dakota					
Tennessee					
Texas*	Yes[†]	Yes		Yes	Yes
Utah					
Vermont					
Virgin Islands					
Virginia	Yes[†]			Yes	
Washington					
West Virginia					
Wisconsin					
Wyoming	Yes				Yes
Total	**20**	**13**	**2**	**22**	**9**

* Refer to introductory text to this table for more information on this state's regulations.

[†] In many cases, clerkships must take place in hospitals affiliated with LCME-accredited medical schools or ACGME-accredited residency programs. These states require additional and/or more specific criteria for evaluation.

Note: All information should be verified with the licensing board; medical licenses are granted to those physicians meeting all state requirements—at the discretion of the board.

Additional Policies Concerning IMGs and DOs

A number of state medical boards have additional graduate medical education (GME) and specialty certificate policies for international medical graduates (IMGs). Fifteen states have requirements for appointment to GME programs other than requiring an Educational Commission for Foreign Medical Graduates (ECFMG) certificate or a limited license.

Seven boards—Connecticut, Maine, Nebraska, Ohio, Oklahoma, Oregon, and Rhode Island—indicated that GME completed in foreign countries other than Canada may be considered for credit toward a license. Specialty certificates of foreign boards, such as the Royal College of Physicians in the United Kingdom, may be accepted for credit toward a license in 11 states.

Thirty-eight medical boards accept GME accredited by the Accreditation Council for Graduate Medical Education (ACGME) for licensure of osteopathic medical graduates.

Additional Notes for Specific Licensing Jurisdictions

Maine—The board may accept GME completed in England, Scotland, and Ireland for credit toward a license, if it is accepted by the specialty board as meeting board eligibility in the United States and notified via certified letter.

Pennsylvania—IMGs seeking appointment to a GME program need a passing score on United States Medical Licensing Examination (USMLE) Steps 1 and 2 (or National Board of Medical Examiners [NBME] Parts I and II or Federation Licensing Examination [FLEX] Component 1) for graduate year 2 medical education; for graduate year 3 and beyond, all parts of USMLE (or NBME or FLEX) are required.

Table 7
Additional Policies Concerning IMGs and DOs

| | Has State Board Requirements for Appointment to GME Program Other Than ECFMG Certificate or Limited License | May Accept GME Completed in Foreign Countries Other Than Canada for Credit Toward a License | May Accept Specialty Certificates of Foreign Boards (eg, Royal College of Physicians of the United Kingdom) for Credit Toward a License | Osteopathic Medical Graduates | |
				ACGME-Accredited GME Accepted	State Osteopathic Board Handles Licensure
Alabama				Yes	
Alaska	Yes (residency permit required)				
Arizona	Yes (residency permit required)				Yes
Arkansas				Yes	
California	Yes				Yes
Colorado				Yes	
Connecticut	Yes (residency intern permit required)	Yes	Yes	Yes	
Delaware					
DC				Yes	
Florida					Yes
Georgia				Yes	
Guam					
Hawaii				Yes	
Idaho				Yes	
Illinois				Yes	
Indiana				Yes	
Iowa				Yes	
Kansas	Yes (residency permit required, and unapproved school must have been in existence at least 15 yrs)			Yes	
Kentucky	Yes (residency permit required for 2nd yr)			Yes	
Louisiana	Yes (passage of FLEX/NBME/USMLE)			Yes	
Maine*		Yes	Yes	Yes	Yes
Maryland				Yes	
Massachusetts				Yes	
Michigan	Yes (certification of medical education)				Yes
Minnesota	Yes (residency intern permit required)			Yes	
Mississippi				Yes	
Missouri	Yes			Yes	
Montana				Yes	
Nebraska		Yes		Yes	
Nevada	Yes				Yes
New Hampshire				Yes	
New Jersey	Yes (residency intern permit required)			Yes	
New Mexico					Yes
New York			Yes	Yes	
North Carolina				Yes	
North Dakota				Yes	
Ohio		Yes	Yes	Yes	

(continued on next page)

Table 7 (continued)
Additional Policies Concerning IMGs and DOs

	Has State Board Requirements for Appointment to GME Program Other Than ECFMG Certificate or Limited License	May Accept GME Completed in Foreign Countries Other Than Canada for Credit Toward a License	May Accept Specialty Certificates of Foreign Boards (eg, Royal College of Physicians of the United Kingdom) for Credit Toward a License	Osteopathic Medical Graduates	
				ACGME-Accredited GME Accepted	State Osteopathic Board Handles Licensure
Oklahoma		Yes	Yes		Yes
Oregon		Yes		Yes	
Pennsylvania*	Yes		Yes		Yes
Puerto Rico					
Rhode Island		Yes (UK only)	Yes; may accept certificates of boards in England, Scotland, and Ireland	Yes	
South Carolina				Yes	
South Dakota				Yes	
Tennessee			Yes; specialty board must be AMA-recognized		Yes
Texas	Yes (physician-in-training permit required)			Yes	
Utah				Yes	Yes
Vermont	Yes		Yes; specialty board must be recognized by ABMS, RCPSC, or CFPC		Yes
Virgin Islands					
Virginia				Yes	
Washington				Yes	Yes
West Virginia				Yes	Yes
Wisconsin			Yes		
Wyoming			Yes (at board's discretion)	Yes	
Total	**15**	**7**	**11**	**38**	**13**

Abbreviations

ACGME—Accreditation Council for Graduate Medical Education
ECFMG—Educational Commission for Foreign Medical Graduates
FLEX—Federation Licensing Examination
GME—graduate medical education
NBME—certificate of the National Board of Medical Examiners
USMLE—United States Medical Licensing Examination

* Refer to introductory text to this table for more information on this state's regulations.

Note: All information should be verified with the licensing board; medical licenses are granted to those physicians meeting all state requirements—at the discretion of the board.

Accredited Subspecialties and Nonaccredited Fellowships That Satisfy GME Requirements for Licensure

Both the AMA and the Accreditation Council for Graduate Medical Education (ACGME) define a residency as graduate medical education (GME) that takes place in any of the medical specialties with ACGME Program Requirements (eg, internal medicine, pediatrics, surgery). Beginning in 2000, the ACGME has used the term fellowship to denote GME in ACGME-accredited subspecialty programs (eg, cardiovascular disease, hand surgery, rheumatology) that is beyond the requirements for eligibility for first board certification in the discipline.

All state medical boards accept residency education in specialty programs accredited by the ACGME as satisfying their GME requirements for licensure. Fifty-one jurisdictions—all except Arkansas, Montana, and Puerto Rico—accept residency education in subspecialty programs accredited by ACGME as satisfying their GME requirements for licensure.

Ten boards accept clinical fellowships not accredited by ACGME, and three boards—Hawaii, New York, and North Carolina—may accept research fellowships not accredited by ACGME to satisfy the GME requirement for licensure.

Table 8
Accredited Subspecialties and Nonaccredited Fellowships That Satisfy Graduate Medical Education Requirements for Licensure

	Accepts Subspecialty GME Accredited by ACGME	Accepts Clinical Fellowships **Not** Accredited by ACGME	Accepts Research Fellowships **Not** Accredited by ACGME
Alabama	Yes		
Alaska	Yes		
Arizona	Yes		
Arkansas			
California MD and DO	Yes		
Colorado	Yes		
Connecticut	Yes		
Delaware	Yes		
DC	Yes		
Florida	Yes		
Georgia	Yes	Yes	
Guam	Yes		
Hawaii	Yes	Yes (with board approval)	Yes (with board approval)
Idaho	Yes		
Illinois	Yes		
Indiana	Yes		
Iowa	Yes		
Kansas	Yes		
Kentucky	Yes		
Louisiana	Yes		
Maine	Yes		
Maryland	Yes	Yes (with board approval)	
Massachusetts	Yes		
Michigan	Yes		
Michigan DO	Only if AOA-accredited		
Minnesota	Yes		
Mississippi	Yes		
Missouri	Yes	Yes	
Montana			
Nebraska	Yes		
Nevada	Yes		
New Hampshire	Yes		
New Jersey	Yes		
New Mexico	Yes		
New York	Yes	Yes	Yes
North Carolina	Yes	Yes (with board approval)	Yes (with board approval)
North Dakota	Yes		
Ohio	Yes	Yes (with board approval)	
Oklahoma	Yes		
Oregon	Yes		
Pennsylvania	Yes		
Puerto Rico			
Rhode Island	Yes	Yes (with board approval)	
South Carolina	Yes		
South Dakota	Yes		

(continued on next page)

Table 8 (continued)
Accredited Subspecialties and Nonaccredited Fellowships That Satisfy Graduate Medical Education Requirements for Licensure

	Accepts Subspecialty GME Accredited by ACGME	Accepts Clinical Fellowships **Not** Accredited by ACGME	Accepts Research Fellowships **Not** Accredited by ACGME
Tennessee	Yes		
Texas	Yes	Yes (if in Texas and board-approved)	
Utah	Yes	Yes (if combined with an ACGME-accredited program)	
Vermont	Yes		
Virgin Islands	Yes		
Virginia	Yes		
Washington MD and DO	Yes		
West Virginia	Yes		
Wisconsin	Yes		
Wyoming	Yes		
Total	**51**	**10**	**3**

Abbreviations

ACGME—Accreditation Council for Graduate Medical Education
GME—graduate medical education

* Refer to introductory text to this table for more information on this state's regulations.

Note: All information should be verified with licensing board; medical licenses are granted to those physicians meeting all state requirements—at the discretion of the board.

Licensure Requirement Exemptions for Eminent Physicians and Medical School Faculty

Seventeen boards license physicians through recognition of eminence in medical education or medical practice. Physicians appointed to a medical school faculty are excused from the graduate medical education (GME) requirement for limited licensure in 20 states and from the examination requirement for limited licensure or teaching certification in 19 states. These faculty appointees would, however, receive a limited license or similar credential.

Table 9
Licensure Requirement Exemptions for Eminent Physicians and Medical School Faculty

	License Physicians Through Recognition of Eminence in Medical Education or Practice	Physicians Appointed to a Medical Faculty Are Excused From...		Notes/Comments
		...the GME Requirement for Limited Licensure	...the Examination Requirement for Limited Licensure	
Alabama		Yes	Yes	
Alaska				
Arizona				
Arkansas				
California DO	Yes	Yes	Yes	
California MD	Yes	Yes	Yes	1-yr medical faculty certificate, for practice only at the medical school or a formally affiliated teaching hospital
Colorado				Distinguished foreign physicians are invited to serve on faculty; temporary licensure may not exceed 5 years
Connecticut		Yes	Yes	
Delaware				
DC	Yes			
Florida		Yes	Yes	Physicians appointed to a medical faculty are eligible for a special license, with which they may practice only at the designated facility/institution
Georgia		Yes	Yes	Physicians appointed to a medical faculty are excused from the GME requirement for limited licensure for teaching only
Guam				
Hawaii				
Idaho				
Illinois				
Indiana				
Iowa	Yes	Yes	Yes	Physicians appointed to a medical faculty are eligible for a special license, with which they may practice only at the designated facility/institution. Time spent on a special license can be applied to the GME requirements for permanent licensure
Kansas				
Kentucky	Yes	Yes	Yes	Physicians appointed to a medical faculty are eligible for a special license, with which they may practice only at the designated facility/institution
Louisiana	Yes	Yes	Yes	A physician licensed through recognition of eminence in medical education must be approved as a tenured professor/associate professor by a Louisiana medical school
Maine				
Maryland	Yes	Yes	Yes	
Massachusetts				
Michigan (MD and DO)	Yes (limited)	Yes	Yes	Only IMGs with an appointment to an approved program
Minnesota				
Mississippi				
Missouri	Yes		Yes	
Montana	Yes			An IMG seeking a restricted license must have published in an English-language, peer-reviewed medical journal
Nebraska				
Nevada	Yes			
New Hampshire	Yes			A courtesy license for educational purposes is provided to eminent physicians under limited circumstances

(continued on next page)

Table 9 (continued)

Licensure Requirement Exemptions for Eminent Physicians and Medical School Faculty

| | License Physicians Through Recognition of Eminence in Medical Education or Practice | Physicians Appointed to a Medical Faculty Are Excused From... | | Notes/Comments |
		...the GME Requirement for Limited Licensure	...the Examination Requirement for Limited Licensure	
New Jersey				
New Mexico				
New York				
North Carolina	Yes	Yes	Yes	Also excused from ECFMG certification requirement
North Dakota				
Ohio		Yes	Yes	Physicians appointed to a medical faculty are eligible for a visiting medical faculty certificate, with which they may practice only at the school or teaching hospitals affiliated with the school. This nonrenewable certificate is valid 1 year or duration of the appointment, whichever is shorter
Oklahoma				
Oregon		Yes		IMGs who are not eligible for licensure may be granted a Limited License, Medical Faculty (LL,MF) if appointed to a full-time medical school faculty position under direction of the department head. LL,MF may be granted annually for 4 years, during which the applicant must pass USMLE Steps 1, 2, and 3 or have passed FLEX or the National Boards. The physician would then be eligible for licensure.
Pennsylvania DO				
Pennsylvania MD	Yes	Yes		Physicians appointed to a medical faculty are eligible for a visiting medical faculty certificate, with which they may practice only at the school or teaching hospitals affiliated with the school. This nonrenewable certificate is valid 1 year or duration of the appointment, whichever is shorter
Puerto Rico				
Rhode Island	Yes	Yes	Yes	Distinguished foreign physicians recommended by the medical school dean may serve on faculty; academic limited registration may be renewed for a maximum of 5 years
South Carolina				
South Dakota				
Tennessee		Yes	Yes	
Texas	Yes	See note	See note	There are several types of limited licenses, each with different requirements and characteristics. Contact the board for more information.
Utah				
Vermont		Yes	Yes	
Virgin Islands				
Virginia	Yes	Yes	Yes	
Washington				
West Virginia		Yes	Yes	
Wisconsin				
Wyoming				Exemption granted at Board's discretion
Total	**17**	**20**	**19**	

Note: All information should be verified with licensing board; medical licenses are granted to those physicians meeting all state requirements—at the discretion of the board.

Teaching (Visiting Professor) Licenses

Forty jurisdictions issue teaching (visiting professor) licenses, with fees ranging from $0 to $400.

Table 10
Teaching (Visiting Professor) Licenses

	Teaching (Visiting Professor) License Granted	Notes
Alabama	Yes	
Alaska		
Arizona	Yes, $100	Education Teaching Permit, granted for 5 days, $100. Teaching licenses, within Board-approved medical school or GME program, $225; valid 1 year and may be renewed for up to 4 years.
Arizona DO	Yes, $318	Education Teaching Permit, granted for 5 days, $106
Arkansas	Yes, $400	Education license must be renewed annually
California	Yes	Renewable certificates of registration are awarded on an individual basis for 1 to 5 years to physicians who do not immediately meet licensure requirements and who have been offered full-time teaching positions in California medical schools. Biennially renewable faculty permits are awarded on an individual basis to academically eminent physicians for whom the medical school has assumed direct responsibility. The holder may practice medicine only within the sponsoring medical school and affiliated institutions.
California DO		
Colorado	Yes, $100	
Connecticut	Yes, $0	
Delaware		
DC		
Florida	Yes, $100	A visiting faculty certificate, valid for 180 days, is granted to MDs/DOs who are graduates of an accredited medical school or its equivalent and hold a valid current license to practice medicine in another US jurisdiction. The certificate authorizes practice only in conjunction with teaching duties at an accredited Florida medical/osteopathic school or in its main teaching hospitals. No more than three physicians per year per institution may hold this certificate; the certificate can be granted to a physician only once in a given 5-year period.
Florida DO	Yes, $400	(See above note)
Georgia	Yes	Teacher's license for faculty of approved Georgia medical schools.
Guam		
Hawaii		
Hawaii DO		
Idaho		
Illinois	Yes	Visiting Professor Permits for a maximum of 2 years are issued to persons receiving faculty appointments to teach in either a medical or osteopathic school. Visiting Physician Permits for up to 180 days are issued to persons receiving an invitation or appointment to study, demonstrate, or perform a specific medical or osteopathic subject or technique in medical/osteopathic schools; hospitals; or facilities operated pursuant to the Ambulatory Surgical Treatment Center Act.
Indiana	Yes, $100	Visiting professor license granted to an institution for a specific physician to whom it has granted a visiting faculty appointment. Institution must certify the physician's qualifications; physician's practice limited to the institution for designated period not to exceed 1 yr
Iowa	Yes	Special license or temporary license, depending on applicant's qualifications and the teaching activity in Iowa
Kansas	Yes, $25	
Kentucky	Yes, $300	
Louisiana	Yes	
Maine	Yes, $0	
Maine DO	Yes, $50	
Maryland	Yes, $332	Limited 1-yr license for graduate teaching
Massachusetts	Yes, $250	Temporary registration is issued to physicians who hold a temporary faculty appointment at a Massachusetts medical school, are substituting temporarily for a fully licensed Massachusetts physician, or are enrolled in a CME course that requires Massachusetts licensure.

(continued on next page)

Table 10 (continued)
Teaching (Visiting Professor) Licenses

	Teaching (Visiting Professor) License Granted	Notes
Michigan	Yes, $170	For teaching/research appointment at approved educational program
Michigan DO	Yes, $170	For teaching/research appointment at approved educational program
Minnesota		
Mississippi		
Missouri	Yes	
Montana		Refer to 37-3-305, MCA
Nebraska	Yes, $25	Temporary visiting faculty permits for medical school faculty
Nevada		
Nevada DO	Yes, $200	Six-month maximum (considered special license)
New Hampshire	Yes, $75	
New Jersey		
New Mexico	Yes, $100	
New Mexico DO		
New York		
North Carolina	Yes, $150	Limited faculty license for medical school faculty
North Dakota		
Ohio	Yes, $125	Visiting Medical Faculty certificate and Special Activities certificates are $125
Oklahoma		
Oklahoma DO		
Oregon	Yes, $175	Limited license (LL) is issued for Visiting Professor (VP) and Medical Faculty (MF). LL-VP is valid for a 1-year teaching position and may be renewed for 1 additional year. LL-MF is valid for a full-time faculty position offered by the dean of the medical school and may be renewed for 3 additional years.
Pennsylvania	Yes	Institutional License allows a qualified person to teach and/or practice medicine for a period of time not to exceed 3 years in one of the Commonwealth's medical colleges, its affiliates, or community hospitals. Temporary License allows the licensee to teach medicine and surgery or participate in a medical procedure necessary for the well-being of a specified patient within the Commonwealth. Applicants for a temporary license must hold an unrestricted license in another state, territory, possession, or country.
Pennsylvania DO		
Puerto Rico	Yes	
Rhode Island	Yes, $150	
South Carolina		
South Dakota		Teaching or visiting professor licenses, permits, or certificates are not issued
Tennessee	Yes, $50	
Tennessee DO		
Texas	Yes, $110	
Utah		
Vermont		
Vermont DO		
Virgin Islands	Yes	
Virginia	Yes, $55	Limited license for fellowship and teaching positions

(continued on next page)

Table 10 (continued)
Teaching (Visiting Professor) Licenses

	Teaching (Visiting Professor) License Granted	Notes
Washington	Yes (limited)	Teaching/Research limited licenses may be granted for teaching (visiting professor) with 1) a letter of nomination by the dean of the University of Washington medical school or CEO of a hospital or other appropriate health care facility and 2) proof of current licensure in another state or country
Washington DO		
West Virginia	Yes, $150	Limited medical school faculty license
West Virginia DO		
Wisconsin	Yes, $110	Visiting professor license for 2-year period
Wyoming		
Total	**40**	

Note: All information should be verified with licensing board; medical licenses are granted to those physicians meeting all state requirements—at the discretion of the board.

Resident/Fellow Physician Licenses

Sixty-four jurisdictions issue educational licenses, permits, certificates, or registration to resident/fellow physicians in graduate medical education (GME) programs, with fees ranging from $0 to $300 per year. (The GME program director generally provides a list of residents/fellows and any other required information directly to the licensing jurisdiction.) In 37 of those jurisdictions, residents/fellows must obtain a new permit/license when changing residency/fellowship programs within the state.

Medical boards in 14 states require that prospective residents have passed United States Medical Licensing Examination (USMLE) Step 1 to receive a permit/license. California, Mississippi, Montana, North Dakota, and Utah require passage of Steps 1 and 2.

Nineteen states require that resident/fellow physicians obtain full licensure (not limited or training licenses) at some point in their training (usually after having completed a certain number of years of GME).

Additional Notes for Specific Licensing Jurisdictions

California—Permits are awarded on an individual basis for a maximum of 5 years to noncitizen physicians for postgraduate work in a California medical school.

IMGs must submit an application to determine that all core requirements have been met before they may begin training in California.

Illinois—Limited temporary licenses (valid for 6 months) are awarded to persons in non-Illinois residency programs who are accepted for a specific period of time to perform a portion of that program at a clinical residency program in Illinois due to the lack of adequate facilities in their state.

Visiting Resident Permits are issued for 180 days to persons who have been invited or appointed for a specific period of time to perform a portion of that clinical resi-dency program under the supervision of an Illinois-licensed physician in an Illinois patient care clinic or facility affiliated with the out-of-state GME program.

Massachusetts—Limited registration is issued to physicians enrolled in accredited residency programs and physicians enrolled in fellowships at hospitals with accredited residency programs in the area of the applicant's specialty.

Mississippi—Institutional license is issued to interns and IMG physicians providing health care in state institutions. Applicants are not required to meet all requirements for permanent unrestricted licensure.

Restricted temporary license is issued to physicians enrolled in first year of GME at the University of Mississippi School of Medicine for practice limited to that school.

Addictionology Fellowship License is issued to physicians admitted for treatment in a board-approved drug and/or alcohol addiction treatment program or to physicians enrolled in fellowship of addictionology of the Mississippi State Medical Association Impaired Professionals Program.

Oregon—Limited license, Fellow granted for 1 year and renewed for 1 additional year. Limited license, Postgraduate granted annually until training is completed.

Pennsylvania—Interim Limited License (up to 12 consecutive months) is issued to physicians providing medical service other than at the training location of the licensee's accredited GME program.

Graduate License allows the licensee to participate for a period of up to 12 consecutive months in GME within the complex of the hospital to which the licensee is assigned and any satellite facility or other training location used in the program.

South Dakota—Resident physicians practicing within the confines of their residency program are not required to obtain a certificate from the board.

A resident physician who wishes to practice on an irregular basis outside their program may apply for a resident certificate if they have completed at least 1 year of GME and remain enrolled in good standing in their program until successful completion. To apply for this certificate, they must meet South Dakota's examination requirements for completion of the entire USMLE within a 7-year period and passing of each step within three attempts. The fee for this certificate is $50.

Table 11
Resident/Fellow Physician Licenses

	Licenses, Permits, Certificates, & Registration	Must Obtain New Permit/License When Changing Residency Programs Within State	Prospective Residents Applying for License Must Have Passed USMLE Step 1	Full licensure required at any point during training?	Notes
Alabama	Yes				Limited license for residency education only
Alaska	Yes				Residency permits for up to 36 mos to physicians in accredited residency programs in the US
Arizona	Yes, $50/yr	Yes	Yes		Education Training Permit, granted for 5 days.
Arizona DO	Yes	Yes			Education Training Permit, granted for 5 days, $106
Arkansas	Yes				Education license must be renewed annually
California*	Yes		Yes (and Step 2)	Yes; after 2 yrs (3 yrs for IMGs)	
California DO				Yes; prior to 3rd yr	No CME required
Colorado	Yes, $10	Yes			Training license valid for duration of program; renews every 3 yrs
Connecticut	Yes, $0	Yes			
Delaware	Yes, $14	Yes			Training license must be renewed annually
DC	Yes, $50	Yes	Yes	Yes	
Florida*	Yes, $200	Yes			
Florida DO	Yes, $100	Yes			Training registration number (for interns, residents, and fellows)
Georgia	Yes, $100				Board must be notified of resident changing program within state
Guam	Yes	Yes	Yes	Yes; after 3 yrs	
Hawaii	Yes, $75				
Hawaii DO	Yes, $75				
Idaho	Yes, $10	Yes		Yes (see note)	After 1 yr GME (US/Canadian graduates), 3 yrs GME (IMGs)
Illinois*	Yes	Yes			
Indiana	Yes, $100	Yes	Yes		Resident permit good for 1 yr, may be renewed annually
Iowa	Yes, $205	Yes			Resident physician license for GME in board-approved pgm under supervision of licensed physician. Issued for full length of pgm.
Kansas	Yes, $40	Yes			
Kentucky	Yes, $75	Yes	Yes		Institutional Practice Limited License or Residency Training License to physicians beyond first year of GME while still in training
Louisiana	Yes, $25	Yes			Intern registration for first 12 mos of GME after completing medical school
Maine	Yes, $100	Yes	Yes		Educational permits for 1 yr in a specific training program, renewable for 7 yrs
Maine DO	Yes, $200	Yes			Temp. educational permits for 1 yr in a specific training pgm only
Maryland	Yes, $100	Yes			Registration of med school grads in GME programs
Massachusetts*	Yes, $100	Yes	Yes	Yes; after 6 yrs	
Michigan	Yes, $170	Yes		Yes; after 6 yrs	Limited annual license for up to 6 yrs for GME, renewable each year; includes controlled substance license
Michigan DO	Yes, $170	Yes		Yes; after 6 yrs	Limited annual license for up to 6 yrs for GME; Includes controlled substance license
Minnesota	Yes	Yes			

(continued on next page)

Table 11 (continued)
Resident/Fellow Physician Licenses

	Licenses, Permits, Certificates, & Registration	Must Obtain New Permit/License When Changing Residency Programs Within State	Prospective Residents Applying for License Must Have Passed USMLE Step 1	Full licensure required at any point during training?	Notes
Mississippi*	Yes, $50/$200		Yes (and Step 2)	Yes; after 5 yrs	
Missouri	Yes, $30	Yes			Temporary licenses issued to interns, residents, and fellows only
Montana	Yes, $100/$50		Yes (and Step 2)		Refer to 37-3-305, MCA
Nebraska	Yes, $25	Yes		Yes; after 5 yrs	Temporary educational permits for residents
Nevada	Yes, $425	Yes		Yes (see note)	Limited 1-yr license for clinical residents ($300 initial, $50 renewal, $75 criminal background investigation). Full licensure usually for fellows/chief residents; depends on program needs
Nevada DO	Yes, $200	Yes			
New Hampshire	Yes, $35	Yes	Yes		
New Jersey	Yes, $50	Yes		Yes; after 5 yrs	Residency training permit required for unlicensed residents in GY2+
New Mexico	Yes, $10		Yes	Yes; after 8 yrs	
New Mexico DO	Yes, $25				
New York	Yes, $105				Requires limited permit for all medical school graduates except individuals in ACGME- or AOA-accredited residency programs. Requires ECFMG certificate from all IMGs for limited permit.
North Carolina	Yes, $100 (permit); $125 (registration)	Yes			Limited license to resident physicians (ineligible for licensure by endorsement)
North Dakota	Yes, $25		Yes (and Step 2)		Limited license for residents in clinical program, renewable annually
Ohio	Yes, $75 (initial) $35 (renewal)	Yes		Yes; after 6 yrs	Training certificate or full license mandatory for interns, residents, and clinical fellows.
Oklahoma	Yes, $200	Yes	Yes (and Step 2)		
Oklahoma DO	Yes			Yes; after 1 yr	
Oregon*	Yes, $185	Yes			
Pennsylvania*	Yes, $30				Graduate license renewal fee is $15
Pennsylvania DO	Yes, $30	Yes			Temporary license for GME valid for up to 12 mos; renewal fee $25
Puerto Rico	Yes				Internship/residency licenses to qualified applicants enrolled in an ACGME-accredited residency program who have successfully completed the first part of the medical board examination (basic sciences) or its equivalent (NBME, FLEX, or USMLE)
Rhode Island	Yes, $40	Yes		Yes; after 5 yrs	Limited medical registration to interns, residents, or fellows. Practice limited to the designated institution and must be under the supervision of a staff physician licensed in RI.
South Carolina	Yes, $150	Yes			Limited licenses for residency programs or limited practices renewable on a yearly basis
South Dakota*					(See note)
Tennessee	Yes, $25	Yes			
Tennessee DO	Yes, $50				
Texas	Yes, $144	Yes			

(continued on next page)

Table 11 (continued)
Resident/Fellow Physician Licenses

	Licenses, Permits, Certificates, & Registration	Must Obtain New Permit/License When Changing Residency Programs Within State	Prospective Residents Applying for License Must Have Passed USMLE Step 1	Full licensure required at any point during training?	Notes
Utah	Yes, $200		Yes (and Step 2)		
Vermont	Yes, $70				Limited license to interns, residents, fellows, or house officers enrolled in ACGME-accredited residency programs and working under supervision of licensed physician at a state-licensed institution or clinic
Vermont DO	Yes, $70				
Virgin Islands	Yes				For residents, institutional license only
Virginia	Yes, $55				Limited license for fellowship and teaching positions. Temporary licenses (renewable annually) to interns, residents, and fellows in accredited programs in Virginia
Washington	Yes, $385				Limited license to physicians in GME and teaching/research at state institutions and city/county health departments
Washington DO	Yes, $300				Limited licensure for GME only
West Virginia					
West Virginia DO	Yes, $50			Yes; after 1 yr	1-yr limited medical registration for interns
Wisconsin	Yes, $10			Yes; after 5 yrs	Temporary educational certificates for residency education after first year
Wyoming	Yes, $25			Yes; after 1 yr	
Total	**65**	**38**	**15**	**19**	

* Refer to introductory text to this table for more information on this state's regulations.

Note: All information should be verified with licensing board; medical licenses are granted to those physicians meeting all state requirements—at the discretion of the board.

Contact Information for State Medical/Osteopathic Boards

Allopathic Boards

Alabama State Board of Medical Examiners
(334) 242-4116
www.albme.org

Alaska State Medical Board
(907) 269-8163
www.dced.state.ak.us/occ/pmed.htm

Arizona Medical Board
(480) 551-2700
www.azmd.gov

Arkansas State Medical Board
(501) 296-1802
www.armedicalboard.org

Medical Board of California
(916) 263-2389
www.medbd.ca.gov

Colorado Board of Medical Examiners
(303) 894-7690
www.dora.state.co.us/medical

Connecticut Medical Examining Board
(860) 509-7648
www.dph.state.ct.us

Delaware Board of Medical Examiners
(302) 744-4500
www.dpr.delaware.gov

District of Columbia Board of Medicine
(202) 724-8800
www.dchealth.dc.gov

Florida Board of Medicine
(850) 245-4131
www.doh.state.fl.us

Georgia Composite State Board of Medical Examiners
(404) 656-3913
www.medicalboard.state.ga.us

Guam Board of Medical Examiners
(671) 735-7406

Hawaii Board of Medical Examiners
(808) 586-2689
www.ehawaii.gov

Idaho State Board of Medicine
(208) 327-7000
www.bom.state.id.us

Illinois Medical Licensing Board
(217) 557-3209
www.idfpr.com

Medical Licensing Board of Indiana
(317) 234-2060
www.in.gov/pla/medical.htm

Iowa Board of Medical Examiners
(515) 281-6641
www.medicalboard.iowa.gov

Kansas Board of Healing Arts
(785) 296-8561
www.ksbha.org

Kentucky Board of Medical Licensure
(502) 429-7150
http://kbml.ky.gov

Louisiana State Board of Medical Examiners
(504) 568-6820 x262
www.lsbme.org

Maine Board of Licensure in Medicine
(207) 287-3601
www.docboard.org/me/me_home.htm

Maryland Board of Physicians
(410) 764-4777
www.mbp.state.md.us

Massachusetts Board of Registration in Medicine
(617) 654-9800
www.massmedboard.org

Michigan Board of Medicine
(517) 373-6873
www.michigan.gov/healthlicense

Minnesota Board of Medical Practice
(612) 617-2130
www.bmp.state.mn.us

Mississippi State Board of Medical Licensure
(601) 987-3079
www.msbml.state.ms.us

Missouri State Board of Registration for the Healing Arts
(573) 751-0098
www.pr.mo.gov/healingarts.asp

Montana Board of Medical Examiners
(406) 841-2364
www.discoveringmontana.com/dli/bsd/license/bsd_boards/med_board/board_page.asp

Nebraska Board of Medicine and Surgery
(402) 471-2118
www.hhs.state.ne.us

Nevada State Board of Medical Examiners
(775) 688-2559
www.medboard.nv.gov

New Hampshire Board of Medicine
(603) 271-1205
www.state.nh.us/medicine

New Jersey State Board of Medical Examiners
(609) 826-7100
www.state.nj.us/lps/ca/medical.htm

New Mexico Medical Board
(505) 476-7221
www.state.nm.us/nmbme

New York State Board of Medicine
(518) 474-3817 x560
www.op.nysed.gov

North Carolina Medical Board
(919) 326-1100 ext 218
www.ncmedboard.org

North Dakota State Board of Medical Examiners
(701) 328-6500
www.ndbomex.com

State Medical Board of Ohio
(614) 466-3934
www.med.ohio.gov

Oklahoma State Board of Medical Licensure and Supervision
(405) 848-6841
www.okmedicalboard.org

Oregon Board of Medical Examiners
(503) 229-5770
www.bme.state.or.us

Pennsylvania State Board of Medicine
(717) 783-1400
www.dos.state.pa.us

Board of Medical Examiners of Puerto Rico
(787) 782-8949 or 782-8937

Rhode Island Board of Medical Licensure and Discipline
(401) 222-3855
www.health.ri.gov/hsr/bmld

South Carolina Board of Medical Examiners
(803) 896-4500
www.llr.state.sc.us/pol/medical

South Dakota State Board of Medical and Osteopathic Examiners
(605) 367-7781
www.state.sd.us/dcr/medical

Tennessee Board of Medical Examiners
(615) 532-3202
www.state.tn.us/health

Texas State Board of Medical Examiners
(512) 305-7010
www.tmb.state.tx.us

Utah Department of Commerce
(801) 530-6621
www.dopl.utah.gov

Vermont Board of Medical Practice
(802) 657-4220
http://healthvermont.gov/hc/med_board/bmp.aspx

Virginia Board of Medicine
(804) 367-4600
www.dhp.virginia.gov

Virgin Islands Board of Medical Examiners
(340) 774-0117

Washington Medical Quality Assurance Commission
(360) 236-4790
www.doh.wa.gov

West Virginia Board of Medicine
(304) 558-2921 x 227
www.wvdhhr.org/wvbom

State of Wisconsin Medical Examining Board
(608) 266-2112
http://drl.wi.gov

Wyoming Board of Medicine
(307) 778-7053
http://wyomedboard.state.wy.us

Osteopathic Boards

Arizona Board of Osteopathic Medical Examiners
(480) 657-7703 x22
www.azdo.gov

Osteopathic Medical Board of California
(916) 263-3100
www.ombc.ca.gov

Florida Board of Osteopathic Medicine
(850) 245-4161
www.doh.state.fl.us/mqa

Maine Board of Osteopathic Licensure
(207) 287-2480
www.maine.gov/osteo

Michigan Board of Osteopathic Medicine and Surgery
(517) 373-6873
www.michigan.gov/healthlicense

Nevada State Board of Osteopathic Medicine
(702) 732-2147
www.osteo.state.nv.us

New Mexico Board of Osteopathic Medical Examiners
(505) 476-4695
www.rld.state.nm.us

Oklahoma Board of Osteopathic Examiners
(405) 528-8625
www.docboard.org

Pennsylvania State Board of Osteopathic Medicine
(717) 783-4858
www.dos.state.pa.us

Tennessee State Board of Osteopathic Examiners
(615) 741-4540
www.state.tn.us/health

State of Utah Department of Commerce
(801) 530-6621
www.dopl.utah.gov

Vermont Board of Osteopathic Physicians and Surgeons
(802) 828-2367
www.sec.state.vt.us

Washington Board of Osteopathic Medicine and Surgery
(360) 236-4943
www.doh.wa.gov

West Virginia Board of Osteopathy
(304) 723-4638
www.wvbdosteo.org